John Bower
Co. I

NO. 9

AMERICAN PRACTICAL NAVIGATOR

AN EPITOME OF NAVIGATION AND NAUTICAL ASTRONOMY

ORIGINALLY BY

NATHANIEL BOWDITCH, LL. D.

Published by the UNITED STATES HYDROGRAPHIC OFFICE under the authority of the SECRETARY OF THE NAVY

UNITED STATES
GOVERNMENT PRINTING OFFICE
WASHINGTON : 1943

For sale by Hydrographic Office, Navy Department, Washington, D. C., also by the Superintendent of Documents
Government Printing Office, Washington, D. C. - - - Price, $2.70

STATUTES OF AUTHORIZATION

There shall be a Hydrographic Office attached to the Bureau of Navigation in the Navy Department, for the improvement of the means for navigating safely the vessels of the Navy and of the mercantile marine, by providing, under the authority of the Secretary of the Navy, accurate and cheap nautical charts, sailing directions, navigators, and manuals of instructions for the use of all vessels of the United States, and for the benefit and use of navigators generally (R. S. 431).

The Secretary of the Navy is authorized to cause to be prepared, at the Hydrographic Office attached to the Bureau of Navigation in the Navy Department, maps, charts, and nautical books relating to and required in navigation, and to publish and furnish them to navigators at the cost of printing and paper, and to purchase the plates and copyrights of such existing maps, charts, navigators, sailing directions, and instructions, as he may consider necessary, and when he may deem it expedient to do so, and under such regulations and instructions as he may prescribe (R. S. 432).

NATHANIEL BOWDITCH (1773–1838)

Nathaniel Bowditch was born on March 26, 1773, at Salem, Mass. Circumstances forced him to educate himself in spare time after he was 10 years old, which he did with such zeal and ability that at the age of 21 he was unusually well informed and an outstanding mathematician.

In 1795, Bowditch went to sea on his first of four voyages as supercargo and captain's writer. A fifth voyage he made as master and part owner of a ship, returning to Salem in 1803, to retire to his studies and the insurance business.

Early during these voyages, Bowditch became keenly interested in navigation and missed no opportunity to take observations of and to study the movements of celestial bodies. The most recent volume on navigation at the time was Hamilton Moore's "Navigator," published in London. Many errors were known to exist in the book. To have exact tables for his work, Bowditch commenced the laborious task of recomputing Moore's tables. He found the book poorly arranged for practical navigation, with inadequate tables, and to contain numerous errors. One error was said to be so serious as to have caused the loss of two ships at sea. When he communicated his findings to the American publisher of the book, Mr. Edmund Blunt of Newburyport, Mass., who was about to publish a third edition in this country, Mr. Blunt urged Bowditch to take several copies of Moore's book on his next voyage to correct it for the third edition. The task involved such extensive revision that Bowditch decided to write his own book, and to "put down in the book nothing I can't teach the crew." On that trip it is said that every man of the crew of 12, including the ship's cook, became able to take and calculate lunar observations and plot the daily position of the ship.

In 1802, Mr. Blunt published the first edition of the American Practical Navigator, which was received with such great acclaim by the maritime world that over 30,000 copies in 10 editions were sold prior to Bowditch's death. In 1866, the United States Hydrographic Office bought the copyright and since that time has published the book, revising it completely from time to time to keep step with the modern changes in navigation methods.

Death at 65 on March 16, 1838, closed a record of wonderful achievement during a life of stainless integrity. Many honors had been conferred upon him by his fellow men. The following eulogy was written by the Salem Marine Society:

"In his death a public, a national, a human benefactor has departed. Not this community nor our country only, but the whole world has reason to do honor to his memory. When the voice of eulogy shall be still, when the tears of sorrow shall cease to flow, no monument will be needed to keep alive his memory among men; but as long as ships shall sail, the needle point to the north, and the stars go through their wonted courses in the heavens, the name of Dr. Bowditch will be revered as of one who has helped his fellowmen in time of need, who was and is a guide to them over the pathless oceans, and one who forwarded the great interests of mankind."

PART I

TEXT AND APPENDICES

PART II

TABLES

HYDROGRAPHIC OFFICE MANUALS OF NAVIGATION AND NAUTICAL ASTRONOMY

Besides the present epitome, entitled the "American Practical Navigator," the Hydrographic Office issues related works to aid in the practice of navigation, which are titled and numbered as follows:

Catalog No.	Title of book
66	Arctic Azimuth Tables giving True Bearings of the Sun and the other celestial bodies within ecliptic limits, for parallels of latitude between 70° and 88° N.
71	Azimuth Tables, giving the True Bearings of the Sun at Intervals of Ten Minutes between Sunrise and Sunset, for Parallels of Latitude between 71° N. and 71° S. (Can also be applied to the moon, planets, and stars, where declinations do not exceed 23° N. or S.)
120	The Azimuths of Celestial Bodies whose declinations range from 24° to 70°, for parallels of latitude extending to 70° from the equator.
127	Star Identification Tables, giving simultaneous values of declination and hour angle for values of latitude, altitude, and azimuth, ranging from 0° to 80° in latitude and altitude, and 0° to 180° in azimuth.
208	Navigation Tables for Mariners and Aviators. Working from an assumed position this small book of tables affords a means of determining (*a*) the Sumner line, (*b*) the compass error, (*c*) the meridian altitude, (*d*) the great circle course and distance, and (*e*) the identification of stars.
211	Dead Reckoning Altitude and Azimuth Table. Working from the dead reckoning position this small book of tables has the same uses as H. O. 208. The solution is uniform under all conditions.
214	Tables of Computed Altitude and Azimuth, for rapidly finding line of position. Consists of 8 volumes, each covering a belt of 10 degrees of latitude. A uniform process adopted by most mariners and aviators. Azimuth is given for every 4 minutes of time.
217	Manual of Maneuvering Board. This book gives essential problems in maneuvering. The determination of proper course, speed, and distance involved, constitute the relative movement, or maneuvering problems, which are readily solved here in 28 cases of illustrated examples.

The chapter containing weather material was submitted to the Weather Bureau of the Department of Agriculture for comment, and acknowledgments are accordingly made to them.

CONTENTS

PART I

PART II

ABBREVIATIONS USED IN THIS WORK

Alt. (or *h*)	Altitude.
a. m	Ante meridian.
Amp	Amplitude.
App	Apparent.
App. t	Apparent time.
Ast	Astronomical.
Ast. t	Astronomical time.
Aug	Augmentation.
Az. (or Z)	Azimuth.
C (or Co)	Course.
Cn	Course through 360°.
C. C	Chronometer correction.
C−W	Chronometer *minus* watch.
Chro. t	Chronometer time.
Co. L	Co. latitude.
Col	Column.
Corr	Correction.
Cos	Cosine.
Cosec	Cosecant.
Cot	Cotangent.
d (or Dec.)	Declination.
D (or D. Lo)	Difference longitude.
Dep	Departure.
Dev	Deviation.
Diff	Difference.
Dist	Distance.
DL	Difference latitude.
D. R	Dead reckoning.
E., Ely	East, easterly.
Eq. t	Equation of time.
F	Longitude factor.
f	Latitude factor.
G. (or Gr.)	Greenwich.
G. A. T	Greenwich apparent time.
G. C. T	Greenwich civil time.
G. H. A	Greenwich hour angle.
G. S. T	Greenwich sidereal time.
h	Altitude.
H	Meridian altitude.
h_c	Computed altitude.
h_o	Sextant altitude with all corrections applied.
h_s	Sextant altitude.
H. A. (or *t*)	Hour angle.
Hav	Haversine.
H. D	Hourly difference.
H. E	Height of eye.
H. P. (or Hor. par.)	Horizontal parallax.
Hr-s	Hour-s.
H. W	High water.
I. C	Index correction.
Int	Intercept.
L. (or Lat.)	Latitude.
L. A. N	Local apparent noon.
L. A. T	Local apparent time.
L. C. T	Local civil time.
L. S. T	Local sidereal time.
Lo. (or Long.)	Longitude.
Log	Logarithm.
Lun. Int	Lunitidal interval.
L. W	Low water.
m	Meridional difference.
Merid	Meridian or noon.
Mag	Magnetic.
Mid	Middle.
Mid. L or Lm	Middle latitude.
M. T	Mean time.
nat	Natural.
N., Nly	North, northerly.
N. A. (or Naut. Alm.)	Nautical Almanac.
Np	Neap.
Obs	Observation.
p (or P. D.)	Polar distance.
p. c	Per compass.
P. D. (or *p*)	Polar distance.
p. m	Post meridian.
p. & r	Parallax and refraction.
Par	Parallax.
R. A	Right ascension.
R. A. M. S	Right ascension mean sun.
Red	Reduction.
Ref	Refraction.
S., Sly	South, southerly.
S. D	Semidiameter.
Sec	Secant.
Sid	Sidereal.
Sid. T. of 0^h G. C. T. or (R. A. M. S. $+12^h$)	Sidereal time of 0^h civil time at Greenwich.
Sin	Sine.
Spg	Spring.
t	Hour angle.
T	Time.
Tab	Table.
Tan	Tangent.
Tr. (or Trans.)	Transit.
Var	Variation.
Vert	Vertex or vertical.
W., Wly	West, westerly.
W. T	Watch time.
z	Zenith distance.
Z	Azimuth.
Zn	Azimuth measured through 360° from north.
Z. D	Zone description.
Z. T	Zone time.
θ	Auxiliary angle.

SYMBOLS

☉	The Sun.
☾	The Moon.
✳	A Star or Planet.
$\overline{☉}$ $\overline{☾}$	Alt. upper limb.
$\underline{☉}$ $\underline{☾}$	Alt. lower limb.
°	Degrees.
′	Minutes of Arc.
″	Seconds of Arc.
^{h}	Hours.
^{m}	Minutes of Time.
^{s}	Seconds of Time.
$\sim$	Sum, or difference.

GREEK LETTERS

Α α	Alpha.
Β β	Beta.
Γ γ	Gamma.
Δ δ	Delta.
Ε ε	Epsilon.
Ζ ζ	Zeta.
Η η	Eta.
Θ θ	Theta.
Ι ι	Iota.
Κ κ	Kappa.
Λ λ	Lambda.
Μ μ	Mu.
Ν ν	Nu.
Ξ ξ	Xi.
Ο ο	Omicron.
Π π	Pi.
Ρ ρ	Rho.
Σ σ (ς)	Sigma.
Τ τ	Tau.
Υ υ	Upsilon.
Φ φ	Phi.
Χ χ	Chi.
Ψ ψ	Psi.
Ω ω	Omega.

INDEX TO PART I

CHAPTER I

NAVIGATION DEFINITIONS

Navigation is the science which affords the knowledge necessary to conduct a vessel from point to point on the earth's surface, and to enable the mariner to determine, with a sufficient degree of accuracy, the position of his vessel at any time. Its two branches are geo-navigation and celo-navigation.

Geo-navigation is that part of navigation in which position is determined from relation to earthly objects. When position is directly ascertained from visible objects, or by radio bearings of known points, or by soundings of the depths of the sea, it is called **piloting.** When position is deduced by totaling the distances on courses run from a geographical position, it is called **dead reckoning.**

Celo-navigation or **nautical astronomy** is that part of navigation in which position is determined by observation of celestial objects—the sun, moon, planets, or stars.

The **earth** is an oblate spheroid, being a nearly spherical body slightly flattened at the poles. Its longer or equatorial axis measures 7,927 statute or 6,884 nautical miles, and its shorter or polar axis measures 7,900 statute or 6,860.5 nautical miles. The shape is so nearly a sphere that for practical purposes of navigation it is assumed to be a perfect sphere. (See fig. 1.)

The **axis of rotation** is the diameter of the earth about which it rotates. The ends of this axis are called the **North Pole** and **South Pole.**

A **great circle** is a circle on the earth's surface formed by the intersection of the earth's surface with a plane passed through the earth's center. A **small circle** is any circle on the earth's surface formed by the intersection of the earth's surface with a plane not passing through the center of the earth.

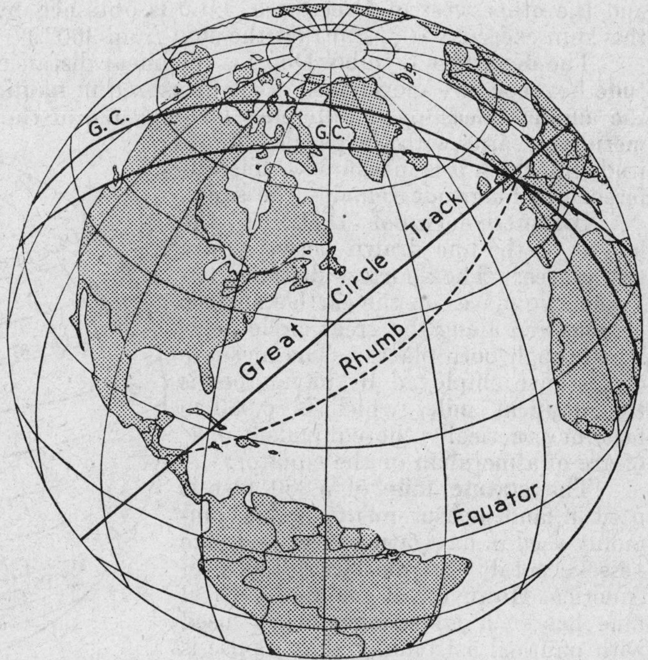

FIGURE 1.

The **Equator** is that great circle of the earth formed by the intersection with the earth's surface of a plane perpendicular to the axis of rotation at its midpoint. All points on the equator are therefore 90° from either pole.

Meridians are great circles of the earth which pass through the poles. The plane of any meridian includes the axis of rotation, is bisected by it, and is perpendicular to the plane of the equator. The half of a celestial meridian which passes through the position of the observer is referred to as the **upper branch** of the meridian, the lower branch being on the opposite side of the earth's axis. When speaking of a meridian the **upper branch** is meant unless the lower branch is specified.

The **prime meridian** is the meridian used as a line of origin for the measurement of longitude. The prime meridian accepted by most nations is that which passes through the observatory at Greenwich, England.

Parallels of latitude are small circles of the earth whose planes are parallel to the plane of the equator.

The **latitude** (symbol L) of a place on the surface of the earth is its angular distance north or south of the equator, measured by the arc of the meridian of the place contained between the place and the equator. With the equator as the origin, latitude is measured from 0° to 90° north or south. (See figure 2.)

The **difference of latitude** (symbol D. L.) between any two places is the angular measure of the arc of a meridian intercepted between their parallels of latitude. Between two places on the same side of the equator their latitudes are subtracted to obtain D. L. Between two places on opposite sides of the equator their latitudes are added to obtain D. L.

The **longitude** (symbol Lo) of a place is its angular distance east or west of the prime meridian, or is the measure of the arc of the equator intercepted between the **prime meridian** (Greenwich) and the meridian of the place, measured to eastward or westward from 0° at Greenwich to 180°. (See figure 3.)

The **difference of longitude** (symbol DLo) between two places is the smaller arc of the equator intercepted between their meridians. If both places are east or west of Greenwich, DLo is obtained by subtracting their longitudes. If one place is east and the other west of Greenwich, DLo is obtained by adding their longitudes. (If this sum exceeds 180°, subtract the sum from 360°.)

The **departure** (symbol Dep.) is the linear distance measured on a parallel of latitude between two meridians. It is measured in **nautical miles** to distinguish it from the angular measure or difference of longitude of the arc. Departure between two meridians varies with the parallel of latitude on which it is measured, while difference of longitude remains the same.

Distance (symbol Dist.) is the length of the line drawn between any two places. The shortest distance between two places on the earth's surface is measured along the great circle passing through both places. The measure of distance employed by navigators is the **nautical mile,** which is 6,080.20 feet, or practically the equivalent of 1′ of arc of a meridian or the equator.

The **statute mile** of 5,280 feet is used in land measurements, and is commonly used in navigating river and lake vessels, notably on the Great Lakes of America. However, at sea the nautical mile has such advantages when used with nautical astronomy that its use is almost universal.

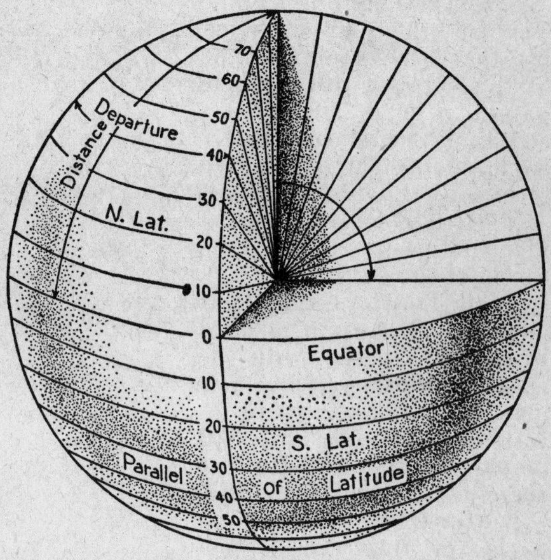

FIGURE 2.

The nautical mile is about one-seventh more than the statute mile, or the statute mile is approximately one-eighth shorter than the nautical mile.

The **knot** (symbol kt or kts) is the unit of speed used in navigation and is equal to 1 nautical mile per hour.

The **course** (symbol C or Co) is the angle which the center line of a vessel makes with the meridian. Course is measured from 0° at North clockwise 360°. In some calculations it is desirable to measure course from the North or South points to either East or West. In such cases the course is expressed in terms of the proper origin as follows:

C=N 25° E., or C_n= 25°.
C=N 25° W., or C_n=335°.
C=S 15° E., or C_n=165°.
C=S 15° W., or C_n=195°.

The **great circle track** between any two places is the route between the two places along the circumference of the great circle which passes through both places. See figure 1. From the properties of a great circle (which is a circle on the earth's surface formed by the intersection of the surface with a plane passed through its center) the distance between two points measured on a great-circle track is shorter than the distance along any other line joining them. Except when the two points are on the same meridian or both lie on the equator, a great circle track will intersect each intervening meridian at a different angle and will differ from the rhumb line, due to the convergence of meridians toward the poles. To follow a great-circle track, therefore, it is necessary to change the compass course periodically to agree with the angle of the track with the meridian at that point. When two points are in different hemispheres the angle that the great-circle track between them makes with successive meridians will increase on one side of the equator and decrease on the other. Laid on a Mercator chart the track has a double curvature.

Rhumb line, loxodromic curve, or **equiangular spiral** is a curved line which cuts all meridians at the same angle. Along a meridian or along the equator the rhumb line coincides with the great-circle track. At all other times it will lie nearer the equator than the great-circle track.

Direction is a point on the horizon towards which a vessel is moving and it is essentially a line. The direction of a line passing through a point on the earth is the inclination of this line to the meridian and is measured clockwise from 000° to 360°.

Heading.—A vessel's heading is the direction in which the ship heads, or points at any particular time and is the angle of the fore and aft line with the meridian.

Heading and **course** are not always the same thing, as when a vessel bucks an adverse wind, or strong tide, and attempts to make good, say for example, a true course east; then to offset strong northerly winds and swift southerly current, it becomes necessary to point the ship's head to northeast. In this case the heading is 045° and the course is 090°.

The **course** of a vessel is the direction given for the ship's movement or progress.

FIGURE 3.

Bearing is the angle between the meridian (north-south line) and the direction in which the ship is required to proceed. Bearings measured from the meridian are known as true bearings. A compass bearing is the angle between the direction of compass north and south and the direction of a place or object. Compass bearings must be corrected for both deviation and variation to get a true bearing.

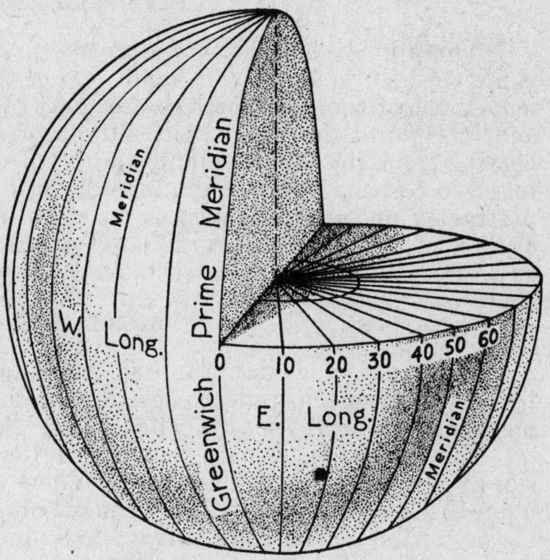

CHAPTER II

NAVIGATION INSTRUMENTS AND ACCESSORIES

DIVIDERS OR COMPASSES

This instrument consists of two legs movable about a joint, so that the points at the extremities of the legs may be set at any required distance from each other. It is used to take and transfer distances and to describe arcs and circles. When used for the former purpose it is termed **dividers,** and the extremities of both legs are metal points; when used for describing arcs or circles, it is called a **compass,** and one of the metal points is replaced by a pencil or pen.

PARALLEL RULERS

Parallel rulers consist of a pair of rulers connected together by metal strips in such a manner as to allow freedom of movement of each member of the pair parallel to the other. They are used for drawing lines parallel to each other in any direction, and are particularly useful in transferring the rhumb-line on the chart to the nearest compass-rose to ascertain the course, or to lay off bearings and courses.

PROTRACTOR

A **protractor,** in its simplest form, is a graduated arc of flat material used to lay down angular measures on a plane surface or chart. A protractor with one stationary and two movable arms for extending the angles from the arc is called a **three-armed protractor.** This protractor is used for plotting the position of the ship, or sounding boat. (For full description see chapter on Marine Surveying.)

UNIVERSAL DRAFTING MACHINE

This appliance consists of a protractor carried by a parallel-motion linkage which is fastened to the upper left-hand edge of the chart board. The linkage permits the movement of the protractor to any part of the chart without change of orientation, and, therefore, the instrument affords great convenience in laying off a course or bearing from any chosen point, and in the parallel transfer of a straight line to any required position. Of the graduated rulers supplied, any two can be mounted on the protractor, one at right angles to the other if desired, to render convenient the plotting of lines of position. The graduated protractor-rim or compass-rose can be clamped as desired, and hence oriented to coincide with the north and south direction on the chart (see fig. 2).

SPEED MEASUREMENT

The speed of a vessel through the water and the distance traveled are measured by various mechanical means described in the following paragraphs. A special instrument for measuring speed is called a **log.** Speeds are recorded in knots.

The **taffrail log** is a mechanical contrivance for registering the distance actually run by a vessel through the water. There are various types of taffrail logs which act upon the same principle. They consist of a registering device, a fly or rotator, and a log or towline. The rotator is a small spindle with a number of spiral fins. When drawn through the water in the direction of its axis, it rotates about that axis after the manner of a screw propeller. The rotator is towed from the vessel by means of a log or towline from 30 to 100 fathoms in length, made fast at its apex. The line is of special make, so that the turns of the rotator are transmitted through it to the worm shaft of the register, to which the inboard end of the line is attached. The registering

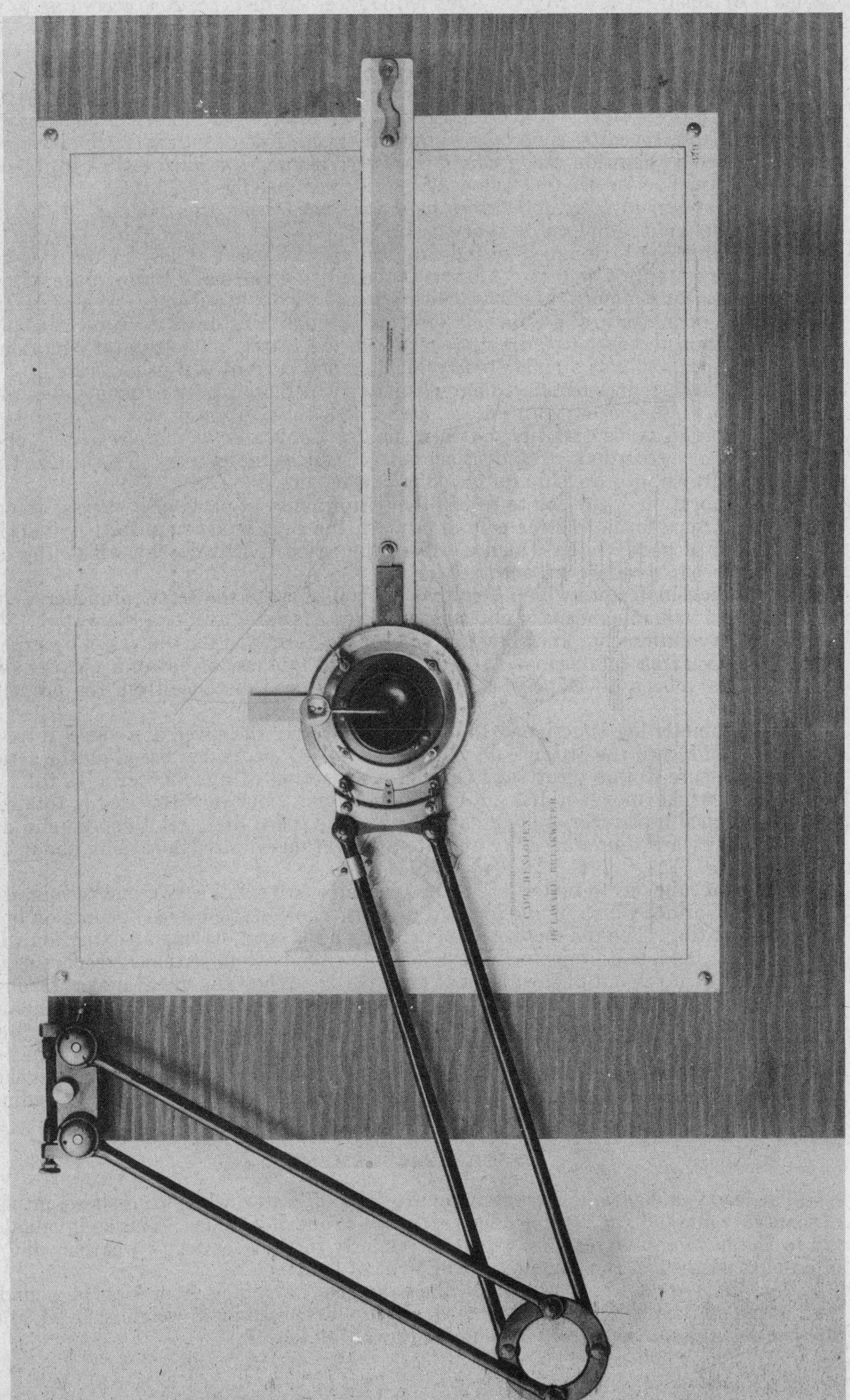

FIGURE 2.—Universal drafting machine

device is so constructed as to show upon a dial face, the distance run, according to the number of turns of its worm shaft. The register is carried at some convenient point on the vessel's quarter. It is frequently found expedient to rig it out upon a small boom, so that the rotator will be towed clear of the wake.

The **taffrail log** affords only an approximate means of determining the vessel's speed through the water. The normal percentage of error in the instrument may be determined from repeated runs over known distances free of currents. Other errors may be caused by bent fins, fins fouled by seaweed or refuse, mechanical wear of parts, too short a tow line, or use in a following or head sea (see figs. 3 and 4).

Electrical registers are sometimes used for transferring the readings of the mechanical register to a dial on or near the bridge.

The **Forbes log** is designed to indicate the vessel's speed at any moment as well as record the distance traveled. A bronze tube is fitted vertically through the bottom of the vessel near the point about which the vessel pivots in turning. Water passing through two openings in the tube acts to rotate a small rotator in the tube at a speed dependent upon the speed of the vessel through the water. The rotator's motion is transferred by spindle to a magneto in which a small current is thus generated. The voltage of this current is registered on voltmeters which are placed at points about the ship convenient to the navigator's use, and which are calibrated to read directly in knots. Rotation is also transferred to a small commutator which electrically operates the distance recorders located adjacent to the speed indicators. The bronze tube can be withdrawn into the ship for cleaning and repairs.

The calibration of this log to record the performance of particular vessels, according to the varying forms of stream lines beneath the hull, is accomplished by varying the selection of gear wheels which compose the respective trains by which the distance and speed recorders are actuated.

Revolution indicators which record the revolutions of the screw propeller afford in a steamer a valuable means of determining a vessel's speed through the water. The number of revolutions per knot must be carefully determined for the vessel by experiment under varying conditions of speed, draft, and foulness of bottom. Various instruments have been developed for indicating speed and distance from the propeller revolutions.

The **pitometer log** is designed to indicate accurately the speed of a vessel through the water and record the distance traveled. The speed element is based on the action of water pressure from a pitot tube causing a deflection of mercury in a U tube or manometer, which moves a dial graduated in knots. Distance traveled is totalized by a mechanical integrator and cam attached to the speed dial. Both speed and distance readings are reproduced by repeaters in various desired locations about the vessel (see fig. 5).

The **pitot tube** or rod meter (see figure) contains two small tubes, one terminating in a dynamic orifice which points forward, the other in a static orifice opening on both sides of a flat tip. The rod meter is supported by a sea cock, having an extension with a watertight gland, and projects about 3 feet below the bottom so that it reaches water unaffected by movement of the vessel at any speed. When the vessel moves through the water, the dynamic orifice receives a pressure which is greater than the comparatively constant pressure on the static orifice. The difference between the two pressures is a function of the vessel's speed and is independent of roll, pitch, or variation in draft. The water pressures from the rod meter are transmitted to the mercury manometer which is so calibrated as to indicate the vessel's speed in knots. Readings below about 5 knots are less accurate than for higher speeds.

DEPTH MEASUREMENT

The **lead** is a device, for ascertaining the depth of water, which consists essentially of a suitably marked line, having a lead attached to one of its ends. It is an invaluable aid to the navigator in shallow water particularly in thick or foggy weather, and is often of service when the vessel is out of sight of land.

Two leads are used for soundings, the **hand lead,** weighing from 7 to 14 pounds, with a line marked to about 25 fathoms, and the **deep-sea lead,** weighing from 30 to 100 pounds, the line being 100 fathoms or upward in length.

FIGURE 3.—Taffrail log.

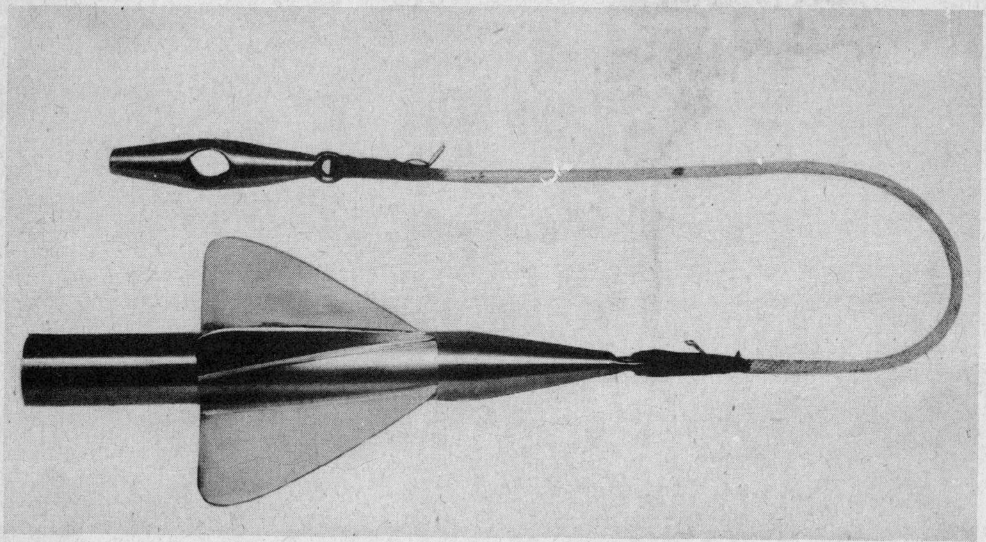

FIGURE 4.—Taffrail log rotator.

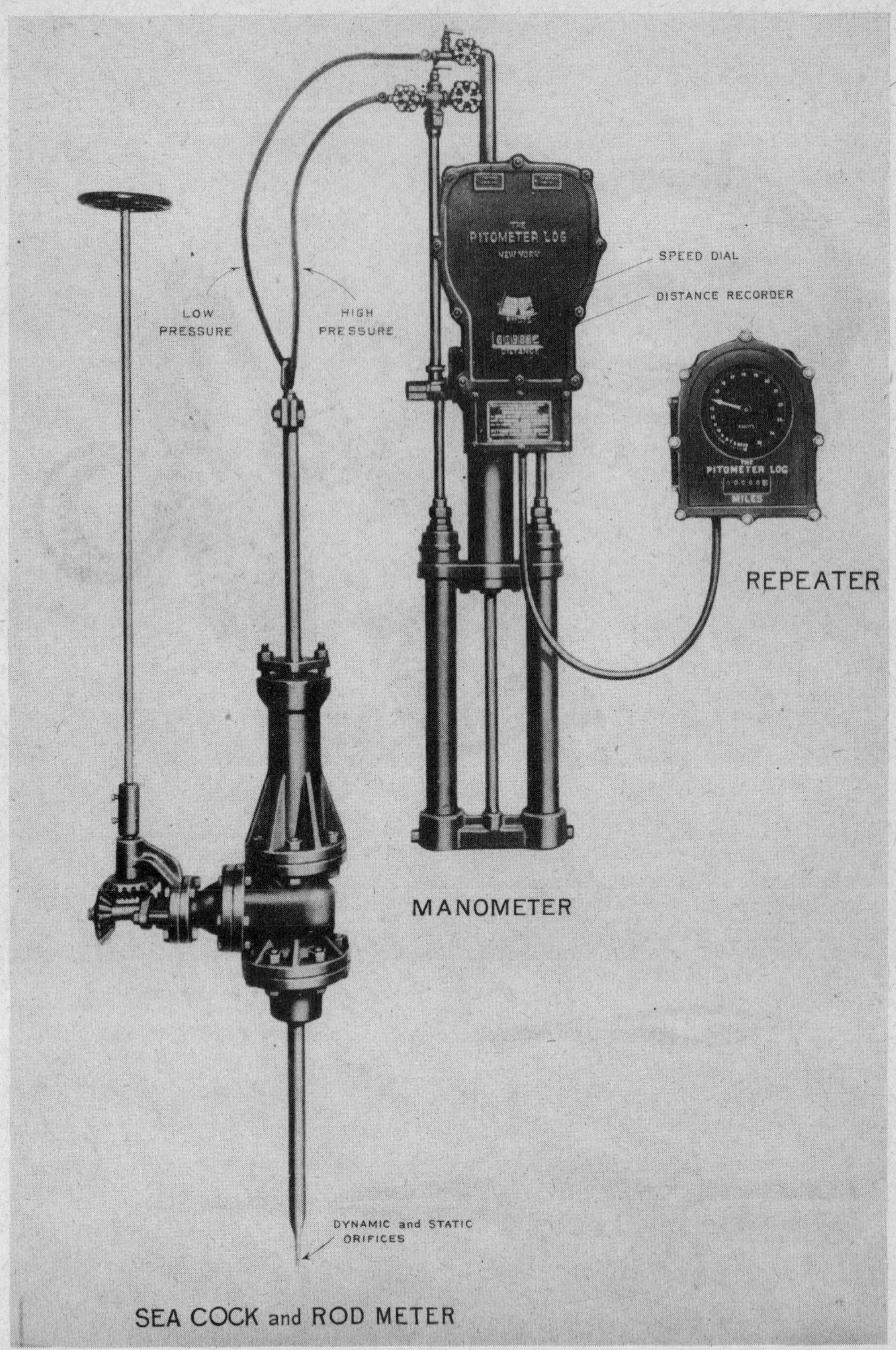

FIGURE 5.—Pitometer.

Lines are generally marked as follows:

2 fathoms from the lead, with 2 strips of leather.
3 fathoms from the lead, with 3 strips of leather.
5 fathoms from the lead, with white rag.
7 fathoms from the lead, with a red rag.
10 fathoms from the lead, with leather having a hole in it.
13 fathoms from the lead, same as at 3 fathoms.
15 fathoms from the lead, same as at 5 fathoms.
17 fathoms from the lead, same as at 7 fathoms.
20 fathoms from the lead, with 2 knots.
25 fathoms from the lead, with 1 knot.
30 fathoms from the lead, with 3 knots.
35 fathoms from the lead, with 1 knot.
40 fathoms from the lead, with 4 knots.
And so on.

Fathoms which correspond with the depths marked are called **marks;** the intermediate fathoms are called **deeps;** the only fractions of a fathom used are a half and a quarter.

A practice sometimes followed is to mark the hand-lead line in feet around the critical depths of the vessel by which it is to be used.

Lead lines should be measured frequently while wet and the correctness of the marking verified. The distance from the leadsman's hand to the water's edge should be ascertained in order that proper allowance may be made therefor in taking soundings at night.

The deep-sea lead may be **armed** by filling with tallow a hole hollowed out in its lower end, by which means a sample of the bottom is brought up.

The **sounding machine** has advantages over the deep-sea lead, for which it is a substitute, in that soundings may be obtained at great depths and with rapidity and accuracy without stopping the vessel. It consists essentially of a stand holding a reel upon which is wound the sounding wire, and which is controlled by a suitable brake. Crank handles or motors are provided for reeling in the wire after the sounding has been taken. Attached to the outer end of the wire is the lead, which has a cavity at its lower end for the reception of the tallow for arming. Above the lead is a cylindrical case containing the depth-registering mechanism; various devices are in use for this purpose, all depending, however, upon the increasing pressure of the water with increasing depths.

In the Lord Kelvin machine a slender glass tube is used, sealed at one end and open at the other, and coated inside with a chemical substance which changes color upon contact with sea water. This tube is placed, closed end up, in the metal cylinder; as it sinks the water rises in the tube, the contained air being compressed with a force dependent upon the depth. The limit of discoloration is marked by a clearly defined line, and the depth of the sounding corresponding to this line is read off from a scale. Tubes that have been used in comparatively shallow water may be used again where the water is known to be deeper.

A tube whose inner surface is ground has been substituted for the chemical-coated tube, ground glass, when wet, showing clear. The advantage of such a tube is that it may be used an indefinite number of times if thoroughly dried. To facilitate drying, a rubber cap is fitted to the upper end, which, when removed, admits circulation of the air through the tube.

As a substitute for the glass tubes a mechanical **depth recorder** contained in a suitable case has been used. In this device the pressure of the water acts upon a piston against the tension of a spring. A scale with an index pointer records the depth reached. The index pointer must be set at zero before each sounding.

Since the action of the sounding machine, when glass tubes are used, depends upon the compression of the air, the barometric pressure of the atmosphere must be taken into account when accurate results are required. The correction consists in *increasing* the indicated depth by a fractional amount according to the following table:

Bar. reading	Increase
"	
29. 75	One-fortieth.
30. 00	One-thirtieth.
30. 50	One-twentieth.
30. 75	One-fifteenth.

Sounding tubes at times are subject to certain defects, which, operating singly or in combination, may give wrong results. Salt deposits are sometimes found inside the ground glass tubes, causing moisture to creep up indicating larger readings. The bore is not always truly cylindrical. Chemical-coated tubes deteriorate with age and a true reading is difficult to make. Errors as much as 20 percent have been noted. Navigators approaching the 100-fathom curve sometimes feel secure when no bottom is obtained, but a leaky tube may indicate no bottom when the water has much less depth, resulting sometimes in disaster. Before beginning the soundings for a landfall it is advisable to stop the vessel for an up and down cast, in order to test the accuracy of the tubes under the prevailing conditions. It will not be necessary to get bottom, but run out 60 or 70 fathoms of wire, then read the tube for a check on the wire register.

The **sonic** and **supersonic depth finders.**—Each type varies considerably in detail but all are based on the discovery that a sound made under water will reflect from the ocean bottom an echo which can be received by a microphone. If the velocity of sound in water is known, and the interval of time between the generation of the sound and the receipt of the echo is measured, the depth can be determined by the formula, depth=velocity×one-half the time interval between sound and echo.

The velocity of sound in sea water varies with the temperature, salinity, and pressure, but an average value of 4,800 feet per second is sufficiently accurate for navigational depth finding. This velocity is 800 fathoms per second. An elapsed time of 1 second between sound and echo would therefore indicate a depth of 400 fathoms.

The essential parts of all echo sounding depth finders are an oscillator for producing sound under water, hydrophones for receiving the echo from the bottom, and a recorder or depth indicator with its necessary electrical attachments.

Sonic depth finders use a sound in the audible range. The sound may be made by a mechanical hammer striking the hull or by an oscillator built into the hull and driven by the reaction between an alternating current and a direct current field. The echo is received in a microphone and may be heard in ear phones or amplified and the energy used to operate a light or mechanical depth indicator.

Supersonic depth finders use a sound in the high pitch range above audibility. The sound emanates from a diaphragm in contact with the water. The diaphragm is vibrated by the contraction of quartz crystals in an electric circuit. The same diaphragm receives the echo, which is amplified and the energy used to operate a light to indicate depth. In some cases, a pencil also makes a graphic record of the depth.

The mechanism in general operates as follows: A constant speed motor rotates a shaft once a second. An arm on the shaft carries a contact maker and a light. The light travels in a circle just under a transparent scale divided into 400 divisions representing fathoms. As the light passes the zero reading, the contact closes and a signal is transmitted. The energy from the echo received flashes the light. The reading on the scale that is illuminated at that instant by the flash of light is the depth. For depths exceeding 400 fathoms, the number of revolutions the arm makes before the flash must be counted and the corresponding amount added to the reading. Readings are continuous and are sufficiently accurate in shoal or deep water without necessity of reducing the speed of the vessel.

THE MARINER'S COMPASS

The **mariner's compass** is an instrument consisting either of a single magnet, or, more usually, of a group of magnets, which, being attached to a graduated circle pivoted at the center and allowed to swing freely in a horizontal plane, has a tendency, when not affected by disturbing magnetic features within the ship, to lie with its magnetic axis in the plane of the earth's magnetic meridian, thus affording a means of determining the azimuth, or horizontal angular distance from that meridian, of the ship's course and of all visible objects, terrestrial or celestial.

The circular card of the compass is divided on its periphery into 360°. For sailing ships, it is sometimes numbered from 0° at North and South to 90° at East and West; or into 32 divisions of 11¼° each, called *points*, the latter being further divided into *half-points* and *quarter-points*. The system of numbering the degrees from 0° to 360°, always increasing toward the right, is shown in figure 7.

Compass points.—The four principal points are called *cardinal points* and are named North, South, East, and West; each differs in direction from the adjacent one by 90°, or 8 points. Midway between the cardinal points, at an angular distance of 45°, or 4 points, are the *inter-cardinal* points, named according to their position Northeast, Southeast, etc. Midway between each cardinal and inter-cardinal point, at an angular distance of 22½°, or 2 points, is a point whose name is made up of a combination of that of the cardinal with that of the inter-cardinal point: North-Northeast, East-Northeast, East-Southeast, etc. At an angular distance of 1 point, or 11¼°, from each cardinal and inter-cardinal point (and therefore midway between it and the 22½°-division last described) is a point which bears the name of that cardinal or inter-cardinal point joined by the word *by* to that of the cardinal point in the direction of which it lies: North by East, Northeast by North, Northeast by East, etc.

The names of the whole points, together with fractional points, are given in Table 2, which gives also the degrees, minutes, and seconds from North or South to which each division corresponds. The process of naming the points as indicated in this table is called **"boxing the compass."**

The compass card is mounted in a bowl which is carried in *gimbals*, thus enabling the card to retain a horizontal position while the ship is pitching and rolling. A vertical black line called the **lubber's line** is marked on the inner surface of the bowl. The compass is so mounted that a line joining its pivot with the lubber's line is parallel to the keel line of the vessel. Thus the lubber's line always indicates the compass direction of the ship's head by marking the position of the ship's head with reference to the compass card. It serves as a reading mark for the helmsman.

According to the purpose which it is designed to fulfill, a compass is designated as a *Standard*, *Steering*, or *Boat Compass*.

There are two types of magnetic compass in use, the *liquid* and the *dry;* in the former the bowl is filled with liquid, the card being thus partially buoyed with consequent increased ease of working on the pivot, and the liquid further serving to decrease the vibrations of the card when deflected by reason of the motion of the vessel or other cause. On account of its advantages the liquid compass is generally used.

The **Navy service 7½-inch liquid compass.**—This consists of a skeleton card 7½ inches in diameter, made of tinned brass, resting on a pivot in liquid, with provisions for two pairs of magnets symmetrically placed (see fig. 7).

The magnet system of the card consists of four cylindrical bundles of steel wires. These wires are magnetized as a bundle between the poles of a powerful electro-magnet. They are afterwards placed in a cylindrical case, sealed, and secured to the card. Steel wires made up into a bundle were adopted because they are more homogeneous, can be more perfectly tempered, and for the same weight give greater magnetic power than a solid steel bar.

Two of the magnets are placed parallel to the north and south diameter of the card, and on the chords of 15° (nearly) of a circle passing through their extremities. These magnets penetrate the air vessel, to which they are soldered, and are further secured to the bottom of the ring of the card. The other two magnets of the system are placed parallel to the longer magnets on the chords of 45° (nearly) of a circle passing through their extremities and are secured to the bottom of the ring of the card.

The card is of a curved annular type, the outer ring being convex on the upper and inner side, and is graduated to read to degrees, with legible figures at each 10°, for use in reading bearings by an azimuth circle or in laying the course to degrees.

The card is provided with a concentric spheroidal air vessel to buoy its own weight and that of the magnets, allowing a pressure of between 60 and 90 grains on the pivot at 60° F. The weight of the card in air is 3,060 grains. The air vessel has within it a hollow cone, open at its lower end, and provided with the pivot bearing or cap containing a sapphire. The sapphire rests upon a gunmetal pivot with an iridium cap, and thus supports the card. The cap is provided with adjusting screws for accurately centering the card. The pivot is fastened to the center of the bottom of the bowl by a flanged plate and screws. Through this plate and the bottom of the bowl are two small holes which communicate with the expansion chamber and admit of a circulation of the liquid between it and the bowl.

FIGURE 6.—Mariners illuminated pelorus.

The card is mounted in a bowl of cast bronze, the glass cover of which is closely packed with rubber, preventing the evaporation or leakage of the liquid, which entirely fills the bowl. This liquid is composed of 45 percent pure alcohol and 55 percent distilled water, and remains liquid below −10° F.

The lubber's line is a fine line drawn on an enameled plate on the inside of the bowl, the inner surface of the latter being covered with an insoluble white paint.

Beneath the bowl is a metallic self-adjusting expansion chamber of elastic metal, by means of which the bowl is kept constantly full without the show of bubbles or the development of undue pressure caused by the change in volume of the liquid due to changes of temperature. In some types, the expansion chamber has a glass bottom and a mica top so that light may be transmitted from bottom to top through the compass bowl, and the compass card thus be illuminated from below instead of from above.

The rim of the compass bowl is made rigid and its outer edge machined strictly to gauge so that an azimuth circle can be fitted snugly onto it.

The **dry compass.**—The Lord Kelvin compass, which may be regarded as one of the standard for the dry type, consists of a strong paper card with the central parts cut away and its outer edge stiffened by a thin aluminum ring. The pivot is fitted with an iridium point, upon which rests a small light aluminum boss fitted with a sapphire bearing. Radiating from this boss are 32 silk threads whose outer ends are made fast to the inner edge of the compass card; these threads sustain the weight of the suspended card, and as they possess some elasticity, tend to decrease the shocks due to motion.

Eight small magnetized steel wire needles, 3¼ to 2 inches long, are usually secured to two parallel silk threads, and are slung from the aluminum rim of the card by other silk threads which pass through eyes in the ends of the outer pair of needles. The needles are below the radial threads, thus keeping the center of gravity low.

The **azimuth circle.**—This is a necessary fitting for all compasses employed for taking bearings—that is, noting the directions—of either celestial or terrestrial objects. The instrument varies widely in its different forms; the essential features which all share consist in (*a*) a pair of sight vanes, or equivalent device, at the extremities of the diameter of a circle that revolves concentrically with the compass bowl, the line of sight thus always passing through the vertical axis of the compass; and (*b*) a system, usually of mirrors and prisms, by which the point of the compass card cut by the vertical plane through the line of sight—in other words, the compass direction—is brought into the field of view of the person making the observation. In some circles, for observing azimuths of the sun advantage is taken of the brightness of that body to reflect a pencil of light upon the card in such a manner as to indicate the bearings. (See figs. 6 and 8).

The azimuth circles should be tested occasionally for accuracy. This can best be done by mounting a standard compass on a tripod in a nonmagnetic spot on shore, in a locality where the variation has been accurately determined. The observed compass bearing of the sun should, of course, be the same as the computed magnetic bearing at any instant, the difference between the two, if any, being equal to the error of the compass or, what is more likely, the error of the azimuth circle. Any doubt in the matter may be removed by the use of two or more compasses. It will be frequently found that the error of the azimuth circle varies with the sun's altitude; this is due to the fact that the axis of the mirror is not normal to the plane passing through the sun, the five-sided prism, and the center of the mirror.

Binnacles.—Compasses are mounted for use in stands known as **Binnacles**, of which there are two principal types—the *Compensating* and the *Noncompensating Binnacle*, so designated according as they are or are not equipped with appliances by which the deviation of the compass, or error in its indications, due to disturbing magnetic features within the ship may be compensated.

Binnacles may be of wood or of some nonmagnetic metal. All contain a compass chamber within which the compass is suspended in its gimbal ring. The knife-edges upon which the gimbal ring is suspended rests in V-shaped bearings. An appropriate method is supplied for centering the compass. A hood is provided for the protection of the compass and for lighting it at night. Binnacles must be rigidly secured to the

FIGURE 7.—United States Navy compass.

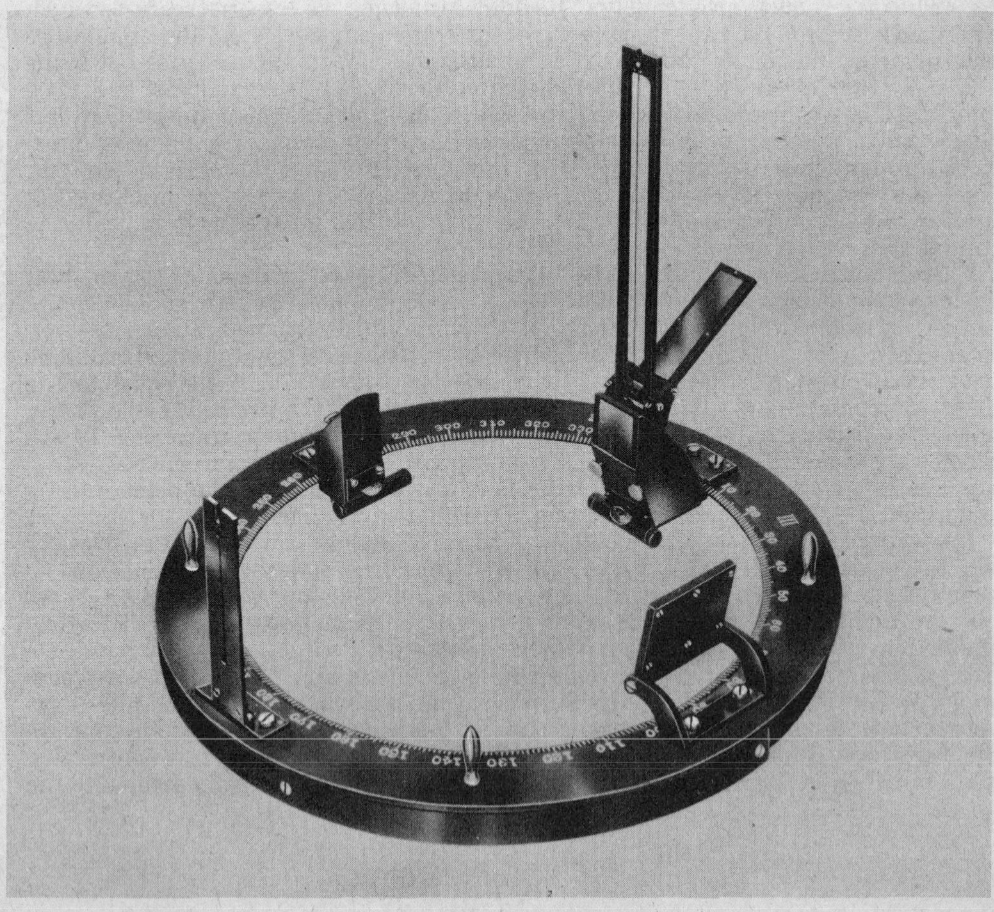

FIGURE 8.—Azimuth circle

deck of the vessel in such position that the lubber's line of the compass gives true indications of the direction of the vessel's head.

The position of the various binnacles on shipboard and the height at which they carry the compass must be chosen with regard to the purpose which the compass is to serve, having in mind the magnetic conditions of the ship.

Compensating binnacles contain the appliances for carrying the various correctors used in the compensation of the deviation of the compass. These consist of (*a*) a system of permanent magnets for semicircular deviation, placed in a magnetic chamber lying immediately beneath the compass chamber, so arranged as to permit variation in the height and number of the magnets employed; (*b*) a pair of arms projecting horizontally from the compass chamber and supporting masses of soft iron for quadrantal deviation; (*c*) a central tube in the vertical axis of the binnacle for a permanent magnet used to correct the heeling error; and (*d*) an attachment, sometimes fitted, for securing a vertical soft-iron rod, or **"Flinders bar,"** used in certain cases for correction of a part of the semicircular deviation. An explanation of the various terms here used, together with the method of compensating the compass, will be given in chapter III.

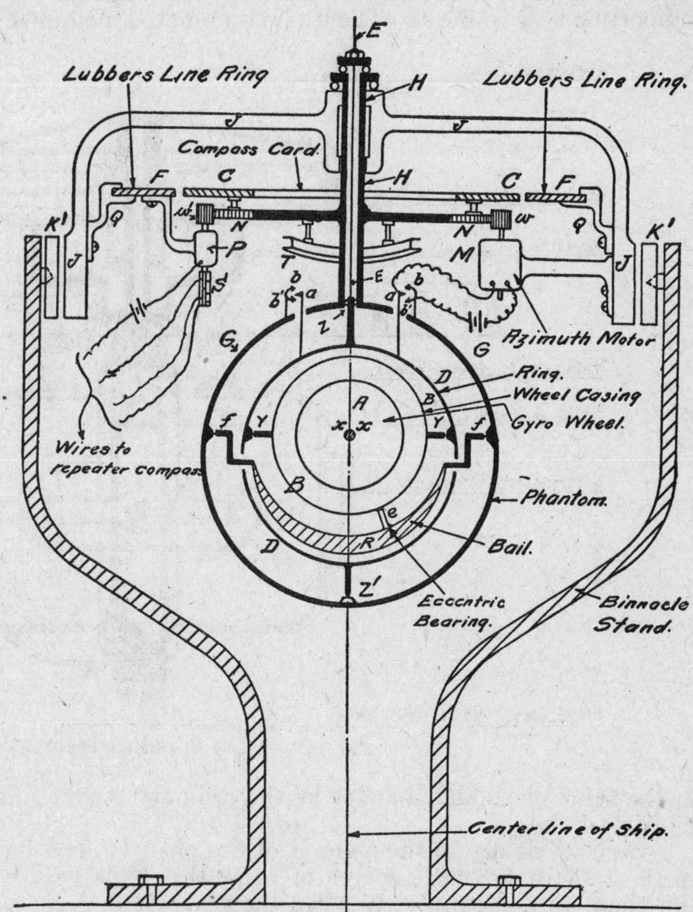

FIGURE 10.

The gyrocompass.—This compass utilizes the principle of the gyroscope to indicate the true north. It consists essentially of a rapidly spinning rotor, usually driven by a three-phase alternating current of electricity, at a rate varying according to the type, from 6,000 to 21,000 revolutions per minute, and so suspended that it automatically places its axis approximately in the direction of the geographical meridian and permits of the reading of the heading of the ship, unaffected by any magnetic influence, from a graduated compass card like that in use on magnetic compasses. From the "master compass," which may be located in a compartment below, electrical connections are made to "repeating compasses" on the bridge, in the conning tower, or in the steering-engine room, so that the ship's true heading may be transmitted to any desired part of the vessel. (See fig. 12.)

The action of the gyrocompass, affected as it is by the earth's rotation under it, conforms to Foucault's general law that "a spinning body tends to swing around so as to place its axis parallel to the axis of any impressed forces, and so that its direction of rotation is the same as that of the impressed forces." By means of a suitable damping device, the axis of the gyrocompass is caused to settle on or very

541524 O - 43 - 3

close to the true meridian. Small corrections, depending upon the latitude, course, and speed are introduced automatically or by hand.

The construction of one of the standard types of this compass is shown in the accompanying illustration, figure 10. The gyroscope wheel A is mounted to spin on a horizontal axis, *xx*, within the casing B, which is pivoted on the horizontal axis YY through its center of gravity and carried by the frame or vertical ring D. The ring D is suspended by the tortionless strand E and guided by bearings ZZ′ to allow a free oscillation of limited amount about its vertical axis ZZ′ within the frame or phantom G.

The phantom G has a hollow stem H to which the strand E is attached at its upper end, and the stem forms a journal for rotation in azimuth with respect to the supporting base frame J. The frame is mounted in gimbal rings K′K′ on the binnacle

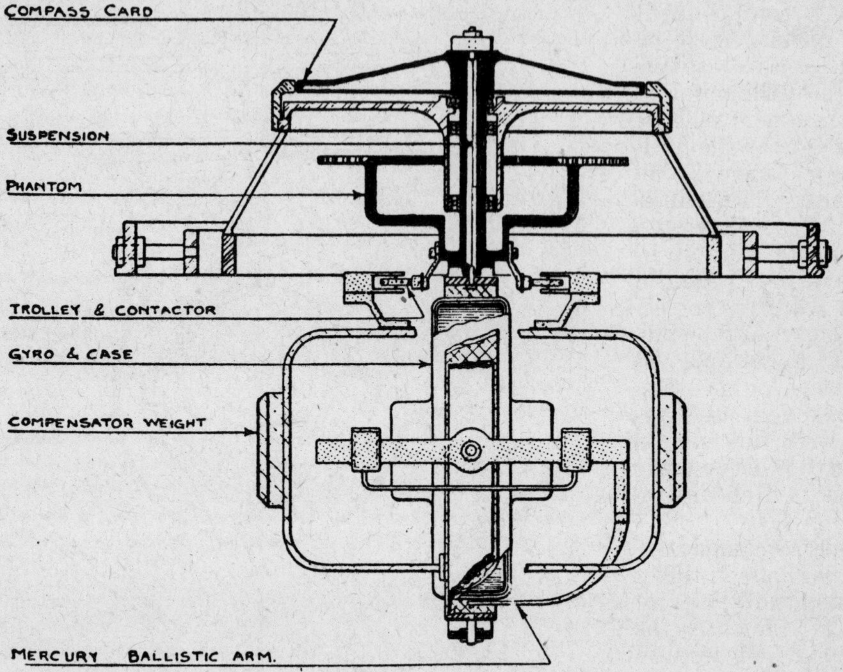

FIGURE 11.—Master compass, east elevation.

in the same or similar manner as the ordinary magnetic compass is mounted in its binnacle stand.

Secured rigidly to the stem H of the phantom is a large wheel, NN, having 360 teeth, 1 tooth for each degree of azimuth. This gear wheel can only move with the phantom and conversely when the gear wheel, NN, is moved the phantom must move.

Rigidly secured to the frame J, and thus fixed relatively to the ship is a motor, M, whose small spur wheel *w* engages with the teeth of NN. Mounted rigidly on NN is the compass card CC graduated to 360°. Flush with the surface of the compass card is a flat ring, FF, on which is engraved the lubber's line. FF is supported by brackets, QQ, on the frame J. Rigidly secured to the lubber's ring FF is a transmitter P whose function is to transmit electrically to the repeater compass at the helmsman, or to the pelorus repeaters, any movement made by the compass card CC.

The wheel A together with the wheel casing B and the ring D is called the sensitive element. As a matter of fact, and most important, the sensitive element is the real gyroscopic compass, and all the other mechanism is installed simply to reproduce the exact movement, headings, or readings of the sensitive element in azimuth without interfering with it. Attached to the sensitive element, on the vertical posts, *a*, *a*, as shown, are two electrical trolley contacts, *a*, *a*, which make a light electrical contact with double stationary contacts *bb′*, *bb′*, carried by the phantom. The object of this mechanism is to make the phantom carrying the compass card follow exactly every movement in azimuth of the axis of gyro wheel and thus register in degrees either the heading (course) of the ship or the direction in which the gyro axis, *xx*, is pointing relative to the meridian. Furthermore, this movement, by means of the repeating transmitter, P, is sent to every steering compass, bridge pelorus, and repeater compass in the ship. This work is performed without any interference with the freedom of action of the sensitive element except that of the very light touch of the electrical contacts *aa* and *bb′ bb′*.

In order to introduce the horizontal couple necessary to suppress the oscillations in azimuth which would otherwise constantly attend the operation of this mechanism, the pivot *e*, connecting the heavy bail R to the rotor casing B, is placed slightly eccentrically, at a distance from the vertical axis of the rotor of about one-eighth inch. As the bail is pivoted at the points *ff*, which are above its center of gravity, its natural tendency is to hang vertically downwards. There are slots in D which allow B to do this. The tendency of the rotor A to keep its position in space as the earth rotates under it causes the axis *xx* to tilt and the bail to be raised from its normal position, and the eccentricity of the pin *e*, by which the bail is raised, causes the gravity couple on B to have a horizontal component. This component provides the necessary vertical precession to produce a spiral motion of the axis by which it reaches its rest point. This point is always to the east of north by a small amount which varies as the tangent of the geographical latitude, and it has a slight altitude from the horizon, excepting when the instrument is located on the equator. This error, together with that arising through the speed and course of the ship, is semiautomatically allowed for; and the errors produced by rolling and pitching are also mechanically corrected by the application of stabilizing gyroscopes and counterweights.

The bail R has been successfully replaced by pivoting on the same bearing, *ff*, a ballistic consisting of mercury contained in a pair of iron boxes joined by a steel pipe (fig. 11). These are connected to the gyro case by an arm and roller engaging in the same manner as the upper part of the pivot, *e*.

The mercury in the containers fills them to a level that is in the same horizontal plane as the center of the gyro spinning axle. Secured to the containers, but above the spinning axle, are compensating weights to counteract the weight of the mercury, containers, and pipe below the spinning axle. Consequently, when the spinning axle is parallel to the horizon the entire system is nonpendulous and in a state of equilibrium.

Each of the three chambers into which each box is subdivided communicates by a valve to the steel connecting pipe, so that one, two, or three chambers may be put into action according to the requirements arising from change of latitude. By means of this adjustment in the distribution of the weight of the mercury content in the containers and the pipe joining them, the ballistic deflection can be made practically correct in any latitude, instead of being deficient or excessive in all latitudes except the one for which the design is originally made.

Gyrocompass advantages.—The Gyrocompass seeks the true meridian, hence all bearings, and courses shown by it are *true*. No variation or deviation is applied, as this compass does not depend on the earth's magnetic field for its directive force, nor is it affected by the magnetism of the ship. Its directive force is much stronger than that of the magnetic compass, but this strength which is greatest at the equator, decreases with an increase in latitude until at the pole it becomes zero.

Disadvantages.—Its mechanism is delicate and complicated, hence gets out of order, requiring expert attention. It needs a constant source of electrical power. The magnetic compass of the ship must be ready at all times to be used in case the gyro is not in operating condition.

Gyro pilot.—By being employed to actuate a contact maker, which would cause the rudder to respond instantly to slight variations of the vessel's head from the prescribed course, the gyrocompass has lent itself to the production of the gyro pilot for mechanical steering, and likewise to the mechanical recording of the course pursued.

The **pelorus.**—This instrument consists of a circular flat metallic ring, mounted in gimbals, upon a vertical standard at some point on board ship affording a clear view for taking bearings. The inner edge of this ring is engraved in degrees—the 360° and the 180° marks indicating a fore-and-aft line parallel to the keel of the ship.

FIGURE 12.—Gyrocompass.

Within this ring a ground-glass dial is pivoted concentrically. This ground-glass dial has painted upon it a compass rose divided into points and subdivisions and into 360°. This dial is capable of revolution, but may be clamped to the outside ring. Pivoted concentrically with the flat ring and the glass dial is a horizontal bar carrying at both of its extremes a sight vane, or, mounted upon the bar and parallel to it, a telescope containing cross wires. This sight-vane bar can be clamped in any position independently of the ground-glass dial, which can be moved freely beneath it. An indicator showing the direction the sight-vane bar points can be read upon the compass card on the glass dial.

The pelorus is used for taking bearings of distant objects, and, at times, may be more convenient than the standard compass for that purpose because of the better view commanded by its position, and because it may be made to eliminate compass errors from observed bearings, thus reducing the bearings observed to magnetic or true bearings. If the glass dial be revolved until the degree of demarcation, which is coincident with the right-ahead marking on the flat ring, is the same as that which points to the lubber's line of the standard compass, then all directions indicated by the glass will be parallel to the corresponding directions of the standard compass, and all bearings taken by the pelorus will be identical with those taken by the compass (leaving out of the question the difference due to the distance which separates them). If it is known that the ship's compass has a certain error due to deviation of the compass and if the glass dial be set to allow for this deviation, then all bearings read from the pelorus will be magnetic. If the dial be set allowing for both deviation and variation of the compass, then all bearings read will be true. It should be noted, however, that the bearings taken by pelorus will be accurate only when the vessel is on her exact course by standard compass. For this reason it is usual to take a bearing by pelorus, at the same time noting the heading by standard compass, and clamping the sight vane; then, moving the glass dial until the direction opposite the dead-ahead mark is the same as that noted by the standard compass, the bearing observed (corrected for the variation and for the deviation of the heading at the instant of observation) will be the true bearing.

The pelorus described above is fitted for illuminating the glass dial from below in order to facilitate night work.

Peloruses whose dials are controlled by a master gyroscopic compass of course indicate at once the true bearing of the object observed. The repeating compasses that are provided with gyro compasses and which may be placed in advantageous positions for a clear view, have rendered the pelorus of much less use. These compasses are arranged in such a way that when the compass is not operating the card may be turned by hand and used like a pelorus.

When fitted with a telescope the pelorus may be used to take the azimuth of stars.

The standard compass is usually located in the ship in the central fore-and-aft line which is established from the builders' marks placed in that vicinity. The standard compass being located, all peloruses may be oriented from it by any one of the following methods:

(*a*) By making the azimuth of a celestial body, taken by the pelorus, coincide with the simultaneous azimuth of the same body taken by the standard compass.

(*b*) By a similar process with distant objects; and the parallax may be entirely eliminated in an apparently near object, in view of the moderate distance that usually separates the two instruments on board ship.

(*c*) By reciprocal bearings between the correct instrument and the instrument to be established; it is evident that if the lubber lines of the two instruments are both in the direction of the keel line, the bearing of the sight vane of each from the other (one being reversed) should coincide.

(*d*) By computing the angle subtended at the pelorus by the fore-and-aft line through the pelorus and the line drawn through the pelorus to the jack staff, and setting the pelorus at this angle and sighting on the jack staff.

MANEUVERING BOARD

The **maneuvering board** is a form of plotting sheet issued by the Hydrographic Office to assist in readily solving problems arising in steering a ship to its anchorage, or problems of relative movement between ships or planes, etc. It can be affixed to a portable drawing board on the bridge of a ship so as to be convenient to the officer directing the movements of the ship.

The board is a plotting sheet consisting of 10 concentric circles spaced 1 inch apart. The outer circle is a full line and is graduated clockwise from 0° to 360°, each 10° reading being indicated in bold-faced type. Inside the circle in small type are the reciprocal readings. The inner circle is also a full line. The eight other circles are dotted lines, each dot representing 1° of arc. Dotted radial lines are drawn at each 10° of arc. At the intersection of the horizontal and vertical lines with the concentric circles the circles are numbered from 1 to 10. The dots of the radial lines further divide each space into 10 equal parts.

The following scales are printed on the board so that suitable speed and distance scales for any problem may be used: Scales—2:1, 3:1, 4:1, 5:1, a logarithmic scale, and a nomogram for quick solution of time, speed, and distance problems.

Various adaptations of the maneuvering board, with the circular part pivoted, with a ruler pivoted at the center, inner and outer scales, etc., are devised for graphical solution of plane triangles, and are called tactical boards or plotting boards.

The H. O. issues publication No. 217, Maneuvering Board Manual, illustrating the ready solution of 28 cases of tactical problems.

THE NAVIGATOR'S CHART

A **nautical chart** is a miniature representation upon a plane surface, in accordance with a definite system of projection or development, of a portion of the navigable waters of the world. It generally includes the outline of the adjacent land, together with the surface forms and artificial features that are useful as aids to navigation, and sets forth the depths of water, especially in the near approaches to the land, by soundings that are fixed in position by accurate determinations. Except in charts of harbors or other localities so limited that the curvature of the earth is inappreciable on the scale of construction, a nautical chart is always framed over with a network of parallels of latitude and meridians of longitude in relation to which the features to be depicted on the chart are located and drawn; and the mathematical relation between the meridians and parallels of the chart and those of the terrestrial sphere determines the method of measurement that is to be employed on the chart and the special uses to which it is adapted.

Chart making presents the problem of representing the surface of a sphere upon a plane surface. The surface of a sphere is said to be undevelopable because no part of the surface can be spread out on a plane without some tearing or stretching. This can be readily seen by attempting to flatten out a section of a hollow rubber ball. The surface of a cone or cylinder, however, can be spread upon a plane or is developable. To make charts upon which the contours of the objects on the earth's surface maintain true relations, the surface of the sphere is projected upon the surface of cylinders, cones, or planes, which are then developed upon the plane or chart. Each system of projection has certain features which make it preferable for certain uses.

There are four principal systems of chart projection in use: (*a*) the **Mercator,** (*b*) the **polyconic,** (*c*) the **gnomonic,** and (*d*) the **Lambert.** Of these the Mercator is by far the most generally used for purposes of navigation proper, while the other three types have special purposes such as: plotting original surveys, facilitating great-circle sailing, plotting radio bearings, and for aviation purposes.

The **Mercator projection.**—This projection is similar in design to those that are developed geometrically upon a plane surface of a cylinder which is tangent to the earth at the equator, but it differs from a true geometric projection in that all points of this projection are computed and it has a scale varying as the secant of the latitude, the *rhumb line* or *loxodromic curve* (Chap. I) appears as a right line preserving the same angle of bearing with respect to the intersected meridians as does the vessel's track.

In order to realize this condition, the line of tangency, which coincides with the earth's equator, being the circumference of a right section of the cylinder, will appear as a right line on the development, while the series of elements of the cylinder corresponding to the projected terrestrial meridians will appear as equidistant right lines, parallel to each other and perpendicular to the equator of the chart, maintaining the same relative positions and the same distance apart on the equator as the meridians have on the terrestrial spheroid. The series of terrestrial parallels will also appear as a system of right lines parallel to each other and to the equator, and will so intersect the meridians as to form a system of rectangles whose altitudes, for successive intervals of latitude, must be variable, increasing from the equator in such manner that the angles made by the rhumb line with the meridian on the chart may maintain the required equality with the corresponding angles on the spheroid.

Meridional parts.—At the equator a degree of longitude is equal to a degree of latitude, but in receding from the equator and approaching the pole, while the degrees of latitude remain always of the same length (save for a slight change due to the fact that the earth is not a perfect sphere), the degrees of longitude become less and less, thus the degree of longitude at 70° north is about 20 nautical miles.

Since, in the Mercator projection, the degrees of longitude are made to appear everywhere of the same length, it becomes necessary, in order to preserve the proportion that exists at different parts of the earth's surface between degrees of latitude and degrees of longitude, that the former be increased from their natural lengths, and such increase must become greater and greater the higher the latitude.

The length of the meridian, as thus increased between the equator and any given latitude, expressed in minutes at the equator as a unit, constitutes the number of **meridional parts** corresponding to that latitude. The Table of Meridional Parts or Increased Latitudes (Table 5), computed for every minute of latitude between 0° and 80°, affords facilities for constructing charts on the Mercator projection and for solving problems in Mercator sailing.

Mercator chart construction.—If the chart for which a projection is to be made includes the equator, the values to be measured off are given directly by Table 5. If the equator does not come upon the chart, then the parallels of latitude to be laid down should be referred to a *principal parallel*, preferably the lowest parallel to be drawn on the chart. The distance of any other parallel of latitude from the principal parallel is then the difference of the values for the two taken from Table 5.

The values so found may either be measured off, without previous numerical conversion, by means of a diagonal scale constructed on the chart, or they may be laid down on the chart by means of any properly divided scale of yards, meters, feet, or miles, after having been reduced to the scale of proportions adopted for the chart.

If, for example, it be required to construct a chart on a scale of one-quarter of an inch to 5 minutes of arc on the equator, a diagonal scale may first be constructed, on which 10 meridional parts, or 10 minutes of arc on the equator, have a length of half an inch.

It may often be desirable to adapt the scale to a certain allotment of paper. In this case, the lowest and the highest parallels of latitude may first be drawn on the sheet on which the transfer is to be made. The distance between these parallels may then be measured, and the number of meridional parts between them ascertained. Dividing the distance by this number will then give the length of one meridional part, or the quantity by which *all* the meridional parts taken from Table 5 must be multiplied. This quantity will represent the *scale of the chart*. If it occurs that the limits of longitude are a governing consideration, the case may be similarly treated.

Example.—Let a projection be required for a chart of 14° extent in longitude between the parallels of latitude 20°30′N. and 30°25′N., and let the space allowable on the paper between these parallels measure 10 inches.

Entering the column in Table 5 headed 20°, and running down to the line marked 30′ in the side column, will be found 1248.9; then, entering the column 30°, and running down to the line 25′ will be found 1905.5. The difference, or 1905.5−1248.9=656.6, is the value of the meridional arc between these latitudes, for which 1′ of arc of the equator is taken as the unit. On the intended projection, therefore, 1′ of arc of longitude will measure $\frac{10^{\text{in.}}}{656.60}=.0152$ inch, which will be the scale of the chart. For the sake of brevity call it 0.015. By this quantity all the values derived from Table 5 will have to be multiplied before laying them down on the projection, if they are to be measured on a diagonal scale of 1 inch.

Draw in the center of the sheet a straight line, and assume it to be the middle meridian of the chart. Construct very carefully on this line a perpendicular near the lower border of the sheet, and assume this perpendicular to be the parallel of latitude 20°30′; this will be the southern inner neat line of the chart From the intersection of the lines lay off on the parallel, on each side of the middle meridian, 7° of longitude, or distances each equal to 0.015×60×7=6.3 inches; and through the points thus obtained draw lines parallel to the middle meridian, and these will be the eastern and western neat lines of the chart.

In order to construct the parallel of latitude for 21°00′, find in Table 5, the meridional parts for 21°00′, which are 1280.8. Subtracting from this number the number for 20°30′, and multiplying the difference by 0.015, we obtain 0.478 inch, which is the distance on the chart between 20°30′ and 21°00′. On the meridians lay off distances equal to 0.478 inch, and through the three points thus obtained draw a straight line, which will be the parallel of 21°00′.

Proceed in the same manner to lay down all the parallels answering to full degrees of latitude; the distances will be respectively:

$0^{in}.015 \times (1344.9 - 1248.9) = 1.440$ inches.
$0^{in}.015 \times (1409.5 - 1248.9) = 2.409$ inches.
$0^{in}.015 \times (1474.5 - 1248.9) = 3.384$ inches, etc.

Thus will be shown the parallels of latitude 22°00′, 23°00′, 24°00′, etc. Finally, lay down in the same way the parallel of latitude 30°25′, which will be the northern inner neat line of the chart. (For south latitude reverse the procedure.)

A degree of longitude will measure on this chart $0^{in}.015 \times 60 = 0^{in}.9$. Lay off, therefore, on the lowest parallel of latitude drawn on the chart, on a middle one, and on the highest parallel, measuring from the middle meridian toward each side, the distances of $0^{in}.9$, $1^{in}.8$, $2^{in}.7$, $3^{in}.6$, etc., in order to determine the points where meridians answering to full degrees cross the parallels drawn on the chart. Through the points thus found draw the meridians. Draw then the outer neat lines of the chart at a convenient distance outside of the inner neat lines, and extend to them the meridians and parallels. Between the inner and outer neat lines of the chart subdivide the degrees of latitude and longitude as minutely as the scale of the chart will permit, the subdivision of the degrees of longitude being found by dividing the degrees into equal parts, and the subdivisions of the degrees of latitude being accurately found in the same manner as the full degrees of latitude previously described, though it will generally be found sufficiently exact to make even subdivisions of the degrees, as in the case of the longitude.

The subdivisions between the two eastern as well as those between the two western neat lines will serve for measuring or estimating terrestrial distances. Distances between points bearing north and south of each other may be ascertained by referring them to the subdivisions between the same parallels. Distances represented by lines at an angle to the meridians (loxodromic lines) may be measured by taking between the dividers a small number of the subdivisions near the middle latitude of the line to be measured, and stepping them off on that line. If, for instance, the terrestrial length of a line running at an angle to the meridians between the parallels of latitude of 24°00′ and 29°00′ be required, the distance shown on the neat space between 26°15′ and 26°45′ (=30 nautical miles) may be taken between the dividers and stepped off on that line.

Coast lines and other positions are plotted on the chart by their latitude and longitude. A chart may be transferred from any other projection to that of Mercator by drawing a system of corresponding parallels and meridians over both charts so close to each other as to form minute squares, and then the lines and characters contained in each square of the map to be transferred may be copied by the eye in the corresponding squares of the Mercator projection.

Since the unit of measure, the mile or minute of latitude, has a different value in every latitude, there is an appearance of distortion in a Mercator chart that covers any large extent of surface; for instance, an island near the pole will be represented as being much larger than one of the same size near the equator, due to the progressive magnification necessary to preserve the character of the projection.

The **polyconic projection.**—This projection is based upon the development of the earth's surface on a series of cones, a different one for each parallel of latitude, each one having the parallel as its base, and its vertex in the point where a tangent to the earth at that latitude intersects the earth's axis produced. The degrees of latitude and longitude on this chart are projected in their true length, and the general distortion of the figure is less than in any other method of projection, the relative magnitudes being closely preserved.

A straight line on the polyconic chart represents a near approach to a great circle, making a slightly different angle with each successive meridian as the meridians converge toward the pole and are theoretically curved lines; but it is only on charts of large extent that this curvature is apparent. The parallels are also curved, this fact being apparent to the eye upon all excepting the largest scale charts.

This method of projection is especially adapted to the plotting of original surveys.

Gnomonic projection.—This is based upon a system in which the plane of projection is tangent to the earth at some given point. The eye of the observer is situated at the center of the sphere, where, being at once in the plane of every great circle, it will see all such circles projected as straight lines where the visual rays passing through them intersect the plane of projection. In a gnomonic chart the straight line between any two points represents the arc of a great circle, and is therefore the shortest line between those points. Gnomonic charts are mostly used to afford a ready means of finding the course and distance at any time in great circle sailing. They are not used for general navigation purposes except in the polar regions, for which latitudes a Mercator chart cannot be readily constructed.

When the plane of projection is tangent at the pole the chart is called a **polar chart,** upon which the meridians appear as straight lines radiating symmetrically from the pole, and the parallels appear as concentric circles whose center is the pole.

Lambert projection.—This is based upon the development of the earth's surface on the surface of a cone which intersects the spheroid at two parallels, which are called the standard parallels for the area represented. On the two selected parallels, arcs of longitude are represented in their true lengths, or to exact scale. Between these standard parallels the scale will be too small and beyond them too large, but for charts of average small areas the percentage of error is negligible. All meridians are straight lines which meet in a common point beyond the limits of the chart. The parallels are concentric circles whose center is at the point of intersection of the meridians. Meridians and parallels intersect at right angles, and the angles formed by any two lines on the earth's surface are correctly represented on this projection.

The projection is called a *conformal* projection or development, because of the property that all small or elementary figures found or drawn upon the surface of the earth retain their original forms upon the projection.

Great circle courses on this chart intersect each meridian at a different angle but as laid on the chart they are practically a straight line. This feature has made the Lambert projection well suited for aviation charts.

Greenwich meridian.—The nautical charts published by the United States and by most foreign governments use the meridian which passes through the observatory at Greenwich, England, as a base or origin for longitude. Other meridians used in addition by other countries are: The meridian of Pulkowa Observatory in longitude 30°19′40″ east of Greenwich, by the U. S. S. R.; the meridian of the Observatory of Paris in longitude 2°20′14.6″ east of Greenwich, by France; the meridian of the Observatory of Lisbon Castle in longitude 9°07′54.86″ west of Greenwich, by Portugal; and the meridian of San Fernando Observatory of Cadiz in longitude 6°12′20″ west of Greenwich, by Spain, in some of the older charts.

Bottom characteristics.—The following table shows the qualities of the bottom, as expressed on charts of various nations:

United States	English and Japanese	French	Italian	Spanish	German
Clay------Cl.	Clay------Cy. or cl.	Argile------Arg.	Argila------arg.	Arcillo or Barro-Arc.	Lehm------L.
Coral------Co.	Coral----Co. or crl.	Corail------Cor.	Casájo------Co.	Coral------Cl.	Korallen------Kor.
Gravel------G.	Gravel------G. or g.	Gravier------Gr.	Rena or Ghiaja-gh.	Casájo------Co.	Kies------K.
Mud------M.	Mud------M. or m.	Vase- ------V.	Fango------f.	Fango or Luno---F.	Schlamm------Schl.
Rocky------rky.	Rock------R. or rk.	Roche------R.	Roccia------r.	Piedra or Roca--P.	Felsig------fls.
Sand------S.	Sand------S. or s.	Sable------S.	Sábbia or Aréna-s.	Arena------A.	Sand------Sd.
Shells------Sh.	Shells------Sh. or sh.	Coquille---Coq.	Conchiglia------c.	Conchuela------Ca.	Muscheln------M.
Stones------St.	Stones------St. or st.	Pierre------Pi.	Pietre------p.	Piedra------P.	Steine------St.
Weed------Wd.	Weed---Wd. or wd.	Herbe------H.	Alga------alg.	Alga------Alg.	Gras------Grs.
Fine------fne.	Fine------f.	Fin------fin.	Fino------fin.	Fina------f.	Fein------f.
Coarse------crs.	Coarse------c.	Gros------g.	Grosso------gr.	Gruesa------g.	Grob------gb.
Stiff------stf.	Stiff------st. or stf.	Dure------d.	Tenace------	Tenaz------	Schlick------Sk.
Soft------sft.	Soft------so. or sft.	Molle------m.	Molle------ml.	Blando------bdo.	Weich------wch.
Black------bk.	Black-----bl. or blk.	Noir------n.	Nero------ner.	Negro------n.	Schwarz------s.
Red------rd.	Red------rd.	Rouge------r.	Rosse------	Rojo------r.	Rot------r.
Yellow------yl.	Yellow------y.	Jaune------j.	Giallo------gl.	Amarillo------amo.	Gelb------g.
Gray------gy.	Gray------gy.				

Depth measures.—The following table shows the units of measure employed in expressing the soundings on modern nautical charts of foreign nations together with their equivalent unit of measure used on the charts published by the United States:

Nationality of chart	Unit of soundings	Equivalent in United States units		Nationality of chart	Unit of soundings	Equivalent in United States units	
		Feet	Fathoms			Feet	Fathoms
Argentine	Braza	6. 000	1. 000	Japanese	Metre	3. 281	0. 547
Belgian	Metre	3. 281	. 547	Norwegian	Metre	3. 281	. 547
British	Fathom	6. 000	1. 000		or favn	6. 176	1. 029
Chilean	Metro	3. 281	. 547	Portuguese	Metro	3. 281	. 547
Danish	favn	6. 176	1. 029	Russian	Sajene	6. 000	1. 000
	or Metre	3. 281	. 547		or Metre	3. 281	. 547
Dutch	vadem	5. 905	. 984	Spanish	Metro	3. 281	. 547
	or metre	3. 281	. 547	Swedish	Metre	3. 281	. 547
French	Metre	3. 281	. 547		or famn	5. 844	. 974
German	Metre	3. 281	. 547	Yugoslav	Metre	3. 281	. 547
Italian	Metre	3. 281	. 547				

THE BAROMETER

The **barometer** is an instrument for measuring the pressure of the atmosphere, and is of great service to the mariner in affording a knowledge of existing meteorological conditions and of the probable changes therein. There are two classes of barometer—**mercurial** and **aneroid.**

Barometric pressure is measured in inches, or by the centimeter-gram-second unit of pressure, which is the dyne per square centimeter. This unit is so small, that a practical unit one million times larger, called a BAR, is substituted. The bar is equivalent to one thousand millibars.

A millibar is equal to the pressure of 1,000 dynes per square centimeter. The average pressure at sea level is 760 m. m., or 1,013 millibars, or 29.91 inches.

The **mercurial barometer.**—This instrument, invented by Torricelli in 1643, indicates the pressure of the atmosphere by the height of a column of mercury.

If a glass tube of uniform internal diameter somewhat more than 30 inches in length and closed at one end be completely filled with pure mercury, and then placed, open end down, in a cup of mercury (the open end having been temporarily sealed to retain the liquid during the process of inverting), it will be found that the mercury in the tube will fall until the top of the column is about 30 inches above the level of that which is in the cup, leaving in the upper part of the tube a vacuum. Since the weight of the column of mercury thus left standing in the tube is equal to the pressure by which it is held in position—namely, that of the atmospheric air—it follows that the height of the column is subject to variation upon variation of that pressure; hence the mercury falls as the pressure of the atmosphere decreases and rises as that pressure increases. The mean pressure of the atmosphere is roughly 15 pounds to the square inch; the mean height of the barometer is about 30 inches.

In the practical construction of the barometer the glass tube which contains the mercury is encased in a brass tube, the latter terminating at the top in a ring to be used for suspension, and at the bottom in a flange, to which the several parts forming the cistern are attached. The upper part of the brass tube is partially cut away to expose the mercurial column for observation; abreast this opening is fitted a scale for measuring the height, and along the scale travels a *vernier* for exact reading; the motion of the vernier is controlled by a rack and pinion, the latter having a milled head accessible to the observer, by which the adjustment is made. In the middle of the brass tube is fixed a thermometer, the bulb of which is covered from the outside but open toward the mercury, and which, being nearly in contact with the glass tube, indicates the temperature of the mercury and not that of the external air. The central position of the column is selected in order that the mean temperature may be obtained—a matter of importance, as the temperature of the mercurial column must be taken into account in every accurate application of its reading.

In the arrangement of further details mercurial barometers are divided into two classes, according as they are to be used, as **standards** (fig. 14) on shore, or as **sea barometers** (fig. 13) on shipboard.

In the standard barometer the scale and vernier are so graduated as to enable an observer to read the height of the mercurial column to the nearest 0.002 inch, while in the sea barometer the reading cannot be made closer than 0.01 inch.

The instruments also differ in the method of obtaining the true height of the mercurial column at varying levels of the liquid in the cistern. It is evident that as the mercury in the tube rises, upon increase of atmospheric pressure, the mercury in the cistern must fall; and, conversely, when the mercurial column falls the amount of fluid in the cistern will thereby be increased and a rise of level will occur. As the height of the mercurial column is required above the existing level in the cistern, some means must be adopted to obtain the true height under varying conditions. In the standard barometer the mercury of the cistern is contained in a leather bag, against the bottom of which presses the point of a vertical screw, the milled head of the screw projecting from the bottom of the instrument and thus placing it under control of the observer. By this means the surface of the mercury in the cistern (which is visible through a glass casing) may be raised or lowered until it exactly coincides with that level which is chosen as the zero of the scale, and which is indicated by an ivory pointer in plain view.

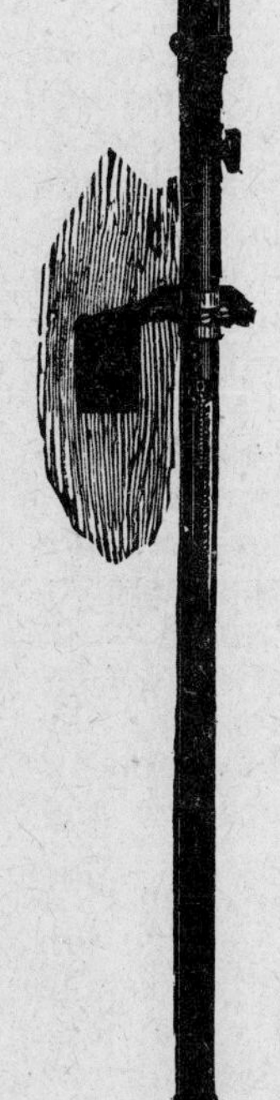

Figure 13.

Figure 14.

In the sea barometer there is no provision for adjusting the level of the cistern to a fixed point, but compensation for the variable level is made in the scale graduations; a division representing an inch on the scale is a certain fraction short of the true inch, proper allowance being thus made for the rise in level which occurs with a fall of the column, and for the reverse condition.

Further modification is made in the sea barometer to adapt it to the special use for which intended. The tube toward its lower end is much contracted to prevent the oscillation of the mercurial column known as "pumping," which arises from the motion of the ship; and just below this point is a trap to arrest any small bubbles of air from finding their way upward. The instrument aboard ship is suspended in a revolving center ring, in gimbals, supported on a horizontal brass arm which is screwed to the bulkhead; a vertical position is thus maintained by the tube at all times.

The **vernier** is an attachment for facilitating the exact reading of the scale of the barometer and is also applied to many other instruments of precision, as, for example, the sextant and theodolite. It consists of a metal scale similar in general construction to that of the instrument to which it is fitted, and arranged to move alongside of and in contact with the main scale.

The general principle of the vernier requires that its scale shall have a total length exactly equal to some whole number of divisions of the scale of the instrument and that this length shall be subdivided into a number of parts equal to 1 more or 1 less than the number of divisions of the instrument scale which are covered; thus, if a space of 9 divisions of the main scale be designated as the length of the vernier, the vernier scale would be divided into either 8 or 10 parts.

Suppose that a barometer scale be divided into tenths of an inch and that a length of 9 divisions of such a scale be divided into 10 parts for a vernier (fig. 15); and suppose that the divisions of the vernier be numbered consecutively from zero at the origin to 10 at the upper extremity. If, now, by means of the movable rack and pinion, the bottom or zero division of the vernier be brought level with the top of the mercurial column, and that division falls into exact coincidence with a division of the main scale, then the height of the column will correspond with the scale reading indicated. In such a case the top of the vernier will also exactly coincide with a scale division, but none of the intermediate divisions will be evenly abreast of such a division; the division marked "1" will fall short of a scale division by one-tenth of 1 division of the scale, or by 0.01 inch; that marked "2" by two-tenths of a division, or 0.02 inch; and so on. If the vernier, instead of having the zero coincide with a scale division, has the division "1" in such coincidence, it follows that the mercurial column stands at 0.01 inch above that scale division which is next below the zero; for the division "2," at 0.02 inch; and similarly for the others. In the case portrayed in figure 15, the reading of the column is 29.81 inches, the scale division next below the zero being 29.80 inches, while the fact that the first division is abreast a mark of the scale shows that 0.01 inch must be added to this to obtain the exact reading.

Had an example been chosen in which 8 vernier divisions covered 9 scale divisions—that is, where the number of vernier divisions was 1 less than the number of scale divisions covered—the principle would still have applied. But, instead of the length of 1 division of the vernier falling short of a division of the scale by one-tenth the length of the latter, it would have fallen beyond by one-eighth. To read in such a case it would therefore be necessary to number the vernier divisions from up downward and to regard the subdivisions as 1/80 instead of 0.01 inch.

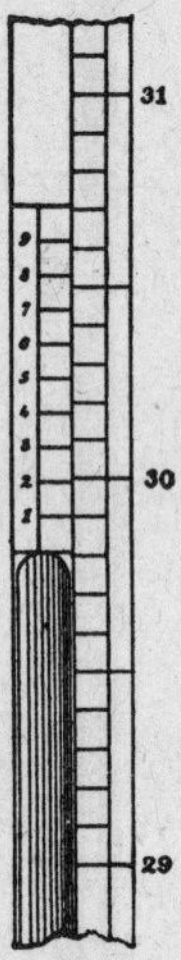

It is a general rule, that the smallest measure to which a vernier reads is equal to the length of 1 division of the scale divided by the number of divisions of the vernier; hence, by varying either the scale or the vernier, the desired subdivision may be obtained.

The sea barometer is arranged as described for the instrument assumed in the illustration; the scale divisions are tenths of an inch, and the vernier has 10 divisions, whence it reads to 0.01 inch. It is not necessary to seek a closer reading, as complete accuracy is not attainable in observing the height of a barometer on a vessel at sea, nor is it essential. The standard barometer on shore, however, is capable of very exact reading; hence each scale division is made equal to half a tenth, or 0.05 inch, while a vernier covering 24 such divisions is divided into 25 parts; hence the column may be read to 0.002 inch.

FIGURE 15.

To adjust the vernier for reading the height of the mercurial column the eye should be brought exactly on a level with the top of the column; that is, the line of sight should be at right angles to the scale. When properly set, the front and rear edges of the vernier and the uppermost point of the mercury should all be in the line of sight. A piece of white paper, held at the back of the tube so as to reflect the light, assists in accurately setting the vernier by day, while a small bull's-eye lamp held behind the instrument enables the observer to get a correct reading at night. When observing the barometer it should hang freely, not being inclined by holding or even by touch, because any inclination will cause the column to rise in the tube.

Other things being equal, the mercury will stand higher in the tube when it is warm than when it is cold, owing to expansion. For the purposes of comparison all barometric observations are reduced to a standard which assumes 32° F. as the temperature of the mercurial column, and 62° F. as that of the metal scale; it is therefore important to make this reduction, as well as that for instrumental error, in order to be enabled to compare the true barometric pressure with the normal that may be expected for any locality. The following table gives the value of this correction for each 2° F., the plus sign showing that the correction is to be added to the reading of the ship's barometer and the minus sign that it is to be subtracted:

Temperature	Correction	Temperature	Correction	Temperature	Correction	Temperature	Correction
°	*Inch*	°	*Inch*	°	*Inch*	°	*Inch*
20	+0. 02	40	−0. 03	60	−0. 09	80	−0. 14
22	+. 02	42	−. 04	62	−. 09	82	−. 14
24	+. 01	44	−. 04	64	−. 09	84	−. 15
26	+. 01	46	−. 05	66	−. 10	86	−. 15
28	. 00	48	−. 05	68	−. 10	88	−. 16
30	. 00	50	−. 06	70	−. 11	90	−. 16
32	−. 01	52	−. 06	72	−. 12	92	−. 17
34	−. 02	54	−. 07	74	−. 12	94	−. 17
36	−. 02	56	−. 07	76	−. 13	96	−. 18
38	−. 03	58	−. 08	78	−. 13	98	−. 18

As an example, let the observed reading of the mercurial barometer be 29.95 inches, and the temperature as given by the attached thermometer 74°; then,

	″
Observed height of the mercury	29. 95
Correction for temperature (74°)	−0. 12
Height of the mercury at standard temperature	29. 83

Millibar readings.—The diagram below enables the mariner to convert millibars and millimeters into inches and vice versa.

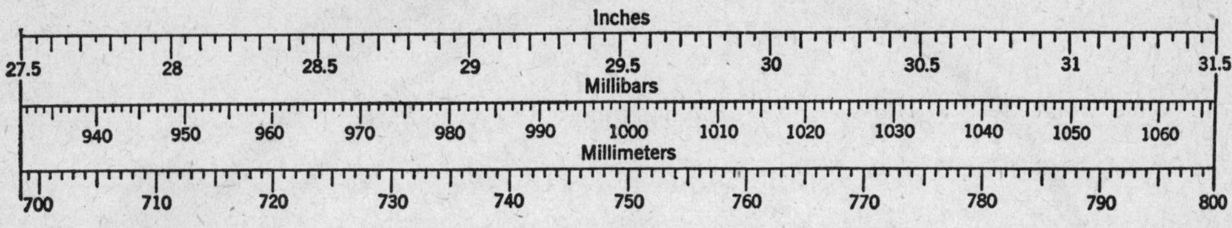

36

The **aneroid barometer.**—This is an instrument in which the pressure of the air is measured by means of the elasticity of a plate of metal. It consists of a cylindrical brass box, the metal in the sides being very thin; the contained air having been partially, and in some instruments completely, exhausted, the box is hermetically sealed. When the pressure of the atmosphere increases the inclosed air is compressed, the capacity of the box is diminished, and the two flat ends approach each other; when the pressure of the atmosphere decreases, the ends recede from one another in consequence of the rebound of the spring as external pressure is released. By means of a combination of levers, this motion of the ends of the box is communicated to an index pointer which travels over a graduated dial plate, the mechanical arrangement being such that the motion of the ends of the box is magnified many times, a very minute movement of the box making a considerable difference in the indication of the pointer. The graduations of the aneroid scale are obtained by comparison with the correct readings of a standard mercurial barometer under normal and reduced atmospheric pressure (see fig. 16).

The thermometer attached to the aneroid barometer is more for convenience in indicating the temperature of the air, but as regards the instrument itself no correction for temperature can be applied with certainty. Aneroids, as now manufactured, are compensated for temperature by the use of different metals having unequal coefficients of expansion, or by other means. They ought, therefore, to show the same pressure at all temperatures.

The aneroid barometer, from its small size and the ease with which it may be transported, can often be usefully employed under circumstances where a mercurial barometer would not be available. It also has an advantage over the mercurial instrument in its greater sensitiveness, and the fact that it gives earlier indications of change of pressure. It can, however, be relied upon only when frequently compared with a standard mercurial barometer; moreover, considerable care is required in its handling; while slight shocks will not ordinarily affect it, a severe jar or knock may change its indications by a large amount.

When in use the aneroid barometer may be suspended vertically or placed flat, but changing from one position to another ordinarily makes a sensible change in the readings; the instrument should always, therefore, be kept in the same position, and the errors determined by comparisons made while occupying its customary place.

Barometer comparison.—To determine the reliability of the ship's barometer, whether mercurial or aneroid, comparisons should from time to time be made with a standard barometer. Nearly all instruments read either too high or too low by a small amount. These errors arise, in a mercurial barometer, from the improper placing of the scale, lack of uniformity of caliber of the glass tube, or similar causes. In order to reduce mercurial barometer readings to a common standard, the barometer readings should be corrected for temperature of mercury column, for height of barometer

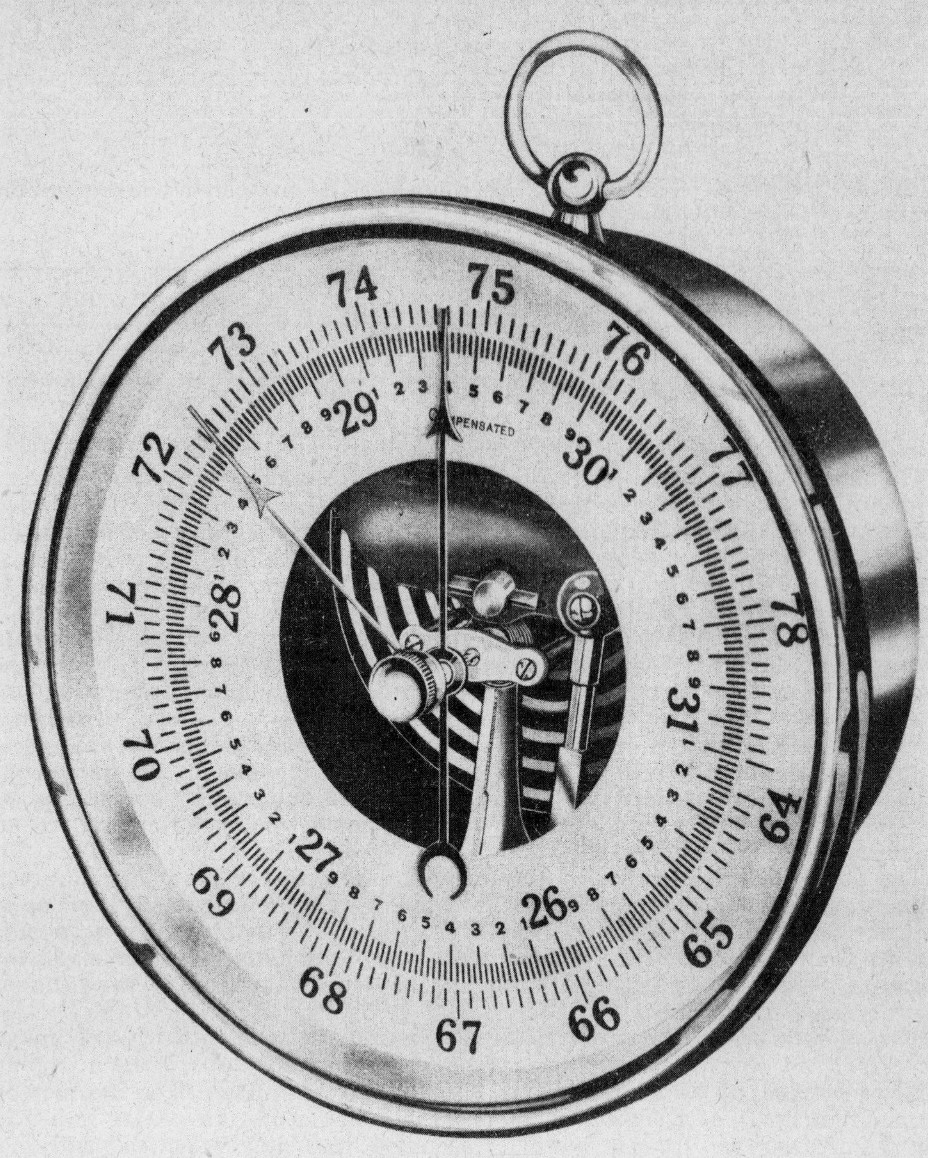

FIGURE 16.—Aneroid barometer.

above sea level, and for correction to reduce observed reading to standard gravity. In an aneroid barometer, which is less accurate and in which there is even more necessity for frequent comparisons, errors may be due to derangement of any of the various mechanical features upon which its working depends. The errors of the barometer should be determined for various pressure readings, as they are seldom the same at all parts of the scale.

In the principal ports of the world standard barometers are observed at specified times each day, and the readings, reduced to zero and to sea level, are published. Readings of a barometer on shipboard in these ports may be made at the specified hours, and the observing officer may thus, by comparing his readings with the official readings, secure a correction for his instrument. In the United States the Weather Bureau makes official comparisons of ships' barometers. The readings of the barometers to be compared are entered on cards furnished for the purpose. These cards are sent to the Weather Bureau office, where the comparison is made, and the ships are then informed as to the corrections obtained.

The reduction of the mercurial to standard gravity for 30 inches from latitude 0° to 10° is −0.08 inch, latitude 15° is −0.07 inch, latitude 20° is −0.06 inch; latitude 25° is −0.05 inch; latitude 30° is −0.04 inch; latitude 35° is −0.03 inch; latitude 40° is −0.01 inch; latitude 45° is 0.0 inch; latitude 50° is +0.01 inch; and latitude 60° is +0.04 inch.

Aneroid barometers may be adjusted for instrumental error by moving the index hand, but this is usually done only in the case of errors of considerable magnitude and should not be done promiscuously as it may result in damage to the instrument.

Determination of heights by barometer.—The barometer may be used to determine the difference in heights between any two stations by means of the difference in atmospheric pressure between them. An approximate rule is to allow 0.0011 inch for each difference in level of 1 foot, or, more roughly, 0.01 inch for every 9 feet.

A very exact method is afforded by Babinet's formula. If B_0 and B represent the barometric pressure (corrected for all sources of instrumental error) at the lower and at the upper stations respectively, and t_0 and t the corresponding temperatures of the air, and C a computed value; then,

$$\text{Diff. in height} = C \times \frac{B_0 - B}{B_0 + B}.$$

If the temperatures be taken by a Fahrenheit thermometer,

$$C \text{ (in feet)} = 52{,}494 \left(1 + \frac{t_0 + t - 64}{900}\right);$$

if a centigrade thermometer is used,

$$C \text{ (in meters)} = 16{,}000 \left(1 + \frac{2\ (t_0 + t)}{1000}\right).$$

The **barograph.**—The barograph is an aneroid barometer provided with a lever which records variation of pressure on a revolving drum driven by clock work. It enables an observer to detect casual errors in the reading of the marine barometer and also gives a continuous record of barometric pressure for reference.

THE THERMOMETER

The **thermometer** is an instrument for indicating temperature. It is constructed on the principle that bodies expand with increase of temperature and contract with decrease. In its most usual form the thermometer consists of a bulb filled with mercury, connected with a tube of very fine cross-sectional area upon which a scale is etched. The liquid column rises or falls in the tube according to the volume of the mercury due to the actual degree of heat, the height of the mercury indicating upon the scale the temperature. The mercury contained in the tube moves in a vacuum produced by the expulsion of the air through boiling the mercury and then closing the top of the tube by means of the blowpipe.

There are two classes of thermometer, distinguished according to the method of graduating the scale as follows: The **Fahrenheit,** in which the freezing point of water is placed at 32° and its boiling point (under normal atmospheric pressure) at 212°; the **centigrade,** in which the freezing point is at 0° and the boiling point at 100°. The Fahrenheit thermometer is generally used in the United States and England. Tables will be found in this work for the interconversion of the two scale readings (Table 16).

The thermometer is a valuable navigational instrument not only by reason of the aid it affords in judging meteorological conditions from the temperature of the air and the amount of moisture it contains, but also for the evidence it furnishes at times, through the temperature of the sea water, of the ship's position and the probable current that is being encountered.

Hygrometer.—The thermometers employed in determining the temperature of the air (wet and dry bulb) and of the water at the surface, should be mercurial, and of some standard make, with the graduation etched upon the glass stem; they should be compared with accurate standards, and should be accompanied by a tabulation showing the variation of their readings from the true throughout the scale.

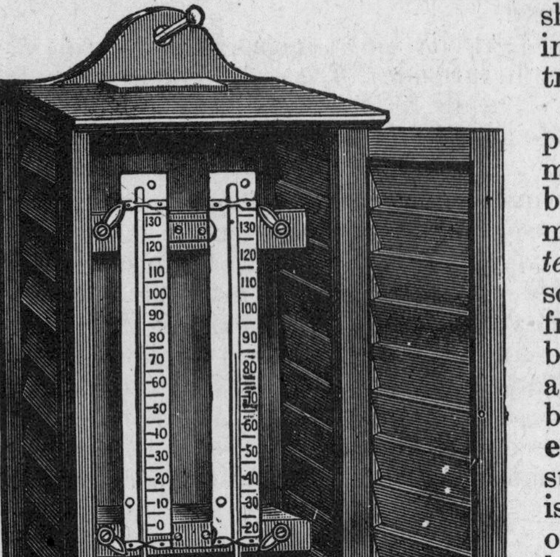

FIGURE 17.

The dry-bulb thermometer gives the temperature of the free air. The wet-bulb thermometer, an exactly similar instrument, the bulb of which is surrounded by an envelope of moistened cloth, gives what is known as the *temperature of evaporation*, which is always somewhat less than the temperature of the free air. Provided the ventilation of the wet bulb is vigorous, the difference of the temperatures shown by the dry bulb and the wet bulb, called, when in combination, a **hygrometer,** will indicate how near the air is to the state of saturation; that is, how near the air is to that point at which condensation will occur and some of its moisture (water vapor) be precipitated in the form of liquid. With the envelope of the wet bulb removed, the two thermometers should read precisely the same; otherwise they are practically useless.

The two thermometers, the wet and the dry bulb, should be hung within a few inches of each other, and the surroundings should be as far as possible identical. In practice the two thermometers are generally inclosed within a small lattice case, such as that shown in figure 17; the case should be placed in a position on deck remote from any source of artificial heat, sheltered from the direct rays of the sun, and from the rain and spray, but freely exposed to the circulation of the air; the door should be kept closed except during the process of reading. The cloth envelope of the wet bulb should be a single thickness of fine muslin, tightly stretched over the bulb, and tied with a fine thread. The wick which serves to carry the water from the cistern to the bulb should consist of a few threads of lamp cotton, and should be of sufficient length to admit of 2 or 3 inches being coiled in the cistern. The muslin envelope of the wet bulb should be at all times thoroughly moist, but not dripping.

When the temperature of the air falls to 32° F. the water in the wick freezes, the capillary action is at an end, the bulb in consequence soon becomes quite dry, and the thermometer no longer shows the temperature of evaporation. At such times the bulb should be thoroughly wetted with ice-cold water shortly before the time of observation, using for this purpose a camel's hair brush or feather; by this process the temperature of the wet bulb is temporarily raised above that of the dry, but only for a brief time, as the water quickly freezes; and inasmuch as evaporation takes place from the surface of the ice thus formed precisely as from the surface of the water, the thermometer will act in the same way as if it had a damp bulb.

The wet-bulb thermometer can not properly read higher than the dry, and if the reading of the wet bulb should be the higher, it may always be attributed to imperfections in the instruments.

Relative humidity.—Knowing the temperature of the wet and dry bulbs, the relative humidity of the atmosphere at the time of observation may be found from the following table:

Temperature of the air, dry-bulb thermometer	Difference between dry-bulb and wet-bulb readings									
	1°	2°	3°	4°	5°	6°	7°	8°	9°	10°
°	*Percent*	*Percent*	*Percent*	*Percent*	*Percent*	*Percent*	*Percent*	*Percent*	*Percenl*	*Percent*
24	87	75	62	50	38	26				
26	88	76	65	53	42	30				
28	89	78	67	56	45	34	24			
30	90	79	68	58	48	38	28			
32	90	80	70	61	51	41	32	23		
34	90	81	72	63	53	44	35	27		
36	91	82	73	64	55	47	38	30	22	
38	92	83	75	66	57	50	42	34	26	
40	92	84	76	68	59	52	44	37	30	22
42	92	84	77	69	61	54	47	40	33	26
44	92	85	78	70	63	56	49	43	36	29
46	93	85	79	72	65	58	51	45	38	32
48	93	86	79	73	66	60	53	47	41	35
50	93	87	80	74	67	61	55	49	43	37
52	94	87	81	75	69	63	57	51	46	40
54	94	88	82	76	70	64	59	53	48	42
56	94	88	82	77	71	65	60	55	50	44
58	94	89	83	78	72	67	61	56	51	46
60	94	89	84	78	73	68	63	58	53	48
62	95	89	84	79	74	69	64	59	54	50
64	95	90	85	79	74	70	65	60	56	51
66	95	90	85	80	75	71	66	61	57	53
68	95	90	85	81	76	71	67	63	58	54
70	95	90	86	81	77	72	68	64	60	55
72	95	91	86	82	77	73	69	65	61	57
74	95	91	86	82	78	74	70	66	62	58
76	95	91	87	82	78	74	70	66	63	59
78	96	91	87	83	79	75	71	67	63	60
80	96	92	87	83	79	75	72	68	64	61
82	96	92	88	84	80	76	72	69	65	62
84	96	92	88	84	80	77	73	69	66	63
86	96	92	88	84	81	77	73	70	67	63
88	96	92	88	85	81	77	74	71	67	64
90	96	92	88	85	81	78	74	71	68	65

The table may be readily understood. For example, if the temperature of the air (dry bulb) be 60°, and the temperature of evaporation (wet bulb) be 56°, the difference being 4°, look in the column headed "Temperature of the air" for 60°, and for the figures on the same line in column headed 4°; here 78 will be found, which means that the air is 78 percent saturated with water vapor; that is, that the amount of water vapor present in the atmosphere is 78 percent of the total amount that it could carry at the given temperature (60°). This total amount, or saturation, is thus represented by 100, and if there occurred any increase of the quantity of vapor beyond this point, the excess would be precipitated in the form of liquid. Over the ocean's surface the relative humidity is generally about 90 percent, or even higher in the doldrums; over the land in dry winter weather it may fall as low as 40 percent.

The **dew point.**—This is the temperature at which the moisture suspended in the atmosphere will commence to condense to form dew. The difference between the readings of the dry-bulb and wet-bulb thermometers may also be employed to find the temperature of the dew point, since the factor by which this difference must be multiplied in order to give the difference between the dry-bulb thermometer and the dew point has been tabulated as follows:

541524 O - 43 - 4

Dew-point factors

Dry bulb, °F.	Factor	Dry bulb, °F.	Factor	Dry bulb, °F.	Factor
10	8. 78	43	2. 20	65	1. 82
12	8. 78	44	2. 18	66	1. 81
14	8. 76	45	2. 16	67	1. 80
16	8. 70	46	2. 14	68	1. 79
18	8. 50	47	2. 12	69	1. 78
20	8. 14	48	2. 10	70	1. 77
22	7. 60	49	2. 08	72	1. 75
24	6. 92	50	2. 06	74	1. 73
26	6. 08	51	2. 04	76	1. 71
28	5. 12	52	2. 02	78	1. 69
30	4. 15	53	2. 00	80	1. 68
32	3. 32	54	1. 98	82	1. 67
33	3. 01	55	1. 96	84	1. 66
34	2. 77	56	1. 94	86	1. 65
35	2. 60	57	1. 92	88	1. 64
36	2. 50	58	1. 90	90	1. 63
37	2. 42	59	1. 89	92	1. 62
38	2. 36	60	1. 88	94	1. 60
39	2. 32	61	1. 87	96	1. 59
40	2. 29	62	1. 86	98	1. 58
41	2. 26	63	1. 85	100	1. 57
42	2. 23	64	1. 83		

Thus, in the former example, if the table of dew-point factors be entered with the temperature of the dry bulb (60° F.), the factor 1.88 will be found on the same line. This factor, multiplied by 4°, the difference between the readings of the dry-bulb and wet-bulb thermometers, will give 7½°, which is the amount that the temperature of the dew point is below the temperature of the air (dry bulb). The temperature of the dew point would therefore be 52½° F.

Surface temperature.—This is obtained either by dipping up a sample of the surface water in a canvas bucket, or from readings obtained from the condenser-intake.

When employing the first method, a canvas bucket having some vertical stiffening and an extra middle ring to prevent collapsing when entering the water is desirable. The bucket, containing no residual water, should be thrown overboard well forward, and clear of any discharge pipes. After sample of water is obtained, haul bucket up quickly, and carry to a sheltered spot where the original temperature of water sample will not be affected by wind or sunshine. Place thermometer in bucket and stir contents with it, keeping the bulb submerged. Then read temperature to nearest tenth of a degree, still keeping the bulb submerged.

Theoretically the condenser-intake temperature is not surface temperature, but the water is usually so well stirred up by wave action that its temperature is essentially uniform to that depth. It is a much simpler and shorter means of obtaining water temperatures. The only errors of importance come from the imperfect installation of the intake thermometer, which should be mounted on the centrifugal pump or between the pump and the ship's side, where true sea water temperatures will be given.

THE LOG BOOK

The **log book** is an official record of the vessel's cruise authenticated by the signatures of watch officers, the navigator, and commanding officer; and, as such, is an important accessory in navigation. In its navigational aspect it should afford among other things all the data from which the position of the ship is established by the method of dead reckoning and should comprise a record of meteorological observations, which should be made not only for the purpose of foretelling the weather during the voyage, but also for contribution to the general fund of marine meteorology.

A convenient form for recording the navigational data and meteorological data, which is employed for the log books of United States naval vessels, is shown on page 51; besides the tabulated matter thus arranged, to which one page of the log is in part devoted, another page bears a narrative of the navigational and other events of the day, written by watches and signed by the proper officers. The Navy Regulations prescribe in detail and at length the matter to be entered in the log.

LOG OF THE UNITED STATES SHIP ______________________
(Name) (Identification Number)

AT
EN ROUTE FROM ______________ TO ______________, ________ 19____
(Day) (Date) (Month)

ZONE DESCRIPTION ________ ______________, ________ *U. S. Navy, Commanding.*

Hour	"All Shaft" Average Revolutions	By Revs.		By Log		Course (P. C.)	Wind		Barometer		Temperature			Weather, by Symbols	Clouds			Visibility	Sea	
		Nautical Miles	Tenths	Nautical Miles	Tenths	Gyro___ Mag.___ (Indicate which)	Direction	Force	Height in Inches	Reading At. Ther.	Air, Dry Bulb	Air, Wet Bulb	Water at Surface		Form	Moving From—	Amount		Condition	Swells From—
	1	2	3	4	5	6	7	8	9	10	11	12	13	14	15	16	17	18	19	20
A.M.																				
1																				
2																				
3																				
4																				
5																				
6																				
7																				
8																				
9																				
10																				
11																				
12																				

8 a.m. { Latitude ________
Longitude ________

Noon { Latitude ________
Longitude ________

8 p.m. { Latitude ________
Longitude ________

Current { Set ________
Drift ________

GYROCOMPASS IN USE

Error ________

STANDARD MAG. COMPASS

Compass No. ________
S. H. ________
Error ________
Variation ________
Deviation ________

Fuel { Received ________
Expended ________
On hand ________

Water { Distilled ________
Received ________
Expended ________
On hand ________

BEFORE LEAVING PORT

Draft for'd ________
Draft aft. ________

AFTER ENTERING PORT

Draft for'd ________
Draft aft. ________

MAGAZINE TEMPERATURES:

Maximum ________
Minimum ________

DRILLS AND EXERCISES

Division	*Morning*	*Afternoon*
1		
2		
3		
4		
5		
6		
7		
8		
9		

Hour	1	2	3	4	5	6	7	8	9	10	11	12	13	14	15	16	17	18	19	20
P.M.																				
13																				
14																				
15																				
16																				
17																				
18																				
19																				
20																				
21																				
22																				
23																				
24																				

SUBMERGED RUN DATA—SUBMARINES

	1	2	3	4	5
Run No. (Serial)					
Time to submerge					
Greatest depth					

The Beaufort Wind Scale

Beaufort No.	Seaman's description of wind	Deep sea signs	Mode of estimating for average sized sailing trawler	Miles per hour (statute)†	Miles per hour (nautical)	Meters per second	Equivalent pressure in millibars* (10^3 dynes per cm^2)	Terms used in U. S. Weather Bureau forecasts
0	**Calm**	Sea smooth as a mirror	No headway	Less than 1	Less than 1	Less than 0.3	Less than 0.005	Light.
1	**Light air**	Small waveletlike scales; no foam crests	Sufficient to give good steerage way to fishing smacks, with "wind free."	1–3	1–3	0.3–1.5	0.005–0.03	
2	**Light breeze**	Waves short; crests begin to break	Fishing smacks with topsails and light canvas, "full and by," make up to 2 knots.	4–7	4–6	1.6–3.3	0.03–0.1	
3	**Gentle breeze**	Foam has glassy appearance, not yet white	Smacks begin to heel over slightly under topsails and light canvas, make up to 3 knots, "full and by."	8–12	7–10	3.4–5.4	0.1–0.2	Gentle.
4	**Moderate breeze**	Waves now longer; many white horses	Good working breeze; smacks heel over considerably on a wind under all sail.	13–18	11–16	5.5–8.0	0.2–0.5	Moderate.
5	**Fresh breeze**	Waves pronounced and long; white foam crests	Smacks shorten sail	19–24	17–21	8.1–10.7	0.5–1.0	Fresh.
6	**Strong breeze**	Larger waves form; white foam crests all over	Smacks double-reef gaff mainsail	25–31	22–27	10.8–13.8	1–1.5	Strong.
7	**Moderate gale**	Sea heaps up; wind blows foam in streaks	Smacks remain in harbor, and those at sea lie to	32–38	28–33	13.9–17.1	1.5–2	
8	**Fresh gale**	Height of waves and crests increasing	Smacks take shelter if possible	39–46	34–40	17.2–20.7	2–3	Gale.
9	**Strong gale**	Foam is blown in dense streaks		47–54	41–47	20.8–24.4	3–4.5	
10	**Whole gale**	High waves with long overhanging crests; large foam patches.		55–63	48–55	24.5–28.3	4.5–6	Whole gale.
11	**Storm**	High waves; ships in sight hidden in troughs		64–75	56–65	28.4–33.5	6–8	
12	**Hurricane**	Sea covered with streaky foam; air filled with spray.		Above 75	Above 65	33.6 or above	Above 8	Hurricane.

* 1 millibar equals approximately 10 kilograms per square meter or 2 pounds per square foot.

† Approximate velocity equivalents at a height of 33 feet above sea level. Values deduced from observations made at British coastal stations.

True direction and force of wind.—When steaming or sailing with any considerable speed, the apparent direction and force of the wind, as determined from a vane flag, or pennant aboard ship, may differ materially from the true direction and force, the reason being that the air appears to come from a direction and with a force dependent, not only upon the wind itself, but also upon the motion of the vessel. For instance, suppose that the wind has a velocity of 20 knots (force 5), and take the case of two vessels, each steaming 20 knots, the first with the wind dead aft, the second with the wind dead ahead. The former vessel will be moving with the same velocity as the air and in the same direction; the velocity of the wind relatively to the ship will thus be zero; on the vessel an apparent calm will prevail and the pennant will hang up-and-down. The latter vessel will be moving with the same velocity as the air, but in the opposite direction; the relative velocity of the two will thus be the sum of the two velocities, or 40 knots, and on the second vessel the wind will apparently have the velocity corresponding very nearly with a fresh gale. Again, it might be shown that in the case of a vessel steaming west at the rate of 20 knots, with the wind blowing from north with the velocity of 20 knots, the velocity with which the air strikes the ship as a result of the combined motion will be 28 knots, and the direction from which it comes will be northwest. If, therefore, the effect of the speed of the ship is neglected the wind will be recorded as northwest, force 7, when in reality it is north, force 5.

In order to make a proper allowance for this error and arrive at the true direction and force of the wind, a vector diagram or the traverse tables may be used. The known factors are, the course and speed of own vessel, and the apparent force and direction of wind: The resultant is the true force and direction of wind.

Weather Symbols.—To designate the state of the weather a series of letters devised according to the Beaufort notation is employed. The system employed in the United States is as follows:

STATE OF WEATHER

(Letters to be used in recording the weather)

b.—Blue sky, cloudless.
bc.—Blue sky with detached clouds.
c.—Sky mainly cloudy.
d.—Drizzling, or light rain.
e.—Wet air, without rain.
f.—Fog, or foggy weather.
g.—Gloomy, or dark, stormy-looking weather.
h.—Hail.
l.—Lightning.
m.—Misty weather.
o.—Overcast.
p.—Passing showers of rain.
q.—Squally weather.
r.—Rainy weather, or continuous rain.
s.—Snow, snowy weather, or snow falling.
t.—Thunder.
u.—Ugly appearance, or threatening weather.
v.—Variable weather.
w.—Wet, or heavy dew.
z.—Hazy weather.

Great intensity of any weather feature may be indicated by an underline thus: *r*., heavy rain.

Clouds.—The atmosphere holds in suspension a limited quantity of water vapor in an invisible state. When the temperature is lowered, the capacity to hold this water is reduced. For example, in a place over the ocean where the atmospheric pressure is lower than that of surrounding areas, the ascending air carries with it a large quantity of water vapor resulting from the evaporation of the water. As this column of water vapor and air rises, it expands with loss of heat, owing to the rarer air of the upper regions. This loss, together with the low temperature of these upper regions, causes the vapor to condense as a cloud. The cloud may keep its level, or increase its altitude depending upon the vertical velocity of the air and the size of the cloud. The amount of water either as liquid or ice in the air is small, the cloud not giving off the water as rain, or hail, or snow, but being only the visible marker of the place where condensation is going on. The following are the principal forms of clouds, named in the order of the altitude above the earth at which they usually occur, beginning with the most elevated. The symbols by which each is designated follows its name.

1. **Cirrus (Ci.).**—*Detached clouds of delicate and fibrous appearance, often showing a featherlike structure, generally of a whitish color.* Cirrus clouds take the most varied shapes, such as isolated tufts, thin filaments on a blue sky, threads spreading out in the form of feathers, curved [or straight] filaments ending in tufts, sometimes called

Cirrus uncinus, etc.; they are sometimes arranged in parallel belts which cross a portion of the sky in a great circle, and by an effect of perspective appear to converge toward a point on the horizon, or, if sufficiently extended, toward the opposite point also. (Ci.-St. and Ci.-Cu., etc., are also sometimes arranged in similar bands.)

2. **Cirro-stratus (Ci.-St.).**—*A thin, whitish sheet of clouds* sometimes covering the sky completely and giving it only a milky appearance (it is then called *Cirro-nebula*), at other times presenting, more or less distinctly, a formation like a tangled web. This sheet often produces halos around the sun and moon. (See fig. 18.)

FIGURE 18.—Cirro-stratus clouds.

3. **Cirro-cumulus (Ci.-Cu.), Mackerel Sky.**—*Small globular masses or white flakes without shadows, or showing very slight shadows, arranged in groups and often in lines.*

4. **Alto-stratus (A.-St.).**—*A thick sheet of gray or bluish color*, sometimes forming a compact mass of dark gray color and fibrous structure. At other times the sheet is thin, resembling thick Ci.-St., and through it the sun or the moon may be seen dimly gleaming as through ground glass. This form exhibits all changes peculiar to Ci.-St., but from measurements its average altitude is found to be about one-half that of Ci.-St.

5. **Alto-cumulus (A.-Cu.), Great Waves.**—*Largish globular masses, white or grayish, partly shaded, arranged in groups or lines, and often so closely packed that their edges appear confused.* The detached masses are generally larger and more compact (resembling St.-Cu.) at the center of the group, but the thickness of the layer varies. At times the masses spread themselves out and assume the appearance of small waves or thin slightly curved plates. At the margin they form into finer flakes (resembling Ci.-Cu.). They often spread themselves out in lines in one or two directions.

6. **Strato-cumulus (St.-Cu.).**—*Large globular masses or rolls of dark clouds often covering the whole sky, especially in winter.* Generally St.-Cu. presents the appearance of a gray layer irregularly broken up into masses of which the edge is often formed of smaller masses, often of wavy appearance resembling A.-Cu. Sometimes this cloud-form presents the characteristic appearance of great rolls arranged in parallel lines and pressed close up against one another. In their centers these rolls are of a dark color. Blue sky may be seen through the intervening spaces which are of a much

lighter color. (Roll-cumulus in England, Wulst-cumulus in Germany.) St.-Cu. clouds may be distinguished from Nb. by their globular or rolled appearance, and by the fact that they are not generally associated with rain.

7. **Nimbus (Nb.), rain clouds.**—*A thick layer of dark clouds, without shape* and with ragged edges, from which *steady* rain or snow usually falls. Through the openings in these clouds an upper layer of Ci.-St. or A.-St. may be seen almost invariably. If a layer of Nb. separates into shreds in a strong wind, or if small loose clouds are visible floating underneath a large Nb., the cloud may be described as *Fracto-nimbus* (Fr.-Nb.) ("Scud" of sailors).

8. **Cumulus (Cu.), wool-pack clouds.**—*Thick clouds of which the upper surface is domeshaped and exhibits protuberances while the base is horizontal.* These clouds appear to be formed by a diurnal ascensional movement which is almost always noticeable. When the cloud is opposite the sun, the surfaces facing the observer have a greater brilliance than the margins of the protuberances. When the light falls aslant, as is usually the case, these clouds throw deep shadows; when, on the contrary, the clouds are on the same side of the observer as the sun, they appear dark with bright edges.

True Cumulus has well-defined upper and lower limits, but in strong winds a broken cloud resembling Cumulus is often seen in which the detached portions undergo continual change. This form may be distinguished by the name *Fracto-cumulus* (Fr.-Cu.).

9. **Cumulo-nimbus (Cu.-Nb.)**, the **thunder-cloud; shower-cloud.**—*Heavy masses of cloud rising in the form of mountains, turrets, or anvils, generally surmounted by a sheet or screen of fibrous appearance (false Cirrus) and having at its base a mass of cloud similar to nimbus.* From the base local showers of rain or snow (occasionally of hail or soft hail) usually fall. Sometimes the upper edges assume the compact form of Cumulus, and form massive peaks round which delicate "false Cirrus" floats. At other times the edges themselves separate into a fringe of filaments similar to Cirrus clouds. This last form is particularly common in spring showers.

The front of thunder clouds of wide extent frequently presents the form of a large arc spread over a portion of a uniformly brighter sky.

10. **Stratus (St.).**—*A uniform layer of cloud resembling a fog but not resting on the ground.* When this sheet is broken up into irregular shreds in a wind, or by the summits of mountains, it may be distinguished by the name *Fracto-stratus* (Fr.-St.).

The attention of mariners is especially called to the value of observations of cirrus as this form of cloud is often closely connected with barometric depressions. If the Cirrus occurs in radiating bands crossing the sky, the point of convergence of these bands should be noted; if in the form of a cloud bank, or sheet, upon the horizon, the center, or point of greatest density of this bank should be observed. These points will sometimes serve to indicate in a general manner the direction of the center of any cyclonic disturbance.

In the scale for the amount of clouds 0 represents a sky which is cloudless and 10 a sky which is completely overcast.

Fog and cloud.—Clouds differ from fog, only in location Each is caused by the cooling of the atmosphere below the dew point, the cloud resulting from vertical convection is separated from the earth's surface, but fog induced by low temperatures at the surface remains there during the process of formation. Fog is made up of droplets of water condensed and floating in the air near the surface, while clouds are particles of water or ice condensed and floating in the air far above the surface.

Haze.—Haze is the obscurity of the air, which may occur in dry weather. It is sometimes caused by smoke or dust, or due to irregularities of density, causing irregular refraction of the rays of light by which distant objects are seen.

Water spouts.—Water spouts are tornadoes or whirlwinds which occur at sea. The spouts are conical with the point downward. They usually cause a rain cloud to be drawn down as a tapering funnel to the surface of the water. They should not be approached closely.

St. Elmo's fire.—Atmospheric electricity of low intensity is frequently sufficient to induce on masts, yards, and occasionally on stays or other parts of a vessel, a greater amount of electricity than the attenuated object can hold and what is called a **brush discharge** takes place without audible noise, but frequently with a feebly luminous glow.

Aurora Borealis.—This is a beautiful phenomenon seen in the sky most frequently in high latitudes, but occasionally in other parts of the earth. It is classified as glows, arches, curtains, streamers, and corona. The color is usually white, but red, yellow, and green, are also common auroral colors. The curtain of light hangs parallel to the magnetic dipping needle. Auroras are more numerous during years of greatest sun-spots. Brilliant shifting auroras are always accompanied by magnetic storms which would indicate they are due to atmospheric electrical discharges.

Halos and Coronas.—These rings or circles are seen around or some distance from the sun or moon. The halos result from the refraction of light in ice crystals, which compose the highest cirrus cloud and are more or less colored.

Mirage.—The refraction and reflection of light rays through air adjacent to the earth's surface which has air layers of different temperatures or humidity, hence different densities, often give rise to distorted, displaced, or inverted images; this phenomenon is termed mirage. Suitable atmospheric conditions may occur in any region, but are most frequent over hot deserts. The image when seen across water is generally raised and is called looming, or the coming into sight of objects normally below the horizon. Sometimes two or more images of the same object are seen.

Visibility.—The following numerical scale is used in the United States Navy to indicate the distance away at which a prominent object can be seen under different atmospheric conditions:

Fog and Visibility Scale

[Numerals to be used in recording visibility]

0.—Prominent objects not visible at 50 yards.
1.—Prominent objects not visible at 200 yards.
2.—Prominent objects not visible at 500 yards.
3.—Prominent objects not visible at ½ mile.
4.—Prominent objects not visible at 1 mile.
5.—Prominent objects not visible at 2 miles.
6.—Prominent objects not visible at 4 miles.
7.—Prominent objects not visible at 7 miles.
8.—Prominent objects not visible at 20 miles.
9.—Prominent objects visible above 20 miles.

State of the Sea is expressed by the following scale:

Scale	Description	Height of wave	Scale	Description	Height of wave
0	Calm sea	0 or less than 1 foot.	5	Very rough sea	8 to 12 feet.
1	Smooth sea	1 to 2 feet.	6	High sea	12 to 20 feet.
2	Slight sea	2 to 3 feet.	7	Very high sea	20 to 40 feet.
3	Moderate sea	3 to 5 feet.	8	Precipitous sea	40 feet and over.
4	Rough sea	5 to 8 feet.	9	Confused sea	Record chief direction.

Character of the sea swell is expressed by the following scale:

	Low	Moderate	Heavy	
0–None.	1. Short or average. 2. Long.	3. Short. 4. Average. 5. Long.	6. Short. 7. Average. 8. Long.	9. Confused.

Direction from which swell is coming should be recorded.

Confused swell should be recorded as "confused northeast," if coming from direction of northeast.

HYDROGRAPHIC OFFICE PUBLICATIONS

There are various publications issued by the United States Hydrographic Office dealing with special features of navigation, which should be regularly consulted. Among the most important of these are:

Pilot Charts (surface) of the various oceans. These are published monthly for the North Atlantic, Central American waters, North Pacific and Indian Oceans, and quarterly for the South Atlantic and South Pacific Oceans.

The Pilot Chart had its inception through the researches of Lt. Matthew Fontaine Maury, United States Navy, who, while in charge of this office during the early part of the nineteenth century, sought to expedite ocean passages through the collection of oceanographical and meteorological information from vessels, and the graphical presentation of these data on appropriate charts. The Pilot Chart today is the outgrowth of the pioneer work undertaken by Maury, aptly known as The Pathfinder of the Seas.

The Pilot Charts show the average winds, percentages of calms and gales, fog areas and percentages, magnetic variations, ocean currents, routes to be followed by steam and sailing vessels, and many other features that assist the navigator in choosing the safest and most expeditious routes. Articles of timely interest to the seafarer are published on the backs of the Pilot Charts.

Pilot Charts (upper air), monthly, for the North Atlantic and North Pacific Oceans. These charts, similar in design to the surface Pilot Charts, furnish the aviator with information regarding the structure and conditions of the atmosphere at four levels, namely, the surface, 2,500, 5,000, and 10,000 feet, as well as other data relating to oceanic circulation, isogonic lines, isothermal lines of air and water, air routes, and articles of interest to the aviator.

Hydrographic Bulletin, weekly, supplementing the Pilot Charts. The Bulletin contains accounts of obstructions and dangers along the coasts and the principal ocean routes. It also contains items relating to navigation, oceanography, and other scientific phenomena based largely on the contributions from the cooperating observers of the Hydrographic Office.

Radio Aids to Navigation (HO 205) contains a complete list of radio stations throughout the world which perform services of value to navigators upon the high seas and their adjacent waters, including direction-finding stations, radiobeacons, and stations broadcasting navigational warnings, time-signals, distress signals, and weather. Detailed and general information for the various radio services are included, as well as international and various national regulations on radio traffic.

Naval Air Pilots.—Publications designed primarily to furnish, in a convenient form, information of assistance to pilots in the navigation of aircraft when on extended flights *outside of the United States.*

Material for these publications is usually divided into two parts.

Part I contains general information concerning routes, weather, flying conditions, also useful tables.

Part II contains detailed information of airports and seaplane anchorages, the descriptive matter being supplemented with sketches and photographs.

Daily Memorandum, carrying a synopsis of all important information relating to dangers and aids to navigation, including reports of ice, derelicts, etc., received up to 4 p. m. of the day of issue. Its more urgent reports are also broadcasted by radio.

Notice to Mariners, weekly, giving changes in aids to navigation (lights, buoys, and harbor construction), dangers to navigation (rocks, shoals, banks, bars), important new soundings, and, in general, all such facts as affect mariners' charts, manuals, and pilots or sailing directions.

Sailing Directions or books treating of certain divisions of the navigable waters of the globe, containing description of coast lines, harbors, and dangers; information of winds, currents, and tides; directions for approaching and entering harbors; and much other information to mariners that cannot be shown on charts or is not published elsewhere.

Light Lists giving detailed information of the position and character of lights, with a brief description of the lighthouses and of any accompanying fog signals. They relate to the lights of the world, except those of the United States and its possessions, for which the U. S. Coast Guard publishes a list.

Radio Information, relating to dangers to vessels either from collision with floating or fixed obstructions or inadequacy of or changes in aids to navigation, is collected and disseminated in certain zones on the Atlantic, Pacific, and Gulf coasts of the United States, and the Great Lakes, by the Hydrographic Office and the Naval Communication Service. Like service for the benefit of navigation is performed by other nations.

CHAPTER III

THE COMPASS ERROR

CAUSES OF THE ERROR

Magnetic poles.—The properties of magnets are such that when two magnets are near enough together to exert a mutual influence, those poles which possess like magnetism repel each other, and those which possess unlike magnetism attract each other.

The earth is a magnetized body, and acts like a great spherical magnet with poles of unlike magnetism situated within the Arctic and Antarctic circles close to 71° N. 96° W. and 73° S., 156° E. of Greenwich, respectively. In common with magnets, the earth is surrounded by a region in which magnetic influence is exercised upon the compass, giving the magnetic needle a definite direction in each locality and causing the end which we name the north pole of the compass to be directed in general toward the region of the magnetic pole in the geographical north, and the south end toward the region of the magnetic pole in the geographical south.

The north end of the compass—north-seeking, as it is sometimes designated for clearness—will be that end which has opposite polarity to the earth's north magnetic pole, or, otherwise stated, which possesses like magnetism with the earth's south magnetic pole.

Variation of compass.—By reason of the fact that the magnetic pole in each hemisphere differs in geographical position by a large and unequal amount from the geographical pole, we are made aware that the earth is not magnetized symmetrically with reference to the geographical poles. Hence the directive influence of the earth's magnetism will not in general cause the compass needle to point in the direction of the true meridian, but each compass point will differ from the corresponding true point by an amount varying according to the geographical locality. The angle representing this difference is the **variation of the compass,** sometimes called by surveyors the **magnetic declination.** It is the angle between the plane of the true meridian and a vertical plane passing through a freely suspended magnetic needle influenced solely by the earth's magnetism.

The variation not only changes as one travels from place to place on the earth, being different in different localities, but in every locality, besides the minor periodic movements of the needle known as the diurnal, monthly, and annual variations, which are not of material concern to the mariner, there is a progressive change which extends through centuries of time and amounts to large alterations in the pointing of the compass. In taking account of the effect produced by the variation of the compass, the navigator must therefore be sure that the variation used is correct not only for the *place*, but also for the *time* under consideration. Variation should be taken from the latest magnetic data available. The amount and direction of the variation for most localities on the earth's surface have been ascertained, and will be found marked on charts. The annual change in variation is also indicated, so that the variation may be corrected to date.

Occasionally the magnetic needle is subject to spasmodic fluctuations of the earth's magnetism lasting from a brief period to several days. These are called *magnetic storms*, and are due to sudden changes in the electric currents which circulate within the earth and in the region surrounding the earth. They come apparently at random, and may occur nearly simultaneously over the whole world or be restricted to a certain region. The range of their effect upon the compass does not often exceed the half of a degree in the lower latitudes, and hence the navigator need only be concerned with them in the higher latitudes where he may look to the aurora as an indication of their occurrence.

H. O. Chart 2406. **Variation of compass for 1940.**

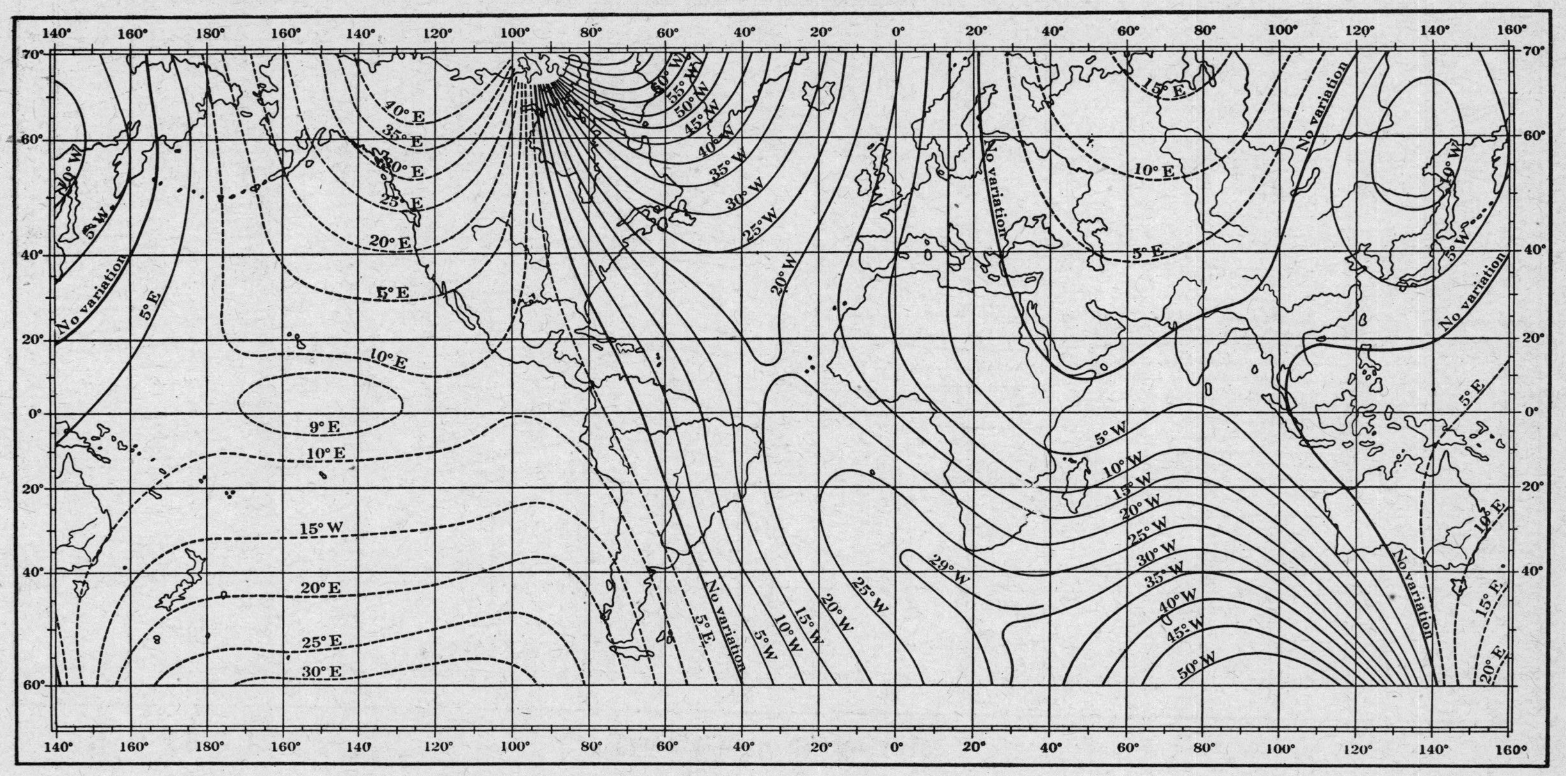

H. O. Chart 1700.

The magnetic dip for 1940.

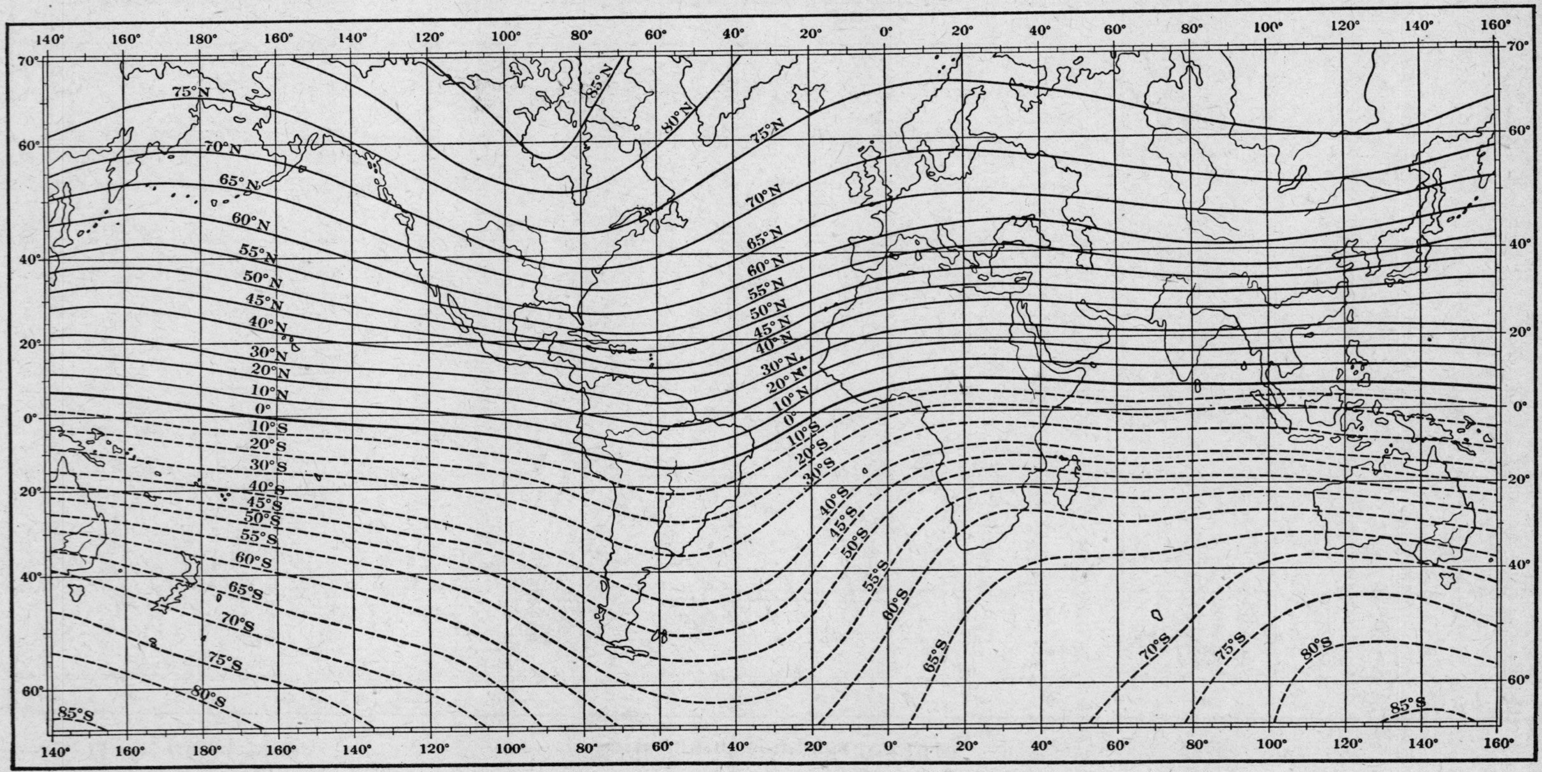

Local disturbance.—Besides the error thus produced in the indications of the compass, a further one, due to **local attraction,** may arise from extraneous influences due to natural magnetic attraction in the vicinity of the vessel. Instances of this are quite common when a ship is in port, as it may be in close proximity to vessels, docks, machinery, or other masses of iron or steel. It is also encountered in the shallow waters of the sea in localities where the mineral substances in the earth itself possess magnetic qualities—as, for example, at certain places in Lake Superior, Alaska, Iceland, Bermuda, and at others off the coast of Australia. When due to the last-named cause, it may be a source of great danger to the mariner, but, fortunately, the number of localities subject to local attraction is limited. The amount of this error can seldom be determined except by survey; if known, it might properly be included with the variation and treated as a part thereof.

Deviation of compass.—In addition to the variation, the compass ordinarily has a still further error in its indications, which arises from the effect exerted upon it by masses of magnetic metal within the ship itself. This is known as the **deviation of the compass.** For reasons that will be explained later, it differs in amount for each heading of the ship, and, further, the character of the deviations undergoes modification as a vessel proceeds from one geographical locality to another.

APPLYING THE COMPASS ERROR

From what has been explained, it may be seen that there are three systems by which *direction* may be expressed.

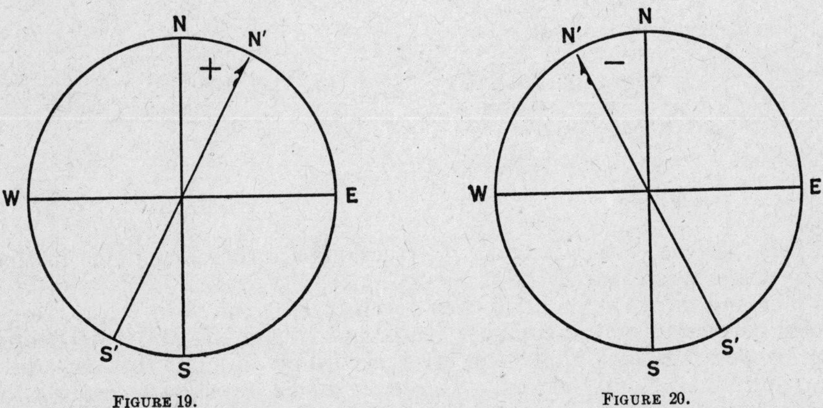

FIGURE 19. FIGURE 20.

True (symbol T or t), when referring to angles measured from the earth's geographic meridian called true north.

Magnetic (symbol mag.), when referring to angles measured from the earth's magnetic meridian called magnetic north. Magnetic and true bearings differ by the amount of the **variation** in that locality.

Compass (symbol P. S. C.), when referring to angles measured from the north point of the compass card. Compass readings differ from magnetic by the **deviation** on that heading of the ship, and from true by the **compass error** which is the algebraic sum of the deviation and variation as explained later.

The necessity for conversion of compass readings from one system to another occurs frequently. Directions on charts are usually true directions, and require application of variation and deviation before being used on the compass, or vice versa. The rules for applying corrections must be carefully learned.

Deviation is called easterly and marked plus (+), or westerly and marked minus (−), according to whether the local magnetic effect is such as to draw the compass needle to the right (east) or left (west) of the earth's magnetic meridian (magnetic north). In figure 19 the compass needle is drawn 20° to the right of the magnetic needle. Therefore, the deviation on that heading of the vessel is 20° E. or +20°. In figure 20 the compass needle is drawn 20° to the left of the magnetic needle or, −20°.

Variation is likewise called easterly and marked plus (+), or westerly and marked minus (−), according to whether the direction of the earth's magnetic meridian at that place is to the right (east) or left (west) of the earth's true meridian. In figure 21 the magnetic meridian (magnetic north) is 20° to the left (west) of the true meridian. Therefore, the variation is 20° W. or −20°. In figure 22 the variation is 15° E. or +15°.

The compass error, being the algebraic sum of the variation and deviation, is likewise marked easterly (+) or westerly (−) according to whether the total magnetic effect draws the compass needle to the right (east) or left (west) of the earth's true meridian. In figure 21, C. E.=−20° (var.)+10° (dev.)=−10° or 10° W. In figure 22 C. E.=+15° (var.)+10° (dev.)=+25° or 25° E.

In applying corrections to the compass always imagine yourself to be at the center of the compass card looking out toward the periphery in the given direction. From this position the numbers always increase toward the right (except from 360° to 0°). The least correct system of directions is that of the compass, the next is

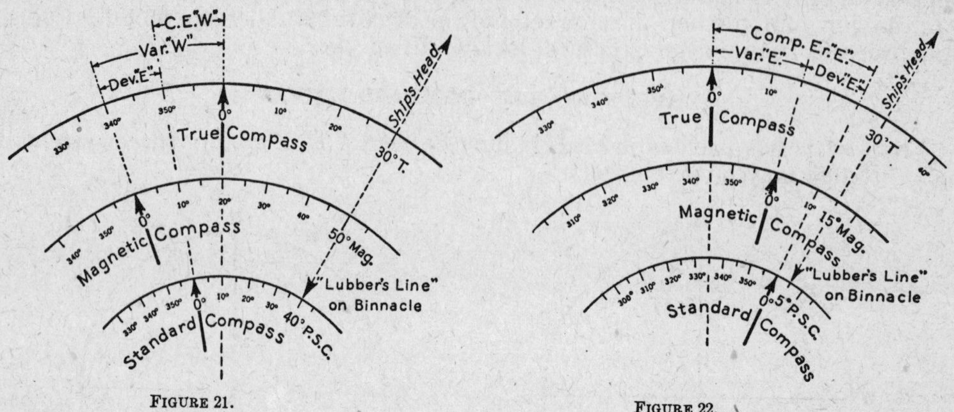

FIGURE 21.

FIGURE 22.

magnetic; the perfect system is true. Corrections are therefore made in that order, compass to magnetic to true.

The plus and minus signs have been given to east and west errors, respectively, to facilitate correction of the compass readings to magnetic and true readings. In *correcting compass readings* apply the error according to sign; that is, add easterly errors and subtract westerly errors. To *reduce a true or magnetic reading* to a compass reading reverse the signs of the correction; that is, subtract easterly and add westerly errors.

In figure 22 note the following:

Given compass course=5° (note lubber's line).
Magnetic course=5°+10° (E. dev.)=15°.
True course=5°+10° (E. dev.)+15° (E. var.)=30°.

To reverse the process.

Given true course=30° (note ship's head).
Magnetic course=30°−15° (E. var.)=15°.
Compass course=30°−15° (E. var.)−10° (E. dev.)=5°.

The thumb rule "true, right, east" may be of assistance. Interpreted it means, if the more correct course is to the right (greater) the error is east; if the error is east, the more correct course is to the right (greater). The reverse is obvious—that, if the more correct course is to the left (less) the error is west; if the error is west the more correct course is to the left (less).

Careful study of the following examples will aid in making the subject clear:

Examples.—A bearing taken by a compass free from deviation is 76°; variation, 5° W.; required the true bearing. 71°.

A vessel steers 153° by compass; deviation on that heading, 3° W.; variation in the locality, 12° E.; required the true course. 162°.

It is desired to steer the magnetic course 322°; deviation, 4° E.; required the course by compass. 318°.

True course to be made, 55°; deviation, 7° E.; variation, 14° W.; required the course by compass. 62°.

A vessel passing a range whose direction is known to be 200°, magnetic, observes the bearing by compass to be 178°; required the deviation. 22° E.

The sun's observed bearing by compass is 91°; it is found by computation to be 84° (true); variation, 8° W.; required the deviation. 1° E.

FINDING THE COMPASS ERROR

The variation of the compass for any given locality is found from the charts. A nautical chart always contains information from which the navigator is enabled to ascertain the variation for any place within the region embraced and for any year. Besides the information thus to be acquired from local charts, a special world magnetic chart, H. O. No. 2406, is published showing the variation at all points on the earth's surface.

The deviation of the compass, varying as it does for every ship, for every heading, and for every geographical locality, must be determined by the navigator, for which purpose various methods are available.

Whatever method is used, the ship must be swung in azimuth and an observation made on each of the headings upon which the deviation is required to be known. If a new iron or steel ship is being swung for the first time, observations should be made on each of the twenty-four 15° rhumbs into which the compass card is divided. At later swings, especially after correctors have been applied, or in the case of wooden ships, twelve 15° rhumbs will suffice—or, indeed, only six. In case it is not practicable to make observations on exact 15° rhumbs, they should be made as near thereto as practicable and plotted on the Napier diagram (to be explained hereafter), whence the deviations on exact 15° rhumbs may be found.

In swinging ship for deviations the vessel should be on an even keel and all movable masses of iron in the vicinity of the compass secured as for sea, and the compass accurately centered in the binnacle. The vessel, upon being placed on any heading, should be steadied there for 3 or 4 minutes before the observation is made, in order that the compass card may come to rest and the magnetic conditions assume a settled state. To assure the greatest accuracy the ship should first be swung to starboard, then to port, and the mean of the two deviations on each course taken. Ships may be swung under their own steam, or with the assistance of a tug, or at anchor, where the action of the tide tends to turn them in azimuth (though in this case it is difficult to get them steadied for the requisite time on each heading), or at anchor, by means of springs and hawsers.

The deviation of all compasses on the ship may be obtained from the same swing, it being required to make observations with the standard only. To accomplish this it is necessary to record the ship's head by all compasses at the time of steadying on each even rhumb of the standard; applying the deviation, as ascertained, to the heading by standard, gives the magnetic heads, with which the direction of the ship's head by each other compass may be compared, and the deviation thus obtained. Then a complete table of deviations may be constructed as explained later.

There are four methods for ascertaining the deviations from swinging, namely: by **reciprocal bearings,** by **bearings of the sun,** by **ranges,** and by a **distant object.**

Reciprocal bearings.—One observer is stationed on shore with a spare compass placed in a position free from disturbing magnetic influences; a second observer is at the standard compass on board ship. At the instant when ready for observation a signal is made, and each notes the bearing of the other. The bearing by the shore compass, reversed, is the magnetic bearing of the shore station from the ship, and the difference between this and the bearing by the ship's standard compass represents the deviation of the latter.

In determining the deviations of compasses placed on the fore-and-aft amidship line, when the distribution of magnetic metal to starboard and port is symmetrical, the shore compass may be replaced by a dumb compass, or pelorus, or by a theodolite in which, for convenience, the zero of the horizontal graduated circle may be termed north; the reading of the shore instrument will, of course, not represent magnetic directions, but by assuming that they do we obtain a series of fictitious deviations, the mean value of which is the error common to all. Upon deducting this error from each of the fictitious deviations, we obtain the correct values.

If ship and shore observers are provided with watches which have been compared with one another, the times may be noted at each observation, and thus afford a means of locating errors due to misundertsanding of signals.

Example.—Having swung a vessel for deviation of the standard compass by the method of reciprocal bearings, find the deviation of the standard compass on 13 headings from 0° to 180°.

Time			Vessel head by P. S. C.	Simultaneous bearings—				(3) Reciprocal of (2)		Deviation of standard compass (3)−(1)	
				(1) of shore compass from standard compass		(2) of standard compass from shore compass					
h	m	s	°	°	′	°	′	°	′	°	′
2	32	05	0	217	30	35	15	215	15	−2	15
2	36	20	15	207	30	26	20	206	20	−1	10
2	41	30	30	200	15	21	50	201	50	+1	35
2	46	00	45	197	00	18	45	198	45	+1	45
2	52	00	60	188	50	10	50	190	50	+2	00
2	57	00	75	186	30	8	50	188	50	+2	20
3	02	00	90	185	40	9	40	189	40	+4	00
3	07	30	105	185	40	10	00	190	00	+4	20
3	11	30	120	187	10	13	30	193	30	+6	20
3	16	00	135	186	15	12	10	192	10	+5	55
3	21	10	150	191	10	15	10	195	10	+4	00
3	25	30	165	191	00	14	20	194	20	+3	20
3	31	10	180	196	30	18	30	198	30	+2	00

Bearings of the sun.—This method requires that on each heading a bearing of the sun be observed by compass and the time noted at the same moment by a chronometer or watch. By means which will be explained in the chapter on azimuth, the true bearing of the sun may be ascertained from the known data, and this, compared with the compass bearing, gives the total compass error; deducting from the compass error the variation, there remains the deviation. The variation used may be that given by the chart, or, in the case of a compass affected only by symmetrically placed iron or steel, may be considered equal to the mean of all the total errors. Other celestial bodies may be observed for this purpose in the same manner as the sun.

This method is important as being the most convenient one available for determining the compass error at sea.

When adjusting compasses much time will be saved by the following simple modification of a detail. Instead of tabulating magnetic azimuths for given stated times in advance, draw on cross-section paper a curve whose ordinates are minutes of local apparent time and whose abscissas are degrees of magnetic azimuth; that is, true azimuth corrected for variation. Then for any given instant (the navigator's watch being set to local apparent time) the magnetic azimuth may be read directly from the curve. The difference between the magnetic azimuth of the sun and its compass bearing is, of course, the deviation of the compass on that particular heading.

Ship's head by standard compass	Times of observation by watch	Watch correction on L. A. T.	L. A. T. of observation	Azimuth of sun by standard compass	True azimuth of sun by azimuth tables	Error of compass	Variation	Deviations of compass
°	h m s		h m s	° ′	° ′	° ′		° ′
0	7 43 00	Error of watch on L. A. T., 3 m. 20 s. To be added to watch time of observation.	7 46 20	112 00	102 02	− 9 58	Mean of 24 equidistant azimuths, column 5 = 120° 32′; Mean of the corresponding azimuths of column 6 = 113° 46′; Variation by observation + constant A = −6° 46′; * Constant A (apply when found accurately) = − 18′; Variation by observation = −6° 28′ (To be applied to error of compass)	− 3 30
15	7 47 25		7 50 45	113 10	102 49	−10 21		− 3 53
30	7 51 55		7 55 15	114 30	103 38	−10 52		− 4 24
45	7 57 00		8 00 20	116 30	104 33	−11 57		− 5 29
60	8 01 50		8 05 10	120 10	105 26	−14 44		− 8 16
75	8 06 42		8 10 02	124 00	106 20	−17 40		−11 12
90	8 11 46		8 15 06	128 20	107 19	−21 01		−14 33
105	8 17 10		8 20 30	131 20	108 21	−22 59		−16 31
120	8 23 10		8 26 30	133 20	109 32	−23 48		−17 20
135	8 28 42		8 32 02	133 10	110 38	−22 32		−16 04
150	8 33 41		8 37 01	128 40	111 39	−17 01		−10 33
165	8 39 10		8 42 30	123 30	112 48	−10 42		− 4 14
180	8 45 10		8 48 30	117 30	114 04	− 3 26		+ 3 02
195	8 50 42		8 54 02	113 15	115 17	+ 2 02		+ 8 30
210	8 56 41		9 00 01	109 00	116 37	+ 7 37		+14 05
225	9 00 46		9 04 06	103 30	117 33	+14 03		+20 31
240	9 04 47		9 08 07	106 30	118 28	+11 58		+18 26
255	9 08 46		9 12 06	109 40	119 25	+ 9 45		+16 13
270	9 13 47		9 17 07	113 10	120 38	+ 7 28		+13 56
285	9 19 50		9 23 10	118 40	122 09	+ 3 29		+ 9 57
300	9 24 40		9 28 00	124 50	123 23	− 1 27		+ 5 01
315	9 29 45		9 33 05	129 00	124 42	− 4 18		+ 2 10
330	9 34 15		9 37 35	133 10	125 54	− 7 16		− 0 48
345	9 38 40		9 42 00	135 50	127 05	− 8 45		− 2 17

L. A. T. by chron.:

	h m s	
Chron	12 32 27	Lat. 39° N.
C. C	+ 5 03.7	Long. 76°24′ W.
G. C. T. Apr. 7	12 37 30.7	Declination 6°39′ N.
Eq. t	(−) 2 19.7	
G. A. T	12 35 11	
Long. W	5 05 36	
L. A. T	7 29 35	
Watch	7 26 15	
Error of w. on L. A. T., slow	3 20	

*The constant A is a constant error usually attributed to faulty fittings in the compass card or accessories, or to the lubbers line being slightly offset from the center line of the ship. (See Constant Deviation, p. 72.)

Ranges.—In many localities there are to be found natural or artificial range marks which are clearly distinguishable, and which when in line lie on a known magnetic bearing. By steaming about on different headings and noting the compass bearing of the ranges each time of crossing the line that they mark, a series of deviations may be obtained, the deviation of each heading being equal to the difference between the compass and the magnetic bearing. The range marks should not be too close together.

Distant object.—A conspicuous object is selected which must be at a considerable distance from the ship and upon which there should be some clearly defined point for taking bearings. The direction of this object by compass is observed on successive headings. Its true or magnetic bearing is then found and compared with the compass bearings, whence the deviation is obtained.

The true or the magnetic bearing may be taken from the chart. The magnetic bearing may also be found by setting up a compass ashore, free from foreign magnetic disturbance, in range with the object and the ship, and observing the bearing of the object; or the magnetic bearing is approximately the mean of the compass bearings on all headings, or the mean of the compass bearings on the cardinal or intercardinal points.

In choosing an object for use in this method care must be taken that it is at such a distance that its bearing from the ship does not practically differ as the vessel swings in azimuth. If the ship is swung at anchor, the distance should be not less than 6 miles. If swung under way, the object must be so far that the parallax (the tangent of which may be considered equal to half the diameter of swinging divided by the distance) shall not exceed about 30′.

541524°—43——5

Example.—The following compass bearings were taken on a distant church spire:

Vessel's head	Compass bearing of object	Deviation	Magnetic bearing
°	°	° ′	°
0	224	1 52 E.	224
45	223	2 52 E.	223
90	221	4 52 E.	221
135	225	0 52 E.	225
180	227	1 08 W.	227
225	228	2 08 W.	228
270	230	4 08 W.	230
315	229	3 08 W.	229
			(Mean) 225°52′

The mean of all compass bearings will be the magnetic bearing, and the difference between the compass bearing and the magnetic bearing will be the deviation for the point on which the vessel was heading. In this example the correct magnetic bearing is 225°52′. On heading 0°, 225°52′—224° (compass bearing) gives deviation 1°52′ E. and so on.

In all of the methods described it will be found convenient to arrange the results in tabular form. In one column record the ship's head by standard compass, and abreast it in successive columns the observations from which the deviation is determined on that heading, and finally write the deviation itself. When the result of the swing has been worked up, another table is constructed showing simply the headings and the corresponding deviations. This is known as the **deviation table** of the compass. If compensation is to be attempted, this table is the basis of the operation; if not, the deviation tables of the standard and steering compass should be posted in such place as to be accessible to all persons concerned with the navigation of the ship.

Deviation table.—Let it be assumed that a deviation table has been found and that the values are as follows:

Deviation table

Ship's head by standard compass		Deviation	Ship's head by standard compass		Deviation
	°	° ′		°	° ′
North	0	—15 29	South	180	+17 52
	15	—14 53		195	+23 47
	30	—13 16		210	+27 07
NE	45	—11 19	SW	225	+25 35
	60	— 9 59		240	+21 57
	75	— 9 42		255	+15 54
East	90	— 9 06	West	270	+ 9 56
	105	— 9 01		285	+ 1 56
	120	— 7 51		300	— 4 09
SE	135	— 5 54	NW	315	—10 20
	150	— 2 16		330	—13 37
	165	+ 8 29		345	—16 01

Testing deviation table.—With a well-adjusted compass, the deviations on N. and E. should equal the deviations on S. and W. with the signs changed. The mean of the deviations on NE. and SW. should equal the mean of the deviations on SE. and NW. with the signs changed.

From the table above the amount of deviation is found on each compass heading. Knowing the ship's head by compass, it is easy to pick out the corresponding deviation, and thus to obtain the magnetic heading. But, if given the magnetic direction in which it is desired to steer, to find the corresponding compass course, the problem is not so simple, for deviations on magnetic headings are not given, and where the errors are large it may not be assumed that they are the same as on the corresponding compass headings. For example, with the deviation table just given, suppose it is required to determine the compass heading corresponding to 165°, magnetic.

The deviation corresponding to 165°, per compass, is +8½°. If we apply this to 165°, magnetic, we have 156½° as the compass course. But, consulting the table, it may be seen that the deviation corresponding to 156½°, per compass, is +2½°, and therefore, if we steer that course the magnetic direction will be 159°, and not 165°, as desired.

A way of arriving at the correct result is to make a series of trials until a course is arrived at which fulfills the conditions. Thus, in the example given:

First trial	°
Mag. course desired	165
Try dev. on 165°	8½ E.
Trial comp. course	156½
Dev. on 156½°	2½ E.
Mag. course made good	159

Since this assumption carries the course 6° too far to the left, assume next a deviation on a course 3½° farther to the right than the one used here.

Second trial	°
Mag. course desired	165
Try dev. on 160°	5 E.
Trial comp. course	160
Dev. on 160°	5 E.
Mag. course made good	165

This happens to be exactly the compass course required. But it often occurs that further trials may be necessary.

The Napier diagram.—A much more expeditious method for the solution of this problem is afforded by the **Napier diagram,** and as that diagram also facilitates a number of other operations connected with compass work it should be clearly understood by the navigator. This admits of a graphic representation of the table of deviations of the compass by means of a curve. Besides furnishing a ready means of converting compass into magnetic courses and the reverse, one of its chief merits is that if the deviation has been determined on a certain number of headings it enables one to obtain the most probable value of the deviation on any other course that the ship may head. The last-named feature renders it useful in making a table of deviations of compasses other than the standard when their errors are found.

The Napier diagram (fig. 23) represents the margin of a compass card cut at the north point and straightened into a vertical line; for convenience, it is usually divided into two sections, representing, respectively, the eastern and western semicircles. The vertical line is of a convenient length and divided into 24 equal parts corresponding to each 15° of the compass, beginning at the top with north and continuing around to the right; it is also divided into 360°, which are appropriately marked.

To obtain a complete curve, a sufficient number of observations should be taken while the ship swings through an entire circle. Generally, observations on every alternate 15° rhumb are enough to establish a good curve, but in cases where the maximum deviation reaches 40° it is preferable to observe on every 15° rhumb.

The curve shown in the full line on figure 23 corresponds to the table of deviations given on page 64.

From compass course to find the magnetic course.—Through the point of the vertical line representing the given compass course draw a line parallel to the *dotted* lines until the curve is intersected, and from the point of intersection draw another line parallel to the plain lines; the point on the scale where this last line cuts the vertical line is the magnetic course sought. The correctness of this solution will be apparent when we consider that the 60° triangles are equilateral, and therefore the distance measured along the vertical side will equal the distance measured along the inclined sides—that is, the deviation; and the direction will be correct, for the construction is such that magnetic directions will be to the right of compass directions when the deviation is easterly and to the left if westerly.

From magnetic course to find compass course.—The process is the same, excepting that the first line drawn should follow, or be parallel to, the *plain* lines, and the second, or return line, should be parallel to the dotted; and a proof similar to that previously employed will show the correctness of the result. As an example, the problem given above may be solved by the diagram, and the result will be found to accord with the solution previously given.

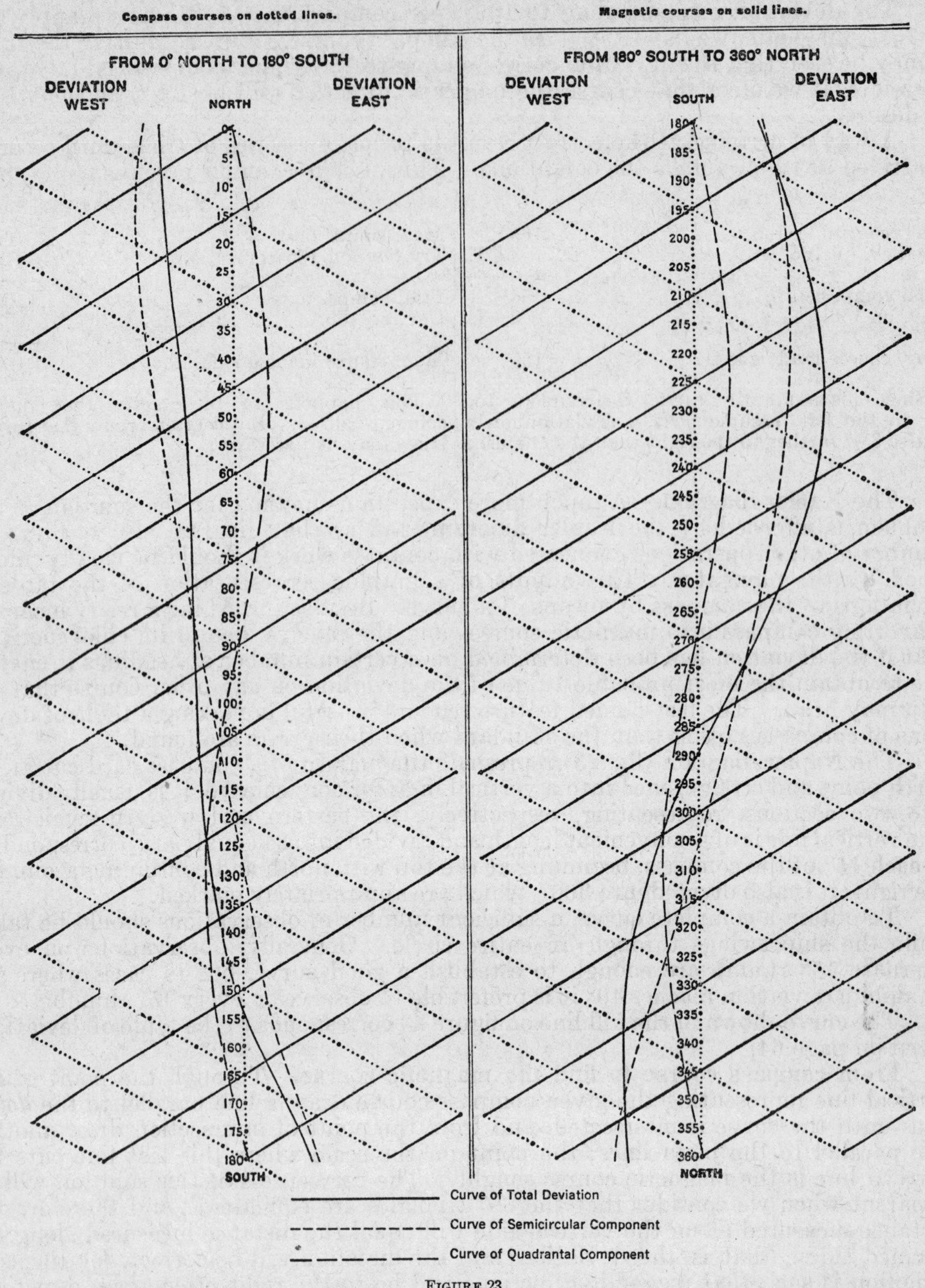

FIGURE 23.

The vertical line is intersected at each 15° rhumb by two lines inclined to it at an angle of 60°, that line which is inclined upward to the right being drawn plain and the other dotted.

The following rhyme will be helpful with the diagram:

From compass course, magnetic to gain,
Depart by dotted, return by plain.
From magnetic course, to course allotted.
Depart by plain, return by dotted.

To plot curve on Napier diagram.—If the deviation has been observed with the ship's head on given *compass* courses (as is usually the case with the standard compass), measure off on the vertical scale the number of degrees corresponding to the deviation and lay it down—to the right if easterly and to the left if westerly—on the *dotted* line passing through the point representing the ship's head; or, if the observation was not made on an even 15° rhumb, then lay it down on a line drawn parallel to the dotted ones through that division of the vertical line which represents the compass heading; if the deviation has been observed with the ship on given *magnetic* courses (as when deviations by steering compass are obtained by noting the ship's head during a swing on even 15° rhumbs of the standard), proceed in the same way, excepting that the deviation must be laid down on a *plain* line or a line parallel thereto. Mark each point thus obtained with a dot or small circle, and draw a free curve passing, as nearly as possible, through all the points.

THE THEORY OF DEVIATION

Features of the earth's magnetism.—It has already been stated that the earth acts like a great spherical magnet, with a pole in each hemisphere which is not coincident with the geographical pole; it has also a magnetic equator which lies close to, but not coincident with, the geographical equator. (Shown on H. O. Dip Chart No. 1700.)

A magnetic needle freely suspended at a point on the earth's surface, and undisturbed by any other than the earth's magnetic influence, will lie in the plane of the magnetic meridian and at an angle with the horizon depending upon the geographical position.

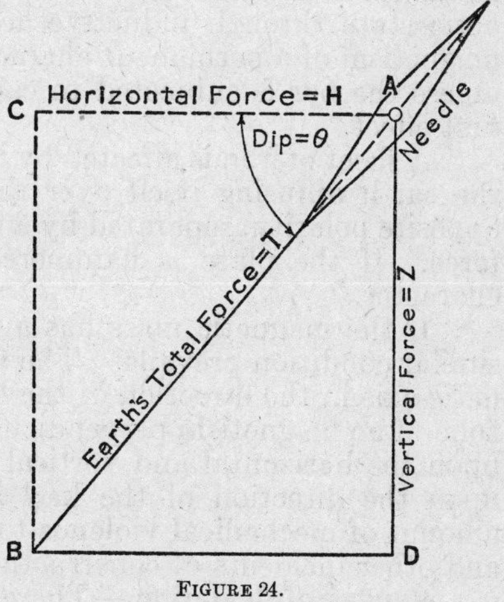

FIGURE 24.

The magnetic elements of the earth which must be considered are shown in figure 24. The earth's **total force** is represented in direction and intensity by the line AB. Since compass needles are mechanically arranged to move only in a horizontal plane, it becomes necessary, when investigating the effect of the earth's magnetism upon them, to resolve the total force into two components which in the figure are represented by AC and AD. These are known, respectively, as the **horizontal** and **vertical components** of the earth's total force, and are usually designated as H and Z. The angle CAB, which the line of direction makes with the plane of the horizon, is called the **magnetic dip,** and denoted by θ.

It is clear that the horizontal component will reduce to zero at the magnetic poles, where the needle points directly downward, and that it will reach a maximum at the magnetic equator, where the free needle hangs in a horizontal direction. The reverse is true of the vertical component and of the angle of dip.

Dip and horizontal intensity charts.—The dip may be found from H. O. Chart No. 1700 and the horizontal intensity from H. O. Chart No. 1701. The vertical intensity is equal to the horizontal intensity $\times$ tangent dip. The total intensity= $\sqrt{H^2+Z^2}$. The *vertical intensity* is given on H. O. Chart 1702.

Induction.—When a piece of unmagnetized iron or steel is brought within the influence of a magnet, certain magnetic properties are immediately imparted to the former, which itself becomes magnetic and continues to remain so as long as it is within the sphere of influence of the permanent magnet; the magnetism that it acquires under these circumstances is said to be *induced*, and the properties of *induction* are such that that end or region which is nearest the pole of the influencing magnet will take up a polarity opposite thereto. If the magnet is withdrawn, the induced magnetism is soon dissipated. If the magnet is brought into proximity again, but with its opposite pole nearer, magnetism will again be induced, but this time its polarity will be reversed. A further property is that if a piece of iron or steel, while temporarily possessed of magnetic qualities through induction, be subjected to blows, twisting, or mechanical violence of any sort, the magnetism is thus made to acquire a permanent nature.

The softer the metal, from a physical point of view, the more quickly and thoroughly will induced magnetism be dissipated when the source of influence is withdrawn; hard metal, on the contrary, is slow to lose the effect of magnetism imparted to it in any way. Hence, in regarding the different features which affect deviation, it is usual to denominate as hard iron that which possesses retained magnetism of a stable nature, and as soft iron that which rapidly acquires and parts with its magnetic qualities under the varying influences to which it is subjected.

Magnetism acquired by steel vessels in building.—The inductive action of the earth's magnetism affects all iron or steel within its influence, and the amount and permanency of the magnetism so induced depends upon the position of the metal with reference to the earth's total force, upon its character, and upon the degree of hammering, bending, and twisting that it undergoes.

An iron bar held in the line of the earth's total force instantly becomes magnetic; if held at an angle thereto it would acquire magnetic properties dependent for their amount upon its inclination to the line of total force; when held at right angles to the line there would be no effect, as each extremity would be equally near the poles of the earth and all influence would be neutralized. If, while such a bar is in a magnetic state through inductive action, it should be hammered or twisted, a certain magnetism of a permanent character is impressed upon it, which is never entirely lost unless the bar is subjected to causes equal and opposite to those that produced the first effect.

A sheet of iron is affected by induction in a similar way, the magnetism induced by the earth diffusing itself over the entire plate and separating itself into regions of opposite polarity, separated by a neutral area at right angles to the earth's line of total force. If the plate is hammered or bent, this magnetism takes up a permanent character.

If the magnetic mass has a third dimension, and assumes the form of a ship, a similar condition prevails. The whole takes up a magnetic character; there is a magnetic axis in the direction of the line of total force, with poles at its extremities and a zone of no magnetism perpendicular to it. The distribution of magnetism will depend upon the horizontal and vertical components of the earth's force in the locality and upon the direction of the keel in building; its permanency will depend upon the amount of mechanical violence to which the metal has been subjected by the riveting and other incidents of construction, and upon the nature of the metal employed.

Causes of deviation.—There are three influences that operate to produce deviation; namely, (*a*) **subpermanent magnetism;** (*b*) **transient magnetism induced in vertical soft iron,** and (*c*) **transient magnetism induced in horizontal soft iron.** Their effect will be explained.

Subpermanent magnetism is the name given to that magnetic force which originates in the ship while building, through the process explained in the preceding article. After the vessel is launched and has an opportunity to swing in azimuth, the magnetism thus induced will suffer material diminution until, after the lapse of a certain time, it will settle down to a condition that continues practically unchanged. The magnetism that remains is denominated subpermanent. The vessel will then approximate to a permanent magnet, in which the north polarity will lie in that region which was north in building and the south polarity (that which exerts an attracting influence on the north pole of the compass needle) in the region which was south in building.

Transient magnetism induced in vertical soft iron is that developed in the soft iron of a vessel through the inductive action of the vertical component only of the earth's total force, and is transient in nature. Its value or force in any given mass varies with and depends upon the value of the vertical component at the place, and is proportional to the sine of the dip, being a maximum at the magnetic pole and zero at the magnetic equator.

Transient magnetism induced in horizontal soft iron is that developed in the soft iron of a vessel through the inductive action of the horizontal component only of the earth's total force, and is transient in nature. Its value or force in any given mass varies with and depends upon the value of the horizontal component at the place, and is proportional to the cosine of the dip, being a maximum at the magnetic equator and reducing to zero at the magnetic pole.

The needle of a compass in any position on board ship will therefore be acted upon by the earth's total force, together with the three forces just described. The poles of these forces do not usually lie in the horizontal plane of the compass needle, but as this needle is constrained to act in a horizontal plane, its movements will be affected solely by the horizontal components of these forces, and its direction will be determined by the resultant of those components.

The earth's force operates to retain the compass needle in the plane of the magnetic meridian, but the resultant of the three remaining forces, when without this plane, deflects the needle, and the amount of such deflection constitutes the deviation.

Classes of deviation.—Investigation has developed the fact that the deviation produced as described is made up of three parts, which are known respectively as **semicircular, quadrantal,** and **constant** deviation, the latter being the least important. A clear understanding of the nature of each of these classes is essential for a comprehension of the methods of compensation.

Semicircular deviation is that due to the combined influence, exerted in a horizontal plane, of the subpermanent magnetism of a ship and of the magnetism induced in soft iron by the vertical component of the earth's force. If we regard the effect of these two forces as concentrated in a single resultant pole exerting an attracting influence upon the north end of the compass needle, it may be seen that there will be some heading of the ship whereon that pole will lie due north of the needle and therefore produce no deviation. Now consider that from this position the ship's head swings in azimuth to the right; throughout all of the semicircle first described an easterly deviation will be produced, and, after completing 180°, the pole will be in a position diametrically opposite to that from which it started, and will again exert no influence that tends to produce deviation. Continuing the swing, throughout the next semicircle the direction of the deviation produced will be always to the westward, until the circle is completed and the ship returns to her original neutral position. From the fact that this disturbing cause acts in the two semicircles with equal and opposite effect as easterly in one semicircle and westerly in the other, it is given the name of *semicircular* deviation.

In figure 23 a curve is depicted which shows the deviations of a semicircular nature separated from those due to other disturbing causes, and from this the reason for the name will be apparent.

Returning to the two distinct sources from which the semicircular deviation arises, it may be seen that the force due to subpermanent magnetism remains constant regardless of the geographical position of the vessel; but since the horizontal force of the earth, which tends to hold the needle in the magnetic meridian, varies with the magnetic latitude, the deviation due to the subpermanent magnetism varies inversely as the horizontal force, or as $\frac{1}{H}$. This may be readily understood if it is considered that the stronger the tendency to cling to the direction of the magnetic meridian the less will be the deflection due to a given disturbing force. On the other hand, that part of the semicircular deviation due to magnetism induced in vertical soft iron varies as the earth's vertical force, which is proportional to the sine of the dip; its effect in producing deviation, as in the preceding case, varies inversely as the earth's horizontal force—that is, inversely as the cosine of the dip; hence the ratio representing the change of deviation arising from this cause on change of latitude is $\frac{\sin \theta}{\cos \theta}$, or $\tan \theta$.

If, then, we consider the change in the semicircular deviation due to a change of magnetic latitude, it will be necessary to separate the two factors of the deviation and to remember that the portion produced by subpermanent magnetism varies as $\frac{1}{H}$, and that due to vertical induction as $\tan \theta$. But for any consideration of the effect of this class of deviation in one latitude only, the two parts may be joined together and regarded as having a single resultant.

Assuming that all the forces tending to produce semicircular deviation are concentrated in a single pole exerting an influence on the north pole of the compass, it will be seen that this can be resolved into a horizontal and a vertical component, just as the earth's magnetic force is illustrated in figure 24. It is now evident, therefore, that the horizontal component of this single magnet may be resolved into two components—one fore-and-aft and one athwartship; in this case, the semicircular forces will be represented by two magnets, one fore-and-aft and the other athwartship, and compensation may be made by two separate magnets lying respectively in the direction stated, but with their north or repelling poles in the position occupied by the south or attracting poles of the ship's force.

Figure 25 represents the conditions that have been described. Let O be the center of the compass, XX′ and YY′, respectively, the fore-and-aft and athwartship lines of the ship, and OS the direction in which the attracting pole of the disturbing force is exerted. Now, if OP be laid off on the line OS, representing the amount of the disturbing force according to some convenient scale, then O*b* and O*c*, respectively, represent, on the same scale, the resolved directions of that force in the keel line and in the transverse line of the ship. Each of these resolved forces will exert a maximum effect when acting at right angles to the needle, the athwartship one when the ship heads north or south by compass, and the longitudinal one when the heading is east or west. On any other heading than those named the deviation produced by each force will be a fraction of its maximum whose magnitude will depend upon the azimuth of the ship's head. The maximum deviation produced, therefore, forms in each case a basis for reckoning all of the various effects of the disturbing force, and is called a *coefficient*.

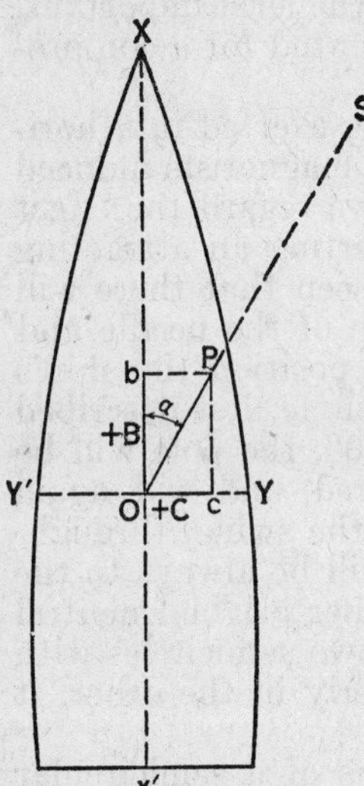

FIGURE 25.

The coefficient of semicircular deviation produced by the force in the fore-and-aft line is called B, and is reckoned as positive when it attracts a north pole toward the bow, negative when toward the stern; that produced by the athwartship force is C, and is reckoned as positive to starboard and negative to port. These coefficients are expressed in degrees.[1]

The coefficient B is approximately equal to the deviation on east; or to the deviation on west with reversed sign; or to the mean of these two. Thus in the ship having the table of deviations previously given (on page 64), B is equal to $-9° 06'$, or to $9° 56'$, or to $\frac{1}{2}(-9° 06'-9° 56')=-9° 31'$.

The coefficient C is approximately equal to the deviation on north; or to the deviation on south with reversed sign; or to the mean of these two. In the example C is equal to $-15° 29'$, or to $-17° 52'$, or to $\frac{1}{2}(-15° 29'-17° 52')=-16° 40'$.

The value of the subpermanent magnetism remaining practically constant under all conditions, it will not alter when the ship changes her latitude; but that due to induction in vertical soft iron undergoes a change when, by change of geographical position, the vertical component of the earth's force assumes a different value, and in such case the correction by means of one or a pair of permanent magnets will not remain effective. If, however, by series of observations in two magnetic latitudes, the values of the coefficients can be determined under the differing circumstances, it is possible, by solving equations, to determine what effect each force has in producing the semicircular deviation. Having done this, the subpermanent magnetism can be corrected by permanent magnets after the method previously described, and the vertical induction in soft iron can be corrected by a piece of vertical soft iron placed in such a position near the compass as to produce an equal but opposite force to the ship's vertical soft iron. This last corrector is called a **Flinders bar**.

[1] It should be remarked that in a mathematical analysis of the deviations it would be necessary to distinguish between the *approximate coefficients*, B and C, here described, as also A, D, and E, to be mentioned later, and the *exact coefficients* denoted by the corresponding capital letters of the German alphabet, which latter are in reality the *forces* producing those deviations expressed in terms of the "mean force to north" (λH), as unit. In the practical discussion of the subject here given, the question of the difference need not be entered into further.

Having thus opposed to each of the component forces a corrector of magnetic character identical with its own, a change of latitude will make no difference in the effectiveness of the compensation, for in every case the modified conditions will produce identical results in the disturbing and in the correcting force.

Quadrantal deviation is that which arises from horizontal induction in the soft iron of the vessel through the action of the horizontal component of the earth's total force. Let us consider, in figure 26, the effect of any piece of soft iron which is symmetrical with respect to the compass—that is, which lies wholly within a plane passing through the center of the needle in either a fore-and-aft or an athwartship direction. It may be seen (*a*) that such iron produces no deviation on the cardinal points (for on north and south headings the fore-and-aft iron, though strongly magnetized, has no tendency to draw the needle from a north-and-south line, while the athwartship iron, being at right angles to the meridian, receives no magnetic induction, and therefore exerts no force; and on east and west headings similar conditions prevail, the athwartship and the fore-and-aft iron having simply exchanged positions); and (*b*) the direction of the deviation produced is opposite in successive quadrants. The action of unsymmetrical soft iron is not quite so readily apparent, but investigation shows that part of its effect is to produce a deviation which becomes zero at the intercardinal points and is of opposite name in successive quadrants. From the fact that deviations of this class change sign every 90° throughout the circle, they gain the name of *quadrantal deviations.* One of the curves laid down in the Napier diagram (fig. 23) is that of quadrantal deviations, whence the nature of this disturbance of the needle may be observed. It will be noted from the diagram that quadrantal deviation is zero on headings, north, east, south, and west magnetic.

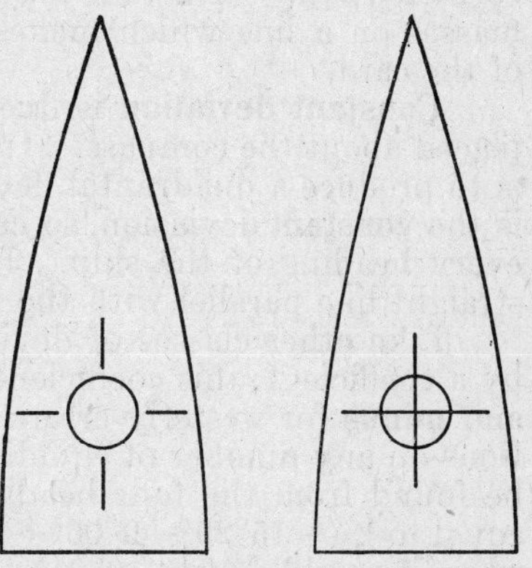

FIGURE 26.

All deviations produced by soft iron may be considered as fractions of the maximum deviation due to that disturbing influence; and consequently the maximum is regarded as a coefficient, as in the case of semicircular deviations. The coefficient due to symmetrical soft iron is designated as D, and is considered positive when it produces easterly deviations in the quadrant between north and east; the coefficient of deviations arising from unsymmetrical soft iron is called E, and is reckoned as positive when it produces easterly deviations in the quadrant between NW. and NE.; this latter attains importance only when there is some marked inequality in the distribution of metal to starboard and to port, as in the case of a compass placed off the amidship line.

D is approximately equal to the mean of the deviations on NE. and SW.; or to the mean of those on SE. and NW., with sign reversed; or to the mean of those means. In the table of deviations given on page 64, D is equal to ½ (−11° 19′+25° 35′)= +7° 08′, or to ½ (+5° 54′+10° 20′)=+8° 07′; or to ½ (7° 08′+8° 07′)=+7° 37′. By reason of the nature of the arrangement of iron in a ship, D is almost invariably positive.

E is approximately equal to the mean of the deviations on north and south; or to the mean of those on east and west with sign reversed; or to the mean of those means. In the example, E is equal to ½ (−15°29′+17°52′)=+1°11′; or to ½ (+9°06′ −9°56′)=−0°25′; or to ½ (+1°11′−0°25′)=+0°23′.

Quadrantal deviation does not, like semicircular, undergo a change upon change of magnetic latitude; being due to induction in horizontal soft iron, the magnetic force exerted to produce it is proportional to the horizontal component of the earth's magnetism; but the directive force of the needle likewise depends upon that same component; consequently, as the disturbing force exerted upon the needle increases, so does the power that holds it in the magnetic meridian, with the result that on any given heading the deflection due to soft iron is always the same.

Quadrantal deviation is corrected by placing masses of soft iron (usually two hollow spheres in the athwartship line, at equal distances on each side of the compass), with the center of mass in the horizontal plane of the needle. The distance is made such that the force exerted exactly counteracts that of the ship's iron. As the correcting effect of this iron will, like the directive force and the quadrantal disturbing force, vary directly with the earth's horizontal component, the compensation once properly made will be effective in all latitudes, provided that the compass needles are short and, consequently, exercise little or no induction on the quadrantal correctors

With compasses such as the United States Navy standard 7½-inch liquid compass, the needles of which are long and powerful, it will usually be found that the position of the spheres must be changed with change of latitude. This may be accounted for by the magnetism induced in the spheres by the compass needles at the same time and in the same manner as the earth's force. In this case the quadrantal correcting force is the resultant of the constant force due to the induction of the needles in the spheres and the variable force (the earth's horizontal force, H, varying with change in magnetic latitude) due to the induction of the earth in the spheres. This resultant of these two forces is a variable force, and, after a given quadrantal deviation is corrected in one latitude by this force, the balance will be changed upon going into another latitude and the correction will fail to hold good.

In practice, the quadrantal deviation due to unsymmetrical iron is seldom corrected; the correction may be accomplished, however, by placing the soft iron masses on a line which makes an angle to the athwartship line through the center of the card.

Constant deviation is due to induction in horizontal soft iron unsymmetrically placed about the compass. It has already been explained that one effect of such iron is to produce a quadrantal deviation, represented by one coefficient E; another effect is the **constant** deviation, so called because it is uniform in amount and direction on every heading of the ship. If plotted on a Napier diagram, it would appear as a straight line parallel with the initial line of the diagram.

Like other classes of deviation, the effect of the disturbing force is represented by a coefficient; this coefficient is designated as A, and is considered **plus** for easterly and **minus** for westerly errors. It is approximately equal to the mean of the deviations on any number of equidistant headings. In the case previously given, it might be found from the four headings, north, east, south, and west, and would then be equal to $\frac{1}{4}(-15°29'-9°06'+17°52'+9°56')=+0°48'$; or from all of the 24 headings, when it would equal $-0°01'$.

For the same reason as in the case of E, the value of A is usually so small that it may be neglected; it only attains a material size when the compass is placed off the midship line, or for some similar cause.

Like quadrantal deviation, since its force varies with the earth's horizontal force, the constant deviation will remain uniform in amount in all latitudes.

No attempt is made to compensate for this class of error.

Coefficients.—The chief value of coefficients is in mathematical analyses of the deviations and their causes. It may, however, be a convenience to the practical navigator to find their approximate values by the methods that have been given, in order that he may gain an idea of the various sources of the error, with a view to ameliorating the conditions, when necessary, by moving the binnacle or altering the surrounding iron. The following relation exists between the coefficients and the deviation:

$$d=A+B\sin z'+C\cos z'+D\sin 2z'+E\cos 2z',$$

where d is the deviation, and z' the ship's heading by compass, measured from compass north.

Mean directive force.—The effect of the disturbing forces is not confined to causing deviations; it is only those components acting at right angles to the needle which operate to produce deflection; the effect of those acting in the direction of the needle is exerted either in increasing or diminishing the directive force of the compass, according as the resolved component is northerly or southerly.

It occurs, with the usual arrangement of iron in a vessel, that the mean effect of this action throughout a complete swing of the ship upon all headings is to reduce the directive force—that is, while it varies with the heading, the average value upon all azimuths is **minus** or southerly. The result of such a condition is unfavorable from the fact that the compass is thus made more "sluggish," is easily disturbed and does not return quickly to rest, and a given deflecting force produces a greater deviation when the directive force is reduced. The usual methods of compensation largely correct this fault, but do not entirely do so; it is therefore the case that the mean combined horizontal force of earth and ship to north is generally less than the horizontal force of the earth alone; but it is only in extreme cases that this deficiency is serious.

Heeling error.—This is an additional cause of deviation that arises when the vessel heels to one side or the other. Heretofore only those forces have been considered which act when the vessel is on an even keel; but if there is an inclination from the vertical certain new forces arise, and others previously inoperative become effective. These forces are (*a*) the vertical component of the subpermanent magnetism acquired in building; (*b*) the vertical component of the induced magnetism in vertical soft iron, and (*c*) the magnetism induced by the vertical component of the earth's total force in iron which, on an even keel, was horizontal. The first two of these disturbing causes are always present, but, when the ship is upright, have no tendency to produce deviation, simply exerting a downward pull on one of the poles of the needle; the last is a new force that arises when the vessel heels.

The maximum disturbance due to heel occurs when the ship heads north or south. When heading east or west there will be no deviation produced, although the directive force of the needle will be increased or diminished. The error will increase with the amount of inclination from the vertical.

For the same reason as was explained in connection with semicircular deviations, that part of the heeling error due to subpermanent magnetism will vary, on change of latitude, as $\frac{1}{H}$, while that due to vertical induction will vary as $\tan\theta$. In south magnetic latitude the effect of vertical induction will be opposite in direction to what it is in north magnetic latitude.

The heeling error is corrected by a permanent magnet placed in a vertical position directly under the center of the compass. Such a magnet has no effect upon the compass when the ship is upright; but since its force acts in an opposite direction to the force of the ship which causes heeling error, is equal to the latter in amount, and is exerted under the same conditions, it affords an effective compensation. For similar reasons to those affecting the compensation of B and C, the correction by means of a permanent magnet is not general and must be rectified upon change of latitude.

PRACTICAL COMPENSATION

In the course of explanation of the different classes of deviation occasion has been taken to state generally the various methods of compensating the errors that are produced. The practical methods of applying the correctors will next be given.

Order of correction.—The following is the order of steps to be followed in each case. It is assumed that the vessel is on an even keel, that the compass is properly centered in the binnacle, that all surrounding masses of iron or steel are in their normal positions, all correctors removed, and that the binnacle is one in which the semicircular deviation is corrected by two sets of permanent magnets at right angles to each other.

In order to ascertain if the compass is properly centered in the binnacle, the heeling corrector may be temporarily placed in its tube and drawn from its lowest to its highest position; if no deflection is shown by the needle the compass is properly centered; if not it should be adjusted by the screws provided for the purpose.

1. Place quadrantal correctors by estimate.
2. Correct semicircular deviation.
3. Correct quadrantal deviation.
4. Swing ship for residual deviations.

The heeling corrector may be placed at any time after the semicircular and quadrantal errors are corrected. A Flinders bar can be put in place only after observations in two latitudes.

The ship is first placed on some magnetic cardinal point. If north or south, the only force (theoretically speaking) which tends to produce deflection of the needle will be the athwartship component of the semicircular force, whose effect is represented by the coefficient C. If east or west, the only deflecting force will be the fore-and-aft component of the semicircular force, whose effect is represented by the coefficient B. This will be apparent from a consideration of the direction of the forces producing deviation, and is also shown by the equation connecting the terms (where A and E are zero):

$$d = B \sin z' + C \cos z' + D \sin 2z'.$$

If the ship is headed north or south, z' being equal to 0° or 180°, the equation becomes $d = \pm C$. If on east or west, z' being 90° or 270°, we have $d = \pm B$.

This statement is exact if we regard only the forces that have been considered in the problem, but experience has demonstrated that the various correctors when in place create certain additional forces by their mutual action, and in order to correct the disturbances thus accidentally produced, as well as those due to regular causes, it is necessary that the magnetic conditions during correction shall approximate as closely as possible to those that exist when the compensation is completed; therefore the quadrantal correctors should first be placed on their arms at the positions which it is estimated that they will occupy later when exactly located. An error in the estimate will have but slight effect under ordinary conditions. It should be understood that the placing of these correctors has no corrective effect while the ship is on a cardinal point. Its object is to create at once the magnetic field with which we shall have to deal when compensation is perfected.

This having been done, proceed to correct the semicircular deviation. If the ship heads north or south, the force producing deflection is, as has been stated, the athwartship component of the semicircular force, which is to be corrected by permanent magnets placed athwartships; therefore enter in the binnacle one or more such magnets and so adjust their height that the heading of the ship by compass shall agree with the magnetic heading. When this is done all the deviation on that azimuth will be corrected.

Similarly, if the ship heads east or west, the force producing deviation is the fore-and-aft component of the semicircular force, and this is to be corrected by entering fore-and-aft permanent magnets in the binnacle and adjusting the height so that the deviation on that heading disappears.

With the deviation on two adjacent cardinal points corrected, the semicircular force has been completely compensated. Next correct the quadrantal deviation. Head the ship NE., SE., SW., or NW. The coefficients B and C having been reduced to zero by compensation, and $2z'$, on the azimuths named, being equal to 90° or 270°, the equation becomes $d = \pm D$. The soft-iron correctors are moved in or out from the positions in which they were placed by estimate until the deviation on the heading (all of which is due to quadrantal force) disappears. The quadrantal disturbing force is then compensated.

Determination of magnetic headings.—To determine when a ship is heading on any given magnetic course, and thus to know when the deviation has been corrected and the correctors are in proper position, four methods are available:

(*a*) **Swinging ship.**—Obtain by the best available method the deviations on a sufficient number of compass courses to construct a curve on the Napier diagram for one quadrant, and thus find the compass headings corresponding to two adjacent magnetic cardinal points and the intermediate intercardinal point, as north, northeast, and east, magnetic, or if time permits make a complete swing. Then put the ship successively on these courses, noting the corresponding headings by some other compass, and when it is desired to head on the various magnetic azimuths during the process of correction the ship may be steadied upon them by the auxiliary compass. Variations of this method will suggest themselves and circumstances may render their adoption convenient. The compass courses corresponding to the magnetic directions may be obtained from observations made with the auxiliary compass itself, or while making observations with another compass the headings by the auxiliary may be noted and a curve for the latter constructed, as explained on page 65, and the required headings thus deduced.

(*b*) **Azimuths.**—Ascertain in advance the true bearing of the sun at frequent intervals during the period which is to be devoted to the compensation of the compasses; apply to these the variation and obtain the magnetic bearings; record the time and bearings in a convenient tabular form, or, better still, plot a curve of magnetic azimuths of the sun on cross-section paper, the coordinates being local apparent time and magnetic bearings of the sun. Set the watch accurately for the local apparent time; then when it is required to steer any given magnetic course, set that point of the pelorus for the ship's head and set the sight vanes for the magnetic bearing of the sun corresponding to the time by watch. Maneuver the ship with the helm until the sun comes on the sight vanes, when the azimuth of the ship's head will be that which is required. The sight vanes must be altered at intervals to accord with the curve or table of times and bearings.

(*c*) Construct a curve or table showing times and corresponding magnetic bearings of the sun, and also set the watch, as explained for the previous method. Then place the sight vanes of the azimuth circle of the compass at the proper angular distance to the right or left of the required azimuth of the ship's head; leave them so set and maneuver the ship with the helm until the image of the sun comes on with the vanes. The course will then be the required one. As an example, suppose that the curve or table shows that the magnetic azimuth of the sun at the time given by the watch is N. 87° E., and let it be required to head magnetic north; when placed upon this heading, therefore, the sun must bear 87° to the right or east of the direction of the ship's head; when steady on any course, turn the sight vane to the required bearing relative to the keel. If on N. 11° W., for example, turn the circle to N. 76° E.; leave the vane undisturbed and alter course until the sun comes on. The magnetic heading is then north, and adjustment may be made accordingly.

(*d*) When ranges are available, they may be utilized for determining magnetic headings.

Summary of corrections.—To summarize, the following is the process of correcting a compass for a single latitude, where magnets at right angles are employed for compensating the semicircular deviation and where the disturbances due to unsymmetrical soft iron are small enough to be neglected.

First. All correctors being clear of the compass, place the quadrantal correctors in the position which it is estimated that they will occupy when adjustment is complete. The navigator's experience will serve in making the estimate, or if there seems no other means of arriving at the probable position they may be placed at the middle points of their supports.

Second. Steady the ship on magnetic north, east, south, or west, and hold on that heading by such method as seems best. By means of permanent magnets alter the indications of the compass until the heading coincides with the magnetic course. If heading north, magnets must be entered north ends to starboard to correct easterly deviation and to port to correct westerly, and the reverse if heading south. If heading east, enter north ends forward for easterly and aft for westerly deviations, and the reverse if heading west. (Binnacles differ so widely in the methods of carrying magnets that details on this point are omitted. It may be said, however, that the magnetic intensity of the correctors may be varied by altering either their number or their distance from the compass; generally speaking, several magnets at a distance are to be preferred to a small number close to the compass.)

Third. Steady the ship on an adjacent magnetic cardinal point and correct the compass heading by permanent magnets to accord therewith in the same manner as described for the first heading.

Fourth. Steady the ship on an intercardinal point (magnetic) and move the quadrantal correctors away from or toward the compass, keeping them at equal distances therefrom, until the compass and magnetic headings coincide.

Fifth. If time permits, it is very important that the ship should next be steadied on opposite cardinal and semicardinal points and *one-half* of the remaining deviation corrected by changing the position or number of the correctors.

The compensation being complete, the navigator should proceed immediately to swing ship and make a table of the residual deviations. Though the remaining errors will be small, it is seldom that they will be reduced to zero, and it must never be assumed that the compass may be relied upon without taking the deviation into account. Observations on eight equidistant points will ordinarily suffice for this purpose.

Compensation while cruising.—Every effort should be made to keep at least the standard and steering compasses compensated, as it is always easier to keep the compasses compensated than to keep a deviation table correct, at hand, and in use.

The following **rectangular method,** is one method by which the compasses may be kept practically compensated and, after the data are once obtained, it requires very little time or trouble.

After the first compensation is completed, or while it is being done, head the ship north or south and move the athwartship magnets up exactly 1 inch, noting by the bearing of the sun or of a distant object, the amount and direction of the effect on the compass. Then repeat the observation, lowering the magnets 1 inch, and noting the effect. Then head the ship east or west and take the same observations with the fore-and-aft magnets. Then head on an intercardinal point and record the effect of moving spheres first in and then out an inch from the correct position.

The record would then take this form:

Date ------ Latitude ------ Longitude ------

H ------ θ ------

On north, raising B magnets (6 bundles) 1 inch (from 9.85 to 8.85) causes 12°30′ easterly deviation, therefore a movement of 1/10 inch causes 1°15′ Ely.

Lowering B magnets (6 bundles) 1 inch (from 9.85 to 10.85) causes 10°15′ westerly deviation, therefore a movement of 1/10 inch causes 1°2′ Wly.

On east, raising C magnet (2 bundles) 1 inch (from 10.45 to 9.45) causes 8°15′ westerly deviation, therefore a movement of 1/10 inch causes 0°50′ Wly.

Lowering C magnet (2 bundles) 1 inch (from 10.45 to 11.45) causes 6°30′ easterly deviation, therefore a movement of 1/10 inch causes 0°39′ Ely.

On northeast, moving spheres in 1 inch (from 10.6 to 9.6) causes 4°15′ westerly deviation, therefore a movement of 1/10 inch causes 0°25′ Wly.

Moving spheres out 1 inch (from 10.6 to 11.6) causes 3°20′ easterly deviation, therefore a movement of 1/10 inch causes 0°20′ Ely.

If now it is found at any time that there is, say, 1°45′ easterly on east, it is evident that raising the C magnets 2/10 inch will correct it, and careful observations on two adjacent cardinal points and an intercardinal point are enough to recompensate. This may ordinarily be done at no expense of time and with little trouble. More confidence may be felt in the result if observations for deviations are afterwards obtained on the four cardinal points and the mean of the results on opposite courses taken for the true value; this must be done if the variation is uncertain. A new set of data observations should be taken after a large change of magnetic latitude, but it will usually be found that the changes are slight.

Theoretically the quadrantal deviation, once corrected, should remain at zero. It will usually be found, however, that the position of the spheres must be changed with change of latitude. A convenient way of dealing with this is to construct a curve showing the positions of the spheres for varying values of H. A similar curve showing the position of the heeling magnet is also convenient.

Whenever the position of any corrector is changed, a note showing new position, date, latitude, longitude, H and θ should be made on one of the blank leaves of the compass record. A complete record of this kind will be found of the utmost value in keeping track of the compasses.

Correcting heeling error.—The heeling error may be corrected by a method involving computation, together with certain observations on shore. A more practical method, however, is usually followed, though its results may be less precise. The heeling corrector is placed in its vertical tube, N. end uppermost in north latitudes, as this is almost invariably the required direction; the ship being on a course near north or south and rolling, observe the vibrations of the card, which, if the error is material, will be in excess of those due to the ship's real motion in azimuth; slowly raise or lower the corrector until the abnormal vibrations disappear, when the correction will be made for that latitude; but it must be readjusted upon any considerable change of geographical position.

In making this observation care must be taken to distinguish the vessel's "yawing" in a seaway from the apparent motion due to heeling error; for this reason it may be well to have an assistant to watch the ship's head and keep the adjuster informed of the real change in azimuth, by which means the latter may better judge the effect of the heeling error.

In the case of a sailing vessel, or one which for any reason maintains a nearly steady heel for a continuous period, the amount of the heeling error may be exactly ascertained by observing the azimuth of the sun, and corrected with greater accuracy than is possible with a vessel which is constantly rolling.

Flinders bar.—The simplest method that presents itself for the placing of the Flinders bar is one which is available only for a vessel crossing the magnetic equator. Magnetic dip charts of the world show the geographical positions at which the dip becomes zero—that is, where a freely suspended needle is exactly horizontal and where there exists no vertical component of the earth's total magnetic force. In such localities it is evident that the factor of the semicircular deviation due to vertical induction disappears and that the whole of the existing semicircular deviation arises from subpermanent magnetism. If, then, when on the magnetic equator the compass be carefully compensated, the effect of the subpermanent magnetism will be exactly opposed by that of the semicircular correcting magnets. Later, as the ship departs from the magnetic equator, the semicircular deviation will gradually acquire a material value, which will be known to be due entirely to vertical induction, and if the Flinders bar be so placed as to correct it, the compensation of the compass will be general for all latitudes.

In following this method it may usually be assumed that the soft iron of the vessel is symmetrical with respect to the fore-and-aft line and that the Flinders bar may be placed directly forward of the compass or directly abaft it, disregarding the effect of components to starboard or port. It is therefore merely necessary to observe whether a vertical soft iron rod must be placed forward or abaft the compass to reduce the deviation, and, having ascertained this fact, to find by experiment the exact distance at which it completely corrects the deviation.

The Flinders bar frequently consists of a bundle of soft iron rods contained in a case, which is secured in a vertical position near the compass, its upper end level with the plane of the needles; in this method, the distance remaining fixed, the intensity of the force that it exerts is varied by increasing or decreasing the number of rods; this arrangement is more convenient and satisfactory than the employment of a single rod at a variable distance.

The United States Navy Flinders bar, type II, is made of carefully annealed pure soft iron, 2 inches in diameter, total length 24 inches, consisting of pieces 12 inches, 6 inches, 3 inches, 1½ inches, and ¾ inch (2 of these) long. Hardwood blocks of the same dimensions are used to support the proper length of Flinders bar at the top of a fixed brass tube, which is secured ordinarily at the forward end of the binnacle in the fore-and-aft line.

It should be noted, however, that it is extremely difficult to get soft iron rods of a satisfactory quality, for, after being placed, they seldom fail to take up more or less subpermanent magnetism. This magnetism, due to shock of gunfire, vibration while cruising or on speed trials, etc., is subject to greater and more erratic changes than that of the harder portion of the hull, and its proximity to the compass intensifies the effect of the variations in its magnetic properties.

When it is not possible to correct the compass at the magnetic equator there is no ready practical method by which the Flinders bar may be placed; the operation will then depend entirely upon computation, and as a mathematical analysis of deviations is beyond the scope laid out for this work the details of procedure will not be gone into; the general principles involved are indicated, and students seeking more must consult the various works that treat the subject fully.

It has been explained that each coefficient of semicircular deviation (B and C) is made up of a subpermanent factor varying as $\frac{1}{H}$ and of a vertical induction factor varying as $\tan \theta$. If we indicate by B_S and B_V or C_S and C_V, respectively, the parts due to each force when $H=1$ and $\theta=45°$, then for any other H and θ we may write the equations of the coefficients:

$$B=B_S\times\frac{1}{H}+B_V\times\tan\theta;\text{ and }C=C_S\times\frac{1}{H}+C_V\times\tan\theta.$$

Now if we distinguish by the subscripts $_1$ and $_2$ the values in the first and in the second position of observation, respectively, of those quantities that vary with the magnetic latitude, we have:

$$B_1=B_S\times\frac{1}{H_1}+B_V\times\tan\theta_1,\ B_2=B_S\times\frac{1}{H_2}+B_V\times\tan\theta_2;$$

$$C_1=C_S\times\frac{1}{H_1}+C_V\times\tan\theta_1,\ C_2=C_S\times\frac{1}{H_2}+C_V\times\tan\theta_2.$$

The values of the coefficients in both latitudes are found from the observations made for deviations; the values of the horizontal force and of the dip at each place are known from magnetic charts; hence for the first pair of equations just given: Errors on E–W heading

$$B_V\tan\theta_2=\frac{(B_1H_1-B_2H_2)\tan\theta_2}{H_1\tan\theta_1-H_2\tan\theta_2}\qquad \frac{B_S}{H_2}=\frac{B_2\tan\theta_1-B_1\tan\theta_2}{\tan\theta_1-\frac{H_2}{H_1}\tan\theta_2}$$

and for the second pair, errors on N–S heading

$$C_V\tan\theta_2=\frac{(C_1H_1-C_2H_2)\tan\theta_2}{H_1\tan\theta_1-H_2\tan\theta_2}\qquad \frac{C_S}{H_2}=\frac{C_2\tan\theta_1-C_1\tan\theta_2}{\tan\theta_1-\frac{H_2}{H_1}\tan\theta_2}$$

This gives the errors due to vertical soft iron and subpermanent magnetism respectively *in the second latitude* when the vessel is on the indicated magnetic headings. Correct these errors respectively by the Flinders bar and the small permanent magnets; but since, as before stated, horizontal soft iron may usually be regarded as symmetrical, C_V is assumed as zero and the bar placed in the midship line.

The adjustment for change of latitude.—The compensation of quadrantal deviation, once properly made, remains effective in all latitudes, excepting as noted on pages 71 and 72; but unless a Flinders bar is used a correction of the semicircular deviation made in one latitude will not remain accurate when the vessel has materially changed her position on the earth's surface. With this in mind the navigator must make frequent observations of the compass error during a passage and must expect that the table of residual deviations obtained in the magnetic latitude of compensation will undergo considerable change as that latitude is departed from. The new deviations may become so large that it will be found convenient to readjust the semicircular correcting magnets. This process is very simple.

When correctors at right angles are used, provide for steadying the ship, by an auxiliary compass or by the pelorus, upon two adjacent magnetic cardinal points. Put the ship on heading north or south (magnetic), and raise or lower the athwartship magnets or alter their number until the deviation disappears; then steady on east or west (magnetic) and similarly adjust the fore-and-aft magnets. Swing ship for a new table of residual deviations.

It must be borne in mind that the compensation of the compass is not an exact science and that the only safeguard is unceasing watchfulness on the navigator's part. As the ship's iron is partly "hard" and partly "soft," the subpermanent magnetism may change appreciably from day to day, especially in a new ship as the magnetism absorbed in building "shakes out." After a ship has been in service for 1 or 2 years, the magnetic conditions may be said to be "settled." They undergo changes, however, to a greater or less extent, on account of the following influences or conditions:

(1) Continuous steaming on one general course for several days, especially in rough weather, or lying alongside a dock on one heading for a long period.

(2) Extensive alterations or repairs in the vicinity of the compass. The use of scaling hammers about the deck have caused a change in the compass.

(3) Steaming with boilers under forced draft where the funnel is near the compass has been known to cause a change of more than 10°, the retained magnetism being "cooked out."

(4) A grounded searchlight circuit has caused a change in the compass.

(5) Ships have reported changes of as much as 7° when struck by lightning or after passing through very severe thunderstorms.

The binnacle fittings must be carefully inspected from time to time to see that the correctors have not changed position. At least once a year the quandrantal correctors should be examined for polarity. This can be done by moving them, one at a time, as close to the compass as practicable and then revolving them slowly about the vertical axis; if the compass is deflected, the magnetism should be removed by bringing the sphere to a low red heat and then letting it cool slowly.

There is little excuse for large deviations in a standard or steering compass, and they should not be allowed to exist.

No matter how well a compass may be adjusted observations for deviation should be made during every watch. Special observations should be made after any change of course exceeding 15°. Retained magnetism cannot be compensated.

541524°—43——6

CHAPTER IV

PILOTING

Piloting, in the sense given the word by modern and popular usage, is the art of conducting a vessel in channels and harbors and along coasts, where landmarks and aids to navigation are available for fixing the position, and where the depth of water and dangers to navigation are such as to require a constant watch to be kept upon the vessel's course and frequent changes to be made therein.

Piloting is the most important part of navigation and the part requiring the most experience and nicest judgment. An error in position on the high seas may be rectified by later observation, but an error in position while piloting usually results in disaster. Therefore the navigator should make every effort to be proficient in this important branch, bearing in mind that a modern vessel is usually safe on the high seas and in danger when approaching the land and making the harbor.

Requisites.—The navigator should have ready on approaching the land the charts of the coast and the largest scale detail charts of the locality at which he expects to make his landfall, the sailing directions, the light and buoy list, and the tide and current tables, all corrected for the latest information from the Notices to Mariners and other sources. The usual instruments employed in navigation should be at hand and in good working order. The most important instrument—the sounding machine or fathometer—should be in place and in working order at least a day before the land is to be made. *The importance of the soundings when making a landfall cannot be exaggerated.* The latest deviation table for the standard compass must be at hand.

Laying the course.—Mark a point upon the chart at the ship's position; then mark another point for which it is desired to steer; join the two by a line drawn with the parallel ruler, and, maintaining the direction of the line, move the ruler until its edge passes through the center of the compass rose and note the direction. If the compass rose indicates *true* directions, this will be the true course, and must be corrected for variation and deviation (by applying each in the *opposite* direction to its name) to obtain the compass course; if it is a *magnetic* rose, the course need be corrected for deviation only.

Before putting the ship on any course a careful look should be taken along the line over which it leads to be assured that it clears all dangers.

Fixing position methods.—A navigator in sight of objects whose positions are shown upon the chart may locate his vessel by any one of the following basic methods: (*a*) cross bearings of two known objects; (*b*) the bearing and distance of a known object; (*c*) the bearing of a known object and the angle between two known objects; (*d*) two bearings of a known object separated by an interval of time, with the run during that interval; (*e*) sextant angles between three known objects. Besides the foregoing there are two methods by which, without obtaining the precise position, the navigator may assure himself that he is clear of any particular danger. These are: (*f*) the danger angle; (*g*) the danger bearing.

The choice of the method will be governed by circumstances, depending upon which is best adapted to prevailing conditions.

Radio compass stations and **Radio direction finders** now enable the navigator to obtain bearings far beyond the range of visibility, and also at night or in a fog. The use of radio bearings is but an extension of the basic methods just listed, which methods will be described in detail first.

Cross bearings.—Choose two objects whose position on the chart can be unmistakably identified and whose respective bearings from the ship differ, as nearly as possible by 90°; observe the bearing of each, either by compass or pelorus, taking one as quickly as possible after the other; see that the ship is on an even keel at the time the observation is made, and, if using the pelorus, be sure also that she heads exactly on the course for which the pelorus is set. Correct the bearings so that they will be either true or magnetic, according as they are to be plotted by the true or magnetic compass rose of the chart—that is, if observed by compass, apply deviation and variation to obtain the true bearing, or deviation only to obtain the magnetic. If observed by pelorus, that instrument should be set for the true or magnetic heading, according to which reading is required, and no further correction will be necessary. Draw on the chart, by means of the parallel rulers, lines which shall pass through the respective objects in the direction that each was observed to bear. As the ship's position on the chart is known to be at some point on each of these lines, it must be at their intersection, the only point that fulfills both conditions.

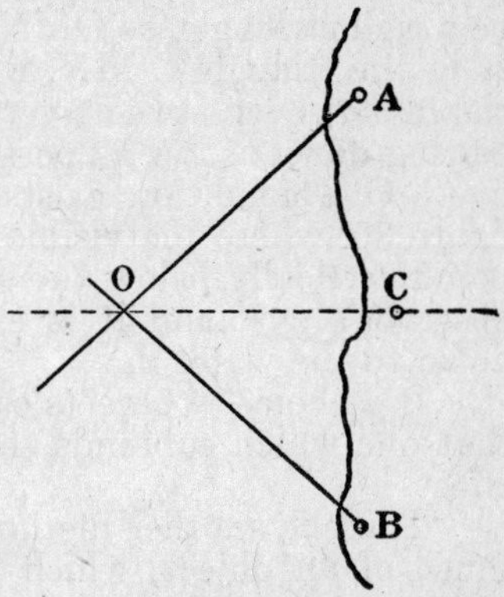

FIGURE 27.

In figure 27, if A and B are the objects and OA and OB the lines passing through them in the observed directions, the ship's position will be at O, their intersection.

When a third object is available a bearing of that may be taken and plotted. If this line intersects at the same point as the other two (as the bearing OC of the object C in the figure), the navigator may have a reasonable assurance that his "fix" is correct; if it does not, it indicates an error somewhere, and it may have arisen from inaccurate observation, incorrect determination or application of the deviation, or a fault in the chart.

If it be possible to avoid it, objects should not be selected for cross bearings which subtend an angle at the ship of less than 30° or more than 150°, as, when the lines of bearing approach parallelism, a small error in an observed bearing gives a large error in the result. For a similar reason objects near the ship should be taken in preference to those at a distance.

What may be considered as a form of this method can be used when only one known object is in sight by taking, at the same instant as the bearing, an altitude of the sun or other heavenly body and noting the time; work out the sight and obtain the line of position, and the intersection of this with the direction line from the object will give the observer's position in the same way as from two terrestrial bearings.

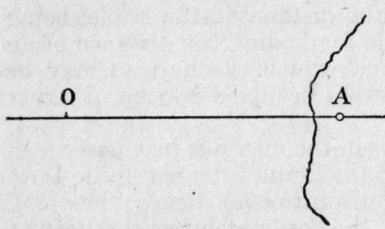

FIGURE 28.

Bearing and distance of a known object.—When only one object is available, the ship's position may be found by observing its bearing and distance. Follow the preceding method in the manner of taking, correcting, and plotting the bearing; then, on this line, lay off the distance from the object, which will give the point occupied by the observer. In figure 28, if A represents the object and AO the bearing and distance, the position sought will be at O.

The stadimeter is an instrument similar to a sextant, employed in the United States Navy, reading directly the distance of the object observed when set for the height of the object.

Range-finding instruments are used in the United States Navy for readily finding the distance of an observed object, and these instruments do not require knowledge of the height of the object.

It is not ordinarily easy to find directly the distance of an object at sea. The most accurate method is when its height is known and it subtends a fair-sized angle from the ship, in which case the angle may be measured by a sextant and the distance computed or taken from a table. Table 9 of this work gives distances up to 5 miles, corresponding to various heights and angles. Table 10 gives distances up to

85 miles for elevations up to 15,500 feet, and Captain Lecky's "Danger Angle and Offshore Distance Tables" carries the computation much further. The use of this method at great distances must not be too closely relied upon, as small errors, such as those due to refraction, may throw out the results to a material extent, but it affords an excellent approximation; and, as this method of fixing position is employed only when no other is available, the best possible approximation has to suffice.

In measuring vertical angles, strictness requires that the observation should be so made that the angle at the foot of the object should equal 90° and that the triangle be a right triangle, as OMN, figure 29, where the line OM is truly horizontal, and not as in the triangle O′MN, where the condition is not fulfilled. This error is inappreciable, however, save at very close distances, when it may be sufficiently corrected by getting down as low as possible on board the vessel, so that the eye is near the water line. One condition exists, however, where the error is material—that shown in figure 30, where the visible shore line is at M′, a considerable distance from M, the point vertically below the summit. In this case there is nothing to mark M in the observer's eye, and it is essential that all angles be measured from a point close down to the water line.

If a choice of objects can be made, the best results will be obtained by observing that one which subtends the greatest angle, as small errors will then have the least effect.

There is another method, known as Buckner's method, for determining the distance of an object, which is available under certain circumstances. This consists

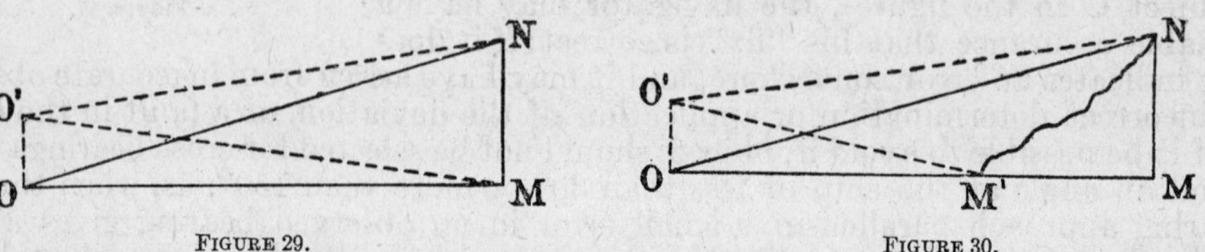

FIGURE 29. FIGURE 30.

in observing, from a position aloft, the angle between the object and the line of the sea horizon beyond. By reference to Table 11 will be found the distance in yards corresponding to different angles for various heights of the observer from 20 to 120 feet. The method is not accurate beyond moderate distances (the table being limited to 5,000 yards) and is obviously only available for finding the distance of an isolated object, such as an islet, vessel, or target, over which the horizon may be seen. In employing this method the higher the position occupied by the observer the more precise will be the results.

In observing small angles, such as those that occur in the methods just described, it is sometimes convenient to measure them *on and off* the limb of the sextant. First look at the bottom of the object and reflect the top down into coincidence; then look through the transparent part of the horizon glass at the top and bring the bottom up by its reflected ray. The mean of the two readings will be the true angle, the index correction having been eliminated by the operation.

When the methods of finding distance by a vertical or a horizon angle are not available, it must be obtained by such means as exist. Estimate the distance by the appearance; take a sounding, and note where the depth falls upon the line of bearing; at night, if atmospheric conditions are normal, consider that the distance of a light when sighted is equal to its maximum range of visibility, remembering that its range is stated for a height of eye of 15 feet; or employ such method as suggests itself under the circumstances, regarding the result, however, as an approximation only.

The bearing of a known object and the angle between two known objects.—This method is seldom employed, as the conditions always permit of cross bearings being taken, and the latter is generally considered preferable.

Take a bearing of a known object by compass or pelorus and observe the sextant angle between some two known objects. The line of bearing is plotted as in former methods. In case one of the objects of the observed angle is that whose bearing is taken, the angle is applied, right or left as the case may be, to the bearing; thus giving the direction of the second object, which is plotted from the compass rose and parallel rulers. If the object whose bearing is taken is not one of the objects of the angle, lay off the angle on a three-armed protractor, or piece of tracing paper, and swing it (keeping the legs or lines always over the two objects) until it passes over the line of bearing, which defines the position of the ship; there will, except in special cases, be two points of intersection of the line with the circle thus described, and the navigator must know his position with sufficient closeness to judge which is correct.

Two bearings of a known object.—This is a most useful method, which is frequently employed, certain special cases arising thereunder being particularly easy of application. The process is to take a careful bearing and at the same moment read the patent log; then, after running a convenient distance, take a second bearing and again read the log, the difference in readings giving the intervening run; when running at a known speed, the time interval will also afford a means for determining the distance run.

The problem is as follows: In figure 31, given OA, the direction of a known object, A, at the first observation; PA, the direction at the second observation; and OP, the distance traversed between the two; to find AP, the distance at the second observation.

Knowing the angle POA, the angular distance of the object from right ahead at the first bearing; OPA, the angular distance from right astern at the second bearing; and OP, the distance run; we have by plane trigonometry:

$$PAO = 180° - (POA + OPA); \text{ and}$$

$$AP = OP \times \frac{\sin POA}{\sin PAO}.$$

If, as is frequently the case, we desire to know the distance of passing abeam we have:

$$AQ = AP \times \sin OPA.$$

FIGURE 31.

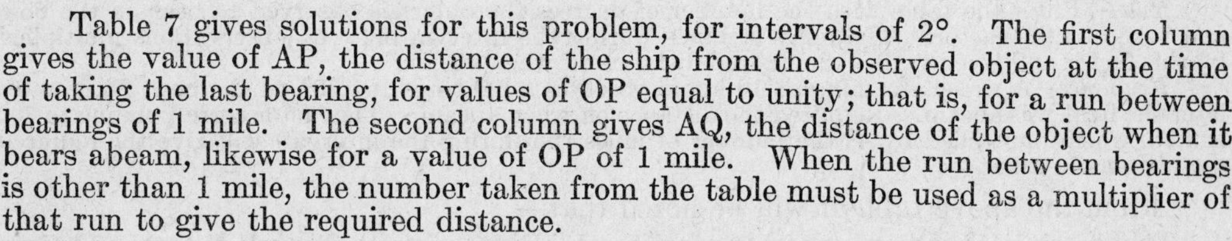

Table 7 gives solutions for this problem, for intervals of 2°. The first column gives the value of AP, the distance of the ship from the observed object at the time of taking the last bearing, for values of OP equal to unity; that is, for a run between bearings of 1 mile. The second column gives AQ, the distance of the object when it bears abeam, likewise for a value of OP of 1 mile. When the run between bearings is other than 1 mile, the number taken from the table must be used as a multiplier of that run to give the required distance.

Example.—A vessel on a course 128° takes the first bearing of an object at 154°, and the second at 182°, running in the interval 0.8 mile. Required the distance at which she will pass abeam.

Difference between course and first bearing, 26°.
Difference between course and second bearing, 54°.
Multiplier from second column, Table 7, 0.76.
0.8 mile×0.76=0.6 mile, distance of passing abeam.

As has been said, there are certain special cases of this problem where it is exceptionally easy of application; these arise when the multiplier is equal to unity and the distance run is therefore equal to the distance from the object. When the angular distance on the bow at the second bearing is twice as great as it was at the first bearing, the distance of the object from the ship *at second bearing* is equal to the run, the multiplier being 1.0. For if, in figure 32, when the ship is in the first position, O, the object

A bears $\alpha°$ on the bow, and at the second position, P, $2\alpha°$, we have in the triangle APO, observing that $APO=180°-2\alpha$, and $POA=\alpha$:

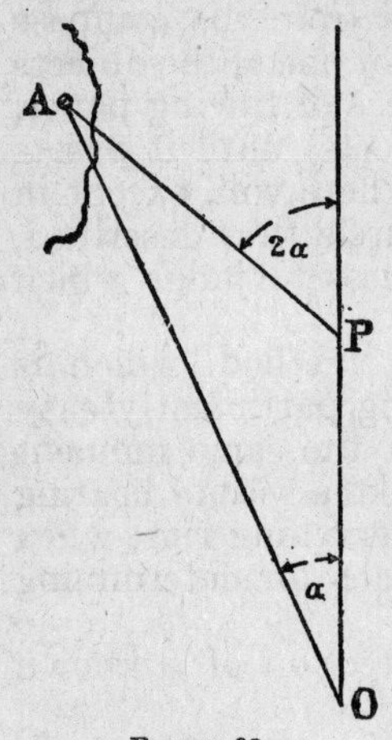

FIGURE 32.

$$PAO=180°-(POA+APO),$$
$$=180°-(\alpha+180°-2\alpha),$$
$$=\alpha.$$

Or, since the angles at O and A are equal to each other, the sides OP and AP are equal or the distance at second bearing is equal to the run. This is known as *doubling the angle on the bow.*

Bow and beam bearing.—A case where this holds good is familiar to every navigator as the *bow and beam bearing,* where the first bearing is taken when the object is broad on the bow (45° from ahead) and the second when it is abeam (or 90° from ahead). In that case the distance at second bearing and the distance abeam are identical and equal to the run between bearings.

Bearings of objects are frequently given with reference to the fore and aft line of the vessel. They are known as **relative bearings.** The terms **on the bow, beam,** or **quarter,** mean 4 points or 45°, 8 points or 90°, and 12 points or 135°, from the ship's head.

The following table is taken from the table of natural tangents (Table 31), and is useful for finding the distance from an object when abeam, by the distance run between the beam bearing and any other bearing before or abaft the beam.

°		°		°		°		°	
35	0. 70	45	1. 00	55	1. 43	65	2. 14	75	3. 73
36	. 73	46	1. 04	56	1. 48	66	2. 25	76	4. 01
37	. 75	47	1. 07	57	1. 54	67	2. 36	77	4. 33
38	. 78	48	1. 11	58	1. 60	68	2. 48	78	4. 70
39	. 81	49	1. 15	59	1. 66	69	2. 61	79	5. 14
40	. 84	50	1. 19	60	1. 73	70	2. 75	80	5. 67
41	. 87	51	1. 23	61	1. 80	71	2. 90	81	6. 31
42	. 90	52	1. 28	62	1. 88	72	3. 08	82	7. 12
43	. 93	53	1. 33	63	1. 96	73	3. 27	83	8. 14
44	. 97	54	1. 38	64	2. 05	74	3. 49	84	9. 51

Rule.—Enter the table with the number of degrees the object is observed to bear on the bow and take out the factor. The miles steamed during the interval between observations multiplied by this factor will give in miles the desired distance off when abeam.

Example.—A vessel steaming at 10 knots observes a light bearing 70° on the bow, 24 minutes later the light was abeam. Required the distance off when abeam. The factor corresponding to 70° is 2.75, which multiplied by 4 (the number of miles run during the interval) will give the required quantity as 11 miles.

From the above table it will be noted that—

First bearing 45° on bow; second bearing abeam. Distance steamed equals distance off object.

First bearing 63½° on bow; second bearing abeam. Twice distance steamed equals distance off object.

First bearing 71½° on bow; second bearing abeam. Three times distance steamed equals distance off object.

Distance passed abeam.—When the first bearing is 26½° from ahead, and the second 45°, the distance *at which the object will be passed abeam* will equal the run between bearings. This is true of any two such bearings whose natural cotangents differ by unity, and the following table is a collection of solutions of this relation in which the pairs of bearings are such that, when observed in succession from ahead upon the same fixed object, the distance run between the bearings will be equal to the distance of the fixed object when it bears abeam, provided that a steady course has been steered, unaffected by current or drift.

The marked pairs will probably be found the most convenient ones to use, as they involve whole degrees only.

When the fixed object bears as per any entry of the first column, take the time and the reading of the patent log. Repeat this procedure on reaching the bearing of the adjacent entry in the second column. The difference of the patent-log readings will be the distance at which the fixed object will be passed abeam.

Bearings from ahead (Relative)

First	Second	First	Second	First	Second
°	°	°	°	°	°
20	29¾	28	48½	37	71¾
21	31¾	*29	51	38	74¼
*22	34	30	53¾	39	76¾
23	36¼	31	56¼	*40	79
24	38¾	*32	59	41	81¼
*25	41	33	61½	42	83½
26	43½	34	64¼	43	85¾
26½	45	35	66¾	*44	88
*27	46	36	69¼	*45	90

This general solution includes the 26½°–45° rule as well as the seven-tenths rule to be explained later; furthermore, it has the advantage that the approximate determination of the distance offshore, at which the fixed object will be passed, need not wait for the 45° bearing.

There are two whole-degree pairs by which such a determination can be made before the 45° bearing is reached. It is possible to get five whole-degree bearings on observations by the time the fixed object bears 30° forward of the beam, as follows: 22°–34°, 25°–41°, 27°–46°, 29°–51°, 32°–59°. Of these, the last three should be reasonably accurate; the acuteness of the first angle in all such observations accounts for the discrepancies noted in practice. The use of the table given above may be found to be more convenient than the methods of plotting about to be described, and the use of Table 7; but it does not take the place of those methods. Table 7 covers all combinations of bearings in which the first bearing is taken when the object is 20° or more on the bow.

The seven-tenths rule.—If bearings of the fixed object be taken at two (2) and four (4) points on the bow (22½° and 45°), seven-tenths (0.7) of the run between bearings will be the distance at which the point will be passed abeam.

From the combination of the seven-tenths rule and the 26½°–45° rule, there follows an interesting corollary, i. e., if bearings of an object at 22½° and 26½° on the bow be taken, then seven-thirds (7/3) of the distance run in the interval will be the distance when abeam.

If a bearing is taken when an object is two (2) points (22½°) forward of the beam, and the run until it bears abeam is measured, then its distance when abeam is seven-thirds (7/3) of the run. This rule, particularly, is only approximate.

In case the 45° bearing on the bow is lost, in order to find the distance abeam that the object is passed, note the time when the object bears 26½° forward of the beam, and again when it has the same bearing abaft the beam; the distance run in this interval is the distance of the object when it was abeam.

To steer an arc course in order to round a light, point, or other object, without fixes, and be sure the course itself does not decrease the initial distance, proceed as follows if there is no current, for which allowance must be made. Stand on course until the light is at the required distance, determined by one or more of the methods described. Immediately bring the light abeam, and do not let it get forward of the beam again, then the course will not decrease the initial distance. When the light is one-half point abaft the beam again bring it abeam; hold course until it is again one-half point abaft the beam, repeating this procedure until the light is rounded. A polygon is thus described, whose nearest approach to the light is the initial distance. The number of sides of the polygon may be increased indefinitely, so that the light may be rounded, by changing the course just enough to keep the light abeam, after it is first brought abeam.

Graphic methods.—There are graphic methods of solving this problem that are considered by some more convenient than the use of multipliers. Draw upon the chart the lines OA and PA (fig. 33), passing through the object on the two observed bearings; set the dividers to the distance run, OP; lay down the parallel rulers in a direction parallel to the course and move them toward or away from the observed object until some point is found where the distance between the lines of bearing is exactly equal to the distance between the points of the dividers; in the figure this occurs when the rulers lie along the line OP, and therefore O represents the position of the ship at the first bearing and P at the second. For any other positions—O′P′, O″P″—the condition is not fulfilled.

A graphic method often used to fix the vessel's approximate position by successive bearings on the same object, is to "run up" previous bearings to the time of the last one.

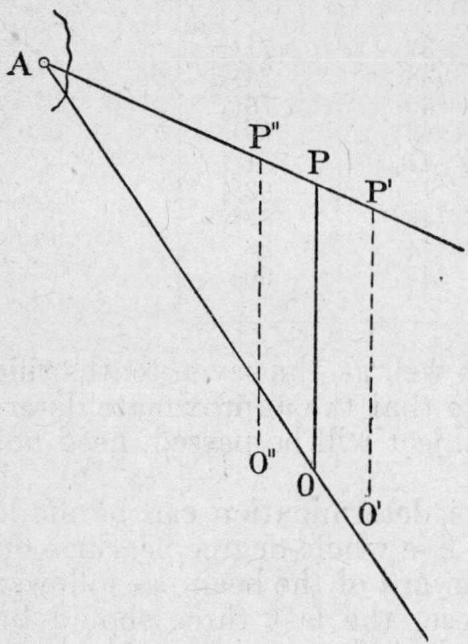

FIGURE 33.

In figure 34 taking XY as the course of the vessel proceeding past an object O, lay off OZ parallel to XY. Considering OA as the first bearing, at the time the second bearing OB is observed, compute the distance made good during the time interval between the two bearings. Measure this distance off along OZ, giving the point P, from which lay down the line PA′, parallel to OA. The intersection of PA′ with OB is the approximate fix of the vessel. Similarly, at the time of the third bearing OC, compute and lay off the distances made since the first and second bearings, and lay down the "run up" bearings P′A″ and QB′.

Another graphic solution is given by the maneuvering board and the various modifications of it that are in use among navigators.

The method of obtaining position by two bearings of the same object is one of great value by reason of the fact that it is frequently necessary to locate the vessel when there is but one landmark in sight. Careful navigators seldom, if ever, miss the opportunity for a bow and beam bearing in passing a lighthouse or other well-plotted object; it involves little or no trouble, and always gives a feeling of added security, however little the position may be in doubt. If about to pass an object abreast of which there is a danger—a familiar example of which is when a lighthouse marks a point off which are rocks or shoals—a good assurance of clearance should be obtained before bringing it abeam, either by doubling the angle on the bow, or, if the object be sighted in time, by using any of the pairs of bearings tabulated above.

Error of fix.—It must be remembered that, however convenient, the fix obtained by two bearings of the same object will be in error unless the course and distance are correctly estimated, the course "made good" and the distance "over the ground" being required. Difficulty will occur in estimating the exact course when there is bad steering, a cross current, or when a ship is making leeway; errors in the allowed run will arise when the vessel is being set ahead or back by a current or when the logging is inaccurate. A current directly with the course of the ship, if unallowed for, will give a determination of position too close to the object observed; and a current directly against the course of the ship, if unallowed for, will give a determination of position too far away from the object observed. The existence of such a current *will not be* revealed by taking more than two successive bearings. All such observations will place the ship on the same apparent course, which course will be parallel to the course made good and to the course steered but in error in its distance from the observed object by an amount dependent upon the ratio of the speed of ship over ground to the speed of ship by log. A current oblique to the course of the ship will give a determination of position which will be erroneous. The existence of such a current but not its amount *will be* revealed by taking more than two observations; in this case, following the usual method of plotting, the determination resulting from any two successive bearings will fail to agree with the determination from any other two. If, in such a case, the observed bearings be drawn upon the chart and the distances run by log between them be laid down on the scale of the chart upon a piece of paper, a course may be found by trial, upon which course the intervals of run correspond with the intervals between the lines of bearing. The apparent course thus determined, which

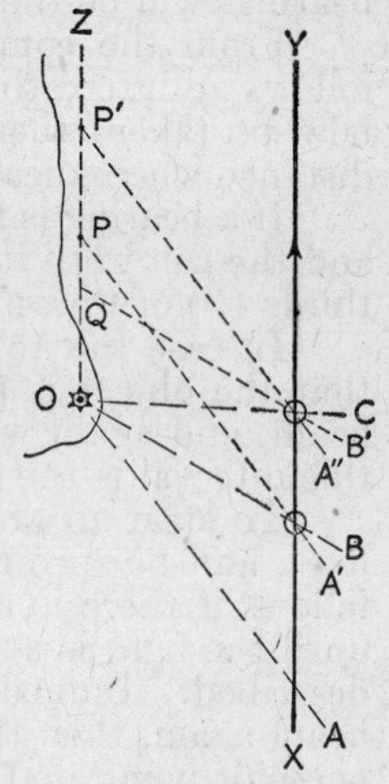

FIGURE 34.

must always be oblique to the course steered, will be parallel to the course actually being made good, but will be in error in its distance from the observed object by an amount dependent upon the ratio of the speed of ship over the ground to the speed of ship by log. If there is an apparent shortening of the distance run from earlier to later observations, or a shortening of the time if the speed is invariable, there is a component of set toward the fixed object. Therefore, if in a current of any sort, due allowance must be made, and it should be remembered that more dependence can be placed upon a position fixed by simultaneous bearings or angles, when two or more objects are available, than by two bearings of a single object.

At 2^h 00^m p. m. a bearing observed on a lighthouse was 344° when the vessel was steaming 270° (true) at 12 knots, a 3 knot tide was setting the vessel northeast (45°). At 2^h 20^m the lighthouse bore 10° true. Plot position (fig. 35).

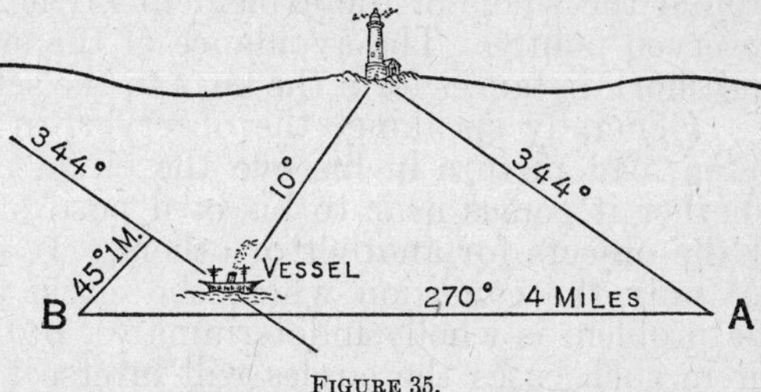

FIGURE 35.

Sextant angles between three known objects.—This method, involving the solution of the *three-point problem*, will, if the objects be well chosen, give the most accurate results of any. It is largely employed in surveying, because of its precision; and it is especially valuable in navigation, because it is not subject to errors arising from imperfect knowledge of the compass error, improper logging, or the effects of current, as are the methods previously described.

Three objects represented on the chart are selected and the angles measured with sextants of known index error between the center one and each of the others. Preferably there should be two observers and the two angles be taken simultaneously, but one observer may first take the angle which is changing more slowly, then take the other, then repeat the first angle, and consider the mean of the first and last observations as the value of the first angle. The position is usually plotted by means of the three-armed protractor. Set the right and left angles on the instrument, and then move it over the chart until the three beveled edges pass respectively and simultaneously through the three objects. The center of the instrument will then mark the ship's position which may be pricked on the chart or marked with a pencil point through the center hole. When the three-armed protractor is not at hand, the tracing-paper protractor will prove an excellent substitute, and may in some cases be preferable to it, as, for instance, when the objects angled on are so near the observer as to be hidden by the circle of the instrument. A graduated circle printed upon tracing paper permits the angles being readily laid off, but a plain piece of tracing paper may be used and the angles marked by means of a small protractor. The tracing-paper protractor permits the laying down, for simultaneous trial, of a number of angles, where special accuracy is sought.

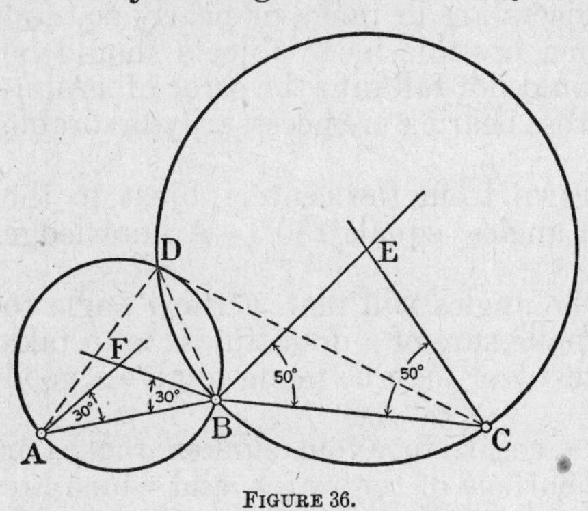

FIGURE 36.

The three-point problem, by which results are obtained in this method, is: to find a point such that three lines drawn from this point to three given points shall make given angles with each other.

Let A, B, and C, in figure 36, be three fixed objects on shore, and from the ship, at D, suppose the angles CDB and ADB are found equal, respectively, to 40° and 60°.

With the complement of CDB, 50°, draw the lines BE and CE; the point of intersection will be the center of a circle, on some point of whose circumference the ship must be. Then, with the complement of the angle ADB, 30°, draw the lines AF and BF, meeting at F, which point will be the center of another circle, on some point of whose circumference the ship must be. Then D, the point of intersection of the circumference of the two circles, will be the position of the ship.

The correctness of this solution may be seen as follows: Take the first circle, DBC; in the triangle EBC, the angle at E, the center, equals $180° - 2 \times 50° = 2$

(90°—50°), twice the complement of 50°, which is twice the observed angle; now if the angle at the center subtended by the chord BC equals twice the observed angle, then the angle at any point on the circumference subtended by that chord, which equals half the angle at the center, equals the observed angle; so the required condition is fulfilled. Should either of the angles exceed 90°, the excess of the angle over 90° must be laid off on the opposite side of the lines joining the stations.

The intersection of the circles becomes less sharp as the centers E and F approach each other; and finally the problem becomes indeterminate when the centers coincide—that is, when the three observed points and the observer's position all fall upon the same circumference; the two circles then coincide and there is no intersection. Such a case is called a "revolver" or "swinger," because the protractor will swing around the whole of the explement of the arc ABC, everywhere passing through the observed points. The avoidance of the swinger and the employment of large angles and short distances form the keys to the selection of favorable objects.

Generally speaking, the observer, in judging which objects are the best to be taken, can picture in his eye the circle passing through the three points and note whether it comes near to his own position. If it does, he must reject one or more of the objects for another or others. It should be remembered that he must avoid not only the condition where the circle passes exactly through his position (when the problem is wholly indeterminate), but also all conditions approximating thereto, for in such cases the circles will intersect at a very acute angle, and the inevitable small errors of the observation and plotting will produce large errors in the resulting fix.

Without giving an analysis of reasons, which may be found in various works that treat the problem in detail, the following may be enumerated as the general conditions which result in a *good* fix:

(*a*) When the center object of the three lies between the observer and a line joining the other two, or lies nearer than either of the other two.

(*b*) When the sum of the right and left angles is equal to or greater than 180°.

(*c*) When two of the objects are in range, or nearly so, and the angle to the third is not less than 30°.

(*d*) When the three objects are in the same straight line.

A condition that limits all of these is that angles should be large—at least as large as 30°—excepting in the case where two objects are in range or nearly so, and then the other angle must be of good size. When possible, near objects should be used rather than distant ones. The navigator should not fall into the error of assuming that objects which would give good cuts for a cross bearing are necessarily favorable for the three-point solution.

In a revolver, the angle formed by lines drawn from the center object to the other two, added to the sum of the two observed angles, equals 180°. A knowledge of this fact may aid in the choice of objects.

If in doubt as to the accuracy with which the angles will plot, a third angle to a fourth object may be taken. Another way to make sure of a doubtful fix is to take one compass bearing, by means of which even a revolver may be made to give a good position.

The danger angle.—When steaming along a coast, to avoid sunken rocks, or shoals, or dangerous obstructions at or below the surface of the water, and which are marked on the chart, the navigator may pass these at any desired distance by using what is known as a **danger angle,** of which there are two kinds, namely, the horizontal and vertical danger angles. The former requires two well-marked objects indicated on the chart, lying in the direction of the coast, and sufficiently distant from each other to give a fair-sized horizontal angle; the latter requires a well-charted object of known height.

In figure 37, let AMB be a portion of the coast along which a vessel is steaming on the course CD; A and B two prominent objects shown on the chart; S and S′ are two outlying shoals, reefs, or dangers. In order to pass outside of the danger S′ take the middle point of the danger as a center and the given distance from the center it is desired to pass as radius, and describe a circle. Pass a circle through A and B tangent to the seaward side of the first circle. To do this, it is only necessary to join A and B and draw a line perpendicular to the middle of AB, and then ascertain by trial the location of the center of the circle EAB. Measure the angle AEB, set the sextant to this angle, and remembering that AB subtends the same angle at all points of the arc AEB, the ship will be outside the arc AEB, and clear the danger S′, as long as AB does not subtend an angle greater than AEB, to which the sextant is set. At the same time in order to avoid the danger S, take the middle point of the danger S and with the desired distance as a radius describe a circle. Pass a second circle through A and B tangent to this circle at G, measure the angle AGB with a protractor, then, as long as the chord

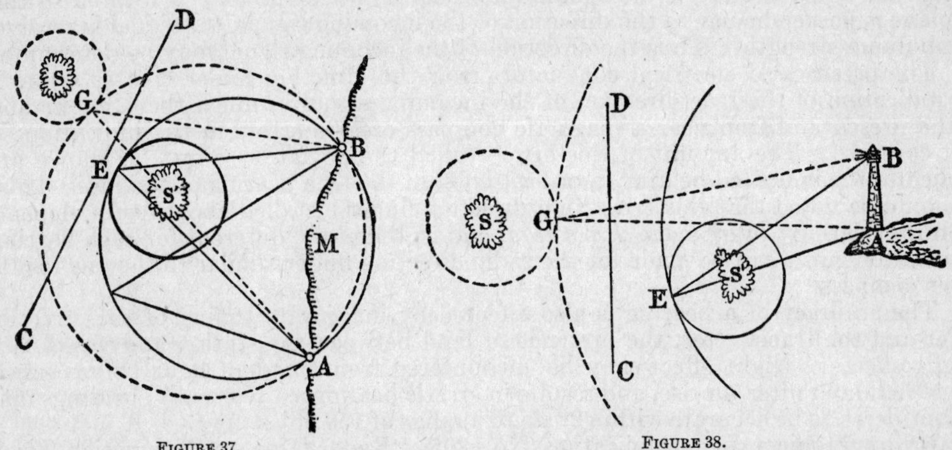

FIGURE 37. FIGURE 38.

AB subtends an angle greater than AGB, the ship will be inside the circle AGB. Therefore, the ship will pass between the dangers S and S′ as long as the angle subtended by AB is less than AEB and greater than AGB.

The vertical danger angle involves the same general principle, as can be readily seen without explanation by reference to the figure 38 in which AB represents a vertical object of known height.

The danger bearing.—This is a method by which the navigator is warned by a compass bearing when the course is leading into danger. Suppose a vessel to be steering a course, as indicated in figure 39, along a coast which must not be approached within a certain distance, the landmark A being a guide. Let the navigator draw through A the line XA, clear of the danger at all points, and note its direction by the compass rose; then let frequent bearings be taken as the ship proceeds, and so long as the bearings YA, ZA, are to the *right* of XA he may be assured that he is on the *left* or safe side of the line.

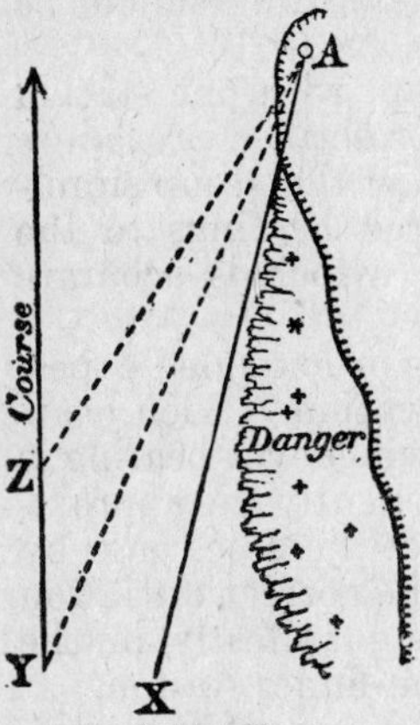

FIGURE 39.

If, as in the case given, there is but one object in sight and that nearly ahead, it would be very difficult to get an exact position, but this method would always show whether or not the ship was on a good course, and would, in consequence, be of the greatest value. And even if there were other objects visible by which to get an accurate fix it would be a more simple matter to note, by an occasional glance over the sight vane of the pelorus or compass, that the ship was making good a safe course than to be put to the necessity of plotting the position each time.

It will occasionally occur that two natural objects will so lie that when in range they mark a danger bearing; advantage should be taken of all such, as they are easier to observe than a compass bearing; but if in a locality with which the navigator has not had previous acquaintance the compass bearing of all ranges should be observed and compared with that indicated on the chart in order to make sure of the identity of the objects. The utility of ranges, either artificial or natural, as guides in navigation, extends also to established lines of bearing giving the true or magnetic direction of fixed objects, such as lines of bearing limiting the sectors of navigational lights.

Radio bearings may be employed in determining a vessel's position, utilizing the basic methods described above. They are particularly useful during fog or periods of reduced visibility, and when beyond visible range of the shore.

Radio bearings may be obtained through the use of radio-direction finders on board ship, radio-direction-finder stations on shore, and special radio beacons on shore.

A radio-direction finder is basically a radio receiving set, equipped with a special loop type of antenna mounted on a dummy compass and capable of being rotated in azimuth. When the plane of the loop is parallel to the direction of the incoming signal, the signal is received at maximum strength; when the loop is rotated so that its plane is perpendicular to the direction of the incoming signal, the signal is received at minimum strength. Thus the direction of the incoming signal may be determined.

The presence of electrical conductors near the direction finder creates errors in the indication of the true direction of the incoming signal in much the same manner as the presence of iron near a magnetic compass creates errors in the indications of that compass. The amount of this error (called the deviation) must be known and applied to the indicated bearing in order to obtain the true bearing of the radio signal. It should be noted that this error, in a direction finder installed aboard ship, depends upon the bearing *relative to the ship's head*, and is, therefore, different for each bearing. A deviation curve can be made for the radio direction finder similar to the one for the ship's compass.

The accuracy of a bearing is also affected by inaccurate tuning of the direction finder and the transmitter, the presence of land between the station and vessel, and "night effect." Night effect may be encountered from one-half hour before sunset to one-half hour after sunrise, and results in erratic bearings. Normally, bearings may be considered to be accurate within 2° up to a range of 150 miles.

Hydrographic Office Publication No. 205, "Radio Aids to Navigation," sets forth, in detail, the regulations and procedure concerning radio bearings and lists the location, frequency, and other details of all stations which may be employed by a navigator in determining his position by radio. A copy of this book should be in the radio room or on the bridge for ready reference.

In order to obtain a bearing from a radio-direction-finder station ashore, the procedure laid down in Hydrographic Office Publication No. 205 must be followed. Stated briefly, a ship desiring a bearing calls the direction-finder station on the prescribed frequency, the station replies and directs the vessel to send M. O.'s. The vessel transmits M. O.'s for 50 seconds, the station then informs the vessel of her true bearing from the station. Bearings reported by the station as "doubtful" should be used with great caution.

In certain areas two or three stations may operate as a group, with one station as the master or control station of the group. By following the prescribed procedure a vessel may request her bearings from all or a number of stations of the group simultaneously. The master station in this case transmits the desired bearings to the vessel. Group bearings of this type give the navigator a "fix" which is accurate within small limits.

Certain direction-finder stations, particularly those on islands or extended capes, are equipped to furnish two corrected true bearings for any observation. Such bearings when furnished ships may differ by approximately 180° and whichever bearing is suitable should be used. Mariners receiving bearings which are evidently the approximate reciprocal of the correct bearing should not attempt to correct these bearings by applying 180° correction, as such a correction would not include the correct deviation error at the direction-finder station. Vessels receiving bearings manifestly in the wrong semicircle should request the other bearings from the direction-finder station.

Radio-direction-finder sets aboard ship enable bearings to be taken of transmissions by radio beacons, other ships, aircraft, and shore stations. The bearings obtained are relative bearings and the true bearings are found by applying the ship's heading and the deviation error to the bearings obtained.

In some sets the operator cannot tell from which side of the ship the signals are coming. If in doubt, another bearing should be taken a short time later, after the ship has steamed a short distance and the direction the bearing is changing noted.

Radio-beacons have been established at appropriate places along the coast line. These beacons are mechanically operated to send out radio waves of approximately uniform strength in all directions. Vessels equipped with radio-direction finders can take their own bearings of these radio beacons at any time. Each radio beacon has a characteristic signal to facilitate identification by the navigator. The location of the beacons and the characteristics of each may be found in Hydrographic Office Publication No. 205.

Plotting radio bearings.—Radio bearings are plotted on the chart and used to obtain a "fix" in the same manner as visual bearings are plotted. They may be used separately when no other bearings are available, or they may be combined with visual bearings having due regard for the possible inaccuracies of the radio bearing.

A track of a radio wave between the transmitter and a receiver is a great circle track. It can be plotted directly upon a gnomonic or Lambert chart, but to plot it on the more generally used Mercator chart, a correction must be applied to convert the great circle bearing to a rhumb line. Table 1 is a conversion table for this purpose. The explanation of Table 1 should be read carefully before applying corrections. The correction to a radio bearing when the distance is less than 50 miles is negligible and is not usually applied. For distances over 50 miles, however, the correction may make an appreciable difference in the plotted position.

Radio bearings are not absolutely accurate, due to any of the reasons more fully discussed in Hydrographic Office Publication No. 205. However, barring unusual conditions the bearings given by shore stations may be considered accurate to within 2°. In plotting it is suggested that lines be drawn upon both sides of each radio bearing at an angular distance from the bearing equal to the estimated probable error. In case of intersecting radio bearings the ship's most probable position is in the area inclosed by these outer lines.

Soundings.—The practice should be followed of employing one or two leadsmen to take and report soundings continuously while in shoal water or in the vicinity of dangers. The soundings must not be regarded as fixing a position, but they afford a check upon the positions obtained by other methods. An exact agreement with the soundings on the chart need not be expected, as there may be some little inaccuracies in reporting the depth on a ship moving with speed through the water, or the tide may cause a discrepancy, or the chart itself may lack perfection; but the soundings should agree in a general way, and a marked departure from the characteristic bottom shown on the chart should lead the navigator to verify his position and proceed with caution; especially is this true if the water is more shoal than expected.

But if the soundings in shallow water when landmarks are in sight serve merely as an auxiliary guide, those taken (usually with the sonic depth finder, sounding machine, or deep-sea lead) when there exist no other means of locating the position, fulfill a much more important purpose. In thick weather, when approaching or running close to the land, and at all times when the vessel is in less than 100 fathoms of water and her position is in doubt, soundings should be taken continuously and at regular intervals, and, with the character of the bottom, systematically recorded. By laying the soundings on tracing paper, along a line which represents the track of the ship according to the scale of the chart, and then moving the paper over the chart, keeping the various courses parallel to the corresponding directions on the chart, until the observed soundings agree with those laid down, the ship's position will then be approximately determined.[1] While some localities, by the sharpness of the characteristics of their soundings, lend themselves better than others to accurate determinations by this method, there are few places where the navigator cannot at least keep out of danger by the indications, even if they tell him no more than that the time has come when he must anchor or lie off till conditions are more favorable.

Lights.—Before coming within range of a light the navigator should acquaint himself with its characteristics, so that when sighted it will be recognized. The charts, sailing directions, and light lists give information as to the color, character, and range of visibility of the various lights. Care should be taken to note all of these and compare them when the light is seen. If the light is of the flashing, quick flashing, or occulting variety the duration of its periods should be noted with a stop watch to identify it. If a fixed light, a method that may be employed to make sure that it is not a vessel's light is to descend several feet immediately after sighting it and observe if it disappears from view; a navigational light will usually do so, excepting in misty weather, while a vessel's light will not. The reason for this is that navigational lights

[1] It is possible to fit a line of soundings in several positions on a chart, so caution should be used with this plan.

are as a rule sufficiently powerful to be seen at the farthest point to which the ray can reach without being interrupted by the earth's curvature. They are therefore seen at the first moment that the ray reaches an observer on a ship's deck, and are cut off if he lowers the eye. A vessel's light, on the other hand, is usually limited by its intensity and does not carry beyond a distance within which it is visible at all heights.

Care must be taken to avoid being deceived on first sighting a light, as there are various errors into which the inexperienced may fall. The glare of a powerful light is often seen beyond the distance of visibility of its direct rays by the reflection downward from particles of mist in the air; the same mist may also cause a white light to have a distinctly reddish tinge, or it may obscure a light except within short distances. When a light is picked up at the extreme limit at which the height of the observer will permit, a fixed light may appear flashing, as it is seen when the ship is on the crest of a wave and lost when in the hollow or trough.

Many lights are made to show different colors in different sectors within their range, and by consulting the chart or books the navigator may be guided by the color of the sector in which he finds himself; in such lights one color is generally used on bearings whence the approach is clear, and another covers areas where dangers are to be encountered.

The visibility of lights is usually stated for an assumed height of the observer's eye of 15 feet, and must be modified accordingly for any other height. But it should be remembered that atmospheric and other conditions considerably affect the visibility, and it must not be positively assumed, on sighting a light, even in perfectly clear weather, that a vessel's distance is equal to the range of visibility; it may be either greater or less, as the path of a ray of light near the horizon receives extraordinary deflection under certain circumstances; the conditions governing this deflection are discussed in chapter X.

Buoys.—While buoys are valuable aids, the navigator should always employ a certain amount of caution in being guided by them. In the nature of things it is never possible to be certain of finding buoys in correct position, or, indeed, of finding them at all. Heavy seas, strong currents, ice, or collisions with passing vessels may drag them from their places or cause them to disappear entirely, and they are especially uncertain in unfrequented waters, or those of nations that do not keep a good lookout upon their aids to navigation. When, therefore, a buoy marks a place where a ship must be navigated with caution, it is well to have a danger angle or bearing as an additional guide instead of placing too much dependence upon the buoy being in place.

Different nations adopt different systems of coloring for their buoys. The following system has been adopted by the United States:

In approaching the channel, etc., from seaward, red buoys, with even numbers, will be found on the starboard side.

In approaching the channel, etc., from seaward, black buoys, with odd numbers, will be found on the port side.

Buoys painted with red and black horizontal stripes will be found on obstructions, with channel ways on either side of them, and may be left on either hand in passing.

Buoys painted with white and black perpendicular stripes will be found in mid-channel, and must be passed close-to to avoid danger.

All other distinguishing marks to buoys will be in addition to the foregoing, and may be employed to mark particular spots.

Perches, with balls, cages, etc., will, when placed on buoys, be at turning points, the color and number indicating on what side they shall be passed.

Nun buoys, properly colored and numbered, are usually placed on the starboard side, and can buoys on the port side of channels.

Day beacons (except such as are on the sides of channels, which will be colored like buoys) are constructed and distinguished with special reference to each locality and particularly in regard to the background upon which they are projected.

Fogs and fog signals.—As with lights, the navigator should, in a fog, acquaint himself with the characteristics of the various sound signals which he is likely to pick up, and when one is heard its periods should be timed and compared with those given in the light lists to insure its proper identity.

Experiment has demonstrated that sound is conveyed through the atmosphere in a very uncertain way; that its intensity is not always increased as its origin is approached; and that areas within its range at one time will seem silent at another and that the apparent direction and distance of the sound must not be closely relied upon. Add to these facts the possibility that, for some cause, the signal may not be working as it should be, and we have reason for observing the rule to proceed with the utmost caution when running near the land in a fog.

The transmission of sound through water from the submarine bells and oscillators [2] that have been installed on many light vessels, and at points of danger, is much more certain than the transmission of sound through air, and can be received in such a way by vessels equipped with submerged microphones on each side as to enable the direction of the submarine bell to be approximately determined.

Characteristic radio signals are automatically transmitted continuously during thick or foggy weather from radiobeacon stations in many parts of the world; the bearing of such a station may be read from a ship's radiocompass.

The method of plotting soundings on a tracing cloth will give a valuable indication of position. Moreover soundings will warn the navigator of the approach to shallow water, when, if his position is at all in doubt, it is wisest to anchor before it becomes too late.

It is worth remembering that when in the vicinity of a bold bluff shore vessels are sometimes warned of a too close approach by having their own fog signals echoed back from the cliffs; indeed, from a knowledge of the velocity of sound in air (1,100 feet per second), it is possible to gain some rough idea of the distance in such a case.

A rough distance can be estimated with this formula—

$$\text{Dist. in ft. from cliff} = \frac{\text{No. of elapsed seconds} \times 1{,}100}{2}$$

The velocity of sound in water is about 4,900 feet per second.

Radio beacon stations are now equipped with fog-signaling apparatus and send out simultaneous radio and sound signals. The distance from the sending station is found by noting the elapsed interval between the time of arrival of radio signal and sound signal, and multiplying this interval, expressed in seconds, by the velocity per second of sound in air (1,100 feet), or the velocity per second of sound in water (4,800 feet), according as the sound signals are received through air or through water.

By thus determining the distance from a fog-signal station to different positions between which the course and distance are known, the position of the vessel could be approximately found in a manner analogous to that which would apply in figure 31 if the distances AO and AP were known in addition to the length and direction of OP.

Bell buoys, whistle buoys, foghorns (either operated by compressed air or by hand), sirens, steam whistles, explosions (usually from a gun), all depend upon the transmission of sound through the air and are often unreliable. Apart from the influence of the wind and with no apparent reason, large zones of silence often occur at varying directions and different distances from the origin of a sound, so entire dependence can never be placed upon these fog signals.

The wind may throw the sound up or down, depending upon circumstances, so lookouts should be stationed aloft, on the bridge, and on deck.

A fog sometimes creeps imperceptibly shoreward, unobserved at first by the lightkeeper, while a vessel enveloped in the fog confidently approaches the land, depending upon a signal which is not being sounded.

Tides and currents.—The information relating to the tides given on the chart and in other publications should be studied, as it is of importance for the navigator to know not only the height of the tide above the plane of reference of the chart, but also the direction and force of the tidal current.

The plane of reference adopted for soundings varies with different charts; the United States charts for the Atlantic coast are given for mean low water. Charts of the Pacific coast of the United States, Hawaiian Islands, Philippine Islands, and Alaska are given for the mean of the lower low waters. Hydrographic Office charts from Puget Sound to Alaska are given for low water ordinary springs. British charts in those places where the diurnal inequality is considerable, use the level of Indian Spring low water which is about the lowest possible low water.

[2] Submarine oscillators have been heard at distances exceeding 25 miles and submarine bells have been heard at distances exceeding 15 nautical miles.

When traversing waters in which the depth exceeds the vessel's draft by only a small margin, account must be taken of the fact that strong winds or a high barometer may cause the water to fall below even a very low plane of reference. On coasts where there is much diurnal inequality in the tides the amount of rise and fall can not be depended upon, and additional caution is necessary.

A careful distinction should be made between the vertical *rise and fall* of the tide, which is marked at the transition periods by a stationary height, or *stand*, and the tidal current, which is the horizontal transfer of water as a result of the difference of level, producing the *flood and ebb*, and the intermediate condition, or *slack*. It seldom occurs that the turn of the tidal stream is exactly coincident with the high and low water, and in some channels the current may outlast the vertical movement which produces it by as much as three hours, the effect being that when the rise is at a stand the tidal stream is at its maximum and when the current is slack the rise or fall is going on with its greatest rapidity. Care must be taken to avoid confounding the two.

The effect of this tide wave in causing currents may be illustrated by two simple cases:

(1) Where there is a small tidal basin connected with the sea by a large opening.

(2) Where there is a large tidal basin connected with the sea by a small opening.

In the first case the velocity of the current in the opening will have its maximum value when the height of the tide within is changing most rapidly, i. e., at a time about midway between high and low water. The water in the basin keeps at approximately the same level as the water outside. The flood stream corresponds with the rising and the ebb with the falling of the tide.

In the second case the velocity of the current in the opening will have its maximum value when it is high water or low water without, for then there is the greatest head of water for producing motion. The flood stream begins about 3 hours after low water, and the ebb stream about 3 hours after high water, slack water thus occuring about midway between the tides.

Along most shores which lack features like bays and tidal rivers, the current usually turns soon after high water and low water.

The swiftest current in straight portions of tidal rivers is usually in the middle of the stream, but in curved portions the most rapid current is toward the outer edge of the curve, and here the water will be deepest. The pilot rule for best water is to follow the ebb-tide reaches.

Countercurrents and eddies may occur near the shores of straits, especially in bights and near points. A knowledge of them is useful in order that they may be taken advantage of or avoided.

A swift current often occurs in the narrow passage connecting two large bodies of water, owing to their considerable difference of level at the same instant. The several passages between Vineyard Sound and Buzzards Bay are cases in point. In the Woods Hole Passage the maximum strength of the tidal streams occurs near high and low water.

Tide rips are made by a rapid current setting over an irregular bottom, as at the edges of banks where the change of depth is considerable.

Generally speaking, the rise and fall and strength of current are at their minimum along straight stretches of coast upon the open ocean, while bays, bights, inlets, and large rivers operate to augment the tidal effects, and it is in the vicinity of these that the highest tides and strongest currents are found. The navigator need not be surprised in cruising along a coast to notice that the vessel is set more strongly toward or from the shore in passing an indentation, and that the evidences of tide will appear more marked near the mouth. Usually more complete data are furnished in charts and tide tables regarding the rise and fall, and it frequently occurs that the information regarding the tidal current is comparatively meager; the navigator must take every means to ascertain the direction and force of the tidal and other currents, either from the set shown between successive well-located positions of the ship, or by noting the ripple of the water around buoys, islets, or shoals, the direction in which vessels at anchor are riding, and the various other visible effects of the current.

Current arrows on the chart must not be regarded as indicating absolutely the conditions that are to be encountered. They represent the mean of the direction and force observed, but the observations upon which they are based may not be complete, or there may be reasons that bring about a departure from the normal state.

Charts.—The chart should be carefully studied, and among other things all of its notes should be read, as valuable information may be given in the margin which it is not practicable to place upon the chart abreast the locality affected.

The navigator will do well to consider the source of his chart and the authority upon which it is based. Confidence is always felt in a chart issued by the government of the more important maritime nations which maintain well-equipped offices for the special purpose of acquiring and treating hydrographic information. Always note the character of the survey from which the chart has been constructed; and, finally, take care that the chart is of recent issue or bears correction of a recent date.

Proceed with caution when the chart of the locality is based upon an old survey, or one whose source does not carry with it the presumption of accuracy. Although the original survey was a good one, a sandy bottom, in a region where the currents are strong or the seas heavy, is liable to undergo in time marked changes; and where the depth is affected by the deposit or removal of silt, as in the vicinity of the estuaries of large river systems, the behavior is sometimes most capricious. Large blank spaces on the chart where no soundings are shown may be taken as an indication that no soundings were made, and are to be regarded with suspicion, especially if the region abounds in reefs or pinnacle rocks, in which case only the closest sort of a survey can be considered as revealing all the dangers. All of these facts must be duly weighed.

When navigating by landmarks the chart of the locality which is on the largest scale should be used. The hydrography and topography in such charts appear in greater detail, and bearings and angles may be plotted with increased accuracy.

Summation.—The navigator must know the exact draft of the ship when approaching the land. Details should be studied of the charts required to be used and the charts should be read in such a way that a mental picture will be formed of how the land and the various aids to navigation will look when sighted, remembering that the position of the sun at different times of day, or the position of the moon at night, affects the appearance of the land as presented to the navigator approaching from seaward. Study must be made of the day, night, and fog characteristics of all aids to navigation in the locality. The state of the tide and the force and direction of the current at all times when in pilot waters must be known. The navigator, in making a plan for entering a strange port, should give very careful previous study to the chart, and should carefully select what appear to be the most suitable marks for use, also providing substitutes for use in case those selected as most suitable should prove unreliable by not being recognized with absolute certainty. Buoys seen at a distance, in approaching a channel, are often difficult to place or identify, because all may appear equally distant, though in reality far apart. Ranges should be noted, if possible, and the lines drawn, both for leading through the best water in channels and also for guarding against particular dangers. For the latter purpose, safety bearings should in all cases be laid down where no suitable ranges offer. The courses to be steered in entering should also be laid down and distances marked thereon. If intending to use the sextant and danger angle in passing dangers, and especially in passing between dangers, the danger circles should be plotted and regular courses planned, rather than to run haphazard by the indications of the angle alone, with the possible trouble to be apprehended from wild steering at critical points.

The vessel's position should not be allowed to be in doubt at any time, even in entering ports considered safe and easy of access, and should be constantly checked by continuing to use for this purpose those marks concerning which there can be no doubt until others are unmistakably recognized.

The ship should ordinarily steer exact courses and follow exact lines as planned from the chart, changing course at exact points, and, where the distances are considerable, the position on the line should be checked at frequent intervals, recording the time and the reading of the patent log. This is desirable, even where it may seem unnecessary for safety; because, if running by the eye alone and the ship's exact position be suddenly required, as in a sudden squall, fixing at that particular moment might be impossible.

The habit of running exact courses with precise changes of courses will be found most useful when it is desired to enter port or pass through inclosed waters during

541524°—43——7

fog by means of the buoys; here safety demands that the buoys be made successively, to do which requires, if the fog be dense, very accurate courses and careful attention to the times, rate of speed, and the set of the current. Failure to make a buoy as expected leaves no safe alternative but to anchor at once.

It is useful to remember that in passing between dangers where there are no suitable leading marks, as, for instance, between two islands or an island and the main shore, with dangers extending from both, a midchannel course may be steered by the eye alone with great accuracy, as the eye is able to estimate very closely the position midway between visible objects.

In piloting among coral reefs or banks, a time should be chosen when the sun will be astern, conning the vessel from aloft or from an elevated position forward. The line of demarcation between the deep water and the edges of the shoals, which generally show as green patches, is indicated with surprising clearness. This method is of frequent application in the numerous passages of the Florida keys.

Changes of course should in general be made by exact amounts, naming the new course or the amount of the change desired, rather than by ordering the helm to be put over and then steadying when on the desired heading, with the possibility of the attention being diverted and so forgetting in the meantime that the ship is still swinging. The helmsman, knowing just what is desired and the amount of change to be made, is thus enabled to act more intelligently and to avoid wild steering, which in narrow channels is a very positive source of danger.

Coast piloting involves the same principles and requires that the ship's positions be continuously determined or checked as the landmarks are passed. On well-surveyed coasts there is a great advantage in keeping near the land, thus holding on to the marks and the soundings, and thereby knowing at all times the position, rather than keeping offshore and losing the marks, with the necessity of again making the land from vague positions, and perhaps the added inconvenience of fog or bad weather, involving a serious loss of time and fuel.

The route should be planned for normal conditions of weather with suitable variations where necessary in case of fog or bad weather or making points at night, the courses and distances, in case of regular runs over the same route, being entered in a notebook for ready reference, as well as laid down on the chart. The danger circles for either the horizontal or the vertical danger angles should be plotted, wherever the method can be usefully employed, and the angles marked thereon; many a mile may thus be saved in rounding dangerous points, with no sacrifice in safety. Ranges should also be marked in, where useful for positions or for safety, and also to use in checking the deviation of the compass by comparing, in crossing, the compass bearing of the range with its magnetic bearing, as given by the chart.

In proceeding to sea from an anchorage, it is well for the navigator to select natural ranges that suggest themselves from his chart or from the natural features of the land that surrounds the harbor. From these ranges it can be told when the vessel stops, goes ahead, or how the vessel is turning. By continuous use of ranges, a vessel can clear the harbor without the use of bearings plotted on the chart.

Changes of course will in general be made with mark or object abeam, the position (a new "departure") being then, as a rule, best and most easily obtained.

Lead and sounding machine.—In making the land in a fog the sounding machine must be kept going at intervals of half an hour some hours before it is expected that soundings can be obtained. Several soundings taken at random will not locate a ship, but on the contrary may lead to disaster. In using the sounding machine be careful that the man handling the tube does not invert the tube when taking it from the tube case, as this would allow water to run toward the closed end of the tube, causing a discoloration of the coating and thus bring about an incorrect sounding. It is also essential that the lead be cleanly and freshly armed for each cast. The bottom having been picked up, a graphic record of the soundings may be laid down on tracing cloth and an approximation made of the position of the ship. Keep a sharp lookout for any landmarks that might show up during a momentary lifting of the fog and have keen ears listening for an aerial or submarine fog signal. Having picked up any such signal, make sure to ascertain exactly what landmark it is. From now on proceed with caution and determine whether it is better to anchor or to proceed through the harbor channel in the fog. If, having approached the land

and failed to hear fog signals at the time they were expected to be heard, and the soundings indicate a dangerous proximity to shore, the only safe course is either to anchor or to stand off. When running slowly in a fog (which caution, as well as the law, requires that one should do) it must be borne in mind that the relative effect of current is increased; for instance, the angle of deflection from the course caused by a cross set is greater at low than at high speed. It is worth remembering that when in the vicinity of a bold bluff shore vessels are sometimes warned of a too-close approach by having their own fog signals echoed back from the cliffs; indeed, from a knowledge of the velocity of sound it is possible to gain some rough idea of the distance in such a case. Great caution must be used in approaching a bold coast in a fog and, unless soundings can be got that will reasonably assure the navigator of his distance from the coast, the only safe course is to stand off, if the depth of the water does not permit of anchoring.

The best aids at the disposal of the navigator when running in a fog are the sounding machine and the hand lead, and the navigator will do well to make great use of them. Even in clear weather the sounding machine may be a great aid to the navigator in verifying his position.

In approaching the land and entering harbors, the navigator must bear in mind that rules of the road in inland waters sometimes differ from those used on the high sea, and should inform himself of the boundaries of the waters where different rules of the road obtain.

Records.—It will be found a profitable practice to pay careful attention to the recording of the various matters relating to the piloting of the ship. A notebook should be kept at hand on deck or on the bridge, in which are to be entered all bearings or angles taken to fix the position, all changes of course, important soundings, and any other facts bearing upon the navigation. (This book should be different from the one in which astronomical sights and offshore navigation are worked.) The entries, though in memorandum form, should be complete; it should be clear whether bearings and courses are true, magnetic, or by compass; and it is especially important that the time and patent log readings should be given for each item recorded. The value of this book will make itself apparent in various directions; it will afford accurate data for the writing of the ship's log; it will furnish interesting information for the next run over the same ground; it will provide a means by which, if the ship be shut in by fog, rain, or darkness, or if there be difficulty in recognizing landmarks ahead, the last accurate fix can be plotted and brought forward; and, finally, if there should be a mishap, the notebook would furnish evidence as to where the trouble had been.

The chart on which the work is done should also be made an intelligible record, and to this end the pencil marks and lines should not be needlessly numerous, heavy, or long. In plotting bearings, draw lines only long enough to cover the probable position. Mark intersections or positions by drawing a small circle around them, and writing neatly abreast them the time and patent-log reading. Indicate the courses and danger bearings by full lines and mark them appropriately, preferably giving both magnetic (or true) and compass directions. A great number of lines extending in every direction may lead to confusion; however remote the chance may seem, the responsibilities of piloting are too serious to run even a small risk.

Finally, on anchoring, record and plot the position by bearings or angles taken after coming to; observe that the berth is a safe one, or, if in doubt, send a boat to sound in the vicinity of the ship to make sure.

CHAPTER V

THE SAILINGS

In considering a vessel's position at sea with reference to any other place, either one that has been left or one toward which the vessel is bound, five terms are involved—the **course,** the **distance,** the **difference of latitude,** the **difference of longitude,** and the **departure.** The solutions of the various problems that arise from the mutual relation of these quantities are called **sailings.**

Kinds of sailings.—When the only quantities involved are the course, distance, difference of latitude, and departure, the process is denominated **plane sailing.** In this method the earth is regarded as a plane, and the operation proceeds as if the vessel sailed always on a perfectly level surface. When two or more courses are thus considered, they are combined by the method of **traverse sailing.** It is evident that the number of **miles** of latitude and departure can thus be readily deduced; but, while one mile always equals one minute in difference of latitude, one mile of departure corresponds to a difference of longitude that will vary with the latitude in which the vessel is sailing. Plane sailing therefore furnishes no solution where difference of longitude is considered, and for such solution resort must be had to one of several methods, which, by reason of their taking account of the spherical figure of the earth, are called **spherical sailings.**

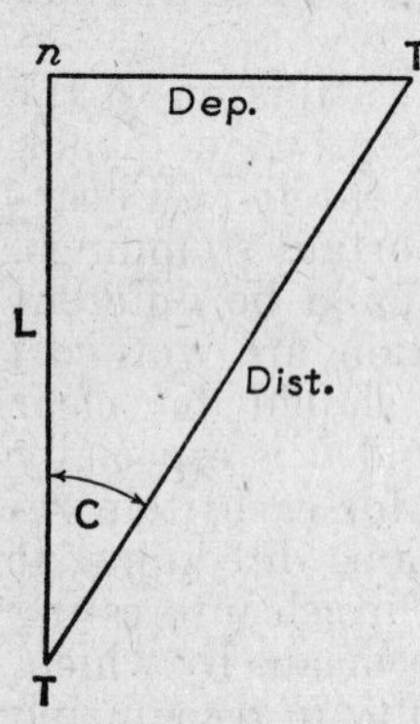

FIGURE 40.

When a vessel sails on an east or west course along a parallel of latitude, the method of converting departure into difference of longitude is called **parallel sailing.** When the course is not east or west, and thus carries the vessel through various latitudes, the conversion may be made either by **middle latitude sailing,** in which it is assumed that the whole run has been made in the mean latitude, or by **Mercator sailing,** in which the principle involved in the construction of the Mercator chart is utilized.

Great circle sailing deals with the courses and distances between any two points when the track followed is a great circle of the terrestrial sphere. A modification of this method which is adopted under certain circumstances is called **composite sailing.**

PLANE SAILING

In plane sailing, the curvature of the earth being neglected, the relation between the elements of the rhumb track joining any two points may be considered from the plane right triangle formed by the meridian of the place left, the parallel of the place arrived at, and the rhumb line. In figure 40, T is the point of departure; T′, the point of destination; T*n*, the meridian of departure; T′*n*, the parallel of destination; and TT′, the rhumb line between the points. Let T′T*n* represent the course (C); TT′ the distance (Dist.); T*n* the difference of latitude (L) and T′*n* the departure (Dep). Then from the triangle TT′*n*, we have the following:

$$\sin C=\frac{\text{Dep.}}{\text{Dist.}};\qquad \cos C=\frac{\text{D L}}{\text{Dist.}};\qquad \tan C=\frac{\text{Dep.}}{\text{D L}}.$$

From these equations are derived the following formulas for working the various problems that may arise in plane sailing:

Given	Required	Formulas	
Course and distance	Difference of latitude	$D\,L = \text{Dist.} \cos C.$	Log D L = log Dist. + log cos C.
	Departure	$\text{Dep.} = \text{Dist.} \sin C.$	Log Dep. = log Dist. + log sin C.
Difference of latitude and departure.	Course	$\tan C = \frac{\text{Dep.}}{D\,L}.$	Log tan C = log Dep. − log D L.
	Distance	$\text{Dist.} = \frac{\text{Dep.}}{\sin C}.$	Log Dist. = log Dep. − log sin C.
Course and difference of latitude	Distance	$\text{Dist.} = \frac{D\,L}{\cos C}.$	Log Dist. = log D L − log cos C.
	Departure	$\text{Dep.} = D\,L \tan C.$	Log Dep. = log D L + log tan C.
Course and departure	Distance	$\text{Dist.} = \frac{\text{Dep.}}{\sin C}.$	Log Dist. = log Dep. − log sin C.
	Difference of latitude	$D\,L = \frac{\text{Dep.}}{\tan C}.$	Log D L = log Dep. − log tan C.
Distance and difference of latitude	Course	$\cos C = \frac{D\,L}{\text{Dist.}}.$	Log cos C = log D L − log Dist.
	Departure	$\text{Dep.} = \text{Dist.} \sin C.$	Log Dep. = log Dist. + log sin C.
Distance and departure	Course	$\sin C = \frac{\text{Dep.}}{\text{Dist.}}.$	Log sin C = log Dep. − log Dist.
	Difference of latitude	$D\,L = \text{Dist.} \cos C.$	Log D L = log Dist. + log cos C.

The solution of the plane right triangle may be accomplished either by plane trigonometry, by traverse table (Table 3), or by construction. If the former method is adopted, the logarithms of numbers may be found in Table 32, and of the functions of angles in Table 33. A more expeditious method is available, however, in the traverse table, which gives by inspection the various solutions. Table 3 contains values for each unit of distance from 1 to 600, and for each degree of the course. The method of solving by construction consists in laying down the various given terms by scale upon a chart or plain paper, and measuring thereon the required terms.

Of the various problems that may arise, the first two given in the foregoing table are of much the most frequent occurrence. In the first, the given quantities are course and distance, and those to be found are difference of latitude and departure; this is the case where a navigator, knowing the distance run on a given course, desires to ascertain the amount made good to north or south and to east or west. In the second case the conditions are reversed; this arises where the course and distance between two points are to be obtained from their known difference of latitude and departure.

Example.—A vessel steams N. 5° E., 188 miles. Required the difference of latitude and the departure.

By computation

Dist.	188	log	2. 27416
C	5°	log cos	9. 99834
DL	187.3	log	2. 27250
Dist.	188	log	2. 27416
C	5°	log sin	8. 94030
Dep.	16.4	log	1. 21446

By inspection

In Table 3, find the course 5°; it occurs at the top of the page, therefore take the names of the columns from the top; opposite 188 in the Dist. column will be seen Lat. 187.3 and Dep. 16.4.

Example.—A steamer is bound to a port which is 136 miles to the north and 203 miles to the west of the vessel's position. Required the course and distance.

By computation

Dep.	203	log	2. 30750
DL	136	log	2. 13354
C	N. 56°11′ W. (304°)	log tan	0. 17396
Dep.	203	log	2. 30750
C	56°11′	log sin	9. 91951
Dist.	244.3	log	2. 38799

By inspection

Enter Table 3 and turn the pages until a course is found whereon the numbers 136 and 203 are found abreast each other in the columns marked respectively Lat. and Dep. This occurs most nearly at the course 56°, the angle being taken from the bottom, because the appropriate names of the columns are found there. The course is therefore (304°). Interpolating for intermediate values, the corresponding number in the Dist. column is about 244.3.

Example.—As a result of a day's run a vessel changes latitude 244 miles to the south and makes a departure of 171 miles to the east. What is the course and distance made good?

By computation

Dep.	171	log	2. 23300
DL	244	log	2. 38739
C S. 35°02′ E. (145°)		log tan	9. 84561
Dep.	171	log	2. 23300
C	35°02′	log sin	9. 75895
Dist.	297.9	log	2. 47405

By inspection

Enter Table 3 and the nearest agreement will be found on course S. 35° E. (145°), the appropriate names being found at the top of the page. The nearest corresponding Dist. is 298 miles.

TRAVERSE SAILING

A **traverse** is an irregular track made by a vessel in steaming on several different courses, and the method of **traverse sailing** consists in finding the difference of latitude and departure corresponding to several courses and distances and reducing all to a single equivalent course and distance. This is done by determining the distance to north or south and to east or west made good on each course, taking the algebraic sum of these various differences of latitude and departure and finding the course and distance corresponding thereto. The work can be most expeditiously performed by adopting a tabular form for the computation and using the traverse tables.

Example.—A ship sails 158°, 15 miles; 135°, 34 miles; 259°, 16 miles; 293°, 39 miles; 169°, 40 miles. Required the course and distance made good.

Courses	Dist.	N.	S.	E.	W.
158°	15		13. 9	5. 6	
135°	34		24. 0	24. 0	
259°	16		3. 1		15. 7
293°	39	15. 2			35. 9
169°	40		39. 3	7. 6	
		15. 2	80. 3	37. 2	51. 6
			15. 2		37. 2
192°	66. 7		65. 1		14. 4

The result of the various courses is, therefore, to carry the vessel 192°, 66.7 miles from the original position.

PARALLEL SAILING

Thus far the earth has been regarded as an extended plane, and its spherical figure has not been taken into account; it has thus been impossible to consider one of the important terms involved—namely difference of longitude. **Parallel sailing** is the simplest of the various forms of spherical sailing, being the method of interconverting departure and difference of longitude when the ship sails upon an east or west course, and therefore remains always on the same parallel of latitude.

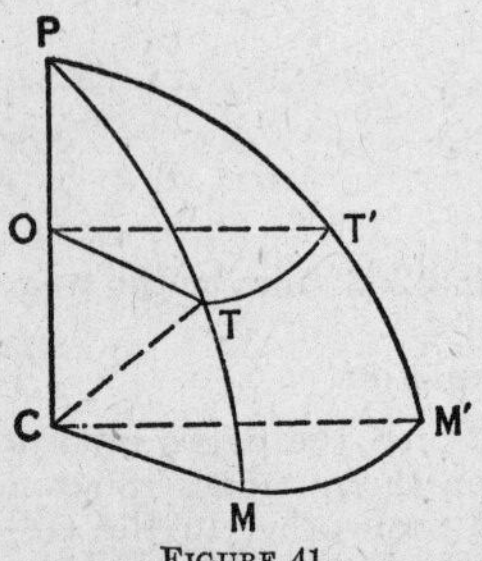

FIGURE 41.

In figure 41, T and T′ are two places in the same latitude; P, the adjacent pole; TT′, the arc of the parallel of latitude through the two places; MM′, the corresponding arc of the equator intercepted between their meridians PM and PM′; and TT′, the departure on the parallel whose latitude is TCM=OTC, and whose radius is OT.

Let D.Lo represent the arc of the equator MM′ which is the measure of MPM′, the difference of longitude of the meridians PM and PM′; R, the equatorial radius of the earth, CM=CT; r, the radius OT of the parallel TT′; and L, the latitude of that parallel.

Then, since TT′ and MM′ are similar arcs of two circles, and are therefore proportional to the radii of the circles, we have:

$$\frac{TT'}{MM'}=\frac{OT}{CM}; \text{ or, } \frac{\text{Dep.}}{\text{D.Lo}}=\frac{r}{\text{R.}}$$

From the triangle COT, r=R cos L; hence

$$\frac{\text{Dep.}}{\text{D.Lo}}=\frac{\text{R cos L}}{\text{R}}; \text{or, D.Lo=Dep. sec L; or, Dep.=D.Lo cos L.}$$

Thus the relations are expressed between *minutes* of longitude and *miles* of departure.

Two cases arise under parallel sailing: first, where the difference of longitude between two places on the same parallel is given, to find the departure; and, second, where the departure is given, to find the difference of longitude.

In working these problems, the computation can be made by logarithms; but the traverse table may be conveniently employed. This table is based upon the formulas,

$$\text{DL=Dist. cos C, and Dist.=DL sec C.}$$

Substitute for the column marked Lat. the departure, for that marked Dist. the difference of longitude, and for the course at top and bottom of the page the latitude. The table then becomes available for making the required conversions.

Example.—A ship in the latitude of 49°30′ sails directly east until making good a difference of longitude of 3°30′. Required the departure.

By computation

L	49°30′	log cos	9. 81254
D.Lo.	210′	log	2. 32222
Dep.	136. 4	log	2. 13476

By inspection

Enter Table 3 with the latitude as C and the difference of longitude as Dist. As the table is computed only to single degrees, we must find the numbers in the pages of 49° and 50° and take the mean. Corresponding to Dist. 210 in the former is Lat. 137.8, and in the latter Lat. 135.0. The mean, which is the required departure, is 136.4.

Example.—A ship in the latitude of 38° sails due west a distance of 215.5 miles. Required the difference of longitude.

By computation

L	38°	log sec	0. 10347
Dep.	215. 5	log	2. 33345
D. Lo.	273′.5 / 4°33′.5	log	2. 43692

By inspection

Enter Table 3 with the latitude, 38°, as a course Corresponding with the number 215.5 in column of Lat., is 273.5 in the column of Dist. This is the required difference of longitude, being equal to 4°33′.5.

MIDDLE LATITUDE SAILING

When a ship follows a course obliquely across the meridians of longitude, the latitude, as well as the longitude, changes continually. With reference to two places situated on the same side of the equator, considering the earth to be of spherical form, the middle latitude is defined as the latitude of the parallel passing midway between them; its value is therefore half the sum of the latitudes of the two places. When the places are situated on opposite sides of the equator, the track connecting them is regarded as being divided into two separate parts by the point where it crosses the equator, and the simple "middle latitude" is replaced by the "half latitude" of each of the places.

Middle latitude sailing is that form of spherical sailing which is founded on the assumption that the length in miles of the arc of the parallel of middle latitude of two places intercepted between their meridians of longitude is nearly equal to the departure. This relation would be exact if the rate of convergence of the meridians of longitude were uniform, like the rate of approach of the equal sides of an isosceles plane triangle. It has been shown, however, that the departure varies as the cosine of the latitude. Consequently, the distance apart, on successive parallels of latitude, of two given meridians of longitude varies like the values given in a table of natural cosines, such as Table 31, and not by uniform increments for uniform changes of the angle of latitude; and hence, to be exact in getting the difference of longitude made good in steaming along a given track, it would be necessary to multiply the departure between the terminal points of the track by the natural secant, or reciprocal of the natural cosine of the latitude of some parallel whose angular distance from the equator is such that its natural secant is the mean or average of the natural secants of all the values of the latitude passed through in proceeding between the limiting parallels of the track.

In middle latitude sailing, having found the mean of the latitudes, the solution is identical with that of parallel sailing, substituting the middle latitude for the single latitude therein employed.

Example.—A vessel in Lat. 42° 30′ N., Long. 58° 51′ W., steams 146°, 300 miles. Required the latitude and longitude arrived at.

From Table 3: Course 146°, Dist., 300, is found Lat., 248.7 S. (4° 08′.7), Dep., 167.8 E.

Latitude left,	42° 30′.0 N.		Latitude left,	42° 30′ N.
DL,	4 08 .7 S.		Latitude arrived at,	38 21 N.
Latitude arrived at,	38 21 .3 N.			2)80 51
			Mid. latitude,	40 25 N.

Enter Table 3 with the middle latitude, 40°, as a course; the difference of longitude (Dist.) corresponding to the departure (Lat.) 167.8 is 219.0; entering with 41°, it is 222.4; the mean is 220.7 (3° 40′.7).

Longitude left,	58° 51′.0 W.
D.Lo,	3 40 .7 E.
Longitude arrived at,	55 10 .3 W.

Example.—A ship in Lat. 39° 42′ S., Long. 3° 31′ E., sails S. 42° W (222°), 236 miles. Required the latitude and longitude arrived at.

From Table 3: Course, S. 42° W., Dist., 236 miles; is found Lat., 175.4 S. (2° 55′.4), Dep., 157.9 W.

Latitude left,	39° 42′.0 S.		Latitude left,	39° 42′ S.
DL,	2 55 .4 S.		Latitude arrived at,	42 37 S.
Latitude arrived at,	42 37 .4 S.			2)82 19
			Mid. latitude,	41 09 S.

From Table 3: Mid. Lat. (course), 41°, Dep. (Lat.), 157.9; is found D.Lo (Dist.), 209.3 (3° 29′.3).

Longitude left,	3° 31′.0 E.
D.Lo,	3 29 .3 W.
Longitude arrived at,	0 01 .7 E.

Example.—A vessel leaves Lat. 49° 57′ N., Long. 15° 16′ W., and arrives at Lat. 47° 18′ N. Long. 20° 10′ W. Required the course and distance made good.

Latitude left	49° 57′ N.		Longitude left,	15° 16′ W.
Latitude arrived at,	47 18 N.		Longitude arrived at,	20 10 W.
DL,	{2° 39′ / 159′} S.		D.Lo,	{4° 54′ / 294′} W.
	2)97° 15′ N.			
Mid. latitude,	48 38 N.			

From Table 3: Mid. Lat. (course), 49°, D.Lo (Dist.), 294; is found Dep. (Lat.), 192.9.

From Table 3: DL 159 S., Dep. 192.9 W., is found course S. 51° W., Dist., 251 miles.

Middle latitude should not be used when the latitudes are of opposite name; if of different names and the distance is small, the departure may be assumed equal to the difference of longitude, since the meridians are sensibly parallel near the equator; but if the distance is great the two portions of the track on opposite sides of the equator must be treated separately.

The assumption upon which middle latitude sailing is based—that the conversion may be made as if the whole distance were sailed upon a parallel midway between the latitudes of departure and destination—while sufficiently accurate for moderate distances, may be materially in error where the distances are large. The amount by which the difference of longitude is affected by taking the middle latitude, L_o, in place of the latitude of conversion L_c (that is, in some selected latitude where the true difference of longitude equals the departure times the sec L_c), is considered to be immaterial for distances ranging up to 200 nautical miles, but for distances of 600 nautical miles the default from accuracy would be of the order of 1 percent when the middle latitude is as great as 60°. In such case, either the method of Mercator sailing must be employed, or else the correction given in the following table should be applied to the mean latitude to obtain what may be termed the latitude of conversion, being that latitude in which the required conditions are accurately fulfilled. The table is computed from the formulas:

$$\text{Cos } L_c = \frac{\text{D. L.}}{m}$$

$$\text{Corr.} = L_m - \text{Cos } L_c$$

where L_c represents the latitude of conversion, L_m the mean or middle latitude, and m the meridional parts between the latitudes of departure and destination.

Mid. Lat.	*Difference of latitude*															Mid. Lat.
	1°	2°	3°	4°	5°	6°	7°	8°	9°	10°	12°	14°	16°	18°	20°	
°	′	′	′	′	′	′	′	′	′	′	′	′	′	′	′	°
15	−86	−85	−84	−83	−81	−79	−76	−73	−69	−65	−56	−46	−34	−21	−6	15
18	−67	−67	−66	−65	−63	−61	−59	−56	−53	−50	−43	−34	−23	−12	1	18
21	−54	−54	−53	−52	−51	−49	−47	−44	−42	−39	−32	−24	−15	−5	7	21
24	−44	−44	−44	−42	−41	−40	−38	−36	−33	−31	−24	−17	−8	1	12	24
30	−31	−30	−29	−29	−28	−26	−24	−23	−20	−18	−12	−6	1	11	21	30
35	−23	−22	−21	−21	−19	−18	−17	−15	−12	−10	−5	2	10	18	28	35
40	−17	−16	−15	−14	−13	−12	−10	−8	−6	−4	2	8	16	25	34	40
45	−12	−11	−11	−10	−8	−7	−5	−3	−1	1	7	14	22	31	41	45
50	−8	−8	−7	−6	−5	−3	−1	1	3	6	12	20	28	38	49	50
55	−5	−5	−4	−3	−2	0	2	5	7	10	17	25	35	46	58	55
58	−4	−3	−3	−1	0	2	4	7	10	13	20	29	39	51	64	58
60	−3	−3	−2	−1	1	3	5	8	11	14	22	32	43	55	69	60
62	−3	−2	−1	0	2	4	7	9	13	17	25	35	46	60	75	62
64	−2	−1	0	1	3	5	8	11	14	18	27	38	50	65	81	64
66	−2	−1	0	2	4	6	9	12	16	20	30	42	55	71	89	66
68	−1	0	1	2	5	7	10	14	18	22	33	46	61	78	98	68
70	−1	0	1	3	5	8	12	16	20	25	37	51	67	87	109	70
72	0	0	2	4	6	10	13	18	23	28	41	57	76	97	123	72

Example.—A vessel sails from Lat. 10° 13′ S. to Lat. 20° 21′ S., making a departure of 432 miles. Required the difference of longitude.

Latitude left,	10° 13′	S.
Latitude arrived at,	20 21	S.
	2)30 34	
Mid. latitude, (L_m)	15 17	S.
Correction,	− 1 05	
L_c,	14 12	S.

For Mid. Lat. 15° and Diff. of Lat. 10°. Correction, −65′

L_c	14° 12′	log sec	. 01348
Dep.	432	log	2. 63548
D.Lo	445′.6	log	2. 64896

MERCATOR SAILING

Mercator sailing is the method by which values of the various elements are determined from considering them in the relation in which they are plotted upon a chart constructed according to the Mercator projection.

Upon the Mercator chart, the meridians being parallel, the arc of a parallel of latitude is shown as equal to the corresponding arc of the equator; the length of every such arc is, therefore, expanded; and, in order that the rhumb line may appear as a straight line, the meridians are also expanded by such amount as is necessary to preserve, in any latitude, the proper proportion existing between a unit of latitude and a unit of longitude. The length of small portions of the meridian thus increased are called **meridional parts**, and these, computed for every minute of latitude from 0° to 80°, form the table of meridional parts (Table 5), by means of which a Mercator chart may be constructed and all problems of Mercator sailing may be solved.

In the triangle ABC (fig. 42), the angle ACB is the course, C; the side AC, the distance, Dist.; the side BC, the difference of latitude, DL; and the side AB, the departure, Dep. Then corresponding to the difference of latitude BC in the latitude under consideration, if CE be laid off to represent the meridional difference of latitude, *m*, completing the right triangle CEF, EF will represent the difference of longitude, D.Lo. The triangle ABC gives the relations involved in plane sailing as previously described; the triangle CEF affords the means for the conversion of departure and difference of longitude by mercator sailing.

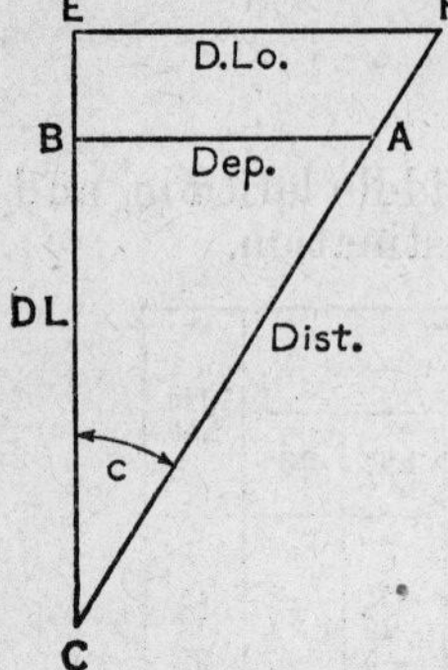

FIGURE 42.

To find the arc of the expanded meridian intercepted between any two parallels, or the *meridional difference of latitude*, when both places are on the same side of the equator, subtract the meridional parts of the lesser latitude, as given by Table 5, from the meridional parts of the greater; the remainder will be the meridional difference of latitude; but if the places are on different sides of the equator, the sum of the meridional parts will be the meridional difference of latitude.

To solve the triangle CEF by the traverse tables it is only necessary to substitute meridional difference for Lat., and difference of longitude for Dep. Where long distances are involved, carrying the computation beyond the limits of the traverse table, as frequently occurs in this method, either of two means may be adopted: the problems may be worked by trigonometrical formulas, using logarithms, or the given quantities involved may all be reduced by a common divisor until they fall within the traverse table, and the results, when obtained, correspondingly increased. The former method is generally preferable, especially when the distances are quite large and accurate results are sought. The formulas for the various conversions are as follows:

$$\tan C = \frac{D.Lo}{m};\ D.Lo = m \tan C;\ m = D.Lo \cot C.$$

When not to use mercator sailing.—The above formulas should not be used when the course approaches 90° or 270° because the tangents of angles near 90° vary rapidly in value, and any error in the value of the course produces a large error in the computed value of the Diff. Long. It is better to use Middle Lat. Sailing in such cases. The following are examples under Mercator sailing:

Example.—A ship in Lat. 42° 30′ N., Long. 58° 51′ W., sails 146°, 300 miles. Required the latitude and longitude arrived at.

From Table 3: Course 146°, Dist., 300; is found Lat. 248′.7 (4° 08′.7 S.)

Latitude left,	42° 30′.0 N.	Merid. parts,	+2806. 4
DL,	4 08 .7 S.		
Latitude arrived at,	38 21 .3 N.	Merid. parts,	−2480. 8
		m,	325. 6

By computation

m	325.6	log	2. 51268
C	34°	log tan	9. 82899
D.Lo	219′.6 (3° 39′.6)	log	2. 34167
Longitude left,		58° 51′.0 W.	
D.Lo,		3 39 .6 E.	
Longitude arrived at,		55 11 .4 W.	

Example.—A vessel in Lat. 4° 37′ S., Long. 21° 05′ W., steams 346°, 450.4 miles. Required the latitude and longitude arrived at.

From Table 3: Course (N.) 14° (W.), Dist., 450.4; is found Lat. 437 N. (7° 17′).

Latitude left,	4° 37′ S.	Merid. parts,	+275.4
DL,	7 17 N.		
Latitude arrived at,	2 40. 0 N.	Merid. parts,	+159.0
		m,	434. 4

By computation

m	434. 4	log	2. 63789
C	14°	log tan	9. 39677
D.Lo	108′.3 (1° 48′.3)	log	2. 03466

By inspection

From Table 3: Course, 14°, *m* (Lat.), 434.4, is found D.Lo (Dep.) 108′.3 W., or 1° 48′.3.

Longitude left,	21° 05′.0 W.
D.Lo,	1 48 .3 W.
Longitude arrived at,	22 53 .3 W

Example.—Required the course and distance by rhumb line from a point in Lat. 42° 03′ N., Long. 70° 04′ W., to another in Lat. 36° 59′ N., Long. 25° 10′ W.

Lat. departure,	42° 03′ N.	Merid. pts.,	+2770. 1	Long. departure,	70° 04′ W.	
Lat. destination,	36 59 N.	Merid. pts.,	−2377. 3	Long. destination,	25 10 W.	
DL	5° 04′ S.=304′	*m*,	392. 8	D.Lo	44° 54′ / 2694′ E.	
D.Lo	2694	log	3. 43040			
m	392. 8	log	2. 59417			
C	S.81°42′ E.(98°.3)	log tan	. 83623	log sec.	. 84056	
DL	304′			log	2. 48287	
Dist.	2106			log	3. 32343	

The course is S. 81°42′ E. (98°) and the distance is 2,106 miles. Since the figures involved are large, it is best to employ only the method by computation. The formula by which the Dist. is obtained comes from plane sailing.

GREAT CIRCLE SAILING

The shortest distance between any two points on the earth's surface is measured by the arc of the great circle which passes through those points; and the method of sailing in which the arc of a great circle is employed for the track of the vessel, taking advantage of the fact that it is the shortest route possible, is denominated **great circle sailing.**

It frequently happens when a great circle route is laid down that it is found to lead across the land, or to carry the vessel into a region of dangerous navigation or extreme cold which it is expedient to avoid; in such a case a certain parallel should be fixed upon as a limit of latitude, and a route laid down such that a great circle is followed as far as the limiting parallel, then the parallel itself, and finally another great circle to the port of destination. Such a modification of the great circle method is called **composite sailing.**

The **rhumb line** which cuts all the meridians at the same angle, has been employed as a track by navigators on account of the ease with which it may be laid down on a Mercator chart. But as it is a longer line than the great circle between the same points, navigators use the latter wherever practicable. On the Mercator chart, however, the arc of a great circle joining two points (unless both are on the equator or both on the same meridian) will not be projected as a straight line, but as a curve.

It should be clearly understood that it is the rhumb line which is in fact the indirect route, and that in following the great circle the vessel is always heading for the port, exactly as if it were in sight, while on the course which is shown as a straight line on the Mercator chart the vessel never heads for the port until at the very end of the voyage.

On the equator and on any meridian, the great circle and the rhumb coincide; therefore near the equator, parallel sailing is about as short as great circle sailing. The Mercator course or rhumb line that traverses close to the direction of north and south is nearly as short as the great circle.

As the great circle makes a different angle with each meridian that is crossed, it becomes necessary to make frequent changes of the vessel's course; in practice, the course is a series of chords or rhumb lines joining the various points on the great circle track. For small distances the G. C. and rhumb are about the same.

If, while endeavoring to follow a great circle, the ship is driven from it, as by unfavorable weather, it will not serve the purpose to return to the old track at convenience, but it is required that another great circle be laid down, joining the actual position in which the ship finds herself with the port of destination.

Methods.—The methods of determining the great circle course may be divided generally into three classes; namely, by *great circle sailing charts*, by *computation*, and by the methods of the *time azimuth.*

Great circle charts.—Of the available methods, that by means of charts especially constructed for the purpose is considered greatly superior to all others.

A series of great circle charts covering the navigable waters of the globe are published by the United States Hydrographic Office. Being on the gnomonic projection, all great circles are represented as straight lines, and it is only necessary to join any two points by such a line to represent the great circle track between them. The course and distance are readily obtainable by a method explained on the charts. The track may be transferred to a chart on the Mercator projection by plotting a number of its points by their coordinates and joining them with a curved line.

The navigator who contemplates the use of great circle tracks will find it of the greatest convenience to be provided with these gnomonic charts for the regions which the vessel is to traverse.

Computation.—This method consists in determining a series of points on the great circle by their coordinates of latitude and longitude, plotting them upon a Mercator chart, and tracing the curve that joins them. The first point determined is the **vertex,** or point of highest latitude, even when, as sometimes occurs, it falls without that portion of the great circle which joins the points of departure and destination.

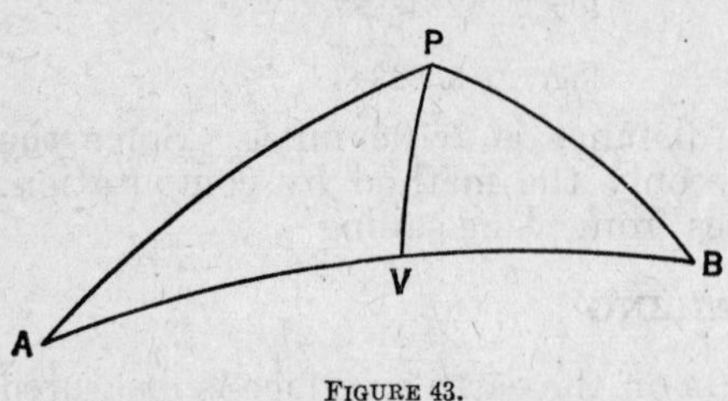

FIGURE 43.

In figure 43, A represents the point of departure; B, the point of destination; AVB, the great circle joining them, with its vertex at V; and P, the pole of the earth.

Let C_A=PAB, the initial course;
C_B=PBA, the final course;
L_A, L_V, L_B=the latitudes of the respective points A, V, B=(90°−PA), (90°−PV), (90°−PB).
Lo_{AB}, Lo_{AV}, Lo_{BV}=the differences of longitude between A and B, A and V, B and V, respectively,=APB, APV, BPV.
D=the great circle distance between A and B; and
φ=an auxiliary angle introduced for the computation.

Then:

$$\tan \varphi = \cos Lo_{AB} \cot L_B;$$
$$\cot C_A = \cot Lo_{AB} \cos (L_A + \varphi) \operatorname{cosec} \varphi;$$
$$\cot D = \cos C_A \tan (L_A + \varphi);$$
$$\cos L_V = \sin C_A \cos L_A;$$
$$\cot Lo_{AV} = \tan C_A \sin L_A.$$

By these formulas are determined the initial course and the total distance by great circle; also the latitude of the vertex and its longitude with respect to A. By interchanging the subscript letters $_A$ and $_B$ throughout, we should obtain the final course, and the longitude of the vertex with respect to B; also the same total distance and latitude of the vertex as before. When the point of destination is on the equator, this formula is indeterminate. Resort must then be had to the haversine formula.

In performing this computation, strict regard must be had to the signs of the quantities. If the points of departure and destination are in contrary latitudes, the latitude of one of these points must be regarded as negative with respect to the other, and they must be marked with opposite signs. Should Lo_{AV} or Lo_{BV} assume a negative value, it indicates that the vertex does not lie between A and B, and is to be laid off accordingly.

To find other points of the great circle, M, N, etc., let their latitudes be represented by L_M, L_N, etc., and their longitudes from the vertex by Lo_{VM}, Lo_{VN}, etc.; then,

$$\tan L_M = \tan L_V \cos Lo_{VM}, \text{ or, } \cos Lo_{VM} = \tan L_M \cot L_V;$$
$$\tan L_N = \tan L_V \cos Lo_{VN}, \text{ or, } \cos Lo_{VN} = \tan L_N \cot L_V;$$

and so on. By these formulas intervals of longitude from the vertex of 5°, 10°, or any amount, may be assumed, and the corresponding latitudes deduced; or any latitude may be assumed and its corresponding interval of longitude from the vertex found. Two positions will result from each solution, and the appropriate ones may be chosen by keeping in mind the signs involved.

Example.—Given two places, one in Lat. 40° N., Long. 70° W., the other in Lat. 30° S., Long. 10° W., find the great circle distance between them; also the initial course, and the longitude of equator crossing.

$$L_A=+40°;\ L_B=-30°;\ Lo_{AB}=60°$$

Lo_{AB}	60°	cos	9.69897	cct	9.76144						
L_B	− 30°	cot (−)	.23856								
L_A	+ 40°							cos	9.88425	sin	9.80807
φ	− 40° 54′	tan (−)	9.93753	cosec(−)	.18393						
$(L_A+\varphi)$	− 0° 54′			cos	9.99995	tan (−)	8.19616				
C_A	131° 24′ *or* S. 48° 36′ E.			cot (−)	9.94532	cos (−)	9.82041	sin	9.87513	tan (−)	.05472
D	89° 24′ *or* 5,364 miles					cot	8.01657				
L_V	+ 54° 56′							cos	9.75938		
Lo_{AV}	− 53° 54′									cot (−)	9.86279

The initial course is S. 48°36′ E. (131°) and the distance 5,364 nautical miles. (It may be found that the course by rhumb line is S. 38°45′ E. (141°), and the distance 5,386 miles.) The vertex of the great circle is in Lat. 54°56′ N., and is 53°54′ in longitude from the point A, in a direction away from B; hence it is in Long. 123°54′ W. To find the longitude of equator crossing let $L_M=0°$; then in the equation,

$$\cos Lo_{VM}=\tan L_M \cot L_V,$$

since $\tan L_M$ equals zero, $\cos Lo_{VM}$ also equals zero, or the longitude interval from the vertex is 90°, which is evident from the properties of the great circle: therefore the longitude of equator crossing is 123°54′ W.−90°=33°54′ W.

Alternative formulas for finding the distance and course.—The following formula obtained from the expression, $\text{hav } z=\text{hav }(L\sim d)+\cos L \cos d \text{ hav } t$, (page 182) by putting $z=D$, $L=L_A$, $d=L_B$, and $t=Lo_{AB}$, is generally preferred for computing the great-circle distance, being a general expression for finding the third side of a spherical triangle in which two sides and the included angle are given: With this formula no account need be taken of algebraic signs.

$$\text{hav } D=\text{hav }(L_A\sim L_B)+\cos L_A \cos L_B \text{ hav } Lo_{AB}.$$

The distance D=AB having been found, the three sides of the spherical triangle APB become known, as well as the angle at P, hence the initial and final courses may be found from the proportionality between the sines of the angles of the triangle and the sines of the opposite sides,

$$\sin C_A=\frac{\sin P\times\sin PB}{\sin AB}=\frac{\sin Lo_{AB}\cos L_B}{\sin D}=\sin Lo_{AB}\cos L_B \operatorname{cosec} D.$$

$$\sin C_B=\frac{\sin P\times\sin PA}{\sin AB}=\frac{\sin Lo_{AB}\cos L_A}{\sin D}=\sin Lo_{AB}\cos L_A \operatorname{cosec} D.$$

The solution of the foregoing example for the required distance, initial and final courses, would be as follows:

$Lo_{AB}=60°$	log hav	9.39794	log sin	9.93753	log sin	9.93753
$L_A=40°$ N.	log cos	9.88425			log cos	9.88425
$L_B=30°$ S.	log cos	9.93753	log cos	9.93753		
	θ log hav	9.21972				
	θ nat hav	0.16585				
$L_A\sim L_B=70°$	nat hav	0.32899				
Distance, D=89° 24½′ =5364½ nautical miles.	nat hav	0.49484	log cosec	0.00002	log cosec	0.00002
			log sin C_A	9.87508	log sin C_B	9.82180
			Course, C_A	131° 24½′	C_B	318° 26′

Time azimuth methods.—A convenient method of obtaining the initial and final courses in great circle sailing is afforded by the azimuth tables and graphic methods which are prepared for the solution of the *time azimuth* problem. It will be found by comparison that if the latitude of the point of departure be substituted for the latitude of the observer in that problem, the latitude of destination for the declination of the celestial body, and the longitude interval for the hour angle, the solution for the initial course will coincide with that for the azimuth; by interchanging the latitudes of the points of departure and destination the final course will be similarly obtained. Advantage may be taken of the various methods provided for facilitating the determination of the azimuth to ascertain the great circle courses from one point to another.

COMPOSITE SAILING

When, for any reason, it is impracticable or unadvisable to follow the great circle track to its highest latitude, a limiting parallel is chosen and the route modified accordingly. This method is called **composite sailing.**

The shortest track between points where a fixed latitude is not exceeded is made up as follows:

1. A great circle through the point of departure tangent to the limiting parallel.
2. A course along the parallel.
3. A great circle through the point of destination tangent to the limiting parallel.

The composite track may be determined by *great circle chart* or by *computation*, or by *graphic approximation.*

On a **great circle chart,** draw lines from the points of departure and destination, respectively, tangent to the limiting parallel; transfer these great circles to a Mercator chart in the usual manner, by the coordinates of several points, including in each case the point of tangency to the parallel. Follow the first great circle to the parallel; then follow the parallel; then the second great circle. Determine great circle courses and distances from the gnomonic chart as thereon described; determine the distance along the parallel by parallel sailing.

Computation.—The problem consists in finding the great circles which pass, respectively, through the points of departure and destination and have their vertices in the latitude of the limiting parallel. Resuming the designation of terms already employed we have:

$$\cos Lo_{VA} = \tan L_A \cot L_V;$$
$$\cos Lo_{VB} = \tan L_B \cot L_V;$$

where Lo_{VA} and Lo_{VB} represent the distances in longitude from A and from B to the respective points of tangency; other features of each of the great circles may be determined in the usual manner.

EXAMPLE: A vessel in Lat. 30° S., Long., 18° W., steams to a point in Lat. 39° S., Long. 145° E., and it is decided not to go south of the parallel of 55° S. Find the longitude of reaching that parallel and the longitude at which it should be left.

L_A = 30° S.; L_B = 39° S.; L_V = 55° S.
Lo_A = 18° W.; Lo_B = 145° E.

L_A	30°	tan 9.76144	L_B	39°	tan 9.90837
L_V	55°	cot 9.84523	L_V	55°	cot 9.84523
Lo_{VA}	66° 09′ E.	cos 9.60667	Lo_{VB}	55° 27′ W.	cos 9.75360
Lo_A	18 00 W.		Lo_B	145 00 E.	
Lo_V	48 09 E.		Lo_V	89 33 E.	

Graphic approximation.—The composite track may be obtained by drawing a straight line between the given points on a Mercator chart and erecting at its middle point a perpendicular, which should be extended until it intersects the limiting parallel. Then through this intersection and the two points describe the arc of a circle, and this will approximate to the shortest distance within the assigned limit of latitude.

A terrestrial globe may be employed for the determination of the composite track; the method of its use will suggest itself.

Another approximation is obtained by joining the two points with a single great circle, and following this to its intersection with the limiting parallel; thence steaming along the parallel until the great circle is again intersected; then resuming the circle and following it to the destination.

CHAPTER VI

DEAD RECKONING

Dead reckoning is the process by which the position of a vessel at any instant is found by applying to the last well-determined position the run that has since been made, using for the purpose the ship's course and the distance indicated by the log.

Positions by dead reckoning, differ from those determined by bearings of terrestrial objects or by observations of celestial bodies in being less exact, as the correctness of dead reckoning depends upon the accuracy of the estimate of the run, and this is always liable to be at fault to a greater or less extent. The course made good by a ship may differ from that which is believed *being made* good, by reason of imperfect steering, improper allowance for compass error, the leeway (caused by the wind), and also the effects of unknown currents; the allowed distance over the ground may be in error on account of inaccurate logging and unknown currents.

Notwithstanding its recognized defects as compared with the more exact methods, the dead reckoning is an invaluable aid to the navigator. It affords a means of plotting the position of the ship at any desired time between astronomical determinations; it also gives an approximate position at the moment of taking astronomical observations which is a great convenience in working up those observations; and finally it affords the only available means of determining the location of a vessel at sea during those periods (which may continue for several days together) when the weather is such as to render the observation of celestial bodies an impossibility.

Taking departure.—Before losing sight of the land, and preferably while objects remain in good view, it is the duty of the navigator to **take a departure**; this consists in fixing the position of the ship by the best means available, and using this position as the origin for dead reckoning. There are two methods of reckoning the departure. The first and simpler consists in taking from the chart the latitude and longitude of the position found, and applying the future run thereto. The other requires that the bearing and distance of an object of known latitude and longitude be found; the position of the object then forms the basis of the reckoning, and the *reversed* direction of the bearing, with the distance, forms the first course and distance; thus it may be considered that the vessel starts from the position of the object and steams to the position where the bearing was taken; the correction for deviation in such a case should be that due to the heading of the vessel when the bearing was taken. Each time that a new position is determined it is used as a new departure for the dead reckoning.

This meaning of the term **departure** should not be confounded with the other, which refers to the distance run toward east or west.

Methods.—The working of dead reckoning merely involves an application of the methods of traverse sailing and middle latitude sailing.

The various compass courses are set down in a column, and abreast each are written the errors by reason of which the course steered by compass differs from the true course made good over the ground; thence the true course made good is determined and recorded; next, the distance is written in, and afterwards, by means of Table 3, the difference of latitude and departure are found, separate columns being kept for distances to the north, south, east, and west.

When the position of the vessel at any moment is required, add up all the differences of latitude and departure, and write in the column of the greater, the difference between the northing and southing, and the easting and westing. Apply the difference of latitude to the latitude of the last determined position, which will give the latitude by D. R., and from which may be found the middle latitude; with the middle latitude find the difference of longitude corresponding to the departure, apply this to the longitude of last position, and the result will be the longitude by D. R.

The employment of the tabular form will be found to facilitate the work and guard against errors. It will be a convenience to include in that form columns showing the hour, together with the reading of the patent log (if used) each time that the course is changed or the dead reckoning worked up.

Use the course to the nearest degree and distance to nearest tenth of a mile. Get latitude and dep. to the nearest tenth of a mile.

Example.—At noon, a vessel took departure from Barnegat Lighthouse (Lat. 39° 45′.9 N., Long. 74° 06′.4 W.), bearing by compass 236°, distant 9 miles; vessel steered on courses in table until noon next day. A current set NE. magnetic at 1.5 knots throughout the 24 hours. Wind as in table. Find the dead reckoning position at noon, and the course and distance to Cape Hatteras Lighthouse (Lat. 35° 15′.3 N., Long. 75° 31′.3 W.).

Wind	Compass course	Var.	Dev.	Leeway	Compass error	True courses	Distances	Diff. of Lat.		Departure	
								N.	S.	E.	W.
South	56°	10° W.	5° E.		5° W.	51°	9	5. 7		7. 0	
S	118°	10° W.	3° W.	5°	18° W.	100°	42		7. 3	41. 4	
S	124°	10° W.	5° E.	5°	10° W.	114°	38		15. 5	34. 7	
S	112°	10° W.	3° W.	5°	18° W.	94°	34		2. 4	33. 9	
N	225°	9° W.	4° E.	5°	10° W.	215°	48		39. 3		27. 5
N	237°	9° W.	3° W.	5°	17° W.	220°	69		52. 9		44. 4
Current	45°	10° W.			10° W.	35°	36	29. 5		20. 6	
									117. 4	137. 6	71. 9
								35. 2	35. 2	71. 9	
								DL=	82. 2	65. 7	=Dep.

Lat. Barnegat Light 39° 45′.9 N. Long. 74° 06′.4 W.
DL. 1 22 .2 S. Diff. Long. 1 24 .5 E.

Lat. (noon) 38 23 .7 N. Long. (noon) 72 41 .9 W.
39 45 .9 N.

2)78 09 .6

Middle Lat.= 39 04 .8 N.

Enter traverse Table 3 with Mid. Lat. 39° and Dep. 65.7 in Lat. column, then in Dist. column is found 84.5 or Diff. Long. 84′.5 or 1° 24′.5 E. To find course and distance made good, enter Table 3, and look for place where DL 82′.2 and Dep. 65′.7 are side by side. This is found under course S. 39° E. (141°); abreast these numbers is distance 105.

Therefore course and distance made good is 141°, 105 miles.

		Mer. parts		
Lat. of vessel	38° 23′.7 N.	2483′.9	Long.	72° 41′.9 W.
Lat. C. Hatteras	35 15 .3 N.	2249 .4	Long.	75 31 .3 W.
Diff. Lat.	3 08 .4 S. or 188′.4	m= 234 .5	Diff. Long.	2 49 .4 W. or 169′.4

Tan. Co. = Diff. Long. ÷ m   Dist. = Sec. Co. × Diff. Lat.

Diff. Long. 169.4= log. 2.22891
m= log. 2.37014

Course S. 35° 51′ W. (216°) tan 9.85877 ---------- secant .09119
Diff. Lat. 188′.4 2.27508

Dist.=232.4 log. 2.36627

Therefore course and dist. to Cape Hatteras is 216°, 232.4 miles.

Example.—Steaming from Norfolk to Block I. Sound, about 1 p. m., took departure from Cape Charles light vessel (Lat. 37° 05′.3 N., Long. 75° 43′.5 W.), compass bearing 271°, distant 8 miles, ship's head 90°, dev. 4° W. var. 5° W. Steamed thence till noon next day on the following courses and distances which, with other data, will be found in the form. Required the latitude and longitude in by D. R., course and distance from the light vessel by D. R., and course and distance from the noon position to a point in Block I. Sound, in Lat. 41° 15′ N., Long. 71° 10′ W., by middle latitude sailing.

Wind	Compass course	Var.	Dev.	Leeway	True courses	Distances	Diff. of Lat.		Departure	
							N.	S.	E.	W.
	True bearing Lt. vessel reversed=				82°	8	1. 1	--------	7. 9	--------
NW.	84°	5° W.	4° W.	0°	75	10	2. 6	--------	9. 7	--------
NW.	79	5 W.	4 W.	0	70	15	5. 1	--------	14. 1	--------
NW.	67	5 W.	3 W.	0	59	40	20. 6	--------	34. 3	--------
NW.	20	6 W.	1 E.	5	20	48. 5	45. 6	--------	16. 6	--------
N.	286	6 W.	3 E.	5	278	12	1. 7	--------	--------	11. 9
NW.	57	7 W.	2 W.	5	53	12	7. 2	--------	9. 6	--------
NE.	87	7 W.	4 W.	8	84	20	2. 1	--------	19. 9	--------
NE.	311	7 W.	2 E.	5	301	10	5. 2	--------	--------	8. 6
						DL=	91. 2	N	112. 1	20. 5
									20. 5	
								Dep.=	91. 6	E.
								D. Lo.	116	E.

Course by D. R. =45°. Distance 129 miles.

Lat. left	=37° 05′. 3 N.	Long. left	=75° 43. 5′ W.
Run D. L.	= 1 31 . 2 N.	D Lo.	= 1 56.0 E.
Lat. arrived	=38 36 . 5 N.	Long.	=73 47. 5 W.
Mid. Lat.	=37 50 . 9 N.		

Lat. of point	=41° 15′. 0 N.	Long. of point	=71° 10′. 0 W.
Lat. in	=38 36 . 5 N.	Long. in	=73 47 . 5 W.
Diff. Lat.	= 2 38 . 5 N.	Diff. Long.	= 2 37 . 5 E.
	= 158 . 5 N.		= 157 . 5 E.
Mid. Lat.	=39 55 . 7 N.	Dep.	= 120 . 8 E.

True course to point=37°
Dist.=199. 2 miles.

Example.—A steamer's position by observation at noon, patent log reading 27.3, is Lat. 49° 15′ N., Long. 7° 32′ W. Thence compass course is 262°, the compass error on course is 20° W., until 12.30, at which time, patent log reading 33.9, the course is then changed to 260° (*p. c.*), with same error. At 4.12, patent log 80.5, sights are taken from which it is found that the true longitude is 8° 46′ W., and the compass error 19° W. At 6.15, patent log reading 6.1, a sight is taken from which it is found that the true latitude is 48° 34′.5 N. At 8 p. m. the patent log reads 27.5. Required the positions by D. R. at each sight and at 8 o'clock.

Time	Compass course	Error	True course	Pat. Log.	Dist.	S.	W.	D. Lo.
Noon.				27. 3				
12. 30	262°	20° W.	242°	33. 9	6. 6	3. 1	5. 8	
4. 12	260°	20° W.	240°	80. 5	46. 6	23. 3	40. 3	
						26. 4	46. 1	70. 3
6. 15	260°	19° W.	241°	6. 1	25. 6	12. 4	22. 4	34. 1
8. 00	260°	19° W.	241°	27. 5	21. 4	10. 4	18. 7	27. 9

	Latitude		*Longitude*
By obs. at noon,	49° 15′.0 N.		7° 32′.0 W.
Run to 4.12 sight,	26 .4 S.	Mid. L., 49°	1 10 .3 W.
By D. R. at 4.12 sight,	48 48 .6 N.		8 42 .3 W.
By obs. at 4.12 sight,			
Run to 6.15 sight,	12 .4 S.	Mid. L., 49°	8 46 .0 W.
			34 .1 W.
By D. R. at 6.15 sight,	48 36 .2 N.		9 20 .1 W.
By obs. at 6.15 sight,	48 34 .5 N.		
Run to 8 p. m.,	10 .4 S.	Mid. L., 48°	27 .9 W.
By D. R. at 8 p. m.,	48 24 .1 N.		9 48 .0 W.

Current allowance.—When a vessel is sailing in a known current whose strength may be estimated with fair accuracy, a more correct position may be arrived at by regarding the set and drift of the current as a course and distance to be regularly taken account of in the dead reckoning.

541524 O - 43 - 8

Example.—A vessel in the Gulf Stream at a point where the current is estimated to set 48° at the rate of 1.8 miles an hour, steams 183° (true), making 9.5 knots through the water for 3^h 30^m. Middle latitude 35°. Required the course and distance made good.

	True course	Dist.	N.	S.	E.	W.	D. Lo.
Run	183°	33. 3		33. 3		1. 7	
Current	48°	6. 3	4. 2		4. 7		
Made good	174°	29. 3		29. 1	3. 0		3. 7

Current finding.—It is usual, upon obtaining a good noon position by observation, to compare that position with the one obtained by dead reckoning, and to attribute such discrepancy as may be found to the effects of **current.** It has been pointed out that causes other than the motion of the water tend to make the dead reckoning inaccurate, so that it must not be assumed that currents proper are thus determined with complete correctness.

Current is said to have **set** and **drift,** referring respectively to the direction toward which it is flowing and the velocity with which it moves.

In calculating current by the method of comparing positions by observation with those by D. R., the navigator must make a limit to the periods during which the dead reckoning has been brought forward independently, without receiving any corrections due to new points of departure. In case it is desired to find the current covering a period during which fresh departures have been used, as from noon to noon, find the algebraical sums of all the differences of latitude and longitude from the table, and apply these to the latitude and longitude of original departure—that of the preceding noon; this gives the position from the ship's run proper, and the difference between this and the position by observation gives the set and drift for the 24 hours; if an allowance has been made for current, as explained in the preceding article, that must be omitted in bringing up the position which is to take account of the run only.

Day's run.—It is usual to compute, each day at noon, the vessel's total run for the preceding 24 hours. Having the positions at noon of each day, the course and distance between them is found. The position by observation is used in each case, if such has been found; otherwise, the position by dead reckoning is used.

Example.—At noon, January 22, the position of a vessel by observation was Lat. 35°10′ N., Long. 134°01′ W. During the next 24 hours, the run by D. R. was 60.1 miles north and 153.2 miles east. At noon, January 23, the position by observation was Lat. 36°03′ N., Long. 131°14′ W. Required the position by D. R. at the latter time; also the run and current for the 24 hours.

	Latitude		*Longitude*
By obs., noon, 22d,	35° 10′.0 N.	Mid. L., 36°	134° 01′.0 W.
Run,	1 00 .1 N.	Dep., 153.2 E.	3 09 .4 E.
By D. R., noon, 23d,	36 10 .1 N.	D.Lo., 189.4 E.	130 51 .6 W.
By obs., noon, 23d,	36 03 .0 N.	D.Lo., 22.4 W.	131 14 .0 W.
Current,	7 .1 S.	Dep., 18.1 W.	22 .4 W.

Current for 24 hours, 7.1 S., 18.1 W.=249°,
19.4 miles.
Current per hour, 249°, 0.8 mile.

	Latitude		*Longitude*
By obs., noon, 23d,	36° 03′.0 N.	Mid. L., 36°	131° 14′.0 W.
By obs., noon, 22d,	35 10 .0 N.	D.Lo., 167.0 E.	134 01 .0 W.
Run,	0 53 .0 N.	Dep., 135.1	2 47 .0 E.

Run for 24 hours, 53′.0 N., 135′.1 E.=68°, 146 miles.

CHAPTER VII

NAUTICAL ASTRONOMY, DEFINITIONS

Nautical astronomy has been defined as that branch of the science of navigation in which the position of a vessel is determined by observations of celestial objects—the sun, moon, planets, or stars.

The celestial sphere.—An observer upon the surface of the earth views the heavenly bodies as if situated upon the surface of a vast hollow sphere, of which the eye is the center. This apparent vault has no existence, and only the relative directions can be determined of the celestial bodies—not their distances from each other, or from the observer. But by adopting an imaginary spherical surface of an infinite radius, the eye of the observer being at the center, the places of the heavenly bodies can be projected upon this **celestial sphere,** at points where the lines joining them with the center intersect the surface of the sphere. Since the center of the earth is the point from which all angular distances are measured, the observer, placed there, will find projected on the celestial sphere, not only the celestial bodies, but the imaginary points and circles of the earth's surface. The actual position of the observer on the surface will be projected in a point called the **zenith;** the meridians, equator, and all other lines and points may also be projected.

The **geographical position** of a celestial body is the point on the surface of the earth that has the body in its zenith, or it is the substellar, subsolar or sublunar point. Its latitude is defined by the declination and its longitude by the Greenwich hour angle of the celestial body.

An observer on the earth's surface is constantly changing position with relation to the celestial bodies projected on the sphere, thus giving to the latter an apparent motion. This is due to three causes: first, the diurnal motion of the earth, arising from its rotation upon its axis; second, the annual motion of the earth, arising from its motion about the sun in its orbit; and third, the actual motion of these celestial bodies. The changes produced by the diurnal motion are different for observers at different points upon the earth, and depend upon the latitude and longitude of the observer. But the changes arising from the other causes named are independent of the observer's position, and may be considered at any instant in their relation to the center of the earth. To this end the elements necessary for any computation are tabulated in the *Nautical Almanac* from data based upon the laws which have been found by long series of observations to govern the actual and apparent motion of the various bodies.

The **zenith** of an observer on the earth's surface is the point of the celestial sphere vertically overhead. The **nadir** is the point vertically beneath (not used in navigation).

The **celestial horizon** is the great circle of the celestial sphere formed by passing a plane through the center of the earth at right angles to the line which joins that point with the zenith of the observer. The celestial horizon differs somewhat from the **visible horizon,** which is that line appearing to an observer at sea to mark the intersection of earth and sky. This difference arises from two causes: first, the eye of the observer is always elevated above the sea level, thus permitting him a range of vision exceeding 90° from the zenith; and second, the observer's position is on the surface instead of at the center of the earth. These causes give rise, respectively, to **dip of the horizon** and **parallax,** which will be explained later.

In figure 44 the celestial sphere is considered to be projected upon the celestial horizon, represented by NESW.; the zenith of the observer is projected at Z, and that pole of the earth which is elevated above the horizon, assumed for illustration to be the north pole, appears at P, the *elevated pole* of the celestial sphere. The other pole is not shown in the figure.

The **Equinoctial,** or **celestial equator,** is the great circle formed by extending the plane of the earth's equator until it intersects the celestial sphere. It is shown in the figure in the line EQW. The equinoctial intersects the horizon in E and W, its east and west points.

Hour circles or **celestial meridians** are great circles of the celestial sphere passing through the poles; they may be formed by extending the planes of the respective terrestrial meridians until they intersect the celestial sphere. In the figure, PB, PS, PB′, are hour circles, and that one, PS, which contains the zenith and is formed by the projection of the terrestrial meridian of the observer, intersects the horizon in N and S, its north and south points. The **upper branch** of the celestial meridian is that half which lies on the same side of the poles as the zenith. The opposite half is the lower branch.

Vertical circles, or **circles of altitude**, are great circles of the celestial sphere which pass through the zenith and nadir; they are secondary to the horizon. In the figure, ZH, WZE, NZS, are projections of such circles, which being at right angles to the plane of projection, appear as straight lines. The vertical circle NZS, which passes through the poles, coincides with the meridian of the observer. The vertical circle WZE, whose plane is at right angles to that of the meridian, intersects the horizon in its eastern and western points, and, therefore, at the points of intersection of the equinoctial and celestial horizon; this circle is distinguished as the **prime vertical.**

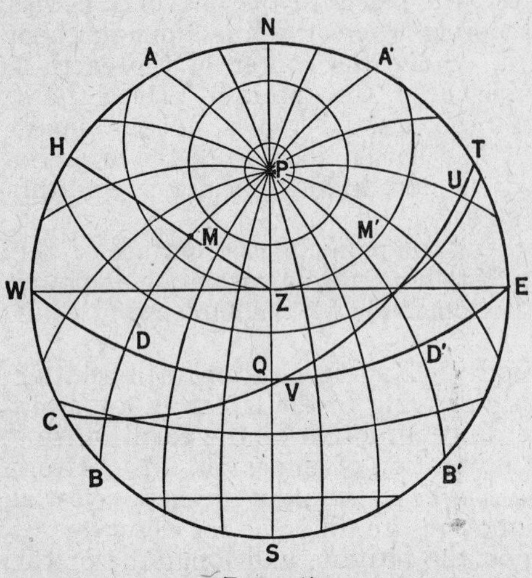

FIGURE 44.

The **declination** of any point on the celestial sphere is its angular distance from the equinoctial, measured upon the hour circle which passes through that point; it is designated as *north* or *south* according to the direction of the point from the equinoctial; it is customary to regard north declinations as positive (+), and south declinations as negative (−). In the figure, DM is the declination of the point M. Declination upon the celestial sphere corresponds with latitude upon the earth.

Parallels of declination are small circles whose planes are parallel to the plane of the equinoctial. Parallels of latitude are small circles whose planes are parallel to the plane of the equator.

The **polar distance** of any point is its angular distance from the pole (generally, the elevated pole of an observer), measured upon the hour circle passing through the point; it must therefore equal 90° *minus* the declination, if measured from the pole of the same name as the declination, or 90° *plus* the declination, if measured from the pole of opposite name. The polar distance of the point M from the elevated pole P is PM.

The **altitude** of any point on the celestial sphere is its angular distance from the horizon, measured upon the vertical circle passing through the point; it is regarded as positive when the body is on the same side of the horizon as the zenith. The altitude of the point M is HM.

The **zenith distance** of any point is its angular distance from the zenith, measured upon the vertical circle passing through the point; the zenith distance of any point which is above the horizon of an observer must equal 90° *minus* the altitude. The zenith distance of M, in the figure, is ZM.

The **hour angle** of any point is the angle at the pole between the meridian of the observer and the hour circle passing through that point; it may also be regarded as the arc of the equinoctial intercepted between those circles. It is measured toward the west as a positive direction through 24^h, or 360°, which constitutes the interval between the successive returns to the meridian, due to the diurnal rotation of the earth, of any point in the celestial sphere. The hour angle of M is the angle QPD, or the arc QD.

The **Greenwich hour angle** (G. H. A.) of a celestial body is the angle at the pole between the meridian of Greenwich and the hour circle of the body.

The **azimuth** of a point on the celestial sphere is the angle at the zenith between the meridian of the observer and the vertical circle passing through the point; it may also be regarded as the arc of the horizon intercepted between those circles. It is measured from either the north or the south point of the horizon (usually that one of the same name as the elevated pole) to the east or west through 180°, and is named accordingly; as, N. 60° W., or S. 120° W., (300°). The azimuth of M is the angle NZH, or the arc NH, from the north point; or it is the angle SZH, or the arc SH, from the south point of the horizon.

The **amplitude** of a point is the angle at the zenith between the prime vertical and the vertical circle of the point; it is measured from the east or the west point of the horizon through 90°, as W. 30° N. It is closely allied with the azimuth and may always be deduced therefrom. In the figure, the amplitude of H is the angle WZH, or the arc WH. The amplitude is used only with reference to points in the horizon.

The **ecliptic** is the great circle representing the path in which, by reason of the annual revolution of the earth, the sun appears to move on the celestial sphere; the plane of the ecliptic is inclined to that of the equinoctial at an angle of 23° 27½′, and this inclination is called the **obliquity of the ecliptic.** The ecliptic is represented by the great circle CVT.

The **equinoxes** are those points at which the ecliptic and the equinoctial intersect, and when the sun occupies either of these positions the days and nights are of equal length throughout the earth. The **Vernal equinox** is that one at which the sun appears to an observer on the earth when passing from southern to northern declination, and the **autumnal equinox** that one at which it appears when passing from northern to southern declination. The vernal equinox is also designated as the **first point of Aries,** and is used as an origin for reckoning right ascension; it is indicated in the figure at V.

The **solstices** are points of the ecliptic at a distance of 90° from the equinoxes, at which the sun attains its highest declination in each hemisphere. They are called the *summer* and the *winter solstice*. The summer solstice is indicated in the figure at U.

The **right ascension** of a point is the angle at the pole between the hour circle of the point and that of the first point of Aries; it may also be regarded as the arc of the equinoctial intercepted between those circles. It is measured from the first point of Aries to the eastward as a positive direction, through 24 hours (0^h–24^h), or 360°. The right ascension of the point M′ is VD′.

Celestial latitude is measured to the north or south of the ecliptic upon great circles secondary thereto. **Celestial longitude** is measured upon the ecliptic from the first point of Aries as an origin, being regarded as positive to the eastward throughout 360°. This system of reference is not used in navigation.

Coordinates.—In order to define the position of a point in space, a system of lines, angles, or planes, or a combination of these, is used to refer it to some fixed line or plane adopted as the primitive; and the lines, angles, or planes by which it is thus referred are called *coordinates*.

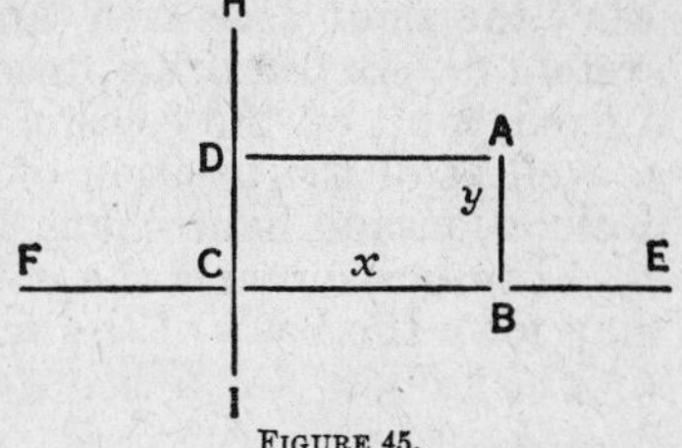

FIGURE 45.

In figure 45 is shown a system of rectilinear coordinates for a plane. A fixed line FE is chosen, and in it a definite point C, as the *origin*. Then the position of a point A is defined by $CB=x$, the distance from the origin, C, to the foot of a perpendicular let fall from A on FE; and by $AB=y$, the length of the perpendicular. The distance x is called the *abscissa* and y the *ordinate*. Assuming two intersecting right lines FE and HI as standard lines of reference, the location of the point A is defined by its distance from each in a direction parallel to the other.

An exemplification of this system is found in the chart, on which FE is represented by the equator, HI by the prime meridian; the coordinates x and y being the longitude and latitude of the point A.

The great circle is to the sphere what the straight line is to the plane; hence, to define the position of a point on the surface of a sphere, some great circle must be selected as the primary, and some particular point of it as the origin. Thus, in figure

46, which represents the case of a sphere, some fixed great circle, Q′CBQ, is selected as the circle of reference and called the *primary;* and a point C is chosen as the origin. Then to define the position of any point A, the abscissa x equals the distance from C to the point B, where the secondary great circle through A intersects the primary; the ordinate y equals the distance of A from the primary, measured on the secondary—that is, x=CB and y=AB.

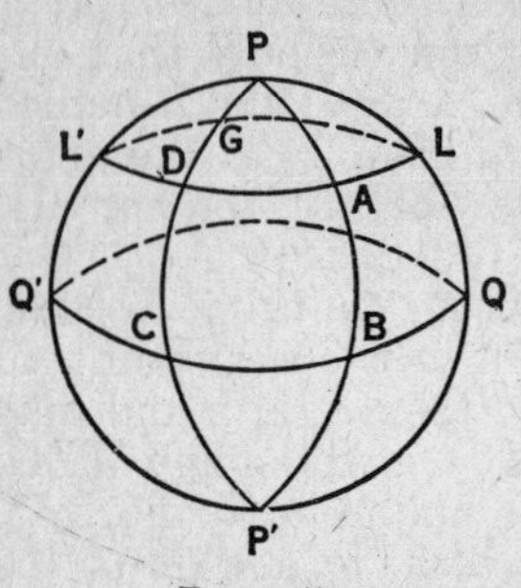

FIGURE 46.

In the case of the earth, the primary selected is the equator (its plane being perpendicular to the earth's axis), and upon this are measured the abscissas, while upon the secondaries to it are measured the ordinates of all points on the earth's surface. The initial point for reference on the equator is determined by the *prime meridian* chosen. West longitudes and north latitudes are called *positive*, east longitudes and south latitudes, *negative.*

In the case of the celestial sphere, there are four systems of coordinates in use for defining the position of any point; these vary according to the circle adopted as the primary and the point used as an origin. They are as follows:

1. Altitude and azimuth.
2. Declination and hour angle.
3. Declination and right ascension.
4. Celestial latitude and longitude (not used in navigation).

Altitude and azimuth.—In this system the primary circle is the celestial horizon, the secondaries to which are the vertical circles, or circles of altitude. The horizon is intersected by the celestial meridian in its northern and southern points, of which one—usually that adjacent to the elevated pole—is selected as an origin for reckoning coordinates. The azimuth indicates in which vertical circle the point to be defined is found, and the altitude gives the position of the point in that circle. In figure 44 the point M is located, according to this system, by its azimuth NH and altitude HM.

Declination and hour angle.—In this system the primary circle is the equinoctial, the secondaries to which are the hour circles. The point of origin is that intersection of the equinoctial and the observer's celestial meridian which is above the horizon. The hour angle indicates in which declination circle the point to be defined is found, and the declination gives the position of the point in that circle. In figure 44 the point M is located, according to this system, by its hour angle QD and declination DM.

Declination and right ascension.—In this system the primary and secondaries are the same as in the system just described, but the point of origin differs, being assumed to be at the first point of Aries, or vernal equinox. The right ascension indicates in which declination circle the point to be defined may be found, and the declination gives the position in that circle. In figure 44 the point M′ is located by VD′, the right ascension, and D′M′, the declination. It should be noted that this system differs from the preceding in that the position of a point is herein referred to a fixed point on the celestial sphere and is independent of the zenith of the observer as well as of the position of the earth in its diurnal motion, while, in the system of declination and hour angle, both of these are factors in determining the coordinates.

The horizon and the equinoctial are of especial importance to the navigator, as they form the basis of the systems of coordinates used.

Summary

Reference circles		Coordinates measured	
Primary	Secondary	Primary	Secondary
Horizon	Vertical circles.	Azimuth	Altitude.
Equinoctial	Hour circles.	Hour angle	Declination.
Do	Do.	Right ascension	Do.

Relation between hour angle and azimuth.—When H. A. is less than 180°, azimuth is west. When H. A. is between 180° and 360°, azimuth is east.

PROJECTIONS OF ASTRONOMICAL TRIANGLE

In figure 44 the triangle PMZ is the **astronomical triangle**, and is the triangle which the navigator solves to find latitude and longitude. This solution is reached through the use of formulas of spherical trigonometry, in which if any three parts of a triangle are known, the unknown parts may be obtained.

The spherical or astronomical triangle may be projected on the plane of the meridian, the horizon, or the equinoctial. The choice of projection is determined by the method of solution to be used. The three projections are shown below.

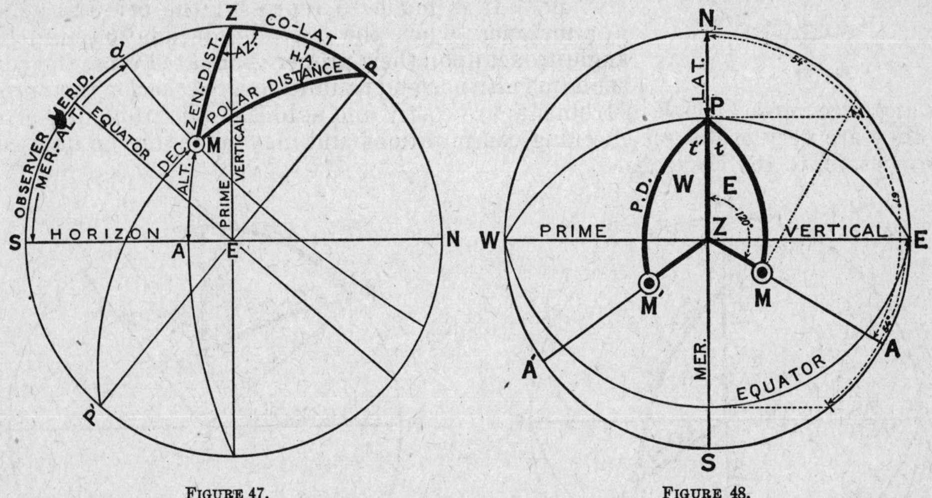

FIGURE 47. FIGURE 48.

Figures 47, 48, and 49 are projections of the astronomical triangle on the plane of the meridian, the horizon, and the equinoctial, respectively, in which the following lettering is used.

P=Elevated pole.
Z=Zenith of the observer.
M or M′=Celestial body.
PM=Polar distance=(90°−declination).
ZM=Zenith distance=(90°−altitude).
PZ=Co-latitude=(90°−PN) or (90°−latitude).
Angle MPZ=Hour angle.
Angle PZM=Azimuth.
Angle ZMP=Position angle (seldom used in navigation).

In figure 47, if the body (M) were on the meridian of the observer, as at d, the triangle would be a straight line PZd.

In figure 48 the astronomical triangle may be constructed as follows:

Suppose that in latitude 54° N. an altitude of 67° is measured, and an azimuth of 120°. Since the latitude is 54° the pole may be placed on the meridian NZS by measuring 54° from north and dropping a perpendicular to the meridian, because the latitude of the observer is equal to the altitude of the elevated pole (it is 90° from N to Z). The equinoctial passes through the east and west point, and since the declination of the zenith is equal to the latitude of the place, by laying off 54° from E. and dropping a perpendicular on the meridian, the position of the equator on the meridian is determined. Now lay off the azimuth 120° from north; draw from Z through 120° line ZA. Lay off from A the altitude 67°, drop perpendicular on ZA, and locate body at M. When the body is at M, the hour angle t is east; when the body is at M′, the hour angle t′ is west.

In figure 49 the astronomical triangle is projected on the plane of the equinoctial, but this projection is more frequently used as a time diagram. The pole P, being at the center of the projection, causes all meridians to be represented by diameters of the circle representing the equinoctial. Therefore, the hour angle between any two meridians may be readily shown in units of arc or time, as will be further explained in the chapter on time.

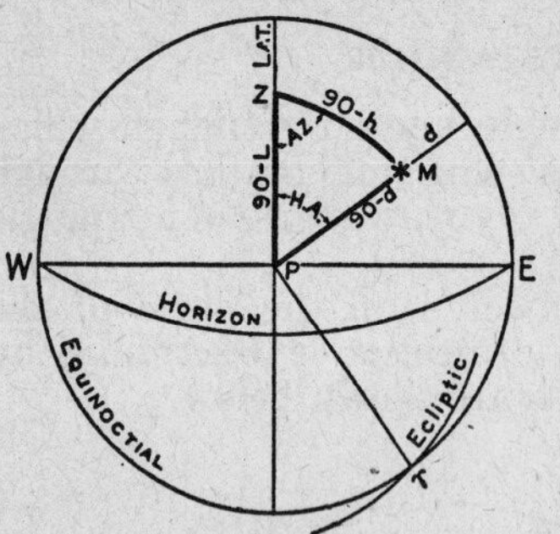

FIGURE 49.

In figures 50 and 51, the values of the sides of the astronomical triangle are shown in the terms used by the navigator.

Figure 52 represents one of the instruments that has been devised for mechanically solving the astronomical triangle. It is made to represent the celestial sphere. For instance, when the latitude, declination, and hour angle are set upon their proper graduated arcs, the corresponding altitude and azimuth may be read on their proper arcs and vice versa. Such instruments are costly and subject to instrumental errors, but they are very useful for checking computations and may some day be devised in a form useful to the navigator.

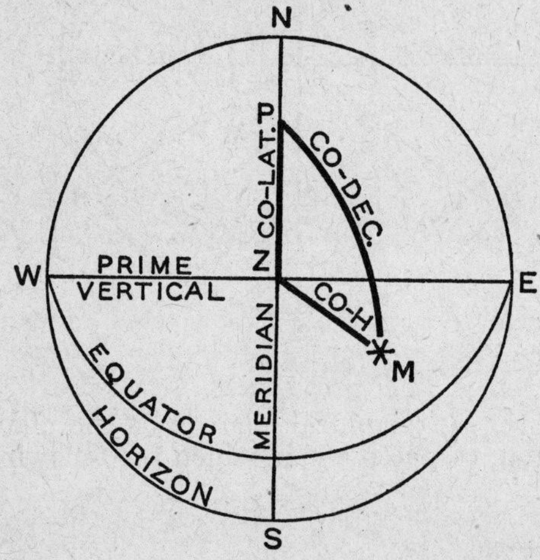

FIGURE 50.

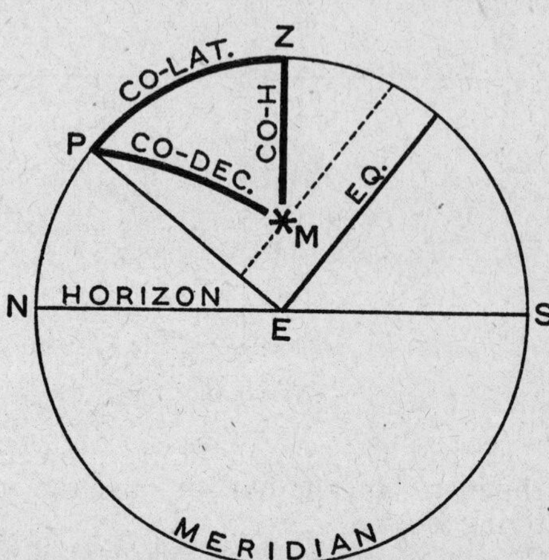

FIGURE 51.

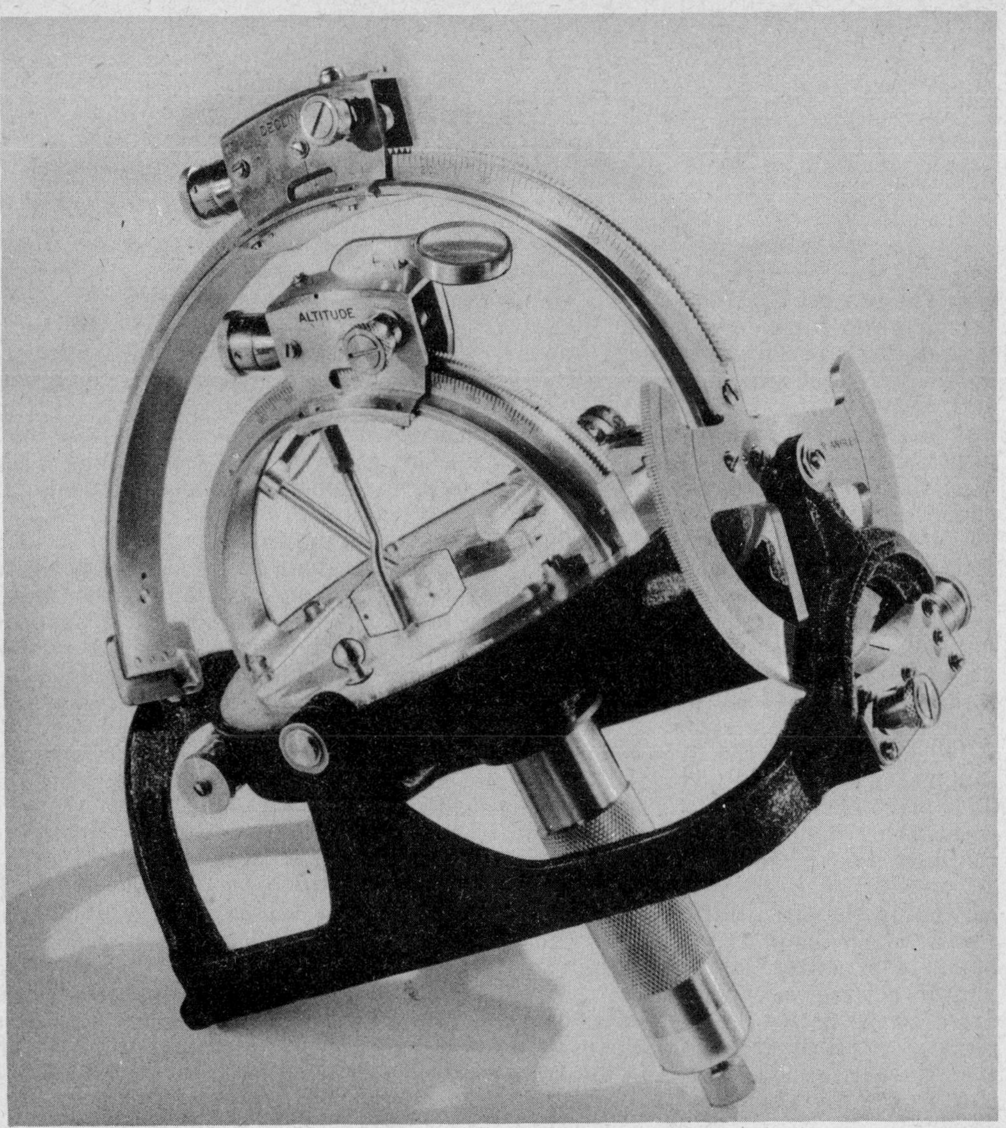

FIGURE 52.—Computing instrument.

CHAPTER VIII

NAUTICAL ASTRONOMY INSTRUMENTS

THE SEXTANT

The **sextant** is an instrument for measuring the angle between two objects by bringing into coincidence at the eye of the observer rays of light received directly from the one and by reflection from the other, the measure being afforded by the inclination of the reflecting surfaces. By reason of its small dimensions, its accuracy, and, above all, the fact that it does not require a permanent or a stable mounting but is available for use under the conditions existing on shipboard, it is a most important instrument for the purposes of the navigator. While the sextant is not capable of the same degree of accuracy as fixed instruments, its measurements are sufficiently accurate for navigation.

Description.—A modern form of the sextant is represented in figure 53. The frame is of brass or some similar alloy. The graduated arc, AA, generally of silver, is marked in appropriate divisions; in the finer sextants, each division represents 10′, and the vernier affords a means of reading to 10″. A wooden handle, H, is provided for holding the instrument. The **index mirror,** M, and **horizon mirror,** *m,* are of plate glass, and are silvered, though the upper half of the horizon glass is left plain to allow direct rays to pass through unobstructed. To give greater distinctness to the images, a small **telescope,** E, is placed in the line of sight; it is supported in a ring, K, which can be moved by a screw in a direction at right angles to the plane of the sextant, thus shifting the axis of the telescope, and therefore the plane of reflection. This plane always remains parallel to that of the instrument, the motion of the telescope being intended merely to regulate the relative brightness of the direct and reflected image. In the ring, K, are small screws for the purpose of adjusting the telescope by making its axis parallel with the plane of the sextant. The vernier is carried on the end of an index bar pivoted beneath the index mirror, M, and thus travels along the graduated scale, affording a measure for any change of inclination of the index mirror. The index mirror, M, is attached to the head of the index bar, with its surface perpendicular to the plane of the instrument; an adjusting screw is fitted at the back to permit of adjustment to the perpendicular plane. The fixed glass *m*, half silvered and half plain, is called the **horizon glass,** as it is through this that the horizon is observed in measuring altitudes of celestial bodies; it is provided with screws, by which its perpendicularity to the plane of the instrument may be adjusted. At P and Q are colored glasses of different shades, which may be used separately or in combination to protect the eye from the intense light of the sun. In order to observe with accuracy and make the images come precisely in contact, a **tangent screw** is fixed to the index, by means of which the latter may be moved with greater precision than by hand; but this screw does not act until the index is fixed by the screw C at the back of the sextant; when the index is to be moved any considerable amount, the screw C is loosened; when it is brought near to its required position the screw must be tightened, and the index may then be moved gradually by the tangent screw.

Besides the telescope, E, the instrument is usually provided with an inverting telescope, and a tube without glasses; also, with a cap carrying colored glasses, which may be put on the eye end of the telescope, thus dispensing with the necessity for the use of the colored shades, P and Q, and eliminating any possible errors which might arise from nonparallelism of their surfaces.

The latest type of sextant (see fig. 53) furnished to the United States Navy is fitted with an endless tangent screw which carries a micrometer drum from which the seconds of arc are read. By pressure of the thumb the tangent screw is released

FIGURE 53.—Sextant.

and the index bar may be moved to any position on the arc by hand, where the tangent screw is again thrown into gear by releasing the pressure of the thumb. The endless tangent screw is accomplished by cutting the edge of the arc with the worm teeth into which the tangent screw gears. At night the reading of this sextant is facilitated by a small electric light carried on it and supplied by a battery contained in the handle.

The ordinary **vernier** is an attachment facilitating exact readings of scale of a sextant, by which aliquot parts of the smallest divisions of the graduated scale are measured. The principle of the sextant vernier is almost identical with that of the barometer vernier, a complete description of which was given under that subject in chapter II. The arc of a sextant is usually divided into 120 or more parts, each division representing 1°; each of these degree divisions is further subdivided to an extent dependent upon the accuracy of reading of which the sextant is capable. In the instruments for finer work, the divisions of the scale correspond to 10′ each and the vernier covers a length corresponding to 59 such divisions, which is subdivided into 60 parts, thus permitting a reading of 10″; all sextants are not so closely graduated.

Whatever the limits of subdivision, all sextants are fitted with verniers which contain one more division than the length of scale covered, and in which, therefore, scale-readings and vernier-readings increase in the same direction—toward the left hand. To read any sextant, it is necessary to observe the scale division next below, or to the right of, the zero of the vernier, and to add thereto the angle corresponding to that division of the vernier scale which is most nearly in exact coincidence with a division of the instrument scale.

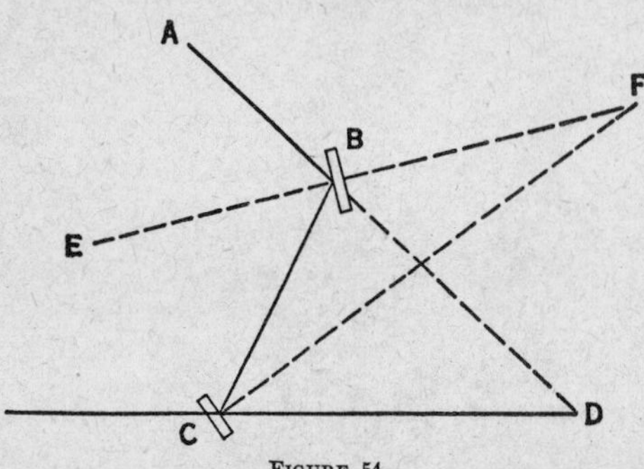

FIGURE 54.

Optical principle.—When a ray of light is reflected from a plane surface, the angle of incidence is equal to the angle of reflection. From this it may be proved that when a ray of light undergoes two reflections in the same plane with two plane mirrors the angle between its first and its last direction is equal to twice the inclination of the reflecting surfaces. Upon this fact the construction of the sextant is based.

In figure 54, let B and C represent, respectively, the index mirror and horizon mirror of a sextant; draw EF perpendicular to B, and CF perpendicular to C; then the angle CFB represents the inclination of the two mirrors. Suppose a ray to proceed from A and undergo reflection at B and at C, its last direction being CD; then ADC is the angle between its first and last directions, and it is desired to prove that ADC=2 CFB.

From the equality of the angles of incidence and reflection:

$$ABE=EBC, \text{ and } ABC=2\ EBC;$$
$$BCF=FCD, \text{ and } BCD=2\ BCF.$$

From geometry:

$$ADC=ABC-BCD=2\ (EBC-BCF)=2\ CFB,$$

which is the relation to be proved.

In the sextant, since the index mirror is immovably attached to the index arm, which also carries the vernier, it follows that no change can occur in the inclination between the index mirror and the horizon mirror, excepting such as is registered by the travel of the vernier upon the scale.

If, when the index mirror is so placed that it is nearly parallel with the horizon mirror, an observer directs the telescope toward some well-defined object, there will be seen in the field of view two separate images of the object; and if the inclination of the index mirror be slightly changed by moving the index bar, it will be seen that while one of the images remains fixed the other moves. The fixed image is the direct one seen through the unsilvered part of the horizon glass, while the movable image is due to rays reflected by the index and horizon mirrors. When the two images coincide these mirrors must be parallel (assuming that the object is sufficiently distant to disregard the space which separates the mirrors); in this position of the index mirror the vernier indicates the true zero of the scale. If, however, instead of observing a single object, the instrument is so placed that the direct ray from one object appears in coincidence with the reflected ray of a second object, then the true angle between the objects will be twice the angle of inclination between the mirrors. or twice the angle measured by the vernier from the true zero of the scale. To avoid the necessity of doubling the angle on the scale, the latter is so marked that each half degree appears as a whole degree, whence its indications give the whole angle directly.

Sextant adjustments.—The theory of the sextant requires that the following conditions be fulfilled for accurate indications:

(*a*) The two surfaces of each mirror and shade glass must be in parallel planes.

(*b*) The graduated arc or limb must be a plane, and its graduations, as well as those of the vernier, must be exact.

(*c*) The axis must be at the center of the limb, and perpendicular to the plane thereof.

(*d*) The index and horizon glasses must be perpendicular, and the line of sight parallel to the plane of the limb.

Of these, only the last named ordinarily require the attention of the navigator who is to make use of the sextant; the others, which may be called the *permanent adjustments*, should be made before the instrument leaves the hands of the maker, and with careful use will never be deranged.

The **index mirror adjustment** consists in making the reflecting surface of this mirror perpendicular to the plane of the sextant. To test this, set the index near the middle of the arc, then, placing the eye very nearly in the plane of the sextant and close to the index mirror, observe whether the direct image of the arc and its image reflected from the mirror appear to form one continuous arc; if so, the glass is perpendicular to the plane of the sextant; if the reflected image appears to droop from the arc seen directly, the glass leans backward; if it seems to rise, the glass leans forward. The adjustment is made by the screws at the back of the mirror.

The **horizon mirror adjustment** consists in making the reflecting surface of this mirror perpendicular to the plane of the sextant. The index mirror having been adjusted, if, in revolving it by means of the index arm, there is found one position in which it is parallel to the horizon glass, then the latter must also be perpendicular to the plane of the sextant. In order to test this, put in the telescope and direct it toward a star; move the index until the reflected image appears to pass the direct image; if one passes directly over the other the mirrors must be parallel; if one passes on either side of the other the horizon glass needs adjustment, which is accomplished by means of the screws attached.

The sea horizon may be used also for making this adjustment. Hold the sextant vertically and bring the direct and the reflected images of the horizon line into coincidence; then incline the sextant until its plane makes but a small angle with the horizon; if the images still coincide the glasses are parallel; if not, the horizon glass needs adjustment.

The **telescope adjustment** must be made so that, in measuring angular distances, the line of sight, or axis of the telescope, shall be parallel to the plane of the instrument, as a deviation in that respect, in measuring large angles, will occasion a considerable error. To avoid such error, a telescope is employed in which are placed two wires, parallel to each other and equidistant from the center of the telescope; by means of these wires the adjustment may be made. Screw on the telescope, and turn the tube containing the eyeglass till the wires are parallel to the plane of the instrument; then select two clearly defined objects whose angular distance must be not less than 90°, because an error is more easily discovered when the angle is great; bring the reflected image of one object into exact coincidence with the direct image of the other at the inner wire; then, by altering slightly the position of the instrument, make the objects appear on the other wire; if the contact still remains perfect, the axis of the telescope is in its right position; but if the two objects appear to separate or lap over at the outer wire the telescope is not parallel, and it must be rectified by turning one of the two screws of the ring into which the telescope is screwed, having previously loosened the other screw; by repeating this operation a few times the contact will be precisely the same at both wires, and the axis of the telescope will be parallel to the plane of the instrument.

Another method is to place the sextant upon a table in a horizontal position, look along the plane of the limb, and make a mark upon a wall, or other vertical surface, at a distance of about 20 feet; draw another mark above the first at a distance equal to the height of the axis of the telescope above the plane of the limb; then so adjust the telescope that the upper mark, as viewed through the telescope, falls midway between the wires. Some sextants are accompanied by small sights whose height is exactly equal to the distance between the telescope and the plane of the limb; by the use of these, the necessity for employing the second mark is avoided and the adjustment can be very accurately made.

Errors.—The errors which arise from defects in the *permanent adjustments* of the sextant may be divided into three classes, namely: errors due to faulty centering of the axis, called **eccentricity;** errors of graduation; and errors arising from lack of parallelism of surfaces in index mirror and in shade glasses.

The errors due to eccentricity and faulty graduation are constant for the same angle, and should be determined once for all at some place where proper facilities for doing the work are at hand; these errors can only be ascertained by measuring known angles with the sextant. If angles of 10°, 20°, 30°, 40°, etc., are first laid off with a theodolite or similar instrument and then measured by the sextant, a table of errors of the sextant due to eccentricity and faulty graduation may be made, and the error at any intermediate angle found by interpolation; this table will include the error of graduation of the theodolite and also the error due to inaccurate reading of the sextant, but such errors are small. Another method for determining the combined errors of eccentricity and graduation is by measuring the angular distance between stars and comparing the observed and the computed arc between them, but this process is liable to inaccuracies by reason of the uncertainty of allowances for atmospheric refraction.

Errors of graduation, when large, may be detected by "stepping off" distances on the graduated arc with the vernier; place the zero of the vernier in exact coincidence with a division of the arc, and observe whether the final division of the vernier also coincides with a division of the arc; this should be tried at numerous positions of the graduated limb, and the agreement ought to be perfect in every case.

The error due to a prismatic index mirror may be found by measuring a certain unchangeable angle, then taking out the glass and turning the upper edge down, and measuring the angle again; half the difference of these two measures will be the error at that angle due to the mirror. From a number of measures of angles in this manner, a table similar to the one for eccentricity and faulty graduation can be made; or the two tables may be combined. When possible to avoid it, however, no sextant should be used in which there is an index mirror which produces a greater error than that due to the probable error of reading the scale. Mirrors having a greater angle than 2″ between their faces are rejected for use in the United States Navy. Index mirrors may be roughly tested by noting if there is an elongated image of a well-defined point at large angles.

Since the error due to a prismatic horizon mirror is included in the index correction, and consequently applied alike to all angles, it may be neglected.

Errors due to prismatic shade glasses can be determined by measuring angles with and without the shade glasses and noting the difference. They may also be determined, where the glasses are so arranged that they can be turned through an angle of 180°, by measuring the angle first with the glass in its usual position and then reversed, and taking the mean of the two as the true measure.

Index error.—The index error of a sextant is the error of its indications due to the fact that when the index and horizon mirrors are parallel the zero of the vernier does not coincide with the zero of the scale. Having made the adjustments of the index and horizon mirrors and of the telescope, as previously described, it is necessary to find that point of the arc at which the zero of the vernier falls when the two mirrors are parallel, for all angles measured by the sextant are reckoned from that point. If this point is to the left of the zero of the limb, all readings will be too great; if to the right of the zero, all readings will be too small.

If desirable that the reading should be zero when the mirrors are parallel, place the zero of the vernier on zero of the arc; then, by means of the adjusting screws of the horizon glass, move that glass until the direct and reflected images of the same object coincide, after which the perpendicularity of the horizon glass should again be verified, as it may have been deranged by the operation. This adjustment is not essential, since the correction may readily be determined and applied to the reading. The sextant should never be relied upon for maintaining a constant index correction, and the error should be ascertained frequently. It is good practice to verify the correction each time a sight is taken.

The **index correction** may be found by a star, by the sea horizon, or by the sun.

Bring the direct and reflected images of a star into coincidence, and read off the arc. The index correction is numerically equal to this reading, and is positive or negative according as the reading is on the right or left of the zero.

The same method may be employed, substituting for a star the sea horizon, though this will be found somewhat less accurate.

Measure the apparent diameter of the sun by first bringing the upper limb of the reflected image to touch the lower limb of the direct image, and then bringing the lower limb of the reflected image to touch the upper limb of the direct image.

Denote the readings in the two cases by r and r'; then, if S=apparent diameter of the sun, and R=the reading of the sextant when the two images are in coincidence, we have:

$$r = R + S,$$
$$r' = R - S,$$
$$R = \tfrac{1}{2}(r + r').$$

As R represents the *error*, the *correction* will be −R. Hence the rule: Mark the readings when *on* the arc with the *negative* sign; when *off*, with the *positive* sign; then the index correction is one-half the algebraic sum of the two readings.

Example.—The sun's diameter is measured for index correction as follows: On the arc, 31′ 20″; off the arc, 33′ 10″. Required the correction.

On the arc,	−31′	20″
Off the arc,	+33	10
2)	+ 1	50
I. C.,	+ 0	55

From the equations previously given, it is seen that, $S = \frac{1}{2}(r - r')$; hence, if the observations are correct, it will be found that the sun's semidiameter, as given in the Nautical Almanac for the day of observation, is equal to one-fourth the algebraic difference of the readings. If required to obtain the index correction with great precision, several observations should be taken and the mean used, the accuracy being verified by comparing the tabulated semidiameter with the value of the semidiameter obtained by observing the diameter. If the sun is low, the horizontal semidiameter should be observed, to prevent the error that may arise from unequal refraction

Use of the sextant.—To measure the angle between any two visible objects, point the telescope toward the lower one, if one is above the other, or toward the left-hand one, if they are in nearly the same horizontal plane. Keep this object in direct view through the unsilvered part of the horizon glass, and move the index arm until the image of the other object is seen by a double reflection from the index mirror and the silvered portion of the horizon glass. Having gotten the direct image of one object into nearly exact contact with the reflected image of the other, clamp the index arm and, by means of the tangent screw, complete the adjustment so that the contact may be perfect; then read the limb.

In measuring the altitude of a celestial body above the sea horizon, it is necessary that the angle shall be measured to that point of the horizon which lies vertically beneath the object. To determine this point, the observer should move the instrument slightly to the right and left of the vertical, swinging it about the line of sight as an axis, taking care to keep the object in the middle of the field of view. The object will appear to describe the arc of a circle, and the lowest point of this arc marks the true vertical.

The shade glasses should be employed as may be necessary to protect the eye when observing objects of dazzling brightness, such as the sun, or the horizon when the sun is reflected from it at a low altitude. Care must be taken that the images are not too bright or the eye will be so affected as to interfere with the accuracy of the observations.

Choice of sextants.—The choice of a sextant should be governed by the kind of work which is required to be done. In rough work, such as surveying, where angles need only be measured to the nearest 30″ the radius may be as small as 6 inches, which will permit easy reading, and the instrument can be correspondingly lightened. Where readings to 10″ are desired, as in precise astronomical work, the radius should be about 7½ inches, and the instrument, to be strongly built, should weigh about 3½ pounds.

The parts of an instrument should move freely, without binding or gritting. The eyepieces should move easily in the telescope tubes; the bracket for carrying the telescope should be made strong. It is found that the parallelism of the line of sight is destroyed in focusing the eyepiece, either on account of the looseness of the fit or because of the telescope bracket being weak. The vernier should lie close to the limbs to prevent parallax in reading. If it is either too loose or too tight at either extremity of its travel, it may indicate that the pivot is not perpendicular. The balls of the tangent screw should fit snugly in their sockets, so that there may be no lost motion.

Where possible, the sextant should always be submitted to expert examination and test as to the accuracy of its permanent adjustments before acceptance by the navigator.

The modern sextants have endless tangent screws and are fitted with micrometers reading to 10″ of arc. They also have electric light attachments for use at night.

Resilvering mirrors.—Occasion may arise for resilvering the mirrors of a sextant, as they are liable to be damaged by dampness or other causes. For this purpose some clean tin foil and mercury are required. Upon a piece of glass about 4 inches square place a piece of blotting paper of slightly less dimensions; on this blotter lay a piece of tin foil whose dimensions exceed by about a quarter of an inch in each direction those of the glass to be silvered; smooth out the foil carefully by rubbing; put a drop of mercury on the foil and spread it with the finger over the entire surface, being careful that none shall find its way under the foil; then put on a few more drops of mercury until the whole surface is fluid. The mirror which is to be silvered having been carefully cleaned chemically with dilute nitric acid or alcohol should be laid upon a piece of tissue paper which is slightly larger than the foil; place both, paper side down, on the tin-mercury amalgam and withdraw the tissue paper from between the amalgam and mirror, a gentle pressure being kept upon the mirror to avoid the formation of bubbles; finally, place the mirror face downward and leave it in an inclined position to allow the surplus mercury to flow off, the latter operation being hastened by a strip of tin foil at its lower edge, and by placing a small weight on the mirror. After 5 or 6 hours the tin foil around the edges may be removed, and the next day a coat of any good commercial varnish or lacquer should be applied. For a horizon mirror care must be taken to avoid silvering the plain half. The mercury drawn from the foil should not be placed with clean mercury with a view to use in the artificial horizon or the whole will be spoiled.

Octants and quintants.—The sextant is an instrument whose arc covers one-sixth of a complete circle, and which is capable of measuring an angle of 120°. Other instruments are made, identical in principle with the sextant, and which differ from that instrument only in the length of the arc. These are the **octant** an eighth of a circle, by which angles may be measured to 90°, and the **quintant** a fifth of a circle, which measures angles up to 144°. The distinction between these instruments is not always carefully made.

Bubble sextant.—In this instrument a bubble arrangement is used to represent an artificial horizon, so that when the natural horizon is indistinct or invisible, as in hazy weather or when in an airplane high above the earth's surface, observations may still be made. The bubble is difficult to control owing to the motion of the ship or airplane, and consequently errors in the measured altitude of a celestial body are liable to be greater than when the visible horizon is used. It is primarily used in aircraft navigation where extreme accuracy is not so essential.

THE ARTIFICIAL HORIZON

The artificial horizon is a small, rectangular, shallow basin of mercury, over which, to protect the mercury from agitation by the wind, is placed a roof consisting of two plates of glass at right angles to each other. The mercury affords a perfectly horizontal surface which is at the same time an excellent mirror. The different parts of an artificial horizon are furnished in a compact form, a metal bottle being provided for containing the mercury when not in use, together with a suitable funnel for pouring.

If MN, in figure 55, is the horizontal surface of the mercury; S′B a ray of light from a celestial object, incident to the surface at B; BA the reflected ray; then an observer at A will receive the ray BA as if it proceeded from a point S″, whose angular depression, MBS″, below the horizontal plane is equal to the altitude, MBS′, of the object above that plane. If, then, SA is a direct ray from the object parallel to S′B, an observer at A can measure with the sextant the angle SAS″=S′BS″=2 S′BM, by bringing the image of the object reflected by the index mirror into coincidence with the image S″ reflected by the mercury and seen through the horizon glass. The instrumental measure, corrected for index error, will be double the apparent altitude of the body.

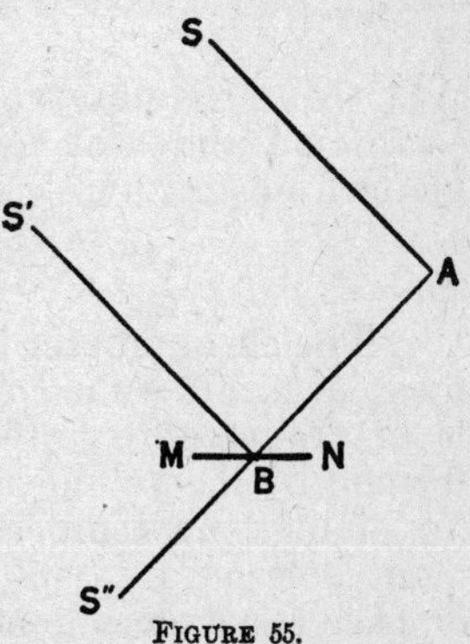

FIGURE 55.

The sun's altitude will be measured by bringing the lower limb of one image to touch the upper limb of the other. Half the corrected instrumental reading will be the apparent altitude of the sun's *lower* or *upper* limb, according as the lower or upper limb of the *reflected* image was the one employed in the observation.

In the morning with closing suns, the upper limb is observed, but with opening suns the lower limb is observed, while in the afternoon with closing suns the lower limb is observed and with opening suns the upper limb is observed When using an inverted telescope, it is the reflected image that moves in the field of view, and when the reflected is above the direct, upper limbs are used, and when the reflected is below the direct, lower limbs are used.

In observations of the sun with the artificial horizon, the eye is protected by a single dark glass over the eyepiece of the telescope through which direct and reflected rays must pass alike, thereby avoiding the errors that might possibly arise from a difference in the separate shade glasses attached to the frame of the sextant.

The glasses in the roof over the mercury should be made of *plate glass*, with *perfectly parallel faces*. If they are at all prismatic, the observed altitude will be erroneous. The error may be removed by observing a second altitude with the roof reversed, and, in general, by taking one-half of a set of observations with the roof in one position and the other half with the roof reversed. On the rare occasions when the atmosphere is so calm that the unsheltered mercury will remain undisturbed, most satisfactory observations may be made by leaving off the roof.

In setting up an artificial horizon, care should be taken that the basin is free from dust and other foreign matter, as small particles floating upon the surface of the mercury interfere with a perfect reflection. The basin should be so placed that its longer edge lies in the direction in which the observed body will bear at the middle of the observations. The spot selected for taking the sights should be as free as possible from vibration, and precautions should be taken to shelter the horizon from the wind, as the mere placing of the roof will not ordinarily be sufficient to accomplish this. Embedding the roof in earth serves to keep out the wind, while setting the whole horizon upon a thick towel or a piece of such material as heavy felt usually affords ample protection from wind, tends to reduce the vibrations from mechanical shocks, and also aids in keeping out the moisture from the ground. In damp climates the roof should be kept dry by wiping, or the moisture deposited from the inclosed air will form a cloud upon the glass.

541524 O - 43 - 9

Molasses, oil, or other viscous fluid may be employed as a substitute for mercury.

Example.—Observed the double altitude of the sun's upper limb from an artificial horizon, I. C. −1′; S. D. of sun 16′.

	Sextant double altitude		
	90°	50′	
	90	40	
	90	30	
	90	20	
	90	10	
(Mean)	90°	30′	
I. C.	−	1	
	2)90	29	
obs. alt.	45°	14′	30″
Ref. (Tab. 22)		−	58
Par. (Tab. 20)		+	6
S. D.		−16	00 (N. A.)
True alt.	44	57	38

When a star is observed with the artificial horizon, the only corrections are the index correction and that for refraction. The artificial horizon is seldom if ever used in modern navigation.

CHRONOMETERS

The **chronometer** is a type of clock which has special attachments to insure the most accurate time keeping under the varying conditions met at sea. A variable lever provides for uniform pressure of the mainspring. A special expansion balance, formed by a combination of metals of different coefficients of expansion, compensates for changes in temperature. Special gimbals, mounted in a case, keep the instrument horizontal in spite of the ship's movement in a seaway. A specially fitted box or case, in a permanent position, protects the instrument from radical changes in temperature and from shock.

The chronometer is used by the navigator to determine the civil time of the meridian of Greenwich, England, which is the basic time used for observations of celestial bodies in determining the ship's position at sea. Since the accuracy of the work depends largely upon the accuracy of the chronometers they are treated with great care.

Chronometers that are used in the naval service are issued to ships by the Naval Observatory at Washington, D. C. Before issue their accuracy is thoroughly tested. They are set to Greenwich civil time and should be kept running constantly. After a period of 3 to 4 years, or in case of derangement, a chronometer should be returned to the Naval Observatory for cleaning and adjustment. No attempts to repair a chronometer should be made on board ship.

Chronometer rate.—Since it is impossible to make a perfect instrument, a normal chronometer will gain or lose a small amount each day. The amount of the gain or loss for one day is called the **rate.** It should be uniform from day to day. The rate is called positive and marked (+) when the chronometer is gaining on the Greenwich civil time, and is called negative and marked (−) when losing on the Greenwich civil time.

The **chronometer error** is the difference between the chronometer time indicated and the Greenwich civil time. The error, as the result of the daily rate, is changing daily, and so must be computed daily and recorded in the chronometer record book. It is marked positive or negative as the chronometer is fast or slow on the Greenwich civil time. The size of the error is of little importance as long as it can be accurately computed at any moment.

The **chronometer correction** is the chronometer error with the sign reversed, so that when applied to the chronometer reading the corresponding Greenwich civil time is obtained. Great care must be taken in the use of the signs of the error and correction. It is much safer to mark the error "fast" or "slow," and to apply it accordingly, knowing that the terms always apply to the chronometer's reading with respect to Greenwich civil time.

FIGURE 56.—Chronometer.

Time signals.—In order to keep account of the rate and error of a chronometer some means must be provided for periodic comparison with a more accurate time recorder. At astronomical observatories special clocks are regulated by the most refined observations of celestial bodies. The results of their account are made available daily to all ships and stations, by means of radio and telegraph time signals. These signals permit the modern navigator to make a daily comparison of his chronometers with the most accurate time recorders made.

Before radio was in general use, ships compared their chronometers each time they were in port; and, by means of daily comparison of the two or three chronometers kept on board, they kept the best possible account of the rate during the voyage. To facilitate comparisons in port a visual time signal was used. This was usually a large ball or shape hoisted in a conspicuous place ashore, and released at the instant of receipt of the telegraphic time signal. Visual time signals are still in use in some ports.

United States time signals.—The Naval Observatory at Washington, D. C., is the origin of all Government time signals broadcast in the United States and its possessions, excepting the Philippine Islands. During the transmission of the time signal, the radio stations at Arlington and Annapolis are automatically controlled by wire from the Naval Observatory transmitting device. The San Francisco signals are controlled by a similar device located at the Mare Island Navy Yard. That device is synchronized with the Washington signal by means of a stroboscopic dial and rotating motor coils. The time signals sent from Honolulu and Balboa, C. Z., are automatic rebroadcasts of the Washington signals.

In the Philippine Islands, time signals are broadcast by the Manila Central Observatory through the naval radio station at Cavite (Los Banos), P. I.

The transmission of signals begins at 55 minutes 0 seconds of some hour, and continues for 5 minutes. Signals are transmitted on every second during that time, except that there is no signal on the 29th second of any minute, nor on certain seconds at the ends of the minutes, as shown in the following diagram:

Minute	Second										
	50	51	52	53	54	55	56	57	58	59	60
55	—		—	—	—	—					—
56	—	—		—	—	—					—
57	—	—	—		—	—					—
58	—	—	—	—		—					—
59	—										—

The dashes in the above diagram indicate seconds on which signals are transmitted. The seconds marked "60" are the zero seconds of the following minutes. All seconds from 0 to 50, inclusive, are transmitted except the 29th second, as explained above. The dash on the beginning of the hour (shown as 59 minutes 60 seconds above) is much longer than the others (i. e., 1.3 seconds).

In all cases the beginnings of the dashes indicate the beginnings of the seconds, and the ends of the dashes are without significance.

It will be noted that the number of dashes sounded in the group at the end of any minute indicates the number of minutes of the signal yet to be sent.

Repetitions.—In case of the failure of a signal, it is repeated 1 hour later.

Hack or comparing watch.—In order to avoid derangement, the chronometers should never be removed from the permanent box in which they are kept on shipboard. When it is desired to mark a certain instant of time, as for an astronomical observation or for obtaining the chronometer error by time signal, the time is marked by a "hack" (an inferior chronometer used for this purpose only), or by a comparing watch. Careful comparisons are taken—preferably both before and afterwards—and the chronometer time at the required instant is thus deduced. The following is the method of making such a comparison. Chronometers beat in half seconds and the tick is readily heard. Noting the chronometer time, the navigator decides upon a chronometer time about a minute in advance at which to compare the watch with the chronometer. Select a time when the chronometer will read an even minute, or half minute, and then put this chronometer time down on paper. Listen to the beating to get the cadence. When the second hand is on 20 seconds begin to count with the cadence of the chronometer, 20, half, 1, half, 2, half, 3, half, 4, half, and so on, then while counting in unison with the beating, shift the eyes to the second hand of the watch. At the count of "30" the selected instant has arrived then put down the reading of the watch. With practice an observer can carry the count of the beat for an indefinite period without looking at the chronometer face providing the tick can be heard. An expert will be able to carry the count for a half minute or more during which time the tick has not been heard.

C−W.—The correction represented by the chronometer time minus the watch time (12 hours being added to the former when necessary to make the subtraction possible) is referred to as C−W. Most errors in this comparison are made by reading the minutes incorrectly.

Suppose, for example, the chronometer and watch are compared and their indications are as follows:

Chro. t.,	5^h	27^m	30^s
W. T.,	2	36	45.5
C−W,	2	50	44.5

If then a sight is taken when the watch shows $3^h\ 01^m\ 27^s.5$, then,

W. T.,	3^h	01^m	$27^s.5$
C−W,	2	50	44 .5
Chro. t.,	5	52	12 .0

It may occur that the values of C−W, as obtained from comparisons before and after marking the desired time, will vary; in that case the value to be used will be the mean of the two, if the time marked is about midway between comparisons, but if much nearer to one comparison than the other, allowance should be made accordingly.

Thus suppose, in the case previously given, a second comparison had been taken after the sight as follows:

Chro. t.,	6^h	12^m	45^s
W. T.,	3	21	59.5
C−W,	2	50	45.5

The sight having been taken at about the middle of the interval, the C−W to be used would be the mean of the two, or $2^h\ 50^m\ 45^s.0$.

Assume that the second comparison showed the following:

Chro. t.,	6^h	38^m	25^s
W. T.,	3	47	39
C−W,	2	50	46

Then, the sight having been taken when only about one-third of the interval had elapsed between the first and second comparisons, it would be assumed that only one-third of the total change in the C−W had occurred up to the time of sight, and the value to be used would be $2^h\ 50^m\ 45^s.0$.

It is considered good practice always to subtract watch time from chronometer time, whatever the relative values, and to employ C−W invariably as an additive correction. It is equally correct to take the other difference, W−C, and make it subtractive; it may sometimes occur that a few figures will thus be saved, but a chance for error arises from the possibility of inadvertently using the wrong sign, which is almost impossible by the other method. Thus, the following example may be given:

Comparison	C,	10^h	57^m	38^s	W,	11^h	42^m	35^s
	W,	11	42	35	C,	10	57	38
	C−W,	11	15	03	W−C,	0	44	57
Sight	W,	11	50	21	W,	11	50	21
	C−W,	11	15	03	W−C,	0	44	57
	C,	11	05	24	C,	11	05	24

Determining the rate.—It is not required that either the error or the rate shall be zero, but in order to be enabled to determine the correct time it is essential that both rate and error be known and that the rate shall have been uniform since its last determination.

Since all chronometers are subject to some variation in rate under the changeable conditions existing on shipboard, it is desirable to ascertain a new rate as often as possible. The process of obtaining a rate involves the determination of the error on two different occasions separated by an interval of time of such length as may be convenient; the change of error during this interval, divided by the number of days, gives the daily rate. With radio signals available the chronometer rate should be checked daily.

Example.—On March 10, at noon, found chronometer No. 576 to be 0^m $32^s.5$ fast of G. C. T.; on March 20, at noon, the same chronometer was 0^m $48^s.0$ fast of G. C. T. What was the rate?

Error, March 10^d 12^h,	$+0^m$ $32^s.5$
Error, March 20^d 12^h,	+0 48.0
Change in 10 days,	+ 15.5
Daily rate,	+ $1^s.55$

The chronometer is therefore *gaining* $1^s.55$ per day.

Determining error from rate.—The error on any given day being known, together with the daily rate, to find the error on any other day it is only necessary to multiply the rate by the number of days that may have elapsed and to apply the product with proper sign to the given error.

Example.—On December 17 a chronometer is 3^m $27^s.5$ slow of G. C. T. and losing $0^s.47$ daily. What is the error on December 26?

Daily rate,	$-0^s.47$	Error Dec. 17,	-3^m $27^s.5$
No. days,	9	Correction,	− 4.2
Corr.,	−4.23	Error Dec. 26,	−3 31.7

The chronometer is therefore *slow* of G. C. T. on December 26, 3^m $31^s.7$, or the chronometer correction is indicated as, −Corr. (slow) 3^m $31^s.7$.

Example.—January 1, 1937, the 10 p. m. (22^h) radio signal was received from Arlington, the hack chronometer reading 3^h 25^m 12^s, a comparison was then made with the ship's chronometer reading 3^h 01^m $10^s.5$ when hack read 3^h 30^m 00^s. On January 10, the noon radio signal from Arlington was received with hack reading 5^h 25^m 04^s. A comparison was made with the hack and the ship's chronometer, hack reading 5^h 30^m 10^s and ship's chronometer reading 5^h 01^m 12^s. Required the rate of the hack and the ship's chronometer.

Signal Jan. 1

G. C. T.	3^h	00^m	00^s
Hack	3	25	12
Hack		25	12 (fast)

Comparison Jan. 1

Hack	3^h	30^m	00^s
Corr. (fast) −		25	12
G. C. T.	3	04	48.0
Chron.	3	01	10.5
Chron.		3	37.5 (slow)

Signal Jan. 10		*Comparison Jan. 10*	
G. C. T.	$17^h\ 00^m\ 00^s$	Hack	$5^h\ 30^m\ 10^s$
Hack	5 25 04	Corr. (fast) −	25 04
Hack	25 04 (fast)	G. C. T.	17 05 06
		Chron.	5 01 12
		Chron.	3 54 (slow)

Signal Jan. 10, G. C. T.	$17^h\ 00^m\ 00^s$
Signal Jan. 1, G. C. T.	3 00 00
Diff. of time	14 00 00 = $8^d.583$

Jan. 1, chron. (slow)	$3^m\ 37^s.5$	Hack fast	$25^m\ 12^s$
Jan. 10, chron. (slow)	3 54 .0	Hack fast	25 04
Chronometer losing	16 .5	Hack losing	08

$$\text{Chron. rate} = (-)\ \frac{16.5^s}{8^d.583} = (-)\ 1^s.9 \qquad \text{Hack rate} = (-)\ \frac{8^s}{8^d.583} = (-)\ 0^s.9$$

Comparison of chronometers.—Two or more chronometers are usually carried aboard ship. They are compared with each other daily so that any change in the rate of the one being used as the Standard chronometer can be detected. The instrument considered as the best is regarded as the Standard, and each of the others is compared to it. It is usual to designate the Standard as "A," and the others as "B," "C," etc. The comparison between any two chronometers is made in the same manner as was described for the "hack" chronometer.

The following form represents the method of recording comparisons used by the United States naval service:

Date at Ship	Daily chronometer comparisons					Max. Min. Diff.	Mean Daily Temp.	Memoranda of errors and rates		
	Chro.	Chro. B with Standard A	2d Diff.	Chro. C with Standard A	2d Diff.			A, No. *777*	B, No. *1509*	C, No. *1802*
17	A	*1-13-40*		*1-14-20*		68°				
	B & C	*1-12-21.5*		*1-13-00*		60°	64°	*Severe electrical storm*		
	Diff.	*1-18.5*		*1-20*		8°				
18	A	*1-16-30*		*1-17-00*		70°		*Compared with 1200 Arlington time signal.*		
	B & C	*1-15-10*		*1-15-41*		65°	67°	*12m 33s fast*	*11m 13s fast*	*11m 14s fast*
									Daily rate	
	Diff.	*1-20*	*+1s.5*	*1-19*	*−1s.0*	5°		*+1s.0*	*−1s.5*	*−2s.0*
19	A	*1-15-30*		*1-15-30*		72°		*Compared with 1200 Arlington time signal*		
	B & C	*1-14-08.5*		*1-14-12*		63°	68°	*12m 34s fast*	*11m 11s.5 fast*	*11m 12s.0 fast*
									Daily rate	
	Diff.	*1-21.5*	*+1s.5*	*1-18*	*−1s.0*	9°		*+1s.0*	*−1s.5*	*−2s.0*

The *second difference* in the form is the difference between the comparisons of the same instruments for 2 successive days. When a vessel is equipped with only one chronometer there is nothing to indicate any irregularity that it may develop at sea—and even the best instruments may undergo changes from no apparent cause. When there are two chronometers, the second difference, which is equal to the algebraic difference between their daily rates, remains uniform as long as the rates remain uniform, but changes if one of the rates undergoes a change; in such a case, there is no means of knowing which chronometer has departed from its expected performance, and the navigator must proceed with caution, giving due faith to the indications of each. If, however, there are three chronometers, an irregularity on the part of one is at once located by a comparison of the second differences. Thus, if the predicted rates of the chronometers were such as to give for the second difference of A−B, $+1^s.5$, and of A−C, $-0^s.5$, suppose on a certain day those differences were $+4^s.5$ and $-0^s.5$, respectively; it would at once be suspected that the irregularity was in B, and that that chronometer had lost 3^s on its normal rate during the preceding day. Suppose, however, the second differences were $+4^s.5$ and $+2^s.5$; it would then be apparent that A had gained 3^s.

Example.—On January 22, 1937, at 10 p. m. (22^h) or (G. C. T. January 23, 3^h), when the radio signal from Arlington was received, the hack chronometer read $3^h\ 06^m\ 45^s$. A few minutes later the hack chronometer was compared with the three chronometers of the ship A, No. 777; B, No. 1509; and C, No. 1802, as follows:

Chron. A, $3^h\ 37^m\ 10^s$	Chron. B, $3^h\ 24^m\ 29^s$	Chron. C, $3^h\ 28^m\ 10^s$
Hack Chron. 3 31 22	Hack 3 32 30	Hack 3 33 38

Find error of chronometers on G. C. T.

When the 10 p. m. (22^h) radio signal received from Arlington on January 12 (G. C. T. January 13, 3^h), the three chronometers had errors as follows, Chron. A, $12^m\ 23^s$ fast; Chron. B, $0^m\ 40^s$ fast; Chron. C, $0^m\ 22^s$ slow. Find rate of each chronometer.

(Arlington) Jan. 22, 22^h = G. C. T. Jan. 23, $3^h\ 00^m\ 00^s$
Hack chron. Jan. 23, 3 06 45

Hack 0 06 45 (fast)

Comparisons

Hack chron.,	$3^h\ 31^m\ 22^s$	Hack	$3^h\ 32^m\ 30^s$	Hack	$3^h\ 33^m\ 38^s$
Chron., fast,	− 6 45	(Fast)	− 6 45	(Fast)	− 6 45
G. C. T.	3 24 37	G. C. T.	3 25 45	G. C. T.	3 26 53
Chron. A	3 37 10	Chron. B	3 24 29	Chron. C	3 28 10
Jan. 23, Chron. A (fast)	12 33	Chron. B (slow)	1 16	Chron. C (fast)	1 17
Jan. 13, Chron. A (fast)	12 23	Chron. B (fast)	0 40	Chron. C (slow)	0 22
Chron. A (gains)	10	Chron. B (loses)	1 56	Chron. C (gains)	1 39
Chron. A (rate)	$\frac{10^s}{10^d}=(+)1^s$	Chron. B (rate)	$\frac{116^s}{10^d}=(-)11^s.6$	Chron. C (rate)	$\frac{99^s}{10^d}=(+)9^s.9$

Care of chronometers on shipboard.—In the front of the chronometer record book, which is supplied with each chronometer, there is a complete set of rules for the care, winding, and transportation of the chronometer. The following is a brief summary:

The box in which the chronometers are kept should have a permanent place as near as practicable to the center of motion of the ship, and where it will be free from excessive shocks and jars, such as those that arise from the engines or from the firing of heavy guns; the location should be one free from sudden and extreme changes of temperature, and as far removed as possible from masses of vertical iron. The box should contain a separate compartment for each chronometer, and each compartment should be lined with baize cloth padded with curled hair, for the double purpose of reducing shocks and equalizing the temperature within. An outer cover of baize cloth should be provided for the box, and this should be changed or dried out frequently in damp weather. The chronometers should all be placed with the XII mark in the same position.

For transportation for short distances by hand, an instrument should be rigidly clamped in its gimbals, for if left free to swing, its performance may be deranged by the violent oscillations that are imparted to it.

For transportation for a considerable distance, as by express, the chronometer should be allowed to run down, and should then be dismounted and the balance corked.

The chronometer should never be removed from its case, nor from the place of its usual stowage, except in case of unusual necessity. The chronometer should never be "set" on board.

Winding.—Chronometers are ordinarily constructed to run for 56 hours without rewinding, and an indicator on the face shows how many hours have elapsed since the last winding. To insure a uniform rate, they must be wound regularly every day, and, to avoid the serious consequences of their running down, the navigator should take some means to guard against neglecting this duty through a fault of memory. To wind, turn the chronometer gently on its side, enter the key in its hole and push it home.

Steady the instrument with the hand and wind to the left, the last half turn being made so as to bring up gently against the stop. After winding, cover the keyhole and return the instrument to its natural position. Chronometers should be wound in the same order to prevent omissions, and the precaution taken to inspect the indicators, as a further assurance of the proper performance of the operation.

After winding each day, the comparisons should be made, and, with the readings of the maximum-and-minimum thermometer and other necessary data, recorded in a book kept for the purpose.

The maximum-and-minimum thermometer is one so arranged that its highest and lowest readings are marked by small steel indices that remain in place until reset. Every chronometer box should be provided with such an instrument, as a knowledge of the temperature to which chronometers have been subjected is essential in any analysis of the rate. To draw down the indices for the purpose of resetting, a magnet is used. This magnet should be kept at all times at a distance from the chronometers.

Temperature curves.—Notwithstanding the care taken to eliminate the effect of a change of temperature upon the rate of a chronometer, it is rare that an absolutely perfect compensation is attained, and it may be assumed that the rates of all chronometers vary somewhat with the temperature. Where the voyage of a vessel is a long one and marked changes of climate are encountered, the accumulated error from the use of an incorrect rate may be very material, amounting to several minutes difference of longitude. Careful navigators will take every means to guard against such an error. By the employment of a *temperature curve* in connection with the chronometer rate the most satisfactory results are obtained.

There should be furnished with each chronometer a statement showing its daily rate under various conditions of temperature; and this may be supplemented by the observations of the navigator during the time that the chronometer remains on board ship. With all available data a temperature curve should be constructed which will indicate graphically the performance of the instrument. It is most convenient to employ for this purpose a piece of "profile paper," on which parallel lines are ruled at equal intervals at right angles to each other. Let each horizontal line represent, say, a degree of temperature, numbered at the left edge, from the bottom up; draw a vertical line in red ink to represent the zero rate, and let all rates to the right be *plus*, or gaining, and those to the left *minus*, or losing; let the intervals between vertical lines represent intervals of rate (as one-tenth of a second) numbered at the top from the zero rate; then on this scale plot the rate corresponding to each temperature; when there are several observations covering one height of the thermometer, the mean may be used. Through all the plotted points draw a fair curve, and the intersection of this curve with each temperature line gives the mean rate at that temperature. The mean temperature given by the maximum and minimum thermometer shows the rate to be used on any day.

CHAPTER IX

TIME AND THE NAUTICAL ALMANAC

Time and the Nautical Almanac are two very important subjects to be mastered in the study of nautical astronomy, as they enter into every operation for the astronomical determination of a ship's position. They will be treated in conjunction, as the two are interdependent.

METHODS OF RECKONING TIME

The instant at which any point of the celestial sphere is on the meridian of an observer is the time of **transit, culmination,** or **meridian passage** of that point; when the passage is over that half of the meridian which contains the zenith, it is designated as *upper* transit; when over the half containing the nadir, as *lower* transit.

Three different kinds of time are employed in astronomy—(*a*) **apparent** or **solar time,** (*b*) **mean time,** and (*c*) **sidereal time.** These depend upon the hour angle of the points to which they respectively refer. The point of reference for apparent or solar time is the *center of the sun;* for mean time, an imaginary point called the **mean sun;** and for sidereal time, the **vernal equinox,** also called the **first point of Aries.**

The unit of time is the *day*, which is the period between two successive transits over the same branch of the meridian of the point of reference. The day is divided into 24 equal parts, called *hours;* and each hour is divided into 60 equal parts, called *minutes;* and each minute into 60 equal parts, called *seconds.*

Apparent or **solar time.**—The hour angle of the center of the sun affords a measure of **apparent** or **solar time.** An **apparent solar day** at any place is the interval of time between two successive lower transits of the center of the sun over the meridian of that place, and the time of day is the hour angle of the center of the sun plus 12 hours. The apparent solar day is the most natural and direct measure of time, and is the unit of time adopted by the navigator at sea. Apparent noon is the instant at which the center of the sun is on the observer's meridian, and, is the time when the latitude can be most readily determined.

Since, the intervals between the successive returns of the sun to the same meridian are not equal, apparent time can not be taken as a standard to which clocks and chronometers may be regulated. The apparent day varies in length from two causes: first, the sun does not move in the equinoctial, the great circle whose plane is perpendicular to the axis of rotation of the earth, but in the ecliptic; and, secondly, the sun's motion in the ecliptic is not uniform. Sometimes the sun describes an arc of 57′ of the ecliptic, and sometimes an arc of 61′ in a day. At the points where the ecliptic and equinoctial intersect, the direction of the sun's apparent motion is inclined at an angle of 23°27′ to the eauinoctial, while at the solstices the motion is in a direction parallel to the equinoctial.

Mean time.—To avoid the irregularity of time caused by the lack of uniformity in the sun's motion, a fictitious sun, called the **mean sun,** is assumed to move in the *equinoctial* with a uniform eastward velocity that equals the *mean velocity of the true sun in the ecliptic.*

Mean time is measured by the hour angle of the center of the mean sun. A **mean solar day** at any place is the interval of time between two successive lower transits of the mean sun over the meridian of that place, and coincides with the civil day of the same date.

Mean time lapses uniformly; at certain times it agrees with apparent time, while sometimes it is behind, and at other times in advance of it, to the extent of about 16 minutes. It is this time that is measured by watches and clocks in ordinary use, and to this the chronometers used by navigators are regulated.

Mean time can not be determined by direct observation, but may be found indirectly by correcting observations of the sun for the equation of time, or by converting to mean time, sidereal time determined by observations of stars.

Equation of time.—The difference between apparent and mean time is called the equation of time. By this quantity, the conversion from one to the other of these times may be made. Its magnitude and the direction of its application may be found for any moment from the Nautical Almanac. It is zero about December 24, April 15, June 14, and September 1.

Sidereal time.—This is the hour angle of the **first point of Aries.** This point, which is identical with the **vernal equinox,** is the origin of all measurements of right ascension of the celestial bodies. Since the position of the point is fixed in the celestial sphere and does not, like the sun, moon, and planets, have actual or apparent motion therein, it shares in this respect the properties of the fixed stars. It may be said that intervals of sidereal time are those which are measured by the stars.

Sidereal time is reckoned on the equator from the meridian, westward around the entire circle from 0^h to 24^h. It is equal to the right ascension of the meridian. When a celestial body is on the meridian, its right ascension is equal to the sidereal time.

A **sidereal day** at any place is the interval of time between two successive upper transits of the first point of Aries across the meridian of that place. **Sidereal noon** is the instant at which the hour circle of the first point of Aries coincides with the meridian. In order to interconvert sidereal and mean times an element is tabulated in the Nautical Almanac. This is the **sidereal time of 0^h civil time at Greenwich,** which is also the **right ascension of the mean sun** increased by 12 hours.

The **civil day** commences at midnight and comprises the 24 hours until the following midnight. The hours run in a continuous series from 0 to 24; but as ordinarily used in civil life, the hours are counted from 0 to 12 in two series, the first running from midnight to noon, and the second from noon to midnight, thus dividing the day into two periods of 12 hours each in which the hours are respectively marked a. m. (ante meridian) and p. m. (post meridian). In navigation, however, the hours are marked 0 to 24.

The **astronomical day** begins at midnight on the civil day of the same date. It is exactly the same as the civil day, but the hours are marked continuously from 0^h to 24^h. There is no a. m. or p. m. marking. The astronomical day is employed in tabulating the data given in the American Nautical Almanac.

Hour angle.—The hour angle of a celestial body is the angle at the pole between the hour circle of the celestial body and the celestial meridian of the observer. It is measured by the arc of the celestial equator between the hour circle and that half of the celestial meridian which passes through the zenith and extends from pole to pole, and is reckoned positively toward the west throughout the entire 24 hours, although, for bodies east of the meridian, it is often measured toward the east, as local hour angle 97° E. (See definition for G. H. A. on page 114.)

In figure 57 let P be the pole of the celestial sphere, of which VMQ is the equator, PQ the celestial meridian, and PM, PS, PV the hour circles of the mean sun, a celestial body, and the first point of Aries, respectively.

Then QPM, or its arc QM, is the hour angle of the mean sun; QPS, or QS, the hour angle of the celestial body; QPV, or QV, the hour angle of the first point of Aries, or the sidereal time; VPQ, or VQ, the right ascension of the meridian; VPS, or VS, the right ascension of the celestial body; and VPM, or VM, the right ascension of the mean sun.

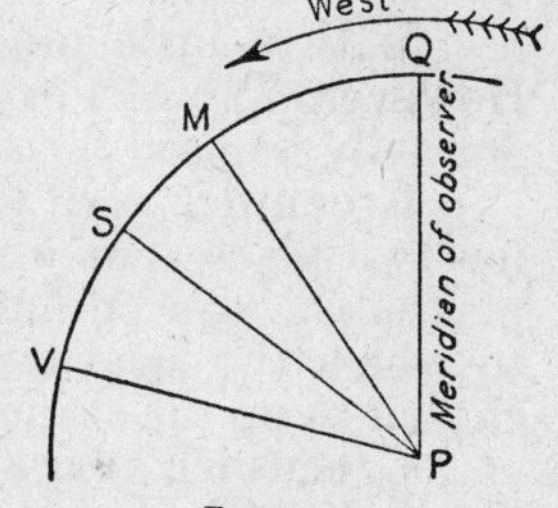

FIGURE 57.

Units of angular measure—Arc and time.—In navigation so far we have used the degrees of arc as a unit of angular measure. Latitude and longitude are usually expressed in terms of arc. Hour angle, right ascension, and time of day, however, are usually expressed in terms of time. The relation between the two systems of units is based on the fact that the sun makes one complete apparent revolution of the 360° of longitude of the earth in 24 hours. Therefore, 1 hour equals 15°.

Time is subdivided: 1 hour equals 60 minutes, 1 minute equals 60 seconds; and is designated as ^{h} ^{m} ^{s}.

Arc is similarly subdivided: 1 degree equals 60 minutes, 1 minute equals 60 seconds, and is designated as ° ′ ″.

Therefore, the ratio of 1 to 15 is maintained in referring time to arc, i. e., $1^{h}=15°$, $1^{m}=15'$, $1^{s}=15''$.

However, $1^{h}=60^{m}=15°$; therefore $1°=4^{m}$ and likewise $1'=4^{s}$; thus, the ratio of 1 to 4 is maintained in referring arc to time.

Conversion of arc to time.—(1) Divide the given number of degrees by 15 to obtain the corresponding number of hours; multiply the remaining degrees by 4 and denote the product as minutes. (2) When minutes and seconds of arc are involved continue the process by dividing the minutes of arc by 15 and adding the quotient to the product obtained in (1) to obtain the total minutes of time; multiply the remainder by 4 and denote the product as seconds of time. (3) Divide the seconds of arc by 15 extending the division to decimals desired, and add the quotient to the product in (2) to obtain the total seconds of time.

Example.—Convert 65° 21′ 27″ to units of time.

$\frac{65}{15}=4^{h}$ and 5° remainder; $4\times5°$ 20^{m}, or $65°=4^{h}\ 20^{m}$

$\frac{21'}{15}=1^{m}$ and 6′ remainder; $4\times6'$ 24^{s}, or $21'=$ $1^{m}\ 24^{s}$

$\frac{27''}{15}=1^{s}.8$ or $27''=$ $1^{s}.8$

Answer $4^{h}\ 21^{m}\ 25^{s}.8$

Conversion of time to arc.—(1) Multiply the given number of hours by 15 to obtain the corresponding number of degrees of arc; (2) divide the minutes of time by 4, add the quotient to the product in (1) to obtain the total degrees of arc, multiply the remainder by 15 and denote the product as minutes of arc; (3) divide the seconds by 4, add the quotient to the product in (2) to obtain the total minutes of arc, multiply the remainder by 15 to obtain the seconds of arc.

Example.—Convert $4^{h}18^{m}19^{s}$ to units of arc.

$4^{h}\times15=60°$ 60°

$\frac{18^{m}}{4}=4°$ and 2^{m} remainder; $2^{m}\times15=30'$ 4° 30′

$\frac{19^{s}}{4}=4'$ and 3^{s} remainder; $3^{s}\times15=45''$ 4′ 45″

Answer 64° 34′ 45″

Example.—Convert arc to time or time to arc.

46° 24′ 32″ equals $3^{h}\ 05^{m}\ 38^{s}.13$
139° 03′ 18″ equals $9^{h}\ 16^{m}\ 13^{s}.2$
204° 47′ 57″ equals $13^{h}\ 39^{m}\ 11^{s}.8$

With a little practice the entire process of conversion can be made mentally. However, Table 34 or 42 gives the corresponding values of arc and time and should normally be used for all problems of conversion in order to avoid errors.

Greenwich civil time.—Since the hour angle of the mean sun at a given instant for two places not on the same meridian is different, the local civil times at these places will also be different. It is therefore necessary to have a standard meridian to which the local civil times can be referred, hence the meridian of Greenwich is chosen to be the standard meridian.

Greenwich hour angle.—There is recorded in the Nautical Almanac the Greenwich hour angle (G. H. A.) of the sun, moon, stars, and planets, which may be found directly for any given G. C. T. by means of interpolation, without recourse to the equation of time, or the position of the vernal equinox. (See G. H. A., page 114.)

Time at different meridians.—The hour angle of the true sun at any meridian when increased by 12 hours is the **local apparent time;** that of the mean sun, when increased by 12 hours, the **local civil time;** that of the first point of Aries, the **local sidereal time.** The similarly treated hour angles of the same bodies and point from

Greenwich are, respectively, the **Greenwich apparent time, Greenwich civil time,** and **Greenwich sidereal time.** The difference between the solar or sidereal time at any meridian and that of Greenwich is equal to the longitude of that place from Greenwich expressed in time; the conversion from time to arc may be effected by a simple mathematical calculation or by the use of Table 42.

Greenwich time, which at any fixed observatory is obtained by applying the longitude to the local time, on board ship is usually taken from the chronometer set to the Greenwich civil time.

In comparing corresponding times of different meridians the most easterly meridian may be distinguished as that at which the time is *greatest* or *latest*.

In figure 58 PM and PM′ represent the celestial meridians of two places, PS the hour circle through the sun, and PG the Greenwich meridian; let T_G=the Greenwich time=GPS+12^h;

T_M=the corresponding local time at all places on the meridian PM=MPS+12^h;

T_M'=the corresponding local time at all places on the meridian PM′=M′PS +12^h;

Lo=west longitude of meridian PM=GPM; and

Lo′=east longitude of meridian PM′=GPM′.

If west longitudes and hour angles be reckoned as positive, and east longitudes and hour angles as negative, we have:

$$Lo = T_G - T_M; \text{ and}$$
$$Lo' = T_G - T_M'; \text{ therefore}$$
$$Lo - Lo' = T_M' - T_M.$$

Thus it may be seen that the difference of longitude between two places equals the difference of their local times. This relation may be shown to hold for any two meridians whatsoever.

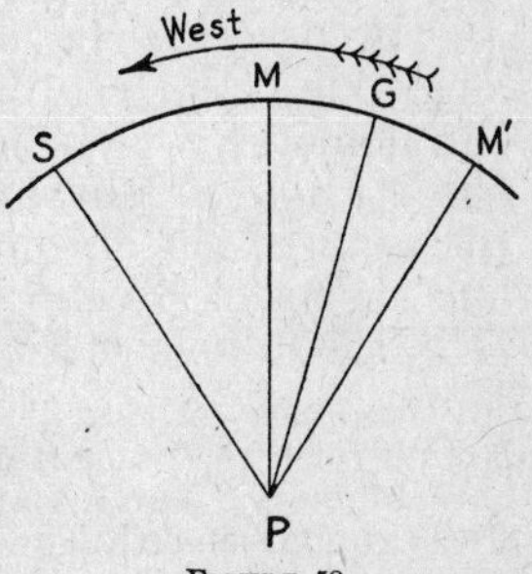

Both local and Greenwich times in the above formulas must be reckoned westward, always from their respective meridians and from 0^h to 24^h.

The formula $Lo = T_G - T_M$ is true for any kind of time, solar or sidereal; or, in general terms, T_G and T_M are the hour angles of any point of the sphere at the two meridians whose difference of longitude is Lo. S may be the sun (true or mean) or the vernal equinox.

FIGURE 58.

Finding Greenwich time and date.—The solution of nearly every problem in celestial navigation requires reference to data contained in the American Nautical Almanac. This data is tabulated for various celestial bodies in such a way that it may be found for any instant of Greenwich civil time. It becomes essential, therefore, that the navigator become thoroughly familiar with the method of finding the Greenwich civil time and date.

The first operation necessary is to deduce from a knowledge of the approximate local civil time and longitude, the corresponding Greenwich date and approximate time expressed in hours, from 0 to 24. This is essential since a chronometer dial is usually marked from 0 to 12 hours, and may, therefore, be 12 hours in error on the astronomical time used in the almanac. If the approximate Greenwich civil time shows it to be afternoon in Greenwich, 12 hours must be added to the chronometer reading.

From the formula $T_G = T_M + Lo$, and remembering that west longitudes are positive and east longitudes are negative, we have the following rule for converting local to Greenwich time:

> To local civil time, *add* longitude if west, *subtract* if east, the result being the corresponding Greenwich civil time.

The result of any conversion is readily checked by remembering the following rhyme:

Longitude west, Greenwich time best,
Longitude east, Greenwich time least.

The following four examples illustrate the four possible cases in which the Greenwich date may be: the same as the local date, 1 day later, or, 1 day earlier; and also indicate when it becomes necessary to add 12 hours to the chronometer reading.

1. Longitude 90° W., L. C. T. about 10:30 a. m., April 15, chronometer reads $4^h\ 27^m$.

Approx. L. C. T.	$15^d\ 10^h\ 30^m$	Chron.	$4^h\ 27^m$
Longitude west (+)	6 00	Add	12
Approx. G. C. T.	15 16 30	G. C. T.	16 27 April 15.

Same date but add 12^h to chronometer.

2. Longitude 90° E., L. C. T. about 2 p. m., August 5, chronometer reads $8^h\ 02^m$.

Approx. L. C. T.	$5^d\ 14^h\ 00^m$ (converting p. m.)	Chron.	$8^h\ 02^m$
Long. east (−)	6 00	G. C. T.	8 02 August 5.
Approx. G. C. T.	5 8 00		

Same date and chronometer face is correct.

3. Longitude 90° W., L. C. T. about 10:30 p. m April 15, chronometer reads $4^h\ 29^m$.

Approx. L. C. T.	$15^d\ 22^h\ 30^m$ (converting p. m.)	Chron.	$4^h\ 29^m$
Long. west (+)	6 00	G. C. T.	4 29 April 16.
Approx. G. C. T.	16 4 30		

One day later and chronometer face is correct.

4. Longitude 90° E., L. C. T. about 4:30 a. m., August 5., chronometer reads $10^h\ 34^m$.

Approx. L. C. T.	$5^d\ 4^h\ 30^m$	Chron.	$10^h\ 34^m$
Long. east (−)	6 00	Add	12
Approx. G. C. T.	4 22 30	G. C. T.	22 34 August 4.

One day earlier and add 12^h to chronometer.

In practice the navigator always knows his approximate local civil time and longitude. To record the instant of his observation he will use a watch, or a hack chronometer, which he can compare with the ship's chronometer before or after the observation to obtain a C–W. From the chronometer record book he will obtain the error of the chronometer on Greenwich civil time for that date, then proceed to find the exact Greenwich civil time corresponding to the watch time of his observation as in the following example.

Example.—About $3^h\ 25^m$ p. m., March 21, local civil time, a ship's D. R. longitude was 60° 30′ W. when the navigator took a sight of the sun using a watch which had been compared with the chronometer. Watch time of sight was $3^h\ 27^m\ 30^s$, C–W was $4^h\ 05^m\ 56^s$, chronometer was slow $2^m\ 14^s$ on Greenwich Time. Find the Greenwich date and civil time.

Approximate civil time	$21^d\ 15^h\ 25^m$
Longitude west (+)	4 02
Approximate G. C. T	21 19 27 (Add 12^h to chronometer reading)

To find exact G. C. T.:

W	$3^h\ 27^m\ 30^s$
C–W	4 05 56
Chron.	7 33 26
Corr. (slow) +	2 14
Chron.	7 35 40 (Add 12^h)
Greenwich civil time	19 35 40 March 21.

Standard time.—This is the local civil time of meridians, known as standard meridians, located 15° of longitude apart commencing with the meridian of Greenwich as the initial meridian. The time of a standard meridian is used for the convenience of railways and in the affairs of everyday life in a locality extending as nearly as practicable 7½° each side of the standard meridian. The system of standard time zones has been extended over the oceanic areas, and the keeping of standard time at sea has been instituted in most navies of the world.

Time zone chart.—The surface of the globe is conceived to be divided into 24 zones, each bounded by meridians 15° of arc or one hour of time apart in longitude. The initial zone is the one which has the meridian of Greenwich running through the middle of it, and the meridians 7½° east of Greenwich and 7½° west of Greenwich,

H. O. Chart 5192.

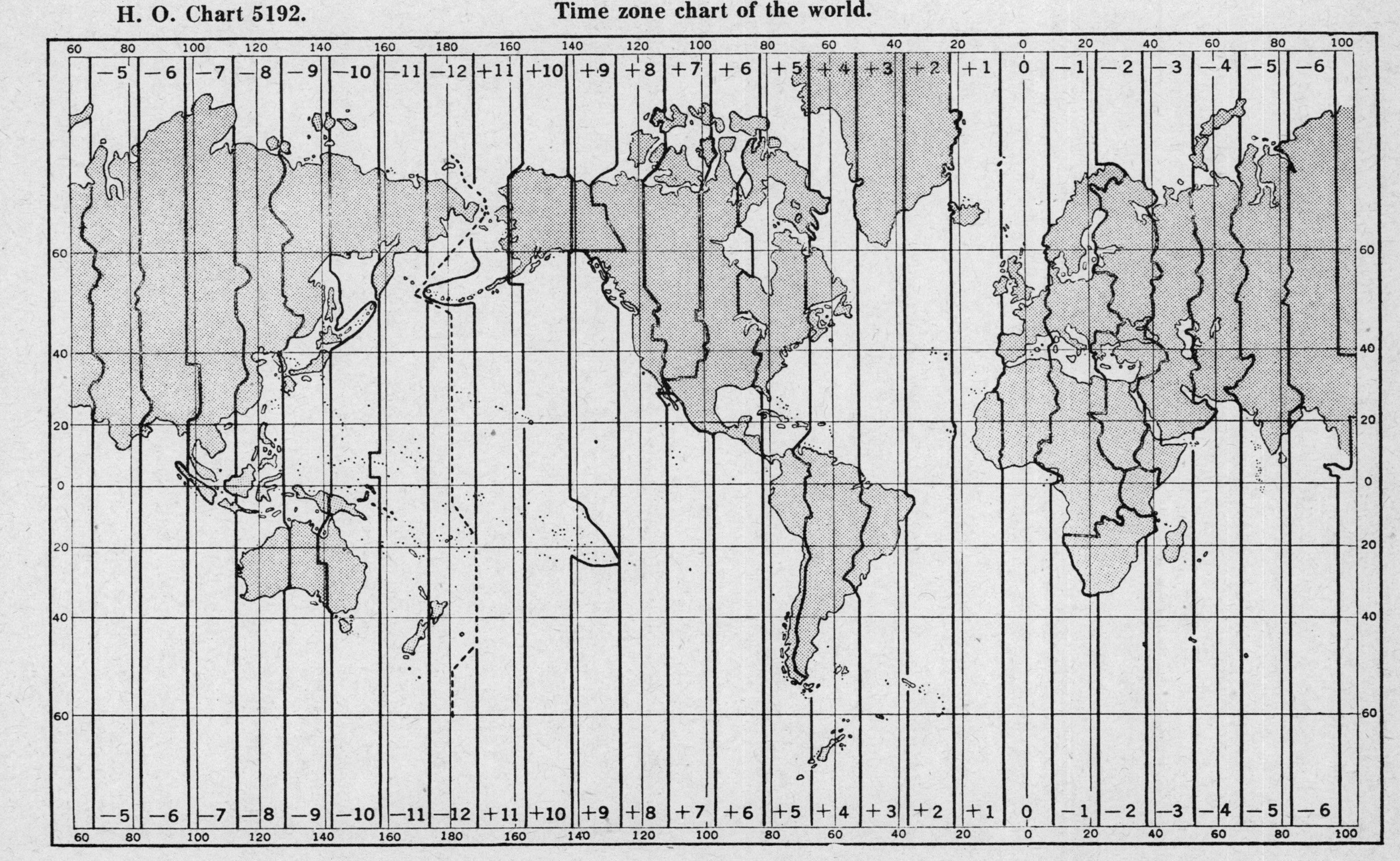

Time zone chart of the world.

marking its eastern and western limits. It is called the **"zero zone"** because the difference between the standard time of this zone and Greenwich civil time is zero. And each of the zones in turn is designated by a number representing the number of hours by which the standard time of the zone differs from Greenwich civil time.

The zones lying in east longitude from the zero zone are numbered in sequence from 1 to 12, and are called minus zones, because, in each of them, the zone number must be subtracted from the standard time in order to obtain the Greenwich civil time. The zones lying in west longitude from the zero zone are numbered in sequence from 1 to 12, and are called plus zones, because, in each of these zones, the zone number must be added to the standard time in order to obtain the Greenwich civil time. The time kept in any zone is the standard time of its central meridian.

The twelfth zone is divided medially by the 180° meridian (the line separating the meridians of east longitude from the meridians of west longitude), and the terms "minus" and "plus" are used in the halves of this zone which lie in the east longitude and west longitude, respectively.

Zone time is the time of the zone in which the ship happens to be and is reckoned from 0^h to 24^h. If the ship is in longitude 49°45′ E., the zone in which it is situated lies between longitude 37°30′ E. and 52°30′ E., or zone −3.

The number of a zone prefixed by the plus sign, thus (+), or by the minus sign, thus (−), constitutes the **"zone description"** of the time of that zone, abbreviated as Z. D.; thus Lon. 99°25′ E. is −7; Lon. 128°05′ W. is +9; Lon. 173°45′ E. is −12.

In the vicinity of the land, the boundaries between zones are modified so as to be in accord with the boundaries of the countries or regions using corresponding times, as shown in the Hydrographic Office Chart of the Time Zones of the World (H. O. Chart No. 5192).

The ship's time of vessels of the United States Navy at sea is kept by observing the following rules:

(1) Instead of adjusting the ship's time to apparent time at noon each day, the clock is adjusted to the standard time of the successive zones as they are entered, although the instant at which the alteration is made need not necessarily be that at which the vessel passes from one zone to another; the change of time will invariably be 1 hour, the minutes and seconds remaining unaffected, with the exception of the cases covered by rule 5.

(2) The "zone description" (Z. D.) of the time that is being kept is marked in a conspicuous manner on such of the ship's clocks as may be designated by the commanding officer.

(3) All entries of time in the ship's log books and records are accompanied by the "zone description" of the time being kept.

(4) In all official correspondence, when the time is referred to, the "zone description" is added.

(5) When a vessel is in a harbor or within the territorial limits of a country where the legal time differs from the standard time zone system, the exact amount in hours, minutes, and seconds which it differs from Greenwich civil time is given with its appropriate sign of plus (+) or minus (−).

In observing the foregoing rules regarding recording of "zone description" it should be borne in mind that the "zone description" is the correction that must be applied to the ship's time to obtain the corresponding Greenwich civil time.

The use of the 24-hour day, with the time expressed as a four figure group, the first two figures denoting the hour and the second two figures denoting the minutes, is authorized for the naval service in correspondence as well as dispatches, using the civil day commencing at midnight, expressed as 0000.

Example.—The navigator of a vessel steaming in longitude 62° E. desires a comparison of the watch with the chronometer to find the error of the watch on G. C. T. and also on the zone time. Watch reading $7^h\ 33^m\ 12^s$ (approximately zone time); chronometer reading $3^h\ 35^m\ 10^s$; chronometer error $1^m\ 20^s$ fast.

Chron.	3^h	35^m	10^s		G. C. T.	3^h	33^m	50^s	
Corr. fast. (−)		1	20		Long. 62° E. (Z. D.−4)+	4			(sign rev.)
G. C. T	3	33	50		Zone time	7	33	50	
Watch	7	33	12		Watch time	7	33	12	
Watch fast	3	59	22	on G. C. T.	Watch slow			38	on zone time.

The central meridian of any zone is converted into time, and this is used to find the G. C. T. regardless of what the longitude may be within the limits of the zone. The L. C. T. of a zone cannot differ more than 30^m from zone time.

Example.—In longitude 62° E., the navigator makes an observation of the sun at W. T. 7^h 35^m 10^s; watch slow 38^s on zone time. Find G. C. T.; Zone time, and L. C. T., of observation. Watch is 3^h 59^m 22^s fast on G. C. T.

Watch	7^h 35^m 10^s		Watch	7^h 35^m 10^s		G. C. T.	3^h 35^m 48^s
Fast on G. C. T.	3 59 22		Error (slow) +	38		Long. 62° E.,	4 08 00
G. C. T.	3 35 48		Zone time	7 35 48		L. C. T.	7 43 48
			Z. D.	−4			
			G. C. T.	3 35 48			

Day and date at 180° meridian.—When crossing the 180° meridian in steaming westward, *add* 1 day to the date, if steaming eastward, *subtract* 1 day, at the same time changing the name of the longitude.

Example.—A vessel in west longitude steaming westward and approaching the 180° meridian, keeps local civil time which is about 12^h slow of G. C. T. at the same instant of time; now suppose at 4 p. m. (or 16^h) on December 7, the vessel is in 179°50′ W., but at 5 p. m. (17^h) the vessel arrives in 179°50′ E. It is required to find the date at the last position.

L. C. T. Dec. 7	16^h 00^m 00^s	
Long. west (+),	11 59 20	
G. C. T., Dec. 8	3 59 20	
1^h later	1 00 00	
G. C. T., Dec. 8	4 59 20	
Long. east (−),	+11 59 20	(rev. sign.)
L. C. T., Dec. 8	16 58 40	

This date at about 5 p. m. goes ahead 1 day.

Suppose the vessel is in 179°50′ E., at 9 a. m., July 4, but at 10 a. m. is in longitude 179°50′ W.; required the date at the last position.

L. C. T., July 4	9^h 00^m 00^s	
Long. east (−),	11 59 20	
G. C. T., July 3	21 00 40	
1^h later	1 00 00	
G. C. T., July 3	22 00 40	
Long. west (+)	−11 59 20	(rev. sign.)
L. C. T., July 3	10 01 20	

This date now goes back a day at 10 a. m.

THE NAUTICAL ALMANAC

The American Ephemeris and Nautical Almanac is the complete astronomical work issued for the use of astronomers, by the Naval Observatory. It is also used by surveying parties and observatories where the most precise values are required. It is divided into seven parts as follows: Part I. Ephemerides of the Sun, Moon, and Planets for the Meridian of Greenwich. Part II. Ephemerides of the Fixed Stars. Part III. Eclipses and Occultations. Part IV. Physical Ephemerides of Sun, Moon, and Planets. Part V. The Satellites of the Planets. Part VI. Ten Miscellaneous Tables Such as Sunrise and Sunset, Conversion of Sidereal to Mean Time and Vice Versa, Azimuth of Polaris, etc. Part VII. Ephemerides of the Sun, Moon, and Planets for the Meridian of Washington. A study of the practical use of the tables for all precise observations should be made from explanations given in that work.

The American Nautical Almanac is a smaller abridged book of values taken from the above Ephemeris and Nautical Almanac and is designed especially for the use of navigators.[1] All values are referred to Greenwich civil time and date. Quantities

[1] For description of Air Almanac used by aviators, see page 203.

are given to a degree of accuracy comparable with that attainable in sextant observations, usually to 0′.1 of arc, or to 1^s of time. It contains for the sun, sidereal time of 0^h civil time at Greenwich (R. A. M. S.$+12^h$), equation of time, declination, and Greenwich hour angle, with means for readily interpolating for any G. C. T. of the proper date.

It contains for the moon, the right ascension, declination, and Greenwich hour angle, together with the phases and time of transit of Greenwich meridian. It contains for the stars, the right ascension, declination, and Greenwich hour angle, with interpolation tables for utilizing the Greenwich civil time of any day; and there is also given the same data for the planets Venus, Mars, Saturn, and Jupiter.

It contains information on eclipses of sun and moon with accompanying charts and also phenomena of planetary configurations.

There are also several miscellaneous tables, such as sunrise, sunset, and twilight tables, moonrise and moonset tables; time of culmination and elongation of Polaris; Greenwich hour angle of Polaris; latitude by Polaris; azimuth of Polaris; sidereal to mean time; mean time to sidereal; table of proportional parts; conversion of arc and time; corrections to observed altitude of sun, stars and moon, and bubble sextant corrections of sun, stars, and moon.

To find from the Nautical Almanac a required element for any given time and place, it is first necessary to convert the local civil time to Greenwich civil time (G. C. T.) and date. Then take from the almanac, for the nearest given *preceding* instant, the required quantity, together with its corresponding "hourly" or "2-hourly difference," noting the name or sign in each case. Multiply the "hourly difference" by the number of hours and fraction of an hour, corresponding to the interval between the time for which the quantity is given in the almanac and the time for which required; apply the correction thus obtained, having regard to its sign. The correction may also be taken from the table of proportional parts in the almanac.

A modification of this rule may be adopted if the time for which the quantity is desired falls considerably nearer a *subsequent* time given in the almanac than it does to one preceding; in this case the interpolation may be made backward, the sign of application of the correction being reversed.

Example.—At a place in Long. 81° 15′ W., April 17, 1937, find the sun's declination and the equation of time at apparent noon.

Long. = 81° 15′ W. = 5^h 25^m G. A. T. = 17^d 17^h 25^m = 17^d $17^h.42$.

G. A. T., 17^d,	17^h 25^m 00^s	Eq. t., 17^d 16^h,	0^m $23^s.7$	H. D.,	$+0^s.6$
Eq. t.,	− 24. 6	Corr.,	+ .9	Int.	$1^h.42$
G. C. T., 17^d,	17 24 35. 4	Eq. t., 17^d 17^h 25^m,	0 24.6	Corr.,	$+0^s.852$
	$=17^h.41$		(Add to MEAN time.)		
Dec., 17^d 16^h,	10° 29. 2 N.	H.D.,	+0′.9		
Corr.,	+ 1. 3	G. C. T. Int.,	$1^h.41$		
Dec., 17^d 17^h $24^m.6$	10 30. 5 N.	Corr.,	+1′.269		

Example.—At a place in long. 81° 15′ E., April 17, 1937, find the sun's declination and the equation of time at apparent noon.

Long. = 81° 15′ E. = 5^h 25^m G. A. T. = 17^d 6^h 35^m = 17^d $6^h.58$

G. A. T., 17^d	6^h 35^m 00^s	Eq. t., 17^d 6^h	0^m $17^s.9$	H. D.,	$0^s.6$
Eq. t.,	− 0 18 .2	Corr.,	+ 0 .3	Int.	$0^h.58$
G. C. T., 17^d	6 34 41 .8	Eq. t., 17^d 6^h 35^m,	0 18 .2	Corr.	$+0^s.348$
	$=6^h.58$		(Add to MEAN time.)		
Dec., 17^d 6^h	10° 20′.4 N.	H. D.,	+0′.9		
Corr.,	+ .5	G. C. T. Int.	$0^h.58$		
Dec., 17^d 6^h 34.7^m	10° 20′.9 N.	Corr.,	+0′.522		

Example.—April 15, 1937, at 11^h 55^m 30^s a. m., local civil time, in longitude 81° 15′ W., required the declination, the equation of time, local hour angle, of the sun, and the right ascension, declination, G. H. A., and semidiameter of the moon and Jupiter.

Local civil time,	15^d 11^h 55^m 30^s
Longitude,	+5 25 00
Greenwich civil time,	15 17 20 30
	15^d 17^h $20^m.5$
	15^d $17^h.34$

For the Sun

Dec., $15^d\ 16^h$	9° 46′.7 N.	G. H. A. $15^d\ 16^h$,	59° 58′.8	Eq. t., $15^d\ 16^h$	$0^m\ 04^s.9$
Corr.,	+ 1 .2	Corr. $1^h\ 20^m\ 30^s$,	20 07 .5	Corr.,	− 0 .8
Dec.,	9 47 .9 N.	G. H. A.,	80 06 .3 W.	Eq. t.,	0 04 .1
H. D.,	+ 0′.9	Long.,	81 15 .0 W.	H. D.,	$0^s.6$
G. C. T. Int.,	$1^h.34$	L. H. A.,	1 08 .7 E.	G. C. T. Int.	$1^h.34$
Corr.,	+ 1′.206	or,	358 51 .3 W.	Corr.,	− $0^s.804$
				(SUBTRACT from MEAN time.)	

For the Moon

R. A., $15^d\ 17^h$,	$5^h\ 49^m\ 38^s$	G. H. A. $15^d\ 17^h$,	11° 01′.5	Dec., $15^d\ 17^h$,	22° 25′.1 N.	S. D.	16′.2
Corr., $20^m.5$	53 .3	Corr., $20^m.5$	4 55.0	Corr., $20^m.5$	0′.6	H. P.	59 .5
R. A.,	5 50 31 .3	G. H. A.,	15 56.5 W.	Dec.,	22° 24′.5 N.		
		Long.,	81 15.0 W.				
		L. H. A.,	65 18.5 E.				
		or,	294 41.5 W.				

For Jupiter

R. A. 15^d	$19^h\ 51^m\ 35^s$	Dec. 15^d,	21° 05′.3 S.	G. H. A. 15^d,	264° 50′.2	Var. per min.,	15′.0372
Corr. $17^h.34$,	+ 16 .6	Corr. $17^h.34$,	− 0 .7	Corr. $17^h\ 20^m.5$,	260 46 .1	Corr. 17^h,	255° 37′.9
						Corr. $20^m.5$,	5 08 .2
R. A.,	19 51 51 .6	Dec.,	21 04 .6 S.		525 36 .3 W.	Corr.,	260 46 .1
				(Subtract),	360°		
Tab. VII, for diff.,	23	Tab. VII, for diff.,	0 .9				
12^h (230),	$11^s.5$	12^h (90),	.45′	G. H. A.,	165 36 .3 W.		
$5^h\ 20^m$,	5 .1	$5^h\ 20^m$,	.20	Long.,	81 15 .0 W.		
Corr. $17^h\ 20^m$,	16 .6	Corr. $17^h\ 20^m$,	.65	L. H. A.,	84 21 .3 W.		

The G. H. A. may be found as follows:

G. C. T.,	$17^h\ 20^m\ 30^s$	
R. A. M. S.$+12^h$,	13 30 56 .0	
Corr. G. C. T.,	2 50 .9	(Tab. 39)
G. S. T.,	30 54 16 .9	
R. A. Jupiter,	19 51 51 .6	
G. H. A.,	11 02 25 .3 W.	
Arc,	165° 36′ 19″. W.	

Example.—January 15, 1937, in long. 122° 10′ E.; local civil time $18^h\ 56^m\ 10^s$; find the right ascension, declination, and local hour angle of the star Aldebaran:

L. C. T.,	$18^h\ 56^m\ 10^s$	G. H. A. Jan. 15,	45° 56′.4	Corr. $10^h\ 47^m$	162° 11′.6
Long. E.,	8 08 40	Corr. $10^h\ 47^m\ 30^s$,	162 19 .1	Corr. 30^s,	7 .5
G. C. T.,	10 47 30	G. H. A.,	208 15 .5 W.	Corr. $10^h\ 47^m\ 30^s$	162 19 .1
		Long.,	122 10 .0 E.		
		L. H. A.,	330 25 .5 W.		
Jan. 15, R. A.,	$4^h\ 32^m\ 20^s.6$	Or	29 34 .5 E.		
Jan. 15, Dec.,	16° 23′.1 N.				

Transit of star, planet or moon—For a star, the Nautical Almanac tabulates the G. C. T. of transit at Greenwich of the bright stars used in navigation. This time is given to the nearest minute and for the first day of each month. A correction table for any other date is also given. Having found the G. C. T. of Greenwich for the required date, the L. C. T. of local transit for that date may be found by applying a correction to the local longitude. It is to be added for east longitude and subtracted for west longitude. Having found the L. C. T. of local transit, apply the longitude in time to obtain the G. C. T. of local transit.

Example.—On April 10, 1937 in long. 74° 30′ W. find G. C. T. of local transit of Sirius.

Star Sirius

Approx. G. C. T. of Gr. transit Apr. 1	$18^h\ 04^m\ 00^s$
Corr. for Apr. 10,	− 0 35 00
Approx. G. C. T. of Gr. transit Apr. 10,	17 29 00
Corr. for long. page 2, N. A. (74°30′ W.$=4^h\ 58^m$)	− 49
L. C. T. of local transit,	17 28 11
Long. W.,	4 58 00
G. C. T. of local transit,	22 26 11

Planets.—The Nautical Almanac gives for each day of the year the G. C. T. of Greenwich transit to the nearest minute. For the G. C. T. of Greenwich transit for the given date, the local civil time of local transit may be obtained by a simple interpolation for longitude between the given date and the adjacent date, interpolating forward for west longitude and backward for east longitude.

Example.—April 16, 1937, in Long. 67°45′ E., chronometer slow, $1^m\ 05^s$; C−W, $7^h\ 33^m\ 42^s$; find the watch time of transit of the planet Jupiter.

Approx. G. C. T. of Greenwich transit Apr. 16,		6^h	16^m	00^s
Corr. for longitude $4^h\ 31^m$ E. (p. 2, N. A.),	+			45
L. C. T. of local transit,		6	16	45
Long. E.,		4	31	00
G. C. T. of local transit, Apr. 16,		1	45	45
Chron. slow,	−		1	05
Chron. at local transit,		1	44	40
C−W (subtract)		7	33	42
Approx. watch time of local transit		6	10	58

Moon.—Finding the local transit of the moon is similar to that of a planet, but the change in right ascension is rapid, therefore the daily difference in the G. C. T. of Greenwich transits are larger and the variation per hour is given, plus for west longitude and minus for east longitude.

Example.—On July 2, 1937, in Long. 30° W.; chronometer fast $1^m\ 30^s$; C−W $2^h\ 03^m\ 10^s$; find the watch time of local transit of the moon.

Approx. G. C. T. of Gr. transit, July 2,		6^h	25^m	00^s
Corr. long. var. $2^m.2 \times 2^h = 4^m.4$	+		4	24
Approx. L. C. T. of local transit,		6	29	24
Long. W.,		2		
Approx. G. C. T. of local transit,		8	29	24
Chron. fast,	+		1	30
Chron. at local transit,		8	30	54
C−W (subtract)		2	03	10
Approx. watch time of local transit,		6	27	44

Conversion of time.—This is the process by which any instant of time that is defined according to one system of reckoning may be defined according to some other system; and also by which any interval of time expressed in units of one system may be converted into units of another.

Sidereal and mean time.—Civil time is the hour angle of the mean sun increased by 12^h; sidereal time is the hour angle of the first point of Aries. Since the right ascension of the mean sun is the angular distance between the hour circles of the first point of Aries and of the mean sun, civil time may be converted into sidereal time by subtracting 12^h from it and adding to the remainder the right ascension of the mean sun; and similarly, sidereal time may be converted into civil time by subtracting from it the right ascension of the mean sun increased by 12^h.

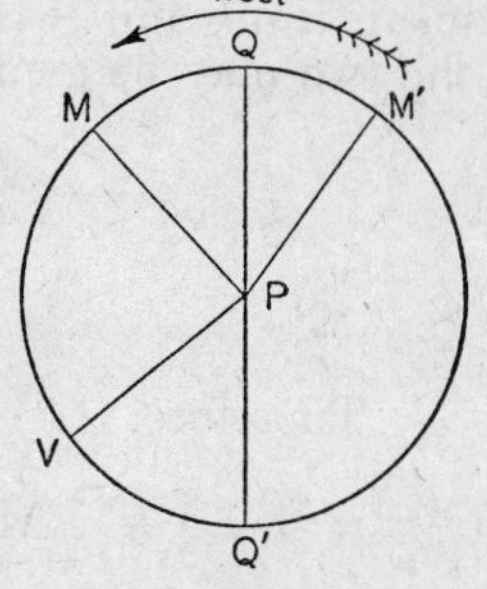

FIGURE 59.

This is explained in figure 59, which represents a projection of the celestial sphere upon the equator. If P be the pole; QPQ′, the meridian; V, the first point of Aries; M, the position of the mean sun (west of the meridian); then QPV, or the arc QV, is the sidereal time; QPM, or the arc QM, is the civil time diminished by 12^h; and VPM, or the arc VM, is the right ascension of the mean sun. From this it will appear that:

$$QV = QM + VM, \text{ or}$$

$$\text{Sidereal time} = \text{Civil time} - 12^h + \text{Right ascension of mean sun, or}$$

$$\text{Sidereal time} + 24^h = \text{Civil time} + \text{Right ascension of mean sun} + 12^h.$$

If the mean sun be on the opposite side of the meridian, at M′, then the civil time equals $12^h - M'Q$. In this case:

$$QV = VM' - M'Q, \text{ or}$$
$$\text{Sidereal time} = \text{Right ascension of mean sun} - (12^h - \text{Civil time}),$$
$$= \text{Right ascension of mean sun} + \text{Civil time} - 12^h, \text{ or}$$
$$\text{Sidereal time} + 24^h = \text{Right ascension of mean sun} + 12^h + \text{Civil time}.$$

Right ascension being measured to the east and hour angle to the west, the sidereal time will therefore always equal the sum of these two; but 24^h must be subtracted when the sum exceeds that amount.

From the preceding equations, there is given:

$$QM = QV - VM; \text{ and}$$
$$M'Q = VM' - QV, \text{ or}$$
$$(12^h - M'Q) = (24^h + QV) - (VM' + 12^h).$$

From this it may be seen that the civil time always equals the sidereal time *minus* the right ascension of the mean sun increased by 12^h (R. A. M. S.$+12^h$), but the former must be increased by 24^h when necessary to make the subtraction possible.

Apparent and mean time.—Apparent time is the angle between the meridian and the hour circle which contains the center of the sun; mean time is the angle between the meridian and the hour circle which contains the mean sun. Since the equation of time represents the angle between the hour circles of the mean and apparent suns, it is clear that the conversion of mean time to apparent time may be accomplished by the application of the equation of time, with its proper sign, to the mean time; and the reverse operation by the application of the same quantity, in an opposite direction, to the apparent time.

The resemblance of these operations to the interconversion of mean and sidereal times may be observed if, in figure 59, we assume that PV is the hour circle of the true sun, PM remaining that of the mean sun; then the arc QM will be the mean time; QV, the apparent time; and VM, the equation of time; whence we have as before:

$$QV = QM + VM, \text{ or}$$
$$\text{Apparent time} = \text{Mean time} + \text{Equation of time};$$

the equation of time will be positive or negative according to the relative position of the two suns.

Sidereal and mean time intervals.—The sidereal year consists of 366.25636 sidereal days or of 365.25636 mean solar days. If, therefore, M be any interval of mean time, and S the corresponding interval of sidereal time, the relations between the two may be expressed as follows:

$$\frac{S}{M} = \frac{366.25636}{365.25636} = 1.0027379;$$

$$\frac{M}{S} = \frac{365.25636}{366.25636} = 0.9972696.$$

Therefore,

$$S = 1.0027379\ M = M + .0027379\ M;$$
$$M = 0.9972696\ S = S - .0027304\ S.$$

If $M = 24^h$, $S = 24^h + 3^m\ 56^s.6$; or, in a mean solar day, sidereal time gains on mean time $3^m\ 56^s.6$, the gain each hour being $9^s.8565$.

If $S = 24^h$, $M = 24^h - 3^m\ 55^s.9$; or, in a sidereal day, mean time loses on sidereal time $3^m\ 55^s.9$, the loss each hour being $9^s.8296$.

If M and S be expressed in hours and fractional parts thereof,

$$S = M + 9^s.8565\ M;$$
$$M = S - 9^s.8296\ S.$$

Tables for the conversion of the intervals of mean into those of sidereal time and the reverse are based upon these relations. Tables 38 and 39 of this work give the values for making these conversions, and similar tables are to be found in the Nautical Almanac.

Converting mean solar into sidereal time.—Apply to the local civil time the longitude, adding if west and subtracting if east, and thus obtain the Greenwich civil time. Take from the Nautical Almanac the sidereal time of 0^h civil time at Greenwich (R. A. M. S.$+12^h$), and correct it for the Greenwich civil time by the supplementary table at the foot of the main table, or by tables in the Nautical Almanac, or Table 39 (Bowditch), or by the hourly difference of $9^s.857$. Add to the local civil time this corrected value of the R. A. M. S.$+12^h$, rejecting 24^h if the sum is greater than that amount. The result will be the local sidereal time.

Example.—April 22, 1937, in long. 81°15′ W., the local civil time is $2^h\ 00^m\ 00^s$ p. m. Required the corresponding local sidereal time.

L. C. T.,	$22^d\ 14^h\ 00^m\ 00^s$	R. A. M. S.$+12^h$, $22^d\ 0^h$,	$13^h\ 58^m\ 31^s.9$	L. C. T.,	$14^h\ 00^m\ 00^s$
Long., +	5 25 00	Red. for $19^h\ 25^m$ (Tab. 39), +	3 11 .4	R. A. M. S.$+12^h$ +	14 01 43.3
G. C. T.,	22 19 25 00	R. A. M. S.$+12^h$, $19^h\ 25^m$,	14 01 43 .3	L. S. T.,	4 01 43.3

Example.—April 22, 1937, in long. 75° E., the local civil time is $4^h\ 00^m\ 00^s$ a. m. Required the local sidereal time.

L. C. T.,	$22^d\ 4^h\ 00^m\ 00^s$	R. A. M. S.$+12^h$, $21^d\ 0^h$,	$13^h\ 54^m\ 35^s.3$	L. C. T. 22^d,	$4^h\ 00^m\ 00^s$
Long., −	5 00 00	Red. for 23^h (Tab. 39), +	3 46 .7	R. A. M. S.$+12^h$,	13 58 22.0
G. C. T.,	21 23 00 00	R. A. M. S.$+12^h$, 23^h,	13 58 22 .0	L. S. T.,	17 58 22.0

In these examples the reduction of the R. A. M. S.$+12^h$ has formed a separate operation in order to make clear the process. It would be better to add together directly L. C. T., R. A. M. S.$+12^h$, and Reduction.

Converting sidereal into mean solar time.—Take from the Nautical Almanac the sidereal time of 0^h civil time at Greenwich (R. A. M. S.$+12^h$) and apply to it the reduction for longitude, either by Table 39 or by the hourly difference of $9^s.857$, and the result will be the local sidereal time of 0^h local civil time, which is equivalent to the local sidereal time at the instant of 0^h local civil time. Subtract this from the given local sidereal time (adding 24^h to the latter if necessary), and the result will be the interval from 0^h local civil time, expressed in units of sidereal time. Convert this sidereal time interval into a mean time interval by subtracting the reduction as given by the table in the Nautical Almanac, or Table 38, or by the hourly difference of $9^s.830$; the result will be the local civil time.

If the sidereal interval is less than $3^m\ 56^s.555$, there will be two mean times corresponding to the given sidereal time, one a few minutes after the preceding 0^h, and the other a few minutes before the following 0^h, the mean time interval between these two mean times being $23^h\ 56^m\ 04^s.09$. The mean time, approximately known, will show which one is to be taken.

Example.—April 22, 1937, about 4 a. m. in Long. 75° E., the local sidereal time is $17^h\ 58^m\ 22^s.0$. What is the local civil time?

L. S. T.	$17^h\ 58^m\ 22^s.0$	R. A. M. S.$+12^h$ Gr. $22^d\ 0^h$,	$13^h\ 58^m\ 31^s.9$
L. S. T. of 0^h L. C. T.	$13^h\ 57^m$ 42 .6	Red. for-5^h long. (Tab. 39), −	49 .3
Sid. interval from 0^h L. C. T.	4 00 39 .4	R. A. M. S.$+12^h$, local 0^h, (or L. S. T. of 0^h L. C. T.)	13 57 42 .6
Red. for sid. interval (Tab. 38),	39 .4		
L. C. T., 22^d,	4 00 00 .0		

Example.—April 22, 1937, about 2 p. m., at a place in Long. 81° 15′ W., the sidereal time is $4^h\ 01^m\ 43^s.3$. What is the corresponding civil time?

L. S. T.$+24^h$ if necessary for the following subtraction:	$28^h\ 01^m\ 43^s.3$	R. A. M. S.$+12^h$ Gr. $22^d\ 0^h$	$13^h\ 58^m\ 31^s.9$
L. S. T., of 0^h L. C. T.	13 59 25 .3	Red. for $+5^h\ 25^m$ long. (Tab. 39) +	0 53 .4
Sid. interval from 0^h L. C. T.,	14 02 18 .0	R. A. M. S.$+12^h$, local 0^h (or L. S. T. of 0^h L. C. T.)	13 59 25 .3
Red. for sid. interval (Tab. 38),−	2 18 .0		
L. C. T., 22^d,	14 00 00		

Converting mean into apparent time and the reverse.—Find the Greenwich time corresponding to the given local time. If apparent time is given, find the Greenwich apparent time and take the equation of time from the almanac using Greenwich apparent time as Greenwich civil time. Apply equation of time with sign reversed. If mean time, find the Greenwich civil time, correct the equation of time for the required instant and apply it with its proper sign to the given time.

Example.—April 21, 1937, in Long. 81° 15′ W., find the local apparent time corresponding to a local civil time of $3^h\ 05^m\ 00^s$ p. m.

L. C. T.,	$21^d\ 15^h\ 05^m\ 00^s$	L. C. T.,	$21^d\ 15^h\ 05^m\ 00^s$	Eq. t., 20^h,	$1^m\ 18^s.7$
Long., W.,	+ 5 25 00	Eq. t.,	+ 1 18 .9	Corr.,	0 .2
G. C. T.,	21 20 30 00	L. A. T.,	21 15 06 18 .9	Eq. t.,	1 18 .9
				H. D.,	+ $0^s.5$
				Int.,	+ $0^h.5$
				Corr.,	+ $0^s.25$
				(Add to MEAN time.)	

Example.—April 3, 1937, in Long. 81° 15′ E., the local apparent time is $8^h\ 45^m\ 00^s$ a. m. Required the local civil time.

L. A. T.,	$3^d\ 8^h\ 45^m\ 00^s$	L. A. T.,	$3^d\ 8^h\ 45^m\ 00^s$	Eq. t., 2^h,	$3^m\ 32^s.2$
Long., E.,	− 5 25 00	Eq. t.,	+ 3 31 .3	Corr.,	− 0 .9
G. A. T.,	3 3 20 00	L. C. T.,	3 8 48 31 .3	Eq. t.,	3 31 .3
				H. D.,	− $0^s.7$
				Int.,	− $1^h.33$
				Corr.,	− $0^s.93$
				(Add to APPARENT time.)	

Finding hour angle of a body from the time, and the reverse.—In figure 59, if M and M′ represent the positions of celestial bodies instead of those of the mean sun as before assumed, then the hour angles of the bodies will be QM and 24^h−M′Q, respectively, and their right ascensions will be VM and VM′.

As before,

$$\begin{aligned} QV &= QM + VM, \\ &= VM' - M'Q; \\ QM &= QV - VM; \\ M'Q &= VM' - VQ, \text{ or} \\ (24^h - M'Q) &= (24^h + QV) - VM'. \end{aligned}$$

Thus, the sidereal time is equal to the sum of the right ascension of the body and its hour angle, subtracting 24^h when the sum exceeds that amount; and the hour angle equals the sidereal time minus the right ascension of the body, 24^h being added to the former when necessary to render the subtraction possible.

Example.—In Long. 81° 15′ W., on April 25, at 1937, $12^h\ 10^m\ 30^s$ local civil time, find the hour angle of Sirius.

L. C. T.,	$12^h\ 10^m\ 30^s$	L. C. T.,	$12^h\ 10^m\ 30^s.0$	or H. A. M. S.,	$0^h\ 10^m\ 30^s.0$ W.
Long.,	+ 5 25 00	R. A. M. S., $+12^h$,	+14 10 21 .5	or R. A. M. S.,	2 10 21 .5
G. C. T.,	17 35 30	Red. $17^h\ 35^m.5$ G. C. T. (Tab. 39),	+ 2 53 .4		2 53 .4
		L. S. T. increased by 24^h,	26 23 44 .9	L. S. T.,	2 23 44 .9
		R. A. Sirius,	− 6 42 23 .4	R. A. Sirius	6 42 23 .4
		H. A. Sirius,	19 41 21 .5 W.	H. A.,	4 18 38 .5 E.

Example.—May 9, 1937, Arcturus being $2^h\ 27^m\ 42^s.5$ east of the meridian, find the local sidereal time.

	$24^h\ 00^m\ 00^s.0$	H. A., ✳	$21^h\ 32^m\ 17^s.5$
H. A.,	2 27 42 .5 E.	R. A., ✳	+14 12 50 .3
H. A.,	21 32 17 .5 W.	L. S. T.,	11 45 07 .8

Or thus:

H. A., ✳	− $2^h\ 27^m\ 42^s.5$
R. A., ✳	+14 12 50 .3
L. S. T.,	11 45 07 .8

Diagrams.—Many navigators find the conversion of time simplified and more easily grasped by roughly plotting the elements as they are presented in any given case, in a figure drawn on the plane of the celestial equator. Noting the known elements and the elements required to be found, a study of the figure shows very quickly how to combine the known elements to get the unknown elements.

Following this method the examples given under the paragraphs on conversion of mean, apparent, and sidereal times are here solved as an alternative to the preceding treatment, since it is found that, for many who have learned this method of procedure in the beginning, every difficulty in reckoning or converting time has been obviated. Although the explanation may appear long, the actual plotting and solution of any given case takes only a few minutes when the method is understood. In the figures, P represents the elevated pole; Q, the intersection of the upper branch of the local meridian with the equator, and Q′ the intersection of the lower branch of the local meridian with the equator; G, the intersection of the upper branch of the meridian of Greenwich with the equator, and G′ the intersection of the lower branch of the meridian of Greenwich with the equator; V, the first point of Aries (Vernal Equinox); S_m, the mean sun; S_a, the apparent sun; and $*$, a star or planet.

FIRST EXAMPLE UNDER "MEAN SOLAR TO SIDEREAL TIME"

(See fig. 60.)

Draw a circle to represent the plane of the celestial equator, P being the projection of the pole, and PQ the projection of the upper branch of the local meridian, and PQ′ the projection of the lower branch of the local meridian. From P draw the projection of the hour circle of the Greenwich meridian which (since the longitude is west) is laid off to the right or eastward of the upper branch of the local meridian so that the arc QG equals the longitude. The arrow indicates westerly direction and shows the direction in which the hour circles of the celestial bodies move around the circle on the earth's axis. The L. C. T. being 14^h, we lay off the hour circle of the mean sun to the westward of the lower branch of the local meridian so that the arc $Q'GS_m$ equals the L. C. T. It is seen at once from the figure that the G. C. T. (the position of the hour circle of the mean sun, S_m, with reference to the lower branch of the Greenwich meridian) is the arc $G'Q'GQS_m$, which equals Long.+L. C. T. Having found the G. C. T., the R. A. M. S.$+12^h$ at that instant is found from the Nautical Almanac (taken out for the day and corrected for the G. C. T.) which, in this case, is $14^h\ 01^m\ 43^s.3$. The correction is (+) or additive to the angle which represents the R. A. M. S.$+12^h$ for 0^h civil time at Greenwich because this angle has been increased by this amount owing to the gain of the Vernal Equinox over the mean sun for the angle through which the mean sun has traveled from the lower branch of the Greenwich meridian. The mean sun is to the eastward of the Vernal Equinox by the amount of its right ascension. Therefore lay off PV, the hour circle of the Vernal Equinox, so that the arc VS_m equals the R. A. M. S. Since the L. S. T. equals the H. A. of the Vernal Equinox, it is at once apparent from the figure that the L. S. T. equals R. A. M. S.+H. A. mean sun, or R. A. M. S.$+12^h$+L. C. T.

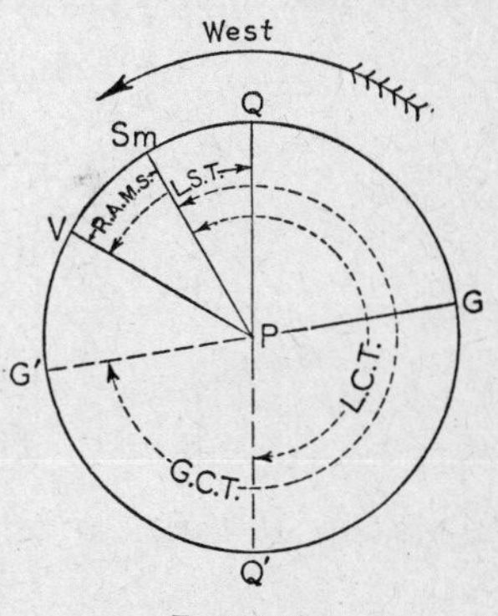

FIGURE 60.

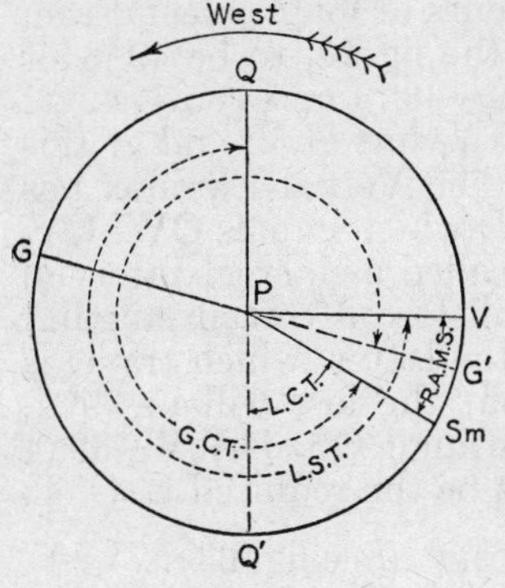

FIGURE 61.

SECOND EXAMPLE UNDER "MEAN SOLAR TO SIDEREAL TIME" (See fig. 61)

Draw a circle to represent the plane of the celestial equator. Project the pole P and upper branch of the local meridian PQ, and the lower branch of the local meridian PQ′. Draw the arrow pointed west to show the direction in which the hour circles move. Since the longitude is east, the Greenwich meridian is to the westward of the local meridian, and PG, the upper branch of the Greenwich meridian, is drawn so that the arc QG equals 5^h (75°) of longitude. Since the L. C. T. is $4^h\ 00^m\ 00^s$ lay off the arc $Q'S_m$, equal to 4^h, (60°) and draw PS_m the hour circle of the mean sun. It is apparent from the figure that, since the mean sun must travel around the arc to the west from S_m to G′ to make the time 0 hours civil time on April 22 at Greenwich, the date must be April 21, and the G. C. T. is 23 hours. For this Greenwich date, take, from the Nautical Almanac (corrected for G. C. T.), the R. A. M. S. $+12^h$ equal to $13^h\ 58^m\ 22^s.0$ and, therefore, the R. A. M. S. is $1^h\ 58^m\ 22^s.0$, which is the amount the hour circle of the mean sun is to the eastward of the hour circle of the

Vernal Equinox. The correction is + or additive for the reason given in the preceding example. Lay off the arc S_mV equal to the R. A. M. S. and draw the hour circle of the Vernal Equinox PV. An inspection of the figure shows us that the L. S. T. is the arc QGV which is equal to the L. C. T.+R. A. M. S.+12^h.

FIRST EXAMPLE UNDER "SIDEREAL TO MEAN SOLAR TIME" (See fig. 62)

Draw the figure as shown, laying off the east longitude, equal to 5^h (75°), to the westward from Q, and thus finding the Greenwich meridian G. The given L. S. T. being $17^h\ 58^m\ 22^s$, lay off QGV equal to this amount for the purpose of determining the position of V, the Vernal Equinox or first point of Aries, for the instant desired. The problem is to plot the position of the mean sun at this instant, and thence find its angular removal from the lower branch, PQ′, of the local meridian, or the L. C. T. The Nautical Almanac gives the sidereal time of 0^h civil time at Greenwich, and, on April 22, this is found to be $13^h\ 58^m\ 31^s.9$. By laying off this amount GV_1, to the westward from G, the position of the Vernal Equinox or first point of Aries at the instant of 0^h G. C. T. is found to be at V_1. To find the position of the Vernal Equinox or first point of Aries at the instant of 0^h L. C. T. the angle QV_2 must be found, which will be less than GV_1, since the first point of Aries always advances faster toward the

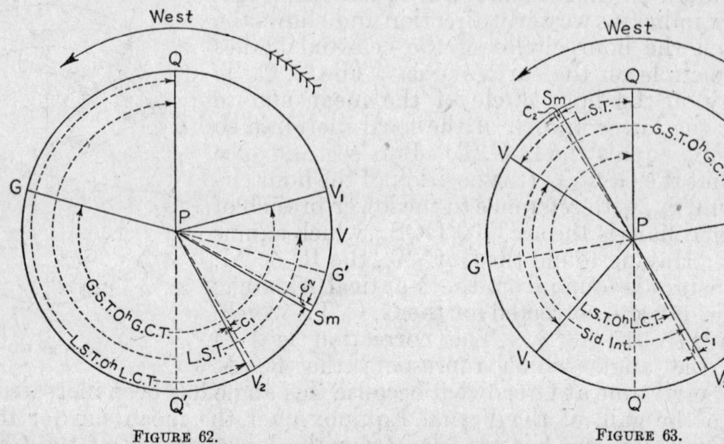

FIGURE 62. FIGURE 63.

west than the mean sun. The amount of this gain of the Vernal Equinox over the mean sun depends on the angular distance through which the mean sun has traveled; that is, in this case from Q to G, the angular amount of 5 hours of longitude. From Table 39 the gain, which is represented by the sector C_1 in the figure, to be $49^s.3$ for the 5 hours, so that QV_2 equals $GV_1-49^s.3$, or $13^h\ 58^m\ 31^s.9-49^s.3$ or $13^h\ 57^m\ 42^s.6$. For the instant of time desired, the Vernal Equinox is not at V_2 but at V, and at this instant the position of the mean sun, S_m, is to be found. The Vernal Equinox has moved from V_2 to the westward to V or through the arc V_2V, which equals $QV-QV_2$ or $17^h\ 58^m\ 22^s.0-13^h\ 57^m\ 42^s.6$ or $4^h\ 00^m\ 39^s.4$, which is called a sidereal interval. During this travel of the Vernal Equinox the mean sun will lose a certain angular amount on the Vernal Equinox, depending on the travel of the latter, which travel is $4^h\ 00^m\ 39^s.4$. From Table 38, for this travel it is found that the loss will be $39^s.4$, which is represented by the sector C_2 in the figure, so that the angle QS_m is $V_2V-39^s.4$ or $4^h\ 00^m\ 39^s.4-39^s.4$, or $4^h\ 00^m\ 00^s$, which the figure shows to be the required L. C. T.

SECOND EXAMPLE UNDER "SIDEREAL TO MEAN SOLAR TIME" (See fig. 63)

Draw the figure as shown, laying off the west longitude equal to $5^h\ 25^m$ (81° 15′), to the eastward from Q, and thus finding the Greenwich meridian G. The problem is similar to the preceding one except that the correction, C_1, represents an increase in the L. S. T. of 0^h L. C. T., since the Vernal Equinox has gained a certain amount on the mean sun during the travel of the sun to the westward from G to Q. For the travel of V_2 to V, the mean sun will fall back a certain amount in relation to the Vernal Equinox, which is represented by the correction C_2, and hence $V_2V-C_2=Q'S_m$=L. C. T.

FIRST EXAMPLE UNDER "HOUR ANGLE OF A BODY FROM THE TIME" (See fig. 64)

Draw the figure as explained above, using longitude 5^h west (75°), and L. C. T., $12^h(+)$. Then G. C. T. equals 12+5 or $17^h(+)$ (255°) of April 25. For this instant of time the mean sun is plotted at S_m. Knowing the positions of G, Q, and S_m, the problem is to find the position of the given star on the diagram, and thence its local hour angle. If there can be found the relative angles from the mean sun and from the star to some third object, there can be plotted this third object and the required hour angle of the star found. The third object is the first point of Aries or Vernal Equinox, and the angles from the mean sun and from the star are the right ascensions of the mean sun and the star. The right ascension of the mean sun increased by 12^h is found from the Almanac, not for the instant required, but for 0^h G. C. T. of the date. The right ascension of the mean sun found by subtracting 12^h from this quantity must be increased by a correction for the time elapsed since 0^h of Greenwich civil

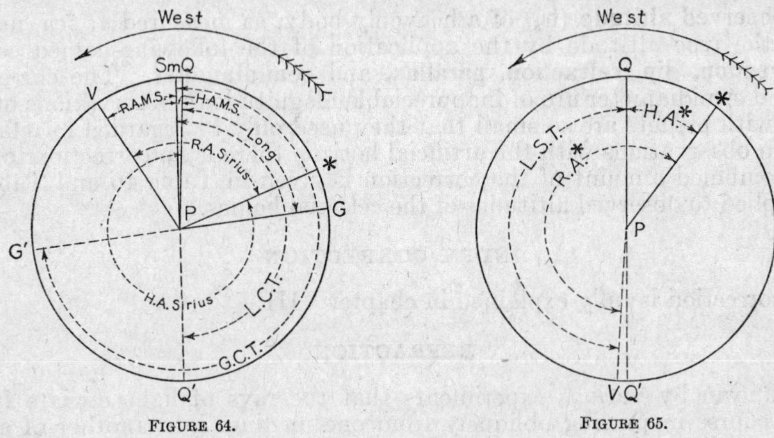

FIGURE 64. FIGURE 65.

time; that is, for the G. C. T. corresponding to the given L. C. T. In the problem the corrected R. A. M. S. is approximately 2^h. Therefore, to find the position of the Vernal Equinox at the required instant, S_mV is laid off from S_m, 2^h to the westward. From the Almanac, the R. A. of the star is found to be 6^h 42^m and, accordingly, V$\ast$ must be laid off 6^h 42_m to the eastward. The required local hour angle of the star is then Q$\ast$ which equals $QS_m+VS_m-V\ast$, or H. A. M. S.+R. A. M. S.−R. A.$\ast$.

SECOND EXAMPLE UNDER "HOUR ANGLE OF A BODY FROM THE TIME" (See fig. 65)

Draw the figure as before. The problem is, knowing the position of the star at a certain instant, to find the L. S. T. Accordingly, the position of the star must be plotted first, and then that of the Vernal Equinox. The local hour angle of the latter is the required L. S. T.

The hour angle of the star is given approximately as 2^h (30°), bearing east from the meridian, so $Q\ast=2^h$ is laid off to the east from Q. Now find from the Almanac the R. A. of the $\ast$ which is approximately 14 hours (210°), and lay off $\ast$V equal to 14^h to the westward from $\ast$. The L. S. T. is then QV, which equals the R. A.$\ast$− H. A.$\ast$, or 14^h-2^h or 12^h.

When doubt exists as to the Greenwich date, the navigator, by plotting the data in exactly the same way as explained above, can at once remove all doubt on the subject and can get the correct G. C. T.

From the above it is noted that right ascension fixes celestial bodies with relation to the vernal equinox and with relation to other celestial bodies, while the hour angle expresses the relation of celestial bodies to the observer's meridian. In plotting the position of sun, moon, star, or planet, from the celestial sphere to the terrestrial sphere, the declination of the body and its Greenwich hour angle must be known for the desired instant of Greenwich civil time.

CHAPTER X

OBSERVED ALTITUDE CORRECTIONS

The true altitude (h_o) of a heavenly body at any place on the earth's surface is the altitude of its center, as it would be measured by an observer at the center of the earth, above the plane passed through the center of the earth at right angles to the direction of the zenith.

The observed altitude (h_s) of a heavenly body, as measured at sea, may be converted to the true altitude by the application of the following-named corrections: **Index correction, dip, refraction, parallax,** and **semidiameter.** The corrections for parallax and semidiameter are of inappreciable magnitude in observations of the fixed stars, and with planets are so small that they need only be regarded in refined calculations. In observations with the artificial horizon there is no correction for dip.

The combined amount of the correction is given in Table 40 and Table 41 and may be applied to observed altitudes of the celestial bodies.

INDEX CORRECTION

This correction is fully explained in chapter VIII.

REFRACTION

It is known by various experiments that the rays of light deviate from their rectilinear course in passing obliquely from one medium into another of a different density; if the latter be more dense, the ray will be bent toward the perpendicular to the line of junction of the media; if less dense, it will be bent away from that perpendicular.

The ray of light before entering the second medium is called the **incident** ray; after it enters the second medium it is called the **refracted** ray, and the difference of direction of the two is called the **refraction.**

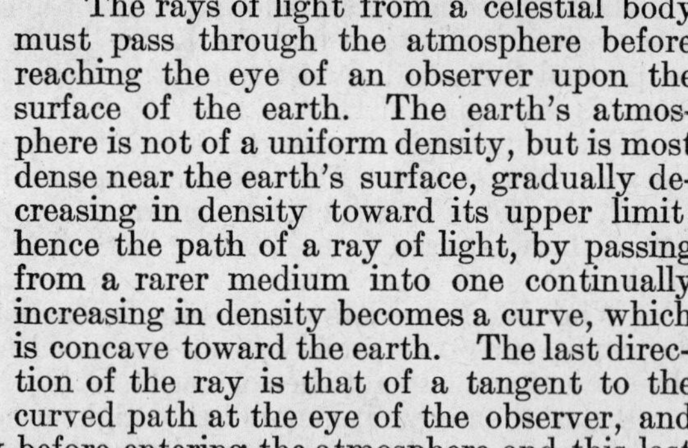

FIGURE 66.

The rays of light from a celestial body must pass through the atmosphere before reaching the eye of an observer upon the surface of the earth. The earth's atmosphere is not of a uniform density, but is most dense near the earth's surface, gradually decreasing in density toward its upper limit; hence the path of a ray of light, by passing from a rarer medium into one continually increasing in density becomes a curve, which is concave toward the earth. The last direction of the ray is that of a tangent to the curved path at the eye of the observer, and the difference of the direction of the ray before entering the atmosphere and this last direction constitutes the refraction.

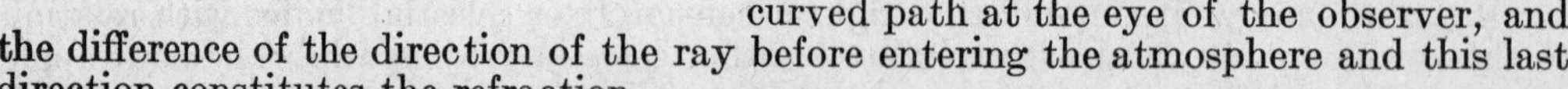

To illustrate this, consider the earth's atmosphere as shown in figure 66; let SB be a ray from a star S, entering the atmosphere at B, and bent into the curve BA; then the apparent direction of the star is AS′, the tangent to the curve at the point A, the refraction being the angle between the lines BS and AS′. If CAZ is the vertical line of the observer, by a law of optics the vertical plane of the observer which contains the tangent AS′ must also contain the whole curve BA and the incident ray BS. Hence refraction increases the apparent altitude of a star without affecting its azimuth.

Refraction at the zenith is nothing. The less the altitude the more obliquely the rays enter the atmosphere and the greater will be the refraction. At the horizon the refraction is the greatest.

The refraction for a mean state of the atmosphere (barometer 30^{in}, Fahr. thermometer 50°) is given in Table 22 and the combined refraction and sun's parallax in Table 23.

Since the amount of the refraction depends upon the density of the atmosphere, and the density varies with the pressure and the temperature, which are indicated by the barometer and thermometer, the *true* refraction is found by applying to the mean refraction the corrections to be found in Tables 24 and 25; these are deduced from Bessel's formulas. Under certain conditions of the atmosphere a very extraordinary deflection occurs in rays of light which reach the observer's eye from the visible horizon, the amount of which is not covered by the ordinary corrections for pressure and temperature; on account of it, altitude less than 5° should be avoided.

Example.—Required the refraction for the apparent altitude 5°, when the thermometer is at 20° and the barometer at 30^{in}.67.

Mean refraction by Table 22 is,	9′ 52″
Correction for height of barometer is,	+ 13
Correction for the temperature,	+ 42
True refraction,	10 47

The correction for refraction should always be subtracted, as also that for combined refraction and parallax of the sun; the correction for combined refraction and parallax of the moon is invariably additive.

DIP

Dip of the horizon is the angle of depression of the visible sea horizon below the true horizon, due to the elevation of the eye of the observer above the level of the sea.

In figure 67 suppose A to be the position of an observer whose height above the level of the sea is AB. CAZ is the true vertical at the position of the observer, and AH is the direction of the true horizon, S being an observed heavenly body. Draw ATH′ tangent to the earth's surface at T. Disregarding refraction, T will be the most distant point visible from A. Owing to refraction, however, the most distant visible point of the earth's surface is more remote from the observer than the point T, and is to be found at a point T′, in figure 68. But to an observer at A the point T′ will appear to lie in the direction of AH″, the tangent at A to the curve AT′. If the vertical plane were revolved about CZ as an axis, the line AH would generate the plane of the true horizon, while the point T′ would generate a small circle of the terrestrial sphere called the **visible or sea horizon.** The **dip of the horizon** is HAH″, being the angle between the true horizon and the apparent direction of the sea horizon. Values of the dip are given in Table 18 for various heights of the observer's eye, and in the computation of the table, allowance has been made for the effect of atmospheric refraction as it exists under normal conditions.

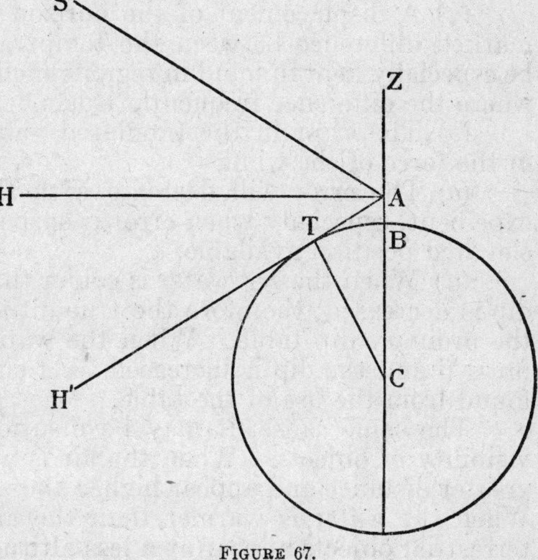

FIGURE 67.

The fact must be emphasized, that under certain conditions the deflection of the ray in its path from the horizon to the eye is so irregular as to give a value of the dip widely different from that which is tabulated for the mean state of atmosphere. These irregularities usually occur when there exists a material difference between the temperature of the sea water and that of the air, and they attain a maximum value in calm or nearly calm weather, when the lack of circulation permits the air to arrange itself in a series of horizontal strata of different densities, the denser strata being below when the air is warmer, and the reverse condition obtaining when the air is cooler. The effect of such an arrangement is that a ray of light from the horizon in passing through media of different densities undergoes a refraction quite unlike that which occurs in the atmosphere of much more nearly homogeneous density that exists under normal conditions.

Various methods have been suggested for computing the amount of dip for different relative values of temperature of air and water, but none of these afford a satisfactory solution. It is far more convenient to measure the dip with special instruments or attachments to the sextant when abnormal conditions are suspected. If instruments are not available, then the navigator should resort to a number of measurements of the altitude.

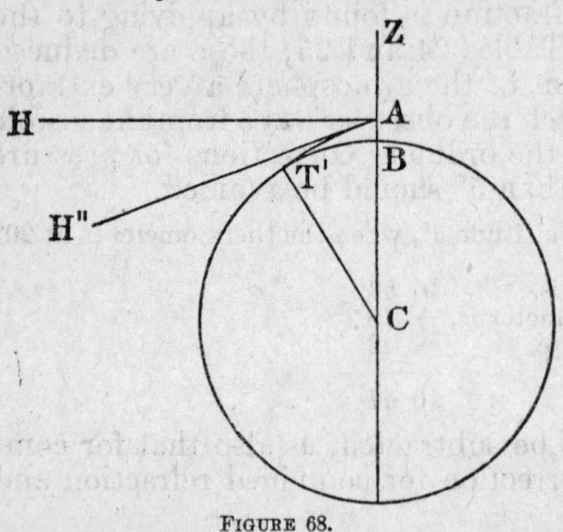

FIGURE 68.

The difference between the actual value of the dip and the tabulated value may be very large occasionally, as reliable observations have placed it above 10′ and even as high as 32′. Such large differences are, however, very rare over the greater part of the oceans, but should be guarded against when in a calm or with wind not more than 1 or 2 of Beaufort scale, and particularly when mirage effects are noticeable. An investigation by the Carnegie Institution of Washington in the course of the Magnetic Survey of the Oceans showed the actual value of the dip to differ not more than 2′½ from the tabulated value in 5,000 determinations, excepting on one occasion when a difference of 10′.6 was found.

The following rules may indicate to the navigator the conditions under which caution must be observed, and the direction of probable error:

(*a*) A displacement of the horizon should always be suspected when there is a marked difference between the temperatures of air and sea water; this fact should be especially kept in mind in regions such as those of the Red Sea and the Gulf Stream, where the difference frequently exists.

(*b*) The error in the tabulated value of the dip will diminish with an increase in the force of the wind.

(*c*) The error will decrease with the height of the observer's eye; hence it is expedient, especially when error is suspected, to make the observation from the most elevated position available.

(*d*) When the sea water is colder than the air the visible horizon is raised and the dip is decreased; therefore the true altitude is greater than that given by the use of the ordinary dip table. When the water is warmer than the air, the horizon is depressed and the dip is increased. At such times the altitude is really less than that found from the use of the table.

The same cause, it may be mentioned here, affects the kindred matter of the visibility of objects. When the air is warmer, terrestrial objects are sighted from a greater distance and appear higher above the horizon than under ordinary conditions. When the water is warmer than the air, the distance of visibility is reduced, and terrestrial objects appear at a less altitude.

What has been said heretofore about the dip supposes the horizon to be free from all intervening land or other objects; but it often happens that an observation is required to be taken from a vessel steaming along shore or at anchor in harbor, when the sun is over the land and the shore is nearer the ship than the visible sea horizon would be if it were unconfined; in this case the dip will be different from that of Table 18 and will be greater the nearer the ship is to that point of the shore to which the sun's image is brought down. In such case Table 19 gives the dip at different heights of the eye and at different distances of the ship from the land.

The dip is always to be subtracted from the observed altitude.

PARALLAX

The **parallax** of a celestial body is, in general terms, the angle between two straight lines drawn to the body from different points. But in Nautical Astronomy **geocentric parallax** is alone considered, this being the difference between the positions of a celestial body as seen at the same instant from the center of the earth and from a point on its surface.

The zenith distance of a body, S (fig. 69), seen from A, on the surface of the earth, is ZAS; seen from C it is ZCS; the **parallax** is the difference of these angles, ZAS−ZCS=ASC.

Parallax in altitude is, then, the angle at the celestial body subtended by the radius of the earth.

If the celestial body is in the horizon as at H′ the radius, being at right angles to AH′, subtends the greatest possible angle at the star for the same distance, and this angle is called the **horizontal parallax.** The parallax is less as the body is farther from the earth, as will be evident from the figure.

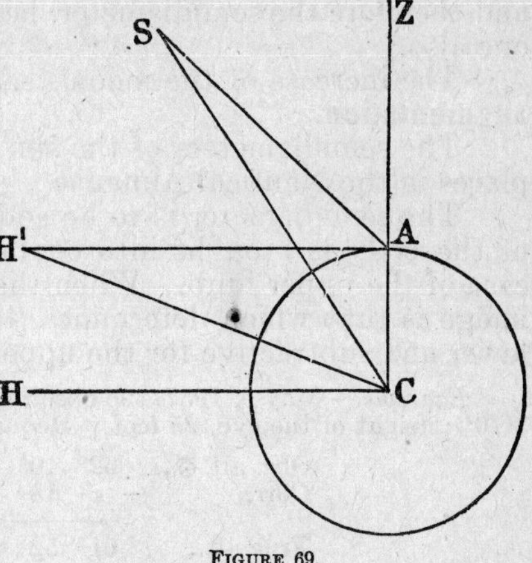

FIGURE 69.

Let par.=parallax in altitude, ASC;
Z=SAZ, the apparent zenith distance (corrected for refraction);
R=AC, the radius of the earth; and
D=CS, the distance of the object from the center of the earth.

Then, since SAC=180°−SAZ, the triangle ASC gives:

$$\sin \text{par.} = \frac{R \sin Z}{D}.$$

If the object is in the horizon at H′, the angle AH′C is the horizontal parallax, and denoting it by H. P. the right triangle AH′C gives:

$$\sin \text{H. P.} = \frac{R}{D}.$$

Substituting this value of $\frac{R}{D}$ in the above,

$$\sin \text{par.} = \sin \text{H. P.} \sin Z.$$

If h=SAH′, the apparent altitude of the celestial body, then Z=90°−h; hence,

$$\sin \text{par.} = \sin. \text{H. P.} \cos h.$$

Since par. and H. P. are always small, the sines are nearly proportional to the angles; hence,

$$\text{par.} = \text{H. P.} \cos h.$$

The Nautical Almanac gives the horizontal parallax of the moon, as well as of the planets Venus, Mars, Jupiter, and Saturn.

In Table 20 will be found the values of the sun's parallax for altitude intervals of 5° or 10°, while Table 23 contains the combined values of the sun's parallax and the refraction.

Parallax is always additive; combined parallax and refraction is subtractive for the sun.

SEMIDIAMETER

The **semidiameter** of a celestial body is half the angle subtended by the diameter of the visible disk at the eye of the observer. For the same body the semidiameter varies with the distance; thus, the difference of the sun's semidiameter at different times of the year is due to the change of the earth's distance from the sun; and similarly for the moon and the planets.

In the case of the moon, the earth's radius bears an appreciable and considerable ratio to the moon's distance from the center of the earth; hence the moon is materially nearer to an observer when in or near the zenith than when in or near the horizon, and therefore the semidiameter, besides having a menstrual change, has a semidiurnal one also.

The increase of the moon's semidiameter due to increase of altitude is called its **augmentation.**

The semidiameters of the sun, moon, and planets are given in their appropriate places in the Nautical Almanac.

The semidiameter is to be added to the observed altitude in case the lower limb of the body is brought into contact with the horizon, and to be subtracted in the case of the upper limb. When the artificial horizon is used, the limb of the *reflected* image is that which determines the sign of this correction, it being additive for the lower and subtractive for the upper.

Example.—May 6, 1937, the observed altitude of the sun's upper limb was 62° 10′ 40″; I. C., + 3′10″; height of the eye, 25 feet. Required the true altitude.

Obs. alt. $\overline{\odot}$,	62° 10′ 40″	I. C.,	+ 3′ 10″
Corr.,	− 18 04		
		S. D. (Naut. Alm.),	−15′ 53″
True alt.,	61 52 36″	dip. (Tab. 18),	− 4 54
		p. & r. (Tab. 23),	− 27
			−21 14
		Corr.,	−18′ 04″

Example.—The altitude of Sirius as observed with an artificial horizon was 50° 59′ 30″; I. C., −1′30″. Required the true altitude.

Obs. 2 alt. ✳,	50° 59′ 30″
I. C., −	1 30
	2)50 58 00
Obs. alt.,	25 29 00
ref. (Tab. 22), −	2 02
True alt.,	25 26 58

Example.—April 16, 1937, observed altitude of Venus 53°26′10″; I. C., +2′30″; height of eye, 20 feet. Required the true altitude.

Obs. alt. ✳,	53° 26′ 10″	par. (Tab. 21),	+0′ 17″	Hor. Par. (Naut. Alm.), 0′.46
Corr.,	− 2 19	I. C.,	+2 30	
True alt.,	53 23 51		+2 47	
		dip, (Tab. 18),	−4′ 23″	
		ref. (Tab. 22),	− 43	
			−5 06	
		Corr.,	−2′ 19″	

The corrections for dip, parallax, refraction, and semidiameter, which must be applied to the observed altitude of a star or of the sun's lower limb in order to obtain the true altitude, have been combined in Table 40, and for the moon's upper and lower limb in Table 41, and will henceforth be used in all subsequent problems. This is done to save the time and labor involved in referring to separate tables of these corrections.

The tabulated correction for an observed altitude of a star combines the mean refraction and the dip; and that for the observed altitude of the sun's lower limb, the mean refraction, the dip, the parallax, and the mean semidiameter, which is taken as 16′. A supplementary table, taking account of the variation of the sun's semidiameter in the different months of the year, is given in connection with the main table.

Thus, in the example on page 160, when variations from the mean state of the atmosphere (barometer 30 inches, Fahr. thermometer 50°) are left out of consideration, proceed as follows:

Measured altitude (h_s)		☉ =	40° 04′ 00″
		I. C.=+	3 00
Correction from Table 40, altitude, and height of eye 20 feet	+10′.6		40° 07′ .0
Supplementary Table for June 21	− 0 .2		10 4
True altitude (h_o)			40 17 .4

And, in the last example on page 161, with the horizontal parallax 54′.2 and the observed altitude corrected for index error, obtain the correction of the measured altitude of the moon from table 41, as follows:

Measured altitude (h_s)		☽ =	59° 06′ 40″
		I. C.=+	2 00
			59 08 .7
Correction from Table 41	+12′.5	+	8 .2
Supplementary Table, correcting for height of eye 19 feet	− 4 .3		
True altitude (h_o)			59 16 .9

The following drawing illustrates the application of Table 8, Table 11, Table 18, and Table 19 of Part II.

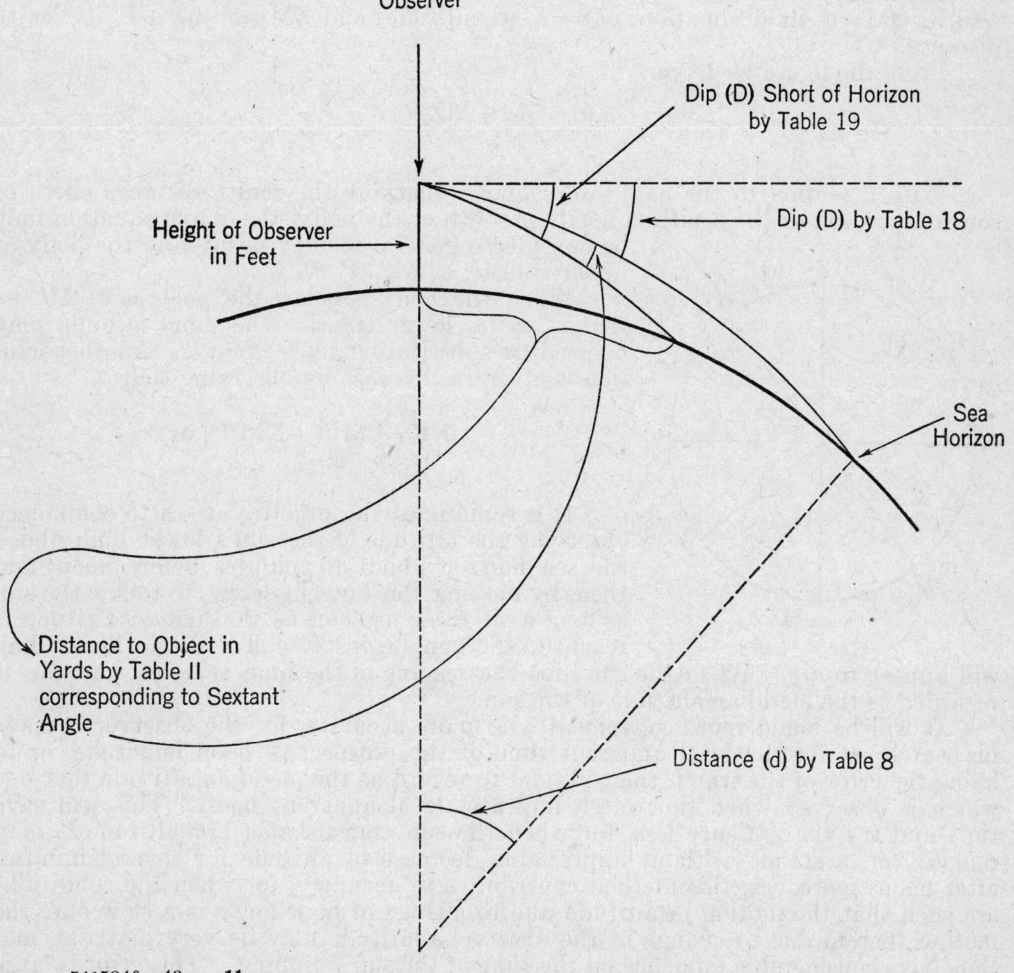

541524°—43——11

CHAPTER XI

LATITUDE

BY MERIDIAN ALTITUDE

The latitude of a place on the surface of the earth, being its angular distance from the equator, is measured by an arc of the meridian between the zenith and the equator, and hence is equal to the declination of the zenith; therefore, if the zenith distance of any heavenly body when on the meridian be known, together with the declination of the body, the latitude can be found.

Let figure 70 represent a projection of the celestial sphere on the plane of the meridian NZS; O, the center of the sphere; NS, the horizon; P and P′, the poles of the sphere; QOQ′, the equator; Z, the zenith of the observer. Then, by the above definition, ZQ will be the latitude of the observer; and NP, the altitude of the elevated pole, will also equal the latitude.

Let M be the position of a celestial body north of the equator, but south of the zenith; QM$=d$, its declination; MS$=h$, its altitude; and ZM$=z=90°-h$, its zenith distance.

From the figure we have:

$$QZ=QM+MZ, \text{ or}$$
$$L=d+z.$$

With attention to the names of z and d, marking the zenith distance north or south according as the zenith is north or south of the body, the above equation may be considered general for any position of the body at upper transit, as M, M′, M″.

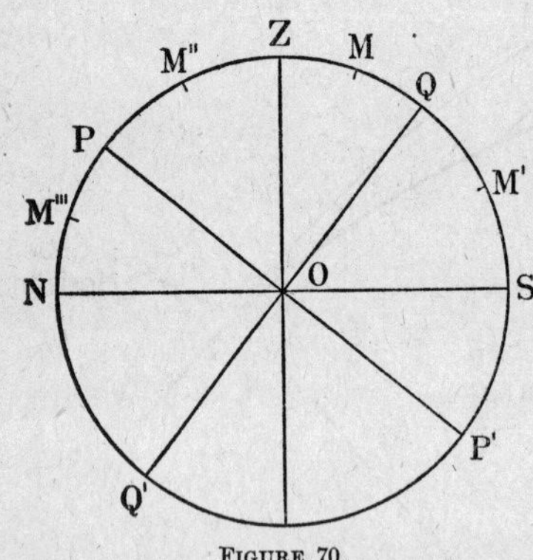

FIGURE 70.

When the body is below the pole, as at M‴—that is, at its lower transit—the same formula may be used by substituting $180°-d$ for d. Another solution is given in this case by observing that:

$$NP=PM'''+NM''', \text{ or}$$
$$L=p+h.$$

It is sometimes the practice at sea to commence observing the altitude of the sun's lower limb above the sea horizon about 10 minutes before noon, and then, by moving the tangent-screw, to follow the sun as long as it rises; as soon as the highest altitude is reached, the sun begins to fall and the lower limb will appear to *dip*. When the sun dips the reading of the limb is taken, and this is regarded as the meridian altitude of the sun.

It will be found more convenient, and more accurate, for the observer to have his watch set for the local apparent time of the prospective noon longitude, or to know the error of the watch thereon, and to regard as the *meridian* altitude that one which is observed when the watch indicates local apparent noon. This will save time and try the patience less, for when the sun transits at a low altitude it may remain "on a stand" without appreciable decrease of altitude for several minutes after noon; moreover, this method contributes to accuracy, for when the conditions are such that the motion in altitude due to change of hour angle is a slow one, the motion therein due to change of the observer's latitude may be very material, and thus have considerable influence on the time of the sun's dipping. This error is large enough to take account of in a fast-moving vessel making a course in which there is a good deal of northing or southing.

Finding time of transit.—In observing the altitude of any other celestial body than the sun, the watch time of transit is previously computed and the meridian altitude taken by time rather than by dipping. This is especially important with the moon, whose rapid motion in declination may introduce still another element of inaccuracy.

The watch time of transit for the sun, or other celestial body, may be found by the forms given below, knowing the D. R. longitude, the chronometer error, and the amount that the watch is slow of the chronometer. In this connection, see page 216 describing another method of setting the watch to L. A. T.

Sun			Stars, Planets, Moon		h m s
L. A. T. noon,		12h 00m 00s	L. S. T. transit		(Right ascension.)
Long. (+if west),	±	______	Long. (+if west),	±	______
G. A. T.,			G. S. T.,		
Eq. t.,	±	______	Sid. t. of 0h G. C. T.	−	______
G. C. T.,			Sid. int. from 0h.		
C. C. (sign reversed),	∓	______	Red. (Tab. 38),	−	______
Chro. time,			G. C. T.,		
C−W,	−	______	C. C. (sign reversed),	∓	______
Watch time noon,			Chro. time,		
			C−W,	−	______
			Watch time transit,		

Example.—June 1, 1937, at 10h 30m a. m., a vessel was in latitude 32°30′ N.; longitude 118° 30′ W.; course 258°, speed 16 knots, chron. fast 1m 10s; C−W 7h 49m 10s. Find watch time of local apparent noon.

Co.	Dist.	D. L.	Dep.	D. Long.
258°	24′	5′.0	23.5	27′.8

Long.,	118° 30′ W.
Run (D. Long.),	27 .8 W.
D. R. Long.,	118° 57′.8 W. at noon=7h 55m 51s

		h	m	s
L. A. T. noon,		12	00	00
Long. W.,	+	7	55	51
G. A. T.,		19	55	51
Eq. t.,	−		2	20
G. C. T.,		19	53	31
C. C. (rev.),	+		1	10
Chron.,		19	54	41
C−W,		7	49	10
Watch time of noon,		12	05	31

The vessel now steams 5m.5 more to get to the 12h 05m longitude, or the additional change in longitude is 1′.7 to the westward, so that the new D. R. longitude is 118° 59′.5 W. (7h 55m 58s). The process can be repeated again using this last longitude for a second estimate of the watch time of noon.

The Greenwich hour angle, given in the Nautical Almanac, may be used in place of apparent time. When the sun is on the meridian, its G. H. A. is equal to the longitude of the place. Take from the Almanac for the proper date the G. H. A. nearest to, but less than the D. R. longitude and note the corresponding G. C. T. Subtract this G. H. A. from the D. R. longitude and this difference in arc, converted into time from the table in the Almanac "corr. to G. H. A." gives the Greenwich civil time of local apparent noon.

D. R. Long.,	118°57′.8 W.		
June 1, G. H. A.,	90 35 .3 W.	=G. C. T.,	18h 00m 00s
Diff.,	28 22 .5	=Corr.,	1 53 30 (N. A.)
		G. C. T.,	19 53 30 of local apparent noon.

Example.—Jan. 15, 1937, in longitude 67° 30′ W., to find the watch time of transit of star α Virginis (Spica), chron. slow $1^m 06^s$; C−W $3^h 59^m 00^s$.

L. S. T. transit,	13^h	21^m	$53^s.6$	=R. A.
Long., W.,	4	30	00 .0	
G. S. T.,	17	51	53 .6	
R. A. M. S.+12^h,	7	36	06 .2	(Jan. 15)
Sid. Int.,	10	15	47 .4	
Red. Tab. 38,	−	1	40 .9	
G. C. T.,	10	14	06 .5	
C. C. (rev.),	−	1	06 .0	
Chron.,	10	13	00 .5	
C−W.,	− 3	59	00 .0	
W. T. of transit,	6	14	00 .5	

or the approximate time of transit to the nearest minute may be found as follows from the Nautical Almanac.

G. C. T. of transit, Jan. 1,	6^h	40^m	00^s	
Corr. for Jan. 15,	−	55	00	(N. A. p. 213)
G. C. T. of transit,	5	45	00	
Corr. for Long. $4^h.5$ W.,	−		44 .4	(N. A. Corr. for Lo. tab., p. 2)
L. C. T. of transit,	5	44	15 .6	
Long., W.,	4	30	00 .0	
G. C. T. of local transit,	10	14	15 .6	
Chron. error (rev.),	−	1	06 .0	
Chron. at local transit,	10	13	09 .6	
C−W.,	− 3	59	00 .0	
Watch time, of transit,	6	14	09 .6	

Finding latitude.—From the observed altitude deduce the true altitude, and thence the true zenith distance. Mark the zenith distance north if the zenith is north of the body when on the meridian, south if the zenith is south of the body.

Take out the declination of the body from the Nautical Almanac for the time of meridian passage, having regard for its proper sign or name.

The algebraic sum of the declination and zenith distance will be the latitude. Therefore, add together the zenith distance and the declination if they are of the same name, but take their difference if of opposite names; this sum or difference will be the latitude, which will be of the same name as the greater.

If the altitude of a celestial body is observed when the body is exactly on the meridian, the latitude obtained is accurate because the sight obtained is independent of any error in the dead reckoning position and any error in time will affect only slightly the value of the declination used. For practical purposes, work all observations for latitude to the nearest tenth of a minute of arc.

Example.—At sea, June 21, 1937, in Long. 60° W., the observed meridian altitude of the sun's lower limb was 40° 04′; sun bearing south; I. C., +3′.0· height of the eye, 20 feet· required the latitude.

h_s,	40° 04′.0	(Tab. 40),	+15′.0	Dec. 16^h, 23° 26′.8 N.	G. A. T.,	16^h 00^m
Corr., +	13 .4	Add. corr.,	− 0 .2		Eq. t.,	01
		H. E.,	− 4 .4			
h_o	40 17 .4	I. C.,	+ 3 .0		G. C. T.,	16^h 01^m
z,	49° 42′.6 N.	Corr.,	+13 .4			
d,	23 26 .8 N.					
L,	73 09 .4 N.					

Example.—At sea, April 14, 1937, in Long. 140° E., the observed meridian altitude of the sun's lower limb was 81° 15′.5; sun bearing north; I. C., −2′.5; height of the eye, 20 feet; find latitude.

h_s,	81° 15′.5	(Tab. 40),	+15′.8	Long. 140° E.=9^h 20^m.		L. A. noon,	12^h 00^m
Corr., +	8′.9	Add. corr.,	0 .0	Dec. 2^h,	9° 12′.5 N.	Long., E.,	9^h 20^m
		H. E.,	− 4 .4				
h_o,	81° 24′.4	I. C.,	− 2 .5	H. D., +	0′.9	G. A. T.,	2^h 40^m.0
				G. C. T.,	0^h.7	Eq. t., +	.5
z,	8° 35′.6 S.	Corr.,	+ 8 .9				
d,	9 13 .1 N.			Corr., +	.6	G. C. T.,	2 40 .5
							= 2^h.7
L,	0 37 .5 N.			Dec.,	9° 13′.1 N.		

Example.—At sea, May 15, 1937, in Long. 0°, the observed meridian altitude of the sun's lower limb was 30° 13′.2; sun bearing north; I. C., +1′.5; height of the eye, 15 feet; find latitude.

h_s,	30° 13′.2	(Tab. 40),	+14′.4	G. A. T. noon,	12^h 00^m
Corr., +	12 .0	Add. corr.,	− .1	Eq. t., −	4
		H. E.,	− 3 .8		
h_o,	30 25 .2	I. C.,	+ 1 .5	G. C. T.,	11^h 56^m=11^h.9
				Dec. 10^h,	18° 48′. 8 N.
z,	59° 34′.8 S.	Corr.,	+12 .0		
d,	18 49 .9 N.			H. D.,	0′.6
				G. C. T..	1^h.9
L,	40 44 .9 S.				
				Corr., +	1′.1
				Dec.,	18° 49′.9 N.

Example.—January 1, 1937, the observed meridian altitude of the star Sirius bearing south was 53° 23′.7; I. C.,+1′.0; height of eye, 30 feet; find latitude.

h_s,	53° 23′.7	(Tab. 40),	−0′.7	Dec. Sirius, 16° 37′.8 S.
Corr., −	5 .1	H. E.,	−5 .4	
		I. C.,	+1 .0	
h_o,	53 18 .6			
		Corr.,	−5 .1	
z,	36° 41′.4 N.			
d,	16 37 .8 S.			
L,	20 03 .6 N.			

Example.—June 13, 1937, in Long. 65° W., in a high northern latitude, the meridian altitude of the sun's lower limb was 8° 16′.2 below the pole; height of eye, 20 feet; I. C., 0′.0; find latitude.

h_s,	8° 16′.2	(Tab. 40),	+9′.8	Long. 65° W=4^h 20^m			
Corr., +	5 .2	Add., corr.	−0 .2	G. A. T. of lower culmination, 4^h 20^m;			
		H. E.,	−4 .4	Eq. t.−15^s			
h_o,	8 21 .4			Approx. G. C. T. 4^h.3			
		Corr.,	+5 .2			H. D.,	0′.1
z,	81° 38 .6 S.			Dec. 4^h,	23° 11′.3 N.	G. C. T.,	0^h.3
180°−d,	156 48 .7 N.						
				p,	66° 48′.7	Corr.,	0′.03
Lat.,	75 10 .1 N.			180°−d,	156° 48′.7		

Alternative method

h,	8° 21′.4
p,	66 48 .7
Lat.,	75 10 .1 N.

Example.—July 17, 1937, in Long. 80° W., the observed meridian altitude of the moon's upper limb bearing north was 59° 06′.7; I. C.+2′.0; height of eye, 19 feet; find the latitude.

h_s,	59° 06′.7	H. P., 54′.2		G. C. T. of Gr. transit,	19^h 32^m	Long. 80° W=5^h.33	
I. C., +	2 .0	Dec. 18^d, 1^h,	20° 32′.2 S.	Corr. for Long., +	11	Var. per hr.,	2^m
		Corr. 3^m,	.2				
	59 08 .7			L. C. T. of local transit,	19 43	Corr.,	10^m.66
Corr., +	8 .2	Dec.,	20° 32′.4 S.	Long. W.,	5 20		
h_o,	59 16 .9	(Tab. 41),	+12′.5	G. C. T. local transit,	1^h 03^m July 18.		
		H. E.,	− 4 .3				
z,	30 43 .1 S.						
d,	20 32 .4 S.	Corr.,	+ 8 .2				
L,	51 15 .5 S.						

Example.—At sea, October 3, 1937, in Long. 75° E., the observed meridian altitude of Jupiter, bearing south, was 51° 25′.3; height of eye 30 feet; I. C.+3′.0; find latitude.

h_s	51° 25′.3	(Tab. 40),	−0′.8	G. C. T. of Gr. Transit,	18^h 31^m
Corr.,	− 3 .2	H. E.,	−5 .4	Corr. Long. 5^h E.,	+ 1
		I. C.,	+3 .0		
h_o,	51 22 .1			L. C. T. of local transit,	18 32
		Corr.,	−3 .2	Long. E.,	5 00
z,	38 37 .9 N.				
d,	22 40 .5 S.			G. C. T. of local transit,	13 32=13^h.5
Lat.,	15 57 .4 N.				

Dec. 0^h,	22° 40′.8 S.	Diff. 24^h,	0′.5
Corr. 13^h.5,	− 3		
		Corr. 12^h,	.25
Dec.	22 40 .5 S.	Corr. 1^h 32^m,	.03 Page 154 N. A.
		Corr.,	.28

Example.—At sea January 2, 1937, in D. R. Lat. 33° 17′ N.; Long. 45° 17′ W.; the sextant altitude of sun's lower limb bearing south at dip was 33° 35′.5; I. C.−1′.0; height of eye 31 feet; watch 12^h 01^m 01^s; C−W 3^h 03^m 09^s; chron. slow 1^m 05^s; find latitude.

W.,	12^h 01^m 01^s	h_s,	33° 35′.5	(Tab. 40),	+14′.7	Dec. 14^h,	22° 55′.5 S.
C−W.,	3 03 09	Corr., +	8 .6	Add. corr.,	+ 0 .3	Corr. 1^h,	.2
				H. E.,	− 5 .4		
Chron.,	15 04 10	h_o,	33 44 .1	I. C.,	− 1 .0	Dec.,	22 55 .3 S.
C. C. (slow), +	1 05						
		z,	56 15 .9 N.	Corr.,	+ 8 .6	H. D.,	0′.2
G. C. T.,	15 05 15	d,	22 55 .3 S.			G. C. T.,	1^h.1
		Lat.,	33 20 .6 N.			Corr.,	.22

Plotting the above example by intercept, for position line.

D. R. Lat.,	33° 17′.0 N.
Dec.,	22 55 .3 S.
z,	56 12 .3
h_c,	33 47 .7
h_o,	33 44 .1
Int.,	3 .6 away from 180°

From D. R. Lat. 33° 17′ N; Long. 45° 17′ W., 3.6 miles away from sun on azimuth 180° draw position line perpendicular to the azimuth.

Constant.—In working the meridian altitude for latitude it is convenient to arrange the terms beforehand so that the computation is completed with the exception of applying the constant to the observed altitude, which gives at once the latitude. It is assumed that the noon longitude by dead reckoning is accurately enough known to correct the declination, also the approximate meridian altitude for its correction; if the latter is not known, it may readily be found from the declination and approximate latitude.

Generally speaking,

$$\begin{aligned} \text{Lat.} &= \text{Zenith distance} + \text{Dec.}, \\ &= 90° - \text{True Alt.} + \text{Dec.}, \\ &= 90° - (\text{Obs. alt.} + \text{Corr.}) + \text{Dec.}, \\ &= (90° + \text{Dec.} - \text{Corr.}) - \text{Obs. alt.}, \end{aligned}$$

in which the quantity (90° + Dec. − Corr.) may be termed a *constant* (K) for the meridian altitude of the day, as it remains the same regardless of what the observed altitude may prove to be. The constant having been worked up before the observation is made, the latitude will be known as soon as the observed altitude is applied.

To avoid the confusion that might arise from the necessity of combining the terms *algebraically* according to their different names it may be convenient to divide the problem into four cases and lay down rules for the *arithmetical* combination of the terms disregarding their respective names as follows:

Case I. Lat. and Dec. same name, Lat. greater, ±90°+Dec.−Corr.−Obs. alt.
Case II. Lat. and Dec. same name, Dec. greater, −90°+Dec.+Corr.+Obs. alt.
Case III. Lat. and Dec. opposite names, +90°−Dec.−Corr.−Obs. alt.
Case IV. Lat. and Dec. same name, lower transit, +90°−Dec.+Corr.+Obs. alt.

The correctness of such an arrangement will become readily apparent from an inspection of figure 70. The assumption has been made that the correction to the observed altitude is positive; when this is not true the sign of the correction must be reversed.

As examples of this method, the first, second, fourth, and fifth of the examples previously given illustrating the meridian altitude will be worked, using the constant; the details by which Corr. and Dec. are obtained are omitted, being the same as in the originals.

1st Example		2d Example		4th Example		5th Example	
	Case I		*Case II*		*Case III*		*Case IV*
	+ 90° 00′.0		−90° 00′.0		+90° 00′.0		+90° 00′.0
Dec.,	+ 23 26 .8	Dec.,	+ 9 13 .1	Dec.,	−16 37 .8	Dec.,	−23 11 .3
Corr.,	− 13 .4	Corr.,	+ 8 .9	Corr.,	+ 5 .1	Corr.,	+ 5 .2
Constant,	+113 13 .4	Constant,	−80 38 .0	Constant,	+73 27 .3	Constant,	+66 53 .9
h_s,	− 40 04 .0	h_s,	+81 15 .5	h_s,	−53 23 .7	h_s,	+ 8 16 .2
Lat.,	73 09 .4 (N.)	Lat.,	0 37 .5 (N.)	Lat.,	20 03 .6 (N.)	Lat.,	75 10 .1 (N.)

REDUCTION TO THE MERIDIAN

Should the meridian altitude be lost, owing to clouds or for other reason, altitudes may be taken near the meridian and the times noted by a watch compared with the chronometer, from which, knowing the longitude, the hour angle may be deduced.

If the observations are within 28^m from the meridian, before or after, the correction to be applied to the observed altitude to reduce it to the meridian altitude may be found by inspection of Tables 29 and 30. Table 29 contains the variation of the altitude for one minute from the meridian, expressed in seconds and tenths of a second. Table 30 contains the product obtained by multiplying the square of the minutes and seconds by the change of altitude in one minute.

Let a=change of altitude (in seconds of arc) in one minute from the meridian:
H=meridian altitude;
h_o=corrected altitude at observation; and
t=interval from meridian passage.

The value of the "reduction to the meridian" altitude for any observed ex-meridian altitude is found by the formula:

$$H=h_o+at^2,$$

a being found in Table 29, and at^2 in Table 30; hence the following rule:

Find the hour angle of the body in minutes and seconds of time or find the value in arc. Take from Table 29 the value of a corresponding to the declination and the latitude. Take from Table 30 the value of at^2 corresponding to the a thus found and to the interval in minutes and seconds of time, or in arc, from meridian passage. This quantity will represent the amount in minutes and tenths of arc necessary to reduce the corrected altitude at the time of observation to the corrected altitude at the meridian passage; *it is always additive when the body is near upper transit,* and *always subtractive when near lower transit.*

Table 29 includes values of the latitude up to 60°, and those of the declination up to 63°, thus taking in all frequented waters of the globe and all celestial bodies that the navigator is likely to employ. No values of a are given when the altitudes are above 86° or below 6°, as the method of reduction to the meridian is not accurate when the body transits very near the zenith, and the altitudes are questionable when very low. In case it is desired to find the change of altitude in one minute from noon for conditions not given in the tables, it may be computed by the formula:

$$a = \frac{1''.9635 \cos L \cos d}{\sin (L \sim d)}$$

Due regard must be paid to the names of the declination and latitude in working this formula; if they are of opposite names, then L and d are added together to obtain $L \sim d$.

Table 30 contains values of at^2 up to the limits within which the method is considered to apply with a fair degree of accuracy. When beyond the limit of the table, it would seem preferable to employ any altitude and azimuth formula, described hereafter, and then lay down a regular line of position.

When employing the method of reduction to the meridian the resulting latitude is that of the vessel at the instant of observation, and to bring it up to noon the run must be applied. The declination should properly be corrected for the instant of observation; with the sun or a planet, it is sufficiently accurate to use the declination at meridian passage, unless the interval from the meridian be quite large; but the moon's declination changes so rapidly that the exact time of observation must be used in its correction when working with this body.

Example.—In D. R Lat. 47° S., having previously worked up the constant for meridian altitude, 78° 42′.2, observed altitude of sun near meridian, 31° 11′ 50″; Dec. 11° N.; watch time $11^h\ 40^m\ 21^s$, watch fast of L. A. T., 07^s; find the latitude.

Watch time,	$11^h\ 40^m\ 21^s$	h_s,	31° 11′.8	a (Tab. 29),	1″.6
Watch fast,	− 07	at^2,	+ 10 .4		
L. A. T.,	11 40 14	Mer. alt.,	31 22 .2	at^2 (Tab. 30),	1″.0 = 6′.5
		Constant,	78 42 .2		.6 = 3 .9
t,	$0^h\ 19^m\ 46^s$ E.				
or Arc.,	4° 56′.5	Lat.,	47 20 .0 S.		1 .6 = 10 .4

Example.—At sea, July 12, 1937, in D. R. Lat. 50° N., Long. 40° W., observed circummeridian altitude of the sun's lower limb, 61° 48′ 30″, chronometer $2^h\ 41^m\ 39^s$; chro. corr., $-2^m\ 26.3^s$, I. C., −3′ 0″; height of the eye, 15 feet. Find the latitude.

Chron.,	$2^h\ 41^m\ 39^s$	h_s,	61° 48′.5	Dec. 14^h,	21° 59′.3 N.
Corr.,	− 2 26 .3	Corr.,	+ 8 .5		
				H. D.,	− 0′.3
G. C. T.,	14 39 12 .7	h_o,	61 57 .0	G. C. T. Int.,	$0^h.65$
G. H. A., 14^h	28° 38′.5	(Tab. 40),	+ 15′.5	Corr.,	− 0′.19
Corr., 39^m	9 45 .0	Add. corr.,	− 0 .2		
Corr., $12^s.7$,	3 .2	H. E.	− 3 .8	Dec.,	21° 59′.1 N.
		I. C.,	− 3 .0		
G. H. A.,	38 26 .7 W.				
Long.,	40 00 .0 W.	Corr.,	+ 8 .5		
L. H. A. (t),	1 33 .3 E.				

h_o,	61° 57′.0	a (Tab. 29),	2″.5
at^2, +	1 .6	at^2 (Tab. 30),	2″.0 = 1′.3
H,	61 58 .6		0 .5 = 0 .3
z,	28 01 .4 N.		2 .5 = 1 .6
d,	21 59 .1 N.		
L,	50 00 .5 N.		

The method of reduction to the meridian is not used so much nowadays, since in a uniform process for the solution of any sight, regardless of the celestial body's position with relation to the meridian, it is better to solve in this case also for a line of position. (See page 177.)

Example.—At sea July 1, 1937, p. m. in D. R. Lat. 2° 00′.0 N.; Long. 99° 19′ W.; the sextant altitude of the star β Crucis bearing southward near the meridian was 28° 46′.0; I. C. +1′.0; height of eye 30 ft.; watch $6^h\ 00^m\ 30^s$; C−W $6^h\ 59^m\ 30^s$; chron. fast $6^m\ 15^s$; find latitude by reduction to the meridian.

W,	$6^h\ 00^m\ 30^s$	h_s,	28° 46′.0	(Tab. 40),	−1′.8	Dec.✳	59° 21′.2 S.
C−W,	6 59 30	Corr.,	−6 .2	H. E.,	−5 .4		
				I. C.,	+1 .0		
Chron.,	1 00 00	h_o,	28 39 .8				
Fast,	−6 15	at^2,	+2 .4	Corr.,	−6 .2		
G. C. T.,	0 53 45 (2 July)	H,	28 42 .2				
G. H. A. 0^h,	88° 35′.6	z,	61 17 .8 N.				
Corr., 53^m,	13 17 .2	d,	59 21 .2 S.				
Corr. 45^s,	11 .3						
		Lat.,	1 56 .6 N.				
G. H. A.,	102 04 .1 W.						
Long.,	99 19 .0 W.						
L. H. A.,	2 45 .1 W.						

$a=1''.2$ (Tab. 29).
$at^2=2'.4$ (Tab. 30).

Diagram—Advantages are gained in working out **meridian altitudes** and **reductions to the meridian,** in finding the *constant* (k) for a meridian altitude or a reduction to the meridian, and in predicting the approximate altitude of a body to be observed on or near the meridian, by projecting, in a quickly and roughly drawn diagram on the plane of the meridian of the observer, the known data entering into the problem. The diagram or figure will show at once how to combine the data to find the required result, and its use tends greatly to accuracy. It is only necessary to know the meaning of the terms already defined and to remember the single principle **that the latitude of a place is equal to the declination of its zenith.**

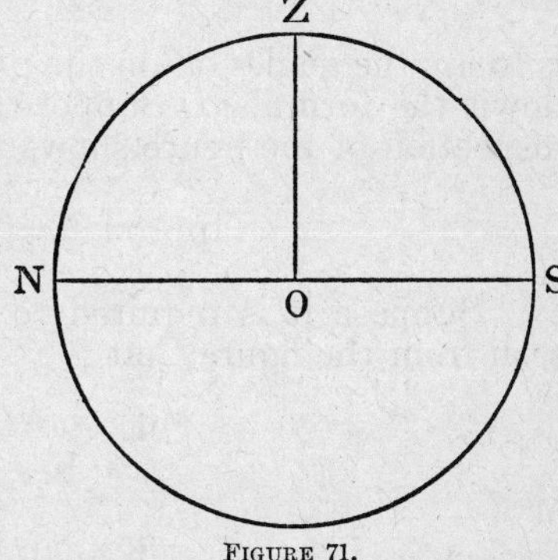

FIGURE 71.

In every case draw a circle (a rough approximation will do) *to represent the plane of the meridian,* as in figure 71. The center O is the position of the observer. Draw a horizontal line through O, marking its intersection with the circumference on the right-hand side S and on the left-hand side N. Erect a perpendicular to this line at O and mark its intersection with the circumference Z. The line NS is the horizon; Z is the zenith. The arc ZS is that portion of the meridian between the zenith and the south point of the horizon; the arc ZN is that portion of the meridian between the zenith and the north point of the horizon. If the meridian altitude of a body is known (i. e., its altitude above the horizon on the meridian), and if it is known whether it bears to the southward or to the northward, its position can be projected at once on the figure. Having the position of the heavenly body on the meridian and knowing the declination of the body, it is evident where to draw in the projection of the equator. Having the projection of the equator, the angular distance between the equator and the zenith (i. e., the declination of the zenith) is the latitude.

Thus in figure 72, supposing the meridian altitude of any celestial body, M, has been observed, and that at the time of observation it was bearing south; also that the declination, *d*, of the body was south. It is known that the true altitude, h, = observed altitude ± altitude corr. Since the body bears south, if the true altitude is h, the position of the body, M, can be located by laying off the arc SM=h, or by drawing OM so that the angle SOM=h. This gives the position of the celestial body on the meridian. Since this body is south of the equator by the amount of the declination, the position of the equator may be drawn by laying off the angle MOQ=d. OQ is the projection of the equator, and the arc ZQ (or the angle ZOQ), being the **declination of the zenith** is equal to the latitude. The formula for finding the latitude may be written by inspection of the figure:

$$L=90°-(h+d)=90°-h-d. \tag{1}$$

Since h=obs. alt. ± corr.,

$$L=90°-\text{obs. alt.}\pm\text{corr.}-d. \tag{2}$$

By a similar process formulas may be written for determining the *approximate altitude* of the celestial body when on the meridian and for getting a noon *constant* (K). The former is necessary to get the altitude correction before taking the sight; the latter, so that the latitude may be obtained as soon as the altitude is read from the sextant. In these cases the D. R. latitude and longitude, which have to be worked out in advance for noon, are used. The longitude is used to get the correction to be applied to the equation of time to get the G. C. T. of local apparent noon in order to get the correct declination at local apparent noon at the noon position. Knowing the approximate latitude and the declination, they are projected on the figure in this way. If the latitude is north, the zenith is to the northward of the equator by the amount of the latitude, and to get the position of the equator lay off the angle ZOQ=Lat. If the latitude were south, the equator would of course be on the north side of the zenith by the amount of the latitude, and OQ would be on the north side of the circle. Having the position of the equator, draw in the position of the celestial body by laying it off to the north side or to the south side of the equator according to the amount and direction of its declination. The angle between the horizon and the celestial body will be the altitude of the body. This is the usual method of plotting, and all that has to be done is to lay the angles off on the proper sides, marking them appropriately, and then write down the formulas. Suppose it is required to find the approximate noon altitude. An inspection of the figure shows that

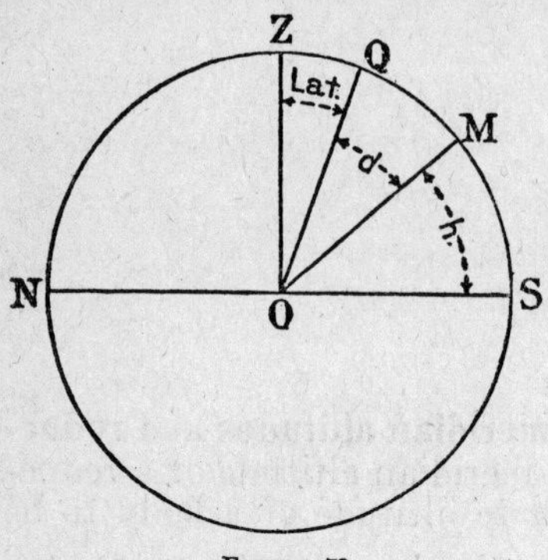

FIGURE 72.

$$\text{approx. } h = 90° - (L + d), \text{ where L is the D. R. Lat.} \quad (3)$$

Suppose it is required to find the constant (K) for a meridian altitude. It is seen from the figure that

$$L = 90° - h - d = 90° - \text{obs. alt.} \pm \text{corr.} - d$$
$$= K - \text{obs. alt. } (h_s)$$

or

$$K = 90° \pm \text{corr.} - d. \quad (4)$$

In the same way any combination may be plotted, and the correct formulas may be written out at once. Suppose on a certain day it is found that at noon the position will be approximately Lat. 10° S., Long. 30° 15′ W., and that the declination of the sun at noon, corrected for G. C. T. of local apparent noon at the noon position, is 20° 30′ .0 S., and it is desired to find the approximate noon altitude and obtain the constant K. Draw the circle representing the plane of the meridian (see fig. 73), draw NS representing the horizon, and OZ representing the line to the zenith. Since the approximate latitude is 10° S, the equator must be 10° north of the zenith, and OQ is drawn to the north of Z so that the angle ZOQ=10°. OQ is then the projection of the equator. The body being 20° 30′ south of the equator, lay off OM so that the angle QOM=20° 30′. SOM will be the approximate altitude, and the formula for it is

$$\text{approx. } h = 90° + L - d, \quad (5)$$

it is also seen that

$$L = h + d - 90° = \text{obs. alt.} \pm \text{corr.} + d - 90° = K + \text{obs. alt.}$$

or

$$K = \pm \text{corr.} + d - 90°.$$

If, instead of the formulas for a meridian altitude, the formulas for a reduction to the meridian are required, there is no change in the figure or the method. The altitude observed before or after noon is corrected to make it the noon altitude by the formula $h = h' + at^2$, where h is the noon altitude, h' the altitude observed t minutes before or after noon, and a the rate of change of altitude near noon. So that in the case shown in figure 73

$$L=h+d-90°=h'+at^2+d-90°$$

$$=\text{obs. alt.}\pm\text{corr.}+at^2+d-90°$$

$$=K+\text{obs. alt.}(h_s) \qquad (6)$$

or

$$K=\pm\text{corr.}+at^2+d-90°.$$

The formula for the approximate value of h, as shown in (5), is used for getting the altitude correction in this case, as the slight difference in altitude makes no change in the correction.

The formula for latitude, given in equation (6), is the formula for the latitude at noon at the point where the observation was taken. But a vessel steaming on a course does not remain at that point, and what is desired is the correct latitude of the vessel's position at noon. If L′ represents the latitude of the place where the observation was taken and L the latitude of the place where the vessel is at noon, then $L=L'\pm\triangle L$, where $\triangle L$ is the change in latitude from the time of observation until noon. This is taken from the traverse tables. But from equation (6) it is seen that $L'=\text{obs. alt.}\pm\text{corr.}+at^2+d-90°$

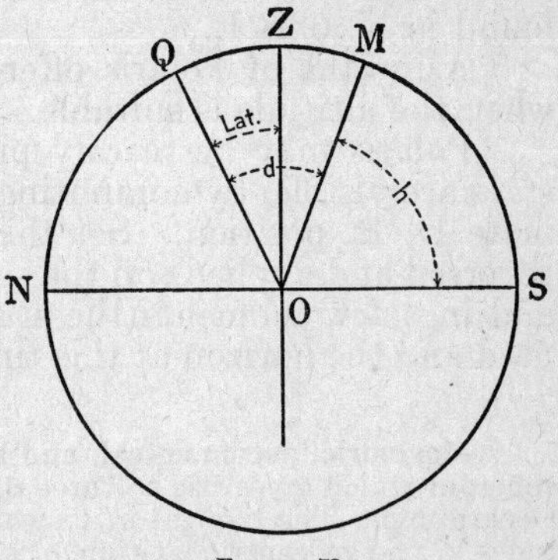

FIGURE 73.

$$\therefore L=L'\pm\triangle L=\text{obs. alt.}\pm\text{corr.}+at^2+d-90°\pm\triangle L.$$

$$=K+\text{obs. alt.}$$

or

$$K=\pm\text{corr.}+at^2+d-90°\pm\triangle L.$$

Polaris method.—This method, confined to northern latitudes, is available when the star Polaris and the horizon are distinctly visible, the time of the observation being noted at the moment the altitude is measured. The altitude of pole=Latitude of place.

Reduce the observed altitude of Polaris to the true altitude.

Reduce the time of observation to the local sidereal time.

With this sidereal time take out the correction from Table I (Nautical Almanac), and add it to or subtract it from the true altitude, according to its sign. The result is the approximate latitude of the place.

Example.—June 10, 1937, at about 22^h 30^m (10^h 30^m p. m.), local civil time, when the Greenwich civil time is June 11, 3^h 36^m 30^s, in longitude 74° west of Greenwich, suppose the true altitude of Polaris to be 39°46′, required the latitude of the place.

		h	m	s
G. C. T., June 11		3	36	30
R. A. M. S.+12^h		17	15	40
Reduction (Table 39) for G. C. T	+		0	36
G. S. T		20	52	46
Longitude, 74° W		4	56	00
L. S. T		15	56	46
			°	′
True altitude			39	46.0
Corr. (Table I, Nautical Almanac)	+		0	51.6
Latitude			40	37.6N.

Alternative method.—The above example may also be worked by finding the Greenwich hour angle of Polaris in the Nautical Almanac for the proper G. C. T. then using the hour angle as an argument and entering Table III (N. A.), take out the correction to be applied to the true altitude to give latitude.

By entering Table IV (N. A.) with the same argument of hour angle and also with the latitude, the azimuth may be obtained.

G. H. A. for 0^h, G. C. T. June 11,	233° 44′.3 W.	(N. A. page 261.)
Corr. for $3^h\ 36^m\ 30^s$	54 16 .4	
G. H. A.,	288 00 .7 W.	
Long.,	74 00 .0 W.	
L. H. A.,	214 00 .7 W.	
True altitude,	39° 46′.0	
Corr. L. H. A. (Tab. III, N. A.) +	51 .4	
Lat.,	40 37 .4 N.	

With L. H. A. 214° and Lat. 40°.6 as arguments in Tab. IV (N. A.) the azimuth found is N. 0°.8 E.

Azimuths of Polaris offer a ready means of checking the error of the compass when the altitude is suitable.

Polaris may be readily picked up in the sextant glass at twilight, before other stars are visible, by computing beforehand the altitude of the star from the approximate D. R. position. Set this altitude (with the sign of correction from Table 40 reversed and applied) on the sextant, then look toward the north point of the horizon, and in a few moments the star will be seen in the telescope. No shade glasses are used and the horizon at this time is often very clear and distinct.

Geocentric, astronomical, and geographic latitudes.—The shape of the earth is that of an oblate spheroid which gives rise to three different kinds of latitude namely, Geocentric, Astronomical, and Geographic. The navigator, in working sights for latitude, is interested only in geographical latitudes. The geocentric latitude of a place is the angle subtended at the center of the earth, between the plane of the equator and the radius of the earth, which passes through the place. The astronomical latitude is the angle between the plumb line, or line of action of gravity at the observer's station and the plane of the equator. It is measured on the celestial sphere, along the meridian from the equator to the zenith. Suppose an observer is at a point O (fig. 73a) which is a meridian section of the earth, with the oblateness exaggerated, the geocentric latitude is the angle OCQ. If a plumb line is continued downward to the equator to point A, then angle OAQ is the astronomical latitude. From figure 73a, the astronomical latitude is noted to be greater than the geocentric,

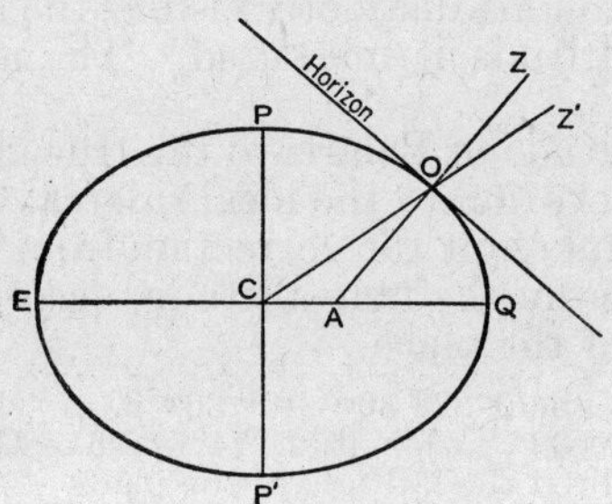

FIGURE 73A.

because $\angle OAQ$ is equal to $\angle OCQ + \angle COA$, except when the observer is at the pole or the equator, when the two kinds of latitude become equal. The greatest difference between them anywhere on the earth is only about 11′ (in lat. 45°). The direction of the plumb line in many places is often affected also by the gravitational pull of the mass in high mountains in the vicinity, or by the density of rock below the surface, but the deflection of the vertical is never more than a few seconds of arc. After the astronomical latitude is corrected for these local irregularities, it is then called the geographical latitude. For all practical purposes of navigation astronomical and geographical latitude is the same. It is geographical latitude that is always determined at sea. Charts and maps are graduated and corrected for geographical latitude. Geocentric latitude is not used. The adoption of geographic latitude makes unnecessary any further consideration of the ellipticity of the earth's meridian in astronomical work at sea. However, when working with geographical latitude, it is much more simple to assume that the zenith direction passes through the center of the earth.

CHAPTER XII

LONGITUDE

The **longitude** of a position on the earth's surface is measured by the arc of the equator intercepted between the Greenwich, or prime meridian, and the meridian passing through the place, or it is the difference between the hour angle of a celestial body from the Greenwich meridian and its hour angle at the same instant from the local meridian. Longitude at sea is determined by means of chronometers corrected for error by frequent radio time signals, and the sextant.

Time sight.—The method used for finding longitude at sea is that of the "time sight." The altitude of the body above the sea horizon is measured with a sextant and the chronometer time noted. The problem consists in finding the hour angle from given values of altitude, latitude, and polar distance. Of the three elements, altitude, declination, and latitude used in the solution of the astronomical triangle, the only uncertain element is the latitude. Results are most accurate when the body is on or near the prime vertical, as then an error in latitude has the least effect.

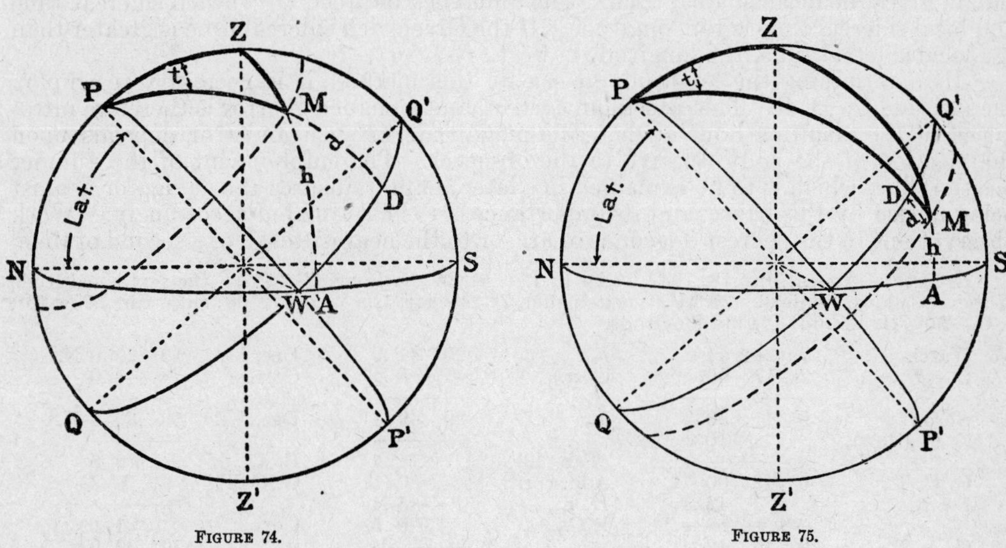

FIGURE 74. FIGURE 75.

In figures 74 and 75 are given:

AM$=h$, the altitude of the body M;
DM$=d$, the declination; and
Q′Z=L, the latitude of the place.

In the astronomical triangle PMZ there may be found from the foregoing:

ZM$=z$, the zenith distance of the body,$=90°-h$;
PM$=p$, the polar distance,$=90°\pm d$; and
PZ=co. L, the co-latitude of the place,$=90°-$L.

From these data it is required to find the angle MPZ, the hour angle of the body,$=t$. This is given by the formula:

$$\sin^2 \tfrac{1}{2}\, t=\frac{\cos \frac{1}{2}\,(h+L+p) \sin \frac{1}{2}\,(L+p-h)}{\cos L \sin p}.$$

If $s=\frac{1}{2}(h+L+p)$, this becomes:

$$\sin^2 \tfrac{1}{2} t = \sec L \operatorname{cosec} p \cos s \sin (s-h).$$

Since $\sin^2 \frac{1}{2} t = \frac{1-\cos t}{2} = \text{haversine } t$, then:

$$\text{hav } t = \sec L \operatorname{cosec} p \cos s \sin (s-h).$$

The polar distance is obtained by adding the declination to 90° when of different name from the latitude, and subtracting it from 90° when of the same name. Like latitude and altitude, it is always positive.

If the sun is the body observed, the resulting hour angle is expressed as local apparent time either a. m. or p. m. according as the altitude is observed in the forenoon or afternoon, or it is expressed in arc. For any other celestial body the local hour angle found may be an angle either east or west of the meridian according as the body is rising or setting. The value of the hour angle is taken from the haversine table (Tab. 34) either in time or arc. The difference between the Greenwich apparent time as deduced from the watch time and the local apparent time as deduced from the sun observation, is the longitude; or the difference between the Greenwich hour angle in arc, as taken from the Nautical Almanac for the G. C. T., and the deduced local hour angle in arc, is also the longitude.

The hour angle of a star, a planet, or the moon, added to its right ascension when west of the meridian at observation, or subtracted therefrom when east of the meridian, gives the local sidereal time. The difference between Greenwich sidereal time and local sidereal time is the longitude. If the Greenwich sidereal time is greater than the local sidereal time, the longitude is west.

In determining the longitude at sea by this method, it is necessary to employ the latitude by D. R. This is seldom correct, and a chance of error is therefore introduced in the resulting hour angle. The magnitude of such an error depends upon the position of the body relative to the observer. The employment of the Sumner position line, which is to be explained in a later chapter, insures the navigator against being misled by this cause, and its importance is to be estimated accordingly. Work observations to the nearest 6 seconds of arc, or to the nearest tenth of a second of time.

Example.—At sea May 18, 1937, in D. R. Lat. 41°34′ N. Long. 33°27′ W. the sextant altitude of the sun's lower limb was 29°41′.0; watch time $7^h\ 24^m\ 44^s$; C—W $2^h\ 17^m\ 06^s$ chro. corr. slow 10^s; I. C.—30″; H. E. 30 ft. Find longitude.

Watch,	$7^h\ 24^m\ 44^s$	h_s,	29° 41′.0	Dec. 8^h,	19° 29′.0 N.
C.—W.,	2 17 06	Corr.,	+8 .4	Corr.,	+1 .0
Chro.,	9 41 50	h_o,	29 49 .4	Dec.,	19 30 .0 N.
C. C. (slow),	+10				
		(Tab. 40),	+14′.4	H. D.,	+0′.6
G. C. T.,	9 42 00	Add. corr.,	−0 .1	G. C. T.,	$1^h.7$
Eq. t.,	+3 42 .4	H. E.,	−5 .4		
		I. C.,	−0 .5	Corr.,	1 .0
G. A. T.,	9 45 42 .4			p,	=70° 30′.0
		Corr.,	+8 .4		

h,	29° 49′ 24″		
L,	41 34 00	sec,	0.12599
p,	70 30 00	cosec,	0.02565
	2)141 53 24		
s,	70 56 42	cos,	9.51386
$s-h$,	41 07 18	sin,	9.81800
L. H. A.,	$4^h\ 27^m\ 54^s.2$ E.	hav. t.,	9.48350
L. A. T.,	7 32 05 .8		
G. A. T.,	9 45 42 .4		
Long.,	2 13 36 .6 W.		
or,	33° 24′.2 W.		

Eq. t., 8^h=	$+3^m\ 42.5^s$
Corr.,	−.1
Eq. t., =	$+3^m\ 42.4^s$

This example may be worked by taking directly the G. H. A. from the Nautical Almanac as follows:

G. C. T.,	$9^h\ 42^m\ 00^s$
G. H. A. 8^h,	300° 55′.6
Corr. $1^h\ 42^m$,	25 30 .0
G. H. A.,	326 25 .6 W.

From the above computation hav. t=9.48350, then the value of the local hour angle in arc is 66° 58′.5 E., there is then obtained,

G. H. A.,	326° 25′.6 W.
L. H. A.,	66 58 .5 E.
	393 24 .1 W.
(Subtract)	360°
Long.,	33° 24′.1 W.

Example.—At sea April 16, 1937, p. m. in Lat. 11° 47′ S; Long. 0° 50′ E, by D. R. the observed altitude of the star Aldebaran west of the meridian was 23° 13′ 20″; chron. $6^h\ 58^m\ 29^s$; chron. fast $2^m\ 27^s$; I. C. −2′; height eye 26 feet; find longitude.

Chron.,	$6^h\ 58^m\ 29^s$	h_s,	23° 13′.3	R. A.✳	$4^h\ 32^m\ 19^s.2$
C. C. (fast),	− 2 27	Corr.,	− 9 .3	Dec.✳	16° 23′.0 N.
				p,	106° 23′.0
G. C. T.,	18 56 02	h_o,	23 04 .0		
R. A. M. S.+12^h,	13 34 52.6				
Corr. G. C. T. (Tab. 39),	3 06.6	(Tab. 40),	− 2′.3		
		H. E.,	− 5 .0		
G. S. T.,	8 34 01.2	I. C.,	− 2 .0		
R. A.✳,	4 32 19.2				
		Corr.,	− 9 .3		
G. H. A.,	4 01 42.0 W.				

h,	23° 04′ 00″		
L,	11 47 00	sec,	0.00925
p,	106 23 00	cosec.,	0.01800
	2) 141 14 00		
s,	70 37 00	cos,	9.52099
$s-h$,	47 33 00	sin,	9.86798
L. H. A.,	$4^h\ 05^m\ 39^s$ W.	hav. t.,	9.41622
G. H. A.,	4 01 42 W.		
Long.,	0 03 57 E.		
or,	0° 59′.3 E.		

or the G. H. A. may be taken directly from the Nautical Almanac under the star Aldebaran for April 16, as follows:

G. C. T.,	$18^h\ 56^m\ 02^s$
G. H. A., Apr. 16,	135° 38′.3
Corr. $18^h\ 56^m$,	284 46 .6
Corr. 2^s,	.5
G. H. A.,	60° 25 .4 W.
L. H. A.,	61 24 .8 W.
Long.,	0 59 .4 E.

From the above computation, hav. t.=9.41622, then the value of the local hour angle in arc is 61° 24′.8 W.

Example.—December 11, 1937, in D. R. position Lat. 35° 00′ N.; Long. 140° 12′ W., about $5^h 45^m$ p. m., observed the planet Jupiter bearing southwestward, altitude 26° 28′ 40″, I. C. +1′ 30″; height eye 36 ft.; watch $5^h 48^m 03^s$; C−W, $8^h 20^m 45^s$; chron. slow $0^m 02^s$. Find longitude.

W. T.,		5^h 48^m 03^s	
C−W.,		8 20 45	
Chron.,		2 08 48	
Corr. (slow),	+	02	
G. C. T. Dec. 12,		2 08 50	
G. H. A. Dec. 12,		139° 48′.4	
Corr. 2^h,		30 03 .8	
Corr. 8^m,		2 00 .2	
Corr. 50^s,		12 .5	
G. H. A.,		172 04 .9	W.

Var. per min. 15′.0319	
For 15′.03, 2^h,	30° 03′.6
Corr. .0019,	.2
Corr. 2^h,	30 03 .8

Dec. Dec. 12,		20° 59′.8 S.	Diff. 24^h=2′.5
Corr.,	−	.2	Prop. Pts., .2
Dec.,		20 59 .6	

For 2^h	
15:03	=30° 03′.6
15:04	=30 04 .8
Diff. =	1′.2

For 15.0319=.19×1.2=.22

h_s,		26° 28′.7
Corr.,	−	6 .3
h_o,		26 22 .4
Tab. 40,	−	1′.9
H. E.,	−	5 .9
I. C.,	+	1 .5
Corr.,	−	6 .3

h,	26°	22′	24″		
L,	35	00	00	sec.,	0.08664
p,	110	59	36	cosec.,	0.02983
	2)172	22	00		
s,	86	11	00	cos.,	8.82324
s−*h*,	59	48	36	sin.,	9.93669
L. H. A.,	31°	50′.3 W.		hav. t.,	8.87640
G. H. A.,	172	04 .9 W.			
Long.,	140	14 .6 W.			

Alternative method for the above example,

h_o,	26° 22′	24″			
z,	63 37	36	nat. hav.,	27789	(subtract.)
(L∼*d*),	55° 59′.6		nat. hav.,	22035	
			nat. hav.,	05754	
			log. hav.,	8.75997	
Lat.	35° 00′	00″N.	sec.,	0.08664	
Dec.,	20 59	36 S.	sec.,	0.02983	
L. H. A.,	31° 50′.4 W.		log. hav.,	8.87644	
G. H. A.,	172 04 .9 W.				
Long.,	140 14 .5 W.				

The nat. hav. of (L∼d), the secant of latitude, and the secant of declination, can be looked up before the sextant altitude is taken.

The formula for this alternative method is derived as follows:

On page 182, there is given,

$$\text{hav. } \theta = \cos. \text{ L} \cos. \text{ d hav. t} \quad (1)$$

$$\text{hav. z} = \text{hav. (L} \sim \text{d)} + \text{hav. } \theta \quad (2)$$

from (1) $\text{hav. t} = \text{hav. } \theta \text{ sec. L sec. d}$

from (2) $\text{hav. z} - \text{hav. (L} \sim \text{d)} = \text{hav. } \theta$

The "time sight" to give a longitude is generally used only when the latitude has been accurately determined. When latitude is not accurately known modern navigators prefer to use one of the several short methods to obtain a "line of position." When two or more such "lines of position," resulting from approximately simultaneous observations of as many celestial bodies, are plotted on the chart, they should cross in a point, which at once fixes both the longitude and latitude. This procedure will be explained in a later chapter.

CHAPTER XIII

AZIMUTH

The **azimuth** of a body is the arc of the horizon intercepted between the meridian and the vertical circle passing through the body. Azimuth, in most cases, is measured from 0° to 360°, clockwise from the north. Sometimes it is measured from the north point of the horizon in north latitude and from the south point in south latitude through 180° to the east or west. Thus, if the bearing of a body is NW., its azimuth would be N. 45° W. in north, or S. 135° W. in south latitude. Measured clockwise through 360° this bearing is 315°.

The azimuth of a celestial body is frequently determined at sea. The comparison of the true bearing with a bearing by compass affords the only means of finding the error of the compass, due to variation and deviation.

The Azimuth Tables (H. O. Pub. No. 71) give the azimuth of the sun at rising and setting and can be used for finding the compass error.

The **amplitude** is the arc measured between the position of the body when its true altitude is zero and the east or west point of the horizon. The amplitude is measured from the east point at rising, or from the west point at setting, toward the north or south according as the declination of the observed body is north or south.

Amplitudes are seldom used in modern practice.

The method of obtaining compass error by amplitudes consists in observing the compass bearing of the celestial body when its center is in the true horizon. Since the body can only be referred to the visible horizon and being subject to vertical displacement due to refraction, parallax and dip, an observation taken near the visible horizon requires a small correction. The true amplitude is given in Table 27 and the correction to the observation is given in Table 28. To the observed amplitude, apply the correction at rising in north latitude, or at setting in south latitude to the right, and at setting in north latitude or at rising in south latitude to the left.

Example.—At sea in Lat. 25° 03′ S., the observed bearing of the star Venus in the visible horizon at rising was E. 18° 30′ N., declination 21°.7 N.; find the compass error.

Enter Table 27, with latitude 25° and declination 21°.7 and true amplitude is E. 24°.1 N.; enter Table 28 with the same arguments and the correction to the observation is 0°.3; since the latitude is south and the body rising, the correction is applied to the left.

Obs. amp.,	E. 18°.5 N.
Correction,	.3 (left)
Compass amp.,	E. 18 .8 N.
True amp.,	E. 24 .1 N.
Error,	5 .3 W.

TIME AZIMUTHS

The true azimuth of a celestial body can be computed for any instant of time. This fact is utilized to obtain the compass error by comparing an azimuth observed by compass with the azimuth computed for the time of the observation.

Any celestial body bright enough to be observed with the azimuth circle may be selected, but the conditions are best when the altitude is low. The local hour angle and declination of the body and the observer's latitude are obtained, from which the azimuth is computed. Take a bearing of the body, bisecting the body if its disc is appreciable. Note the watch time of the observation. Find the G. C. T., and then the local hour angle. The declination is taken from the almanac, and the observer's latitude from the chart.

To solve the triangle:

Let $S = \frac{1}{2}$ sum of polar distance and co-lat.

$D = \frac{1}{2}$ difference of polar distance and co-lat.

$\frac{1}{2}t = \frac{1}{2}$ hour angle.

$Z =$ true azimuth.

$$\text{Then, } \tan X = \sin D \operatorname{cosec} S \cot \tfrac{1}{2}t;$$

$$\tan Y = \cos D \sec S \cot \tfrac{1}{2}t;$$

$$Z = X + Y, \text{ or } X \sim Y.$$

541524°—43——12

First case.—If the half-sum of the polar distance and co-lat. is *less* than 90°: take the sum of the angles X and Y, if the polar distance is *greater* than the co-lat.; take the difference, if the polar distance is *less* than the co-lat.

Second case.—If the half-sum of the polar distance and co-lat. is *greater* than 90°: always take the difference of X and Y, which subtract from 180°, and the result will be the true azimuth.

In either case, mark the true azimuth N. or S. according to the latitude, and E. or W. according to the hour angle. It may sometimes be convenient to use the supplement of the true azimuth by subtracting it from 180° and reversing the prefix N. or S., in order to make it correspond to the compass azimuth when the latter is less than 90°.

Example.—At sea Dec. 3, 1937, in Lat. 30° 25′ N., Longitude 81° 27′.8 W., the observed bearing of the sun's center was 135° 30′; watch 9^h 10^m 19^s; C–W 5^h 25^m 51^s; chron. fast 0^m 09^s; corrected declination 22° 06′.2 S.; find compass error.

W.,	9^h 10^m 19^s	Co. lat.,	59° 35′.0	½ t,	19° 57′.3	Cot,	0.43999	Cot,	0.43999
C.−W.,	5 25 51	p,	112 06 .2	S,	85 50 .6	Cosec.,	0.00114	Sec.,	1.13976
				D,	26 15 .6	Sin,	9.64586	Cos,	9.95269
Chron.,	14 36 10	p+co. lat.,	171 41 .2						
C. C. (fast),	−09			x,	50 42	Tan,	0.08699	Tan,	1.53244
		S,	85 50 .6	y,	88 19				
G. C. T.,	14 36 01								
		p−co. lat.,	52° 31 .2	x+y,	139 01				
G. H. A. 14^h,	32° 32′.8								
Corr. 36^m,	9 00 .0	D,	26 15 .6						
Corr. 1^s,	0 .3								
G. H. A.,	41 33 .1 W.			True azimuth,	139° 01′				
Long.,	81 27 .8 W.			Compass azimuth,	135 30				
				Compass error,	3 31 E.				
L. H. A. (t),	39 54 .7 E.								
½ t,	19 57 .3								

Example.—At sea in Lat. 2° 16′ N., the observed bearing of the sun's center was N. 85° 15′ E., the local hour angle was 56° 04′ E., and the corrected declination was 7° 38′ N.; find the compass error.

Co. lat.,	87° 44′	½ t,	28° 02′	Cot,	0.27372	Cot,	0.27372
p,	82 22	S,	85 03	Cosec.,	0.00162	Sec.,	1.06406
		D,	2 41	Sin,	8.67039	Cos,	9.99952
p+co. lat.,	170 06						
		x,	5 03	Tan,	8.94573	Tan,	1.33730
S,	85 03	y,	87 22				
Co. lat.−p,	5° 22′	y−x,	82 19				
D,	2 41						
		True azimuth,	82° 19′				
		Comp. azimuth,	85 15				
		Compass error,	2 56 W.				

Example.—At sea, in Lat. 16° 32′ S., the observed bearing of Venus was N. 56° 00′ W. (304°), the local hour angle was 66° 52′.8 W., and the corrected declination was 23° 12′.0 N.; find the compass error.

Co. lat.,	73° 28′	½ t,	33° 26′.4	Cot,	0.18021	Cot,	0.18021
p,	113 12	S,	93 20 .0	Cosec.,	0.00074	Sec.,	1.23549
		D,	19 52 .0	Sin,	9.53126	Cos,	9.97335
p+co. lat.,	186 40						
		x,	27 16 .0	Tan,	9.71221	Tan,	1.38905
S,	93 20	y,	87 40 .0				
p−co. lat.,	39° 44′	y−x,	60 24				
D,	19 52	Z,	119° 36′				

True azimuth,	S. 119° 36′ W. (299° 36′)
Compass azimuth,	S. 124 00 W. (304 00)
Compass error,	4 24 W.

ALTITUDE AZIMUTHS

When the local time is computed from an observed altitude, as in the "time sight", the true azimuth can also be computed from the formula given below. This true azimuth compared with the observed azimuth by compass will determine the compass error.

There are given the altitude h, the latitude L, and the polar distance p, to compute the azimuth Z from the formula hav Z=sin (s−L) sin (s−h) sec. h sec. L, in which s=½(h+L+p). The resulting azimuth is to be reckoned from the north in north latitude and from the south in south latitude.

Example.—At sea, in lat. 30° 25′.0 N.; the observed bearing of the sun's center was 135°.5; the corrected altitude was 24° 59′.0 and the corrected declination was 22° 06′.2 S; find the compass error.

h,	24° 59′ 00″	sec,	0.04267			
L,	30 25 00	sec,	0.06431			
p,	112 06 12					
2)	167 30 12					
s,	83 45 06					
s−h,	58 46 06	sin,	9.93201	True azimuth,	139° 01′	
s−L,	53 20 06	sin,	9.90425	Compass azimuth,	135 30	
Z,	139° 01′	hav,	9.94324	Compass error,	3 31 E.	

TIME AND ALTITUDE AZIMUTHS

When, at the time of observing the compass bearing of a celestial body, the altitude is measured and the exact time is noted, the true azimuth may be computed without any knowledge of the latitude. The declination of the body is corrected for time of sight and the local hour angle is found. The azimuth is then determined from the formula.

$$\text{Sin } Z = \sin t \cos d \sec h$$

Example.—At sea, Dec. 3, 1937, in lat. 30° 25′.0 N.; long. 81° 27′.8 W.; the observed bearing of the sun's center was 135°.5; its altitude was 24° 59′.0; hour angle 39° 54′.7, and corrected declination was 22° 06′.2 S.; find compass error. (See example under Altitude Azimuth and first example of Time Azimuth, also example on page 181.)

t,	39° 54′.7	sin,	9.80727	True azimuth,	139° 01′
d,	22 06 .2	cos,	9.96685	Compass azimuth,	135 30
h,	24 59 .0	sec,	0.04267		
				Compass error,	3 31 E.
Z, S.	40° 59′ E.	sin,	9.81679		

This method has a defect in that there is nothing to indicate whether the computed azimuth is measured from the north or south point of the horizon, but as the approximate azimuth is always known at sea, cases are rare when the solution will be in question. If the approximate azimuth is not known, the altitude on the prime vertical can be computed by the formula: sin h=sin d cosec L. If the observed altitude is less than the computed one on the prime vertical, the bearing of the sun is on the side of the elevated pole. Thus, if the computed altitude on the prime vertical is 30° 50′ and the observed altitude is 29° 10′, the bearing would be north and east in the northern hemisphere for a rising celestial body. (See fig. 76.)

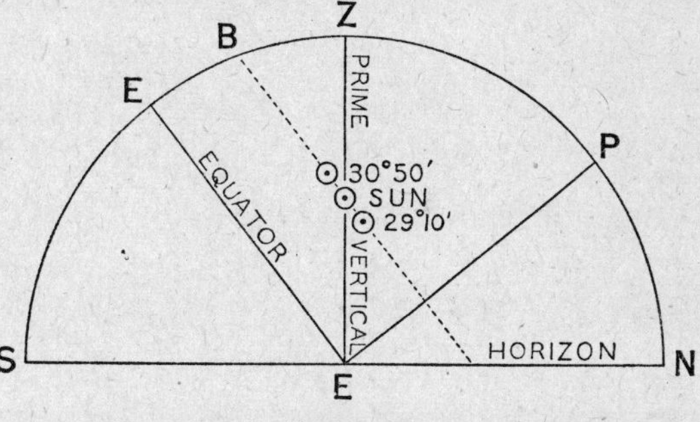

FIGURE 76.

AZIMUTH TABLES

On account of the convenience they afford, the Hydrographic Office publishes two volumes of azimuth tables which are preferred by the navigator to the laborious method of computation, as given in the preceding examples. In these tables, the values of azimuth are tabulated for various probable combinations of latitude and declination in whole degrees for every 10 minutes of time. Hydrographic Office Publication No. 71 was computed primarily for use with the sun, but this table may be used for any other celestial body whose declination is less than 23°. Hydrographic Office Publication No. 120 is used for the azimuths of celestial bodies that have declinations of 24° to 70° and is used for stars, planets, and the moon. In many cases values of azimuth can be taken directly by inspection from the tables, and for other cases resort must be had to interpolation.

Example.—Find the true azimuth in Lat. 37° 17′ N.; Dec. 3° 36′. 3 S., and t, 4^h 28^m.7 E.

	t	*d*	*L*	
t, 4^h 28^m.7 E.	108° 06′	108° 06′	108° 06′	Base, 108° 06′
d, 3° 36′.3 S.	106 24	108 54	108 24	Corr., − 55
L, 37° 17′.0 N.				
	− 1 42	+ 48	+ 18	Z=N 107 11 E.
	− 102	× .6	× .3	Z_n, (107° 11′)
	× .87			
		+ 28.8	+ 5.4	
	714	+ 5.4		
	816			
		+ 34.2		
	− 88.74	− 88.74		
		Corr., − 54.54		

On page 210 under Short Tabular Methods, it will be noted that azimuth may be readily found for every 4 minutes of time, (1°), from the series of 8 books (H. O. Pub. No. 214), covering declinations of sun, moon, and bright navigable stars, for all navigable latitudes.

CHAPTER XIV

THE SUMNER LINE

DESCRIPTION OF THE LINE OF POSITION

The method of navigation involving the use of the Sumner line, or line of position, takes its name from Capt. Thomas H. Sumner, an American shipmaster, who discovered it and published it to the world. As a proof of its value, the incident which led to its discovery may be related:

"Having sailed from Charleston, S. C., November 25th, 1837, bound for Greenock, a series of heavy gales from the westward promised a quick passage; after passing the Azores the wind prevailed from the southward, with thick weather; after passing longitude 21° W. no observation was had until near the land, but soundings were had not far, as was supposed, from the bank. The weather was now more boisterous and very thick, and the wind still southerly; arriving about midnight, December 17th within 40 miles, by dead reckoning, of Tuskar light, the wind hauled SE. true, making the Irish coast a lee shore; the ship was then kept close to the wind and several tacks made to preserve her position as nearly as possible until daylight, when, nothing being in sight, she was kept on ENE. under short sail with heavy gales. At about 10 a. m. an altitude of the sun was observed and the chronometer time noted; but, having run so far without observation, it was plain the latitude by dead reckoning was liable to error and could not be entirely relied upon.

"The longitude by chronometer was determined, using this uncertain latitude, and it was found to be 15′ E. of the position by dead reckoning; a second latitude was then assumed 10′ north of that by dead reckoning, and toward the danger, giving a position 27 miles ENE. of the former position; a third latitude was assumed 10′ farther north, and still toward the danger, giving a third position ENE. of the second 27 miles. Upon plotting these three positions on the chart, they were seen to be in a straight line, and this line passed through Smalls light.

"It then at once appeared that the observed altitude must have happened at all of the three points and at Smalls light and at the ship at the same instant."

Then followed the conclusion that, although the absolute position of the ship was uncertain, she must be somewhere on that line. The ship was kept on the course ENE., and in less than an hour Smalls light was made, bearing ENE. ½E. and close aboard.

The latitude by dead reckoning was found to be 8′ in error, and if the position given by that latitude had been assumed correct, the error would have been 8 miles too far S., and 31′30″ of longitude too far W., and the result to the ship might have been disastrous had this wrong position been adopted. This represents one of the practical applications of the Sumner line.

The **line of position** represents the most important principle in modern navigation. The special methods used for determining a latitude, or a longitude, can now be worked to give a line of position. It is no longer necessary to wait for the observed body to be on the meridian, or on the prime vertical. The meridian altitude, the reduction to the meridian, and a single longitude have lost their former importance.

The properties of the line of position will now be explained.

Equal altitude circles.—In figure 77, if EE′E″ represent the earth projected upon the horizon of a point A, and if it be assumed that, at some particular instant of time, a celestial body is in the zenith of that point, then the true altitude of the body as observed at A will be 90°. In such a case the great circle EE′E″, which forms the horizon of A, will divide the earth into two hemispheres, and from any point on the surface of one of these hemispheres the body will be visible, while over the whole of the other hemisphere it will be invisible. The great circle EE′E″, from the fact of its marking the limit of illumination of the body, is termed the *circle of illumination*, and from any point on its circumference the true altitude of the center of the body will be zero. On any small circle of the sphere BB′B″, CC′C″, DD′D″, whose plane is parallel to the plane of the circle of illumination and which lies within the hemisphere throughout which the body is visible, it will be apparent that the true altitude of the body at any point of the circumference of one of these circles is equal to its true altitude at any other point of the same circumference; thus the altitude of the body at B is equal to its altitude at B′ or B″, and its altitude at D is the same as at D′ or D″.

It follows that at any instant of time there is a series of positions on the earth at which a celestial body appears at the same given altitude, and these positions lie in the circumference of a circle described upon the earth's surface whose center is at that position which has the body in the zenith, and whose radius depends upon the zenith distance, or—what is the same thing—upon the altitude. Such circles are termed **circles of equal altitude.** It is important to note that an observer making an instantaneous transit through the latitudes and longitudes passed over by any rhumb line drawn within the hemisphere of illumination, through the point A, will experience no astronomical difference with reference to the observed body in the zenith of A, save an altitude difference.

The data for an astronomical sight comprise merely the time, declination, and altitude. The first two fix the position of the body and may be regarded as giving the latitude and longitude of that point on the earth in whose zenith the body is found; the zenith distance (the complement of the altitude) indicates the distance of the observer from that point; but there is nothing to show at which of the numerous positions fulfilling the required conditions the observation may have been taken. A number of navigators may measure the same altitude of a body at the same instant of time, at places thousands of miles apart; and each proceeds to work out his position with identical data, so far as this sight is concerned. It is therefore clear that *a single observation is not enough in itself to locate the point occupied by the observer*, and it becomes necessary, in order to fix the position, to employ a second circle, which may be either that of another celestial body or that of the same body given by an observation when it is in the zenith of some other point than when first taken; knowing that the point of observation lies upon each of two circumferences, it is only possible that it can be at one of their two points of intersection; and since the position of the ship is always known within fairly close limits, it is easy to choose the proper one of the two. Figure 78 shows the plotting of observations of two bodies vertically over the points A and A′ upon the earth, the zenith distances corresponding respectively to the radii AO and A′O.

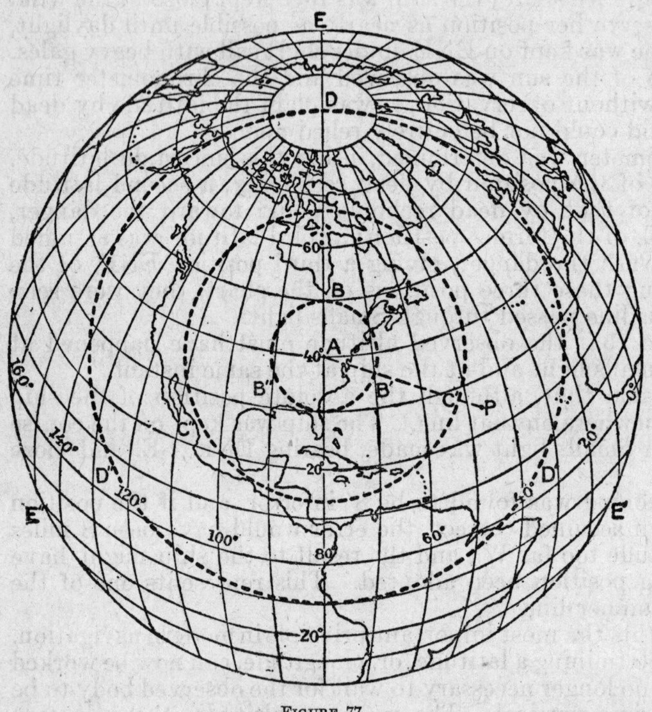

FIGURE 77.

The Sumner line of position.—In practice, under the conditions existing at sea, it is never necessary to determine the whole of a circle of equal altitude, as a very small portion of it will suffice for the purposes of navigation; the position is always known within a distance which will seldom exceed 30 miles under the most unfavorable conditions, and which is usually very much less; in the narrow limits thus required, the arc of the circle will practically coincide with the tangent at its middle point, and may be regarded as a straight line. Such a line, comprising so much of the circle of equal altitude as covers the probable limits of position of the observer, is called a **Sumner line,** or **line of position.**

The latter designation has a more extended meaning, embracing any line, straight or curved, which forms a locus of the ship's position, whether it be obtained from observations of celestial bodies, or from bearings or distances of terrestrial objects.

Since the direction of a circle at any point—that is, the direction of the tangent—must be perpendicular to the radius at that point, it follows that *the position line always lies in a direction at right angles to that in which the body bears from the observer.* Thus, in figure 78, it may be seen that $m\ m'$ and $n\ n'$, the extended position lines corresponding to the bodies at A and A′, are respectively perpendicular to the bearings of the bodies OA and OA′. This fact has a most important application in the employment of the position line.

Uses of the position line.—The position line is valuable because it gives to the navigator a knowledge of all of the probable positions of the vessel, while a sight worked with a single assumed latitude or longitude gives but one of the probable positions; it must be recognized that, in the nature of things, an error in the assumed coordinate will almost invariably exist, and its possible effect should be taken into consideration; the line of position reveals the difference of longitude due to an error in the latitude, or the reverse.

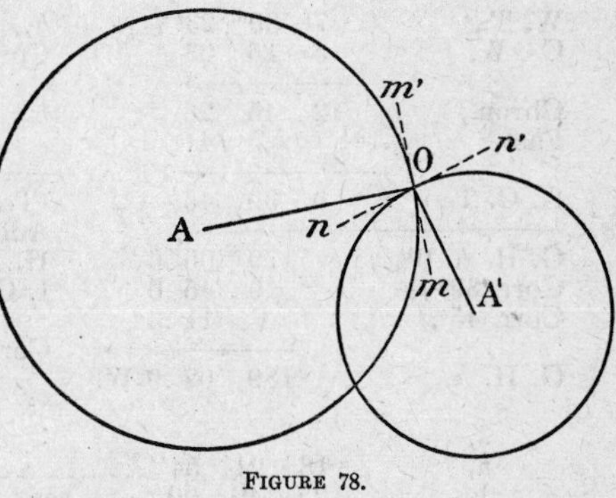

FIGURE 78.

Since the position line is at right angles to the azimuth or bearing, it may be seen that *when the body bears east or west—that is, when it is on the prime vertical—the resulting line runs north and south, coinciding with a meridian. When the body bears north or south, or is on the meridian, the position line runs east and west, and coincides for a short length with a parallel of latitude. Any intermediate bearing gives a position line inclined to both meridians and parallels.*

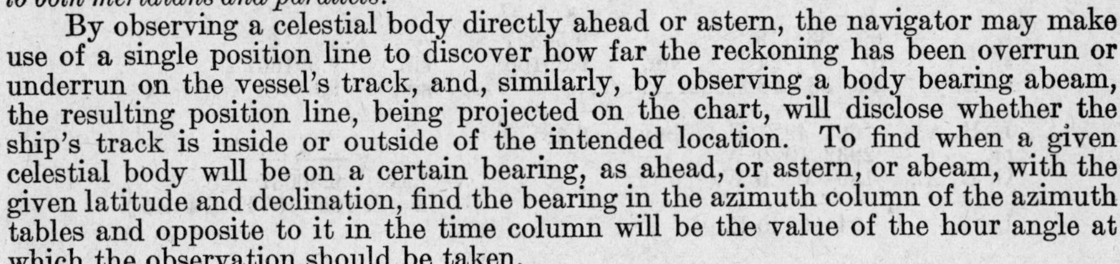

By observing a celestial body directly ahead or astern, the navigator may make use of a single position line to discover how far the reckoning has been overrun or underrun on the vessel's track, and, similarly, by observing a body bearing abeam, the resulting position line, being projected on the chart, will disclose whether the ship's track is inside or outside of the intended location. To find when a given celestial body will be on a certain bearing, as ahead, or astern, or abeam, with the given latitude and declination, find the bearing in the azimuth column of the azimuth tables and opposite to it in the time column will be the value of the hour angle at which the observation should be taken.

The greatest benefit to be derived from the line of position is when two lines are worked and their intersection found. The two lines may be given by different bodies, which is generally preferable, or two different lines may be obtained from the same body from the observations taken at different times. The position given by the intersection of two lines is more accurate the more nearly the lines are at right angles to each other, as an error in one line thus produces less effect upon the result. When two observations of the same body are taken, the position of the vessel at the time of first sight must be brought forward to that at the second in considering the intersection; if, for example, a certain line is determined, and the vessel then steams 27 miles 315°, it is evident that the new position is on a line parallel with the first and 27 miles 315° from it; a second line being obtained, the intersection of this with the first line as corrected for the run, gives the "fix," or position of the vessel. Besides the employment of two or three lines for intersection with each other, a single line may be made to serve various useful purposes for the navigator. The line of position should not be advanced more than five hours of run.

METHODS OF DETERMINATION

The best means for finding the line of position is to determine by any well selected method the altitude and azimuth of a given celestial body, at any given point on the earth, at any given instant of time. The difference between the computed altitude and the corrected observed altitude is the altitude intercept. Now lay off from the assumed geographical point, along the line of the direction of the azimuth of the celestial body at the time of the sight, the determined altitude intercept or distance to the line of position. This was not exactly the method employed by Captain Sumner on the occasion of the discovery of the process. He assumed two values of latitude about 20 to 50 miles apart, then worked two "time sights" which gave two different values for the longitude at two different latitudes. In this way, two points were fixed and the line joining them gave the line of position.

The usual method adopted where a "time sight" is computed is to assume a latitude, then work a longitude and an azimuth. This gives one point on the position line. The line of position is then drawn through the determined point at right angles to the direction of the azimuth.

Example.—April 3, 1937, about 7^h 30^m a. m., in D. R. Lat. 25° 40′ S., Long. 104° 00′ E., the sextant altitude of the sun's lower limb was 18° 14′.0; I. C. −1′; height of eye, 19 ft; watch 7^h 30^m 23^s; C−W 5^h 15^m 03^s; chron. fast 5^m 41^s; find line of position. (Example plotted fig. 79.)

W. T.,	7^h 30^m 23^s	h_s,		18° 14′.0	Dec. 0^h,		5° 04′.0 N.
C−W,	5 15 03	Corr.,	+	7 .9	Corr.,	+	.7
Chron.,	12 45 26	h_o,		18 21 .9	Dec.,		5 04 .7 N.
Fast,	− 5 41						
G. C. T.,	0 39 45	(Tab. 40),	+	13′.2	H. D.,		1′.0
		Add. corr.,		0 .0	G. C. T.,		.7
G. H. A. 0^h,	179° 06′.6	H. E.,	−	4 .3			
Corr. 39^m,	9 45 .0	I. C.,	−	1 .0	Corr.,	+	.7
Corr. 45^s,	11 .3						
		Corr.,	+	7 .9			
G. H. A.,	189 02 .9 W.						

		H. A.		*Az.*	
h,	18° 21′ 54″			sec,	0.02270
L,	25 40 00	sec,	0.04512	sec,	0.04512
p,	95 04 42	cosec,	0.00171		
	2) 139 06 36				
s,	69 33 18	cos,	9.54321		
$s-h$,	51 11 24	sin,	9.89166	sin,	9.89166
$s-L$,	43 53 18			sin,	9.84089
L. H. A.,	66° 49′.1 E.	hav,	9.48170		
or,	293° 10′.9 W.				
G. H. A.,	189 02 .9 W.			hav	9.80037
				Z=S. 105° 15′ E. (74° 45′)	
Long.,	104 08 .0 E.				

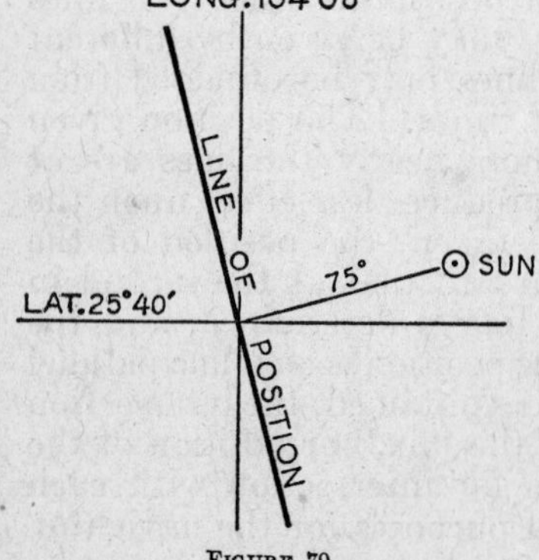

FIGURE 79.

Draw position line through Lat. 25° 40′ S.; Long. 104° 08′ E., at right angles to the azimuth S. 105°.2 E. (74°.8.)

Where a reduction to the meridian is used, a longitude is assumed and a latitude and azimuth are computed. The line of position is then drawn through this determined point, at right angles to the direction of the azimuth.

Example.—At sea, July 12, 1937, in Lat. 50° N.; Long. 41° 26′.7 W.; observed a circum-meridian altitude of the sun's lower limb 61° 46′ 10″; chron. time 2^h 41^m 39^s; chron. fast 2^m $26^s.3$; I. C.—3′ 00″; height of eye 30 feet; find the line of position.

Chron.,	2^h 41^m $39^s.0$	h_s,	61° 46′.2	Dec. 14^h,	21° 59′3 N.
Fast,	− 2 26 .3	Corr.,	+ 6 .9		
				H. D.,	− 0 .3
G. C. T.,	14 39 12 .7	h_o,	61 53 .1	G. C. T.,	$0^h.7$
G. H. A. 14^h,	28° 38′.5	(Tab. 40),	+ 15′.5	Corr.,	− 0 .2
Corr.39^m,	9 45 .0	Add. corr.,	− 0 .2	Dec.,	21° 59′.1 N.
Corr. $12^s.7$,	3 .2	H. E.,	− 5 .4	a (Tab. 29)	2″.5
		I. C.,	− 3 .0		
G. H. A.,	38 26 .7 W.				2″.0=4′.8
Long.,	41 26 .7 W.	Corr.,	+ 6 .9	at^2 (Tab. 30)	0 .5=1 .2
L. H. A.,	3 00 .0 E.				2 .5=6′.0

h_o,	61° 53′.1	t,	3° 00′ 00″	sin,	8.71880
at^2,	+ 6 .0	d,	21 59 06	cos,	9.96722
		h,	61 53 06	sec,	0.32675
H,	61 59 .1				
				sin,	9.01277
z,	28° 00′.9 N.			Z=S. 5° 54′ E. (174°)	
Dec.,	21 59 .1 N.				
Lat.,	50 00 .0 N.				

Draw position line through Lat. 50° 00′.0 N.; Long. 41° 26′.7 W.; at right angle to the azimuth 174°.

Saint Hilaire method.—This is a method of finding the line of position in which the course of procedure is the same, whatever the position of the observed body in the heavens may be, provided that the sextant altitude of the celestial body is measured at a known instant of time, from some D. R. position.

In figure 77, the circumference of a circle of position is represented as having been laid down from A, the geographical position of the observed body, as a center, with a radius AC′ equal to the zenith distance of the observed celestial body; but it is evident that a small arc of the circumference, not differing sensibly from a straight line within the extent of a line of position may be determined in the following manner from a neighboring geographical position, as at P, inside or outside of the circumference and at or near the position of the ship as given by dead reckoning:

From the D. R. position P, compute the altitude (or zenith distance) and the azimuth of the body A.

Take the difference, in minutes of arc (nautical miles), between this zenith distance AP due to the observer's assumed position, and the zenith distance AC′ found from the true altitude of observation.

Lay off this difference, which is called the *altitude-difference,* or *intercept,* from the assumed position P either *away from* or *toward* the observed celestial body according as the true altitude by observation is *less* or *greater* than the altitude at the assumed position, and through the point thus reached draw a line at right angles to the bearing or azimuth.

The line so drawn will be a tangent to the circumference of the circle of position and will be so nearly coincident with this circumference throughout such length as the position line need have, in all those cases in which the zenith distance is as great as 10°, that the tangent itself may be taken as the true line of position. The only computation that occurs under this method is in computing the length and bearing of the great-circle arc joining the dead reckoning position P with the geographical position A, which is always in a latitude equal to the declination of the observed celestial body at the instant of observation and in a longitude equal to the Greenwich hour angle of the body. In the case of the sun the Greenwich hour angle is indicated directly in arc, or by Greenwich apparent time, and in the case of any other celestial body the Greenwich hour angle is found as heretofore explained.

The fundamental formula for solving the astronomical triangle is:

$$\sin h = \sin L \sin d + \cos L \cos d \cos t,$$

which is often preferred for the computation of the altitude from the latitude, declination, and hour angle.

Since the above equation requires for its solution both logarithms, and natural sines and cosines, the following modification is adopted, called the sine-cosine formula:

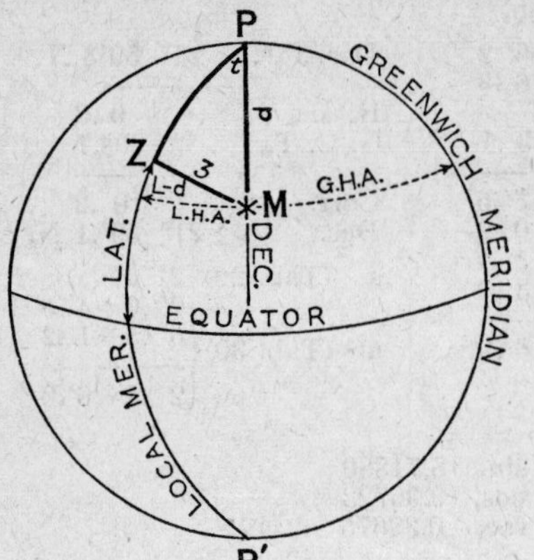

FIGURE 80.

$$A = \sin L \sin d, \quad B = \cos L \cos d \cos t;$$

hence,

$$\sin h = A + B.$$

When latitude and declination are of contrary name then $\sin h = A - B$.

With the use of haversine tables, the most convenient process for the navigator is the cosine haversine formula, given as follows,

$$\text{hav } z = \text{hav } (L \sim d) + \cos L \cos d \text{ hav } t.$$

in which,

$$\text{hav } \theta = \cos L \cos d \text{ hav } t;$$

then,

$$\text{hav } z = \text{hav } (L \sim d) + \text{hav } \theta.$$

When latitude and declination are of the same name $(L \sim d)$ is subtracted. For the azimuth there is used the formula,

$$\sin Z = \sin t \cos d \sec h,$$

Example.—December 11, 1937, in D. R. position Latitude 35° 00′ N., Longitude 140° 12′ W.; about $5^h\ 45^m$ p. m., observed the planet Jupiter, bearing southwestward, sextant altitude 26° 28′ 40″, I. C. +1′30″ height eye 36 feet; watch $5^h\ 48^m\ 03^s$; C—W $8^h\ 20^m\ 45^s$; chronometer slow $0^m\ 02^s$. Required the line of position. (See plot in fig. 81.)

Var. per min. 15′.0319		2^h	
For 15′ 03, 2^h, 30° 03′.6		15′.03,	30° 03′.6
Corr. .0019,	.2	15 .04,	30 04 .8
Corr. 2^h,	30 03 .8	Diff.,	1 .2
			.19
		Corr.,	.22

W. T.,	$5^h\ 48^m\ 03^s$				
C—W,	8 20 45				
Chron.,	2 08 48				
Corr.,	+ 02				
G. C. T., Dec. 12,	2 08 50				
G. H. A. Dec. 12,	139° 48′.4				
Corr. 2^h,	30 03 .8				
Corr. 8^m,	2 00 .2				
Corr. 50^s,	12 .5				
G. H. A.,	172 04 .9 W.				
Long.,	140 12 .0 W.				
L. H. A.,	31 52 .9 W.			cos,	9.92898
Lat.,	35° 00′00″N.	sin,	9.75859	cos,	9.91336
Dec.,	20 59 36 S.	sin,	9.55420	cos,	9.97017
		log A,	9.31279	log B,	9.81251
		A,	0.20549	B,	0.64940
				A,	0.20549
h_c=26° 21′.2=nat. sin A—B				A—B,	0.44391

Dec. 12^d,	20°59′.8 S	Diff.,	2′.5
Corr., —	.2	Prop. P.,	.2
Dec.,	20 59 .6		

h_s		26° 28′.7
Corr.,	—	6 .4
h_o		26 22 .3
(Tab. 40),	—	2′.0
I. C.,	+	1 .5
H. E.,	—	5 .9
Corr.,	—	6.4

or, by the cosine haversine formula:

		Altitude		Azimuth	
t,	31° 52′ 54″	hav,	8.87755	sin,	9.72278
L,	35 00 00N.	cos,	9.91336		
d,	20 59 36S.	cos,	9.97017	cos,	9.97017
		log hav θ,	8.76108		
		nat. hav θ,	.05769		
L∼d,	55° 59′ 36″	nat. hav,	.22035		
z	63 38 45	nat. hav,	.27804		
h_c	26° 21′.2			sec,	.04766
h_o,	26 22 .3				
				sin,	9.74061
Int.,	1 .1 towards 213°.4			Az. S	33° 24′ W.
				or N.	146° 36′ W. (213°.4)

From Lat. 35°00′.0 N., Long. 140°12′.0 W., lay off the azimuth line N. 146°.6 W. (213°.4) and from this position measure 1.1 miles along the azimuth line towards the planet Jupiter. Through this latter point, draw a line of position at right angles to the azimuth.

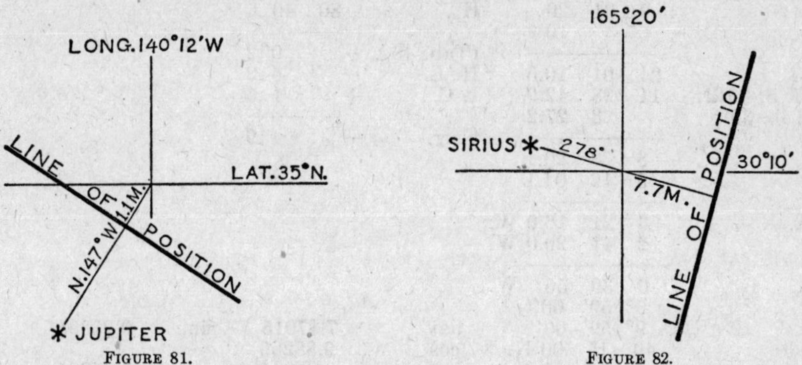

FIGURE 81.

FIGURE 82.

It will be noted that in the above example the latitude and declination are of contrary name, hence latitude and declination are added to give L∼*d*.

Example.—May 1, 1937, in D. R. position Lat. 30° 10′.3 S., Long. 165° 20′.2 E.; observed the star Sirius, bearing northwestward, sextant altitude 47° 12′ 10″; I. C. −1′ 00″; watch $7^h 05^m 23^s$ p. m.; C−W $0^h 58^m 39^s$; chronometer fast $0^m 02^s$; height of eye 26 feet; find line of position.

W. T.,	$7^h 05^m 23^s$	h_s,	47° 12′.2	Dec.✳,	16° 38′.0 S.		
C−W,	0 58 39	Corr.,	− 6.9				
Chron.,	8 04 02	h_o,	47 05.3				
Fast,	− 02						
		(Tab. 40),	− 0′.9				
G. C. T.,	8 04 00	I. C.,	− 1.0				
		H. E.,	− 5.0				
G. H. A. May 1,	117° 54′.4 W.						
Corr. $8^h 04^m$,	121 19.9	Corr.,	6.9				
					Alt.		*Az.*
G. H. A.,	239 14.3 W.	*t*,	44° 34′ 30″	hav	9.15786	sin	9.84624
Long.,	165 20.2 E.	L,	30 10 18 S.	cos	9.93678		
		d,	16 38 00 S.	cos	9.98144	cos	9.98144
L. H. A.,	44 34.5 W.			hav *θ*	9.07608		
				nat. hav *θ*	0.11915		
		L∼d	13 32 18	nat. hav	0.01389		
		z	42 47 00	nat. hav	.13304	cosec.	0.16798
		h_c	47° 13′.0				
		h_o	47 05.3			sin	9.99566
		Intercept.,	7.7 away from 278°			Z=N. 81° 55′ W. (278°)	

From Lat. 30° 10′.3 S., Long. 165° 20′.2 E., plot azimuth line N. 82° W. (278°). From D. R. position, lay off 7.7 miles along the azimuth line in a direction away from the star Sirius. Through this latter position, draw at right angles to the azimuth line, the required line of position. (See plot in fig. 82).

Example.—March 15, 1937, in D. R. position Lat. 40° 15′ N., Long. 40° 20′ W., observed the star Capella bearing northwestward, sextant altitude 80° 45′ 30″; I. C.+1′ 30″; height of eye 40 feet; watch $6^h\ 20^m\ 00^s$ p. m.; C−W $2^h\ 41^m\ 20^s$; chronometer fast 10^s; required line of position.

W. T.	$6^h\ 20^m\ 00^s$	H_s,		80° 45′.5	R. A. Capella,	$5^h\ 12^m\ 04^s.1$
C−W	2 41 20	Corr.	−	4 .9	Dec. Capella,	45° 56′.3 N.
Chron.	9 01 20	H_o,		80 40 .6		
Fast,	− 10	(Tab. 40,)	−	0′.2		
G. C. T.	21 01 10.0	H. E.	−	6 .2		
R. A. M. S.+12^h,	11 28 42.9	I. C.	+	1 .5		
Corr. (Tab. 39),	3 27.2	Corr.	−	4 .9		
G. S. T.	8 33 20.1					
R. A.✱	5 12 04.1					
G. H. A.	3 21 16.0 W.					
Long.	2 41 20.0 W.					
L. H. A.	0 39 56 W.					
or Arc,	9° 59′ 00″			*Alt.*		*Az.*
t,	9° 59′ 00″	hav		7.87915	sin,	9.23895
L,	40 15 00 N.	cos		9.88266		
d,	45 56 18 N.	cos		9.84225	cos,	9.84225
		hav θ		7.60406		
		nat. hav θ		.00402		
(L∼*d*),	5° 41′ 18″	nat. hav		.00247		
z,	9 14 30	nat. hav		.00649	cosec.,	0.79427
h_e	80° 45′.5				sin,	9.87547
h_o	80 40 .6					
Int.	4.9	away from 311°				Z=N. 48° 39′ W. (311°.4)

From D.R. Lat. 40° 15′N., Long. 40° 20′ W.; plot azimuth line 311°; lay off point 4.9 miles away from star Capella along azimuth line. Draw position line through this latter point, perpendicular to the azimuth line.

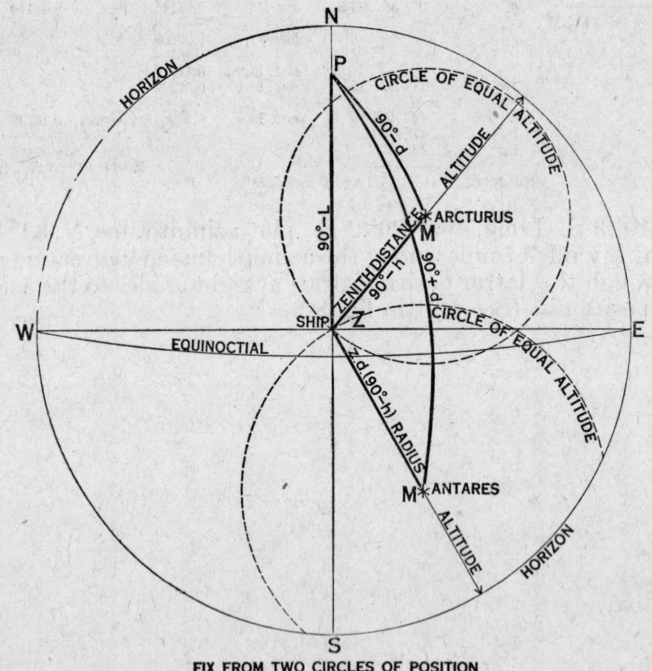

FIX FROM TWO CIRCLES OF POSITION

The following is an example of simultaneous observations of two stars:

Example.—During morning twilight on July 3, 1937, in D. R. position, Latitude 30° 08′.0 S.; Longitude 140° 42′.0 W.; observed simultaneous observations of the star Hamal bearing northeastward, sextant altitude 25° 26′ 00″, G. C. T. 14^h 08^m 32^s, and the star Achernar bearing southeastward, sextant altitude 55° 15′ 00″; G. C. T. 14^h 09^m 08^s; height of eye 25 feet; I. C. 0′ 0″; find position. (See plot of example in fig. 82a.)

Hamal

G. C. T.,	14^h 08^m 32^s	h_s,	25° 26′.0	Dec., 23° 10′.0 N.			
		Corr.,	— 7 .0				
G. H. A. July 3, 0^h,	249° 41′.2						
Corr. 14^h 08^m,	212 34 .8	h_o,	25 19 .0				
Corr. 32^s,	8 .0						
					Altitude		*Azimuth*
	462 24 .0						
(Subtract),	360°	L. H. A.,	38° 18′ E.	hav,	9.03186	sin,	9.79224
		Lat.,	30 08 S.	cos,	9.93695		
G. H. A.,	102 24 .0 W.	Dec.,	23 10 N.	cos,	9.96349	cos,	9.96349
Long.,	140 42 .0 W.						
				hav,	8.93230		
L. H. A.,	38 18 .0 E.						
				nat. hav,	.08556		
		(L∼d),	53 18	nat. hav,	.20119		
		z,	64 45 .2	nat. hav,	.28675	cosec.	0.04361
		h_c,	25° 14′.8			sin,	9.79934
		h_o,	25 19 .0			Z=N. 39° E.	
		Int.,	4 .2 towards 39°				

Achernar

G. C. T.,	14^h 09^m 08^s	h_s,	55° 15′.0	Dec., 57° 32′.9 S.			
		Corr.,	— 5 .6				
G. H. A. July 3, 0^h,	256° 45′.2						
Corr. 14^h 09^m,	212 49 .9	h_o,	55 09 .4				
Corr. 08^s,	2 .0						
					Altitude		*Azimuth*
	469 37 .1						
(Subtract),	360°	L. H. A.,	31° 04′.9 E.	hav,	8.85607	sin,	9.71287
		Lat.,	30 08 .0 S.	cos,	9.93695		
G. H. A.,	109 37 .1 W.	Dec.,	57 32 .9 S.	cos,	9.72964	cos,	9.72964
Long.,	140 42 .0 W.						
				hav,	8.52266		
L. H. A.,	31 04 .9 E.						
				nat. hav,	.03331		
		(L∼d),	27 24 .9	nat. hav,	.05616		
		z,	34 48 .5	nat. hav,	.08947	cosec.,	0.24349
		h_c,	55 11 .5			sin,	9.68600
		h_o,	55 09 .4			Z=S. 29° E. (151°)	
		Int.,	2 .1 away from 151°				

From D. R. Lat. 30° 08′ S., Long. 140° 42′ W., plot azimuth 39°; lay off 4.2 miles towards star Hamal and draw position line through this latter point at right angles to the azimuth. From same D. R. position, plot azimuth 151° and lay off 2.1 miles away from star Achernar, and through this last point, at right angles to the azimuth, draw the position line. The intersection of the two position lines is the "fix" or the vessel's position.

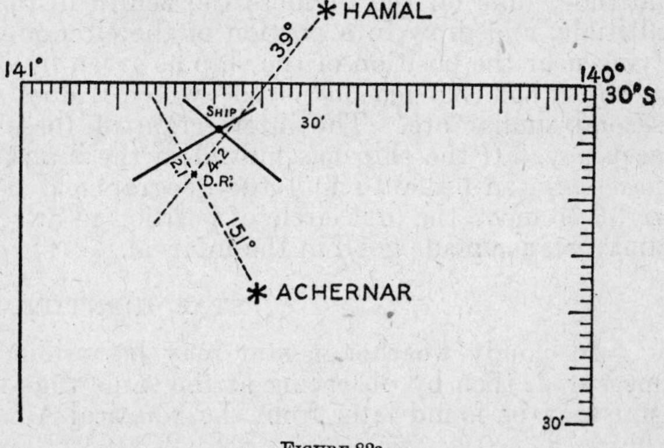

FIGURE 82a.

Should the meridian altitude be observed and worked by the cosine-haversine method, the local hour angle of the celestial body is 0°. Then, since the haversine of 0° is equal to zero, the equation reduces to

$$\text{hav } z = \text{hav } (L \sim d)$$

$$z = L \sim d$$

which gives at once or, the usual formula $L = d + z$ for finding the latitude from a meridian altitude. By this we note the full interpretation of a meridian altitude, which is that it gives the latitude of the intersection with the local meridian of a line of position tangent to a parallel of latitude.

In addition to the simplicity which arises from always working by the same process, the navigator has, by this method, the further practical advantage of being able to do the most of the work of obtaining the line of position before taking the observation, since, in clear weather, he may, in selecting the assumed D. R. position, assume an hour angle and compute the time the chronometer or watch should show at the instant when the celestial body has this hour angle, and then observe the altitude at this instant; or, if anything happens to make him a few seconds late in getting the altitude, he may alter the assumed longitude by a corresponding amount so as to make the hour angle correct, then the rest of the work holds good.

After correcting the observed altitude and obtaining from it the true altitude, no more time need subsequently elapse in determining the line of position than is necessary to take the difference between the altitudes found by computation and by observation and to rule a line at right angles to the bearing of the observed body through the point found by laying off this altitude-difference as an intercept from the assumed position.

Zenith Distance less than 10°.—It has been implied that when the altitude of the observed body is greater than 80° and, therefore, the zenith distance or radius of the circle of position is less than 10°, the tangent drawn to the circumference to represent the position line could no longer be regarded as coinciding throughout its proper length with the arc of the circumference. When the zenith distance is 10°, the departure of the tangent from the circumference is one-tenth of a mile at a distance of 10 miles from the theoretical point of tangency and seven-tenths of a mile at a distance of 30 miles from the theoretical point of tangency. These departures are doubled when the zenith distance is reduced to 5°, and they are nearly 10 times the amounts stated for 10° when the zenith distance is shortened to 1°.

There is no occasion for resorting to the procedure of laying down a straight line as a substitute for an arc of the actual circle of position when the zenith distance is only a few degrees in length. In such cases the best results are found by drawing the required short arcs of the circles of position directly on the navigator's chart. For instance, it happens in crossing the tropical zone that, for a day or so, the sun is very near the zenith—perhaps not more than 1° away on one day and 2° or 3° on another. In such circumstances, having a chart of suitable scale, plot the sun's geographical position with Greenwich hour angle as longitude and declination as latitude, take on the dividers the zenith distance, or complement of the corrected altitude, and draw in a portion of the circumference of the actual circle of position lying near the position of the ship as given by dead reckoning. Then wait until the azimuth has changed 30° or so—which it does very rapidly near noon—and draw a second similar arc. The intersection of these arcs gives the ship's position with accuracy. If the ship has moved in the interval between the two sights, it will be necessary, in order to find the geographical position at the instant of the second sight, to move the first circle of position in direction and amount equal to the course and distance made good in the interval.

STAR IDENTIFICATION

In cloudy weather, a star may be visible through the clouds and its altitude measured, then by observing at the same time its compass bearing, the name of the star may be found later from the Nautical Almanac.

Example.—During evening twilight on October 7, 1937, in D. R. position Lat. 15° 05′ N., Long. 76° 40′ W., a star is observed through a break in the clouds and the following data recorded, watch $6^h\ 06^m\ 20^s$. C—W $5^h\ 10^m\ 06^s$; chronometer fast $10^m\ 06^s$; sextant altitude 20° 55′.0; I. C.+1′ height eye 36 feet, bearing of star by gyro 285° (N. 75° W.). Identify the star.

W.,	$6^h\ 06^m\ 20^s$
C.—W.,	5 10 06
Chro.,	11 16 26
Fast,	— 10 06
G. C. T.,	23 06 20
R. A. M. S.+12^h,	1 00 53
Corr. (Tab. 39),	3 48
G. S. T.,	24 11 01
Long. W.,	5 06 40
L. S. T.	19 04 21
(Approx.) t*,	4 51 09 W.

h_s, 20° 55′.0	
corr., —7.4	
h_o, 20 47.6	
hav Z (75)°,	9.56889
cos L (15° 05′),	9.98477
cos h (20° 47′.6),	9.97075
log hav,	9.52441
nat. hav,	.33451
(L—h_o) 5° 42′.6 nat. hav,	.00248
p 70° 58′.3 nat. hav,	.33699
Dec. 19° 01.7 N.	

h_o,	20° 47′.6		
z,	69° 12′.4	nat. hav,	.32250
(L∼d),	3 56.7	nat. hav,	.00118
		nat. hav,	.32132
		log hav,	9.50693
		L 15° 05′ N. sec.,	.01523
		d 19 02 N., sec.,	.02442
		hav, t	9.54658
			t=$4^h\ 51^m\ 09^s$ W.

(Approx.) R. A.*, 14 13 12
(Approx.) Dec.*, 19° 02′ N. } Enter Nautical Almanac in star list with this R. A. and Dec. and the star is identified as Arcturus.

Example.—At dawn on November 20, 1937, in D. R. Lat. 27° 35′ N., Long. 71° 34′.5 W., a star is observed through a break in the clouds and the following data recorded: Watch $6^h\ 10^m\ 28^s$ C—W $4^h\ 40^m\ 42^s$; chronometer slow 10^s, sextant altitude 28° 24′.0; I. C.—1′; height eye 40 feet; bearing of star by gyro 120°. Required to identify the unknown star.

W.	$6^h\ 10^m\ 28^s$
C—W.,	4 40 42
Chron.,	10 51 10
Slow	+10
G. C. T.,	10 51 20
R. A. M. S.+12^h,	3 54 22
Corr. (Tab. 39),	1 47
G. S. T.,	14 47 29
Long. W.,	4 46 18
L. S. T.,	10 01 11
(Approx.) t*,	3 22 56 E.

h_s, 28° 24′.0	
Corr., —9.0	
h_o, 28° 15′	
hav Z (120°),	9.87506
cos L (27° 35)	9.94760
cos h_o (28° 15′)	9.94492
hav,	9.76758
nat. hav,	.58557
L—h_o (0° 40′) nat. hav,	.00003
p 99° 51′.5 nat. hav,	.58560
Dec. 9 51.5 S.	

h_o,	28° 15′		
z,	61 45	nat. hav,	.26334
L∼d,	37 27	nat. hav,	.10306
		nat. hav,	.16028
		log hav,	9.20488
		L 27° 35′ N. sec.,	.05240
		d 9° 52 S. sec.,	.00647
		log hav,	9.26375
			t=$3^h\ 22^m\ 56^s$ E.

(Approx.) R. A.*, 13 24 07
(Approx.) Dec.*, 9° 52′. S. } Enter Nautical Almanac in star list with R. A.* and the Dec.* and the star is identified as Spica.

When the value of p (polar distance) is over 90°, the declination has the opposite name from the latitude.

OTHER METHODS FOR ALTITUDE AND AZIMUTH

There are many other good methods for determining the value of altitude and azimuth of celestial bodies, and one process is perhaps as adaptable as any other. All methods carry out the same plan as in the St. Hilaire process, of computing an azimuth, and an altitude to compare with the observed altitude. Several of these methods lend themselves conveniently to tabulation in forms which make the computation short, quick, and simple. These will be discussed in the following chapter.

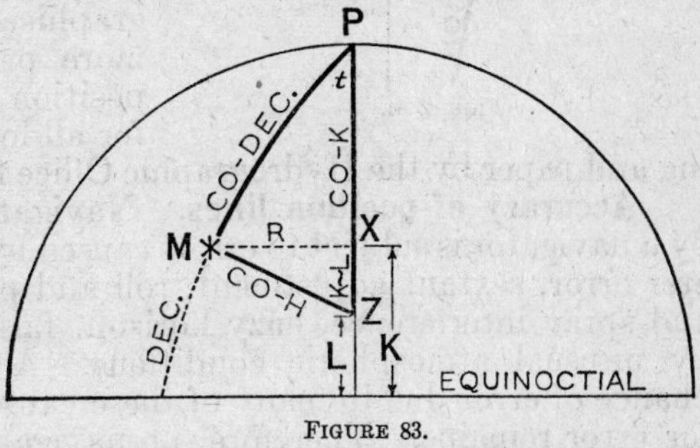

FIGURE 83.

But one process will be given here as an example. In figure 83, let P represent the pole; Z, zenith; angle PZM, azimuth, called Z; M, celestial body; L, latitude observer; d, declination of body; t, local hour angle; H, altitude of body; R, perpendicular let fall from M on meridian; X, intersection of R with PZ; K, arc from X to equinoctial. There is then derived the following formula:

In triangle PMX

$$\text{cosec. R} = \text{cosec. } t \text{ sec. } d.$$

$$\text{cosec. K} = \frac{\text{cosec. } d}{\text{sec. R}}$$

In triangle ZMX

$$\text{cosec. H}_c = \text{sec. R sec. (K} \sim \text{L)}$$

$$\text{cosec. Z} = \frac{\text{cosec. R}}{\text{sec. H}_c}$$

Example.—January 1, 1937, in Latitude 10° 10′ S., Longitude 9° 00′.8 E.; observed altitude of planet Venus bearing southwestward 41° 46′ 10″; watch time 6^h 25^m 10^s p. m.; C—W 11^h 23^m 57^s; chronometer slow 10^s; height of eye 36 feet; I. C.—1′; find line of position. (See plot in fig. 84.)

W. T.	6^h 25^m 10^s	h_s,	41° 46′.2	R. A. Venus,	21^h 47^m 52^s	Diff.	268		
C−W,	11 23 57	Corr.	− 8.0	Corr.	+ 3 19	*p. p.*	199^s $=3^m$ 19^s		
Chron.	17 49 07	h_o,	41 38.2	R. A.	21 51 11				
Slow,	+ 10								
G. C. T.	17 49 17	(Tab. 40),	− 1′.1						
R. A. M. S.+12^h	6 40 54.4	H. E.	− 5.9	Dec. Venus,	15° 07′.3 S.	Diff.	25′.7		
Corr. (Tab. 39)	2 55.7	I. C.	− 1.0	Corr.	− 19.0	*p. p.*	19′.0		
G. S. T.	24 33 07.1	Corr.	− 8.0	Dec.	14 48.3 S.				
R. A. Venus	21 51 11.0								
G. H. A.	2 41 56.1 W.								
Long.	0 36 03.0 E.								
L. H. A.	3 17 59.1 W.								
or *t* (arc)	49° 29′ 46″ W.								
t,	49° 29′ 46″ W.	cosec.	.11898						
Dec.	14 48 18 S.	sec.	.01466	cosec.	.59255	*Altitude*		*Azimuth*	
(R)*		cosec.	.13364	sec.	.16881	sec.	.16881	cosec.	.13364
K,	22° 08′.6 S.			cosec.	.42374				
Lat.	10 10.0 S.								
K∼L,	11 58.6					sec.	.00956		
h_c,	41° 32′.6					cosec.	.17837	sec.	.12583
h_o,	41 38.2					Z=S. 79° 10′ W. (259°)		cosec.	.00781
Int.	5.6 toward 259°								

K is named the same as the declination.
K∼L is added if of *contrary* name and subtracted if of *same* name.
*It is never necessary to evaluate the angle R.

In the above example, plot from D. R. position latitude 10° 10′ S., longitude 9° 01′ E., the azimuth line 259°, lay off from this position 5.6 miles toward the planet Venus; through this latter position, draw the position line perpendicular to the azimuth line.

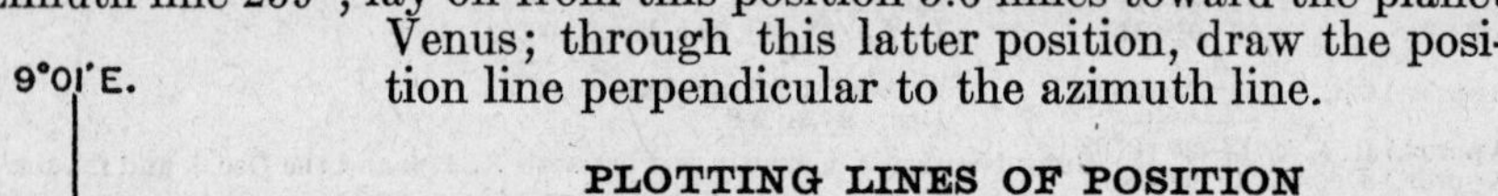

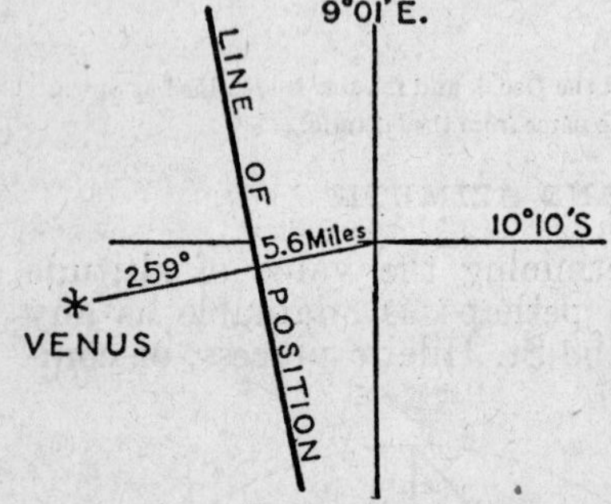

FIGURE 84.

PLOTTING LINES OF POSITION

Having computed the data for a line of position by any of the foregoing methods, or by any of the newer short methods described in the next chapter, the problem remains to place the lines on the chart and select the most probable position of the vessel. The intersection of two or more lines may be plotted graphically, or computed. The former is by far the more practical method and to facilitate plotting position line, plotting sheets upon an ample scale for all localities have been provided at cost of printing and paper by the Hydrographic Office for the use of navigators.

Accuracy of position lines.—Navigation at sea is not exact. Any sight taken by a navigator is subject to errors caused by such things as, personal eyesight, chronometer error, sextant adjustment, roll and pitch of the vessel while taking sights, wind and spray interference, hazy horizon, false horizon, or abnormal refraction caused by unusual atmospheric conditions. A skilled navigator can greatly reduce the chance of error due to many of these causes, but can never rest assured that no cause for error remains. Therefore, no navigator should assume that his observations are perfect and his position exact, even though three position lines do cross in a point. Perhaps a reasonable allowance for these unknown errors is 2 miles. There are many occasions in navigation where such an allowance must be given consideration in estimating the most probable position of the ship.

Single line of position.—Any single line of position represents a locus of the possible positions of the vessel at the instant of the observation. It is plotted on the chart from the geographic position used in the computation by measuring the altitude difference in the proper direction along the azimuth line drawn through the position, and erecting the line of position perpendicular to the azimuth line. If the D. R. position was used, the intersection of the azimuth line and position line, called the **computed point** represents the most probable position, *providing no circumstances of current, weather, or other observation are available to aid the navigator in making a better estimate.*

Since the line may be in error as much as 2 miles, dotted lines drawn parallel to the position line and 2 miles on either side of it will limit the area of the most probable position, or if the circumstances mentioned above exist, the area within 2 miles of the computed point becomes the most probable area in which the exact position is located.

Two lines of position from simultaneous sights.—Two or more lines of position which have been obtained from simultaneous observations, using the same geographic position, are plotted singly from that position and their intersection fixes the position of the ship within reasonable limits. The nearer the lines are at right

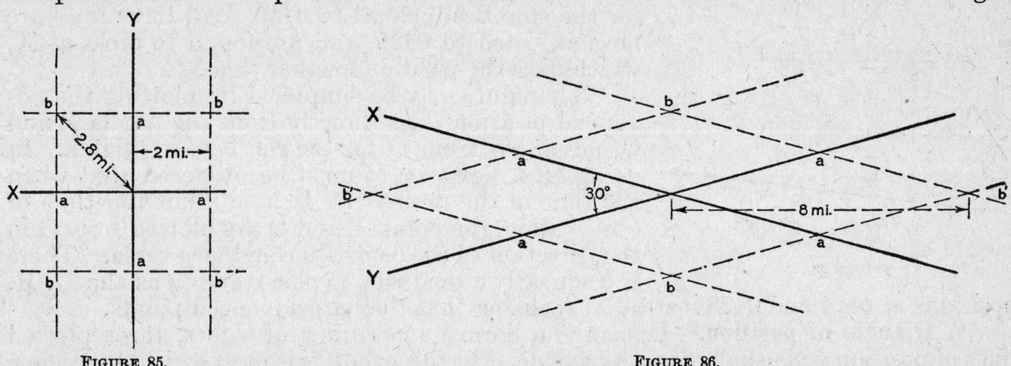

FIGURE 85. FIGURE 86.

angles to each other, the less effect a possible error may have on the position. As before, draw dotted lines parallel to, and 2 miles on each side of each line. The inclosed parallelogram represents the most probable area in which the exact position is located.

In figure 85 (lines of position x and y at right angles to each otner), if one line is in error 2 miles, the position must be at one of the points *a*, while if both lines are in error 2 miles the position must be at one of the points *b*, a maximum error of about 2.8 miles. Similarly in figure 86 (lines of position x and y intersecting at an angle of 30°), if both lines are in error 2 miles, the positions *b'* may be in error as much as 8 miles. Intersections less than 30° introduce greater possible errors and should be avoided if possible.

A running fix.—When two observations of the same or different bodies are made at different times, one line of position may be advanced or retarded parallel to itself along the course line of the vessel, an amount equal to the estimated run over the ground of the ship for that interval, to obtain what is called a **running fix.** Such a fix is not as accurate as one obtained from simultaneous, or nearly simultaneous, observations, since its accuracy depends on the accuracy of the estimated course and distance made good between the observations.

In figure 87 let A be the D. R. position at 0730, at which time the sun was observed on the prime vertical and the position line cd plotted. The point A′ is the computed point. Let B be the D. R. position at 0930 when another observation gave the position line ef. The line cd is advanced parallel to itself the length A′B′ = to AB, the estimated run of the vessel from 0730 to 0930. The intersection X of the advanced line c′d′ and the plotted line ef is the running fix for 0930.

FIGURE 87.

Three lines—taken in succession.—Every navigator prefers to take his own sights, which makes it obviously impossible to obtain two or more simultaneous observations. The ordinary procedure is to observe each suitable star in turn as the horizon clears in the morning, or as it becomes visible at night. The time between sights will vary considerably, depending on the length of twilight and on weather and cloud conditions. Each sight is worked using the corresponding time, but the same D. R. position is adopted for all sights. A previously plotted D. R. position may be used, but more frequently the D. R. position at the time of the last sight is used and the plot for the other sights run up as a running fix to that time.

In figure 88, three stars, A, B, and C were observed successively at 0424, 0428, and 0430, and their position lines Aa, Bb, Cc were plotted from the 0430 D. R. position used in the computations for all stars. The triangle abc results which must now be corrected for the difference in time used. The point A is the computed point for the star A at 0424. Advance A parallel to the course line the distance AA′ equal to the run of the vessel at 15 knots for 6 minutes or 1.5 miles. Draw A′X parallel to Aa. A′X now represents the position line for the star A advanced to 0430. In the same manner advance B to B′ 0.5 mile for the 2-minute run between sights and B′X represents the position line for the star B advanced to 0430. All three lines are now adjusted to 0430, and are found to cross at X, which fixes the position for that time.

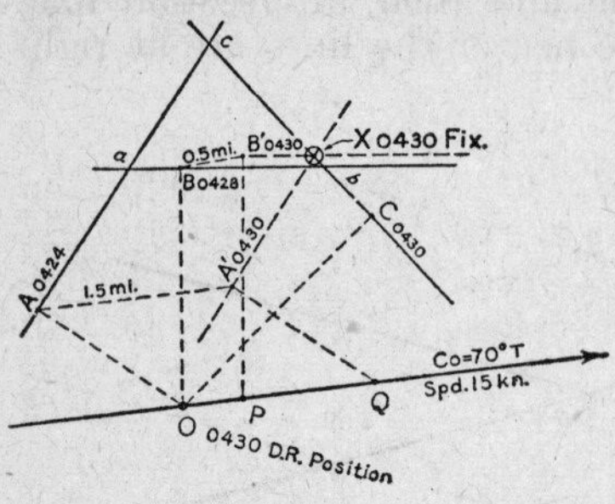

FIGURE 88.

The figure may be simplified by plotting the advanced position lines directly from the points P and Q, advanced from O for the run between sights. In doing this, however, it must be observed that when the time of the desired fix is later than the time of observation, the points P and Q are plotted from O in the direction of the course line and vice versa. There is frequently a tendency to plot P and Q as the D. R. positions at 0424 and 0428 instead of realizing that they are advanced points.

A triangle of position.—Due to the normal inaccuracy of sights, three plotted lines of position will usually form a triangle. In this event, it is most logical to assume that some type of error is mutual to all sights and therefore should be applied equally to all either away or toward the star, but not away from some and toward others. For any triangle there are four points equidistant from all three lines, one inside and three outside the triangle, found by laying the bisectors of the internal and external

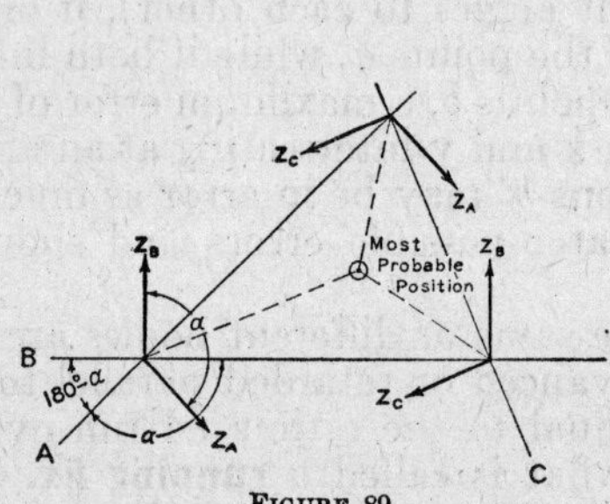

FIGURE 89.

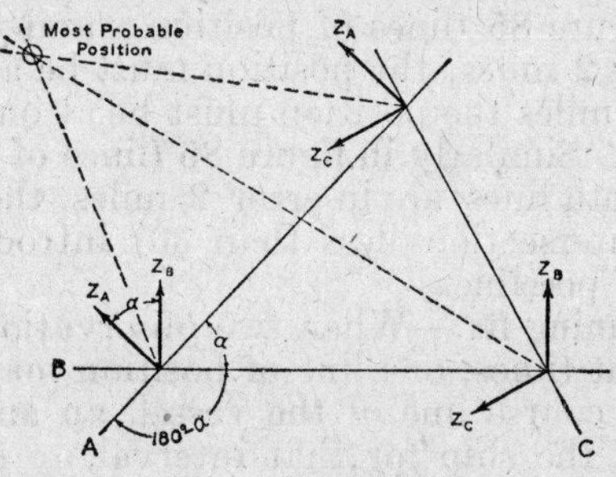

FIGURE 90.

angles. Assuming the error of each line to be in the same direction from its star, the following method will determine the point representing the most probable position.

In figures 89 and 90, at the vertices of the triangles draw in the vectors $Z_A Z_B$ and Z_C to represent the azimuth lines of the respective bodies. At each vertex bisect the smaller of the two angles formed by the azimuth lines. If this angle is called α, it will be noted that one of the angles of the triangle at that vertex equals α and the other $180° - \alpha$. The bisector will always bisect the angle equal to $180° - \alpha$.

The mathematical proof for this method may be found in the Hydrographic Review, volume VIII, No. 2 of November 1931, under the article "Accurate Determination of the Position at Sea."

COMPUTING INTERSECTION OF POSITION LINES

The finding of the intersection of two position lines by computation is divided into two cases:

Case I. When one line lies in a 45°–225° direction, and the other in a 135°–315° direction, as shown in figure 91.

Case II. When both lie in a 45°–225°, or both in a 135°–315° direction, as shown in figure 92.

If each position line is defined by the latitude and longitude of one of its points and the azimuth of the celestial body at right angles to whose true bearing the line runs, then, by means of Table 35, find the longitude of any other point on such a line when its difference of latitude from the known point has been ascertained. The numbers in Table 35 are values of the longitude factor, here denoted by the letter F. They vary with the latitude of the observer and the celestial body's azimuth at right angles to the direction of the line, and express the change in longitude due to a change of 1′ in latitude along any given line. So that the difference of latitude between any two points of a line, being multiplied by the longitude factor, will give the difference of longitude between those points.

In figures 91 and 92 considering the position lines $A_1 A_2$ and $B_1 B_2$ there represented to be defined by the azimuth at right angles to each and the latitudes and longitudes of the points A_1 and B_1, respectively, there will be shown the relations which exist for determining the latitude and longitude of the fix at their intersection by means of the tabulated longitude factors. The line PO drawn perpendicular to the parallel of latitude through the points A_1 and B_1, the latitude of the intersection is the distance OP from the common latitude of A_1 and B_1, and its longitude is the distance A_1 O from A_1 and B_1 O from B_1. Let F_1 and F_2 represent the longitude factors from Table 35 for the position lines $A_1 A_2$ and $B_1 B_2$. Since F_1 is the difference of longitude corresponding to a change of 1′ of latitude along the line $A_1 A_2$, the difference of longitude A_1 O is equal to F_1 multiplied by the number of minutes of latitude in the length OP. Therefore,

$$A_1 O = OP \times F_1; \text{ and } B_1 O = OP \times F_2;$$

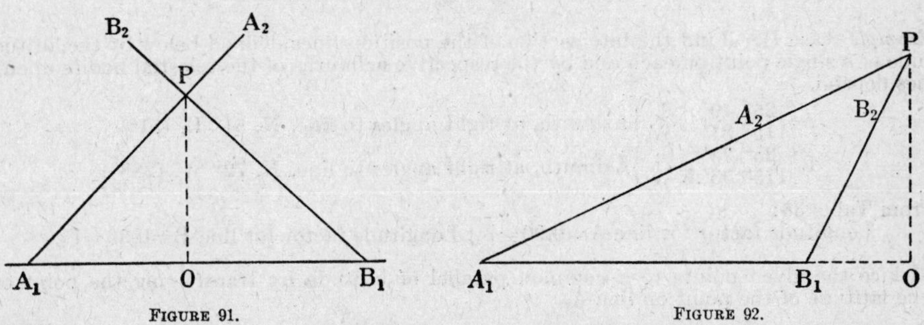

FIGURE 91. FIGURE 92.

and, since the known difference of longitude between the points A_1 and B_1 is composed of the sum of A_1 O and B_1 O in case I, and the difference of A_1 O and B_1 O in case II, we have

$$A_1 O + B_1 O = A_1 B_1 = OP \times F_1 + OP \times F_2 = OP\ (F_1 + F_2), \text{ in case I, and}$$
$$A_1 O - B_1 O = A_1 B_1 = OP \times F_1 - OP \times F_2 = OP\ (F_1 - F_2), \text{ in case II.}$$

Placing the known quantities on the right-hand side of the equations, thus:

$$OP = \frac{A_1 B_1}{F_1 + F_2}, \text{ in case I, and } OP = \frac{A_1 B_1}{F_1 - F_2}, \text{ in case II.}$$

There is obtained the difference of latitude from the common parallel of A_1 and B_1 to the point of intersection by dividing the known difference of longitude between the points A_1 and B_1 by the sum of the longitude factors of the respective position lines in case I and by their difference in case II.

Having determined OP and hence the latitude of the point of intersection of the position line, multiply OP by F_1 to get the difference of longitude A_1O, and apply that difference to the known longitude of A_1 to find the longitude of the point of intersection P; and also, as a check, multiply OP by F_2 to get the difference of longitude B_1O, which, being applied to the longitude of B_1, gives again the longitude of the point of intersection, P.

Summary.—Make a rough sketch of the position lines whose intersection is to be fixed in latitude and longitude, classifying them under case I, or case II.

Take from Table 35 the longitude factors F_1 and F_2, respectively, for the position lines.

If the given coordinates of the points on the two lines have not a common latitude, reduce them to a common latitude by multiplying the difference between the latitudes of the points on the two lines by the longitude factor of one of the lines, and apply the product to the longitude of the point on that line. The sketch will show whether the difference of longitude is to be added or subtracted, and the result will be the longitude of a point of this line on the common parallel of latitude.

The difference between the longitudes of the points of the two position lines, on the common parallel, divided by the sum of the longitude factors (F_1+F_2), is the difference of latitude between the point of intersection and the common parallel, when the lines are classified under case I; and the difference between the longitudes of the points of the two position lines, on the common parallel, divided by the difference of the longitude factors (F_1-F_2), is the difference of latitude between the point of intersection and the common parallel, when the lines are classified under case II.

The sketch shows whether the intersection of the position lines lies to the northward or southward of the common parallel, and whether the difference of latitude is added or subtracted from the latitude of the common parallel.

Having found the difference of latitude between the point of intersection of the position lines and the common parallel, multiply this difference by the longitude factor of each line and apply the products each to the longitude of its corresponding line on the common parallel. The products are applied in opposite directions in case I, and both of them give the same longitude for the point of intersection; and the products are applied in the same direction in case II, and in this case also both of them must give the same longitude for the point of intersection.

Example (case I).—Find the intersection of the position lines defined below by the latitude and longitude of a single point on each and by the respective azimuths of the celestial bodies upon which the lines depend.

A $\begin{cases} 25° 40' & S. \\ 115° 31' & W. \end{cases}$ Azimuth, at right angles to line, N. 51° E. (51°)

B $\begin{cases} 25° 25' & S. \\ 115° 33'.5 & W. \end{cases}$ Azimuth, at right angles to line, N. 72° W. (288°)

From Table 35:

Longitude factor for line A=0.90=F_1; Longitude factor for line B=0.36=F_2.

Reduce the given points to a common parallel of latitude by transferring the point on line B to the latitude of the point on line A,

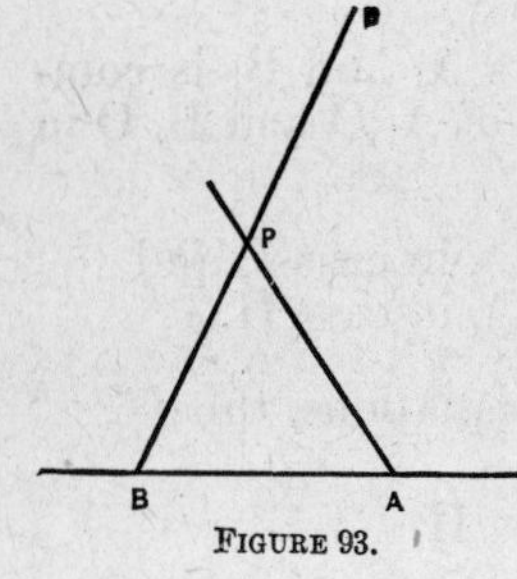

FIGURE 93.

(25° 40′ S.−25° 25′ S.)$\times F_2$=15′×0.36= 5′.4 W.
115° 33′.5 W.

115° 38′.9 W.

Hence for the point on the line B at which the latitude is the same as the latitude of the point on the line A,

B $\begin{cases} 25° 40' & S. \\ 115° 38'.9 & W. \end{cases}$ Azimuth, at right angles to line, N. 72° W. (288°).

There are now two position lines, under case I, whose common latitude is 25°40′ S. and whose longitudes on the common parallel are:

115° 38′.9 W.
115° 31′.0 W.

7′.9=Diff. Long. on common parallel.

$$\frac{7.9}{F^1+F^2}=\frac{7.9}{.90+.36}=\frac{7.9}{1.26}=6.27 \text{ Diff. Lat. between intersection and common parallel.}$$

Corrections in longitude:

$6.27\times F_1=6.27\times 0.90=5'.64$; $6.27\times F_2=6.27\times 0.36=2.26$

Long. A,	115° 31′.0 W.	Long. B,	115° 38′.9 W.	Lat. common parallel,	25° 40′.0 S.
Diff. Long.,	5 .6 W.	Diff. Long.,	2 .3 E.	Diff. Lat.,	6 .3 N.
Intersection,	115 36 .6 W.		115 36 .6 W.		25 33 .7 S.

Example (case II).—Find the intersection of the position lines defined below:

A $\begin{cases} 49° 30' & N. \\ 5\ \ 24.8 & W. \end{cases}$ Azimuth, at right angles to line, N. 81° W. (279°)

B $\begin{cases} 49° 30' & N. \\ 5\ \ 25.8 & W. \end{cases}$ Azimuth, at right angles to line, N. 31° W. (329°).

A sketch of the lines show them to be under case II.

From Table 35:

Longitude factor for line A=0.24=F_1 and longitude factor for line B=2.57=F_2.

Diff. Long. on common parallel=5° 25′.8−5° 24′.8=1′.0.

$\frac{1.0}{F_2-F_1}=\frac{1.0}{2.57-0.24}=\frac{1.0}{2.33}=0.42$= Diff. Lat. between intersection and common parallel.

Corrections in longitude.

$0.42\times F_1=0.42\times 0.24=0.1$; $0.42\times F_2=0.42\times 2.57=1.1$

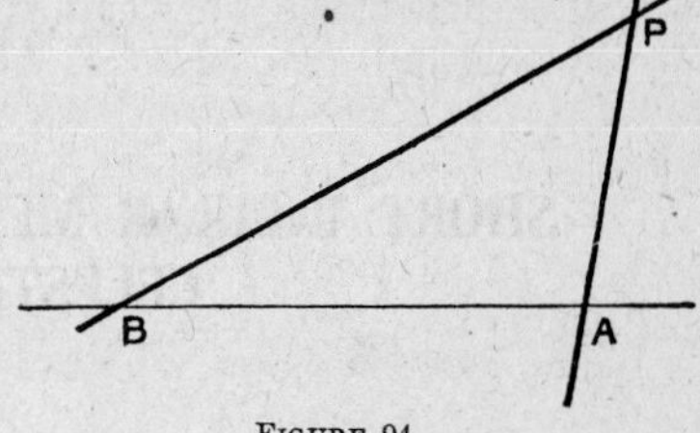

FIGURE 94.

Long. A,	5° 24′.8 W.	Long. B,	5° 25′.8 W.	Lat. common parallel,	49° 30′.0 N.
Diff. Long.,	0 .1 E.	Diff. Long.,	1 .1 E.	Diff. Lat.,	0 .4 N.
Intersection,	5 24 .7 W.		5 24 .7 W.		49 30 .4 N.

CHAPTER XV

SHORT TABULAR METHODS FOR SOLVING OBSERVATIONS OF CELESTIAL BODIES IN NAVIGATION

Description.—For many years, time and study have been devoted toward practical ways of producing for the navigator convenient epitomized tables for solving the astronomical triangle for the required elements, by means of a shorter process than that usually employed in logarithmic computation.

Up to the present time, the only element of the triangle that can be directly measured is the sextant altitude, hence there has been developed but two methods for obtaining line of position. One of these is called the longitude or "time sight" method, whereby hour angle and azimuth are determined; the other is the St. Hilaire or intercept method, in which altitude and azimuth are found. This latter method is the one generally adopted.

In the former method the oblique spherical astronomical triangle is solved directly for a local hour angle and azimuth of the celestial body, while in the latter method, the spherical triangle is divided into two right spherical triangles by dropping from the observed body on the meridian an auxiliary perpendicular arc, or dropping the auxiliary perpendicular arc from the zenith on the circle of declination. Either one of the methods of dividing the triangle produce a similar solution, or identical result in obtaining the desired computed altitude or azimuth.

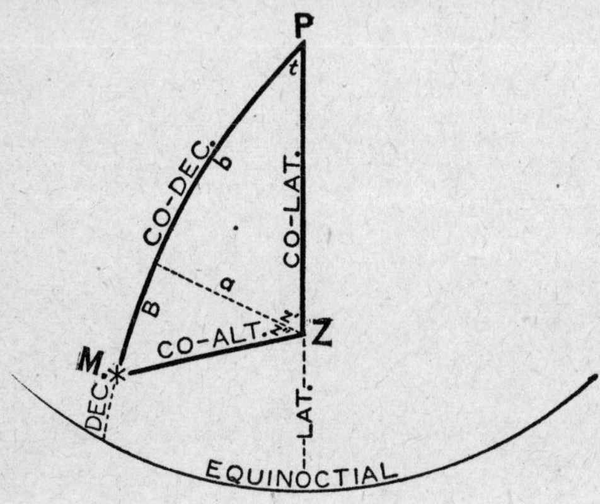

FIGURE 95. (H. O. Pub. No. 208).

The method of splitting the oblique spherical triangle into two right triangles is as old as the science of geometry or trigonometry, yet this is the one and only process that has been adopted by every foreign author in over a century of time. Such men as Towson (England), Kelvin (England), Souillagouet (France), Fuss (Russia), Delafon (France), Bertin (France), Aquino (Brazil), Smart and Shearme (England), Newton and Pinto (Portugal), Ogura (Japan), and others have utilized the split triangle. The later American publications follow along similar lines, with only slight alterations in the compilation of the table. No book is strictly the work of any one individual author, for all involve the principles which are the results of years of general development in the science of navigation.

The Hydrographic Office has issued a few publications of this nature, such as Publications Nos. 208, 211, and 214. The publication No. 211 is not a tabulated method, but a convenient collection of logarithmic functions of cosecants, termed A values, and logarithmic secants, termed B values.

For all of the tabulated methods, some assumed position must be selected; for the longer logarithmic computation, the dead-reckoning positions may be utilized. A dead-reckoning position is convenient for plotting two or more stars; otherwise there is no particular advantage in its use. The following examples will illustrate the publications now issued by the Hydrographic Office:

H. O. PUBLICATION NO. 208

(ALTITUDE—AZIMUTH)

At sea, January 15, 1934, about $5^h\ 30^m$ p. m. in D. R. latitude 20° N.; longitude 170° E.; observed simultaneous altitudes of the planet Venus bearing southwestward, sextant altitude 31° 40′ 00″, watch $6^h\ 07^m\ 35^s$, and the star Aldebaran bearing northeastward, sextant altitude 41° 05′ 00″, watch $6^h\ 08^m\ 00^s$. Watch keeping G. C. T., slow 5^s. I. C. 0′ 00″ H. E. 500 feet. Find position of air vessel.

VENUS

Watch,	$6^h\ 07^m\ 35^s$	H. A. Var. per min.	Sext. alt.,	31° 40′.0	Corr.,	− 7′.4
Corr.,	$+5^s$		Corr.,	−23 .5	H. E.,	−16 .1
G. C. T.,	$6^h\ 07^m\ 40^s$	15′.044	True alt.,	31° 16′.5	Corr.,	−23 .5
G. H. A. Jan. 15,	148° 51′.8					
Corr. 6^h,	90 15 .8		Dec.,	10° 37′.5 S.	P. P.	
Corr. $7^m\ 40^s$,	1 55 .4		Corr.,	−3 .5	13.7	
G. H. A.,	241° 03′.0 W.		Dec.,	10° 34′.0 S.		
Long.,	169° 57′.0 E.					

L. H. A.	51° W.	dec.	10° 34′.0 S.				
Lat.	20° N.	b,	59° 57′.4 N.	A16549	C 137	Z′	67°.1 N.
				B11967	D 9933	Z″	49 .6 N.
		d+b,	49° 23′.4 N.	A+B28516	C+D70		N. 116°.7 W.
h_c	31° 14′.3						
h_o	31 16 .5						
Int.	2′.2 toward N. 117° W.						

b takes name of Lat.
Z′ takes name of b.
Z″ takes name of d+b.

ALDEBARAN

G. C. T.,	$6^h\ 08^m\ 05^s$	Sext. alt.,	41° 05′.0	Corr.,	− 7′.0
		Corr.,	−23 .1	H. E.,	−16 .1
G. H. A. Jan. 15,	45° 42′.8				
Corr. $6^h\ 08^m$,	92 15 .1	True alt.,	40° 41′.9	Corr.,	−23 .1
Corr. 5^s,	1 .3				
		Dec.,	16° 22′.8 N.		
G. H. A.,	137° 59′.2 W.				
Long.,	170 00 .8 E.				

L. H. A.,	308° W.	dec.,	16° 22′.8 N.				
Lat.,	20° N.	b,	59° 24′.5 N.	A17259	C 130	Z′	66°.4 N.
				B 1350	D 9404	Z″	18 .9 N.
		d+b,	75° 47′.3 N.	A+B18609	C+D9534		N. 85°.3 E.
h_c	40° 39′.3						
h_o	40 41 .9						
Int.	2′.6 toward N. 85° E.						

Hour angles between 0° and 180° are named W. and between 180° and 360° are named E. with respect to naming Z.

The detailed procedure for the observation Venus is illustrated only and values for star Aldebaran are found in a similar manner. Enter Table I, with arguments H. A. 51°; latitude 20° take out b, A, C, Z′, combine b, and dec. name b same as latitude obtain d+b. Enter Table II, with d+b and take out B, D, C+D, and Z″. Add A+B and take from Table II, the computed altitude. For star Aldebaran enter Table I with argument H. A. 308° W. latitude 20° take out b, A, C, Z′ combine b, and declination for d+b. Enter Table II with d+b as argument and take B, D, and Z″. Add A+B and take from Table II the computed altitude, add Z for azimuth. On the parallel of latitude 20° N. longitude 169° 57′ .0 E. lay down azimuth N. 117° W. plot line of position 2.2 miles toward Venus along azimuth line and at right angles to azimuth of Venus.

In latitude 20° N. longitude 170° 00′ .8 E., lay down azimuth N. 85° E. plot line of position at right angles to azimuth 2.6 miles toward star Aldebaran.

The intersection of the position lines is the position of the vessel.

H.O. PUBLICATION No. 208

Table I

L° \ t°	309° b	51° A	C	Z′	308° b	52° A	C	Z′	L° \ t°
	° ′			°	° ′			°	
0	90 0.0	20113	110	90.0	90 0.0	21066	103	90.0	0
1	88 24.7	20103	110	88.8	88 22.6	21055	104	88.7	1
2	86 49.4	20072	110	87.5	86 45.2	21022	104	87.4	2
3	85 14.4	20022	110	86.3	85 8.1	20969	104	86.2	3
4	83 39.6	19953	111	85.1	83 31.2	20894	105	84.9	4
5	82 5.1	19863	111	83.9	81 54.7	20797	105	83.6	5
6	80 31.1	19753	112	82.6	80 18.7	20681	106	82.4	6
7	78 57.6	19626	113	81.4	78 43.3	20543	107	81.1	7
8	77 24.7	19481	114	80.2	77 8.5	20387	108	79.9	8
9	75 52.4	19317	115	79.1	75 34.4	20213	109	78.7	9
10	74 20.9	19136	116	77.9	74 1.1	20019	110	77.5	10
11	72 50.1	18940	118	76.7	72 28.7	19808	112	76.3	11
12	71 20.2	18726	119	75.6	70 57.2	19580	113	75.1	12
13	69 51.3	18498	121	74.5	69 26.7	19337	115	73.9	13
14	68 23.2	18257	123	73.4	67 57.2	19077	117	72.8	14
15	66 56.2	18001	125	72.3	66 28.8	18805	119	71.6	15
16	65 30.2	17732	127	71.2	65 1.6	18519	121	70.6	16
17	64 5.3	17452	129	70.1	63 35.5	18219	123	69.5	17
18	62 41.6	17160	131	69.1	62 10.6	17909	125	68.4	18
19	61 18.9	16860	134	68.1	60 47.0	17589	128	67.4	19
20	59 57.4	16549	137	67.1	59 24.5	17259	130	66.4	20
21	58 37.1	16230	140	66.1	58 3.4	16919	133	65.4	21
22	57 18.0	15902	142	65.2	56 43.5	16573	136	64.4	22
23	56 0.0	15568	145	64.2	55 24.9	16219	139	63.4	23
24	54 43.3	15228	148	63.3	54 7.6	15858	143	62.5	24
25	53 27.8	14881	152	62.4	52 51.6	15493	146	61.6	25

Table II—*d*~*b*

′	31° h_e 31° B	Z″ 58° D	40° h_e 40° B	Z″ 49° D	49° h_e 49° B	Z″ 40° D	59° h_e 59° B	Z″ 30° D	71° h_e 71° B	Z″ 18° D	75° h_e 75° B	Z″ 14° D	°
0	28816	221	19193	76	12222	9939	6693	9779	2433	9537	1506	9428	1.0
1	28795	221	19178	76	12211	9939	6686	9778	2429	9537	1502	9428	1.0
2	28774	221	19163	76	12200	9939	6678	9778	2424	9536	1499	9427	1.0
3	28753	220	19148	75	12189	9938	6671	9778	2420	9536	1495	9427	1.0
4	28732	220	19133	75	12178	9938	6663	9778	2416	9535	1492	9426	.9
5	28711	220	19118	75	12167	9938	6656	9777	2411	9535	1489	9426	.9
6	28690	220	19103	75	12156	9938	6648	9777	2407	9535	1485	9425	.9
7	28669	219	19088	74	12145	9937	6640	9777	2403	9534	1482	9425	.9
8	28648	219	19073	74	12134	9937	6633	9776	2398	9534	1479	9424	.9
9	28627	219	19058	74	12123	9937	6625	9776	2394	9533	1475	9423	.9
10	28607	218	19043	74	12113	9937	6618	9776	2390	9533	1472	9423	.8
11	28586	218	19028	73	12102	9936	6610	9776	2385	9532	1469	9422	.8
12	28565	218	19013	73	12091	9936	6603	9775	2381	9532	1465	9422	.8
13	28544	218	18998	73	12080	9936	6595	9775	2377	9532	1462	9421	.8
14	28523	217	18983	73	12069	9936	6588	9775	2372	9531	1459	9421	.8
15	28502	217	18968	72	12058	9935	6580	9774	2368	9531	1455	9420	.8
16	28481	217	18953	72	12047	9935	6573	9774	2364	9530	1452	9420	.7
17	28461	216	18939	72	12036	9935	6565	9774	2360	9530	1449	9419	.7
18	28440	216	18924	72	12025	9935	6558	9774	2355	9530	1445	9419	.7
19	28419	216	18909	71	12015	9934	6550	9773	2351	9529	1442	9418	.7
20	28398	216	18894	71	12004	9934	6543	9773	2347	9529	1439	9418	.7
21	28378	215	18879	71	11993	9934	6535	9773	2343	9528	1435	9417	.7
22	28357	215	18864	71	11982	9934	6528	9772	2338	9528	1432	9417	.6
23	28336	215	18849	70	11971	9933	6520	9772	2334	9527	1429	9416	.6
24	28315	214	18834	70	11960	9933	6513	9772	2330	9527	1426	9416	.6
25	28295	214	18820	70	11949	9933	6505	9772	2326	9527	1422	9415	.6
26	28274	214	18805	70	11939	9933	6498	9771	2321	9526	1419	9415	.6
27	28253	214	18790	69	11928	9932	6490	9771	2317	9526	1416	9414	.6
28	28233	213	18775	69	11917	9932	6483	9771	2313	9525	1412	9414	.5
29	28212	213	18760	69	11906	9932	6475	9770	2309	9525	1409	9413	.5

The azimuth is reckoned from the north when in north latitude, from the south when in south latitude, toward the east when body is rising or is east of the meridian, toward the west when body is setting or is west of the meridian. **In zero latitude the azimuth takes the name of the declination.**

PLOT OF ADJACENT PROBLEM

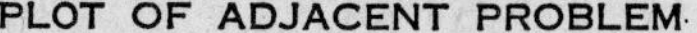

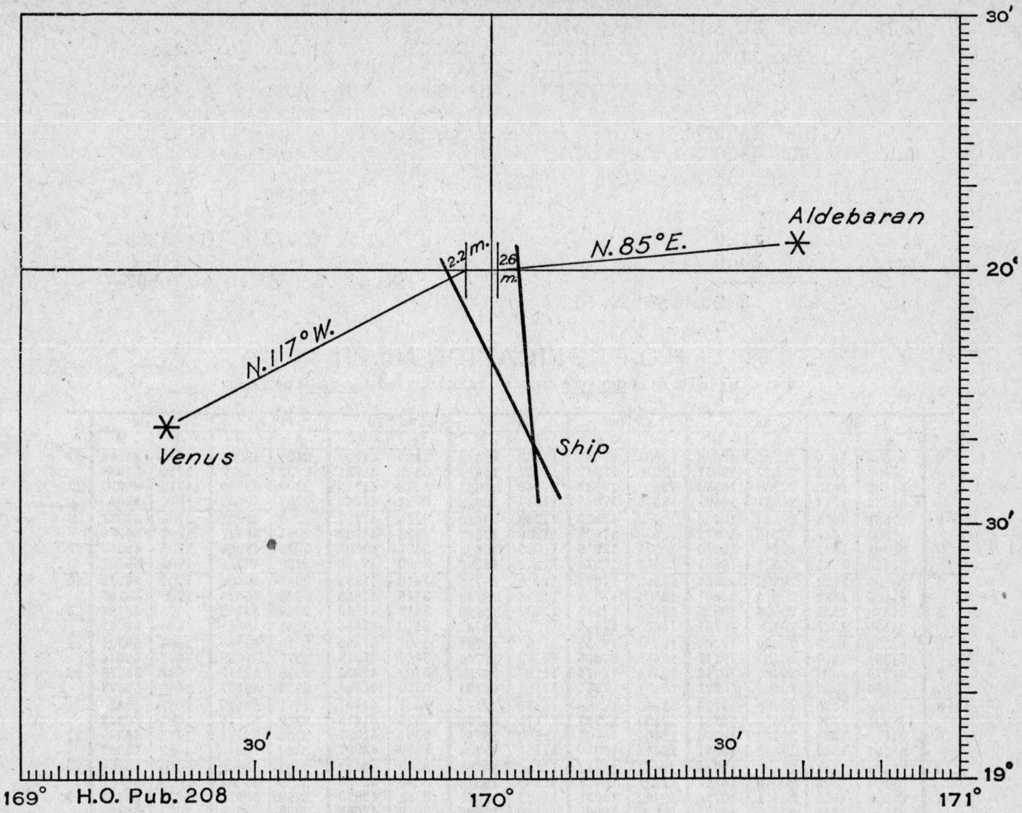

FIGURE 98.

H. O. PUBLICATION NO. 211

(ALTITUDE—AZIMUTH)

At sea, May 15, 1934, about $7^h\ 30^m$ p. m. in D. R. latitude 40° 43′ N.; longitude 68° 30′ W., observed simultaneous altitudes of star Vega, bearing northeastward, sextant altitude 14° 39′ 30″ and the star Procyon bearing southwestward, sextant altitude 26° 40′ 40″; watch keeping G. C. T. $0^h\ 34^m\ 24^s$ (May 16), watch slow 3^s; H. E. 35 feet; I. C. 0′ 0″. Required position of vessel.

Watch,	$0^h\ 34^m\ 24^s$
Corr., +	3^s
G. C. T.,	$0^h\ 34^m\ 27^s$

VEGA

Dec. 38° 43′.0 N.				
G. C. T. $0^h\ 34^m\ 27^s$				
G. H. A. May 16,	314° 20′.0			
Corr. $0^h\ 34^m$,	8 31 .4			
Corr. 27^s,	6 .8			
G. H. A.,	322 58 .2 W.			
Long.,	68 30 .0 W.			
L. H. A.,	254 28 .2 W.			
L. H. A.,	105 31 .8 E.			
Sextant alt.,	14° 39′.5		Alt.,	−3′.7
Corr.,	− 9 .5		H. E.,	−5′.8
True alt.,	14 30 .0		Corr.,	−9 .5

PROCYON

Dec. 5° 23′.7 N.			
G. C. T. $0^h\ 34^m\ 27^s$			
G. H. A. May 16,	119° 03′.0		
Corr. $0^h\ 34^m$,	8 31′.4		
Corr. 27^s,	6 .8		
G. H. A.,	127 41 .2 W.		
Long.,	68 30 .0 W.		
L. H. A.,	59 11 .2 W.		
Sextant alt.,	26° 40′.7	Alt.,	−1′.9
Corr.,	− 7 .7	H. E.,	−5′.8
True alt.,	26 33 .0	Corr.,	−7 .7

VEGA

L. H. A. 105° 31′.8 E.	A 1616				
Dec. 38° 43′.0 N.	B 10777	A 20379		*Alt.*	*Az.*
	A 12393	B 18081		B 18081	A 12393
K 108° 28′.5 N.		A 2298			
Lat. 40 43 .0 N.					
K–L 67 45 .5				B 42192	
h_c 14° 27′.0				A 60273	B 1396
h_o 14 30 .0			N. 50° 56′ E. =		A 10997
Int. 3 .0 toward N. 51° E.					

H.O. PUBLICATION No. 211

WHEN LHA (E OR W) IS GREATER THAN 90°, TAKE "K" FROM BOTTOM OF TABLE

′	14° 00′		38° 30′		48° 30′		50° 30′		67° 30′		71° 30′		74° 00′		′
′	A	B	A	B	A	B	A	B	A	B	A	B	A	B	′
0	61632	1310	20585	10646	12554	17873	11259	19649	3438	41716	2304	49852	1716	55966	30
	61607	1311	20577	10651	12549	17881	11254	19657	3436	41731	2302	49871	1714	55988	
1	61582	1313	20569	10656	12543	17888	11249	19664	3433	41746	2300	49890	1712	56010	29
	61556	1314	20561	10661	12538	17895	11244	19672	3431	41762	2298	49909	1710	56032	
2	61531	1316	20553	10666	12532	17902	11239	19680	3428	41777	2296	49928	1709	56054	28
	61506	1317	20545	10671	12526	17909	11233	19687	3425	41792	2294	49947	1707	56076	
3	61481	1319	20537	10676	12521	17916	11228	19695	3423	41808	2292	49966	1705	56099	27
	61455	1321	20529	10681	12515	17924	11223	19703	3420	41823	2290	49985	1703	56121	
4	61430	1322	20522	10686	12510	17931	11218	19710	3418	41838	2287	50004	1701	56143	26
	61405	1324	20514	10691	12504	17938	11213	19718	3415	41853	2285	50023	1700	56165	
5	61380	1325	20506	10696	12499	17945	11207	19726	3412	41869	2283	50042	1698	56187	25
	61355	1327	20498	10701	12493	17952	11202	19733	3410	41884	2281	50061	1696	56209	
6	61330	1329	20490	10706	12487	17959	11197	19741	3407	41899	2279	50080	1694	56231	24
	61304	1330	20482	10711	12482	17966	11192	19749	3404	41915	2277	50098	1692	56254	
7	61279	1332	20474	10716	12476	17974	11187	19756	3402	41930	2275	50117	1691	56276	23
	61254	1333	20466	10721	12471	17981	11181	19764	3399	41945	2273	50137	1689	56298	
8	61229	1335	20458	10726	12465	17988	11176	19772	3397	41961	2271	50156	1687	56320	22
	61204	1336	20450	10731	12460	17995	11171	19779	3394	41976	2269	50175	1685	56342	
9	61179	1338	20442	10736	12454	18002	11166	19787	3391	41991	2266	50194	1683	56365	21
	61154	1340	20435	10741	12448	18010	11161	19795	3389	42007	2264	50213	1682	56387	
10	61129	1341	20427	10746	12443	18017	11156	19803	3386	42022	2262	50232	1680	56409	20
	61104	1343	20419	10751	12437	18024	11150	19810	3384	42038	2260	50251	1678	56431	
11	61079	1344	20411	10756	12432	18031	11145	19818	3381	42053	2258	50270	1676	56454	19
	61054	1346	20403	10761	12426	18038	11140	19826	3379	42068	2256	50289	1674	56476	
12	61029	1348	20395	10767	12421	18045	11135	19834	3376	42084	2254	50308	1673	56498	18
	61004	1349	20387	10772	12415	18053	11130	19841	3373	42099	2252	50327	1671	56521	
13	60979	1351	20379	10777	12410	18060	11124	19849	3371	42115	2250	50346	1669	56543	17
	60954	1352	20371	10782	12404	18067	11119	19857	3368	42130	2248	50365	1667	56565	
14	60929	1354	20364	10787	12398	18074	11114	19864	3366	42145	2246	50385	1665	56588	16
	60904	1356	20356	10792	12393	18081	11109	19872	3363	42161	2243	50404	1664	56610	
15	60879	1357	20348	10797	12387	18089	11104	19880	3360	42176	2241	50423	1662	56632	15
	60855	1359	20340	10802	12382	18096	11099	19888	3358	42192	2239	50442	1660	56655	
16	60830	1360	20332	10807	12376	18103	11094	19895	3355	42207	2237	50461	1658	56677	14
	60805	1362	20324	10812	12371	18110	11088	19903	3353	42223	2235	50480	1657	56700	
17	60780	1364	20316	10817	12365	18117	11083	19911	3350	42238	2233	50499	1655	56722	13
	60755	1365	20309	10822	12360	18125	11078	19918	3348	42254	2231	50519	1653	56745	
18	60730	1367	20301	10827	12354	18132	11073	19926	3345	42269	2229	50538	1651	56767	12
	60706	1368	20293	10832	12349	18139	11068	19934	3342	42285	2227	50557	1650	56790	
19	60681	1370	20285	10838	12343	18146	11063	19942	3340	42300	2225	50576	1648	56812	11
	60656	1372	20277	10843	12338	18154	11057	19949	3337	42316	2223	50596	1646	56835	
20	60631	1373	20269	10848	12332	18161	11052	19957	3335	42331	2221	50615	1644	56857	10
	60607	1375	20261	10853	12327	18168	11047	19965	3332	42347	2218	50634	1642	56880	
21	60582	1377	20254	10858	12321	18175	11042	19973	3329	42362	2216	50653	1641	56902	9
	60557	1378	20246	10863	12316	18182	11037	19980	3327	42378	2214	50673	1639	56925	
22	60533	1380	20238	10868	12310	18190	11032	19988	3324	42393	2212	50692	1637	56947	8
	60508	1381	20230	10873	12305	18197	11027	19996	3322	42409	2210	50711	1635	56970	
23	60483	1383	20222	10878	12299	18204	11021	20004	3319	42424	2208	50730	1634	56992	7
	60459	1385	20214	10883	12293	18211	11016	20012	3317	42440	2206	50750	1632	57015	
24	60434	1386	20207	10888	12288	18219	11011	20019	3314	42455	2204	50769	1630	57038	6
	60410	1388	20199	10894	12282	18226	11006	20027	3312	42471	2202	50788	1628	57060	
25	60385	1390	20191	10899	12277	18233	11001	20035	3309	42486	2200	50808	1627	57083	5
	60360	1391	20183	10904	12271	18240	10996	20043	3306	42502	2198	50827	1625	57106	
26	60336	1393	20175	10909	12266	18248	10991	20050	3304	42518	2196	50846	1623	57128	4
	60311	1394	20167	10914	12260	18255	10986	20058	3301	42533	2194	50866	1621	57151	
27	60287	1396	20160	10919	12255	18262	10980	20066	3299	42549	2192	50885	1619	57174	3
	60262	1398	20152	10924	12249	18269	10975	20074	3296	42564	2190	50905	1618	57196	
28	60238	1399	20144	10929	12244	18277	10970	20082	3294	42580	2188	50924	1616	57219	2
	60213	1401	20136	10934	12238	18284	10965	20089	3291	42596	2185	50943	1614	57242	
29	60189	1403	20128	10939	12233	18291	10960	20097	3289	42611	2183	50963	1612	57265	1
	60164	1404	20121	10945	12227	18298	10955	20105	3286	42627	2181	50982	1611	57287	
30	60140	1406	20113	10950	12222	18306	10950	20113	3283	42642	2179	51002	1609	57310	0
	A	B	A	B	A	B	A	B	A	B	A	B	A	B	
′	165° 30′		141° 00′		131° 00′		129° 00′		112° 00′		108° 00′		105° 30′		′

ALWAYS TAKE "Z" FROM BOTTOM OF TABLE, EXCEPT WHEN "K" IS SAME NAME AND GREATER THAN LATITUDE, IN WHICH CASE TAKE "Z" FROM TOP. OF TABLE

PROCYON

L. H. A.	59° 11′.2 W.	A 6610					
dec.	5 23 .7 N.	B 193	A 102704		*Alt.*		*Az.*
		A 6803	B 28513		B 28513		A 6803
K	10° 26′.5 N.		A 74191				
Lat.	40 43 .0 N.						
K–L	30 16 .5				B 6368		
h_s	26° 36′.5				A 34881		B 4862
h_o	26 33 .0			N. 107° W. =			A 1941
Int.	3 .5 away from N. 107° W.						

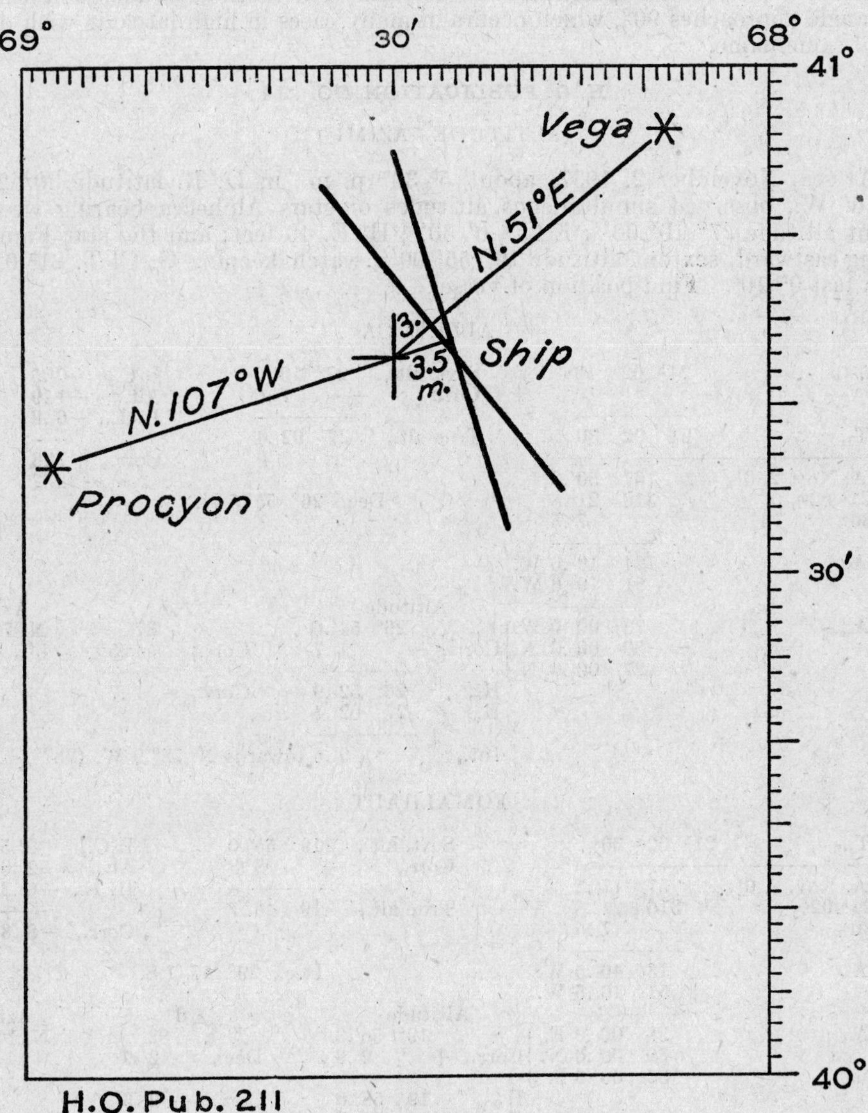

FIGURE 103.

Only the observation of the star Vega is illustrated in the sample page, but the observation for star Procyon is found in a similar way.

Enter the table with local hour angle 105° 31′.8 and take out A 1616; enter table with declination 38°43′; find value of B 10777 and A 20379, add A and B of H. A. and dec. and get A 12393; search in tables for B value 18081 corresponding to this A value 12393. Copy this B value 18081 for getting altitude and the A value 12393 for obtaining azimuth. Subtract this latter B value 18081 from A value 20379 obtained from declination and get A value 2298; this is the K value 108° 28′.5 and is named the same as declination. Combine K with D. R. latitude and get K–L; find in table the B value 42192 for K–L (67° 45′.5), add the B values 18081 and 42192 for the A value 60273 of the computed altitude 14° 27′.0; find the corresponding B value 1396 for the azimuth, subtract this B value 1396 from A value 12393 and get an A value 10977 for azimuth.

Plot both position lines from the D. R. position; the intersection of the position lines is the most probable position of the vessel. The method is not good when the hour angle approaches 90°, which occurs in many cases in high latitude with declination of same name.

H. O. PUBLICATION NO. 214

(ALTITUDE—AZIMUTH)

At sea, November 2, 1937, about $5^h\ 30^m$ p. m., in D. R. latitude 30° 29′ N.; 51° 10′ W., observed simultaneous altitudes of stars Alphecca bearing westward, sextant altitude 27° 10′ 00″; I. C.+0′ 30″; H. E. 40 feet; and the star Fomalhaut bearing eastward, sextant altitude 19° 55′ 00″; watch keeping G. C. T. $21^h\ 02^m\ 40^s$; watch fast $0^m\ 10^s$. Find position of vessel.

ALPHECCA

Watch,	$21^h\ 02^m\ 40^s$	Sext. alt.,	27° 10′.0	I. C.,	+0′.5
Corr.,	— 10	Corr.,	— 7 .6	Alt.,	−1 .9
				H. E.,	−6 .2
G. C. T.,	21 02 30	True alt.,	27 02 .4		
				Corr.,	−7′.6
G. H. A. Nov. 2, 0^h,	167° 50′.3				
Corr. $21^h\ 02^m$,	316 21 .8	Dec., 26° 55′.5 N.			
Corr. 30^s,	7 .5				
G. H. A.,	124° 19 .6 W.				
Long.,	51 19 .6 W.				

			Altitude	Δd	Azimuth
L. H. A.,	73 00 .0 W.		26° 54′.6	37′	N. 72°.9 W.
Lat.,	30 00 .0 N.	Corr.,	— 1 .7	Corr., 4′.5	
Dec.,	27 00 .0 N.				
		H_c,	26 52 .9	Corr., — 1 .7	
		H_o,	27 02 .4		
		Int.,	9 .5 towards N. 72°.9 W. (287°)		

FOMALHAUT

G. C. T.,	$21^h\ 02^m\ 30^s$	Sext. alt.,	19° 55′.0	I. C.,	+0′.5
		Corr.,	— 8 .3	Alt.,	−2 .6
G. H. A. Nov. 2, 0^h,	57° 17′.2			H. E.,	−6 .2
Corr. $21^h\ 02^m$,	316 21 .8	True alt.,	19 46 .7		
Corr. 30^s,	7 .5			Corr.,	−8 .3
G. H. A.,	13 46 .5 W.	Dec., 29° 57.′1 S.			
Long.,	51 46 .5 W.				

			Altitude	Δd	Azimuth
L. H. A.,	38 00 .0 E.		19° 56′.3	82	N. 145°.4 E.
Lat.,	30 00 .0 N.	Corr.,	+ 2 .3	Dec., 2′.9	
Dec.,	30 00 .0 S.				
		H_c,	19 58 .6	Corr., + 2 .3	
		H_o,	19 46 .7		
		Int.,	11 .9 away from N. 145°.4 E. (145°)		

Enter table in case of star Alphecca with latitude 30°; declination 27° same name and hour angle 73° and take out tabulated altitude 26° 54′.6 and difference for 1′ of declination .37′ and azimuth 72°.9. Since the tabulated value of declination is too large by 4′.5, a correction is made for this amount of declination. The difference for 1′ of declination is .37′ and .37×4′.5 is the correction to apply to the tabulated value to give the true altitude for latitude 30°; H. A. 73° and declination 26° 55′.5. This multiplication is automatically made for any value by a table on the back cover.

H.O. Pub. 214

LATITUDE 30°. DECLINATION SAME NAME AS LATITUDE

26° 00′			26° 30′			27° 00′			27° 30′			H.A.
Alt.		Az.	Alt.		Az.	Alt.		Az.	Alt.		Az.	
° ′	Δd Δt	°	° ′	Δd Δt	°	° ′	Δd Δt	°	° ′	Δd Δt	°	°
29 02.3	37 84	75.0	29 13.3	36 84	74.5	29 24.0	36 83	74.0	29 34.7	35 83	73.4	**70**
28 12.2	37 84	74.6	28 23.2	37 83	74.1	28 34.1	36 83	73.6	28 44.9	36 83	73.0	1
27 22.1	37 83	74.2	27 33.3	37 83	73.7	27 44.3	37 83	73.2	27 55.3	36 83	72.7	2
26 32.2	38 83	73.9	26 43.5	37 83	73.4	26 54.6	37 83	72.9	27 05.7	37 82	72.3	3←
25 42.3	38 83	73.5	25 53.7	38 83	73.0	26 05.0	37 83	72.5	26 16.2	37 82	72.0	4
24 52.5	39 83	73.1	25 04.1	38 83	72.6	25 15.5	38 82	72.1	25 26.9	37 82	71.6	**75**
24 02.8	39 83	72.7	24 14.5	39 82	72.2	24 26.1	38 82	71.7	24 37.6	38 82	71.2	6
23 13.3	39 82	72.3	23 25.1	39 82	71.8	23 36.9	39 82	71.3	23 48.5	38 82	70.8	7
22 23.8	40 82	72.0	22 35.8	40 82	71.5	22 47.7	39 82	71.0	22 59.5	39 82	70.5	8
21 34.5	40 82	71.6	21 46.6	40 82	71.1	21 58.6	40 82	70.6	22 10.6	39 81	70.1	9
20 45.2	41 82	71.2	20 57.5	41 82	70.7	21 09.7	40 81	70.2	21 21.8	40 81	69.7	**80**
19 56.1	41 82	70.8	20 08.5	41 82	70.3	20 20.9	41 81	69.8	20 33.1	40 81	69.3	1
19 07.1	42 82	70.4	19 19.6	42 81	69.9	19 32.1	41 81	69.4	19 44.5	41 81	68.9	2
18 18.2	42 81	70.0	18 30.9	42 81	69.5	18 43.5	42 81	69.0	18 56.1	42 81	68.5	3
17 29.4	43 81	69.6	17 42.3	43 81	69.1	17 55.1	42 81	68.6	18 07.8	42 80	68.1	4
16 40.8	43 81	69.2	16 53.8	43 81	68.7	17 06.8	43 80	68.2	17 19.6	43 80	67.7	**85**
15 52.3	44 81	68.8	16 05.5	44 80	68.3	16 18.6	43 80	67.8	16 31.6	43 80	67.3	6
15 03.9	44 80	68.4	15 17.3	44 80	67.9	15 30.5	44 80	67.4	15 43.7	44 80	66.9	7
14 15.7	45 80	67.9	14 29.2	45 80	67.4	14 42.6	45 80	67.0	14 55.9	44 79	66.5	8
13 27.6	45 80	67.5	13 41.2	45 80	67.0	13 54.8	45 79	66.6	14 08.4	45 79	66.1	9
12 39.7	46 80	67.1	12 53.5	46 80	66.6	13 07.2	46 79	66.2	13 20.9	46 79	65.7	**90**

From latitude 30° N.; longitude 51° 19′.6 W., lay off azimuth line N. 73° W. (287°). From this position lay off 9.5 miles toward the star; draw line of position through this latter point at right angles to azimuth.

In case of star Fomalhaut enter table at latitude 30°, declination 30° (contrary name), and hour angle 38°, pick out altitude 19° 56′.3; Δd .82 and azimuth 145°.4. Since the declination is 29° 57′.1, it is smaller by 2′.9 than 30°. Then correction is .82×2′.9=+2′.3; plus because decreasing declinations show increasing altitudes. The computed or tabular altitude is then 19° 58′.6.

From latitude 30° N.; longitude 51° 46′.5 W., lay down azimuth 145° and from this position plot a point, 11.9 miles away from star Fomalhaut and through this point at right angles to the azimuth draw the line of position. The intersection of the position lines is the position of ship.

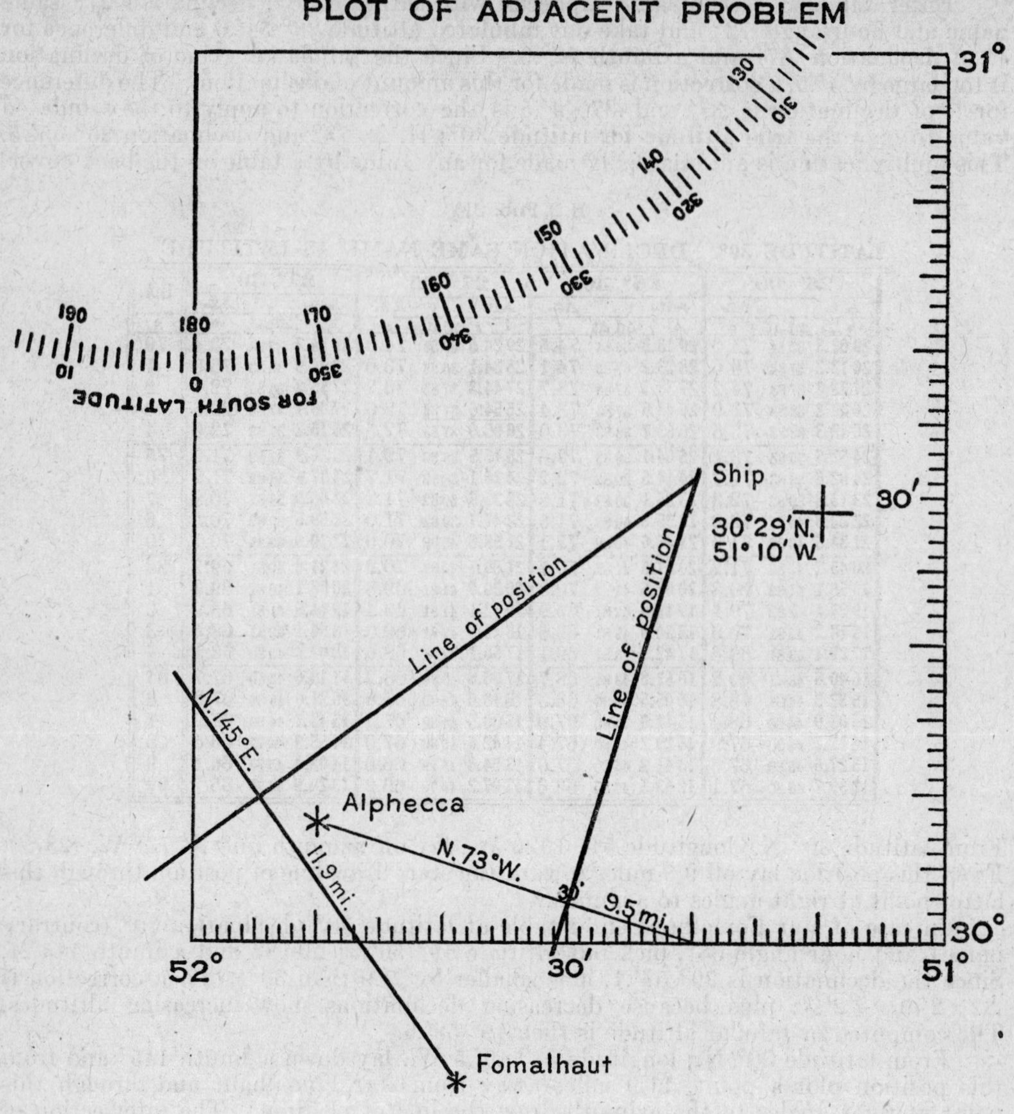
PLOT OF ADJACENT PROBLEM
31°
130
310
140
320
150
330
160
340
190
180
170
10
0
350
FOR SOUTH LATITUDE
Ship
30′
30°29′N.
51° 10′W.
Line of position
Line of position
N.145°E.
Alphecca
11.9mi.
N.73°W.
30′
9.5mi.
30°
52°
30′
51°
Fomalhaut

FIGURE 100.

The American Air Almanac

This type of Almanac is designed especially for the use of aviators, but with a very few alterations, it would be convenient also for surface navigators. It was first developed at the Hydrographic Office in 1932, but perfected and published later by the Naval Observatory. It affords simple and quick results and offers a ready means in dealing with celestial bodies for all types of aircraft. The quantities in this Almanac are tabulated to 1′ of arc and can be used by surface craft in open waters, providing that the limitations of the Almanac are understood without danger of introducing any serious error, but the Almanac should not be used near land except with caution, because the error resulting from its use is not the only error to be expected in the observed position, but also all other unavoidable errors occurring in any sight observed with sextant. The Air Almanac is conveniently arranged for every day in the year, to give all data, for Sun, G. H. A. ♈, Planets, Moon, sunrise, sunset, moonrise, moonset, twilight, Semidiameter of Sun and Moon and Moon's parallax; all arranged *on one* sheet. Corrections for any Greenwich Civil Time interval for Sun, Planets, and Moon are given on the front inside cover. On the back inside cover an alphabetical list of the stars are tabulated indicating the stars hour angle (S. H. A.) which is equal to (360°−R. A.) also the declination and magnitude. The error in any interpolated Greenwich hour angle of a celestial body depends upon the number of quantities that form it and is never larger than 1′.8 and the average error is 0′.5 except certain star hour angles shown in parentheses. The error resulting from the use of this Almanac in a position determined by two simultaneous observations will rarely be as large as 5 miles.

Hour Angle of Sun.—The Greenwich hour angle of the sun at any given instant of G. C. T. is found by adding the G. H. A. for the preceding hour taken from the tabulated data of the daily sheet for every 10 minutes of time, to the correction for the sun's motion in the odd minutes and seconds taken from the interpolation table for the sun. The Greenwich hour angle of the celestial body from the Greenwich meridian (G. H. A.) is tabulated in arc for every 10 minutes of G. C. T. For the exact instant of observation, the correction to G. H. A. is found by inspection from a G. H. A. interpolation table on the inside front cover of the Almanac. To find the local hour angle, apply the observer's longitude, subtracting in west longitude from the G. H. A. to which 360° is added if necessary, but adding in east longitude and subtracting 360° from the resulting sum if necessary.

Example.—In Long. 120° W., at G. C. T. $21^h\ 24^m\ 37^s$, find the G. H. A. and L. H. A. of the Sun on January 1, 1943.

G. C. T.	$21^h\ 24^m\ 37^s$	
G. H. A. $21^h\ 20^m$	139° 07′	(Daily p. m. sheet)
Corr. $4^m\ 37^s$	1 09	(Choose upper of two adjacent values from table on inside front cover when argument is an exact tabulated value)
G. H. A. $21^h\ 24^m\ 37^s$	140 16 W.	
Long.	120 00 W.	
L. H. A.	20 16 W.	

Example.—In Long. 23° 30′ E., at G. C. T. $08^h\ 23^m\ 47^s$; find the G. H. A. and L. H. A. of Moon, on January 1, 1943.

G. C. T.	$08^h\ 23^m\ 47^s$	
G. H. A. $08^h\ 20^m$	16° 17′	(Daily a. m. sheet)
Corr. $3^m\ 47^s$	55	(From inside front cover)
Corr. H. A. ☾	0	(Additional correction on a. m. sheet in lower right hand corner due to irregularity of the moon's motion. This correction must always be made)
G. H. A. $08^h\ 23^m\ 47^s$	17 12 W.	
Long.	23 30 E.	
L. H. A.	40 42 W.	

Example.—In Long. 45° E., at G. C. T. $16^h\ 37^m\ 40^s$ find the G. H. A. and L. H. A. of the planet Saturn on January 1, 1943.

G. C. T.	$16^h\ 37^m\ 40^s$	
G. H. A. $16^h\ 30^m$	282° 44′	
Corr. $7^m\ 40^s$	1 55	(Corr. inside front cover)
G. H. A. $16^h\ 37^m\ 40^s$	284 39 W.	
Long.	45 00 E.	
L. H. A.	329 39 W.	

The correction for the same example taken from the American Nautical Almanac for January 1, 1943, is as follows:

Saturn, Jan. 1, G. C. T.	$16^h\ 37^m\ 40^s$	Var. per min. 15′0438
G. H. A. 0^h	34° 30′.6	
Corr. for Planets 16^h	240 42 .2	Corr. 15′0400=9° 16′.5
		Corr. 15′0500=9° 16′.8
Corr. for Planets 37^m	9 16 .6	Corr. 15′0438=9° 16′.6
Corr. for Planets 40^s	10 .0	
G. H. A. $16^h\ 37^m\ 40^s$	284 39 .4 W.	

The G. H. A. of a star=G. H. A. Aries plus Star hour angle (S. H. A.).

The S. H. A. for any star can be determined by subtracting stars R. A. from 360°.

Example.—In Long. 169° 20′ W., at G. C. T. $15^h\ 21^m\ 10^s$, find the G. H. A. and L. H. A. and Declination of Star Sirius on January 1, 1943.

G. C. T.	$15^h\ 21^m\ 10^s$	
G. H. A. ♈, $15^h\ 20^m$	330° 24′	(From p. m. daily sheet)
Corr. $1^m\ 10^s$	0 18	(Inside front cover)
G. H. A. ♈	330 42	
S. H. A. Sirius	259 20	(Inside back cover) Dec. 16° 38′ S.
G. H. A. Sirius	590 02 W.	
Long.	169 20 W.	
	420 42 W.	
	−360	
L. H. A. Sirius	60 42 W.	

Correction to Altitudes.—All observed altitudes must be corrected for refraction, and the Moon for parallax. If the upper or lower limb of the Sun or Moon is observed, the correction for semidiameter must be made and observations utilizing the horizon must be corrected for Dip.

Example.—On January 1, 1943, an observation of the sun's lower limb utilizing the horizon, h_s 47° 10′, I. C.+1′, height of eye 36 feet, find true altitude (h_o).

H. O. PUB. No. 9

h_s	47° 10′	I. C.	+ 1′.0	
Corr.	+10.6	Alt.	+15 .2	(Tab. 40)
		Date	+ 0 .3	
h_o	47 20.6	Ht. eye	− 5 .9	
		Corr.	+10 .6	

AIR ALMANAC

h_s	47° 10′	I. C.	+1′	
Corr.	+10	Dip	−6	(Cover)
		S. D.	+16	(a. m. page)
h_o	47 20	Ref.	−1	(Cover)
		Corr.	+10	

Example.—January 1, 1943, the sextant altitude of the moon's lower limb was 23° 30′.0; I. C.—1′; H. E. 60 ft., G. C. T. $11^h\ 40^m\ 00^s$ find true alt. (h_o) of moon.

H. O. PUB. NO. 9

h_s	23° 30′	I. C.	−1′.0	
		H. A. corr.	+66 .8	(Tab. 41)
Corr.	+58 .2	H. E.	−7 .6	
h_o	24 28 .2	Corr.	+58 .2	

(From Nautical Almanac, H. P.=58′)

AIR ALMANAC

h_s	23° 30′	I. C.	−1′	
		Ref.	−2	(Cover)
Corr.	+58	S. D.	+16	(a. m. page)
		Paral.	+53	(a. m. page)
h_o	24 28	Dip.	−8	(cover)
		Corr.	+58	

When using a bubble octant for celestial observations, the errors to be corrected for stars and planets are for refraction only, which is found on back cover of Air Almanac, but for the moon, corrections are made for refraction and parallax.

Example.—January 1, 1943, the altitude of star Arcturus was measured with a bubble octant flying at 20,000 feet. H_s 45° 15′; I. C. 0′.

H_s	45° 15′	Ref. −1′.0 (Back cover)
Corr.	−1	
H_o	45 14	

The Polaris table printed on back of star diagram of Air Almanac gives for values of L. H. A. ♈, the correction which must be applied to the true altitude of Polaris to determine the latitude of place.

Example.—January 1, 1943, flying at 5,000 feet in Long. 75° W. the observed altitude of Polaris with bubble octant was (h_s) 45° 20′ at G. C. T. $22^h\ 50^m\ 10^s$. What is the latitude?

G. C. T.	$22^h\ 50^m\ 10^s$	h_s	45° 20′	
G. H. A. ♈, $22^h\ 50^m$	83° 13′	Ref.	−1	
Corr. 10^s	03			
		h_o	45 19	
G. H. A. ♈	83 16 W.	L. H. A. ♈, 8° 16′	−57	(Inside back cover)
Long.	75 00 W.			
		Lat.	44 22 N.	
L. H. A. ♈	8 16 W.			

Diagram.—The diagram on the right side of a. m. sheet indicates a locality in the region of the ecliptic, where the sun, moon, and planets are found. Four bright stars are also selected, Aldebaran (Dec.+16°). Regulus (Dec.+12°), Spica (Dec. −10°) and Antares (Dec.−26°). The moon is shown in its different phases, together with 5 planets, Mercury ☿, Venus ♀, Mars ♂, Jupiter ♃, and Saturn ♄, unless they are within 5° of the Sun. The position of the Vernal Equinox (♈) is shown for reference. The diagram is 360° long and represents a complete circle around the sky, the two ends of the diagram represent a point on the sky 180° from the Sun. At any given time only half of the region on the diagram is visible so that the region near the center is rising in the East and the region marked West is setting in the west.

Example.—January 1, 1943, the diagram shows that at sunrise Mars and Antares are about 30° westward of the Sun, Mars is 4° northeastward of Antares. The Moon is in the last quarter and is a few degrees northward of the star Spica, both of these bodies are eastward and close to the meridian. The star Regulus is about three hours westward of the meridian and low down near the horizon is the planet Jupiter. Halfway between the Sun and Jupiter is the local meridian. At sunrise Venus and Mercury lie about 10° and 18° eastward of the Sun and set a little later than the Sun. Away in the eastward is the star Aldebaran and the planet Saturn lying 3° northwestward of it. A few hours after sunset the brilliant Jupiter rises in the east, followed 3 hours later by the rising of Regulus.

On the p. m. side of the daily sheet is given the local civil time of sunrise, sunset, moonrise, moonset, and time of civil twilight (sun 6° below horizon), for latitudes from 60° N. to 60° S. The duration of dawn is obtained by subtracting its beginning from the time of sunrise and the ending of evening twilight by adding its duration to the time of sunset. The time given for twilights are for local time and must be corrected for any standard or zone time.

541524°—43——14

Example.—Find the 75° standard time of dawn and twilight in Lat. 37°30′ N.; Long. 77° W. on June 1, 1943.

	Sunrise	Dawn	Sunset	Twilight
L. C. T. from p. m. page	07^h 15^m	30^m	16^h 52^m	30^m
Corr. for 2° of Long. W. of 75° mer	+8		+8	
75° Standard time	07 23		17 00	
Duration of dawn and twilight	−30		+30	
Standard time of beginning and end of twilight	06 53		17 30	

There are three stages in the period of twilight:

Civil Twilight (given in Air Almanac) which begins and ends when the sun's center is 6° below the horizon, is the time when the horizon grows *indistinct* in the evening or begins to get clear in the morning. (The one used in practical navigation observations.)

Nautical Twilight begins or ends when the sun's center is 12° below the horizon.

Astronomical Twilight as given in the American Nautical Almanac begins and ends when the sun's center is 18° below the horizon at which time absolute darkness is assumed to begin or end, so far as the sun is concerned.

Table.—There is also a table given in the Air Almanac for corrections to times of sunrise, sunset, dawn, and twilight for heights in feet from 250 to 40,000 feet.

Example.—In the above example for Lat. 37°30′ N.; Long. 77° W. find sunrise, sunset, dawn, and twilight for a plane flying at 40,000 feet.

	Sunrise	Dawn	Sunset	Twilight
75° standard time	0723	30^m	1700	30^m
Corr. from height table 40,000 ft	−22		+22	
75° standard time	0701		1722	

1730 + 8^m = 1738 = end of twilight at 40,000 ft.

Above example 0653 − 8^m at 40,000 ft. = 0645 beginning of twilight.

The columns for Moonrise and Moonset are for the time of transit, Greenwich meridian. Since the time of the moon's movements are one hour later from day to day, interpolation for longitude of observer in the different latitudes is given in the last column "Diff."

Example.—January 1, 1943, find the zone time of moonrise and moonset in Lat. 58° N., Long. 132° W.

	Moonrise	Moonset
G. C. T. for Lat. 58° N	01^h 39^m	12^h 32^m
Corr. for 132° × Diff. column (81^m and 23^m) / 360°	+30	+8
L. C. T	02 09	12 40
Corr. for +9 zone (3° or 12^m E.)	−12	−12
Zone time of rise or set	01 57	12 28

Example in navigation with the Air Almanac.—On January 1, 1943, the S. S. *Elmcoll* on a voyage from Seattle to the Pacific, in D. R. Lat. 45° N., Long. 150° W., desired morning sights of certain stars for a fix of position.

	Sunrise	Twilight
Morning twilight Lat. 45° L. C. T	07^h 38^m	34^m
Duration twilight	34	
Time beginning of twilight	07 04	
Long. 150° W	10 00	
G. C. T	17 04	
G. H. A. ♈ 17^h (p. m. sheet)	355° 28′	
Corr. 4^m	1 00	
G. H. A. ♈	356 28 W.	
Long	150 00 W.	
L. H. A. ♈	206 28	

Place 45° template on Star Finder (H. O. 2102C) and set arrow on rim to read L. H. A. ♈, 206°30′.

Select from "Star Finder."

Polaris, bearing N., h, 45° Z, 000°.
Arcturus, bearing S., h, 64° Z, 165°.
Vega, bearing E., h, 37° Z, 70°.
Regulus, bearing W., h, 33° Z, 253°.

The navigator should be on the bridge about watch time 0645, or G. C. T. 16ʰ 45ᵐ; I. C. +1′.0″; height of eye, 30 feet.

Sights as follows January 1, 1943:

Stars	*G. C. T.*	h_s	*Dec.*
Polaris	16ʰ 55ᵐ 20ˢ	44° 06′	
Arcturus	16 58 12	63 37	19° 29′ N
Regulus	17 01 43	33 27	12 15 N.
Vega	17 04 41	37 50	38 44 N.

POLARIS

					Ref. −1′
G. C. T.	16ʰ 55ᵐ 20ˢ	h_s	44° 06′		I. C. +1
		Corr.	−5		Dip. −5
G. H. A. ♈, 16ʰ 50ᵐ	352° 58′				
Corr. 05ᵐ 20ˢ	1 20	h_o	44 01		Corr. −5
G. H. A. ♈	354 18 W.	Corr. L. H. A. ♈	+1 00 (Table Air Alm.)		
Long.	150 00 W.				
		Lat.	45° 01′. N.		
L. H. A. ♈	204 18 W.				

ARCTURUS		REGULUS		VEGA	
G. C. T.	16ʰ 58ᵐ 12ˢ	G. C. T.	17ʰ 01ᵐ 43ˢ	G. C. T.	17ʰ 04ᵐ 41ˢ
G. H. A. ♈ 16ʰ 50ᵐ	352° 58′	G. H. A. ♈ 17ʰ	355° 28′	G. H. A. ♈ 17ʰ	355° 28′
Corr. 08ᵐ 12ˢ	2 03	Corr. 01ᵐ 43ˢ	26	Corr. 04ᵐ 41ˢ	1 10
G. H. A. ♈	355 01		355 54		356 38
S. H. A.	146 44		208 40		81 15
G. H. A. ✱	501 45		564 34		437 53
Less	360		−360		−360
G. H. A. ✱	141 45 W.		204 34 W.		77 53 W.
Long.	150 00 W.				
L. H. A. ✱	8 15 E.				

ARCTURUS

a (Tab. 29)	Lat. 45°, Dec. 19°.5 } = 3″	h_s	63° 37′	I. C., Dip. } −4′
at^2 (Tab. 30)	3″, L. H. A. 8° 15′ } = +54′			Ref. −1
	=33ᵐ or 1089″	Corr.	−5	Corr. −5
		h_o	63 32	
		at^2	+54	
		H.	64 26	
		z,	25 34 N.	
		d,	19 29 N.	
		Lat.	45 03 N.	} Mean Lat. 45° 02′ N.
		Polaris, Lat.	45 01 N.	

REGULUS

h_s	33° 27′	I. C. } Dip }	−4′
Corr.	−5	Ref.	−1
		Corr.	−5
h_o	33 22		
z,	56 38	nat. hav.	22500 } sub-
(L∼d)	32 47	nat. hav.	07964 } tract
		nat. hav.	14536
		log hav.	9.16244
Lat.	45° 02′ N.	sec.	15077
Dec.	12 15 N.	sec.	1000
L. H. A.	54° 37′ W.	log hav.	9.32321
G. H. A.	204 34 W.		
Long.	149 57 W.		

VEGA

h_s	37° 50′	I. C. } Dip }	−4′
Corr.	−5	Ref.	−1
		Corr.	−5
h_o	37 45		
z,	52 15	nat. hav.	19389
(L∼*d*)	6 18	nat. hav.	302
		nat. hav.	19087
		log hav.	9.28074
Lat.	45° 02′ N.	sec.	15077
Dec.	38 44 N.	sec.	10787
L. H. A.	72° 06′ E.	log hav.	9.53938
G. H. A.	77 53 W.		
Long.	149 59 W.		

Mean Long. 149° 58′ W.

Fix Lat. 45° 02′ N., Long. 149° 58′ W.

About 0910 on course 260° in Lat. 44° 58′ N.; 150° 24′ W. at G. C. T. 19^h 11^m 25^s simultaneous observations were taken of the moon's upper limb, h_s 31° 50′ and the sun's lower limb h_s 11° 20′; I. C. + 1′.0; H. E. 30 ft. Find position of vessel.

MOON

I. C. } Dip }	−4′	G. C. T.	19^h 11^m 25^s
Par.	+49	G. H. A. 19^h 10^m	173° 18′
Ref.	−2	Corr. 1^m 25^s	0 21
S. D.	−16		
		G. H. A. Moon	173° 39′ W.
Corr.	+27	Dec.	8° 47′ S.
h_s	31° 50′		
h_o	32 17		
z,	57 43	nat. hav.	23295
(L∼*d*)	53 45	nat. hav.	20435
			02860
		log hav.	8.45637
Lat.	44° 58′ N.	sec.	15026
Dec.	8 47 S.	sec.	512
L. H. A.	23 20 W.	hav.	8.61175
G. H. A.	173 39 W.		
Long.	150° 19′ W.		

SUN

I. C. } Dip }	−4′	G. C. T.	19^h 12^m 14^s
Ref.	−5	G. H. A. 19^h 10^m	106° 38′
		Corr. 2^m 14^s	34
S. D.	+16		
		G. H. A.	107 12 W.
Corr.	+7	Dec.	23 02 S.
h_s	11° 20′		
h_o	11 27		
z,	78 33	nat. hav.	40074
(L∼*d*)	68 00	nat. hav.	31270
		nat. hav.	08804
		log hav.	8.94468
Lat.	44 58 N.	sec.	15026
Dec.	23 02 S.	sec.	3608
L. H. A.	43° 09′ E.	hav.	9.13102
G. H. A.	107 12 W.		
Long.	150 21 W.		

Mean Long. 150° 20′ W.

Run-Course 260°; 40m to noon, D. L. 7′; D. R. Long. noon 151° 16′ W.

Noon, D. R. Long.	151° 16′			
Jan. 1, G. H. A. Sun	151 37	for G. C. T.	22^h 10^m 00^s	
Difference	21	(Corr. front cover)	−1 23	
		G. C. T. of L. A. noon	22 08 37	Dec. 23° 01′ S.

Observation at G. C. T. 22^h 08^m 37^s sun's lower limb h_s 22° 00′.

h_s	22° 00′	I. C. } Dip. }	−4′		
Corr.	+09	Ref.	−3′	Long. 0910	150° 20′ W.
h_o	22 09	S. D.	+16′	Run to noon D. Lo.	56 W.
z,	67 51 N.	Corr.	+9′	D. R. Long. noon	151 16 W.
d,	23 01 S.				
Lat.	44 50 N.				

Since the D. L. is 7′, then Lat. 44° 50′+7′=Lat. 44° 57′ N. and Long. 150° 20′ W. as the true fix at 0910.

Run to afternoon Sun sight, Course 260°, Dist. 31 miles, Lat. D. R. 44° 45′ N., Long. 151° 58′ W. G. C. T. $00^h\ 19^m\ 34^s$ January 2, sun lower limb h^s 16° 04′; I. C.+1′; H. E. 30 ft.

SUN

h_s	16° 04′	I. C. / Dip.	−4′	G. C. T.	$00^h\ 19^m\ 34^s$
Corr.	+8	Ref.	−4	G. H. A. $00^h\ 10^m$,	181° 36′
		S. D.	+16	Corr. $09^m\ 34^s$,	2° 24
h_o	16 12				
		Corr.	+8	G. H. A. Sun	184 00 W.
z,	73 48	n. hav.	36050		Dec. 23° 01′S.
(L∼d)	67 46	n. hav.	31081		
			04969		
		log hav.	8. 69627		
Lat.	44° 45′N.	sec.	14863		
Dec.	23 01 S.	sec.	03603		
L. H. A.	32 01 W.	log hav.	8. 88093		
G. H. A.	184 00 W.				
Long.	151 59 W.	D. R. Lat.	44° 45′ N.		

Prepare now the evening twilight sights; run to 1630, course 260°, 31m. D. L. 5′.4; Dep. 30.5; D. Lo. 43′; D. R. Lat. 44° 40′ N., Long. 152° 42′ W.

	Sunset	
	$16^h\ 30^m$	
Twilight duration	34	
End of twilight	17 04	
Long.	10 11 W.	
G. C. T.	3 15	Jan. 2
G. H. A. ♈, $3^h\ 10^m$	148° 23′	
Corr. 5^m	1 15	
G. H. A. ♈	149 38	
	+360	
	509 38 W.	
Long.	152 42 W.	
L. H. A. ♈	356 56	

Set "Star Finder" with template, Lat. 45° N. and arrow at L. H. A. ♈, 356° 56′, and note the following stars for observation.

Polaris, bearing N., h, 45°, Z, 000°
Deneb Kaitos, bearing S., h, 26°, Z, 166°
Aldebaran, bearing E., h, 25°, Z, 092°
Vega, bearing W., h, 33°, Z, 294°

The following stars were observed:

G. C. T. (January 2)	*Stars*	h_s	*Dec.*
$03^h\ 26^m\ 15^s$	Vega	31° 54′	38° 44′ N.
03 29 40	Deneb Kaitos	26 30	18 18 S.
03 32 38	Polaris	45 40	
03 36 20	Aldebaran	28 35	16 24 N.

Find the ship's position at G. C. T. 0331. This steamer is making 0′.4 S. per minute and 0′.23 W., or 0ˢ.9 W.

POLARIS

G. C. T.	$03^h\ 32^m\ 38^s$	h_s	45° 40′	I. C. } Dip }	−4′
G. H. A. ♈ $03^h\ 30^m$	153° 24′	Corr.	−5	Ref.	−1
Corr. $02^m\ 38^s$	40				
		h_o	45 35	Corr.	−5
G. H. A. ♈	154 04 W.	Corr.	−55 (Air Almanac)		
Long.	152 42 W.				
		Lat.	44 40 N.		
L. H. A. ♈	1 22				

DENEB KAITOS

G. C. T.	$03^h\ 29^m\ 40^s$		
G. H. A. ♈ $03^h\ 20^m$	150° 54′		
Corr. $09^m\ 40^s$	2 25		
G. H. A. ♈	153 19		
S. H. A.✳	349 49		
G. H. A.✳	503 08 W.		
Long.	152 42 W.		
L. H. A.✳	350 26 W.		
or	9 34 E.	hav.	7.84221
Lat.	44° 40′ N.	Cos	9.85200
Dec.	18 18 S.	Cos	9.97746
		hav.	7.67167
			.00470
			.27275
(L∼d),	62 58		
(L∼d),	63 34		.27745

Reduction to mer.	+36	h_s	26° 30′	I. C. } Dip }	−4′
h_o	26 24	Corr.	−6	Ref.	−2
H.	27 00	h_o	26° 24′		
				Corr.	−6
z.	63 00 N.	Or by			
d.	18 18 S.	Tab. 29, a=1″.5			
		Tab. 30=1″.5×$(38^m)^2$=			
Lat.	44 42 N.	1″.5×1444=+36′ Red.			

Polaris Lat. 44° 40′ N.
Deneb Kaitos Lat. 44° 42′ N. } Mean Lat. 44° 41′ N.

VEGA

G. C. T.	$03^h\ 26^m\ 15^s$
G. H. A. ♈ $03^h\ 20^m$	150° 54′
Corr. $06^m\ 15^s$	1 34
G. H. A. ♈	152 28
S. H. A. Vega	81 15
G. H. A. Vega	233 43 W.

ALDEBARAN

G. C. T.	$03^h\ 36^m\ 20^s$
G. H. A. ♈ $03^h\ 30^m$	153° 24′
Corr. $06^m\ 20^s$	1 35
G. H. A. ♈	154 59
S. H. A. ✳	291 50
G. H. A.✳	86 49 W.

VEGA

		I. C.} Dip.}	−4′	
H_s	31° 54′			
Corr.	−6	Ref.	−2	
h_o	31 48	Corr.	−6	
z,	58 12	n. hav.		23652
(L∼*d*)	5 57	n. hav.		00269
		n. hav.		23383
		log. hav.		9. 36890
Lat.	44 41 N.	sec.		. 14813
Dec.	38 44 N.	sec.		. 10787
L. H. A.	80° 59′ W.	hav.		9. 62490
G. H. A.	233 43 W.			
Long.	152° 44′ W.			
Run	+1 W.	for 5^m at $0^s.9=5\times.9=4^s=1'$		
Long.	152 45 W.			

ALDEBARAN

H_s	28° 35′		
Corr.	−6		
H_o	28° 29′		
z,	61 31	n. hav.	26155
(L∼*d*)	28 17	n. hav.	05969
		n. hav.	20186
		log hav.	9. 30505
Lat.	44 41 N.	sec.	. 14813
Dec.	16 24 N.	sec.	. 01804
L. H. A.	65 55 E.	hav.	9. 47122
G. H. A.	86 49 W.		
Long.	152 44 W.		
Run	−1 W.	for $5^m=4^s$ or −1′	
Long.	152 43 W.		

Mean Longitude = 152° 44′ W.
Latitude = 44 41 N.

From morning star fix G. C. T.	$17^h.0$	= Long.	149° 58′ W.
To evening star fix G. C. T.	$27^h.5$	= Long.	152 44 W.
Difference	10 . 5		2° 46′ = 11^m

In $10^h.5$ change in long. = 11^m, then in 24^h = 25 minutes.
Set ship's clocks back 25^m due to run westward.
Set course for the night 260°, speed 14 knots.

GREENWICH A. M. 1943 JANUARY 1 (FRIDAY)

GCT	☉ SUN GHA	SUN Dec.	♈ GHA	MARS 1.7 GHA	MARS Dec.	JUPITER −2.2 GHA	JUPITER Dec.	SATURN 0.0 GHA	SATURN Dec.	◑ MOON GHA	MOON Dec.
h m	° ′	° ′	° ′	° ′	° ′	° ′	° ′	° ′	° ′	° ′	° ′
0 00	179 14	S23 05	99 46	209 51	S22 16	346 25	N21 59	34 31	N19 36	255 25	S 5 25
10	181 44		102 17	212 21		348 56		37 01		257 50	27
20	184 14		104 47	214 51		351 26		39 31		260 15	29
30	186 43	· ·	107 18	217 21	· ·	353 57	· ·	42 02	· ·	262 40 ·	30
40	189 13		109 48	219 51		356 27		44 32		265 05	32
50	191 43		112 18	222 21		358 57		47 03		267 30	34
1 00	194 13	S23 05	114 49	224 51	S22 16	1 28	N21 59	49 33	N19 36	269 55	S 5 36
10	196 43		117 19	227 21		3 58		52 04		272 20	38
20	199 13		119 50	229 51		6 29		54 34		274 45	39
30	201 43	· ·	122 20	232 21	· ·	8 59	· ·	57 05	· ·	277 10 ·	41
40	204 13		124 50	234 52		11 30		59 35		279 35	43
50	206 43		127 21	237 22		14 00		62 05		282 01	45
2 00	209 13	S23 05	129 51	239 52	S22 16	16 31	N21 59	64 36	N19 36	284 26	S 5 47
10	211 43		132 22	242 22		19 01		67 06		286 51	48
20	214 13		134 52	244 52		21 32		69 37		289 16	50
30	216 43	· ·	137 23	247 22	· ·	24 02	· ·	72 07	· ·	291 41 ·	52
40	219 13		139 53	249 52		26 33		74 38		294 06	54
50	221 43		142 23	252 22		29 03		77 08		296 31	55
3 00	224 13	S23 05	144 54	254 52	S22 17	31 34	N21 59	79 38	N19 36	298 56	S 5 57
10	226 43		147 24	257 22		34 04		82 09		301 21	5 59
20	229 13		149 55	259 53		36 34		84 39		303 46	6 01
30	231 43	· ·	152 25	262 23	· ·	39 05	· ·	87 10	· ·	306 11 ·	03
40	234 13		154 55	264 53		41 35		89 40		308 36	04
50	236 42		157 26	267 23		44 06		92 11		311 01	06
4 00	239 12	S23 05	159 56	269 53	S22 17	46 36	N21 59	94 41	N19 36	313 26	S 6 08
10	241 42		162 27	272 23		49 07		97 12		315 51	10
20	244 12		164 57	274 53		51 37		99 42		318 16	11
30	246 42	· ·	167 27	277 23	· ·	54 08	· ·	102 12	· ·	320 42 ·	13
40	249 12		169 58	279 53		56 38		104 43		323 07	15
50	251 42		172 28	282 23		59 09		107 13		325 32	17
5 00	254 12	S23 04	174 59	284 53	S22 17	61 39	N21 59	109 44	N19 36	327 57	S 6 19
10	256 42		177 29	287 24		64 10		112 14		330 22	20
20	259 12		180 00	289 54		66 40		114 45		332 47	22
30	261 42	· ·	182 30	292 24	· ·	69 11	· ·	117 15	· ·	335 12 ·	24
40	264 12		185 00	294 54		71 41		119 45		337 37	26
50	266 42		187 31	297 24		74 12		122 16		340 02	27
6 00	269 12	S23 04	190 01	299 54	S22 18	76 42	N21 59	124 46	N19 36	342 27	S 6 29
10	271 42		192 32	302 24		79 12		127 17		344 52	31
20	274 12		195 02	304 54		81 43		129 47		347 17	33
30	276 42	· ·	197 32	307 24	· ·	84 13	· ·	132 18	· ·	349 42 ·	34
40	279 12		200 03	309 54		86 44		134 48		352 07	36
50	281 42		202 33	312 25		89 14		137 19		354 32	38
7 00	284 12	S23 04	205 04	314 55	S22 18	91 45	N21 59	139 49	N19 36	356 57	S 6 40
10	286 42		207 34	317 25		94 15		142 19		359 22	41
20	289 11		210 04	319 55		96 46		144 50		1 47	43
30	291 41	· ·	212 35	322 25	· ·	99 16	· ·	147 20	· ·	4 12 ·	45
40	294 11		215 05	324 55		101 47		149 51		6 37	47
50	296 41		217 36	327 25		104 17		152 21		9 02	49
8 00	299 11	S23 04	220 06	329 55	S22 18	106 48	N21 59	154 52	N19 36	11 27	S 6 50
10	301 41		222 37	332 25		109 18		157 22		13 52	52
20	304 11		225 07	334 55		111 49		159 52		16 17	54
30	306 41	· ·	227 37	337 25	· ·	114 19	· ·	162 23	· ·	18 42 ·	56
40	309 11		230 08	339 56		116 49		164 53		21 07	57
50	311 41		232 38	342 26		119 20		167 24		23 32	6 59
9 00	314 11	S23 04	235 09	344 56	S22 18	121 50	N21 59	169 54	N19 36	25 57	S 7 01
10	316 41		237 39	347 26		124 21		172 25		28 22	03
20	319 11		240 09	349 56		126 51		174 55		30 47	04
30	321 41	· ·	242 40	352 26	· ·	129 22	· ·	177 26	· ·	33 12 ·	06
40	324 11		245 10	354 56		131 52		179 56		35 37	08
50	326 41		247 41	357 26		134 23		182 26		38 02	10
10 00	329 11	S23 03	250 11	359 56	S22 19	136 53	N21 59	184 57	N19 36	40 27	S 7 11
10	331 41		252 41	2 26		139 24		187 27		42 52	13
20	334 11		255 12	4 57		141 54		189 58		45 17	15
30	336 41	· ·	257 42	7 27	· ·	144 25	· ·	192 28	· ·	47 42 ·	17
40	339 10		260 13	9 57		146 55		194 59		50 07	18
50	341 40		262 43	12 27		149 26		197 29		52 32	20
11 00	344 10	S23 03	265 13	14 57	S22 19	151 56	N21 59	199 59	N19 36	54 57	S 7 22
10	346 40		267 44	17 27		154 26		202 30		57 22	24
20	349 10		270 14	19 57		156 57		205 00		59 47	25
30	351 40	· ·	272 45	22 27	· ·	159 27	· ·	207 31	· ·	62 12 ·	27
40	354 10		275 15	24 57		161 58		210 01		64 37	29
50	356 40		277 46	27 27		164 28		212 32		67 02	31
12 00	359 10	S23 03	280 16	29 57	S22 19	166 59	N21 59	215 02	N19 36	69 27	S 7 32

☾ Par.

Alt. °	Corr. + ′
0	
	58
8	
	57
13	
	56
17	
	55
20	
	54
23	
	53
25	
	52
27	
	51
29	
	50
31	
	49
33	
	48
35	
	47
36	
	46
38	
	45
40	
	44
41	
	43
43	
	42
44	
	41
45	
	40
47	
	39
48	
	38
49	
	37
51	
	36
52	
	35
53	
	34
54	
	33
56	
	32
57	
	31
58	
	30
59	
	29
60	
	28
61	
	27
62	
	26
64	
	25
65	
	24
66	
	23
67	
	22
68	
	21
69	
	20
70	
	19
71	
	18
72	
	17
73	
	16
74	
	15
75	
	14
76	
	13
77	
	12
78	
	11
79	
	10
80	

SD, ☉ 16

SD, ☾ 16

Corr. HA ☾

Int. m	Corr. ′
0	
	0
10	

East
180°
Aldebaran
SATURN
90°
♈
MERCURY
VENUS
0° ☉
MARS
Antares
Spica
90°
Regulus
JUPITER
180°
West

GREENWICH P. M. 1943 JANUARY 1 (FRIDAY)

GCT	☉ SUN GHA	SUN Dec.	♈ GHA	MARS 1.7 GHA	MARS Dec.	JUPITER -2.2 GHA	JUPITER Dec.	SATURN 0.0 GHA	SATURN Dec.	☽ MOON GHA	MOON Dec.
h m	° ′	° ′	° ′	° ′	° ′	° ′	° ′	° ′	° ′	° ′	° ′
12 00	359 10	S23 03	280 16	29 57	S22 19	166 59	N21 59	215 02	N19 36	69 27	S 7 32
10	1 40		282 46	32 28		169 29		217 33		71 51	34
20	4 10		285 17	34 58		172 00		220 03		74 16	36
30	6 40	• •	287 47	37 28	• •	174 30	• •	222 33	• •	76 41	• 38
40	9 10		290 18	39 58		177 01		225 04		79 06	39
50	11 40		292 48	42 28		179 31		227 34		81 31	41
13 00	14 10	S23 03	295 18	44 58	S22 19	182 02	N21 59	230 05	N19 36	83 56	S 7 43
10	16 40		297 49	47 28		184 32		232 35		86 21	45
20	19 10		300 19	49 58		187 03		235 06		88 46	46
30	21 40	• •	302 50	52 28	• •	189 33	• •	237 36	• •	91 11	• 48
40	24 10		305 20	54 58		192 04		240 06		93 36	50
50	26 40		307 50	57 28		194 34		242 37		96 01	52
14 00	29 09	S23 03	310 21	59 59	S22 20	197 04	N21 59	245 07	N19 36	98 26	S 7 53
10	31 39		312 51	62 29		199 35		247 38		100 51	55
20	34 09		315 22	64 59		202 05		250 08		103 16	57
30	36 39	• •	317 52	67 29	• •	204 36	• •	252 39	• •	105 41	• 7 59
40	39 09		320 23	69 59		207 06		255 09		108 06	8 00
50	41 39		322 53	72 29		209 37		257 39		110 30	02
15 00	44 09	S23 02	325 23	74 59	S22 20	212 07	N21 59	260 10	N19 36	112 55	S 8 04
10	46 39		327 54	77 29		214 38		262 40		115 20	05
20	49 09		330 24	79 59		217 08		265 11		117 45	07
30	51 39	• •	332 55	82 29	• •	219 39	• •	267 41	• •	120 10	• 09
40	54 09		335 25	85 00		222 09		270 12		122 35	11
50	56 39		337 55	87 30		224 40		272 42		125 00	12
16 00	59 09	S23 02	340 26	90 00	S22 20	227 10	N21 59	275 13	N19 36	127 25	S 8 14
10	61 39		342 56	92 30		229 41		277 43		129 50	16
20	64 09		345 27	95 00		232 11		280 13		132 15	18
30	66 39	• •	347 57	97 30	• •	234 41	• •	282 44	• •	134 40	• 19
40	69 09		350 27	100 00		237 12		285 14		137 04	21
50	71 39		352 58	102 30		239 42		287 45		139 29	23
17 00	74 09	S23 02	355 28	105 00	S22 20	242 13	N21 59	290 15	N19 36	141 54	S 8 24
10	76 39		357 59	107 30		244 43		292 46		144 19	26
20	79 08		0 29	110 00		247 14		295 16		146 44	28
30	81 38	• •	3 00	112 31	• •	249 44	• •	297 46	• •	149 09	• 30
40	84 08		5 30	115 01		252 15		300 17		151 34	31
50	86 38		8 00	117 31		254 45		302 47		153 59	33
18 00	89 08	S23 02	10 31	120 01	S22 21	257 16	N22 00	305 18	N19 36	156 24	S 8 35
10	91 38		13 01	122 31		259 46		307 48		158 48	36
20	94 08		15 32	125 01		262 17		310 19		161 13	38
30	96 38	• •	18 02	127 31	• •	264 47	• •	312 49	• •	163 38	• 40
40	99 08		20 32	130 01		267 18		315 20		166 03	42
50	101 38		23 03	132 31		269 48		317 50		168 28	43
19 00	104 08	S23 02	25 33	135 01	S22 21	272 18	N22 00	320 20	N19 36	170 53	S 8 45
10	106 38		28 04	137 32		274 49		322 51		173 18	47
20	109 08		30 34	140 02		277 19		325 21		175 43	48
30	111 38	• •	33 04	142 32	• •	279 50	• •	327 52	• •	178 07	• 50
40	114 08		35 35	145 02		282 20		330 22		180 32	52
50	116 38		38 05	147 32		284 51		332 53		182 57	54
20 00	119 08	S23 01	40 36	150 02	S22 21	287 21	N22 00	335 23	N19 36	185 22	S 8 55
10	121 38		43 06	152 32		289 52		337 53		187 47	57
20	124 08		45 36	155 02		292 22		340 24		190 12	8 59
30	126 38	• •	48 07	157 32	• •	294 53	• •	342 54	• •	192 36	• 9 00
40	129 08		50 37	160 02		297 23		345 25		195 01	02
50	131 37		53 08	162 32		299 54		347 55		197 26	04
21 00	134 07	S23 01	55 38	165 03	S22 22	302 24	N22 00	350 26	N19 36	199 51	S 9 06
10	136 37		58 09	167 33		304 55		352 56		202 16	07
20	139 07		60 39	170 03		307 25		355 27		204 41	09
30	141 37	• •	63 09	172 33	• •	309 56	• •	357 57	• •	207 06	• 11
40	144 07		65 40	175 03		312 26		0 27		209 30	12
50	146 37		68 10	177 33		314 56		2 58		211 55	14
22 00	149 07	S23 01	70 41	180 03	S22 22	317 27	N22 00	5 28	N19 36	214 20	S 9 16
10	151 37		73 11	182 33		319 57		7 59		216 45	17
20	154 07		75 41	185 03		322 28		10 29		219 10	19
30	156 37	• •	78 12	187 33	• •	324 58	• •	13 00	• •	221 35	• 21
40	159 07		80 42	190 04		327 29		15 30		223 59	22
50	161 37		83 13	192 34		329 59		18 00		226 24	24
23 00	164 07	S23 01	85 43	195 04	S22 22	332 30	N22 00	20 31	N19 36	228 49	S 9 26
10	166 37		88 13	197 34		335 00		23 01		231 14	27
20	169 07		90 44	200 04		337 31		25 32		233 39	29
30	171 37	• •	93 14	202 34	• •	340 01	• •	28 02	• •	236 03	• 31
40	174 07		95 45	205 04		342 32		30 33		238 28	33
50	176 37		98 15	207 34		345 02		33 03		240 53	34
24 00	179 07	S23 01	100 46	210 04	S22 22	347 33	N22 00	35 34	N19 36	243 18	S 9 36

Lat.	Sunrise	Twilt.	Moonrise	Diff.
N °	h m	m	h m	m
60	9 03	57	1 43	83
58	8 46	51	39	81
56	32	47	36	79
54	19	43	34	76
52	8 08	40	31	75
50	7 59	38	29	73
45	38	34	24	70
40	22	31	21	66
35	7 08	28	17	64
30	6 56	26	14	61
20	35	24	09	57
10	6 17	23	05	53
0	5 59	22	1 01	50
10	43	23	0 57	47
20	24	25	52	44
30	5 02	27	48	40
35	4 49	29	45	38
40	34	32	42	35
45	4 17	36	38	32
50	3 55	43	34	29
52	44	48	32	27
54	32	53	30	25
56	18	61	27	24
58	3 02	72	25	21
60	2 42	95	0 22	18
S				

Lat.	Sunset	Twilt.	Moonset	Diff.
N °	h m	m	h m	m
60	15 04	57	12 28	20
58	21	51	32	23
56	35	47	36	25
54	48	43	40	27
52	15 58	40	43	29
50	16 08	38	46	30
45	28	34	52	34
40	45	31	12 57	37
35	16 59	28	13 02	39
30	17 11	26	06	42
20	32	24	13	45
10	17 50	22	19	49
0	18 07	22	24	52
10	25	23	30	55
20	18 43	25	36	59
30	19 05	27	43	63
35	18	29	47	65
40	33	32	52	67
45	19 50	37	13 57	70
50	20 12	44	14 04	73
52	23	49	06	76
54	35	54	10	77
56	20 49	61	13	80
58	21 05	73	17	82
60	21 25	96	14 22	85
S				

GREENWICH A. M. 1943 JANUARY 2 (SATURDAY)

GCT h m	⊙ SUN GHA ° ′	Dec. ° ′	♈ GHA ° ′	MARS 1.7 GHA ° ′	Dec. ° ′	JUPITER −2.2 GHA ° ′	Dec. ° ′	SATURN 0.0 GHA ° ′	Dec. ° ′	☾ MOON GHA ° ′	Dec. ° ′
0 00	179 07	S23 01	100 46	210 04	S22 22	347 33	N22 00	35 34	N19 36	243 18	S 9 36
10	181 36		103 16	212 34		350 03		38 04		245 43	38
20	184 06		105 46	215 04		352 33		40 34		248 07	39
30	186 36	· ·	108 17	217 35	· ·	355 04	· ·	43 05	· ·	250 32	· 41
40	189 06		110 47	220 05		357 34		45 35		252 57	43
50	191 36		113 18	222 35		0 05		48 06		255 22	44
1 00	194 06	S23 00	115 48	225 05	S22 23	2 35	N22 00	50 36	N19 36	257 47	S 9 46
10	196 36		118 18	227 35		5 06		53 07		260 11	48
20	199 06		120 49	230 05		7 36		55 37		262 36	49
30	201 36	· ·	123 19	232 35	· ·	10 07	· ·	58 07	· ·	265 01	· 51
40	204 06		125 50	235 05		12 37		60 38		267 26	53
50	206 36		128 20	237 35		15 08		63 08		269 50	54
2 00	209 06	S23 00	130 50	240 05	S22 23	17 38	N22 00	65 39	N19 36	272 15	S 9 56
10	211 36		133 21	242 35		20 09		68 09		274 40	58
20	214 06		135 51	245 06		22 39		70 40		277 05	9 59
30	216 36	· ·	138 22	247 36	· ·	25 10	· ·	73 10	· ·	279 30	·10 01
40	219 06		140 52	250 06		27 40		75 41		281 54	03
50	221 36		143 23	252 36		30 11		78 11		284 19	04
3 00	224 06	S23 00	145 53	255 06	S22 23	32 41	N22 00	80 41	N19 36	286 44	S10 06
10	226 36		148 23	257 36		35 11		83 12		289 09	08
20	229 06		150 54	260 06		37 42		85 42		291 33	09
30	231 35	· ·	153 24	262 36	· ·	40 12	· ·	88 13	· ·	293 58	· 11
40	234 05		155 55	265 06		42 43		90 43		296 23	13
50	236 35		158 25	267 36		45 13		93 14		298 48	14
4 00	239 05	S23 00	160 55	270 07	S22 23	47 44	N22 00	95 44	N19 36	301 12	S10 16
10	241 35		163 26	272 37		50 14		98 14		303 37	18
20	244 05		165 56	275 07		52 45		100 45		306 02	19
30	246 35	· ·	168 27	277 37	· ·	55 15	· ·	103 15	· ·	308 27	· 21
40	249 05		170 57	280 07		57 46		105 46		310 51	23
50	251 35		173 27	282 37		60 16		108 16		313 16	24
5 00	254 05	S23 00	175 58	285 07	S22 24	62 47	N22 00	110 47	N19 36	315 41	S10 26
10	256 35		178 28	287 37		65 17		113 17		318 06	28
20	259 05		180 59	290 07		67 48		115 48		320 30	29
30	261 35	· ·	183 29	292 37	· ·	70 18	· ·	118 18	· ·	322 55	· 31
40	264 05		185 59	295 07		72 48		120 48		325 20	32
50	266 35		188 30	297 38		75 19		123 19		327 44	34
6 00	269 05	S22 59	191 00	300 08	S22 24	77 49	N22 00	125 49	N19 36	330 09	S10 36
10	271 35		193 31	302 38		80 20		128 20		332 34	37
20	274 05		196 01	305 08		82 50		130 50		334 59	39
30	276 35	· ·	198 32	307 38	· ·	85 21	· ·	133 21	· ·	337 23	· 41
40	279 05		201 02	310 08		87 51		135 51		339 48	42
50	281 34		203 32	312 38		90 22		138 21		342 13	44
7 00	284 04	S22 59	206 03	315 08	S22 24	92 52	N22 00	140 52	N19 35	344 37	S10 46
10	286 34		208 33	317 38		95 23		143 22		347 02	47
20	289 04		211 04	320 08		97 53		145 53		349 27	49
30	291 34	· ·	213 34	322 38	· ·	100 24	· ·	148 23	· ·	351 51	· 50
40	294 04		216 04	325 09		102 54		150 54		354 16	52
50	296 34		218 35	327 39		105 25		153 24		356 41	54
8 00	299 04	S22 59	221 05	330 09	S22 24	107 55	N22 00	155 55	N19 35	359 06	S10 55
10	301 34		223 36	332 39		110 26		158 25		1 30	57
20	304 04		226 06	335 09		112 56		160 55		3 55	10 59
30	306 34	· ·	228 36	337 39	· ·	115 26	· ·	163 26	· ·	6 20	·11 00
40	309 04		231 07	340 09		117 57		165 56		8 44	02
50	311 34		233 37	342 39		120 27		168 27		11 09	03
9 00	314 04	S22 59	236 08	345 09	S22 25	122 58	N22 00	170 57	N19 35	13 34	S11 05
10	316 34		238 38	347 39		125 28		173 28		15 58	07
20	319 04		241 09	350 09		127 59		175 58		18 23	08
30	321 34	· ·	243 39	352 40	· ·	130 29	· ·	178 29	· ·	20 48	· 10
40	324 04		246 09	355 10		133 00		180 59		23 12	11
50	326 34		248 40	357 40		135 30		183 29		25 37	13
10 00	329 04	S22 59	251 10	0 10	S22 25	138 01	N22 00	186 00	N19 35	28 02	S11 15
10	331 34		253 41	2 40		140 31		188 30		30 26	16
20	334 03		256 11	5 10		143 02		191 01		32 51	18
30	336 33	· ·	258 41	7 40	· ·	145 32	· ·	193 31	· ·	35 16	· 19
40	339 03		261 12	10 10		148 03		196 02		37 40	21
50	341 33		263 42	12 40		150 33		198 32		40 05	23
11 00	344 03	S22 58	266 13	15 10	S22 25	153 04	N22 01	201 02	N19 35	42 30	S11 24
10	346 33		268 43	17 40		155 34		203 33		44 54	26
20	349 03		271 13	20 11		158 04		206 03		47 19	27
30	351 33	· ·	273 44	22 41	· ·	160 35	· ·	208 34	· ·	49 43	· 29
40	354 03		276 14	25 11		163 05		211 04		52 08	31
50	356 33		278 45	27 41		165 36		213 35		54 33	32
12 00	359 03	S22 58	281 15	30 11	S22 25	168 06	N22 01	216 05	N19 35	56 57	S11 34

☾ Par.

Alt. °	+ Corr. ′
0	
	59
8	
	58
13	
	57
17	
	56
20	
	55
22	
	54
25	
	53
27	
	52
29	
	51
31	
	50
33	
	49
34	
	48
36	
	47
38	
	46
39	
	45
41	
	44
42	
	43
44	
	42
45	
	41
46	
	40
48	
	39
49	
	38
50	
	37
51	
	36
53	
	35
54	
	34
55	
	33
56	
	32
57	
	31
58	
	30
60	
	29
61	
	28
62	
	27
63	
	26
64	
	25
65	
	24
66	
	23
67	
	22
68	
	21
69	
	20
70	
	19
71	
	18
72	
	17
73	
	16
74	
	15
75	
	14
76	
	13
77	
	12
78	
	11
79	
	10
80	

SD ⊙ ′ 16

SD ☾ ′ 16

Corr. HA ☾

Int. m	− Corr. ′
0	
	0
10	

East
180°
Aldebaran
SATURN
90°
♈
MERCURY
VENUS
0°
⊙
MARS
Antares
☾
Spica
90°
Regulus
JUPITER
180°
West

GREENWICH P. M. 1943 JANUARY 2 (SATURDAY)

GCT h m	☉ SUN GHA ° ′	SUN Dec. ° ′	♈ GHA ° ′	MARS 1.7 GHA ° ′	MARS Dec. ° ′	JUPITER −2.2 GHA ° ′	JUPITER Dec. ° ′	SATURN 0.0 GHA ° ′	SATURN Dec. ° ′	MOON GHA ° ′	MOON Dec. ° ′
12 00	359 03	S22 58	281 15	30 11	S22 25	168 06	N22 01	216 05	N19 35	56 57	S11 34
10	1 33		283 46	32 41		170 37		218 36		59 22	35
20	4 03		286 16	35 11		173 07		221 06		61 47	37
30	6 33	· ·	288 46	37 41	· ·	175 38	· ·	223 36	· ·	64 11	· 39
40	9 03		291 17	40 11		178 08		226 07		66 36	40
50	11 33		293 47	42 41		180 39		228 37		69 00	42
13 00	14 03	S22 58	296 18	45 12	S22 26	183 09	N22 01	231 08	N19 35	71 25	S11 43
10	16 33		298 48	47 42		185 40		233 38		73 50	45
20	19 03		301 18	50 12		188 10		236 09		76 14	46
30	21 33	· ·	303 49	52 42	· ·	190 41	· ·	238 39	· ·	78 39	· 48
40	24 02		306 19	55 12		193 11		241 09		81 04	50
50	26 32		308 50	57 42		195 41		243 40		83 28	51
14 00	29 02	S22 58	311 20	60 12	S22 26	198 12	N22 01	246 10	N19 35	85 53	S11 53
10	31 32		313 50	62 42		200 42		248 41		88 17	54
20	34 02		316 21	65 12		203 13		251 11		90 42	56
30	36 32	· ·	318 51	67 42	· ·	205 43	· ·	253 42	· ·	93 07	· 57
40	39 02		321 22	70 12		208 14		256 12		95 31	11 59
50	41 32		323 52	72 43		210 44		258 43		97 56	12 01
15 00	44 02	S22 58	326 22	75 13	S22 26	213 15	N22 01	261 13	N19 35	100 20	S12 02
10	46 32		328 53	77 43		215 45		263 43		102 45	04
20	49 02		331 23	80 13		218 16		266 14		105 09	05
30	51 32	· ·	333 54	82 43	· ·	220 46	· ·	268 44	· ·	107 34	· 07
40	54 02		336 24	85 13		223 17		271 15		109 59	08
50	56 32		338 55	87 43		225 47		273 45		112 23	10
16 00	59 02	S22 57	341 25	90 13	S22 26	228 18	N22 01	276 16	N19 35	114 48	S12 11
10	61 32		343 55	92 43		230 48		278 46		117 12	13
20	64 02		346 26	95 13		233 19		281 16		119 37	15
30	66 32	· ·	348 56	97 43	· ·	235 49	· ·	283 47	· ·	122 02	· 16
40	69 02		351 27	100 14		238 19		286 17		124 26	18
50	71 32		353 57	102 44		240 50		288 48		126 51	19
17 00	74 01	S22 57	356 27	105 14	S22 27	243 20	N22 01	291 18	N19 35	129 15	S12 21
10	76 31		358 58	107 44		245 51		293 49		131 40	22
20	79 01		1 28	110 14		248 21		296 19		134 04	24
30	81 31	· ·	3 59	112 44	· ·	250 52	· ·	298 50	· ·	136 29	· 25
40	84 01		6 29	115 14		253 22		301 20		138 53	27
50	86 31		8 59	117 44		255 53		303 50		141 18	28
18 00	89 01	S22 57	11 30	120 14	S22 27	258 23	N22 01	306 21	N19 35	143 43	S12 30
10	91 31		14 00	122 44		260 54		308 51		146 07	31
20	94 01		16 31	125 14		263 24		311 22		148 32	33
30	96 31	· ·	19 01	127 45	· ·	265 55	· ·	313 52	· ·	150 56	· 34
40	99 01		21 32	130 15		268 25		316 23		153 21	36
50	101 31		24 02	132 45		270 56		318 53		155 45	37
19 00	104 01	S22 57	26 32	135 15	S22 27	273 26	N22 01	321 24	N19 35	158 10	S12 39
10	106 31		29 03	137 45		275 57		323 54		160 34	41
20	109 01		31 33	140 15		278 27		326 24		162 59	42
30	111 31	· ·	34 04	142 45	· ·	280 57	· ·	328 55	· ·	165 23	· 44
40	114 01		36 34	145 15		283 28		331 25		167 48	45
50	116 31		39 04	147 45		285 58		333 56		170 12	47
20 00	119 01	S22 56	41 35	150 15	S22 27	288 29	N22 01	336 26	N19 35	172 37	S12 48
10	121 31		44 05	152 46		290 59		338 57		175 01	50
20	124 00		46 36	155 16		293 30		341 27		177 26	51
30	126 30	· ·	49 06	157 46	· ·	296 00	· ·	343 57	· ·	179 50	· 53
40	129 00		51 36	160 16		298 31		346 28		182 15	54
50	131 30		54 07	162 46		301 01		348 58		184 39	56
21 00	134 00	S22 56	56 37	165 16	S22 28	303 32	N22 01	351 29	N19 35	187 04	S12 57
10	136 30		59 08	167 46		306 02		353 59		189 28	12 59
20	139 00		61 38	170 16		308 33		356 30		191 53	13 00
30	141 30	· ·	64 08	172 46	· ·	311 03	· ·	359 00	· ·	194 17	· 02
40	144 00		66 39	175 16		313 34		1 31		196 42	03
50	146 30		69 09	177 46		316 04		4 01		199 06	05
22 00	149 00	S22 56	71 40	180 17	S22 28	318 35	N22 01	6 31	N19 35	201 31	S13 06
10	151 30		74 10	182 47		321 05		9 02		203 55	07
20	154 00		76 41	185 17		323 35		11 32		206 20	09
30	156 30	· ·	79 11	187 47	· ·	326 06	· ·	14 03	· ·	208 44	· 10
40	159 00		81 41	190 17		328 36		16 33		211 09	12
50	161 30		84 12	192 47		331 07		19 04		213 33	13
23 00	164 00	S22 56	86 42	195 17	S22 28	333 37	N22 01	21 34	N19 35	215 58	S13 15
10	166 30		89 13	197 47		336 08		24 04		218 22	16
20	169 00		91 43	200 17		338 38		26 35		220 47	18
30	171 30	· ·	94 13	202 47	· ·	341 09	· ·	29 05	· ·	223 11	· 19
40	173 59		96 44	205 17		343 39		31 36		225 35	21
50	176 29		99 14	207 48		346 10		34 06		228 00	22
24 00	178 59	S22 56	101 45	210 18	S22 28	348 40	N22 01	36 37	N19 35	230 24	S13 24

Lat. °	Sun-rise h m	Twlt. m	Moon-rise h m	Diff. m
N				
60	9 03	57	3 06	87
58	8 46	51	3 00	84
56	32	47	2 55	81
54	19	43	50	79
52	8 08	40	46	77
50	7 59	38	42	75
45	39	34	34	71
40	22	31	27	68
35	7 08	28	21	66
30	6 56	26	15	64
20	35	24	2 06	61
10	17	23	1 58	57
0	6 00	22	51	54
10	5 43	23	44	51
20	25	25	36	48
30	5 03	27	28	44
35	4 50	29	23	41
40	36	32	17	39
45	4 18	36	10	37
50	3 56	43	1 03	33
52	45	47	0 59	32
54	34	52	55	30
56	20	60	51	28
58	3 04	71	46	26
60	2 44	93	0 40	24
S				

Lat. °	Sun-set h m	Twlt. m	Moon-set h m	Diff. m
N				
60	15 05	57	12 48	26
58	22	50	12 55	29
56	36	46	13 01	31
54	49	43	07	33
52	15 59	40	12	34
50	16 09	38	16	36
45	29	34	26	40
40	16 46	31	34	42
35	17 00	28	41	45
30	12	26	48	46
20	32	24	13 58	50
10	17 51	22	14 08	53
0	18 08	22	16	56
10	25	23	25	59
20	18 43	25	35	61
30	19 05	27	46	64
35	18	29	52	67
40	32	32	14 59	69
45	19 50	37	15 07	72
50	20 12	43	17	76
52	22	48	22	77
54	34	53	27	79
56	20 48	60	33	81
58	21 04	72	39	83
60	21 24	94	15 47	85
S				

INTERPOLATION OF GHA

SUN, PLANETS, ♈

Int. m s	Corr. ° ′
00 00	0 00
01	0 01
05	0 02
09	0 03
13	0 04
17	0 05
21	0 06
25	0 07
29	0 08
33	0 09
37	0 10
41	0 11
45	0 12
49	0 13
53	0 14
57	0 15
01 01	0 16
05	0 17
09	0 18
13	0 19
17	0 20
21	0 21
25	0 22
29	0 23
33	0 24
37	0 25
41	0 26
45	0 27
49	0 28
53	0 29
57	0 30
02 01	0 31
05	0 32
09	0 33
13	0 34
17	0 35
21	0 36
25	0 37
29	0 38
33	0 39
37	0 40
41	0 41
45	0 42
49	0 43
53	0 44
57	0 45
03 01	0 46
05	0 47
09	0 48
13	0 49
17	0 50
21	

Int. m s	Corr. ° ′
03 17	0 50
21	0 51
25	0 52
29	0 53
33	0 54
37	0 55
41	0 56
45	0 57
49	0 58
53	0 59
57	1 00
04 01	1 01
05	1 02
09	1 03
13	1 04
17	1 05
21	1 06
25	1 07
29	1 08
33	1 09
37	1 10
41	1 11
45	1 12
49	1 13
53	1 14
57	1 15
05 01	1 16
05	1 17
09	1 18
13	1 19
17	1 20
21	1 21
25	1 22
29	1 23
33	1 24
37	1 25
41	1 26
45	1 27
49	1 28
53	1 29
57	1 30
06 01	1 31
05	1 32
09	1 33
13	1 34
17	1 35
21	1 36
25	1 37
29	1 38
33	1 39
37	1 40
41	

Int. m s	Corr. ° ′
06 37	1 40
41	1 41
45	1 42
49	1 43
53	1 44
57	1 45
07 01	1 46
05	1 47
09	1 48
13	1 49
17	1 50
21	1 51
25	1 52
29	1 53
33	1 54
37	1 55
41	1 56
45	1 57
49	1 58
53	1 59
57	2 00
08 01	2 01
05	2 02
09	2 03
13	2 04
17	2 05
21	2 06
25	2 07
29	2 08
33	2 09
37	2 10
41	2 11
45	2 12
49	2 13
53	2 14
57	2 15
09 01	2 16
05	2 17
09	2 18
13	2 19
17	2 20
21	2 21
25	2 22
29	2 23
33	2 24
37	2 25
41	2 26
45	2 27
49	2 28
53	2 29
57	2 30
10 00	

MOON

Int. m s	Corr. ° ′
00 00	0 00
02	0 01
06	0 02
10	0 03
14	0 04
18	0 05
22	0 06
26	0 07
31	0 08
35	0 09
39	0 10
43	0 11
47	0 12
51	0 13
55	0 14
01 00	0 15
04	0 16
08	0 17
12	0 18
16	0 19
20	0 20
24	0 21
29	0 22
33	0 23
37	0 24
41	0 25
45	0 26
49	0 27
53	0 28
58	0 29
02 02	0 30
06	0 31
10	0 32
14	0 33
18	0 34
22	0 35
26	0 36
31	0 37
35	0 38
39	0 39
43	0 40
47	0 41
51	0 42
55	0 43
03 00	0 44
04	0 45
08	0 46
12	0 47
16	0 48
20	0 49
24	

Int. m s	Corr. ° ′
03 20	0 49
24	0 50
29	0 51
33	0 52
37	0 53
41	0 54
45	0 55
49	0 56
53	0 57
58	0 58
04 02	0 59
06	1 00
10	1 01
14	1 02
18	1 03
22	1 04
27	1 05
31	1 06
35	1 07
39	1 08
43	1 09
47	1 10
51	1 11
56	1 12
05 00	1 13
04	1 14
08	1 15
12	1 16
16	1 17
20	1 18
25	1 19
29	1 20
33	1 21
37	1 22
41	1 23
45	1 24
49	1 25
54	1 26
58	1 27
06 02	1 28
06	1 29
10	1 30
14	1 31
18	1 32
23	1 33
27	1 34
31	1 35
35	1 36
39	1 37
43	

Int. m s	Corr. ° ′
06 39	1 37
43	1 38
47	1 39
52	1 40
56	1 41
07 00	1 42
04	1 43
08	1 44
12	1 45
16	1 46
20	1 47
25	1 48
29	1 49
33	1 50
37	1 51
41	1 52
45	1 53
49	1 54
54	1 55
58	1 56
08 02	1 57
06	1 58
10	1 59
14	2 00
18	2 01
23	2 02
27	2 03
31	2 04
35	2 05
39	2 06
43	2 07
47	2 08
52	2 09
56	2 10
09 00	2 11
04	2 12
08	2 13
12	2 14
16	2 15
21	2 16
25	2 17
29	2 18
33	2 19
37	2 20
41	2 21
45	2 22
50	2 23
54	2 24
58	2 25
10 00	

Correction to be added to GHA for interval of GCT

STARS

No.	Name	Mag.	SHA ° ′	Dec. ° ′	No.	Name	Mag.	SHA ° ′	Dec. ° ′
1	Achernar . .	0. 6	336 07	S57 32	12	Dubhe . . .	2. 0	194 56	N62 03
2	Acrux. . . .	1. 1	174 08	S62 47	13	Fomalhaut. .	1. 3	16 23	S29 56
3	Aldebaran. .	1. 1	291 50	N16 24	14	Peacock . . .	2. 1	54 43	S56 55
4	Alpheratz . .	2. 2	358 39	N28 47	15	Pollux. . . .	1. 2	244 32	N28 10
5	Altair. . . .	0. 9	63 00	N 8 43	16	Procyon . . .	0. 5	245 55	N 5 22
6	Antares . . .	1. 2	113 31	S26 18	17	Regulus . . .	1. 3	208 40	N12 15
7	Arcturus . .	0. 2	146 44	N19 29	18	Rigel	0. 3	282 03	S 8 16
8	Betelgeux . .	0. 1–1. 2	271 59	N 7 24	19	Rigil Kent. .	0. 3	141 04	S60 36
9	Canopus . .	−0. 9	264 20	S52 40	20	Sirius	−1. 6	259 20	S16 38
10	Capella . . .	0. 2	281 53	N45 57	21	Spica	1. 2	159 27	S10 52
11	Deneb . . .	1. 3	50 08	N45 05	22	Vega	0. 1	81 15	N38 44

Complete Star List on inside back cover.

POLARIS

LHA ♈	Corr.	LHA ♈	Corr.	LHA ♈	Corr.	LHA ♈	Corr.	LHA ♈	Corr.	LHA ♈	Corr.
° ′	′	° ′	′	° ′	′	° ′	′	° ′	′	° ′	′
358 56		89 43		128 40		178 28		270 37		309 39	
	−54		−26		+14		+54		+26		−14
1 02		90 46		129 39		180 37		271 41		310 37	
	−55		−25		+15		+55		+25		−15
3 20		91 48		130 38		182 56		272 43		311 36	
	−56		−24		+16		+56		+24		−16
5 52		92 50		131 37		185 31		273 46		312 35	
	−57		−23		+17		+57		+23		−17
8 45		93 52		132 36		188 27		274 48		313 34	
	−58		−22		+18		+58		+22		−18
12 11		94 53		133 36		191 57		275 49		314 34	
	−59		−21		+19		+59		+21		−19
16 47		95 53		134 37		196 37		276 50		315 34	
	−60		−20		+20		+60		+20		−20
35 41		96 53		135 37		215 51		277 51		316 34	
	−59		−19		+21		+59		+19		−21
40 16		97 53		136 38		220 31		278 51		317 34	
	−58		−18		+22		+58		+18		−22
43 42		98 53		137 39		224 00		279 51		318 35	
	−57		−17		+23		+57		+17		−23
46 35		99 52		138 41		226 56		280 50		319 37	
	−56		−16		+24		+56		+16		−24
49 07		100 51		139 44		229 31		281 49		320 39	
	−55		−15		+25		+55		+15		−25
51 25		101 50		140 46		231 51		282 48		321 41	
	−54		−14		+26		+54		+14		−26
53 31		102 48		141 50		233 59		283 47		322 44	
	−53		−13		+27		+53		+13		−27
55 30		103 47		142 54		236 00		284 46		323 48	
	−52		−12		+28		+52		+12		−28
57 21		104 45		143 58		237 53		285 44		324 52	
	−51		−11		+29		+51		+11		−29
59 07		105 42		145 04		239 40		286 42		325 56	
	−50		−10		+30		+50		+10		−30
60 48		106 40		146 10		241 23		287 40		327 02	
	−49		− 9		+31		+49		+ 9		−31
62 25		107 38		147 16		243 01		288 37		328 08	
	−48		− 8		+32		+48		+ 8		−32
63 59		108 35		148 24		244 36		289 35		329 15	
	−47		− 7		+33		+47		+ 7		−33
65 29		109 32		149 32		246 08		290 32		330 22	
	−46		− 6		+34		+46		+ 6		−34
66 57		110 30		150 42		247 36		291 30		331 31	
	−45		− 5		+35		+45		+ 5		−35
68 22		111 27		151 52		249 02		292 27		332 41	
	−44		− 4		+36		+44		+ 4		−36
69 44		112 24		153 03		250 26		293 24		333 51	
	−43		− 3		+37		+43		+ 3		−37
71 05		113 21		154 16		251 48		294 21		335 03	
	−42		− 2		+38		+42		+ 2		−38
72 24		114 18		155 30		253 08		295 18		336 16	
	−41		− 1		+39		+41		+ 1		−39
73 41		115 15		156 45		254 26		296 15		337 30	
	−40		0		+40		+40		0		−40
74 57		116 12		158 01		255 42		297 12		338 46	
	−39		+ 1		+41		+39		− 1		−41
76 11		117 09		159 19		256 58		298 09		340 03	
	−38		+ 2		+42		+38		− 2		−42
77 24		118 06		160 39		258 11		299 06		341 22	
	−37		+ 3		+43		+37		− 3		−43
78 36		119 03		162 01		259 24		300 03		342 43	
	−36		+ 4		+44		+36		− 4		−44
79 46		120 00		163 25		260 35		301 00		344 06	
	−35		+ 5		+45		+35		− 5		−45
80 56		120 57		164 51		261 46		301 57		345 31	
	−34		+ 6		+46		+34		− 6		−46
82 05		121 55		166 20		262 55		302 55		346 58	
	−33		+ 7		+47		+33		− 7		−47
83 12		122 52		167 51		264 03		303 52		348 28	
	−32		+ 8		+48		+32		− 8		−48
84 19		123 50		169 26		265 11		304 49		350 02	
	−31		+ 9		+49		+31		− 9		−49
85 25		124 47		171 04		266 17		305 47		351 39	
	−30		+10		+50		+30		−10		−50
86 31		125 45		172 47		267 23		306 45		353 20	
	−29		+11		+51		+29		−11		−51
87 36		126 43		174 34		268 29		307 43		355 06	
	−28		+12		+52		+28		−12		−52
88 40		127 42		176 27		269 33		308 41		356 57	
	−27		+13		+53		+27		−13		−53
89 43		128 40		178 28		270 37		309 39		358 56	

CORRECTIONS FOR HEIGHT

TO TIMES OF SUNRISE, SUNSET, AND TWILIGHT

JANUARY

Height in feet	250		500		1000		2000		5000		10000		15000		20000		25000		30000		35000		40000	
Latitude	S	T	S	T	S	T	S	T	S	T	S	T	S	T	S	T	S	T	S	T	S	T	S	T
	m	*m*	*m*	*m*	*m*	*m*	*m*	*m*	*m*	*m*	*m*	*m*	*m*	*m*	*m*	*m*	*m*	*m*	*m*	*m*	*m*	*m*	*m*	*m*
N60°	3	0	5	0	7	0	10	1	15	2	21	3	26	5	29	6	32	8	35	9	38	10	40	11
55	3	0	4	0	5	0	8	1	12	1	17	3	20	4	23	5	26	6	28	8	30	9	32	10
50	2	0	3	0	4	0	6	0	10	1	14	2	17	3	20	4	22	5	24	7	26	8	28	9
40	2	0	3	0	4	0	5	0	8	1	12	2	14	2	16	3	18	4	20	6	21	7	22	8
20	2	0	2	0	3	0	4	0	6	1	9	2	11	2	13	3	14	4	15	4	16	5	18	6
0	1	0	2	0	3	0	4	0	6	1	8	2	10	2	12	3	13	4	14	4	15	5	16	6
20	1	0	2	0	3	0	4	0	6	1	9	2	11	2	13	3	14	4	16	4	17	5	18	6
40	2	0	3	0	4	0	5	0	8	1	12	2	14	3	17	4	18	5	20	6	22	7	23	8
50	2	0	3	0	5	0	7	0	11	2	15	3	19	4	22	5	24	7	26	9	29	10	30	11
55	3	0	4	0	6	0	8	1	13	2	18	4	23	6	26	8	29	10	32	13	35	15	37	16
S60	4	0	5	0	8	0	11	1	17	3	25	6	31	9	36	12	40	15	45	19	48	22	52	25

REFRACTION

A. *Total correction.*—For use with H. O. 208, H. O. 211, H. O. 214, and the Polaris Table. Subtract from observed altitude.

Height in feet	Observed altitude						
	5°	10°	15°	20°	30°	45°	60°
	′	′	′	′	′	′	′
0	10	5	4	3	2	1	1
5,000	8	5	3	2	1	1	0
10,000	7	4	3	2	1	1	0
15,000	6	3	2	2	1	1	0
20,000	5	3	2	1	1	1	0
25,000	4	2	2	1	1	0	0
30,000	3	2	1	1	1	0	0
35,000	3	2	1	1	1	0	0
40,000	2	1	1	1	0	0	0

B. *Adjustment.*—For use with A. N. T. (H. O. 218 and Astrograph. Apply to observed altitude with sign given.

Height in feet	Observed altitude						
	5°	10°	15°	20°	30°	45°	60°
	′	′	′	′	′	′	′
0	−1	−1	0	0	0	0	0
5,000	0	0	0	0	0	0	0
10,000	+1	+1	0	0	0	0	0
15,000	2	1	+1	+1	0	0	0
20,000	2	2	1	1	+1	0	0
25,000	3	2	1	1	1	0	0
30,000	3	3	2	1	1	0	0
35,000	4	3	2	1	1	+1	0
40,000	+4	+3	+2	+2	+1	+1	0

DIP

Subtract from altitude observed with *sea horizon.*

Height	Corr.	Height	Corr.	Height	Corr.	Height	Corr.
Ft.	′	*Ft.*	′	*Ft.*	′	*Ft.*	′
0		**160**		**620**		**1380**	
	1		13		25		37
2		**180**		**670**		**1460**	
	2		14		26		38
6		**210**		**730**		**1540**	
	3		15		27		39
12		**250**		**780**		**1620**	
	4		16		28		40
21		**280**		**840**		**1700**	
	5		17		29		41
31		**310**		**900**		**1790**	
	6		18		30		42
43		**350**		**960**		**1870**	
	7		19		31		43
58		**390**		**1030**		**1960**	
	8		20		32		44
75		**430**		**1090**		**2060**	
	9		21		33		45
93		**480**		**1160**		**2150**	
	10		22		34		46
114		**520**		**1230**		**2250**	
	11		23		35		47
137		**570**		**1310**		**2340**	
	12		24		36		48
162		**620**		**1380**		**2440**	

STARS

Alphabetical order							Order of SHA						
Name		Mag.	SHA		Dec.		SHA		Dec.		RA		Name
			°	′	°	′	°	′	°	′	h	m	
Acamar		3.4	315	59	S40	32	14	31	N14	54	23	02	Markab
Achernar	1	0.6	336	07	S57	32	16	23	S29	56	22	54	**Fomalhaut**
Acrux	2	1.1	174	08	S62	47	28	51	S47	14	22	05	Al Na'ir
Adhara	†	1.6	255	54	S28	54	34	39	N 9	37	21	41	Enif
Aldebaran	3	1.1	291	50	N16	24	50	08	N45	05	20	39	**Deneb**
Alioth		1.7	167	07	N56	16	54	43	S56	55	20	21	Peacock
Al Na'ir		2.2	28	51	S47	14	63	00	N 8	43	19	48	**Altair**
Alnilam	†	1.8	276	40	S 1	14	77	04	S26	22	18	52	Nunki
Alphard	†	2.2	218	48	S 8	25	81	15	N38	44	18	35	**Vega**
Alphecca	†	2.3	126	56	N26	54	84	54	S34	25	18	20	Kaus Aust.
Alpheratz	4	2.2	358	39	N28	47	91	11	N51	30	17	55	Etamin
Al Suhail		2.2	223	31	S43	12	96	56	N12	36	17	32	Rasalague
Altair	5	0.9	63	00	N 8	43	97	34	S37	04	17	30	Shaula
Antares	6	1.2	113	31	S26	18	103	13	S15	39	17	07	Sabik
Arcturus	7	0.2	146	44	N19	29	(109	21)	S68	55	16	43	α Tri. Aust.
ε Argus		1.7	234	39	S59	20	113	31	S26	18	16	26	**Antares**
Bellatrix	†	1.7	279	29	N 6	18	120	46	S22	28	15	57	Dschubba
Betelgeux	8	0.1–1.2	271	59	N 7	24	126	56	N26	54	15	32	Alphecca
Canopus	9	−0.9	264	20	S52	40	(137	17)	N74	23	14	51	Kochab
Capella	10	0.2	281	53	N45	57	141	04	S60	36	14	36	**Rigil Kent.**
Caph		2.4	358	28	N58	50	146	44	N19	29	14	13	**Arcturus**
θ Centauri		2.3	149	10	S36	05	149	10	S36	05	14	03	θ Centauri
β Crucis		1.5	168	54	S59	23	159	27	S10	52	13	22	**Spica**
γ Crucis		1.6	173	00	S56	48	159	35	N55	13	13	22	Mizar
Deneb	11	1.3	50	08	N45	05	167	07	N56	16	12	52	Alioth
Deneb Kait.	†	2.2	349	49	S18	18	168	54	S59	23	12	44	β Crucis
Denebola	†	2.2	183	28	N14	53	173	00	S56	48	12	28	γ Crucis
Dschubba		2.5	120	46	S22	28	174	08	S62	47	12	23	**Acrux**
Dubhe	12	2.0	194	56	N62	03	183	28	N14	53	11	46	Denebola
Enif		2.5	34	39	N 9	37	194	56	N62	03	11	00	Dubhe
Etamin		2.4	91	11	N51	30	208	40	N12	15	10	05	**Regulus**
Fomalhaut	13	1.3	16	23	S29	56	218	48	S 8	25	9	25	Alphard
Hamal	†	2.2	329	01	N23	12	(221	50)	S69	29	9	13	Miaplacidus
Kaus Aust.		2.0	84	54	S34	25	223	31	S43	12	9	06	Al Suhail
Kochab		2.2	(137	17)	N74	23	234	39	S59	20	8	21	ε Argus
Marfak		1.9	309	56	N49	40	244	32	N28	10	7	42	**Pollux**
Markab		2.6	14	31	N14	54	245	55	N 5	22	7	36	**Procyon**
Miaplacidus		1.8	(221	50)	S69	29	255	54	S28	54	6	56	Adhara
Mizar		2.4	159	35	N55	13	259	20	S16	38	6	43	**Sirius**
Nunki		2.1	77	04	S26	22	264	20	S52	40	6	23	**Canopus**
Peacock	14	2.1	54	43	S56	55	271	59	N 7	24	5	52	**Betelgeux**
Polaris		2.1	(333	57)	N89	00	276	40	S 1	14	5	33	Alnilam
Pollux	15	1.2	244	32	N28	10	279	29	N 6	18	5	22	Bellatrix
Procyon	16	0.5	245	55	N 5	22	281	53	N45	57	5	12	**Capella**
Rasalague	†	2.1	96	56	N12	36	282	03	S 8	16	5	12	**Rigel**
Regulus	17	1.3	208	40	N12	15	291	50	N16	24	4	33	**Aldebaran**
Rigel	18	0.3	282	03	S 8	16	309	56	N49	40	3	20	Marfak
Rigil Kent.	19	0.3	141	04	S60	36	315	59	S40	32	2	56	Acamar
Ruchbah		2.8	339	29	N59	56	329	01	N23	12	2	04	Hamal
Sabik		2.6	103	13	S15	39	(333	57)	N89	00	1	44	**Polaris**
Shaula		1.7	97	34	S37	04	336	07	S57	32	1	36	**Achernar**
Sirius	20	−1.6	259	20	S16	38	339	29	N59	56	1	22	Ruchbah
Spica	21	1.2	159	27	S10	52	349	49	S18	18	0	41	Deneb Kait.
α Tri. Aust.		1.9	(109	21)	S68	55	358	28	N58	50	0	06	Caph
Vega	22	0.1	81	15	N38	44	358	39	N28	47	0	05	Alpheratz

SHA=360°−RA GHA*=GHA♈+SHA*

CHAPTER XVI

THE PRACTICE OF NAVIGATION AT SEA

The methods for working dead reckoning and the solution of examples for the various methods of determining latitude, longitude, azimuth, hour angle, altitude, line of position, and the final fix of the ship's position have been given in the previous chapters. The practical application of these principles and methods to the ever varying circumstances encountered daily at sea are determined by the navigator. In this chapter an outline of the average day's work, with examples, will be given.

Minimum program for day's work.—The following program represents a minimum of work and celestial observations that should be accomplished daily at sea during clear weather in order to keep a continuous accurate record of the position of the ship. Cloudy and overcast weather may, at any time, reduce this program, in which case the dead reckoning position must be relied upon.

Departure and continuous dead reckoning plot of position.

Star observations during morning twilight, for a fix from two or more lines of position.

Sun observation on or near prime vertical for longitude, or at other time for a line of position.

Azimuth observation of the sun to find the compass error, either in conjunction with the sun sight or as a separate time azimuth observation.

Computation of the interval to noon, watch time of local apparent noon, and constants for meridian or ex-meridian sights.

Meridian or ex-meridian observation of the sun for noon latitude line. Running fix or cross with Venus line for noon fix. Determine the day's run, the set and drift of current since the previous noon.

At least one sun observation during the afternoon for use in case stars are not available at twilight.

Azimuth observation of sun for compass error.

Star observations during twilight for a fix from two or more lines of position.

The observations may be worked out by any method the navigator prefers, either by computation or by any of the short tabular methods described in the previous chapter. Some of the latter provide a more universal solution than the methods of computation, and since they eliminate much of the mathematical work with its consequent chances of errors these methods are becoming increasingly popular with navigators. The explanations and examples in this publication are confined to the methods for which tables are available in **part II.**

Accuracy.—Exact results are not attainable at sea; chronometer error, sextant error, refraction error and errors of observation are all variable. No navigator should assume that his position is not liable to some error for which a reasonable allowance is about 2 miles. Ways of plotting this allowance have been previously discussed under Lines of Position.

It is probably best to work all sights for altitude to the nearest tenth of a minute of arc, and for longitude to the nearest tenth of a second of time.

Position lines.—The navigator must remember that a single observation will not give a definite "fix," but will give a position line which passes through the observer's position at right angles to the azimuth. If two position lines are determined simultaneously, the observer's position must be at their intersection. If only one celestial body is visible such as the sun, only one position line is obtainable and it will be necessary to wait until the sun has changed about 30° in azimuth before taking another observation with which to make a running "fix" from the first observation.

Many times during daylight a position line of the moon makes an excellent cut with the sun. The planet Venus, when near quadrature can be observed all day, and is utilized to give a position line which cuts with lines of the sun or moon. During twilight, stars, planets, and the moon are available to select for suitable lines of position. Three stars whose azimuth differ by 120° give a good "fix." The position lines may not intersect in a point and a triangle will be formed, in which case the most probable position is the meeting point of the bisectors of the internal or external angles of the triangle as previously explained. It may be inside or outside of the triangle.

Navigator's work book.—Every navigator should keep a navigation note book in which he keeps a complete record of all that pertains to the navigation of the vessel when not running on bearings of the land. The entries should be neat, legible, orderly, and intelligible to any person who has reason to refer to it. All observations should be entered with their computations by either logarithms or tables. Every operation pertaining to the working of the sights should appear in this book.

It is well to observe a systematic form of work for each type of sight, always writing the different terms in the same position on the page as this plan will lessen the chance for error and tends to make the book more clear. The navigator can make up his own work form by having printed a desirable one for the various sights, or by having a rubber stamp made of the form desired.

Departure and dead reckoning.—When starting on a voyage between ports, a good departure is taken from one or more well determined landmarks. This is used as the origin of dead reckoning, which with frequent new departures from each "fix" by observation, is kept progressively plotted up to the point of destination. From the dead reackoning plot, the navigator can determine at any instant, with a fair degree of accuracy, the vessel's position at any instant. When taking the departure, record the reading of the patent log. Note the hourly reading of the log for information relative to the speed of the vessel; also read the log when each observation for position is made. If a vessel does not use a form of patent log, but estimates the speed by revolutions of the engines, the noting of the time is essential.

Time to observe stars.—Twilight begins in the morning and ends in the evening when the sun's center is about 18° below the horizon. When the sun is about 6° below the horizon, the horizon ceases to be visible in the sextant. This indicates the approximate time that stars should be observed. The Nautical Almanac gives the approximate local civil time of sunrise and the beginning of morning twilight or the time of sunset and the end of evening twilight. If one third of the duration of twilight be subtracted from the time of sunrise or added to the time of sunset, the approximate time to make observations is obtained. The interval during which both stars and horizon are clearly visible is relatively short. The navigator should familiarize himself with the location of the suitable stars beforehand and be prepared to make observations systematically and quickly. As each star is observed the exact time and the approximate azimuth are noted.

It is good practice to make three or more successive observations of each star and use the average of the altitudes observed and the times recorded for the solution.

Star identification.—By means of the navigational star chart of the Nautical Almanac most of the stars may be readily identified, or from the Hydrographic Office Star Finder No. 2102, the approximate altitudes and azimuths of celestial bodies may be found for the time at which observations will be made. This information is also given in Hydrographic Office Publication No. 127, Star Identification Tables, and it may be computed as shown on page 187. By selecting certain bright stars well located in azimuth and listing their altitudes and azimuths, the stars are readily identified in the heavens and are easily picked up in the sextant by setting the listed altitude on the sextant and looking in the true direction of the star.

Morning star sights.—It has been pointed out that when the celestial body is on the meridian, a true latitude is obtained with the line of position running east and west through this latitude. When the body is on the prime vertical and the observation is worked as a "time sight," a true longitude is obained with the line of position running north and south through this longitude. Observations taken when the celestial body is away from the meridian or prime vertical, give neither the true latitude nor the true longitude but furnish only a line of position running perpendicular to the celestial body's azimuth. Therefore, a "time sight" rarely gives the true longitude, but provides only a line of position similar to any of the shorter tabulated methods which work well for all conditions and positions of the celestial bodies in the heavens. *The time sight is used here only when the latitude is known to be correct.*

541524°—43——15

Stars should be selected for observation whose azimuths are at least 30° apart in order to get the best "fix." Stars on or near the meridian, or prime vertical should always be utilized when possible.

Polaris should be observed at dawn for a latitude line of position. Stars observed nearly eastward or westward of the meridian, and worked with the latitude given by Polaris would give a good longitude, or the computed altitude and azimuth of these observed stars would give intersecting position lines for a good "fix." The altitude of Polaris can be computed beforehand from the approximate D. R. position, then set on the sextant and the star Polaris readily picked up in the telescope by looking in the

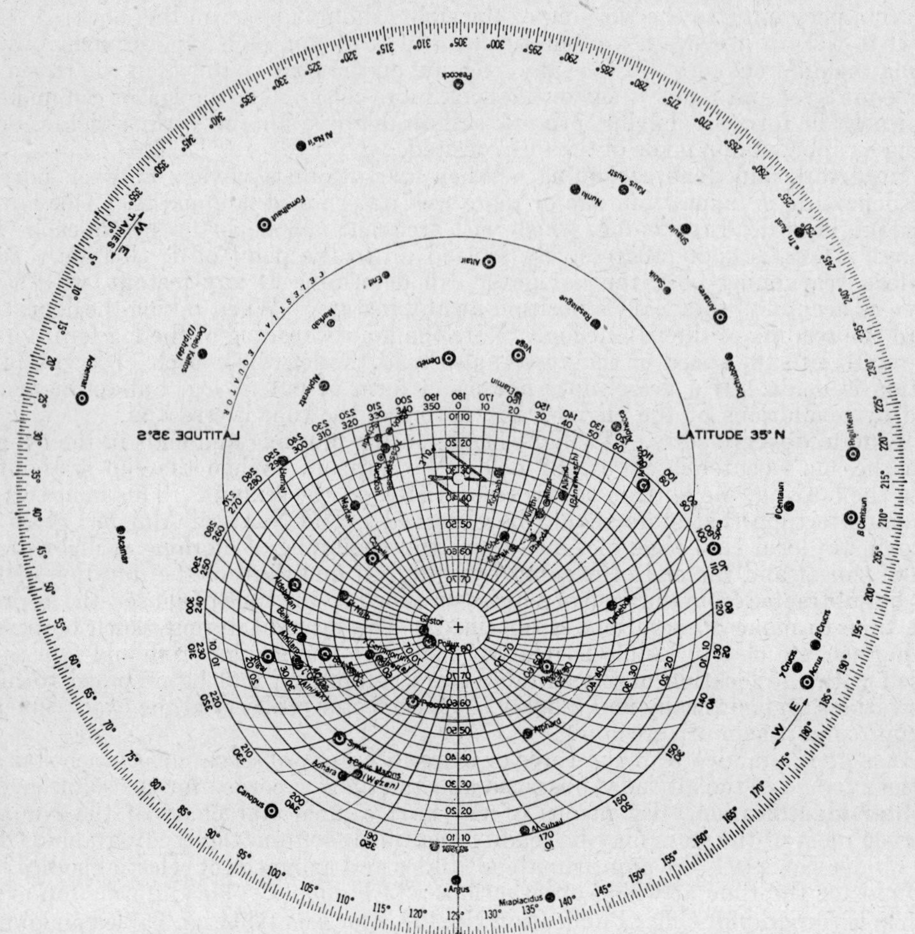

FIGURE 105.—Star Finder H. O. 2102C.
(Letters Patent No. 2304797.)

direction of north. It may be especially desirable to do this in the evening when the horizon tends to become dark before Polaris is clearly visible to the naked eye.

Before beginning to work up the morning observations, the navigator compares his watch with the chronometer to get his C—W. In some vessels a hack chronometer, which is first compared with the standard chronometer, is used in the chart house. The date, the error on G. C. T., and the rate are kept on a slip of paper in the back of the hack case. However, on most vessels, the navigator makes a direct comparison of his watch at the place where the standard chronometer is stowed. The C—W and chronometer error are entered in the work book. From the log book the courses and distances run from the last "fix" are entered. The new D. R. position for the time of sights is either worked up by computation or plotted on the chart. The observed altitudes with corresponding watch times are entered and the compass bearing of an observed body is noted to find the compass error. The computations are then made of the sights to determine a line of position for each observed body. The true azimuth may be found by computation or from azimuth tables. The intersection of the lines of position is either computed, or plotted directly on the chart for the morning "fix." From the morning "fix" the set and drift of current since the last "fix" may be obtained.

Moon observations.—During the night the gleam upon the water directly below the moon may define the horizon and permit an observation for altitude when it is impossible to take a sight of any other body. During daylight the moon is often visible and its position line may give a good cut with the position line of the sun.

Owing to its nearness to the earth and the rapidity with which it changes right ascension and declination, the various corrections entailed render observations somewhat longer to work out and more liable to error than for other bodies. The navigator will usually pass the moon by if other celestial bodies are available.

Morning sun line.—The best time for the morning observation to give a good longitude is when the sun is on the prime vertical. This position of the sun may be observed within reasonable limits from the compass, or the approximate time may be determined as follows: enter the sun azimuth tables with the D. R. latitude and the sun's declination as arguments; in the declination column locate azimuth 90°, and note the corresponding apparent time. This is the approximate time the sight should be taken, but the exact watch time can be obtained also.

Suppose the 8 a. m. D. R. position on July 19, 1937, is Lat. 35° N., Long. 65°15′ W. The noon declination of the sun is found to be about 21° N. and the apparent time on the prime vertical is found to be about 8^h10^m a. m. The navigator now compares his watch with the chronometer and applies the chronometer correction when the chronometer reads, say, $11^h59^m30^s$ and the watch reads $7^h\ 15^m\ 12^s$. From the almanac the declination and equation of time for Greenwich civil noon on July 19 are Dec. 20°53′ N., Eq. t. 6^m07^s subtractive from mean time.

	h	m	s
Chron. at comparison	11	59	30
Chron. correction (slow)	+	1	13
G. C. T. at comparison	12	00	43
Eq. t	—	6	07
G. A. T. at comparison	11	54	36
Longitude 65°15′ W	4	21	00
L. A. T. of 8 a. m. position	7	33	36
W. T. at comparison	7	15	12
Watch slow of L. A. T. at 8 a. m	0	18	24
L. A. T. of sun on prime vertical	8	10	00
W. T. to take observation	7	51	36

When the latitude and declination are of contrary name, the sun crosses the prime vertical before rising, in which case the observation is taken as soon as the sun is sufficiently high in altitude to eliminate uncertain refraction.

A sight of the sun on the prime vertical gives a good longitude, the use of which will make the computation of the watch time of L. A. N. more accurate.

Other observations of the sun may be made at any time when accurate positions are required, as when in dangerous waters or making a landfall. The position line of any previous observation may be advanced to the time of the last observation to obtain a running fix. This work is usually done on the chart or on plotting sheets, but may be done by computation using the longitude factor found in Table 35.

Azimuth for compass error.—Coincident with one of the morning observations, the azimuth of the body may be observed by compass. The computed azimuth of the body for that instant compared with the azimuth as observed by compass will give the compass error. More frequently a separate observation of the compass azimuth of the sun is taken, and a "time azimuth" computed, from which the compass error is obtained.

Interval to noon.—W. T. of L. A. N.: The next important step is to determine the watch time of local apparent noon at which time the sun will be on the meridian and a meridian observation will be taken for latitude. From the sun sight on the prime vertical, or the a. m. observation, there is obtained the local hour angle. The course and speed of the vessel to noon must be known. If the current in longitude is established by the morning observation and it is assumed that it will continue without much change until noon it should also be applied. When a vessel does not change in longitude between the morning sight and noon, as when its course is north or south, it is carried by the earth's rotation toward the sun's hour circle at the rate of 15° or 900′ per hour, and the elapsed time from the morning sight to the meridian altitude sight is the value of the local hour angle at the a. m. observation. Should the vessel change longitude due to the course, the speed, and the current, it moves towards or away from the sun at a greater or less rate than 900′ per hour. If the hour angle at the a. m. observation, expressed in minutes of arc, is divided by the rate in minutes of arc at which the ship approaches the sun, the result will be the number of hours between the sight and noon, or the interval to noon.

Example.—The watch time of a. m. sight is $7^h\ 59^m\ 43^s$ and the observed local hour angle is $3^h\ 34^m\ 02^s$ E. The course is 81° T., speed 15 knots, current 0′.5 E. Find the interval to noon and the watch time of local apparent noon.

$t=3^h\ 34^m\ 02^s=53°\ 30'.5=3210'.5.$

Course	*Distance*	*D. Lo.*	*Current*
81°	15′	19′ E.	0.5 E.

Rate of approach 900′+19′+.5′ (Easterly movement increases rate). Interval to noon $\frac{3210'.5}{919.5}=$ $3^h.491=3^h\ 29^m\ 28^s$

W. T. of sight =	7^h	59^m	43^s
Interval to noon =	3	29	28
W. T. of L. A. N. =	11	29	11

If the watch is set ahead 31 minutes, it will be 11 seconds fast of local apparent noon.

Example by noon interval table.—In the example that follows in a day's work at sea, it will be noted that the L. A. T. of the $9^h\ 30^m$ a. m. observation is $9^h\ 41^m\ 03^s.4$, or the hour angle is $2^h\ 18^m\ 56^s.6$ E. or $2^h.316$. The hourly change in longitude and current to the eastward is 14′.3. The factor from the noon interval table (Table 37) is .98436. $2^h.316\times.98436=2^h.28$ or $2^h\ 16^m\ 48^s$ which is the interval to local apparent noon. When $t=2^h\ 16^m\ 48^s$ E. then the watch and the G. C. T. are:

Watch	9^h	30^m	00^s	G. C. T.	14^h	17^m	10^s
Noon interval	2	16	48		2	16	48
W. T. of L. A. N.	11	46	48	G. C. T. of L. A. N.	16	33	58

Vessels steaming eastward set the clocks ahead, while those steaming westward set the clocks back by the amount of the change in longitude, or to agree with the zone time of the time zone entered. As the change of time is usually made between 11:00 a. m. and noon, it will be noted that the elapsed time between the time of the a. m. sight and the new watch time of noon will be more than the watch face shows by the amount the watch has been set back, and the difference must be allowed for in computing the run to noon.

If the vessel has been making eastings, the clocks will be set ahead and the elapsed time between sights will be less than the watch face shows by the amount the watch has been set ahead. The time cannot be computed exactly, but it can be approximated closely. The navigator can now set the watches and clocks for the coming local apparent noon position. A convenient way to set the watch is as follows: Having looked at the chronometer and found that it reads $4^h\ 07^m\ 10^s$, set the watch to the correct L. A. T. of the noon position when the chronometer reads $4^h\ 10^m\ 00^s$.

Reading of chronometer when watch is to be set	4^h	10^m	00^s
Chronometer fast on G. C. T.	−		30
G. C. T. at which watch is to be set for L. A. T.	16	09	30. 0
Eq. T. corrected for long. of noon position	+	11	32. 3
G. A. T. of the time watch is to be set	16	21	02. 3
Long. of noon position	4	45	26. 8
Watch face should read	11	35	35. 5

The watch is now to be set so that at $4^h\ 10^m\ 00^s$ by chronometer the watch face will show as near $11^h\ 35^m\ 36^s$ as possible. Since the second hand cannot be set exactly, it can be set so that it will be 30 seconds or less fast or slow on the desired time. The number of seconds the watch is fast or slow on L. A. T. should be noted as it will help in taking near noon sights to get the correct L. A. T.

Noon constant.—Between 11^h and noon, allowing for gain or loss due to run, the navigator sets the clocks for L. A. T. of the D. R. noon position. He now works up his constants for his reduction to the meridian and meridian altitude. A complete description of how to obtain and apply the constants is contained in the chapter on latitude.

Noon sights.—A few minutes before noon, observations are made for a meridian altitude to give latitude. If the weather is cloudy, observations for a reduction to the meridian are made.

The planet Venus can often be observed at noon and a line of position obtained to cross with that of the noon sun line to obtain an excellent fix. Compute the altitude and azimuth of Venus for the noon position. Set the altitude on the sextant and by looking toward the true direction of the planet, it will be seen in the field of the telescope on the horizon.

The position line of the morning sun sight may also be advanced as a running fix at noon. Or, with the correct noon latitude, find by how many minutes it differs from the D. R. noon latitude and multiply this difference by the longitude factor to get the correction to be applied to the morning longitude by observation run up to noon, to get the accepted noon longitude.

The position lines are now plotted and the noon position is compared with the previous noon position (or the point of departure) and the true course and distance made good is determined.

If the vessel is steaming on the great circle track that requires a change of compass course, the new course is laid out as soon as the true noon position is obtained.

Current.—The set and drift of the current may be found by comparing the noon positions as found by observation and by dead reckoning. To current is attributed all discrepancies found between the D. R. position and the observed position, but this error also includes such things as faulty steering, wrong allowance for compass error, and inaccurate estimate of the vessel's speed over the ground.

Blank forms for the noon report are shown in a sample page from the log book under Instruments and Accessories in Navigation (chap. II).

Afternoon sights.—A sun sight is observed in the afternoon for line of position and compass error. Lines of position obtained at noon may be run up to the p. m. observation with allowance made for current found at noon. Preparations are made for star sights at twilight and the time of sunset is determined. The star finder is set to select favorable bearing stars with their altitudes, or the local sidereal time of sunset is determined to identify the stars from the navigational star chart in the Nautical Almanac. The navigator can compute the altitude of Polaris for the D. R. position at twilight or the local hour angle, or local sidereal time of sunset may be found and from Table I and Table III of the Nautical Almanac, the correction for latitude may be found. With the almanac correction, index correction, and height of eye corrections, having all signs reversed and applied to the D. R. latitude, the approximate altitude of Polaris is found. With this altitude set on the sextant, Polaris is picked up in the telescope bearing north. The horizon being clear and distinct, no shade glass is used. At the same time, its true azimuth may be found from the Nautical Almanac, its compass bearing observed, and the compass error determined.

The following examples illustrate a day's work for the navigator at sea. The "time sight" and cosine haversine formulas are used in the computations for determining the lines of position, but any good method, including any of the short cut navigational tables, may be substituted for them.

Example 1.—On October 4, 1937, a steamer left Hampton Roads for Lisbon on a great circle course. The distance was 3,120 miles. From Hampton Roads to point of departure, the distance was 25 miles. At 5 p. m. with Cape Henry Light bearing 301° (mag.) distance 8.3 miles took departure, set course 77° (p. s. c.) (Var. 8° W., Dev. 3° W.) patent log reading 0, (The point of departure is lat. 36°52′.0 N., longitude 75°51′.1 W.). The chronometer was 30^s fast on G. C. T. At about 5^h 30^m a. m. the navigator decided to take sights of two stars for position. When the chronometer read 10^h 03^m 00^s the watch was set for local civil time. At about 5^h 30^m a. m. simultaneous observations were made of star Polaris, alt. 38°21′35″, W. T. 5^h 32^m 12^s, C—W, 4^h 51^m 45^s; and star Regulus bearing southeast, alt. 34°42′48″; W. T. 5^h 28^m 50^s; I. C.+0′30″; H. E. 40 feet; compass bearing of Regulus 113°; patent log 147. The vessel continued on same course and speed (11.7 knots) until 9:30 a. m. when an observation of the sun's lower limb was taken, alt. 36°11′06″; W. T. 9^h 30^m 00^s; C—W, 4^h 47^m 40^s; patent log 193; sun's azimuth p. s. c. 146° vessel's head 77°.

Perform a. m. part of day's work.

The vessel continues on same course and speed. When the chronometer reads 4^h 10^m 00^s at what time should the watch be set for local apparent time of noon? If the watch is set 24 seconds fast on L. A. T. of noon position, work out constants for observations for latitude to be taken at 15^m, 10^m, and 5^m before noon and at noon. The observed altitudes near noon were as follows:

15^m before 46°29′55″; 10^m before 46°34′25″; 5^m before 46°36′40″. The noon altitude was 46°37′ 25″, with the patent log reading 220 miles. About noon a sight was obtained of the planet Venus bearing southwestward, sextant altitude 48°59′0, I. C. +30″; H. E. 40 feet; watch 12^h 05^m 18^s; C−W, 4^h 45^m 08^s, chron. fast 30^s.

Complete the day's work for noon.

At noon course was changed to 84° p. s. c., Var. 11° W.; Dev. 4° W. Steamed until 3 p. m. when at watch time 3^h 00^m 10^s; C−W, 4^h 42^m 20^s; observed altitude of sun's lower limb 27°49′05″; I. C.+0′30″, H. E. 40 feet; patent log 255 miles; compass bearing of sun 252°, vessel's head 84°.

Find position at 3 p. m.

The vessel continues on same course and speed until 6:00 p. m. when star observations were taken on star Polaris for latitude; altitude 38°44′10″; W .T. 6^h 01^m 00^s; C−W, 4^h 38^m 56^s; compass bearing of Polaris 16°.5, vessel's head 84°; and on star Arcturus, bearing north westward, altitude 25°55′35″; W. T. 6^h 05^m 00^s, C−W, 4^h 38^m 52^s; I. C.+0′30″; H. E. 40 feet, patent log 290 miles. Course and speed remaining the same, find D. R. position at 8 p. m. (See plot fig. 106.)

October 5, 1937.—A. M. Work

From the Nautical Almanac the navigator notes the time of sunrise and determines on a position about $5^h 30^m$ a. m. From 5 p. m., October 4, to 5:30 a. m., October 5=$12^h.5$. $12^h.5 \times 11$ knts.7=146.3 miles.

True course	Distance	N.	E.	D. Lon.
66°	146.3	59.5	133.6	168′.1

Long. of departure, 75° 51′ 03″ W.
Change in longitude, 2° 45′ 36″ E.
73 05 27 W.
=4^h 52^m 22s

168′.1=2° 48′ 06″=$11^m 12^s.4$
D. Long. per hour=13′.4=$53^s.6$
$\frac{11^m.21}{60}$ of $53^s.6=10^s$; $11^m\ 12^s.4-10^s=11^m\ 02^s.4$
therefore the watch is set ahead $11^m\ 02^s.4$
$11^m\ 02^s.4$=2° 45′ 36″

Set watch when
C. T., $10^h\ 03^m\ 00^s$
C. C., — 30
G. C. T., 10 02 30
Long. W., 4 52 22
L. C. T., 5 10 08

Course	Var.	Dev.	Compass error	True course	Dist.	N.	E.	D. Lo.
77°	8° W.	3° W.	11° W.	66°	147	59.8	134.3	169

Point of departure Lat., 36° 52′.0 N. Long., 75° 51′.1 W.
D. L., 59 .8 N. D. Lo., 2 49 .0 E.
D. R. position at 5^h 30 a. m. Lat., 37° 51′.8 N. Long., 73° 02′.1 W.=$4^h\ 52^m\ 08^s.4$

Star.	R. A.	Dec.	Alt.
Regulus	$10^h\ 05^m\ 03^s.5$	12° 16′.3 N.	34° 42′ 48″
Polaris	------------	------------	38° 21′ 35″

Regulus
W. T., $5^h\ 28^m\ 50^s$
C.—W., 4 51 45
Chron., 10 20 35
Corr., — 30
G. C. T., 10 20 05
R. A. M. S.+12^h, 0 53 00.1
Corr. (Tab. 39), 1 41.8
G. S. T., 11 14 46.9
R. A. ✱, 10 05 03.5
G. H. A., 1 09 43.4 W.

Az. from table, N. 102° E.

h_s 34° 42′.8
Corr., — 7 .1
h_o, 34 35 .7

h, 34° 35′ 42″
L, 37 55 00
p, 77 43 42
150 14 24
s, 75 07 12
s—h 40 31 30

L. H. A., $3^h\ 41^m\ 48^s.5$ E.
or, 20 18 11 .5 W.
G. H. A., 25 09 43 .4 W
Long. { 4 51 31 .9 W. / 72° 53′.0 W.

(Tab. 40) —1′.4
H. E., —6 .2
I. C., + .5
Corr., —7 .1

sec., .10298
cosec, .01004
cos, 9.40958
sin, 9.81276
hav, 9.33536

Polaris
W. T., $5^h\ 32^m\ 12^s$
C—W, 4 51 45
Chron., 10 23 57
Corr., — 30
G. C. T., 10 23 27.0
R. A. M. S.+12^h, 0 53 00.4
Corr. (Tab. 39), 1 42.3
G. S. T., 11 18 09.4
Long., 4 52 08.4 W.
L. S. T., 6 26 01.

h_s, 38° 21′.6
Corr., — 7.0
h_o, 38 14 .6
Corr. Tab. I. N. A., —19′.6
h_o 38° 14′ 6
Corr., — 19 .6
Lat., 37 55 .0 N.

(Tab. 40), —1′.3
H. E., —6 .2
I. C., + .5
Corr., —7 .0

True position, $5^h\ 30^m$ a. m. Lat., 37° 55′.0 N. Long., 72° 53′.0 W.
D. R. position, $5^h\ 30^m$ a. m. Lat., 37 51 .8 N. Long., 73 02′.1 W.

D. L., 3 .2 N. D. Long., 9 .1 E.

Drift per hour in longitude, $\frac{9.1}{12.5}$=0′.7 E.

Regulus, true bearing $5^h\ 30^m$,	102°
Regulus, compass bearing $5^h\ 30^m$,	113°
Compass error,	11° W.
Variation from chart,	8° W.
Deviation of compass,	3° W. (on heading 77° (p. s. c.))

Run to observation of sun at $9^h\ 30^m$ a. m.

Course	Var.	Dev.	Compass error	True course	Dist.	D. Lat.	Dep.	D. Lo.
77°	8° W.	3° W.	11° W.	66°	46′	18′.7	42.0	53′.3 E.

Lat. by obs. $5^h\ 30^m$ a. m., Lat.,	37° 55′.0 N.	Long.,	72° 53′.0 W.	
Run, D. L.,	18 .7 N.	D. Lo.,	53 .3 E.	
D. R. position, $9^h\ 30^m$, Lat.,	38° 13′.7 N.	Long.,	71 59 .7 W.	$=4^h\ 47^m\ 59^s$

October 5, 1937.—Sun Sight

W. T.,	$9^h\ 30^m\ 00^s$		
C−W,	4 47 40		
Chron.,	2 17 40		
Corr.,	− 30		
G. C. T.,	14 17 10	$=14^h.29$	
Eq. t,	+ 11 30.6		
G. A. T.,	14 28 40.6		
Long.,	4 47 59.0		
L. A. T.,	9 40 41.6		
t,	= 2 19 18.4 E.		
Arc,	= 34° 49′ 36′ E.		

h_s,	36° 11′.1	(Tab. 40),	+14′.8
Corr.,	+ 9 .1	H. E.,	− 6 .2
		I. C.,	+ .5
h_o,	36° 20′.2	Corr.,	+ 9 .1

			Altitude		Azimuth
t,	$2^h\ 19^m\ 18^s.4$	hav,	8.95211	sin,	9.75671
L,	38° 13′ 42″ N.	cos,	9.89517		
d,	4 42 48 S.	cos,	9.99853	cos,	9.99853
		hav,	8.84581		
		nat. hav,	.07011		
L∼d,	42° 56′ 30″	nat. hav,	13398		
z,	53 42 50	nat. hav,	20409	cosec.,	0.09363
h_c,	36° 17′.2			sin,	9.84887
h_o,	36 20 .2			Z.,	S 44° 55′ E.
				or,	135°
Int.,	3 .0 towards 135°				

Dec. 14^h,	4° 42′.5 S.	
Corr.,	+ 0 .3	
Dec.,	4 42 .8 S.	
Eq. t, 14^h,	$11^m\ 30^s.4$	
Corr.,	+ .2	
Eq. t,	+11 30 .6	

With distance 3′ on course 135° or bearing of sun.

Co.	Dist.	D. L.	Dep.	D. Long.
135°	3′.0	2′.1	2.1	2′.7

(Tab. 35), long. factor,	1′.3	D. R. lat.,	38° 13′.7 N.	Long.,	71° 59′.7 W.
D. lat.,	2 .1	D. L.,	2 .1 S.	D. long.,	2 .7 E.
Corr. in long.,	2 .7 E.	Position point used if line is plotted,	38 11 .6 N.	Long.,	71 57 .0 W.
		Corr. to long. to correspond with D. R. lat.,			2 .7 E.
		9^h 30^m a. m. D. R. lat. 38° 13′.7 N.		Long.,	71 54 .3 W. = 4^h 47^m $37^s.2$

True bearing of sun,	135°
Compass bearing of sun,	146
Compass error,	11° W.
Variation by chart,	8° W.
Deviation of compass on C. 66° T.,	3° W.

9^h 30^m a. m. observation, G. A. T.,	14^h 28^m $40^s.6$
9^h 30^m a. m. long. by observation,	4 47 37 .2
9^h 30^m a. m. observation L. A. T.,	9 41 03 .4
9^h 30^m a. m. observation the W. T., =	9 30 00 .0
9^h 30^m a. m. the watch is slow on L. A. T.	11 03 .4

October 5, 1937.—Work from 9^h 30^m to Noon

Course 66° true, speed 11.7 knots: Northing per hour 4′.76. Eastings per hour = 10.69. D. Long. = 13′.6.

Change in Long. per hour due to speed of vessel	13′.6 E.	Change in Long. from 9^h 30^m to 11^h = 14′.3 × $1^h.5$ = 21′.4 =	1^m $25^s.6$
Change in Long. per hour due to current	.7 E.	Watch slow on L. A. T. at 9^h 30^m	11 03 .4
Vessel changes Long. per hour	14 .3 E.	11 a. m. watch is slow on L. A. T.	12 29 .0
Time to noon = $1^h - 12^m$ 29^s = 47^m 31^s = $0^h.79$		Chg. in Long. from 11^h to 12^h,	0 45 .2
Chg. in Long. from 11^h to 12^h = .79 × 14.3 = 11′.3 = 0^m $45^s.2$		Total amount watch is set ahead	13 14 .2

Time of run from 9^h 30^m to noon is 13^m $14^s.2$ less than 2^h 30^m = 2^h 16^m $45^s.8$ = $2^h.28$.
Change in Lat. from 9^h 30^m to noon is $2^h.28$ × 4′.76 = 10′.8 N. Chg. in Long. $2^h.28$ × 14.3 = 32′.6 E.

9^h 30^m D. R. Lat.,	38° 13′.7 N.	Long.,	71° 59′.7 W.	Long. by obs.,	71° 54′.3 W.	G. A. T.,	16^h 45^m $26^s.8$
Run to noon D. L.,	10 .8 N.	D. Lo.,	32 .6 E.	D. Lo.,	32 .6 E.	Eq. *t*.,	− 11 32 .4
Noon D. R. Lat.,	38 24 .5 N.	Long.,	71 27 .1 W.	Long.,	71 21 .7 W.	G. C. T.,	16 33 54 .4
				9^h 30^m run to noon = 4^h 45^m $26^s.8$		(Used in noon Lat. obs.)	

Set watch to L. A. T. when			
Chron.,	4^h	10^m	00^s
Corr.,	−		30
G. C. T.,	16	09	30.0
Eq. t,	+	11	32.3
G. A. T.,	16	21	02.3
Long.,	4	45	26.8
L. A. T.,	11	35	35.5

Dec. 16^h,	4° 44′.5 S.	
Corr.,	+ .6	
Dec.,	4 45 .1 S.	

Eq. t,	+ 11^m $31^s.9$
Corr.,	+ .4
Eq. t,	+ 11 32 .3

In setting watch left an error making watch 24^s fast on L. A. T.
$L=90°-d-h$, or approx. $h=90°-(d+L)$

d,	4° 45′
L,	38 25
d+L,	43 10
Approx. h=46° 50′	

d,	4° 45′.1
corr.,	+ 9 .5
d+corr.,	4 54 .6

Corr. (Tab. 40) Approx. h=46° 50′	+15′.2
H. E.,	− 6 .2
I. C.,	+ .5
Total corr.,	+ 9 .5

L=L′ ± △ L; L′=90°−d−obs. alt.−at² ± corr. to alt. ∴ L=90°−d−at² ± Corr. to alt. ± △ L−obs. alt.=K−obs. alt., or K=90°−d−at² ± corr. to alt. ± △ L; since vessel is making northing △L in this case is (+)

$$\triangle L=\frac{4'.8}{4},\frac{4'.8}{6},\frac{4'.8}{12}=1'.2;\ 0'.8;\ 0'.4$$

If watch is 24^s fast, the observations should be taken at watch	11^h 45^m 24^s	11^h 50^m 24^s	11^h 55^m 24^s	12^h 00^m 24^s
But chg. in Long. from these watch times to noon= $\frac{14'.3}{4}$, $\frac{14'.3}{6}$, $\frac{14'.3}{12}$ =3′.5; 2′.4; 1′.2	0 14	0 09	0 05	0 00
Hence watch times to take observations are	11 45 38	11 50 33	11 55 29	12 00 24
For Lat. 38°. 4 N., and Dec. 4.° 8 S., from (Tab. 29) a=2″. 3 and (Tab. 30) at²	− 0° 8′.6	− 3′.8	− 0′.9	− 0′.0
△L	+ 0 1 .2	+ 0 .8	+ 0 .4	+ 0 .0
d+Corr.	− 4° 54′.6	− 4° 54′.6	− 4° 54′.6	− 4° 54′.6
	5° 02′.0	4° 57′.6	4° 55′.1	4° 54′.6
∴ K	84° 58′.0	85° 02′.4	85° 04′.9	85° 05′.4
Obs. Alts.,	46 29 .9	46 34 .4	46 36 .7	46 37 .4
Noon Lat. by Obs.,	38 28 .1	38 28 .0	38 28 .2	38 28 .0

Mean,	38° 28′.1
Noon Lat. by D. R.,	38 24 .5
D. L.,	3 .6
Long. factor (Tab. 35),	1 .3
Corr. in Long.,	4 .7 E.
Noon Long. by a. m. obs.,	71° 21′.7 W.
True Long. at noon,	71° 17′.0 W.=4^h 45^m 08^s

Watch,	12h 05m 18s	R. A. Venus,	10h 55m 16s
C−W,	4 45 08	Corr.,	3 13
Chron.,	16 50 26	R. A.,	10 58 29
Corr.,	− 30		
G. C. T.,	16 49 56	h_s,	48° 59′.0
R. A. M. S+12h,	0 53 00.1	Corr., −	6 .5
Corr. (Tab. 39),	2 45.9	h_o,	48 52 .5
G. S. T.,	17 45 42		
R. A.✳,	10 58 29		
G. H. A.,	6 47 13 W.		

	276s	Dec.,	8° 10′.6 N.
P. P.,	138	Corr.,	18 .5
(N. A. Tab. VII)	55	Dec.,	7 52 .1 N.
Corr.,	193s	p.,	82° 07′.9

	26′.4
P. P.,	13 .2
(N. A. Tab. VII)	5 .3
Corr.,	18′.5

		H. A.		Az.	
h,	48° 52′ 30″			sec,	0.18197
L,	38 28 06	sec,	0.10626	sec,	0.10626
p,	82 07 54	cosec,	0.00411		
	169 28 30				
s,	84 44 15	cos,	8.96247		
s−h,	35 51 45	sin,	9.76778	sin,	9.76778
s−L,	46 16 09			sin,	9.85890
L. H. A.,	2h 02m 05s.2 W.	hav,	8.84062		
G. H. A.,	6 47 13 .0 W.			hav,	9.91491
Long.,	4 45 07 .8 W.				Z=N. 130° W.
=	71° 17′.0 W.				or 230°

Lat. (departure),	36° 52′.0 N.	Long.,	75° 51′.1 W.
Lat. in,	38 28 .1 N.	Long.,	71 17 .0 W.
D. L.,	1 36 .1 N.	D. Lo.,	4 34 .1=274′.1
			Dep.=217
Course made good,	66° 237 miles		
Dist. to pt. of Dep.,	25		
Total distance made,	262		
Dist. to destination,	3120		
Dist. to go,	2858		

Lat. by obs.,	38° 28′.1 N.	Long.,	71° 17′.0 W.
Lat. by D. R.,	38 24 .5 N.	Long.,	71 27 .1 W.
D. L.,	3 .6 N.	D. Lo.	10 .1 E.
		Dep.,=	7.9

Current 8.6 miles. Set 66°
Drift 8.6 miles=1.3 knts.

From Chart Course 69° (true) Var. 11° W.
Dev. 4° W. Compass Course=84°

Run to 3 p. m. observation of sun.

Compass Course	Var.	Dev.	Compass Error	True Course	Dist.	D. Lat.	Dep.	D. Lo.
84°	11° W.	4° W.	15° W.	69°	35′	12′.5	32.7	41′.8

Noon Lat., 38° 28′.1 N. Long. 71° 17′.0 W.
D. L. (run), 12 .5 N. D. Long. 41 .8 E.

D. R. Lat., 38 40 .6 N. Long., 70 35 .2 W. = 4^h 42^m $20^s.8$

W. T. 3^h 00^m 10^s
C—W 4 42 20

Chron. 7 42 30
Fast, −30

G. C. T., 19 42 00
Eq. t., + 11 34.6

G. A. T., 19 53 34.6
Long. W., 4 42 20.8

L. A. T., 15 11 13.8
t = 3 11 13.8 W.

h_s, 27° 49′.1
Corr., +8 .6

h_o, 27 57 .7

(Tab. 40). +14′.3
H. E., − 6 .2
I. C., + .5

Corr. + 8.6

Dec. 18^h, 4° 46′.4 S.
Corr., 1 .7

Dec., 4 48 .1 S.

Eq. t. $+11^m$ $33^s.4$
Corr., +1 .2

Eq. t., 11 34 .6

t, 3^h 11^m $13^s.8$ — *Alt.* hav., 9.21535 — *Az.* sin 9.86976
L, 38° 40′ 36″ N. — cos 9.89248
d, 4 48 06 S. — cos 9.99847 — cos 9.99847

hav 9.10630

nat. hav., .12773
L∼d 43° 28′ 42″ nat. hav., .13719

z., 61 57 20 nat. hav., .26492 cosec 0.05425

h_c, 28° 02′.7
h_o 27 57 .7 sin 9.92248

Z = S 57° W.
or 237°

Int., 5.0 away on reverse bearing of sun.
Reverse bearing of sun = 57°

True course	Dist.	D. L.	Dep.	D. Long.
57°	5′.0	2′.7	4.2	5′.4

D. R. Lat., 38° 40′.6 N. Long., 70° 35′.2 W.
D. L., 2 .7 N. D. Lo., 5 .4 E.

Point used if line is plotted, Lat., 38 43 .3 N. Long., 70 29 .8 W.
(Tab. 35), Long. factor .83 Corr. to long. to correspond with D. R. Lat., 2 .2 E.
D. L., 2′.7

3 p. m., D. R. Lat. 38°40′.6 N., Long., 70 27 .6 W.

Corr. in long., 2 .2 E.

Sun's true bearing, 3 p. m., 237°
Compass bearing 252

Compass error., 15° W.
Variation (chart) 11° W.

Deviation, 4° W. on heading 84° (p. s. c.)

Run to 6 p. m. observation.

Compass	Var.	Dev.	Compass Error	True Course	Dist.	D. L.	Dep.	D. Lo.
84°	11° W.	4° W.	15° W.	69°	35′	12′.5	32.7	41′.8

3 p. m. D. R. Lat.,	38° 40′.6 N.		Long.,	70° 27′.6 W.
Run D. L.,	12 .5 N.		D. lo.,	41 .8 E.
6 p. m. D. R. Lat.,	38 53 .1 N.		Long.,	69 45 .8 W. = $4^h\ 39^m\ 03^s.2$

Polaris

W. T.,	$6^h\ 01^m\ 00^s$	h_s,	38° 44′.2	(Tab. 40),	−1′.2
C−W.,	4 38 56	Corr.,	−6 .9	H. E.,	−6 .2
				I. C.,	+ .5
Chron.,	10 39 56	h_o,	38 37 .3		
Fast,	−30			Corr.,	−6 .9
G. C. T.,	22 39 26				
G. H. A. Oct. 5,	347° 34′.2	h_o,	38° 37′.3		
Corr. $22^h\ 39^m$,	340 40 .8	Corr.,	+ 12 .7 (Tab. III, N. A.)		
Corr. 26^s,	6 .5				
	688 21 .5	Lat.,	38 50 .0 N.		
	−360°				
G. H. A.,	328 21 .5 W.				
Long.,	69 45 .8 W.				
L. H. A.,	258 35 .7 W.				

True bearing Polaris,	1°.3 (Tab. IV, N. A.)
Compass bearing Polaris,	16°.5
Compass error,	15 .2 W.
Var. from chart,	11 .2 W.
Deviation,	4 .0 W. on vessel heading 84° (p. s. c.)

			Arcturus				
W. T.,	$6^h\ 05^m\ 00^s$	h_s,	25° 55′.6	(Tab. 40),	−2′.0	Dec.,	19° 30′.5 N.
C−W.,	4 38 52	Corr.,	−7 .7	H. E.,	−6 .2	p,	70° 29′.5
				I. C.,	+ .5		
Chron.,	10 43 52	h_o,	25 47 .9				
Fast,	−30			Corr.,	−7 .7		
G. C. T.,	22 43 22						

G. H. A. Oct. 5,	160° 02′.8
Corr. $22^h\ 43^m$,	341 41 .0
Corr. 22^s,	5 .5
	501 49 .3
(Subtract),	(360°)
G. H. A.	141 49 .3 W.

h,	25° 47′ 54″		
L,	38 50 00	sec,	.10848
p,	70 29 30	cosec,	.02567
	135 07 24		
s,	67 33 42	cos,	9.58171
s−h,	41 45 48	sin,	9.82351
L. H. A.,	72° 05′.4 W.	hav,	9.53937
G. H. A.,	141 49 .3 W.		
Long.,	69 43 .9 W.		

Azimuth from tables N. 85° W. (275°).

Cape Razo Light, entrance to Lisbon is in 38°42′ N., Long. 9°29′ W. Difference of longitude from 6 p. m. position is 4^h. Open azimuth tables to Lat. 39° N. dec. 39° and time 4^h and the great circle course is found to be N. 70° E. Changed course to 70° true Var. 13° W. Dev. 4° W.

Position at 6 p. m. by obs. Lat. 38°50′.0 N.; Long. 69°43′.9 W.
Run to 8 p. m.

True course	Dist.	D. L.	Dep.	D. Lo.
70°	23′	7′.9	21.6	27′.8

6 p. m. Lat.,	38° 50′.0 N.	Long.,	69° 43′.9 W.
Run D. L.,	7 .9 N.	D. Lo.,	27 .8 E.
8 p. m. D. R. Lat.,	38 57 .9 N.	Long.,	69 16 .1 W.

Course for night 87° (p. s. c.)

Example 2.—The U. S. S. *Alden* en route from Batavia, Java, to Aden, Arabia, was at 0530 zone time (-6^h) August 28, 1937, by D. R.—from last fix 36 hours previously—in Lat. 5° S.; Long. 95° E. The course was 304° (gyro) and speed 15 kts. The last azimuth showed the gyro error to be zero. The following sights were taken of star Achernar bearing southwestward, sextant altitude 31°20′30″; watch time $5^h\ 06^m\ 05^s$; C−W. $6^h\ 05^m\ 03^s$; chron. fast $5^m\ 02^s$; I. C. −1′.0; height of eye, 31 feet; the star Deneb Kaitos bearing 251° (gyro), sextant altitude 39°16′10″; W. T. $5^h\ 17^m\ 57^s$; the moon's lower limb, sextant altitude 60° 27′.48″; bearing northwestward; W. T. $5^h\ 30^m\ 01^s$. The watch was set to approximate zone time. Find fix at 0530, also the set and drift of current.

Continued same course and speed and at W. T. $7^h\ 29^m\ 55^s$ an observation was taken of sun's lower limb, sextant altitude 25°18′50″, bearing by gyro 77°; vessel's head by gyro 304° and by standard compass 305°½; variation 3°½ W. Find sun's position line, error of gyro, and deviation of standard compass; the 0800 position and interval to and watch time of local apparent noon.

Continued on same course and speed when meridian altitude of sun's lower limb was observed, sextant altitude 75°58′10″. Find running fix of L. A. N. and position of vessel at 1200.

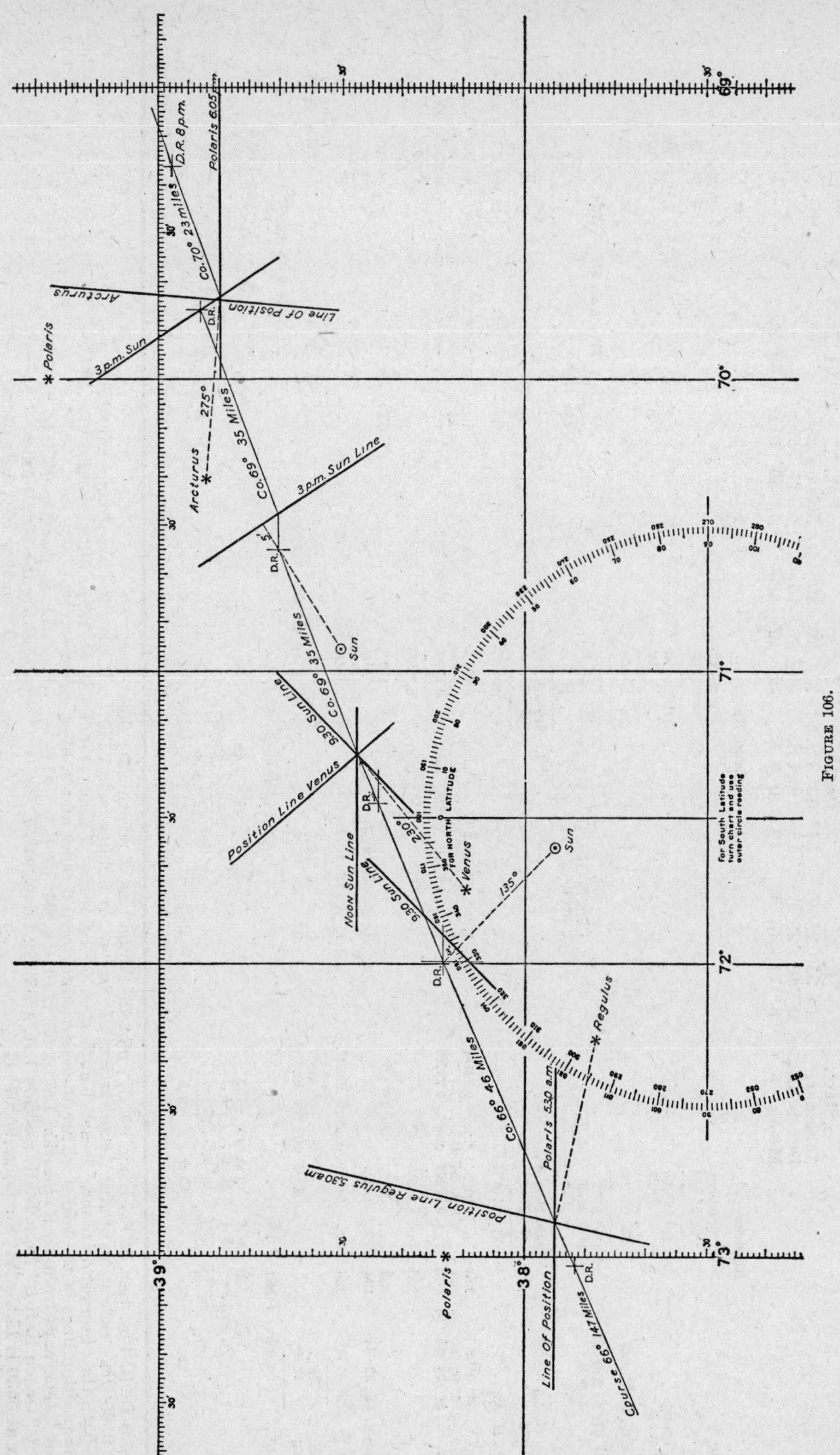
Polaris 6.05 p.m.
D.R. 8 p.m.
Co. 70° 23 miles
Arcturus
Line of Position
3 p.m. Sun
Polaris
275°
Co. 69° 35 Miles
Arcturus
3 p.m. Sun Line
D.R.
Sun
Co. 69° 35 Miles
930 Sun Line
Position Line Venus
D.R.
230°
Venus
Noon Sun Line
930 Sun Line
135°
Sun
D.R.
Regulus
Co. 66° 46 Miles
Polaris 530 a.m.
Position Line Regulus 530 a.m.
Polaris
Line Of Position
D.R.
Course 66° 147 Miles
FOR NORTH LATITUDE
For South Latitude turn chart and use outer circle reading
69°
70°
71°
72°
73°
39°
38°

FIGURE 106.

Continued same course and speed. The sky became overcast, the middle of the afternoon, but cleared somewhat shortly before sunset. Sights were obtained of celestial bodies as follows: the star Altair, sextant altitude 43°37′25″, bearing by gyro 75°; W. T. $18^h\ 12^m\ 02^s$; the star Nunki, sextant altitude 53°48′10″; bearing by gyro 132°.5; W. T. $18^h\ 20^m\ 00^s$ and the star Vega, sextant altitude 42°51′20″ bearing by gyro 26°; W. T. $18^h\ 23^m\ 58^s$. Find fix at 1820; set and drift of current since morning fix and position to report at 2000.

Stars.	R. A.	Dec.	Alt.	W. T.	H. P.
Achernar,	$1^h\ 35^m\ 25^s.7$	57° 32′.8 S.	31° 20′ 30″	$5^h\ 06^m\ 05^s$	
Deneb Kaitos,	0 40 29 .6	18 19 .4 S.	39 16 10	5 17 57	
Moon,	3 11 46 .5	19 40 .3 N.	60 27 48	5 30 01	59′.2

Achernar

W. T., $5^h\ 06^m\ 05^s$
C.–W., 6 05 03
Chron., 11 11 08
Fast., – 5 02
G. C. T. Aug. 27, 23 06 06
G. H. A. Aug. 27, 310° 57′.2
Corr. $23^h\ 06^m$, 347 26 .9
Corr. 06^s, 1 .5
G. H. A., 298 25 .6 W.
Long., 95 00 .0 E.
L. H. A., 33 25 .6 W.

t, 33° 25′.6 W. hav., 8.91753 sin, 9,74104
L, 5° 00′ 00″ S. cos, 9.99834
d, 57 32 48 S. cos, 9.72966 cos, 9.72966
hav., 8.64553
nat. hav., .04421
L∼d, 52 32 48 nat. hav., .19595
z, 58° 41′.3 nat. hav., .24016 cosec, .06837
h_c, 31 18 .7 sin, 9.53907
h_o, 31 12 .4 Z=S. 20° W. (200°)
Int., 6 .3 away from Z (200°).

h_s, 31° 20′.5 (Tab. 40), –1′.7
Corr., – 8 .1 H. E., –5 .4
I. C., –1 .0
h_o, 31 12 .4 Corr., –8 .1

Deneb Kaitos

$5^h\ 17^m\ 57^s$
6 05 03
11 23 00
– 5 02
23 17 58
324° 41′.2
Corr. $23^h\ 17^m$, 350 12 .4
Corr. 58^s, 14 .5
315 08 .1 W.
95 00 .0 E.
50 08.1 W.

t, 50° 08′.1 W. hav., 9.25409 sin, 9.88511
L, 5° 00′ 00″ S. cos, 9.99834
d, 18 19 24 S. cos, 9.97740 cos, 9.97740
hav., 9.22983
.16976
L∼d, 13 19 24 .01346
z, 50° 41′.2 .18322 cosec, .11143
h_c, 39 18 .8 sin, 9.97394
h_o, 39 08 .6 Z=S. 70°.4 W. (250°)
Int., 10 .2 away from Z (250°).

h_s, 39° 16′.2 (Tab. 40) –1′.2
Corr., – 7 .6 H. E., –5 .4
I. C., –1 .0
h_o, 39 08 .6 Corr., –7 .6

Moon

$5^h\ 30^m\ 01^s$
6 05 03
11 35 04
– 5 02
23 30 02
G. H. A. 23^h., (Aug. 27) 273° 07′.1
Corr. 30^m., 7 13 .1
Corr. 02^s., .5
280 20 .7 W.
95 00 .0 E.
15 20 .7 W.

t, 15° 20′.7 W. hav., 8.25103 sin, 9.42264
L, 5° 00′ 00″ S. cos, 9.99834
d, 19 40 18 N. cos, 9.97389 cos, 9.97389
hav., 8.22326
.01672
L∼d, 24 40 18 .04564
z, 28° 55′.2 .06236 cosec, .31552
hc., 61 04 .8 sin, 9.71205
h_o., 61 06 .3 Z=N. 31° W. (329°)
Int. 1 .5 toward Z (329°)

h_s, 60° 27′.8 (Tab. 41), +44′.9
I. C., – 1 .0 H. E., – 5 .4
60 26, 8 Corr., +39 .5
Corr., + 39. 5
h_o, 61 06. 3

From D. R. Pos. Lat. 5° S.; Long. 95° E., plot the Moon line of position for 0530.
At 0506 the observation of star Achernar was 24^m before, or 6 miles from 0530 D. R. position along course 304°.
At 0518 the observation of star Deneb Kaitos was 12^m before, or 3 miles from 0530, D. R. position along course 304°.
The position lines of the two stars are then carried forward 6 miles and 3 miles, respectively.
Plot "Achernar" from D. R. position Lat. 4°57′ S.; Long. 94°55′ E.
Plot "Deneb Kaitos" from D. R. position Lat. 4°58′ S.; Long. 94°57′ E.
Fix at 0530 is Lat. 4°54′ S.; Long. 95°07′ E.

From D. R. position 0530 to fix
Current=50°, 9 miles.
$9^m \div 36^h = .25^m$ drift per hr.

A. M. SUN LINE

Run to 0730

Co.	Dist.	D. L.	Dep.	D. Lo.
304°	30′	16′.8	24.9	25′.0

Position at 0530 Lat.,	4° 54′.0 S.	Long.,	95° 07′ E.
Run D. L.,	16 .8 N.	D. Lo.,	25′ W.
D. R. position 0730 Lat.,	4 37 .2 S.	Long.,	94 42 E. = $6^h\ 18^m\ 48^s$

W. T.,	$7^h\ 29^m\ 55^s$	h_s,	25° 18′.8	Dec. 0^h,	9° 57′.0 N.	Eq. t,	$-1^m\ 23^s.0$
C−W,	6 05 03	Corr.,	+ 7 .6	Corr.,	− 1 .3	Corr.,	− 1 .1
Chron.,	13 34 58	h_o,	25 26 .4	Dec.,	9 55 .7 N.	Eq. t,	−1 21 .9
Fast,	− 5 02				H. D.		H. D.
G. C. T. Aug. 28,	1 29 56 = $1^h.5$	(Tab. 40),	+ 14′.1				
Eq. t,	− 1 21.9	Add. Corr.,	− 0 .1		0′.9		$0^s.7$
		H. E.,	− 5 .4	G. C. T.,	$1^h.5$	G. C. T.,	$1^h.5$
G. A. T.,	1 28 34.1	I. C.,	− 1 .0				
Long., E.	6 18 48.0			Corr.,	1 .3	Corr.,	1 .1
		Corr.,	+ 7′.6				

L. A. T.,	7 47 22 .1						
t,	4 12 37 .9 E.	hav,	9.43812	sin,	9.95049	Sun's bearing by gyro.,	77° 00′
L,	4° 37′ 12″.0 S.	cos,	9.99859			Sun's true bearing,	76 42
d,	9 55 42 .0 N.	cos,	9.99345	cos,	9.99345		
						Gyro. error,	0 18 W.
		hav,	9.43016				
						Ship's head by gyro.,	304° 00′
		nat. hav,	.26925			Gyro error,	18′ W.
L~d,	14° 32′ 54″	nat. hav,	.01604				
						Gyro.,	303 42
z.	64° 34′.2	nat. hav,	.28529	cosec,	.04426	Ship's head (p. s. c.),	305 30
h_c,	25° 25′.8			sin,	9.98820	Error,	1 48 W.
h_o,	25 26 .4			Z=76° 42′		Variation from chart,	3 30 W.
Int.,	0 .6 towards Z 77°					Deviation (ship's head),	1 42 E.

Run to 0800

Co.	Dist.	D. L.	Dep.	D. Lo.
304°	7′.5	4′.2	6.2	6′.2

Lat. at 0730,	4° 37′.2 S.	Long.,	94° 42′.0 E.
Run D. L.,	4 .2 N.	D. Lo.,	6 .2 W.
Position at 0800 Lat.,	4 33 S.	Long.,	94 35 .8 E.

Noon interval

Time of a. m. sun sight, $4^h\ 12^m\ 37^s.9 = 4^h.21$

	Course	Dist.	D. L.	Dep.	D. Lo.
	304°	15′	8′.4	12.4 W.	
Current,	50°	.25	0 .2 N.	0.2 E.	
			8 .6	12.2	12′.23

Noon int. factor (Tab. 37) = 1.01378

	h	m	s
A. m. sight,	$4^h.21$		
	4^h	16^m	05^s
W. T., (obs.)	7	29	55
W. T., of L. A. noon	11	46	00
C−W,	6	05	03
Chron.,	5	51	03
Fast	−	5	02
G. C. T., of L. A. noon	5	46	01

	Co.	Dist.	D. L.	Dep.	D. Lo.
From 1146 to 1200 = 14^m and $\frac{14}{60} \times 15$kts = 3′.5	304°	3′.5	2′.0	2.9	2′.9

Run from 0800 to 1200.

		Dist.	D. L.	Dep.	D. Lo.
Course	304°	60′	33′.6	49.7	49′.8
Current	50°	1	0.6	0.8	0.8

0800 Pos. Lat.,	4° 33′.0 S.	Long.,	94° 35′.8 E.
Run D. L.,	33 .6 N.	D. Lo.,	49 .8 W.
1200 D. R. Pos. Lat.,	3 59 .4 N.	Long.,	93 46′.0 E.
Run 14^m,	2 .0 S.		2 .9 E.
	4 01 .4 S.		93 48 .9 E.
Current,	.6 N.		.8 E.
1146 Pos. Lat.,	4 00 .8 S.	Long.,	93 49 .7 E. point to advance morning sun line for running fix.

Meridian altitude

h_s,	75° 58′.2
Corr., +	9 .3
h_o,	76 07 .5
z,	13 52 .5 S.
Dec.,	9 51 .9 N.
Lat.,	4 00 .6 S.

(Tab. 40),	+15′.8
Add. corr.,	− 0 .1
H. E.,	− 5 .4
I. C.,	− 1 .0
Corr.,	+ 9 .3

Dec. 4^h,	9° 53′.5 N.
Corr.,	1 .6
Dec.,	9 51 .9 N.

	H. D.
	0′.9
G. C. T.,	$1^h.77$
Corr.,	1 .6

Running fix, Lat.,	4° 00′.6 S.	Long.,	93° 49′.7 E.
Run to 1200, D. L.,	2 .0 N.	D. long.,	2 .9 W.
1200 position, Lat.,	3 58 .6 S.	Long.,	93 46 .8 E.

Run from 1200 to 1820

Co.	Dist.	D. L.	Dep.	D. Long.
304°	95′	53′.1	78.8	79′.0

	Lat.		Long.
1200 pos., Lat.,	3° 58′.6 S.	Long.,	93° 46′.8 E.
Run, D. L.,	53 .1 N.	D. long.,	1 19 .0 W.
1820 D. R. pos., Lat.,	3 05 .5 S.	Long.,	92 27 .8 E.

Stars	R. A.	Dec.	Alt.	W. T.
Altair,	19h 47m 46s.5	8° 42′.4 N.	43° 37′.4	6h 12m 02s
Nunki,	18 51 26 .1	26° 22′.5 S.	53 48 .2	6 20 00
Vega,	18 34 51 .2	38° 43′.8 N.	42 51 .3	6 23 58

	Altair		*Nunki*		*Vega*
W. T.,	18h 12m 02s		18h 20m 00s		18h 23m 58s
C—W,	6 05 03		6 05 03		6 05 03
Chron.,	12 17 05		12 25 03		12 29 01
Fast.	− 5 02		− 5 02		− 5 02
G. C. T. Aug. 28,	12 12 03		12 20 01		12 23 59
G. H. A. " "	38° 51′.1		52° 56′.2		57° 05′.0
Corr. 12h 12m,	183 30 .1	Corr. 12h 20m,	185 30 .4	Corr. 12h 23m,	186 15 .5
Corr. 3s,	.8	Corr. 1s,	.3	Corr. 59s,	14 .8
G. H. A.,	222 22 .0 W.		238 26 .9 W.		243 35 .3 W.
Long.,	92 27 .8 E.		92 27 .8 E.		92 27 .8 E.
L. H. A.,	314 49 .8 W.		330 54 .7 W.		336 03 .1 W.
t,	45 10 .2 E.		29 05.3 E.		23 56 .9 E.

Altair

t,	45° 10′ .2 E.	hav,	9.16878	sin,	9.85076
L,	3° 05′ 30″ S.	cos,	9.99936		
d,	8 42 24 N.	cos,	9.99496	cos,	9.99496
		hav,	9.16310		
		nat. hav,	.14558		
L∼d,	11 47 54	nat. hav,	.01056		
z	46° 33′.0	nat. hav,	.15614	cosec.	13908
h_c	43 27 .0			sin,	9.98480
h_o	43 30 .0			Z=75°	
Int.,	3 .0 towards 75°				

h_s	43° 37′.4	(Tab. 40),	−1′.0
Corr.,	− 7 .4	H. E.,	−5 .4
		I. C.,	−1 .0
h_o,	43 30 .0	Corr.,	−7 .4

Nunki

t,	29° 05′ .3 E.	hav,	8.79979	sin,	9.68678
L,	3° 05′ 30″ S.	cos,	9.99936		
d,	26 22 30 S.	cos,	9.95226	cos,	9.95226
		hav,	8.75141		
		nat. hav,	.05642		
L∼d,	23 17 00	nat. hav,	.04072		
z,	36° 19′ .2	nat, hav,	.09714	cosec,	22747
h_c,	53 40′.8			sin,	9.86651
h_o	53 41 .1			Z=S 47° E. (133°)	
Int.,	0 .3 towards 133°				

h_s,	53° 48′.2	(Tab. 40),	−0′.7
Corr.,	− 7 .1	H. E.,	−5 .4
		I. C ,	−1 .0
h_o,	53 41 .1	Corr.,	−7 .1

Vega

t,	23° 56′ .9 E.	hav,	8.63391	sin,	9.60844
L,	3° 05′ 30″ S.	cos,	9.99936		
d,	38 43 48 N.	cos,	9.89215	cos,	9.89215
		hav,	8.52542		
		nat. hav,	.03353		
L∼d,	41 49 18	nat. hav,	.12739		
z	47° 18′.0	nat. hav,	.16092	cosec,	.13376
h_c	42° 42′.0			sin,	9.63435
h_o	42 43 .8			Z=25°.5	
Int.,	1 .8 towards 25°.5				

h_s,	42° 51′.3	(Tab. 40),	−1′.1
Corr.,	− 7 .5	H. E.,	−5 .4
		I. C.,	−1 .0
h_o,	42 43 .8	Corr.,	−7 .5

Fix at 1820 Lat. 3° 04′ S., Long. 92° 29′ E. "Altair" position line is carried forward 2 miles and "Vega" position line is moved backward 1 mile to bring all position lines to 1820

Run to 2000

Co	Dist.,	D. L.,	Dep.,	D. Lo.,
304°	25′	14′.0	20.7	20′.7

1820 Pos.,	Lat., 3° 04′ S.	Long., 92° 29′ 0 E.	1820,	D. R., 3° 05′.5 S.	Long., 92° 27′.8 E.
Run,	D. L., 14 N.	D. Lo., 20 .7 W.	Run,	D. L., 14 .0 N.	D. Lo., 20 .7 W.
2000 Pos.,	Lat., 2 50 S.	Long., 92° 08 .3 E.	2000 D. R.,	Lat. 2 51 .5 S.	Long., 92 07 .1 E.

Set=39°
Drift .13 per hour

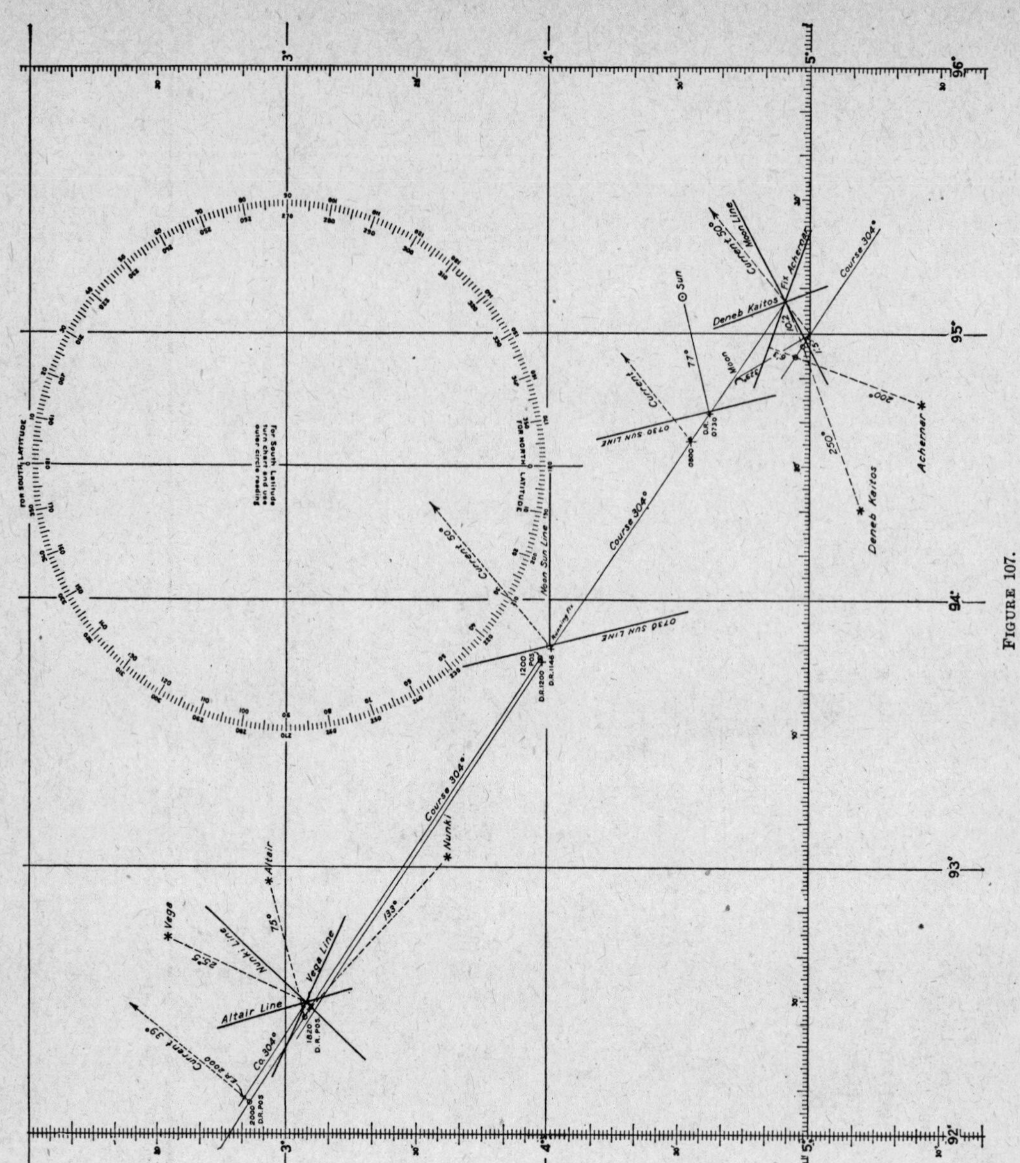
3°
4°
5°
96°
95°
94°
93°
92°
For South Latitude
For North Latitude
0730 Sun Line
Noon Sun Line
Course 304°
Current 50°
Current
Moon Line
Fix Achernar
Deneb Kaitos
Course 304°
Sun
Moon
77°
250°
200°
Achernar
Deneb Kaitos
Nunki
Altair
Vega
Altair Line
Vega Line
Nunki Line
133°
75°
255
Co. 304°
Current 39°
D.R. Pos.
2000

FIGURE 107.

CHAPTER XVII

MARINE SURVEYING

Hydrography has been authoritatively defined as that branch of science which deals with the measurement and description of the physical features of that portion of the earth's surface which embraces the oceans, seas, lakes, rivers and other waters, and their adjoining coastal areas, with special reference to their use for the purpose of navigation.

It embraces the carrying out of marine surveys, including triangulation, topography sounding, magnetic and astronomical work; the study of tides, tidal streams and currents, also of oceanography and meteorology so far as they affect navigation; the construction, the compilation and publication of nautical charts, sailing directions, light lists, tide tables, radio signal lists, notices to mariners, and other useful information for navigators.

From the foregoing definition it may be seen that the execution of marine surveys and the various steps required to construct the nautical chart amount to a complex and exacting science requiring specialized training and involving large expenditures of funds.

It is not deemed appropriate to include in this volume a complete treatise on marine surveying, as this subject is treated in more detail in Hydrographic Office Publication No. 215, "Hydrographic and Geodetic Surveying Manual." The discussion will be limited to simple methods and procedures intended to enable the mariner to conduct reconnaissance surveys of heretofore uncharted waters, and to obtain and record in a suitable form new data for the correction and improvement of existing charts. The accuracy and completeness of any such survey or report furnished by a mariner will redound to his credit as having rendered a valuable service to all navigators.

INSTRUMENTS EMPLOYED IN MARINE SURVEYING

Transits and theodolites.—The **surveyor's transit** (fig. 108), and similar instruments of higher precision called **theodolites** (fig. 109), are employed for the accurate measurement of horizontal and vertical angles, by observing in each of two opposite positions of the horizontal axis, namely, with the circle left and the telescope direct, as in figure 108, and also with the circle right and the telescope inverted.

The telescope carries cross hairs in the common focus of the object glass and the eyepiece, and is so mounted as to have motion about two axes at right angles to each other. The planes of motion may be made truly vertical and horizontal, respectively, by means of levels and adjusting screws. When so adjusted, the instrument is capable of measuring angles in these planes by means of graduated circles and verniers read under microscopes.

The telescope is carried in the V bearings of two standards rigidly attached to the upper plate, which also carries two levels at right angles to each other and also two, sometimes three, verniers at equal intervals about the circle. This part of the instrument, consisting of the telescope, the standards, the upper plate and the attached levels and verniers, is called the *alidade.*

When the clamp seen at the right-hand edge of the plate is released, the alidade may be rotated in azimuth about the vertical axis. As it rotates, the attached verniers are carried around the periphery and just above a graduated circle situated below and within the turned-down edges of the upper plate. This is the lower plate, or the *horizontal circle.* It has the general form of a shallow cup with the upper edge graduated from 0° to 360°, and like the alidade is free to rotate about the vertical axis when its clamp, seen below, is released. There are, therefore, 2 motions in azimuth, that of the alidade, called the *upper motion*, and that of the horizontal circle, called the *lower motion*. The lower motion is clamped to the axis, and the upper motion is clamped to the lower motion. All clamping arrangements include slow-motion tangent screws for perfecting pointings and settings.

Most transits and theodolites carry a *vertical circle* or arc for the measurement of altitudes. The better instruments have two, sometimes three, verniers, with microscopes attached.

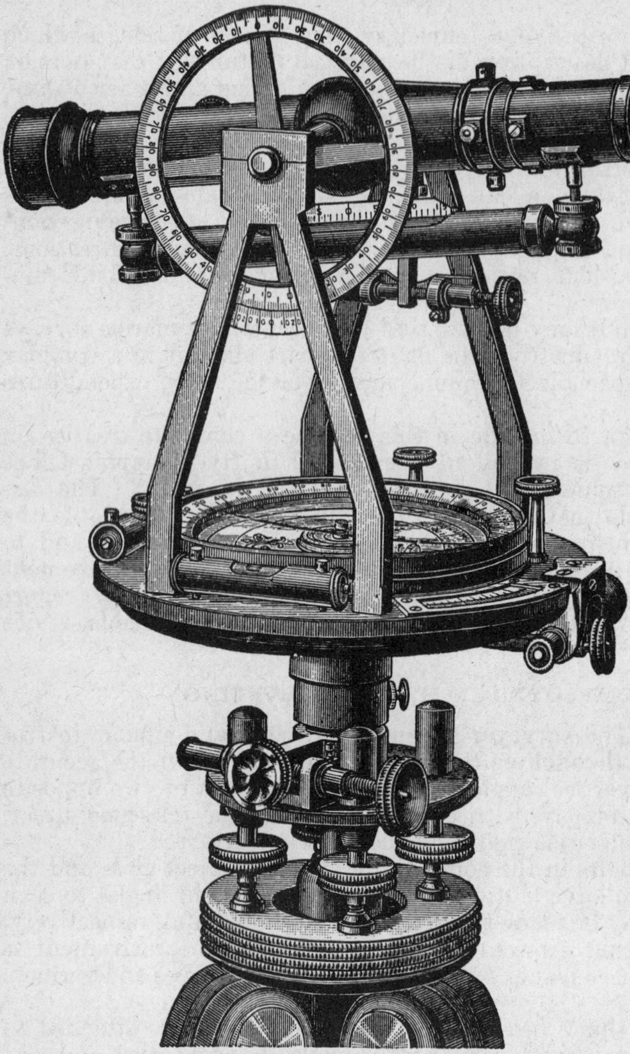

FIGURE 108.

Figure 108 shows a transit fitted with a *compass needle and circle*, distinct from the plate circle, for reading magnetic bearings. Usually the circle is provided with a rack and pinion by means of which the magnetic variation may be set off by rotating the zero of the circle. When this has been done, the readings of the needle will be true bearings.

The lighter instruments of this class are nearly always fitted with *stadia wires* parallel to the horizontal cross hair and equidistant from it, enabling the observer to read the distance to an object by means of the interval intercepted on a *stadia rod* held at the object.

This instrument is called a *transit* because the telescope is capable of being *transited*, that is, turned completely about its horizontal axis; or a *telemeter*, in reference to its distance-reading or stadia fittings; or a *tachymeter*, in reference to its quick furnishing of the three coordinates of distance, azimuth, and elevation.

A plane may be determined by two intersecting perpendicular lines, or by three points. Corresponding to the first determination, four leveling screws are used, as in figure 108; corresponding to the second, three leveling screws are used, as in the larger instruments of this class.

Adjustments of the transit.—The fundamental principle in the construction, use, and adjustment of a transit is that errors are disclosed in double their true magnitudes by reversal of the instrument.

To make the plane of the plate bubbles perpendicular to the vertical axis.—Rotate the alidade until the bubble vials (of a four-screw transit) are parallel to both sets of opposite leveling screws. By means of the leveling screws, letting off on one and taking up on its opposite, and keeping both snug but not tight, bring both bubbles to the center. Rotate the alidade 180° and note the new positions of the bubbles.

FIGURE 109.—Theodolite.

Correct one-half of the error by means of the leveling screws and the remainder by raising or lowering one end of each bubble vial by means of the adjusting screw. The bubbles should now remain stationary in all positions of the alidade. If they do not, repeat the adjustment until they satisfy the test. It is advisable to protect the instrument from both sun and wind.

To make the line of sight perpendicular to the horizontal axis of the telescope.—The previous adjustment having been made, set a pin on the line of sight about 300 feet distant, with both motions clamped. Transit the telescope and set a pin in the opposite direction. Free the upper (or the lower) motion, and rotate the alidade until the line of sight falls upon the first pin. Clamp, transit again, and set a third pin on the line of sight beside the second one. Set a fourth pin at one-fourth of the distance from the third pin to the second one, and bring the line of sight to this position by shifting the reticule laterally. This will require a slight loosening of the top and bottom screws and a simultaneous letting off and tightening up of the opposing lateral screws. Test the adjustment until it may be considered perfect.

To make the horizontal axis of the telescope perpendicular to the axis of the instrument.—The previous adjustments having been made, sight on a small fixed "high point," near at hand and perhaps 45° in elevation, and with both motions clamped establish a "low point," as a pin in the ground, in the same apparently vertical plane. Free the upper (or the lower) motion, rotate the alidade 180°, transit the telescope, and again set on the high point. Lower the telescope and establish a second low point beside the first. Half way between these stick a pin. Raise or lower one end of the horizontal axis until by repeated tests the high point and the mean low point are found to be in the same vertical plane.

To make the axis of the telescope parallel to the line of sight.—Set two pegs in nearly level ground about 300 feet apart. Set up the transit at about half the length of the telescope from one of the pegs. Holding a leveling rod vertically on the first peg, look at it through the object end of the telescope and make a pencil mark on it in the center of the small field of view, taking care that the bubble of the telescope level is at the center at the moment. Again, with the bubble still in the center, sight on the rod held on the second peg, and make a second mark, or, better, set a target where the horizontal cross hair falls. Call the first reading a and this one b. The first, a, is the height of instrument, and the second, b, is the rod reading. Go to the distant peg and obtain another height of instrument, a', and another rod reading, b'. From the mean of the heights of instrument subtract the mean of the rod readings, and call the difference d. Move the target by the amount d from the b' reading, upward when d is positive, downward when d is negative. The target will then be in the same horizontal plane with the horizontal cross hair of the instrument. Set the cross hair on the target, and raise or lower one end of the level vial until the bubble comes to the center of the vial.

When this adjustment has been made, the transit may be used to run lines of levels. At this point the vernier of the vertical circle, if it does not read zero when the telescope bubble is in its central position, may be adjusted; but in general, with transits having a full vertical circle, it is better not to disturb the vernier, relying upon the easy method of finding an index correction, for any particular series of observations, by observing a *double altitude* of some small definite object, first with the telescope direct and second with the telescope inverted.

To remove the parallax of the eyepiece.—Turn the telescope toward the sky and bring the object glass slide all or nearly all the way in. Move the eyepiece backward and forward through the position of maximum distinctness, and decide upon some mean position in which the wires appear as black and distinct as possible. The instrument is now nearly in sidereal focus. Point upon a star or upon some distant terrestrial object, either centrally or slightly to one side, and clamp the telescope. Perfect the object glass focus and the eyepiece focus alternately until the wires appear to be motionless and as distinct as possible when the eye is moved from side to side or up and down before the eyepiece. The adjustment is now made for distant objects and for the particular observer, the focus of the eyepiece depending upon the eyes of the observer; and will be found to be suitable for triangulation work with an instrument of high precision. But in work in which the sights are short it may be advisable to modify the adjustment slightly, in order to obtain the maximum distinctness at medium ranges.

Telemeter and stadia equipment.—Any telescope fitted with stadia wires may be regarded as a telemeter, but little success would attend its use unless it were provided with a stable support. Instruments of this character designed to be held in the hand are useful in sketching.

A transit fitted with stadia wires is a very useful instrument for reading distances up to about 1,200 feet, using a *stadia rod* or board having no divisions less than 0.1 foot.

Let c=distance from the center of a transit to the objective,
f=focal length of the objective,
i=vertical interval between the cross-wires,
s=space intercepted on a rod held vertically,
and d=horizontal distance from the center of the transit to the rod.

Then

$$d=\frac{f}{i}\,s+(f+c).$$

If $(f+c)$ is not furnished by the manufacturer, c may be measured directly, and f may be found by measuring from cross wires to objective when the latter is in sidereal focus. The term $(f+c)$ is about 9 inches in most transits.

If this term is disregarded in the formula it will be seen that the coefficient of s is simply the factor by which rod readings are multiplied to give distances. In many transits it is made 100, approximately, and the *stadia constant* furnished by the manufacturer is 1 percent of this factor.

Example.—The reading on a stadia rod graduated in feet and tenths is 662, the lower wire standing at the 2-foot mark and the upper at 8.62 feet. The stadia constant is 0.995, and $(f+c)$ is 9 inches. What is the distance?

$$d=662.75\text{ ft.}-\tfrac{1}{2}\%\text{ of }662\text{ ft.}=659+\text{ft.}$$

In this brief treatment it is deemed inexpedient to discuss the reduction of inclined stadia sights.

The sextant.—For the description and the adjustments of the sextant see chapter VIII. Its use in minor hydrographic surveys will be discussed later in the present chapter.

To observe a horizontal angle with a transit or theodolite.—Clamp the upper plate to the lower plate with the zero of the A-vernier near the zero of the horizontal circle, and perfect the coincidence by means of the tangent screw. This is called *setting the zeros*, for at the same time the zero of the B-vernier will nearly coincide with 180° on the circle. Read the B-vernier. Then the initial setting, *corrected for eccentricity*, is the mean of the reading of the A-vernier and the angle obtained by subtracting 180° from the reading of the B-vernier.

Next, with the upper motion clamped and the lower motion free, sight the object considered to be the **origin of directions,** clamp the lower motion, and perfect the pointing with the lower motion tangent screw. Free the upper motion. The instrument is now ready for observing the relative directions of all other objects in sight. They are usually observed successively, in what is called a *round of angles*, from 0° to 360°, when again, if the instrument has remained in adjustment, the origin should read 0°, A-vernier. This test, called *checking the zeros*, should be made several times while taking the round of angles, if much time elapses in the process.

In pointing upon any one of these objects the upper motion is clamped lightly, and the vertical wire is made to bisect the object with precision by using the upper motion tangent screw. In taking single angles, or *cuts*, usually only the A-vernier is read, and the recorded angle is the travel of the A-vernier. In taking repeated or *multiple angles*, however, both verniers are read and recorded. In such a case the total angle is the mean of the travels of the verniers between their initial and final positions, and the resulting multiple angle is the total angle divided by the number of repetitions.

To repeat an angle, having made the first measure of it, called the *1-time angle*, leave the upper motion clamped, free the lower motion, and point again upon the origin. Free the upper motion and point upon the second object. The plate reading will now be a 2-time angle. Do not stop to read it, but continue to the end of the series as quickly as possible, while the instrument remains in adjustment. If the series consists of 2n repetitions, reverse the telescope after the nth pointings, thereby eliminating most of the instrumental errors.

The Wye Level.—This is an instrument constructed for the sole purpose of measuring the difference of elevation between any two stations that are equally distant from it. It consists of a sensitive bubble and in the same vertical plane a telescopic line of sight parallel both to the equipotential surface of the bubble and to the longitudinal axis of the bubble. The telescope is solidly mounted in wyes supported on a tripod, and when not locked in position is capable of rotation about its longitudinal axis, a motion necessary for adjusting the line of sight to the centers of the pivot rings.

FIGURE 110.

When the telescope is lifted out of the wyes and turned end for end, any lack of parallelism between the line of sight and the plane defined by the bubble will become apparent in double its magnitude, and may be adjusted out by raising or lowering one end of the bubble tube by half the amount required to bring the bubble to the center. Or the peg adjustment for the transit may be applied.

The axes of telescope and bubble should lie in the same vertical plane. If they do not, this may be discovered by rotating the telescope slightly in the wyes. If the bubble tends to run toward one end, the adjustment to the same plane may be made by means of the lateral adjusting screw of the vial.

The action of the four leveling screws is like that of the transit. These screws, however, play no necessary part in the adjustment. But by means of the adjustment similar to that for the transit, the axis of the wyes may be made perpendicular to the vertical axis of the instrument, thus permitting the telescope to be turned in any direction without releveling.

The wye level is used principally for finding the elevation of bench marks above the datum of soundings and for finding the differences of elevation of stakes on the base line. This kind of leveling is called **differential leveling,** as distinguished from **trigonometric leveling,** which depends upon computed or scaled distances and vertical angles. The requirement of *equal* distances, in the differential method, is designed to eliminate corrections for refraction and the curvature of the earth's surface.

Astronomical transit instruments.—Various instruments are employed for the astronomical determinations necessary in a marine survey. Among these are the *zenith telescope* and *portable transit.* While differing in detail they consist essentially of a telescope mounted upon a horizontal axis placed truly in the prime vertical, thus insuring the revolution of the line of collimation in the meridian; a vertical graduated circle and vernier are supplied, affording a measure of altitude; in the focus are a number of equidistant vertical cross hairs or lines; a small lamp is so placed that its rays illuminate the cross hairs and render possible observations at night. Latitude is obtained by observing the meridian altitude of stars; hour angle (and thence local sidereal time) by observing the times of their meridian transit, which is taken as the mean of the times of passing all of the vertical cross hairs.

Excepting in surveys of a most accurate nature, the astronomical determination of position by the sextant and artificial horizon is regarded as satisfactory.

The three-armed protractor (station pointer).—This is an instrument whereby positions are plotted on the principle of the "three-point problem," of which an explanation is given in chapter IV. It consists (fig. 110) of a graduated circle with three arms pivoted at the center; each arm has one edge that is a true rule, the direction of which always passes through the center of the circle. The middle arm is immovably fixed at the zero of the scale; the right and left arms each revolve about the center on their own sides, and are provided with verniers giving the angular distance from the middle arm. The protractor being set for the right and left angles, is so moved that the three arms pass through the respective stations, when the center will mark the position of the observer. Center pieces of various forms are provided, being cylindrical plugs made to fit into a socket at the pivot. By employing one or the other of them the position of the true center may be pricked with a needle, dotted with a pencil, or indicated by cross hairs. Adjustable arms are provided which can be fitted to the ends of the ordinary arms when working with distant signals.

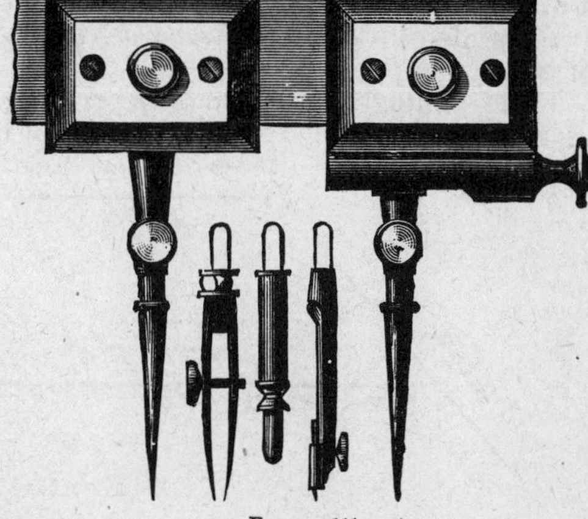

FIGURE 111

The most valuable use of the three-armed protractor is in plotting the positions of soundings taken on shipboard or in boats, where sextant angles between signals are observed. It may occur, however, that certain shore stations will be located by its use.

As this instrument cannot be made with both right and left arms capable of being set to small angles down to 0°, the manufacturers make protractors with either small right or small left angles. Surveying parties should be equipped with both. In default of a three-armed protractor, a piece of tracing paper may be made to answer its purpose. To use the tracing paper, draw a line, making a dot on it to represent the center station, and with the center of an ordinary protractor on the dot, lay off the two observed angles right and left of the line; then, laying the tracing paper on the plan, move it about till the three lines pass exactly through the three stations observed. The dot from which they were laid off will be on the position of the observer, and may be pricked lightly through or marked underneath in pencil.

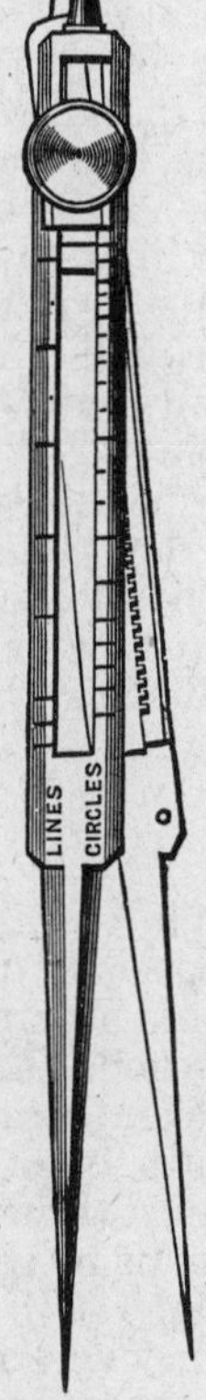

FIGURE 112

The beam compass.—This instrument (fig. 111) is employed in chart drafting and performs the functions of compasses and dividers when the distance that must be spanned is beyond the limits of those instruments in their ordinary form. It consists of a bar of wood or metal upon which two instruments termed beam heads may slide easily. A clamping screw attached to one side of the beam head will fix it in any part of its course along the beam. Upon each head a socket is constructed to carry a plain point, exchangeable for an ink or a pencil point. To secure accuracy, the beam head placed at the end of the beam has a fine adjustment, which moves the point a short distance to correct any error in the first rough setting of the instrument. This adjustment generally consists of a milled-head screw, which passes through a nut fixed upon the end of the beam head, which it carries with its motion.

Proportional dividers.—These are principally employed for reducing or enlarging drawings. They consist (fig. 112) of two narrow flat pieces of metal called legs, which turn upon a pivot movable in the direction of their length. The ends of both legs are shaped into points like those of ordinary dividers. When the pivot is fixed at the middle of the legs, any distance measured by the points at one end is equal to that measured by those at the other; for any other location of the pivot, however, the distances thus measured will not be equal, but with a given setting of the pivot any distance measured by one end bears a fixed ratio to that measured by the other. The path of travel of the pivot is graduated so that the ratio may be given any desired value. Being adjusted in this respect, if a distance is taken off a chart with the legs at one end of the instrument, then those at the other end will show the same distance on the scale of a chart enlarged or reduced in the proportion represented by the ratio for which the pivot was set.

The pantograph.—Whereas proportional dividers are capable of locating only discrete points of a design on a smaller or larger scale, the **pantograph,** shown diagrammatically in figure 113 is capable of reducing or enlarging the design continuously. The principle involved is that of the parallelogram linkage, in which the conditions to be satisfied are, first that the opposite sides must be equal and parallel; and second, that the points P, P′, and P″, respectively, the pivot, the pencil (or metal) point, and the metal (or pencil) point, must be in line. These conditions are satisfied continuously by graduating the movable bar and the two bars that it joins, and by making equal settings.

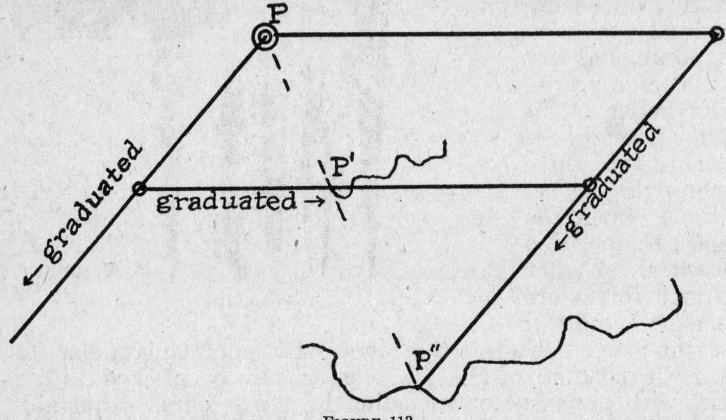

FIGURE 113.

METHODS EMPLOYED IN A HYDROGRAPHIC SURVEY

Before beginning a survey a general reconnaissance of the field is made to gain information necessary for the economical conduct of the survey, and especially to select such sites for *triangulation stations* as will effectively *control* the whole area of the survey by a *net of well-conditioned triangles*, quadrilaterals, and polygons, the quadrilaterals and polygons, of course, being composed of triangles as elementary units. A triangle is usually regarded as well-conditioned when the length of one side, called the *base*, is known, and when the position of the station or third vertex opposite the base is such that the lines of direction to it, drawn from the ends of the base, intersect at an angle, called the *receiving* angle, lying between 30° and 150°.

When the possibilities of obtaining a strong net are known, a site somewhere in the area, should be selected for measuring, an initial unit of length called the **base line,** so situated and of such length and azimuth as will afford a strong connection with one side of the triangulation net. If the field is extensive the matter of **check base lines,** their connection with the triangulation net, and their availability for later extensions of the net in both directions, should be considered.

Every survey is by custom referred to a station of known latitude and longitude, called the **survey origin,** and is oriented by means of an observed **azimuth** controlling the directions of all sides of the triangulation net. If these elements are lacking, they may be found by star observations described elsewhere in this book. It may be assumed that a radio set is available for receiving the time signals of a known meridian.

The observation for azimuth should be made with a transit, if one is available, by turning a multiple angle between a circumpolar star and a triangulation station, marking the time of each pointing on the star in order to enable its azimuth to be computed. When the time is not known precisely, errors in the computation of the azimuth of the star may be minimized by observing at the time of either elongation, when the star will apparently remain on the vertical cross wire for some minutes.

It is considered best to observe the azimuth over some long side of the triangulation net. If there is a lighthouse, it may well be considered as a triangulation station and be used as a mark during azimuth observations. When there is no lighthouse, some other conspicuous and permanent object should be connected with the triangulation net for later use as a *chart origin*.

The base line.—That the base line is truly the unit of distance of the whole survey, permitting the omission of all other linear measurements between stations, may be illustrated by cases in which surveys proceed upon an assumed or uncertain length of the base line. For instance, if a base line roughly measured as 1,000 feet in length, and so used to plot a survey, were afterwards found to be only 999 feet long, all computed distances could be corrected by reducing each by 1 part in 1,000, and the survey sheet itself could be rectified by drawing on it a new scale 1 part in 999 longer than the original scale.

If a steel tape is used, the **measurement of the base line** should be made on a rainy day or at night, when the temperature of the tape can be found with some degree of precision. The coefficient of expansion of steel may be taken as 1 part in 160,000 per degree Fahrenheit of variation from the standard temperature, which is usually 60° F. The exact manner of applying the tape, whether or not conforming to the conditions described in its certificate of standardization, should be described in detail in the record of the base line measurement, in order that corrections for sag, stretch, and temperature may be computed later.

Such extreme precautions are unnecessary when the tape metal is **invar,** a nickel alloy of steel having a coefficient of expansion about one-eleventh as great as that of ordinary tape steel.

Let B be the whole length of metal, excluding stray line, used in the measurement of a base line; a the coefficient of expansion; t_m the mean temperature during the measurement; and t_o the temperature of standardization.

Then

$$\text{temperature correction} = +(t_m - t_o)aB.$$

Anticipating the possible lack of a certificate of standardization, it is suggested that the base line be measured with the tape laid flat and stretched with a tension of 15 pounds, for a 100-foot tape, or 30 pounds, for a 300-foot tape, the temperature being recorded at each application.

If the measurement must be made over water, or swampy or rough terrain, it will be necessary to suspend the tape in a catenary and to make a correction for sag to each tape length; or else to make a substitute tape which, when used in a catenary, will span a horizontal distance determinable by measurement with the standard tape laid flat.

If the part of a tape between end marks weighs P pounds and is L feet long, laid flat, the reduction in length when the tape is suspended at the end marks by supports in the same horizontal plane, and subjected to a tension of T pounds, is

$$\text{reduction for sag (feet)} = \frac{L}{24}\left(\frac{P}{T}\right)^2.$$

A *substitute tape,* about 300 feet long, may be made over any level place of this extent where the standard tape may be laid flat, by stretching piano wire over tripods having board tops with a nail hole drilled in the center of each, marking the piano wire by soldering on sleeves at the nail holes, plumbing down from the sleeves to the ground, and measuring the effective horizontal interval on the ground by use of the standard tape. To obtain a steady invariable tension a loop in one end of the piano wire may be placed over the nail in the rear tripod head, and the wire may be stretched past the nail in the forward tripod head by attaching and suspending a 14-pound lead, taking care to minimize friction by placing a small roller under the wire near the edge of the board. As the tripod legs, in use, may be thrust far into the mud, it will be necessary to suspend the lead as high as possible.

When for any reason the existing conditions do not permit of a direct measurement being made along the line between the two base stations, recourse must be had to a *broken base;* that is, one in which the length of the base is obtained by reduction from the measured length of two or more auxiliary lines. Necessity for resorting to a broken base arises frequently when the two stations are situated on a curving shore line and the straight line between them passes across water, or where wooded or unfavorable country intervenes, or where a stream must be crossed. The most common form of broken base is that in which the auxiliary lines run from each extremity of the base at an acute angle and intersect; in addition to measuring each of these lines the angle formed by their intersection or else the angles formed by them with the base line must be observed and the true length of the base deduced by solution of the triangle. The form that is most frequently used where only a short section of the base is incapable of measurement (as is the case where a deep stream flows across) is that of an auxiliary right triangle whose base is the required distance along the base line and altitude a distance measured along a line perpendicular thereto to some convenient point; by this measured distance and the angles which are observed, the triangle is solved and the length of the unmeasured section determined.

In a survey of considerable extent, where good means are at hand for the correct determination of latitude and longitude, the measurement of a base line and an azimuth may be dispensed with, and, instead, the positions of the two stations which are most widely separated may be determined astronomically and plotted; the triangulation is then plotted upon any assumed scale, and when it has been brought up to connect the two stations the true scale and a mean value of the azimuth are adopted. This is called the method of an *astronomical base.*

Signals.—All points in the survey whose positions are to be located from other stations, or from which other positions are to be located, must be marked by signals of such character as will render them distinguishable at the distance from which they are to be observed.

A vessel regularly fitted out for surveying would carry scantlings, lumber, bolts, nuts, nails, whitewash, and sheeting for the erection of signals; however meager the equipment, the whitewash and sheeting (or some substitute for sheeting, preferably half of it white and half dark in color) should be provided, if possible, before beginning any surveying work. Regular tripod signals, which are quickly erected and are visible, under favorable circumstances, for many miles, are often employed to mark the main triangulation stations; among other advantages the tripod form permits the occupation with the theodolite of the exact center of the station, and avoids the necessity of a *reduction to center.* Signals on secondary stations take an innumerable variety of forms, the requirement being only that they shall be visible wherever needed; a whitewashed spot on a rock, a whitewashed trunk of a tree, a whitewashed cairn of stones, a sheeting flag, a piece of sheeting wrapped about a bush, or hung, with stones attached, over a cliff, or a whitewashed barrel or box filled with rocks or earth and surmounted by a flag, suggest some of the secondary signals that may be employed; sometimes objects are found that are sufficiently distinct in themselves to be used as signals without marking, as a cupola or tower, a hut, a lone tree, or a bowlder; but it is seldom that an object is not rendered more conspicuous by the flutter of a flag above it, or by the dead-white ray reflected from a daub of whitewash.

For convenience, each signal is given some short name of three letters by which it is designated in the records.

For the sake of economy in both time and labor, steel towers of the sectional built-up type are being extensively employed by hydrographic parties for survey signals. They are very easily erected and dismounted, easily transported, offer little resistance to gales of wind, and are more permanent and satisfactory than signals of wood.

The main triangulation.—The points selected as stations for the main triangulation outline the whole area to be surveyed; they are close enough together to afford an accurate means of plotting all intermediate stations of the secondary triangulation; and they are so placed with relation to one another that the triangles or quadrilaterals derived from them are well conditioned. The points are generally so chosen that small angles will be avoided. In order to fulfill the other conditions, it frequently becomes necessary to carry forward the triangulation by means of stations located on points a considerable distance inland, such as mountain peaks, which would not otherwise be regarded as properly within the limits of the survey.

Great care should be taken in observing all angles upon which the main triangulation is based; the best available instrument should be employed; angles taken with a theodolite or transit should be repeated, and observed with telescope direct and reversed, and the mean result taken; if the sextant is used, a number of separate observations of each angle should be taken and averaged for the most probable value. It must be remembered that while, in any other part of the work, an error in an angle affects only the results in its immediate vicinity, an error in the main triangulation goes forward through all the plotting that comes after it.

It occurs frequently that the purposes of the survey are sufficiently well fulfilled by a graphic plotting of the main triangulation, but where more rigorous methods prevail, the results are obtained by computation. The sum of the angles of each triangle is taken, and if it does not exactly equal 180° plus its spherical excess, the values are adjusted to make them comply with this condition. In cases where the triangulation stations form a series of quadrilaterals, the angles of each quadrilateral are adjusted so as to form a perfect geometrical figure. Allowance is made for the curvature of the earth where the area of triangles is sufficiently large to render it expedient to do so. The lengths of the various sides and the relative latitudes and longitudes of the several stations are then computed. Each station may then be plotted in its latitude and longitude on a polyconic projection, and a delineation of the triangulation system may thus be obtained free from the accumulated errors of a graphic plotting.

The spherical excess of a triangle is approximately 1¾ seconds per 100 square nautical miles of its area.

It is not deemed advisable, in this brief treatment, to illustrate forms for the adjustment of quadrilaterals and polygons; nor to include tables, based on the figure and dimensions of the earth, that would be required for the computation of spherical excess, geodetic latitudes, longitudes, and azimuths, and the elements of polyconic projections. Lacking these forms, formulas, and tables, the computations and plotting will necessarily go forward as outlined in the paragraphs devoted to Survey Sheets.

When the true center of a triangulation station cannot be occupied, an *eccentric station* close at hand may be occupied instead, and the directions so observed to other stations may be corrected to the true center by means of the formula

$$C''=d \cot 1'' \frac{\sin a}{K},$$

in which d is the eccentric distance, a is the direction from the eccentric station to any distant station as found by setting the zeros on the true center and turning to the true station, K is the approximate distance to the latter, and C'', in seconds, is the required correction to the direction a. The algebraic sign of the correction is the same as that of $\sin a$. The value used for K is obtained by a preliminary solution of the triangle of which it is a side. The true values of the central angles are now found by combining the corrected directions, and with these the triangles having the true center as a vertex are computed anew.

The value of d is found by measurement or by scaling on a large-scale drawing.

The usual observations at a triangulation station may be classed as follows:

(*a*) Main triangulation angles, multiple angles, each with its explement.

(*b*) Secondary triangulation angles.

(*c*) Single cuts to signals, beacons, buoys, and landmarks.

(*d*) Tangents to islands, shoals, and reefs; vertical angles to those nearest.

(*e*) Horizontal and vertical angles to peaks.

(*f*) References for the station, designed to assist in its restoration in case of the destruction of the center mark. This includes a sketch and a description of the station and the vicinity.

The secondary triangulation.—The points of the secondary triangulation are located by angles from the main triangulation stations; these angles, having less dependent upon them, need not be repeated. A graphic plotting of these stations, without computation, will suffice.

Astronomical work.—This comprises the determination of the correct latitude and longitude of some point of the survey, and of the true direction of some other point from the observation spot, thus furnishing an origin from which all positions and all directions can be determined either graphically or by computation.

The methods of finding latitude, longitude, and the true azimuth of a terrestrial object are given in previous chapters. The feature that distinguishes such work in surveying from that of determining the position of a ship at sea lies in the greater care that is taken to eliminate possible errors.

The results should therefore be based upon a very large number of observations, employing the best instruments that are available, and the various sights being so taken that probable errors are offset in reckoning the mean.

By taking a number of sights the observer arrives at the most probable result of which his instruments and his own faculties render him capable; but this result is liable to an error whose amount is indeterminate and which is equal to the algebraic sum of a number of small errors due, respectively, to his instruments (which must always lack perfection in some details), to an improper allowance for refraction under existing atmospheric conditions, and to his own personal error. Assuming, as we may, that the personal error is approximately constant, these three causes give rise to an error by which all altitudes appear too great or too small by a uniform but unknown amount. Let us assume, for an illustration, that this error has the effect of making all altitudes appear 30″ too great; if an observer attempted to work his latitude from the meridian altitude of a star bearing south, the result of this unknown error would give a latitude 30″ south of the true latitude; if another star to the southward were observed, this mistake would be repeated; but if a star to the north were taken, the resulting latitude would be 30″ to the north. It is evident, therefore, that the true latitude will be the mean of the results of observation of the northern and the southern star, or the mean of the average of several northern stars and the average of several southern stars. A similar process of reasoning will show that errors in the determination of hour angle are offset by taking the mean of altitudes of objects respectively east and west of the meridian.

It must be remembered that the uniformity of the unknown error only exists where the altitude remains approximately the same, as instrumental and refraction errors may vary with the altitude; another condition of uniformity requires that the instrument and the observer remain the same, and that all observations be taken about the same time, in order that atmospheric conditions remain unchanged; to preserve uniformity, if the artificial horizon is used, the same end of the roof should always be the near one to the observer; in taking the sun, however, as the personal error may not be the same for approaching as for separating limbs, every series of observations should be made up of an equal number of sights taken under each condition.

With this in mind, a general rule adopted is that astronomical determinations shall be based upon the mean of observations, under similar conditions, of bodies whose respective distances from the zenith are nearly equal, and which bear in opposite directions therefrom.

This condition eliminates the sun from availability for observations for latitude, though it properly admits the use of that body for longitude where equal altitudes or single a. m. and p. m. sights are taken. Opposite stars of approximately equal zenith distance should always be used for latitude, circum-meridian altitudes being observed during a few minutes before and after transit; excellent results are also obtained from stellar observations for longitude; but very low stars should be avoided, on account of the uncertainty of refraction, and likewise very high ones, as the reflection from the index mirror of the sextant may not be perfectly distinct when the ray strikes at an acute angle.

If there is telegraphic or radio communication, an endeavor should be made to obtain a time signal from a reliable source, instead of depending upon the chronometers.

Topography.—In general, topography is a term referring to the visible forms of shore lines, landmarks, streams, hills, and mountains.

The survey of a shore line is usually accomplished by plane table, or by vertical aerial photography, when airplanes are available; or by traversing the shore and taking three-point fixes at intervals, sketching in the intermediate portions. A considerable measure of control is also afforded by tangents and other cuts from triangulation stations.

The positions and elevations of nearby hills may be determined by transit cuts or by transit and stadia, but those of conspicuous inland peaks are best determined by horizontal and vertical theodolite angles at triangulation stations. The most important distances are computed, and the less important are scaled.

Let

A feet=height of eye of observer at station A,
B feet=height of ground or target at station B,
d nautical miles=distance from A to B=6080 d feet,

and

V=vertical angle of B above the *true horizon*,

Then the height of B above A, expressed in feet, is

$$B-A=6080\ d \tan v+0.76d^2,$$

in which the last term is the correction for curvature of the earth combined with that for refraction. This correction is always positive, whether v is positive or negative; and tan v has the sign of v.

To modify the formula for use with a sextant, let v' be the vertical angle above the *sea horizon*, and D the dip of the sea horizon in seconds.

Then

$$B-A=6080\ d \tan (v'+D)+0.76d^2,$$

in which

$$D=-58''.82\sqrt{A}.$$

Small streams are surveyed with sufficient accuracy for chart purposes by running a few lines of soundings in the navigable part, in or parallel to the axes of the principal reaches, and estimating distances to shore at intervals.

The heights of hills within a reasonable distance from shore may be determined with an *aneroid barometer;* or this instrument may be used to check heights obtained by sextant elevations.

Summits of definite and recognizable shape should be shown by *sketch contours* surrounding a dot at the exact position of the apparent summit.

Survey sheets.—The approximate extent of the survey being known, it will be found expedient, without waiting for astronomical and base line results, to make a *station sheet* large enough to embrace the whole area and on the scale intended to be used in sounding, with the intention of plotting stations and cuts on it from day to day, and to serve as a master sheet for sectional sheets of various kinds, by pricking through stations, meridians, and parallels.

To obviate shrinkage and variations in scale, it is best to reduce the positions of triangulation and other important stations to a system of rectangular coordinates with axes through the origin, and to place on the sheet a grid of pencil squares 1,000 to 10,000 feet on a side, for the easy and accurate plotting of stations in their proper squares.

Boat sheets need not be made large, if care is taken in the placement of subsidiary stations to serve their respective sounding areas. In addition, each boat sheet, when issued, should bear such pencil lines, to be followed by sounding boats, as will insure a uniform development of the hydrography. Other lines, calling for closer examination and development of shoals and channels, may be added after obtaining the first general spread. To facilitate this study during the progress of the work, it is good practice to ink in soundings and to pencil in tentative fathom lines daily.

Shore lines are often plotted on the station sheet, but when there are several observers **shore line sheets** will be required, unless equipment is at hand for vertical photography. These are simply replicas of the station sheet, and are intended for the plotting of successive three-point fixes along the shore in sufficient number to enable the shore line to be well delineated from point to point, with the aid of tangents from the triangulation stations and tangents and sketches forward and backward from the shore line stations.

541524°—43——17

The positions of inland peaks and of distant conspicuous objects may be plotted on special small-scale *topographic sheets*.

The approaches to a harbor or anchorage will naturally be sounded by the ship. For this a *ship's sheet* of smaller scale than the boat sheets (1: 60,000 is often suitable) will be needed.

The final plot of the whole survey will usually be made on one or more *smooth sheets*, on a system of plane coordinates, or on a system of geographical coordinates, if preferred, provided that the necessary tables based on the form and dimensions of the earth are at hand.

Hydrography.—The correct delineation of the hydrographic features being one of the most important objects of the survey, great care should be devoted to this part of the work. Soundings are run in one or more series of parallel lines, the direction and spacing of which depend upon the scope of the survey. It is usual for one series of lines to extend in a direction normal to the general trend of the shore line. In most cases a second series runs perpendicular to the first, and in surveys of important bodies of water still other series of lines cross the system diagonally. In developing rocks, shoals, or dangers the direction of the lines is so chosen as will best illustrate the features of the bottom. When lines cross, the agreement of the reduced soundings at their intersection affords a test of the accuracy of the work.

As the depth of water increases, if there is no reason to suspect dangers, the interval between lines may be increased.

Lines are run by the ship or boat in such manner as to follow as closely as possible the scheme of sounding that has been laid out. The position is located by angles at the beginning of each line, at each change of course, at frequent intervals along the line, and at the point where each line is finished. Soundings taken between *positions* are plotted by the time intervals.

There are a number of methods for determining positions while sounding, which may be described briefly as follows:

By two sextant angles.—Two observers with sextants measure simultaneously the angles between three objects of known position, and the position is located by the three-point problem. This is the method most commonly employed in boat work, and has the great advantage that the results may be plotted at once on the working sheet in the boat and the lines as run thus kept nearly in coincidence with those laid out in the scheme. A study of the three-point problem (ch. IV) will give the considerations that must govern in the selection of objects.

By two transit angles.—Two stations on shore are occupied by observers with transits, and at certain instants, indicated by a signal from the ship or boat, they observe the angular distance thereof from some known point. The intersection of the direction lines thus given is at the required position. This method is expeditious where the signals are small or not numerous. Its disadvantage is that the plotting can not be kept up as the work proceeds.

By sextant and transit angle.—An observer on shore occupies a station with a transit and cuts in the ship or boat, while one on board takes a sextant angle between two objects, of which one should preferably be the occupied station. It is plotted by laying off the direction line from the transit station and finding with a three-armed protractor or piece of tracing paper at what point of that line the observed angle between the objects is subtended. Its advantages and disadvantages are the same as those of the preceding method.

By radio-acoustic sound ranging (phonotelemetry).—Because of the limitations and delays attendant upon marine hydrographic surveying operations by conditions of visibility, resort may be had to hydrophone location, especially for locating offshore soundings. By this method sound is caused to be transmitted through the water from the position required to be fixed to each of two hydrophones suitably placed in known positions. The observer's vessel is also equipped with a hydrophone, and the time of receipt by this hydrophone of the sound of the explosion of a bomb near the vessel is recorded on the vessel's chronograph, which also receives indications, by radio transmission from each of the fixed hydrophone stations, of the time when the sound of the explosion has reached it. The transmission interval of the radio signal being exceedingly minute and consequently negligible, the record of the chronograph affords the means of telling the interval of time required for the sound of the explosion to travel from the observer's vessel to each of the fixed hydrophone stations, and hence, knowing the velocity of sound through the water (about 800 fathoms per second) the distance of the observing vessel from each of the locations in which these selected stations are known to be.

In running lines of soundings offshore, where signals are lost sight of, another method is to get an accurate departure, before dropping the land, by the best means that offers, keeping careful note of the dead reckoning, and on running in again, to get a position as soon as possible, note the drift and reconcile the plotting of intermediate soundings accordingly. Where circumstances require, the position may be located by astronomical observations as usually taken at sea.

A careful record of soundings must be kept, showing the time of each (so that proper tidal correction may be applied), the depth, the character of bottom, and all data required to plot the position.

The wire drag.—The use of the lead in hydrographic surveying does not absolutely establish a definite available depth, as pinnacle obstructions may exist which are not detected by that means. This is particularly true of rocky localities and those of coral formation.

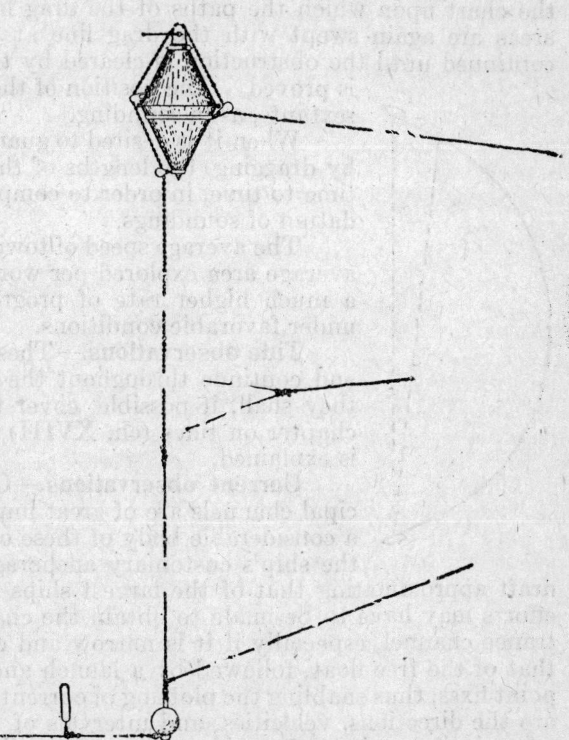

FIGURE 114

In order to guarantee a certain depth of water for purposes of navigation, it has become the practice to tow through the waters to be examined a line of wire or cable suspended at that depth.

The drag or sweep consists essentially of a horizontal member, known as the bottom wire, which is a long steel line composed of 50-foot sections coupled together with swivels and shackles. It is supported at each terminal from an 80-pound buoy by a chain stirrup line whose length may be adjusted from 20 to 50 feet. There are smaller buoys placed at intervals varying from 150 to 450 feet, according to local conditions, which support the wire by means of steel-cable stirrup lines, adjustable in length like the chain stirrup lines on the terminal buoys. At intermediate 50-foot connections, cedar toggles or floats, which have a little more buoyancy than is sufficient to support the wire between the stirrup lines, are attached by means of snap hooks. To prevent the bottom wire from sagging back as the drag is towed transversely to its own length by the bridles fastened at the terminals, a leaden weight of 165 pounds is suspended from each of the terminal stirrup lines, and a weight of 20 pounds from each of the intermediate stirrup lines. The length of the drag may be varied through a wide range to suit the conditions existing in the localities to be examined. Any multiple of 50 feet may be used, but it is in general found best to use, in each division between two towing launches, eight sections with stirrup line supports at their ends, each composed of from three to seven 50-foot units. The towing launches use tow lines about 200 feet in length bridled to the terminal stirrup lines with attachments at the top and bottom. During the towing, as long as the drag is free, the line of supporting buoys will trace out a parabolic curve on the surface of the water; but if progress should be interrupted by a pinnacle of rock rising in its path above the depth to which the drag line is set, the parabolic curve of the line of buoys will immediately become broken into the form of a V, whose angle will correspond in position with the position of the pinnacle. The presence of any such obstruction is also registered by the spring balance usually attached to the towline at a convenient position near the towing vessel. If the shape of the obstruction is such as to allow the drag line to ride upward upon it, as may be with boulders and shoals, an additional indication of its presence is afforded by the falling over of the supporting buoys when the stirrup lines are relieved of strain by the grounding of the weights attached to them.

In such cases a tender should be in readiness to proceed to the indicated point for the purpose of taking position angles to locate the spot and also soundings to ascertain the characteristics of the obstruction. Such localities are plotted upon the chart upon which the paths of the drag line are being mapped, and later these areas are again swept with the drag line at a lesser depth; and this procedure is continued until the obstruction is cleared by the drag line, and thus the least depth is proved. The position of the drag is determined by observers with sextants, as in sounding.

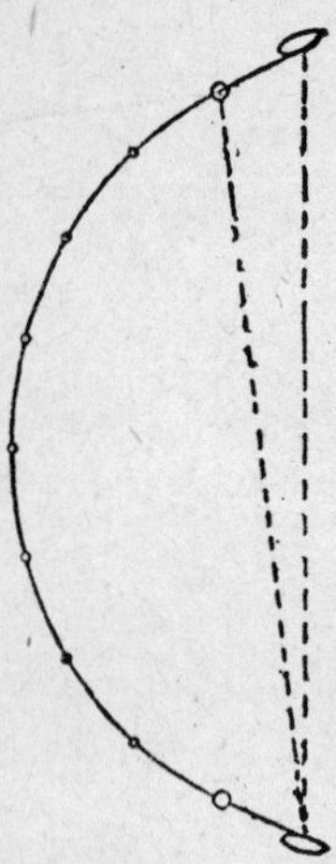

When it is desired to guarantee a specified depth of clear channel by dragging, the lengths of the stirrup lines must be adjusted, from time to time, in order to compensate for the height of tide above the datum of soundings.

The average speed of towing is about 1.5 knots per hour, and the average area explored per working day is 1.5 square miles, although a much higher rate of progress is usually attained in open areas under favorable conditions.

Tide observations.—These should begin as early as practicable and continue throughout the survey, it being most important that they shall, if possible, cover the period of a lunar month. In the chapter on tides (ch. XVIII) the nature of the data to be obtained is explained.

Current observations.—Observations of currents in the principal channels are of great importance. In the course of the survey a considerable body of these observations may be easily obtained at the ship's customary anchorage, by means of a cord and a spar of draft approximating that of the largest ships frequenting the locality. But special efforts may have to be made to obtain the characteristics of the currents in the entrance channel, especially if it is narrow and crooked. For this the best method is that of the free float, followed by a launch and located from time to time by three-point fixes, thus enabling the plotting of current vectors. The quantities most wanted are the directions, velocities, and intervals of time following high water, of the currents during periods of maximum strength, called the *strength of flood* and the *strength of ebb*, respectively.

Magnetic measurements.—Lacking special magnetic instruments for the precise determination of the magnetic variation (declination), or the horizontal intensity of the earth's magnetic force, and the magnetic inclination, or dip, it is still regarded as essential to measure the element most useful in navigation, namely the variation (*declination*) by the best means available. The Navy service 7½-inch compass is suitable for this purpose, for observations ashore over any line of the triangulation net. When only a limited number of observations can be made, they are best made at about 11 a. m., when the *change of the declination* is at a minimum. But the better plan is to observe an equal number of short series for several days between 7 and 9 o'clock in the morning and between 1 and 2 o'clock in the afternoon; that is, at times of eastern and western elongation, respectively.

Running survey.—Where time permits only a superficial examination of a coast line or water area, or where the interests of navigation require no more, recourse is had to a *running survey*, in which shore positions are determined and soundings are made while the ship steams along the coast, stopping only at what are regarded as principal turning points to fix the position, and in which the assistance of boat or shore parties may or may not be employed.

In this method the ship starts at one end of the field from a known position, fixed either by astronomical observations or by angles or bearings of terrestrial objects having a determined location. Careful compass bearings or sextant angles are taken from this position to all objects ashore which can be recognized, and a series of direction lines is thus obtained. The ship then steams along the coast, at a convenient distance therefrom, keeping accurate account of the run by compass courses and engine turns. From time to time other series of bearings or angles are taken upon those objects ashore which are to be located, the direction lines are plotted from the estimated position of the ship, and the various objects are located by the intersections with their other direction lines. While the ship is under way, soundings are taken at regular intervals and plotted from the dead reckoning. As frequently as circumstances permit, the ship is stopped and its position located by the best available means, and the intervening dead reckoning reconciled for any current that may be found.

If a steam launch can be employed in connection with a running survey, it is usually sent to run a second line inshore of the ship. The boat's position is obtained by bearings and masthead angles of the ship, or by such other means as offer. The duty of the boat is to take a series of soundings and to collect data for shore line and topography.

If circumstances allow the landing of a shore party, its most important duty is to mark the various objects on shore by some sort of signals which will render them unmistakable. Beyond this, it can perform such of the duties assigned to shore parties in a regular survey as opportunity permits.

Sailing directions.—The data gathered in a marine hydrographic survey, besides that which goes to make up the fair plotting sheets by graphical representation, should include sailing directions and supplementary descriptive information of advantage in piloting and the practice of navigation. Important among the kinds of descriptive information to be dealt with in this manner may be mentioned—

(*a*) Aspect of the land from seaward.

(*b*) Directions for clearing outlying dangers.

(*c*) Description of the shores and points of land and of prominent and useful marks.

(*d*) Description of aids to navigation.

(*e*) Anchorages, bearings for anchoring, nature of holding ground, effect of wind, swell, and current.

(*f*) Local winds and weather and conditions of visibility of objects.

(*g*) Offshore and inshore currents and their effects on navigation, tidal currents, including interval between high water and the turn of the currents.

(*h*) Local maritime signals. Quarantine and port regulations.

(*i*) Pilots.

(*j*) Available marks or ranges (prominent and permanent), both for courses and changes in courses.

(*k*) Maximum draft, that can be carried through channels or into port.

(*l*) Ports, towns, and shore settlements. Appearance, population, wharves, cargo-handling facilities, repair facilities, supplies, communications (radio, telegraph, cable, railroad, and steamship), sanitation, hospitals, special regulations.

MINOR HYDROGRAPHIC SURVEYS

So much surveying work of genuine service can be done with the limited equipment normally carried by most vessels for navigational purposes only that it seems appropriate to outline the manner in which this equipment may be utilized in minor hydrographic surveys.

By the use of a launch or pulling boat equipped with a steering compass, lead lines, two sextants, a sounding platform, a chart board, a chart or plotting sheet (called a *boat sheet*), and a three-arm protractor, a boat officer and his crew are prepared for various hydrographic tasks, such as running lines of soundings in channels, developing uncharted shoals, and locating new aids to navigation. With the same equipment, and in addition a steel tape, also materials for constructing tripods and other simple signals, a complete reconnaissance survey may be made of a harbor or anchorage of which no chart exists.

Harbor chart amendments.—The harbor chart, though based upon an original good survey, may sometimes require amendments, due to the destruction of old marks or the addition of new, to the silting or scouring of channels, to the displacement of buoys by storms, and so on. The positions of most of the marks in a harbor may be verified or established anew by cross-bearings from two positions of the ship at anchor, if sufficiently far apart, and if well established in position by sextant angles between principal points of the chart. The sextant angles and bearings, both those used to fix the position of the ship and those used to establish new objects, should be observed, not at random, but according to a system enabling the easy combination of angles and bearings and the final reference of all directions to a single controlling direction, which may be the bearing of some distant object.

When the only available direction instruments are sextants and compasses (the pelorus being regarded as an adjunct to the ship's compass), the following procedure will minimize the accumulation of errors:

(*a*) Establish a reference bearing to some distant object.

(*b*) With a sextant measure three or four adjacent angles all around the horizon and back to the first object. All of the objects should be as distant as possible, provided that they are distinct. Adjust the angles so that their sum will be 360°. The sextant angles being recorded from left to right, add the adjusted value of the first angle to the reference bearing and obtain a second reference bearing. To this add the second angle for a third reference bearing; and so on.

(*c*) Again with the sextant, taking the objects between the first two reference bearings, measure, for each object, the angle from the first reference object to it and also the angle from it to the second reference object. Adjust the sum of each pair of angles to the adjusted value of the first reference angle.

(*d*) Continue in like manner with the objects lying between the remaining reference bearings.

It is obvious that for work of this precision the ship must be in irons.

In reporting positions of new marks the mariner should keep in mind the principle that *the positions of marks charted or proposed to be charted should be of higher precision than ship's positions dependent thereon.*

It may not be practicable to find two anchorages for the ship. In that case three well established shore points should be occupied with sextants, and the cuts obtained from at least two of the stations should be crossed with those obtained on the ship, not only to give location and check for each object to be located, but to check the error of the ship's compass on the standard bearing, which can be done if the true azimuth of any direction observed ashore is known and is related to the direction of the ship by an observed angle.

Again, it may be found that the most practicable method of locating new features is the independent location of each by a three-point fix, or rather an n-point fix, to strengthen a possible three-point fix and to provide a check.

With reference to any newly discovered danger in a harbor or in the approaches, the chart-making organization is seldom content merely with a copy of the chart showing the plotted position of the danger, but desires also the fix angles by means of which the danger was plotted. A three-point fix at the spot, or an intersection by three cuts, is most satisfactory. To facilitate obtaining the three cuts the spot may be marked by a temporary buoy. The vicinity should always be searched for companion dangers.

When channels are found to have silted up or scoured out since the making of the chart, satisfactory corrections may be obtained by running channel lines of soundings, that is, one line in the axis of the channel, and one or more on either side, at slow speed and with frequent fixes.

Intercept and floating signal methods.—When chart or triangulation control for the location of soundings, shore line, and navigation marks is lacking, and when the erection of shore control stations is impracticable, the method of surveying by polar coordinates and intercepts is still available. The position of the ship's anchorage is found by astronomical observations. Directions of objects to be located are found by means of compass and pelorus. Distances are found by rangefinder or by *intercept methods.*

In any intercept method there is an object of known height or width (I) which viewed from an unknown distance (D), subtends an angle (θ) observed with a sextant or transit. The distance intercepted, conveniently called the *intercept,* may be *vertical,* as the height of a mast, pole, or lighthouse; or *horizontal,* as the length of the ship or the distance between two flags a tape length apart. Strictly speaking, the intercept I is not necessarily the longest dimension of the object sighted, but only that component of it which is perpendicular to the line of sight, in magnitude equal to the longest dimension multiplied by the sine of its inclination to the line of sight. With this proviso the distance D may be found approximately by either of the formulae

$$D = I \cot \theta, \text{ or } D = \tfrac{1}{2} I \cot \tfrac{1}{2} \theta.$$

The factor cot θ, by which the known intercept I must be multiplied to obtain the unknown distance D, is large and rapidly varying when θ is small. For observations with a sextant it is considered inadvisable to use this method when θ is less than half a degree, the multiplier then being 115 plus or minus 4 per minute of the error in observing θ. Within this limit, however, fair results may be obtained if the following precautions are observed:

Use as great an intercept as is practicable, θ increasing nearly with I. Provide targets of similar size and shape, but of contrasting colors. Use a telescope, and read sextant angles both on and off the arc. For the greater distances use horizontal rather than vertical intercepts, to avoid refraction disturbances and to gain greater length of intercept.

Within the limit mentioned the length of sounding lines that can be run, radiating from the ship, when bearings are obtained from the ship and distances are obtained by observations of masthead angles is 115 times the height of the mast; and the uncertainty in distance is 4 times the height of the mast. Suppose that a launch has run nearly this distance, and that the boat officer, finding that the vertical angle is about to go below 30°, drops a buoy, and without changing course or speed, continues the line to the end, ceasing, however, to observe vertical angles, relying on dead reckoning beyond the buoy. The line finished, he turns to the next line and heads for the ship at the same uniform speed, until he has obtained several positions having masthead angles greater than 30′.

At this point the boat officer may discontinue the line and go to the buoy to obtain the best possible position of it. Having obtained it and plotted it on his sheet, he has gained a serviceable horizontal intercept, namely the distance from the ship to the buoy, to assist him in locating points on other sounding lines, distant from the ship, provided that they are not too near the first line. In this way, by planting temporary buoys as may be needed, a harbor of considerable size may be sounded. It is evident that locations would be improved if fixed objects, instead of buoys, were used.

A better though somewhat more elaborate method consists in providing signals for three-point fixes over any partial area about to be sounded. Counting as one signal the ship, placed in irons and located on the sheet for the day's sounding work, anchor two wherries in line with the ship, or better, in such positions that the curved line through ship and wherries shall be convex to the proposed sounding area. Locate the wherries by bearings and taut-wire distances from the ship, if practicable. Otherwise, locate the nearer wherry by bearing and masthead angle, and the second by bearing from the ship and cut from an anchored position of the launch, the latter determined by bearing from the ship and angle at the launch between the ship and the previously located wherry.

The methods under this heading are admittedly of last resort.

CHAPTER XVIII

TIDES

Definitions.—Tidal phenomena are presented to the observer under two aspects—as alternate elevations and depressions of the sea, and as recurrent inflows and outflows of streams. The word **tide,** in common and general usage, is made to refer without distinction to both the vertical and horizontal motions of the sea, and confusion has sometimes arisen from this double application of the term; in its strict sense, this word may be used only with reference to the changes of elevation, while the recurrent streams are properly distinguished as **tidal currents.**

The tide rises until it reaches a maximum height called **high water** or **high tide,** and then falls to a minimum level called **low water** or **low tide;** that period at high or low water marking the transition between the tides, during which no vertical change can be detected, is called **stand.**

Of the tidal currents, that which arises from a movement of the water in a direction, generally speaking, from the sea toward the land, is called **flood,** and that arising from an opposite movement, **ebb;** the intermediate period between the currents, during which there is no horizontal motion, is distinguished as **slack. Set** and **drift** are terms applicable to the tidal currents, the first referring to the direction and the second to the velocity.

Care should be taken to avoid confusing the terms relating to tides with those which relate to tidal currents.

Cause.—The cause of the tides is the periodic disturbance of the ocean from its position of equilibrium brought about through the periodic differences of attraction upon the water particles of the earth by the moon, and to lesser degree, by the sun, on account of their relative periodic movements. The tide-producing force of the moon upon a particle of unit mass on the surface of the earth is the difference between the moon's attraction upon the given unit mass and the moon's attraction upon the entire earth; and it is likewise with the sun, only the magnitude of the mean tide-producing force is in this case reduced to about two-fifths of the tide-producing force of the moon, because of the comparative remoteness of the sun from the earth.

A particle which has a tide-producing body in its zenith or in its nadir experiences, as the result of the attraction of the tide-producing body, an effect only in the vertical direction as if the intensity of gravity were momentarily lessened; and a particle which has the tide-producing body in its horizon, being then practically at the same distance from the tide-producing body as the center of the earth, experiences, as the result of the attraction of the tide-producing body, an effect which is practically all in the vertical direction as if the intensity of gravity were momentarily increased. But when the tide-producing body is in any other situation with reference to an attracted particle, the attraction is partly directed in a vertical line toward the center of the earth and partly in a horizontal direction along the surface of the earth. The vertical components of the attractions of the tide-producing bodies can not create any sensible disturbance on the existing oceans; but the horizontal components of such attractions, tending to produce horizontal movements oscillating back and forth on the surface of the earth, are effective in the production of the tides, and, by acting upon portions of the oceans that are susceptible of taking up stationary oscillations in approximate unison with the period of the tide-producing forces, give rise to the dominant tides.

The peculiarities that characterize the tides of many localities are caused by modifications resulting from reflections and interferences suffered by the dependent waves generated by the dominant tides. Theory is not yet sufficiently advanced to render practicable the prediction of the tides where no observations have been made; but by theory, supplemented by the observation of actual tidal conditions in a given locality during a certain period of time, very accurate predictions of the time and height of the tides can be made for that locality.

Establishment.—High and low water occur, on the average of the 29 days comprising a lunar month, at about the same intervals after the transit of the moon over the meridian. These nearly constant intervals, expressed in hours and minutes, are known, respectively, as the **high-water lunitidal interval** and **low-water lunitidal interval.**

The interval between the moon's meridian passage at any place and the time of the next succeeding high water, as observed on the days when the moon is at full or change, is called the **vulgar** (or **common**) **establishment** of that place, or, sometimes, simply the establishment. This interval is frequently spoken of as the **time of high water on full and change days** (abbreviated "H. W. F. & C."); for since, on such days the moon's two transits (upper and lower) over the meridian occur about midnight and noon, the vulgar establishment then corresponds closely with the local times of high water. When more extended observations have been made, the average of all high-water lunitidal intervals for at least a lunar month is taken to obtain what is termed, in distinction to the vulgar establishment, the **corrected establishment** of the port, or **mean high-water lunitidal interval.** In defining the tidal characteristics of a place some authorities give the corrected establishment, and others the vulgar establishment, or "high water, full and change"; computations based upon the former will more accurately represent average conditions, though the two intervals seldom differ by a large amount.

Having determined the time of high water by applying the establishment to the time of moon's transit, the navigator may obtain the time of low water with a fair degree of approximation by adding or subtracting $6^h\ 13^m$ (one-fourth of a mean lunar day); but a closer result will be given by applying to the time of transit the **mean low-water lunitidal interval,** which occupies the same relation to the time of low water as the mean high-water lunitidal interval, or corrected establishment, does to the time of high water.

Range.—The **range** of the tide is the difference in height between low water and high water. This term is often applied to the difference existing under average conditions, and may in such a case be designated as the **mean range** or **mean rise and fall** to distinguish it from the **spring range** or **neap range**, which are the ranges at spring and neap tides, respectively.

Spring and neap tides.—At the times of new and full moon the relative positions of sun and moon are such that the high water produced by one of those bodies occurs at the same time as that produced by the other, and so also with the low waters; the tides then occurring, called **spring tides,** have a greater range than any others of the lunar month, and at such times the highest high tides as well as the lowest low tides are experienced, the tidal range being then at its maximum. At the first and third quarters of the moon the positions are such that the high tide due to one body occurs at the time of the low tide due to the other, so that the two actions are opposed; this causes the **neap tides,** which are those of minimum range, the high waters being lower and the low waters higher than at other periods of the month.

Since the horizontal motion of the water depends directly upon the rise and fall of the tides, it follows that the currents will be greatest at springs and least at neaps.

The effect of the moon's being at full or change is not felt at once in all parts of the world, and the greatest range of tides does not generally occur until one or two days thereafter; thus, on the Atlantic coast of North America, the highest tides are experienced one day, and on the Atlantic coast of Europe two days afterwards, though on the Pacific coast of North America they occur nearly at full and change.

The nearer the moon is to the earth the stronger is its attraction, and as it is nearest in perigee the tides will be larger then on that account, and consequently less in apogee. For a like reason, the tides will be increased by the sun's action when the earth is near its perihelion, about the 1st of January, and decreased when near its aphelion, about the 1st of July.

The height of the tides at any place may undergo modification on account of strong prevailing winds or abnormal barometric conditions, a wind blowing off the shore or a high barometer tending to reduce the tides, and the reverse. The effect of atmospheric pressure is to create a difference of about 2 inches in the height of tide for every tenth of an inch of difference in the barometer.

Priming and lagging.—The **tidal day** is the variable interval, averaging $24^h\ 50^m$, between two alternate high or low waters. The amount by which corresponding tides grow later day by day—that is, the amount by which the tidal day exceeds 24^h—is called the **daily retardation.** When the sun's tidal effect is such as to shorten the lunitidal intervals, thus reducing the length of the tidal day and causing the tides to occur earlier than usual, there is said to be a **priming** of the tide; when, from similar causes, the interval is lengthened, there is said to be a **lagging.**

Types of tides.—The observed tide is not a simple wave; it is a compound of several elementary undulations, rising and falling from the same common plane, of which two can be distinguished and separated by a simple grouping of the data. These two waves are known as the **semidiurnal** and the **diurnal** tides, because the first, if alone, would give two high and two low waters in a day, while the second would give but one high and one low water in an equivalent period of time. In nearly all ports these two tides coexist, but the proportion between them varies remarkably for different seas. The effect of the combination of these two types of tide is to produce a **diurnal inequality,** both in the height of two consecutive high or low waters, and in the intervals of time between their occurrence. The height of the diurnal wave may be regarded as reaching a maximum fortnightly, soon after the moon attains its extreme declination and is therefore near one of the tropics. The tides that then occur are denominated *tropic tides.*

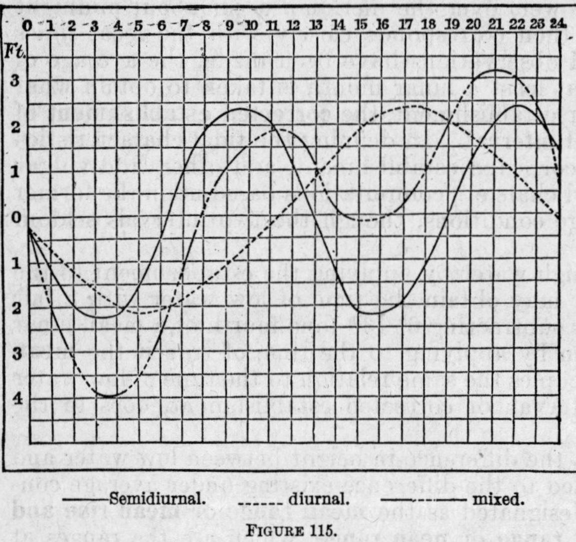

FIGURE 115.

In undertaking to investigate the tides of a port it is important to ascertain as early as possible the form of the tide; that is, whether it resembles the semidiurnal, the diurnal, or the mixed type; because not only may this information be of scientific value, but the knowledge thus gained at the outset will enable the observer to fix upon the best method of keeping the record.

The type forms referred to are illustrated in the diagram in figure 115, where the waves are plotted in curves, using the times as abscissæ and the heights as ordinates. In this diagram, the curve traced in the full line is a tide wave of the semidiurnal type; that traced by the dotted line one of the diurnal; while the broken line is one of the mixed type, in this case the compound of the two others.

In order to determine the type to which the tide of any port belongs, it is usually only necessary to make hourly observations for a day or two at the date of the moon's maximum declination, and to repeat the series about a week later, when the moon crosses the equator. The reported irregularities of the rise and fall at any place should not deter persons from careful investigation. When analyzed, even the most complicated of tides are found to follow some general law.

Tidal currents.—It should be clearly borne in mind by the navigator that the periods of *flood* and *ebb* currents do not necessarily coincide with those of rising and falling tides, and that, paradoxical though it may seem at first thought, the inward set of the surface current does not always cease when the water has attained its maximum height, nor the outward set when a minimum height has been reached. Under some circumstances it may occur that *stand* and *slack* will be simultaneous, while other conditions may produce a maximum current at stand, with a maximum rate of rise or fall at slack water.

The varying effects which will be produced according to local conditions may be considered by the comparison of two tidal basins, to one of which the tide wave has access from the sea by a channel of ample capacity, while the other has an entrance that is narrow and constricted. In the first case, the process of filling or emptying the basin keeps pace with the change of level in the sea and is practically completed as soon as the height without becomes stationary; in this case slack and stand occur nearly at the same time, as do flood and rise and ebb and fall. In the second case, the limited capacity of the entrance will not permit the basin to fill or empty as rapidly as the tide changes its level without; hence there is still a difference of level to produce a current when the vertical motion in either direction has ceased on the outside, and for a considerable time after motion in the reverse direction has been in progress; under extreme conditions it may even occur that a common level will not be established until mid-tide, and therefore the surface current at some places will ebb until 3 hours after low water and flow until 3 hours after high water.

Localities that partake of the nature of the first case are those upon open coasts and wide-mouthed bights. Examples of the latter class will be found in narrow bays and long channels.

Tide tables.—The most exact method of ascertaining the times of high and low water and other features of the tides will be by reference to the worlds *tide tables* and every navigator must provide himself with this publication. The United States Coast and Geodetic Survey publishes annually, in advance, tables giving, for every day in the year, the predicted time and height of the tides at certain principal ports of the world, and from these, by a simple reduction, the times and heights at a multitude of other ports may readily be obtained. Separate tables giving data pertaining to tidal currents along the coasts of the United States are also published. General tide tables are also published by the Governments of other maritime nations, and special tables are to be had for many particular localities.

TIDAL OBSERVATIONS

Since navigators will frequently have opportunity to observe tidal conditions, either in connection with a hydrographic survey or otherwise, at places where existing knowledge of the tides is incomplete, an understanding of the methods employed in tidal observations may be important.

For the proper study of tides, frequent and continuous observations are necessary; it will not suffice to observe the heights of the high and low waters only, even if they present themselves as distinct phases, but the whole tidal curve for each day should be developed by recording the height of water at intervals, which, preferably, should not exceed 30 minutes. Observations, to be complete, must cover a whole lunar month; or, if it be impracticable to observe the tides at night, the day tides of 2 lunar months may be substituted.

When made for the purposes of a hydrographic survey, the tidal observations are used to correct the soundings, and care must be taken to make sure that the gage is placed in a situation visited by the same form of tide as that which occurs at the place where soundings are being made. It will not answer, for instance, to correct the soundings upon an inlet bar by tidal observations made within the lagoon with which this inlet communicates, because the range of the tide within the lagoon is less than upon the outside coast. A partial obstruction, like a bridge, or a natural contraction of the channel section, while it may not reduce the total range of the tide or materially affect the time of high or low tides, will alter the relative heights above and below at intermediate stages, so that the hydrographer must be careful to see that no such obstruction intervenes between his field of work and the gage.

Tidal currents.—Observations for tidal currents should be made with the same regularity as for tides; the intervals need not ordinarily be more frequent than once in every half hour. They should always be made at the same point or points, which should be far enough from shore to be representative of the conditions prevailing in the navigable waters. The ordinary log may be employed for measuring the current, but it is better to replace the chip by a pole weighted to float upright at a depth of about 15 feet; the line should be a very light one, and buoyed at intervals by cork floats to keep it from sinking; the set of the current should be noted by a compass bearing of the direction of the pole at the end of the observation.

Record.—The record of observations should be kept clearly and in complete form. It should include a description of the locality of observation, the nature of gage and of instruments used for measuring currents, and the exact position of both tidal and current stations, together with situation and height of bench mark. The time of making each observation should be shown, and data given for reduction to some standard time. In extended tidal observations the meteorological conditions should be carefully recorded, the instruments used for the observations being properly compared with standards.

There are frequently remarkable facts in reference to tides and currents to be obtained from persons having local knowledge; these should be examined and recorded. The date and circumstances of the highest and lowest tides ever known form important items of information.

Reference planes.—The **plane of reference** is the plane to which soundings and tidal data are referred. One of the principal objects of observing tides when making a survey is to furnish the means for reducing the soundings to this plane. Four planes of reference are used, namely, mean low water, mean low water springs, mean lower low waters, and the harmonic or Indian tide plane.

Mean low water is a plane whose depression below mean sea level corresponds with half the mean semidiurnal range, while the depression of **mean low water springs** corresponds with half the mean range of spring tide; **mean lower low water** depends upon the diurnal inequality in high and low water; the **harmonic** or **Indian tide plane** was adopted as a convenient means of expressing something of an approximation to the level low water of ordinary spring tides, but where there is a large diurnal inequality in low waters it falls considerably below the true mean of such tides.

As these planes may differ considerably, it is important to ascertain which plane of reference is adopted before making use of any chart or considering data concerning the tides.

The following planes of reference are used:

Mean low water.—United States (Atlantic coast), Argentina, Sweden, and Norway.

Mean lower low water.—(Pacific coast).

Mean low water springs.—Great Britain, Germany, Denmark, Italy, Brazil, and Chile.

Lowest low water springs.—Portugal.

Low water Indian spring.—India and Japan.

Lowest low water.—France, Spain, Greece.

The tides are subject to so many variations dependent upon the movements of the sun and moon, and to so many irregularities due to the action of winds and river outflows, that a very long series of observations would be necessary to fix any natural plane. In consideration of this, and keeping in view the possibilities of repetitions of the surveys or subsequent discoveries within the field of work, it is necessary to define the position of the plane of reference which has resulted from any series of observations. This is done by leveling from the tide gage to a permanent bench, precisely as if the adopted plane were arbitrary.

Bench mark.—The plinth of a lighthouse, the water table of a substantial building, the base of a monument, and the like, are proper benches; and when these are not within reach a mark may be made on a rock not likely to be moved or started by the frost, or, if no rock naturally exists in the neighborhood, a block of stone buried below the reach of frost and plowshare should be the resort. When a bench is made on shore it should be marked by a circle of 2 or 3 inches diameter with a cross in the center indicating the reference point. The levelings between this point and the gage should be run over twice and the details recorded. A bench made upon a wharf or other perishable structure is of little value, but in the absence of permanent objects it is better than nothing. The marks should be cut in, if on stone, and if on wood, copper nails should be used. Bench marks consisting of standard metal disks with inscriptions indicating their purpose are now used in naval surveys and by the Coast and Geodetic Survey. The bench must be sketched and carefully described, and its location marked on the hydrographic sheet, with a statement of the relative position of the plane of reference.

The leveling from the bench mark to the tide gage may be done, when a leveling instrument is not available, by measuring the difference of height of a number of intermediate points by means of a long straight-edged board, held horizontal by the aid of a carpenter's spirit level, or even a plummet square, taking care to repeat each step with the level inverted end for end. A line of sight to the sea horizon, when it can be seen from the bench across the tide staff, will afford a level line of sufficient accuracy, especially when observed with the telescope. It may often be convenient to combine these methods.

Tide gages.—The staff gage is the simplest device for measuring the heights of tides, and in perfectly sheltered localities it is the best. It consists of a vertical staff graduated upward in feet and tenths, and so placed that its zero shall lie below the lowest tides. The same gage may also be used where the surface is rough, if a glass tube with a float inside is secured alongside of the staff, care being taken to practically close the lower end of the tube so as to exclude undulations; readings may also be made by noting the point midway between the crest and trough of the waves.

A staff gage should always be erected for careful tidal observations, even where other classes of gage are to be employed, as it furnishes a standard for comparison of absolute heights, and also serves to detect any defects in the mechanical details upon which all other gages are to a greater or less extent dependent.

Where there is considerable swell, and where, from the situation of the gage or the great range of the tide (making it inconvenient for the observer to see the figures in certain positions) the staff gage cannot be used, recourse must be had to the **box gage.** This gage consists of a vertical box, closed at the bottom, with a small hole in the lower part which admits sufficient water to keep the level within equal to the mean level without but which does not permit the admission of water with sufficient rapidity to be affected by the waves. Within the box is a copper float; in some cases this float carries a graduated vertical rod whose position with reference to a fixed point of the box affords a measure for the height of the water; in other gages of this class the float is attached to a wire or cord which passes over pulleys and terminates in a counterpoise, an index attached to the wire or cord indicating the height of the tide on a fixed scale. A **tape gage** is a form of box gage in which the float is supported by a graduated tape which moves over a fixed index.

A form of box gage adapted especially for use in the rough waters on shoals offshore consists of a white-pine pole staff, cross section 1 by 1 inch, with rounded edges, graduated on each of the four sides in feet and two-tenths with the zero (0) at the top, and set in a hollow cylindrical white-pine float 1½ inches outside diameter and seven-eighths inch inside diameter. The float should be thoroughly covered with shellac and liquid paraffin. The length of the rod will depend upon the range of tide in the locality where it is to be used, and the length of the float should be about four-tenths that of the rod. The float well consists of a 2-inch iron pipe, the bottom of which is set in a 1,000-pound concrete block to serve as an anchor. The pipe should be long enough to reach above the ordinary waves at high tide, and a one-fourth inch hole should be drilled in the side several feet above the concrete anchor. A cap with a square hole for the staff is to be screwed on top of the pipe after the float staff has been placed inside. Just below the cap, a 2-inch flange for the attachment of guy wires may be screwed on the pipe, and four small sheaves, one for each guy wire, secured to this flange by wire loops. The top of the pipe is to be secured by four guy wires of No. 6 wire with leads making an angle of 60° or more with the vertical. The end of each guy wire is to be anchored with concrete blocks, giving a total weight of about 2,000 pounds to each anchor. For convenience in handling, each concrete block may be cast with wire-rope loops projecting. After the anchors have been set, the guy wires are led through the sheaves at the top of the float pipe and drawn taut, a fence-wire stretcher being convenient for the purpose.

A **pressure gage** is an instrument for determining the tide by measuring the variation in the pressure at the bottom, due to the rise and fall of the water. Although the results are much less reliable than those obtained by a plain staff, the gage is serviceable in obtaining the approximate tides on shoals where the water is too deep to erect an ordinary tide gage. A simple form of this gage consists of a strong rubber bag connected with a flexible airtight tube, which may be made in sections like garden hose. The upper end of the tube has a stopcock and a pressure gage. The rubber bag is encased in an iron box, which is nearly watertight so as to exclude the influence of short-period waves. The iron box containing the inflated bag is lowered to the bottom. The rise and fall of the tide is then indicated by the changes in pressure as shown by the gage at the upper end of the connecting tube. Several other types of pressure gages have been used from time to time.

The **automatic gage.**—This gage requires a box and float similar to those used for a box gage. The motion of the float in rising and falling with the tide is communicated to a pencil which rests upon a moving sheet of paper; uniform motion is imparted to the paper by the revolution of a cylinder driven by clockwork; the motion of the pencil due to the tide is in a direction perpendicular to the direction of motion of the paper, and a curve is thus traced, of which one coordinate is time and the other height. In some types of the automatic gage the record is traced upon a roll of paper of sufficient length to contain a month of record; in other types, single sheets designed to include several days of record are changed on the gage at more or less frequent intervals.

Another type of automatic gage prints on a paper tape the date, the time, and the stage of the tide at short intervals.

The automatic gage, besides giving a perfectly continuous record, has the further merit of requiring but little of the observer's time. But its indications, both of time and heights, should be checked by occasional comparisons with the standard clock and the staff gage, the readings of which should be noted by hand at appropriate points of the graphic record.

CHAPTER XIX

OCEAN CURRENTS

An **ocean current** is a progressive horizontal motion of the water occurring throughout a region of the ocean, as a result of which all bodies floating therein are carried with the stream.

The **set** of a current is the direction toward which it flows, and its **drift,** the velocity of the flow.

Cause.—The principal cause of the surface currents is the wind. Every breeze sets in motion, by its friction, the surface particles of the water over which it blows; this motion of the upper stratum is imparted to the stratum next beneath, and thus the general movement is communicated, each layer of particles acting upon the one below it, until a current is established. The direction, depth, strength, and permanence of such a current will depend upon the direction, steadiness, and force of the wind; all, however, subject to modification on account of extraneous causes, such as the intervention of land or shoals and the meeting of conflicting currents.

Another cause in the generation of ocean currents is the difference in density of the sea water in different regions, as a result of which a set is produced from the less dense toward the more dense, in the effort to establish equilibrium of pressure; the difference of density may be due to temperature, the warmer water near the equator being less dense than the colder water of higher latitudes; or it may be created by a difference in the amount of contained saline matter, resulting from evaporation, freezing, or other causes. A further factor that may have influence upon ocean currents is the difference of pressure exerted by the atmosphere upon the water in different regions. But neither of the last-mentioned causes may be regarded as of great importance when compared with the influence, direct and indirect, of the wind.

Submarine currents.—In any scientific investigation of the circulation of ocean waters it is necessary to take account of the submarine currents as well as those encountered upon the surface; but for the practical purposes of the navigator the surface currents alone are of interest.

Determination methods.—The methods of determining the existence of a current, with its set and drift, may be divided into three classes; namely, (*a*) by observations from a vessel occupying a stationary position not affected by the current; (*b*) by comparison of the position of a vessel under way as given by observation with that given by dead reckoning; and (*c*) by the drift of objects abandoned to the current in one locality and reappearing in another.

Of these methods the first named, by observations from a vessel at anchor, is by far the most accurate and reliable, but being possible only under special circumstances is not often available. The most valuable information about ocean currents being that which pertains to conditions in the open sea, the great depths there existing usually preclude the possibility of anchoring a vessel; vessels especially fitted for the purpose have at times, however, carried out current observations with excellent results; notable achievements in this direction are those of the survey of the Gulf Stream, made by the United States Navy acting under the Coast and Geodetic Survey, during which the vessel was anchored and observations were made in positions where the depths reached to upward of 2,000 fathoms.

The method of determining current from a comparison of positions obtained respectively by observation and by dead reckoning is the one upon which our knowledge must largely depend. This method is always subject to some inaccuracy and the results are frequently quite erroneous, for the so-called current is thus made to embrace not only the real *set* and *drift,* but also the errors of observation and dead reckoning. In the case of a modern steamer accurately steered and equipped with good instruments for determining the speed through the water as well as the position by astronomical observations, the current may be arrived at by this method with an approximate degree of accuracy. It is not always possible, however, to keep an exact reckoning, and this is especially true in sailing vessels, where the conditions render it difficult to determine correctly the position by dead reckoning, this source of error may be combined with faulty instrumental determinations, giving apparent currents differing widely from those that really exist.

Some knowledge regarding ocean currents has been derived from the observed drift of objects from one to another locality such as by bottles thrown overboard from vessels, also from derelicts, drifting buoys, and pieces of wreckage. The deductions to be drawn from such drift are of a general nature only. The point of departure, point of arrival, and elapsed time are all that are positively known. The route followed and the set and drift of current at different points are not indicated, and in the case of objects floating otherwise than in a completely submerged condition account must be taken of the fact that the drift is influenced by the wind.

Atlantic Ocean currents.—A consideration of the currents of the Atlantic most conveniently begins with a description of the **equatorial currents**. The effect of the northeast and southeast trade winds is to form two great drift currents, setting in a westerly direction across the Atlantic from Africa toward the American continent, whose combined width covers at times upward of 50 degrees of latitude. These are distinguished as the **north** and **south equatorial currents,** according as they arise from the trade winds of the Northern or Southern Hemisphere.

The **south equatorial current** is the more extensive of the two. It has its origin off the continent of Africa south of the Guinea coast, and begins its flow with a velocity that averages about 0.6 of a knot; it maintains a general set of west, the portion near the equator acquiring later, however, a northerly component, while the drift steadily increases until, on arriving off the South American coast, a rate of 2.5 knots is not uncommon. At Cape San Roque the current bifurcates, the main or equatorial branch flowing along the Guiana coast, while the other branch is deflected to the southward.

The **north equatorial current** originates to the northward of the Cape Verde Islands and sets across the ocean in a direction that averages due west in latitude 15°, with a velocity of 0.7 of a knot.

An **equatorial counter current** is found between the north and south equatorial currents, setting to the eastward under the propelling force of the southwest monsoon, which prevails over an elongated area of varying extent lying north of the equator and stretching westward from the southwestern part of the salient extension of the continent of Africa. The extent and strength of this current thus varies with the seasonal extent of the monsoon area, being a maximum in July and August, when its effect is apparent from longitude 50° W. to the Gulf of Guinea, while at its minimum, in November and December, its influence is but slight and prevails for only a limited distance from the African coast.

To the westward of the region of the equatorial counter current the north and the south equatorial currents unite. A large part of the combined stream flows into the Caribbean Sea through the various passages between the Windward Islands, takes up a course first to the westward and then to the northward and westward, finally arriving off the extremity of the Yucatan peninsula; from here some of the water follows the shore line of the Gulf of Mexico, while another portion passes directly toward the north coast of Cuba; by the reuniting of these two branches in the Straits of Florida there is formed the most remarkable of all ocean currents—the **Gulf Stream.**

From that portion of the combined equatorial currents which fails to find entrance to the Caribbean Sea a current of moderate strength and volume takes its course along the north coasts of Porto Rico, Haiti, and Cuba, flows between the island of Cuba and the Bahamas, and joins the Gulf Stream off the Florida coast, thus adding its waters to those of the branch of the equatorial current which has arrived at the same point by way of the Caribbean, the Yucatan Passage, and the Gulf; and, in a similar manner, further accessions to the Gulf Stream are received to the northward of the Bahama Islands from those portions of the circulatory drift of the North Atlantic Ocean which hold their course to the eastward of that group of islands.

The Gulf Stream.—This stream which has its origin, as has been described, in the Straits of Florida, flows in a direction that averages true north as far as the parallel of 31°, then curves sharply to 68° until reaching the latitude of 32°, when a direction a little to the north of 45° is assumed and maintained as far as Cape Hatteras; at this point its axis is about 40 miles off shore, while its inner edge is approximately 20 miles off shore. Thus far in its flow the average position of the maximum current is from 11 to 20 miles outside the 100-fathom curve, disregarding the irregularities of the latter; and the width of the stream—about 40 miles—is nearly uniform. From off Hatteras the stream broadens rapidly and curves more to the eastward, seeking deeper water; its northern limit may be stated to be 60 to 80 miles off Nantucket Shoals and 120 to 150 miles to the southward of Nova Scotia, in which latter place is has expanded to a width of about 250 miles.. Farther on its identity as the Gulf Stream is lost, but its general direction is preserved in a current to be described later.

The water of the Gulf Stream is of a deep indigo-blue color, and its junction with ordinary sea water may be plainly recognized; in moderate weather the edges of the stream are marked by ripples; in cool regions the evaporation from its surface, due to difference of temperature between air and water, is apparent to the eye; the stream carries with it a quantity of weed known as "gulf weed," which is familiar to all who have navigated its waters.

In its progress from the tropics to higher latitudes the transit is so rapid that time is not given for more than a partial cooling of the water, and it is therefore found that the Gulf Stream is very much warmer than the neighboring waters of the seas through which it flows. This warm water is, however, divided by bands of markedly cooler water which extend in a direction parallel to the axis and are usually found near the edges of the stream of warm water. The most abrupt change from warm to cold water occurs on the inshore side, where the name of the **cold wall** has been given to that band which has appeared to some oceanographers to form the northern and western boundary of the stream.

The investigations of Pillsbury tend to prove that the thermometer is only an approximate guide to the direction and velocity of the current. Though it indicates the limits of the stream in a general way, it must not be assumed that the greatest velocity of flow coincides with the highest temperature, nor that the northeasterly set will be lost when the thermometer shows a region of cold sea water.

Pillsbury has also demonstrated that in the vicinity of the land there is a marked variation in the velocity of current at different hours of the day, which may amount to upward of 2 knots, and which is due to the elevation and depression of the sea as a result of tidal influences, the maximum current being encountered at a period which averages about 3 hours after the moon's transit. Another effect noted is that at those times when the moon is near the equator the current presents a narrow front with very high velocity in the axis of maximum strength, while at periods of great northerly or southerly declination the front broadens, the current decreasing at the axis and increasing at the edges. These tidal effects are not observed in the open sea.

The velocity of the Gulf Stream varies with the seasons, following the variation in the intensity of the trade winds, to which it largely owes it origin. The drift of the current under average conditions may be stated as follows:

Between Key West and Habana: Mean surface velocity in axis of maximum current, 2.2 knots; allowance to be made by a vessel crossing the entire width of the stream, 1.1 knots.

Off Fowey Rocks: Mean surface velocity in axis, 3.5 knots; allowance in crossing, 2.2 knots.

Off Cape Hatteras: Mean surface velocity in axis, upward of 2 knots; allowance in crossing the stream, 1.5 knots between the 100-fathom curve and a point 40 miles outside that curve.

After passing beyond the longitude of the easternmost portions of North America, it is generally regarded that the **Gulf Stream,** as such, ceases to exist; but by reason of the prevalence of westerly winds the direction of the set toward Europe is continued until the continental shores are approached, when the current divides, one branch going to the northeastward and entering the Arctic regions and the other running off toward the south and east in the direction of the African coast. These currents have received, respectively, the designations of the **Easterly, Northeast,** and **Southeast Drift Currents.**

The effect of the **Southeast Drift Current** is to create a general circulation of the surface waters of the North Atlantic, in a direction coinciding with that of the hands of a watch, about the periphery of a huge ellipse, whose limits of latitude may be considered as 20° N. and 40° N., and which is bounded in longitude by the eastern and western continents. The central space thus inclosed, in which no well-marked currents are observed, and in the waters of which great quantities of the Sargasso or gulf weed are encountered, is known as the **Sargasso Sea.**

The Southeast Drift Current carries its waters to the northwest coast of Africa, whence they follow the general trend of the land from Cape Spartel to Cape Verde. From this point a large part of the current is deflected to the eastward close along the upper Guinea coast. The stream thus formed, greatly augmented at certain seasons by the prevailing monsoon and by the waters carried eastward with the Equatorial Counter Current, is called the **Guinea Current.** A remarkable characteristic of this current is the fact that its southern limit is only slightly removed from the northern edge of the west-moving Equatorial Current, the effect being that the two currents flow side by side in close proximity, but in diametrically opposite directions.

The Arctic or Labrador Current. This current sets out of Davis Strait, flows southward down the coasts of Labrador and Newfoundland, passing along the eastern shoulder of the Grand Bank to its southern confines and to a variable extent beyond, according to the season, into the region between the parallels of 41° and 42° of latitudes where, upon encountering the Gulf Stream drift, it turns to the eastward, acquiring a movement parallel with the direction of progress of the Gulf Stream waters toward the northward and eastward. It brings with it the ice so frequently met at certain seasons off Newfoundland.

Rennells Current was formerly represented as a temporary but extensive stream setting at times from the Bay of Biscay toward the west and northwest across the English Channel and to the westward of Cape Clear. The most recent investigations fail to reveal such a feature, but disclose only a narrow current of reaction moving northward along the coast of France when the winds have forced the waters above the usual level at the head of the Gulf of Gascoyne.

Of the two branches of the South Equatorial Current which are formed by its bifurcation off Cape San Roque, the northern one, setting along the coasts of northeastern Brazil and of Guiana and contributing to the formation of the Gulf Stream, has been described; the other, known as the **Brazil Current,** flows to south and west, along the southeastern coast of Brazil, as far as the neighborhood of the island of Trinidad; here it divides, one part continuing down the coast and having some slight influence as far as the latitude of 45° S., and the other curving around toward east.

The last-mentioned branch of the Brazil Current is called the **Southern Connecting Current** and flows toward the African coast in about the latitude of Tristan da Cunha. It then joins its waters with those of the general northerly current that sets out of the Antarctic region, forming a current which flows to the northward along the southwest African coast and eventually connects with the Southern Equatorial Current, thus completing the surface circulation of the South Atlantic.

There is another current whose effects are felt in the Atlantic. It originates in the Pacific and flows around Cape Horn, and will be described in connection with the currents of the Pacific Ocean.

Pacific Ocean currents.—As in the Atlantic, the waters of the Pacific Ocean, in the region between the tropics, have a general drift toward the westward, due to the effect of the trade winds, the currents produced in the two hemispheres being denominated, respectively, the **North** and the **South Equatorial Currents.** These are separated, as also in the case of the Atlantic, by an east-setting stream, about 300 miles wide, whose mean position is a few degrees north of the equator, and which receives the name of the **Equatorial Counter Current.**

The major portion of the **North Equatorial Current,** after having passed the Marianas, flows toward the eastern coast of Taiwan in a 292° direction, whence it is deflected northward, forming a current which is sometimes called the **Japan Stream,** but which more frequently receives its Japanese name of **Kuroshiwo,** or "black stream." This current, the waters of which are dark in color and contain a variety of seaweed similar to "gulf weed," carries the warm tropical water at a rapid rate to the northward and eastward along the coasts of Asia and its off-lying islands, presenting many analogies to the Gulf Stream of the Atlantic.

The limits and volume of the Kuroshiwo vary according to the monsoon, being augmented during the season of southwesterly winds and diminished during the prevalence of those from northeast. The current sets to the north along the east coast of Taiwan (Formosa), and in about latitude 26° N. changes its course to northeast, arriving at the extreme southwestern point of Japan by a route to westward of the Sakishima and Nansei Shoto. A branch makes off from the main stream to follow northward along the west coast of Japan, entering the Sea of Japan by the Tsushima Kaikyo; but the principal current bends toward the east, flows through Osumi Kaikyo and the passages between the Tokara Gunto, and runs parallel to the general trend of the south shores of the Japanese islands of Kiushu, Shikoku, and Honshu, attaining its greatest velocity between Bungo Suido and Kii Suido, where its average drift is between 2 and 3 knots. Continuing beyond the southeastern extremity of Honshu, the direction of the stream becomes somewhat more northerly, and its width increases, with consequent loss of velocity. In the Kuroshiwo, as in the Gulf Stream, the temperature of the sea water is an approximate, though not an exact, guide as to the existence of the current.

Near longitude 146° or 147° E. and north of the 40° parallel the Kuroshiwo divides into two parts. One of these, called the **Kamchatka Current,** flows to the northeast in the direction of the Aleutian Islands, and its influence is felt to a high latitude. The second branch continues as the main stream, and maintains a general easterly direction to the 180° meridian, where it is merged into the north and northeast drift currents which are generally encountered in this region.

A cold **countercurrent to the Kamchatka Current** sets out of Bering Sea and flows to the south and west close to the shores of the Kuril Islands, Hokushu and Honshu, sometimes, like the Labrador Current in the Atlantic, bringing with it quantities of Arctic ice. This is often called by its Japanese name of **Oyashiwo.**

On the Pacific coast of North America, from about latitude 50° N. to the mouth of the Gulf of California, latitude 23° N., a cold current, 200 or 300 miles wide, called the **California Current,** flows with a mean speed of .8 knot, being generally stronger near the land than at sea. It follows the trend of the land in a 158° direction as far as Point Conception (south of Monterey), when it begins to bend toward a 202° direction, and then to a 248° direction, off Capes San Blas and San Lucas, ultimately joining the great North Equatorial Current.

On the coast of Mexico, from Cape Corrientes (lat. 20° N.) to Cape Blanco (Gulf of Nicoya), there are alternate currents extending over a space of more than 300 miles in width, which appear to be produced by the prevailing winds. During the dry season—January, February, and March—the currents generally set toward southeast; during the rainy season—from May to October—especially in July, August, and September, the currents set to northwest, particularly from Cosas Island and the Gulf of Nicoya to the parallel of 15°.

The **South Equatorial Current** prevails between limits of approximate latitude 4° N. and 10° S., in a broad region extending from the American continent almost to the 180° meridian, setting always to the west and with slowly increasing velocity. In the neighborhood of the Fiji Islands this current divides; one part, known as the **Rossel Current,** continues to the westward, following a route marked by the various passages between the islands, and later acquiring a northerly component and setting through Torres Strait and along the north coast of New Guinea; the other part, called the **Australia Current,** sets toward south and west, arriving off the east coast of Australia, along which it flows southward to about latitude 35° S., whence it bends toward southeast and east and is soon after lost in the currents due to the prevailing wind.

The general drift current that sets to the north out of the Antarctic regions is deflected until, upon gaining the regions to the southwest of Patagonia, it has acquired a nearly easterly set; in striking the shores of the South American continent it is divided into two branches.

The first, known as the **Cape Horn Current,** maintains the general easterly direction, and its influence is felt, where not modified by winds and tidal currents, throughout the vicinity of Cape Horn, and, in the Atlantic Ocean, off the Falkland Islands and eastern Patagonia.

The second branch flows northeast in the direction of Valdivia and Valparaiso, follows generally the direction of the coast lines of Chile and Peru (though at times setting directly toward the shore in such manner as to constitute a great danger to the navigator) and forms the important current which has been called variously the **Peruvian, Chilean,** or **Humboldt Current.** The principal characteristic of the **Peruvian Current** is its relatively low temperature. The direction of the waters between Pisco and Payta is between north and northwest; near Cape Blanco the current leaves the coast of America and bears toward the Galapagos Islands, passing on both the northern and southern sides; here it sets toward 292° and 270°; beyond the meridian of the Galapagos it widens rapidly, and the current is lost in the equatorial current, near Long. 108° W. As often happens in similar cases, the existence of a countercurrent has been proved on different occasions; this sets toward the south, is very irregular, and extends only a little distance from shore.

Indian Ocean currents.—In this ocean the currents to the north of the equator are very irregular; the periodical winds, the alternating breezes, and the changes of monsoon produce currents of a variable nature, their direction depending upon that of the wind which produces them, and upon the form of neighboring coasts.

There is, in the Indian Ocean south of the equator, a regular **Equatorial Current** which, by reason of owing its source to the southeast trade winds, corresponds with the South Equatorial Currents of the Atlantic and Pacific. The limits of this west-moving current vary with the longitude as well as with the season. Upon reaching about the meridian of Rodriguez Island (63° E.), a branch makes off toward the south and west, flowing past Mauritius, then to the south of Madagascar (on the meridian of which it is 480 miles broad), and thereafter, rapidly diminishing its breadth, forming part of the **Agulhas Current** a little to the south of Port Natal.

The main equatorial current continues westward until passing the north end of Madagascar, where encountering the obstruction presented by the African continent, it divides, one branch following the coast in a northerly the other in a southerly direction. The former, in the season of the southwest monsoon, is merged into the general easterly and northeasterly drift that prevails throughout the ocean from the northern limit of the Equatorial Current on the south, as far as India and the adjacent Asiatic shores on the north; but during the northeast monsoon, when there exists in the northern regions of the Indian Ocean, a westerly drift current analogous to the North Equatorial Currents produced in the Atlantic and Pacific by the northeast trades, there is formed an east-setting **Equatorial Counter Current,** which occupies a narrow area near the equator and is made up of the waters accumulated at the western continental boundary of the ocean by the drift currents of both hemispheres.

The southern branch of the Equatorial Current flows to the south and west down the Mozambique Channel, and, being joined in the neighborhood of Port Natal by the stream which arrives from the open ocean, there is formed the warm **Agulhas Current,** which possesses many of the characteristics of the Gulf and Japan streams. This current skirts the east coast of South Africa and attains considerable velocity over that part between Port Natal and Algoa Bay. During the summer months its effects are felt farther to the westward; during the winter it diminishes in force and extent. The meeting of the Agulhas Current with the cold water of higher latitudes is frequently denoted by a broken and confused sea.

Upon arriving at the southern side of the Agulhas Bank the major part of the current is deflected to the south, and then curves toward east, flowing back into the Indian Ocean with diminished strength and temperature on about the parallel of latitude 40° S., where its influence is felt as far as the 80° meridian. A small part of the stream which reaches Agulhas Bank continues across the southern edge of that bank before turning to the southward and eastward to rejoin the major part.

Along the parallel of latitude 40° S. between Africa and Australia, there is a general easterly set, due to the branch of the Agulhas Current already described, to the continuation of the drift current from the Atlantic which passes to southward of the Cape of Good Hope, and to the westerly winds which largely prevail in this region. At Cape Leeuwin, the southwestern extremity of Australia, this east-setting current is divided into two branches; one, going north along the west coast of Australia, blends with the Equatorial Current nearly in the latitude of the Tropic of Capricorn; the other preserves the direction of the original current and has the effect of producing an easterly set along the south coast of Australia.

As in the other oceans, a general northerly current is observed to set into the Indian Ocean from the Antarctic regions.

Seasonal changes.—In all oceans the currents are subject to seasonal changes, due to freezing and melting, evaporation and rainfall, and seasonal variations of insolation and atmospheric circulation.

CHAPTER XX

OCEAN WAVES

Waves arise from causes such as: the wind over the sea, the tide producing forces of the sun and moon, and the activity of submarine volcanoes and earthquakes. Each cause produces a different type of wave.

The most common type in the open sea is the wave caused by the wind. Wind does not blow at a constant velocity but always in irregular gusts, and these gusts subject the ocean surface to irregular unequal pressures which deform it from a level surface into one of **troughs** and **crests.** The size of ocean waves depend upon the strength of the wind, its duration, and the extent of open waters over which it blows. From observation it is found that the length of waves are increased when the length of fetch, or the length of the sheet of water to windward, is increased, and the wave raising power of the wind is greater when acting upon water already in waves than upon approximately smooth water. The energy of a wave, and consequently its destructive force, depends upon its length, height, and velocity.

The **length** of a wave is the horizontal distance from trough to trough, or from crest to crest.

The **height** of a wave is the vertical distance measured from the bottom of the trough to the top of the crest.

The **period** of a wave is the time interval in seconds between the passage of two successive crests past a fixed point.

The **velocity** of a wave is the rate at which its crest moves forward, or the velocity equals the length divided by the period. An approximate velocity in foot-seconds is equal to the square root of the length times 5.12, thus for a wave having a length of 400 feet, the velocity is $\sqrt{5.12 \times 400} = 45$ feet per second, or about 26 knots. By another form of approximation, the velocity in knots very nearly equals three times the period in seconds.

When a wave is first formed in the open sea it is short and steep, but continual wind increases the length and height and decreases the period. This action causes the undulations to advance, and increase in size until the limit of the wave height for the given velocity is reached, provided that the fetch and depth of water body are sufficiently great. The increase in the size of the wave is not simply proportional to the duration. At first the increase is rapid and then it proceeds more slowly. With strong winds the limiting height of the wave has been found to be 1.5 times the square root of the fetch in nautical miles, but 50 feet has been found to be the ultimate limit found in deep water in the open sea. However two high waves intersecting, or a high wave breaking along a coastline, may thrust a peak much higher than 50 feet.

In the trade wind belt the maximum height of wave for a given strength of wind is soon reached and although the wind may continue steadily with the same force for days there is no increase in the size of the waves. In general, the velocity of the wind in statute miles an hour, divided by 2.05, gives the height of the wave in feet. The longest wave recorded is one 2,600 feet in length with a period of 23 seconds. The longest waves ever encountered in the South Pacific were of lengths varying from 600 to 1,000 feet with periods from 11 to 14 seconds. Waves 500 to 600 feet in length are sometimes met with in the Atlantic but generally they are from 150 to 300 feet with periods from 6 to 8 seconds.

In all types of waves, the wave form moves away over the surface of the water, while the individual water particles move but a comparatively short distance. In typical waves of oscillation in deep water each water particle moves through a circular orbit, the particle moves forward on the crest of the wave, down on the back, backward in the trough, and upward on the wave front. In deep water, waves have no motion of translation. The theoretical form of these waves are profiles of trochoidal curves, or the curves which would be described by points within a circle which is rolling along the under side of a straight line. If the sea is disturbed by waves having a height of 20 feet and a length of 400 feet the water particles at the surface move in circles, having a diameter of 20 feet. The disturbance set up by the wave motion extends for some distance below the surface but the size of the orbits, through which the water particles move, decreases rapidly with increase in depth and the trochoid becomes flatter and flatter. At a depth equal to one wave length, it is less than a five hundredth part of what it was at the surface, so that water at that depth may be considered undisturbed and the motion associated with the largest ocean waves is inappreciable at even modest depths.

Waves from deep water are modified as they get into shoal water. When the depth is reduced to less than one-half the wave length the orbit of the particles commence to become flat. The period of the wave remains unchanged, but the length and speed are increased. The wave becomes higher and shorter, the crest arches forward and finding itself unsupported by sufficient water on the front, dashes downward with a roar producing a wave broken into surf. An individual breaking wave is called a **breaker**.

As soon as waves arise in the sea they are propagated very many miles from the place from which they originate. As the waves move beyond the wind swept region they become gradually lessened in height and give rise to the gentle undulation known as the **swell** or **ground swell**. The term swell is also used to denote the gradual dying down of waves that the winds in the immediate locality had previously set up. In the open sea, the swell is not a very prominent feature; along exposed coasts, however, it frequently assumes very considerable importance in connection with shipping. Ports along the coast of Portugal and Northern Africa have been at times completely isolated as a result of swells from storms off the coast of Ireland, a thousand miles distant.

A **submarine earthquake** may produce several types of waves. First the short and quick oscillations, which travel toward the surface with the velocity of sound in water, causing any overlying vessel to feel a sharp and violent shock like the ship striking a reef. Such shocks may be so severe as to hurl the vessel out of the water. Other groups of waves are produced by the dislocation of the sea bottom. The uplifted portion of the sea bottom raises a mound of water above the general surface of the sea and the settling back of this water generates a great wave of translation which traverses the ocean with a high velocity. Sometimes several such waves are produced. The behavior of many earthquake waves upon reaching the coast suggest that they partake of the character of oscillatory waves, the water particles moving backward in a sort of great trough toward the oncoming wave crest.

In **submarine volcanic explosions,** there is produced a sharp and powerful shock corresponding to earthquake effect, small jets of water may be shot into the air but there soon follows a doming or upswelling of the ocean surface and finally the whole mass of upraised water may be hurled into the air by the escaping gases. The back falling mass of water will tend to produce waves, some being waves of translation, some of oscillation, and some compound waves.

On the open sea the height of earthquake and explosion waves quickly diminish and since the lengths are very great, they soon become so low and flat as to be unnoticed by vessels. But when they enter shallow water, they act like other waves, the height increasing until the wave form breaks to produce a gigantic surf. The velocity of these waves is great as they may travel 10,000 miles in 24 hours. An instance is recorded in which a velocity of 900 miles an hour was attained. Their periods range from 15 minutes to 1 or 2 hours. Heights attained by an earthquake wave when it reaches the coast may be as much as 50 feet. In 1868, an earthquake on the coast of Peru resulted in large waves, one of which submerged the mainland 55 feet above high water. A United States war vessel was carried a quarter of a mile inland at Arica, where it remained until another great wave carried it farther inland in 1877. This last was the wave caused by the Iquique earthquake which was reported of a wave height of 25 to 80 feet.

CHAPTER XXI

WINDS

Wind is air in approximately horizontal motion. Observations of the wind should include its true direction, and its force or velocity. The direction of the wind is designated by the point of the compass from which it proceeds. The force of the wind is at sea ordinarily expressed in terms of the Beaufort scale, each degree of this scale corresponding to a certain velocity in nautical or statute miles per hour, as explained in chapter II, or it may also be expressed directly in nautical or statute miles per hour.

The cause of wind.—Winds are produced by differences of atmospheric pressure, which are for the most part primarily attributable to differences of temperature.

To understand how the air can be set in motion by these differences of pressure, it is necessary to have a clear conception of the nature of air itself.

The atmosphere which completely envelops the earth may be considered a sea of air at the bottom of which we live. It extends upward to a considerable height, the density constantly diminishing as the altitude increases, but being still appreciable at 150 to 200 miles or more.

The air is a mixture of transparent gases which, like all gases, is elastic and highly compressible. Although extremely light, it has a definite weight which can be measured. A cubic foot of air at ordinary pressure and temperature weighs 1.22 ounces, or about one seven hundred and seventieth part of the weight of an equal volume of water. In consequence of this weight the air exerts a certain pressure upon the surface of the earth, amounting on the average to 15 pounds per square inch. To accurately measure this pressure, which is constantly undergoing slight changes, a mercurial barometer is used (ch. II). This is an instrument in which the weight of a column of mercury is balanced against the weight of the outside air pressing against the column at one end. The height of the column of mercury which the weight of the air will support at any particular time and place is called the atmospheric or barometric pressure at that time and place. Instead of saying that the pressure of the atmosphere is a certain number of pounds per square inch, it is customary to say that it is a certain number of inches of mercury, meaning that a column of air of given cross section extending from the barometer to the upper limit of the atmosphere supports a column of mercury of the same cross section and the stated number of inches in height.

When air that is not confined is heated, it increases in volume. When cooled, its volume is diminished. Suppose now that the atmosphere over any considerable region of the earth's surface is maintained at a higher temperature than that of the air surrounding it. The warmed air will expand and the increase in volume will result in a flow outwards at higher altitudes toward places where the air at the surface is cooler. Since this overflow of air at high altitudes relieves the regions underneath of some of the weight of air pressing down upon them, the pressure in these regions is diminished, and the reading of the barometer decreases. On the other hand, the regions which are cooler at the surface and toward which the overflow of air has taken place now have more air pressing down upon them. Consequently, in these cooler regions the barometer rises. As the result of this difference of pressure between the warm and the cool regions there will tend to be a movement of surface air away from the region of high pressure and toward the region of low.

If the temperature of the atmosphere at any given altitude were everywhere the same, there would be no tendency for the air to move from one place to another. It would lie at rest on the earth's surface—sluggish, torpid, and oppressive. There would be no winds. This fortunately is not the case. The air over certain regions of the earth is *continually* warmer than the air over other regions due to one cause or another. Over certain parts of the earth the air is *periodically* warmer than the air over other parts because the changing declination of the sun results in the seasons, summer and winter. There are other temperature differences which arise as some regions absorb more heat from the sun during the day or lose more heat by radiation at night than do other regions. These various temperature differences give rise to barometric pressure differences, which lead to a flow of the air. The wind circulations which actually result, however, are profoundly influenced by effects of the rotation of the earth and by other factors; and in general the winds do not blow directly and steadily from colder to warmer regions. As is to be expected, the periodical variations in the distribution of temperature, repeated season by season, give rise to similar periodical variations in the distribution of pressure.

Normal Distribution of Pressure.—The winds, while due primarily to differences of temperature, stand in more apparent relation to differences of pressure, and it is from this point of view that they are ordinarily studied.

Since the winds and weather over any region are closely related to the distribution of atmospheric pressure over that region, a study of pressure distribution gives an insight into the weather conditions which prevail. Consequently, most countries issue daily charts that show the pressure distribution on that particular day; and charts have been prepared for nearly all regions of the globe showing the average reading of the barometer for certain common periods, such as the month, the season, and the year. On such a chart all points which have the same reading of the barometer are joined by a line called an **isobar.** The charts are known as isobaric charts.

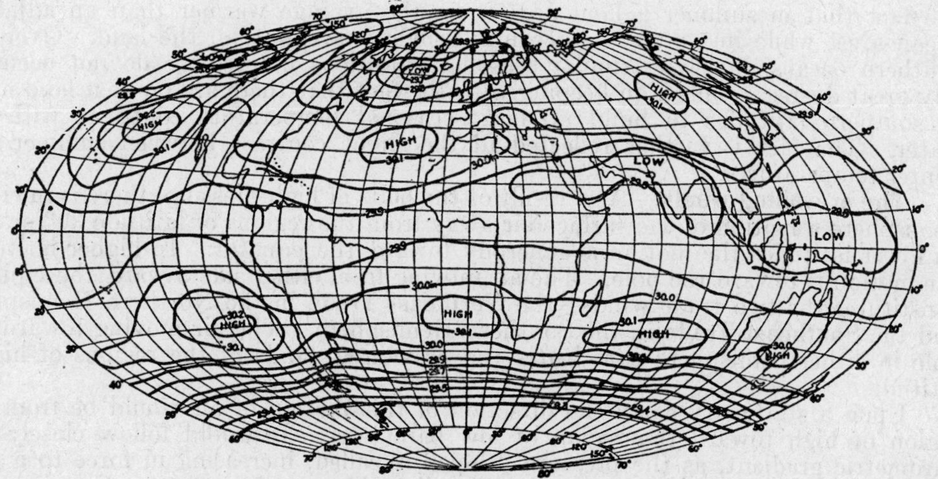

FIGURE 116.—Isobaric chart for the year.

The isobaric chart for the year (fig. 116) reveals several important characteristics. First, along the equator there is a belt of relatively low pressure encircling the globe with barometer reading 29.90 inches. This belt contains two well-defined minima reading 29.80 inches, one over the region of the East Indies, the other over India, Arabia, and the Sudan. Second, on either side of this belt of low pressure is a belt of high pressure. That in the Northern Hemisphere lies mostly between latitudes 30° N. and 40° N. with three well-defined centers of maximum pressure, one over the eastern Pacific reading 30.20 inches, the second over the Azores reading 30.10 inches, and the third over Siberia reading 30.10 inches. The belt of high pressure in the Southern Hemisphere roughly follows parallel 30° S. It also has three centers of maximum pressure, one in the eastern Pacific, the second in the eastern Atlantic, and the third in the Indian Ocean. A third characteristic to be noted from the isobaric chart for the year is that beyond the belt of high pressure in either hemisphere the pressure diminishes toward the pole. In the Southern Hemisphere the decrease in pressure toward the pole is regular and very marked. The pressure decreases from an average somewhat above 30.00 inches along latitude

30° S. to an average about 29.30 inches along latitude 60° S. In the Northern Hemisphere, however, the decrease in pressure toward the pole is less regular and not so great. Two centers of low pressure reading approximately 29.70 inches are well defined, one over the North Pacific near the Aleutian Islands, the other over the North Atlantic near Iceland. North of these centers the pressure increases again.

While the pressure belts which stand out on the isobaric chart (fig. 116) represent average pressure distribution for the year, these belts are rarely continuous on any given day. They are usually broken up into detached areas of high or low pressure by secondary circulations of the atmosphere. (See Cyclonic storms, ch. XXII.)

Seasonal variations of pressure.—As might be expected from its close relation to the temperature, the system of general pressure distribution exhibits a tendency to follow the sun's motion in declination, the barometric equator occupying in July a position slightly to the northward of its position in January. In either hemisphere, moreover, the pressure over the land during the winter season is decidedly above the annual average, during the summer season decidedly below it; the extreme variations occurring in the case of continental Asia, where the mean monthly pressure ranges from about 30.50 inches during January to about 29.50 inches during July. Over the northern ocean, on the other hand, conditions are reversed, the summer pressures being here somewhat the higher. Thus, in January the Icelandic and the Aleutian Islands minima intensify to a depth of about 29.50 inches, while in July these minima fill up and are almost obliterated. This characteristic is associated with the gales which are frequent and violent over the higher northern latitudes in winter time and comparatively rare in summer. The reason for the seasonal reversal of relative pressure over adjacent continents and oceans is to be found in the fact that in summer a land area is on the average warmer than an adjacent ocean area, while in winter the ocean is usually warmer than the land. Over the southern oceans, however, similar seasonal variations in pressure do not occur to any great degree. This is in keeping with the fact that there are no vast land areas in southern latitudes to build up large seasonal temperature contrasts with the water. The fact is further reflected in the slight contrast between summer and winter temperatures.

The prevailing winds.—As a result of the belts of high pressure, there is in either hemisphere a motion of the surface air away from the regions of latitude 30° or 35°. In lower latitudes the motion is generally toward the equator. In higher latitudes the motion is toward the pole. The air moving from either side toward the equator constitutes the two trade winds—the **Northeast Trade** in the Northern Hemisphere and the **Southeast Trade** in the Southern Hemisphere. The air moving toward the pole in either hemisphere constitutes the prevailing winds of the regions of higher latitude.

Upon a stationary earth the direction of this motion of air would be from the region of high toward the region of low barometer. It would follow closely the barometric gradient, as the pressure "slope" is called, increasing in force to a gale where the gradient is steep, decreasing to a light breeze where the gradient is weak, and sinking to a calm where there is no gradient. The earth, however, is in rapid rotation, and this rotation exerts an influence on all horizontal motions upon its surface, whatever their direction, tending to divert them to the *right* in the Northern Hemisphere and to the *left* in the Southern Hemisphere. The air set in motion by the difference of pressure is thus constantly turned aside from its natural course down the barometric gradient, and the direction of the wind at any point, instead of being identical with that of the gradient at that point tends to be at right angles to the gradient although because of friction the wind at the surface of the earth crosses the gradient at a varying angle which is usually between 45° and 90°. Here it should be noted that when the wind is deflected 90° from the barometric gradient, it blows parallel to the isobars. As a result of the earth's rotation, therefore, the northerly winds which one would naturally expect to find on the equatorial side of the belt of high pressure in the northern hemisphere become northeasterly—the **Northeast Trades.** The southerly winds on the polar side become southwesterly—the prevailing westerly winds of northern latitudes. Similarly, in the Southern Hemisphere the southerly winds blowing from the belt of high pressure toward the equator become southeasterly—the **Southeast Trades;** and the northerly winds blowing toward the South Pole become northwesterly—the prevailing westerly winds of southern latitudes.

The relation here described as existing between the distribution of atmospheric pressure and the direction of the wind is of the greatest importance. It may be briefly stated as follows:

In the Northern Hemisphere stand with the face to the wind; in this position the region of high barometer lies on your left hand and somewhat in front of you; the region of low barometer on your right hand and somewhat behind you.

In the Southern Hemisphere stand with the face to the wind; in this position the region of high barometer lies on your right hand and somewhat in front of you; the region of low barometer on your left hand and somewhat behind you.

This relation holds, not only in the case of the general distribution of pressure and circulation of the atmosphere, but also in the case of the special conditions of high and low pressure which usually accompany severe gales.

The trade winds.—The trade winds blow from the belts of high pressure toward the equatorial belt of low pressure—in the Northern Hemisphere from the northeast, in the Southern Hemisphere from the southeast. Over the eastern half of each of the great oceans they extend considerably farther from the equator and their original direction inclines more toward the meridian than in midocean, where the direction is more from the east. The trade winds are ordinarily looked upon as the most constant of winds for they sometimes blow for days or even weeks with slight variation in direction or strength. However, their uniformity should not be exaggerated. There are times when the trade winds weaken or shift. There are regions where their steady course is deformed, notably among the island groups of the South Pacific, where the trades during January and February are practically nonexistent. They attain their highest development in the South Atlantic and in the South Indian Ocean. They are everywhere fresher during the winter than during the summer season. The regions of the trade winds are not often invaded by cyclonic storms. The majority of cyclonic disturbances that do occur within these regions are of the typhoon or hurricane type. They are mostly confined in point of time to the late summer and autumn months of the respective hemispheres, and in scene of action to the western portion of the several oceans. The South Atlantic Ocean alone enjoys complete immunity from tropical cyclonic storms.

The doldrums.—The equatorial girdle of low pressure occupies a position between the high-pressure belt of the Northern and the similar belt of the Southern Hemisphere. Throughout the extent of this barometric trough the pressure, save for the slight diurnal oscillation, is practically uniform, and decided barometric gradients do not exist. Here, accordingly, the winds sink to stagnation, or rise at most only in fitful breezes, coming first from one point of the compass, then from another. The air is hot and sultry. The sky is often overcast and showers and thunderstorms are frequent. The region throughout which these conditions prevail consists of a wedge-shaped area, the base of the wedge resting in the case of the Atlantic Ocean on the coast of Africa and in the case of the Pacific Ocean on the coast of America, the axis extending westward. The position and extent of the belt vary somewhat with the season. Throughout February and March it is found immediately north of the equator and is of inappreciable width, vessels following the usual sailing routes frequently passing from trade to trade without interruption in both the Atlantic and the Pacific Oceans. In July and August it has migrated to the northward, the axis extending east and west along the parallel of 7° N., and the belt itself covering several degrees of latitude, even at its narrowest point. At this season of the year, also, the Southeast Trades blow with diminished freshness across the equator and well into the Northern Hemisphere, where they are diverted by the effect of the earth's rotation into southerly and southwesterly winds. The so-called southwest monsoons of the African and Central American coasts arise partly from this diversion of the Southeast Trades.

The horse latitudes.—On the outer margin of the trades, corresponding vaguely with the belt of high pressure in either hemisphere, is a second region throughout which the barometric gradients are faint and undecided and the winds correspondingly light and variable. These regions of light and variable winds where the pressure is relatively high are the so-called **horse latitudes**, or calms of Cancer and of Capricorn.

Unlike the doldrums, however, the weather here is clear and fresh, and the periods of stagnation are intermittent rather than continuous, showing none of the persistency which is so characteristic of the equatorial regions. The explanation of this difference is to be found in the fact that over the equatorial belt of calms the humid surface air becomes heated which causes it to expand and rise. Cooling accompanies this process and results in the condensation of water vapor as cloud and rain. In the horse latitudes, on the other hand, there are no general rising currents of air to result in condensation of water vapor. It is generally inferred that the air in the horse latitudes is descending for its humidity is remarkably low.

The prevailing westerly winds.—On the polar side of the high-pressure belt in either hemisphere the barometric pressure again diminishes. The currents of air set in motion along these gradients toward the pole, diverted by the earth's rotation to the right of their initial course in the Northern Hemisphere, appear as southwesterly winds; in the Southern Hemisphere, diverted to the left, the poleward currents appear as northwesterly winds. These two wind systems are the **prevailing westerlies** of the temperate zones.

Only in the Southern Hemisphere do these winds exhibit a persistency approaching that of the trade winds. Their course in the Northern Hemisphere is subject to frequent interruption by secondary wind circulations. The tabulated results for the portion of the North Atlantic included between the parallels 40° and 50° N., and the meridians 10° W. and 50° W., show that winds from the western semicircle (south to north-northwest) comprise about 74 percent of the whole number of observations, their relative frequency being somewhat higher in winter than in summer. The average force of these winds decreases from force 6 (Beaufort scale) in winter to force 4 in summer. In the Southern Hemisphere, on the other hand, such variations over the sea are not apparent. Here the westerlies blow throughout the year with a steadiness little less than that of the trade winds in lower latitudes, and with a force which, though fitful, averages 5 or 6, Beaufort scale, their boisterous nature having given the name **"Roaring Forties"** to the latitudes in which they are most frequently observed.

The explanation of this striking difference in the extratropical winds of the two hemispheres is found in the distribution of atmospheric pressure and in the widely different variations which this latter undergoes in different parts of the globe. In the comparatively landless Southern Hemisphere the average yearly atmospheric pressure south of parallel 30° diminishes much more rapidly poleward and has fewer irregularities due to continental interference than in the Northern Hemisphere. The system of steep and persistent gradients which thus exists gives rise to the comparatively strong and persistent northwest and west winds of the "Roaring Forties."

The monsoon winds.—The air over the land is warmer in summer and colder in winter than that over the adjacent oceans. During the former season the continents thus become the seat of areas of relatively low pressure; during the latter, of relatively high. Pressure gradients, directed outward during the winter, inward during the summer, are thus established between the land and the sea, which exercise the greatest influence over the winds prevailing in the region adjacent to the coast.

The most striking illustration of winds of this class is presented by the **monsoons** (*mausim*, season) of the China Sea and of the Indian Ocean. In January abnormally low temperatures and high pressure obtain over the Asiatic plateau, high temperatures and low pressure over Australia and the nearby portion of the Indian Ocean. As a result of the baric gradients thus established, the southern and eastern coast of the vast Asiatic continent and the seas adjacent thereto are swept by an outflowing current of air, which, diverted to the right of the gradient by the earth's rotation, appears as a northeast wind, covering the China Sea and the northern Indian Ocean. Upon entering the Southern Hemisphere, however, the earth's rotation which hitherto deflected the moving air to the right of the gradient now serves to deflect it to the left; and here, accordingly, we have the monsoon appearing as a northwest wind, covering the Indian Ocean as far south as latitude 10°, the Arafura Sea, and the northern coast of Australia.

In July these conditions are reversed. Asia is now the seat of high temperature and correspondingly low pressure, while Australia and the Indian Ocean have a relatively low temperature and high pressure, although the departure from the annual average is by no means as pronounced in the case of Australia and the Indian Ocean as in the case of Asia. The barometric gradients now lead northward across the equator and are directed toward the interior of Asia, giving rise to a system of winds whose direction is southeast in the Southern Hemisphere, deflected to southwest in the Northern.

The northeast (winter) monsoon blows in the China Sea usually from October to April. It is known as the dry or fair weather monsoon. It is marked by a steadiness similar to that of the trade winds, and it often attains the force of a moderate gale. The southwest (summer) monsoon usually occurs from May to September. It breaks with great severity on some coasts accompanied by heavy squalls and thunderstorms. The rainfall during this season is much heavier than during the northeast monsoon. As the season advances and the southwest monsoon becomes established, squalls and rain become less frequent. In some places the monsoon then blows as a light breeze, unsteady in direction, sometimes sinking to a calm. In other places it prevails with fresh velocities throughout the season, being infrequently interrupted by calms, or by winds from other directions. The tropical cyclonic storms of this region, locally known as **typhoons**, occur most frequently during the season of the southwest monsoon, although their occurrence may extend well into the season of the winter monsoon.

Land and sea breezes.—Corresponding with the seasonal contrast of temperature and pressure over land and water, there is a diurnal contrast which exercises a similar though more local effect. In summer particularly the land over its whole area is warmer than the sea by day, colder than the sea by night. The variations of pressure thus established, although small, suffice to evoke a system of littoral breezes directed landward during the daytime, seaward during the night. These land and sea breezes usually penetrate to a distance of about 30 miles on and off shore, and extend to a height of a few hundred feet.

The sea breeze begins in the morning hours—from 9 to 11 o'clock—as the land warms. In the late afternoon it dies away. In the evening the land breeze springs up, and blows gently out to sea until morning. In the Tropics this process is repeated day after day with great regularity. In higher latitudes the land and sea breezes are often masked by winds of cyclonic origin.

Temperature, pressure, and wind relations.—In the preceding articles of this chapter the most important effects of temperature and pressure distribution upon the surface winds of the globe have been discussed. There are other important relations between temperature, pressure, and wind which can not be described here at length. If discussions are desired of local phenomena, such as mountain and valley breezes, glacier winds, whirlwinds, and so on, they may be found in a modern textbook of meteorology.

There are certain other aspects of the general circulation of the atmosphere, that should be briefly summarized. One of these is the effect of land areas upon the high-pressure belt in either hemisphere and upon the trade winds and prevailing westerlies. A continent in summer, since it is relatively warmer than adjacent oceans, becomes the seat of an area of low pressure. Therefore, wherever a high-pressure belt crosses a continent, the belt in summer is interrupted by the area of low pressure over the land. The interrupted belts of high pressure then appear as elliptical areas over the oceans, especially in the Northern Hemisphere where the continents are vast. Similarly, the low-pressure area and the local winds of a continent serve to modify greatly the systems of trade winds and prevailing westerlies wherever they cross the land. Another aspect of the general circulation that should be briefly discussed is the formation of the five persistent centers within the two belts of high pressure. On page 269 six centers of maximum pressure were pointed out. One of these, that over Siberia, exists only during the winter. The remaining five rarely disappear entirely. They are called the semipermanent **"highs."** All five are centered over oceans, and they occur only where a distinctly cold ocean current crosses one of the two belts of high pressure. Finally, it should be noted that the earth's rotation diverts the air flowing outwards from an area of high pressure, so that in the Northern Hemisphere as one rounds the area on the east the direction of the wind is successively northwesterly, northerly, and northeasterly, thus introducing air from the Temperate Zone into the region of the trade winds. Similarly, as one rounds a high-pressure area on the west the wind direction is successively southeasterly, southerly, and southwesterly, introducing air from the trade region into the Temperate Zones. It is seen that the wind circulation about an area of high pressure in the Northern Hemisphere is clockwise, a circulation opposite to that around a cyclone in this hemisphere. Such areas are therefore known as **anticyclones.** In the Southern Hemisphere an analogous circulation occurs about the centers of maximum pressure.

Backing and veering wind.—When the wind changes in a clockwise direction, that is N-E-S-W; it is said to *veer* when it changes in the reverse direction N-W-S-E; it is said to *back*. These terms are used both in the Northern and Southern Hemispheres.

CHAPTER XXII

CYCLONIC STORMS

Variations of atmospheric pressure.—The prevailing distribution of atmospheric pressure previously described (chap. XXI) and the attendant circulation of the winds are those which become evident after the effects of many disturbing causes have been eliminated by the process of averaging observations covering an extended period of time. However, conditions over the globe do not always conform to these averages. On some days pressure and winds may be distributed much as they appear on a chart of averages. More frequently, however, the actual conditions in various localities lie to one side or the other of the averages, and it is sometimes difficult to distinguish the features which the averages bring out.

Confining our attention for the time being to the subject of atmospheric pressure, it may be said that this, at any given point on the earth's surface, is in a constant state of change, the mercurial barometer rarely becoming stationary, and then only for a few hours in succession. The variations which the pressure undergoes may be divided into two classes, viz, periodic, or those which are continuously in operation, repeating themselves within fixed intervals of time, long or short; and nonperiodic or accidental, which occur irregularly, and are of varying duration and extent.

Periodic variations.—Of the periodic class of changes the most important are the seasonal, which have been already to some extent described, and the diurnal. The latter consists of the daily occurrence of two barometric maxima, or points of highest pressure, with two intervening minima. Under ordinary circumstances, with the atmosphere free from disturbances, the barometer each day attains its first minimum about 4 a. m. As the day advances the pressure increases, and a maximum, or point of greatest pressure, is reached about 10 a. m. From this time the pressure diminishes, and a second minimum is reached about 4 p. m., after which the mercury again rises, reaching its second maximum about 10 p. m. The range of this diurnal oscillation is greatest at the equator, where it amounts to about ten hundredths (0.10) of an inch. It diminishes with increased latitude, and near the poles it seems to vanish entirely. In middle latitudes it is much more apparent in summer than in winter.

Nonperiodic variations.—The equatorial slope of the belt of high pressure which encircles the globe in either hemisphere near latitudes 30° to 35° is characterized by the marked uniformity of its meteorological conditions, the temperature, wind, and weather changes proper to any given season repeating themselves as day succeeds day with almost monotonous regularity. Here the diurnal oscillation of the barometer constitutes the main variation to which the atmospheric pressure is subjected. On the polar slope of these belts conditions are very different, the elements which go to make up the daily weather here passing from phase to phase without regularity, with the result that no two days are precisely alike; and as regards atmospheric pressure, it may be said that in marked contrast with the uniformity of the torrid zone, the barometer in the temperate zone is constantly subjected to nonperiodic or accidental fluctuations of such extent that the periodic dirunal variation is scarcely apparent, the mercurial barometer at a given station frequently rising or falling several tenths of an inch in 24 hours.

The explanation of this rapid change of conditions in the higher latitudes is found in the approach and passage of extensive areas of alternately high and low pressure, which affect alike, although to a different degree, all the barometers coming within their scope. The general direction of motion of these areas is that of the prevailing winds. In the latitudes which are under consideration, therefore, their movement is in general from west to east though often with a large north or south component.

Cyclonic and anticyclonic circulations.—A central area of low pressure is surrounded by a system of winds which exhibit a tendency to draw in toward the center but at the same time circulate about it; the direction of this circulation being in the Northern Hemisphere *opposite* to the motion of the hands of a watch. A rotation of this kind is defined as "cyclonic" rotation, and the area of low pressure is termed a "cyclone." In the Southern Hemisphere cyclonic rotation is directed in the opposite sense, that is, *with* the motion of the hands of a watch.

Around the center of an area of high pressure a similar system of winds will be found, but blowing in the reverse direction. Here the barometric gradients are directed radially outward, with the result that in place of an inflow we have an outflow, the circulatory motion being right handed or *with* the hands of a watch in the Northern Hemisphere, left handed or *against* the hands of a watch in the Southern.

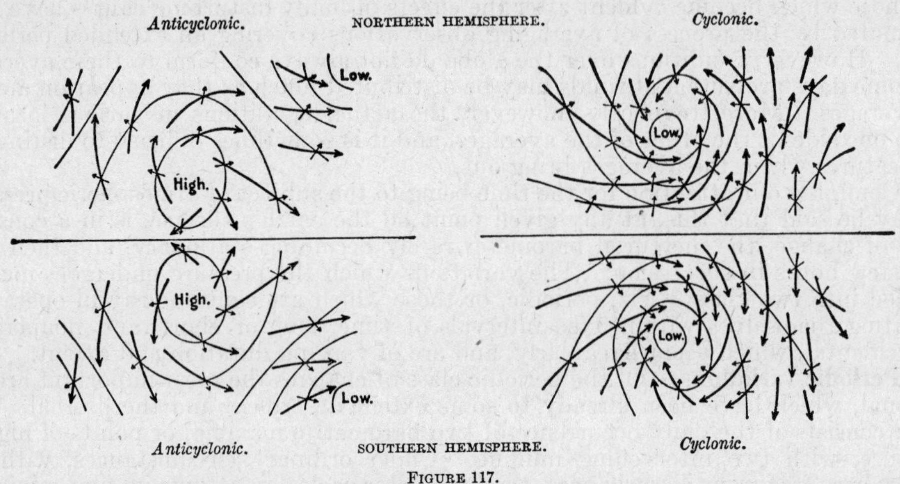

FIGURE 117.

The light arrows show the direction of the gradients; the heavy arrows the direction of the winds.

A rotation of this kind is said to be "anticyclonic," and the area of high pressure is termed an "anticyclone."

All these features are shown in the accompanying diagram (fig. 117), which exhibits the general character of cyclonic (around a LOW) and anticyclonic (around a HIGH) circulations in the Northern and Southern Hemispheres, respectively. The closed curves represent the isobars, or lines along which the barometric pressure is the same; the short arrows show the direction of the gradients, which are everywhere at right angles to the isobars; the long arrows give the directions of the winds, deflected by the earth's rotation to the right of the gradients in the Northern Hemisphere, to the left in the Southern.

Features of cyclonic and anticyclonic regions.—Certain features of the two areas may here be contrasted. In the anticyclonic, the successive isobars are as a rule far apart, showing weak gradients and consequently light winds. In the cyclonic area, on the other hand, the successive isobars are usually crowded together, showing steep gradients and strong winds.

The anticyclonic area is a region of outflowing winds, as shown in figure 117. The divergence of the wind streams at sea level necessitates a compensating downward flow of air from aloft. Since descending air is compressed and consequently is heated, a condition favoring the dissipation of clouds results. The cyclonic area, however, is a region of inflowing winds. The convergence of the winds at sea level demands that there be a general tendency for an upward movement of air. Since ascending air expands and consequently cools, the formation of clouds and precipitation is favored. These considerations explain why in general the approach and presence of anticyclonic areas are in most cases attended by fair weather, although they are not infrequently characterized by scattered showers, whereas the progress of cyclonic areas is usually accompanied by thickly overcast skies, more or less continuous rain, and the generally foul weather which characterizes the ordinary storm at sea.

Classification of cyclones.—Cyclones have been classified in various ways. According to duration they are known as semipermanent and migratory; according to season of occurrence, as winter and summer; or according to zone of origin, as tropical and extratropical.

There are several semipermanent cyclones in different parts of the world, the most prominent of which are, in the Northern Hemisphere, the so-called Icelandic and Aleutian lows, and in the Southern Hemisphere those of Ross Sea and Weddell Sea. The Aleutian low is active during winter only.

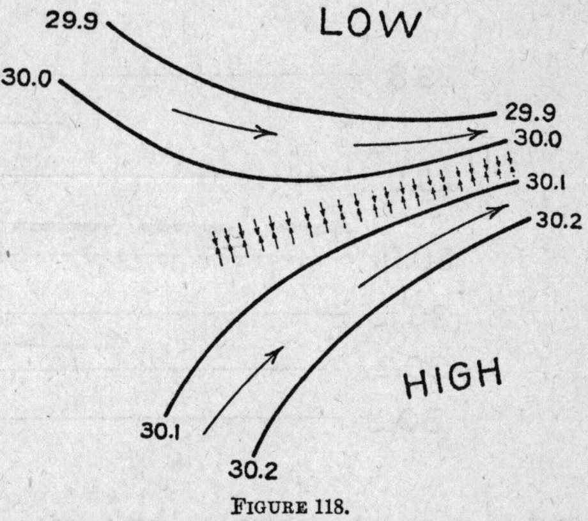

FIGURE 118.

The regions occupied by the semipermanent cyclones constitute what may be called the "graveyards" of the migratory cyclones. Many of the traveling cyclones move directly into these areas, merging with and reinforcing the semipermanent cyclones, and at the same time losing their own identity. In fact it may be said that the semipermanent cyclones are maintained largely by the tendency for the migratory ones, after they have attained their maximum intensity, to collect in certain favored regions, where they often come virtually to a standstill. The areas so favored are zones where the thermal differences between the polar regions and the relatively warm open oceans are sharply concentrated. Such a condition in itself leads to the development and perpetuation of a cyclonic circulation with attendant low pressure.

The two general types of migratory cyclonic storms, known as tropical and extratropical, though chiefly distinguished from one another by the zone of origin, also differ from one another in size, structure, intensity, direction of movement, the distribution of temperature and rainfall within the storm area, and the way in which they are maintained or dissipated. Storms of the latter class—that is, extratropical—are by far the more numerous, being of daily occurrence in middle and northern latitudes. Their number, as well as intensity, is greater, however, in the colder seasons of the year. Their place of origin is not restricted and they may and do form over the continents, though in much larger numbers over the oceans. Generally, but not always, they increase in intensity on passing from the continents to the oceans and diminish in energy on passing from the oceans to the continents.

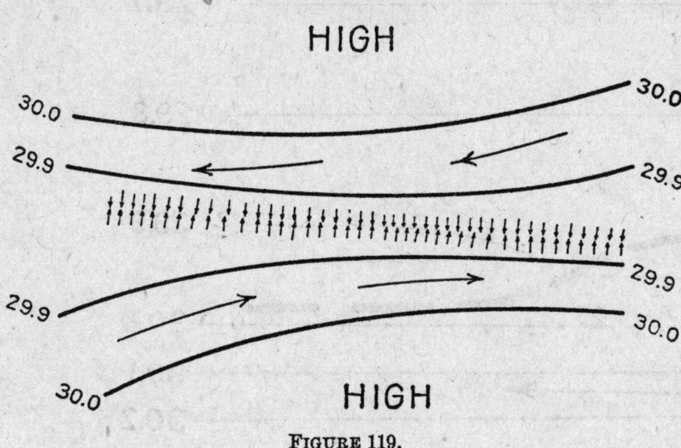

FIGURE 119.

Formation and development of extratropical cyclones.—The great majority of extratropical cyclones do not form haphazardly within the circulation of the prevailing westerlies but at special points where a convergence of wind streams occurs. Two types of pressure distribution favoring convergence are shown in figures 118 and 119. In one case the air currents are flowing almost in the same direction; in the other they flow in almost opposite directions. The bringing-together of air currents which have originated in widely separated regions and which consequently possess differing properties leads to the development of a comparatively narrow zone, generally less than 100 miles in width, in which there is a rapid transition of temperature from one air current or "air mass" to the other. The formation of such a zone or "**front**," as it is termed, is the prelude to the development of an extratropical cyclone.

541524°—43——19

This preliminary stage is shown in figure 120. Here the converging of two distinct air currents, both of which are flowing towards the east has concentrated the temperature and density differences in a narrow zone represented by the heavy dashed line. The air current to the north of the front is relatively cold and dry, being characteristically of polar or sub-polar origin, and it is moving comparatively slowly, as indicated by the widely separated isobars. On the other hand, that to the south of the front is relatively warm and moist being characteristically of tropical or sub-tropical origin,

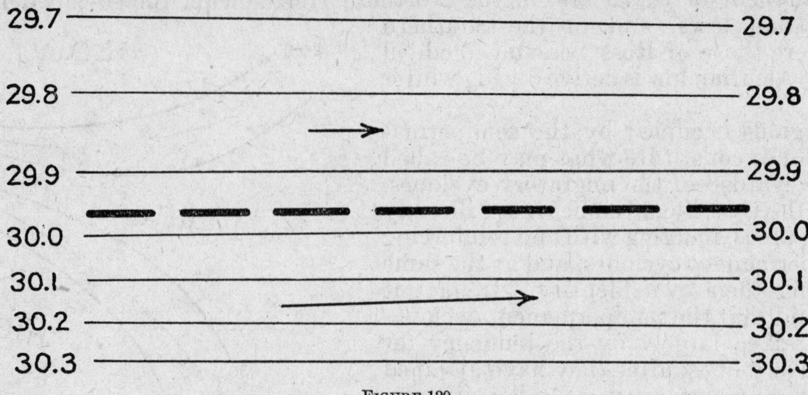

FIGURE 120.

and it is moving comparatively rapidly as indicated by the closely spaced isobars. The boundary between the air masses is not vertical. On the contrary, because of the density differences between the air masses, the frontal surface assumes a gentle slope (on the order of 1/100), the polar air lying under the tropical air in the form of a thin wedge.

The next stage is the development of cyclonic rotation at some point along the boundary. This tends to distort the front and cause it to exhibit a wave-like corrugation, as illustrated in figure 121. Occasionally further intensification of the cyclonic rotation fails to take place, and the wave travels rapidly along the front in an easterly

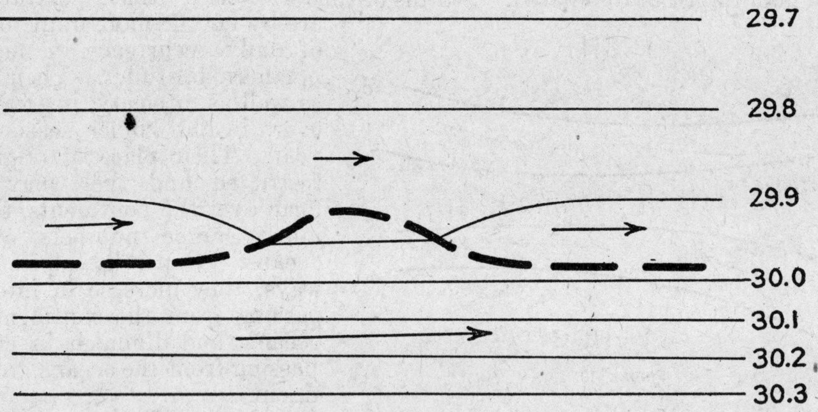

FIGURE 121.

direction, at the same time maintaining its flat character. Almost invariably, however, the cyclonic rotation, once it has been concentrated, intensifies progressively. This leads to a closed circulation with accompanying closed isobars and increased barometric gradients. The originally flat wave becomes more pronounced, and a center of low pressure appears at its crest. This stage is illustrated in figure 122.

The cyclones thus formed at a front have at first an oblong shape. Later they become more circular. They intensify quickly and move rapidly. As they intensify, the increasing circulation around the center tends to fold up the front and consequently to narrow the tongue of warm air, which is termed the "warm sector" of the cyclone. The air within the warm sector is raised from the ground, whence it flows away above the body of cold air which lies ahead of the wave. Eventually the front is doubled up on itself, and the center of low pressure is completely surrounded at

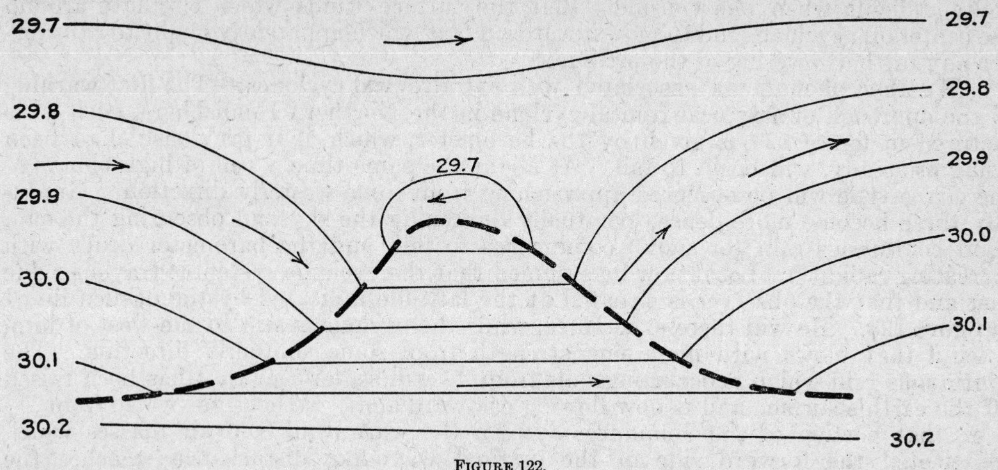

FIGURE 122.

the ground by the cold air. When this stage has been reached the cyclone is said to be **"occluded."** It now begins to resemble more and more a circular vortex and to lose intensity. Thereafter it gradually fills up and disappears, merges with a semi-permanent system, or is absorbed by a newer and more vigorous cyclone which has

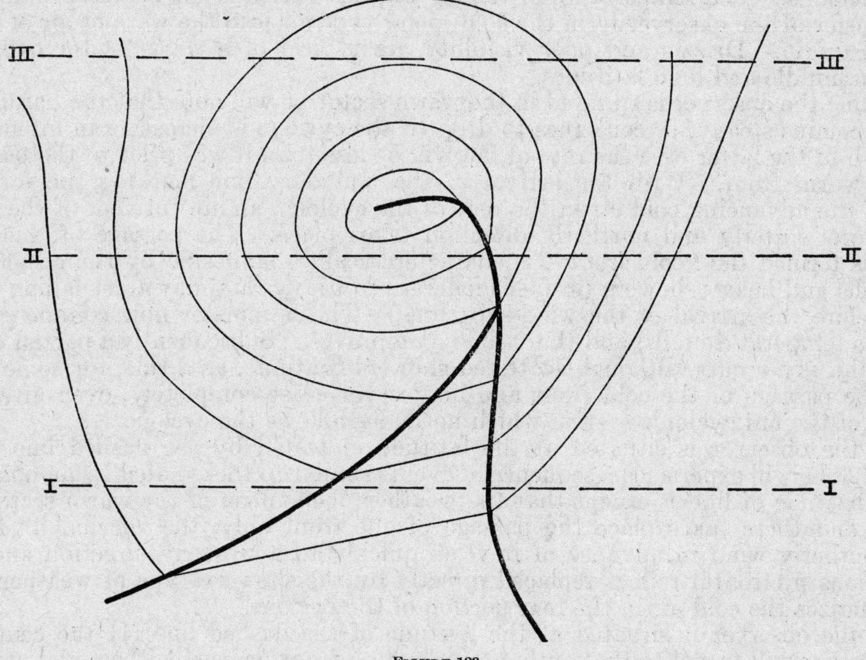

FIGURE 123.

developed at some other point on the front. A partly occluded cyclone is shown in figure 123.

The ascent of the air in the warm sector and its replacement at the surface by the cold air constitutes a process which is continually furnishing kinetic energy to the cyclonic system. The resulting gain of energy is manifested by the increasing strength of the circulation as the cyclone becomes occluded. The steepening barometric gradients associated with this development necessitate a lowering of the pressure at the center of the cyclone. However, the mechanism through which the removal of air from the region above a cyclone is achieved is by no means thoroughly understood and has never been satisfactorily explained. The problem is seen to be especially difficult when one considers that the surface winds which circulate around the center of a cyclone tend to blow inwards, a fact which apparently ought to counteract any further lowering of the pressure.

Weather phenomena associated with extratropical cyclones.—The first warning of the approach of a typical frontal cyclone in the Northern Hemisphere, such as is pictured in figure 123, is given by the barometer, which, if it previously had been rising or steady, will begin to fall. At about the same time a veil of high clouds of the cirrus type will be observed approaching from some westerly direction. Gradually these become more dense, eventually darkening the sky and obscuring the sun. Soon continuous rain (or snow) commences to fall, and the barometer drops with increasing rapidity. Let it now be assumed that the cyclonic system is traveling due east and that the observer is situated at the latitude indicated by the dashed line I in figure 123. He will there experience, while the cyclone is still to the west of him, a wind that blows with increasing strength from some southerly direction. The continuous rain which is occurring falls from "warm sector" air that has been raised off the earth's surface and is now flowing eastward aloft. When the "warm front"—i. e., that portion of the boundary between the warm and cold air masses which constituted the forward side of the original wave-like disturbance—reaches the observer, the rate of fall of the barometer abruptly decreases, and a quick, though not necessarily pronounced, *veer* of the wind to a more westerly direction occurs. At this juncture the nature of the weather also changes. The continuous rain ceases, and in its place a very fine drizzle accompanied by poor visibility (sometimes by fog) characteristically sets in. The drizzle falls from an unbroken layer of low-lying stratus clouds. The temperature of the air will have risen a few degrees, indicating the transfer of the observer from the cold, polar-type air into the warmer air of more tropical origin. Drizzle and poor visibility are typical of a warm sector over the ocean in middle and high latitudes.

While the observer is situated in the warm sector he will note that the barometer either remains steady, or continues to drop (if the cyclone is increasing in intensity), although in the latter case the rate of fall will be less than it was prior to the passage of the warm front. With the arrival of the boundary line marking the forward edge of the advancing cold air in the rear of the cyclone, an abrupt veer of the wind to a more westerly and northerly direction takes place. The passage of this line, which is termed the **"cold front,"** is characteristically manifested by the occurrence of squalls and heavy showers (in fact moderate to heavy rain may start falling some time before the arrival of the wind-shift line.) The barometer now commences to rise, the temperature falls, and the visibility improves. Subsequently a partial clearing of the sky occurs, although scattered showers continue, as a rule, for some time after the passage of the cold front and may never cease completely, even after the arrival of the anticyclonic system which normally follows the cyclone.

If the observer is situated at the latitude indicated by the dashed line II in figure 123 he will experience a sequence of events similar to those noted by an observer at the latitude of line I, except that the weather phenomena of the warm sector are absent and there takes place the passage of one front only, the "occluded" front. The southerly wind in advance of it veers quickly to a westerly direction and the continuous prefrontal rain is replaced directly by the showery type of weather that characterizes the cold air in the rear portion of the cyclone.

If the observer is situated at the latitude of the dashed line III the center of low pressure will travel to the south of him and no front passage with sudden veering of the wind will be experienced. Instead the wind, which may originally have set in from a southerly or easterly direction gradually *backs* through north to northwest. The barometer exhibits no abrupt or discontinuous change in its rate of fall but rather a relatively gradual transition from falling to rising. The character of the weather also undergoes a comparatively slow change from precipitation of a continuous type to a showery type as the wind backs to the northwest.

The general sequences of weather phenomena described in the preceding paragraphs apply to the typical extratropical cyclone of the winter season in middle and high latitudes of the Northern Hemisphere. Naturally each individual storm differs somewhat in form from the model depicted in figure 123. However, there is one feature that is common to the structure of all young extratropical cyclones. It is an absence of symmetry and the presence of lines of discontinuity, in other words, fronts. On this account changes in the wind and in the state of the weather do not take place progressively over an extended interval of time but with a suddenness which is often surprising. Thus, a gentle westerly wind may be replaced by a northerly gale within the space of a few minutes.

Once an extratropical cyclone has become entirely occluded it has attained the last stage of its life history. It is then said to be an old cyclone. It assumes an almost symmetrical structure and the frontal system associated with it gradually dissolves. No longer do we find several distinct systems of clouds and precipitation which were characteristic of the partly occluded cyclone. The weather throughout the area surrounding the center becomes essentially uniform and tends towards the pure shower type.

Tropical cyclonic storms.—Tropical cyclones, in contrast to extratropical cyclones do not occur frequently. They form only over certain well-defined and limited water areas of the Tropics and quickly lose energy on reaching a large land surface. They also lose energy, although more slowly, as they progress toward middle latitudes over the oceans, usually at the same time expanding in size. On nearing or reaching the higher latitudes of the ocean a cyclone of tropical origin either dissipates or takes on the characteristics of an extratropical storm.

Tropical cyclones are confined mostly to six fairly distinct regions of great or small extent, four in the Northern Hemisphere and two in the Southern. These regions are (1) the entire West Indian region, including the Caribbean Sea, the Gulf of Mexico, and the waters east of Florida, in addition to much of the ocean east of the Antilles; (2) the southeastern North Pacific, known as the Mexican west coast region; (3) the Far East, which includes the entire area west of the Marianas and the Caroline Islands, across the Philippines and the China Sea, and northwestward to China and Japan; (4) the Arabian Sea and the Bay of Bengal; (5) a great stretch of ocean in the vicinity of and to the east of Madagascar, including the Mauritius and other islands; (6) the general region embracing Australian waters and eastward, including the archipelagoes to or beyond mid-Pacific.

The occurrence of tropical cyclones in the different months and for the six general regions is shown in the following table.

Occurrence of tropical cyclones of the six regions

	Jan.	Feb.	Mar.	Apr.	May	June	July	Aug.	Sept.	Oct.	Nov.	Dec.	Annual average number	Length of record (years)
Region I:														
North Atlantic Ocean	0	0	0	0	4	24	25	71	112	91	23	2	7	50
Region II:														
Southeastern North Pacific Ocean	0	0	0	0	3	17	17	25	50	26	2	1	5	27
Region III:														
North Pacific Ocean (Far East)	15	8	11	13	26	36	109	151	129	117	59	37	20	36
Region IV:														
Arabian Sea	x	x	x	x	5	11	3	0	2	10	8	2	2	23
Bay of Bengal	x	x	x	x	21	42	65	55	70	51	37	17	10	36
Region V:														
South Indian Ocean	113	115	98	68	25	3	x	x	x	7	33	58	7	70
Region VI:														
Australian waters to 160° E. longitude	54	49	58	29	7	7	x	x	x	4	10	22	3	84
South Pacific Ocean east of 160° E. longitude	69	47	64	18	2	2	x	x	x	4	8	31	2	105

x, Rare.

The number of tropical cyclones varies greatly from year to year. This irregularity in annual frequency is shown for three of the six regions of occurrence in the following tables. The greatest irregularity is shown for the North Atlantic, where the annual occurrence as indicated by the specific 10 years (1927–1936) itemized in the table, ranged between 2, in 1929 and 1930, and 21, in 1933. Data for the 50-year period 1887–1936, summarized in the table, are from the records of the United States Weather Bureau. The table of eastern North Pacific tropical cyclones, covering the 27-year period 1910–1936, is compiled also from the records of the Weather Bureau. The table of typhoons in the western part of the North Pacific Ocean extends over the 36-year period 1901–1936, and is compiled largely from the records of the Zi-Ka-wei Observatory, Shanghai, China, the Weather Bureau, Manila, P. I., and the Central Meteorological Observatory, Kobe, Japan.

Occurrence of North Atlantic tropical cyclones, 1887–1936

	1887–1926	1927	1928	1929	1930	1931	1932	1933	1934	1935	1936	Total
May	1	0	0	0	0	0	1	1	1	0	0	4
June	17	0	0	1	0	1	0	1	1	0	3	24
July	18	0	0	0	0	1	0	3	1	0	2	25
August	46	1	2	0	1	1	3	7	2	2	6	71
September	85	3	3	1	1	3	3	5	2	1	5	112
October	74	2	1	0	0	1	3	4	3	2	1	91
November	19	1	0	0	0	1	1	0	1	0	0	23
December	2	0	0	0	0	0	0	0	0	0	0	2
Total	262	7	6	2	2	8	11	21	11	5	17	352

Average annual number, 7.

Occurrence of tropical cyclones of Eastern North Pacific, 1910–1936

	1910–1926	1927	1928	1929	1930	1931	1932	1933	1934	1935	1936	Total
May	0	0	1	1	0	0	0	1	0	0	0	3
June	7	2	2	1	1	0	1	1	0	0	2	17
July	11	2	1	0	0	1	0	1	1	0	0	17
August	12	1	1	2	1	1	2	1	0	2	2	25
September	32	3	3	3	0	4	1	0	1	0	3	50
October	17	1	2	0	3	0	0	0	1	0	2	26
November	2	0	0	0	0	0	0	0	0	0	0	2
December	1	0	0	0	0	0	0	0	0	0	0	1
Total	82	9	10	7	5	6	4	4	3	2	9	141

Average annual number, 5.

Occurrence of typhoons of the North Pacific, 1901–1936

	1901–1926	1927	1928	1929	1930	1931	1932	1933	1934	1935	1936	Total
January	13	0	0	0	0	1	0	0	0	0	1	15
February	7	0	0	0	0	0	0	0	1	0	0	8
March	7	1	0	0	1	0	1	0	1	0	0	11
April	10	0	0	0	1	0	1	0	0	1	0	13
May	21	1	1	1	1	0	0	0	0	0	1	26
June	31	1	0	3	0	0	0	1	0	0	0	36
July	79	2	4	5	5	0	2	4	1	2	5	109
August	121	4	3	2	2	5	3	1	4	3	3	151
September	93	4	3	7	1	4	1	4	6	4	2	129
October	78	5	3	5	1	4	3	4	6	4	4	117
November	40	2	2	2	1	3	1	2	2	1	3	59
December	27	0	0	0	0	1	1	0	4	3	1	37
Total	527	20	16	25	13	18	13	16	25	18	20	711

Average annual number, 20.

Many tropical cyclones originate in the more or less definite region known as the **"doldrums,"** that narrow belt lying between the northeast and southeast trade winds. It is a region characterized by sultry air and calms or light and baffling breezes, interrupted by frequent rains, thunderstorms, and squalls.

The South Atlantic Ocean is free from cyclones of tropical origin, the reason being that the Atlantic doldrums are almost entirely north of the equator, their southernmost position, which occurs in March, being commonly between latitude 3° N. and the equator. They rarely reach south of that latitude and, if so, only for a brief period.

The origin of tropical cyclones is obscure in some of the details but the absence of such storms from the continental regions of the Tropics and their early disintegration after passing from the sea to the land go to show that their maintenance is dependent on a supply of water vapor, which in the doldrums is present in the atmosphere in large amounts. The vapor-laden and heated air of these regions is underrun and forced upward by adjacent denser air—denser because drier and cooler. Thus is begun that process which later results in a continuing system of winds blowing around a moving center and constituting a tropical cyclone.

The developing storm drifts slowly westward with the current of free air and with this current it deviates more and more away from the equator after arriving at the western margin of the adjacent semipermanent "high." Here the winds turn poleward, as before explained, and this fact is reflected in the tracks of tropical cyclones, the centers of which commonly follow the free-air currents of the general circulation.

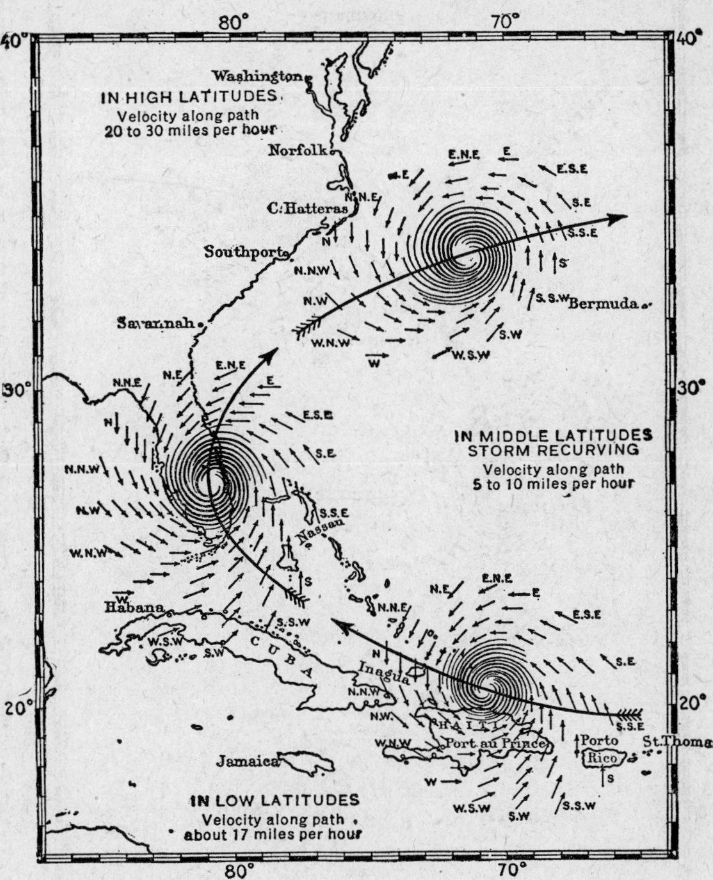

FIGURE 124.—Characteristic track and wind system of tropical cyclone of Northern Hemisphere.

Fully developed, the tropical cyclone consists of a well-defined area, more or less circular in shape, throughout which the atmospheric pressure diminishes rapidly on all sides toward the center or point of lowest barometer, the rate of this diminution amounting in the case of severe storms to 0.01 or even 0.02 of an inch for each mile of approach. Within this area of barometric depression the winds blow with great force, the velocity of the moving air increasing with the steepness of the barometric slope or gradient, the direction, however, as previously explained being not toward but around the center. At the center itself—the point of lowest pressure—is a region seldom more than 10 or 20 miles in diameter throughout which calm or light air prevails. Here, too, the dense canopy of cloud which overhangs the storm area is pierced, forming the so-called **"eye of the storm."** The seas within this area are violent and confused, sweeping in from all sides with overwhelming violence. The gale winds, high seas, and torrents of rain which usually accompany tropical cyclones often cause great damage to coastal regions and to shipping in the path of the storm.

The size of tropical cyclones varies greatly. In the case of West Indian hurricanes, considering the area in which winds of gale force prevail, the average diameter is some 300 miles. The diameter of the area of destructive winds is, however, much smaller. The size of the vortex, or calm area, likewise varies. It rarely exceeds 15 to 20 miles in diameter and may be as little as 7 miles

The usual track of the tropical cyclone resembles a parabola, of which the first branch of ten has its extremity in the region of the doldrums, as already explained, and the second branch, running to the east and north, has its extremity in middle latitudes. Here the storm either dissipates or takes on the form of an extra-tropical cyclone.

Figure 124 illustrates the typical parabolic track of a tropical cyclone of the Northern Hemisphere with its attendant system of winds blowing counterclockwise and directed somewhat toward the center. The angle between the wind direction and the isobars seems to vary in the different quadrants. In several West Indian hurricanes that have been studied this angle was found to be greatest in the right hand rear quadrant, and least in the left-hand front quadrant. The statement is frequently met with that in cyclones of the South Indian Ocean the northeasterly and easterly winds (understood to mean before the storm recurves) seldom, if ever, blow around the center but almost directly toward it. These winds correspond in part to those of the right-hand rear quadrant of tropical cyclones of the Northern Hemisphere, in which quadrant as just stated, the inclination toward the center was also found to be greatest.

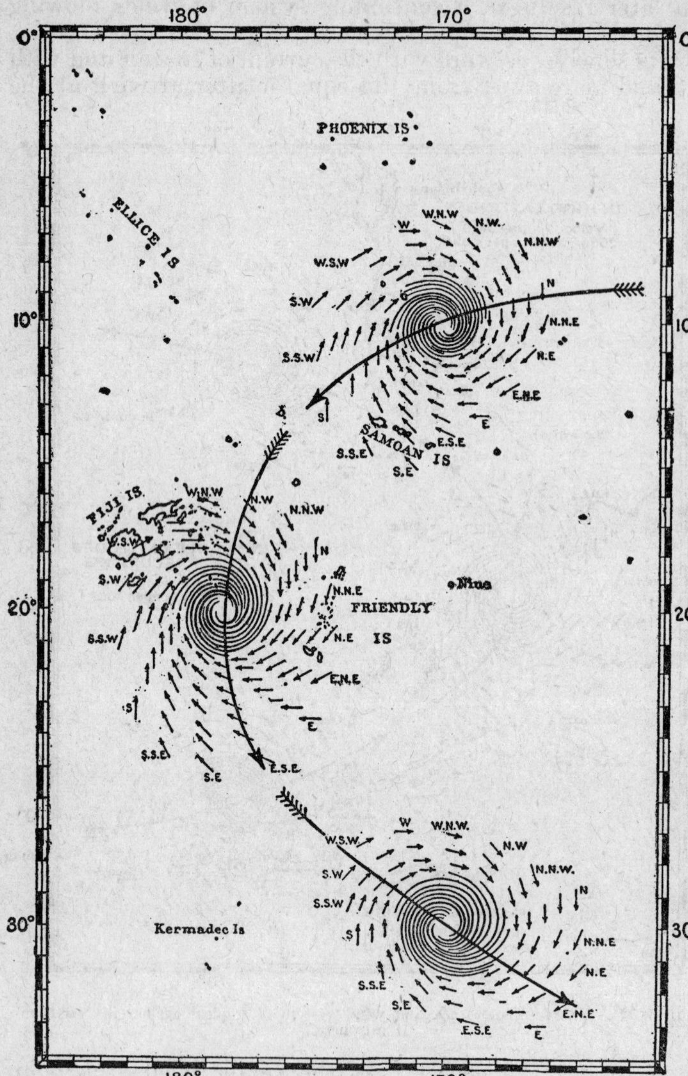

FIGURE 125.—Characteristic track and wind system of tropical cyclone of Southern Hemisphere.

It will be noted from figure 124 that in portions of both right-hand quadrants the winds blow in the general direction of the line of advance of the storm. It is these violent, sustained winds, sometimes blowing in one direction for several days, that cause the storm waves and swells so destructive on the coasts visited by tropical storms. Careful observations made by use of tide gauges on the coast of the Gulf of Mexico show that the highest storm tide occurs in front of tropical storms and immediately to the right of the line of advance of the center.

In the Southern Hemisphere the winds blow in a clockwise direction about the center of a cyclone. Here again, the average track of a tropical cyclone, arising in the region of doldrums, leads westerly at first. Its constantly increasing poleward component, however, carries it southwest, then south, and it finally recurves toward a southeasterly direction. In figure 125 is shown a characteristic track and wind system of a tropical cyclone in the Southern Hemisphere.

Although the average tracks of tropical cyclones in either hemisphere, arising in the doldrums, lead westward and poleward in a parabolic curve until in middle latitudes they recurve eastward, many individual cyclones deviate widely from the average. In the Northern Hemisphere, and possibly in the Southern also, the general direction of the first part of the track varies in different parts of the cyclone season, as does also the latitude of the vertex, or point where the track recurves to the eastward. In the case of West Indian hurricanes the average direction of the first branch in the early part of the season, June and July is about 315°. The direction of the first branch of August hurricane tracks is about 281°.

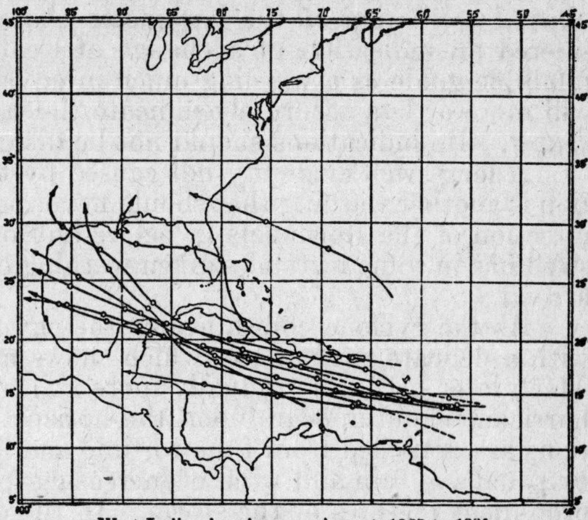

West Indian hurricanes. August, 1900 to 1921.

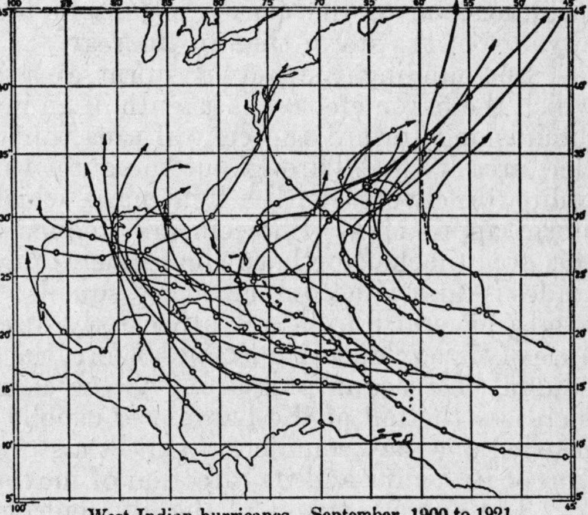

West Indian hurricanes. September, 1900 to 1921.

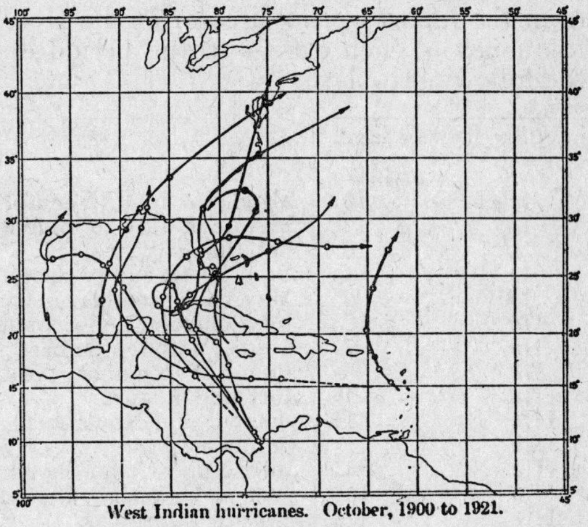

West Indian hurricanes. October, 1900 to 1921.

FIGURE 126.

With the advance of the season the direction of the first branch of the track inclines more and more to the northward and the latitude of recurve moves southward. The result is that the storms of September have generally recurved and started on the second branch of the track. Those which originated well out in the Atlantic have for the most part recurved near or to the east of the Bahama Islands, and the second branch has been about equal in length to the first. On the other hand, those which formed in the Caribbean Sea have generally recurved in the Gulf of Mexico and dissipated soon afterwards over the southern United States. In the case of October and November hurricanes the first part of the track had a 338° direction and the recurve was effected at still lower latitudes. Practically all storms of the period recurved and generally the second branch of the track was longer than the first. In these months, also, the presence of large anticyclones to the northward sometimes forces the tropical cyclone from a normal track, in extreme cases even causing it to move in such a way as to form a loop in its track. A study of the charts in figure 126 will reveal the characteristics of West Indian hurricane tracks just discussed. In figure 127 typhoons of the North Pacific have been classified according to average tracks. The percent frequency of each class and the period of the year during which typhoons are likely to follow that track are given in the table before the figure.

Early indications of tropical cyclones.—As will be explained later the modern development of radio weather reports at sea has made it possible for organized weather services to locate tropical cyclones when they develop and to issue warnings to shipping as to their size and probable movement. Although this advance has made it unnecessary for each ship to depend entirely upon its own observations and knowledge to avoid damage from the storm, it is still desirable that the rules for establishing the existence of a tropical cyclone and for locating its center be discussed.

These conditions are frequently accompanied by an unsteady barometer sometimes a little higher than usual.

During the season of tropical storms any interruption in the regularity of the diurnal oscillation of the barometer characteristic of low latitudes should be considered an indication of a change of weather. The barometer is by no means an infallible guide as a warning much in advance, but after the beginning of a storm it will more or less accurately indicate the rapidity of approach and distance from the center. Its indications should not be disregarded.

A long swell evidently not caused by the winds blowing at the place of observation is another warning that should never be overlooked. Frequently a swell from the direction of the storm sets in before any other indication becomes marked. Such a swell has in some instances given warning of a tropical cyclone days in advance of its arrival.

As the cyclone comes nearer the sky becomes overcast and remains so, at first with a delicate cirrus haze, which shows no disposition to clear away at sunset, but which later becomes gradually more and more dense until the dark mass of the true hurricane cloud appears upon the horizon. From the main body of this cloud portions are detached from time to time and drift across the sky, their progress marked by squalls of rain and wind of increasing force. Rain, indeed, forms one of the most prominent features of the storm. In the outer portions it is fine and mistlike, with occasional showers, these later increasing in frequency and in copiousness. In the neighborhood of the center it falls in torrents. The rain area extends farther in advance of the storm than in the rear.

Surrounding the actual storm area is a territory of large extent throughout which the barometer reads a tenth of an inch or more below the average, the pressure diminishing toward the central area, but with no such rapidity as is noted within that area itself. Throughout the outer ring unsettled weather prevails. The sky is ordinarily covered with a light haze, which increases in density as the center of the storm approaches. Showers are frequent. Throughout the northern semicircle of this area (in the Northern Hemisphere) the wind rises to force 6 or 8—the "reinforced trades"—and is accompanied by squalls; throughout the other semicircle unsettled winds, generally from a southeasterly direction, prevail. Usually after the appearance of cirrus clouds, sometimes before, the barometer shows an unmistakable although gradual decrease in pressure. As the clouds grow thicker and lower and the wind increases the fall of the barometer usually becomes more rapid. When this stage is reached one may confidently expect a storm, and observations to determine the location of its center and its direction of movement should be begun.

The average tracks of the different classes of typhoons are the result of a study of 244 of these storms which occurred during the period 1884–1897, and are taken from the report of the director of the Hongkong Observatory for 1897. The relative frequency of each class and the period during which it is apt to occur are given in the following table:

Class	Frequency	Period
	Percent	
I*aα*	10	Middle of June to end of September.
I*aβ*	12	Middle of July to middle of October.
1*b*	0	Late in the year.
1*c*	4	June to the end of September.
I*d*	2	May to September, inclusive.
II*a*	2	July, August, and September.
II*b*	7	August and September.
II*c*	3	June to September. Maximum in July.
II*d*	4	July and August.
III*a*	1½	October and November.
III*b*	1	October.
III*c*	4	July, August, and September.
III*d*	15	June to October. Most frequent in August and September.
III*e*	12½	May to December.
IV*aα*	8½	May to December. Rare in August.
IV*aβ*	3	Beginning and end of typhoon season.
IV*b*	4½	September 1 to December 1. Most common in November.
IV*c*	4	Beginning and end of typhoon season. Most frequent in May.
IV*d*	1	April and December.

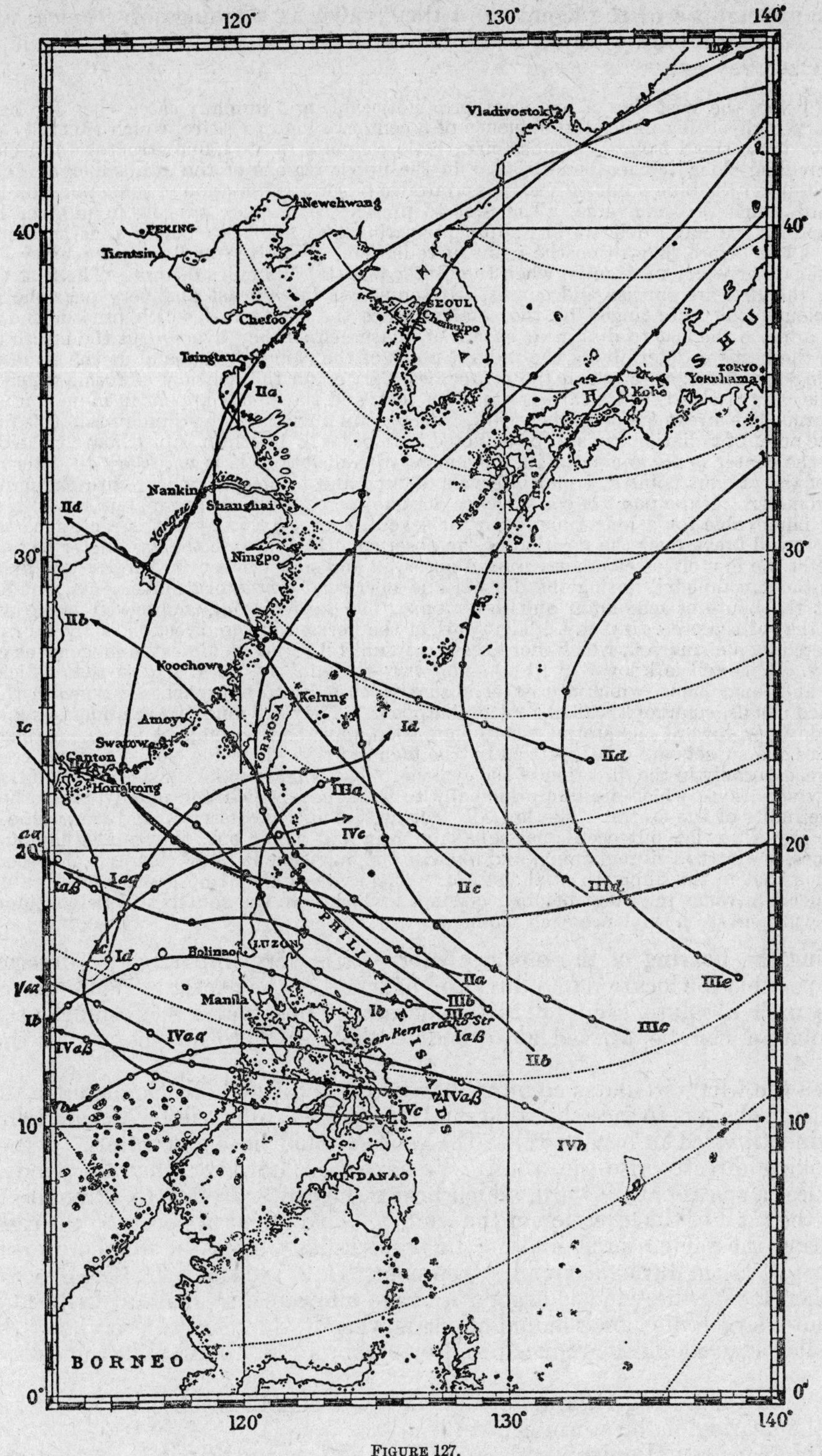
Vladivostok
Newchwang
PEKING
Tientsin
Chefoo
SEOUL
Chemulpo
Tsingtau
TOKYO
Yokohama
Kobe
Nagasaki
Nankin
Shanghai
Ningpo
Foochow
Kelung
FORMOSA
Amoy
Swatow
Canton
Hongkong
Bolinao
LUZON
Manila
PHILIPPINE ISLANDS
San Bernardino Str
MINDANAO
BORNEO
120°
130°
140°
40°
30°
20°
10°
0°

FIGURE 127.

The appearance of the clouds and their value as warnings of tropical cyclones is described as follows by Faura in Cyclones of the Far East, by Jose Algué, of the Manila Observatory:

Long before the least sign of bad weather is noticeable and in many cases when the barometer is still very high—being under the influence of a center of high pressure, which generally precedes a tempest—these small isolated clouds (cirri, little clouds of a very fine structure and clear opal color resembling elongated feathers) appear in the upper regions of the atmosphere. They seem to be piled up on the blue vault of heaven and drawn out in the direction of some point on the horizon toward which they converge. The first to present themselves are few in number but well defined and of the most delicate structure, appearing like filaments bound together but whose visibility is lost before they reach the point of radiation. We often had an opportunity to watch them at the observatory of Manila, when the center was still 600 miles distant. The best times for observing the cirri are sunrise and sunset. If the sun is in the east and very near the horizon, the first clouds which are tinged by the solar rays are the cirro-strati which precede the cyclone, and they are also the last to disappear at sunset, inasmuch as they overspread the horizon. Such times are the best for determining the radiant point of the cloud streaks and at the same time for ascertaining the direction in which the center lies. Later on the delicacy of form, which characterizes this class of clouds in its earliest stages, is lost, and the clouds appear in more confused and tangled forms, like streamers of feather work, with central nuclei, which still maintain this direction, so that the point of radiation can still be detected. In order to ascertain approximately the direction in which the center is advancing in its movement of translation, it is necessary to determine the changes of the radiant point at equal intervals of time and to compare them with the movements of the barometer. If the point of convergence does not perceptibly change its position, but remains fixed and immovable for a long time, even for several consecutive days, it is almost certain that the tempest will break over the position of the observer. In this case the barometer begins to fall shortly after the first cirrus clouds have been observed and sometimes even before. At first it falls slowly, without completely losing the diurnal and nocturnal oscillatory movements, but changing somewhat the hours of maximum and minimum. The daily reading is observed to be each day less than that of the preceding day. That part of the horizon in the direction of the storm begins to be covered by a cirrus veil, which increases slowly until it forms an almost homogeneous covering of the sky. This veil is known by the name "cirro-pallium" of Poëy, and is that which causes the solar and lunar halos, which are never absent when a storm approaches. Beneath the veil a few isolated clouds, commonly called "cotton," appear. They are much more numerous and larger on the side lying toward the storm, where they soon appear as a compact mass. At such times the sunrises and sunsets are characterized by the high red tint which the clouds assume, resembling a great fire, especially in the direction of the cyclone. The wind remains fixed at one point, showing only a few variations, which are due principally to the squalls,which continually exert their force within the limits of the storm. The low, or "cotton," clouds successively and from time to time cover the sky, throwing out occasional squalls of rain and wind; but, the squalls having passed, a lull ensues, the cirrus veil remaining, and likewise the hurricane bank of clouds, which seems fixed to the same spot in the direction of the storm. This state of the atmosphere continues until the bank of clouds invades the point of observation, in which case the squalls will be continuous and the wind will increase in violence each moment.

Fixing the bearing of the storm center.—It is very important to determine as early as possible the location and direction of travel of the center. While this can not be done with absolute accuracy with one set of observations, a sufficiently close approximation can be arrived at to enable the vessel to maneuver to the best advantage.

Since the wind circulates counterclockwise in the Northern Hemisphere, the rule in that hemisphere is to face the wind, and the storm center will be on the right hand. If the wind traveled in exact circles, the center would be eight points to the right when looking directly into the wind. We have seen, however, that the wind follows more or less a spiral path inward, which brings the center from 8 to 12 points (90° to 135°) to the right of the direction of the wind. The number of points to the right may vary during the same storm, and as the wind usually shifts in squalls its direction should not be taken during a squall. Ten points (112°) to the right (left in south latitude) when facing the wind is a good average allowance to make if in front of the storm, but a larger allowance should be made when in the rear. If very near the center the allowance should be reduced to 8 or 9 points (90° to 101°) in the front quadrants.

Based on the average, the following rules will enable an observer to fix approximately the bearing of the storm center:

In the **Northern Hemisphere,** stand with the face to the wind; the center of the cyclone will bear approximately 10 points to the observer's right.

In the **Southern Hemisphere,** stand with the face to the wind; the center of the cyclone will bear approximately ten points (112°) to the observer's left.

It may be noted here that the storm center almost always bears very close to 8 points (90°) from the direction of movement of the lower clouds of the cyclone. Therefore, when the direction of movement of the lower clouds can be observed it may serve as a more accurate indication of the bearing of the center than does the direction of surface wind.

Further assistance in locating the approximate position of the storm center may be obtained in some instances by observations of the clouds. When the sky first becomes overcast with the characteristic veil of cirrus the storm center will most probably lie in the direction of the greatest density of the cloud. Later when the hurricane cloud appears over the horizon it will be densest at the storm center. The hurricane cloud, sometimes called the **"bar of the cyclone,"** is a dense mass of rain cloud formed about the center of the storm, giving the appearance of a huge bank of black clouds resting upon the horizon. It may retain its form unchanged for hours. It is usually most conspicuous about sunrise or sunset. When it is possible to observe this cloud the changes in its position at intervals of a few hours will enable the observer to determine the direction of movement of the storm.

Although the approximate bearing of the storm center is a comparatively easy matter to determine, and the direction in which the center is moving may be estimated with fair accuracy from the charted paths of similar storms (see figs. 126 and 127) it is by no means an easy matter for the observer to estimate his distance from the storm center. The following old table from Piddington's "Horn Book" may serve as a guide, but it can only give an imperfect estimate of the distance and too much reliance must not be placed upon it:

Average fall of barometer per hour	Distance in miles from center
From 0.02 to 0.06 inch	From 250 to 150.
From .06 to .08 inch	From 150 to 100.
From .08 to .12 inch	From 100 to 80.
From .12 to .15 inch	From 80 to 50.

This table assumes that the vessel is hove-to in front of the storm and that the latter is advancing directly toward it.

With storms of varying area and different intensities the lines of equal barometric pressure (isobars) must lie much closer together in some cases than in others, so that it is possible only to guess at the distance of the center by the height of the mercury or its rate of fall.

A further source of error arises because storms travel at varying rates of progression. In the Tropics this ranges from 5 to 20 miles per hour, generally decreasing as the storm track turns poleward and recurves, increasing again as it reaches higher latitudes. In the North Atlantic its rate of progression may amount to as much as 50 miles per hour. Within the Tropics the storm area is usually small, the region of violent winds seldom extending more than 150 miles from the center. The unsettled state of the barometer described heretofore is usually found in the area between 500 and 1,000 miles in advance of the center. This gives place at a distance of 300 or 400 miles to a slow and steady fall of the mercurial column. When the region of violent winds extending about 150 miles from the center is reached, the barometer falls rapidly as the center of the storm comes on, this decrease within the violent area sometimes amounting to 2 inches.

Because of this very steep barometric gradient the winds blow with greater violence and are more symmetrically disposed around the center of a tropical cyclone than is the case with the less intense cyclones of higher latitudes. After a tropical cyclone has recurved it gradually widens out and becomes less severe, and its velocity of translation increases as its rotational energy grows more moderate. Its center is no longer a well-defined area of small size marked by a patch of clear sky and near which the winds blow with the greatest violence. Out of the Tropics the strongest winds are often found at some distance from the center.

Handling the vessel within the storm area.—If, from the weather indications given above and such others as his experience has taught him, the navigator is led to believe that a tropical cyclone is approaching, he should at once—

First. Determine the bearing of the center.
Second. Estimate its distance.
Third. Plot its apparent path.

The first two of the above determinations will locate the approximate position of the center, which should be marked on the chart. The relation between the position of the ship and the position and prospective track of the center will indicate the proper course to pursue (*a*) to enable the vessel to keep out of or escape from the dangerous semicircle and to avoid the center of the storm; (*b*) to enable the vessel to ride out the storm in safety if unable to escape from it.

Should the ship be to the westward of the storm center before the path has recurved, it may be assumed that the latter will draw nearer more or less directly. It then becomes of the utmost importance to determine its path and so learn whether the vessel is in the right or left semicircle of the storm area.

The right and left semicircles lie on the right and left hands, respectively, of an observer standing on the storm track and facing in the direction the center is moving. *Prior to recurving,* the winds in that semicircle of the storm which is more remote from the equator (the right-hand semicircle in the Northern Hemisphere, the left-hand semicircle in the Southern) are liable to be more severe than those of the opposite semicircle. A vessel hove-to in the semicircle adjacent to the equator has also the advantage of immunity from becoming involved in the actual center itself, inasmuch as there is a distinct tendency of the storm to move away from the equator and to recurve. For these reasons the more remote semicircle (the right hand in the Northern Hemisphere, the left hand in the Southern Hemisphere) has been called the **dangerous,** while that semicircle adjacent to the equator (the left hand in the Northern Hemisphere, the right hand in the Southern Hemisphere) is called the **navigable.**

In order to determine the path of the storm and consequently in which semicircle the ship finds herself, it is necessary to wait until the wind shifts. When this occurs, plot a new position of the center 10 points (112°) to the right of the new direction of the wind as before, and the line joining these two positions will be the *probable* path of the storm. If the ship has not been stationary during the time between the two sets of observations (as will indeed never be the case unless at anchor), allowance must be made for the course and distance traveled in the interim.

Two bearings of the center with an interval between of from 2 to 3 hours will, in general, be sufficient to determine the course of the storm, provided an accurate account is kept of the ship's way, but if the storm be moving slowly a longer interval will be necessary.

Should the wind not shift, but continue to blow steadily with increasing force, and with a falling barometer, it may be assumed that the vessel is on or near the storm track. Owing to the slow advance of storms in the Tropics, a vessel might come within the disturbed area through overtaking the center. In such a case a slight decrease in speed would probably be all that would be necessary, but it should be borne in mind that the storm path is by no means constant either in speed or direction, and that it is particularly liable to recurve away from the equator.

A vessel hove-to in advance of a tropical cyclonic storm will experience a long heavy swell, a falling barometer with torrents of rain, and winds of steadily increasing force. The shifts of wind will depend upon the position of the vessel with respect to the track followed by the storm center. Immediately upon the track, the wind will hold steady in direction until the passage of the central calm, the "eye of the storm," after which the gale will renew itself, but from a direction opposite to that which it previously had. To the right of the track, or in the *right-hand semicircle* of the storm the wind, as the center advances and passes the vessel, will constantly shift to the right, the rate at which the successive shifts follow each other increasing with the proximity to the center; in this semicircle, then, in order that the wind shall draw aft with each shift, and the vessel not be taken aback, a *sailing vessel* must be hove-to on the starboard tack; similarly, in the left-hand semicircle, the wind will constantly shift to the left, and here a *sailing vessel* must be hove-to on the port tack so as not to be taken aback. These two rules hold alike for both hemispheres and for *cyclonic* storms in all latitudes.

It must not be forgotten that the shifts of wind will only occur in the above order when the vessel is stationary. When the course and speed are such as to maintain a constant relative bearing between the ship and storm center, there will be no shift of wind. Should the vessel be outrunning the storm, the wind will indeed shift in the opposite direction to that given, and a navigator in the right semicircle, for

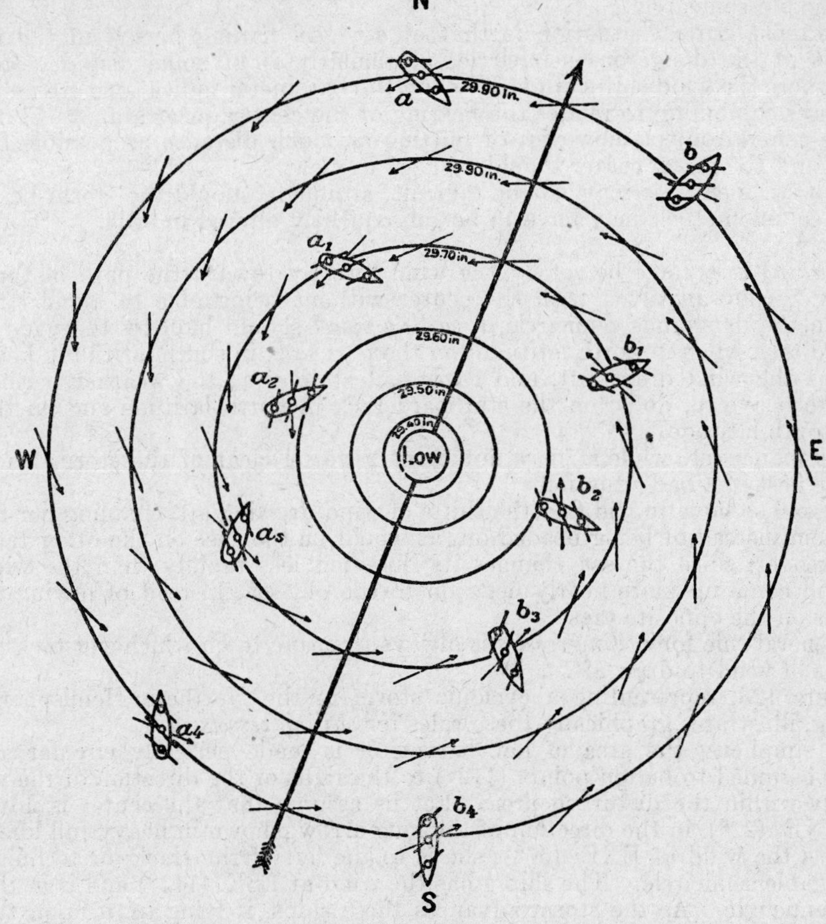

FIGURE 128.

instance, judging only by the shifts of wind without taking into account his own run, might imagine himself on the opposite side. In such a case the barometer must be the guide. If it falls, one is approaching the center; if it rises, one is receding.

An examination of figure 128 shows how this is. A vessel hove to at the position marked *b*, and being passed by the storm center, will occupy successive positions in regard to the center from *b* to *b*4, and will experience shifts of wind, as shown by the arrows, from East through South to SW. On the other hand, if the storm center be stationary or moving slowly and a vessel be overtaking it along the line from *b*4 to *b*, the wind will back from SW. to East, and is likely to convey an entirely wrong impression as the location and movement of the center.

Hence it is recommended that a vessel suspecting the approach or proximity of a cyclonic storm should stop (if a sailing ship heave to on the starboard tack) for a while until the path of the center is located by observing the shifts of the wind and the behavior of the barometer.

If the wind remains steady in direction and increases in force in heavy squalls while the barometer falls rapidly, say, at a greater rate than 0.03 of an inch per hour, the vessel is probably on or near the track of the storm and in advance of the center.

In this position, with plenty of sea room, the proper course is to run with the wind well on the starboard quarter, if north of the equator, and on the port quarter if south. The vessel will thus be in the navigable semicircle and be constantly increasing her distance from the center. The wind will draw more forward as she recedes from the center, but the compass course first set should be adhered to until well clear.

The procedure is the same if the observations place the ship anywhere within the navigable semicircle.

The most critical situation is that of a vessel finding herself in the forward quadrant of the dangerous semicircle, particularly if at some distance from the center, where the wind shifts but slowly and the barometer indications are undecided, both causes combining to render the bearing of the center uncertain.

The general object, however, of putting as much distance as possible between the ship and the storm center should be kept in view.

With steamers this may not be difficult, although, should the storm be recurving, the course first set may have to be subsequently altered in order to continue to draw away.

A *sailing vessel* will be set by the wind directly toward the path of the storm and may become involved with the center without being able to avoid it. If so caught in the dangerous semicircle, a *sailing vessel* should haul by the wind on the starboard tack when in north latitude (on the port tack in south latitude), keep coming up as the wind draws aft, and carry sail as long as the weather permits. If obliged to heave to, do so on the starboard tack in north latitude and on the port tack in south latitude.

This maneuver, while it may not carry a vessel clear of the storm track, will make the best of a bad situation.

A vessel so hove to will find the shifts of wind drawing aft, enabling her to come up to them instead of being headed off, as would be the case on the other tack.

Moreover, since the sea changes its direction less rapidly than the wind, the vessel will come up more nearly head on to the old sea, instead of having it more abeam as on the opposite tack.

A general rule for *sailing vessels* is always to heave to on whichever tack permits the shifts of wind to draw aft.

Figure 128, representing a cyclonic storm in the Northern Hemisphere after recurving, illustrates graphically these rules for *sailing vessels*.

For simplicity the area of low barometer is made perfectly circular and the center is assumed to be ten points (112°) to the right of the direction of the wind at all points within the disturbed area. Let us assume that the center is advancing about NNE. (22°), in the direction of the long arrow, shown in heavy full line. The ship *a* has the wind at ENE. (67°); she is to the left of the track, or technically in the navigable semicircle. The ship *b* has the wind at ESE. (112°) and is in the dangerous semicircle. As the storm advances these ships, if lying to, *a* upon the port tack, *b* upon the starboard tack, as shown, take with regard to the storm center the successive positions a_1, a_2, etc., b_1, b_2, etc., the wind of ship *a* shifting to the left, of ship *b* to the right, or in both cases drawing aft, and thus diminishing the probability of either ship being struck aback, with possible serious damage to spars and rigging, a danger to which a vessel lying to on the opposite tack (i. e., the starboard tack in the left-hand semicircle or the port tack in the right-hand semicircle) is constantly exposed, the wind in the latter case tending constantly to draw forward. This ship *b* is continually beaten by wind and sea toward the storm track. The ship *a* is drifted away from the track and should she be able to carry sail would soon find better weather by running off to the westward.

Should steamers find it necessary to heave to the method of doing so must depend upon the position within the storm area.

A steamer is concerned more with the damage resulting from heavy seas than from wind; furthermore a steamer is not dependent for the course upon the direction of the wind, but is free to maneuver to keep away from the storm center, where the heaviest and most confused seas are found, unless other circumstances, such as proximity to the land, prevent.

If unable to escape from the storm, and this can be done only in low latitudes when the storm covers a comparatively limited area, the principal object of a steamer is to avoid the center of the storm.

Referring to figure 128, it is obvious that in the Northern Hemisphere if a steamer finding herself in the left-hand (**navigable**) semicircle at *a* or *a*–1 should obey the rule for sailing vessels and heave to on the port tack, her head will lie *toward* the storm track and the greatest danger. On the other hand, under the same circumstances, if the steamer heaves to on the starboard tack, her head will lie *away* from the storm track and such headway as is made will all be in the direction of safety.

Following the same reasoning, a steamer in the Northern Hemisphere caught in the right-hand (**dangerous**) semicircle at *b*, *b*–1 (fig. 128) and obliged to heave to should do so head to sea, because in this case both the wind and sea are constantly beating her toward the storm track, and then lying to, head to sea, less leeway will be made than in any other position.

Many steamers behave better when hove to with the sea astern, or on the quarter, but the adoption of this method must depend upon the position of the vessel within the storm area. Referring again to figure 128, it will be clearly seen that, in the Northern Hemisphere, if in the forward quadrant of the left-hand semicircle at positions *a*, *a*–1, a steamer may safely heave to with the sea astern or on the starboard quarter. This course, however, should never be attempted when in the forward quadrant of the right-hand semicircle (positions *b*, *b*–1) for the reason that any headway made would be, in all probability, toward the storm center where the high and confused seas would be likely to inflict damage.

If, in spite of all endeavors, the storm center should pass directly over a vessel she will experience a short period of calm, but the seas will be high, confused, and dangerous, being swept in from all directions. After a short interval the wind will burst with hurricane force from a point directly opposite to that from which it was blowing before, and the vessel must be prepared to meet it and to avoid being caught aback.

Maneuvering rules.—The rules for maneuvering, so far as they may be generalized, are:

NORTHERN HEMISPHERE

Right or dangerous semicircle.—Steamers: Bring the wind on the starboard bow, make as much way as possible, and if obliged to heave to, do so head to sea. Sailing vessels: Keep close-hauled on the starboard tack, make as much way as possible, and if obliged to heave to, do so on the starboard tack.

Left or navigable semicircle.—Steam and sailing vessels: Bring the wind on the starboard quarter, note the course and hold it. If obliged to heave to, steamers may do so stern to sea; sailing vessels on the port tack.

On the storm track, in front of center.—Steam and sailing vessels: Bring the wind two points (22°) on the starboard quarter, note the course and hold it, and run for the left semicircle, and when in that semicircle maneuver as above.

On the storm track, in rear of center.—Avoid the center by the best practicable route, having due regard to the tendency of cyclones to recurve to the northward and eastward.

SOUTHERN HEMISPHERE

Left or dangerous semicircle.—Steamers: Bring the wind on the port bow, make as much way as possible, and if obliged to heave to do so head to sea. Sailing vessels: Keep close-hauled on the port tack, make as much way as possible, and if obliged to heave to do so on the port tack.

Right or navigable semicircle.—Steam and sailing vessels: Bring the wind on the port quarter, note the course and hold it. If obliged to heave to, steamers may do so stern to sea; sailing vessels on the starboard tack.

On the storm track, in front of center.—Steam and sailing vessels: Bring the wind two points (22°) on the port quarter, note the course and hold it and run for the right semicircle, and when in that semicircle maneuver as above.

541524°—43——20

On the storm track, in rear of center.—Avoid the center by the best practicable route, having due regard to the tendency of cyclones to recurve to the southward and eastward.

The above rules depend, of course, upon having sea room. In case land interferes, a vessel should heave to, as recommended for the semicircle in which she finds herself.

Weather forecasting.—Until the invention of the telegraph, forecasts of the weather were necessarily based upon weather indications at the observer's position only. After years of close observation of the weather, mariners, for example, grew familiar with the indications afforded by the barometer, the winds, the clouds, and other signs until they could foretell the approach of severe storms. They lacked sufficient knowledge, however, to forecast in detail the common day to day changes of weather, wind, and temperature. With modern improvements the forecaster who must forecast entirely from local indications may after long experience tell with accuracy the weather for his locality a short period in advance of its arrival. Since he has no information of current weather a few hundred miles away, his forecast

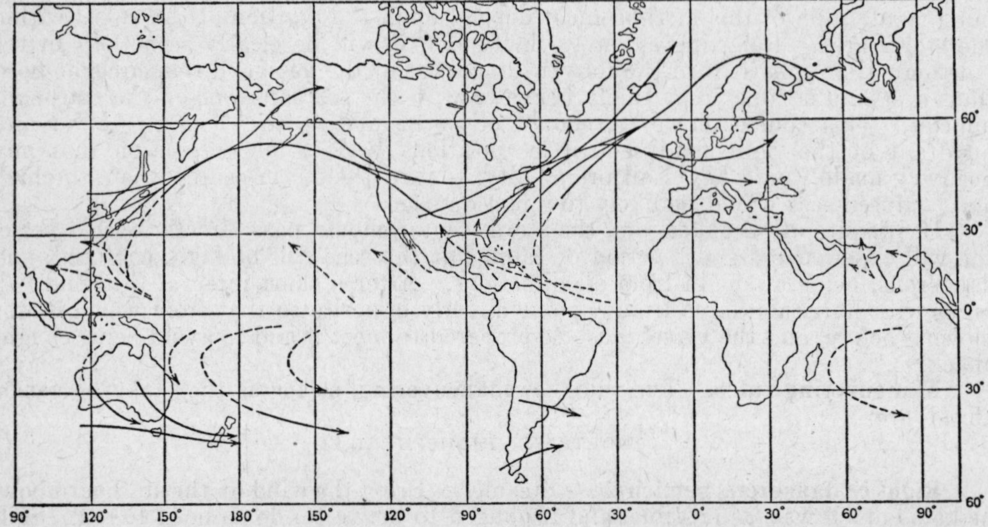

FIGURE 129.—Best known storm tracks of world. (Dotted lines, tropical cyclones; solid lines, extra-tropical cyclones.)

is limited in range of time to the ensuing few hours, rarely beyond 24 hours, and in space usually to the area within a few miles of his place of observation. Moreover, since cloud forms and other weather characteristics that forerun certain changes in one locality often precede quite different weather in another locality, the method of forecasting from local indications can be used to a great extent only by one who has had long experience in the place for which he is forecasting. In order to forecast in detail from local indications, the forecaster must usually have available for ready reference accurate records of past fluctuations of barometric pressure, wind, temperature, and humidity, and changes in cloud forms with the weather attending them. Modern meteorological instruments make it possible to keep continuous records of many important weather elements automatically. Some elements, such as the appearance of the sky, can be recorded only by personal observation. Each day the forecaster studies the current records of his instruments, observes closely the cloud forms and the direction of movement of the different layers, the appearance of the sky, and certain other indications, and compares them with records of past weather. With sufficient experience he is able to recognize significant characteristics in the present weather and from these to foretell the weather which is to be expected during the next few hours. There are other factors affecting local weather which must be studied by the forecaster. Among these are the topography of his locality and the meteorological conditions in the air far above the surface. Daily data of winds, temperatures, pressures, and humidities in the upper layers of the atmosphere are of very great importance, and their use in local forecasting is increasing.

The method now most commonly used in forecasting weather is based upon the use of daily weather maps. (See fig. 130.) Most of the large countries have established Government weather services each of which, after a study of the current weather map, publishes daily by telegraph and radio a forecast of weather for the ensuing 24 hours or more over its territory and adjacent waters

The method of making forecasts can be discussed but briefly here. Reports of local weather conditions from many stations scattered over the country and from ships at sea are telegraphed several times daily to the central office of the weather service. In the United States and Europe four observations a day are available. After these simultaneous reports are plotted on charts, the forecaster draws the isobars and fronts after having studied all the information available. This information

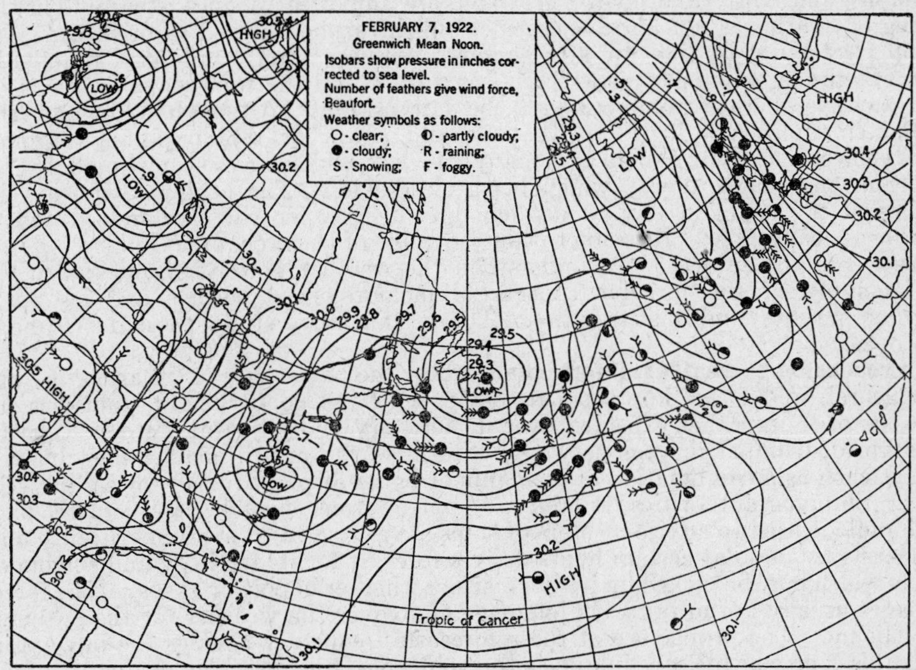

FIGURE 130.—Daily weather map.

consists of barometric pressure, temperatures, dew points, wind direction, wind velocity, state of the sky, the clouds, the pressure tendencies, pilot balloon observations showing wind direction and velocity at different levels, and available airplane observations giving pressures, temperatures, and humidities at different levels up to 4 or 5 kilometers. After having studied all these data carefully he is able to determine the different air masses involved and to picture the atmospheric processes taking place. Methods have also been developed whereby the movement of fronts and centers may be calculated from the pressures and pressure tendencies. Also, studies have shown when to expect the genesis and dissipation of fronts and highs and lows. The forecaster with his previous study and experience is able then to make reliable deductions as to the movements of and changes in the fronts, highs and lows and their effect on subsequent weather processes.

By use of a weather map forecasts can be made for a larger territory and for longer periods of time than is possible using local indications alone. Forecasts for the ensuing 24 to 36 hours can usually be made from a weather map. Attempts have been made to forecast over a longer range of time. Forecasts exceeding in time the ensuing 36 hours can sometimes be made with confidence but they must be expressed in very general terms. Long-range forecasts of elements such as temperature and rainfall covering a month or a season in a general way have been made at times based upon averages or other factors, but these are worthless in forecasting the weather on any particular day.

When very detailed forecasts of weather are required it is usually necessary to combine the use of the two methods described above. A weather map interpreted in the light of local observations makes it possible for a forecaster to draw very definite inferences of ensuing winds and weather giving approximate times of occurrence and other details. Here, again, careful and continuous study of local observations and experience in recognizing local indications are essential. The forecaster must observe almost hourly the significant features of weather, especially of clouds and wind, in the locality for which he is forecasting. Local forecasts in detail made in this manner have become very important at large aviation bases since the development of aerial navigation.

As explained in preceding articles the factors which determine weather are numerous and vast, and many of them are imperfectly understood. The forecasting of weather is not an exact science which can be reduced to brief laws. Proficient forecasting is, like an art, acquired through study and long practice. A glance at the barometer or at a "high" or a "low" on the weather map is not sufficient to say whether tomorrow will be fair or foul. Although a high or rising barometer typically brings fair weather, and a low or rapidly falling barometer usually means a storm, there are many "highs" which are accompanied by wind and rain, and many "lows" which bring clear skies. The beginner who attempts to foretell the common day to day changes in weather will find indeed that the weather is changeable. It is not within the scope of these chapters to give a detailed discussion of the subject. To understand the weather better it is necessary to go into a study of the broader aspects of meteorological science and its kindred subjects, physics and mathematics. The reader may study these from modern textbooks.

Broadcasting weather information.—For the assistance of marine, aviation, agricultural, and other interests, almost every large country now publishes daily forecasts of the weather expected over its territory and adjacent waters. The forecasts are distributed in various ways. Storm warnings are made public by visual signals, such as a combination of pennants or lights displayed from towers in various ports. Shipping authorities on land are kept informed by telegraph and telephone, while radio is used to advise masters of ships at sea. Almost every maritime country broadcasts by radio at certain hours daily a forecast for its territory and surrounding waters which may be picked up by the mariner whether in port or at sea. The forecast messages usually are in ordinary language and cover the weather for the ensuing 12 to 24 hours. The proper use of these forecasts frequently enables the navigator to adjust his course or his schedule so as to avoid gales, thick weather, or fog. Information regarding the time and other particulars of the distribution of weather advices may be obtained by writing to the weather services of the various countries.

There are many times when the individual, the mariner or the aviator, for example, needs more definite information of approaching weather than can be included in the forecast from a central office. The best source of this information is a weather map of the region. Many countries therefore broadcast daily in addition to the message containing forecasts in ordinary language, a collection of synoptic reports in simple figure code from which the mariner or the aviator may draw up maps for his own use. These coded synoptic reports usually contain the following data from simultaneous observations taken at a number of representative land stations and ships: (1) Name of station or position of ship; (2) direction and force of wind; (3) state of weather; (4) barometric pressure reduced to sea level; (5) visibility; and (6) current temperature. From these data the mariner is able to construct in a few minutes a weather map and draw therefrom certain conclusions for himself. It is unlikely that the average mariner will care to go sufficiently into a study of forecasting to enable him to foretell the small everyday changes in weather, but he may without extensive study recognize on the weather map the severe cyclonic storms which may prove dangerous. He may also, after some experience, come to recognize various types of "lows" and recall the winds and weather which usually attend the respective quadrants of these types in different regions of the globe.

A forecasting service carried on from a vessel at sea is very valuable over those parts of oceans not covered by forecasts from land weather services. In regions subject to tropical storms, known as hurricanes, typhoons, etc., there is an organized service for giving warning of the location and movements of such storms to vessels in the vicinity. Ship masters can render aid of high value to meteorological services which issue warnings of tropical storms by observing the provision of article 34 of the Convention for Safety of Life at Sea, signed in London on May 31, 1929, which imposes the duty on ship masters to give notice to competent authorities when a dangerous tropical storm is met

CHAPTER XXIII

ICE MOVEMENT IN THE NORTH ATLANTIC OCEAN

Ice.—Vessels crossing the Atlantic Ocean between Europe and the ports of the United States and British America are liable to encounter icebergs or extensive fields of compact ice, which are carried southward from the Arctic region by the ocean currents. It is in the vicinity of the Great Bank of Newfoundland that these masses of ice appear in the greatest numbers and drift farthest southward. The accompanying charts show the changeable area in which icebergs and field ice have been reported by mariners in the years 1912 and 1919 to 1923 in the months of April May, and June, when they occur in the greatest number.

The amount of ice and its location and movement are so variable from year to year, while the region occupied in its formation and transportation is so vast and so little under special observation, that no successful system of prediction has as yet been instituted. The most that can be said now is that after an exceptionally open winter in the Arctic we may expect the ice to come south earlier and in greater quantity. After such a winter the East Greenland current starts the ice stream around Cape Farewell from 1 to 3 months earlier, and this advancing of the season is reflected by a corresponding advance in the Labrador Current and on the Newfoundland Bank. The greatest calving at the glaciers of Greenland follows the breaking up of the shore ice, and hence the bergs also start southward earlier and with more freedom after an open winter.

In April, May, and June icebergs have been seen as far south as latitude 37°50′ N. and as far east as longitude 38° W. Exceptional drifts have occurred almost down to latitude 30° N., and between longitudes 10° and 75° W., in these months as well as during other seasons of the year. Between Newfoundland and the 40° parallel floating ice may be met in any month, but not often from August to December. On the Great Bank of Newfoundland bergs generally move southward. Those that drift westward of Cape Race usually pass between Green and St. Pierre banks. The Virgin Rocks are generally surrounded by ice until the middle of April or the beginning of May.

Icebergs origin.—Most of the bergs which annually appear in the North Atlantic originate on the western coast of Greenland; a few come from the east coast and from Hudson Bay. A small but productive glacier in southern Greenland yields the bluish bergs which are so hard to see at night. The largest bergs come from the glaciers at Umanak Fjord and Disko Bay (Lat. 69° to 71°), and their height above water will rise to 500 feet; but as they lose in mass from that time forward, we cannot expect to find them of such gigantic height when they finally appear near the Newfoundland Bank.

A huge ice sheet, formed from compressed snow, covers the whole of the interior of Greenland. The surface of this enormous glacier, only occasionally interrupted by protruding mountain tops, rises slightly toward the interior and forms a watershed between the east and west coasts, which is estimated to be from 8,000 to 10,000 feet above the sea. The outskirts of Greenland, as they are called, consist of a fringe of islands, mountains, and promontories surrounding the vast ice-covered central portion and varying in width from a mere border up to 80 miles. Upon the west side, below the parallel of 73° of latitude, it has an average width of about 50 miles and extends with little interruption from Cape Farewell to Melville Bay, a distance of something over 1,000 miles.

Everywhere this mountainous belt is penetrated by deep fjords, which reach to the inland ice, and are terminated by the perpendicular fronts of huge glaciers, while in some places the ice comes down in broad projections close to the margin of the sea. All of these glaciers are making their way toward the sea, and, as their ends are forced out into the water, they are broken off and set adrift as bergs. This process is called **calving.** The size of the pieces set adrift varies greatly, but a berg from 60 to 100 feet to the top of its walls, whose spires or pinnacles may reach from 200 to 250 feet in height and whose length may be from 300 to 500 yards, is considered to be of ordinary size in the Arctic. These measurements apply to the part

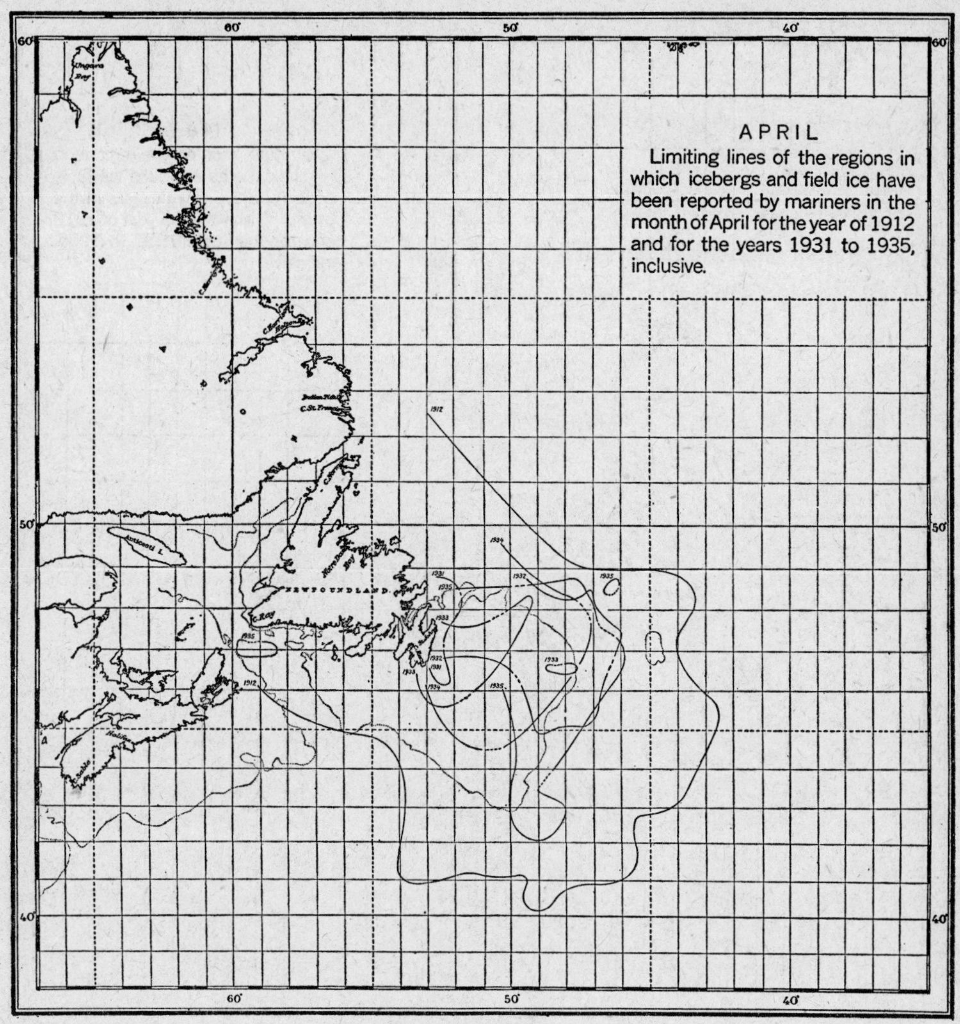

APRIL
Limiting lines of the regions in which icebergs and field ice have been reported by mariners in the month of April for the year of 1912 and for the years 1931 to 1935, inclusive.
60°
50°
40°
NEWFOUNDLAND

FIGURE 131.

above water, which is about one-eighth or one-ninth of the whole mass. Many authors give the depth under water as being from eight to nine times the height above; this is incorrect, as measurements above and below water should be referred to mass and not to height.

Bergs are being formed all the year round, but in greater numbers during the summer season; and thousands are set adrift each year.

Once adrift in the Arctic they find their way into the Labrador Current and begin their journey to the southward. It is not an unobstructed drift, but one attended with many stoppages and mishaps. Many ground in the Arctic Basin and break up there; others reach the shores of Labrador, where from one end to the other they continually ground and float; some break up and disappear entirely, while others get safely past and reach the Grand Bank. The whole coast of Labrador is cut up by numerous islands, bays, and headlands, shoals and reefs, which makes the journey of all drift a long one, and adds greatly to the destruction of the bergs by stoppages and by causing them to break up. Disintegration is also hastened by their breaking away from the floe ice, for detached bergs will melt and break up rapidly even in high latitudes during the summer.

Ice-bearing currents.—The Labrador Current passes to the southward along the coasts of Baffin Land and Labrador, and, although it occasionally ceases altogether,

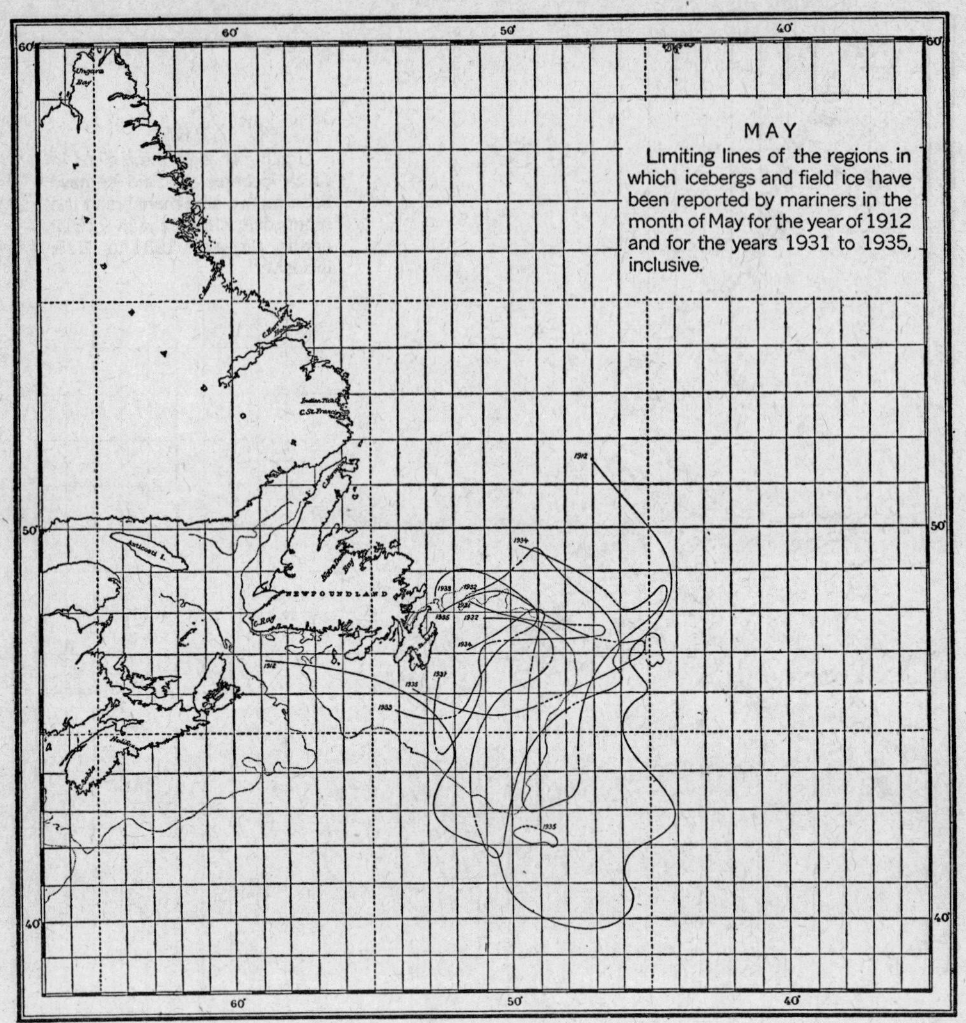
MAY
Limiting lines of the regions in which icebergs and field ice have been reported by mariners in the month of May for the year of 1912 and for the years 1931 to 1935, inclusive.
NEWFOUNDLAND
Anticosti I.
60°
50°
40°

FIGURE 132.

its usual rate is from 10 to 36 miles per day. Near the coast it is very much influenced by the winds, and reaches its maximum rate after those from the northward. The general drift of the current is to the southward, as shown by the passage of many icebergs, although occasions have arisen on which these have been observed to travel northward without any apparent reason. The breadth and depth of the current are not known, but it is certain that it pours into the Atlantic enormous masses of water for which compensation is derived from the warm waters of the Atlantic and from the East Greenland Current that flows around Cape Farewell. The flow of the Polar Current down the east coast of Greenland has been abundantly demonstrated by the drift of vessels that have been beset in the ice pack to the eastward of Greenland. This current turns around Cape Farewell, with an ice stream 60 miles wide, and then takes a northwesterly direction along the Greenland coast as far as the Arctic Circle, where it meets the southerly current from Baffin Bay.

Drift and iceberg characteristics.—Not all the bergs made in any one season find their way south during the following one, for only a small percentage of them ever reach trans-Atlantic routes. So many delays attend their journey and so irregular and erratic is it that many bergs seen in any one season may have been made several seasons before. If bergs on their calving at once drifted to the southward and met with no obstructions their journey of about 1,200 to 1,500 miles would occupy from 4 to 5 months, reckoning the drift of the Labrador Current at 10 miles a day, which may be making it too little. Then, if bergs were liberated principally in July and August they should reach trans-Atlantic routes in December and January, while we know this to be the rare exception. It is then seen what an important bearing the shores of Labrador have in arresting their flow, when it is known that bergs are generally most plentiful in the late spring and early summer months off the Bank.

All bergs do not follow the same course when set adrift from their parent glaciers, for, like floating bodies at the head of a river, some will go direct to the mouth, others will go but a short distance and lodge, others will accomplish half the journey and remain until another freshet again floats them, so that in the end the debris will be composed in part of that of several years' production.

Bergs, when first liberated on the west Greenland shore, are out of the strongest sweep of the southerly current, and they may take some months to find their way out of Davis Strait, while again others may at once drift into the current and move unobstructed until dissipated in the Gulf Stream. The difference in time of two bergs reaching a low latitude, which were set adrift the same day, may cover a period of 1 or 2 years.

Field ice also offers an obstruction to bergs, and a close season in the Arctic may prevent their liberation to a great extent, though, from their deep submersion, they act as ice plows and aid materially in breaking up the vast fields of ice which so often close the Arctic Basin.

Ice fields are more affected by wind than bergs. Bergs owe their drift almost entirely to current, so that they will often be noticed forcing their way through immense fields of heavy ice and going directly to windward. Advantage is taken of this by vessels in ice fields, which often moor to bergs and are towed for miles through ice in which they could not otherwise make any headway. This is accomplished by sinking an ice anchor into them, and using a strong towline, and as the berg advances open water is left to leeward while the loose ice floats past on both sides. For the same reason vessels, when beset by field ice, run from the lee of one berg to that of another, as leads may offer themselves.

Instances are not rare where icebergs were seen to drift toward north, making 15 to 24 miles a day, near the tail of the Bank and to the eastward of Cape Race.

All ice is brittle, especially that in bergs, and it is wonderful how little it takes to accomplish their destruction. A blow of an ax will at times split them, and the report of a gun, by concussion, will accomplish the same end. They are more apt to break up in warm weather than cold, and whalers and sealers note this before landing on them, when an anchor is to be planted or fresh water to be obtained. On the coast of Labrador in July and August, when it is packed with bergs, the noise of rupture is often deafening, and those experienced in ice give them a wide berth.

When they are frozen the temperature is very low, so that when their surface is exposed to a thawing temperature the tension of the exterior and interior is very different. Then, too, during the day water made by melting finds its way into the crevices, freezes, and hence expands, and, acting like a wedge, forces the berg into fragments. It is the greatly increased surface which the fragments expose to the melting action of the oceanic waters that accounts for the rapid disappearance of the ice after it has reached the northern edge of the warm circulatory drift currents of the North Atlantic Ocean. If these processes of disintegration did not go on and large bergs should remain intact, several years might elapse before they would melt, and they would ever be present in the transoceanic routes. In fact, instances are on record in which masses of ice, escaping the influences of swift destruction or possessing a capability for resisting them, have, by phenomenal drifts, passed into European waters and been encountered from time to time throughout that portion of the ocean which stretches from the British Isles to the Azores.

Icebergs assume the greatest variety of shapes, from those approximating to some regular geometric figure to others crowned with spires, domes, minarets, and peaks, while others still are pierced by deep indentations or caves. Small cataracts fall from the large bergs, while from many icicles hang in clusters from every projecting ledge. They frequently have outlying spurs under water, which are as dangerous as any other sunken reefs. For this reason it is advisable for vessels to

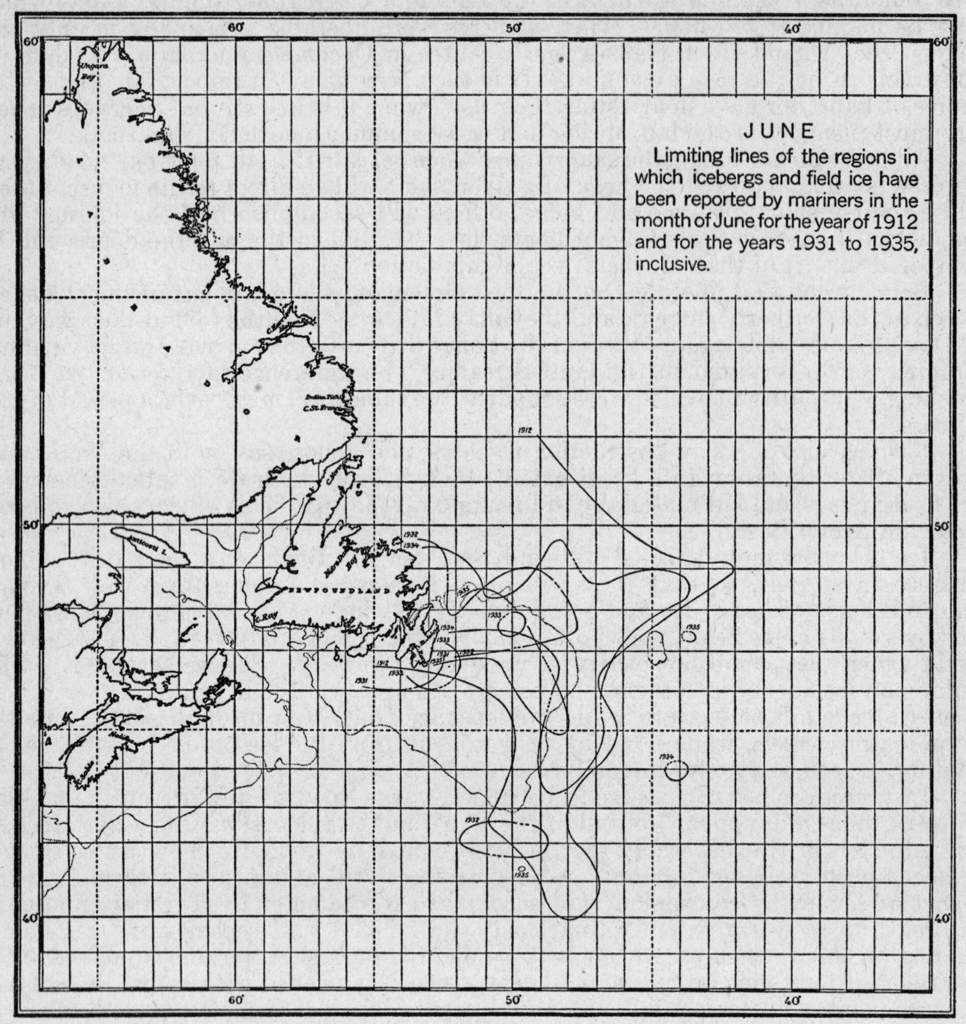
JUNE
Limiting lines of the regions in which icebergs and field ice have been reported by mariners in the month of June for the year of 1912 and for the years 1931 to 1935, inclusive.
60°
50°
40°
NEWFOUNDLAND
1912
1931
1932
1933
1934
1935

FIGURE 133.

give them a wide berth, for there are cases on record where vessels were seriously damaged by striking when apparently clear of the berg. Among these is that of the British steamship *Nessmore,* which ran into a berg in latitude 41°50′ N., longitude 52° W., and stove in her bows. On docking the vessel a long score was found extending from abreast the forerigging all of the way aft, just above the keel. Four frames were broken and the plates were almost cut through. The ship evidently struck a projecting spur after the helm had been put over, as there was clear water between the vessel and the berg after the first collision.

It is generally best to go to windward of an iceberg, because the disintegrated fragments will have a tendency to drift to leeward while open water will be found to windward. Serious injury has occurred to vessels through the breaking up or capsizing of icebergs. Often the bergs are so nicely balanced that the slightest melting of their surfaces causes a shifting of the center of gravity and a consequent turning over of the mass into a new position, and this overturning also frequently takes place when bergs, drifting with the current in a state of delicate equilibrium, touch the ocean bottom.

Field Ice.—Field ice is formed throughout the region from the Arctic Ocean to the shores of Newfoundland and yearly leaves the shore to find its way into the path of commerce. Starting with the Arctic field ice and coming to the southward, this ice is found growing lighter, both in thickness and in quantity, until it disappears entirely. Ice made in the Arctic is heavier and has lived through a number of seasons. After the short summer in high latitudes ice begins to form on all open water, increasing several feet in thickness each season. Much of this remains north during the following summer, and, though it melts to some extent, it never entirely disappears, so that each succeeding winter adds to its thickness.

This continues from year to year until it reaches 12 or 15 feet in thickness, often more. If it remained perfectly quiet it would be of uniform thickness, increasing with the latitude, but it is in a state of almost continual motion, often a very violent one, which causes it to raft and pile until it becomes full of hummocks and other irregularities. Immense fields are detached from the shore and from other fields, and under the influence of winds, currents, and tides are set in motion and kept continually drifting from place to place; after a snow, thaw, or piling the whole becomes cemented together into solid pieces, when under the influence of a low temperature. The space of open water between the fields becomes frozen, joining smaller fields, and making a solid pack which will remain so until the elements again break it to pieces. Along the shores from headland to headland the bays and inlets often remain solid for years, almost invariably through the Arctic winter, but in Baffin Bay and Davis Strait open water can be found at intervals all the year round.

Ice becomes rafted in a variety of ways. If two fields are adrift the one to windward will drift down on the one to leeward; the one which is rougher on its surface gives the wind a better hold and drifts the faster; fields may be impelled towards each other by winds from contrary directions. Ice that is secure to the shore is rafted on its seaward edge from contact with that which is adrift. Fields in drifting often have a turning motion, which is caused by contrary currents, or one variable in strength at different places, or by the friction of a field coming in contact with another field afloat or one attached to the shore. This rotary motion is especially dangerous when a vessel finds itself between two fields. A heavy gale will break up the strongest fields at times and cause them to raft and form hummocks.

Small fragments of bergs find themselves mingled with Arctic fields and become frozen fast. These, when liberated to the southward, are called **growlers,** and form low, dark, indigo colored masses, which are just awash and rounded on top like a whale's back. They are very dangerous when in ice fields which have become loose enough to permit the passage of vessels through them, and should always be looked for; they can be seen apparently rising and sinking as the sea breaks over them.

During the spring and summer months the bergs, aided by a rise of temperature, so cut up and weaken the ice fields that much ice is loosened and begins drifting out of the Arctic basin. This is joined by that brought from the waters of Spitzbergen by the East Greenland Current, near the 63° parallel, whence it flows down the eastern coast of North America, reaching Cape Chidley about October or November. By this time the remaining ice in the Arctic is being cemented into solid fields, while the ice cap is being daily extended to the southward. As fast as fields are detached the open water freezes, and these masses are forced to the southward and cannot rejoin the solid pack. With a westerly wind ice formed in Hudson Strait and adjacent waters is swept out and joins the Arctic ice, differing from it only in being a little lighter.

Ice begins to form at Cape Chidley about the middle of October, at Belle Isle about November 1, and by the middle of November or 1st of December, the whole coast is solidly frozen. The dates given are approximate and vary from year to year, with many marked exceptions.

The string of ice along the coast of Labrador extends from headland to headland, including the outlying islands, and starting from the heads of the bays works its way out to seaward, forming by the middle of December an impassible barrier to the shore which will probably not be permanently broken until the latter part of

April. This ice varies in thickness from 12 feet at the northern extreme to 3 or 4 feet at the southern. During the entire winter the Arctic drift is finding its way down the coast, and is being continually reinforced by fields broken from the Labrador ice. These continue to the southward in the Labrador Current on an average of about 10 miles a day, reaching Belle Isle between the middle of January and the middle of February.

The best example on record of a continued drift from the Arctic is that of Captain Tyson. On October 14, 1871, he and a party of 19 others were separated from the United States surveying ship *Polaris*, in latitude 77° or 78° N., just south of Littleton Island, and, being unable to regain the ship, remained on the floe and accomplished one of the most wonderful journeys. After a drift of over 1,500 miles fraught with danger from beginning to end, they were picked up about 6 months later, April 30, 1872, by the *Tigress*, a sealing steamer from Newfoundland, near the Strait of Belle Isle, in latitude 53°35′ N., and carried safely into port.

Much delay in the southward movement of the drift will be caused by winds from the southward of west, as field ice is affected more by wind than current. The prevailing wind and weather will influence the drift very greatly. Strong northerly or northwest winds will increase its speed, but contrary winds will hold it back. The string of shore ice keeps the northern ice off the coast and in the current. At times westerly winds will also send the Labrador ice off the coast and leave it entirely clear, but this does not happen often. Still the outer Labrador ice is constantly being added to the Arctic flow. Frequently the bays remain frozen over until June; again, they are cleared some years in April, making a large variation. During the drift the wind from northwest to southwest will clear the ice off the coast and leave a line of open water, but the ice will be set on the coast by a northeast wind and be rafted and piled. The appearance of the ice when it reaches Belle Isle and to the southward would be a fair indication of the weather it had encountered on its way down. The rougher the ice the more severe the weather. This floating ice string extends approximately 200 miles offshore in the latitude of Cape Harrison, and spreads more during its drift, though narrower farther north. One small stream finds its way through the Strait of Belle Isle, while the greater part continues toward the northern limit of the Gulf Stream. By the middle of January the shores of Newfoundland and Gulf of St. Lawrence are full of ice, which has been frozen there and are opened or closed by a favorable or adverse wind. Navigation in the River St. Lawrence is closed about the middle of November and does not open until about May. A wind from northwest to southwest will clear the eastern coast of Newfoundland, while the Gulf of St. Lawrence may remain full of ice until the 1st of May. Even after this date much ice is found in the Gulf until July, and by August or earlier the field ice is replaced in the Strait of Belle Isle by bergs.

In the bight from Cape Bauld to Fogo Island a string of ice is often found joining these points, hemming in the shore for weeks at a time.

With each northwest or westerly wind the ice is cleared off the Newfoundland coast, except from some of the deeper bays, and carried out to sea, and frequently before the Arctic and Labrador ice has passed Belle Isle the Newfoundland ice has found its way as far south as latitude 45°. In the same way the Labrador ice sometimes precedes the Arctic ice, while all may arrive at nearly the same time. Ice fields often lose their identity, as coming from any one particular place, by the constant intermingling on its southern journey with ice made in a lower latitude.

With easterly winds the field ice and icebergs may block the harbors on the east coast of Newfoundland until June or even July, but these harbors are usually open in May.

Ice leaving the gulf and river St. Lawrence flows southward through Cabot Strait. This strait is never frozen over completely, but vessels not specially built to encounter ice cannot navigate it safely between the beginning of January and the last of April on account of the heavy drift ice which blocks the passage. Nearly every spring, from about the middle of April to the middle of May, a great rush of ice out of the Gulf of St. Lawrence causes a block between St. Paul Island and Cape Ray. This block, which sometimes lasts for 3 or 4 weeks, and completely prevents the passage of ships, is known as the *bridge*. It is recorded that 300 vessels have at one time been detained by this obstacle.

The ice usually passes out of Cabot Strait in the direction of Banquereau Bank, with its eastern edge extending halfway between Scatari and St. Pierre Islands. Its path broadens after it is through the strait and is principally governed by the winds, but under the influence of the current alone, it drifts southwestward, and in latitude 45° may be from 10 to 75 miles in width. Much of this ice is very heavy and prevents the passage through it of all vessels that are not specially built to encounter ice.

Ice fields assume a variety of shapes, depending upon the influence of winds and currents, and upon their shape on being set adrift. Those loosened in the Arctic meet with so many vicissitudes that they have entirely lost their original form when a low latitude is reached, while those from Newfoundland may remain approximately intact. Their extent is governed by the same rules and varies from a few scattered pieces to several hundred miles in length.

From off Belle Isle the field ice finds its way south toward the Gulf Stream where no definite shape can be given it. In appearance, if heavy ice, it will be white covered with snow, and visible at a long distance; even in foggy weather it can often be seen for some distance. It is full of hummocks and its surface is very uneven; blocks have been piled upon each other, others stood on end, and the whole mass will form an impenetrable field, through which vessels cannot force their way.

If the ice is lighter the pans will be smoother and more even, the angles ground down by friction and turned up at the edges like so many large pond lilies. If compact, no water is seen; if loose, wide leads may extend through the whole, or a little water be seen surrounding each cake.

The appearance must decide whether a vessel is warranted in trying to force her way through. In a smooth sea, where doubt exists, should a vessel go dead slow into the mass, there will be but little danger in attempting it, and if too heavy she can haul out. Often the weather edge is the heaviest from being rafted, when to leeward it may be scattering. An ice field will often form a good lee for riding out a gale of wind, as it will break the force of the sea. But care is necessary not to lie too close, for the pans are often given such a force that they will stave in the bows of the strongest vessel.

A high temperature will soften field ice and make it very rotten, so that the slightest motion will cause it to fall to pieces. On reaching the waters of the Gulf Stream or a warmer atmospheric temperature it begins to melt, gets soft and spongy, and left in a calm will disappear slowly. But, fortunately, there is seldom a time when there is not a swell on the sea, and this soon breaks the pans into small pieces, thus bringing a greater surface in contact with the melting agency. A heavy gale will in a few hours sometimes cause the destruction of a large field by fracture, friction, and continued motion, just as a calm, cold night may unite it in a solid mass. Bergs plow their way through fields, break them up, and scatter the pieces, as in the Arctic. Snow preserves them and often gives the pans the appearance of standing well out of water, and is misleading in this particular. By melting and afterwards freezing it adds to the thickness of the ice.

Ice disappearance.—The advancing ice will have reached, in the month of April, the northern average limit of the Gulf Stream; and, having spread itself along this line both east and west of the fiftieth meridian, it enters the final stage of disintegration and rapid disappearance.

After reaching this limit of southward movement, many bergs, on account of their deep immersion, find their way to the westward to a limited extent, even within the current of the Gulf Stream.

The locality in which ice of all kinds is most apt to be found during the months of April, May, and June lies between latitude 42° and 45° N. and longitude 47° and 52° W. Here the Gulf Stream and the Labrador Current meet, and the movement of the ice is influenced sometimes by the one and sometimes by the other of these currents.

Besides the three charts of monthly limits for April, May, and June, a fourth chart is presented showing the general limits within which icebergs and field ice have been encountered during the same months.

Signs of the proximity of ice.—The proximity of ice is indicated by the following-described signs:

Before field ice is seen from deck the ice blink will often indicate its presence. On a clear day over an ice field on the horizon the sky will be much paler or lighter in color and is easily distinguished from that overhead, so that a sharp lookout should be kept and changes in the color of the sky noted.

On clear nights, especially when the moon is up, the sky along the horizon in the direction of the ice is markedly lighter than the rest of the horizon. This effect can

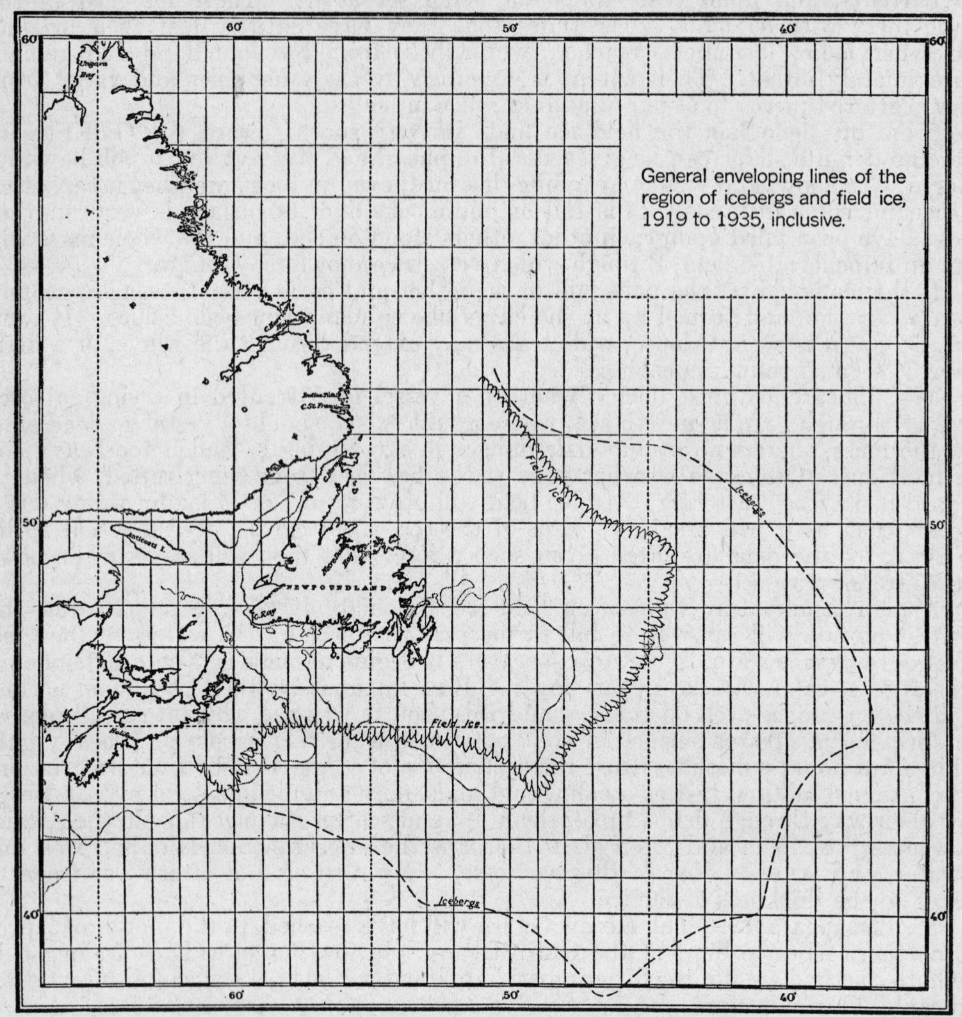

FIGURE 134.

be noted before the ice is sighted. On a clear, dark starlight night, an iceberg is rarely discernible at a greater distance than a quarter of a mile.

On a clear day icebergs can be seen at a long distance, owing to their brightness; during foggy weather, they may not be perceptible beyond the range of 100 yards, and, when the fog is dense, their first appearance is in the form of a luminous, white object if the sun is shining, but, if the sun is not shining, as a dark, sombre mass with a narrow streak of blackness at the waterline.

They can sometimes be detected by the echo from the steam whistle or the fog horn. In that case, by noting the time between the blast of a whistle and the reflected sound, the distance of the berg, in feet may be approximately found by multiplying by 550. The absence of echo is by no means proof that no bergs are near, for unless there is a fairly vertical wall, no return of the sound waves can be expected.

The presence of icebergs is often made known by the noise of their breaking up and falling to pieces. The cracking of the ice or the falling of pieces into the sea makes a noise like breakers or a distant discharge of guns, which may often be heard a short distance.

The absence of swell or wave motion in a fresh breeze is a sign that there is land or ice on the weather side.

The appearance of herds of seal or flocks of murre far from land is an indication of the proximity of ice.

The temperature studies made during the ice patrol show that no definite temperature effects of the air can be attributed to the presence of icebergs. Also that if there are temperature effects of sea water due to icebergs they are not distinguishable from the irregular variations observed.

In the ice zone ice is more likely to be found in cold water than in warm. So when encountering water below 40° in spring and below 50° in early summer, it is well to be on guard for ice. In foggy weather it is advisable to keep in water above 50° while crossing the ice zone, thereby avoiding both ice and fog.

A reliable sign of icebergs being near is the presence of calf ice. When such pieces occur in a curved line, as they may do, especially in calm weather, the parent berg is on the concave side of the curve.

No ship captain can afford to trust any of the above-named signs to the exclusion of a good lookout.

A remarkable optical phenomenon was observed one day by the ice patrol of 1914 when an iceberg which was ordinarly below the horizon was seen raised above it, at one time inverted and at another time erect. This phenomenon was observed near the Gulf Stream.

Information regarding ice conditions.—The Hydrographic Office and its branch offices receive and disseminate daily by radio the latest information regarding ice and other obstructions to navigation, being furnished with the reports of passing vessels and the ice patrol ships of the United States Coast Guard, as long as such are in service. They also distribute the publications of the Hydrographic Office dealing with this topic, namely, the Daily Memorandum, Hydrographic Bulletin (weekly), and the Pilot Chart of the North Atlantic Ocean (monthly).

APPENDIX I

EXTRACTS FROM THE AMERICAN NAUTICAL ALMANAC FOR THE YEAR 1937, WHICH HAVE REFERENCE TO THE EXAMPLES FOR THAT YEAR GIVEN IN THIS WORK

SUN, 1937

G. C. T.	Equation of time	Sun's Declination	Sun's G. H A.	Equation of time	Sun's Declination	Sun's G. H. A.
	April, Saturday 3			June, Sunday 13		
	m s	° ′	° ′	m s	° ′	° ′
0	−3 33.7	+5 4.0	179 6.6	+0 17.7	+23 10.7	180 4.4
2	3 32.2	5 5.9	209 7.0	0 16.7	23 11.0	210 4.2
4	3 30.7	5 7.8	239 7.3	0 15.6	23 11.3	240 3.9
6	3 29.2	5 9.8	269 7.7	0 14.6	23 11.6	270 3.7
8	3 27.7	5 11.7	299 8.1	0 13.6	23 11.9	300 3.4
10	3 26.2	5 13.6	329 8.4	0 12.5	23 12.1	330 3.1
12	3 24.7	5 15.5	359 8.8	0 11.5	23 12.4	0 2.9
14	3 23.3	5 17.4	29 9.2	0 10.4	23 12.7	30 2.6
16	3 21.8	5 19.3	59 9.6	0 9.4	23 13.0	60 2.4
18	3 20.3	5 21.2	89 9.9	0 8.4	23 13.3	90 2.1
20	3 18.8	5 23.2	119 10.3	0 7.3	23 13.5	120 1.8
22	3 17.3	5 25.1	149 10.7	0 6.3	23 13.8	150 1.6
H. D.	0.7	1.0	... .. .	0.5	0.1	... .. .
	Wednesday 14			Monday 21		
0	−0 29.9	+9 10.7	179 52.5	−1 24.7	+23 26.6	179 38.8
2	0 28.6	9 12.5	209 52.8	1 25.8	23 26.7	209 38.6
4	0 27.3	9 14.3	239 53.2	1 26.9	23 26.7	239 38.3
6	0 26.1	9 16.1	269 53.5	1 27.9	23 26.7	269 38.0
8	0 24.8	9 17.9	299 53.8	1 29.0	23 26.7	299 37.7
10	0 23.6	9 19.7	329 54.1	1 30.1	23 26.8	329 37.5
12	0 22.3	9 21.5	359 54.4	1 31.2	23 26.8	359 37.2
14	0 21.1	9 23.3	29 54.7	1 32.3	23 26.8	29 36.9
16	0 19.8	9 25.1	59 55.0	1 33.3	23 26.8	59 36.7
18	0 18.5	9 26.9	89 55.4	1 34.4	23 26.8	89 36.4
20	0 17.3	9 28.7	119 55.7	1 35.5	23 26.8	119 36.1
22	0 16.1	9 30.5	149 56.0	1 36.6	23 26.8	149 35.8
H. D.	0.6	0.9	... .. .	0.5	0.0	... .. .
	Thursday 15			July, Monday 12		
0	−0 14.8	+9 32.3	179 56.3	−5 21.2	+22 4.1	178 39.7
2	0 13.6	9 34.1	209 56.6	5 21.9	22 3.4	208 39.5
4	0 12.3	9 35.9	239 56.9	5 22.5	22 2.7	238 39.4
6	0 11.1	9 37.7	269 57.2	5 23.2	22 2.0	268 39.2
8	0 9.9	9 39.5	299 57.5	5 23.8	22 1.4	298 39.0
10	0 8.6	9 41.3	329 57.8	5 24.5	22 0.7	328 38.9
12	0 7.4	9 43.1	359 58.2	5 25.1	22 0.0	358 38.7
14	0 6.2	9 44.9	29 58.5	5 25.8	21 59.3	28 38.5
16	0 4.9	9 46.7	59 58.8	5 26.4	21 58.6	58 38.4
18	0 3.7	9 48.4	89 59.1	5 27.1	21 57.9	88 38.2
20	0 2.5	9 50.2	119 59.4	5 27.7	21 57.2	118 38.1
22	0 1.3	9 52.0	149 59.7	−5 28.3	+21 56.5	148 37.9
H. D.	0.6	0.9	... .. .	0.3	0.3	... .. .
	May, Tuesday 18					
0	+3 43.2	+19 24.6	180 55.8			
2	3 43.0	19 25.7	210 55.8			
4	3 42.8	19 26.8	240 55.7			
6	3 42.7	19 27.9	270 55.7			
8	3 42.5	19 29.0	300 55.6			
10	3 42.4	19 30.1	330 55.6			
12	3 42.2	19 31.2	0 55.5			
14	3 42.0	19 32.3	30 55.5			
16	3 41.8	19 33.4	60 55.5			
18	3 41.7	19 34.5	90 55.4			
20	3 41.5	19 35.6	120 55.4			
22	3 41.3	19 36.7	150 55.3			
H. D.	0.1	0.6	... .. .			

SEMIDIAMETER

Apr. 1	16.03
11	15.99
21	15.94
May 1	15.90
11	15.86

Corr. to G. H. A.

Min. or Sec.	Corr. for Minutes	Corr. for 1 Hour +Minutes	Corr. for Sec's.
	° ′	° ′	′
0	0 0.0	15 0.0	0.0
1	0 15.0	15 15.0	0.3
2	0 30.0	15 30.0	0.5
3	0 45.0	15 45.0	0.8
4	1 0.0	16 0.0	1.0
5	1 15.0	16 15.0	1.3
6	1 30.0	16 30.0	1.5
7	1 45.0	16 45.0	1.8
8	2 0.0	17 0.0	2.0
9	2 15.0	17 15.0	2.3
10	2 30.0	17 30.0	2.5
11	2 45.0	17 45.0	2.8
12	3 0.0	18 0.0	3.0
13	3 15.0	18 15.0	3.3
14	3 30.0	18 30.0	3.5
15	3 45.0	18 45.0	3.8
16	4 0.0	19 0.0	4.0
17	4 15.0	19 15.0	4.3
18	4 30.0	19 30.0	4.5
19	4 45.0	19 45.0	4.8
20	5 0.0	20 0.0	5.0
21	5 15.0	20 15.0	5.3
22	5 30.0	20 30.0	5.5
23	5 45.0	20 45.0	5.8
24	6 0.0	21 0.0	6.0
25	6 15.0	21 15.0	6.3
26	6 30.0	21 30.0	6.5
27	6 45.0	21 45.0	6.8
28	7 0.0	22 0.0	7.0
29	7 15.0	22 15.0	7.3
30	7 30.0	22 30.0	7.5
31	7 45.0	22 45.0	7.8
32	8 0.0	23 0.0	8.0
33	8 15.0	23 15.0	8.3
34	8 30.0	23 30.0	8.5
35	8 45.0	23 45.0	8.8
36	9 0.0	24 0.0	9.0
37	9 15.0	24 15.0	9.3
38	9 30.0	24 30.0	9.5
39	9 45.0	24 45.0	9.8
40	10 0.0	25 0.0	10.0
41	10 15.0	25 15.0	10.3
42	10 30.0	25 30.0	10.5
43	10 45.0	25 45.0	10.8
44	11 0.0	26 0.0	11.0
45	11 15.0	26 15.0	11.3
46	11 30.0	26 30.0	11.5
47	11 45.0	26 45.0	11.8
48	12 0.0	27 0.0	12.0
49	12 15.0	27 15.0	12.3
50	12 30.0	27 30.0	12.5
51	12 45.0	27 45.0	12.8
52	13 0.0	28 0.0	13.0
53	13 15.0	28 15.0	13.3
54	13 30.0	28 30.0	13.5
55	13 45.0	28 45.0	13.8
56	14 0.0	29 0.0	14.0
57	14 15.0	29 15.0	14.3
58	14 30.0	29 30.0	14.5
59	14 45.0	29 45.0	14.8
60	15 0.0	30 0.0	15.0

NOTE.—The Equation of Time is to be applied to the G. C. T. in accordance with the sign as given

G. C. T.	Equation of Time	Sun's Declination	Sun's G. H. A.	Equation of Time	Sun's Declination	Sun's G. H. A.
	Aug. Wednesday 25			**Aug. Sunday 29**		
h	m s	° ′	° ′	m s	° ′	° ′
0	−2 13.3	+10 59.5	179 26.7	−1 5.4	+9 35.8	179 43.6
2	2 11.9	10 57.8	209 27.0	1 4.0	9 34.0	209 44.0
4	2 10.6	10 56.1	239 27.4	1 2.5	9 32.3	239 44.4
6	2 9.2	10 54.4	269 27.7	1 1.0	9 30.5	269 44.8
8	2 7.8	10 52.6	299 28.1	0 59.5	9 28.7	299 45.1
10	2 6.5	10 50.9	329 28.4	0 58.1	9 27.0	329 45.5
12	2 5.1	10 49.2	359 28.7	0 56.6	9 25.2	359 45.9
14	2 3.7	10 47.5	29 29.1	0 55.1	9 23.4	29 46.2
16	2 2.4	10 45.8	59 29.4	0 53.6	9 21.6	59 46.6
18	2 1.0	10 44.0	89 29.7	0 52.1	9 19.8	89 47.0
20	1 59.6	10 42.3	119 30.1	0 50.6	9 18.1	119 47.4
22	1 58.3	10 40.6	149 30.4	0 49.1	9 16.3	149 47.7
H. D.	0.7	0.9	... ..	0.7	0.9	... ..
	Thursday 26			**Monday 30**		
0	−1 56.9	+10 38.8	179 30.8	−0 47.6	+9 14.5	179 48.1
2	1 55.5	10 37.1	209 31.1	0 46.1	9 12.7	209 48.5
4	1 54.1	10 35.4	239 31.5	0 44.6	9 10.9	239 48.9
6	1 52.7	10 33.6	269 31.8	0 43.1	9 9.1	269 49.2
8	1 51.3	10 31.9	299 32.2	0 41.6	9 7.4	299 49.6
10	1 49.9	10 30.2	329 32.5	0 40.1	9 5.6	329 50.0
12	1 48.5	10 28.4	359 32.9	0 38.6	9 3.8	359 50.4
14	1 47.1	10 26.7	29 33.2	0 37.1	9 2.0	29 50.7
16	1 45.7	10 25.0	59 33.6	0 35.5	9 0.2	59 51.1
18	1 44.3	10 23.2	89 33.9	0 34.0	8 58.4	89 51.5
20	1 42.9	10 21.5	119 34.3	0 32.5	8 56.6	119 51.9
22	1 41.5	10 19.7	149 34.6	0 31.0	8 54.8	149 52.3
H. D.	0.7	0.9	... ..	0.8	0.9	... ..
	Saturday 28			**Tuesday 31**		
0	−1 23.0	+9 57.0	179 39.3	−0 29.4	+8 53.0	179 52.6
2	1 21.5	9 55.2	209 39.6	0 27.9	8 51.2	209 53.0
4	1 20.1	9 53.5	239 40.0	0 26.4	8 49.4	239 53.4
6	1 18.6	9 51.7	269 40.3	0 24.9	8 47.6	269 53.8
8	1 17.2	9 50.0	299 40.7	0 23.3	8 45.8	299 54.2
10	1 15.7	9 48.2	329 41.1	0 21.8	8 44.0	329 54.6
12	1 14.2	9 46.4	359 41.4	0 20.3	8 42.2	359 54.9
14	1 12.8	9 44.7	29 41.8	0 18.7	8 40.4	29 55.3
16	1 11.3	9 42.9	59 42.2	0 17.2	8 38.6	59 55.7
18	1 9.9	9 41.1	89 42.5	0 15.6	8 36.8	89 56.1
20	1 8.4	9 39.4	119 42.9	0 14.1	8 35.0	119 56.5
22	−1 6.9	+9 37.6	149 43.3	−0 12.5	+8 33.2	149 56.9
H. D.	0.7	0.9	... ..	0.8	0.9	... ..
	October, Tuesday 5					
0	+11 19.9	−4 29.0	182 50.0			
2	11 21.4	4 31.0	212 50.4			
4	11 22.9	4 32.9	242 50.7			
6	11 24.4	4 34.8	272 51.1			
8	11 25.9	4 36.8	302 51.5			
10	11 27.4	4 38.7	332 51.8			
12	11 28.9	4 40.6	2 52.2			
14	11 30.4	4 42.5	32 52.6			
16	11 31.9	4 44.5	62 53.0			
18	11 33.4	4 46.4	92 53.3			
20	11 34.9	4 48.3	122 53.7			
22	11 36.3	4 50.2	152 54.1			
H. D.	0.7	1.0	... ..			

SEMIDIAMETER

		′
Aug.	1	15.79
	11	15.81
	21	15.84
	31	15.88

Corr. to G. H. A.

Min. or Sec.	Corr. for Minutes	Corr. for 1 Hour +Minutes	Corr. for Sec's.
	° ′	° ′	′
0	0 0.0	15 0.0	0.0
1	0 15.0	15 15.0	0.3
2	0 30.0	15 30.0	0.5
3	0 45.0	15 45.0	0.8
4	1 0.0	16 0.0	1.0
5	1 15.0	16 15.0	1.3
6	1 30.0	16 30.0	1.5
7	1 45.0	16 45.0	1.8
8	2 0.0	17 0.0	2.0
9	2 15.0	17 15.0	2.3
10	2 30.0	17 30.0	2.5
11	2 45.0	17 45.0	2.8
12	3 0.0	18 0.0	3.0
13	3 15.0	18 15.0	3.3
14	3 30.0	18 30.0	3.5
15	3 45.0	18 45.0	3.8
16	4 0.0	19 0.0	4.0
17	4 15.0	19 15.0	4.3
18	4 30.0	19 30.0	4.5
19	4 45.0	19 45.0	4.8
20	5 0.0	20 0.0	5.0
21	5 15.0	20 15.0	5.3
22	5 30.0	20 30.0	5.5
23	5 45.0	20 45.0	5.8
24	6 0.0	21 0.0	6.0
25	6 15.0	21 15.0	6.3
26	6 30.0	21 30.0	6.5
27	6 45.0	21 45.0	6.8
28	7 0.0	22 0.0	7.0
29	7 15.0	22 15.0	7.3
30	7 30.0	22 30.0	7.5
31	7 45.0	22 45.0	7.8
32	8 0.0	23 0.0	8.0
33	8 15.0	23 15.0	8.3
34	8 30.0	23 30.0	8.5
35	8 45.0	23 45.0	8.8
36	9 0.0	24 0.0	9.0
37	9 15.0	24 15.0	9.3
38	9 30.0	24 30.0	9.5
39	9 45.0	24 45.0	9.8
40	10 0.0	25 0.0	10.0
41	10 15.0	25 15.0	10.3
42	10 30.0	25 30.0	10.5
43	10 45.0	25 45.0	10.8
44	11 0.0	26 0.0	11.0
45	11 15.0	26 15.0	11.3
46	11 30.0	26 30.0	11.5
47	11 45.0	26 45.0	11.8
48	12 0.0	27 0.0	12.0
49	12 15.0	27 15.0	12.3
50	12 30.0	27 30.0	12.5
51	12 45.0	27 45.0	12.8
52	13 0.0	28 0.0	13.0
53	13 15.0	28 15.0	13.3
54	13 30.0	28 30.0	13.5
55	13 45.0	28 45.0	13.8
56	14 0.0	29 0.0	14.0
57	14 15.0	29 15.0	14.3
58	14 30.0	29 30.0	14.5
59	14 45.0	29 45.0	14.8
60	15 0.0	30 0.0	15.0

Note.—The Equation of Time is to be applied to the G. C. T. in accordance with the sign as given

541524°—43——21

SUN, 1937

Day of Month	Sidereal Time of 0h Civil Time at Greenwich (R. A. M. S. +12h)					
	January	February	March	April	June	October
	h m s	h m s	h m s	h m s	h m s	h m s
1	6 40 54.4	8 43 7.6	10 33 31.1	12 35 44.3	16 36 14.1	0 37 13.9
2	6 44 50.9	8 47 4.2	10 37 27.7	12 39 40.8	16 40 10.7	0 41 10.4
3	6 48 47.5	8 51 0.7	10 41 24.2	12 43 37.4	16 44 7.2	0 45 7.0
4	6 42 44.0	8 54 57.3	10 45 20.8	12 47 33.9	16 48 3.8	0 49 3.5
5	6 56 40.6	8 58 53.8	10 49 17.3	12 51 30.5	16 52 0.3	0 53 0.1
6	7 0 37.1	9 2 50.4	10 53 13.9	12 55 27.0	16 55 56.9	0 56 56.6
7	7 4 33.7	9 6 46.9	10 57 10.5	12 59 23.6	16 59 53.4	1 0 53.2
8	7 8 30.2	9 10 43.5	11 1 7.0	13 3 20.1	17 3 50.0	1 4 49.7
9	7 12 26.8	9 14 40.1	11 5 3.6	13 7 16.7	17 7 46.6	1 8 46.3
10	7 16 23.4	9 18 36.6	11 9 0.1	13 11 13.2	17 11 43.1	1 12 42.8
11	7 20 19.9	9 22 33.2	11 12 56.7	13 15 9.8	17 15 39.7	1 16 39.4
12	7 24 16.5	9 26 29.7	11 16 53.2	13 19 6.3	17 19 6.3	1 20 35.9
13	7 28 13.0	9 30 26.3	11 20 49.8	13 23 2.9	17 23 32.8	1 24 32.5
14	7 32 9.6	9 34 22.8	11 24 46.3	13 26 59.5	17 27 29.4	1 28 29.0
15	7 36 6.2	9 38 19.4	11 28 42.9	13 30 56.0	17 31 25.9	1 32 25.6
22				13 58 31.9		
25				14 10 21.5		

Correction for Longitude from Greenwich

Longitude	0h	1h	2h	3h	4h	5h	6h	7h	8h	9h	10h	11h
m	m s	m s	m s	m s	m s	m s	m s	m s	m s	m s	m s	m s
0	0 0.0	0 9.9	0 19.7	0 29.6	0 39.4	0 49.3	0 59.1	1 9.0	1 18.9	1 28.7	1 38.6	1 48.4
5	0 0.8	0 10.7	0 20.5	0 30.4	0 40.2	0 50.1	1 0.0	1 9.8	1 19.7	1 29.5	1 39.4	1 49.2
10	0 1.6	0 11.5	0 21.4	0 31.2	0 41.1	0 50.9	1 0.8	1 10.6	1 20.5	1 30.4	1 40.2	1 50.1
15	0 2.5	0 12.3	0 22.2	0 32.0	0 41.9	0 51.7	1 1.6	1 11.5	1 21.3	1 31.2	1 41.0	1 50.9
20	0 3.3	0 13.1	0 23.0	0 32.9	0 42.7	0 52.6	1 2.4	1 12.3	1 22.1	1 32.0	1 41.8	1 51.7
25	0 4.1	0 14.0	0 23.8	0 33.7	0 43.5	0 53.4	1 3.2	1 13.1	1 23.0	1 32.8	1 42.7	1 52.5
30	0 4.9	0 14.8	0 24.6	0 34.5	0 44.4	0 54.2	1 4.1	1 13.9	1 23.8	1 33.6	1 43.5	1 53.3
35	0 5.8	0 15.6	0 25.5	0 35.3	0 45.2	0 55.0	1 4.9	1 14.7	1 24.6	1 34.5	1 44.3	1 54.2
40	0 6.6	0 16.4	0 26.3	0 36.1	0 46.0	0 55.9	1 5.7	1 15.6	1 25.4	1 35.3	1 45.1	1 55.0
45	0 7.4	0 17.2	0 27.1	0 37.0	0 46.8	0 56.7	1 6.5	1 16.4	1 26.2	1 36.1	1 46.0	1 55.8
50	0 8.2	0 18.1	0 27.9	0 37.8	0 47.6	0 57.5	1 7.4	1 17.2	1 27.1	1 36.9	1 46.8	1 56.6
55	0 9.0	0 18.9	0 28.7	0 38.6	0 48.5	0 58.3	1 8.2	1 18.0	1 27.9	1 37.7	1 47.6	1 57.5
60	0 9.9	0 19.7	0 29.6	0 39.4	0 49.3	0 59.1	1 9.0	1 18.9	1 28.7	1 38.6	1 48.4	1 58.3

P. P.	
m	s
1	0.2
2	0.3
3	0.5
4	0.7
5	0.8

NOTE.—The correction is to be added to Sidereal Time of 0h Civil Time at Greenwich to obtain Sidereal Time of 0h Civil Time at any longitude west of Greenwich; to be subtracted if the longitude is east of Greenwich.

VENUS, 1937

GREENWICH CIVIL TIME

Date	Right Ascension 0h				Declination 0h			Greenwich H. A. 0h		Var. per Min.	Transit Merid. of Greenwich	
OCTOBER												
	h	m	s	s	°	′	′	°	′	′	h	m
1	10	36	46	278	+9	53.4	25.3	210	7.1	14.9927	10	0
2	10	41	24	278	9	28.1	25.6	209	56.6	14.9928	10	0
3	10	46	2	277	9	2.5	25.8	209	46.3	14.9929	10	1
4	10	50	39	277	8	36.7	26.1	209	36.2	14.9930	10	2
5	10	55	16	276	8	10.6	26.4	209	26.1	14.9931	10	2
6	10	59	52	276	+7	44.2	26.6	209	16.1	14.9932	10	3
7	11	4	28	276	7	17.6	26.8	209	6.3	14.9932	10	4

JUPITER, 1937

GREENWICH CIVIL TIME

Date	Right Ascension 0h				Declination 0h			Greenwich H. A. 0h		Var. per Min.	Transit Merid. of Greenwich	
JANUARY												
	h	m	s	s	°	′	′	°	′	′	h	m
1	18	29	26	60	−23	12.2	0.6	182	52.1	15.0307	11	47
2	18	30	26	60	23	11.6	0.6	183	36.2	15.0307	11	44
3	18	31	26	60	23	11.0	0.7	184	20.3	15.0307	11	41
4	18	32	26	60	23	10.3	0.7	185	4.4	15.0307	11	38
5	18	33	26	60	23	9.6	0.7	185	48.6	15.0307	11	35
APRIL												
11	19	49	57	26	−21	9.1	1.0	261	18.2	15.0366	6	34
12	19	50	23	25	21	8.1	1.0	262	10.9	15.0367	6	30
13	19	50	48	24	21	7.1	0.9	263	3.8	15.0368	6	27
14	19	51	12	23	21	6.2	0.9	263	56.9	15.0369	6	23
15	19	51	35	23	21	5.3	0.9	264	50.2	15.0371	6	20
OCTOBER												
1	19	18	2	14	−22	41.6	0.4	79	48.1	15.0386	18	38
2	19	18	16	15	22	41.2	0.4	80	43.6	15.0385	18	34
3	19	18	31	16	22	40.8	0.5	81	39.0	15.0384	18	31
4	19	18	47	17	22	40.3	0.5	82	34.2	15.0382	18	27
5	19	19	4	17	22	39.8	0.5	83	29.1	15.0381	18	23
DECEMBER												
8	19	58	24	51	−21	9.5	2.4	136	44.0	15.0321	14	51
9	19	59	15	52	21	7.1	2.4	137	30.2	15.0320	14	48
10	20	0	7	53	21	4.7	2.4	138	16.3	15.0320	14	45
11	20	1	0	52	21	2.3	2.5	139	2.4	15.0320	14	42
12	20	1	52	53	20	59.8	2.5	139	48.4	15.0319	14	39

MOON, 1937

Greenwich Civil Time

APRIL 15

G. C. T.	Right Ascension	Declination	Greenwich H. A.
h	h m s	° ′	° ′
0	5 5 19	+22 45. 2	126 24. 4
1	5 7 57	22 45. 3	140 47. 3
2	5 10 34	22 45. 2	155 10. 3
3	5 13 12	22 45. 0	169 33. 4
4	5 15 49	22 44. 6	183 56. 5
5	5 18 27	22 44. 0	198 19. 7
6	5 21 4	22 43. 3	212 42. 8
7	5 23 41	22 42. 4	227 6. 1
8	5 26 17	22 41. 4	241 29. 4
9	5 28 54	22 40. 2	255 52. 7
10	5 31 30	22 38. 8	270 16. 1
11	5 34 6	22 37. 3	284 39. 6
12	5 36 42	22 35. 7	299 3. 1
13	5 39 18	22 33. 9	313 26. 6
14	5 41 53	22 31. 9	327 50. 2
15	5 44 28	22 29. 8	342 13. 9
16	5 47 3	22 27. 5	356 37. 7
17	5 49 38	22 25. 1	11 1. 5
18	5 52 12	22 22. 5	25 25. 3
19	5 54 46	22 19. 8	39 49. 3
20	5 57 20	22 16. 9	54 13. 3
21	5 59 54	22 13. 9	68 37. 4
22	6 2 27	22 10. 7	83 1. 5
23	6 5 0	+22 7. 4	97 25. 7

Multiples of Variation per Minute

m	R.A. s	Dec. ′	H.A. ′
1	3	0.0	14.4
2	5	−0.1	28.8
3	8	0.1	43.2
4	10	0.1	57.6
5	13	0.1	72.0
6	16	0.2	86.4
7	18	0.2	100.7
8	21	0.2	115.1
9	23	0.3	129.5
10	26	0.3	143.9
20	52	0.6	287.8
30	78	0.9	431.8
40	104	1.2	575.7
50	130	−1.5	719.6

JULY 18

G. C. T.	Right Ascension	Declination	Greenwich H. A.
h	h m s	° ′	° ′
0	15 22 13	−20 27. 2	64 49. 8
1	15 24 18	20 32. 2	79 21. 1
2	15 26 22	20 37. 1	93 52. 4
3	15 28 27	20 41. 9	108 23. 7
4	15 30 32	20 46. 6	122 54. 9
5	15 32 37	20 51. 2	137 26. 1
6	15 34 42	20 55. 8	151 57. 3
7	15 36 48	21 0. 2	166 28. 4
8	15 38 53	21 4. 5	180 59. 5
9	15 40 59	21 8. 8	195 30. 6
10	15 43 4	21 12. 9	210 1. 6
11	15 45 10	21 16. 9	224 32. 6
12	15 47 16	21 20. 9	239 3. 6
13	15 49 22	21 24. 7	253 34. 5
14	15 51 29	21 28. 5	268 5. 4
15	15 53 35	21 32. 1	282 36. 3
16	15 55 41	21 35. 7	297 7. 2
17	15 57 48	21 39. 2	311 38. 0
18	15 59 55	21 42. 5	326 8. 8
19	16 2 1	21 45. 8	340 39. 6
20	16 4 8	21 48. 9	355 10. 3
21	16 6 15	21 52. 0	9 41. 0
22	16 8 23	21 55. 0	24 11. 7
23	16 10 30	−21 57. 8	38 42. 3

Multiples of Variation per Minute

m	R.A. s	Dec. ′	H.A. ′
1	2	−0.1	14.5
2	4	0.1	29.0
3	6	0.2	43.5
4	8	0.3	58.1
5	10	0.3	72.6
6	13	0.4	87.1
7	15	0.5	101.6
8	17	0.5	116.1
9	19	0.6	130.6
10	21	0.6	145.2
20	42	1.3	290.3
30	63	2.0	435.5
40	84	2.6	580.6
50	105	−3.2	725.8

H. P. 54.2′

AUGUST 27

G. C. T.	Right Ascension	Declination	Greenwich H. A.
23	3 10 33	+19 37. 0	273 7. 1

m	R.A. s	Dec. ′	H.A. ′
1	2	+0.1	14.4
30	72	4.0	433.1

AUGUST 28

G. C. T.	Right Ascension	Declination	Greenwich H. A.
0	3 13 0	+19 43. 6	287 32. 6

H. P. 59.2′

TRANSIT AT GREENWICH

	h m	Var. per hour m
July 2	6 25	2. 2
17	19 32	2. 0

POLARIS, 1937

Local S. T.	6^h	
m	° ′	
0	−0 26. 2	
		25
10	0 23. 7	
		25
20	0 21. 2	
		26
30	−0 18. 6	
		26
40	0 16. 0	
		26
50	0 13. 4	
		27
60	−0 10. 7	

G. H. A. FOR 0^h G. C. T.

	° ′		° ′
Oct. 1	343 38. 1	Dec. 1	43 46. 2
2	344 37. 1	2	44 45. 5
3	345 36. 2	3	45 44. 8
4	346 35. 2	4	46 44. 1
5	347 34. 2	5	47 43. 4
June 11	233 44. 3		

POLARIS TABLE III

L. H. A.	Corr.
°	° ′
214	0 51. 4
258	0 13. 4
259	0 12. 3

TABLE IV

L. H. A. \ Lat.	40°
°	°
210	+0. 7
220	0. 9

VENUS, 1937

GREENWICH CIVIL TIME

Date	Right Ascension 0^h				Declination 0^h			Greenwich H. A. 0^h		Var. per Min.	Transit Merid. of Greenwich	
	h	m	s	s	°	′	′	°	′	′	h	m
JANUARY												
1	21	47	52	268	−15	7.3	25.7	133	15.5	14.9944	15	7
2	21	52	20	266	14	41.6	26.2	133	7.8	14.9947	15	8
3	21	56	46	264	14	15.4	26.4	133	0.4	14.9951	15	8
FEBRUARY												
14	0	39	4	197	+6	16.1	28.6	133	49.7	15.0067	15	4
15	0	42	21	195	6	44.7	28.3	133	59.6	15.0070	15	4
16	0	45	36	193	7	13.0	28.1	134	10.0	15.0074	15	3

APPARENT PLACES OF STARS, 1937

FOR 0^h GREENWICH CIVIL TIME

No.	Constellation Name	Right Ascension		Jan. 1	Feb. 1	Mar. 1	Apr. 1	May 1	June 1	July 1	Aug. 1	Sept. 1	Oct. 1	Nov. 1	Dec. 1	Dec. 32
		h	m	s	s	s	s	s	s	s	s	s	s	s	s	s
1	α Andr. (*Alpheratz*) . . .	0	5	8.4	8.0	7.8	7.9	8.5	9.3	10.4	11.3	12.0	12.3	12.3	12.0	11.6
2	β Cassiop. (*Caph*)	0	5	49.0	48.1	47.6	47.7	48.4	49.8	51.4	52.8	53.8	54.2	54.0	53.4	52.4
3	β Ceti (*Deneb Kaitos*) . .	0	40	26.7	26.3	26.1	26.1	26.4	27.1	28.1	29.0	29.7	30.1	30.2	29.9	29.6
4	δ Cassiop. (*Ruchbah*) . .	1	21	42.5	41.6	40.7	40.4	40.8	41.9	43.5	45.1	46.5	47.4	47.7	47.4	46.7
5	α Eridani (*Achernar*) . .	1	35	23.5	22.5	21.7	21.1	21.2	21.9	23.1	24.6	25.8	26.6	26.7	26.3	25.4
10	α Tauri (*Aldebaran*). . .	4	32	20.6	20.4	19.9	19.4	19.1	19.3	19.8	20.6	21.6	22.5	23.2	23.7	23.9
17	α Can. Maj. (*Sirius*) . .	6	42	24.7	24.7	24.4	23.8	23.3	23.0	23.1	23.6	24.3	25.1	26.0	26.8	27.3
25	α Leonis (*Regulus*) . . .	10	5	3.1	3.8	4.0	3.9	3.6	3.2	2.9	2.8	3.0	3.4	4.2	5.1	6.1
30	β Crucis	12	44	2.8	4.5	5.5	6.1	6.1	5.7	4.9	4.0	3.3	3.1	3.8	4.8	6.5
33	α Virginis (*Spica*)	13	21	. . .	. . .	. . .	. . .	. . .	. . .	. . .	. . .	. . .	. . .	. . .	. . .	. . .
35	α Bootis (*Arcturus*) . . .	14	12	47.5	48.5	49.4	50.0	50.3	50.3	50.0	49.6	49.2	48.8	48.8	49.2	50.1
38	α Cor. Bor. (*Alphecca*). .	15	32	0.9	1.9	2.8	3.6	4.1	4.3	4.2	3.8	3.3	2.7	2.5	2.7	3.3
54	α Pis. Aus. (*Fomalhaut*) .	22	54	10.8	10.6	10.6	11.0	11.7	12.7	13.7	14.6	15.1	15.1	14.8	14.4	13.9
55	α Pegasi (*Markab*). . . .	23	1	37.7	37.5	37.5	37.8	38.4	39.3	40.3	41.1	41.5	41.6	41.4	41.0	40.7

No.	Declination	Jan. 1	Feb. 1	Mar. 1	Apr. 1	May 1	June 1	July 1	Aug. 1	Sept. 1	Oct. 1	Nov. 1	Dec. 1	Dec. 32	Special Name	Mag.
	°	′	′	′	′	′	′	′	′	′	′	′	′	′		
1	+28	44.8	44.8	44.7	44.6	44.6	44.6	44.7	44.8	44.9	45.0	45.1	45.2	45.1	Alpheratz	2.2
2	+58	48.5	48.5	48.4	48.2	48.1	48.1	48.1	48.3	48.4	48.6	48.7	48.8	48.9	Caph	2.4
3	−18	19.9	20.0	19.9	19.9	19.8	19.6	19.5	19.5	19.4	19.5	19.5	19.6	19.6	Deneb Kaitos. . .	2.2
4	+59	54.9	54.9	54.8	54.7	54.5	54.5	54.5	54.6	54.7	54.8	55.0	55.1	55.2	Ruchbah.	2.8
5	−57	33.6	33.6	33.5	33.3	33.2	33.0	32.9	32.8	32.8	32.9	33.1	33.2	33.3	Achernar.	0.6
10	+16	23.1	23.1	23.1	23.1	23.0	23.1	23.1	23.1	23.2	23.2	23.2	23.2	23.2	Aldebaran	1.1
17	−16	37.8	37.9	38.0	38.0	38.0	37.9	37.8	37.7	37.7	37.6	37.7	37.8	37.9	Sirius.	−1.6
25	+12	16.4	16.3	16.3	16.3	16.3	16.3	16.4	16.4	16.4	16.3	16.2	16.1	16.1	Regulus	1.3
30	−59	20.5	20.6	20.8	20.9	21.1	21.2	21.2	21.2	21.1	21.0	20.8	20.8	20.8	. . . .	1.5
33	−10	. . .	. . .	. . .	. . .	. . .	. . .	. . .	. . .	. . .	. . .	. . .	. . .	. . .	Spica.	1.2
35	+19	30.4	30.3	30.2	30.3	30.3	30.4	30.5	30.5	30.5	30.5	30.4	30.2	30.1	Arcturus	0.2
38	+26	55.4	55.2	55.2	55.2	55.3	55.4	55.5	55.6	55.6	55.6	55.5	55.4	55.2	Alphecca.	2.3
54	−29	57.4	57.4	57.3	57.2	57.1	57.0	56.9	56.9	56.9	57.0	57.1	57.1	57.1	Fomalhaut. . . .	1.3
55	+14	52.1	52.1	52.0	52.0	52.0	52.1	52.2	52.3	52.4	52.5	52.5	52.5	52.5	Markab	2.6

STARS, JANUARY 1937

GREENWICH CIVIL TIME

Star	α Androm. *Alpheratz* Mag. 2.2	β Cassiop. *Caph* Mag. 2.4	β Ceti *Deneb Kait.* Mag. 2.2	δ Cassiop. *Ruchbah* Mag. 2.8	α Eridani *Achernar* Mag. 0.6	α Arietis *Hamal* Mag. 2.2	θ[1] Eridani *Acamar* Mag. 3.4	α Tauri *Aldebaran* Mag. 1.1	α Bootis *Arcturus* Mag. 0.2
R. A.	h m s	h m s	h m s	h m s	h m s	h m s	h m s	h m s	h m s
Jan. 1.0	0 5 8.4	0 5 49.0	0 40 26.7	1 21 42.5	1 35 23.5	2 3 38.7	2 55 54.1	4 32 20.6	14 12 47.5
Declination	° ′	° ′	° ′	° ′	° ′	° ′	° ′	° ′	° ′
Jan. 1.0	+28 44.8	+58 48.5	−18 19.9	+59 54.9	−57 33.6	+23 10.1	−40 33.5	+16 23.1	+19 30.4
Transit	h m	h m	h m	h m	h m	h m	h m	h m	h m
Jan. 1	17 21	17 22	17 57	18 38	18 51	19 20	20 12	21 48	7 31
Date	Greenwich Hour Angle for 0h Greenwich Civil Time								
	° ′	° ′	° ′	° ′	° ′	° ′	° ′	° ′	° ′
1	98 56.5	98 46.3	90 6.9	79 48.0	76 22.7	69 18.9	56 15.1	32 8.4	247 1.7
2	99 55.6	99 45.5	91 6.1	80 47.1	77 21.9	70 18.1	57 14.2	33 7.6	248 0.8
3	100 54.8	100 44.6	92 5.2	81 46.3	78 21.0	71 17.2	58 13.4	34 6.7	249 0.0
4	101 53.9	101 43.8	93 4.3	82 45.4	79 20.2	72 16.3	59 12.5	35 5.9	249 59.1
5	102 53.0	102 42.9	94 3.5	83 44.5	80 19.3	73 15.5	60 11.6	36 5.0	250 58.2
6	103 52.2	103 42.1	95 2.6	84 43.7	81 18.4	74 14.6	61 10.8	37 4.2	251 57.4
7	104 51.3	104 41.2	96 1.8	85 42.8	82 17.6	75 13.8	62 9.9	38 3.3	252 56.5
8	105 50.5	105 40.4	97 0.9	86 42.0	83 16.7	76 12.9	63 9.1	39 2.4	253 55.6
9	106 49.6	106 39.5	98 0.0	87 41.1	84 15.9	77 12.1	64 8.2	40 1.6	254 54.7
10	107 48.8	107 38.7	98 59.2	88 40.3	85 15.0	78 11.2	65 7.4	41 0.7	255 53.9
11	108 47.9	108 37.8	99 58.3	89 39.4	86 14.2	79 10.3	66 6.5	41 59.9	256 53.0
12	109 47.0	109 36.9	100 57.5	90 38.6	87 13.3	80 9.5	67 5.7	42 59.0	257 52.1
13	110 46.2	110 36.1	101 56.6	91 37.7	88 12.5	81 8.6	68 4.8	43 58.1	258 51.3
14	111 45.3	111 35.2	102 55.8	92 36.9	89 11.6	82 7.8	69 3.9	44 57.3	259 50.4
15	112 44.5	112 34.4	103 54.9	93 36.0	90 10.8	83 6.9	70 3.1	45 56.4	260 49.5

GREENWICH CIVIL TIME

JULY 1937

	β Crucis Mag. 1.5	α Eridani *Achernar* Mag. 0.6	α Arietis *Hamal* Mag. 2.2
	h m s	h m s	h m s
	12 44 4.9	1 35 23.1	2 3 39.3
	° ′	° ′	° ′
	−59 21.2	−57 32.9	+23 10.0
	h m	h m	h m
	18 7	7 0	7 28
Date			
	° ′	° ′	° ′
1	87 36.5		
2	88 35.6		
3		256 45.2	243 41.2

AUGUST 1937

Star	α Lyræ *Vega* Mag. 0.1	σ Sagittarii *Nunki* Mag. 2.1	α Aquilæ *Altair* Mag. 0.9
R. A.	h m s	h m s	h m s
Aug. 1.0	18 34 51.7	18 51 26.4	19 47 46.6
Declination	° ′	° ′	° ′
Aug. 1.0	+38 43.7	−26 22.5	+8 42.3
Transit	h m	h m	h m
Aug. 1	21 55	22 11	23 7
Date	Greenwich Hour Angle for 0h		
	° ′	° ′	° ′
26	55 6.7	50 57.9	36 52.9
27	56 5.8	51 57.1	37 52.0
28	57 5.0	52 56.2	38 51.1
29	58 4.1	53 55.4	39 50.3
30	59 3.2	54 54.5	40 49.4

NOVEMBER 1937

Star	α Cor. Bor. *Alphecca* Mag. 2.3	α Pis. Aus. *Fomalhaut* Mag. 1.3
R. A.	h m s	h m s
Nov. 1.0	15 32 2.5	22 54 14.8
Declination	° ′	° ′
Nov. 1.0	+26 55.5	−29 57.1
Transit	h m	h m
Nov. 1	12 50	20 11
Date		
	° ′	° ′
1	166 51.1	56 18.0
2	167 50.3	57 17.2
3	168 49.4	58 16.3

GREENWICH CIVIL TIME

AUGUST 1937

	β Ceti *Deneb Kait.* Mag. 2.2	δ Cassiop. *Ruchbah* Mag. 2.8	α Eridani *Achernar* Mag. 0.6
	h m s	h m s	h m s
	0 40 29.0	1 21 45.1	1 35 24.6
	° ′	° ′	° ′
	−18 19.5	+59 54.6	−57 32.8
	h m	h m	h m
	4 3	4 44	4 58
Date	G. H. A. for 0h		
26	323 42.1	313 22.9	309 58.1
27	324 41.2	314 22.1	310 57.2
28	325 40.4	315 21.2	311 56.3
		July 3	256 45.2

STARS 1937

	α Can. Mai *Sirius*
	° ′
Jan. 1	359 37.4
Mar. 15	71 34.7
May 1	117 54.4

CORRECTION TO BE ADDED TO TABULATED GREENWICH HOUR ANGLE OF STARS

Min.	Hours of Greenwich Civil Time								Sec.	Corr.
	10h	11h	12h	13h	14h	15h	22h	23h		
	° ′	° ′	° ′	° ′	° ′	° ′	° ′	° ′		′
0	150 24.6	165 27.1	180 29.6	195 32.0	210 34.5	225 37.0	330 54.2	345 56.7	0	0.0
1	150 39.7	165 42.1	180 44.6	195 47.1	210 49.5	225 52.0	331 9.3	346 11.7	1	0.3
2	150 54.7	165 57.2	180 59.7	196 2.1	211 4.6	226 7.0	331 24.3	346 26.8	2	0.5
3	151 9.8	166 12.2	181 14.7	196 17.2	211 19.6	226 22.1	331 39.3	346 41.8	3	0.8
4	151 24.8	166 27.3	181 29.7	196 32.2	211 34.7	226 37.1	331 54.4	346 56.8	4	1.0
5	151 39.8	166 42.3	181 44.8	196 47.2	211 49.7	226 52.2	332 9.4	347 11.9	5	1.3
6	151 54.9	166 57.3	181 59.8	197 2.3	212 4.7	227 7.2	332 24.5	347 26.9	6	1.5
7	152 9.9	167 12.4	182 14.9	197 17.3	212 19.8	227 22.2	332 39.5	347 42.0	7	1.8
8	152 25.0	167 27.4	182 29.9	197 32.4	212 34.8	227 37.3	332 54.5	347 57.0	8	2.0
9	152 40.0	167 42.5	182 44.9	197 47.4	212 49.9	227 52.3	333 9.6	348 12.0	9	2.3
10	152 55.1	167 57.5	183 0.0	198 2.4	213 4.9	228 7.4	333 24.6	348 27.1	10	2.5
11	153 10.1	168 12.6	183 15.0	198 17.5	213 19.9	228 22.4	333 39.7	348 42.1	11	2.8
12	153 25.1	168 27.6	183 30.1	198 32.5	213 35.0	228 37.5	333 54.7	348 57.2	12	3.0
13	153 40.2	168 42.6	183 45.1	198 47.6	213 50.0	228 52.5	334 9.7	349 12.2	13	3.3
14	153 55.2	168 57.7	184 0.1	199 2.6	214 5.1	229 7.5	334 24.8	349 27.2	14	3.5
15	154 10.3	169 12.7	184 15.2	199 17.6	214 20.1	229 22.6	334 39.8	349 42.3	15	3.8
16	154 25.3	169 27.8	184 30.2	199 32.7	214 35.2	229 37.0	334 54.9	349 57.3	16	4.0
17	154 40.3	169 42.8	184 45.3	199 47.7	214 50.2	229 52.7	335 9.9	350 12.4	17	4.3
18	154 55.4	169 57.8	185 0.3	200 2.8	215 5.2	230 7.7	335 24.9	350 27.4	18	4.5
19	155 10.4	170 12.9	185 15.3	200 17.8	215 20.3	230 22.7	335 40.0	350 42.5	19	4.8
20	155 25.5	170 27.9	185 30.4	200 32.9	215 35.3	230 37.8	335 55.0	350 57.5	20	5.0
21	155 40.5	170 43.0	185 45.4	200 47.9	215 50.4	230 52.8	336 10.1	351 12.5	21	5.3
22	155 55.5	170 58.0	186 0.5	201 2.9	216 5.4	231 7.9	336 25.1	351 27.6	22	5.5
23	156 10.6	171 13.0	186 15.5	201 18.0	216 20.4	231 22.9	336 40.2	351 42.6	23	5.8
24	156 25.6	171 28.1	186 30.6	201 33.0	216 35.5	231 37.9	336 55.2	351 57.7	24	6.0
25	156 40.7	171 43.1	186 45.6	201 48.1	216 50.5	231 53.0	337 10.2	352 12.7	25	6.3
26	156 55.7	171 58.2	187 0.6	202 3.1	217 5.6	232 8.0	337 25.3	352 27.7	26	6.5
27	157 10.7	172 13.2	187 15.7	202 18.1	217 20.6	232 23.1	337 40.3	352 42.8	27	6.8
28	157 25.8	172 28.2	187 30.7	202 33.2	217 35.6	232 38.1	337 55.4	352 57.8	28	7.0
29	157 40.8	172 43.3	187 45.8	202 48.2	217 50.7	232 53.2	338 10.4	353 12.9	29	7.3
30	157 55.9	172 58.3	188 0.8	203 3.3	218 5.7	233 8.2	338 25.4	353 27.9	30	7.5
31	158 10.9	173 13.4	188 15.8	203 18.3	218 20.8	233 23.2	338 40.5	353 42.9	31	7.8
32	158 26.0	173 28.4	188 30.9	203 33.3	218 35.8	233 38.3	338 55.5	353 58.0	32	8.0
33	158 41.0	173 43.5	188 45.9	203 48.4	218 50.8	233 53.3	339 10.6	354 13.0	33	8.3
34	158 56.0	173 58.5	189 1.0	204 3.4	219 5.9	234 8.4	339 25.6	354 28.1	34	8.5
35	159 11.1	174 13.5	189 16.0	204 18.5	219 20.9	234 23.4	339 40.6	354 43.1	35	8.8
36	159 26.1	174 28.6	189 31.0	204 33.5	219 36.0	234 38.4	339 55.7	354 58.2	36	9.0
37	159 41.2	174 43.6	189 46.1	204 48.6	219 51.0	234 53.5	340 10.7	355 13.2	37	9.3
38	159 56.2	174 58.7	190 1.1	205 3.6	220 6.1	235 8.5	340 25.8	355 28.2	38	9.5
39	160 11.2	175 13.7	190 16.2	205 18.6	220 21.1	235 23.6	340 40.8	355 43.3	39	9.8
40	160 26.3	175 28.7	190 31.2	205 33.7	220 36.1	235 38.6	340 55.8	355 58.3	40	10.0
41	160 41.3	175 43.8	190 46.2	205 48.7	220 51.2	235 53.6	341 10.9	356 13.4	41	10.3
42	160 56.4	175 58.8	191 1.3	206 3.8	221 6.2	236 8.7	341 25.9	356 28.4	42	10.5
43	161 11.4	176 13.9	191 16.3	206 18.8	221 21.3	236 23.7	341 41.0	356 43.4	43	10.8
44	161 26.4	176 28.9	191 31.4	206 33.8	221 36.3	236 38.8	341 56.0	356 58.5	44	11.0
45	161 41.5	176 43.9	191 46.4	206 48.9	221 51.3	236 53.8	342 11.1	357 13.5	45	11.3
46	161 56.5	176 59.0	192 1.5	207 3.9	222 6.4	237 8.8	342 26.1	357 28.6	46	11.5
47	162 11.6	177 14.0	192 16.5	207 19.0	222 21.4	237 23.9	342 41.1	357 43.6	47	11.8
48	162 26.6	177 29.1	192 31.5	207 34.0	222 36.5	237 38.9	342 56.2	357 58.6	48	12.0
49	162 41.6	177 44.1	192 46.6	207 49.0	222 51.5	237 54.0	343 11.2	358 13.7	49	12.3
50	162 56.7	177 59.2	193 1.6	208 4.1	223 6.5	238 9.0	343 26.3	358 28.7	50	12.5
51	163 11.7	178 14.2	193 16.7	208 19.1	223 21.6	238 24.1	343 41.3	358 43.8	51	12.8
52	163 26.8	178 29.2	193 31.7	208 34.2	223 36.6	238 39.1	343 56.3	358 58.8	52	13.0
53	163 41.8	178 44.3	193 46.7	208 49.2	223 51.7	238 54.1	344 11.4	359 13.8	53	13.3
54	163 56.9	178 59.3	194 1.8	209 4.2	224 6.7	239 9.2	344 26.4	359 28.9	54	13.5
55	164 11.9	179 14.4	194 16.8	209 19.3	224 21.8	239 24.2	344 41.5	359 43.9	55	13.8
56	164 26.9	179 29.4	194 31.9	209 34.3	224 36.8	239 39.3	344 56.5	359 59.0	56	14.0
57	164 42.0	179 44.4	194 46.9	209 49.4	224 51.8	239 54.3	345 11.5	0 14.0	57	14.3
58	164 57.0	179 59.5	195 1.9	210 4.4	225 6.9	240 9.3	345 26.6	0 29.1	58	14.5
59	165 12.1	180 14.5	195 17.0	210 19.5	225 21.9	240 24.4	345 41.6	0 44.1	59	14.8
60	165 27.1	180 29.6	195 32.0	210 34.5	225 37.0	240 39.4	345 56.7	0 59.1	60	15.0

APPENDIX II

FORMS FOR WORKING DEAD RECKONING AND ASTRONOMICAL SIGHTS

FORM FOR DAY'S WORK, DEAD RECKONING

Time	Compass Course	Var.	Dev.	Lee-way	Total error	True Course	Patent log	Dist.	N.	S.	E.	W.	Diff. Long.

	Latitude ° ′		*Longitude* ° ′	
Left at departure (or noon)	------	N. *or* S.	------	E. *or* W.
Run to	------	N. *or* S.	------	E. *or* W.
By D. R. at	------	N. *or* S.	------	E. *or* W.
Run to	------	N. *or* S.	------	E. *or* W.
By D. R. at	------	N. *or* S.	------	E. *or* W.

FORM FOR TIME SIGHT OF SUN'S LOWER LIMB (LINE OF POSITION)

	h. m. s.		° ′ ″
W. T.,	---------	Obs. alt.,	⊙ ---------
C–W, +	---------	Corr.,	± ---------
Chro. t.,	---------	*h*	---------
C. C., ±	---------		′ ″
G. C. T.,	---------	Corr. (Tab. 40)	---------
Eq. t., ±	---------	H. E.	---------
		I. C.	---------
G. A. T.,	---------	Corr.	---------

	° ′ ″			*m. s.*
Dec.	--------- N. *or* S.		Eq. t.	---------
	″			*s*
H. D.	± ---------		H. D.	± ---------
	h.			*h*
G. C. T. Int.	---------		G. C. T. Int.	---------
	′ ″			*s*
Corr.	± ---------		Corr.	± ---------
	° ′ ″			*m. s.*
Dec.	--------- N. *or* S.		Eq. t.	---------
	° ′ ″			
p	---------			

	° ′ ″	H. A.		Az.	
h	---------			sec.	---------
L	---------	log sec.	---------	sec.	---------
p	---------	log cosec.	---------		
2)	---------				
s	---------	log cos	---------		
s–h	---------	log sin	---------	sin	---------
s–L	---------			sin	---------
	h. m. s.				
G. A. T	---------				
L. A. T.	---------	log hav. *t*.	---------	log hav. Z,	---------
				Z	=---------

Long { h. m. s. --------- / ° ′ ″ --------- } E. *or* W.

Plot line of position through D. R. Lat. and computed longitude, perpendicular to azimuth.

ALTERNATIVE FORM FOR TIME SIGHT (LINE OF POSITION)

	h. m. s.		° ′		*H. A.* (Subtract)		*Az.*		° ′
W. T.,	--------	h_s,	--------					Dec.,	-------- N. *or* S.
C−W,	+ --------	Corr.,	--------					Eq. t.,	--------
		h_o,							
Chron.,	--------	z.,	--------	nat. hav.,	--------	cosec,	--------		
C.C.,	--------	L∼d,	--------	nat. hav.,	--------				
G. C. T.,	--------			nat. hav.,					
Eq. T. (R. A. M. S.+12ʰ),	--------								
(Tab. 39), Corr.,	--------			log hav.,	--------				
				Lat. sec.	--------				
G. A. T. (G. S. T.),	--------			dec. sec.,	--------	cos,	--------		
(R. A.✳),	--------								
				log. hav.,	--------				
G. H. A. (time),	--------			L. H. A.	--------	sin,	--------		
G. H. A. (arc),	--------								
L. H. A. (arc),	--------					Sin Z,	--------		
Long.,	-------- E. *or* W.								

FORM FOR TIME SIGHT OF STAR OR PLANET (LINE OF POSITION)

	h. m. s.				° ′		h.m.s.		° ′		
W. T.,	--------			h_s✳	--------	R. A.✳,	--------	Dec.,	---- N. *or* S.		
C−W,	+ --------			Corr.	--------			p.,	----		
Chron.,	--------			h_o,	--------						
C. C.,	± --------			Tab. 40	--------						
G. C. T.,	--------	or, G. C. T.,	--------	H. E.,	--------	h,	--------			log. sec.,	----
R. A. M. S.+12ʰ,	--------			I. C.,	--------	L,	--------	log. sec,	----	log. sec.,	----
Corr. (Tab. 39)	--------	G. H. A.,	--------			p,	--------	log. cosec,	--		
		Corr.,	--------	Corr.,	--------						
G. S. T.,	--------					2),	--------				
R. A. ✳,	--------	G. H. A.,	--------			S,	--------	log. cos,	----		
						S−h,	--------	log. sin,	----	log. sin.,	----
						S−L,	--------			log. sin.,	----
G. H. A.,	-------- E. *or* W.					L. H. A.,	-------- E. *or* W.	log.hav.,	----	log hav	---- = Z
						G. H. A.,	--------				
						Long.,	-------- E. *or* W.				

Plot line of position through D. R. latitude and computed longitude perpendicular to Z

FORM FOR TIME SIGHT OF MOON'S LOWER LIMB (LINE OF POSITION)

	h. m. s.		° ′		*h. m. s.*		° ′
W. T.,	--------	Obs. alt. ☾,	--------	R. A.,	--------	Dec.,	-------- N. *or* S.
C−W,	+ --------	I. C.,	--------		*s*		′
Chro. t.,	--------	Corr. (Table 41),	--------	Corr.,	--------	Corr.,	--------
C. C.,	± --------	H. E.,	--------				
		h,					
G. C. T.,	-------- *or*	G. C. T.,	--------	R. A.,	--------	Dec.,	--------
Sid. t. 0ʰ G. C. T.,	+ --------						
Corr. (Tab. 39),	+ --------	G. H. A.,	--------				
		Corr.,	--------				
G. S. T.,	--------						
R. A. ☾,	--------	G. H. A.,	--------				
G. H. A.,	-------- E. *or* W.						

For the remainder of the work, by which the hour angle and the longitude are found, employ the method given under "Form for Time Sight of a Star (Line of Position)."

FORM FOR MERIDIAN ALTITUDE OF SUN'S LOWER LIMB

	° ′		′		*h. m. s.*		° ′
Obs. alt. ⊙,	--------	Corr. (Tab. 40),	--------	L. A. T.,	--------	Dec.,	-------- N *or* S.
Corr.,	± --------	H. E.,	--------	Long.,	--------		′
		I. C.,	--------				
h,	--------	Corr.,	--------	G. A. T.,	--------	H. D.,	± --------
	° ′			Eq. t.,	--------		*h.*
z,	-------- N. *or* S.			G. C. T.,	--------	G. C. T. Int.,	± --------
d,	-------- N. *or* S.						′
Lat.,	-------- N. *or* S.					Corr.,	± --------
							° ′
						Dec.,	-------- N. *or* S.

FORM FOR MERIDIAN ALTITUDE OF A STAR

	° ′ ″		′		° ′
Obs. alt.,	✳ --------	Corr. (Tab. 40),	--------	Dec.,	-------- N. *or* S.
Corr.,	± --------	H. E.,	--------		
		I. C.,	--------		
h,	--------	Corr.,	--------		
z,	-------- N. *or* S.				
d,	-------- N. *or* S.				
Lat.,	-------- N. *or* S.				

FORM FOR MERIDIAN ALTITUDE OF A PLANET

	° ′			′		h. m.		° ′
Obs. alt., *	--------	Corr. (Tab. 40),	--------	G. C. T., Gr. trans.,	--------	Dec.,	-------- N. or S.
Corr.,	± --------	par.,	+ --------	Corr. for long.,	± --------		′
		I. C.,	+ --------				
h,	--------	H. E.,	--------	L. C. T., local trans.,	--------	Diff. 24^h,	± --------
	° ′			Long.,	± --------		h.
		Corr.,	∓ --------			G. C. T., P. P.,	--------
z,	-------- N. or S.			G. C. T., local trans.,	--------		′
d,	-------- N. or S.					Corr.,	± --------
Lat.,	-------- N. or S.						° ′
						Dec.,	-------- N. or S.

FORM FOR MERIDIAN ALTITUDE OF MOON'S LOWER LIMB

	° ′		° ′		h. m.		° ′
h,	--------	Obs. alt. ☾,	--------	G. C. T. trans.,	--------	Dec.,	-------- N. or S.
	° ′ ″	I. C.,	--------	Corr. for long. (Tab. 26),	± --------		′
z,	-------- N. or S.	Corr. (Tab. 41),	--------	L. C. T., local trans.,	--------	Corr.,	± --------
d,	-------- N. or S.	H. E.,	--------	Long.,	± --------		
Lat.,	-------- N. or S.	Corr.,	--------	G. C. T., local trans.,	--------		° ′
						Dec.,	-------- N. or S.

Mark zenith distance N. or S. according as zenith is north or south of the body observed; mark Dec. according to its name, subtracting it from 180° for cases of lower transit; then, in combining the two for Lat., have regard to their names.

ALTERNATIVE FORM FOR MERIDIAN ALTITUDE OF A BODY

	±90° 00′ 0
Dec.	± ----------
Corr.	± ----------
Constant	± ----------
Obs. Alt.	± ----------
Lat.	---------- N or S.

Rules for signs

Case I.	Lat. & Dec. same name, Lat. greater	+90°+Dec.−Corr.−Alt.
Case II.	Lat. & Dec. same name, Dec. greater	−90°+Dec.+Corr.+Alt.
Case III.	Lat. & Dec. opposite names	+90°−Dec.−Corr.−Alt.
Case IV.	Lower transit	+90°−Dec.+Corr.+Alt.

FORM FOR REDUCTION TO THE MERIDIAN

	h. m. s.						
W. T.,	----------	h_s,	----------	a, =	---------- (Tab. 29)		
C−W,	----------	Corr.,	----------	at^2,=	---------- (Tab. 30)		
Chron.,	----------	h_o,	----------				
C. C.,	----------			h,	----------	log sec,	----------
G. C. T.,	----------	(Tab. 40),	----------	at^2,	----------		
Eq. t (R. A. M. S.+12^h),	----------	H. E.,	----------				
Corr.,	----------	I. C.,	----------	H,	----------	log sin(t),	----------
G. A. T. (G. S. T.),	----------	Corr.,		z,	---------- N or S		
(R. A.*),	----------			d,	---------- N or S.	log cos,	----------
G. H. A. time,	----------			Lat.,	---------- N or S.	log sin,	----------
G. H. A. Arc,	----------					Z,	----------
Long. D. R.,	----------						
L. H. A.,	----------						
t,	---------- E. or W.						

Plot line of position through Lat. and D. R. Long. perpendicular to Z

FORM FOR THE COMPUTED ALTITUDE AND THE ALTITUDE DIFFERENCE OF THE SUN'S LOWER LIMB FOR LINE OF POSITION

(SINE−COSINE FORMULA)

	h. m. s.				° ′		m. s.
W. T.	----------			Dec.	---------- N. or S.	Eq. t.	----------
C−W	+ ----------				′		s.
Chro. t.	----------			H. D.	± ----------	H. D.	± ----------
C. C.	± ----------				h.		h.
				G. C. T. Int.	----------	G. C. T., Int.	----------
G. C. T.	---------- or,	G. C. T.,	----------		′		s.
Eq. t.	± ----------			Corr.	± ---------- ±	Corr.	± ----------
		G. H. A.,	----------		° ′		m. s.
G. A. T.	----------	Corr., h. m.,	----------				
	----------	Corr., s.,	----------	d,	---------- ±	Eq. t.	----------
Long. (assumed Pos.)	----------	G. H. A.,	----------				

	h. m. s.						
L. A. T.=	----------	----------	----------	log cos	----------	log sin	----------
	° ′						
Obs. alt. ⊙	----------	L± ----------	log sin ----------	±log cos	----------		
		d± ----------	log sin ----------	±log cos	----------	log cos	----------
I. C.	----------		(Sum) log A ----------	±log B	----------		
Corr. (Tab. 40)	----------		A± ----------	B± ----------			
H. E.	----------			A± ----------			
h_o	----------			=A+B	----------	log sec	----------
Computed h	----------	----------	nat. sin,			log sin	----------
Alt. Diff.	---------- (toward or away from Z)					Z,	----------

FORM FOR FINDING THE COMPUTED ALTITUDE AND THE INTERCEPT OF THE SUN'S LOWER LIMB FOR LINE OF POSITION

(COSINE—HAVERSINE FORMULA)

	h. m. s.	
W. T.	--------	
C−W	+ --------	
Chro. t.	--------	
C. C.	± --------	
G. C. T.	--------	
Eq. t.	± --------	
G. A. T.	--------	
Long. (assumed Pos.)	--------	E. *or* W.
	h. m. s.	
L. A. T.=*t*	° ′ ″	
L	--------	
d	--------	
L∾d	--------	
z	--------	
h_o	--------	
h_c	--------	
Int.	--------	(toward or away from Z)

or, G. C. T.	--------
G. H. A.	--------
Corr., h. m	--------
Corr., s	--------
G. H. A.	--------

	° ′	
Dec.	--------	N. *or* S.
H. D. ±	′	

G. C. T.	h. --------	
Corr. ±	′ --------	
C		
d,	° ′	
	± --------	

log hav	--------	log sin	--------
log cos	--------		
log cos	--------	log cos	--------
log hav φ	--------		
nat hav φ	--------		
nat hav	--------		
nat hav	--------	log cosec	--------
		log sin	--------
		Z	--------

	m. s.
Eq. t.	--------
H. D.	± s. --------
G. C. T.	h. --------
Corr.	± s. --------
	m. s.
Eq. t.	--------
	° ′
Obs. alt. ⊙	--------
I. C.	--------
Corr. (Tab. 40).	± --------
H. E.	--------
h_o	--------

FORM FOR THE COMPUTED ALTITUDE AND THE INTERCEPT OF A STAR OR PLANET FOR LINE OF POSITION

(COSINE-HAVERSINE FORMULA)

	h. m. s.	
W. T.,	--------	
C−W.,	+ --------	
Chro. t.,	--------	
C. C.,	± --------	
G. C. T.,	--------	
Sid. t. of 0^h G. C. T.,	+ --------	
Corr. (Tab. 39)	+ --------	
G. S. T.,	--------	
R. A.✱	--------	
G. H. A.✱,	--------	E. *or* W.
Long. of assumed Pos.,	--------	E. *or* W.
L. H. A. (*t*),	{h. m. s. / ° ′ ″	

	° ′
Or, G. C. T.,	--------
G. H. A. 0^h,	--------
Corr. h, m,	--------
Corr. s.,	--------
G. H. A.,	--------

	° ′
Obs. alt.✱	--------
I. C.,	--------
Corr. (Tab. 40)—	--------
Obs. *h*,	--------
	° ′ ″
t,	--------
L,	--------
d,	--------
L∾*d*,	--------
z,	--------
h_c,	--------
h_o,	--------
Int.,	-------- (towards or away)

Log hav,	--------
Log cos,	--------
Log cos,	--------
Log hav,	--------
Nat. hav,	--------
Nat. hav,	--------

	° ′	
Dec.,	--------	N. *or* S
	h. m. s.	
R. A.,	--------	
Log sin,	--------	
Log cos,	--------	
Log cosec,	--------	
Log sin,	--------	
Z,	--------	

Plot line of position through D. R. Lat. and Long. perpendicular to Z, then move line as indicated by intercept.

FORM FOR STAR IDENTIFICATION

	h. m. s.	
W. T.,	--------	
C−W,	+ --------	
Chron.,	--------	
C. C.,	--------	
G. C. T.,	--------	
Sid. t. of 0^h,	--------	
Corr. (Tab. 39),	--------	
G. S. T.,	--------	
Long.,	--------	E. *or* W.
L. S. T.,	--------	
(Approx.) *t*,	--------	
(Approx.) R. A.,	--------	Enter N. A. with coordinates of R. A. and Dec. for identification.
(Approx.) Dec.,	--------	*When *p* is greater than 90° the declination is named contrary to latitude.

h_s,	--------
Corr.,	--------
h_o,	--------
*p,	--------
Dec.,	

(Tab. 40),	--------
H. E.,	--------
I. C.,	--------
Corr.,	--------
hav Z,	--------
cos L,	--------
cos h_o,	--------
log hav,	--------
nat. hav,	--------
(L−h) nat. hav,	--------
nat. hav,	--------

h_o,	--------
z,	--------
L∾d,	--------
L,	--------
Dec.,	--------

nat. hav,	--------	
nat. hav,	--------	
(Subtract),	--------	
nat. hav,	--------	
log hav,	--------	
sec.,	--------	
sec.,	--------	
Log hav,	--------	
t,	--------	E. *or* W.

APPENDIX III

MATHEMATICAL PRINCIPLES USED IN THE SOLUTION OF NAVIGATION PROBLEMS

GEOMETRY

Geometry is the science which treats of the description, properties, and relations of magnitudes, of which there are three kinds; viz, a *line*, which has only length without either breadth or thickness; a *surface*, comprehended by length and breadth; and a *solid*, which has length, breadth, and thickness.

A *point*, considered mathematically, has neither length, breadth, nor thickness; it denotes position simply.

A *line* has length without breadth or thickness.

A *surface* has length and breadth without thickness.

A *solid* has length, breadth, and thickness.

A *straight* or *right line* is the shortest distance between two points on a plane surface.

A *plane surface* is one in which, any two points being taken, the straight line between them lies wholly within that surface.

Parallel lines are such as are in the same plane and if extended indefinitely never meet.

A *circle* is a plane figure bounded by a curved line of which every point is equally distant from a point within called the *center*. The bounding curve of the circle is called the *circumference*.

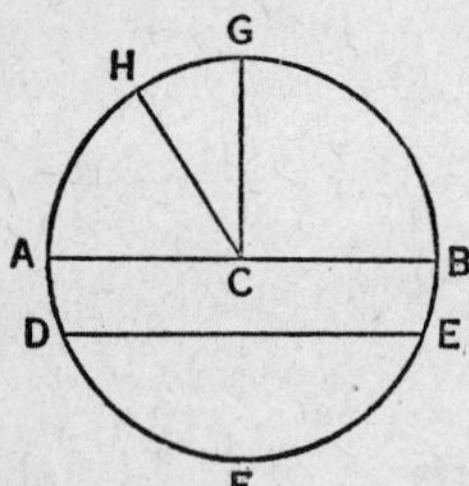

FIGURE 135.

The *radius* of a circle, or *semidiameter*, is a right line drawn from the center to the circumference, as AC (fig. 135); its length is that distance which is taken between the points of the compasses to describe the circle.

A *diameter* of a circle is a right line drawn through the center and terminated at both ends by the circumference, as ACB, its length being twice that of the radius. A diameter divides the circle and its circumference into two equal parts.

An *arc* of a circle is any portion of the circumference, as DFE.

The *chord* of an arc is a straight line joining the ends of the arc. It divides the circle into two unequal parts, called *segments*, and is a chord to them both; thus, DE is the chord of the arcs DFE and DGE.

A *semicircle*, or half circle, is a figure contained between a diameter and the arc terminated by that diameter, as AGB or AFB.

Any part of a circle contained between two radii and an arc is called a *sector*, as GCH.

A *quadrant* is half a semicircle, or one-fourth part of a whole circle, as CAG.

All circles are supposed to have their circumferences divided into 360 equal parts, called degrees; each degree is divided into 60 equal parts, called minutes; and each minute into 60 equal parts, called seconds; an arc is measured by the number of degrees, minutes, and seconds that it contains.

A *sphere* is a solid bounded by a surface of which every point is equally distant from a point within, which, as in the circle, is called the *center*. Substituting *surface* for *circumference*, the definitions of the *radius* and *diameter*, as given for the circle, apply for the sphere.,

An *angle* is the inclination of two intersecting lines, and is measured by the arc of a circle intercepted between the two lines that form the angle, the center of the circle being the point of intersection.

A *right angle* is one that is measured by a quadrant, or 90°. An *acute angle* is one which is less than a right angle. An *obtuse angle* is one which is greater than a right angle.

A *plane triangle* is a figure contained by three straight lines in the same plane.

When the three sides are equal, the triangle is called *equilateral;* when two of them are equal, it is called *isosceles.* When one of the angles is 90°, the triangle is said to be *right-angled.* When each angle is less than 90°, it is said to be *acute-angled.* When one is greater than 90°, it is said to be *obtuse-angled.* Triangles that are not right-angled are generally called *oblique-angled.*

A *quadrilateral* figure is one bounded by four sides. If the opposite sides are parallel, it is called a *parallelogram.* A parallelogram having all its sides equal and its angles right angles is called a *square.* When the angles are right angles and only the opposite sides equal, it is called a *rectangle.*

In a right-angled triangle the side opposite the right angle is called the *hypotenuse,* one of the other sides is called the *base,* and the third side is called the *perpendicular.* In any oblique-angled triangle, one side having been assumed as a base, the distance from the intersection of the other two sides to the base or the base extended, measured at right angles to the latter, is the perpendicular. In a parallelogram, one of the sides having been assumed as the base, the distance from its opposite side, measured at right angles to its direction, is the perpendicular. The term *altitude* is sometimes substituted for *perpendicular* in this sense.

Every section of a sphere made by a plane is a circle. A *great circle* of a sphere is a section of the surface made by a plane which passes through its center. A *small circle* is a section by a plane which intersects the sphere without passing through the center.

A great circle may be drawn through any two points on the surface of a sphere, and the arc of that circle lying between those points is shorter than any other distance between them that can be measured upon the surface. All great circles of a sphere have equal radii, and all bisect each other.

The extremities of that diameter of the sphere which is perpendicular to the plane of a circle are called the *poles* of that circle. In the case of a small circle the poles are named the *adjacent pole* and the *remote pole.* All circles of a sphere that are parallel have the same poles. All points in the circumference of a circle are equidistant from the poles. In the case of a great circle, the poles are 90° distant from every point of the circle.

Assuming any great circle as a *primary,* all great circles which pass through its poles are called its *secondaries.* All secondaries cut the primary at right angles.

Useful formulas derived from geometry.—In these formulas the following abbreviations are adopted:

b, base of triangle or parallelogram.
h, perpendicular of triangle or parallelogram.
l, height of cylinder or cone.
π, ratio of diameter to circumference (= 3.141593).
r, radius of sphere or circle.
d, diameter of sphere or circle.
A, major axis of ellipse.
a, minor axis of ellipse.
s, side of a cube.

Area of parallelogram $= b \times h$.
Area of triangle $= \frac{1}{2} b \times h$.
Area of any right-lined figure = sum of the areas of the triangles into which it is divided.
Sum of three angles of any triangle = 180°.
Circumference of circle $= 2\pi r$, or πd.

Area of circle $= \pi r^2$, or $\frac{\pi d^2}{4}$.

Angle subtended by arc equal to radius = 57°.29578 (called *radian*).

Volume of sphere $= \frac{\pi d^3}{6}$

Surface of sphere $= \pi d^2$, or $4\pi r^2$.

Area of ellipse $= \frac{\pi A a}{4}$

Volume of cube $= s^3$.
Volume of cylinder $=$ Area of base $\times\, l$.

Volume of pyramid or cone $=$ Area of base $\times \frac{l}{3}$.

TRIGONOMETRIC FUNCTIONS

The *trigonometric functions* of the angle formed by any two lines are the *ratios* existing between the sides of a right triangle formed by letting fall a perpendicular from any point in one line upon the other line; no matter what point is chosen for the perpendicular nor which line, the ratios, and therefore the respective functions, will be the same for any given angle.

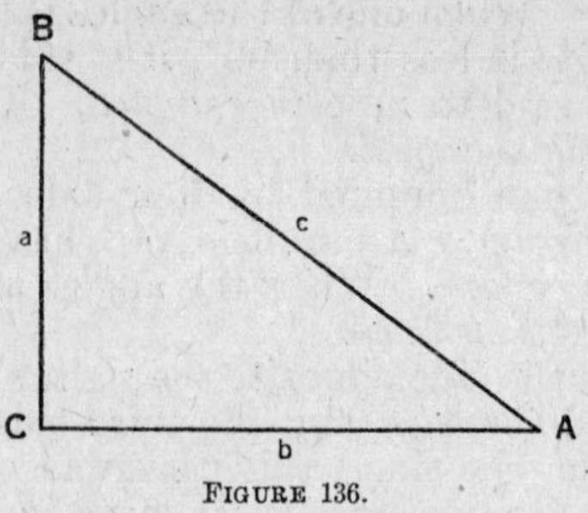

FIGURE 136.

Let ABC (fig. 136) be a plane right triangle in which C is the right angle; A and B, the other angles; *c*, the hypotenuse; *a* and *b* the sides opposite the angles A and B, respectively. In considering the functions of the angle A, its opposite side, *a*, is regarded as the perpendicular, and its adjacent side, *b*, as the base; for the angle B, *b* is the perpendicular and *a* the base. Then the various ratios are designated as follows:

$\frac{a}{c}$, or $\frac{\text{perpendicular}}{\text{hypotenuse}}$, is the *sine* of the angle A, or sin A;

$\frac{b}{c}$, or $\frac{\text{base}}{\text{hypotenuse}}$, is the *cosine* of the angle A, or cos A;

$\frac{a}{b}$, or $\frac{\text{perpendicular}}{\text{base}}$, is the *tangent* of the angle A, or tan A;

$\frac{b}{a}$, or $\frac{\text{base}}{\text{perpendicular}}$, is the *cotangent* of the angle A, or cot A;

$\frac{c}{b}$, or $\frac{\text{hypotenuse}}{\text{base}}$, is the *secant* of the angle A, or sec A;

$\frac{c}{a}$, or $\frac{\text{hypotenuse}}{\text{perpendicular}}$, is the *cosecant* of the angle A, or cosec A;

1—cosine A, is the *versed sine* of A, or vers A.
1—sine A, is the *co-versed sine* of A, or covers A.
½ (1—cosine A) is the haversine of A, or hav A.
The following relations exist between the various functions:

$$\frac{1}{\sin A}=1\div\frac{a}{c}=\frac{c}{a}=\text{cosec } A;$$

$$\frac{1}{\cos A}=1\div\frac{b}{c}=\frac{c}{b}=\sec A;$$

$$\frac{1}{\tan A}=1\div\frac{a}{b}=\frac{b}{a}=\cot A;$$

$$\frac{\sin A}{\cos A}=\frac{a}{c}\div\frac{b}{c}=\frac{a}{b}=\tan A.$$

The cosecant is the reciprocal of the sine, the secant is the reciprocal of the cosine, the cotangent is the reciprocal of the tangent, and the tangent equals the sine divided by the cosine.

The *complement* of an angle is equal to 90° minus that angle, and thus in the triangle ABC the angle B is the complement of A. The *supplement* is equal to 180° minus the angle.

From the triangle ABC, regarding the angle B, we have:

$$\sin B=\frac{b}{c}=\cos A;$$

$$\tan B=\frac{b}{a}=\cot A;$$

$$\sec B=\frac{c}{a}=\text{cosec } A.$$

It may be seen that the sine of an angle is the cosine of the complement of that angle; the tangent of an angle is the cotangent of its complement, and the secant of of an angle is the cosecant of its complement.

The functions of angles vary in sign according to the quadrant in which the angles are located.

Let AA′ and BB′ (fig. 137) be two lines at right angles intersecting at the point

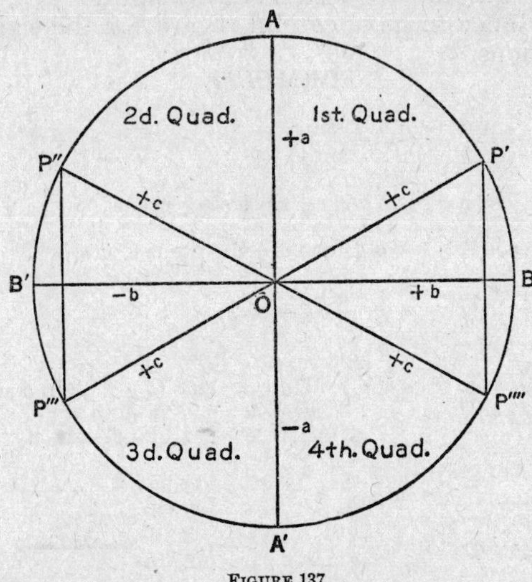

FIGURE 137.

O, and let that point be the center about which a radius revolves from an initial position OB, successively passing the points A, B′, A′. In considering the angle made by this radius at any position, P′, P″, P‴, P⁗, with the line OB, its position of origin, the functions will depend upon the ratios existing between the sides of a right triangle whose base, *b*, will always lie within BB′, and whose perpendicular, *a*, will always be parallel to AA′, while its hypotenuse, *c* (of a constant length equal to that of the radius), will depend upon the position occupied by the radius. Now, if OB and OA be regarded as the positive directions of the base and perpendicular, respectively, and OB′ and OA′ as their negative directions, the sign of the hypotenuse being always positive, the sign of any function may be determined by the signs of the sides of the triangle upon which it depends.

For example, the sine of the angle P″OB is $\frac{a}{c}$, and since *a* is positive the quantity has a positive value; its cosine is $\frac{b}{c}$, and as *b* is measured in a negative direction from O the cosine must therefore be negative.

In the first quadrant, between 0° and 90°, all quantities being positive, all functions will also be positive.

In the second quadrant, between 90° and 180°, sin A $\left(=\frac{a}{c}\right)$ is positive; cos A $\left(=\frac{b}{c}\right)$ has a negative value because *b* is negative; tan A $\left(=\frac{a}{b}\right)$ is also negative because of *b*. The cosecant, secant, and cotangent have, as in all cases, the same signs as the sine, cosine, and tangent, respectively, being the reciprocals of those quantities.

In the third quadrant, between 180° and 270°, sin A $\left(=\frac{a}{c}\right)$ and cos A $\left(=\frac{b}{c}\right)$ are both negative, because both *a* and *b* have negative values; tan A $\left(=\frac{a}{b}\right)$ is positive for the same reason.

In the fourth quadrant, between 270° and 360°, sin A $\left(=\frac{a}{c}\right)$ is negative, cos A $\left(=\frac{b}{c}\right)$ is positive, and tan A $\left(=\frac{a}{b}\right)$ is also negative.

From a consideration of the signs in the manner that has been indicated, the following relations will appear:

$$\sin A=\sin (180°-A)=-\sin (180°+A)=-\sin (360°-A)=-\sin (-A).$$
$$\cos A=-\cos (180°-A)=-\cos (180°+A)=\cos (360°-A)=\cos (-A).$$
$$\tan A=-\tan (180°-A)=\tan (180°+A)=-\tan (360°-A)=-\tan (-A).$$
$$\sin A=\cos (90°-A)=-\cos (90°+A)=-\cos (270°-A)=\cos (270°+A).$$

Any similar relation may be deduced from the figure.

It is of great importance to have careful regard for the signs of the functions in all trigonometrical solutions.

FORMULAS

$$\frac{\sin a}{\sin A}=\frac{\sin b}{\sin B}=\frac{\sin c}{\sin C}$$

$$\cos a=\cos b \cos c+\sin b \sin c \cos A;$$

$$\cos A=-\cos B \cos C+\sin B \sin C \cos a;$$

$$\frac{a+b+c}{2}=s;$$

$$\sin \frac{A}{2}=\sqrt{\frac{\sin (s-b) \sin (s-c)}{\sin b \sin c}};$$

$$\cos \frac{A}{2}=\sqrt{\frac{\sin s \sin (s-a)}{\sin b \sin c}};$$

$$\tan \frac{A}{2}=\sqrt{\frac{\sin (s-b) \sin (s-c)}{\sin s \sin (s-a)}};$$

$$1-\cos A=2 \sin^2\frac{A}{2};$$

$$\text{Hav } a=\text{hav } (b-c)+\sin b \sin c \text{ hav A}$$
$$\text{Hav } \theta=\text{hav A} \sin b \sin c$$
$$\text{Nat hav } a=\text{nat hav } \theta+\text{nat hav } (b-c)$$

A---------	log hav---------	
b---------	log sin---------	
c---------	log sin ---------	
θ---------	log hav---------	nat hav---------
	$(b-c)$---------	nat hav---------
	a---------	nat hav---------

In a right spherical triangle by Napier's analogies:

The sine of the middle part is equal to the product of the tangents of the adjacent parts.

The sine of the middle part is equal to the product of the cosine of the opposite parts.

The differentials are as follows:

$d \sin x=\cos x\, dx$; $d \cos x=-\sin x\, dx$; $d \tan x=\sec^2 x\, dx$; $d \cot x=-\csc^2 x\, dx$; $d \sec x=\tan x \sec x\, dx$; $d \csc x=-\cot x \csc x\, dx$

$\frac{\Delta h}{\Delta t}=-\cos L \sin Z$; L and d constant

$\frac{\Delta h}{\Delta L}=\cos Z$; d and t constant.

$\frac{\Delta h}{\Delta Z}=-\cos h \tan M$; L and d constant

$\frac{\Delta Z}{\Delta L}=-\sec L \cot t$; d and h constant.

$\frac{\Delta Z}{\Delta L}=\tan h \sin Z$; d and t constant.

$\frac{\Delta t}{\Delta L}=-\sec L \cot Z$; d and h constant

$\frac{\Delta Z}{\Delta t}=\cos d \sec h \cos M$; L and d constant.

$\frac{\Delta d}{\Delta t}=\cos d \tan M$; L and h constant.

$\frac{\Delta d}{\Delta Z}=\cos L \sin t$; L and h constant.

LOGARITHMS

In order to abbreviate the tedious operations of multiplication and division with large numbers, a series of numbers, called *logarithms*, was invented by Lord Napier, by means of which the operation of multiplication may be performed by addition, and that of division by subtraction. Numbers may be involved to any power by simple multiplication and the root of any power extracted by simple division.

In Table 32 the logarithms of all numbers from 1 to 9,999 are given. By interpolation a fifth figure may be found which virtually extends the table to include logarithms of numbers from 1 to 99,999.

The method of obtaining the logarithms of numbers, and of obtaining numbers from given logarithms with examples, is fully explained in the Explanation of Tables appearing before Table I of Part II of this publication.

The following additional examples show how multiplication and division are accomplished by use of logarithms.

It may be remarked that in using five-place logarithm tables it is not generally to be expected that results will be exact beyond the fifth figure.

To show the characteristics corresponding to mixed and decimal numbers, the following examples are given:

Mixed number	*Logarithms*	*Decimal number*	*Logarithms*
40943. 0	Log. 4. 61218	0. 40943	Log. 9. 61218−10
4094. 3	Log. 3. 61218	0. 040943	Log. 8. 61218−10
409. 43	Log. 2. 61218	0. 0040943	Log. 7. 61218−10
40. 943	Log. 1. 61218	0. 00040943	Log. 6. 61218−10
4. 0943	Log. 0. 61218	0. 000040943	Log. 5. 61218−10

To perform multiplication by logarithms, add the logarithms of the two numbers to be multiplied and the sum will be the logarithm of their product.

Example I

Multiply 25 by 35

	25	Log. 1. 39794
	35	Log. 1. 54407
Product,	875	Log. 2. 94201

Example II

Multiply 22.4 by 1.8

	22. 4	Log. 1. 35025
	1. 8	Log. 0. 25527
Product,	40. 32	Log. 1. 60552

Example III

Multiply 3.26 by 0.0025

	3. 26	Log. 0. 51322
	0. 0025	Log. 7. 39794
Product,	0. 00815	Log. 7. 91116

Example IV

Multiply 0.25 by 0.003

	0. 25	Log. 9. 39794
	0. 003	Log. 7. 47712
Product,	0. 00075	Log. 6. 87506

In the last example, the sum of the two logarithms is really 16.87506−20; this is the same as 6.87506−10, or, remembering that the quantity is less than unity, simply 6.87506.

To perform division by logarithms, from the logarithm of the dividend subtract the logarithm of the divisor; the remainder will be the logarithm of the quotient.

Example I

Divide 875 by 25

	875	Log. 2. 94201
	25	Log. 1. 39794
Quotient,	35	Log. 1. 54407

Example II

Divide 40.32 by 22.4

	40. 32	Log. 1. 60552
	22. 4	Log. 1. 35025
Quotient,	1. 8	Log. 0. 25527

Example III

Divide 0.00815 by 0.0025

	0. 00815	Log. 7. 91116
	0. 0025	Log. 7. 39794
Quotient,	3. 26	Log. 0. 51322

Example IV

Divide 0.00075 by 0.025

	0. 00075	Log. 6. 87506
	0. 025	Log. 8. 39794
Quotient,	0. 03	Log. 8. 47712

In example III both the divisor and dividend are fractions less than unity, and the divisor is the lesser; consequently the quotient is greater than unity. In example IV both fractions are less than unity; and, since the divisor is the greater, its logarithm is greater than that of the dividend; for this reason it is necessary to borrow 10 in the characteristic before making the subtraction, that is, to regard the logarithm of .00075 as 16.87506−20; hence the quotient is less than unity.

The *arithmetical complement* of the logarithm of a number, usually called the *cologarithm* of the number, and denoted by colog, is the remainder obtained by subtracting the logarithm of the number from the logarithm of unity. It is therefore the logarithm of the reciprocal of the number; and, since the effect of dividing by any number is the same as that of multiplying by its reciprocal, it follows that, in performing division by logarithms, we may either subtract the logarithm of the divisor or add the arithmetical complement of that logarithm. As the addition of a number of quantities can be performed in a single operation, while in subtraction the difference between only two quantities can be taken at a time, it is frequently a convenience to deal with the arithmetical complements rather than with the logarithms themselves.

541524°—43——22

Example I

Divide 875 by 25

875 .... Log. 2. 94201
25 ... Log. 1.39794 .... Colog. 8. 60206

Quotient, 35 .... Log. 1. 54407

Example II

Divide 0.00075 by 0.025

0.00075 .... Log. 6. 87506
0.025 .. Log. 8.39794 .... Colog. 1. 60206

Quotient, 0.03 .... Log. 8. 47712

Example III

Simplify the expression, $\frac{40.32\times.00815}{22.4\times.0025}$

40.32 .... Log. 1. 60552
.00815 .... Log. 7. 91116
22.4 ..... Log. 1.35025 .... Colog. 8. 64975
.0025 .. Log. 7.39794 .... Colog. 2. 60206

Result, 5.868 .... Log. 0. 76849

To perform involution by logarithms, multiply the logarithm of the given number by the index of the power to which the quantity is to be raised; the product will be the logarithm of the power sought.

Example I

Required the square of 18

18 .... Log. 1. 25527
2

Answer, 324 .... Log. 2. 51054

Example II

Required the square of 6.4

6.4 .... Log. 0. 80618
2

Answer, 40.96 .... Log. 1. 61236

Example III

Required the cube of 13

13 .... Log. 1. 11394
3

Answer, 2197 .... Log. 3. 34182

Example IV

Required the cube of 0.25

0.25 .... Log. 9. 39794
3

Answer, 0.015625 .... Log. 8. 19382

In the last example the full product of the multiplication of 9.39794−10 by 3 is 28.19382−30 which is equivalent to 8.19382−10.

To perform evolution by logarithms divide the logarithm of the number by the index of the power; the quotient will be the logarithm of the root sought. If the number whose root is to be extracted is a decimal fraction less than unity, increase the index of its logarithm by adding a number of tens which shall be less by one than the index of the power before making the division.

Example I

Required the square root of 324

324 .... Log. 2)2. 51055

Answer, 18 .... Log. 1. 25527

Example II

Required the cube root of 2197

2197 .... Log. 3)3. 34183

Answer, 13 .... Log. 1. 11394

Example III

Required the square root of 40.96

40.96 .... Log. 2)1. 61236

Answer, 6.4 .... Log. 0. 80618

Example IV

Required the cube root of 0.015625

0.015625 .... Log. 8. 19382
Add 20 to the index .... Log. 3)28. 19382

Answer, 0.25 .... Log. 9. 39794

In the last example the logarithm 8.19382−10 was converted into its equivalent form of 28.19382−30, which, divided by 3, gives 9.39794−10.

To find the logarithm of any function of an angle, Table 33 must be employed. This table is so arranged that on every page there appear the logarithms of all the functions of a certain angle A, together with those at the angles 90−A, 90+A, and 180−A.

A full explanation of the methods of obtaining the logarithms of the functions of angles, with examples, is contained in the Explanation of Tables appearing before Table I of part II of this publication.

USEFUL DATA

Earth's equatorial radius=6378.388 kilometers (3963.34 statute miles.)
Earth's polar radius=6356.909 kilometers (3949.99 statute miles.)----
Earth's compression $=\frac{1}{297}$ log 7.5272436------------------------------
Earth's logarithm of eccentricity log e=8.913804--------------------
(Hayford Spheroid of 1909.)

Earth's polar radius=6,356,583.8 meters (3,949.79 statute miles).
Earth's equatorial radius=6,378,206.4 meters (3,963.23 statute miles).
(Clarke's Spheroid of 1866.)

Earth's compression$=\frac{1}{293.465}$ (Clarke's determination in 1880.)
Earth's eccentricity=0.0822719--------------log 8. 9152513. (Clarke's Spheroid of 1866.)
Number of feet in 1 statute mile=5280-------log 3. 7226339.
Number of feet in 1 nautical mile=6080.27*---log 3. 7839229.
Statute mile=0.868362 nautical mile.
Nautical mile=1.151594 statute miles.
One foot=0.3048006 meter.
Sine of 1″=0.00000485------------------------log 4. 6855749.
Sine of 1′=0.00029089------------------------log 6. 4637261.
The Napierian base ϵ=2.7182818------------log 0. 4342945.
The modulus of common logarithms= 0.4342945--------------------------------log 9. 6377843.
Ratio of diameter to circumference π= 3.14159265--------------------------------log 0. 4971499.
French meter in English feet, 3.2808333-------log 0. 5159842.
French meter in English statute miles, 0.000621370-----------------------------log 6. 7933503.
French meter in nautical miles, 0.000539593----log 6. 7320663.
Atmosphere=15 pounds per square inch or 1 ton per square foot.
1 pound Avoirdupois=7,000 grains Troy.
French gramme=0.00220606 Imperial pound Troy.
French kilogramme=0.0196969 English cwts.

Cubic inch of distilled water, in grains=252.458.
Cubic foot of water, in ounces Troy=908.8488.
Cubic foot of water, in pounds Troy=75.7374.
Cubic foot of water, in ounces Avoirdupois=997.1369691.
Cubic foot of water, in pounds Avoirdupois=62.3210606.
Bar 30.00 in.; ther. 62° F.

Length of pendulum which vibrates seconds at Greenwich, 39.1393 incnes.
Mean distance, earth to moon, 238,857 statute miles.
Mean distance, earth to sun, 92,897,416 statute miles.
Velocity of light, 186,324 statute miles per second.
Velocity of sound in 35 percent salt water, 1,510.4 meters per second.
Velocity of sound in dry air, 1,089 feet per second.

*Minute of arc of a great circle of a sphere whose surface equals that of the Clarke Spheroid of 1866.

APPENDIX IV

MARITIME POSITIONS

MARITIME POSITIONS

EAST COAST OF NORTH AMERICA

Coast	Place	Lat. N. °	Lat. N. ′	Long. W. °	Long. W. ′
Labrador	Nain: S. Channel cairn	56	31	61	40
	Fords Harbor: Lighthouse	56	28	61	09
	Cape Harrigan: Lighthouse	55	51	60	19
	Napakataktalik: Lighthouse	55	33	60	14
	Tikkerasuk I.: Lighthouse	55	20	59	43
	Cutthroat I.: Lighthouse	54	29	57	06
	Packs Harbor Island: Lighthouse	53	51	56	59
	Cape North: Lighthouse	53	46	56	26
	Cartwright: Harbor F. S.	53	43	57	01
	Indian Tickle: White Point Lighthouse	53	34	56	01
	Domino Point: Lighthouse	53	28	55	44
	Double Island: Lighthouse	52	15	55	32
	Belle Isle:				
	North Point Lighthouse	51	53	55	22
	South Point Lighthouse	51	53	55	21
	Saddle I.: Lighthouse	51	43	56	25
	Amour Point: Lighthouse	51	27	56	50
	Greenly Island: Lighthouse	51	22	57	10
Newfoundland	Flower Island: Lighthouse	51	18	56	44
	Cape Norman: Lighthouse	51	38	55	54
	Kirpon Harbor: Lighthouse	51	36	55	27
	Cape Bauld: Lighthouse	51	39	55	25
	Egg Point: Lighthouse	51	21	55	33
	Fox Point: Lighthouse	51	21	55	33
	Canada Bay: Aiguillettes Harbor Lighthouse	50	43	56	06
	Nid Island: Lighthouse	50	42	55	37
	Fourche Harbor: Lighthouse	50	30	56	15
	Orange Bay (Great Harbor Deep): Lighthouse	50	22	56	24
	Jackson Arm: Lighthouse	49	52	56	44
	Western Cove: Lighthouse	49	47	56	37
	Seal Cove: Lighthouse	49	56	56	22
	Coachman Harbor: Lighthouse	50	03	56	04
	La Scie Harbor: Lighthouse	49	58	55	22
	Gull Island: Lighthouse	50	00	55	21
	Nipper Harbor: Lighthouse	49	47	55	50
	Little Bay Island: Lighthouse	49	38	55	46
	Long Island: Lighthouse	49	36	55	34
	Leading (Ladle) Tickles: Lighthouse	49	30	55	24
	Fortune Harbor: Lighthouse	49	32	55	14
	Surgeon Cove Head: Lighthouse	49	31	55	07
	Upper Black I.: Lighthouse	49	25	55	08
	Cabbage Harbor Head: Lighthouse	49	20	55	12
	Grassy Island: Lighthouse	49	16	55	14
	Lower Sandy Point: Lighthouse	49	13	55	17
	Mill Point: Lighthouse	49	09	55	20
	Twillingate: Lighthouse	49	41	54	47
	Bacalhao I.: Lighthouse	49	41	54	33
	Change I. S. end: Lighthouse	49	34	54	24
	Smoker I.: Lighthouse	49	37	54	27
	Rags I.: Lighthouse	49	44	54	15
	Brookes Point: Lighthouse	49	45	54	09
	Cann Island: Lighthouse	49	35	54	10
	Offer Wadham: Lighthouse	49	36	53	45
	Peckford I.: Lighthouse	49	32	53	52
	North Penguin I.: Lighthouse	49	27	53	48
	Stinking I.: Lighthouse	49	10	53	21
	Puffin I.: Lighthouse	49	03	53	32
	Little Dunier I.: Lighthouse	48	41	53	35
	Kings Cove: Lighthouse	48	34	53	19
	Squarey Islet: Lighthouse	48	39	53	08
	Cape Bonavista: Lighthouse	48	42	53	04
	Green I.: Lighthouse	48	30	53	02
	Ragged Island: Lighthouse	48	14	53	27
	Hopeall Head: Lighthouse	47	38	53	34
	Hearts Content: Lighthouse	47	53	53	23
	Port Aux Choix: Lighthouse	50	43	57	20
	Ferolle Point: Old Ferolle Beacon	51	05	56	54
River and Gulf of St. Lawrence	Flat Island: Lighthouse	50	45	58	45
	St. Mary Island: Lighthouse	50	18	59	39
	Natashkwan Point: Lighthouse	50	06	61	43
	Little Natashkwan Harbor: Lighthouse	50	11	61	51
	Quetachua Bay: Front Lighthouse	50	17	62	45
	Walrus Island: Lighthouse	50	12	63	33
	Eskimo Point: Lighthouse	50	15	63	36
	Perroquet I.: Lighthouse	50	13	64	12
River and Gulf of St. Lawrence	Anticosti I.:				
	Heath Point Lighthouse	49	05	61	42
	Bagot Bluff Lighthouse	49	04	62	16
	S. W. Point Lighthouse	49	23	63	36
	Port Menier, rear light	49	50	64	23
	West Point Lighthouse	49	52	64	31
	Cap de Rabast Lighthouse	49	57	64	09
	Carleton Point Lighthouse	49	44	62	56
	Table Head Lighthouse	49	21	61	54
	Carousel I.: Lighthouse	50	05	66	23
	Egg I.: Lighthouse	49	37	67	10
	Pointe des Monts: Lighthouse	49	19	67	22
	Quebec: Observatory (transit inst.)	46	48	71	13
	Cavalier Building, Time Ball	46	48	71	12
	Montreal:				
	Obs. McGill University E. transit pier	45	30	73	35
	Ottawa: Dominion obs. (meridian circle)	45	24	75	43
	Stone Pillar Island: Lighthouse	47	12	70	22
	Cape Dogs: Lighthouse	47	55	69	48
	Father Point: Lighthouse	48	31	68	28
	Cape Chat: Lighthouse	49	05	66	44
	Riviere a la Martre: Lighthouse	49	13	66	09
	Cape Madeleine: Lighthouse	49	15	65	19
Quebec	Fame Point: Lighthouse	49	06	64	36
	Cap des Rosiers: Lighthouse	48	51	64	12
	Perce: Lighthouse	48	30	64	13
	Cap d'Espoir: Lighthouse	48	25	64	19
	Maquereau Point: Lighthouse	48	12	64	46
	Paspebiac Point: Lighthouse	48	01	65	15
	Bonaventure Point: Lighthouse	48	00	65	27
	Little Belledune Point: Lighthouse	47	55	65	54
New Brunswick	Carleton: Tracadigash Point: Lighthouse	48	05	66	08
	Birch Point: Lighthouse	48	01	64	29
	Big Shippigan: Lighthouse	47	43	64	40
	North Tracadie Gully: Lighthouse	47	33	64	51
	Neguac Gully: Lighthouse	47	15	65	00
	Portage I. (front): Lighthouse	47	10	65	03
	Escuminac Point: Lighthouse	47	04	64	48
	Richibucto Head: Lighthouse	46	40	64	43
	Cassie Point: Lighthouse	46	19	64	31
	Shediac: Pointe du Chene Lighthouse	46	15	64	31
	Jourimain I.: Lighthouse	46	09	63	48
	Cape Tormentine: Pier light	46	08	63	47
Nova Scotia	Amet I.: Lighthouse	45	50	63	11
	Caribou Point: Lighthouse	45	46	62	41
	Pictou I.:				
	S. E. Point Lighthouse	45	49	62	31
	W. Point Lighthouse	45	48	62	36
	Pictou Harbor: Lighthouse	45	41	62	40
	Arisaig Point: Lighthouse	45	46	62	10
	Cape George: Lighthouse	45	53	61	54
Newfoundland	Jeans Head: Lighthouse	47	56	53	22
	Hants Harbor: Lighthouse	48	01	53	15
	Baccalieu I.: Lighthouse	48	09	52	48
	Carbonear I.: Lighthouse	47	44	53	09
	Harbor Grace I.: Lighthouse	47	43	53	08
	North Head: Lighthouse	47	33	53	11
	Salmon Cove Point: Lighthouse	47	28	53	09
	Cape St. Francis: Lighthouse	47	49	52	47
	St. Johns Harbor: Fort Amherst Lighthouse	47	34	52	40
	Cape Spear: Lighthouse	47	31	52	37
	Bay Bulls: Lighthouse	47	19	52	45
	Ferryland Head: Lighthouse	47	01	52	51
	Bearcove Point: Lighthouse	46	56	52	53
	Cape Race: Lighthouse	46	39	53	04
	Powles Head: Lighthouse	46	41	53	24
	Cape Pine: Lighthouse	46	37	53	32
	La Haye Point: Lighthouse	46	54	53	37
	Cape St. Mary: Lighthouse	46	49	54	11
	Placentia: Verde Point Lighthouse	47	14	54	00
	Fox I.: Lighthouse	47	21	53	59
	Marticot I.: Lighthouse	47	19	54	34

APPENDIX IV

MARITIME POSITIONS

EAST COAST OF NORTH AMERICA—Continued

Coast	Place	Lat. N. ° ′	Long. W. ° ′
Newfoundland	Long I.: Lighthouse	47 18	54 42
	Iron I.: Lighthouse	47 03	55 07
	Burin I.: Dodding Head Lighthouse	47 00	55 09
	Little St. Lawrence Harbor: Lighthouse	46 54	55 20
	Lamaline Harbor, Allan Island: Lighthouse	46 51	55 48
	Green Island: Lighthouse	46 52	56 05
	Galantry Head: Lighthouse	46 46	56 10
	Plate Point: Lighthouse	46 49	56 24
	Cape Blanc: Lighthouse	47 06	56 24
	Grand Bank: Lighthouse	47 08	55 42
	Garnish: Lighthouse	47 14	55 22
	Long Harbor Point: Lighthouse	47 34	55 07
	St. Jacques I.: Lighthouse	47 28	55 25
	Brunet I., Mercer Head: Lighthouse	47 15	55 52
	Harbor Breton: Lighthouse	47 28	55 48
	Pass I.: Lighthouse	47 29	56 12
	Gaultois Harbor: Lighthouse	47 36	55 54
	Great Jervis Harbor: Lighthouse	47 38	56 09
	New Harbor Island: Lighthouse	47 36	56 38
	Penguin Islands: Lighthouse	47 23	56 59
	Ramea I.: Lighthouse	47 30	57 24
	Boar I.: Lighthouse	47 36	57 35
	Ireland I.: Lighthouse	47 38	58 22
	Christmas Head: Lighthouse	47 40	58 23
	Rose Blanche Point: Lighthouse	47 36	58 41
	Great Burnt Island: Lighthouse	47 36	58 53
	Pitmans I.: Lighthouse	47 35	58 58
	Port Basque: Lighthouse	47 34	59 07
	Cape Ray: Lighthouse	47 37	59 18
	Cape Anguille: Lighthouse	47 54	59 25
	St. George Harbor: Sandy Point Lighthouse	48 27	58 29
	Cape St. George: Lighthouse	48 28	59 15
	Long Point: Lighthouse	48 47	58 46
	Broad Cove: Lighthouse	48 46	58 37
	Little Port: Lighthouse	49 07	58 25
	Frenchmans Head: Lighthouse	49 04	58 10
	Eagle I.: Lighthouse	49 10	58 08
	Woody Point: Lighthouse	49 30	57 54
	Lobster Cove Head: Lighthouse	49 36	57 57
	Cow Head: Lighthouse	49 55	57 49
	Keppel Island: Lighthouse	50 38	57 19
	Rich Point: Lighthouse	50 42	57 24
Nova Scotia	Baccaro Point: Lighthouse	43 27	65 28
	Cape Sable I.: W. Hd. Lt	43 27	65 39
	Bon Portage I.: Lighthouse	43 27	65 45
	Seal I.: Lighthouse	43 24	66 01
	Pubnico Harbor Beach Point: Lighthouse	43 36	65 47
	Peases I.: Lighthouse	43 38	66 02
	Yarmouth, Cape Fourchu: Lighthouse	43 47	66 09
	Cape St. Mary: Lighthouse	44 05	66 13
	Brier I.: Lighthouse	44 15	66 24
	Boars Head: Lighthouse	44 24	66 13
	Prim Point: Lighthouse	44 41	65 47
	Hampton: Lighthouse	44 54	65 21
	Margaretville: Lighthouse	45 03	65 04
	Walton Harbor: Lighthouse	45 14	64 01
	Isle Haute: Lighthouse	45 15	65 00
	Apple River, Cape Capstan: Lighthouse	45 28	64 51
New Brunswick	Fort Folly Point: Lighthouse	45 52	64 34
	Grindstone Island: Lighthouse	45 43	64 37
	Cape Enrage: Lighthouse	45 36	64 47
	Martin Head: Lighthouse	45 29	65 11
	Quaco Head: Lighthouse	45 19	65 32
	Cape Spencer: Lighthouse	45 12	65 55
	St. John: Partridge I. Lighthouse	45 14	66 03
	Time ball	45 17	66 04
	Lorneville, Dock Lt	45 12	66 09
	Musquash: Lighthouse	45 09	66 14
	Lepreau Point: Lighthouse	45 04	66 28
	Wolves I.: Lighthouse	44 56	66 44
	Bliss I.: Lighthouse	45 01	66 51
	St. Andrews: Lighthouse	45 04	67 03
	Chance Harbor: Reef Point Lighthouse	45 08	66 21
New Brunswick	East Quoddy Head: Lighthouse	44 57	66 54
	Grand Manan I.:		
	Swallowtail Lighthouse	44 46	66 44
	Gull Cove Lighthouse	44 38	66 42
	Grand Harbor Lighthouse	44 40	66 45
	S. W. Head Lighthouse	44 36	66 54
	Gannet Rock: Lighthouse	44 31	66 47
	Machias Seal I.: Lighthouse	44 30	67 06
Nova Scotia	Queensport: Rook I. Lighthouse	45 21	61 16
	Canso Harbor: Cutler (Hart) I. Lighthouse	45 21	60 59
	Cranberry I.: Lighthouse	45 20	60 56
	Whitehead I.: Lighthouse	45 12	61 08
	Three Top I.: Lighthouse	45 13	61 10
	Cole Harbor: Front Lighthouse	45 16	61 17
	Berry Head: Lighthouse	45 11	61 19
	Country I.: Lighthouse	45 06	61 33
	Harbor I.: Lighthouse	45 08	61 37
	Isaac Harbor: Lighthouse	45 10	61 40
	Wedge I.: Lighthouse	45 00	61 53
	Liscomb I.: Lighthouse	44 59	61 58
	Marie Joseph Harbor: Thrumcap I. Lighthouse	44 58	62 03
	Beaver Islands:		
	Lighthouse	44 49	62 21
	Harbor: Lighthouse	44 54	62 23
	Sheet Harbor:		
	Passage Lighthouse	44 51	62 27
	Sheet Rock Lighthouse	44 50	62 29
	Tomlees Head: Lighthouse	44 49	62 36
	Pope Harbor: Lighthouse	44 48	62 39
	Wolf Point: Lighthouse	44 45	62 46
	Owls Head: Lighthouse	44 43	62 48
	Egg I.: Lighthouse	44 40	62 52
	Jeddore:		
	Rock Lighthouse	44 40	63 01
	Harbor front Lighthouse	44 43	63 01
	Halifax:		
	Devil I. rear Lighthouse	44 35	63 28
	Post office clock tower	44 39	63 35
	Dockyard Observatory	44 39	63 36
	Mauger Beach Lighthouse	44 36	63 32
	McNab Island Lighthouse	44 37	63 32
	Chebucto Head Lighthouse	44 30	63 31
	Sambro Island:		
	Lighthouse	44 26	63 34
	Harbor Lighthouse	44 28	63 36
	Pennant Harbor: Lighthouse	44 28	63 38
	Betty I. Brig Point: Lighthouse	44 26	63 46
	Prospect Harbor: Sauls I. Lighthouse	44 28	63 47
	Port Dover: Lighthouse	44 29	63 51
	Peggy Point: Lighthouse	44 29	63 55
	Indian Harbor: Paddy Head I. Lighthouse	44 31	63 56
	Croucher I.: Lighthouse	44 38	63 57
	E. Ironbound I.: Lighthouse	44 26	64 05
	Pearl I.: Lighthouse	44 23	64 03
	Chester: Quaker I. Lighthouse	44 31	64 14
	Mahone: Wasthaver I. Lighthouse	44 26	64 20
	Cross I: Lighthouse	44 19	64 10
	Lunenburg: Battery Point Lighthouse	44 22	64 18
	West Ironbound I.: Lighthouse	44 14	64 16
	La Havre: Fort Point Lighthouse	44 17	64 21
	Port Medway: Medway Head Lighthouse	44 06	64 32
	Coffin I.: Lighthouse	44 02	64 37
	Liverpool: Western Head Lighthouse	43 59	64 40
	Spectacle I.: Lighthouse	43 55	64 48
	Little Hope I.: Lighthouse	43 49	64 47
	Port Herbert: Lighthouse	43 49	64 55
	Lockeport: Gull Rock Lighthouse	43 39	65 06
	Shelburne: Sand Spit Lighthouse	43 41	65 19
	Cape Roseway: Lighthouse	43 37	65 16
	Negro Island:		
	Lighthouse	43 30	65 21
	Harbor front Lighthouse	43 33	65 23
	Salvages Rocks: Lighthouse	43 28	65 23
	Port Latour: Page I. Lighthouse	43 29	65 27

MARITIME POSITIONS

EAST COAST OF NORTH AMERICA—Continued

Coast	Place	Lat. N. °	Lat. N. ′	Long. W. °	Long. W. ′
Prince Edward Island	North Point: Lighthouse	47	04	63	59
	Cascumpeque Harbor: Lighthouse	46	48	64	02
	Fish (Bill Hook) I.: Lighthouse	46	35	63	42
	Cape Tryon: Lighthouse	46	32	63	30
	North London: Lighthouse	46	31	63	29
	Tracadie Harbor: Lighthouse	46	25	63	02
	St. Peters Harbor: Lighthouse	46	26	62	45
	Shipwreck Point: Lighthouse	46	28	62	25
	East Point: Lighthouse	46	27	61	58
	Souris: Knights Point Lighthouse	46	21	62	15
	Grand (Boughton) River Banks Point: Lighthouse	46	16	62	25
	Panmure Head: Lighthouse	46	09	62	28
	Murray Harbor, Beach Point: Lighthouse	46	01	62	28
	Cape Bear: Lighthouse	46	00	62	28
	Little Sands: Lighthouse	45	58	62	39
	Wood Island: Lighthouse	45	57	62	45
	Prim Point: Lighthouse	46	03	63	02
	Charlottetown Harbor: Haszard Point: Lighthouse	46	12	63	05
	St. Peter Island: Lighthouse	46	07	63	11
	Sea Cow Head: Lighthouse	46	19	63	48
	Cape Egmont: Lighthouse	46	24	64	08
	West Point: Lighthouse	46	37	64	23
	Miminegash: Lighthouse	46	53	64	14
Cape Breton Island	Pomquet (Bayfield): Lighthouse	45	40	61	44
	Havre Bouche: Lighthouse	45	41	61	31
	North Canso: Lighthouse	45	42	61	29
	Henry Island: Lighthouse	45	59	61	36
	Port Hood: Lighthouse	46	00	61	31
	Mabou: Lighthouse	46	05	61	28
	Sea Wolf (Margaree) I.: Lighthouse	46	21	61	16
	Margaree: Lighthouse	46	26	61	07
	Friar Head: Lighthouse	46	30	61	04
	Grand Etang (Squirrel Pond): Lighthouse	46	33	61	02
	Cheticamp I.: Lighthouse	46	36	61	03
	Cape St. Lawrence: Lighthouse	47	03	60	35
	Cape North: Lighthouse	47	02	60	23
	St. Paul I.:				
	South Point Lighthouse	47	11	60	10
	North Point Lighthouse	47	14	60	08
	White Point: Lighthouse	46	53	60	21
	Neil Harbor: Lighthouse	46	49	60	19
	Ingonish:				
	Island Lighthouse	46	41	60	20
	Harbor Lighthouse	46	38	60	23
	St. Ann Beach Point: Lighthouse	46	18	60	32
	Ciboux Island: Lighthouse	46	23	60	22
	Gillis Point: Lighthouse	46	02	60	46
	Aconi Point: Lighthouse	46	19	60	17
	Sydney Harbor:				
	Edward Point Lighthouse	46	11	60	15
	Flat Point Lighthouse	46	16	60	08
	Lingan Head: Lighthouse	46	14	60	02
	Flint Island: Lighthouse	46	11	59	46
	Scatari Island:				
	W. side Lighthouse	46	00	59	48
	NE. side Lighthouse	46	02	59	41
	Louisburg: Lighthouse	45	54	59	58
	Guion (Guyon) I.: Lighthouse	45	46	60	07
	St. Esprit I.: Lighthouse	45	37	60	29
	Cape Rond: Lighthouse	45	35	60	53
	Green Island: Lighthouse	45	29	60	54
	Balache Point: Lighthouse	45	39	61	25
	Eddy (Sandy): Lighthouse	45	31	61	15
	Guysborough Harbor: Lighthouse	45	23	61	29
Maine	Calais: Astronomical station	45	11	67	17
	Eastport: Cong. Church	44	54	66	59
	West Quoddy Head: Lighthouse	44	49	66	57
	Little River: Lighthouse	44	39	67	11
	Libby Islands: Lighthouse	44	34	67	22
	Petit Manan Island: Lighthouse	44	22	67	52
	Bakers Island: Lighthouse	44	14	68	12
	Mount Desert Rock: Lighthouse	43	58	68	08
	Bangor: Thomas Hill	44	48	68	47
	Belfast: Methodist Church	44	25	69	00
	Rockland: Episcopal Church	44	06	69	07
	Matinicus Rock: Lighthouse	43	47	68	51
	Monhegan Island: Lighthouse	43	46	69	19
	Seguin Island: Lighthouse	43	42	69	46
	Bath: Winter St. Church	43	55	69	49
Maine	Halfway Rock: Lighthouse	43	39	70	02
	Portland:				
	Customhouse	43	39	70	15
	Portland Head Lighthouse	43	37	70	12
	Cape Elizabeth: Lighthouse (east)	43	34	70	12
	Wood Island: Lighthouse	43	27	70	20
	Cape Neddick: Lighthouse	43	10	70	35
	Boon Island: Lighthouse	43	07	70	29
N. H.	Whaleback Reef: Lighthouse	43	04	70	42
	Portsmouth:				
	Navy yard flagstaff	43	05	70	44
	Fort Constitution	43	04	70	43
	Isles of Shoals: White I. Lighthouse	42	58	70	37
Massachusetts	Newburyport:				
	Academy	42	49	70	52
	Plum I. Lighthouse	42	49	70	49
	Ipswich: Lighthouse (rear)	42	41	70	46
	Annisquam Harbor: Lighthouse	42	40	70	41
	Cape Ann: Thatchers I. Lighthouse (N.)	42	38	70	35
	Gloucester:				
	Eastern Point Lighthouse	42	35	70	40
	Ten-pound I. Lighthouse	42	36	70	40
	Bakers Island: Lighthouse	42	32	70	47
	Beverly: Hospital Pt. Lighthouse	42	33	70	51
	Salem: Derbys Wharf Lighthouse	42	31	70	53
	Marblehead: Lighthouse	42	30	70	50
	Cambridge: Harvard Observatory (dome)	42	23	71	08
	Boston:				
	Navy yard flagstaff	42	22	71	03
	The Graves Lighthouse	42	22	70	52
	Lighthouse I. Lighthouse	42	20	70	53
	Minots Ledge: Lighthouse	42	16	70	46
	Plymouth: Gurnet Lighthouse	42	00	70	36
	Barnstable: Sandy Neck Lighthouse	41	43	70	17
	Cape Cod:				
	Highlands Lighthouse	42	02	70	04
	Nauset Beach Lighthouse	41	52	69	57
	Chatham: Lighthouse (south)	41	40	69	57
	Monomoy Point: Old tower	41	34	70	00
	Nantucket:				
	Great Point Lighthouse	41	23	70	03
	South Church	41	17	70	06
	Sankaty Head Lighthouse	41	17	69	58
	Cape Poge: Lighthouse	41	25	70	27
	Tarpaulin Cove: Lighthouse	41	28	70	45
	Vineyard Haven: W. Chop Lighthouse	41	29	70	36
	Gay Head: Lighthouse	41	21	70	50
	Cuttyhunk: Lighthouse	41	25	70	57
	New Bedford: Baptist Church	41	38	70	56
Rhode Island	Sakonnet: Lighthouse	41	27	71	12
	Newport: Flagstaff, torpedo station	41	29	71	20
	Bristol Ferry: Lighthouse	41	39	71	16
	Providence: Brown University Obsy	41	50	71	24
	Beavertail: Lighthouse	41	27	71	24
	Point Judith: Lighthouse	41	22	71	29
	Block Island: Lighthouse (SE.)	41	09	71	33
	Watch Hill Point: Lighthouse	41	18	71	52
Connecticut and New York	Montauk Point: Lighthouse	41	04	71	51
	Stonington: Lighthouse (inner breakwater)	41	20	71	55
	New London: Groton Monument	41	21	72	05
	Race Rock: Lighthouse	41	15	72	03
	Little Gull Island: Lighthouse	41	12	72	06
	Plum Island: Lighthouse, W. pt.	41	10	72	13
	Saybrook: Lighthouse, Lynde Pt.	41	16	72	21
	Falkner Island: Lighthouse	41	13	72	39
	New Haven:				
	Yale Univ. Obs. Transit Inst.	41	19	72	55
	Lighthouse breakwater	41	13	72	57
	Stratford Point: Lighthouse	41	09	73	06
	Bridgeport Harbor: Lighthouse	41	09	73	11
	Eaton Neck: Lighthouse	40	57	73	24
	Shinnecock Bay: Lighthouse	40	51	72	30
	Fire Island: Lighthouse	40	38	73	13
	New York:				
	Navy yard flatstaff	40	42	73	59
	City Hall	40	43	74	00
	Ft. Wadsworth: Lighthouse	40	36	74	03

APPENDIX IV

MARITIME POSITIONS

EAST COAST OF NORTH AMERICA—Continued

Coast	Place	Lat. N. °	Lat. N. ′	Long. W. °	Long. W. ′
Va., Del., Pa., and N. J.	Sandy Hook: Lighthouse (rear)	40	28	74	00
	Navesink Highlands: Lighthouse (S)	40	24	73	59
	Sea Girt: Lighthouse	40	08	74	02
	Barnegat Inlet: Lighthouse	39	46	74	06
	Tuckers Beach: Lighthouse	39	30	74	17
	Absecon Inlet: Lighthouse	39	22	74	25
	Ludlam Beach: Lighthouse	39	10	74	41
	Hereford Inlet: Lighthouse	39	00	74	48
	Cape May: Lighthouse	38	56	74	58
	Philadelphia:				
	Univ. Obs. (dome)	39	58	75	17
	Navy yard flatstaff, League I.	39	53	75	11
	Wilmington: Town Hall	39	44	75	33
	Cape Henlopen: Lighthouse	38	47	75	05
	Fenwick Island: Lighthouse	38	27	75	03
	Assateague Island: Lighthouse	37	55	75	21
	Hog Island: Lighthouse	37	24	75	42
	Cape Charles: Lighthouse	37	07	75	54
Maryland	Baltimore: Johns Hopkins Obs	39	18	76	37
	Annapolis: Naval Academy Obs	38	59	76	29
	Point Lookout: Lighthouse	38	02	76	19
	Washington, D. C.:				
	Navy yard flagstaff	38	52	77	00
	Naval Observatory	38	55	77	04
	Capitol dome	38	53	77	01
	Old Point Comfort: Lighthouse	37	00	76	18
	Norfolk: Navy yard flagstaff	36	50	76	18
	Cape Henry: Lighthouse	36	56	76	00
North Carolina	Currituck Beach: Lighthouse	36	23	75	50
	Bodie Island: Lighthouse	35	49	75	34
	Cape Hatteras: Lighthouse	35	15	75	31
	Ocracoke: Lighthouse	35	07	75	59
	Newbern: Episcopal spire	35	06	77	02
	Cape Lookout: Lighthouse	34	37	76	31
	Beaufort: Courthouse	34	43	76	40
	Cape Fear: Lighthouse	33	51	77	58
	Bald Head: Lighthouse	33	52	78	00
South Carolina	Georgetown:				
	Episcopal Church	33	22	79	17
	Lighthouse, North I.	33	13	79	11
	Cape Romain: Lighthouse	33	01	79	22
	Charleston:				
	Lighthouse, Morris I.	32	42	79	53
	St. Michael's Church	32	47	79	56
	Beaufort: Episcopal Church	32	26	80	40
	Hunting I.: Lighthouse	32	23	80	26
	Hilton Head: Lighthouse (front)	32	10	80	43
Georgia	Tybee Island: Lighthouse (rear)	32	01	80	51
	Savannah: Exchange spire	32	05	81	05
	Sapelo Island: Lighthouse	31	24	81	17
	St. Simon: Lighthouse (rear)	31	08	81	24
	Brunswick: Academy	31	09	81	29
Florida	St. Andrew Sound: Lighthouse	31	00	81	25
	Amelia Island: Lighthouse	30	40	81	27
	Fernandina: Water tower	30	40	81	27
	St. Johns River: Lighthouse	30	24	81	26
	Jacksonville: Methodist Church	30	20	81	39
	St. Augustine:				
	Presbyterian Church	29	53	81	19
	Lighthouse	29	53	81	17
	Mosquito Inlet: Lighthouse	29	05	80	56
	Cape Canaveral: Lighthouse	28	28	80	33
	Jupiter Inlet: Lighthouse	26	57	80	05
	West Palm Beach Cath. Church spire	26	43	80	03
	Hillsboro Inlet: Lighthouse	26	16	80	05
	Fowey Rocks: Lighthouse	25	35	80	06
	Carysfort Reef: Lighthouse	25	13	80	13
	Alligator Reef: Lighthouse	24	51	80	37
	Sombrero Key: Lighthouse	24	37	81	07
	American Shoal: Lighthouse	24	31	81	31
	Sand Key: Lighthouse	24	27	81	53
	Key West: Lighthouse	24	33	81	48
	Rebecca Shoal: Lighthouse	24	35	82	35
	Loggerhead Key: Dry Tortugas Lighthouse	24	38	82	55
	Sanibel Island: Lighthouse	26	27	82	01
	Gasparilla Island: Lighthouse (rear)	26	42	82	16

Coast	Place	Lat. N. °	Lat. N. ′	Long. W. °	Long. W. ′
Florida	Tampa Bay: Egmont Key Lighthouse	27	36	82	46
	Anclote Keys: Lighthouse	28	10	82	51
	Cedar Keys:				
	Ast. station, Depot Key	29	07	83	02
	North Bank No. 1 Lighthouse	29	09	83	06
	St. Marks:				
	Fort St. Marks	30	09	84	13
	Lighthouse	30	04	84	11
	Crooked River: Lighthouse (rear)	29	50	84	42
	Apalachicola: Flagstaff	29	44	84	59
	Cape St. George: Lighthouse	29	35	85	03
	Cape San Blas: Lighthouse	29	40	85	21
	St. Joseph Point: Lighthouse (rear)	29	55	85	23
	Pensacola:				
	Lighthouse	30	21	87	18
	Navy-yard chimney	30	21	87	16
Alabama, Mississippi, and Louisiana	Sand Island: Lighthouse	30	11	88	03
	Mobile Point: Lighthouse	30	14	88	01
	Mobile: Episcopal Church	30	41	88	02
	Horn Island: Lighthouse	30	13	88	29
	Round Island: Lighthouse	30	18	88	35
	Biloxi: Lighthouse	30	24	88	54
	Ship Island: Lighthouse	30	13	88	58
	Cat Island: Lighthouse	30	14	89	10
	Chandeleur: Lighthouse	30	03	88	52
	Mississippi River Mouth:				
	Pass A, Loutre Lighthouse	29	11	89	02
	S. Pass, Lighthouse (rear)	29	01	89	10
	SW. Pass, Lighthouse	28	58	89	23
	New Orleans: United States Mint	29	58	90	03
	Barataria Bay: Lighthouse	29	16	89	57
	Timbalier Island: Lighthouse	29	03	90	21
	Ship Shoal: Lighthouse	28	55	91	04
	Point au Fer Reef Lighthouse	29	22	91	23
	Calcasieu Pass: Lighthouse (rear)	29	47	93	21
	Sabine Bank: Lighthouse	29	28	93	43
	Sabine Pass: Lighthouse	29	43	93	51
Texas	Galveston:				
	Cathedral, N. spire	29	18	94	47
	Bolivar Pt. Lighthouse	29	22	94	46
	Brazos River: Lighthouse	28	57	95	19
	Matagorda: Lighthouse	28	20	96	25
	Aransas Pass: Lighthouse	27	52	97	03
	Brazos Santiago: Lighthouse	26	04	97	10
Mexico	Punta Jerez: Lighthouse	22	54	97	46
	Tampico: Lighthouse	22	16	97	50
	Lobos I.: Lighthouse	21	28	97	13
	Mata Redonda: Lighthouse	21	14	97	24
	Tuxpam: Lighthouse	21	00	97	19
	Tecolutla: Lighthouse	20	30	97	01
	Nautla: Lighthouse	20	16	96	46
	Punta Delgada: Lighthouse	19	51	96	28
	Tacubaya National Observatory (Meridian circle)	19	24	99	12
	Veracruz:				
	Blanquilla Reef: Light	19	14	96	06
	Anegada de Adentro Reef: Light	19	14	96	04
	Verde I.: Light	19	12	96	04
	Sacrificios I.: Light	19	10	96	05
	Lighthouse (Edificio)	19	12	96	08
	Enmedio I.: Light	19	06	95	56
	Blanca Reef: Lighthouse	19	05	96	00
	El Jiote Reef: Lighthouse	19	04	96	00
	Santiaguillo I.: Lighthouse	19	08	95	48
	Roca Partida: Lighthouse	18	44	95	11
	Puerto Mexico W.: Lighthouse	18	09	94	25
	Tonala: Lighthouse	18	12	94	08
	Frontera: Lighthouse	18	39	92	42
	Carmen I.: Lighthouse	18	39	91	51
	Aguada I.: Lighthouse	18	47	91	31
	Champoton River: Lighthouse	19	21	90	43
	Morros Point: Lighthouse	19	41	90	42
	Arcas Cays: Lighthouse (rear)	20	13	91	59
	West Triangles Reef: Lighthouse	20	58	92	19

MARITIME POSITIONS

EAST COAST OF NORTH AMERICA—Continued

Coast	Place	Lat. N.	Long. W.
		° ′	° ′
Yucatan Peninsula	Xicalango: Lighthouse	18 38	91 54
	Campeche: Lighthouse	19 50	90 32
	Celestun: Lighthouse	20 52	90 24
	Arenas Cay: Lighthouse	22 07	91 24
	Sisal: Lighthouse	21 10	90 02
	Progreso: Lighthouse	21 17	89 40
	Alacran Reef: Lighthouse	22 24	89 42
	Merida: Cathedral	20 58	89 37
	Yalkubul Point: Lighthouse	21 31	88 37
	Monte de Cuyo: Lighthouse	21 31	87 41
	Cape Catoche: Lighthouse	21 37	87 04
	Mujeres I.: Lighthouse	21 12	86 43
	Cozumel I.:		
	North Point Lighthouse	20 36	86 44
	South Point Lighthouse	20 16	86 59
	San Miguel Lighthouse	20 31	86 57
	Herrero Point: Lighthouse	19 18	87 27
	Chinchorro Bank: North Cays Lighthouse	18 46	87 19
	Xcalak: Lighthouse	18 14	87 50
Br. Honduras	Rocky Point: Lighthouse	18 22	88 09
	Mauger Cay: Lighthouse	17 37	87 47
	Northern Two Cays: Lighthouse	17 27	87 28
	Half Moon Cay: Lighthouse	17 12	87 32
	Bokel Cay: Lighthouse	17 10	87 54
	Belize: Fort George Lighthouse	17 30	88 11
	East Snake Cay: Lighthouse	16 12	88 31
	Punta Gorda: Lighthouse	16 05	88 49
Honduras	Cape Three Points Lighthouse	15 57	88 36
	Caballos Point: Lighthouse	15 49	87 57
	Tela: Pier light	15 46	87 27
	Utila I. (West): Lighthouse	16 06	87 00
	Swan I.: Lighthouse	17 24	83 56
	False Cape: Lighthouse	15 13	83 23
Nicaragua	Cape Gracias a Dios: Lighthouse	15 00	83 09
	Gorda Point: Lighthouse	14 21	83 12
	Puerto Cabezas: Lighthouse	14 02	83 23
	Quito Sueño Bank: Lighthouse	14 28	81 07
	Serrano Bank: S. W. Cay Lighthouse	14 17	80 24
	Roncador Bank: Lighthouse	13 35	80 04
	Old Providence I.: Lighthouse	13 19	81 23
	St. Andrews I.: Lighthouse	12 36	81 41
	Little Corn I.: Lighthouse	12 18	82 59
	Bluefields Bluff: Lighthouse	12 00	83 41
C. R.	Greytown: Lighthouse	10 56	83 42
	Port Limon: Grape (or Uva) Cay Lighthouse	10 00	83 01
Panama	Cape Toro: Lighthouse	9 22	82 13
	Toro Point: Lighthouse	9 22	79 57
	Colon: East Breakwater Channel light	9 23	79 55
	Isla Grande: Lighthouse	9 38	79 34

WEST COAST OF NORTH AMERICA

Coast	Place	Lat. N.	Long. W.
Alaska	Point Barrow	71 23	156 18
	Icy Cape	70 16	161 47
	Cape Lisburne	68 52	166 06
	Point Hope: Lighthouse	68 20	166 45
	Cape Krusenstern	67 09	163 39
	Chamisso I	66 14	161 45
	CapeEspenberg: Light	66 35	163 40
	DiomedeI. Fairway Rock	65 36	168 40
	Cape Prince of Wales: Light	65 36	168 05
	Grantley Harbor: Light	65 17	166 20
	Point Spencer: Light	65 17	166 50
	King I	64 58	168 02
	Sledge I.: Lighthouse	64 30	166 11
	Nome: Ames Bldg., F. S	64 30	165 24
	Port Safety: Front Light	64 28	164 44
	Cheenik: Light	64 33	163 02
	Golofnin Bay: Light	64 31	162 55
	Whale I.: Lighthouse	63 30	161 59
	Cape Stephens: Lighthouse	63 33	162 18
	Point Romanoff: Lighthouse	63 12	162 50
	Pastolik River: Lighthouse	63 02	163 19
	Cape Romanzof	61 48	166 04
	St. Lawrence I. NE. Cape	63 18	168 42
	St. Matthew I. Cape Upright	60 18	172 04
	Pribilof I., St. George I., Dalnoi Pt	56 36	169 47
	Port Moller Cannery	55 59	160 34
	Ketchikan: Courthouse	55 21	131 39
Aleutian Is.			Long. E.
	Attu I.: Chichagof Harbor Ast. Sta	52 56	173 14
	Kiska I.: Kiska Harbor Ast. Sta	51 59	177 30
	Amchitka I.: Constantine Harbor Ast. Sta	51 23	179 21
			Long. W.
	Adak I.: Unalga Bight, Bay of Is	51 46	176 49
	Atka: Church spire	52 12	174 12
	Nikolski: Church	52 56	168 52
	Dutch Harbor Spithead: Lighthouse	53 53	166 31
	Akutan: Lighthouse	54 09	165 44
	Cape Sarichef: Lighthouse	54 36	164 56
	Unimak I.:		
	Scotch Cap: Lighthouse	54 24	164 45
	Cape Pankof: Lighthouse	54 40	163 04
	Sanak: Lighthouse	54 29	162 44
	Kabuch Point: Lighthouse	54 49	163 21
	Fox I.: Lighthouse	54 57	162 26
	Iliasik I.: Lighthouse	55 02	161 56
	Arch Point: Lighthouse	55 12	161 54
Alaska	Shumagin Is.:		
	Unga Spit	55 24	160 43
	Pirate Cove: Lighthouse	55 22	160 22
	Cape Wedge: Lighthouse	55 18	159 53
	Kukak Bay: Lighthouse	58 20	154 11
	Kodiak I.:		
	Harvester I.: Spit Light	57 38	154 00
	Prokoda I.: Lighthouse	57 54	152 31
	Puffin I.: Lighthouse	57 45	152 26
	Hanin Rocks: Lighthouse	57 50	152 19
	Afognak I.: Cape Tonki Lighthouse	58 21	152 00
	E. Amatuli I.: Lighthouse	58 55	151 58
	Chisik I.: Lighthouse	60 05	152 34
	Kalgin I.: Lighthouse	60 29	151 50
	East Foreland: Lighthouse	60 43	151 25
	Anchor Point: Lighthouse	59 46	151 52
	Seldovia: Gray Cliff Lighthouse	59 27	151 44
	Flat I.: Lighthouse	59 20	152 00
	Pearl I.: Lighthouse	59 07	151 38
	Chugach I.: Lighthouse	59 06	151 27
	Seal Rocks: Lighthouse	59 31	149 38
	Pilot Rocks: Lighthouse	59 44	149 29
	Hive I.: Lighthouse	59 53	149 23
	Point Elrington: Lighthouse	59 56	148 15
	Cape Hinchinbrook: Lighthouse	60 14	146 39
	Johnston Point: Lighthouse	60 29	146 37
	Valdez:		
	Middle Rock Lighthouse	61 05	146 40
	Busby I. Lighthouse	60 54	146 49
	Orca Bay:		
	Gravina Point: Lighthouse	60 37	146 16
	Channel I.: Lighthouse	60 37	145 49
	Egg Islands: Lighthouse	60 22	145 44
	Martin Islands: Lighthouse	60 10	144 37
	Kayak I. Cape St. Elias: Lighthouse	59 48	144 36
	Ocean Cape: Lighthouse	59 32	139 51
	Cape Spencer: Lighthouse	58 12	136 38
	Cape Edward: Lighthouse	57 41	136 15
	Cape Edgecumbe: Lighthouse	57 00	135 51
	Sitka Harbor: Lighthouse	57 03	135 20
	Cape Ommaney: Lighthouse	56 10	134 40
	Point Crowley: Lighthouse	56 07	134 15
	Cape Chacon: Lighthouse	54 41	132 01
Queen Charlotte Is.	Langara I.: Lighthouse	54 15	133 03
	Cape St. James: Lighthouse	51 53	131 02
	Copper Is.: Lighthouse	52 20	131 10
	Low I.: Lighthouse	52 55	131 31
	Kingui I.: Lighthouse	53 01	131 38

MARITIME POSITIONS

WEST COAST OF NORTH AMERICA—Continued

Coast	Place	Lat. N. °	Lat. N. ′	Long. W. °	Long. W. ′
Vancouver Island	Entrance I.: Lighthouse	50	26	128	02
	Lookout I.: Lighthouse	50	00	127	28
	Nootka: San Rafael I. Lighthouse	49	35	126	38
	Estevan Point: Lighthouse	49	22	126	32
	Lennard Island: Lighthouse	49	07	125	56
	Amphitrite Point: Lighthouse	48	55	125	33
	Swale Rock: Lighthouse	48	56	125	13
	Cape Beale: Lighthouse	48	47	125	13
	Pachena Point: Lighthouse	48	44	125	06
	Carmanah: Lighthouse	48	37	124	45
	Sheringham Point: Lighthouse	48	22	123	56
	Race Rocks: Lighthouse	48	18	123	32
	Victoria Harbor: Berens I. Lighthouse	48	25	123	24
	Fiddle Reef: Lighthouse	48	26	123	17
	Discovery I.: Lighthouse	48	25	123	13
Washington	Point Roberts: Lighthouse	48	58	123	05
	Semiamoo Harbor: Lighthouse	49	00	122	47
	Patos Islands: Lighthouse	48	47	122	58
	Smith Island: Lighthouse	48	19	122	51
	West Point: Lighthouse	47	40	122	26
	Seattle: C. S. ast. station	47	36	122	20
	Tacoma: St. Luke's Church	47	16	122	26
	Robinson Pt.: Lighthouse	47	23	122	22
	Bremerton: Navy yard flagstaff	47	34	122	38
	Alki Point: Lighthouse	47	35	122	25
	Point No Point: Lighthouse	47	55	122	32
	Port Townsend: Hudson Pt. Lighthouse	48	07	122	45
	Point Wilson: Lighthouse	48	09	122	45
	New Dungeness: Lighthouse	48	11	123	07
	Port Angeles: Ediz Hook Lighthouse	48	08	123	24
	Slip Point: Lighthouse	48	16	124	15
	Cape Flattery: Lighthouse	48	24	124	44
	Destruction Island: Lighthouse	47	40	124	29
	Grays Harbor: Lighthouse	46	53	124	07
	Willapa Bay: Lighthouse	46	43	124	04
	Cape Disappointment: Lighthouse	46	17	124	03
Oregon	Tillamook Rock: Lighthouse	45	56	124	01
	Cape Meares: Lighthouse	45	29	123	59
	Yaquina Head: Lighthouse	44	41	124	05
	Heceta Head: Lighthouse	44	08	124	08
	Siuslaw Inlet: Light (front)	44	01	124	08
	Umpqua River: Lighthouse	43	40	124	12
	Cape Arago: Lighthouse	43	20	124	22
	Coquille River: Lighthouse	43	07	124	25
	Cape Blanco: Lighthouse	42	50	124	34
California	St. George Reef: Lighthouse	41	50	124	22
	Crescent City: Lighthouse	41	45	124	12
	Redding Rock: Lighthouse	41	20	124	11
	Trinidad Head: Lighthouse	41	03	124	09
	Eureka: Methodist Church	40	48	124	10
	Table Bluff: Lighthouse	40	42	124	16
	Cape Mendocino: Lighthouse	40	26	124	24
	Punta Gorda: Lighthouse	40	15	124	21
	Point Cabrillo: Lighthouse	39	21	123	50
	Point Arena: Lighthouse	38	57	123	44
	Point Reyes: Lighthouse	38	00	123	01
	Point Bonita: Lighthouse	37	49	122	32
	Alcatraz: Lighthouse	37	50	122	25
	Carquinez Strait: Lighthouse	38	04	122	15
	Mare I.: Chron. and time sta. Navy Yard	38	06	122	16
	Berkeley: Univ. of Cal. Obs	37	52	122	16
	San Francisco: W/T Station, K. P. O., east tower	37	32	122	13
	Goat Island: Lighthouse	37	48	122	22
	Mile Rocks: Lighthouse	37	48	122	31
	S. E. Farallon: Lighthouse	37	42	123	00
	Point Montara: Lighthouse	37	32	122	31
	Pigeon Point: Lighthouse	37	11	122	24
	Año Nuevo I.: Lighthouse	37	06	122	20
	Santa Cruz: Lighthouse	36	57	122	02
	Point Pinos: Lighthouse	36	38	121	56
	Point Sur: Lighthouse	36	18	121	54
	Piedras Blancas: Lighthouse	35	40	121	17
	San Luis Obispo: Lighthouse	35	10	120	46
	Point Arguello: Lighthouse	34	35	120	39
California	Point Conception: Lighthouse	34	27	120	28
	Richardson Rock: Lighthouse	34	06	120	31
	Santa Barbara: Lighthouse	34	24	119	43
	Point Hueneme: Lighthouse	34	09	119	13
	Anacapa Island: Lighthouse	34	01	119	22
	Point Fermin: Lighthouse	33	42	118	18
	Los Angeles Harbor: Light (breakwater)	33	43	118	15
	Point Loma: Lighthouse	32	40	117	15
	Santa Catalina I.: Catalina Peak	33	23	118	24
	San Nicolas I.: Summit	33	15	119	31
Lower California	Coronados Islands: North Lighthouse	32	25	117	15
	Todas Santos Islands: Lighthouse	31	49	116	49
	Banda Point: Lighthouse	31	45	116	45
	Santa Rosalia Bay: Obs. cairn	28	40	114	14
	Magdalena Bay: Man of War Cove Light	24	38	112	09
	Cabo Falso: Lighthouse	22	52	109	58
	San Jose del Cabo Bay: W/T station	23	03	109	42
	Prieta Point: Lighthouse	24	13	110	18
	La Paz: Mexican Obs. spot	24	10	110	20
	Port Loreto: Lighthouse	26	01	111	21
	Mulege: El Sombrerito Lighthouse	26	54	111	58
	Santa Rosalia: Mole Light	27	20	112	16
Mexico	Pajaros I.: Lighthouse	27	53	110	52
	Cape Haro: Lighthouse	27	50	110	54
	Lobos I.: Lighthouse	27	20	110	38
	Puerto Yavaros: Lighthouse	26	41	109	31
	Topolobampo: Mole Light	25	35	109	04
	Mazatlan: Creston I. Lighthouse	23	11	106	27
	Maria Madre I.: Balleto Pt. Lighthouse	21	36	106	33
	San Blas: Vigia Hill Lighthouse	21	32	105	19
	Customhouse	21	32	105	17
	Puerto Ballarta: Lighthouse	20	37	105	15
	Cape Corrientes: Lighthouse	20	24	105	43
	Manzanillo: Lighthouse	19	04	104	20
	Punta de Campos: Lighthouse	19	01	104	21
	San Telmo Pt.: Lighthouse	18	19	103	30
	Acapulco: Roqueta I.: Lighthouse	16	49	99	55
	Maldonado: Lighthouse	16	19	98	34
	Port Angeles: Punta Izuca Lighthouse	15	39	96	31
	Morro Ayuca: Lighthouse	15	52	95	47
	Salina Cruz: Lighthouse	16	09	95	11
	Arista: Lighthouse	15	56	93	49
	Puerto de San Benito: Lighthouse	14	42	92	26
Central America	Ocos River: Lighthouse	14	30	92	11
	Champerico: Lighthouse	14	18	91	56
	San Jose: Lighthouse	13	55	90	50
	Acajutla: Lighthouse	13	35	89	49
	Remedios Pt.: Lighthouse	13	31	89	48
	La Libertad: Lighthouse	13	29	89	19
	Amapala Point: Lighthouse	13	09	87	54
	La Union: Lighthouse	13	20	87	51
	Corinto: Cardon Head Lighthouse	12	28	87	13
	San Juan del Sur: Lighthouse	11	15	85	54
	Puntarenas: Pier light	9	58	84	50
	San Lorenzo: Lighthouse	8	12	82	13
	Linartes I.: Lighthouse	8	07	82	15
	Entrada Pt.: Lighthouse	8	05	81	45
	Burica Pt.: Lighthouse	8	01	82	53
	Afuera I.: Lighthouse	7	40	81	38
	Jicarita I.: Lighthouse	7	12	81	48
	Morro Puercos Lighthouse	7	15	80	26
	South Frailes I.: Lighthouse	7	20	80	09
	Cape Mala: Lighthouse	7	28	80	00
	Anton River: Lighthouse	8	11	80	16
	Panama Cathedral, S. tower	8	57	79	32
	Balboa: Pier light	8	57	79	34
	Bona I.: Lighthouse	8	35	79	36
	Pacheca I.: Lighthouse	8	40	79	03
	Flamenco I.: Lighthouse	8	55	79	31
	San Jose I.: Lighthouse	8	13	79	08
	La Palma: Lighthouse	8	25	78	10
	Patiñito I.: Lighthouse	8	16	78	19

MARITIME POSITIONS

WEST INDIA ISLANDS

Coast	Place	Lat. N.		Long. W.	
		°	′	°	′
Bahama Islands	Bahama I.: Lighthouse	26	29	78	41
	Great Isaac: Lighthouse	26	02	79	06
	Gun Cay: Lighthouse	25	34	79	18
	Great Stirrup Cay: Lighthouse	25	50	77	54
	North West Channel: Lighthouse	25	28	78	10
	Andros Island: Fresh Creek Lighthouse	24	44	77	48
	Double-Headed Shot Cays: Lighthouse	23	56	80	28
	Lobos Cay: Lighthouse	22	23	77	35
	Great Inagua Island: Lighthouse	20	56	73	40
	Salt Cay: Lighthouse	21	21	71	12
	Grand Turk: Lighthouse	21	31	71	07
	South Caicos I.: Lighthouse	21	30	71	31
	Castle Island: Lighthouse	22	08	74	20
	Crooked Island: Bird Rock Lighthouse	22	51	74	22
	Long I.: Cape St. Maria Lighthouse	23	40	75	20
	Devil Point: Lighthouse	24	08	75	29
	San Salvador (Watlings): Lighthouse	24	06	74	26
	Eleuthera I.: Lighthouse	24	37	76	08
	Goulding Cay: Lighthouse	25	02	77	35
	Athol Island: Lighthouse	25	05	77	17
	Nassau Harbor: Hog I. Lighthouse	25	06	77	22
	Abaco I. Hole in Wall: Lighthouse	25	51	77	11
	Elbow Cay: Lighthouse	26	31	76	58
Cuba	Cape Maisi: Lighthouse	20	15	74	08
	Port Baracoa: Lighthouse	20	21	74	30
	Port Tanamo: Lighthouse	20	43	75	19
	Nipe Bay: Mayari Point Lighthouse	20	48	75	31
	Moa Grande Cay: Lighthouse	20	42	74	54
	Pt. Lucrecia: Lighthouse	21	05	75	37
	Port Sama: Lighthouse	21	08	75	46
	Port Vita: Lighthouse	21	06	75	58
	Port Gibara: Lighthouse	21	07	76	07
	Port Padre: Lighthouse	21	17	76	32
	Nuevitas: Practicos Pt.: Lighthouse	21	37	77	06
	Pt. Maternillos: Lighthouse	21	40	77	08
	Paredon Grande Cay: Lighthouse	22	29	78	10
	Cay Frances: Lighthouse	22	39	79	14
	Sagua La Grande: Rancheria Pt. Lighthouse	23	05	80	05
	Bahia de Cadiz Cay: Lighthouse	23	13	80	29
	Cruz del Padre Cay: Lighthouse	23	17	80	54
	Piedras Cay: Lighthouse	23	15	81	07
	Diana Cay: Lighthouse (1930)	23	10	81	06
	Matanzas: Maya Point Lighthouse	23	06	81	28
	Habana:				
	Morro Castle Lighthouse	23	09	82	21
	Capitol, dome	23	08	82	22
	Port Mariel: Lighthouse	23	01	82	45
	Cabañas: Lighthouse	23	00	82	59
	Gobernadora Pt.: Lighthouse	23	00	83	13
	Jutias Cay: Lighthouse	22	43	84	01
	Cape San Antonio: Lighthouse	21	52	84	57
	Batabano: Lighthouse	22	41	82	18
	Piedras Cay: Lighthouse	21	58	81	07
	East Guano Cay: Lighthouse	21	40	81	02
	Cienfuegos: Lighthouse	22	02	80	26
	Blanco Cay: Lighthouse	21	38	79	53
	Zarza Blanco Cay: Lighthouse	21	36	79	36
	Breton Cay: Light	21	07	79	27
	Perla Cay: Lighthouse	20	22	77	15
	Cape Cruz: Lighthouse	19	51	77	44
	Santiago de Cuba: Lighthouse	19	57	75	52
	Guantanamo Bay: Lighthouse, Windward Point	19	53	75	10
Jamaica	Grand Cayman: Gorling Bluff: Lighthouse	19	18	81	07
	Cayman Brac: Lighthouse	19	43	79	50
	South Negril Point: Lighthouse	18	15	78	23
	Galina Point: Lighthouse	18	25	76	55
	Morant Point: Lighthouse	17	55	76	11
	Kingston:				
	Plum Point Lighthouse	17	56	76	47
	Fort Augusta Lighthouse	17	58	76	51

Coast	Place	Lat. N.		Long. W.	
		°	′	°	′
Island of Haiti	Navassa I.: Lighthouse	18	24	75	01
	Cape Samana: Lighthouse	19	18	69	09
	Cape Viejo Frances: Lighthouse	19	40	69	55
	Port Plata: Lighthouse	19	49	70	41
	Monte Cristi: Cabra I. Lighthouse	19	54	71	40
	Cape Haitien: Picolet Pt. Lighthouse	19	48	72	12
	Tortuga I:				
	E. Point Lighthouse	20	01	72	38
	W. Point Lighthouse	20	04	72	58
	Cape St. Nicolas Mole: Lighthouse	19	50	73	25
	St. Marc Point: Lighthouse	19	04	72	50
	Arcadian Is.: Lighthouse	18	49	72	39
	Port au Prince:				
	Lamentin Point Lighthouse	18	33	72	24
	Fort Islet Lighthouse	18	34	72	21
	Rochelois Bank: Lighthouse	18	39	73	12
	Cape Dame Maria: Lighthouse	18	37	74	26
	Vache I.: Lighthouse	18	04	73	34
	Cape Jacmel: Lighthouse	18	10	72	32
	Alta Vela I.: Lighthouse	17	28	71	38
	Punta Salinas: Lighthouse	18	12	70	32
	Santo Domingo: Lighthouse	18	28	69	53
	San Pedro de Macoris: Lighthouse	18	26	69	17
	Romana: Lighthouse	18	25	68	57
	Saona I.: Lighthouse	18	07	68	34
Puerto Rico	Mona I.: Lighthouse	18	05	67	51
	Point Borinquen: Lighthouse	18	29	67	10
	Port San Juan: Lighthouse	18	28	66	07
	Cape San Juan: Lighthouse	18	23	65	37
	Cabeza de Perro: Lighthouse	18	15	65	35
	Cabras I.: Lighthouse	18	13	65	36
	Point Tuna: Lighthouse	17	59	65	53
	Arroyo: Point Figuras: Lighthouse	17	57	66	03
	Jobos Harbor: Lighthouse	17	56	66	17
	Muertos I.: Lighthouse	17	54	66	31
	Ponce: Cardona I. Lighthouse	17	58	66	38
	Guanica: Lighthouse	17	57	66	54
	Cape Rojo: Lighthouse	17	56	67	12
	Point Jiguero: Lighthouse	18	22	67	16
Lesser Antilles	Vieques I.: Point Mulas: Lighthouse	18	09	65	27
	Culebrita Island: Lighthouse	18	19	65	14
	Sail Rock: Lighthouse	18	17	65	06
	Buck Island: Lighthouse	18	17	64	54
	St. Thomas:				
	Muhlenfels Pt. Lighthouse	18	19	64	55
	Judge Bergs Lighthouse (front)	18	21	64	56
	St. Croix I.: Hams Bluff Lighthouse	17	46	64	52
	Tortola: Fort Burt	18	25	64	37
	Sombrero: Lighthouse	18	36	63	26
	Anguilla: Customhouse	18	13	63	05
	St. Martin:				
	Fort Marigot Light	18	04	63	06
	Grande Bay Light	18	01	63	04
	St. Bartholomew: Fort Oscar	17	54	62	51
	Saba: Diamond Rock	17	39	63	15
	St. Eustatius: Fort flagstaff	17	29	62	59
	St. Christopher:				
	Basseterre Lighthouse	17	18	62	43
	Booby Island: Center	17	13	62	35
	Nevis: Fort Charles	17	08	62	37
	Barbuda: Flagstaff, Martello Tower	17	36	61	50
	Antigua:				
	English Harbor: Flagstaff, dockyard	17	00	61	46
	Sandy Island: Lighthouse	17	07	61	55
	St. Johns Cathedral	17	06	61	50
	Pillar Rock: Lighthouse	17	06	61	53
	Redonda Islet: Center	16	56	62	21
	Montserrat: Plymouth Wharf	16	42	62	13
	Guadeloupe:				
	Petite Terre: Lighthouse	16	10	61	07
	Pointe a Pitre: Monroux Light	16	13	61	32
	Desirade I: Frigate Bluff	16	18	61	06
	Saintes Islands: Tower on Chameau Hill	15	52	61	36

APPENDIX IV

MARITIME POSITIONS

WEST INDIA ISLANDS—Continued

Coast	Place	Lat. N.	Long. W.
		° ′	° ′
Lesser Antilles	Dominica, Roseau: Fort Young Lighthouse	15 17	61 24
	Aves I.	15 42	63 38
	Martinique:		
	Caravelle Pen. Lighthouse	14 46	60 53
	Fort de France: Lighthouse	14 36	61 04
	St. Lucia:		
	Port Castries Lighthouse	14 02	61 01
	Tapion Rock Lighthouse	14 01	61 01
	Cape Moulá Chique Lighthouse	13 43	60 57
	Barbados:		
	South Pt. Lighthouse	13 03	59 32
	Ragged Pt. Lighthouse	13 10	59 26
	Needham Pt. Lighthouse	13 05	59 37
	St. Vincent: Kingston Lighthouse	13 09	61 15
	Grenadines: Carriacou I. Lighthouse	12 29	61 27
Lesser Antilles	Grenada:		
	St. George Harbor Lighthouse	12 03	61 45
	Saline Point Lighthouse	12 00	61 48
	Tobago I.: Lighthouse	11 10	60 43
	Testigo Grande I.: Village	11 23	63 07
	Los Roques I.: Lighthouse	11 58	66 41
	Aruba I.:		
	Colorado Pt. Lighthouse	12 25	69 52
	Pan de Azucar (Hooiberg)	12 31	70 00
	Oranjestadt Lighthouse	12 31	70 02
	Bonaire I.:		
	Boca Spelonk Lighthouse	12 14	68 12
	Kralendijk Lighthouse	12 09	68 16
	North Point Lighthouse	12 19	68 23
	Little Curacao: Lighthouse	11 59	68 39
	Curacao I.:		
	Santa Anna Harbor Lighthouse	12 06	68 56
	North Point Lighthouse	12 23	69 09

NORTH AND EAST COASTS OF SOUTH AMERICA

Coast	Place	Lat. N.	Long. W.
Colombia	Tesoro I.: Lighthouse	10 14	75 45
	Cartagena:		
	San Domingo Battery Lighthouse	10 26	75 33
	Puerto Colombia: Cupino Beach Lighthouse	11 00	74 57
	Gomez I.: Lighthouse	11 05	74 48
	Santa Marta: Lighthouse	11 15	74 14
	La Hacha: Lighthouse	11 33	72 55
Venezuela	Vela de Coro: Lighthouse	11 28	69 34
	Puerto Cabello: Brava Point Lighthouse	10 30	68 01
	La Guaira: Lighthouse	10 37	66 56
	Carenero: Lighthouse	10 32	66 07
	Guanta Hbr. Pitahaya I.: Lighthouse	10 15	64 36
	Cumana: Lighthouse	10 28	64 12
	Margarita I.:		
	Porlamar Lighthouse	10 57	63 51
	Pampatar Lighthouse	11 00	63 48
	Orinoco River: Point Barima Lighthouse	8 36	60 25
	Carupano: Lighthouse	10 41	63 15
Trinidad	Chacachacare I.: Bocas del Dragon Lighthouse	10 42	61 45
	Trinidad I.:		
	Port of Spain Lighthouse	10 39	61 31
	Port of Spain, St. Vincent Jetty Lighthouse	10 39	61 31
	La Brea Point Lighthouse	10 15	61 38
	Icacos Pt. Lighthouse	10 03	61 56
	Galera Pt. Lighthouse	10 50	60 55
Guiana	Georgetown: Lighthouse	6 50	58 10
	Surinam River: Entrance lighthouse	5 57	55 13
	Paramaribo: Radio masts	5 50	55 10
	Maroni River: Galibi Pt. Lighthouse	5 45	53 59
	Isere Point Lighthouse	5 44	53 48
	Salut Is.: Lighthouse	5 17	52 35
	Enfant Perdu: Lighthouse	5 03	52 21
	Cayenne: Lighthouse	4 56	52 20
Brazil	Amazon River:		
	Bailique I. Lighthouse	1 00	49 56
	Macapa Lighthouse	0 01	51 12
		Lat. S.	Long. W.
	Machadinho I.: Lighthouse	0 09	48 44
	Cape Magoari: Lighthouse	0 17	48 25
	Para River:		
	Soure: Lighthouse	0 42	48 35
	Joannes: Lighthouse	0 51	48 31
	Capim I.: Lighthouse	1 33	48 52
	Arrozal: Lighthouse	1 27	48 42
	Para: Customhouse	1 27	48 30

Coast	Place	Lat. S.	Long. W.
Brazil	Para River—Continued.		
	Point Chapeo Virado: Lighthouse	1 09	48 28
	Gaivotas I.: Lighthouse	0 36	48 03
	Point Atalaia: Lighthouse	0 35	47 19
	Carauassu I.: Lighthouse	0 48	46 38
	Itaculumy Point: Lighthouse	2 10	44 25
	Alcantara Point: Lighthouse	2 25	44 24
	Maranhao I.: San Marcos Fort Lighthouse	2 29	44 17
	Santa Anna: Lighthouse	2 16	43 36
	Preguicas River: Lighthouse	2 34	42 44
	Tutoya River, Papagaio I.: Lighthouse	2 41	42 16
	Pedra do Sal: Lighthouse	2 49	41 45
	Parnahiba River, Amaracao: Lighthouse	2 53	41 39
	Camocim River: Lighthouse	2 51	40 53
	Pt. Mandahu: Melancia Lighthouse	3 11	39 21
	Ceara: Point Mocuripe Lighthouse	3 42	38 28
	Aracaty: Jaguaribe River Lighthouse	4 25	37 45
	Rata Island: Lighthouse	3 49	32 23
	Pico Fernando Noronha	3 51	32 25
	Ponta do Barra Vermelho: Lighthouse	3 53	32 28
	Rocas Reef: Lighthouse	3 52	33 48
	Point Mel: Lighthouse	4 57	36 53
	Macao: Lighthouse	5 06	36 36
	Santo Alberto Point: Lighthouse	5 02	36 01
	Cape Calcanhar: Lighthouse	5 10	35 29
	Cape St. Roque: Lighthouse	5 29	35 16
	Rio Grande do Norte: Ft. Reis Magos Lighthouse	5 45	35 12
	Natal: Cathedral	5 47	35 13
	Cape Bacopary: Lighthouse	6 22	35 00
	Parahiba River, Pedra Secca: Lighthouse	6 57	34 49
	Pt. Pedras: Lighthouse	7 37	34 48
	Pernambuco:		
	Olinda Pt.: Lighthouse	8 01	34 51
	Recife: Lighthouse	8 03	34 52
	Cape St. Agostinho: Lighthouse	8 21	34 57
	Tamandare: Fort Santo Ignacio: Lighthouse	8 46	35 06
	Porto de Pedras: Lighthouse	9 10	35 18
	Maceio:		
	Lighthouse	9 40	35 44
	Verde Point Lighthouse	9 40	35 42
	Jiquia: Church	10 01	36 01
	Samoco: Lighthouse	10 31	36 24
	Aracaju: Cotinguiba River Lighthouse	10 58	37 03
	Garcia de Avila: Lighthouse	12 35	38 00
	Itapoan Point: Piraboca Rock Lighthouse	12 57	38 21
	Mare I.: Tinoaso Point Lighthouse	12 47	38 32

MARITIME POSITIONS

NORTH AND EAST COASTS OF SOUTH AMERICA—Continued

Coast	Place	Lat. S. °	Lat. S. ′	Long. W. °	Long. W. ′
Brazil	Frade I.: Lighthouse	12	49	38	38
	Bahia: Fort San Antonio Lighthouse	13	01	38	32
	Morro de Sao Paulo: Lighthouse	13	23	38	54
	Camamu: Quiepe I.: Lighthouse	13	51	38	57
	Morro Pernambuco: Lighthouse	14	49	39	01
	S. Jorge dos Ilheos: Church	14	48	39	01
	Belmont: Lighthouse	15	51	38	54
	Santa Cruz: Church	16	17	39	01
	Porto Seguro: Lighthouse	16	25	39	04
	Corumbao Point: Lighthouse	16	52	39	06
	Balea Point: Lighthouse	17	41	39	08
	Abrolhos I.: Lighthouse	17	58	38	42
	Rio Doce, Regencia Augusta: Lighthouse	19	37	39	49
	Santa Luzia Point: Lighthouse	20	19	40	16
	Escalvada Islet: Lighthouse	20	43	40	25
	Franceza I.: Lighthouse	20	54	40	45
	Sao Joao da Barra: Lighthouse	21	37	41	01
	Cape St. Thome: Lighthouse	22	03	41	03
	Santa Anna I.: Lighthouse	22	25	41	45
	Point Laginha: Lighthouse	22	54	42	00
	Cape Frio: Lighthouse	23	01	42	00
	Negra Point: Lighthouse	22	57	42	40
	Marica I.: Lighthouse	23	01	42	55
	Rio de Janeiro:				
	Fort Villegagnon Lighthouse	22	55	43	09
	Ilha Fiscal Lighthouse	22	54	43	10
	National Observatory (Since 1921)	22	54	43	13
	Raza I.: Lighthouse	23	04	43	09
	Guaratiba Point: Lighthouse	23	05	43	34
	Marambaia Rock: Lighthouse	23	07	43	50
	Sapetiba Bay: Soco I. Lighthouse	22	57	43	55
	Pino Islet: Lighthouse	23	06	44	07
	Preta Rock: Lighthouse	23	03	44	18
	Ilha Grande:				
	Castelhanos Pt. Lighthouse	23	10	44	06
	Branca I. Lighthouse	23	08	44	20
	Rapada I.: Lighthouse	23	09	44	39
	Parati: Fort	23	12	44	42
	Cape Joatinga: Lighthouse	23	18	44	30
	Ubatuba: Cathedral	23	26	45	04
	Ilha Sao Sebastiao:				
	Canaveiras Point Lighthouse	23	43	45	18
	Boi Point: Lighthouse	23	58	45	15
	Moleques Rock: Lighthouse	23	51	45	24
	Alcatrazes Is., Port I.: Lighthouse	24	06	45	42
	Bertioga: Light	23	52	46	07
	Santos: Moela I. Lighthouse	24	03	46	16
	Lago de Santos: Lighthouse	24	19	46	10
	Conceicao Church	24	11	46	48
	Queimada Grande I.: Lighthouse	24	29	46	41
	Bom Abrigo Lighthouse	25	07	47	52
Brazil	Paranagua Bay, Mel Island:				
	Bixo Pt. Lighthouse	25	30	48	20
	Morro das Conchas Lighthouse	25	32	48	17
	Guaratuba Bay: Caiova I. Lighthouse	25	52	48	33
	Sao Francisco do Sul River: Lighthouse	26	11	48	34
	Paz I.: Lighthouse	26	11	48	29
	Itapacaroya: Church	26	47	48	37
	Itajahy: Cabecudas Point: Lighthouse	26	56	48	37
	Sao Pedro Is.: Lighthouse	27	15	48	26
	Arvoredo I.: Lighthouse	27	18	48	22
	Anhatomirim: Fort Santa Cruz Lighthouse	27	25	48	34
	Florianopolis: Fort Santa Anna Lighthouse	27	35	48	33
	Santa Catharina I. Naufragados Pt.: Lighthouse	27	50	48	36
	Batuba Pt.: Lighthouse	28	17	48	40
	Araras Islet: Lighthouse	28	21	48	39
	Barra Lagoa: Lighthouse (breakwater)	28	32	48	47
	Cape Santa Martha Grande: Lighthouse	28	36	48	49
	Tramandahy: Lighthouse	29	46	50	01
	Cidreira: Lighthouse	30	09	50	12
	Solidao: Lighthouse	30	42	50	29
	Mostardas: Lighthouse	31	15	50	54
	Conceicao: Lighthouse	31	44	51	29
	Rio Grande do Sul: Lighthouse	32	07	52	05
	Sarita: Lighthouse	32	38	52	26
	Albardao: Lighthouse	33	12	52	42
	Chui River: Lighthouse	33	45	53	22
Uruguay	Cape Polonio: Lighthouse	34	25	53	48
	Cape Santa Maria: Lighthouse	34	40	54	09
	San Jose Ignacio Point: Lighthouse	34	51	54	38
	Maldonado Bay: Punta del Este: Lighthouse	34	58	54	57
	Lobos I.: Lighthouse	35	01	54	53
	Punta Negra: Lighthouse	34	54	55	15
	Flores I.: Lighthouse	34	57	55	56
	Punta Brava: Lighthouse	34	56	56	10
	Montevideo: El Cerro: Lighthouse	34	53	56	16
	Panela Rock: Lighthouse	34	55	56	27
	Colonia: Lighthouse	34	28	57	52
	Farallon I.: Lighthouse	34	29	57	56
	Las Vacas River: S. dyke Lighthouse	34	00	58	19

EAST AND SOUTH COASTS OF SOUTH AMERICA

Coast	Place	Lat. S. °	Lat. S. ′	Long. W. °	Long. W. ′
Argentina	Martin Garcia I.: Lighthouse	34	11	58	15
	Buenos Aires: Darsena Norte, Obs. and W/T sta	34	36	58	22
	La Plata:				
	(E. mole) Lighthouse	34	48	57	51
	National Univ. Obs. (mer. circle)	34	55	57	56
	Piedras Point: Lighthouse	35	27	57	09
	Cape San Antonio Lighthouse	36	18	56	46
	Point Medano: Lighthouse	36	53	56	40
	Querandi: Lighthouse	37	28	57	07
	Punta Mogotes: Lighthouse	38	05	57	33
	Quequen: Lighthouse	38	34	58	41
	Claromeco: Lighthouse	38	51	60	03
	Bahia Blanca: Lighthouse	39	00	61	16
	Port Belgrano: Lighthouse	38	53	62	06
	Port Militar: Point Ciguena: Lighthouse	38	56	62	03
	Second Barranca Point: Lighthouse	40	47	62	16
	Rio Negro: Lighthouse	41	04	62	50
	San Matias: Lighthouse	40	49	64	43
	Port San Antonio: Delgado Beacon	40	46	64	55
	Morro Nuevo: Lighthouse	42	52	64	09
Argentina	Madryn: Lighthouse	42	43	65	02
	Ninfas Point: Lighthouse	42	58	64	19
	Blancas I.: Lighthouse	44	47	65	39
	Leones I.: Lighthouse	45	03	65	36
	Raza Islet: Lighthouse	45	06	65	24
	Cape Aristazabal: Lighthouse	45	14	66	35
	Cabo San Jorge: Lighthouse	45	47	67	23
	Cape Blanco: Lighthouse	47	12	65	44
	Port Deseado: Estacion Beacon Light	47	45	65	54
	Penguin I.: Lighthouse	47	55	65	43
	Cape Curioso: Lighthouse	49	11	67	37
	Cape Francisco de Paula	49	45	67	43
	Santa Cruz: Lighthouse	50	09	68	21
	Buen Tiempo: Lighthouse	51	33	68	57
	Port Gallegos:				
	Deseada I. Lighthouse	51	35	69	02
	Convento Beacon light	51	45	68	52
	Virgenes Pt.: Lighthouse	52	20	68	21
	Arenas Point: Lighthouse	53	08	68	13
	Le Maire Str.: Lighthouse	54	47	64	42
	Cape San Pio: Lighthouse	55	04	66	32
	Les Eclaireurs Beacon light	54	52	68	05
	New Year Island: Lighthouse	54	39	64	08

MARITIME POSITIONS

EAST AND SOUTH COASTS OF SOUTH AMERICA—Continued

Coast	Place	Lat. S. ° ′	Long. W. ° ′
Chile	Cape Horn: South Summit (1391)	55 58	67 17
	Magellan Strait: Dungeness Lighthouse	52 24	68 25
	Cape Possession: Lighthouse	52 18	68 57
	Direction Hill: Lighthouse	52 52	69 30
	Delgade Point: Lighthouse	52 28	69 32
	Satellite Point: Lighthouse	52 33	69 40
	Mendez Point: Lighthouse	52 32	69 35
	Cone Hill: Lighthouse	52 40	70 23
	Santa Magdalena I.: Lighthouse	52 55	70 34
Chile	Quartermaster I.: beacon	52 57	70 21
	Magallanes (Punta Arenas): Lighthouse	53 10	70 54
	Tesner Islet: Lighthouse	53 50	70 24
	Cape San Isidro: Lighthouse	53 47	70 58
	English Reach: Rupert I.: Lighthouse	53 40	72 12
	Crooked Reach:		
	Cohorn I.: Lighthouse	53 33	72 20
	Cape Morion: Lighthouse	53 34	72 31

WEST COAST OF SOUTH AMERICA

Coast	Place	Lat. S. ° ′	Long. W. ° ′
Chile	Long Beach:		
	Cape Cooper Key: Lighthouse	53 15	73 13
	Sentinel I.: Lighthouse	53 05	73 35
	San Felix Bay: Lighthouse	52 58	74 05
	Fairway I.: Lighthouse	52 44	73 47
	Evangelistas Is.: Lighthouse	52 24	75 06
	Port Henry: Observation spot	50 00	75 13
	San Pedro I.: Lighthouse	47 43	74 53
	Cape Raper: Lighthouse	46 49	75 37
	Port Melinca: Falsa Isla Point Lighthouse	43 53	73 44
	Guafo Island: Lighthouse	43 34	74 49
	Chiloe I.:		
	Laitec I.: Lighthouse	43 17	73 35
	Punta Corona: Lighthouse	41 47	73 53
	Ahui Point: Lighthouse	41 50	73 52
	Tres Cruces Point: Lighthouse	41 50	73 29
	Port Montt: Lighthouse (mole)	41 29	72 57
	Port Calbuco: Light (mole)	41 46	73 08
	Corvio Bank: Lighthouse	41 50	73 13
	Galera Point: Lighthouse	40 00	73 45
	Port Valdivia:		
	Niebla Pt.: Lighthouse	39 52	73 26
	Port Corral mole light	39 53	73 27
	Mocha I.:		
	Torrecillas Hill: Lighthouse	38 21	73 58
	Anegadiza Point: Lighthouse	38 23	73 52
	Port Lebu: Tucapel Point: Lighthouse	37 37	73 42
	Lavapie Point: Lighthouse	37 08	73 36
	Santa Maria I.: Lighthouse	36 58	73 33
	Lota Bay: Morro Lutrin: Lighthouse	37 05	73 11
	Coronel Bay: Puchoco Pt.: Lighthouse	37 01	73 10
	Gualpen Point: Lighthouse	36 45	73 12
	Tumbes Point: Lighthouse	36 37	73 07
	Quiriquina I.: Lighthouse	36 36	73 03
	Port Talcahuano: Belen Bank Lighthouse	36 42	73 05
	Cerro Verde: Lighthouse	36 44	73 01
	Cape Carranza: Lighthouse	35 33	72 38
	Topocalma Point: Lighthouse	34 09	72 01
	Port San Antonio: Sentinel Hill Lighthouse	33 33	71 39
	Santiago: Nat. Obs. (Quinta Normal)	33 27	70 42
	Curaumilla Point: Lighthouse	33 06	71 45
	Valparaiso: Playa Ancha: Lighthouse	33 01	71 39
	Huevos I.: Lighthouse	31 55	71 33
	Lengua de Vaca: Lighthouse	30 14	71 39
	Coquimbo: Tortuga Pt.: Lighthouse	29 56	71 22
	Pajaros Islets: Lighthouse	29 35	71 33
	Mostacilla Pt.: Lighthouse	29 27	71 20
	Chanaral I.: Lighthouse	29 00	71 36
	Huasco: Mole light	28 28	71 14
Chile	Caldera: Lighthouse	27 03	70 52
	Tetas Point: Lighthouse	23 31	70 39
	Punta Angamos: Lighthouse	23 02	70 32
	Iquique I.:		
	Lighthouse	20 13	70 11
	Pattilliguaje Rocks: Lighthouse	20 12	70 10
	Alacran I.: Lighthouse	18 29	70 21
	Arica: Iron church	18 29	70 20
	Coles Point: Lighthouse	17 42	71 22
Peru	Port Mollendo: Lighthouse	17 01	72 02
	Atico Point: Lighthouse	16 14	73 42
	Point San Juan: Lighthouse	15 21	75 11
	Pisco: Lighthouse	13 42	76 14
	Chincha I.: Lighthouse	13 38	76 25
	Callao:		
	Palominos Rk. Lighthouse	12 08	77 14
	La Punta: Lighthouse	12 05	77 11
	Mazorca I.: Lighthouse	11 23	77 44
	Supe: Tomas Point: Lighthouse	10 49	77 46
	Huarmey: Lagarto Head: Lighthouse	10 06	78 12
	Chimbote landing bridge light	9 05	78 35
	Huanape I.: Lighthouse	8 35	78 57
	Salaverry: Mole light	8 14	78 58
	Pacasmayo: Mole light	7 24	79 33
	Eten: Mole light	6 56	79 51
	Lobos de Afuera I.: Lighthouse	6 56	80 43
	Lobos de Tierra I.: Lighthouse	6 28	80 52
	Paita: Cathedral	5 05	81 07
	Parinas Point: Lighthouse	4 40	81 20
	Talara Bay: Lighthouse	4 34	81 18
Ecuador	Guayaquil Gulf:		
	Santa Clara I.: Lighthouse	3 11	80 25
	Jambeli: Lighthouse	3 14	80 01
	Arena Point: Lighthouse	3 02	80 07
	Machala wireless station	3 16	79 55
	Puna wireless station	2 44	79 53
	Cerro Santa Ana	2 38	79 51
	Isla Verde: Lighthouse	2 11	79 55
	Santa Elena Point: Lighthouse	2 11	81 00
	Manglaralto Point: Lighthouse	1 50	80 45
	La Plata I.: Lighthouse	1 16	81 06
	Cape San Lorenzo: Lighthouse	1 03	80 55
	Manta Bay: Lighthouse	0 57	80 44
	Caraques Bay: Wireless station	0 35	80 23
	Cape Pasado: Lighthouse	0 22	80 30
		Lat. N.	**Long. W.**
	Galera Point: Lighthouse	0 51	80 05
	Esmeraldas: Wireless station	0 59	79 42
Colombia	Tumaco Road: Morro Chico	1 49	78 45
	Buenaventura: Railroad office	3 54	77 05

ISLANDS IN THE ATLANTIC OCEAN

Coast	Place	Lat. N.	Long. W.
Bermuda	St. David Island: Lighthouse	32 22	64 39
	Gibbs Hill: Lighthouse	32 15	64 50
	North Rock: Lighthouse	32 28	64 46
	Ireland I. Casemate Barracks	32 19	64 50
	Hamilton I.: Fort	32 18	64 47
Azores	Corvo I.: Lighthouse	39 40	31 07
	Flores I.:		
	Lagens Point: Lighthouse	39 22	31 11
	Fajem Grande: Lighthouse	39 26	31 16
	Albarnas Point: Lighthouse	39 31	31 15

MARITIME POSITIONS

ISLANDS IN THE ATLANTIC OCEAN—Continued

Coast	Place	Lat. N.	Long. W.
		° ′	° ′
Azores	Fayal I.:		
	Capellinhos Point: Lighthouse	38 36	28 50
	Horta: Santa Cruz Castle	38 32	28 38
	Ribeirnha Point: Lighthouse	38 36	28 36
	Pico I. Areia Larga Point: Lighthouse	38 32	28 32
	San Jorge Island: Lighthouse	38 40	28 13
	Graciosa I.:		
	Fort do Santo: Lighthouse	39 05	28 01
	Rochela Point: Lighthouse	39 03	27 58
	Terceira I.:		
	Serreta Point: Lighthouse	38 46	27 23
	St. Matheo Port: Lighthouse	38 39	27 17
	San Antonio Point: Lighthouse	38 38	27 14
	San Miguel I.:		
	Ferraria Point: Lighthouse	37 51	25 52
	Mosteiros: Lighthouse	37 53	25 50
	Ponta Delgada: Lighthouse	37 44	25 41
	Villa Franca: Lighthouse	37 43	25 27
	Arnel Point: Lighthouse	37 49	25 09
	Santa Maria Island: Lighthouse	36 56	25 10
Madeira	Pargo Point: Lighthouse	32 48	17 16
	Funchal: Fort Ilheu: Lighthouse	32 38	16 55
	Fora I.: Lighthouse	32 43	16 39
	Cima Islet: Lighthouse	33 03	16 16
Canary Islands	Palma I.:		
	Cumplida Point: Lighthouse	28 50	17 47
	Fuencaliente Point: Lighthouse	28 26	17 50
	Hierro: Lighthouse	27 46	17 54
	Gomera I. San Cristoval Point: Lighthouse	28 06	17 06
	Teneriffe:		
	Teno Point: Lighthouse	28 21	16 56
	Anaga: Lighthouse	28 35	16 08
	Rasca Point: Lighthouse	28 00	16 41
	Abona Point: Lighthouse	28 09	16 26
	Santa Cruz: Lighthouse	28 28	16 15
	Gran Canaria I.:		
	Sardinia Point: Lighthouse	28 10	15 43
	Isleta Point: Lighthouse	28 11	15 25
	La Luz E. mole: Lighthouse	28 09	15 25
	Aringa Point: Lighthouse	27 52	15 22
	Morro Colchas Point: Lighthouse	27 44	15 35
	Fuerteventura I.:		
	Jandia Point: Lighthouse	28 03	14 31
	Port Cabras: Lighthouse	28 29	13 51
	Ballena Point: Lighthouse	28 42	14 01
	Lobos I. Martino Point: Lighthouse	28 46	13 49
Cape Verde Is.	St. Antonio I.:		
	Bull Point: Lighthouse	17 07	24 59
	Ponta do Sol: Lighthouse	17 12	25 06
	St. Vincent I.:		
	Ponta Machado: Lighthouse	16 50	25 05
	Passero (Bird) I.: Lighthouse	16 55	25 01
	Porto Grande Light	16 53	25 00

Coast	Place	Lat. N.	Long. W.
		° ′	° ′
Cape Verde Is.	St. Nicolau (St. Nicholas) I.:		
	Ponta do Barril: Lighthouse	16 37	24 25
	Preguica: Lighthouse	16 34	24 16
	Sal I.:		
	North Point: Lighthouse	16 51	22 55
	South Point: Lighthouse	16 34	22 56
	Boavista I. Sal Rei Island: Lighthouse	16 10	22 57
	Maio I.: Lighthouse	15 07	23 13
	St. Thiago I.:		
	Temerosa Point: Lighthouse	14 53	23 30
	Port Praia Front: Lighthouse	14 54	23 31
	St. Thiago I.:		
	Ponta Lobo: Lighthouse	14 59	23 25
	Preta Point: Lighthouse	15 18	23 48
	Fogo I.: San Philipe: Lighthouse	14 53	24 30
	Brava I.: Ponta Jalunga: Lighthouse	14 53	24 39
	St. Paul Rocks: Lighthouse	0 55	29 22
		Lat. S.	Long. W.
South Atlantic Islands	Rocas Reef: Lighthouse	3 52	33 48
	Fernando Noronha I.: Rat I.: Lighthouse	3 49	32 23
	Ascension I.:		
	Fort Thornton	7 55	14 25
	Georgetown: Lighthouse	7 56	14 25
	St. Helena: Jamestown Light	15 55	5 42
	Martin Vaz Rocks: Largest Islet	20 29	28 53
	Trinidad I.: Peak	20 30	29 19
	Tristan da Cunha, NW. point	37 03	12 20
	Gough I. Penguin Islet	40 19	9 55
	Falkland Islands:		
	Port William: Lighthouse	51 39	57 43
	Port Stanley: Town Hall	51 42	57 51
	South Georgia I.:		
	Cape Crew: Lighthouse	54 02	37 08
	Cape Saunders: Lighthouse	54 07	36 38
	Grass I.: Lighthouse	54 09	36 40
	Jason Islet: Lighthouse	54 10	36 30
	King Edward Point: Lighthouse	54 16	36 30
	Long Point: Lighthouse	54 16	36 17
	Shag Rocks, center	53 33	42 01
Antarctic Regions	S. Sandwich Is.: Thule I., Hewison Point	59 28	27 15
	S. Orkney Is.: Coronation I., Mt. Noble	60 40	45 18
	S. Shetland Is.: Port Foster, lighthouse	62 50	60 29
	Palmer Land: Melchior Harbor, Gallows Pt. lighthouse	64 19	62 55
	Peter First I.: Christensen Peak	68 49	90 32
		Lat. N.	Long. E.
	Bouvet I.	54 24	3 27

ATLANTIC COAST OF EUROPE

Coast	Place	Lat. N.	Long. E.
Great Britain	Greenwich: Observatory (Mer. circle)	51 29	0 00
	Cambridge: Obs	52 13	0 06
	Sheerness: Garrison Pt. Lighthouse	51 27	0 45
	North Foreland Lighthouse	51 22	1 27
	South Foreland Lighthouse	51 08	1 22
	Dover: Warden Hotel flagstaff	51 07	1 19
	Dungeness: High Lighthouse	50 55	0 58
	Hastings: West Hill Lighthouse	50 51	0 35
	Beachy Head: Lighthouse	50 44	0 15
		Lat. N.	Long. W.
	Brighton: W. pier light	50 49	0 09
	Nab Tower: Lighthouse	50 40	0 57
	South Sea Castle Lighthouse	50 47	1 05
	Oxford: Univ. Obs	51 46	1 15

Coast	Place	Lat. N.	Long. W.
Great Britain	Portsmouth: Victoria Pier N. light	50 47	1 06
	Southampton: Town pier light	50 54	1 24
	Isle of Wight:		
	St. Catherine Lighthouse	50 34	1 18
	Egypt Pt. Lighthouse	50 46	1 19
	Needles Rock Lighthouse	50 40	1 35
	Hurst: Lighthouse (rear)	50 42	1 33
	Anvil Point: Lighthouse	50 35	1 57
	Portland: N. E. breakwater light	50 35	2 25
	Portland Peninsula: Lighthouse	50 31	2 27
	Berry Head: Lighthouse	50 24	3 29
	Start Point: Lighthouse	50 13	3 38
	Plymouth: Breakwater Lighthouse	50 20	4 09
	Eddystone: Lighthouse	50 11	4 16
	Fowey: St. Catherine Lighthouse	50 20	4 39

MARITIME POSITIONS

ATLANTIC COAST OF EUROPE—Continued

Coast	Place	Lat. N. °	Lat. N. '	Long. W. °	Long. W. '
Great Britain	Falmouth: St. Anthony Pt. Lighthouse	50	09	5	01
	Lizard Head: Lighthouse (E.)	49	58	5	12
	Wolf Rock: Lighthouse	49	57	5	48
	Lands End: Longships Lighthouse	50	04	5	45
	Scilly Isles:				
	Penninis: Lighthouse	49	54	6	18
	Round I. Lighthouse	49	59	6	19
	Bishop Rock Lighthouse	49	52	6	27
	Pendeen: Lighthouse	50	10	5	40
	Godrevy I. Lighthouse	50	15	5	24
	St. Agnes: Beacon	50	18	5	13
	Trevose Head: Lighthouse	50	33	5	02
	Hartlant Point: Lighthouse	51	01	4	32
	Bideford: Braunton Sands: Lighthouse	51	04	4	12
	Bull Point: Lighthouse	51	12	4	12
	Lundy I.:				
	South Lighthouse	51	10	4	40
	North Lighthouse	51	12	4	41
	Ilfracombe: Lantern Hill Lighthouse	51	12	4	07
	Lynmouth: Foreland Pt. Lighthouse	51	15	3	47
	Flatholm: Lighthouse	51	23	3	07
	Blacknore: Lighthouse	51	29	2	48
	Bristol: Cathedral	51	27	2	35
	Newport: West Usk Lighthouse	51	32	3	00
	Cardiff: Bute W. dock lights	51	28	3	10
	Monkstone Rock Lighthouse	51	25	3	06
	Nash Point: Low light	51	24	3	33
	Porthcawl: Breakwater light	51	28	3	42
	Swansea: W. pier light	51	37	3	56
	Mumbles: Lighthouse	51	34	3	58
	Bury Holme: Lighthouse	51	36	4	19
	Caldy Island: Lighthouse	51	38	4	41
	Milford Haven:				
	Great Castle Head Lighthouse	51	43	5	07
	St. Anns: Lighthouse	51	41	5	10
	Skokham I.: Lighthouse	51	42	5	17
	Smalls Rocks: Lighthouse	51	43	5	40
	South Bishop Rock Lighthouse	51	51	5	25
	Strumble Head: Lighthouse	52	02	5	04
	Aberystwith: Pier light	52	24	4	06
	St. Tudwall: Lighthouse	52	48	4	28
	Bardsey I.: Lighthouse	52	45	4	48
	Carnarvon: south pier light	53	09	4	17
	South Stack: Lighthouse	53	18	4	42
	Holyhead: Old pier light	53	19	4	37
	Skerries: Lighthouse	53	25	4	36
	Point Lynus: Lighthouse	53	25	4	17
	Great Ormes Head: Lighthouse	53	21	3	52
	Air Point: Old unused lighthouse	53	21	3	19
	Liverpool: Black Rock Lighthouse	53	27	3	02
	Fleetwood: High light	53	56	3	00
	Walney I.: Lighthouse	54	03	3	11
	Isle of Man:				
	Chicken Rock: Lighthouse	54	02	4	50
	Ayre Point: Lighthouse	54	25	4	22
	Maughold Head: Lighthouse	54	18	4	18
	Douglas Head: Lighthouse	54	09	4	28
	Lang Ness: Lighthouse	54	03	4	37
	St. Bees Head: Lighthouse	54	31	3	38
	Whitehaven: W. pier light	54	33	3	36
	Little Ross I.: Lighthouse	54	46	4	05
	Mull of Galloway: Lighthouse	54	38	4	51
	Killantringan, Black Head: Lighthouse	54	52	5	09
	Corsewall Point: Lighthouse	55	00	5	09
	Ailsa Craig: Lighthouse	55	15	5	06
	Turnberry Point: Lighthouse	55	19	4	50
	Ayr Harbor: Inner light	55	28	4	38
	Troon: Light on pier (W.)	55	33	4	41
	Pladda I.: Lighthouse	55	26	5	07
	Holy I.: S. Lighthouse	55	31	5	04
	Cumbrae I. Lighthouse	55	43	4	58
	Cloch Pt. Lighthouse	55	57	4	53
	Glasgow: Observatory	55	53	4	18
	Davarr I. Lighthouse	55	26	5	32
	Sanda I.: Ship Rock: Lighthouse	55	16	5	35
	Mull of Cantyre: Lighthouse	55	19	5	48
	Rhinns of Islay: Oversay I.: Lighthouse	55	40	6	31
Great Britain	Sgeirvuile Rock: Lighthouse	55	52	5	50
	Lismore I.: Musdile Islet, lighthouse	56	27	5	36
	Dubh Artach: Lighthouse	56	08	6	38
	Skerryvore: Lighthouse	56	19	7	07
	Ardnamurchan: Lighthouse	56	44	6	13
	Oigh Sgeir: Lighthouse	56	58	6	41
	Barra Head: Lighthouse	56	47	7	39
	Monach Shillay I.: Lighthouse	57	32	7	42
	Ushinish: Lighthouse	57	18	7	12
	Neist Point: Lighthouse	57	25	6	47
	Trodday: Lighthouse	57	43	6	18
	Scalpay I.: Lighthouse	57	51	6	38
	South Rona: Lighthouse	57	35	5	58
	Rudh Re: Lighthouse	57	51	5	49
	Ru Stoer: Lighthouse	58	14	5	24
	Tiumpan Head: Lighthouse	58	16	6	08
	Butt of Lewis: Lighthouse	58	31	6	16
	Loch Carloway: Lighthouse	58	17	6	49
	Flannan I.: Lighthouse	58	17	7	35
	Cape Wrath: Lighthouse	58	38	5	00
	Sule Skerry: Lighthouse	59	05	4	24
	Dunnet Head: Lighthouse	58	40	3	22
	Stroma I.: Lighthouse	58	42	3	07
	Duncansby Head: Lighthouse	58	39	3	01
	Pentland Skerries: Lighthouse	58	41	2	55
	Cantick Head: Lighthouse	58	47	3	08
	Graemsay, Sardside Point Lighthouse	58	56	3	16
	Scapa: Pier light	58	57	2	58
	Copinsay: Lighthouse	58	54	2	40
	Kirkwall pier light	58	59	2	58
	Auskerry I.: Lighthouse	59	02	2	34
	Start Point Lighthouse	59	17	2	22
	North Ronaldsay: Dennis Ness: Lighthouse	59	23	2	23
	Noup Head: Lighthouse	59	20	3	04
	Scaddon: Lighthouse	59	31	1	39
	Skroo: Lighthouse	59	33	1	36
	Sumburg Head: Lighthouse	59	51	1	16
	Bressay: Lighthouse	60	07	1	07
	Balta I.: Lighthouse	60	44	0	48
	Out Skerries: Lighthouse	60	25	0	44
	North Unst: Lighthouse	60	51	0	53
	Noss Head: Lighthouse	58	29	3	03
	Clyth Ness: Lighthouse	58	18	3	13
	Tarbet Ness: Lighthouse	57	52	3	47
	Inverness: Chanonry Point lighthouse	57	34	4	05
	Chromarty: Lighthouse	57	41	4	02
	Covesea Skerries: Lighthouse	57	43	3	20
	Kinnaird Head: Lighthouse	57	42	2	00
	Rattray Head: Lighthouse	57	37	1	49
	Buchanness: Lighthouse	57	28	1	46
	Aberdeen: Girdleness Lighthouse	57	08	2	03
	Tod Head: Lighthouse	56	53	2	13
	Montrose: Scurdyness Lighthouse	56	42	2	26
	Buddonness: Lighthouse (rear)	56	28	2	45
	Dundee: Middle pier light	56	28	2	58
	Bell Rock: Lighthouse	56	26	2	23
	May Island: Lighthouse	56	11	2	33
	Rosyth: Coal jetty light	56	01	3	26
	Inchkeith: Lighthouse	56	02	3	08
	Leith: Martello tower	55	59	3	11
	Edinburg: Royal Obs. Blackford Hill	55	55	3	11
	Fidra I.: Lighthouse	56	04	2	47
	Bass Rock: Lighthouse	56	05	2	38
	Barns Ness: Lighthouse	55	59	2	27
	St. Abbs Head: Lighthouse	55	55	2	08
	Eyemouth: W. pier light	55	52	2	05
	Berwick: Pier light	55	46	1	59
	FarnI.: Longstone: Lighthouse	55	39	1	37
	Coquet I.: Lighthouse	55	20	1	32
	Blyth: High light	55	07	1	29
	St. Mary I.: Lighthouse	55	04	1	27
	North Shields: Rear light	55	00	1	26
	Tyne River: North pier light	55	01	1	24
	Souter Point: Lighthouse	54	58	1	22
	Sunderland: North pier light	54	55	1	21
	Hartlepool: Heugh Lighthouse	54	42	1	11
	River Tees: S. Gare breakwater light	54	39	1	08
	Whitby: West pier lighthouse	54	30	0	37

MARITIME POSITIONS

ATLANTIC COAST OF EUROPE—Continued

Coast	Place	Lat. N.	Long. W.
		° ′	° ′
Great Britain	Scarborough: Vincent pier light	54 17	0 23
	Flamborough Head: Lighthouse	54 07	0 05
	Humber River: Killingholme Lighthouse (rear)	53 39	0 13
		Lat. N.	Long. E.
	Withernsea: Lighthouse	53 44	0 02
	Spurn Point Lighthouse	53 35	0 07
	Cromer: Lighthouse	52 55	1 19
	Haisborough: Lighthouse	52 49	1 32
	Yarmouth: Gorleston S. pier lighthouse	52 34	1 44
	Lowestoft High Light	52 29	1 45
	Southwold: Town pier light	52 20	1 42
	Orfordness: Lighthouse	52 05	1 35
	Harwich: Landguard Point: Lighthouse	51 56	1 19
		Lat. N.	Long. W.
	Fastnet Rock: Lighthouse	51 23	9 36
	Bantry Bay: Roancarrig I. light	51 39	9 45
	Bull Rock: Lighthouse	51 35	10 18
	Skelligs Rock: Lighthouse	51 46	10 32
	Valencia: Cromwell Point Lighthouse	51 56	10 19
	Inishtearaght: Lighthouse	52 05	10 40
	Tralee: Little Samphire: Lighthouse	52 16	9 53
	Shannon River:		
	Kilcradan Head, Lighthouse	52 35	9 43
	Tarbert Lighthouse	52 35	9 22
	Limerick Cathedral	52 40	8 27
	Loop Head: Lighthouse	52 34	9 56
	Galway Bay:		
	Mutton I. Lighthouse	53 15	9 03
	Inisheer I. Lighthouse	53 03	9 31
	Eeragh I. Lighthouse	53 09	9 51
	Slyne Head: Lighthouse	53 24	10 14
	Clare I.: Lighthouse	53 49	9 59
	Black Rock: Lighthouse	54 04	10 19
	Eagle Island: Lighthouse	54 17	10 06
	Broadhaven: Guba Cashel Point: Lighthouse	54 16	9 53
	Sligo: Black Rock Lighthouse	54 18	8 37
	Killybegs: St. John Point: Lighthouse	54 34	8 28
	Rathlin O'Birne: Lighthouse	54 40	8 50
	Aran I.: Lighthouse	55 01	8 34
	Tory I.: Lighthouse	55 16	8 15
	Fanad Head: Lighthouse	55 17	7 38
	Malin Head: Tower	55 23	7 22
	Inishtrahull: Lighthouse	55 26	7 14
	Inishowen: Dunagree Point: E. light	55 14	6 56
	Londonderry: Cathedral	55 00	7 19
	Rathlin I.:		
	W. Lighthouse	55 18	6 17
	E. Lighthouse	55 18	6 10
	Rue Point Lighthouse	55 15	6 11
	Maidens Rock: Lighthouse	54 56	5 44
	Black Head: Lighthouse	54 46	5 41
	Belfast: No. 1, E. side light	54 40	5 49
	Mew I.: Lighthouse	54 42	5 31
	Donaghadee: Pier light	54 39	5 32
	Ardglass: Pier light	54 16	5 37
	Dundrum Bay: St. Johns Point Lighthouse	54 14	5 39
	Carlingford Lough: Haul-bowline Rock: Lighthouse	54 01	6 05
	Drogheda: Sand Hills Lighthouse	53 43	6 15
	Rockabill: Lighthouse	53 36	6 00
	Dublin:		
	Poolbeg Lighthouse	53 21	6 09
	Observatory	53 23	6 20
	Wicklow Head: Lighthouse	52 58	6 00
	Arklow: Church	52 48	6 09
	Wexford: College	52 20	6 28
	Tuskar Rock: Lighthouse	52 10	6 12
	Waterford:		
	Hook Point Lighthouse	52 07	6 56
	Cathedral	52 16	7 06
	Mine Head: Lighthouse	52 00	7 35
	Youghal: Lighthouse	51 57	7 51
	Ballycottin: Lighthouse	51 49	7 59
	Cork (Queenstown): Roche Point light	51 48	8 15
Great Britain	Kinsale: Old Head Lighthouse	51 37	8 32
	Galley Head: Lighthouse	51 32	8 57
	Baltimore Harbor: Barrack Point light	51 28	9 24
	Guernsey Island:		
	Hanois Rock Lighthouse	49 26	2 42
	Platte Fougere: Lighthouse	49 31	2 29
	St. Peter: Belvedere light	49 27	2 32
	Serk Island: Robert Point Lighthouse	49 26	2 21
	Casquets: Lighthouse	49 43	2 23
	Alderney Island: Quenard Point Lighthouse	49 44	2 10
	Jersey Island:		
	Corbiere Rock: Lighthouse	49 11	2 15
	Verclut breakwater light	49 13	2 01
U. S. S. R., White Sea		Lat. N.	Long. E.
	Cape Kanin: Beacon	68 39	43 18
	Mezen: Church	65 50	44 16
	Cape Voronov: Lighthouse	66 31	42 18
	Sosnovetz I.: S. Light	66 29	40 42
	Intzi: Lighthouse	65 58	40 43
	Veprevskoi Pt.: Lighthouse	65 37	39 52
	Modvugski: Lighthouse	64 55	40 17
	Arkhangel:		
	Zaostrovkis I. Lighthouse	64 31	40 33
	Trinity Church	64 32	40 31
	Chesmenskoi: Lighthouse	64 43	36 33
	Kem: Rombaki I. Lighthouse	65 02	35 02
	Sharapov Head: Lighthouse	66 14	34 04
	Kandalaski: Monastery	67 08	32 26
	Cape Orlov: Lighthouse	67 12	41 19
	Cape Gorodetzki: Lighthouse	67 41	41 02
	Sviatoi Nos: Lighthouse	68 09	39 49
	Litzki Point: Lighthouse	68 38	37 50
	Sem I. Kharlov I.: Lighthouse	68 49	37 22
	Podpakhta: Lighthouse	69 11	35 52
	Cape Teriberski: Lighthouse	69 15	35 10
	Kola Inlet: Salni I. Lighthouse	69 08	33 28
Norway	Bokfjord: Lighthouse	69 52	30 13
	Bugones: Oterneset: Lighthouse	69 58	29 40
	Vadso: Mole light	70 04	29 43
	Vardo: Hornoen Lighthouse	70 23	31 10
	Kjolnes: Lighthouse	70 51	29 15
	Sletness: Lighthouse	71 05	28 13
	Helnes: Magero: Lighthouse	71 04	26 10
	Fruholmen: Lighthouse	71 06	23 59
	Hammerfest: Fuglenes: Lighthouse	70 40	23 40
	Hasvik: Lighthouse	70 28	22 10
	Sorvaer Ovre: Lighthouse	70 38	21 59
	Fugloy Kalven: Lighthouse	70 19	20 11
	Torsvag: Lighthouse	70 15	19 30
	Lille Lyngoy: Lighthouse	69 55	18 28
	Hekkingen: Lighthouse	69 36	17 50
	Andenes: Lighthouse	69 19	16 07
	Langenes: Lighthouse	69 02	15 08
	Litloy: Lighthouse	68 36	14 19
	Drogneset: Lighthouse	68 35	14 41
	Lofoten I.:		
	Vaeroy: Lighthouse	67 39	12 44
	Glapen: Lighthouse	67 53	13 03
	Moholmen: Lighthouse	68 09	14 25
	Skraven: Saltvaerholmen Lighthouse	68 09	14 39
	Maloy-Skarholmen: Lighthouse	67 46	14 25
	Landegode: Lighthouse	67 27	14 23
	Grytoy: Lighthouse	67 23	13 51
	Tenholmen: Lighthouse	67 18	13 30
	Kalsholmen: Lighthouse	66 55	13 06
	Myken: Lighthouse	66 46	12 29
	Traenen: Lighthouse	66 26	11 58
	Ytterholmen: Lighthouse	66 01	11 42
	Brynjulfskjaer: Lighthouse	65 39	11 35
	Steinan: Gjeteroen Lighthouse	65 36	11 18
	Sklinna: Lighthouse	65 12	11 00
	Nordoerne: Lighthouse	64 48	10 33
	Gjaeslingene: Lighthouse	64 44	10 52
	Ellingrasa: Lighthouse	64 34	10 49
	Kya: Lighthouse	64 28	10 13
	Buholmrasa: Lighthouse	64 24	10 28
	Halten: Lighthouse	64 10	9 25
	Storskjaer: Lighthouse	64 03	9 51
	Finnvaer: Lighthouse	64 04	9 07

541524°—43——23

APPENDIX IV

MARITIME POSITIONS

ATLANTIC COAST OF EUROPE—Continued

Coast	Place	Lat. N. °	Lat. N. ′	Long. E. °	Long. E. ′
Norway	Asenvagoen: Lighthouse	63	56	9	47
Norway	Tarven: Lighthouse	63	49	9	23
Norway	Sulen: Lighthouse	63	51	8	28
Norway	Sletringen: Lighthouse	63	40	8	16
Norway	Skalmen: Lighthouse	63	28	7	46
Norway	Trondhjem:				
Norway	Observatory	63	26	10	22
Norway	Cathedral	63	26	10	24
Norway	Grip: Lighthouse	63	14	7	37
Norway	Kristiansund: Nordholmen Lighthouse	63	07	7	45
Norway	Hestskjaer: Lighthouse	63	05	7	30
Norway	Kvitholmen Lighthouse	63	01	7	15
Norway	Ona: Lighthouse	62	52	6	33
Norway	Storholmen: Lighthouse	62	38	5	56
Norway	Alnes: Lighthouse	62	29	5	58
Norway	Graesoerne: Lighthouse	62	26	5	46
Norway	Rundo: Lighthouse	62	25	5	35
Norway	Svino: Lighthouse	62	20	5	16
Norway	Krakenes: Lighthouse	62	02	4	59
Norway	Hendanes: Lighthouse	61	58	5	02
Norway	Kvanhovden: Lighthouse	61	42	4	50
Norway	Ytteroerne: Lighthouse	61	34	4	41
Norway	Gjeita: Lighthouse	61	16	4	49
Norway	Utvaer: Lighthouse	61	02	4	30
Norway	Holmengra Lighthouse	60	51	4	39
Norway	Helliso: Lighthouse	60	45	4	43
Norway	Skarvo: Lighthouse	60	30	4	50
Norway	Bergen: Naval School Obs.	60	24	5	18
Norway	Marstenen: Lighthouse	60	07	5	01
Norway	Slottero: Lighthouse	59	54	5	04
Norway	Ryvarden: Lighthouse	59	32	5	14
Norway	Rovaersholmen: Lighthouse	59	27	5	04
Norway	Utsire: Lighthouse	59	18	4	53
Norway	Skudenes: Lighthouse	59	08	5	18
Norway	Hvidingso: Lighthouse	59	04	5	24
Norway	Stavanger: Fjeldoen: Lighthouse	59	05	5	34
Norway	Feistenen: Lighthouse	58	49	5	31
Norway	Obrestad: Lighthouse	58	39	5	34
Norway	Kvasheim: Lighthouse	58	33	5	41
Norway	Egero: Lighthouse	58	26	5	52
Norway	Lille Praestskjaer: Lighthouse	58	19	6	16
Norway	Aensire: Lighthouse	58	16	6	23
Norway	Varnes: Lighthouse	58	11	6	38
Norway	Lister: Lighthouse	58	06	6	34
Norway	Listerrauna: Lighthouse	58	03	6	41
Norway	Lindesnes: Naze: Lighthouse	57	59	7	03
Norway	Ryvingen: Lighthouse	57	58	7	30
Norway	Songvaar: Lighthouse	58	01	7	49
Norway	Kristiansand: Odderoen Lighthouse	58	07	8	00
Norway	Okso: Lighthouse	58	04	8	03
Norway	Homborsund: Lighthouse	58	15	8	32
Norway	Torungen: Inner light	58	24	8	48
Norway	Yttre Mokkalasset: Lighthouse	58	32	9	01
Norway	Lyngor: Lighthouse	58	38	9	09
Norway	Jomfruland: Lighthouse	58	52	9	36
Norway	Tvesten: Lighthouse	58	56	9	57
Norway	Svenoer: Lighthouse	58	58	10	09
Norway	Guldholmen: Lighthouse	59	26	10	35
Norway	Kristiania: University Obs. (mer. circle)	59	55	10	43
Norway	Stromtangen: Lighthouse	59	09	10	50
Norway	Struten: Lighthouse	59	07	10	45
Norway	Fredrikstad: Forstads, Church light	59	12	10	57
Norway	Torbjornskjaer: Lighthouse	59	00	10	47
Norway	Faerder: Lighthouse	59	02	10	32
Sweden	Tjurholm: Lighthouse	58	59	11	06
Sweden	Ursholm: Lighthouse	58	50	10	59
Sweden	Ramskar Rock: Lighthouse	58	46	11	00
Sweden	Vaderobod: Lighthouse	58	33	11	02
Sweden	Hallo: Lighthouse	58	20	11	13
Sweden	Maseskar: Lighthouse	58	06	11	20
Sweden	Hamnskar (Pater Noster) Lighthouse	57	54	11	28
Sweden	Vinga: Lighthouse	57	38	11	36
Sweden	Goteborg W. breakwater light	57	42	11	57
Sweden	Yttre Tistlarna Lighthouse	57	31	11	44
Sweden	Nidingen, Western: Lighthouse	57	18	11	54
Sweden	Varberg: Skrifvareklippan: Lighthouse	57	06	12	13
Sweden	Morups Tange: Lighthouse	56	55	12	22
Sweden	Stutarne: Lighthouse	56	54	12	25
Sweden	Falkenberg:				
Sweden	Mellan Rev. Light	56	53	12	28
Sweden	Church	56	54	12	30
Sweden	Tylo: Lighthouse	56	34	12	43
Sweden	Halmstad:				
Sweden	Breakwater light	56	39	12	51
Sweden	Palace	56	40	12	52
Sweden	Hallands Vadero: Lighthouse	56	27	12	33
Sweden	Torekov: Vingaskar: Lighthouse	56	25	12	36
Sweden	Engelholm: Church	56	15	12	52
Sweden	Kullen: Lighthouse	56	18	12	27
Sweden	Hoganas: Pier light	56	12	12	33
Sweden	Helsingborg: N. mole Lighthouse	56	03	12	41
Sweden	Haken: Lighthouse	55	55	12	44
Sweden	Ven: Lighthouse	55	55	12	40
Sweden	Landskrona: Grasrannan Lighthouse	55	52	12	48
Sweden	Barseback: Lighthouse	55	45	12	54
Sweden	Lund: Royal Univ. Obs. (center)	55	42	13	11
Sweden	Malmo: Pier Lighthouse	55	37	13	00
Sweden	Klagshanm: Wharf light	55	31	12	53
Sweden	Falsterbo: Lighthouse	55	23	12	49
Sweden	Trelleborg: E. pier Lighthouse	55	22	13	09
Sweden	Smygehuk: Lighthouse	55	20	13	22
Sweden	Ystad: Lighthouse (rear)	55	26	13	50
Sweden	Sandhammaren: Lighthouse	55	23	14	11
Sweden	Simrishamn: Lighthouse	55	33	14	22
Sweden	Stenshuvud: Lighthouse	55	40	14	17
Sweden	Ahus: N. jetty front light	55	56	14	19
Sweden	Solvesborg: Timan: Lighthouse	56	01	14	35
Sweden	Hano I. Lighthouse	56	01	14	51
Sweden	Tarno: Lighthouse	56	07	14	58
Sweden	Karlshamn: Ortholm Lighthouse	56	09	14	53
Sweden	Karlskrona: Laboratoriholm light	56	10	15	36
Sweden	Utkilppan Rock: Lighthouse	55	57	15	42
Sweden	Oland I.:				
Sweden	S. point Lighthouse	56	12	16	24
Sweden	Kapelludden: Lighthouse	56	49	16	51
Sweden	N. point Lighthouse	57	22	17	06
Sweden	Kalmar: Church	56	39	16	22
Sweden	Gotland I.:				
Sweden	Hoborg: Lighthouse	56	55	18	09
Sweden	Ostergarns: Lighthouse	57	27	18	59
Sweden	Faro: Lighthouse	57	57	19	21
Sweden	Hallshuk: Lighthouse	57	56	18	45
Sweden	Stenkyrkehuk: Lighthouse	57	49	18	28
Sweden	Stora Karlso: Lighthouse	57	17	17	58
Sweden	Haradskar: Lighthouse	58	09	16	59
Sweden	Arko: Lighthouse	58	29	17	00
Sweden	Oxelo: Harbor light	58	40	17	06
Sweden	Grand Kubben: Lighthouse	58	48	17	45
Sweden	Landsort: Lighthouse	58	44	17	52
Sweden	Huvudskar: Lighthouse	58	58	18	34
Sweden	Gronskar: Lighthouse	59	17	19	02
Sweden	Sandhamn: Lighthouse	59	17	18	55
Sweden	Stockholm: Obs. (mer. circle)	59	21	18	03
Sweden	Svenska Hogarne: Lighthouse	59	27	19	30
Sweden	Soderarm: Lighthouse	59	45	19	25
Sweden	Upsala Univ. Obs. (Transit Ins.)	59	51	17	38
Sweden	Norrtelge: Inn	59	45	18	42
Sweden	Svartklubben: Lighthouse	60	11	18	50
Sweden	Osthammar: Church	60	15	18	23
Sweden	Understen: Lighthouse	60	17	18	55
Sweden	Oregrund: Clock Tower	60	20	18	27
Sweden	Orskar: Lighthouse	60	32	18	23
Sweden	Forsmark: Church	60	22	18	10
Sweden	Bjorn: Lighthouse	60	38	17	59
Sweden	Gavle: Gefle: Church	60	40	17	08
Sweden	Eggegrund: Lighthouse	60	44	17	34
Sweden	Hamrange: Church	60	56	17	03
Sweden	Storjungfrun: Lighthouse	61	10	17	20
Sweden	Soderhamm: Courthouse	61	18	17	04
Sweden	Enanger: Church	61	33	17	02
Sweden	Ago: Lighthouse	61	33	17	28
Sweden	Hudiksvall: Courthouse	61	44	17	08
Sweden	Gran: Lighthouse	62	01	17	38
Sweden	Gnarp: Church	62	03	17	16
Sweden	Bremo: Lighthouse	62	13	17	44
Sweden	Sundsvall: Church	62	23	17	19
Sweden	Astholmsudde: Lighthouse	62	23	17	45
Sweden	Harno: Lighthouse	62	37	18	03
Sweden	Harnosand: Harbor light	62	38	17	58
Sweden	Lungo: Lighthouse	62	39	18	05
Sweden	Hog Bonden: Lighthouse	62	52	18	29
Sweden	Skag: Lighthouse	63	12	19	03

MARITIME POSITIONS

ATLANTIC COAST OF EUROPE—Continued

Coast	Place	Lat. N. °	Lat. N. ′	Long. E. °	Long. E. ′
Sweden	Ornskoldsvik: Pier light	63	17	18	43
	Bonden Rock: Lighthouse	63	26	20	03
	Holmogadd: Lighthouse	63	36	20	45
	Umea: Fjardgrund: Lighthouse	63	40	20	20
	Stora Fjaderagg: Lighthouse	63	48	21	00
	North Ratan: Lighthouse	63	59	20	54
	Vannskar Yttre: Lighthouse	64	09	21	08
	Klubben: Beacon	64	18	21	23
	Bjurokluub: Lighthouse	64	29	21	35
	Ronnskar: Lighthouse	65	02	21	34
	Pitea: Range light	65	19	21	29
	Rodkallen: Lighthouse	65	19	22	22
	Maloren I.: Lighthouse	65	32	23	34
Finland	Tornea: Church	65	50	24	33
	Ajos Holm: Lighthouse	65	40	24	10
	Uleaborg:				
	Church: Lighthouse	65	01	5	29
	Karlo I.: Light	65	02	24	34
	Ulko Kalla: Lighthouse	64	20	23	27
	Hallgrund: Lighthouse	63	39	22	25
	Valsorarne: Lighthouse	63	25	21	04
	Norrskar: Lighthouse	63	14	20	36
	Strommingsbadan: Lighthouse	62	59	20	45
	Salgrund: Lighthouse	62	20	21	12
	Yttergrund: Lighthouse	61	59	21	18
	Sappi (Sebbskar): Lighthouse	61	29	21	21
	Nurmis I.: Lighthouse	61	12	21	20
	Enskar: Isokari Lighthouse	60	43	21	01
	Alan I.: Skalskar, Sodra: Lighthouse	60	25	19	35
	Market Rock: Lighthouse	60	18	19	08
	Gisslan: Islet Lighthouse	60	10	19	18
	Stora Lokskar: Lighthouse	59	59	20	02
	Nyhamn, Lilla Batskar: Lighthouse	59	58	19	57
	Lagskar: Lighthouse	59	50	19	55
	Bogskaren: Lighthouse	59	30	20	21
	Kokarsorn: Lighthouse	59	46	21	01
	Uto: Lighthouse	59	47	21	22
	Selsye I.: Lighthouse	60	04	21	45
	Bengtskar: Lighthouse	59	43	22	30
	Hango Russaro: Lighthouse	59	46	22	57
	Jussaro old lighthouse	59	49	23	34
	Kalbadagrund: Lighthouse	59	52	24	18
	Kyto Karingen: Lighthouse	60	04	24	43
	Helsingfors:				
	Grohara: Lighthouse	60	06	24	59
	Imperial Univ. Obs	60	10	24	57
	Soderskar (Sedersher): Lighthouse	60	07	25	25
	Orrengrun: Lighthouse	60	16	26	26
	North Hogland: Lighthouse	60	06	26	57
	South Hogland: Lighthouse	60	01	27	00
	Frederikshamn: Manniklub: Lighthouse	60	15	27	00
	Veitkari Rock: Lighthouse	60	16	27	14
	Pukionsari: Lighthouse	60	26	27	48
	Galli (Halli) Rock: Lighthouse	60	16	27	14
	Serkoloda (Sarkiluoto): Lighthouse	60	18	28	17
	Stirs Point (Styrsudd): Lighthouse	60	10	29	02
	Rodsher Islet: Lighthouse	59	58	26	42
	Great (East) Tyters: Lighthouse	59	51	27	12
	Sommars I.: Lighthouse	60	12	27	37
	Nerva Islet: Lighthouse	60	15	27	57
	Seskar: Lighthouse	60	02	28	22
U. S. S. R., Baltic Sea	Leningrad: Univ. Obs	59	57	30	18
	Pulkovo Central Obs. (center obs.)	59	46	30	20
	Peterhof: N. pier Lighthouse	59	53	29	55
	Oranienbaum pier light	59	57	29	46
	Kronstadt:				
	Kronslot Is.: Lighthouse	59	59	29	45
	Cathedral	60	00	29	46
	Tolboukin: Lighthouse	60	03	29	33
	Karavalda I. (Shepler): Lighthouse	59	59	29	08
Esthonia	Narva: Lighthouse	59	28	28	02
	North Hoft: Lighthouse	59	41	26	31
	Stenskar: Lighthouse	59	49	26	23
	Ekholm: Lighthouse	59	41	25	48
	Kokskar Islet: Lighthouse	59	42	25	01
	Reval:				
	Tallinn (front): Lighthouse	59	26	24	48
	Cathedral	59	26	24	44
Esthonia	Wulf I. Reef: Lighthouse	59	36	24	44
	Nargen I.: Lighthouse	59	36	24	31
	Cape Sourop (Surop): Lighthouse	59	28	24	23
	Pakerort: Lighthouse	59	23	24	02
	Cape Arabusheren: Lighthouse	59	21	23	52
	Odensholm: Lighthouse	59	18	23	22
	Tahkona (Tachkona Point): Lighthouse	59	05	22	35
	Dagerort: Lighthouse	58	55	22	11
	Ristna Point: Lighthouse	58	56	22	03
	Filsand: Lighthouse	58	23	21	49
	Zerel (Svalferort): Lighthouse	57	55	22	03
	Allirahu (Galliray): Lighthouse	58	10	22	47
	Kubasaar: Lighthouse	58	26	23	18
	Kino I.: Lighthouse	58	06	23	58
	Pernau S. ent. light	58	23	24	29
Latvia	Gainash (Ainazi): Lighthouse	57	52	24	21
	Salacgriva: Lighthouse	57	45	24	22
	Livonia: Dingen-Knan Point: Lighthouse	57	33	24	23
	Dunamund (Daugavgriva): Lighthouse	57	04	24	01
	Riga: St. Peter Cathedral	56	57	24	07
	Messaragotsem Point: Lighthouse	57	22	23	07
	Domesness (Kolkarags): Lighthouse	57	48	22	38
	Michael (Mikelbaka): Lighthouse	57	36	21	59
	Liserort (Oviza): Lighthouse	57	34	21	43
	Windau (Ventspils) (rear): Lighthouse	57	24	21	34
	Backofen (Uzava): Lighthouse	57	13	21	25
	Steinort (Akmenrags): Lighthouse	56	50	21	04
	Libau: (Liepaja) Main: Lighthouse	56	31	20	59
	Pappenze (Pape)	56	09	21	02
Lithuania	Memel: Lighthouse	55	44	21	06
	Nidden: Lighthouse	55	16	21	00
Germany	Brusterort: Lighthouse	54	58	19	59
	Pillau: Lighthouse	54	38	19	54
	Fischausen: W. Gable Church	54	44	20	00
	Konigsberg: University Obs	54	43	20	30
	Tolkemit: Church tower	54	19	19	32
	Kahlberg: Lighthouse	54	23	19	27
	Elbing: Church tower	54	10	19	24
Poland	Neufahrwasser: Lighthouse	54	24	18	40
	Gydnia: Marine Obs	54	31	18	33
	Oxhoft: Lighthouse	54	33	18	34
	Hela: Lighthouse	54	36	18	49
	Jastarnia Pen.: Lighthouse	54	39	18	47
	Rosewie: Lighthouse	54	50	18	20
Germany	Stilo: Lighthouse	54	47	17	44
	Leba:				
	Church Tower	54	45	17	33
	Mole head light	54	46	17	33
	Scholpin: Lighthouse	54	43	17	15
	Jershoft: Lighthouse	54	32	16	33
	Rugenwald: St. Gertrude's Church	54	26	16	25
	Funkenhagen: Lighthouse	54	15	15	52
	Kolberg: Lighthouse	54	11	15	33
	St. George's Church	54	11	15	35
	Gross Horst: Lighthouse	54	06	15	04
Denmark	Bornholm I.:				
	Hammeren Lighthouse	55	17	14	46
	Hammer Odde Lighthouse	55	18	14	47
	Due Odde N. Lighthouse	55	00	15	04
	Christianso I.: Lighthouse	55	19	15	11
	Gjedser: Lighthouse	54	34	11	58
	Moen I.:				
	Lighthouse	54	57	12	32
	Heleharnnakke Lighthouse	55	00	12	31
	Stege: Church spire	54	59	12	17
	Præsto:				
	Naeb: Lighthouse	55	08	12	04
	Church spire	55	07	12	03
	Faxe: E. mole light	55	13	12	10
	Sterns: Lighthouse	55	17	12	27
	Kjoge: N. mole light	55	27	12	12

MARITIME POSITIONS

ATLANTIC COAST OF EUROPE—Continued

Coast	Place	Lat. N. °	Lat. N. ′	Long. E. °	Long. E. ′
Denmark	Copenhagen:				
	University Obs. (center of Obs.)	55	41	12	35
	Trekroner: Battery Lighthouse	55	42	12	37
	Middelgrund Fort Lighthouse	55	43	12	40
	Flakfort: Lighthouse	55	42	12	44
	Kronborg: N E. Castle tower Light house	56	02	12	37
	Nakke Hoved: Lighthouse	56	07	12	21
	Gilleleje: Outer mole Lighthouse	56	08	12	19
	Lysegrund: Lighthouse	56	18	11	48
	Hesselo: Lighthouse	56	12	11	43
	Nordre Rose Lighthouse	55	38	12	41
	Lynæs: W. mole light	55	56	11	52
	Spodsjerg: Lighthouse	55	58	11	51
	Sjaellands Rev.: Lighthouse	56	05	11	13
	Sejro: Lighthouse	55	55	11	05
	Revsnaes: Lighthouse	55	45	10	52
	Kallundborg: E. mole light	55	41	11	05
	Sprogo: Lighthouse	55	20	10	58
	Korsor:				
	Breakwater light: S. end	55	20	11	08
	Agerso: Helleholm: Lighthouse	55	11	11	13
	Omo I.:				
	Lighthouse	55	10	11	08
	Church	55	10	11	09
	Vejro I.: Lighthouse	55	02	11	22
	Vordingborg:				
	Ore: Lighthouse	55	00	11	52
	Waldemar tower: Lighthouse	55	00	11	55
	Hestehoved: Lighthouse	54	50	12	10
	Hyllekrog: Lighthouse	54	36	11	30
	Bandholm: N. mole light	54	50	11	30
	Kragenaes: N. mole light	54	55	11	22
	Taars: Lighthouse	54	53	11	02
	Albuen:				
	Lighthouse	54	50	10	58
	Kjelsnor Lighthouse	54	44	10	43
	Langeland:				
	Tranekjaer Lighthouse	54	59	10	53
	Hov Lighthouse	55	09	10	57
	Franke-Klint Lighthouse	55	10	10	56
	Lohals Lighthouse	55	08	10	54
	Sio I.: Lighthouse	54	57	10	42
	Elsehoved: Lighthouse	55	06	10	47
	Nyborg:				
	Church spire	55	19	10	48
	Jomfruhoj rear light beacon	55	18	10	47
	Knudshoved: Lighthouse	55	17	10	51
	Romso: Lighthouse	55	31	10	48
	Aebelo: Lighthouse	55	39	10	10
	Strib: Lighthouse	55	33	9	45
	Faeno I.: Lighthouse	55	28	9	42
	Skamblingsbanke: Survey monument	55	25	9	34
	Baago I.: Lighthouse	55	18	9	48
	Tvinsbjerg (rear): Lighthouse	55	20	9	55
	Assens:				
	Church tower le	55	16	9	54
	Front range mo light	55	16	9	53
	Helnaes: Lighthouse	55	08	9	59
	Skjoldnaes: Lighthouse	54	58	10	12
	Dybbol: Survey station	54	54	9	45
	Augustenborg: Church	54	57	9	52
	Hojbjerg: Survey station	54	58	9	59
	Aabenraa: Church	55	03	9	25
	Aaro I.: Lighthouse	55	15	9	44
	Aaro Sund: Mole light	55	16	9	43
	Kolding: Castle tower	55	30	9	29
	Borup: E. Lighthouse	55	32	9	41
	Fredericia: N. mole light	55	34	9	45
	Traelle Naes: Lighthouse	55	38	9	52
	Hjarno: Rear range Lighthouse	55	50	10	04
	Horsens:				
	Front range Lighthouse	55	51	9	52
	Frelser Church spire	55	52	9	51
	Samso I.:				
	Vestborg Lighthouse	55	46	10	33
	Ljushage Lighthouse	55	46	10	37
	Kolby Kaas mole light	55	48	10	32
	Hov Harbor: E. mole light	55	55	10	16
	Tuno I.: Lighthouse	55	57	10	27
	Tuno Ron	55	57	10	29
	Aarhus:				
	South Havn: E. mole light	56	09	10	13
	Sletterhage: Lighthouse	56	06	10	31

Coast	Place	Lat. N. °	Lat. N. ′	Long. E. °	Long. E. ′
Denmark	Ebeltoft Bay: Lighthouse	56	14	10	37
	Hjelm I.: Lighthouse	56	08	10	48
	Grenaa Harbor: E. mole light	56	25	10	56
	Fornaes: Lighthouse	56	27	10	58
	Gjerrild: Knudshoved: Lighthouse	56	32	10	50
	Udbyhoj: Lighthouse	56	35	10	19
	Anholt I.: Lighthouse	56	44	11	39
	Hals-Barre: Lighthouse	56	57	10	26
	Hals: Church tower	57	00	10	19
	Laeso, N. W. reef Lighthouse	57	18	10	46
	Nordre Ronner Lighthouse	57	21	10	55
	Frederikshavn: S. light inner mole	57	26	10	33
	Hirsholm: Lighthouse	57	29	10	38
	Skagen:				
	Lighthouse	57	44	10	38
	Harbor: Outer mole S. light	57	43	10	36
	Hirshals: Lighthouse	57	35	9	57
	Rudbjerg-Knude: Lighthouse	57	27	9	47
	Hanstholm: Lighthouse	57	07	8	36
	Lodbjerg: Lighthouse	56	49	8	16
	Bovbjerg: Lighthouse	56	31	8	07
	Lyngvig: Lighthouse	56	03	8	06
	Ringkjobing Church spire	56	05	8	15
	Blaavands-Huk: Lighthouse	55	33	8	05
Germany	Stettin N. Castle tower	53	26	14	34
	Swinemunde: Lighthouse	53	55	14	17
	Usedom: Church tower	53	52	13	55
	Lassan Church tower	53	57	13	51
	Wolgast: Church tower	54	03	13	47
	Greifswald: St. Nicholas Church	54	06	13	23
	Greifswalder Oie: Lighthouse	54	15	13	56
	Granitz: Castle tower	54	23	13	38
	Bergen: Church tower	54	25	13	26
	Sassnitz: New Lighthouse	54	30	13	38
	Kollickerort: Lighthouse	54	34	13	41
	Ranzow: Lighthouse	54	35	13	38
	Cape Arkona: Lighthouse	54	41	13	26
	Dornbusch: Lighthouse	54	36	13	07
	Vierendehl: Upper light	54	26	13	04
	Barhoft (rear): Lighthouse	54	25	13	02
	Stralsund: St. Mary Church	54	19	13	06
	Darsser Ort: Lighthouse	54	28	12	30
	Wustrow:				
	Church	54	20	12	23
	Lighthouse	54	21	12	24
	Warnemunde:				
	Lighthouse	54	11	12	05
	Rostock: St. Peter's Church	54	06	12	09
	Diedrichshagen: Survey station	54	06	11	45
	Basdorf: Survey station	54	08	11	41
	Buk: Lighthouse	54	08	11	42
	Wismar: St. Nicholas Church	53	54	11	28
	Timmendorf: Lighthouse	54	00	11	23
	Hohenschonberg: Survey station	53	59	11	06
	Travemunde: Lighthouse	53	59	10	53
	Burg: Church tower	54	26	11	12
	Pelzer Haken: Lighthouse	54	05	10	52
	Dahmeshoved: Lighthouse	54	12	11	06
	Fehmarn:				
	Staberhuk: Lighthouse	54	24	11	19
	Marienleuchte: Lighthouse	54	30	11	14
	Wester Markelsdorf Lighthouse	54	32	11	04
	Flugge: Lighthouse	54	27	11	01
	Petersdorf: Church tower	54	29	11	04
	Neuland: Lighthouse	54	22	10	36
	Hessenstein tower	54	20	10	33
	Schonberg: Church	54	24	10	22
	Kiel: University Observatory	54	20	10	09
	Bulk Point: Lighthouse	54	27	10	12
	Eckernforde:				
	Lighthouse	54	27	9	51
	Church	54	28	9	50
	Schleimunde: Lighthouse	54	40	10	02
	Kappeln: Church	54	40	9	56
	Schleswig: Cathedral dome	54	31	9	34
	Falshoft: Lighthouse	54	46	9	58
	Holnis: Lighthouse	54	52	9	34
	Flensburg: Nikolav Church	54	47	9	26
Denmark	Guldager: Church	55	32	8	24
	Fano Nordby harbor:				
	Pier (center) light	55	27	8	25
	Church	55	26	8	24
	Mano I: Church spire	55	16	8	32
	Ballum: Church	55	06	8	40

MARITIME POSITIONS

ATLANTIC COAST OF EUROPE—Continued

Coast	Place	Lat. N. °	′	Long. E. °	′
Germany	Rotekliff: Lighthouse	54	57	8	21
	Horum Point: Lighthouse	54	45	8	18
	Fohr: St. Nicholas Church	54	42	8	33
	Galgenberg: Survey station	54	41	8	34
	Amrum I: Lighthouse	54	38	8	21
	Husum: Church	54	29	9	03
	Tonning: Church	54	19	8	56
	Busum: Lighthouse	54	08	8	52
	Helgoland: Lighthouse	54	11	7	53
	Scharhorn: Beacon	53	57	8	25
	Neuwerk: Large Lighthouse	53	55	8	30
	Cuxhaven:				
	Lighthouse	53	52	8	43
	Time ball signal	53	52	8	43
	Stade: Church spire	53	36	9	29
	Steinkirchen: Church	53	34	9	39
	Hamburg:				
	Marine Obs. (transit pier)	53	33	9	58
	Time signal station	52	32	9	58
	Berlin:				
	Urania Obs	52	32	13	22
	Treptow Obs	52	29	13	29
	Hohe Weg: Lighthouse	53	43	8	15
	Bremerhaven:				
	Protestant Church	53	33	8	35
	Rear range light	53	33	8	34
	Wilhelmshaven: Obs. time ball signal	53	31	8	09
	Wangeroog: Lighthouse	53	47	7	54
	Emden: Time ball signal	53	21	7	12
Netherlands	Borkum: West Lighthouse	53	35	6	40
	Rottumeroog: Lighthouse	53	33	6	33
	Schiermonnikoog: South Lighthouse	53	29	6	09
	Ameland: Lighthouse	53	27	5	38
	Terschelling (Brandaris): Lighthouse	53	22	5	13
	Vlieland (Vuurduin): Lighthouse	53	18	5	04
	Eierland: Lighthouse	53	11	4	51
	Texel:				
	Kijkduin: Lighthouse	52	57	4	44
	Zanddijk (front) light beacon	52	53	4	43
	Nieuwe Diep: Time ball signal	52	58	4	47
	Egmond-Aan-Zee: Lighthouse	52	37	4	37
	Amsterdam:				
	W. Church tower	52	22	4	53
	Time ball signal (Meteorological Ins.)	52	23	4	55
	Utrecht: Univ. Obs. (Alta-azimuth pier)	52	05	5	08
	Leiden: Univ. Obs. (Mer. circle)	52	09	4	29
	Ymuiden (Ijmuiden) (rear): Lighthouse	52	28	4	35
	Noordwijk: Lighthouse	52	15	4	26
	Scheveningen: Lighthouse	52	06	4	16
	Hook of Holland: Noordwal (rear) Lighthouse	51	59	4	08
	Rotterdam: Time signal (Gate Bldg.)	51	55	4	30
	Goeree: West Hoofd Lighthouse	51	49	3	52
	North Schouwen: Lighthouse	51	45	3	47
	Domburg: Lighthouse	51	34	3	29
	Westkapelsche Dyke: Lighthouse	51	32	3	26
	Westkapelle: Lighthouse	51	32	3	27
	Flushing (Vlissingen):				
	Time ball station	51	27	3	36
	West Haven Bastion Lighthouse	51	26	3	35
Belgium	Brussels (Uccle): Royal Obs	50	48	4	22
	Antwerp:				
	Notre Dame Cathedral	51	13	4	24
	Escaut: Ft. Ste. Marie, light	51	15	4	18
	Nieuwe Sluis: Lighthouse	51	24	3	31
	Zeebrugge: Mole light	51	21	3	12
	Blankenberge: E. Breakwater Lighthouse	51	19	3	07
	Ostende:				
	E. Breakwater Lighthouse	51	14	2	55
	Nieuport: Lighthouse	51	09	2	44
	La Panne: Lighthouse	51	06	2	35
France	Paris: Observatory	48	50	2	20
	Dunkerque:				
	Tower	51	02	2	23
	Lighthouse	51	03	2	22
	Gravelines: Fort Philippe Lighthouse	51	00	2	07

Coast	Place	Lat. N. °	′	Long. E. °	′
France	Calais:				
	Lighthouse	50	58	1	51
	Saint Inglevert aerial light	50	53	1	45
	Cape Gris Nez: Lighthouse	50	52	1	35
	Boulogne: Chanzy quay light	50	44	1	36
	Cape Alprech: Lighthouse	50	42	1	34
	Touquet Point: Lighthouse	50	31	1	36
	Pointe du Haut Banc: Lighthouse	50	24	1	34
	Pointe Hourdel light	50	13	1	34
	Abbeville Tower	50	07	1	50
	Cayeux: Lighthouse	50	12	1	31
	Dieppe: W. jetty light	50	01	1	05
	Pointe d'Ailly: Lighthouse	49	55	0	58
	St. Valery en Caux: W. jetty light	49	52	0	43
	Fecamp: N. jetty light	49	46	0	22
	Cape d'Antifer: Lighthouse	49	41	0	10
	Cape de La Heve: Lighthouse	49	31	0	04
	Havre: N. cupola Bourse, rear range light	49	30	0	07
	Honfleur: W. jetty light	49	26	0	14
	Trouville: E. jetty light	49	22	0	04
		Lat. N.		Long. W.	
	Caen: Church tower	49	11	0	21
	Pointe de Vere: Lighthouse	49	20	0	31
	Isigny: Rear range light	49	19	1	07
	Carentan: Rear range light	49	20	1	11
	St. Marcouf Islet: Lighthouse	49	30	1	09
	Morsalines: Lighthouse	49	34	1	19
	La Hougue: Lighthouse	49	34	1	16
	Cape Barfleur-Gatteville: Lighthouse	49	42	1	16
	Cape Levi: Lighthouse	49	42	1	28
	Cherbourg:				
	Breakwater, W. head: Light	49	40	1	39
	Marine Obs. time signal	49	39	1	38
	Cape de La Hague: Lighthouse	49	43	1	57
	Port de Dielette: W. jetty light	49	33	1	52
	Cape Carteret: Lighthouse	49	22	1	48
	Coutances: Cathedral tower	49	03	1	27
	Iles Chausey: Lighthouse	48	52	1	49
	Granville: Cape Lihou: Lighthouse	48	50	1	37
	La Pierre de Herpin: Lighthouse	48	44	1	49
	St. Malo: Rochebonne: Lighthouse	48	40	1	59
	Cape Frehel: Lighthouse	48	41	2	19
	Roches Douvres: Lighthouse	49	06	2	49
	Heaux de Brehat: Lighthouse	48	55	3	05
	Les Sept Iles: Lighthouse	48	53	3	29
	Triagoz: Lighthouse	48	52	3	39
	Ile de Bas: Lighthouse	48	45	4	02
	Ile Vierge: Lighthouse	48	38	4	34
	L'Abervrach: Ile Vrach Lighthouse	48	37	4	35
	Ushant I.:				
	Pointe de Creach Lighthouse	48	27	5	08
	Stiff Point Lighthouse	48	29	5	03
	La Jument Rock Lighthouse	48	25	5	08
	Les Pierres Noires: Lighthouse	48	19	4	55
	Trezien: Lighthouse	48	25	4	47
	Corsen Point: Lighthouse	48	25	4	43
	Le Conquet: Kermorvan Point Lighthouse	48	22	4	47
	Pointe St. Mathieu: Lighthouse	48	20	4	46
	Toulinguet Point: Lighthouse	48	17	4	38
	Brest:				
	Portzic Point Lighthouse	48	21	4	32
	Naval School Obs. time signal	48	23	4	30
	Ar-Men Rock: Lighthouse	48	03	5	00
	Ile de Sein: Lighthouse	48	03	4	52
	La Vieille Rock: Lighthouse	48	02	4	45
	Audierne: Trescadec (front) Lighthouse	48	01	4	33
	Penmarc'h (Eckmühl): Lighthouse	47	48	4	22
	Ile Penfret: Lighthouse	47	43	3	57
	Concarneau: Lighthouse	47	53	3	54
	Ile de Groix: Pen Men Lighthouse	47	39	3	30
	Lorient: Church Tower Lighthouse	47	45	3	22
	Belle Ile:				
	Pointe des Poulains Lighthouse	47	23	3	15
	Goulfar Lighthouse	47	19	3	14
	Les Grands Cardinaux: Lighthouse	47	19	2	50

APPENDIX IV

MARITIME POSITIONS

ATLANTIC COAST OF EUROPE—Continued

Coast	Place	Lat. N.		Long. W.	
		°	'	°	'
France	Port Navalo: Lighthouse	47	33	2	55
	Vannes: St. Pierre Church	47	39	2	45
	Croisic: Trehic Jetty Lighthouse	47	18	2	31
	Guerande: Church spire	47	20	2	26
	St. Nazaire: Old Mole Lighthouse	47	16	2	12
	Paimboeuf: Church spire	47	17	2	02
	Nantes: Cathedral	47	13	1	33
	Le Pilier Isle: Lighthouse	47	03	2	22
	Noirmoutier I.: Des Dames Lighthouse	47	01	2	13
	Ile d'Yeu: Petite Foule Lighthouse	46	43	2	23
	St. Gilles Sur Vie: Rear Range Lighthouse	46	42	1	57
	Les Sables d'Olonne: Potence (rear) Lighthouse	46	30	1	46
	Ile de Ré: Les Baleines Lighthouse	46	15	1	34
	La Pallice: N. jetty light	46	10	1	14
	Rochelle: Rear Lighthouse	46	09	1	09
	Ile d'Aix: Lighthouse	46	01	1	11
	Rochefort:				
	Time ball signal	45	56	0	58
	Hospital	45	57	0	58
	Ile d'Oleron: Chassiron Point Lighthouse	46	03	1	25
	La Coubre: Lighthouse	45	42	1	14
	Cordouan Rock: Lighthouse	45	35	1	10
	Gironde River:				
	Terre Negre Lighthouse	45	39	1	06
	Pointe de Grave Lighthouse	45	34	1	04
	Bordeaux (Floirac) Univ. Obs. (mer. circle)	44	50	0	32
	Hourtin: Lighthouse	45	08	1	10
	Cape Ferret: Lighthouse	44	39	1	15
	Contis: Lighthouse	44	06	1	19
	Bayonne: Cathedral	43	29	1	29
	Biarritz: Pointe St. Martin: Lighthouse	43	30	1	33
	St. Jean de Luz: Saint Barbe Lighthouse	43	24	1	40
	Le Socoa: Lighthouse	43	24	1	41
	Abbadia: Hendaye Obs	43	23	1	45
Spain	Cape Higuer: Lighthouse	43	24	1	48
	Port Pasajes: Cape La Plata Lighthouse	43	20	1	56
	San Sebastian: Santa Clara Lighthouse	43	19	2	00
	Guetaria: San Antonio I.: Lighthouse	43	19	2	12
	Zumaya: Lighthouse	43	18	2	15
	Cape Machichaco: Lighthouse	43	27	2	45
	Bilbao: Punta Galea Lighthouse	43	22	3	02
	Castro Urdiales: Breakwater light	43	23	3	13
	Santona: Faro del Caballo	43	27	3	26
	Santander: Cape Mayor Lighthouse	43	29	3	47
	Suances: San Martin de la Arena Lighthouse	43	27	4	03
	San Vicente de la Barquera: Lighthouse	43	24	4	24
	San Emeterio: Lighthouse	43	24	4	32
	Ribadesella: Mt. Somos Lighthouse	43	28	5	04
	Gijon: Santa Catalina Lighthouse	43	33	5	40
	Cape Torres: Lighthouse	43	34	5	42
	Cape San Antonio: Lighthouse	43	36	5	46
	Cape Peñas: Lighthouse	43	39	5	51
	Aviles: Lighthouse	43	36	5	57
	Tapia Isla: Lighthouse	43	34	6	57
	Estaca de Bares: Lighthouse	43	47	7	41
	Cedeira: Lighthouse	43	39	8	05
Spain	Cape Prior: Lighthouse	43	34	8	19
	Ferrol:				
	Arsenal flagstaff, old naval Obs	43	28	8	14
	Cape Priorino Chico Lighthouse	43	27	8	20
	Coruna: Torre Hercules Lighthouse	43	23	8	24
	Sisargas Islands: Lighthouse	43	22	8	51
	Punta Lage: Lighthouse	43	14	9	01
	Cape Villano: Lighthouse	43	10	9	13
	Cape Torinana: Lighthouse	43	03	9	18
	Cape Finisterre: Lighthouse	42	53	9	16
	Insua Pt.: Lighthouse	42	46	9	08
	Cape Corrubedo: Lighthouse	42	35	9	05
	Salvora Isla: Lighthouse	42	28	9	01
	Ons Isla: Lighthouse	42	23	8	56
	Vigo:				
	Monte Faro Lighthouse	42	13	8	55
	Punta Robaleira Lighthouse	42	15	8	52
	Cape Vicos: Lighthouse	42	11	8	53
	Cape Silleiro: Lighthouse	42	06	8	54
Portugal	Cape Montedor: Lighthouse	41	45	8	52
	Boa Nova: Lighthouse	41	12	8	43
	Leixoes: S. mole light	41	11	8	42
	Oporto: Nossa Senhora da Luz Light	41	09	8	41
	Aveiro: Lighthouse	40	38	8	45
	Cape Mondego: Lighthouse	40	11	8	54
	Coimbra: University Obs	40	12	8	26
	Penedo da Saudade: Lighthouse	39	46	9	02
	Farilhao: Lighthouse	39	29	9	33
	Berlenga: Lighthouse	39	25	9	30
	Cape Carvoeiro: Lighthouse	39	22	9	24
	Peniche: Fort Cabanas Light	39	21	9	23
	Cape Roca: Lighthouse	38	47	9	30
	Cape Razo: Lighthouse	38	42	9	29
	Lisbon:				
	Fort Bugio Lighthouse	38	40	9	18
	Tapada Obs. (center of dome)	38	43	9	11
	Customhouse wharf time signal	38	42	9	08
	Cape Espichel: Lighthouse	38	25	9	13
	Setubal: Outao Lighthouse	38	29	8	56
	Cape Sines: Lighthouse	37	57	8	53
	Cape Sardao: Lighthouse	37	36	8	49
	Cape San Vicente: Lighthouse	37	01	9	00
	Sagres: Lighthouse	37	00	8	57
	Lagos:				
	Ponta da Piedade Lighthouse	37	05	8	40
	Cape Carvoeiro do Algarve: Lighthouse	37	05	8	26
	Cape Santa Maria: Lighthouse	36	58	7	52
	Vila Real de Santo Antonio: Lighthouse	37	11	7	25
Spain	Rompido de Cartaya: Lighthouse	37	13	7	08
	Picacho: Lighthouse	37	08	6	49
	Chipiona: Lighthouse	36	44	6	26
	Cadiz:				
	San Sebastian Lighthouse	36	31	6	19
	San Fernando: Naval Obs. (center building)	36	28	6	12
	Cape Trafalgar: Lighthouse	36	11	6	02
	Tarifa: Lighthouse	36	00	5	37
	Carnero Point: Lighthouse	36	04	5	25
	Algeciras: Verde I. Lighthouse	36	07	5	26
	Gibraltar:				
	Dockyard clock tower	36	07	5	21
	Europa Pt. Lighthouse	36	06	5	21
	Doncella Point: Lighthouse	36	25	5	09

COASTS OF THE MEDITERRANEAN, ADRIATIC, AND BLACK SEAS

Coast	Place	Lat. N.		Long. W.	
Spain	Marbella: Lighthouse	36	30	4	53
	Calaburras Point: Lighthouse	36	30	4	38
	Malaga: San Nicolas Battery Lighthouse	36	43	4	25
	Torrox Point: Lighthouse	36	43	3	57
	Cape Sacratif: Lighthouse	36	41	3	28
	Adra: Lighthouse	36	45	3	02
	Almeria: E. breakwater light	36	50	2	28
	Cape Gata: Lighthouse	36	43	2	11
Spain	Mesa de Roldan: Lighthouse	36	56	1	54
	Mazarron: Lighthouse	37	33	1	15
	Cape Tinoso: Lighthouse	37	32	1	06
	Cartagena:				
	Navidad mole light	37	35	0	59
	Escombrera I. Lighthouse	37	33	0	58
	Porman: Lighthouse	37	35	0	50
	Cape Palos: Lighthouse	37	38	0	41
	Hormiga Grande I.: Lighthouse	37	39	0	39

MARITIME POSITIONS

COASTS OF THE MEDITERRANEAN, ADRIATIC, AND BLACK SEAS—Continued

Coast	Place	Lat. N. °	Lat. N. ′	Long. W. °	Long. W. ′
Spain	El Estacio: Lighthouse	37	45	0	44
	Santa Pola: Talayola Tower Lighthouse	38	12	0	31
	Plana (Tabarca) I.: Lighthouse	38	10	0	28
	Alicante: Outer breakwater light	38	20	0	29
	Cape Huertas: Lighthouse	38	21	0	24
	Albir Point: Lighthouse	38	34	0	03
		Lat. N.		Long. E.	
	Morayva Tower	38	41	0	09
	Cape San Antonio: Lighthouse	38	48	0	12
	Denia: Front range light	38	50	0	07
		Lat. N.		Long. W.	
	Gandia: N. mole light	39	00	0	09
	Cape Cullera: Lighthouse	39	11	0	13
	Valencia:				
	Grao Church tower	39	27	0	20
	Lighthouse	39	27	0	18
	Canet: Lighthouse	39	40	0	12
	Burriana: Lighthouse	39	53	0	03
		Lat. N.		Long. E.	
	Castellon de la Plana: Lighthouse	39	58	0	01
	Columbretes I.: Lighthouse	39	54	0	41
	Cape Oropesa: Lighthouse	40	05	0	09
	Peniscola: Lighthouse	40	22	0	24
	Vinaroz: E. mole light	40	28	0	29
	Port Alfaques: Bana Pt. Lighthouse	40	33	0	40
	Cape Tortosa: Lighthouse	40	43	0	54
	Port Fangar: Fango Point Lighthouse	40	47	0	46
	Cape Salou: Lighthouse	41	03	1	10
	Tarragona: Levante mole light	41	06	1	14
	Villanueva y Geltru: Lighthouse	41	13	1	44
	Barcelona:				
	Montjuich Lighthouse	41	22	2	10
	Fabra Obs	41	25	2	08
	Harbor clock tower	41	22	2	11
	Calella: Lighthouse	41	36	2	39
	Cape Tossa: Lighthouse	41	43	2	56
	Palamos: Molino Pt. Lighthouse	41	50	3	08
	Cape San Sebastian: Lighthouse	41	54	3	12
	Meda I.: Lighthouse	42	03	3	13
	Rosas: Ponsella Point Lighthouse	42	15	3	11
	Cadagues: Cala Naus Lighthouse	42	16	3	17
	Cape Creus: Lighthouse	42	19	3	19
	Selva: Sernella Lighthouse	42	21	3	11
France	Cape Bear: Lighthouse	42	31	3	08
	Port Vendres: Fort Fanal Lighthouse	42	31	3	07
	Port Nouvelle: S. jetty light	43	01	3	04
	Brescou: Lighthouse	43	16	3	30
	Cette: (Séte)				
	Mont St. Clair Lighthouse	43	24	3	41
	St. Louis mole light	43	24	3	42
	Aigues Mortes: Espiguette Pt. Lighthouse	43	29	4	09
	La Camargue: Lighthouse	43	21	4	41
	Port Bouc: Lighthouse	43	24	4	59
	Cape Couronne: Lighthouse	43	20	5	03
	Marseilles:				
	Joliette Lighthouse	43	18	5	22
	National Obs. (Mer. circle)	43	18	5	24
	Ile d'If: Lighthouse	43	17	5	20
	Planier I.: Lighthouse	43	12	5	14
	Cassis: Lighthouse	43	13	5	32
	Ciotat: Lighthouse	43	10	5	37
	Grand Rouveau: Lighthouse	43	05	5	46
	Toulon:				
	Rascas Point: Lighthouse	43	04	5	57
	Obs. time signal	43	08	5	55
	St. Mandrier: Lighthouse	43	05	5	56
	Grand Ribaud: Lighthouse	43	01	6	09
	Porquerolles (S.): Lighthouse	42	59	6	12
	Cape Benat: Lighthouse	43	05	6	22
	Levant: Titan: Lighthouse	43	03	6	31
	Cape Camarat: Lighthouse	43	12	6	41
	Rade d'Agay: Baumette Pt. Lighthouse	43	26	6	52
	Cannes mole light	43	33	7	01
	La Garoupe: Lighthouse	43	34	7	08
	Antibes: Lighthouse	43	35	7	08
	Nice: Lighthouse	43	42	7	17

Coast	Place	Lat. N. °	Lat. N. ′	Long. E. °	Long. E. ′
France	Mt. Gros Obs	43	43	7	18
	Villefranche: Cape Ferrat Lighthouse	43	40	7	20
	Monaco: Green light on mole	43	44	7	26
Balearic I.	Iviza I.:				
	Conejera I. Lighthouse	39	00	1	13
	Tagomago I. Lighthouse	39	02	1	39
	Botafoch I. Lighthouse	38	54	1	27
	Cabrera I.: Lighthouse	39	08	2	55
	Majorca:				
	Cape Salinas Lighthouse	39	16	3	03
	Port Pi Lighthouse	39	33	2	37
	Cape Cala Figurea Lighthouse	39	27	2	31
	Cape Llebeitx Lighthouse	39	34	2	18
	Port Soller Lighthouse	39	48	2	41
	Cape Formentor Lighthouse	39	58	3	13
	Cape Pera Lighthouse	39	43	3	29
	Minorca:				
	Cape Caballeria Lighthouse	40	05	4	05
	Port Mahon Lighthouse	39	52	4	18
	Aire I. Lighthouse	39	48	4	18
Sardinia	Cape Spartivento: Lighthouse	38	53	8	51
	Caglairi: Cape San Elia Lighthouse	39	11	9	09
	Carloforte: International Lat. Obs. (Zen. telescope)	39	08	8	19
	Cavoli I.: Lighthouse	39	05	9	32
	Cape Bellavista: Lighthouse	39	56	9	43
	Tavolara I.: Lighthouse	40	55	9	44
	Cape Ferro: Lighthouse	41	09	9	31
	Caprara: Lighthouse	41	07	8	19
	Cape Caccia: Lighthouse	40	34	8	10
	Cape San Marco: Lighthouse	39	52	8	26
	Cape Sandalo: Lighthouse	39	09	8	13
	Razzoli I.: Lighthouse	41	18	9	20
Corsica	Lavezzi I.: Lighthouse	41	20	9	16
	Cape Pertusato: Lighthouse	41	22	9	11
	Vecchio: Point Chiappa Lighthouse	41	36	9	22
	Alistro: Lighthouse	42	16	9	32
	Ile Rousse: Pietra Lighthouse	42	39	8	56
	Bastia: Dragon Mole Lighthouse	42	42	9	27
	Cape Corse: Giraglia I. Lighthouse	43	02	9	24
	Revellata Point: Lighthouse	42	35	8	43
	Ajaccio: Lighthouse	41	55	8	45
	Sanguinaires I.: Lighthouse	41	53	8	36
	Aquila Point: Lighthouse	41	33	8	48
Italy	Cape Arma: Lighthouse	43	49	7	50
	Port Maurizio: S. mole light	43	52	8	02
	Cape Mele: Lighthouse	43	57	8	10
	Cape Vado: Lighthouse	44	15	8	27
	Genoa:				
	Cape Faro Lighthouse	44	24	8	54
	Hydro. Inst. Obs	44	25	8	55
	San Benigno time signal	44	24	8	54
	Portofino: Lighthouse	44	18	9	13
	Tino I.: Lighthouse	44	02	9	51
	Spezia: Santa Maria light	44	04	9	51
	Florence: Arcetri Royal Obs	43	45	11	15
	Meloria Bank: Lighthouse	43	33	10	13
	Livorno: (Piana Rock) breakwater Lighthouse	43	33	10	18
	Vada Rock: Lighthouse	43	19	10	22
	Capraia: Cape Ferraione Lighthouse	43	03	9	51
	Elba I.:				
	Polveraja Lighthouse	42	48	10	07
	Port Ferraio: Stella Fort Lighthouse	42	49	10	20
	Port Longonne: Cape Focardo Lighthouse	42	45	10	25
	Pianosa I.: Lighthouse	42	35	10	06
	Africa Rock: Lighthouse	42	21	10	04
	Palmaiola I.: Lighthouse	42	52	10	29
	Lividonia Pt.: Lighthouse	42	27	11	06
	Giglio I.:				
	Capel rosso: Lighthouse	42	19	10	55
	Fenajo Lighthouse	42	23	10	53
	Port Ercole: Fort La Roca Lighthouse	42	23	11	13
	Giannutri: Punta Rossa Lighthouse	42	14	11	07

MARITIME POSITIONS

COASTS OF THE MEDITERRANEAN, ADRIATIC, AND BLACK SEAS—Continued

Coast	Place	Lat. N.	Long. E.
		° ′	° ′
Italy	Civitavecchia: Darsena Nuova Lighthouse	42 05	11 47
	Cape Linaro: Chiaruccia Tower, old sem.	42 02	11 50
	Fiumara Grande: Lighthouse	41 45	12 13
	Tiber River: Tor San Michele Lighthouse	41 44	12 15
	Rome:		
	Royal Univ. Obs	41 54	12 29
	Vatican Obs	41 54	12 27
	Cape d'Anzio: Lighthouse	41 27	12 37
	Monte Circeo: Lighthouse	41 13	13 04
	Gaeta:		
	Santa Caterina: Lighthouse	41 12	13 35
	Zannone I. Cape Nero: Lighthouse	40 58	13 03
	Ponza I. Guardia Pt.: Lighthouse	40 53	12 57
	Ischia I.:		
	Pt. Imperatore Lighthouse	40 43	13 51
	Ischia Castle Lighthouse	40 44	13 58
	Procida I.: Pioppetto Pt. Lighthouse	40 46	14 01
	Cape Miseno: Lighthouse	40 47	14 05
	Naples:		
	San Gennaro Mole Lighthouse	40 50	14 16
	Capodimonte Obs	40 52	14 15
	Castellamare: Lighthouse	40 42	14 28
	Capri I.:		
	Pt. Carena Lighthouse	40 32	14 12
	Pt. Lo Capo Lighthouse	40 34	14 16
	Campanella: Lighthouse	40 34	14 20
	Cape Orso: Lighthouse	40 38	14 41
	Salerno: Manfredi mole light	40 40	14 45
	Cape Palinuro: Lighthouse	40 01	15 17
	Scalea: Lighthouse	39 49	15 47
	Cape Suvero: Lighthouse	38 57	16 10
	Cape Vaticano: Lighthouse	38 37	15 50
	Scilla:		
	Castle Lighthouse	38 15	15 43
	Cape Peloro Lighthouse (old)	38 16	15 39
	Cape Milazzo Lighthouse	38 16	15 14
	Vulcano I.: Lighthouse	38 22	14 59
	Lipari I.: Pignataro Lighthouse	38 29	14 58
	Salina I.: Lighthouse	38 35	14 52
	Ustica I.:		
	Gavazzi Lighthouse	38 42	13 10
	Cape Zaffarano Lighthouse	38 07	13 32
	Palermo:		
	Main Lighthouse	38 08	13 22
	Royal Obs. (center S. dome)	38 07	13 21
	Cape Gallo: Lighthouse	38 13	13 19
	Cape S. Vito: Lighthouse	38 11	12 44
	Levanzo I.: Grosso Point Lighthouse	38 01	12 20
	Trapani I.: Palumbo Lighthouse	38 00	12 29
	Marettimo I.: Libeccio Lighthouse	37 57	12 03
	Favignana I.: Sottile Pt. Lighthouse	37 56	12 16
	Marsala: Main Lighthouse	37 47	12 26
	Cape Granitola: Lighthouse	37 34	12 39
	Cape Rossello: Lighthouse	37 18	13 27
	Port Empedocle: E. mole	37 17	13 32
	Licata: Lighthouse	37 06	13 57
	Terranova: Lighthouse	37 04	14 15
	Cape Scalambri: Lighthouse	36 47	14 30
	Cozzo Spadaro: Lighthouse	36 41	15 08
	Cape Passero: Lighthouse	36 41	15 09
	Gozo I.: Lighthouse	36 04	14 13
	Malta:		
	Valletta Lighthouse	35 54	14 31
	Dellimara Pt. Lighthouse	35 50	14 34
	Government Palace	35 54	14 31
	Cape Murro di Porco: Lighthouse	37 00	15 20
	Syracuse: Maniaci Lighthouse	37 03	15 18
	Augusta: Dromo Lighthouse	37 13	15 10
	Catania:		
	Sciara Biscari Lighthouse	37 30	15 06
	Royal Obs. (Transit Ins.)	37 30	15 05
	Cape Molini: Lighthouse	37 35	15 11
	Messina:		
	San Raineri Lighthouse	38 12	15 35
	Fort San Salvadore time signal	38 12	15 34
	Cape Armi: Lighthouse	37 57	15 41
	Cape Spartivento: Lighthouse	37 55	16 04
	Punta Stilo: Lighthouse	38 27	16 35
Italy	Cape Rizzuto: Lighthouse	38 54	17 06
	Cape Colonne: Lighthouse	39 01	17 12
	Cotrone: N. harbor breakwater light	39 05	17 08
	Alice Point: Lighthouse	39 24	17 09
	Cape Trionto: Lighthouse	39 37	16 46
	Taranto:		
	Cape San Vito Lighthouse	40 25	17 12
	San Paolo I. Lighthouse	40 26	17 11
	Arsenal time signal	40 28	17 14
	Gallipoli: San Andrea Lighthouse	40 03	17 57
	Cape Santa Maria di Leuca: Lighthouse	39 48	18 22
	Cape Otranto: Lighthouse	40 06	18 31
	S. Cataldo di Lecce: Lighthouse	40 23	18 19
	Brindisi:		
	Pedagne Rock: Lighthouse	40 39	18 00
	Riso Pt. Lighthouse	40 40	17 58
	Cape Gallo: Lighthouse	40 41	17 56
	Bari:		
	San Cataldo Lighthouse	41 08	16 51
	Barletta: Lighthouse	41 20	16 17
	Molfetta: Main Lighthouse	41 12	16 36
	Manfredonia: Main Lighthouse	41 38	15 55
	Vieste: Santa Croce Rock Lighthouse	41 53	16 11
	Pelagosa I.: Lighthouse	42 23	16 15
	Pianosa I.: Lighthouse	42 13	15 45
	Caprara I.: Lighthouse	42 08	15 31
	San Domino I.: Lighthouse	42 06	15 29
	Penna Point: Lighthouse	42 10	14 43
	Pedaso: Lighthouse	43 05	13 51
	Ancona: Cappuccini Lighthouse	43 37	13 31
	Castel di Mezzo: Lighthouse	43 58	12 48
	Cesenatico: Main Lighthouse	44 12	12 24
	Corsini: Main Lighthouse	44 29	12 17
	Maestra Pt.: Lighthouse	44 58	12 29
	Chioggia: Fort S. Felice Lighthouse	45 14	12 17
	Malamocco: Rocchetta Lighthouse	45 20	12 19
	Port Lido: Murano I. Lighthouse	45 27	12 21
	Venice:		
	St. Mark tower	45 26	12 20
	Nautical Inst. Obs	45 26	12 21
	Piave Vecchia: Lighthouse	45 29	12 35
	Grado: Church tower	45 41	13 23
	Monfalcone: Church tower	45 49	13 32
	Trieste:		
	Santa Teresa Lighthouse	45 39	13 45
	Royal Obs	45 39	13 46
	Sottile Pt.: Lighthouse	45 36	13 43
	Capo d'Istria: Galere mole light	45 33	13 44
	Pirano: Madonna Lighthouse	45 32	13 34
	Salvore: Mosche Pt. Lighthouse	45 29	13 29
	Pegolotta: Lighthouse	45 27	13 30
	Parenzo: Cathedral tower	45 14	13 36
	Rovigno: Santa Eufemia Lighthouse	45 05	13 38
	San Giovanni di Pelago: Lighthouse	45 03	13 37
	Peneda Pt.: Lighthouse	44 53	13 45
	Pola:		
	Cape Compare breakwater light	44 53	13 48
	Hydrographic Office Obs. (meridian circle)	44 52	13 51
	Porer Rock: Lighthouse	44 45	13 53
	Nera Pt.: Lighthouse	44 57	14 09
	Fiume:		
	Cathedral tower	45 20	14 27
	Main Lighthouse	45 20	14 25
Yugoslavia	Porto Re: D'Ostro Pt. Lighthouse	45 16	14 34
	Veglia: Breakwater light	45 01	14 35
	Galiola I.: Lighthouse	44 44	14 11
	Sansego I.: Lighthouse	44 31	14 18
	Lussin Piccolo:		
	Poljana Pt.: Lighthouse	44 33	14 26
	Manora Obs	44 32	14 28
	Gruica I.: Lighthouse	44 25	14 34
	Bianchè Pt.: Lighthouse	44 09	14 49
	Zara: Amica Pt. Lighthouse	44 08	15 12
	Port Tajer: Lighthouse	43 51	15 12
	Lucietta Islet: Lighthouse	43 37	15 34
	Mulo I.: Lighthouse	43 31	15 55
	Spalato: Botticella Pt. Lighthouse	43 30	16 26

MARITIME POSITIONS

COASTS OF THE MEDITERRANEAN, ADRIATIC, AND BLACK SEAS—Continued

Coast	Place	Lat. N. ° ′	Long. E. ° ′
Yugoslavia	Lesina I.:		
	Cape Pellegrino Lighthouse	43 12	16 22
	Citta Vecchia, Fortino Pt. Lighthouse	43 11	16 35
	Lissa I.: Stoncica Pt. Lighthouse	43 04	16 15
	Hoste I.: Lighthouse	43 05	16 12
	Tarcola I.: Maestro Point Lighthouse	43 05	16 40
	Cazza I.: Lighthouse	42 45	16 29
	Lagosta I.: Skrigeva Pt. Lighthouse	42 43	16 53
	Lagostini I.: Lighthouse	42 46	17 09
	Alessandria Islet: Lighthouse	42 52	17 26
	San Andrea (Donzella): Lighthouse	42 39	17 57
	Port Gravosa: Pettini Rock Lighthouse	42 39	18 03
	Point d'Ostro: Lighthouse	42 23	18 32
	Cattaro:		
	Pier light	42 26	18 46
	Health office	42 25	18 46
	Port Budua: St. Nicolo I.: Lighthouse	42 15	18 52
	Antivari: Volovica Lighthouse	42 05	19 04
	Dulcigno: Fort Lighthouse	41 56	19 12
Albania	Cape Rodoni: Lighthouse	41 35	19 27
	Durazzo: Lighthouse	41 19	19 27
	Samana Point: Lighthouse	40 48	19 21
	Saseno I.: Lighthouse	40 30	19 16
	Valona Bay: Pelasgia Pt. Lighthouse	40 25	19 30
	Port Palermo: Pyramid	40 03	19 48
Greece	Fano I. Kastri Pt.: Lighthouse	39 51	19 26
	Tignoso I.: Lighthouse	39 47	19 58
	Corfu: Cape Sidero Lighthouse	39 37	19 56
	Sivota I.: Lighthouse	39 24	20 14
	Paxo:		
	Marmori Rocks Lighthouse	39 14	20 09
	Madonna I. Lighthouse	39 12	20 13
	Anti Paxos I.: Novara Point Lighthouse	39 08	20 17
	Santa Maura I.: Levkas Lighthouse	38 51	20 43
	Cape Dukato: Lighthouse	38 34	20 34
	Cape Gheroghambo: Lighthouse	38 11	20 21
	Vardiani I.: Lighthouse	38 08	20 25
	Port Argostoli: Lighthouse	38 11	20 28
	Formicula I.: Lighthouse	38 34	20 52
	Kaloyeros I.: Lighthouse	38 30	21 02
	Astokos: Mole light	38 32	21 05
	Kunelli I.: Lighthouse	38 21	21 04
	Oxia: Lighthouse	38 17	21 06
	Mesolonghion, Sosti I.: Lighthouse	38 19	21 22
	Anti Rhion: Castro Rumelia Lighthouse	38 20	21 45
	Cape Melangari: Lighthouse	38 02	22 51
	Corinth: Mole light	37 57	22 56
	Patras: Saint Nicolas mole light	38 15	21 43
	Cape Papas (Araxos): Lighthouse	38 13	21 22
	Cape Skinari: Lighthouse	37 56	20 42
	Cape Glarenza: Kaufkalida I. Lighthouse	37 56	21 07
	Cape Katakola: Lighthouse	37 38	21 19
	Strovathi I.: Lighthouse	37 15	21 00
	Navarin:		
	Pylos I.: Lighthouse	36 54	21 40
	Mole light	36 55	21 42
	Methoni: Mole light	36 49	21 43
	Sapienza I.: Lighthouse	36 45	21 42
	Koroni: Mole light	36 48	21 58
	Petalidi: Light	36 57	21 56
	Cape Kitries: Lighthouse	36 55	22 08
	Cape Matapan: Lighthouse	36 23	22 29
	Githion: Cranae I. Lighthouse	36 45	22 34
	Mulaos: Mole light	36 45	22 48
	Kythera I.: Cape Spathi Lighthouse	36 22	22 57
	Cape Malea: Lighthouse	36 27	23 13
	Elaphonisi I.: Lighthouse	35 15	23 31
	Gavdos I.: Lighthouse	34 50	24 03
	Kuphonisi: Lighthouse	34 56	26 09
	Cape Sidero: Lighthouse	35 20	26 20
	Dio (Standia) I.: Lighthouse	35 28	25 14
	Cape Drepanos: Lighthouse	35 28	24 15
	Crete: Khania: Mole light	35 31	24 01

Coast	Place	Lat. N. ° ′	Long. E. ° ′
Greece	Kaimeni (Belo Pulo): Lighthouse	36 56	23 27
	Nauplia: Mole light	37 34	22 48
	Cape Zurva: Lighthouse	37 22	23 35
	Agios Georgios: Lighthouse	37 28	23 57
	Lipso I.: Lighthouse	37 57	23 36
	Port Drako:		
	(Piraeus) Themistocles breakwater light	37 56	23 38
	Time ball on lighthouse	37 56	23 38
	Athens: National Obs. (Cercle Syngros)	37 58	23 43
	Phleva I.: Lighthouse	37 46	23 46
	Cape Tamelos: Lighthouse	37 31	24 16
	Seriphos (Serpho) Pt. Spathi: Lighthouse	37 06	24 31
	Pholegandros I. Asproponta Pt.: Lighthouse	36 38	24 52
	Thira I. Cape Akroterion: Lighthouse	36 21	25 22
	Paros I. Cape Korax: Lighthouse	37 09	25 14
	Mykoni I. Cape Armenisti: Lighthouse	37 29	25 19
	Syros I. Cape Trimesson: Lighthouse	37 31	24 53
	Andros I.:		
	Cape Phassa: Lighthouse	37 58	24 43
	Cape Gerias: Lighthouse	37 54	24 58
	Doro I.: Lighthouse	38 09	24 36
	Kaloyeri Rocks: Lighthouse	38 10	25 17
	Prassudo I.: Lighthouse	38 40	24 15
	Skyros I. Lithari Pt.: Lighthouse	38 47	24 41
	Skopelos I. Guruni Head: Lighthouse	39 12	23 36
	Psathura I.: Lighthouse	39 30	24 11
	Kassandra Pt.: Lighthouse	39 58	23 23
	Salonika: White Tower	40 38	22 57
	Lemnos:		
	Kombi I.: Lighthouse	39 47	25 14
	Kastro Lighthouse	39 52	25 03
	Cape Plaka: Lighthouse	40 02	25 27
	Dedeagatch: Lighthouse	40 51	25 52
Turkey	Dardanelles: Cape Helles Lighthouse	40 03	26 11
	Gallipoli: Lighthouse	40 24	26 41
	Erekli: Lighthouse	40 58	27 59
	Stefano Point: Lighthouse	40 57	28 51
	Constantinople: Seraglio Pt. Lighthouse	41 00	28 59
	Skutari: Leander Tower Lighthouse	41 01	29 00
	Kara Burnu: Lighthouse	41 20	28 40
	Cape Kuri: Lighthouse	41 52	28 04
Bulgaria	Megalo-Nisi I.: Lighthouse	42 26	27 42
	Anastasia I.: Lighthouse	42 28	27 33
	Burghaz: E. breakwater light	42 29	27 29
	Cape Emineh: Light	42 43	27 56
	Galata Burnu: Light	43 10	27 57
	Varna: E. breakwater light	43 11	27 57
Rumania	Cape Kaliakra: Lighthouse	43 21	28 30
	Cape Shableh: Lighthouse	43 33	28 38
	Cape Tuzla: Lighthouse	44 00	28 40
	Constantza (Kustenjeh): Lighthouse	44 10	28 41
	Fidonisi I.: Lighthouse	45 15	30 13
U. S. S. R.	Cape Fontana: Lighthouse	46 23	30 45
	Odessa:		
	Univ. Obs. (Mer. circle)	46 29	30 46
	Vorontzovski mole light	46 30	30 46
	Suvorov: Lighthouse	46 37	31 30
	Nikolaieff: Naval Obs	46 58	31 58
	Berdyansk: Upper light	46 46	36 46
	Tendra: (High) Lighthouse	46 19	31 31
	Dzharuilgach Pt.: Lighthouse	46 01	33 04
	Cape Tarkhan: Lighthouse	45 21	32 30
	Cape Khersonese: Lighthouse	44 35	33 23
	Sevastopol: Vladimir Lighthouse	44 37	33 30
	Eupatoria: Lighthouse	45 09	33 16
	Sarich Pt.: Lighthouse	44 23	33 45
	Cape Aitodor: Lighthouse	44 26	34 07
	Cape Meganom: Lighthouse	44 48	35 05
	Cape St. Elias: Lighthouse	45 01	35 26
	Chaudinski: Lighthouse	45 00	35 50
	Kertch: Ravlosk Lighthouse	45 18	36 27

APPENDIX IV

MARITIME POSITIONS

COASTS OF THE MEDITERRANEAN, ADRIATIC, AND BLACK SEAS—Continued

Coast	Place	Lat. N. °	Lat. N. ′	Long. E. °	Long. E. ′
U. S. S. R.	Cape Chardak (Kadosh): Lighthouse	44	06	39	02
	Pitsunda Pt.: Lighthouse	43	09	40	21
	Sukhum Pt.: Lighthouse	42	59	40	59
	Poti: Lighthouse	42	08	41	36
Turkey	Batum: Lighthouse	41	39	41	38
	Trebizond: Lighthouse	41	01	39	46
	Cape Sinub (Sinope): Lighthouse	42	01	35	13
	Cape Injeh: Lighthouse	42	06	34	58
	Cape Kerempeh: Lighthouse	42	01	33	17
	Evlidge: Burnu Lighthouse	41	19	31	26
	Kilia Pt.: Lighthouse	41	10	29	37
	Fanar Burnu: Lighthouse	40	58	29	02
	Marmara I.: Fanar Adasi Lighthouse	40	38	27	45
	Kutali Road: Round Rock Lighthouse	40	31	27	29
Syria, Grecian Arch., and Asia Minor	Tenedos I.: Ponente Pt. Lighthouse	39	50	25	59
	Megalonisi (Sigri I.): Lighthouse	39	13	25	50
	Cape Skammia: Lighthouse	39	23	26	21
	Oghlak: Lighthouse	38	40	26	43
	Smyrna: English consulate flagstaff	38	26	27	09
	Psara I.: Lighthouse	38	32	25	37
	Pasha I.: Lighthouse	38	30	26	18
	Venetiko I.: Lighthouse	38	08	26	02
	Nikaria I.: Cape Papas Lighthouse	37	31	26	00
	Levitha I.: Spano Pt. Lighthouse	37	00	26	32
	Kandeliusa (Madonna I.): Lighthouse	36	30	26	59
	Kos I.: Castle	36	54	27	18
	Rhodes I.: Cape Prasonisi Lighthouse	35	52	27	47
	Port of Rhodes: St. Nicola Fort Lighthouse	36	27	28	14
	Hypsili I.: Lighthouse	36	06	29	41
	Adalia: Lighthouse	36	52	30	47
	Alaya: Cape Kiloarda Lighthouse	36	31	32	02
	Cape Anamur: Lighthouse	36	00	32	50
	Mersina: Lighthouse	36	47	34	37
	Karadash Burnu: Lighthouse	36	32	35	20
	Alexandretta: New lighthouse	36	35	36	09
	Cyprus:				
	Klides I.: Lighthouse	35	41	34	37
	Cape Greco: Lighthouse	34	56	34	06
	Cape Gata: Lighthouse	34	34	33	01
	Ras Ibn Hani: Lighthouse	35	36	35	44
	Ruad I.: Lighthouse	34	51	35	51
	Tripoli: Port Lighthouse	34	28	35	49
	Ramkine I.: Lighthouse	34	30	35	45
	Ras Beirut: Lighthouse	33	54	35	28
	Beirut: Jetty light	33	54	35	31
	Saida (Sidon): Lighthouse	33	34	35	22
	Sur (Tyre): Lighthouse	33	17	35	11
	Akka (Acre): Lighthouse	32	55	35	04
Palestine	Mount Carmel: Lighthouse	32	50	34	58
	Haifa (Khaifa) Castle: Lighthouse	32	49	35	00
	Yafa (Jaffa): Lighthouse	32	03	34	45
Egypt	Port Said: Main Lighthouse	31	16	32	19
	Nile River: Damietta Lighthouse	31	31	31	51
	Cape Brulos (Brullos): Lighthouse	31	36	31	05
	Rosetta: Lighthouse	31	30	30	19
	Alexandria:				
	Eunostos Pt. (Ras-el-Tin) Lighthouse	31	12	29	52
	Cairo: Helwan Obs	29	51	31	20
Libia (Tripoli)	Marsa Tobruk: Ras Allem-el-Milhr Light	32	05	24	00
	Derna: Ras Boasa: Lighthouse	32	46	22	39
	Marsa Susa: Lighthouse	32	54	21	58
	Tolmetta: Lighthouse	32	43	20	56
	Bengasi: Lighthouse	32	07	20	04
	Zuitana (Zuctina): Lighthouse	30	57	20	07
	Cape Misurata: Lighthouse	32	22	15	13
	Lebida (Khoms): Lighthouse	32	39	14	16
	Tripoli: New Lighthouse	32	54	13	11
	Zuara: Lighthouse	32	56	12	07

Coast	Place	Lat. N. °	Lat. N. ′	Long. E. °	Long. E. ′
Tunisia	Zarzis: Lighthouse	33	30	11	07
	Jerba: Ras Turgeuness Lighthouse	33	49	11	03
	Ras Tina: Lighthouse	34	39	10	41
	Sfax: Quay light	34	44	10	46
	Mahedia: Sidi Jabber Lighthouse	35	30	11	05
	Kuriat: Lighthouse	35	48	11	02
	Monastir: Burj el Kelb Lighthouse	35	45	10	50
	Susa (Sousse) Citadel Tower: Lighthouse	35	49	10	38
	Kelibia: Lighthouse	36	50	11	07
Italy	Lampedusa I.: Cape Grecale Lighthouse	35	31	12	38
	Linosa I. Beppe Tuccio: Lighthouse	35	52	12	53
	Pantellaria I. Spadillo Pt.: Lighthouse	36	49	12	01
Tunisia	Cape Bon: Lighthouse	37	05	11	03
	Cape Carthage: Lighthouse	36	52	10	21
	Tunis: Basin light	36	48	10	11
	Plane I. (El Kamela): Lighthouse	37	11	10	20
	Cani Rocks: Lighthouse	37	21	10	08
	Bizerte: E. jetty light	37	17	9	54
	Ras Engela: Lighthouse	37	21	9	44
	Cape Serrat: Lighthouse	37	14	9	13
	Galitona I.: Lighthouse	37	30	8	53
	Tabarca I.: Lighthouse	36	58	8	46
Algeria	La Calle: Lighthouse	36	54	8	27
	Cape Rosa: Lighthouse	36	57	8	14
	Bone: Green entrance light, stone tower	36	54	7	47
	Cape Garde: Lighthouse	36	58	7	47
	Cape Fer: Lighthouse	37	05	7	10
	Stora: Singes I. Lighthouse	36	54	6	53
	Srigina I.: Lighthouse	36	56	6	53
	Point Jerda: Lighthouse	37	01	6	35
	Cape Bougaroni: Lighthouse	37	05	6	28
	Ras Atia: Lighthouse	37	01	6	16
	Djidjelli: Lighthouse	36	50	5	47
	Ras Afia: Lighthouse	36	49	5	42
	Cape Carbon: (High) Lighthouse	36	47	5	06
	Cape Sigli: Lighthouse	36	54	4	46
	Cape Corbelin: Lighthouse	36	55	4	26
	Cape Bengut: Lighthouse	36	55	3	54
	Cape Matifu: Lighthouse	36	49	3	15
	Algiers:				
	Admiralty Peninsula Lighthouse	36	47	3	04
	Bouzareah Obs	36	48	3	02
	Cape Caxine: Lighthouse	36	49	2	57
	Tipaza: Ras el Kalia Lighthouse	36	36	2	27
	Shershel: Joinville I. Lighthouse	36	37	2	11
	Cape Tenez: Lighthouse	36	33	1	21
	Cape Ivi: Lighthouse	36	07	0	14
	Mostaghanem: N. breakwater light	35	56	0	05
		Lat. N.		Long. W.	
	Arzeu Islet: Lighthouse	35	52	0	17
	Abuja Pt.: Lighthouse	35	53	0	28
	Oran: N. mole Lighthouse	35	43	0	39
	Mars-el-Kebir: Fort Lighthouse	35	44	0	42
	Cape Falcon: Lighthouse	35	46	0	48
	Habibas I.: Lighthouse	35	43	1	08
	Rashgun I.: Lighthouse	35	20	1	29
	Nemours: Lighthouse	35	06	1	52
Morocco	Zafarin I. Isabel Segunda: Lighthouse	35	11	2	26
	Melilla: Bonete Tower Lighthouse	35	18	2	56
	Cape Tres Forcas: Lighthouse	35	27	2	59
	Alboran I.: Lighthouse	35	56	3	02
	Velez de la Gomera: Lighthouse	35	10	4	18
	Rio Martin: Lighthouse	35	37	5	16
	Ceuta: Almina: Lighthouse	35	54	5	17
	Malabata Point: Lighthouse	35	49	5	45
	Tangier: Le Charf Lighthouse	35	46	5	47
	Cape Spartel: Lighthouse	35	47	5	55

APPENDIX IV

MARITIME POSITIONS

WEST COAST OF AFRICA

Coast	Place	Lat. N.	Long. W.
		° ′	° ′
Morocco	El Araish (Larache) Punta Nador: Lighthouse	35 12	6 10
	Mehediya: Lighthouse	34 17	6 39
	Rabat: Lighthouse	34 02	6 51
	Cape Fedala: Lighthouse	33 43	7 24
	Dar el Beida: El Hank Lighthouse	33 37	7 39
	Cape Mazighan: Lighthouse	33 15	8 31
	Cape Kantin: Lighthouse	32 32	9 14
	Safi: Customhouse light	32 18	9 15
	Agadir: Minaret	30 25	9 38
	Mogador:		
	Sidi Mogdoul Lighthouse	31 30	9 46
	Battery flagstaff	31 31	9 47
	Cape Sim: Lighthouse	31 24	9 50
	Rio de Oro, Arcipres Grande Pt.: Lighthouse	23 44	15 57
Maur.	Cape Blanco: Lighthouse	20 46	17 03
	Cansado Pt.: Lighthouse	20 51	17 02
	Port Etienne: Lighthouse	20 55	17 03
Senegal	St. Louis: Lighthouse	16 02	16 30
	Cape Verde: Lighthouse	14 43	17 31
	Almadi Rock: Lighthouse	14 44	17 32
	Cape Manuel: Lighthouse	14 39	17 27
	Dakar: S. breakwater light	14 40	17 25
	Rufisque: Lighthouse	14 43	17 18
	Bathurst, Gambia: Lighthouse	13 27	16 34
Guinea	Kasamanze River: Jogue Pt. Lighthouse	12 34	16 49
	Karabane: Lighthouse	12 35	16 44
	Cayo I.: Lighthouse	11 50	16 23
	Tamara I: Lighthouse	9 27	13 50
	Matakong I.: Lighthouse	9 16	13 25
	Cape Sierra Leone: Lighthouse	8 30	13 18
	Freetown: Wharf light	8 30	13 14
Liberia	Monrovia: Cape Mesurado Lighthouse	6 19	10 49
	Grand Bassa Pt.: Lighthouse	5 52	10 04
	Sinu Bay: Lighthouse	4 59	9 02
Ivory Coast	Cape Palmas: Lighthouse	4 22	7 44
	Grand Tabu: Tafu Pt. Lighthouse	4 25	7 22
	Sassandra: Lighthouse	4 57	6 04
	Grand Lahu: Lighthouse	5 08	5 01
	Grand Bassam: Lighthouse	5 12	3 44
	Assini (Assinie): Lighthouse	5 07	3 16
Gold Coast	Axim Bay:		
	Fort St. Anthony	4 52	2 15
	Bobowasi I. Lighthouse	4 52	2 15
	Cape Three Points: Lighthouse	4 45	2 06
	Dix Cove: Fort	4 48	1 57
	Sekondi: Fort Orange Lighthouse	4 56	1 42
	Cape Coast Castle: Lighthouse	5 06	1 14
	Akkra: Fort Jamestown Lighthouse	5 32	0 11
		Lat. N.	Long. E.
	Cape St. Paul: Lighthouse	5 50	0 58
	Lome, Togoland: Lighthouse	6 08	1 17
	Kotonu, Dahomey: Lighthouse	6 21	2 26

Coast	Place	Lat. N.	Long. E.
		° ′	° ′
Nigeria	Lagos R. Beecroft Pt.: Lighthouse	6 24	3 23
	Palm Pt. Cape Formosa: Lighthouse	4 16	6 05
Cameroon	Debundga Pt.: Lighthouse	4 06	8 58
	Fernando Po: Fernanda Pt. Lighthouse	3 46	8 48
	Cape Nachtigal: Lighthouse	3 57	9 13
	Duala: Government flagstaff light	4 03	9 41
Port. Islands	Ilha do Principe: Garca Pt. Lighthouse	1 37	7 27
	Sao Thome:		
	Cabras I. Lighthouse	0 25	6 43
	Ft. San Sebastian	0 21	6 45
	Bata, Rio Muni: Lighthouse	1 52	9 46
	Mosquito Pt.: Lighthouse	1 05	9 26
Gabon	Gombe Pt.: Lighthouse	0 18	9 18
	Libreville: S. jetty light	0 23	9 26
		Lat. S.	Long. E.
	Cape Lopez: Lighthouse	0 38	8 42
	Port Gentil: Iron tower Lighthouse	0 42	8 48
	Sette Cama Light	2 31	9 45
	Mayumba: Lighthouse	3 22	10 39
	Loango, Indian Pt.: Lighthouse	4 39	11 48
	Landana (Lendana): Lighthouse	5 14	12 09
	Kabinda Pt.: Lighthouse	5 33	12 11
	Kongo River:		
	Ponta Padrao Lighthouse	6 04	12 20
	Mouta Secca Pt. Lighthouse	6 07	12 16
Angola	Foreland Bluff: Lighthouse	7 17	12 54
	Ambriz: Lighthouse	7 50	13 06
	Cape Lagosta: Lighthouse	8 46	13 18
	Loanda: Observatory time signal	8 49	13 13
	Palmeirinhas Pt.: Cape Lombo Lighthouse	9 03	13 00
	Porto Amboim: Old Light	10 44	13 45
	Nova Redonda: Lighthouse	11 07	13 53
	Lobito Spit: Lighthouse	12 19	13 36
	Benguela: Lighthouse	12 35	13 18
	Salinas Pt.: Lighthouse	12 50	12 56
	Elephant Bay, Friar Rocks	13 12	12 49
	Giraul Pt.: Lighthouse	15 08	12 07
	Little Fish Bay: Pier light	15 12	12 09
	Great Fish Bay: Tiger Point Lighthouse	16 31	11 44
Southwest Africa	Swakopmund: Lighthouse	22 44	14 31
	Walvis (Walfisch) Bay: Pelican Pt.: Lighthouse	22 54	14 26
	Angra Pequena (Luderitz Bay) Diaz Pt.: Lighthouse	26 38	15 06
	Shark I.: Lighthouse	26 38	15 10
Union of South Africa	Port Nolloth: Beacon light	29 16	16 52
	Dassen I.: Lighthouse	33 26	18 05
	Robben I.: Lighthouse	33 49	18 22
	Green Pt.: Lighthouse	33 54	18 24
	Cape Town:		
	Breakwater light	33 54	18 26
	Royal Observatory (mer. circle)	33 56	18 29
	Slang Kop Pt.: Lighthouse	34 09	18 19
	Cape of Good Hope: Lighthouse	34 21	18 30

EAST COAST OF AFRICA

Coast	Place	Lat. S.	Long. E.
Union of South Africa	Simons Bay: Roman Rocks Lighthouse	34 11	18 27
	Kalk Bay: Breakwater Lighthouse	34 08	18 27
	Danger Pt.: Lighthouse	34 38	19 18
	Cape Agulhas: Lighthouse	34 50	20 01
	Cape St. Blaize: Lighthouse	34 11	22 09
	Aliwal: Mole light	34 11	22 09
	Cape St. Francis: Lighthouse	34 13	24 50
	Cape Recife: Lighthouse	34 02	25 42
	Port Elizabeth: Lighthouse	33 58	25 37
	Bird Island: Lighthouse	33 50	26 17
	Great Fish Pt.: Lighthouse	33 31	27 07

Coast	Place	Lat. S.	Long. E.
Union of South Africa	Hood Point: Lighthouse	33 02	27 54
	East London:		
	Castle Pt. Lighthouse	33 02	27 54
	Bashee River: Lighthouse	32 14	28 55
	Cape Hermes: Lighthouse	31 38	29 33
	Port Shepstone: Lighthouse	30 45	30 28
	Green Point: Lighthouse	30 15	30 47
	Port Natal (Durban):		
	Natal Bluff Lighthouse	29 52	31 04
	Time ball signal	29 53	31 04
	Obsy	29 51	31 00
	Durnford Pt.: Lighthouse	28 55	31 55
	Cape St. Lucia: Lighthouse	28 31	32 24

MARITIME POSITIONS

EAST COAST OF AFRICA—Continued

Coast	Place	Lat. S.	Long. E.
		° ′	° ′
Mozambique	Delagoa Bay: Cape Inhaca Lighthouse	25 58	32 59
	Lourenco Marques: Obsy	25 58	32 36
	Cockburn Lighthouse	25 53	32 54
	Monte Bello: Lighthouse	25 11	33 30
	Zavora Pt.: Lighthouse	24 31	35 12
	Burra Pt.: Lighthouse	23 47	35 32
	Santa Carolina I.: Lighthouse	21 37	35 20
	Bazaruto I.: Lighthouse	21 32	35 29
	Chuluwan (Chiluan) I.: Lighthouse	20 37	34 54
	Macuti Pt.: Lighthouse	19 51	34 54
	Zambezi River: Timbue I.: Lighthouse	18 50	36 22
	Port Chinde: Lighthouse	18 31	36 31
	Vilhena: Lighthouse	18 06	36 55
	Ponta Matirre: Lighthouse	17 17	38 11
	Caldeira Pt.: Lighthouse	16 39	39 30
	Mafamede I.: Lighthouse	16 21	40 02
	Antonio River: Sangage Lighthouse	16 00	40 07
	Infusse: Lighthouse	15 30	40 35
	Mozambique:		
	Tower of Sao Paulo	15 02	40 44
	Memba Bay: Pinda: Lighthouse	14 12	40 43
	Maunhane Pt.: Lighthouse	12 59	40 36
	Porto Amelia: Ponta Romero: Lighthouse	12 57	40 30
	Ibo I.: Lighthouse	12 19	40 40
	Cape Delgado: Lighthouse	10 41	40 38
Zanzibar	Lindi River: Ras Ekapapa: Lighthouse	9 56	39 47
	Fanjove I.: Lighthouse	8 34	39 34
	Mafia I.: Ras Mkumbi: Lighthouse	7 38	39 55
	Ras Kanzi: Lighthouse	7 01	39 33
	Dar es Salaam: Lighthouse	6 48	39 20

Coast	Place	Lat. S.	Long. E.
		° ′	° ′
	Bagamoyo: French Mission	6 26	38 54
Zanzibar	Zanzibar I.:		
	Chumbe: Lighthouse	6 17	39 10
	Pungume I.: Lighthouse	6 26	39 20
	Zanzibar: British consulate	6 10	39 11
	Ras Nungwe: Lighthouse	5 43	39 18
	Mwana Mwana I.: Lighthouse	5 45	39 13
	Ulenge I.: Lighthouse	5 00	39 10
	Pemba I.: Ras Kegomacha: Lighthouse	4 53	39 41
Kenya	Mombasa: Ras Serani: Lighthouse	4 04	39 41
	Malindi: Lighthouse	3 13	40 08
	Lamu: Lighthouse	2 18	40 55
Italian Somaliland	Giumbo: Radio mast	0 15	42 37
		Lat. N.	Long. E.
	Brava: Radio mast	1 06	44 02
	Merka: Radio mast	1 43	44 46
	Cingani: Lighthouse	2 02	45 21
	Mogdishu: Lighthouse	2 02	45 20
	Ras Hafun: Lighthouse	10 26	51 25
	Francesco Crispi (Cape Guardafui): Lighthouse	11 50	51 17
	Sokotra I.: Tamarida mosque	12 39	54 00
Gulf of Aden	Bandar Alulu: Lighthouse	11 59	50 46
	Berbera: Lighthouse	10 25	45 00
	Zeila: Mosque	11 22	43 30
	Mashah I.: Scorpion Pt.: Lighthouse	11 44	43 13
	Jibuti: Ayabela Lighthouse	11 33	43 07
	Ras al Bir: Lighthouse	11 59	43 22

THE RED SEA

Place	Lat. N.	Long. E.
Shab Shakhs: Lighthouse	14 39	41 07
Ummes, Sahirig I.: Lighthouse	15 04	40 29
Shumma I.: Lighthouse	15 32	40 00
Madote I.: Lighthouse	15 35	39 45
Massaua: Governor's Palace	15 37	39 28
Sheikh ul Abu: Lighthouse	16 02	39 26
Difnein I.: Lighthouse	16 37	39 19
Taclai: Lighthouse	17 31	38 50
Port Sudan: White Tomb	19 36	37 14
Sanganeb Reef: Lighthouse	19 43	37 26
Daedalus Shoal: Lighthouse	24 55	35 51
Shadwan I.: Lighthouse	27 27	34 02
Ashrafi Reef: Lighthouse	27 47	33 42

Place	Lat. N.	Long. E.
Ras Gharib: Lighthouse	28 21	33 07
Zafarana: Lighthouse	29 06	32 40
Suez: Port Ibrahim south mole head: Lighthouse	29 56	32 33
Tor: Ruins (fort)	28 14	33 37
Brothers N. Island: Lighthouse	26 19	34 51
Jebel Teir I.: Lighthouse	15 32	41 49
Zebayir I.: Center Peak I.: Lighthouse	15 01	42 09
Abu Ail I.: Lighthouse	14 04	42 49
Mokha: Lighthouse	13 18	43 13
Perim I.: High light	12 39	43 26

ISLANDS OF THE INDIAN OCEAN

Coast	Place	Lat.	Long.
	Laccadive Islands: Minikoi I.: Lighthouse	Lat. N. 8 16	Long. E. 73 01
	Seychelles Islands:	Lat. S.	Long. E.
	Dennis I.: Lighthouse	3 48	55 40
	Mamelle: Lighthouse	4 29	55 32
	Mahe I.: Victoria: Lighthouse	4 37	55 31
	Mauritius:		
	Flat I.: Lighthouse	19 53	57 39
	Port Louis: Royal Alfred Obs.	20 06	57 33
	Fouquet: Grand Port: Lighthouse	20 23	57 46
	Caves Point: Lighthouse	20 11	57 25
	Reunion I.:		
	Pointe des Galets: Lighthouse	20 55	55 17
	St. Paul light	21 00	55 17
	St. Denis: Lighthouse	20 52	55 27
	Bel-Air: Lighthouse	20 53	55 36
	St. Pierre light	21 20	55 29
Madagascar	Antsirana: Lighthouse	12 16	49 17
	Diego Suarez Bay:		
	Nosi Langor: Lighthouse	12 13	49 19
	Cape Mine: Lighthouse	12 14	49 22
	Cape East: Lighthouse	15 15	50 29
	St. Mary I.:		
	Halbrand Pt.: Lighthouse	16 43	50 03
	Port St. Mary: Lighthouse	16 59	49 54
	Ile aux Nattes: Lighthouse	17 07	49 51

Coast	Place	Lat. S.	Long. E.
Madagascar	Tamatave:		
	Tanio Pt.: Lighthouse	18 08	49 25
	Hastie Pt.: Lighthouse	18 09	49 26
	Mananjara: Lighthouse	21 15	48 20
	Itaperina Pt.: Lighthouse	24 59	47 07
	Fort Dauphin: Lighthouse	25 02	47 02
	Tullear Road: Jetty light	23 22	43 39
	Bombetoke Bay:		
	Katsepe Cliffs: Lighthouse	15 43	46 13
	Majunga (Mojonga): Lighthouse	15 44	46 18
	Anorombato Pt.: Lighthouse	15 43	46 18
	Analalava: Lighthouse	14 38	47 46
	Nosi Lava: Lighthouse	14 33	47 36
	Nosi Iranja: Lighthouse	13 35	47 50
	Tani Keli: Lighthouse	13 29	48 14
	Nosi Vorona: Lighthouse	13 25	48 22
	Hell-Ville: Jetty light	13 24	48 17
	Woody I. (Nosi Anambo): Lighthouse	12 16	48 39
	Comoro I.:		
	Johanna I.: Lighthouse	12 09	44 24
	Suadzu I.: Lighthouse	11 41	43 15
	Kerguelen I.: Murray I.: Lighthouse	49 30	70 16
	Cocos (Keeling) I.: Lighthouse	12 05	96 54

MARITIME POSITIONS

SOUTH COAST OF ASIA

Coast	Place	Lat. N. ° ′	Long. E. ° ′
Arabia	Aden:		
	Telegraph station	12 47	44 59
	Ras bin Jarbein clock tower	12 47	44 59
	Ras Marshag Lighthouse	12 46	45 03
	Makatein: Black ruin	13 25	46 27
	Makalla: Lighthouse	14 31	49 07
	Maskat Cove: British Consulate Light	23 37	58 36
	Suwaik: Fort	23 51	57 26
	Sohar: S. E. tower (town hall)	24 22	56 46
	Doha (Al Bida) Ras Nessa Fort)	25 17	51 33
	Bahrein: Portuguese Fort	26 14	50 31
	Ras Tanurah: Beacon	26 37	50 10
	Kuweit Harbor: Ras al Ardh Beacon	29 21	48 06
Persia (Iran)	Shatt Al Arab: Tidal semaphore	29 50	48 43
	Fao: Flagstaff	29 58	48 29
	Ganaveh Light	29 34	50 31
	Abu Shahr (Bushire): Residence flagstaff	28 59	50 50
	Basidu: Chapel	26 39	55 17
	Jezirat Tanb I.: Lighthouse	26 16	55 19
	Henjam:		
	Telegraph flagstaff	26 41	55 54
	Ras Al Mashia: Lighthouse	26 42	55 53
	Kishm: Fort	26 57	56 18
	Bandar Abbas: British Consulate	27 11	56 18
	Little Quoin I.: Lighthouse	26 28	56 33
	Jashk: Lighthouse	25 38	57 46
	Charbar (Chahbar) Telegraph Bldg.: Lighthouse	25 16	60 37
Baluchistan	Gwadar: Telegraph Office	25 07	62 20
	Pasni: Telegraph Office	25 16	63 29
	Ormar: Telegraph Office	25 12	64 37
	Sunmiani: Jams house	25 25	66 36
	Ras Muari (Cape Monze): Lighthouse	24 50	66 40
India	Karachi:		
	Manora Pt. Lighthouse	24 48	66 59
	Observatory	24 50	67 02
	Time ball signal	24 49	66 58
	Mandvi: Fort Lighthouse	22 50	69 20
	Navinar Point: Lighthouse	22 44	69 42
	Rojhi: Lighthouse	22 33	70 01
	Peritan I	22 36	69 56
	Beit Harbor: Lighthouse	22 29	69 06
	Dwarka Point:		
	Lighthouse	22 14	68 57
	Temple spire	22 14	68 59
	Porbandar: Lighthouse	21 38	69 36
	Navibandar: Lighthouse	21 27	69 47
	Mangrol: Lighthouse	21 06	70 07
	Veraval: Lighthouse	20 53	70 22
	Diu Head: Lighthouse	20 41	70 50
	Diu: Forte do Mar Lighthouse	20 43	71 00
	Jafarabad: Lighthouse	20 51	71 22
	Kutpur: Lighthouse	21 02	71 49
	Goapnath: Lighthouse	21 12	72 06
	Piram I.: Lighthouse	21 36	72 21
	Tapti: Lighthouse	21 05	72 37
	Surat: Minaret Adrusah	21 12	72 49
	Daman: Fort light	20 24	72 49
	Arnala: Lighthouse	19 27	72 44
	Bassein: Dongri Lighthouse	19 18	72 48
	Bombay:		
	Prongs Reef Lighthouse	18 53	72 48
	Colaba Observatory (Transit Inst.)	18 54	72 49
	Kundari I.: Lighthouse	18 42	72 49
	Rajpuri Point: Lighthouse	18 17	72 56
	Bankot: Fort Victoria	17 58	73 03
	Hernai (Herni): Lighthouse	17 48	73 06
	Port Dabhol: Lighthouse	17 34	73 09
	Jaigarh: Lighthouse	17 18	73 11
	Ratnagiri: Lighthouse	16 59	73 16
	Rajapur: Lighthouse	16 36	73 19
	Viziadrug: Fort Flagstaff	16 33	73 20
	Deogarh: Lighthouse	16 23	73 22
	Vengurla Rocks: Lighthouse	15 53	73 27
	Vengurla: Lighthouse	15 51	73 36
	Aguada Fort	15 29	73 46
	Goa: St. Denis Church	15 21	73 54
	Marmagao: Chiquilim Point: Lighthouse	15 25	73 50
India	Oyster Rock: Lighthouse	14 49	74 03
	Sadashivgad: Port Karwar Light	14 48	74 07
	Kumpta Point: Lighthouse	14 25	74 22
	Honawar: Monument	14 17	74 27
	Bhatkal: Fort light	13 58	74 31
	Kundapur: Lighthouse	13 38	74 40
	Mulpi (Malpe): Lighthouse	13 20	74 41
	Cahp Rocks: Lighthouse	13 13	74 44
	Mangalore: Lighthouse	12 52	74 50
	Tellicherri: Lighthouse	11 45	75 28
	Kadalur (Cotta Point): Lighthouse	11 28	75 39
	Calicut: Lighthouse	11 15	75 47
	Cochin: Lighthouse	9 58	75 15
	Alleppi: Lighthouse	9 30	76 19
	Quilon: Tangacherri Pt. Lighthouse	8 53	76 34
	Trivandrum: Observatory	8 31	76 57
	Muttum Point: Lighthouse	8 07	77 18
	Cape Comorin: Flagstaff light	8 05	77 33
	Manapad Pt.: Lighthouse	8 22	78 03
	Tiruchendore: Pagoda on point	8 30	78 08
	Tuticorin:		
	Pier light	8 48	78 09
	Hare I.: Lighthouse	8 47	78 11
	Pamban: Lighthouse	9 17	79 13
Ceylon	Manar I.: Lighthouse	9 06	79 42
	Colombo:		
	Clock Tower Lighthouse	6 56	79 51
	Observatory	6 54	79 52
	Barberyn: Lighthouse	6 28	79 58
	Galle: Lighthouse	6 01	80 13
	Dondra Head: Lighthouse	5 55	80 36
	Hambantota: Lighthouse	6 07	81 08
	Great Basses Rocks: Lighthouse	6 11	81 29
	Little Basses Rocks: Lighthouse	6 25	81 44
	Batticaloa: Lighthouse	7 45	81 41
	Foul Point: Lighthouse	8 32	81 19
	Trincomali: Round I. Lighthouse	8 31	81 14
	Muletivu: Lighthouse	9 16	80 48
	Pedro Pt.: Lighthouse	9 49	80 15
	Kankesanturai: Lighthouse	9 49	80 03
	Kovilam: Lighthouse	9 46	79 52
India	Tondi: Lighthouse	9 45	79 00
	Calimere: Lighthouse	10 18	79 51
	Negapatam: Lighthouse	10 46	79 51
	Karikal: Lighthouse	10 55	79 51
	Cuddalore: Lighthouse	11 43	79 47
	Pondicherri: Lighthouse	11 56	79 50
	Mahabalipur Pagoda: Lighthouse	12 37	80 11
	Madras:		
	Main Lighthouse	13 05	80 17
	Observatory	13 04	80 15
	Time ball tower	13 06	80 18
	Pulicat: Lighthouse	13 25	80 20
	Armagon (Armeghon): Lighthouse	13 53	80 12
	Masulipatam: Lighthouse	16 10	81 11
	Sacramento: Lighthouse	16 35	82 17
	Cocanada River: Lighthouse	16 47	82 16
	Vakalapudi: Lighthouse	17 01	82 17
	Vizagapatam: Lighthouse	17 41	83 18
	Bimlipatam: Lighthouse	17 53	83 27
	Santapilli: Lighthouse	18 04	83 38
	Kalingapatam: Lighthouse	18 19	84 08
	Baruva: Lighthouse	18 53	84 36
	Gopalphur: Lighthouse	19 15	84 55
	Puri:		
	Lighthouse	19 48	85 50
	Great temple	19 48	85 49
	False Pt.: Lighthouse	20 20	86 44
	Shortt I.: Lighthouse	20 47	87 04
	Hugli River: Sagar I. Lighthouse	21 40	88 03
	Calcutta:		
	Ft. William time ball	22 33	88 20
	Commissioner's Office time signal	22 34	88 21
	Kutabdia: Lighthouse	21 52	91 50
Burma	Oyster I.: Lighthouse	20 12	92 33
	Savage I.: Lighthouse	20 05	92 54
	Beacon I.: Lighthouse	18 56	93 27

APPENDIX IV

MARITIME POSITIONS

SOUTH COAST OF ASIA—Continued

Coast	Place	Lat. N.	Long. E.
		° ′	° ′
Burma	Bassein River:		
	Alguada Lighthouse	15 42	94 12
	Diamond I. Lighthouse	15 52	94 17
	Andaman I.:		
	Table I. Lighthouse	14 11	93 22
	Port Blair Main Lighthouse	11 41	92 45
	Rangoon River: Elephant Pt. Lighthouse	16 29	96 20
	Rangoon:		
	Great Dragon pagoda	16 48	96 09
	Moulmein River: Green I. Lighthouse	16 04	97 33
	Double I.: Lighthouse	15 52	97 35
	Tavoy River: Reef I. Lighthouse	13 37	98 13
	Mergui:		
	Pagoda	12 26	98 36
	Lighthouse	12 29	98 35
	Pakchan River: Spiteful Rock	9 52	98 27
	Pak Kruen: Lighthouse	9 01	98 19
Straits Settlements (Malaya)	Puket: Lighthouse	7 50	98 26
	Krachome Fai I.: Lighthouse	7 05	99 24
	Kedah River: Lighthouse	6 06	100 17
	Pulo Tikus: Lighthouse	5 29	100 18
	Pulo Penang:		
	Muka Head Lighthouse	5 28	100 11
	Fort Point Lighthouse	5 25	100 21
	Rimau I. Lighthouse	5 14	100 17
	Tanjong Hantu: Lighthouse	4 19	100 34
	Pangkor: Hospital Rock Lighthouse	4 13	100 34
	Pulo Katak: Lighthouse	4 09	100 37
	Kuala Perak: Denison Lighthouse	4 05	100 45
	White Rock: Lighthouse	4 00	100 30
	Bagan Datch: Lighthouse	3 59	100 46
	Selangor River: Lighthouse	3 20	101 15
	Pulo Angsa: Lighthouse	3 11	101 13
	One Fathom Bank: Lighthouse	2 53	101 00
	Port Dickson: Lighthouse	2 31	101 48
	Cape Rachado: Lighthouse	2 24	101 51
	Malakka: St. Paul Hill Lighthouse	2 12	102 15
	Pulo Undan: Lighthouse	2 03	102 20
	Pisang I.: Lighthouse	1 27	103 15
	Sultan Shoal: Lighthouse	1 14	103 39
	Raffles I.: Lighthouse	1 10	103 45
	E. St. John I.: Lighthouse	1 13	101 51
	Singapore:		
	Fort Canning Lighthouse	1 18	103 51

Coast	Place	Lat. N.	Long. E.
		° ′	° ′
Straits Settlements	Pedra Branca: Lighthouse	1 19	104 24
	Rhio Strait:		
	Pan Reef Lighthouse	1 10	104 11
	Pulo Sau Lighthouse	1 03	104 10
	Terkolei Lighthouse	0 57	104 20
	Little Karas I.: Lighthouse	0 44	104 22
	Kentar I.: Lighthouse	0 02	104 47
		Lat. S.	Long. E.
	Linga I.: Lighthouse	0 18	105 00
	Muchi I.: Lighthouse	0 32	104 02
	Berhala I.: Lighthouse	0 52	104 24
Sumatra		Lat. N.	Long. E.
	Pulo Bras: Lighthouse	5 45	95 03
	Pulo Weh: Lighthouse	5 53	95 18
	Pulo Buru: Lighthouse	5 41	95 23
	Jambu Ayer (Diamond Point): Lighthouse	5 17	97 29
	Roesa I.: Lighthouse	5 17	95 12
	Edi: Lighthouse	4 57	97 46
	Sembilan I.: Lighthouse	4 08	98 15
	Diemoer (Jemur) I.: Lighthouse	2 53	100 34
	Brothers (Hiju Kechil): Lighthouse	1 11	103 21
	Durian Strait:		
	N. Brother I. Lighthouse	0 37	103 46
	S. Brother I. Lighthouse	0 33	103 46
		Lat. S.	Long. E.
	Banka I.:		
	Pulo Dapur Lighthouse	3 08	106 31
	Pulo Besar Lighthouse	2 53	106 08
	W. Nangka Lighthouse	2 23	105 45
	Tanjong Kelian Lighthouse	2 05	105 08
	Tanjong Ular Lighthouse	1 58	105 07
	Klabat Bay Lighthouse	1 31	105 41
	Pulo Lepar: Lighthouse	2 57	106 55
	Shoalwater I.: Lighthouse	3 19	107 13
	Pulo Mendanau: Lighthouse	2 53	107 20
	Billiton I.: Langkaus I. Lighthouse	2 32	107 37
	Discovery E. Bank: Lighthouse	3 35	109 10
	Telok Betong: Lighthouse	5 28	105 17
	Flat Cape (Vlakke Hoek): Lighthouse	5 56	104 33
	Kru: Lighthouse	5 11	103 56
	Pulo Pisang: Lighthouse	5 07	103 51
	Bandar Pt.: Lighthouse	4 49	103 20
	Mana River: Lighthouse	4 29	102 54

SOUTHEAST COAST OF ASIA

Coast	Place	Lat. S.	Long E.
Sumatra	Benkulen: Pulo Tikus Lighthouse	3 51	102 11
	Katang Katang I.: Lighthouse	1 53	100 34
	Pulo Niamuk: Lighthouse	1 16	100 18
	Ujung Sungei Bramei: Lighthouse	1 02	100 22
	Pulo Pisang: Lighthouse	1 00	100 20
	Pulo Pandang: Lighthouse	0 57	100 08
	Pulo Karsik: Lighthouse	0 36	100 04
	Pulo Bojo: Lighthouse	0 39	98 31
	Sigata: Lighthouse	0 08	98 12
		Lat. N.	Long. E.
	Pangkai I.: Lighthouse	0 08	99 17
	Pulo Temang: Lighthouse	0 22	99 05
	Pulo Labu: Lighthouse	0 51	98 56
	Hinako (Naku) I.: Lighthouse	0 51	97 20
	Gunong Sitoli: Pt. Mbaa Lighthouse	1 18	97 36
	Tapa Tuan: Lighthouse	3 15	97 11
	Simalur I.: Lighthouse	2 30	96 24
	Karang (Kareung) Pt.: Lighthouse	4 08	96 07
Java		Lat. S.	Long. E.
	First Pt.: Lighthouse	6 45	105 13
	Chilachap: Lighthouse	7 47	109 02
	Balambangan: Lighthouse	8 46	114 31
	Banjuwangi: Lighthouse	8 12	114 23
	Bali I.: Buleleng Lighthouse	8 06	115 05

Coast	Place	Lat. S.	Long. E.
Java	Bansering (front): Lighthouse	8 03	114 25
	Duiven (Tabuan) I.: Lighthouse	8 02	114 28
	Meinderts (Karang Mas): Lighthouse	7 40	114 26
	Sapudi: Lighthouse	7 05	114 16
	Panarukan: Lighthouse	7 41	113 56
	Probolingo (mole): Lighthouse	7 43	113 13
	Pasuruan: Lighthouse	7 37	112 55
	Koko (Zwaanties) Reef: Lighthouse	7 28	113 07
	Surabaya: Wilhelmina Tower	7 12	112 44
	Sembilangan: Lighthouse	7 04	112 41
	Juana: Lighthouse	6 42	111 09
	Mandalike I.: Lighthouse	6 23	110 55
	Semarang: Lighthouse	6 57	110 25
	Pekalongan: Lighthouse	6 51	109 41
	Tegal: Lighthouse	6 51	109 08
	Cheribon: Lighthouse	6 43	108 34
	Boompjes I.: Lighthouse	5 56	108 23
	Tanjong Priok E. mole light	6 05	106 53
	Batavia:		
	W. pier light	6 06	106 48
	Meteorological Obs. (Bamberg transit inst.)	6 11	106 50
	Edam I.: Lighthouse	5 57	106 50
	Etna Bank: Lighthouse	5 18	106 54

MARITIME POSITIONS

SOUTHEAST COAST OF ASIA—Continued

Coast	Place	Lat. S.	Long. E.
		° ′	° ′
Java	North Watcher (Noord Wachter): Lighthouse	5 12	106 28
Java	Payung I.: Lighthouse	5 49	106 33
Java	Babi I.: Lighthouse	5 49	106 17
Java	Toppers I.: Lighthouse	5 54	105 56
Java	Fourth Point: Lighthouse	6 04	105 53
East India Is.	Bawean I.: Sangkapura Lighthouse	5 51	112 39
East India Is.	Lombok: Ampenam Lighthouse	8 34	116 04
East India Is.	Postillon I.: Banawaja: Lighthouse	6 49	119 12
East India Is.	Maria Reigersbergen: Lighthouse	7 51	117 11
East India Is.	Zandbuis Bank: Lighthouse	7 46	117 08
East India Is.	Sumbawa: Kelapa I.: Lighthouse	8 40	119 14
East India Is.	Flores I.: Laboean Badjo: Pier light	8 29	119 53
East India Is.	Sawu I. Kali Menia: Lighthouse	10 26	121 52
East India Is.	Seba: Lighthouse	10 29	121 50
East India Is.	Rotti I. Baa: Lighthouse	10 43	123 03
East India Is.	Semao I. Tanjong Kurong: Lighthouse	10 08	123 27
East India Is.	Timor I.:		
East India Is.	Koepang Ft. Concordia Lighthouse	10 10	123 34
East India Is.	Dilhi Harbor Lighthouse	8 34	125 37
East India Is.	Liran I.: Lighthouse	8 03	125 44
East India Is.	Sermatta I. Maety Miarang (Brisbane) I.: Lighthouse	8 20	128 29
East India Is.	Buru I. Leksoela: Lighthouse	3 48	126 33
East India Is.	Suangi I.: Lighthouse	3 18	127 28
East India Is.	Amboina I.: Lighthouse	3 47	128 05
Celebes	Saleier: Pasi Tanette Lighthouse	5 44	120 30
Celebes	De Bril Bank (Taka Rewataya): Lighthouse	6 05	118 54
Celebes	Dewakang Besar I.: Lighthouse	5 24	118 26
Celebes	Pulo Dayang Dayangan: Lighthouse	5 24	119 11
Celebes	Makassar (Mariso): Lighthouse	5 09	119 24
Celebes	Great Lae Lae Shoal: Lighthouse	5 09	119 23
Celebes	Kapoposang I.: Lighthouse	4 42	118 57
Celebes	Cape Mandar: Lighthouse	3 33	118 56
Celebes	Cape William: Lighthouse	2 38	118 49
Celebes	Palos Bay: Karang Pt.: Lighthouse	0 38	119 44
Celebes	Walea Strait: Lighthouse	0 25	122 25
Celebes	Wangi Wangi: Lighthouse	5 16	123 32
		Lat. N.	Long. E.
Celebes	North Watcher: Lighthouse	0 35	119 48
Celebes	Stroomen Kaap: Lighthouse	1 20	120 48
Celebes	Bulolio Reef: Lighthouse	1 08	122 22
Celebes	Hulawa I.: Lighthouse	0 58	122 54
Celebes	Menado: Lighthouse	1 30	124 50
Celebes	Tanjong Aros: Lighthouse	1 53	125 06
Celebes	Pondang I.: Lighthouse	0 26	124 29
Celebes	Gorontalo: Lighthouse	0 30	123 03
Borneo	Taganak I.: Lighthouse	6 05	118 19
Borneo	Sandakan: Fort Pryer	5 50	118 07
Borneo	Tanjong Unsang: Lighthouse	5 21	119 13
Borneo	Batu Tinagat: Lighthouse	4 13	117 59
Borneo	Tarakan: Mengachu Pt.: Lighthouse.	3 14	117 37
Borneo	Muaras Reef: Lighthouse	1 46	119 02
Borneo	Mangkalihat: Lighthouse	0 59	118 59
		Lat. S.	Long. E.
Borneo	Aru Bank: Lighthouse	2 15	116 39
Borneo	Balabalagan I. Ambo: Lighthouse	2 32	117 57
Borneo	Kota Baru: Lighthouse	3 14	116 14
Borneo	Stagen: Pier light	3 17	116 09
Borneo	Anak Suangi: Lighthouse	3 26	116 02
Borneo	Petang Point: Lighthouse	3 37	115 57
Borneo	Sambergelap I. Boeton Boetona: Lighthouse	3 39	116 36
Borneo	Dwaalder I.: Lighthouse	4 14	116 07
Borneo	Kunwit I.: Lighthouse	4 05	116 02
Borneo	Cape Selatan: Lighthouse	4 11	114 39
Borneo	Serutu I.: Lighthouse	1 43	108 42
		Lat. N.	Long. E.
Borneo	St. Pierre I.: Lighthouse	1 54	108 39
Borneo	S. Natuna I.: Subi Kechil Lighthouse	3 03	108 51
Borneo	Po Point: Lighthouse	1 44	110 31

Coast	Place	Lat. N.	Long. E.
		° ′	° ′
Borneo	Cape Sirik: Lighthouse	2 45	111 21
Borneo	Baram Point: Lighthouse	4 36	113 58
Borneo	Tanjong Lobong: Lighthouse	4 22	113 58
Borneo	Kuraman I.: Lighthouse	5 14	115 08
Borneo	Pappan I.: Lighthouse	5 15	115 16
Borneo	Labuan I.: Ramsay Point Beacon	5 16	115 15
Borneo	Jesselton: Clock tower	5 59	116 05
Philippine Islands	Balabac I.:		
Philippine Islands	Cape Melville: Lighthouse	7 49	117 00
Philippine Islands	Balabac Lighthouse	7 58	117 04
Philippine Islands	Comiran I.: Lighthouse	7 55	117. 13
Philippine Islands	Palawan I.:		
Philippine Islands	Sir Brooke Pt. Lighthouse	8 46	117 49
Philippine Islands	Port Princesa Lighthouse	9 44	118 44
Philippine Islands	Tubbataha Reef: Lighthouse	8 44	119 48
Philippine Islands	Saluag I.: Lighthouse	4 35	119 28
Philippine Islands	Bongao: Lighthouse	5 02	119 46
Philippine Islands	Pearl Bank: Lighthouse	5 50	119 44
Philippine Islands	N. Ubian I.: Lighthouse	6 10	120 28
Philippine Islands	Jolo: Pier light	6 03	121 00
Philippine Islands	Tatalan I.: Lighthouse	6 13	121 50
Philippine Islands	Mataja I.: Lighthouse	6 34	121 42
Philippine Islands	Sibago I.: Lighthouse	6 45	122 24
Philippine Islands	Malamaui I.: Lighthouse	6 45	121 59
Philippine Islands	Zamboanga: Mole light	6 54	122 04
Philippine Islands	Little Santa Cruz I.: Lighthouse	6 53	122 02
Philippine Islands	Port Banga: Lighthouse	7 30	122 25
Philippine Islands	Parang: Lighthouse	7 22	124 16
Philippine Islands	Cotabata: Lighthouse	7 15	125 38
Philippine Islands	Tinaca Pt.: Lighthouse	5 33	125 20
Philippine Islands	Malalag: Lighthouse	6 36	125 25
Philippine Islands	Santa Cruz: Lighthouse	6 49	125 25
Philippine Islands	Davao: Lighthouse	7 04	125 38
Philippine Islands	Cape San Agustin: Lighthouse	6 16	126 11
Philippine Islands	Mati: Lighthouse	6 56	126 14
Philippine Islands	Arangasa I.: Lighthouse	8 53	126 20
Philippine Islands	Cauit Pt.: Lighthouse	9 18	126 12
Philippine Islands	Bocas Grande I. Dahakit Pt.: Light	9 34	125 56
Philippine Islands	Rasa I.: Light	9 48	125 35
Philippine Islands	Surigao: Light	9 47	125 30
Philippine Islands	Agusan River: Light	9 00	125 31
Philippine Islands	Nasipit: Light	8 59	125 20
Philippine Islands	Cagayan: Lighthouse	8 31	124 40
Philippine Islands	Kolambugan: Lighthouse	8 07	123 53
Philippine Islands	Polo Point: Lighthouse	8 36	123 45
Philippine Islands	Tagolo Pt.: Lighthouse	8 44	123 23
Philippine Islands	Negros I. Apo I.: Lighthouse	9 05	123 16
Philippine Islands	Dumaguete: Light	9 19	123 19
Philippine Islands	Port Canoan: Front Light	9 15	123 36
Philippine Islands	Balicasag: Lighthouse	9 31	123 41
Philippine Islands	Amblan Pt.: Lighthouse	9 28	123 13
Philippine Islands	Pescador I.: Lighthouse	9 55	123 20
Philippine Islands	Dumanjug: Lighthouse	10 04	123 26
Philippine Islands	Balamban: Light	10 30	123 43
Philippine Islands	Refugio I.: Lighthouse	10 28	123 27
Philippine Islands	San Carlos wharf light	10 29	123 25
Philippine Islands	Malapascua I.: Lighthouse	11 21	124 07
Philippine Islands	Tanguingui Islet: Lighthouse	11 29	123 43
Philippine Islands	Capitancillo I.: Lighthouse	10 59	124 06
Philippine Islands	Bogo: Light	11 05	124 02
Philippine Islands	Bagacay Pt.: Lighthouse	10 23	124 01
Philippine Islands	Cebu: San Nicholas Church: Lighthouse	10 18	123 53
Philippine Islands	Mactan I. Lauis Ledge: Lighthouse	10 14	123 53
Philippine Islands	Palompon: Light	11 03	124 23
Philippine Islands	Ormoc: Light	11 00	124 36
Philippine Islands	Canigao I.: Lighthouse	10 15	124 45
Philippine Islands	Panaon I. Liloan: Lighthouse	10 10	125 07
Philippine Islands	Maasin: Light	10 38	124 51
Philippine Islands	Malitbog: Light	10 09	124 59
Philippine Islands	Mariquitdaquit I.: Light	11 04	125 09
Philippine Islands	Jinamoc I.: Light	11 16	125 04
Philippine Islands	Tacloban: Lighthouse	11 15	125 00
Philippine Islands	Biliran Strait: Lighthouse	11 27	124 29
Philippine Islands	Suluan I.: Lighthouse	10 45	125 58
Philippine Islands	Divinubo I.: Lighthouse	11 36	125 30
Philippine Islands	Borongan: Light	11 37	125 26
Philippine Islands	Batag I.: Lighthouse	12 40	125 04
Philippine Islands	San Bernardino I.: Lighthouse	12 45	124 17
Philippine Islands	Capul I.: Lighthouse	12 29	124 08
Philippine Islands	Calantas Rock: Lighthouse	12 31	124 05
Philippine Islands	Calbayog: Lighthouse	12 04	124 35

APPENDIX IV

MARITIME POSITIONS

SOUTHEAST COAST OF ASIA—Continued

Coast	Place	Lat. N. ° ′	Long. E. ° ′
Philippine Islands	Catbalogan: Lighthouse	11 47	124 53
	Matabao I.: Lighthouse	12 19	123 49
	San Jacinto: Lighthouse	12 34	123 44
	San Miguel: Lighthouse	12 43	123 35
	Masbate Harbor: Lighthouse	12 23	123 36
	Port Barrera: Colorado Pt.: Lighthouse	12 33	123 23
	Bugui Pt.: Lighthouse	12 36	123 14
	Jintotolo I.: Lighthouse	11 50	123 07
	Port Batan: Floripon Pt.: Lighthouse	11 37	122 29
	Capiz Harbor: Lighthouse	11 37	122 42
	Manigonigo I.: Lighthouse	11 36	123 11
	N. Gigante I.: Lighthouse	11 39	123 22
	Baliguian I.: Lighthouse	11 12	123 20
	Calabazas I.: Lighthouse	11 05	123 01
	Iloilo:		
	Siete Pecados Lighthouse	10 46	122 41
	N. jetty light	10 42	122 35
	Guimaras I.: Lighthouse	10 29	122 28
	Nogas I.: Lighthouse	10 25	121 55
	San Jose, Antique: Tubigan Pt. Lighthouse	10 44	121 56
	Cuyo I.: Lighthouse	10 51	121 00
	Culion I.: Lighthouse	11 54	120 01
	Apo Reef: Lighthouse	12 40	120 25
	Ambulon I.: Lighthouse	12 13	121 01
	Maniguin I.: Lighthouse	11 36	121 42
	Romblon: Agbatan Pt. Reef Lighthouse	12 35	122 16
	Sabang Pt.: Lighthouse	12 36	122 16
	Cobrador I.: Lighthouse	12 40	122 14
	Boac: Light	13 26	121 49
	Balanacan: Light	13 32	121 52
	Santa Cruz: Light	13 30	122 03
	Calapan: Light	13 26	121 11
	Port Galera Light	13 30	120 57
	Escarceo Pt.: Light	13 31	120 59
	Cabra I.: Light	13 53	120 01
	Fortune I.: Light	14 03	120 29
	Cape Santiago: Lighthouse	13 46	120 39
	Balayan: Light	13 56	120 44
	Lemery (Taal): Light	13 53	120 55
	Batangas: Light	13 46	121 02
	Malabrigo Pt.: Lighthouse	13 36	121 16
	Lucena: Lighthouse	13 54	121 36
	Donsol: Light	12 54	123 35
	Sorsogon: Light	12 50	123 47
	Bagatao I.: Lighthouse	12 50	123 47
	Bulan: Light	12 40	123 52
	Gubat: Light	12 56	124 07
	Legaspi: Lighthouse	13 10	123 45
	Sula: Light	13 14	123 52
	Ungay Pt.: Lighthouse	13 11	124 13
	Malinao: Light	13 24	123 43
	Sabang: Light	13 43	123 35
	Virac: Light	13 35	124 14
	Sialat Point: Lighthouse	13 40	124 02
	Ocata: Lighthouse	13 59	123 50
	Canimo: Lighthouse	14 08	123 03
	Tailon I.: Lighthouse	14 25	122 40
	Silangan Pass: Lighthouse	14 00	122 11
	Baliscan I.: Lighthouse	14 15	121 54
	Polillo: Front Light	14 44	121 55
	Cape Engano: Lighthouse	18 35	122 08
	San Vicente: Light	18 31	122 07
	Linao: Lighthouse	18 23	121 36
	Pata Pt.: Lighthouse	18 37	121 09
	Cape Bojeador: Lighthouse	18 31	120 36
	Currimao: Lighthouse	18 01	120 29
	Salomague: Lighthouse	17 46	120 25
	Pandan: Lighthouse	17 32	120 22
	Candon Pt.: Lighthouse	17 12	120 25
	Tagudin: Lighthouse	16 57	120 26
	San Fernando: Front light	16 37	120 18
	San Fernando Pt.: Lighthouse	16 37	120 17
	Dagupan: Pt. Guecet Lighthouse	16 04	120 20
	Bolinao: Lighthouse	16 23	119 55
	Cape Bolinao: Piedra Pt.: Lighthouse	16 19	119 47
	Hermana Mayor I.: Lighthouse	15 48	119 48
	Palauig Pt.: Lighthouse	15 26	119 54
	Caponez I.: Lighthouse	14 55	120 00
	Subic Bay: Sueste Pt.: Lighthouse	14 45	120 11
	Olongapo: Caiman Shoal Lighthouse	14 49	120 16
	Mariveles: Lighthouse	14 26	120 29

Coast	Place	Lat. N. ° ′	Long. E. ° ′
Philippine Islands	Monja I.: Lighthouse	14 23	120 31
	Corregidor I.: Lighthouse	14 23	120 35
	Caballo I.: Lighthouse	14 22	120 37
	San Nicolas Shoal: Lighthouse	14 26	120 46
	Sangley Pt.: Lighthouse	14 30	120 55
	Cavite: Time signal (water tower)	14 29	120 55
	Manila:		
	W. breakwater Lighthouse	14 34	120 57
	Cathedral	14 36	120 58
	Time ball (Observatory)	14 35	120 59
Siam	Mersing: Lighthouse	2 27	103 49
	Anamba I.: Mangkai I. Lighthouse	3 05	105 36
	Pahang R.: Lighthouse	3 33	103 27
	Kuantan R. N. entrance: Light	3 50	103 20
	Sungi Kumama: Lighthouse	4 13	103 27
	Tringano: Fort Lighthouse	5 22	103 08
	Kwala Kelantan: Lighthouse	6 13	102 10
	Tj. Patani: Lighthouse	6 57	101 17
	Singora: Pagoda Hill Lighthouse	7 12	100 36
	Lem Polam Pook Light	8 26	100 12
	Koh Prap Lighthouse	9 16	99 26
	Koh Wang Nai: Lighthouse	9 19	99 54
	Langsuen Riv. S. entrance Lighthouse	9 56	99 08
	Koh Rang-Pratad Light	10 07	99 13
	Metaphon I. Lighthouse	10 27	99 15
	Bangkok:		
	Tide signal station	13 28	100 35
	Wat Cheng	13 45	100 30
	Asadang Prapakar: Lighthouse	13 11	100 48
	Koh Phra: Lighthouse	12 38	100 51
	Koh Chuen: Lighthouse	12 31	100 56
	Koh Samet: Lighthouse	12 35	101 27
	Prasa River: Entrance Light	12 42	101 42
	Lem Sing Lighthouse	12 28	102 04
	Koh Chik Lighthouse	12 18	102 14
	Koh Chang: Lighthouse	12 10	102 19
	Lem Noob: Lighthouse	12 10	102 24
	Koh Tron: Lighthouse	10 01	104 00
	Nui Nai Pt.: Lighthouse	10 21	104 25
	Pulo Obi: Lighthouse	8 26	104 50
Indo-China	Condore I. Haon Bai Kan I.: Lighthouse	8 40	106 42
	Mirador Pt.: Light	10 16	106 45
	Kua Tieu: Norodom Bank Light	10 15	106 47
	Kua Dong Tranh: Lighthouse	10 23	106 52
	Saigon: Cathedral	10 47	106 42
	C. St. James Lighthouse	10 20	107 04
	Vung Pt.: Lighthouse	10 23	107 03
	Kega Point: Lighthouse	10 42	107 59
	Fanthit: Lighthouse	10 55	108 06
	Cape Padaran: Lighthouse	11 22	109 01
	Fan Rang: Lighthouse	11 35	109 03
	Kamranh: Hon Chut I. Lighthouse	11 47	109 13
	Chut Pt.: Lighthouse	12 13	109 12
	Hon Lon: Lighthouse	12 12	109 20
	Cape Varella: Lighthouse	12 54	109 27
	Gambir I.: Lighthouse	13 37	109 21
	Kin Hon: Lighthouse	13 46	109 15
	Vung Moë: Lighthouse	14 15	109 11
	Cape Batangan: Lighthouse	15 15	108 56
	Kulao Rei: Lighthouse	15 24	109 08
	Tien Sha: Lighthouse	16 08	108 19
	Tourane:		
	Observatory I.: Lighthouse	16 07	108 13
	Cape Tourane Lighthouse	16 08	108 19
	Dong Hoi River: Beacon light	17 29	106 37
	Bien Shon I.: Lighthouse	19 20	105 49
	Hon Dau I.: Lighthouse	20 40	106 49
	Lakh Huen: Lighthouse	20 50	106 53
	Haifong: Observation pagoda	20 52	106 41
	Norway I.: Lighthouse	20 37	107 09
China	Hainan Island:		
	Lamko Pt. Light	20 00	109 42
	Hoihow: Fort A Light	20 03	110 20
	Hoihow: Harbor Light	20 01	110 16
	Cape Cami: Lighthouse	20 13	109 55
	Nauchow I.: Lighthouse	20 54	110 36
	Green Hill: Lighthouse	21 06	110 33
	Portalis Point: Lighthouse	21 10	110 22
	Gap Rock: Lighthouse	21 49	113 56

MARITIME POSITIONS

EAST COAST OF ASIA

Coast	Place	Lat. N.		Long. E.	
		°	′	°	′
China	Great Ladrone I.: Highest summit	21	57	113	43
	Koho Pt.: Lighthouse	22	07	113	37
	Macao: Fort Guia Lighthouse	22	12	113	33
	Ki au I.: Lighthouse	22	26	113	40
	Wangmun: Lighthouse	22	35	113	37
	Sampanchau: Lighthouse	22	43	113	39
	Canton: Dutch Folly S. beacon light	23	07	113	15
	Tongku: Lighthouse	22	23	113	53
	Lantau I.: Lighthouse	22	13	114	01
	Mawan I.: Lighthouse	22	21	114	03
	Kapsing I.: Lighthouse	22	20	114	04
	Green I.: Lighthouse	22	17	114	07
	Hongkong:				
	Cathedral	22	17	114	09
	Observatory (transit inst.)	22	18	114	10
	Victoria Park Flagstaff	22	17	114	09
	Cape Collinson: Lighthouse	22	16	114	16
	Lamtong I: Lighthouse	22	14	114	17
	Waglan I.: Lighthouse	22	11	114	18
	Chilang Pt.: Lighthouse	22	39	115	34
	Breaker Point: Lighthouse	22	56	116	30
	Good Hope Cape: Lighthouse	23	14	116	48
	Sugarloaf I.: Lighthouse	23	20	116	46
	Swatow: Light	23	21	116	40
	Lamocks I.: Main Lighthouse	23	16	117	17
	Chapel I.: Lighthouse	24	10	118	13
	Tsingseu I.: Lighthouse	24	22	118	07
	Amoy: Semaphore Station	24	27	118	04
	Taitan I.: Lighthouse	24	23	118	10
	Dodd I.: Lighthouse	24	26	118	30
	Ockseu I.: Lighthouse	25	00	119	27
	Turnabout I.: Lighthouse	25	26	119	56
	Tungkuen: Lighthouse	25	58	119	59
	Pagoda Rock: Lighthouse	25	59	119	27
	Mamoi Rock: Lighthouse	25	59	119	26
	Tung Yung I.: Lighthouse	26	23	120	30
	Spider I.: Lighthouse	26	31	120	04
	Incog I.: Lighthouse	26	59	120	28
	Middle I.: Lighthouse	27	53	121	08
	Shroud I.: Lighthouse	27	38	121	03
	Peiyushan (Shaho) I.: Lighthouse	28	53	122	16
	Tongting I.: Lighthouse	29	52	122	35
	Loka I.: Lighthouse	29	58	122	27
	Square I.: Lighthouse	30	00	121	45
	Tiger I.: Lighthouse	29	58	121	44
	Steep I.: Lighthouse	30	13	122	35
	Elgar I.: Lighthouse	30	26	122	31
	West Volcano I.: Lighthouse	30	21	121	51
	Rugged I. S. W. Horn: Lighthouse	30	36	121	58
	Bonham I.: Lighthouse	30	37	122	25
	Button Rock: Lighthouse	30	38	122	22
	North Saddle I.: Lighthouse	30	52	122	40
	Gutzlaff I.: Lighthouse	30	49	122	10
	Kiutoan: Beacon light	31	19	121	40
	Shaweishan I.: Lighthouse	31	25	122	14
	Shanghai: Time signal (French Concession)	31	14	121	29
	Woosung Lighthouse	31	23	121	30
	Kiachow:				
	Arkona I.: Lighthouse	36	03	120	19
	Yunui San: Lighthouse	36	03	120	17
	Horseshoe Reef: Lighthouse	36	05	120	17
	Taikung Tao: Lighthouse	35	58	120	29
	Chalien Tao: Lighthouse	35	54	120	52
	Shantung Promontory:				
	(S. E.) Lighthouse	36	54	122	32
	(N. E.) Lighthouse	37	24	122	42
	Weihaiwei: Flagstaff Point: Lighthouse	37	30	122	08
	Chefoo:				
	Kungtungtao I.: Lighthouse	37	34	121	31
	New mole light	37	33	121	23
	Tower Hill: Lighthouse	37	33	121	24
	Time signal	37	33	121	23
	Howki I. (Miaotao): Lighthouse	38	04	120	39
	Chimatao Promontory: Lighthouse	37	41	120	13
	Taku: Bar range rear light	38	58	117	41
	Haiho River: Tangku Tidal Sta	39	00	117	42
	Shaluitien (Tsaofeitien) I.: Lighthouse	38	56	118	31
	Chinwangtao: Pier light	39	55	119	38
	Liautishan Promontory: Lighthouse	38	43	121	08
	Ryojun Ko (Port Arthur):				
	Rokobi: Lighthouse	38	48	121	15
	Dairen: S.: Lighthouse	38	56	121	40

Coast	Place	Lat. N.		Long. E.	
		°	′	°	′
China	San Shan Tao: Light	38	52	121	49
	Thornton Haven: Lighthouse	39	04	123	09
	Antung: Talutao I. Lighthouse	39	45	123	45
	Newchwang: Bar Signal Station	40	38	122	10
Taiwan (Formosa)	Pescadores I.:				
	Kita Jima: Lighthouse	23	47	119	35
	Fuon: Lighthouse	23	32	119	31
	Sabo Sho (Three I): Lighthouse	23	32	119	43
	Litsitah Pt.: Lighthouse	23	34	119	27
	Tokitsu Sho: Lighthouse	23	16	119	40
	Wan Kan Banks: Lighthouse	23	32	120	02
	Anpei (Amping): Lighthouse	23	01	120	10
	Takau: Lighthouse	22	37	120	15
	Haikan Wan: Kaiko (rear): Lighthouse	22	05	120	43
	Goaram Pii (Garan Bi): Lighthouse	21	54	120	51
	Taito: Lighthouse	22	46	121	09
	Sansendai: Lighthouse	23	08	121	25
	Hoaren Kan: Lighthouse	23	59	121	37
	Peitau Kaku: Lighthouse	25	08	121	55
	Kiirun:				
	Kelung, Banjintai Bi Lighthouse	25	09	121	44
	Puki Kaku: Lighthouse	25	18	121	31
	Tansui: Lighthouse	25	11	121	25
	Pakusa Pt.: Lighthouse	25	02	121	04
Chosen (Korea)	Kotan Misaki: Lighthouse	35	22	129	22
	Cape Tikmenev: Lighthouse	35	30	129	27
	Changii Kutsu (Cape Clonard): Lighthouse	36	05	129	34
	Yonshu Kutsu: Lighthouse	37	03	129	26
	Chumonjin Kutchi: Lighthouse	37	54	128	50
	Suon Kutchi (Cape Duroch): Lighthouse	38	42	128	23
	Gensan: Breakwater light	39	10	127	27
	Karumappo Pt.: Lighthouse	39	12	127	29
	Defosses Pt.: Lighthouse	39	17	127	34
	Moisyeeva Pt. (Panyansomu Kuchi): Lighthouse	39	48	127	40
	Mayan To (Gontcharof I.): Lighthouse	40	00	128	12
	Song Chin (Sonjin): Lighthouse	40	40	129	12
	Kilchu Peninsula: Lighthouse	40	39	129	12
	Musu Kutchi: Lighthouse	40	50	129	44
	Cape Kozakof: Lighthouse	41	23	129	47
	Komarusan Kutchi: Lighthouse	41	45	129	52
	Chonjin Bay N. breakwater light	41	47	129	50
	Ijin Rock: Lighthouse	42	05	130	07
	Chosan Bay Nan To: Lighthouse	42	14	130	31
U. S. S. R., Siberia, Pacific Shores	Expedition Bay, Nazimof Pt.: Lighthouse	42	38	130	49
	Cape Gamof: Lighthouse	42	33	131	12
	Bruce Point: Lighthouse	42	53	131	28
	Skripley I.: Lighthouse	43	02	131	57
	Pospyelov Pt.: Lighthouse	43	04	131	53
	Cape Tokarevski: Lighthouse	43	04	131	50
	Vladivostok:				
	Cape Goldobin: Lighthouse	43	05	131	53
	Alekseev Hill Ast. Sta	43	07	131	53
	Askold I.: Lighthouse	42	44	132	21
	Povorotni: Lighthouse	42	40	133	03
	Cape Nizmennui: Lighthouse	43	31	135	09
	Chikhachev I.: Lighthouse	43	41	135	17
	Olga Bay, N. shore: Lighthouse	43	44	135	14
	Cape Byelkin (Disappointment): Lighthouse	45	49	137	41
	Cape St. Nikolaya: Lighthouse	48	58	140	24
	Imperial Harbor, Milyutin Pt.: Lighthouse	49	03	140	20
	Cape Jonquieres: Lighthouse	50	53	142	07
	Castries Bay:				
	Klosterkamp: Lighthouse	51	25	140	53
	Klikoff Pt.: Lighthouse	51	28	140	46
	Amur River: Nikolaevsk: Lighthouse	53	08	140	43
	Kamchatka:				
	Petropavlovsk (rear): Lighthouse	53	00	158	39
	Dalni Point: Lighthouse	52	53	158	43
Japan	Notoro Misaki: Lighthouse	44	06	144	14
	Atoiya Misaki: Lighthouse	44	27	146	34
	Cape Keramoi: Lighthouse	43	29	145	32
	Nemoro Ko: Lighthouse	43	20	145	35
	Noshappu Zaki: Lighthouse	43	23	145	49

541524°—43——24

APPENDIX IV

MARITIME POSITIONS

EAST COAST OF ASIA—Continued

Coast	Place	Lat. N. °	Lat. N. ′	Long. E. °	Long. E. ′
Japan (Hokushu)	Otchishi Zaki: Lighthouse	43	10	145	31
	Akkeshi: Lighthouse	42	56	144	52
	Kushiro Saki: Lighthouse	42	58	144	23
	Yerimo Saki: Lighthouse	41	55	143	15
	Urakawa: Lighthouse	42	10	142	47
	Mororan: Lighthouse	42	21	140	56
	Chikyu Misaki: Lighthouse	42	18	141	00
	Yesan Saki: Lighthouse	41	48	141	10
	Shiokubi Saki: Lighthouse	41	43	140	57
	Hakodate: Lighthouse	41	47	140	42
	Kattoshi Saki: Lighthouse	41	45	140	36
	Shirakami Saki: Lighthouse	41	24	140	11
Japan (S. W. Islands)	Agincourt I.: Lighthouse	25	38	122	04
	Naha: Tsuken Shima: Lighthouse	26	14	127	57
	Sachibaru Zachi (Cape Abbey): Lighthouse	26	12	127	40
	Miyegushiku Fort Lighthouse	26	13	127	40
	Iye Shima: Lighthouse	26	43	127	45
	Sotsuko Saki: Lighthouse	28	15	129	08
	Naze: Borose Zaki Lighthouse	28	27	129	31
	Yaku Shima, Mi Saki: Lighthouse	30	23	130	23
	Nishinoomote: Lighthouse	30	44	131	00
Chosen (Korea)	Shurerii I.: Lighthouse	39	41	124	24
	Teifa To: Lighthouse	39	26	124	35
	Daido:				
	Chinnampo Lighthouse	38	43	125	24
	Oondogu Lighthouse	38	39	125	13
	The Sisters Lighthouse	38	41	125	00
	Su Do (Sei Tau) Lighthouse	38	33	124	46
	Soi Chong To: Lighthouse	37	46	124	44
	Jinsen:				
	(Chemulpo) S. breakwater light	37	28	126	36
	Sho Getsubi To Lighthouse	37	28	126	36
	Hachibi To (Yodolmi) Lighthouse	37	21	126	30
	Kito Chosi Sho (N. Watcher Rocks) Lighthouse	37	20	126	29
	Haku Gan (White Rocks) Lighthouse	37	14	126	25
	Fu To (Warren I.) Lighthouse	37	09	126	21
	An To: Lighthouse	36	57	126	10
	Ferrieres I. (Bundegi): Lighthouse	36	56	125	47
	Kakureppi (Clifford I.): Lighthouse	36	38	125	33
	O To (Baker I.): Lighthouse	36	39	126	00
	Ochon To (Guerin I.): Lighthouse	36	08	125	58
	Kunsan: Rock off N. Brown I. Light	35	58	126	33
	Tarunu To: Lighthouse	35	52	126	19
	Kunnoroku To: Lighthouse	35	06	125	59
	Amutei To (South Twin): Lighthouse	34	52	126	09
	Mokpo: Lighthouse	34	46	126	23
	Irikobari Somu (Pinnacle I.): Lighthouse	34	47	125	47
	Jiihaa To: Lighthouse	34	42	126	14
	Megunyaguto (Washington Strait): Lighthouse	34	34	126	18
	Kacha To: Lighthouse	34	27	126	03
	Kakyo To (Ross I.): Lighthouse	34	05	125	06
	Chu To (Bamboo I.): Lighthouse	34	13	125	51
	Chanjiku Channel: Hacho To: Lighthouse	34	19	126	05
	Oryogu To: Lighthouse	34	17	126	28
	Shoan Group: Cheki To Lighthouse	34	06	126	36
	Stanley I. (Sho Bo To): Lighthouse	34	14	126	46
	Quelpart I. Saishu: Lighthouse	33	31	126	33
	Giffard I. (Mara To): Lighthouse	33	07	126	15
	Beaufort I. (Gyu To): Lighthouse	33	29	126	58
	Tonai Kai (Port Hamilton): Lighthouse	34	00	127	19
	Kommo I. Sori Do: Lighthouse	34	25	127	48
	Reisu: Lighthouse	34	44	127	45
	Samzenpo: Lighthouse	34	56	128	03
	Cho Do: Lighthouse	34	45	128	25
	Shomaifutsu: Lighthouse	34	37	128	33
	Sentinel I. (Ari Somu): Lighthouse	34	32	128	43
	Toguyogu (Bonifay I.): Lighthouse	34	50	128	27
	Mado Sho (Frederick Rock): Lighthouse	35	06	128	41
Chosen	Puto Suido (Sir H. Parker Sound): Lighthouse	35	05	128	40
	Katoku To: Lighthouse	34	59	128	50
	Choragu Somu (Deer I.): Lighthouse	35	03	129	05
	Fusan:				
	Chebipaui Rocks Lighthouse	35	06	129	03
	Uno Se Lighthouse	35	06	129	04
Japan (Hokushu)	Fukuyama: Lighthouse	41	25	140	06
	Tsugaru Strait: Ko Shima Lighthouse	41	22	139	49
	Yesashi: Lighthouse	41	52	140	06
	Okushiri: Inaho Misaki Lighthouse	42	15	139	34
	Benkei Saki: Lighthouse	42	50	140	11
	Iwanai: Lighthouse	43	00	140	30
	Kamoi Misaki: Lighthouse	43	20	140	21
	Hiyori Yama: Lighthouse	43	14	141	01
	Otaru: North breakwater Lighthouse	43	12	141	01
	Ishikara: W. entrance Lighthouse	43	15	141	21
	Mashike: Lighthouse	43	51	141	31
	Yangishiri Jima: Lighthouse	44	26	141	25
	Teshio Gawa: Lighthouse	44	53	141	44
	Rishiri Shima: Lighthouse	45	15	141	14
	Wakkanai: Lighthouse	45	26	141	39
	Soya Misaki: Lighthouse	45	31	141	56
Sakhalin	Nishi Notoro Misaki: Lighthouse	45	54	142	05
	Soni Misaki: Lighthouse	46	03	141	55
	Hinode Bana (Todo Shima): Lighthouse	46	15	141	16
	Kinushi Misaki: Lighthouse	46	36	141	49
	Korsakov (Kushunkotan): Lighthouse	46	40	142	45
Japan (Honshu)	Tsuno Shima: Lighthouse	34	21	130	51
	Kottoi: Lighthouse	34	19	130	53
	Hamada: Uma Shima Lighthouse	34	54	132	03
	Hino Misaki: Lighthouse	35	26	132	38
	Jizo Saki: Lighthouse	35	34	133	20
	Sakai: Lighthouse	35	33	133	15
	Saigo Misaki: Lighthouse	36	10	133	20
	Kyoga Misaki: Lighthouse	35	47	135	13
	Tateishi Zaki: Lighthouse	35	46	136	01
	Tsuruga: Lighthouse	35	40	136	04
	Kanaiwa: Lighthouse	36	36	136	35
	Shiroo: Lighthouse	36	44	136	41
	Fukura: Lighthouse	37	05	136	43
	Saruyama Zaki: Lighthouse	37	19	136	43
	Rokugo Saki: Lighthouse	37	32	137	19
	Nanao:				
	Kannon Point Lighthouse	37	06	137	03
	Matsuga Point Lighthouse	37	06	136	58
	Fushiki: Lighthouse	36	48	137	04
	Uwozu: Lighthouse	36	49	137	24
	Sado Shima:				
	Hime Saki Lighthouse	38	05	138	34
	Hajiki Zaki Lighthouse	38	20	138	31
	Niigata: Old Lighthouse	37	56	139	04
	Nezugaseki: Lighthouse	38	34	139	32
	Sakata: Old Lighthouse	38	55	139	49
	Funakawa: Lighthouse	39	52	139	50
	Nyudo Saki: Lighthouse	40	00	139	42
	Tairadate: Lighthouse	41	11	140	38
	Aomori: W. breakwater Lighthouse	40	50	140	44
	Oma Zaki: Lighthouse	41	33	140	55
	Shiriya Saki: Lighthouse	41	26	141	28
	Todo Saki: Lighthouse	39	33	142	05
	O Shima: Lighthouse	38	50	141	39
	Kinka San: Lighthouse	38	17	141	36
	Shioya Saki: Lighthouse	37	00	140	59
	Inubo Saki: Lighthouse	35	42	140	52
	Katsuura Wan: Lighthouse	35	08	140	19
	Nojima Zaki: Lighthouse	34	54	139	53
	Suno Saki: Lighthouse	34	59	139	45
	Tateyama: Lighthouse	34	59	139	51
	Fort 2: Lighthouse	35	19	139	45
	Tokyo:				
	Old No. 2 Battery	35	38	139	46
	University Obs. (at Azabu)	35	39	139	45
	Haneda: Lighthouse	35	32	139	48
	Yokohama: N. breakwater Lighthouse	35	27	139	40

MARITIME POSITIONS

EAST COAST OF ASIA—Continued

Coast	Place	Lat. N.	Long. E.
		° ′	° ′
Japan (Honshu)	Yokosuka: N. E. breakwater (E.) Lighthouse	35 19	139 40
	Fort No. 3: Lighthouse	35 18	139 44
	Kannon Zaki: Lighthouse	35 15	139 45
	Ashika Jima: Lighthouse	35 13	139 44
	Tsurugi Saki: Lighthouse	35 09	139 41
	Joga Shima: Lighthouse	35 08	139 37
	Inatori: Lighthouse	34 47	139 03
	Kazahaya Saki: Lighthouse	34 48	139 23
	Mikomoto Shima: Lighthouse	34 34	138 57
	Miyake Jima: Lighthouse	34 06	139 29
	Iro Saki: Lighthouse	34 36	138 51
	Shimizu: De Bana Lighthouse	35 00	138 32
	Omai Saki: Lighthouse	34 36	138 14
	Kaketsuka: Lighthouse	34 39	137 49
	Kami Shima: Lighthouse	34 33	136 59
	Kadoishi: Lighthouse	34 42	136 59
	Mayeshiba: Lighthouse	34 47	137 20
	Nomaga Zaki: Lighthouse	34 45	136 51
	Nagoya: W. breakwater Lighthouse	35 02	136 51
	Yokkaichi: Lighthouse	34 58	136 39
	Niye Saki: Lighthouse	34 42	136 32
	Suga Shima: Lighthouse	34 30	136 55
	Toba: Lighthouse	34 29	136 51
	Anori Saki: Lighthouse	34 22	136 55
	Ko Shima: Lighthouse	34 14	136 49
	Tsuru Shima: Lighthouse	33 37	135 57
	Kantori Zaki: Lighthouse	33 35	135 58
	Kashino Saki: Lighthouse	33 28	135 52
	Shio Misaki: Lighthouse	33 26	135 45
	Ichie Zaki: Lighthouse	33 35	135 24
	Tanabe, Aizu Gawa: Lighthouse	33 43	135 22
	Susami: Lighthouse	32 33	135 31
	Hino Misaki: Lighthouse	33 53	135 04
	Tomoga Shima: Lighthouse	34 17	135 00
	Sakai: Lighthouse	34 35	135 27
	Kizu Gawa: Lighthouse	34 37	135 27
	Osaka: N. breakwater Lighthouse	34 38	135 24
	Wada Misaki: Lighthouse	34 39	135 11
	Kobe:		
	E. breakwater (S.) Lighthouse	34 40	135 12
	Time signal	34 41	135 11
Japan (Honshu)	Yesaki: Lighthouse	34 36	134 59
	Komatsushima: Lighthouse	34 01	134 36
	Muroto Zaki: Lighthouse	33 15	134 10
	Ashizuri Misaki: Lighthouse	32 43	133 01
	Kanai Saki: Lighthouse	32 45	132 48
	Mizunoko Shima: Lighthouse	33 03	132 11
	Sada Misaki: Lighthouse	33 20	132 01
	Seki Zaki: Lighthouse	33 16	131 54
	Ya Shima: Lighthouse	33 43	132 08
	He Saki: Lighthouse	33 58	131 01
	Moji Saki: Lighthouse	33 58	130 58
	Moji: Time signal	33 57	130 57
	Yamazokono Hana: Lighthouse	33 55	130 55
	Kata Shima: Lighthouse	33 58	130 51
	Mutsure Shima (Rockuren): Lighthouse	33 59	130 52
	Futaoi Shima: Lighthouse	34 06	130 47
	Okino Shima: Lighthouse	34 15	130 06
	Tsu Shima: Lighthouse	34 05	129 13
	Yara Zaki: Lighthouse	34 12	129 18
	Mitsu Shima: Lighthouse	34 43	129 27
	Yeboshi Shima: Lighthouse	33 41	129 59
	Wakamiya: Lighthouse	33 52	129 41
	Futagami Jima: Lighthouse	33 36	129 33
	Koshiki Shima: Lighthouse	33 18	129 10
	Shiro Se: Lighthouse	33 11	128 48
	Goto I.: Ose Saki Lighthouse	32 37	128 36
	Odate Shima: Lighthouse	33 01	129 26
	Nagasaki:		
	Io Jima Lighthouse	32 43	129 45
	Obs. time ball signal	32 44	129 52
Japan (Kyushu)	Gotsu Sho: Lighthouse	32 34	130 06
	Kuchinotsu: Lighthouse	32 36	130 12
	Yu Shima: Lighthouse	32 36	130 20
	Shimabara: Lighthouse	32 47	130 23
	Miike: Lighthouse	33 00	130 23
	Misumi: Lighthouse	32 37	130 26
	Nagasaki Bana: Lighthouse	32 07	130 06
	Tsurikake Saki: Lighthouse	31 38	129 41
	Bono Misaki: Lighthouse	31 15	130 13
	Kagoshima: Benten Fort Lighthouse	31 36	130 34
	Sata Misaki: Lighthouse	30 59	130 39

ISLANDS OF THE PACIFIC

Coast	Place	Lat.	Long.
		Lat. N.	Long. W.
	Malpelo I. Summit 1,200 ft	3 59	81 34
	Cocos I. Chatham Bay	5 33	86 59
		Lat. S.	Long. W.
	Galapagos Islands: Chatham I. Lido Point	0 53	89 37
		Lat. N.	Long. W.
	Christmas I.: Cook I. N. end	1 57	157 28
	Fanning I.: Longitude station near cable office	3 54	159 23
	Washington I. Obs. Spot	4 43	160 25
	Palmyra I	5 52	162 06
	Baker I.	0 13	176 28
	Howland I. Center	0 48	176 38
	Gilbert Islands:	Lat. S.	Long. E.
	Drummond I	1 29	175 11
	Nauru (Pleasant) I. Lighthouse	0 32	166 55
	Marshall Islands:	Lat. N.	Long E.
	Wotje I. Christmas Harbor	9 31	169 51
	Caroline Islands:		
	Kusaie (Ualan) I	5 20	163 00
	Ponape I. Ponape harbor	7 00	158 12
	Truk I. Uman I	7 18	151 53
	Yap I. Tomil harbor	9 30	138 08
	Ulithi I. Mogmog I	10 06	139 43
	Sorol I	8 08	140 25
	Palau (Pelew) Is.:		
	Urukthapel I. Lighthouse	7 15	134 27
	Angaur I	6 53	134 08
	Merir I. Warren Hastings I	4 20	132 19
	Nevil (Lord North) I	3 00	131 11
	Sonserol I	5 20	132 13
	Marianas Islands:	Lat. N.	Long. E.
	Guam: Port Apra Lighthouse	13 27	144 37
	Rota I. Summit	14 09	145 12
	Tinian I	15 00	145 36
	Saipan I	15 11	145 45
	Anatahan I	16 22	145 40
	Sarigan I	16 43	145 47
	Agrigan I	18 47	145 40
	Wake Island	19 17	166 35
	Gaspar Rico Reef	14 34	168 58
		Lat. N.	Long. W.
	Johnston I	16 45	169 31
	Clipperton I	10 17	109 13
	Lisianski I	26 01	173 59
	Midway I.: Lighthouse	28 13	177 23
	Laysan I	25 42	171 44
	Gardner Pinnacles	25 01	168 01
	French Frigate Shoal (120 ft. Islet)	23 48	166 12
	Necker I	23 35	164 41
	Nihoa: Miller Peak	23 03	161 55
Hawaiian Islands	Hawaiian Islands:		
	Kauhola Point Lighthouse	20 15	155 46
	Kukuihaele Lighthouse	20 08	155 33
	Laupahoehoe Point Lighthouse	20 00	155 15
	Pepeekeo Point Lighthouse	19 51	155 05
	Hilo:		
	Paukaa Point Lighthouse	19 46	155 06
	Waiakea Lighthouse	19 44	155 04
	Kalae: Lighthouse	18 55	155 41
	Napoopoo Lighthouse	19 29	155 56
	Kailua: Lighthouse	19 39	156 00

APPENDIX IV

MARITIME POSITIONS

ISLANDS OF THE PACIFIC—Continued

Coast	Place	Lat. N.	Long. W.
		° ′	° ′
Hawaiian Islands	Hawaiian Islands—Continued.		
	Keahole Point Lighthouse	19 44	156 04
	Kawaihae: Lighthouse	20 03	155 50
	Mahukona Lighthouse	20 11	155 54
	Maui I.:		
	Nakalele Head: Lighthouse	21 02	156 36
	Kahului Breakwater Light East	20 54	156 28
	Pauwela Point: Lighthouse	20 57	156 19
	Kauiki Head: Lighthouse	20 45	155 59
	Cape Hanamanioa Lighthouse	20 35	156 25
	Molokini Island: Lighthouse	20 38	156 30
	Lahaina: Lighthouse	20 53	156 41
	Hawea Point Lighthouse	21 00	156 40
	Lanai I.: Kaumalapau Lighthouse (S.)	20 47	157 00
	Molokai I.:		
	Lighthouse	21 13	156 58
	Kaunakakai Lighthouse (front)	21 06	157 01
	Laau Point Lighthouse	21 06	157 19
	Oahu I.:		
	Makapuu Point Lighthouse	21 19	157 39
	Diamond Head Lighthouse	21 16	157 49
	Honolulu Harbor Lighthouse	21 19	157 52
	Barbers Point Lighthouse	21 18	158 07
	Kaena Point Lighthouse	21 35	158 17
	Kauai I.:		
	Kilauea Point Lighthouse	22 14	159 24
	Kahala Point Lighthouse	22 09	159 18
	Nawiliwili Harbor Lighthouse	21 57	159 20
	Makahuena Point Lighthouse	21 52	159 27
	Hanapepe Lighthouse	21 54	159 36
	Kokole Point Lighthouse	21 59	159 46
		Lat. N.	Long. E.
	Marcus I.	24 17	153 58
	Ogasawara Islands (Bonin Is.):		
	Hachijo Jima	33 06	139 46
	Aoga Shima	32 27	139 46
	Tori Shima	30 29	140 19
	Chichi Jima	27 05	142 11
	Haha Jima	26 38	142 09
	Iwo Jima	24 48	141 18
	Marquesas Islands:	Lat. S.	Long. W.
	Nuku Hiva Light	8 55	140 05
	Fatu Hiva	10 32	138 39
	Caroline Atoll: Solar eclipse transit pier	10 00	150 14
	Vostok I.	10 06	152 23
	Flint I.	11 25	151 48
	Malden I.	4 03	155 01
	Starbuck I.	5 37	155 56
	Tongareva I. (Penrhyn)	9 00	158 03
	Jarvis I.	0 23	160 02
	Rakahanga I. (Reirson) Church	10 03	161 06
	Manahiki I. (Humphrey)	10 20	161 01
	Union Group:		
	Fakaofu I.	9 23	171 15
	Nukunono I.	9 12	171 54
	Atafu I.	8 32	172 31
	Phoenix Islands:		
	Canton I.	2 50	171 40
	Enderbury I.	3 08	171 03
	Hull I.	4 30	172 10
	McKean I.	3 37	174 07
	Gardner I.	4 40	174 35
	Ellice Islands:	Lat. S.	Long. E.
	Funafuti I.	8 31	179 13
	Nanomea I.	5 39	176 06
	Solomon Islands:		
	Bougainville I.: Kieta Light	6 13	155 40
	Malaita I. Auki Hbr	8 47	160 43
	New Georgia: Rendova harbor	8 26	157 17
	Florida I.: Lighthouse	9 11	160 13
	Guadalcanal I.: Light	9 25	160 05
	Admiralty Is.: Nares harbor	1 56	146 40
	New Britain Islands:		
	Rabaul: Simpson harbor	4 12	152 12
	New Guinea Islands:		
	Aru Is. Wamar I. Dobo Light	5 45	134 13
	Panjang I. Lighthouse	3 00	132 18
	Secar Bay, F. S. at Kokas	2 43	132 25
	Doom I.: Sorong Lighthouse	0 53	131 14

Coast	Place	Lat. S.	Long. E.
		° ′	° ′
	New Guinea Islands—Continued.		
	Menukwari Road: Light	0 52	134 03
	Beliao I.: Friederich Wilhelm Lighthouse	5 13	145 49
	Station Point Lighthouse	7 45	147 39
	Nateara Reef Lighthouse	9 32	147 08
	Cape Vogel Lighthouse	9 40	149 59
	Merauke River Lighthouse	8 30	140 22
	Rossel I.: East point	11 23	154 18
	Coringa I.: Chilcott Islet	16 55	150 00
	Cato I.	23 15	155 32
	Santa Cruz Islands:		
	Obelisk I.	9 51	167 07
	Ndeni: Graciosa Bay	10 44	165 49
	New Hebrides Islands:		
	Efate I.: Fila Light	17 44	168 19
	Pango Point Light	17 47	168 16
	Eromanga I.: Dillon Bay	18 48	168 58
	Fiji (Viti) Islands:	Lat. S.	Long. W.
	Wailangilala I. Light	16 46	179 07
	Vanua Levu: Cape Undu Light	16 08	179 57
		Lat. S.	Long. E.
	Savusavu Bay Light	16 50	179 15
	Koro I. Light	17 23	179 22
	Wakaya Reef Light	17 41	179 04
	Ovalau I.: Levuka harbor rear Light	17 41	178 50
	Viti Levu:		
	Nasilai Reef Lighthouse	18 08	178 41
	Suva: (rear) Lighthouse	18 06	178 25
	Navula Reef Lighthouse	17 55	177 13
	Na Koro Koro Lighthouse	17 39	177 23
	North Astrolabe Reef Lighthouse	18 38	178 33
	Kandavu I: Cape Washington Lighthouse	19 07	177 57
	Samoa Islands:	Lat. S.	Long. W.
	Aunuu I. Lighthouse	14 17	170 33
	Pago Pago: Breaker Point Lighthouse	14 17	170 40
	Upulo I.: Apia, rear Lighthouse	13 50	171 45
	Society Islands: Tahiti I.:		
	Venus Point Lighthouse	17 29	149 29
	Papeete front Lighthouse	17 32	149 34
	Pitcairn I.: Bounty Bay	25 04	130 05
	Henderson I.: South Point	24 25	128 19
	Tuamotu Archipelago:		
	Fakarava I. Lighthouse Rotoava	16 02	145 36
	Marokau I.	18 00	142 14
	Toau I.	15 50	146 03
	Makatea I.	15 50	148 12
	Gambier I.: Mangareva I.	23 07	134 57
	Juan Fernandez I.: Lighthouse	33 38	78 50
	Mas Afuera I.	33 46	80 46
	San Ambrosio I.	26 20	79 54
	Sala y Gomez I.	26 27	105 28
	Easter I.: Cook Bay	27 09	109 26
	Rapa I.	27 36	144 17
	Tubuai (Austral) I.	23 22	149 28
	Cook Islands:		
	Mitiero Islands	20 01	157 34
	Rarotonga I. Light	21 12	159 46
	Mangaia I. Light	21 50	158 00
	Tonga Islands:		
	Vavau Neiafu Light	18 39	173 59
	Malinoa Islet Light	21 02	175 08
	Tongatabu I.: Nukualofa Light	21 08	175 12
	Niue I.: Alofi Light	19 02	169 55
	Kermadee Islands: Raoul I.	29 15	177 55
	New Caledonia:	Lat. S.	Long. E.
	Cape Ndua Lighthouse	22 24	166 56
	Bulari Pass: Amedee I. Lighthouse	22 29	166 29
	Tabu Reef Lighthouse	22 29	166 28
	Noumea:		
	Ducrot Peak Lighthouse	22 16	166 26
	Denouel Point Lighthouse	22 17	166 27
	Semaphore Lighthouse	22 16	166 27
	Burail Bay Lighthouse	21 37	165 27
	Norfolk I.: Sydney Bay	29 04	167 58

MARITIME POSITIONS

AUSTRALIA

Coast	Place	Lat. S.	Long. E.
		° ′	° ′
South Coast	Glenelg: Lighthouse	35 00	138 30
South Coast	Cape Jervis: Lighthouse	35 37	138 06
South Coast	Port Victor: Lighthouse	35 35	138 38
South Coast	Cape Jaffa: Lighthouse	36 58	139 36
South Coast	Rivoli Bay: Penguin I	37 31	140 01
South Coast	Cape Banks: Lighthouse	37 54	140 23
South Coast	Cape Northumberland: Lighthouse	38 04	140 40
South Coast	Cape Nelson: Lighthouse	38 26	141 33
South Coast	Portland:		
South Coast	Whaler Point Lighthouse	38 20	141 36
South Coast	Railroad jetty light	38 21	141 37
South Coast	Port Fairy: Griffiths Island Lighthouse	38 24	142 15
South Coast	Warrnambool (front): Lighthouse	38 24	142 29
South Coast	Cape Otway: Lighthouse	38 52	143 31
South Coast	Eagle Nest Point: Lighthouse	38 28	144 06
South Coast	Lonsdale Point: Lighthouse	38 17	144 37
South Coast	Gellibrand Point: Lighthouse	37 53	144 55
South Coast	Melbourne: Observatory	37 50	144 58
South Coast	Arthurs Seat: Lighthouse	38 21	144 56
South Coast	Cape Schanck: Lighthouse	38 30	144 53
South Coast	Port Western: Round I. Lighthouse	38 31	145 07
South Coast	Cape Liptrap: Lighthouse	38 55	145 56
South Coast	Citadel I.: Lighthouse	39 07	146 13
South Coast	Southeast Point: Lighthouse	39 08	146 25
South Coast	Waterloo Point: Lighthouse	39 05	146 26
South Coast	Cliffy I.: Lighthouse	38 57	146 42
South Coast	Cape Everard: Lighthouse	37 48	149 16
South Coast	Gabo I.: Lighthouse	37 34	149 55
South Coast	Green Cape: Lighthouse	37 16	150 05
South Coast	Eden: Lookout Point Lighthouse	37 04	149 55
East Coast	Montagu I.: Lighthouse	36 14	150 14
East Coast	Ulladulla: Warden Head Lighthouse	35 22	150 31
East Coast	Point Perpendicular: Lighthouse	35 05	150 50
East Coast	Crookhaven R.: Lighthouse	34 54	150 47
East Coast	Kiama: Lighthouse	34 40	150 53
East Coast	Kembla: Lighthouse	34 29	150 56
East Coast	Wollongong: Lighthouse	34 25	150 56
East Coast	Port Jackson: Macquarie Lighthouse	33 51	151 17
East Coast	Sydney: Observatory	33 52	151 12
East Coast	Barrenjoey Head: Lighthouse	33 35	151 20
East Coast	Norah Head: Lighthouse	33 17	151 36
East Coast	Newcastle:		
East Coast	Nobby Head Lighthouse	32 55	151 48
East Coast	S. Breakwater Lighthouse	32 55	151 48
East Coast	Stephens Point: Lighthouse	32 45	152 13
East Coast	Port Stephens: Lighthouse	32 43	152 11
East Coast	Sugar Loaf Point: Lighthouse	32 26	152 34
East Coast	Cape Hawke Harbor: Lighthouse	32 11	152 32
East Coast	Crowdy Head: Lighthouse	31 51	152 46
East Coast	Port Macquarie: Tacking Point Lighthouse	31 29	152 57
East Coast	Smoky Cape: Lighthouse	30 56	153 06
East Coast	Southwest Rocks: Lighthouse	30 53	153 03
East Coast	South Solitary I.: Lighthouse	30 12	153 17
East Coast	Woolgoolga: Lighthouse	30 06	153 13
East Coast	Clarence Riv.: South Head Lighthouse	29 25	153 23
East Coast	Richmond River: North Head Lighthouse	28 51	153 37
East Coast	Cape Byron: Lighthouse	28 37	153 39
East Coast	Fingal Head: Lighthouse	28 11	153 35
East Coast	Brisbane:		
East Coast	Observatory: Time signal	27 28	153 02
East Coast	Comboyuro: Lighthouse	27 04	153 23
East Coast	Cape Moreton: Lighthouse	27 02	153 28
East Coast	Bribie I.: Lighthouse	26 53	153 09
East Coast	Caloundra Head: Lighthouse	26 48	153 09
East Coast	Double I.: Point Lighthouse	25 56	153 13
East Coast	Cape Sandy: Lighthouse	24 44	153 13
East Coast	Woody I.: North Bluff Lighthouse	25 15	152 58
East Coast	Lady Elliot I.: Lighthouse	24 07	152 45

NEW ZEALAND

Place	Lat. S.	Long. E.
Cape Maria Van Dieman: Lighthouse	34 28	172 39
Cape Brett: Lighthouse	35 11	174 21
Whangarei: Sugar Loaf I.: Lighthouse	35 52	174 31
Marsden: Wharf light	35 50	174 30
Maro Tiri I.: Lighthouse	35 53	174 47
Burgess I.: Lighthouse	35 54	175 07
Flat Rock: Lighthouse	36 27	174 55
Tiri-tiri Matangi: Lighthouse	36 36	174 54
Motukorea I.: Lighthouse	36 49	174 54
Auckland:		
Bean Rocks Lighthouse	36 50	174 52
Electric time signal	36 50	174 46
Rangitoto I.: Lighthouse	36 47	174 49
Thames: Goods Wharf Lighthouse	37 08	175 33
Cuvier I.: Lighthouse	36 27	175 47
Ohena I.: Lighthouse	36 44	175 54
East Cape: Lighthouse	37 41	178 34
Gable I.: Lighthouse	38 32	178 18
Tuahina Pt.: Lighthouse	38 42	178 04
Gisborne: S. Breakwater Lighthouse	38 41	178 02
Portland I.: Lighthouse	39 18	177 53
Wairoa River: Lighthouse	39 03	177 26
Ahuriri:		
Napier Bluff Lighthouse	39 29	176 55
Castle Point: Lighthouse	40 55	176 14
Cape Palliser: Lighthouse	41 37	175 19
Port Nicholson:		
Pencarrow Head: Lighthouse	41 22	174 51
Somes I. Lighthouse	41 15	174 52
Wellington:		
Queens Wharf Lighthouse	41 17	174 47
Mt. Cook Initial Sta	41 18	174 47
Observatory	41 17	174 46
Karori Rock: Lighthouse	41 21	174 40
North Head: Lighthouse	39 57	174 59
Patea River: Lighthouse	39 47	174 31
Cape Egmont: Lighthouse	39 17	173 46
Waitara: F. S. and Light	38 50	174 14
Manukau:		
Paratutai I.: Lighthouse	37 03	174 31
Destruction Gully Lighthouse	37 02	174 35
Kaipara:		
Pouto Pt. Lighthouse	36 21	174 12
North Head Lighthouse	36 23	174 08
Bush End Point: Farewell Spit Lighthouse	40 33	173 02
Nelson: Bowlder Bank Lighthouse	41 15	173 17
Okure Point: Lighthouse	40 58	173 46
French Pass: Lighthouse	40 55	173 50
Stephens I.: Lighthouse	40 40	174 01
Nine Pin Rock: Lighthouse	40 55	174 04
Jackson Head: Lighthouse	40 59	174 20
Brothers, North I.: Lighthouse	41 06	174 27
Picton Harbor: Wharf light	41 17	174 02
Alapawa I.: Lighthouse	41 12	174 19
Cape Campbell: Lighthouse	41 43	174 18
Godley (Cachalot Head): Lighthouse	43 36	172 49
Lyttleton: E. Breakwater Light	43 37	172 44
Akaroa Head: Lighthouse	43 54	173 00
Timaru: Bluff Lighthouse	44 23	171 18
Jacks Point: Lighthouse	44 27	171 18
Oamaru: South Head Lighthouse	45 07	171 01
Moeraki: Lighthouse	45 24	170 53
Otago Harbor:		
Signal Station F. S	45 47	170 44
Hayward Point Lighthouse	45 46	170 43
Cape Saunders: Lighthouse	45 53	170 45
Nugget Point: Lighthouse	46 27	169 51
Waipapapa Pt.: Lighthouse	46 40	168 52
Dog I.: Lighthouse	46 40	168 26
Awarua (Bluff) Harbor, Stirling Point: Lighthouse	46 37	168 23
Campbelltown: Bluff Signal Station	46 37	168 20
Stewart I.: Akers Point: Lighthouse	46 54	168 11
Center I.: Lighthouse	46 28	167 52
Puysegur: Lighthouse	46 10	166 38
Queenstown: U. S. (Transit of Venus) station	45 02	168 40
Grey River: S. breakwater light	42 26	171 13
Cape Foulwind: Lighthouse	41 45	171 28
Buller River: W. breakwater light	41 43	171 36
Kahurangi Point: Lighthouse	40 46	172 13

APPENDIX IV

MARITIME POSITIONS

AUSTRALIA

Coast	Place	Lat. S. °	Lat. S. ′	Long. E. °	Long. E. ′
North Coast	Cape Don: Lighthouse	11	18	131	46
	Port Darwin:				
	Point Charles Lighthouse	12	23	130	38
	Emery Point Lighthouse	12	27	130	49
	Cape Leveque: Lighthouse	16	23	122	55
	Gantheaume Pt.: Lighthouse	17	58	122	11
	Broome: Mangrove Point Lighthouse	17	58	122	14
	Cape Bossut: Lighthouse	18	43	121	39
	Bedout I.: Lighthouse	19	35	119	06
	Mount Blaze: Lighthouse	19	59	119	[illegible]
	Port Hedland: Tidal staff light	20	18	118	35
	Port Walcott: Jarman I. Lighthouse	20	39	117	13
	N. Sandy I.: Lighthouse	21	06	115	39
	Ashburton Road: Onslow jetty light	21	41	115	00
	Anchor I.: Lighthouse	21	32	114	46
	Viaming Head: Lighthouse	21	48	114	06
	Point Cloates: Lighthouse	22	41	113	41
West Coast	Babbage I.: Lighthouse	24	52	113	38
	Cape Inscription: Lighthouse	25	29	112	58
	Geraldton: Moore Point Lighthouse	28	47	114	35
	Rottnest I.: Lighthouse	32	00	115	30
	Bathurst Pt.: Lighthouse	31	59	115	32
	Freemantle: Lighthouse	32	03	115	44
	Woodman Point: Lighthouse	32	08	115	47
	Bunbury (main) Lighthouse	33	19	115	39
	Busselton: Inner pier Lighthouse	33	38	115	21
	Cape Naturaliste: Lighthouse	33	32	115	02
	Cape Leeuwin: Lighthouse	34	22	115	09
	Princess Royal: King Pt. Light house	35	03	117	55
	Break Sea I.: Lighthouse	35	04	118	03
South Coast	Port Eyre: Lighthouse	32	00	132	26
	St. Francis I.: Lighthouse	32	31	133	18
	Murat Bay:				
	West Side Jetty Lighthouse	32	06	133	35
	East Side Jetty Lighthouse	32	08	133	40
	Port Thevenard: Lighthouse	32	09	133	38
	Streaky Bay:				
	Gibson Pt. Lighthouse	32	45	134	14
	Port Blanche: Lighthouse	32	48	134	12
	Flinders I.: Lighthouse	33	41	134	30
	Four Hummocks: Lighthouse	34	46	135	01
	Price I.: Lighthouse	34	42	135	17
	South Neptune I.: Lighthouse	35	20	136	07
	Dangerous Reef: Lighthouse	34	49	136	12
	Cape Donington: Lighthouse	34	44	136	00
	Boston I.: Lighthouse	34	44	135	56
	Port Lincoln: Kirton Point jetty Lighthouse	34	43	135	51

Coast	Place	Lat. S. °	Lat. S. ′	Long. E. °	Long. E. ′
South Coast	Boston Point: Lighthouse	34	39	135	56
	Winceby I.: Lighthouse	34	29	136	17
	Tipara Reef: Lighthouse	34	04	137	24
	Wardang I.: Lighthouse	34	30	137	21
	Corny Point: Lighthouse	34	54	137	01
	Wedge I.: Lighthouse	35	10	136	29
	Althorpe I.: Lighthouse	35	23	136	51
	Kangaroo I.:				
	Cape Borda Lighthouse	35	45	136	35
	Cape Couedic Lighthouse	36	0[illegible]	136	42
	Cape Willoughby Lighthouse	35	51	138	08
	Cape St. Alban Lighthouse	35	49	138	07
	Kingscote Lighthouse	35	40	137	38
	Marsden Pt. Lighthouse	35	34	137	37
	Troubridge Shoal: Lighthouse	35	08	137	50
	Port Wakefield: Lighthouse	34	12	138	08
	Port Adelaide:				
	Wonga Shoal Lighthouse	34	50	138	56
	Semaphore Time Signal	34	50	138	29
	Observatory (mer. circle)	34	56	138	35
East Coast	Bustard Head: Lighthouse	24	01	151	46
	Gatcombe Head: Lighthouse	23	53	151	23
	Cape Capricorn: Lighthouse	23	29	151	14
	Little Sea Hill: Lighthouse	23	30	151	00
	North Reef: Lighthouse	23	11	151	56
	High Peak I.: Lighthouse	21	57	150	43
	Percy Isles: Lighthouse	21	39	150	14
	Flat Top I.: Lighthouse	21	09	149	16
	Kennedy Sound: Shaw Peak	20	28	149	05
	Dent Island: Lighthouse	20	22	148	57
	Port Denison: Lighthouse	20	01	148	17
	Cape Bowling Green: Lighthouse	19	20	147	26
	Cape Cleveland: Lighthouse	19	11	147	01
	Townsville Harbor: W. breakwater Lighthouse	19	15	146	50
	Brook Islands: Lighthouse	18	09	146	19
	North Barnard Islets Lighthouse	17	41	146	11
	Cairns Harbor: Front beacon light	16	55	145	47
	Port Douglas: Island Point Lighthouse	16	29	145	28
	Low Isles: Lighthouse	16	2[illegible]	145	34
	Point Archer: Lighthouse	15	36	145	20
	Coquet I.: Lighthouse	14	32	144	59
	Pipon I.: Lighthouse	14	08	144	31
	Dhu Reef: Lighthouse	14	08	144	00
	Heath Reef: Lighthouse	13	28	143	40
	Chapman Island Lighthouse	12	53	143	35
	Piper Island: Lighthouse	12	15	143	15
	Clerke Island: Lighthouse	11	58	143	17
	Hannibal I.: Lighthouse	11	35	142	56
	Albany Rock: Lighthouse	10	43	142	38
	Wednesday Is.: Lighthouse	10	31	142	19
	Goode I.: Lighthouse	10	33	142	09
	Booby I.: Lighthouse	10	36	141	55

TASMANIA

Place	Lat. S. °	Lat. S. ′	Long. E. °	Long. E. ′
Deal Island: Lighthouse	39	29	147	19
Goose Island: Lighthouse	40	19	147	48
Swan Island: Lighthouse	40	44	148	07
Low Head: Lighthouse	41	03	146	49
Devonport: Time ball signal	41	10	146	24
Mersey Bluff: Lighthouse	41	09	146	24
Emu Bay: Breakwater light	41	03	145	57
Cape Wickham: Lighthouse	39	36	143	57
Currie Harbor: Lighthouse	39	57	143	51
Cape Rochon: Lighthouse	40	24	144	57
Hunter Island: Lighthouse	40	29	144	43
Entrance Islet: Lighthouse	42	12	145	13
Cape Sorell: Lighthouse	42	11	145	11
Maatsuyker Isles: Lighthouse	43	39	146	17
One Tree Point: Lighthouse	43	11	146	59
Hope I.: Lighthouse	43	20	147	03
Cape Bruny: Lighthouse	43	30	147	09
Hobart:				
Iron Pot Is.: Lighthouse	43	04	147	26
Fort Mulgrave Time signal	42	53	147	20
Astronomical Station (Transit Venus)	42	53	147	20
Tasman I.: Lighthouse	43	14	148	02
Cape Forestier: Lighthouse	42	11	148	23
Eddystone Point: Lighthouse	41	00	148	21

THE ARCTIC REGIONS

Coast	Place	Lat. N. °	Lat. N. ′	Long. W. °	Long. W. ′
Hudson Bay and Str.	Cape Walsingham: Extreme	66	00	69	28
	Mill Island: N. pt	64	04	77	50
	Button Islands: Observation Islet	62	35	74	00
	Baffin I.: Monument	62	22	68	46
	Douglas Harbor: Monument	61	55	72	37
	Wakeham Bay: Monument	61	42	71	55
	Fisher Bay: Shepherd I	61	46	72	11
	Nuwuk Is.: N. E. point	62	24	78	00
	Nelson River: Marsh Pt. Beacon	57	03	92	12
	Churchill: Lighthouse	58	47	94	12
Arctic North America	Marble Island: E. end	62	33	91	06
	Cape Kendall: Extreme	63	42	87	15
	Iglooik Island: E. pt	69	21	81	31
	King William I.: Gjoahavn	68	37	95	53
	Victoria Harbor: N. shore	70	09	91	30
	Elizabeth Harbor: Entrance	70	38	92	10
	Port Neill: N. pt. of entrance	73	09	89	00
	Port Bowen: N. cove	73	13	88	54
	Batty Bay: S. pt. of entrance	73	13	91	08
	Port Leopold: Whaler Pt	73	50	90	12

MARITIME POSITIONS

THE ARCTIC REGIONS—Continued

Coast	Place	Lat. N.	Long. W.
		° ′	° ′
Arctic North America	Careys Islands	76 49	73 10
	Discovery Harbor	81 04	64 45
	Alert's Winter Quarters	82 27	61 18
	Cape Joseph Henry: N. extreme	82 40	63 38
	Cape Hecla: N. extreme	82 54	64 45
	Cape Columbia: Extreme	83 07	70 20
	Isachsen I.: N. end	79 23	105 29
	Amund Riognes I.: N. E. part	78 44	98 17
	Lougheed I.: S. end	77 07	104 45
	Melville Island: Winter Harbor	74 46	110 47
	Brock I.: S. W. corner	77 48	115 16
	Prince Patrick I.: S. W. end	77 11	123 45
	Cape Russell	75 11	117 28
	Mercy Bay: W. side	74 08	118 50
	Cape Kellett	71 59	124 55
	Tuktoyaktuk: Flagstaff	69 27	133 03
Arctic Ocean		Lat. N.	Long. E.
	Bear Island (Bjornoya):		
	Austervag W/T sta	74 29	19 10
	West Spitsbergen I. (Svalbard):		
	Green Harbor: W/T sta	78 03	14 14
	London: W/T sta	78 58	12 03
	Longyearbyen: W/T sta	78 13	15 38
	Kotelni I.: Settlement	75 22	137 09
	Cape Chelyuskin	77 41	104 01
	Gulf of Yenesei:		
	Arctic Institute Islands	75 22	81 36
	Port Dickson: W/T station	73 30	80 24
	Golchikha: Chapel and light	71 44	83 28
	Sverdrup I.: Ast. Station	74 33	79 30
	Gulf of Ob:		
	Shokalski I.: Northeast Cape	73 05	74 45
	Nadyrsale Cape: Lighthouse	72 39	72 57
	Yogorski Strait; Village	69 39	60 26
	Vaigach I.: Lighthouse	70 15	58 31
	Pechora: C. Konstonovski Bn	68 18	54 30
	Novaya Zemlya:		
	Cape Cherni	70 49	53 30
	Matochkin Strait: Polar Geophysics Obsy. and W/T sta.	73 16	56 24
	Cape Zhelaniya	76 52	69 00
	Franz Josef Land; Wilczek I	60 45	80 40
	Kanin Nose: Beacon	68 39	43 18
	Mezen: Ephiphany Church	65 50	44 16
	Morzhovetz I.: Lighthouse	66 45	42 28
	Arkhangel: Trinity Church	64 32	40 31
	Zhizhginsk I.: Lighthouse	62 12	36 52
	Onega: St. Michael's Church	63 54	38 08
	Cape Intzi: Lighthouse	65 58	40 43
	Cape Kerets: Lighthouse	65 20	39 43
	Cape Sviatoi: Lighthouse	68 09	39 49
	Cape Tsyip-Navolok: Lighthouse	69 43	33 08
Greenland		Lat. N.	Long. W.
	Cape Morris Jesup	83 39	30 40
	Thank God Harbor	81 38	61 44
	Cape York: Extreme	75 55	65 30
	Upernivik: Flagstaff	72 47	55 53
	Proven: Village	72 20	55 20
	Omenak Island: Village	70 40	51 59
	Godhavn: Gov. Mansion	69 15	53 32
	Jacobshavn	69 13	50 56
	Claushavn	69 07	50 55
	Christianshaab	68 49	51 00
	Egedesminde: Battery F. S	68 43	52 52
	Whalefish Island: Boat Inlet	68 58	53 27
	Holsteinberg: Colonial Bldg	66 57	53 40
	Kangamint	65 48	53 23
	Ny Sukkertop	65 24	52 54
	Godthaab: Flagstaff	64 10	51 45
	Sermelik Fjord: Kasuk Peak	63 29	51 10
	Fiskernaes	63 05	50 43
	Jensen Nunatak: Peak	62 50	48 57
	Ravn Storo: Peak	62 42	50 20
	Frederikshaab: Church	61 59	49 44

Coast	Place	Lat. N.	Long. W.
		° ′	° ′
Greenland	Kangarssuk Havn	61 28	48 51
	Arsuk: Pingo Beacon	61 10	48 26
	Kajartalik Island: Summit	61 09	48 30
	Ivigtuk: House	61 12	48 10
	Bangs Havn: Anchorage	60 47	47 52
	Aurora Harbor	60 48	47 46
	Julianshaab Adm. Bldg	60 43	46 02
	Neunortalik	60 08	45 16
	Frederiksthal	60 00	44 40
	Cape Farewell: Staten Huk	59 49	44 01
	Aleuk Islands: Center	60 09	42 55
	Cape Tordenskjold: Extreme	61 25	42 15
	Cape Bille: Extreme	62 01	42 00
	Cape Juul: Extreme	63 14	40 50
	Cape Lowenorn: Extreme	64 30	39 30
	Dannesbrog Island: Beacon	65 18	38 30
	Ingolsfjeld	66 19	35 11
	Rigny Mount: Summit	69 00	26 10
	Pendulum Islands	74 40	18 17
	Cape Philipp Broke	74 55	17 33
	Cape Bismarck: Extreme	76 47	18 40
	Jan Mayen I.:		
	Mt. Beerenberg, 6,870 ft	71 04	7 36
	Youngs Foreland, or Cape Northeast	71 08	7 26
	Mary Muss Bay	71 00	8 28
	Southwest Cape	70 50	9 01
Iceland	Portland (Dyrhola): Lighthouse	63 24	19 08
	Vestmannaeyja (Heimaey): Lighthouse	63 24	20 17
	Reykjanes: Lighthouse	63 49	22 42
	Sangerdi: Lighthouse	64 02	22 40
	Faxe Bay:		
	Skagi (Skagen): Lighthouse	64 05	22 42
	Reykjavik: Lighthouse	64 09	21 55
	Malarif Point: Lighthouse	64 44	23 48
	Svortuloft: Lighthouse	64 52	24 03
	Ondverdarnes: Lighthouse	64 53	24 03
	Ellidaey I.: Lighthouse	65 09	22 49
	Latrabjarg: Lighthouse	65 30	24 32
	Svalvogar: Lighthouse	65 55	23 51
	Goltr (Galtar): Lighthouse	66 10	23 34
	Arnares: Lighthouse	66 06	23 03
	Straumnaes: Lighthouse	66 26	23 08
	Gjogur: Lighthouse	66 00	21 18
	Grimsey I.: Lighthouse	65 41	21 25
	Kalshamarnes: Lighthouse	66 01	20 26
	Skagata: Lighthouse	66 07	20 06
	Siglunes: Lighthouse	66 11	18 50
	Hrisey I.: Lighthouse	66 01	18 22
	Flatey I.: Lighthouse	66 10	17 51
	Revsnes: Lighthouse	66 32	16 12
	Cape Langanes: Lighthouse	66 23	14 32
	Bjarnarey I.: Lighthouse	65 47	14 19
	Dalatangi: Lighthouse	65 16	13 35
	Vattarnes: Lighthouse	64 56	13 41
	Kampnaes: Lighthouse	64 48	13 51
	Streiteshuk: Lighthouse	64 44	14 00
	Papey I.:		
	Lighthouse	64 35	14 11
	Transit station	64 36	14 09
	Stokksnes: Lighthouse	64 14	14 58
	Hvanney: Lighthouse	64 14	15 12
	Ingolfshofdi:		
	Lighthouse	63 48	16 38
	Transit station	63 48	16 36
	Reythur Fjeld Transit station	64 56	13 41
Faroe Islands	Sumbo. Lighthouse	61 24	6 40
	Galgetange Lighthouse	61 33	6 48
	Nolso: Lighthouse	61 57	6 36
	Borin: Lighthouse	61 57	6 38
	Tofte: Lighthouse	62 05	6 44
	Straender: Lighthouse	62 07	6 45
	Kalso: Lighthouse	62 15	6 39
	Myggenaes: Lighthouse	62 06	7 40

MARITIME POSITION INDEX TO APPENDIX IV

REGIONS, COASTS, AND ISLAND GROUPS

REGIONS, COASTS, AND ISLAND GROUPS—continued

PLACES

PLACES—continued

PLACES—continued

PLACES—continued

PLACES—continued

PLACES—continued

PLACES—continued

PLACES—continued

PLACES—continued

PLACES—continued

PLACES—continued

PLACES—continued

PLACES—continued

PLACES—continued

PLACES—continued

PLACES—continued

PLACES—continued

PLACES—continued

PLACES—continued

PLACES—continued

PLACES—continued

PLACES—continued

PLACES—continued

PLACES—continued

PLACES—continued

541524°—43——26

PLACES—continued

PLACES—continued

PART II.

TABLES.

1

CONTENTS OF PART II.

EXPLANATION OF TABLES.

TABLE 1.—RADIO BEARING CONVERSION.

This table is used to convert the radio or true bearing into the mercator bearing, when it is desired to plot the bearing on a mercator chart. The arguments used to find the correction are the middle latitude between the sending radio station and the vessel's D. R. position, and the difference of longitude between the radio station and the vessel. The sign of the correction is as follows,

In north latitude, when the vessel is $\frac{\text{eastward}}{\text{westward}}$ of the station, the correction is $\frac{\text{additive}}{\text{subtractive}}$.

In south latitude, when the vessel is $\frac{\text{eastward}}{\text{westward}}$ of the station, the correction is $\frac{\text{subtractive}}{\text{additive}}$.

Should the bearing be observed from the vessel, the sign of the correction as given above is reversed.

EXAMPLE: A vessel in D. R. Lat. 38°03′ N.; Long. 55° W.; receives a radio bearing of 118° from Bar Harbor, Maine, radio station (Lat. 44°19′ N.; Long. 68°11′ W.). Find the Mercator bearing.

Bar Harbor station, Lat. 44°19′ N.; Long. 68°11′ W.
Vessel (D. R. position), Lat. 38°03′ N.; Long. 55°00′ W.
Middle Lat. 41°11′ N.; Diff. Long. 13°11′ W.

Enter table with Mid. Lat. 41° and Diff. Long. 13°.2; the correction is +4°.4.
Mercator bearing = Radio bearing plus correction, or 118°+4°.4=122°.4.

The table is computed from the formula, $\tan \text{correction} = \dfrac{\sin \text{Mid. Lat.}}{\cos \dfrac{\text{Diff. Lat.}}{2}} \tan \dfrac{\text{Diff. Long.}}{2}$.

TABLE 2.—CONVERSION OF POINTS TO DEGREES.

This table gives the 32 points of the compass arranged in order from North to East, East to South, South to West, and West to North. The process of naming these points in this order is called "Boxing the Compass." The names of the whole points and fractional points are readily converted by this table into the corresponding degrees, minutes, and seconds, from 0° to 360°.

TABLE 3.—TRAVERSE TABLE, DEGREES.

This table contains the difference of latitude and departure corresponding to distances up to 600 miles and for courses for every degree of the compass. The table may also be employed in the solution of any right triangle. The manner of using these tables is particularly explained under the different problems of Plane, Middle Latitude, and Mercator Sailing in Chapter V, and the interchanges of the designations of the headings of the different columns in order to subserve these various uses, are summarized in the marginal diagram at the foot of each page.

TABLE 4.—CONVERSION OF DEPARTURE INTO DIFFERENCE OF LONGITUDE.

This table is computed from the formula, Departure = Diff. Long. × cosine Mid. Lat., or Diff. Long. $= \dfrac{\text{Dep.}}{\text{cos. Mid. Lat.}}$ The body of the table gives the difference of longitude (D. Lo.) for every mile of departure from one mile to sixty. The middle latitudes are given from 4° to 60°. The table is entered with the arguments, Mid. Lat. at the top of the page, and the Dep. at the side of the page, from which is found the D. Lo.

EXAMPLE: In Mid. Lat. 59°30′, the departure was 30 miles. Find the D. Lo.

Under Mid. Lat. 59°30′ and opposite Dep. 30, is found D. Lo. 59′.1.

EXAMPLE: In Mid. Lat. 54° the D. Lo. was 51.′ Find Dep.

Under Mid. Lat. 54° and in the D. Lo. column is found 51′, opposite in Dep. column is found 30 miles.

TABLE 5.—MERIDIONAL PARTS.

This table contains the meridional parts, or increased latitudes, for every degree and minute to 80°, calculated by the following formula:

$$m=\frac{a}{M}\log\tan\left(45°+\frac{L}{2}\right)-a\left(e^2\sin L+\tfrac{1}{3}e^4\sin^3 L+\tfrac{1}{5}e^6\sin^5 L+\ .\ .\ .\ .\ \right),$$

in which

the Equatorial radius $a=\frac{10800'}{\pi}=3437'.74677$ (log 3.5362739);

M, the modulus of common logarithms=0.4342945;

$\frac{1}{M}=2.3025851$ (log 0.3622157);

c, the *compression* or meridional ellipticity of the earth according to Clarke (1880) $=\frac{1}{293.465}=0.003407562$ (log 7.5324437);

$e=\sqrt{2c-c^2}=0.0824846$ (log 8.9163666);

from which

$\frac{a}{M}=7915'.7044558$ (log 3.8984895);

$ae^2=\ \ 23'.38871$ (log 1.3690072);

$\frac{1}{3}ae^4=\ \ 0'.053042$ (log 8.7246192);

$\frac{1}{5}ae^6=\ \ 0'.000216523$ (log 6.3355038).

The results are tabulated to one decimal place, which is sufficient for the ordinary problems of navigation.

The practical application of this table is illustrated in Chapters II and V, in articles treating of the Mercator Chart and Mercator Sailing.

TABLE 6.—LENGTH OF DEGREES OF LATITUDE AND LONGITUDE.

This table gives the length of a degree in both latitude and longitude at each parallel of latitude on the earth's surface, in nautical and statute miles and in meters, based upon Clarke's value (1866) of the earth's compression, $\frac{1}{299.15}$. In the case of latitude, the length relates to an arc of which the given degree is the center.

TABLE 7.—DISTANCE OF OBJECT BY TWO BEARINGS—DEGREES.

This table has been computed to facilitate the operation of finding the distance from an object by two bearings from a given distance run and course. The arguments are given in degrees; the first column contains the multiplier of the distance run to give the distance of observed object at second bearing; the second, at time of passing abeam.

The method is explained in Chapter IV.

TABLE 8.—DISTANCE OF VISIBILITY OF OBJECTS.

This table contains the distances, in nautical and statute miles, at which any object is visible at sea. It is calculated by the formulæ:

$$d=1.15\sqrt{x},\text{ and }d'=1.32\sqrt{x},$$

in which d is the distance in nautical miles, d' the distance in statute miles, and x the height of the eye or the object in feet.

To find the distance of visibility of an object, the distance given by the table corresponding to its height should be added to that corresponding to the height of the observer's eye.

EXAMPLE: Required the distance of visibility of an object 420 feet high, the observer being at an elevation of 15 feet.

Dist. corresponding to 420 feet,	23.5	naut. miles.
Dist. corresponding to 15 feet,	4.4	naut. miles.
Dist. of visibility,	27.9	naut. miles.

TABLE 9.—DISTANCE BY VERTICAL ANGLES (distance less than 5 miles).

This table gives the distance, up to 5 miles, of an object of known height by the vertical angle that it subtends at the position of the observer. It was computed by the formula

$$\tan\alpha=\frac{h}{d},$$

where α=the vertical angle;
h=the height of the observed object in feet; and
d=the distance of the object, also converted into feet.

No correction for Dip is applied.

The employment of this method of finding distance is explained in Chapter IV.

TABLE 10.—DISTANCE BY VERTICAL ANGLES (distance greater than 5 miles).

This table gives the distance greater than 5 miles of an object of known height by the angle it subtends at the position of the observer. The table comprises heights from 400 to 15,500 feet above the sea and distances from 6 miles to 85 miles. It contains correction tables for refraction and dip, both of which are subtracted from the observed angle after applying the index correction of the sextant. Aircraft using the bubble sextant correct the observed altitude for refraction only. This table is used for angles of elevation, or for those cases where the height of object is greater than height of observer.

EXAMPLE: The altitude of a mountain top 15,000 feet high was observed which gave by sextant an elevation of 1°40′; I. C.+1′; height of eye 35 feet, estimated distance 60 miles. Find the required distance. After applying the index correction of plus 1′ the altitude is 1°41′. From the table, the correction for Dip is −5′.8, and the correction for refraction is −4′.4 or a total of −10′.2. This correction subtracted from 1°41′ gives an angle of elevation of 1°30′.8. Enter table ordinarily with the difference between the height of object and height of eye, but when the height of eye is relatively low this may be disregarded. Therefore under the column for 15,000 feet find the angle nearest 1°31′. By interpolation the distance away is found in the side column to be approximately 67.6 nautical miles.

It must be noted that observed bearings are the same as great circle bearings and are not the same as mercator bearings taken from the chart. The mercator bearing requires a correction similar to the correction of a radio bearing. In most cases this correction can be disregarded, unless the mountain is very far away or the vessel is in high latitudes.

TABLE 11.—HORIZON ANGLES.

This shows the distance in yards corresponding to any observed angle between an object and the sea horizon beyond, the observer being at a known height.

The method of use is explained in Chapter IV.

TABLE 12.—SPEED TABLE.

This table shows the rate of speed, in nautical miles per hour, of a vessel which traverses a measured mile in any given number of minutes and seconds. It is entered with the number of minutes at the top and the number of seconds at the side; under one and abreast the other is the number of knots of speed.

TABLE 13.—TIME—SPEED—DISTANCE TABLE.

This table shows the distance in nautical miles steamed in any part of an hour from 5 knots to 37 knots. It is entered with the number of minutes at the side, with speed in knots at the top, abreast of one and under the other is found the distance in nautical miles.

TABLE 14.—CONVERSION TABLES FOR NAUTICAL AND STATUTE MILES.

TABLE 15.—CONVERSION TABLES FOR METRIC AND ENGLISH LINEAR MEASURE.

TABLE 16.—CONVERSION TABLES FOR THERMOMETER SCALES.

TABLE 17.—REDUCTION OF LOCAL CIVIL TIME TO STANDARD MERIDIAN TIME.

This table contains the reduction to be applied to the local time to obtain the corresponding time at any other meridian whose time is adopted as a standard. The results are given to the nearest minute of time only; being intended for the reduction of such approximate quantities as the time of high water or time of sunset.

TABLE 18.—DIP OF SEA HORIZON.

This table contains the dip of the sea horizon, calculated by the formula:

$$D=58''.8\sqrt{F},$$

in which F=height of the eye above the level of the sea in feet.

It is explained in Chapter X.

TABLE 19.—DIP SHORT OF HORIZON.

This table contains the dip for various distances and heights, calculated by the formula:

$$D=\frac{3}{7}d+0.56514\times\frac{h}{d},$$

in which D represents the dip in miles or minutes, d, the distance of the land in sea miles, and h, the height of the eye of the observer in feet.

TABLE 20.—PARALLAX OF SUN.

This table contains the sun's parallax in altitude computed by the formula:

$$\text{par.} = \sin z \times 8''.75,$$

in which z = apparent zenith distance, the sun's horizontal parallax being 8''.75.
It is explained in Chapter X.

TABLE 21.—PARALLAX OF PLANET.

Parallax in altitude of a planet is found by entering at the top with the planet's horizontal parallax, and at the side with the altitude. In observations at sea, this correction is disregarded.

TABLE 22.—MEAN REFRACTION.

This table gives the refraction, reduced from Bessel's tables, for a mean atmospheric condition in which the barometer is 30.00 inches, and thermometer 50° Fahr.

TABLE 23.—MEAN REFRACTION AND PARALLAX OF SUN.

This table contains the correction to be applied to the sun's apparent altitude for mean refraction and parallax, being a combination of the quantities for the altitudes given in Tables 20 and 22.

TABLES 24, 25.—CORRECTIONS OF REFRACTION FOR BAROMETER AND THERMOMETER.

These are deduced from Bessel's tables. The method of their employment will be evident.

TABLE 26.—REDUCTION FOR MOON'S TRANSIT.

This table was computed by proportioning the daily variation of the time of the moon's passing the meridian.
The numbers taken from the table are to be added to the Greenwich time of moon's transit in west longitude, but subtracted in east longitude.

TABLE 27.—AMPLITUDES.

This table contains amplitudes of heavenly bodies, at rising and setting, for various latitudes and declinations computed by the formula:

$$\sin \text{amp.} = \sec. \text{Lat.} \times \sin \text{dec.}$$

It is entered with the declination at the top and the latitude at the side.
Its use is explained in Chapter XIII.

TABLE 28.—CORRECTION FOR AMPLITUDES OBSERVED ON THE APPARENT HORIZON.

This table gives a correction to be applied to the observed amplitude to counteract the vertical displacement due to refraction, parallax, and dip, when the body is observed with its center in the visible horizon.
The correction is to be applied for the sun, a planet or a star, as follows:

At Rising in N. Lat.
Setting in S. Lat. } apply the correction to the right.

At Rising in S. Lat.
Setting in N. Lat. } apply the correction to the left.

For the moon, apply *half* the correction in the *contrary* manner.

TABLE 29.—CHANGE OF ALTITUDE IN ONE MINUTE FROM MERIDIAN.

This table gives the variation of the altitude of any heavenly body, for one minute of time from meridian passage, for latitudes up to 60°, declinations to 63°, and altitudes between 6° and 86°. It is based upon the method set forth in Chapter XI under "Reduction to the Meridian" and the values may be computed by the formula:

$$a = \frac{1''.9635 \cos L \cos d}{\sin (L - d)},$$

where a = variation of altitude in one minute from meridian,
L = latitude, and
d = declination—positive for same name and negative for opposite name to latitude at upper transit, and negative for same name at lower transit.

The limits of the table take in all values of latitude, declination, and altitude which are likely to be required. In its employment, care must be taken to enter the table at a place where the declination is appropriately named (of the same or opposite name to the latitude); it should also be noted that at the bottom of the last three pages values are given for the variation of a body at *lower* transit, which can only be observed when the declination and latitude are of the same name, and in which case the reduction to the meridian is subtractive; the limitations in this case are stated at the *foot* of the page, and apply to all values below the heavy rules.

TABLE 30.—CHANGE OF ALTITUDE IN GIVEN TIME FROM MERIDIAN.

This table gives the product of the variation in altitude in one minute of a heavenly body near the meridian, by the square of the number of minutes. Values are given in arc for every 5′ from 0° to 7°, or in time for every 20^s from 0^m to 28^m, and for all variations likely to be employed in the method of "reduction to the meridian."

The formula for computing is:

$$\text{Red.} = a \times t^2,$$

where a = variation in one minute (Table 29), and
t = number of minutes (in units and tenths) from time of meridian passage.

The table is entered in the column of the nearest interval of time or arc from meridian, and the value taken out corresponding to the value of a found from Table 29. The units and tenths are picked out separately and combined, each being corrected by interpolation for intermediate intervals of time or arc.

The result in minutes and tenths of arc is the amount to be applied to the observed altitude to reduce it to the meridian altitude, which is always to be added for upper transits and subtracted for lower.

TABLE 31.—NATURAL TRIGONOMETRIC FUNCTIONS.

This table and the explanation thereto, have been prepared and copyrighted by Lyman M. Kells, Willis F. Kern, and James R. Bland, who have supplied them to the Hydrographic Office for use in its publications. Neither the table nor any new feature embodied therein, may be reproduced in any form without the permission of the copyright owners.

Table of natural values of trigonometric functions.—Table 31 contains the numerical values of the sines, cosines, tangents, and cotangents of angles from 0° to 90° at intervals of 1′. In the case of an angle in the range from 0° to 45°, the number of degrees in the angle and the names of the functions are found at the top of the page and the left-hand minute column applies; in the case of angles in the range from 45° to 90°, the number of degrees in the angle and the names of the functions are found at the bottom of the page and the right-hand minute column applies. Interpolation must be carried out without the aid of difference columns or tables of proportional parts.

The following examples illustrate the method of using the tables.

EXAMPLE 1: Find sin 68°28′.

Solution.—We first find the page at the bottom of which 68° appears and then find the row of the 68° block containing 28′ in the right-hand minute column. In this row and in the column having sin at its foot we find 020 to which we must prefix 0.93 to obtain sin 68°28′ = 0.93020.

EXAMPLE 2: Find sin 38°38′27″.

Solution.—Using the tables and computing differences, we find the values exhibited in the following form:

$$\left.\begin{matrix}\left.\begin{matrix}\sin 38°38'00'' \\ \sin 38°38'27''\end{matrix}\right\}27'' \\ \sin 38°39'00''\end{matrix}\right\}60'' \quad \left.\begin{matrix}\left.\begin{matrix}=0.62433 \\ =?\end{matrix}\right\}x \\ =0.62456\end{matrix}\right\}23$$

Hence

$$\frac{x}{23} = \frac{27}{60}, \text{ or } x = \left(\frac{27}{60}\right)23 = 10 \text{ (nearly)}.$$

Therefore

$$\sin 38°38'27'' = 0.62433 + 0.00010 = 0.62443. \quad \textit{Ans.}$$

EXAMPLE 3: If cot θ = 0.37806, find θ.

Solution.—Using the tables and computing differences, we find the values exhibited in the following form:

$$\left.\begin{matrix}\left.\begin{matrix}\cot 69°17'00'' \\ \cot \quad ?\end{matrix}\right\}x \\ \cot 69°18'00''\end{matrix}\right\}60 \quad \left.\begin{matrix}\left.\begin{matrix}=0.37820 \\ =0.37806\end{matrix}\right\}14 \\ =0.37787\end{matrix}\right\}33$$

Hence

$$\frac{x}{60} = \frac{14}{33}, \text{ or } x = \frac{14}{33}(60) = 25'' \text{ (nearly), and } \theta = 69°17'25''. \quad \textit{Ans.}$$

Since cot θ is positive in the third quadrant, we may also write an answer 180° + 69°17′25″ = 249°17′25″.

TABLE 32.—COMMON LOGARITHMS OF NUMBERS.

This table and the explanation thereto, have been prepared and copyrighted by Lyman M. Kells, Willis F. Kern, and James R. Bland, who have supplied them to the Hydrographic Office for use in its publications. Neither the table nor any new features embodied therein, may be reproduced in any form without the permission of the copyright owners.

Additional examples in the use of logarithms are contained in Appendix III of Part I of this publication.

Introduction.—*The power L to which a given number b must be raised to produce a number N is called the logarithm of N to the base b.* This relation expressed in symbols is

$$b^L = N.$$

It appears at once that b must not be unity and it must not be negative. In the following set of tables, 10 is used as base.

Characteristic and mantissa.—The common logarithm of any real, positive number may be written as an integer, positive or negative, plus a positive decimal fraction. The integral part is called the *characteristic* and the decimal part the *mantissa.* The characteristic may be written by using the following rules:

RULE 1: *The characteristic of the common logarithm of a number greater than 1 is obtained by subtracting 1 from the number of digits to the left of the decimal point.*

For example, 68.30 has two digits to the left of its decimal point; hence its characteristic is $2-1=1$. Similarly for 6830, the characteristic is $4-1=3$, for 7.864 it is $1-1=0$, and for 5846300 it is 6.

RULE 2: *The characteristic of the common logarithm of a positive number less than 1 is negative and its magnitude is obtained by adding 1 to the number of zeros immediately following the decimal point.*

If the characteristic of a number is $-n$ (n positive), it should be written in the form $(10-n)-10$. *To obtain directly the logarithm of a number less than 1, subtract from 9 the number of zeros immediately following the decimal point, and write the result before the mantissa and −10 after it.*

For example, 0.000785 has three zeros immediately following the decimal point; hence its characteristic is $-(3+1)=-4$, or $6-10$. Similarly for 0.0000587 the characteristic is $-(4+1)=-5$ or $5-10$, for 0.0287 it is -2 or $8-10$, and for 0.684 it is -1 or $9-10$.

To find the mantissa—Special case.—The mantissa, or decimal part of the logarithm of a number, depends only on the sequence of the digits and not on the position of the decimal point. Table 32 lists the mantissas, accurate to five decimal places, of the logarithms of all integers from 1 to 10,000.

The change in the mantissas of the logarithms is very slow. Consequently the first two digits of the mantissas have been omitted from a large percentage of entries. When these two digits are omitted from an entry, they always appear in the column containing the entry both slightly above it and also slightly below it.

To find the mantissa of the logarithm of a number locate the first three digits of this number in the left-hand column headed *No.*, and the fourth digit in the row at the top of the page. Then the mantissa of the given number containing four significant figures is in the row whose first three figures are the first three significant figures of the given number, and in the column headed by the fourth. Thus to find the logarithm of 76.64 find 766 in the column headed *No.*, and follow the corresponding row to the entry in the column headed by 4. This entry 88446 represents the mantissa required. The first two digits 88 of the mantissa were found in the same column with the considered entry but one space lower, and also in the same column, but seven spaces higher.

Hence, we have

$$\log 76.64 = 1.88446.$$

Interpolation.—When a number contains a fifth significant figure, we find the logarithm corresponding to the first four figures as above and then add an increment obtained by a process called interpolation. This process is based on the assumption that *for relatively small changes in the number N the changes in log N are proportional to the changes in N.* The following example will serve to illustrate the process of interpolation.

The expression *tabular difference* will be used frequently in what follows. The tabular difference, when used in connection with a table, means the result of subtracting the lesser of two successive entries from the greater. These differences have been computed in every case and tabulated in the columns headed "d".

EXAMPLE: Find log 235.47.

Solution.—We first find the logarithms in the following form and then compute the difference indicated:

$$\left.\begin{matrix}\left.\begin{matrix}\log 235.40\\ \log 235.47\end{matrix}\right\}7\\ \log 235.50\end{matrix}\right\}10 \quad \left.\begin{matrix}\left.\begin{matrix}=2.37181\\ =?\end{matrix}\right\}d\\ =2.37199\end{matrix}\right\}18 \text{ (tabular difference).}$$

By the principle of proportional parts, we have

$$\frac{7}{10}=\frac{d}{18}, \quad \text{or } d=\frac{7}{10}(18)=12.6=13 \text{ (nearly).}$$

Adding 0.00013 to 2.37181, we obtain

$$\log 235.47 = 2.37194.$$

The increment 12.6 was rounded off to 13 because we are not justified in writing more than five decimal places in the mantissa.

The essence of this procedure is embodied in the following statement. *To find the logarithm of a number composed of five significant figures, first find the logarithm corresponding to the first four figures and to it add one-tenth of the tabular difference multiplied by the fifth digit.*

To shorten the process of interpolation, 10^5 times each tabular difference occurring in the table has been multiplied by 0.1, 0.2, . . . 0.9, and the results have been tabulated on the right-hand sides of the pages on which these differences occur. The abbreviation Prop. Parts written at the top of the page over these small tables abbreviates the words *proportional parts.* To interpolate in the example just solved, note the tabular difference 18, locate the Prop. Parts table headed 18 and find opposite 7 in its left-hand column the entry 13. In general, this difference should not be computed but should be obtained from the number opposite the fifth digit in the appropriate table of proportional parts.

To find the number corresponding to a given logarithm.—If log $N=L$, the number N is called the *antilogarithm* of L. The sequence of digits of a number N corresponding to a given logarithm L is found from its mantissa, and the decimal point is then placed in accordance with the italicized rules stated above.

EXAMPLE: Given log $N=1.92955$, find N.

Solution.—The mantissa .92955 lies between the entries .92952 and .92957 of Table 32. Using the table and computing the differences indicated, we write the following form:

$$\left.\begin{array}{l}\left.\begin{array}{l}1.92952\\1.92955\end{array}\right\}3\\1.92957\end{array}\right\}5=\begin{array}{l}\left.\begin{array}{l}=\log 85.020\\ \log N\end{array}\right\}x\\=\log 85.030\end{array}\right\}10.$$

Assuming that changes in the logarithm are proportional to the corresponding changes in the number, we write

$$\frac{3}{5}=\frac{x}{10}, \text{ or } x=10\left(\frac{3}{5}\right)=6.$$

Hence

$$N=85.026.$$

The essence of the process of interpolation is indicated in the foregoing procedure. However, in practice, the student should always interpolate by using the table of proportional parts. The fifth figure 6 should have been obtained from the table of porportional parts. In the small Prop. Parts table corresponding to the tabular difference 5, we read either 5 or 6 in the left-hand column opposite the entry 3. However, the 6 must be chosen; for in case there is a choice between two or more entries one of which is opposite a number printed in **boldface,** give preference to the entry opposite the **bold-faced** figure.

RULE: *Whenever a number lying exactly half way between two entries is under consideration* or is the same as two or more adjacent entries, give preference to that character which has a **bold-faced** part nearest the entry.

TABLE 33.—LOGARITHMS OF TRIGONOMETRIC FUNCTIONS.

This table and the explanation thereto, have been prepared and copyrighted by Lyman M. Kells, Willis F. Kern, and James R. Bland, who have supplied them to the Hydrographic Office for use in its publications. Neither the table nor any new features embodied therein, may be reproduced in any form without the permission of the copyright owners.

Table of logarithms of trigonometric functions.—Table 33 gives the logarithms of the sines, cosines, tangents, cotangents, secants, and cosecants of angles at intervals of 1′ from 0° to 90°. The names of the functions written at the top of any page apply to angles having the number of degrees written at the top of the page, and the function names written at the bottom apply to angles having the number of degrees written at the bottom. The left-hand or the right-hand minute column applies according as the number of degrees in the angle is written on the left side or on the right side of the block of numbers under consideration. One of the arrowheads attached to each number representing degrees points toward the column of minutes to be used in connection with an angle involving that number of degrees, the other points toward the row of names to be considered.

For example, to find log sin 32°46′, we find the page at the top of which 32° appears. find the row containing 46 in the left-hand minute column, and read 9.73337 in this row and in the column headed **sin.** The part 9.73 was found above the 46′ entry or it could have been found lower down in the column, and 10 is to be subtracted from every logarithm in the table. Again, to find log tan 142°36′, find the page at the top of which 142° appears, find the row containing 36 in the right-hand minute column, and read 9.88341 in this row and in the column headed **tan.** Hence log tan 142°36′=(−) 9.88341−10. The minus sign in parentheses before the log indicates that a negative number is under consideration. The 9.88 was found three spaces higher in the column, or it could have been found lower in the column.

Given the angle to find the logarithm of a trigonometric function—Interpolation.—The principles involved here are the same as those involved in finding logarithms and antilogarithms of numbers. Interpolation for seconds is accomplished by direct interpolation or by using the columns headed "diff." The following example will illustrate the use of the difference columns.

EXAMPLE: Find log tan 65°42′17″.

Solution.—On the page at the foot of which 65° appears, read opposite the 42′ of the right-hand minute column 533; attach to this the 10.34 found four spaces above this entry, to obtain 10.34533. In the nearest difference column opposite 17″ find 9 and add it to the last figures (33) of 10.34533 and finally subtract 10 from the result to obtain

$$\log \tan 65°42'17'' = 10.34542 - 10 = 0.34542$$

In the process of interpolation for seconds, *the difference column, headed* "diff," *nearest to the column of entries involved should be used. The change for seconds is found in this column opposite a number in the adjacent column equal to the number of seconds in the given angle. This difference is added to or subtracted from the number represented by the last three digits of the entry opposite the given number of minutes according as the entry for the next higher number of minutes is a greater or a lesser one.*

Interpolation by means of the columns headed "diff" involve slight errors which are negligible for most purposes of navigation. To avoid this error, direct interpolation may be used. Let n represent the number of seconds, D the difference between the entry corresponding to the given number of minutes and that corresponding to the next higher number of minutes, and d the required change to be added to or subtracted from the entry opposite the given number of minutes. Then

$$d = \frac{n}{60} D.$$

Given the logarithm of a trigonometric function, to find the angle.—The following example will indicate the procedure necessary to find the angle when the logarithm of a trigonometric function of the angle is given.

EXAMPLE: Find θ if log cos $\theta = 9.85391 - 10$.

Solution.—On the page at the top of which 44° appears, and in the column headed **cos** find the two entries 9.85399 and 9.85386 between which the given logarithm lies. Write $\theta = 44°24' +$ associated with the entry 9.85399. The difference between 9.85399 and the given logarithm is 0.00008; hence enter the adjacent column headed "diff" and opposite the 8 in **boldface** read 39″ in the associated seconds column. Hence

$$\theta = 44°24'39''.$$

In obtaining approximate position, observe only the two digits in **boldface** at the top of the page while leafing through the table in search of the desired page.

RULE: *Whenever,* in the process of finding the appropriate number of seconds, *there is a choice between two or more entries one of which is printed in* **boldface** *always give preference to the* **bold-faced** *entry.*

Here again direct interpolation may be used. For this purpose solve the formula written above, $d = (n/60)D$ for n to obtain

$$n = \frac{d}{D} 60,$$

where n and D have the same meanings as above and d is the difference between the logarithm corresponding to the correct number of minutes and the given logarithm.

TABLE 34.—LOGARITHMIC AND NATURAL HAVERSINES.

The haversine is defined by the following relation:

$$\text{hav. } A = \tfrac{1}{2} \text{ vers. } A = \tfrac{1}{2}(1 - \cos A) = \sin^2 \tfrac{1}{2} A.$$
$$\text{hav. } A = \text{hav. } (360° - A)\text{; thus hav. } 210° = \text{hav. } 150°.$$

It is a trigonometric function which simplifies the solution of many problems in nautical astronomy as well as in plane trigonometry. To afford the maximum facility in carrying out the processes of solution, the values of the natural haversine and its logarithm are set down together in a single table for all values of angle ranging from 0° to 360°, expressed both in arc and in time.

TABLE 35.—THE LONGITUDE FACTOR.

The change in longitude due to a change of 1′ in latitude, called the longitude factor, F, is given in this table at suitable intervals of latitude and azimuth. The quantities tabulated are computed from the formula—

$$F = \text{sec. Lat.} \times \text{cot. Az.}$$

When a time sight is solved with a dead-reckoning latitude, the resulting longitude is only true if the latitude be correct. This table, by setting forth the number of minutes of longitude due to each minute of error in latitude, gives the means of finding the correction to the longitude for any error that may subsequently be disclosed in the latitude used in the computation.

Regarding the azimuth of the observed celestial body as less than 90° and as measured from either the North or the South point of the horizon toward East or West, the rule for determining whether the correction in longitude is to be applied to the eastward or to the westward will be as follows: If the change in latitude is of the same name as the first letter of the bearing, the change in longitude is of the contrary name to that of the second letter, and vice versa.

Thus, if the body bears S. 45° E. and the change in latitude is to the southward, the change in longitude will be to the westward; and, if the change in latitude is to the northward, the change in longitude will be to the eastward.

The convenient application of the longitude factor in finding the intersection of position lines is explained under "Computing the intersection of position lines," chapter XIV.

TABLE 36.—THE LATITUDE FACTOR.

The change in latitude due to a change of 1′ in the longitude, called the latitude factor, *f*, is given in this table at suitable intervals of latitude and azimuth. The quantities tabulated, being the reciprocals of the values of the longitude factor, are computed from the formula—

$$f=\frac{1}{F}=\frac{1}{\text{sec. Lat.}\times\text{cot. Az.}}=\text{cos. Lat.}\times\text{tan. Az.}$$

When an ex-meridian sight is solved with a longitude afterwards found to be in error, this table, by setting forth the number of minutes of latitude due to each 1′ of error in longitude, gives the means of finding the correction in the latitude for the amount of error in the longitude used in the calculation.

Regarding the azimuth of the observed celestial body as less than 90° and as measured from either the North or the South point of the horizon toward East or West, the rule for determining whether the correction in latitude is to be applied to the northward or to the southward is as follows: If the change in longitude is of the same name as the second letter of the bearing, the change in latitude is of the contrary name to the first letter, and vice versa. Thus, if the body bears S. 14° E. and the change in longitude is to the westward, the change in latitude will be to the southward, and, if the change in longitude is to the eastward, the change in latitude will be to the northward.

TABLE 37.—NOON INTERVAL FACTOR.

An important item in the day's work is the proper setting of the watch to show the correct time of local apparent noon, or to find the interval of time from the morning sun observation to local apparent noon. The rate of change of longitude of the sun in its diurnal path from east to west is 900′ per hour. If to this is added the hourly change in longitude of the vessel due to course and speed, combined with the current, when this change of longitude is to the eastward, or if to this is subtracted the hourly change in longitude when speed and current are to the westward, the result will be the rate of approach per hour of the meridian of the sun toward the meridian of the observer. Suppose at watch time $7^h\ 59^m\ 43^s$ (G. C. T. $12^h\ 12^m\ 50^s$) the local observation of sun gave an easterly hour angle of $3^h\ 34^m\ 06^s$ ($3^h.5683$), the vessel changes longitude 19′ every hour to the eastward due to course and speed, and that the current in longitude is 0′.6 eastward; then the interval to noon is $3^h.5683\times\frac{900'}{919'.6}$. From the table for 19′.6, Easterly hourly change in longitude the factor found is .97869 and this number multiplied by the hour angle $3^h.5683$ is the interval to noon.

logarithm of .97869 = 9.99065
logarithm of $3^h.5683$ = 0.55246

logarithm of interval = 0.54311 = $3^h.4923$ = $3^h\ 29^m\ 32^s$

	h	m	s		h	m	s
W. T. obs.	7	59	43	G. C. T. of obs.	12	12	50
Intv. to noon,	3	29	32	Intv. to noon,	3	29	32
W. T. of L. A. noon,	11	29	15	G. C. T. of L. A. noon,	15	42	22

The declination for noon is found in the nautical almanac for G. C. T. $15^h\ 42^m\ 22^s$.

The W. T. of transit of star or planet may be found by multiplying its hour angle by table factor.

TABLE 38.—CONVERSION OF SIDEREAL INTO MEAN SOLAR TIME.

TABLE 39.—CONVERSION OF MEAN SOLAR INTO SIDEREAL TIME.

These tables give, respectively, the reductions necessary to convert intervals of sidereal time into those of mean solar time, and intervals of mean solar into those of sidereal time. The reduction for any interval is found by entering with the number of hours at the top and the number of minutes at the side, adding the reduction for seconds as given in the margin.

The relations between mean solar and sidereal time intervals, and the methods of conversion of these times, are given in Chapter IX.

TABLE 40.—CORRECTIONS TO BE APPLIED TO FIND THE TRUE ALTITUDE OF A STAR AND ALSO OF THE SUN FROM THE OBSERVED ALTITUDE ABOVE THE HORIZON.

This is a consolidated table in which the tabulated correction for an observed altitude of a star combines the mean refraction, and that for an observed altitude of the sun's lower limb combines the mean refraction, the parallax, and the mean semidiameter, which is taken as 16′. The additional correction for the sun takes account of the variation of the sun's semidiameter in the different months of the year. The auxiliary table for height of eye gives the additional corrections for dip. In case the sun's upper limb is observed, then twice the semidiameter obtained from the Nautical Almanac is subtracted from the resulting altitude. This gives the lower limb, then the corrections from this table are supplied as usual.

TABLE 41.—CORRECTIONS TO BE APPLIED TO FIND THE TRUE ALTITUDE OF THE MOON FROM THE OBSERVED ALTITUDE ABOVE THE HORIZON.

In this table, which is to be entered with the observed altitude in the side column and from the top with the horizontal parallax as obtained from the Nautical Almanac for the time of observation, there are set down the corrections to be applied to the observed altitude of the moon's upper limb above the horizon, and also of the lower limb, giving the combined effect of the astronomical refraction for the mean state of the atmosphere. and of the parallax and semidiameter of the moon. The auxiliary table for height of eye gives the correction for dip.

TABLE 42.—CONVERSION OF ARC AND TIME.

This table, which is divided into three parts, contains: First, angular measures of arc from 0° to 360°, with corresponding values expressed in time (hours and minutes); second, angular measures of arc from 0′00″ to 60′00″ with corresponding values expressed in time (minutes, seconds); third, angular measures of arc 0″ to 60″ with corresponding values expressed in decimals of a second of time.

The table will be especially convenient in dealing with longitude and hour angle when converting from time to arc or vice versa.

TABLE 43.—CONVERSION OF LOCAL CIVIL TIME TO GREENWICH CIVIL TIME.

This table is divided into two parts, the upper part is for places in west longitude and the lower for east longitude. The table is entered with local civil or watch time of place then under the column of longitude or time zone of observer is found the G. C. T. for the local date. If the G. C. T. is found where there are italic type in west longitude, then the Greenwich date is one day ahead of the local date, or the next day; if the G. C. T. is found in italic type in east longitude, then the Greenwich date is one day before the local date.

Example: Find the approximate G. C. T. and the date corresponding to a watch time of 11 p. m. on July 1, Long. 136° W.

Enter table with L. C. T. 23^h and under Long. 135°, the G. C. T. is 8^h, since it is found in italic type the date is one day ahead or July 2.

Example: Find the approximate L. C. T. or watch time of Washington, D. C., when it is 4 a. m. watch time July 4, Manila P. I.

Enter table of East Long. with L. C. T. 4^h and under 120° (−8 zone) is found, G. C. T. 20^h in italic type which is G. C. T. 20^h July 3. In the first table (west longitude) look under 75° (+5 zone) for Washington and for G. C. T. 20^h, then under L. C. T. is found 15^h, or 3 p. m. July 3. Whenever G. C. T. is found in italic type, the date for L. C. T. is changed from the date of the known G. C. T.; in other words, it is a reversal of the process.

541524°—43——27

TABLE 1.

Radio Bearing Conversion.

Correction to be applied to radio bearing to convert to mercator bearing.

Difference of longitude

Mid. lat.	1°	1.5°	2°	2.5°	3°	3.5°	4°	4.5°	5°	5.5°	6°	6.5°	7°	7.5°	8°	8.5°	Mid. lat.
°	°	°	°	°	°	°	°	°	°	°	°	°	°	°	°	°	°
4	----	----	----	0.1	0.1	0.1	0.1	0.2	0.2	0.2	0.2	0.2	0.2	0.3	0.3	0.3	4
5	0.1	0.1	0.1	.1	.1	.2	.2	.2	.2	.2	.3	.3	.3	.3	.4	.4	5
6	.1	.1	.1	.1	.2	.2	.2	.2	.3	.3	.3	.3	.4	.4	.4	.5	6
7	.1	.1	.1	.2	.2	.2	.3	.3	.3	.3	.4	.4	.4	.5	.5	.5	7
8	.1	.1	.1	.2	.2	.2	.3	.3	.4	.4	.4	.5	.5	.5	.6	.6	8
9	.1	.1	.1	.2	.2	.2	.3	.3	.4	.4	.5	.5	.6	.6	.6	.7	9
10	.1	.1	.1	.2	.2	.3	.4	.4	.4	.5	.5	.6	.6	.6	.7	.7	10
11	.1	.1	.2	.2	.3	.3	.4	.4	.5	.5	.6	.6	.7	.7	.8	.8	11
12	.1	.1	.2	.3	.3	.4	.4	.5	.5	.6	.6	.7	.7	.8	.8	.9	12
13	.1	.2	.2	.3	.3	.4	.4	.5	.6	.6	.7	.7	.8	.8	.9	1.0	13
14	.1	.2	.2	.3	.4	.4	.5	.6	.6	.7	.7	.8	.8	.9	1.0	1.0	14
15	.1	.2	.3	.3	.4	.4	.5	.6	.6	.7	.8	.8	.9	1.0	1.0	1.1	15
16	.1	.2	.3	.4	.4	.5	.6	.6	.7	.8	.8	.9	1.0	1.0	1.1	1.2	16
17	.2	.2	.3	.4	.4	.5	.6	.6	.7	.8	.9	1.0	1.0	1.1	1.2	1.2	17
18	.2	.2	.3	.4	.5	.5	.6	.7	.8	.8	.9	1.0	1.1	1.2	1.2	1.3	18
19	.2	.2	.3	.4	.5	.6	.6	.7	.8	.9	1.0	1.1	1.1	1.2	1.3	1.4	19
20	.2	.2	.3	.4	.5	.6	.7	.8	.8	.9	1.0	1.1	1.2	1.3	1.4	1.5	20
21	.2	.3	.4	.5	.5	.6	.7	.8	.9	1.0	1.1	1.2	1.2	1.4	1.4	1.5	21
22	.2	.3	.4	.5	.6	.6	.8	.8	.9	1.0	1.1	1.2	1.3	1.4	1.5	1.6	22
23	.2	.3	.4	.5	.6	.7	.8	.9	1.0	1.1	1.2	1.3	1.4	1.5	1.6	1.7	23
24	.2	.3	.4	.5	.6	.7	.8	.9	1.0	1.1	1.2	1.3	1.4	1.5	1.6	1.7	24
25	.2	.3	.4	.5	.6	.7	.8	1.0	1.1	1.2	1.3	1.4	1.5	1.6	1.7	1.8	25
26	.2	.3	.4	.6	.6	.8	.9	1.0	1.1	1.2	1.3	1.4	1.5	1.6	1.8	1.9	26
27	.2	.3	.4	.6	.7	.8	.9	1.0	1.1	1.2	1.4	1.5	1.6	1.7	1.8	1.9	27
28	.2	.4	.5	.6	.7	.8	.9	1.1	1.2	1.3	1.4	1.5	1.6	1.8	1.9	2.0	28
29	.2	.4	.5	.6	.7	.8	1.0	1.1	1.2	1.3	1.4	1.6	1.7	1.8	1.9	2.1	29
30	.2	.4	.5	.6	.8	.9	1.0	1.1	1.2	1.4	1.5	1.6	1.8	1.9	2.0	2.1	30
31	.2	.4	.5	.6	.8	.9	1.0	1.2	1.3	1.4	1.6	1.7	1.8	1.9	2.1	2.2	31
32	.3	.4	.5	.7	.8	.9	1.1	1.2	1.3	1.4	1.6	1.7	1.8	2.0	2.1	2.2	32
33	.3	.4	.6	.7	.8	1.0	1.1	1.2	1.4	1.5	1.6	1.8	1.9	2.1	2.2	2.3	33
34	.3	.4	.6	.7	.8	1.0	1.1	1.2	1.4	1.5	1.7	1.8	2.0	2.1	2.2	2.4	34
35	.3	.4	.6	.7	.9	1.0	1.2	1.3	1.4	1.6	1.7	1.9	2.0	2.2	2.3	2.4	35
36	.3	.4	.6	.7	.9	1.0	1.2	1.3	1.5	1.6	1.8	1.9	2.1	2.2	2.4	2.5	36
37	.3	.4	.6	.8	.9	1.1	1.2	1.4	1.5	1.6	1.8	2.0	2.1	2.2	2.4	2.6	37
38	.3	.5	.6	.8	.9	1.1	1.2	1.4	1.5	1.7	1.8	2.0	2.2	2.3	2.5	2.6	38
39	.3	.5	.6	.8	1.0	1.1	1.2	1.4	1.6	1.7	1.9	2.1	2.2	2.4	2.5	2.7	39
40	.3	.5	.6	.8	1.0	1.1	1.3	1.4	1.6	1.8	1.9	2.1	2.2	2.4	2.6	2.7	40
41	.3	.5	.6	.8	1.0	1.2	1.3	1.5	1.6	1.8	2.0	2.1	2.3	2.5	2.6	2.8	41
42	.3	.5	.7	.8	1.0	1.2	1.3	1.5	1.7	1.8	2.0	2.2	2.3	2.5	2.7	2.8	42
43	.3	.5	.7	.8	1.0	1.2	1.4	1.5	1.7	1.9	2.1	2.2	2.4	2.6	2.7	2.9	43
44	.4	.5	.7	.9	1.1	1.2	1.4	1.6	1.7	1.9	2.1	2.2	2.4	2.6	2.8	3.0	44
45	.4	.5	.7	.9	1.1	1.2	1.4	1.6	1.8	2.0	2.1	2.3	2.5	2.6	2.8	3.0	45
46	.4	.5	.7	.9	1.1	1.3	1.4	1.6	1.8	2.0	2.2	2.3	2.5	2.7	2.9	3.1	46
47	.4	.6	.7	.9	1.1	1.3	1.5	1.7	1.8	2.0	2.2	2.4	2.6	2.8	2.9	3.1	47
48	.4	.6	.8	.9	1.1	1.3	1.5	1.7	1.8	2.1	2.2	2.4	2.6	2.8	3.0	3.2	48
49	.4	.6	.8	1.0	1.1	1.3	1.5	1.7	1.9	2.1	2.3	2.5	2.6	2.8	3.0	3.2	49
50	.4	.6	.8	1.0	1.1	1.3	1.5	1.7	1.9	2.1	2.3	2.5	2.7	2.9	3.1	3.2	50
51	.4	.6	.8	1.0	1.2	1.4	1.6	1.8	2.0	2.1	2.3	2.5	2.7	2.9	3.1	3.3	51
52	.4	.6	.8	1.0	1.2	1.4	1.6	1.8	2.0	2.2	2.4	2.6	2.8	3.0	3.2	3.4	52
53	.4	.6	.8	1.0	1.2	1.4	1.6	1.8	2.0	2.2	2.4	2.6	2.8	3.0	3.2	3.4	53
54	.4	.6	.8	1.0	1.2	1.4	1.6	1.8	2.0	2.2	2.4	2.6	2.8	3.0	3.2	3.4	54
55	.4	.6	.8	1.0	1.2	1.4	1.6	1.8	2.1	2.2	2.4	2.7	2.9	3.1	3.3	3.5	55
56	.4	.6	.8	1.0	1.2	1.4	1.7	1.9	2.1	2.3	2.5	2.7	2.9	3.1	3.3	3.5	56
57	.4	.6	.8	1.1	1.2	1.5	1.7	1.9	2.1	2.3	2.5	2.7	2.9	3.2	3.4	3.6	57
58	.4	.6	.8	1.1	1.3	1.5	1.7	1.9	2.1	2.3	2.6	2.8	3.0	3.2	3.4	3.6	58
59	.4	.6	.8	1.1	1.3	1.5	1.7	1.9	2.2	2.4	2.6	2.8	3.0	3.2	3.4	3.6	59
60	.4	.6	.9	1.1	1.3	1.5	1.7	2.0	2.2	2.4	2.6	2.8	3.0	3.2	3.5	3.7	60

In north latitude when vessel is $\frac{\text{eastward}}{\text{westward}}$ of station, the correction is $\frac{+}{-}$. When shore station gives bearing. Should vessel take bearings on shore stations, the signs are reversed.

TABLE 1.

Radio Bearing Conversion.

Correction to be applied to radio bearing to convert to mercator bearing.

Difference of longitude

Mid. lat.	9°	9.5°	10°	10.5°	11°	11.5°	12°	12.5°	13°	13.5°	14°	14.5°	15°	15.5°	16°	16.5°	Mid. lat.
°	°	°	°	°	°	°	°	°	°	°	°	°	°	°	°	°	°
4	0.3	0.3	0.3	0.4	0.4	0.4	0.4	0.4	0.5	0.5	0.5	0.5	0.5	0.5	0.5	0.6	4
5	.4	.4	.4	.5	.5	.5	.5	.5	.6	.6	.6	.6	.7	.7	.7	.7	5
6	.5	.5	.5	.6	.6	.6	.6	.6	.7	.7	.7	.8	.8	.8	.8	.9	6
7	.6	.6	.6	.6	.7	.7	.7	.8	.8	.8	.9	.9	.9	1.0	1.0	1.0	7
8	.6	.7	.7	.7	.8	.8	.8	.9	.9	.9	1.0	1.0	1.1	1.1	1.1	1.2	8
9	.7	.8	.8	.8	.9	.9	.9	1.0	1.0	1.1	1.1	1.1	1.2	1.2	1.3	1.3	9
10	.8	.8	.9	.9	1.0	1.0	1.0	1.1	1.1	1.2	1.2	1.3	1.3	1.4	1.4	1.5	10
11	.8	.9	1.0	1.0	1.1	1.1	1.2	1.2	1.3	1.3	1.3	1.4	1.5	1.5	1.5	1.6	11
12	.9	1.0	1.0	1.1	1.2	1.2	1.3	1.3	1.4	1.4	1.5	1.5	1.6	1.6	1.7	1.7	12
13	1.0	1.1	1.1	1.2	1.3	1.3	1.4	1.4	1.5	1.5	1.6	1.6	1.7	1.8	1.8	1.9	13
14	1.1	1.2	1.2	1.3	1.4	1.4	1.5	1.5	1.6	1.6	1.7	1.8	1.8	1.9	2.0	2.0	14
15	1.2	1.2	1.3	1.4	1.5	1.5	1.6	1.6	1.7	1.8	1.8	1.9	1.9	2.0	2.1	2.2	15
16	1.2	1.3	1.4	1.5	1.5	1.6	1.7	1.7	1.8	1.9	1.9	2.0	2.1	2.2	2.2	2.3	16
17	1.3	1.4	1.5	1.6	1.6	1.7	1.8	1.8	1.9	2.0	2.1	2.1	2.2	2.3	2.4	2.4	17
18	1.4	1.5	1.6	1.6	1.7	1.8	1.9	1.9	2.0	2.1	2.2	2.3	2.3	2.4	2.5	2.6	18
19	1.5	1.6	1.6	1.7	1.8	1.9	2.0	2.1	2.1	2.2	2.3	2.4	2.5	2.5	2.6	2.7	19
20	1.5	1.6	1.7	1.8	1.9	2.0	2.1	2.2	2.2	2.3	2.4	2.5	2.6	2.7	2.8	2.8	20
21	1.6	1.7	1.8	1.9	2.0	2.1	2.2	2.3	2.3	2.4	2.5	2.6	2.7	2.8	2.9	3.0	21
22	1.7	1.8	1.9	2.0	2.1	2.2	2.3	2.4	2.5	2.5	2.6	2.7	2.8	2.9	3.0	3.1	22
23	1.8	1.8	2.0	2.1	2.2	2.3	2.4	2.5	2.5	2.6	2.7	2.8	3.0	3.1	3.2	3.3	23
24	1.8	1.9	2.0	2.2	2.3	2.4	2.4	2.6	2.7	2.8	2.8	3.0	3.1	3.2	3.3	3.4	24
25	1.9	2.0	2.1	2.2	2.4	2.5	2.5	2.7	2.8	2.9	3.0	3.1	3.2	3.3	3.4	3.5	25
26	2.0	2.1	2.2	2.3	2.4	2.6	2.6	2.8	2.9	3.0	3.1	3.2	3.3	3.4	3.5	3.6	26
27	2.1	2.2	2.3	2.4	2.5	2.6	2.7	2.8	3.0	3.1	3.2	3.3	3.4	3.5	3.7	3.8	27
28	2.1	2.2	2.4	2.5	2.6	2.7	2.9	2.9	3.1	3.2	3.3	3.4	3.5	3.7	3.8	3.9	28
29	2.2	2.3	2.4	2.6	2.7	2.8	2.9	3.0	3.2	3.3	3.5	3.6	3.7	3.8	3.9	4.0	29
30	2.2	2.4	2.5	2.7	2.8	2.9	3.0	3.1	3.3	3.4	3.5	3.6	3.8	3.9	4.0	4.1	30
31	2.3	2.5	2.6	2.7	2.9	3.0	3.1	3.2	3.4	3.5	3.6	3.8	3.9	4.0	4.1	4.3	31
32	2.4	2.5	2.6	2.8	3.0	3.1	3.2	3.3	3.5	3.6	3.7	3.8	4.0	4.1	4.3	4.4	32
33	2.4	2.6	2.7	2.9	3.0	3.2	3.3	3.4	3.6	3.7	3.8	3.9	4.1	4.2	4.4	4.5	33
34	2.5	2.6	2.8	3.0	3.1	3.3	3.4	3.5	3.6	3.8	3.9	4.1	4.2	4.4	4.5	4.6	34
35	2.6	2.7	2.9	3.1	3.2	3.3	3.4	3.6	3.7	3.9	4.0	4.2	4.3	4.5	4.6	4.8	35
36	2.6	2.8	2.9	3.1	3.3	3.4	3.5	3.7	3.8	4.0	4.1	4.3	4.4	4.6	4.7	4.9	36
37	2.7	2.9	3.0	3.2	3.4	3.5	3.6	3.8	3.9	4.1	4.2	4.4	4.5	4.7	4.8	5.0	37
38	2.8	2.9	3.1	3.3	3.4	3.6	3.7	3.8	4.0	4.2	4.3	4.5	4.6	4.8	4.9	5.1	38
39	2.8	3.0	3.2	3.3	3.5	3.7	3.8	4.0	4.1	4.3	4.4	4.6	4.7	4.9	5.1	5.2	39
40	2.9	3.1	3.2	3.4	3.6	3.8	3.9	4.0	4.2	4.4	4.5	4.7	4.8	5.0	5.2	5.3	40
41	3.0	3.1	3.3	3.5	3.6	3.8	3.9	4.1	4.3	4.5	4.6	4.8	4.9	5.1	5.3	5.4	41
42	3.0	3.2	3.4	3.6	3.7	3.9	4.0	4.2	4.4	4.5	4.7	4.9	5.0	5.2	5.4	5.5	42
43	3.1	3.2	3.4	3.6	3.8	4.0	4.1	4.3	4.5	4.6	4.8	5.0	5.1	5.3	5.5	5.7	43
44	3.1	3.3	3.5	3.7	3.9	4.0	4.2	4.3	4.5	4.7	4.9	5.1	5.2	5.4	5.6	5.8	44
45	3.2	3.4	3.5	3.7	3.9	4.1	4.3	4.4	4.6	4.8	5.0	5.2	5.3	5.5	5.7	5.9	45
46	3.2	3.4	3.6	3.8	4.0	4.2	4.3	4.5	4.7	4.9	5.1	5.2	5.4	5.6	5.8	6.0	46
47	3.3	3.5	3.7	3.9	4.1	4.2	4.4	4.6	4.8	4.9	5.1	5.3	5.5	5.7	5.9	6.1	47
48	3.4	3.5	3.7	3.9	4.1	4.3	4.5	4.7	4.8	5.0	5.2	5.4	5.6	5.8	6.0	6.2	48
49	3.4	3.6	3.8	4.0	4.2	4.4	4.5	4.7	4.9	5.2	5.3	5.5	5.7	5.9	6.1	6.3	49
50	3.4	3.6	3.8	4.1	4.2	4.5	4.6	4.8	5.0	5.2	5.4	5.6	5.8	5.9	6.1	6.3	50
51	3.5	3.7	3.9	4.1	4.3	4.5	4.7	4.9	5.1	5.3	5.5	5.7	5.8	6.0	6.2	6.4	51
52	3.6	3.8	4.0	4.2	4.4	4.6	4.7	4.9	5.1	5.3	5.5	5.7	5.9	6.1	6.3	6.5	52
53	3.6	3.8	4.0	4.2	4.4	4.6	4.8	5.0	5.2	5.4	5.6	5.8	6.0	6.2	6.4	6.6	53
54	3.6	3.8	4.1	4.3	4.5	4.7	4.9	5.1	5.3	5.5	5.7	5.9	6.1	6.3	6.5	6.7	54
55	3.7	3.9	4.1	4.4	4.6	4.8	4.9	5.1	5.3	5.5	5.7	6.0	6.2	6.4	6.6	6.8	55
56	3.7	3.9	4.2	4.4	4.6	4.8	5.0	5.2	5.4	5.6	5.8	6.0	6.2	6.4	6.6	6.8	56
57	3.8	4.0	4.2	4.5	4.7	4.9	5.0	5.3	5.5	5.7	5.9	6.1	6.3	6.5	6.7	6.9	57
58	3.8	4.0	4.2	4.5	4.7	4.9	5.1	5.3	5.5	5.7	5.9	6.2	6.4	6.6	6.8	7.0	58
59	3.8	4.1	4.3	4.6	4.8	5.0	5.2	5.4	5.6	5.8	6.0	6.3	6.4	6.7	6.9	7.1	59
60	3.9	4.1	4.3	4.6	4.8	5.0	5.2	5.4	5.6	5.8	6.1	6.3	6.5	6.7	6.9	7.2	60

In south latitude when the vessel is $\frac{\text{eastward}}{\text{westward}}$ of station the correction is $\frac{-}{+}$. When shore station gives bearing. Should vessel take bearing on shore station, the signs are reversed.

TABLE 2.

Conversion of Points to Degrees

	Points.	Angular measure. ° ′ ″
NORTH TO EAST.		
North:		
N¼E	¼	2 48 45
N½E	½	5 37 30
N¾E	¾	8 26 15
N. by E	1	11 15 00
N. by E¼E	1¼	14 03 45
N. by E½E	1½	16 52 30
N. by E¾E	1¾	19 41 15
NNE	2	22 30 00
NNE¼E	2¼	25 18 45
NNE½E	2½	28 07 30
NNE¾E	2¾	30 56 15
NE. by N	3	33 45 00
NE¾N	3¼	36 33 45
NE½N	3½	39 22 30
NE¼N	3¾	42 11 15
NE	4	45 00 00
NE¼E	4¼	47 48 45
NE½E	4½	50 37 30
NE¾E	4¾	53 26 15
NE. by E	5	56 15 00
NE. by E¼E	5¼	59 03 45
NE. by E½E	5½	61 52 30
NE. by E¾E	5¾	64 41 15
ENE	6	67 30 00
ENE¼E	6¼	70 18 45
ENE½E	6½	73 07 30
ENE¾E	6¾	75 56 15
E. by N	7	78 45 00
E¾N	7¼	81 33 45
E½N	7½	84 22 30
E¼N	7¾	87 11 15
SOUTH TO WEST.		
South	16	180 00 00
S¼W	16¼	182 48 45
S½W	16½	185 37 30
S¾W	16¾	188 26 15
S. by W	17	191 15 00
S. by W¼W	17¼	194 03 45
S. by W½W	17½	196 52 30
S. by W¾W	17¾	199 41 15
SSW	18	202 30 00
SSW¼W	18¼	205 18 45
SSW½W	18½	208 07 30
SSW¾W	18¾	210 56 15
SW. by S	19	213 45 00
SW¾S	19¼	216 33 45
SW½S	19½	219 22 30
SW¼S	19¾	222 11 15
SW	20	225 00 00
SW¼W	20¼	227 48 45
SW½W	20½	230 37 30
SW¾W	20¾	233 26 15
SW. by W	21	236 15 00
SW by W¼W	21¼	239 03 45
SW. by W½W	21½	241 52 30
SW. by W¾W	21¾	244 41 15
WSW	22	247 30 00
WSW¼W	22¼	250 18 45
WSW½W	22½	253 07 30
WSW¾W	22¾	255 56 15
W. by S	23	258 45 00
W¾S	23¼	261 33 45
W½S	23½	264 22 30
W¼S	23¾	267 11 15

	Points.	Angular measure. ° ′ ″
EAST TO SOUTH.		
East	8	90 00 00
E¼S	8¼	92 48 45
E½S	8½	95 37 30
E¾S	8¾	98 26 15
E. by S	9	101 15 00
ESE¾E	9¼	104 03 45
ESE½E	9½	106 52 30
ESE¼E	9¾	109 41 15
ESE	10	112 30 00
SE. by E¾E	10¼	115 18 45
SE. by E½E	10½	118 07 30
SE. by E¼E	10¾	120 56 15
SE. by E	11	123 45 00
SE¾E	11¼	126 33 45
SE½E	11½	129 22 30
SE¼E	11¾	132 11 15
SE	12	135 00 00
SE¼S	12¼	137 48 45
SE½S	12½	140 37 30
SE¾S	12¾	143 26 15
SE. by S	13	146 15 00
SSE¾E	13¼	149 03 45
SSE½E	13½	151 52 30
SSE¼E	13¾	154 41 15
SSE	14	157 30 00
S. by E¾E	14¼	160 18 45
S. by E½E	14½	163 07 30
S. by E¼E	14¾	165 56 15
S. by E	15	168 45 00
S¾E	15¼	171 33 45
S½E	15½	174 22 30
S¼E	15¾	177 11 15
WEST TO NORTH.		
West	24	270 00 00
W¼N	24¼	272 48 45
W½N	24½	275 37 30
W¾N	24¾	278 26 15
W. by N	25	281 15 00
WNW¾W	25¼	284 03 45
WNW½W	25½	286 52 30
WNW¼W	25¾	289 41 15
WNW	26	292 30 00
NW. by W¾W	26¼	295 18 45
NW. by W½W	26½	298 07 30
NW. by W¼W	26¾	300 56 15
NW. by W	27	303 45 00
NW¾W	27¼	306 33 45
NW½W	27½	309 22 30
NW¼W	27¾	312 11 15
NW	28	315 00 00
NW¼N	28¼	317 48 45
NW½N	28½	320 37 30
NW¾N	28¾	323 26 15
NW. by N	29	326 15 00
NNW¾W	29¼	329 03 45
NNW½W	29½	331 52 30
NNW¼W	29¾	334 41 15
NNW	30	337 30 00
N. by W¾W	30¼	340 18 45
N. by W½W	30½	343 07 30
N. by W¼W	30¾	345 56 15
N. by W	31	348 45 00
N¾W	31¼	351 33 45
N½W	31½	354 22 30
N¼W	31¾	357 11 15
North	32	360 00 00

TABLE 3.

Difference of Latitude and Departure for 1° (179°, 181°, 359°).

Dist.	Lat.	Dep.	Dist.	Lat.	Dep.	Dist.	Lat.	Dep.	Dist.	Lat.	Dep.	Dist.	Lat.	Dep.
1	1.0	0.0	61	61.0	1.1	121	121.0	2.1	181	181.0	3.2	241	241.0	4.2
2	2.0	0.0	62	62.0	1.1	22	122.0	2.1	82	182.0	3.2	42	242.0	4.2
3	3.0	0.1	63	63.0	1.1	23	123.0	2.1	83	183.0	3.2	43	243.0	4.2
4	4.0	0.1	64	64.0	1.1	24	124.0	2.2	84	184.0	3.2	44	244.0	4.3
5	5.0	0.1	65	65.0	1.1	25	125.0	2.2	85	185.0	3.2	45	245.0	4.3
6	6.0	0.1	66	66.0	1.2	26	126.0	2.2	86	186.0	3.2	46	246.0	4.3
7	7.0	0.1	67	67.0	1.2	27	127.0	2.2	87	187.0	3.3	47	247.0	4.3
8	8.0	0.1	68	68.0	1.2	28	128.0	2.2	88	188.0	3.3	48	248.0	4.3
9	9.0	0.2	69	69.0	1.2	29	129.0	2.3	89	189.0	3.3	49	249.0	4.3
10	10.0	0.2	70	70.0	1.2	30	130.0	2.3	90	190.0	3.3	50	250.0	4.4
11	11.0	0.2	71	71.0	1.2	131	131.0	2.3	191	191.0	3.3	251	251.0	4.4
12	12.0	0.2	72	72.0	1.3	32	132.0	2.3	92	192.0	3.4	52	252.0	4.4
13	13.0	0.2	73	73.0	1.3	33	133.0	2.3	93	193.0	3.4	53	253.0	4.4
14	14.0	0.2	74	74.0	1.3	34	134.0	2.3	94	194.0	3.4	54	254.0	4.4
15	15.0	0.3	75	75.0	1.3	35	135.0	2.4	95	195.0	3.4	55	255.0	4.5
16	16.0	0.3	76	76.0	1.3	36	136.0	2.4	96	196.0	3.4	56	256.0	4.5
17	17.0	0.3	77	77.0	1.3	37	137.0	2.4	97	197.0	3.4	57	257.0	4.5
18	18.0	0.3	78	78.0	1.4	38	138.0	2.4	98	198.0	3.5	58	258.0	4.5
19	19.0	0.3	79	79.0	1.4	39	139.0	2.4	99	199.0	3.5	59	259.0	4.5
20	20.0	0.3	80	80.0	1.4	40	140.0	2.4	200	200.0	3.5	60	260.0	4.5
21	21.0	0.4	81	81.0	1.4	141	141.0	2.5	201	201.0	3.5	261	261.0	4.6
22	22.0	0.4	82	82.0	1.4	42	142.0	2.5	02	202.0	3.5	62	262.0	4.6
23	23.0	0.4	83	83.0	1.4	43	143.0	2.5	03	203.0	3.5	63	263.0	4.6
24	24.0	0.4	84	84.0	1.5	44	144.0	2.5	04	204.0	3.6	64	264.0	4.6
25	25.0	0.4	85	85.0	1.5	45	145.0	2.5	05	205.0	3.6	65	265.0	4.6
26	26.0	0.5	86	86.0	1.5	46	146.0	2.5	06	206.0	3.6	66	266.0	4.6
27	27.0	0.5	87	87.0	1.5	47	147.0	2.6	07	207.0	3.6	67	267.0	4.7
28	28.0	0.5	88	88.0	1.5	48	148.0	2.6	08	208.0	3.6	68	268.0	4.7
29	29.0	0.5	89	89.0	1.6	49	149.0	2.6	09	209.0	3.6	69	269.0	4.7
30	30.0	0.5	90	90.0	1.6	50	150.0	2.6	10	210.0	3.7	70	270.0	4.7
31	31.0	0.5	91	91.0	1.6	151	151.0	2.6	211	211.0	3.7	271	271.0	4.7
32	32.0	0.6	92	92.0	1.6	52	152.0	2.7	12	212.0	3.7	72	272.0	4.7
33	33.0	0.6	93	93.0	1.6	53	153.0	2.7	13	213.0	3.7	73	273.0	4.8
34	34.0	0.6	94	94.0	1.6	54	154.0	2.7	14	214.0	3.7	74	274.0	4.8
35	35.0	0.6	95	95.0	1.7	55	155.0	2.7	15	215.0	3.8	75	275.0	4.8
36	36.0	0.6	96	96.0	1.7	56	156.0	2.7	16	216.0	3.8	76	276.0	4.8
37	37.0	0.6	97	97.0	1.7	57	157.0	2.7	17	217.0	3.8	77	277.0	4.8
38	38.0	0.7	98	98.0	1.7	58	158.0	2.8	18	218.0	3.8	78	278.0	4.9
39	39.0	0.7	99	99.0	1.7	59	159.0	2.8	19	219.0	3.8	79	279.0	4.9
40	40.0	0.7	100	100.0	1.7	60	160.0	2.8	20	220.0	3.8	80	280.0	4.9
41	41.0	0.7	101	101.0	1.8	161	161.0	2.8	221	221.0	3.9	281	281.0	4.9
42	42.0	0.7	02	102.0	1.8	62	162.0	2.8	22	222.0	3.9	82	282.0	4.9
43	43.0	0.8	03	103.0	1.8	63	163.0	2.8	23	223.0	3.9	83	283.0	4.9
44	44.0	0.8	04	104.0	1.8	64	164.0	2.9	24	224.0	3.9	84	284.0	5.0
45	45.0	0.8	05	105.0	1.8	65	165.0	2.9	25	225.0	3.9	85	285.0	5.0
46	46.0	0.8	06	106.0	1.8	66	166.0	2.9	26	226.0	3.9	86	286.0	5.0
47	47.0	0.8	07	107.0	1.9	67	167.0	2.9	27	227.0	4.0	87	287.0	5.0
48	48.0	0.8	08	108.0	1.9	68	168.0	2.9	28	228.0	4.0	88	288.0	5.0
49	49.0	0.9	09	109.0	1.9	69	169.0	2.9	29	229.0	4.0	89	289.0	5.0
50	50.0	0.9	10	110.0	1.9	70	170.0	3.0	30	230.0	4.0	90	290.0	5.1
51	51.0	0.9	111	111.0	1.9	171	171.0	3.0	231	231.0	4.0	291	291.0	5.1
52	52.0	0.9	12	112.0	2.0	72	172.0	3.0	32	232.0	4.0	92	292.0	5.1
53	53.0	0.9	13	113.0	2.0	73	173.0	3.0	33	233.0	4.1	93	293.0	5.1
54	54.0	0.9	14	114.0	2.0	74	174.0	3.0	34	234 0	4.1	94	294.0	5.1
55	55.0	1.0	15	115.0	2.0	75	175.0	3.1	35	235.0	4.1	95	295.0	5.1
56	56.0	1.0	16	116.0	2.0	76	176.0	3.1	36	236.0	4.1	96	296.0	5.2
57	57.0	1.0	17	117.0	2.0	77	177.0	3.1	37	237.0	4.1	97	297.0	5.2
58	58.0	1.0	18	118.0	2.1	78	178.0	3.1	38	238.0	4.2	98	298.0	5.2
59	59.0	1.0	19	119.0	2.1	79	179.0	3.1	39	239.0	4.2	99	299.0	5.2
60	60.0	1.0	20	120.0	2.1	80	180.0	3.1	40	240.0	4.2	300	300.0	5.2
Dist.	Dep.	Lat.	Dist.	Dep.	Lat.	Dist.	Dep.	Lat.	Dist.	Dep.	Lat.	Dist.	Dep.	Lat.

89° (91°, 269°, 271°).

In **Plane Sailing.**	**Dist.**	**Lat.**	**Dep.**
For converting *Dep.* into *Diff. Long.* and *Diff. Long.* into *Dep.* In **Middle Latitude Sailing.**	Diff. Long.	Dep.	
For converting *Dep.* into *Diff. Long.* and *Diff. Long.* into *Dep.* In **Mercator Sailing.**		*m*	Diff. Long.
For multiplication of numbers by sines and by cosines, or solution of plane right-angled triangles.	N.	N×Cos.	N×Sin.
	Hypotenuse.	Side Adj.	Side Opp.

TABLE 3.

Difference of Latitude and Departure for 1° (179°, 181°, 359°).

Dist.	Lat.	Dep.	Dist.	Lat.	Dep.	Dist.	Lat.	Dep.	Dist.	Lat.	Dep.	Dist.	Lat.	Dep.
301	301.0	5.3	361	360.9	6.3	421	420.9	7.3	481	480.9	8.4	541	540.9	9.4
02	302.0	5.3	62	361.9	6.3	22	421.9	7.4	82	481.9	8.4	42	541.9	9.5
03	303.0	5.3	63	362.9	6.3	23	422.9	7.4	83	482.9	8.4	43	542.9	9.5
04	304.0	5.3	64	363.9	6.4	24	423.9	7.4	84	483.9	8.4	44	543.9	9.5
05	305.0	5.3	65	364.9	6.4	25	424.9	7.4	85	484.9	8.5	45	544.9	9.5
06	306.0	5.3	66	365.9	6.4	26	425.9	7.4	86	485.9	8.5	46	545.9	9.5
07	307.0	5.4	67	366.9	6.4	27	426.9	7.5	87	486.9	8.5	47	546.9	9.5
08	308.0	5.4	68	367.9	6.4	28	427.9	7.5	88	487.9	8.5	48	547.9	9.6
09	309.0	5.4	69	368.9	6.4	29	428.9	7.5	89	488.9	8.5	49	548.9	9.6
10	310.0	5.4	70	369.9	6.5	30	429.9	7.5	90	489.9	8.6	50	549.9	9.6
311	311.0	5.4	371	370.9	6.5	431	430.9	7.5	491	490.9	8.6	551	550.9	9.6
12	312.0	5.4	72	371.9	6.5	32	431.9	7.5	92	491.9	8.6	52	551.9	9.6
13	313.0	5.5	73	372.9	6.5	33	432.9	7.6	93	492.9	8.6	53	552.9	9.7
14	314.0	5.5	74	373.9	6.5	34	433.9	7.6	94	493.9	8.6	54	553.9	9.7
15	315.0	5.5	75	374.9	6.5	35	434.9	7.6	95	494.9	8.6	55	554.9	9.7
16	316.0	5.5	76	375.9	6.6	36	435.9	7.6	96	495.9	8.7	56	555.9	9.7
17	317.0	5.5	77	376.9	6.6	37	436.9	7.6	97	496.9	8.7	57	556.9	9.7
18	318.0	5.5	78	377.9	6.6	38	437.9	7.6	98	497.9	8.7	58	557.9	9.7
19	319.0	5.6	79	378.9	6.6	39	438.9	7.7	99	498.9	8.7	59	558.9	9.8
20	320.0	5.6	80	379.9	6.6	40	439.9	7.7	500	499.9	8.7	60	559.9	9.8
321	321.0	5.6	381	380.9	6.6	441	440.9	7.7	501	500.9	8.7	561	560.9	9.8
22	322.0	5.6	82	381.9	6.7	42	441.9	7.7	02	501.9	8.8	62	561.9	9.8
23	323.0	5.6	83	382.9	6.7	43	442.9	7.7	03	502.9	8.8	63	562.9	9.8
24	324.0	5.7	84	383.9	6.7	44	443.9	7.7	04	503.9	8.8	64	563.9	9.8
25	325.0	5.7	85	384.9	6.7	45	444.9	7.8	05	504.9	8.8	65	564.9	9.9
26	326.0	5.7	86	385.9	6.7	46	445.9	7.8	06	505.9	8.8	66	565.9	9.9
27	327.0	5.7	87	386.9	6.8	47	446.9	7.8	07	506.9	8.9	67	566.9	9.9
28	328.0	5.7	88	387.9	6.8	48	447.9	7.8	08	507.9	8.9	68	567.9	9.9
29	328.9	5.7	89	388.9	6.8	49	448.9	7.8	09	508.9	8.9	69	568.9	9.9
30	329.9	5.8	90	389.9	6.8	50	449.9	7.9	10	509.9	8.9	70	569.9	9.9
331	330.9	5.8	391	390.9	6.8	451	450.9	7.9	511	510.9	8.9	571	570.9	10.0
32	331.9	5.8	92	391.9	6.8	52	451.9	7.9	12	511.9	9.0	72	571.9	10.0
33	332.9	5.8	93	392.9	6.9	53	452.9	7.9	13	512.9	9.0	73	572.9	10.0
34	333.9	5.8	94	393.9	6.9	54	453.9	7.9	14	513.9	9.0	74	573.9	10.0
35	334.9	5.8	95	394.9	6.9	55	454.9	7.9	15	514.9	9.0	75	574.9	10.0
36	335.9	5.9	96	395.9	6.9	56	455.9	8.0	16	515.9	9.0	76	575.9	10.1
37	336.9	5.9	97	396.9	6.9	57	456.9	8.0	17	516.9	9.0	77	576.9	10.1
38	337.9	5.9	98	397.9	6.9	58	457.9	8.0	18	517.9	9.0	78	577.9	10.1
39	338.9	5.9	99	398.9	7.0	59	458.9	8.0	19	518.9	9.1	79	578.9	10.1
40	339.9	5.9	400	399.9	7.0	60	459.9	8.0	20	519.9	9.1	80	579.9	10.1
341	340.9	6.0	401	400.9	7.0	461	460.9	8.0	521	520.9	9.1	581	580.9	10.1
42	341.9	6.0	02	401.9	7.0	62	461.9	8.1	22	521.9	9.1	82	581.9	10.2
43	342.9	6.0	03	402.9	7.0	63	462.9	8.1	23	522.9	9.1	83	582.9	10.2
44	343.9	6.0	04	403.9	7.1	64	463.9	8.1	24	523.9	9.1	84	583.9	10.2
45	344.9	6.0	05	404.9	7.1	65	464.9	8.1	25	524.9	9.2	85	584.9	10.2
46	345.9	6.0	06	405.9	7.1	66	465.9	8.1	26	525.9	9.2	86	585.9	10.2
47	346.9	6.1	07	406.9	7.1	67	466.9	8.2	27	526.9	9.2	87	586.9	10.2
48	347.9	6.1	08	407.9	7.1	68	467.9	8.2	28	527.9	9.2	88	587.9	10.3
49	348.9	6.1	09	408.9	7.1	69	468.9	8.2	29	528.9	9.2	89	588.9	10.3
50	349.9	6.1	10	409.9	7.2	70	469.9	8.2	30	529.9	9.2	90	589.9	10.3
351	350.9	6.1	411	410.9	7.2	471	470.9	8.2	531	530.9	9.3	591	590.9	10.3
52	351.9	6.1	12	411.9	7.2	72	471.9	8.2	32	531.9	9.3	92	591.9	10.3
53	352.9	6.2	13	412.9	7.2	73	472.9	8.3	33	532.9	9.3	93	592.9	10.3
54	353.9	6.2	14	413.9	7.2	74	473.9	8.3	34	533.9	9.3	94	593.9	10.4
55	354.9	6.2	15	414.9	7.2	75	474.9	8.3	35	534.9	9.3	95	594.9	10.4
56	355.9	6.2	16	415.9	7.3	76	475.9	8.3	36	535.9	9.4	96	595.9	10.4
57	356.9	6.2	17	416.9	7.3	77	476.9	8.3	37	536.9	9.4	97	596.9	10.4
58	357.9	6.2	18	417.9	7.3	78	477.9	8.3	38	537.9	9.4	98	597.9	10.4
59	358.9	6.3	19	418.9	7.3	79	478.9	8.4	39	538.9	9.4	99	598.9	10.5
60	359.9	6.3	20	419.9	7.3	80	479.9	8.4	40	539.9	9.4	600	599.9	10.5
Dist.	Dep.	Lat.	Dist.	Dep.	Lat.	Dist.	Dep.	Lat.	Dist.	Dep.	Lat.	Dist.	Dep.	Lat.

89° (91°, 269°, 271°).

In **Plane Sailing.**	**Dist.**	**Lat.**	**Dep.**
For converting *Dep.* into *Diff. Long.* and *Diff. Long.* into *Dep.* In **Middle Latitude Sailing.**	Diff. Long.	Dep.	
For converting *Dep.* into *Diff. Long.* and *Diff. Long.* into *Dep.* In **Mercator Sailing.**		*m*	Diff. Long.
	N.	N×Cos.	N×Sin.
For multiplication of numbers by sines and by cosines, or solution of plane right-angled triangles.	Hypotenuse.	Side Adj.	Side Opp.

TABLE 3.

Difference of Latitude and Departure for 2° (178°, 182°, 358°).

Dist.	Lat.	Dep.	Dist.	Lat.	Dep.	Dist.	Lat.	Dep.	Dist.	Lat.	Dep.	Dist.	Lat.	Dep.
1	1.0	0.0	61	61.0	2.1	121	120.9	4.2	181	180.9	6.3	241	240.9	8.4
2	2.0	0.1	62	62.0	2.2	22	121.9	4.3	82	181.9	6.4	42	241.9	8.4
3	3.0	0.1	63	63.0	2.2	23	122.9	4.3	83	182.9	6.4	43	242.9	8.5
4	4.0	0.1	64	64.0	2.2	24	123.9	4.3	84	183.9	6.4	44	243.9	8.5
5	5.0	0.2	65	65.0	2.3	25	124.9	4.4	85	184.9	6.5	45	244.9	8.6
6	6.0	0.2	66	66.0	2.3	26	125.9	4.4	86	185.9	6.5	46	245.9	8.6
7	7.0	0.2	67	67.0	2.3	27	126.9	4.4	87	186.9	6.5	47	246.8	8.6
8	8.0	0.3	68	68.0	2.4	28	127.9	4.5	88	187.9	6.6	48	247.8	8.7
9	9.0	0.3	69	69.0	2.4	29	128.9	4.5	89	188.9	6.6	49	248.8	8.7
10	10.0	0.3	70	70.0	2.4	30	129.9	4.5	90	189.9	6.6	50	249.8	8.7
11	11.0	0.4	71	71.0	2.5	131	130.9	4.6	191	190.9	6.7	251	250.8	8.8
12	12.0	0.4	72	72.0	2.5	32	131.9	4.6	92	191.9	6.7	52	251.8	8.8
13	13.0	0.5	73	73.0	2.5	33	132.9	4.6	93	192.9	6.7	53	252.8	8.8
14	14.0	0.5	74	74.0	2.6	34	133.9	4.7	94	193.9	6.8	54	253.8	8.9
15	15.0	0.5	75	75.0	2.6	35	134.9	4.7	95	194.9	6.8	55	254.8	8.9
16	16.0	0.6	76	76.0	2.7	36	135.9	4.7	96	195.9	6.8	56	255.8	8.9
17	17.0	0.6	77	77.0	2.7	37	136.9	4.8	97	196.9	6.9	57	256.8	9.0
18	18.0	0.6	78	78.0	2.7	38	137.9	4.8	98	197.9	6.9	58	257.8	9.0
19	19.0	0.7	79	79.0	2.8	39	138.9	4.9	99	198.9	6.9	59	258.8	9.0
20	20.0	0.7	80	80.0	2.8	40	139.9	4.9	200	199.9	7.0	60	259.8	9.1
21	21.0	0.7	81	81.0	2.8	141	140.9	4.9	201	200.9	7.0	261	260.8	9.1
22	22.0	0.8	82	82.0	2.9	42	141.9	5.0	02	201.9	7.0	62	261.8	9.1
23	23.0	0.8	83	82.9	2.9	43	142.9	5.0	03	202.9	7.1	63	262.8	9.2
24	24.0	0.8	84	83.9	2.9	44	143.9	5.0	04	203.9	7.1	64	263.8	9.2
25	25.0	0.9	85	84.9	3.0	45	144.9	5.1	05	204.9	7.2	65	264.8	9.2
26	26.0	0.9	86	85.9	3.0	46	145.9	5.1	06	205.9	7.2	66	265.8	9.3
27	27.0	0.9	87	86.9	3.0	47	146.9	5.1	07	206.9	7.2	67	266.8	9.3
28	28.0	1.0	88	87.9	3.1	48	117.9	5.2	08	207.9	7.3	68	267.8	9.4
29	29.0	1.0	89	88.9	3.1	49	148.9	5.2	09	208.9	7.3	69	268.8	9.4
30	30.0	1.0	90	89.9	3.1	50	149.9	5.2	10	209.9	7.3	70	269.8	9.4
31	31.0	1.1	91	90.9	3.2	151	150.9	5.3	211	210.9	7.4	271	270.8	9.5
32	32.0	1.1	92	91.9	3.2	52	151.9	5.3	12	211.9	7.4	72	271.8	9.5
33	33.0	1.2	93	92.9	3.2	53	152.9	5.3	13	212.9	7.4	73	272.8	9.5
34	34.0	1.2	94	93.9	3.3	54	153.9	5.4	14	213.9	7.5	74	273.8	9.6
35	35.0	1.2	95	94.9	3.3	55	154.9	5.4	15	214.9	7.5	75	274.8	9.6
36	36.0	1.3	96	95.9	3.4	56	155.9	5.4	16	215.9	7.5	76	275.8	9.6
37	37.0	1.3	97	96.9	3.4	57	156.9	5.5	17	216.9	7.6	77	276.8	9.7
38	38.0	1.3	98	97.9	3.4	58	157.9	5.5	18	217.9	7.6	78	277.8	9.7
39	39.0	1.4	99	98.9	3.5	59	158.9	5.5	19	218.9	7.6	79	278.8	9.7
40	40.0	1.4	100	99.9	3.5	60	159.9	5.6	20	219.9	7.7	80	279.8	9.8
41	41.0	1.4	101	100.9	3.5	161	160.9	5.6	221	220.9	7.7	281	280.8	9.8
42	42.0	1.5	02	101.9	3.6	62	161.9	5.7	22	221.9	7.7	82	281.8	9.8
43	43.0	1.5	03	102.9	3.6	63	162.9	5.7	23	222.9	7.8	83	282.8	9.9
44	44.0	1.5	04	103.9	3.6	64	163.9	5.7	24	223.9	7.8	84	283.8	9.9
45	45.0	1.6	05	104.9	3.7	65	164.9	5.8	25	224.9	7.9	85	284.8	9.9
46	46.0	1.6	06	105.9	3.7	66	165.9	5.8	26	225.9	7.9	86	285.8	10.0
47	47.0	1.6	07	106.9	3.7	67	166.9	5.8	27	226.9	7.9	87	286.8	10.0
48	48.0	1.7	08	107.9	3.8	68	167.9	5.9	28	227.9	8.0	88	287.8	10.1
49	49.0	1.7	09	108.9	3.8	69	168.9	5.9	29	228.9	8.0	89	288.8	10.1
50	50.0	1.7	10	109.9	3.8	70	169.9	5.9	30	229.9	8.0	90	289.8	10.1
51	51.0	1.8	111	110.9	3.9	171	170.9	6.0	231	230.9	8.1	291	290.8	10.2
52	52.0	1.8	12	111.9	3.9	72	171.9	6.0	32	231.9	8.1	92	291.8	10.2
53	53.0	1.8	13	112.9	3.9	73	172.9	6.0	33	232.9	8.1	93	292.8	10.2
54	54.0	1.9	14	113.9	4.0	74	173.9	6.1	34	233.9	8.2	94	293.8	10.3
55	55.0	1.9	15	114.9	4.0	75	174.9	6.1	35	234.9	8.2	95	294.8	10.3
56	56.0	2.0	16	115.9	4.0	76	175.9	6.1	36	235.9	8.2	96	295.8	10.3
57	57.0	2.0	17	116.9	4.1	77	176.9	6.2	37	236.9	8.3	97	296.8	10.4
58	58.0	2.0	18	117.9	4.1	78	177.9	6.2	38	237.9	8.3	98	297.8	10.4
59	59.0	2.1	19	118.9	4.2	79	178.9	6.2	39	238.9	8.3	99	298.8	10.4
60	60.0	2.1	20	119.9	4.2	80	179.9	6.3	40	239.9	8.4	300	299.8	10.5
Dist.	Dep.	Lat.	Dist.	Dep.	Lat.	Dist.	Dep.	Lat.	Dist.	Dep.	Lat.	Dist.	Dep.	Lat.

88° (92°, 268°, 272°).

In Plane Sailing.	Dist.	Lat.	Dep.
For converting *Dep.* into *Diff. Long.* and *Diff. Long.* into *Dep.* In **Middle Latitude Sailing.**	Diff. Long.	Dep.	
For converting *Dep.* into *Diff. Long.* and *Diff. Long.* into *Dep.* In **Mercator Sailing.**		*m*	Diff Long.
For multiplication of numbers by sines and by cosines, or solution of plane right-angled triangles.	N. / Hypotenuse.	N×Cos. / Side Adj.	N×Sin. / Side Opp.

TABLE 3.

Difference of Latitude and Departure for 2° (178°, 182°, 358°).

Dist.	Lat.	Dep.	Dist.	Lat.	Dep.	Dist.	Lat.	Dep.	Dist.	Lat.	Dep.	Dist.	Lat.	Dep.
301	300.8	10.5	361	360.8	12.6	421	420.7	14.7	481	480.7	16.8	541	540.7	18.9
02	301.8	10.5	62	361.8	12.6	22	421.7	14.7	82	481.7	16.8	42	541.7	18.9
03	302.8	10.6	63	362.8	12.7	23	422.7	14.7	83	482.7	16.8	43	542.7	19.0
04	303.8	10.6	64	363.8	12.7	24	423.7	14.8	84	483.7	16.9	44	543.7	19.0
05	304.8	10.6	65	364.8	12.7	25	424.7	14.8	85	484.7	16.9	45	544.7	19.0
06	305.8	10.7	66	365.8	12.8	26	425.7	14.9	86	485.7	16.9	46	545.7	19.1
07	306.8	10.7	67	366.8	12.8	27	426.7	14.9	87	486.7	17.0	47	546.7	19.1
08	307.8	10.7	68	367.8	12.8	28	427.7	14.9	88	487.7	17.0	48	547.7	19.1
09	308.8	10.8	69	368.8	12.9	29	428.7	15.0	89	488.7	17.0	49	548.7	19.2
10	309.8	10.8	70	369.8	12.9	30	429.7	15.0	90	489.7	17.1	50	549.7	19.2
311	310.8	10.8	371	370.8	12.9	431	430.7	15.0	491	490.7	17.1	551	550.7	19.2
12	311.8	10.9	72	371.8	13.0	32	431.7	15.1	92	491.7	17.1	52	551.7	19.3
13	312.8	10.9	73	372.8	13.0	33	432.7	15.1	93	492.7	17.2	53	552.7	19.3
14	313.8	10.9	74	373.8	13.0	34	433.7	15.1	94	493.7	17.2	54	553.7	19.3
15	314.8	11.0	75	374.8	13.1	35	434.7	15.2	95	494.7	17.2	55	554.7	19.4
16	315.8	11.0	76	375.8	13.1	36	435.7	15.2	96	495.7	17.3	56	555.7	19.4
17	316.8	11.0	77	376.8	13.1	37	436.7	15.2	97	496.7	17.3	57	556.7	19.4
18	317.8	11.1	78	377.8	13.2	38	437.7	15.3	98	497.7	17.3	58	557.7	19.5
19	318.8	11.1	79	378.8	13.2	39	438.7	15.3	99	498.7	17.4	59	558.7	19.5
20	319.8	11.2	80	379.8	13.2	40	439.7	15.3	500	499.7	17.4	60	559.7	19.5
321	320.8	11.2	381	380.8	13.3	441	440.7	15.4	501	500.7	17.5	561	560.7	19.6
22	321.8	11.2	82	381.8	13.3	42	441.7	15.4	02	501.7	17.5	62	561.7	19.6
23	322.8	11.3	83	382.8	13.3	43	442.7	15.4	03	502.7	17.5	63	562.7	19.6
24	323.8	11.3	84	383.8	13.4	44	443.7	15.5	04	503.7	17.6	64	563.7	19.7
25	324.8	11.3	85	384.8	13.4	45	444.7	15.5	05	504.7	17.6	65	564.7	19.7
26	325.8	11.4	86	385.8	13.5	46	445.7	15.6	06	505.7	17.6	66	565.7	19.8
27	326.8	11.4	87	386.8	13.5	47	446.7	15.6	07	506.7	17.7	67	566.7	19.8
28	327.8	11.4	88	387.8	13.5	48	447.7	15.6	08	507.7	17.7	68	567.7	19.8
29	328.8	11.5	89	388.8	13.6	49	448.7	15.7	09	508.7	17.7	69	568.7	19.9
30	329.8	11.5	90	389.8	13.6	50	449.7	15.7	10	509.7	17.8	70	569.7	19.9
331	330.8	11.5	391	390.8	13.6	451	450.7	15.7	511	510.7	17.9	571	570.7	19.9
32	331.8	11.6	92	391.8	13.7	52	451.7	15.8	12	511.7	17.9	72	571.7	20.0
33	332.8	11.6	93	392.8	13.7	53	452.7	15.8	13	512.7	17.9	73	572.7	20.0
34	333.8	11.6	94	393.8	13.7	54	453.7	15.8	14	513.7	17.9	74	573.7	20.0
35	334.8	11.7	95	394.8	13.8	55	454.7	15.9	15	514.7	18.0	75	574.6	20.1
36	335.8	11.7	96	395.8	13.8	56	455.7	15.9	16	515.7	18.0	76	575.6	20.1
37	336.8	11.7	97	396.8	13.8	57	456.7	15.9	17	516.7	18.0	77	576.6	20.1
38	337.8	11.8	98	397.8	13.9	58	457.7	16.0	18	517.7	18.1	78	577.6	20.2
39	338.8	11.8	99	398.8	13.9	59	458.7	16.0	19	518.7	18.1	79	578.6	20.2
40	339.8	11.9	400	399.8	13.9	60	459.7	16.0	20	519.7	18.1	80	579.6	20.2
341	340.8	11.9	401	400.8	14.0	461	460.7	16.1	521	520.7	18.2	581	580.6	20.3
42	341.8	11.9	02	401.8	14.0	62	461.7	16.1	22	521.7	18.2	82	581.6	20.3
43	342.8	12.0	03	402.8	14.0	63	462.7	16.1	23	522.7	18.3	83	582.6	20.3
44	343.8	12.0	04	403.8	14.1	64	463.7	16.2	24	523.7	18.3	84	583.6	20.4
45	344.8	12.0	05	404.8	14.1	65	464.7	16.2	25	524.7	18.3	85	584.6	20.4
46	345.8	12.1	06	405.8	14.2	66	465.7	16.2	26	525.7	18.4	86	585.6	20.5
47	346.8	12.1	07	406.8	14.2	67	466.7	16.3	27	526.7	18.4	87	586.6	20.5
48	347.8	12.1	08	407.8	14.2	68	467.7	16.3	28	527.7	18.4	88	587.6	20.5
49	348.8	12.2	09	408.8	14.3	69	468.7	16.4	29	528.7	18.5	89	588.6	20.6
50	349.8	12.2	10	409.8	14.3	70	469.7	16.4	30	529.7	18.5	90	589.6	20.6
351	350.8	12.2	411	410.7	14.3	471	470.7	16.4	531	530.7	18.5	591	590.6	20.6
52	351.8	12.3	12	411.7	14.4	72	471.7	16.5	32	531.7	18.6	92	591.6	20.7
53	352.8	12.3	13	412.7	14.4	73	472.7	16.5	33	532.7	18.6	93	592.6	20.7
54	353.8	12.3	14	413.7	14.4	74	473.7	16.5	34	533.7	18.6	94	593.6	20.7
55	354.8	12.4	15	414.7	14.5	75	474.7	16.6	35	534.7	18.7	95	594.6	20.8
56	355.8	12.4	16	415.7	14.5	76	475.7	16.6	36	535.7	18.7	96	595.6	20.8
57	356.8	12.4	17	416.7	14.5	77	476.7	16.6	37	536.7	18.7	97	596.6	20.8
58	357.8	12.5	18	417.7	14.6	78	477.7	16.7	38	537.7	18.8	98	597.6	20.9
59	358.8	12.5	19	418.7	14.6	79	478.7	16.7	39	538.7	18.8	99	598.6	20.9
60	359.8	12.5	20	419.7	14.6	80	479.7	16.7	40	539.7	18.8	600	599.6	20.9
Dist.	Dep.	Lat.	Dist.	Dep.	Lat.	Dist.	Dep.	Lat.	Dist.	Dep.	Lat.	Dist.	Dep.	Lat.

88° (92°, 268°, 272°).

In **Plane Sailing.**	**Dist.**	**Lat.**	**Dep.**
For converting *Dep.* into *Diff. Long.* and *Diff. Long.* into *Dep.* In **Middle Latitude Sailing.**	Diff. Long.	Dep.	
For converting *Dep.* into *Diff. Long.* and *Diff. Long.* into *Dep.* In **Mercator Sailing.**		*m*	Diff. Long.
For multiplication of numbers by sines and by cosines, or solution of plane right-angled triangles.	N. / Hypotenuse.	N×Cos. / Side Adj.	N×Sin. / Side Opp.

TABLE 3.

Difference of Latitude and Departure for 3° (177°, 183°, 357°).

Dist.	Lat.	Dep.	Dist.	Lat.	Dep.	Dist.	Lat.	Dep.	Dist.	Lat.	Dep.	Dist.	Lat.	Dep.
1	1.0	0.1	61	60.9	3.2	121	120.8	6.3	181	180.8	9.5	241	240.7	12.6
2	2.0	0.1	62	61.9	3.2	22	121.8	6.4	82	181.8	9.5	42	241.7	12.7
3	3.0	0.2	63	62.9	3.3	23	122.8	6.4	83	182.7	9.6	43	242.7	12.7
4	4.0	0.2	64	63.9	3.3	24	123.8	6.5	84	183.7	9.6	44	243.7	12.8
5	5.0	0.3	65	64.9	3.4	25	124.8	6.5	85	184.7	9.7	45	244.7	12.8
6	6.0	0.3	66	65.9	3.5	26	125.8	6.6	86	185.7	9.7	46	245.7	12.9
7	7.0	0.4	67	66.9	3.5	27	126.8	6.6	87	186.7	9.8	47	246.7	12.9
8	8.0	0.4	68	67.9	3.6	28	127.8	6.7	88	187.7	9.8	48	247.7	13.0
9	9.0	0.5	69	68.9	3.6	29	128.8	6.8	89	188.7	9.9	49	248.7	13.0
10	10.0	0.5	70	69.9	3.7	30	129.8	6.8	90	189.7	9.9	50	249.7	13.1
11	11.0	0.6	71	70.9	3.7	131	130.8	6.9	191	190.7	10.0	251	250.7	13.1
12	12.0	0.6	72	71.9	3.8	32	131.8	6.9	92	191.7	10.0	52	251.7	13.2
13	13.0	0.7	73	72.9	3.8	33	132.8	7.0	93	192.7	10.1	53	252.7	13.2
14	14.0	0.7	74	73.9	3.9	34	133.8	7.0	94	193.7	10.2	54	253.7	13.3
15	15.0	0.8	75	74.9	3.9	35	134.8	7.1	95	194.7	10.2	55	254.7	13.3
16	16.0	0.8	76	75.9	4.0	36	135.8	7.1	96	195.7	10.3	56	255.6	13.4
17	17.0	0.9	77	76.9	4.0	37	136.8	7.2	97	196.7	10.3	57	256.6	13.5
18	18.0	0.9	78	77.9	4.1	38	137.8	7.2	98	197.7	10.4	58	257.6	13.5
19	19.0	1.0	79	78.9	4.1	39	138.8	7.3	99	198.7	10.4	59	258.6	13.6
20	20.0	1.0	80	79.9	4.2	40	139.8	7.3	200	199.7	10.5	60	259.6	13.6
21	21.0	1.1	81	80.9	4.2	141	140.8	7.4	201	200.7	10.5	261	260.6	13.7
22	22.0	1.2	82	81.9	4.3	42	141.8	7.4	02	201.7	10.6	62	261.6	13.7
23	23.0	1.2	83	82.9	4.3	43	142.8	7.5	03	202.7	10.6	63	262.6	13.8
24	24.0	1.3	84	83.9	4.4	44	143.8	7.5	04	203.7	10.7	64	263.6	13.8
25	25.0	1.3	85	84.9	4.4	45	144.8	7.6	05	204.7	10.7	65	264.6	13.9
26	26.0	1.4	86	85.9	4.5	46	145.8	7.6	06	205.7	10.8	66	265.6	13.9
27	27.0	1.4	87	86.9	4.6	47	146.8	7.7	07	206.7	10.8	67	266.6	14.0
28	28.0	1.5	88	87.9	4.6	48	147.8	7.7	08	207.7	10.9	68	267.6	14.0
29	29.0	1.5	89	88.9	4.7	49	148.8	7.8	09	208.7	10.9	69	268.6	14.1
30	30.0	1.6	90	89.9	4.7	50	149.8	7.9	10	209.7	11.0	70	269.6	14.1
31	31.0	1.6	91	90.9	4.8	151	150.8	7.9	211	210.7	11.0	271	270.6	14.2
32	32.0	1.7	92	91.9	4.8	52	151.8	8.0	12	211.7	11.1	72	271.6	14.2
33	33.0	1.7	93	92.9	4.9	53	152.8	8.0	13	212.7	11.1	73	272.6	14.3
34	34.0	1.8	94	93.9	4.9	54	153.8	8.1	14	213.7	11.2	74	273.6	14.3
35	35.0	1.8	95	94.9	5.0	55	154.8	8.1	15	214.7	11.3	75	274.6	14.4
36	36.0	1.9	96	95.9	5.0	56	155.8	8.2	16	215.7	11.3	76	275.6	14.4
37	36.9	1.9	97	96.9	5.1	57	156.8	8.2	17	216.7	11.4	77	276.6	14.5
38	37.9	2.0	98	97.9	5.1	58	157.8	8.3	18	217.7	11.4	78	277.6	14.5
39	38.9	2.0	99	98.9	5.2	59	158.8	8.3	19	218.7	11.5	79	278.6	14.6
40	39.9	2.1	100	99.9	5.2	60	159.8	8.4	20	219.7	11.5	80	279.6	14.7
41	40.9	2.1	101	100.9	5.3	161	160.8	8.4	221	220.7	11.6	281	280.6	14.7
42	41.9	2.2	02	101.9	5.3	62	161.8	8.5	22	221.7	11.6	82	281.6	14.8
43	42.9	2.3	03	102.9	5.4	63	162.8	8.5	23	222.7	11.7	83	282.6	14.8
44	43.9	2.3	04	103.9	5.4	64	163.8	8.6	24	223.7	11.7	84	283.6	14.9
45	44.9	2.4	05	104.9	5.5	65	164.8	8.6	25	224.7	11.8	85	284.6	14.9
46	45.9	2.4	06	105.9	5.5	66	165.8	8.7	26	225.7	11.8	86	285.6	15.0
47	46.9	2.5	07	106.9	5.6	67	166.8	8.7	27	226.7	11.9	87	286.6	15.0
48	47.9	2.5	08	107.9	5.7	68	167.8	8.8	28	227.7	11.9	88	287.6	15.1
49	48.9	2.6	09	108.9	5.7	69	168.8	8.8	29	228.7	12.0	89	288.6	15.1
50	49.9	2.6	10	109.8	5.8	70	169.8	8.9	30	229.7	12.0	90	289.6	15.2
51	50.9	2.7	111	110.8	5.8	171	170.8	8.9	231	230.7	12.1	291	290.6	15.2
52	51.9	2.7	12	111.8	5.9	72	171.8	9.0	32	231.7	12.1	92	291.6	15.3
53	52.9	2.8	13	112.8	5.9	73	172.8	9.1	33	232.7	12.2	93	292.6	15.3
54	53.9	2.8	14	113.8	6.0	74	173.8	9.1	34	233.7	12.2	94	293.6	15.4
55	54.9	2.9	15	114.8	6.0	75	174.8	9.2	35	234.7	12.3	95	294.6	15.4
56	55.9	2.9	16	115.8	6.1	76	175.8	9.2	36	235.7	12.4	96	295.6	15.5
57	56.9	3.0	17	116.8	6.1	77	176.8	9.3	37	236.7	12.4	97	296.6	15.5
58	57.9	3.0	18	117.8	6.2	78	177.8	9.3	38	237.7	12.5	98	297.6	15.6
59	58.9	3.1	19	118.8	6.2	79	178.8	9.4	39	238.7	12.5	99	298.6	15.6
60	59.9	3.1	20	119.8	6.3	80	179.8	9.4	40	239.7	12.6	300	299.6	15.7
Dist.	Dep.	Lat.	Dist.	Dep.	Lat.	Dist.	Dep.	Lat.	Dist.	Dep.	Lat.	Dist.	Dep.	Lat.

87° (93°, 267°, 273°).

In Plane Sailing.	Dist.	Lat.	Dep.
For converting *Dep.* into *Diff. Long.* and *Diff. Long.* into *Dep.* In **Middle Latitude Sailing.**	Diff. Long.	Dep.	
For converting *Dep.* into *Diff. Long.* and *Diff. Long.* into *Dep.* In **Mercator Sailing.**		*m*	Diff. Long.
For multiplication of numbers by sines and by cosines, or solution of plane right-angled triangles.	N. / Hypotenuse.	N×Cos. / Side. Adj.	N×Sin. / Side Opp.

TABLE 3.

Difference of Latitude and Departure for 3° (177°, 183°, 357°).

Dist.	Lat.	Dep.	Dist.	Lat.	Dep.	Dist.	Lat.	Dep.	Dist.	Lat.	Dep.	Dist.	Lat.	Dep.
301	300.6	15.7	361	360.5	18.9	421	420.4	22.0	481	480.3	25.2	541	540.3	28.3
02	301.6	15.8	62	361.5	18.9	22	421.4	22.1	82	481.3	25.2	42	541.3	28.4
03	302.6	15.9	63	362.5	19.0	23	422.4	22.1	83	482.3	25.3	43	542.3	28.4
04	303.6	15.9	64	363.5	19.1	24	423.4	22.2	84	483.3	25.3	44	543.3	28.5
05	304.6	16.0	65	364.5	19.1	25	424.4	22.2	85	484.3	25.4	45	544.3	28.5
06	305.6	16.0	66	365.5	19.2	26	425.4	22.3	86	485.3	25.4	46	545.3	28.6
07	306.6	16.1	67	366.5	19.2	27	426.4	22.3	87	486.3	25.5	47	546.3	28.6
08	307.6	16.1	68	367.5	19.3	28	427.4	22.4	88	487.3	25.5	48	547.2	28.7
09	308.6	16.2	69	368.5	19.3	29	428.4	22.5	89	488.3	25.6	49	548.2	28.7
10	309.6	16.2	70	369.5	19.4	30	429.4	22.5	90	489.3	25.6	50	549.2	28.8
311	310.6	16.3	371	370.5	19.4	431	430.4	22.6	491	490.3	25.7	551	550.2	28.8
12	311.6	16.3	72	371.5	19.5	32	431.4	22.6	92	491.3	25.7	52	551.2	28.9
13	312.6	16.4	73	372.5	19.5	33	432.4	22.7	93	492.3	25.8	53	552.2	28.9
14	313.6	16.4	74	373.5	19.6	34	433.4	22.7	94	493.3	25.9	54	553.2	29.0
15	314.6	16.5	75	374.5	19.6	35	434.4	22.8	95	494.3	25.9	55	554.2	29.0
16	315.6	16.5	76	375.5	19.7	36	435.4	22.8	96	495.3	26.0	56	555.2	29.1
17	316.6	16.6	77	376.5	19.7	37	436.4	22.9	97	496.3	26.0	57	556.2	29.2
18	317.6	16.6	78	377.5	19.8	38	437.4	22.9	98	497.3	26.1	58	557.2	29.2
19	318.6	16.7	79	378.5	19.8	39	438.4	23.0	99	498.3	26.1	59	558.2	29.3
20	319.6	16.7	80	379.5	19.9	40	439.4	23.0	500	499.3	26.2	60	559.2	29.3
321	320.6	16.8	381	380.5	19.9	441	440.4	23.1	501	500.3	26.2	561	560.2	29.4
22	321.6	16.9	82	381.5	20.0	42	441.4	23.1	02	501.3	26.3	62	561.2	29.4
23	322.6	16.9	83	382.5	20.0	43	442.4	23.2	03	502.3	26.3	63	562.2	29.5
24	323.6	17.0	84	383.5	20.1	44	443.4	23.2	04	503.3	26.4	64	563.2	29.5
25	324.6	17.0	85	384.5	20.1	45	444.4	23.3	05	504.3	26.4	65	564.2	29.6
26	325.6	17.1	86	385.5	20.2	46	445.4	23.3	06	505.3	26.5	66	565.2	29.6
27	326.6	17.1	87	386.5	20.3	47	446.4	23.4	07	506.3	26.5	67	566.2	29.7
28	327.6	17.2	88	387.5	20.3	48	447.4	23.4	08	507.3	26.6	68	567.2	29.7
29	328.5	17.2	89	388.5	20.4	49	448.4	23.5	09	508.3	26.6	69	568.2	29.8
30	329.5	17.3	90	389.5	20.4	50	449.4	23.6	10	509.3	26.7	70	569.2	29.8
331	330.5	17.3	391	390.5	20.5	451	450.4	23.6	511	510.3	26.7	571	570.2	29.9
32	331.5	17.4	92	391.5	20.5	52	451.4	23.7	12	511.3	26.8	72	571.2	29.9
33	332.5	17.4	93	392.5	20.6	53	452.4	23.7	13	512.3	26.8	73	572.2	30.0
34	333.5	17.5	94	393.5	20.6	54	453.4	23.8	14	513.3	26.9	74	573.2	30.0
35	334.5	17.5	95	394.5	20.7	55	454.4	23.8	15	514.3	27.0	75	574.2	30.1
36	335.5	17.6	96	395.5	20.7	56	455.4	23.9	16	515.3	27.0	76	575.2	30.1
37	336.5	17.6	97	396.5	20.8	57	456.4	23.9	17	516.3	27.1	77	576.2	30.2
38	337.5	17.7	98	397.5	20.8	58	457.4	24.0	18	517.3	27.1	78	577.2	30.3
39	338.5	17.7	99	398.5	20.9	59	458.4	24.0	19	518.3	27.2	79	578.2	30.3
40	339.5	17.8	400	399.5	20.9	60	459.4	24.1	20	519.3	27.2	80	579.2	30.4
341	340.5	17.8	401	400.5	21.0	461	460.4	24.1	521	520.3	27.3	581	580.2	30.4
42	341.5	17.9	02	401.4	21.0	62	461.4	24.2	22	521.3	27.3	82	581.2	30.5
43	342.5	18.0	03	402.4	21.1	63	462.4	24.2	23	522.3	27.4	83	582.2	30.5
44	343.5	18.0	04	403.4	21.1	64	463.4	24.3	24	523.3	27.4	84	583.2	30.6
45	344.5	18.1	05	404.4	21.2	65	464.4	24.3	25	524.3	27.5	85	584.2	30.6
46	345.5	18.1	06	405.4	21.2	66	465.4	24.4	26	525.3	27.5	86	585.2	30.7
47	346.5	18.2	07	406.4	21.3	67	466.4	24.4	27	526.3	27.6	87	586.2	30.7
48	347.5	18.2	08	407.4	21.4	68	467.4	24.5	28	527.3	27.6	88	587.2	30.8
49	348.5	18.3	09	408.4	21.4	69	468.4	24.5	29	528.3	27.7	89	588.2	30.8
50	349.5	18.3	10	409.4	21.5	70	469.4	24.6	30	529.3	27.7	90	589.2	30.9
351	350.5	18.4	411	410.4	21.5	471	470.4	24.7	531	530.3	27.8	591	590.2	30.9
52	351.5	18.4	12	411.4	21.6	72	471.4	24.7	32	531.3	27.8	92	591.2	31.0
53	352.5	18.5	13	412.4	21.6	73	472.4	24.8	33	532.3	27.9	93	592.2	31.0
54	353.5	18.5	14	413.4	21.7	74	473.4	24.8	34	533.3	27.9	94	593.2	31.1
55	354.5	18.6	15	414.4	21.7	75	474.3	24.9	35	534.3	28.0	95	594.2	31.1
56	355.5	18.6	16	415.4	21.8	76	475.3	24.9	36	535.3	28.1	96	595.2	31.2
57	356.5	18.7	17	416.4	21.8	77	476.3	25.0	37	536.3	28.1	97	596.2	31.2
58	357.5	18.7	18	417.4	21.9	78	477.3	25.0	38	537.3	28.2	98	597.2	31.3
59	358.5	18.8	19	418.4	21.9	79	478.3	25.1	39	538.3	28.2	99	598.2	31.3
60	359.5	18.8	20	419.4	22.0	80	479.3	25.1	40	539.3	28.3	600	599.2	31.4
Dist.	Dep.	Lat.	Dist.	Dep.	Lat.	Dist.	Dep.	Lat.	Dist.	Dep.	Lat.	Dist.	Dep.	Lat.

87° (93°, 267°, 273°).

In Plane Sailing.	Dist.	Lat.	Dep.
For converting *Dep.* into *Diff. Long.* and *Diff. Long.* into *Dep.* In **Middle Latitude Sailing.**	Diff. Long.	Dep.	
For converting *Dep.* into *Diff. Long.* and *Diff. Long.* into *Dep.* In **Mercator Sailing.**		*m*	Diff. Long.
For multiplication of numbers by sines and by cosines, or solution of plane right-angled triangles.	N. Hypotenuse.	N×Cos. Side Adj.	N×Sin. Side Opp.

TABLE 3.

Difference of Latitude and Departure for 4° (176°, 184°, 356°).

Dist.	Lat.	Dep.	Dist.	Lat.	Dep.	Dist.	Lat.	Dep.	Dist.	Lat.	Dep.	Dist.	Lat.	Dep.
1	1.0	0.1	61	60.9	4.3	121	120.7	8.4	181	180.6	12.6	241	240.4	16.8
2	2.0	0.1	62	61.8	4.3	22	121.7	8.5	82	181.6	12.7	42	241.4	16.9
3	3.0	0.2	63	62.8	4.4	23	122.7	8.6	83	182.6	12.8	43	242.4	17.0
4	4.0	0.3	64	63.8	4.5	24	123.7	8.6	84	183.6	12.8	44	243.4	17.0
5	5.0	0.3	65	64.8	4.5	25	124.7	8.7	85	184.5	12.9	45	244.4	17.1
6	6.0	0.4	66	65.8	4.6	26	125.7	8.8	86	185.5	13.0	46	245.4	17.2
7	7.0	0.5	67	66.8	4.7	27	126.7	8.9	87	186.5	13.0	47	246.4	17.2
8	8.0	0.6	68	67.8	4.7	28	127.7	8.9	88	187.5	13.1	48	247.4	17.3
9	9.0	0.6	69	68.8	4.8	29	128.7	9.0	89	188.5	13.2	49	248.4	17.4
10	10.0	0.7	70	69.8	4.9	30	129.7	9.1	90	189.5	13.3	50	249.4	17.4
11	11.0	0.8	71	70.8	5.0	131	130.7	9.1	191	190.5	13.3	251	250.4	17.5
12	12.0	0.8	72	71.8	5.0	32	131.7	9.2	92	191.5	13.4	52	251.4	17.6
13	13.0	0.9	73	72.8	5.1	33	132.7	9.3	93	192.5	13.5	53	252.4	17.6
14	14.0	1.0	74	73.8	5.2	34	133.7	9.3	94	193.5	13.5	54	253.4	17.7
15	15.0	1.0	75	74.8	5.2	35	134.7	9.4	95	194.5	13.6	55	254.4	17.8
16	16.0	1.1	76	75.8	5.3	36	135.7	9.5	96	195.5	13.7	56	255.4	17.9
17	17.0	1.2	77	76.8	5.4	37	136.7	9.6	97	196.5	13.7	57	256.4	17.9
18	18.0	1.3	78	77.8	5.4	38	137.7	9.6	98	197 5	13.8	58	257.4	18.0
19	19.0	1.3	79	78.8	5.5	39	138.7	9.7	99	198.5	13.9	59	258.4	18.1
20	20.0	1.4	80	79.8	5.6	40	139.7	9.8	200	199.5	14.0	60	259.4	18.1
21	20.9	1.5	81	80.8	5.7	141	140.7	9.8	201	200.5	14.0	261	260.4	18.2
22	21.9	1.5	82	81.8	5.7	42	141.7	9.9	02	201.5	14.1	62	261.4	18.3
23	22.9	1.6	83	82.8	5.8	43	142.7	10.0	03	202.5	14.2	63	262.4	18.3
24	23.9	1.7	84	83.8	5.9	44	143.6	10.0	04	203.5	14.2	64	263.4	18.4
25	24.9	1.7	85	84.8	5.9	45	144.6	10.1	05	204.5	14.3	65	264.4	18.5
26	25.9	1.8	86	85.3	6.0	46	145.6	10.2	06	205.5	14.4	66	265.4	18.6
27	26.9	1.9	87	86.8	6.1	47	146.6	10.3	07	206.5	14.4	67	266.3	18.6
28	27.9	2.0	88	87.8	6.1	48	147.6	10.3	08	207.5	14.5	68	267.3	18.7
29	28.9	2.0	89	88.8	6.2	49	148.6	10.4	09	208.5	14.6	69	268.3	18.8
30	29.9	2.1	90	89.8	6.3	50	149.6	10.5	10	209.5	14.6	70	269.3	18.8
31	30.9	2.2	91	90.8	6.3	151	150.6	10.5	211	210.5	14.7	271	270.3	18.9
32	31.9	2.2	92	91.8	6.4	52	151.6	10.6	12	211.5	14.8	72	271.3	19.0
33	32.9	2.3	93	92.8	6.5	53	152.6	10.7	13	212.5	14.9	73	272.3	19.0
34	33.9	2.4	94	93.8	6.6	54	153.6	10.7	14	213.5	14.9	74	273.3	19.1
35	34.9	2.4	95	94.8	6.6	55	154.6	10.8	15	214.5	15.0	75	274.3	19.2
36	35.9	2.5	96	95.8	6.7	56	155.6	10.9	16	215.5	15.1	76	275.3	19.3
37	36.9	2.6	97	96.8	6.8	57	156.6	11.0	17	216.5	15.1	77	276.3	19.3
38	37.9	2.7	98	97.8	6.8	58	157.6	11.0	18	217.5	15.2	78	277.3	19.4
39	38.9	2.7	99	98.8	6.9	59	158.6	11.1	19	218.5	15.3	79	278.3	19.5
40	39.9	2.8	100	99.8	7.0	60	159.6	11.2	20	219.5	15.3	80	279.3	19.5
41	40.9	2.9	101	100.8	7.0	161	160.6	11.2	221	220.5	15.4	281	280.3	19.6
42	41.9	2.9	02	101.8	7.1	62	161.6	11.3	22	221.5	15.5	82	281.3	19.7
43	42.9	3.0	03	102.7	7.2	63	162.6	11.4	23	222.5	15.6	83	282.3	19.7
44	43.9	3.1	04	103.7	7.3	64	163.6	11.4	24	223.5	15.6	84	283.3	19.8
45	44.9	3.1	05	104.7	7.3	65	164.6	11.5	25	224.5	15.7	85	284.3	19.9
46	45.9	3.2	06	105.7	7.4	66	165.6	11.6	26	225.4	15.8	86	285.3	20.0
47	46.9	3.3	07	106.7	7.5	67	166.6	11.6	27	226.4	15.8	87	286.3	20.0
48	47.9	3.3	08	107.7	7.5	68	167.6	11.7	28	227.4	15.9	88	287.3	20.1
49	48.9	3.4	09	108.7	7.6	69	168.6	11.8	29	228.4	16.0	89	288.3	20.2
50	49.9	3.5	10	109.7	7.7	70	169.6	11.9	30	229.4	16.0	90	289.3	20.2
51	50.9	3.6	111	110.7	7.7	171	170.6	11.9	231	230.4	16.1	291	290.3	20.3
52	51.9	3.6	12	111.7	7.8	72	171.6	12.0	32	231.4	16.2	92	291.3	20.4
53	52.9	3.7	13	112.7	7.9	73	172.6	12.1	33	232.4	16.3	93	292.3	20.4
54	53.9	3.8	14	113.7	8.0	74	173.6	12.1	34	233.4	16.3	94	293.3	20.5
55	54.9	3.8	15	114.7	8.0	75	174.6	12.2	35	234.4	16.4	95	294.3	20.6
56	55.9	3.9	16	115.7	8.1	76	175.6	12.3	36	235.4	16.5	96	295.3	20.6
57	56.9	4.0	17	116.7	8.2	77	176.6	12.3	37	236.4	16.5	97	296.3	20.7
58	57.9	4.0	18	117.7	8.2	78	177.6	12.4	38	237.4	16.6	98	297.3	20.8
59	58.9	4.1	19	118.7	8.3	79	178.6	12.5	39	238.4	16.7	99	298.3	20.9
60	59.9	4.2	20	119.7	8.4	80	179.6	12.6	40	239.4	16.7	300	299.3	20.9
Dist.	Dep.	Lat.	Dist.	Dep.	Lat.	Dist.	Dep.	Lat.	Dist.	Dep.	Lat.	Dist.	Dep.	Lat.

86°; (94°, 266°, 274°).

In Plane Sailing.	**Dist.**	**Lat.**	**Dep.**
For converting *Dep.* into *Diff. Long.* and *Diff. Long.* into *Dep.* **In Middle Latitude Sailing.**	Diff. Long.	Dep.	
For converting *Dep.* into *Diff. Lonj.* and *Diff. Long.* into *Dep.* **In Mercator Sailing.**		*m*	Diff Long.
For multiplication of numbers by sines and by cosines, or solution of plane right-angled triangles.	N. Hypotenuse.	N×Cos. Side Adj.	N×Sin. Side Opp.

TABLE 3.

Difference of Latitude and Departure for 4° (176°, 184°, 356°).

Dist.	Lat.	Dep.	Dist.	Lat.	Dep.	Dist.	Lat.	Dep.	Dist.	Lat.	Dep.	Dist.	Lat.	Dep.
301	300.3	21.0	361	360.1	25.2	421	420.0	29.4	481	479.8	33.6	541	539.7	37.7
02	301.3	21.1	62	361.1	25.2	22	421.0	29.4	82	480.8	33.6	42	540.7	37.8
03	302.3	21.1	63	362.1	25.3	23	422.0	29.5	83	481.8	33.7	43	541.7	37.9
04	303.3	21.2	64	363.1	25.4	24	423.0	29.6	84	482.8	33.8	44	542.7	37.9
05	304.3	21.3	65	364.1	25.5	25	424.0	29.6	85	483.8	33.8	45	543.7	38.0
06	305.3	21.3	66	365.1	25.5	26	425.0	29.7	86	484.8	33.9	46	544.7	38.1
07	306.3	21.4	67	366.1	25.6	27	426.0	29.8	87	485.8	34.0	47	545.7	38.2
08	307.2	21.5	68	367.1	25.7	28	427.0	29.9	88	486.8	34.0	48	546.7	38.2
09	308.2	21.6	69	368.1	25.7	29	428.0	29.9	89	487.8	34.1	49	547.7	38.3
10	309.2	21.6	70	369.1	25.8	30	429.0	30.0	90	488.8	34.2	50	548.7	38.4
311	310.2	21.7	371	370.1	25.9	431	430.0	30.1	491	489.8	34.3	551	549.7	38.4
12	311.2	21.8	72	371.1	25.9	32	430.9	30.1	92	490.8	34.3	52	550.7	38.5
13	312.2	21.8	73	372.1	26.0	33	431.9	30.2	93	491.8	34.4	53	551.7	38.6
14	313.2	21.9	74	373.1	26.1	34	432.9	30.3	94	492.8	34.5	54	552.7	38.6
15	314.2	22.0	75	374.1	26.2	35	433.9	30.3	95	493.8	34.5	55	553.6	38.7
16	315.2	22.1	76	375.1	26.2	36	434.9	30.4	96	494.8	34.6	56	554.6	38.8
17	316.2	22.1	77	376.1	26.3	37	435.9	30.5	97	495.8	34.7	57	555.6	38.9
18	317.2	22.2	78	377.1	26.4	38	436.9	30.6	98	496.8	34.7	58	556.6	38.9
19	318.2	22.3	79	378.1	26.4	39	437.9	30.6	99	497.8	34.8	59	557.6	39.0
20	319.2	22.3	80	379.1	26.5	40	438.9	30.7	500	498.8	34.9	60	558.6	39.1
321	320.2	22.4	381	380.1	26.6	441	439.9	30.8	501	499.8	34.9	561	559.6	39.1
22	321.2	22.5	82	381.1	26.6	42	440.9	30.8	02	500.8	35.0	62	560.6	39.2
23	322.2	22.5	83	382.1	26.7	43	441.9	30.9	03	501.8	35.1	63	561.6	39.3
24	323.2	22.6	84	383.1	26.8	44	442.9	31.0	04	502.8	35.2	64	562.6	39.3
25	324.2	22.7	85	384.1	26.9	45	443.9	31.0	05	503.8	35.2	65	563.6	39.4
26	325.2	22.7	86	385.1	26.9	46	444.9	31.1	06	504.8	35.3	66	564.6	39.5
27	326.2	22.8	87	386.1	27.0	47	445.9	31.2	07	505.8	35.4	67	565.6	39.6
28	327.2	22.9	88	387.1	27.1	48	446.9	31.3	08	506.8	35.4	68	566.6	39.6
29	328.2	22.9	89	388.1	27.1	49	447.9	31.3	09	507.8	35.5	69	567.6	39.7
30	329.2	23.0	90	389.0	27.2	50	448.9	31.4	10	508.8	35.6	70	568.6	39.8
331	330.2	23.1	391	390.0	27.3	451	449.9	31.5	511	509.8	35.6	571	569.6	39.8
32	331.2	23.2	92	391.0	27.3	52	450.9	31.5	12	510.8	35.7	72	570.6	39.9
33	332.2	23.2	93	392.0	27.4	53	451.9	31.6	13	511.8	35.8	73	571.6	40.0
34	333.2	23.3	94	393.0	27.5	54	452.9	31.7	14	512.7	35.9	74	572.6	40.0
35	334.2	23.4	95	394.0	27.6	55	453.9	31.7	15	513.7	35.9	75	573.6	40.1
36	335.2	23.4	96	395.0	27.6	56	454.9	31.8	16	514.7	36.0	76	574.6	40.2
37	336.2	23.5	97	396.0	27.7	57	455.9	31.9	17	515.7	36.1	77	575.6	40.2
38	337.2	23.6	98	397.0	27.8	58	456.9	31.9	18	516.7	36.1	78	576.6	40.3
39	338.2	23.6	99	398.0	27.8	59	457.9	32.0	19	517.7	36.2	79	577.6	40.4
40	339.2	23.7	400	399.0	27.9	60	458.9	32.1	20	518.7	36.3	80	578.6	40.5
341	340.2	23.8	401	400.0	28.0	461	459.9	32.2	521	519.7	36.3	581	579.6	40.5
42	341.2	23.9	02	401.0	28.0	62	460.9	32.2	22	520.7	36.4	82	580.6	40.6
43	342.2	23.9	03	402.0	28.1	63	461.9	32.3	23	521.7	36.5	83	581.6	40.7
44	343.2	24.0	04	403.0	28.2	64	462.9	32.4	24	522.7	36.6	84	582.6	40.7
45	344.2	24.1	05	404.0	28.3	65	463.9	32.4	25	523.7	36.6	85	583.6	40.8
46	345.2	24.1	06	405.0	28.3	66	464.9	32.5	26	524.7	36.7	86	584.6	40.9
47	346.2	24.2	07	406.0	28.4	67	465.9	32.6	27	525.7	36.8	87	585.6	40.9
48	347.2	24.3	08	407.0	28.5	68	466.9	32.6	28	526.7	36.8	88	586.6	41.0
49	348.1	24.3	09	408.0	28.5	69	467.9	32.7	29	527.7	36.9	89	587.6	41.1
50	349.1	24.4	10	409.0	28.6	70	468.9	32.8	30	528.7	37.0	90	588.6	41.2
351	350.1	24.5	411	410.0	28.7	471	469.9	32.9	531	529.7	37.0	591	589.6	41.2
52	351.1	24.6	12	411.0	28.7	72	470.9	32.9	32	530.7	37.1	92	590.6	41.3
53	352.1	24.6	13	412.0	28.8	73	471.8	33.0	33	531.7	37.2	93	591.6	41.4
54	353.1	24.7	14	413.0	28.9	74	472.8	33.1	34	532.7	37.2	94	592.6	41.4
55	354.1	24.8	15	414.0	28.9	75	473.8	33.1	35	533.7	37.3	95	593.6	41.5
56	355.1	24.8	16	415.0	29.0	76	474.8	33.2	36	534.7	37.4	96	594.5	41.6
57	356.1	24.9	17	416.0	29.1	77	475.8	33.3	37	535.7	37.5	97	595.5	41.6
58	357.1	25.0	18	417.0	29.2	78	476.8	33.3	38	536.7	37.5	98	596.5	41.7
59	358.1	25.0	19	418.0	29.2	79	477.8	33.4	39	537.7	37.6	99	597.5	41.8
60	359.1	25.1	20	419.0	29.3	80	478.8	33.5	40	538.7	37.7	600	598.5	41.9
Dist.	Dep.	Lat.	Dist.	Dep.	Lat.	Dist.	Dep.	Lat.	Dist.	Dep.	Lat.	Dist.	Dep.	Lat.

86° (94°, 266°, 274°).

In **Plane Sailing.**	**Dist.**	**Lat.**	**Dep.**
For converting *Dep.* into *Diff. Long.* and *Diff. Long.* into *Dep.* **In Middle Latitude Sailing.**	Diff. Long.	Dep.	
For converting *Dep.* into *Diff. Long.* and *Diff. Long.* into *Dep.* **In Mercator Sailing.**		*m*	Diff. Long.
For multiplication of numbers by sines and by cosines, or solution of plane right-angled triangles.	N. Hypotenuse.	N×Cos. Side Adj.	N×Sin. Side Opp.

TABLE 3.

Difference of Latitude and Departure for 5° (175°, 185°, 355°).

Dist.	Lat.	Dep.	Dist.	Lat.	Dep.	Dist.	Lat.	Dep.	Dist.	Lat.	Dep.	Dist.	Lat.	Dep.
1	1.0	0.1	61	60.8	5.3	121	120.5	10.5	181	180.3	15.8	241	240.1	21.0
2	2.0	0.2	62	61.8	5.4	22	121.5	10.6	82	181.3	15.9	42	241.1	21.1
3	3.0	0.3	63	62.8	5.5	23	122.5	10.7	83	182.3	15.9	43	242.1	21.2
4	4.0	0.3	64	63.8	5.6	24	123.5	10.8	84	183.3	16.0	44	243.1	21.3
5	5.0	0.4	65	64.8	5.7	25	124.5	10.9	85	184.3	16.1	45	244.1	21.4
6	6.0	0.5	66	65.7	5.8	26	125.5	11.0	86	185.3	16.2	46	245.1	21.4
7	7.0	0.6	67	66.7	5.8	27	126.5	11.1	87	186.3	16.3	47	246.1	21.5
8	8.0	0.7	68	67.7	5.9	28	127.5	11.2	88	187.3	16.4	48	247.1	21.6
9	9.0	0.8	69	68.7	6.0	29	128.5	11.2	89	188.3	16.5	49	248.1	21.7
10	10.0	0.9	70	69.7	6.1	30	129.5	11.3	90	189.3	16.6	50	249.0	21.8
11	11.0	1.0	71	70.7	6.2	131	130.5	11.4	191	190.3	16.6	251	250.0	21.9
12	12.0	1.0	72	71.7	6.3	32	131.5	11.5	92	191.3	16.7	52	251.0	22.0
13	13.0	1.1	73	72.7	6.4	33	132.5	11.6	93	192.3	16.8	53	252.0	22.1
14	13.9	1.2	74	73.7	6.4	34	133.5	11.7	94	193.3	16.9	54	253.0	22.1
15	14.9	1.3	75	74.7	6.5	35	134.5	11.8	95	194.3	17.0	55	254.0	22.2
16	15.9	1.4	76	75.7	6.6	36	135.5	11.9	96	195.3	17.1	56	255.0	22.3
17	16.9	1.5	77	76.7	6.7	37	136.5	11.9	97	196.3	17.2	57	256.0	22.4
18	17.9	1.6	78	77.7	6.8	38	137.5	12.0	98	197.2	17.3	58	257.0	22.5
16	18.9	1.7	79	78.7	6.9	39	138.5	12.1	99	198.2	17.3	59	258.0	22.6
20	19.9	1.7	80	79.7	7.0	40	139.5	12.2	200	199.2	17.4	60	259.0	22.7
21	20.9	1.8	81	80.7	7.1	141	140.5	12.3	201	200.2	17.5	261	260.0	22.7
22	21.9	1.9	82	81.7	7.1	42	141.5	12.4	02	201.2	17.6	62	261.0	22.8
23	22.9	2.0	83	82.7	7.2	43	142.5	12.5	03	202.2	17.7	63	262.0	22.9
24	23.9	2.1	84	83.7	7.3	44	143.5	12.6	04	203.2	17.8	64	263.0	23.0
25	24.9	2.2	85	84.7	7.4	45	144.4	12.6	05	204.2	17.9	65	264.0	23.1
26	25.9	2.3	86	85.7	7.5	46	145.4	12.7	06	205.2	18.0	66	265.0	23.2
27	26.9	2.4	87	86.7	7.6	47	146.4	12.8	07	206.2	18.0	67	266.0	23.3
28	27.9	2.4	88	87.7	7.7	48	147.4	12.9	08	207.2	18.1	68	267.0	23.4
29	28.9	2.5	89	88.7	7.8	49	148.4	13.0	09	208.2	18.2	69	268.0	23.4
30	29.9	2.6	90	89.7	7.8	50	149.4	13.1	10	209.2	18.3	70	269.0	23.5
31	30.9	2.7	91	90.7	7.9	151	150.4	13.2	211	210.2	18.4	271	270.0	23.6
32	31.9	2.8	92	91.6	8.0	52	151.4	13.2	12	211.2	18.5	72	271.0	23.7
33	32.9	2.9	93	92.6	8.1	53	152.4	13.3	13	212.2	18.6	73	272.0	23.8
34	33.9	3.0	94	93.6	8.2	54	153.4	13.4	14	213.2	18.7	74	273.0	23.9
35	34.9	3.1	95	94.6	8.3	55	154.4	13.5	15	214.2	18.7	75	274.0	24.0
36	35.9	3.1	96	95.6	8.4	56	155.4	13.6	16	215.2	18.8	76	274.9	24.1
37	36.9	3.2	97	96.6	8.5	57	156.4	13.7	17	216.2	18.9	77	275.9	24.1
38	37.9	3.3	98	97.6	8.5	58	157.4	13.8	18	217.2	19.0	78	276.9	24.2
39	38.9	3.4	99	98.6	8.6	59	158.4	13.9	19	218.2	19.1	79	277.9	24.3
40	39.8	3.5	100	99.6	8.7	60	159.4	13.9	20	219.2	19.2	80	278.9	24.4
41	40.8	3.6	101	100.6	8.8	161	160.4	14.0	221	220.2	19.3	281	279.9	24.5
42	41.8	3.7	02	101.6	8.9	62	161.4	14.1	22	221.2	19.3	82	280.9	24.6
43	42.8	3.7	03	102.6	9.0	63	162.4	14.2	23	222.2	19.4	83	281.9	24.7
44	43.8	3.8	04	103.6	9.1	64	163.4	14.3	24	223.1	19.5	84	282.9	24.8
45	44.8	3.9	05	104.6	9.2	65	164.4	14.4	25	224.1	19.6	85	283.9	24.8
46	45.8	4.0	06	105.6	9.2	66	165.4	14.5	26	225.1	19.7	86	284.9	24.9
47	46.8	4.1	07	106.6	9.3	67	166.4	14.6	27	226.1	19.8	87	285.9	25.0
48	47.8	4.2	08	107.6	9.4	68	167.4	14.6	28	227.1	19.9	88	286.9	25.1
49	48.8	4.3	09	108.6	9.5	69	168.4	14.7	29	228.1	20.0	89	287.9	25.2
50	49.8	4.4	10	109.6	9.6	70	169.4	14.8	30	229.1	20.0	90	288.9	25.3
51	50.8	4.4	111	110.6	9.7	171	170.3	14.9	231	230.1	20.1	291	289.9	25.4
52	51.8	4.5	12	111.6	9.8	72	171.3	15.0	32	231.1	20.2	92	290.9	25.4
53	52.8	4.6	13	112.6	9.8	73	172.3	15.1	33	232.1	20.3	93	291.9	25.5
54	53.8	4.7	14	113.6	9.9	74	173.3	15.2	34	233.1	20.4	94	292.9	25.6
55	54.8	4.8	15	114.6	10.0	75	174.3	15.3	35	234.1	20.5	95	293.9	25.7
56	55.8	4.9	16	115.6	10.1	76	175.3	15.3	36	235.1	20.6	96	294.9	25.8
57	56.8	5.0	17	116.6	10.2	77	176.3	15.4	37	236.1	20.7	97	295.9	25.9
58	57.8	5.1	18	117.6	10.3	78	177.3	15.5	38	237.1	20.7	98	296.9	26.0
59	58.8	5.1	19	118.5	10.4	79	178.3	15.6	39	238.1	20.8	99	297.9	26.1
60	59.8	5.2	20	119.5	10.5	80	179.3	15.7	40	239.1	20.9	300	298.9	26.1
Dist.	Dep.	Lat.	Dist.	Dep.	Lat.	Dist.	Dep.	Lat.	Dist.	Dep.	Lat.	Dist.	Dep.	Lat.

85° (95°, 265°, 275°).

In **Plane Sailing.**	**Dist.**	**Lat.**	**Dep.**
For converting *Dep.* into *Diff. Long.* and *Diff. Long.* into *Dep.* In **Middle Latitude Sailing.**	Diff. Long.	Dep.	
For converting *Dep* into *Diff. Long* and *Diff Long.* into *Dep.* In **Mercator Sailing.**		*m*	Diff. Long.
For multiplication of numbers by sines and by cosines, or solution of plane right-angled triangles.	N.	N×Cos.	N×Sin.
	Hypotenuse.	Side Adj.	Side Opp.

TABLE 3.

Difference of Latitude and Departure for 5° (175°, 185°, 355°).

Dist.	Lat.	Dep.	Dist.	Lat.	Dep.	Dist.	Lat.	Dep.	Dist.	Lat.	Dep.	Dist.	Lat.	Dep.
301	299.9	26.2	361	359.6	31.5	421	419.4	36.7	481	479.2	41.9	541	538.9	47.2
02	300.9	26.3	62	360.6	31.6	22	420.4	36.8	82	480 2	42.0	42	539.9	47.2
03	301.8	26.4	63	361.6	31.6	23	421.4	36.9	83	481.2	42.1	43	540.9	47.3
04	302.8	26.5	64	362.6	31.7	24	422.4	37.0	84	482.2	42.2	44	541.9	47.4
05	303.8	26.6	65	363.6	31.8	25	423.4	37.1	85	483.2	42.3	45	542.9	47.5
06	304.8	26.7	66	364.6	31.9	26	424.4	37.1	86	484.2	42.4	46	543.9	47.6
07	305.8	26.8	67	365.6	32.0	27	425.4	37.2	87	485.1	42.4	47	544.9	47.7
08	306.8	26.8	68	366.6	32.1	28	426.4	37.3	88	486.1	42.5	48	545.9	47.8
09	307.8	26.9	69	367.6	32.2	29	427.4	37.4	89	487.1	42.6	49	546.9	47.8
10	308.8	27.0	70	368.6	32.2	30	428.4	37.5	90	488.1	42.7	50	547.9	47.9
311	309.8	27.1	371	369.6	32.3	431	429.4	37.6	491	489.1	42.8	551	548.9	48.0
12	310.8	27.2	72	370.6	32.4	32	430.4	37.7	92	490.1	42.9	52	549.9	48.1
13	311.8	27.3	73	371.6	32.5	33	431.4	37.7	93	491.1	43.0	53	550.9	48.2
14	312.8	27.4	74	372.6	32.6	34	432.3	37.8	94	492.1	43.1	54	551.9	48.3
15	313.8	27.5	75	373.6	32.7	35	433.3	37.9	95	493.1	43.1	55	552.9	48.4
16	314.8	27.5	76	374.6	32.8	36	434.3	38.0	96	494.1	43.2	56	553.9	48.5
17	315.8	27.6	77	375.6	32.9	37	435.3	38.1	97	495.1	43.3	57	554.9	48.5
18	316.8	27.7	78	376.6	33.0	38	436.3	38.2	98	496.1	43.4	58	555.9	48.6
19	317.8	27.8	79	377.6	33.0	39	437.3	38.3	99	497.1	43.5	59	556.9	48.7
20	318.8	27.9	80	378.6	33.1	40	438.3	38.3	500	498.1	43.6	60	557.9	48.8
321	319.8	28.0	381	379.6	33.2	441	439.3	38.4	501	499.1	43.7	561	558.9	48.9
22	320.8	28.1	82	380.5	33.3	42	440.3	38.5	02	500.1	43.8	62	559.9	49.0
23	321.8	28.2	83	381.5	33.4	43	441.3	38.6	03	501.1	43.8	63	560.9	49.1
24	322.8	28.2	84	382.5	33.5	44	442.3	38.7	04	502.1	43.9	64	561.9	49.2
25	323.8	28.3	85	383.5	33.6	45	443.3	38.8	05	503.1	44.0	65	562.9	49.3
26	324.8	28.4	86	384.5	33.6	46	444.3	38.9	06	504.1	44.1	66	563.8	49.3
27	325.8	28.5	87	385.5	33.7	47	445.3	39.0	07	505.1	44.2	67	564.8	49.4
28	326.8	28.6	88	386.5	33.8	48	446.3	39.0	08	506.1	44.3	68	565.8	49.5
29	327.7	28.7	89	387.5	33.9	49	447.3	39.1	09	507.1	44.4	69	566.8	49.6
30	328.7	28.8	90	388.5	34.0	50	448.3	39.2	10	508.1	44.4	70	567.8	49.7
331	329.7	28.8	391	389.5	34.1	451	449.3	39.3	511	509.1	44.5	571	568.8	49.8
32	330.7	28.9	92	390.5	34.2	52	450.3	39.4	12	510.1	44.6	72	569.8	49.9
33	331.7	29.0	93	391.5	34.3	53	451.3	39.5	13	511.0	44.7	73	570.8	49.9
34	332.7	29.1	94	392.5	34.3	54	452.3	39.6	14	512.0	44.8	74	571.8	50.0
35	333.7	29.2	95	393.5	34.4	55	453.3	39.7	15	513.0	44.9	75	572.8	50.1
36	334.7	29.3	96	394.5	34.5	56	454.3	39.7	16	514.0	45.0	76	573.8	50.2
37	335.7	29.4	97	395.5	34.6	57	455.3	39.8	17	515.0	45.1	77	574.8	50.3
38	336.7	29.5	98	396.5	34.7	58	456.3	39.9	18	516.0	45.1	78	575.8	50.4
39	337.7	29.6	99	397.5	34.8	59	457.3	40.0	19	517.0	45.2	79	576.8	50.5
40	338.7	29.6	400	398.5	34.9	60	458.2	40.1	20	518.0	45.3	80	577.8	50.6
341	339.7	29.7	401	399.5	34.9	461	459.2	40.2	521	519.0	45.4	581	578.8	50.6
42	340.7	29.8	02	400.5	35.0	62	460.2	40.3	22	520.0	45.5	82	579.8	50.7
43	341.7	29.9	03	401.5	35.1	63	461.2	40.4	23	521.0	45.6	83	580.8	50.8
44	342.7	30.0	04	402.5	35.2	64	462.2	40.4	24	522.0	45.7	84	581.8	50.9
45	343.7	30.1	05	403.5	35.3	65	463.2	40.5	25	523.0	45.8	85	582.8	51.0
46	344.7	30.2	06	404.5	35.4	66	464.2	40.6	26	524.0	45.8	86	583.8	51.1
47	345.7	30.2	07	405.5	35.5	67	465.2	40.7	27	525.0	45.9	87	584.8	51.2
48	346.7	30.3	08	406.4	35.6	68	466.2	40.8	28	526.0	46.0	88	585.8	51.2
49	347.7	30.4	09	407.4	35.6	69	467.2	40.9	29	527.0	46.1	89	586.8	51.3
50	348.7	30.5	10	408.4	35.7	70	468.2	41.0	30	528.0	46.2	90	587.8	51.4
351	349.7	30.6	411	409.4	35.8	471	469.2	41.1	531	529.0	46.3	591	588.8	51.5
52	350.7	30.7	12	410.4	35.9	72	470.2	41.1	32	530.0	46.4	92	589.7	51.6
53	351.7	30.8	13	411.4	36.0	73	471.2	41.2	33	531.0	46.5	93	590.7	51.7
54	352.7	30.9	14	412.4	36.1	74	472.2	41.3	34	532.0	46.5	94	591.7	51.8
55	353.6	30.9	15	413.4	36.2	75	473.2	41.4	35	533.0	46.6	95	592.7	51.9
56	354.6	31.0	16	414.4	36.3	76	474.2	41.5	36	534.0	46.7	96	593.7	51.9
57	355.6	31.1	17	415.4	36.3	77	475.2	41.6	37	535.0	46.8	97	594.7	52.0
58	356.6	31.2	18	416.4	36.4	78	476.2	41.7	38	536.0	46.9	98	595.7	52.1
59	357.6	31.3	19	417.4	36.5	79	477.2	41.7	39	536.9	47.0	99	596.7	52.2
60	358.6	31.4	20	418.4	36.6	80	478.2	41.8	40	537.9	47.1	600	597.7	52.3
Dist.	Dep.	Lat.	Dist.	Dep.	Lat.	Dist.	Dep.	Lat.	Dist.	Dep.	Lat.	Dist.	Dep.	Lat.

85° (95°, 265°, 275°).

In Plane Sailing.	Dist.	Lat.	Dep.
For converting *Dep.* into *Diff. Long.* and *Diff. Long.* into *Dep.* In **Middle Latitude Sailing.**	Diff. Long.	Dep.	
For converting *Dep.* into *Diff. Long.* and *Diff. Long.* into *Dep.* In **Mercator Sailing.**		*m*	Diff. Long.
For multiplication of numbers by sines and by cosines, or solution of plane right-angled triangles.	N. / Hypotenuse.	N×Cos. / Side Adj.	N×Sin. / Side Opp.

TABLE 3.

Difference of Latitude and Departure for 6° (174°, 186°, 354°).

Dist.	Lat.	Dep.	Dist.	Lat.	Dep.	Dist.	Lat.	Dep.	Dist.	Lat.	Dep.	Dist.	Lat.	Dep.
1	1.0	0.1	61	60.7	6.4	121	120.3	12.6	181	180.0	18.9	241	239.7	25.2
2	2.0	0.2	62	61.7	6.5	22	121.3	12.8	82	181.0	19.0	42	240.7	25.3
3	3.0	0.3	63	62.7	6.6	23	122.3	12.9	83	182.0	19.1	43	241.7	25.4
4	4.0	0.4	64	63.6	6.7	24	123.3	13.0	84	183.0	19.2	44	242.7	25.5
5	5.0	0.5	65	64.6	6.8	25	124.3	13.1	85	184.0	19.3	45	243.7	25.6
6	6.0	0.6	66	65.6	6.9	26	125.3	13.2	86	185.0	19.4	46	244.7	25.7
7	7.0	0.7	67	66.6	7.0	27	126.3	13.3	87	186.0	19.5	47	245.6	25.8
8	8.0	0.8	68	67.6	7.1	28	127.3	13.4	88	187.0	19.7	48	246.6	25.9
9	9.0	0.9	69	68.6	7.2	29	128.3	13.5	89	188.0	19.8	49	247.6	26.0
10	9.9	1.0	70	69.6	7.3	30	129.3	13.6	90	189.0	19.9	50	248.6	26.1
11	10.9	1.1	71	70.6	7.4	131	130.3	13.7	191	190.0	20.0	251	249.6	26.2
12	11.9	1.3	72	71.6	7.5	32	131.3	13.8	92	190.9	20.1	52	250.6	26.3
13	12.9	1.4	73	72.6	7.6	33	132.3	13.9	93	191.9	20.2	53	251.6	26.4
14	13.9	1.5	74	73.6	7.7	34	133.3	14.0	94	192.9	20.3	54	252.6	26.6
15	14.9	1.6	75	74.6	7.8	35	134.4	14.1	95	193.9	20.4	55	253.6	26.7
16	15.9	1.7	76	75.6	7.9	36	135.3	14.2	96	194.9	20.5	56	254.6	26.8
17	16.9	1.8	77	76.6	8.0	37	136.2	14.3	97	195.9	20.6	57	255.6	26.9
18	17.9	1.9	78	77.6	8.2	38	137.2	14.4	98	196.9	20.7	58	256.6	27.0
19	18.9	2.0	79	78.6	8.3	39	138.2	14.5	99	197.9	20.8	59	257.6	27.1
20	19.9	2.1	80	79.6	8.4	40	139.2	14.6	200	198.9	20.9	60	258.6	27.2
21	20.9	2.2	81	80.6	8.5	141	140.2	14.7	201	199.9	21.0	261	259.6	27.3
22	21.9	2.3	82	81.6	8.6	42	141.2	14.8	02	200.9	21.1	62	260.6	27.4
23	22.9	2.4	83	82.5	8.7	43	142.2	14.9	03	201.9	21.2	63	261.6	27.5
24	23.9	2.5	84	83.5	8.8	44	143.2	15.1	04	202.9	21.3	64	262.6	27.6
25	24.9	2.6	85	84.5	8.9	45	144.2	15.2	05	203.9	21.4	65	263.5	27.7
26	25.9	2.7	86	85.5	9.0	46	145.2	15.3	06	204.9	21.5	66	264.5	27.8
27	26.9	2.8	87	86.5	9.1	47	146.2	15.4	07	205.9	21.6	67	265.5	27.9
28	27.8	2.9	88	87.5	9.2	48	147.2	15.5	08	206.9	21.7	68	266.5	28.0
29	28.8	3.0	89	88.5	9.3	49	148.2	15.6	09	207.9	21.8	69	267.5	28.1
30	29.8	3.1	90	89.5	9.4	50	149.2	15.7	10	208.8	22.0	70	268.5	28.2
31	30.8	3.2	91	90.5	9.5	151	150.2	15.8	211	209.8	22.1	271	269.5	28.3
32	31.8	3.3	92	91.5	9.6	52	151.2	15.9	12	210.8	22.2	72	270.5	28.4
33	32.8	3.4	93	92.5	9.7	53	152.2	16.0	13	211.8	22.3	73	271.5	28.5
34	33.8	3.6	94	93.5	9.8	54	153.2	16.1	14	212.8	22.4	74	272.5	28.6
35	34.8	3.7	95	94.5	9.9	55	154.2	16.2	15	213.8	22.5	75	273.5	28.7
36	35.8	3.8	96	95.5	10.0	56	155.1	16.3	16	214.8	22.6	76	274.5	28.8
37	36.8	3.9	97	96.5	10.1	57	156.1	16.4	17	215.8	22.7	77	275.5	29.0
38	37.8	4.0	98	97.5	10.2	58	157.1	16.5	18	216.8	22.8	78	276.5	29.1
39	38.8	4.1	99	98.5	10.3	59	158.1	16.6	19	217.8	22.9	79	277.5	29.2
40	39.8	4.2	100	99.5	10.5	60	159.1	16.7	20	218.8	23.0	80	278.5	29.3
41	40.8	4.3	101	100.4	10.6	161	160.1	16.8	221	219.8	23.1	281	279.5	29.4
42	41.8	4.4	02	101.4	10.7	62	161.1	16.9	22	220.8	23.2	82	280.5	29.5
43	42.8	4.5	03	102.4	10.8	63	162.1	17.0	23	221.8	23.3	83	281.4	29.6
44	43.8	4.6	04	103.4	10.9	64	163.1	17.1	24	222.8	23.4	84	282.4	29.7
45	44.8	4.7	05	104.4	11.0	65	164.1	17.2	25	223.8	23.5	85	283.4	29.8
46	45.7	4.8	06	105.4	11.1	66	165.1	17.4	26	224.8	23.6	86	284.4	29.9
47	46.7	4.9	07	106.4	11.2	67	166.1	17.5	27	225.8	23.7	87	285.4	30.0
48	47.7	5.0	08	107.4	11.3	68	167.1	17.6	28	226.8	23.8	88	286.4	30.1
49	48.7	5.1	09	108.4	11.4	69	168.1	17.7	29	227.7	23.9	89	287.4	30.2
50	49.7	5.2	10	109.4	11.5	70	169.1	17.8	30	228.7	24.0	90	288.4	30.3
51	50.7	5.3	111	110.4	11.6	171	170.1	17.9	231	229.7	24.1	291	289.4	30.4
52	51.7	5.4	12	111.4	11.7	72	171.1	18.0	32	230.7	24.3	92	290.4	30.5
53	52.7	5.5	13	112.4	11.8	73	172.1	18.1	33	231.7	24.4	93	291.4	30.6
54	53.7	5.6	14	113.4	11.9	74	173.0	18.2	34	232.7	24.5	94	292.4	30.7
55	54.7	5.7	15	114.4	12.0	75	174.0	18.3	35	233.7	24.6	95	293.4	30.8
56	55.7	5.9	16	115.4	12.1	76	175.0	18.4	36	234.7	24.7	96	294.4	30.9
57	56.7	6.0	17	116.4	12.2	77	176.0	18.5	37	235.7	24.8	97	295.4	31.0
58	57.7	6.1	18	117.4	12.3	78	177.0	18.6	38	236.7	24.9	98	296.4	31.1
59	58.7	6.2	19	118.3	12.4	79	178.0	18.7	39	237.7	25.0	99	297.4	31.3
60	59.7	6.3	20	119.3	12.5	80	179.0	18.8	40	238.7	25.1	300	298.4	31.4
Dist.	Dep.	Lat.	Dist.	Dep.	Lat.	Dist.	Dep.	Lat.	Dist.	Dep.	Lat.	Dist.	Dep.	Lat.

84°, (96°, 264°, 276°).

In **Plane Sailing.**	**Dist.**	**Lat.**	**Dep.**
For converting *Dep.* into *Diff. Long.* and *Diff. Long.* into *Dep.* In **Middle Latitude Sailing.**	Diff. Long.	Dep.	
For converting *Dep.* into *Diff. Long.* and *Diff. Long.* into *Dep.* In **Mercator Sailing.**		*m*	Diff. Long.
For multiplication of numbers by sines and by cosines, or solution of plane right-angled triangles.	N. Hypotenuse.	N×Cos. Side Adj.	N×Sin. Side Opp.

TABLE 3.

Difference of Latitude and Departure for 6° (174°, 186°, 354°).

Dist.	Lat.	Dep.	Dist.	Lat.	Dep.	Dist.	Lat.	Dep.	Dist.	Lat.	Dep.	Dist.	Lat.	Dep.
301	299.3	31.5	361	359.0	37.7	421	418.7	44.0	481	478.4	50.3	541	538.0	56.5
02	300.3	31.6	62	360.0	37.8	22	419.7	44.1	82	479.4	50.4	42	539.0	56.7
03	301.3	31.7	63	361.0	37.9	23	420.7	44.2	83	480.4	50.5	43	540.0	56.8
04	302.3	31.8	64	362.0	38.0	24	421.7	44.3	84	481.3	50.6	44	541.0	56.9
05	303.3	31.9	65	363.0	38.2	25	422.7	44.4	85	482.3	50.7	45	542.0	57.0
06	304.3	32.0	66	364.0	38.3	26	423.7	44.5	86	483.3	50.8	46	543.0	57.1
07	305.3	32.1	67	365.0	38.4	27	424.7	44.6	87	484.3	50.9	47	544.0	57.2
08	306.3	32.2	68	366.0	38.5	28	425.7	44.7	88	485.3	51.0	48	545.0	57.3
09	307.3	32.3	69	367.0	38.6	29	426.6	44.8	89	486.3	51.1	49	546.0	57.4
10	308.3	32.4	70	368.0	38.7	30	427.6	44.9	90	487.3	51.2	50	547.0	57.5
311	309.3	32.5	371	369.0	38.8	431	428.6	45.1	491	488.3	51.3	551	548.0	57.6
12	310.3	32.6	72	370.0	38.9	32	429.6	45.2	92	489.3	51.4	52	549.0	57.7
13	311.3	32.7	73	371.0	39.0	33	430.6	45.3	93	490.3	51.5	53	550.0	57.8
14	312.3	32.8	74	372.0	39.1	34	431.6	45.4	94	491.3	51.6	54	551.0	57.9
15	313.3	32.9	75	372.9	39.2	35	432.6	45.5	95	492.3	51.7	55	552.0	58.0
16	314.3	33.0	76	373.9	39.3	36	433.6	45.6	96	493.3	51.8	56	553.0	58.1
17	315.3	33.1	77	374.9	39.4	37	434.6	45.7	97	494.3	52.0	57	553.9	58.2
18	316.3	33.2	78	375.9	39.5	38	435.6	45.8	98	495.3	52.1	58	554.9	58.3
19	317.3	33.3	79	376.9	39.6	39	436.6	45.9	99	496.3	52.2	59	555.9	58.4
20	318.2	33.4	80	377.9	39.7	40	437.6	46.0	500	497.3	52.3	60	556.9	58.5
321	319.2	33.6	381	378.9	39.8	441	438.6	46.1	501	498.3	52.4	561	557.9	58.6
22	320.2	33.7	82	379.9	39.9	42	439.6	46.2	02	499.3	52.5	62	558.9	58.7
23	321.2	33.8	83	380.9	40.0	43	440.6	46.3	03	500.2	52.6	63	559.9	58.8
24	322.2	33.9	84	381.9	40.1	44	441.6	46.4	04	501.2	52.7	64	560.9	59.0
25	323.2	34.0	85	382.9	40.2	45	442.6	46.5	05	502.2	52.8	65	561.9	59.1
26	324.2	34.1	86	383.9	40.3	46	443.6	46.6	06	503.2	52.9	66	562.9	59.2
27	325.2	34.2	87	384.9	40.5	47	444.6	46.7	07	504.2	53.0	67	563.9	59.3
28	326.2	34.3	88	385.9	40.6	48	445.5	46.8	08	505.2	53.1	68	564.9	59.4
29	327.2	34.4	89	386.9	40.7	49	446.5	46.9	09	506.2	53.2	69	565.9	59.5
30	328.2	34.5	90	387.9	40.8	50	447.5	47.0	10	507.2	53.3	70	566.9	59.6
331	329.2	34.6	391	388.9	40.9	451	448.5	47.1	511	508.2	53.4	571	567.9	59.7
32	330.2	34.7	92	389.9	41.0	52	449.5	47.2	12	509.2	53.5	72	568.9	59.8
33	331.2	34.8	93	390.8	41.1	53	450.5	47.4	13	510.2	53.6	73	569.9	59.9
34	332.2	34.9	94	391.8	41.2	54	451.5	47.5	14	511.2	53.7	74	570.9	60.0
35	333.2	35.0	95	392.8	41.3	55	452.5	47.6	15	512.2	53.8	75	571.9	60.1
36	334.2	35.1	96	393.8	41.4	56	453.5	47.7	16	513.2	53.9	76	572.8	60.2
37	335.2	35.2	97	394.8	41.5	57	454.5	47.8	17	514.2	54.0	77	573.8	60.3
38	336.1	35.3	98	395.8	41.6	58	455.5	47.9	18	515.2	54.1	78	574.8	60.4
39	337.1	35.4	99	396.8	41.7	59	456.5	48.0	19	516.2	54.3	79	575.8	60.5
40	338.1	35.5	400	397.8	41.8	60	457.5	48.1	20	517.2	54.4	80	576.8	60.6
341	339.1	35.6	401	398.8	41.9	461	458.5	48.2	521	518.1	54.5	581	577.8	60.7
42	340.1	35.7	02	399.8	42.0	62	459.5	48.3	22	519.1	54.6	82	578.8	60.8
43	341.1	35.9	03	400.8	42.1	63	460.5	48.4	23	520.1	54.7	83	579.8	60.9
44	342.1	36.0	04	401.8	42.2	64	461.5	48.5	24	521.1	54.8	84	580.8	61.0
45	343.1	36.1	05	402.8	42.3	65	462.5	48.6	25	522.1	54.9	85	581.8	61.1
46	344.1	36.2	06	403.8	42.4	66	463.4	48.7	26	523.1	55.0	86	582.8	61.3
47	345.1	36.3	07	404.8	42.5	67	464.4	48.8	27	524.1	55.1	87	583.8	61.4
48	346.1	36.4	08	405.8	42.6	68	465.4	48.9	28	525.1	55.2	88	584.8	61.5
49	347.1	36.5	09	406.8	42.8	69	466.4	49.0	29	526.1	55.3	89	585.8	61.6
50	348.1	36.6	10	407.8	42.9	70	467.4	49.1	30	527.1	55.4	90	586.8	61.7
351	349.1	36.7	411	408.7	43.0	471	468.4	49.2	531	528.1	55.5	591	587.8	61.8
52	350.1	36.8	12	409.7	43.1	72	469.4	49.3	32	529.1	55.6	92	588.8	61.9
53	351.1	36.9	13	410.7	43.2	73	470.4	49.4	33	530.1	55.7	93	589.8	62.0
54	352.1	37.0	14	411.7	43.3	74	471.4	49.5	34	531.1	55.8	94	590.7	62.1
55	353.1	37.1	15	412.7	43.4	75	472.4	49.7	35	532.1	55.9	95	591.7	62.2
56	354.0	37.2	16	413.7	43.5	76	473.4	49.8	36	533.1	56.0	96	592.7	62.3
57	355.0	37.3	17	414.7	43.6	77	474.4	49.9	37	534.1	56.1	97	593.7	62.4
58	356.0	37.4	18	415.7	43.7	78	475.4	50.0	38	535.1	56.2	98	594.7	62.5
59	357.0	37.5	19	416.7	43.8	79	476.4	50.1	39	536.0	56.3	99	595.7	62.6
60	358.0	37.6	20	417.7	43.9	80	477.4	50.2	40	537.0	56.4	600	596.7	62.7
Dist.	Dep.	Lat.	Dist.	Dep.	Lat.	Dist.	Dep.	Lat.	Dist.	Dep.	Lat.	Dist.	Dep.	Lat.

84° (96°, 264°, 276°).

In **Plane Sailing.**	Dist.	Lat.	Dep.
For converting *Dep.* into *Diff. Long.* and *Diff. Long.* into *Dep.* In **Middle Latitude Sailing.**	Diff. Long.	Dep.	
For converting *Dep.* into *Diff. Long.* and *Diff. Long.* into *Dep.* In **Mercator Sailing.**		*m*	Diff. Long.
For multiplication of numbers by sines and by cosines, or solution of plane right-angled triangles.	N. Hypotenuse.	N×Cos. Side Adj.	N×Sin. Side Opp.

See page 17, Part II.

TABLE 3.

Difference of Latitude and Departure for 7° (173°, 187°, 353°).

Dist.	Lat.	Dep.	Dist.	Lat.	Dep.	Dist.	Lat.	Dep.	Dist.	Lat.	Dep.	Dist.	Lat.	Dep.
1	1.0	0.1	61	60.5	7.4	121	120.1	14.7	181	179.7	22.1	241	239.2	29.4
2	2.0	0.2	62	61.5	7.6	22	121.1	14.9	82	180.6	22.2	42	240.2	29.5
3	3.0	0.4	63	62.5	7.7	23	122.1	15.0	83	181.6	22.3	43	241.2	29.6
4	4.0	0.5	64	63.5	7.8	24	123.1	15.1	84	182.6	22.4	44	242.2	29.7
5	5.0	0.6	65	64.5	7.9	25	124.1	15.2	85	183.6	22.5	45	243.2	29.9
6	6.0	0.7	66	65.5	8.0	26	125.1	15.4	86	184.6	22.7	46	244.2	30.0
7	6.9	0.9	67	66.5	8.2	27	126.1	15.5	87	185.6	22.8	47	245.2	30.1
8	7.9	1.0	68	67.5	8.3	28	127.0	15.6	88	186.6	22.9	48	246.2	30.2
9	8.9	1.1	69	68.5	8.4	29	128.0	15.7	89	187.6	23.0	49	247.1	30.3
10	9 9	1.2	70	69.5	8.5	30	129.0	15.8	90	188.6	23.2	50	248.1	30.5
11	10.9	1.3	71	70.5	8.7	131	130.0	16.0	191	189.6	23.3	251	249.1	30.6
12	11.9	1.5	72	71.5	8.8	32	131.0	13.1	92	190.6	23.4	52	250.1	30.7
13	12.9	1.6	73	72.5	8.9	33	132.0	16.2	93	191.6	23.5	53	251.1	30.8
14	13.9	1.7	74	73.4	9.0	34	133.0	16.3	94	192.6	23.6	54	252.1	31.0
15	14.9	1.8	75	74.4	9.1	35	134.0	16.5	95	193.5	23.8	55	253.1	31.1
16	15.9	1.9	76	75.4	9.3	36	135.0	16.6	96	194.5	23.9	56	254.1	31.2
17	16.9	2.1	77	76.4	9.4	37	136.0	16.7	97	195.5	24.0	57	255.1	31.3
18	17.9	2.2	78	77.4	9.5	38	137.0	16.8	98	196.5	24.1	58	256.1	31.4
19	18.9	2.3	79	78.4	9.6	39	138.0	16.9	99	197.5	24.3	59	257.1	31.6
20	19.9	2.4	80	79.4	9.7	40	139.0	17.1	200	198.5	24.4	60	258.1	31.7
21	20.8	2.6	81	80.4	9.9	141	139.9	17.2	201	199.5	24.5	261	259.1	31.8
22	21.8	2.7	82	81.4	10.0	42	140.9	17.3	02	200.5	24.6	62	260.0	31.9
23	22.8	2.8	83	82.4	10.1	43	141.9	17.4	03	201.5	24.7	63	261.0	32.1
24	23.8	2.9	84	83.4	10.2	44	142.9	17.5	04	202.5	24.9	64	262.0	32.2
25	24.8	3.0	85	84.4	10.4	45	143.9	17.7	05	203.5	25.0	65	263.0	32.3
26	25.8	3.2	86	85.4	10.5	46	144.9	17.8	06	204.5	25.1	66	264.0	32.4
27	26.8	3.3	87	86.4	10.6	47	145.9	17.9	07	205.5	25.2	67	265.0	32.5
28	27.8	3.4	88	87.3	10.7	48	146.9	18.0	08	206.4	25.3	68	266.0	32.7
29	28.8	3.5	89	88.3	10.8	49	147.9	18.2	09	207.4	25.5	69	267.0	32.8
30	29.8	3.7	90	89.3	11.0	50	148.9	18.3	10	208.4	25.6	70	268.0	32.9
31	30.8	3.8	91	90.3	11.1	151	149.9	18.4	211	209.4	25.7	271	269.0	33.0
32	31.8	3.9	92	91.3	11.2	52	150.9	18.5	12	210.4	25.8	72	270.0	33.1
33	32.8	4.0	93	92.3	11.3	53	151.9	18.6	13	211.4	26.0	73	271.0	33.3
34	33.7	4.1	94	93.3	11.5	54	152.9	18.8	14	212.4	26.1	74	272.0	33.4
35	34.7	4.3	95	94.3	11.6	55	153.8	18.9	15	213.4	26.2	75	273.0	33.5
36	35.7	4.4	96	95.3	11.7	56	154.8	19.0	16	214.4	26.3	76	273.9	33.6
37	36.7	4.5	97	96.3	11.8	57	155.8	19.1	17	215.4	26.4	77	274.9	33.8
38	37.7	4.6	98	97.3	11.9	58	156.8	19.3	18	216.4	26.6	78	275.9	33.9
39	38.7	4.8	99	98.3	12.1	59	157.8	19.4	19	217.4	26.7	79	276.9	34.0
40	39.7	4.9	100	99.3	12.2	60	158.8	19.5	20	218.4	26.8	80	277.9	34.1
41	40.7	5.0	101	100.2	12.3	161	159.8	19.6	221	219.4	26.9	281	278.9	34.2
42	41.7	5.1	02	101.2	12.4	62	160.8	19.7	22	220.3	27.1	82	279.9	34.4
43	42.7	5.2	03	102.2	12.6	63	161.8	19.9	23	221.3	27.2	83	280.9	34.5
44	43.7	5.4	04	103.2	12.7	64	162.8	20.0	24	222.3	27.3	84	281.9	34.6
45	44.7	5.5	05	104.2	12.8	65	163.8	20.1	25	223.3	27.4	85	282.9	34.7
46	45.7	5.6	06	105.2	12.9	66	164.8	20.2	26	224 3	27.5	86	283.9	34.9
47	46.6	5.7	07	106.2	13.0	67	165.8	20.4	27	225.3	27.7	87	284.9	35.0
48	47.6	5.8	08	107.2	13.2	68	166.7	20.5	28	226.3	27.8	88	285.9	35.1
49	48.6	6.0	09	108.2	13.3	69	167.7	20.6	29	227.3	27.9	89	286.8	35.2
50	49.6	6.1	10	109.2	13.4	70	168.7	20.7	30	228.3	28.0	90	287.8	35.3
51	50.6	6.2	111	110.2	13.5	171	169.7	20.8	231	229.3	28.2	291	288.8	35.5
52	51.6	6.3	12	111.2	13.6	72	170.7	21.0	32	230.3	28.3	92	289.8	35.6
53	52.6	6.5	13	112.2	13.8	73	171.7	21.1	33	231.3	28.4	93	290.8	35.7
54	53.6	6.6	14	113.2	13.9	74	172.7	21.2	34	232.3	28.5	94	291.8	35.8
55	54.6	6.7	15	114.1	14.0	75	173.7	21.3	35	233.2	28.6	95	292.8	36.0
56	55.6	6.8	16	115.1	14.1	76	174.7	21.4	36	234.2	28.8	96	293.8	36.1
57	56.6	6.9	17	116.1	14.3	77	175.7	21.6	37	235.2	28.9	97	294.8	36.2
58	57.6	7.1	18	117.1	14.4	78	176.7	21.7	38	236.2	29.0	98	295.8	36.3
59	58.6	7.2	19	118.1	14.5	79	177.7	21.8	39	237.2	29.1	99	296.8	36.4
60	59.6	7.3	20	119.1	14.6	80	178.7	21.9	40	238.2	29.2	300	297.8	36.6
Dist.	Dep.	Lat.	Dist.	Dep.	Lat.	Dist.	Dep.	Lat.	Dist.	Dep.	Lat.	Dist.	Dep.	Lat.

83° (97°, 263°, 277°).

In *Plane Sailing.*	Dist.	Lat.	Dep.
For converting *Dep.* into *Diff. Long.* and *Diff. Long.* into *Dep.* **In Middle Latitude Sailing.**	Diff. Long.	Dep.	
For converting *Dep.* into *Diff. Long.* and *Diff. Long.* into *Dep.* **In Mercator Sailing.**		*m*	Diff. Long.
For multiplication of numbers by sines and by cosines, or solution of plane right-angled triangles.	N. Hypotenuse.	N×Cos. Side. Adj.	N×Sin. Side Opp.

TABLE 3.

Difference of Latitude and Departure for 7° (173°, 187°, 353°).

Dist.	Lat.	Dep.	Dist.	Lat.	Dep.	Dist.	Lat.	Dep.	Dist.	Lat.	Dep.	Dist.	Lat.	Dep.
301	298. 7	36. 7	361	358. 3	44. 0	421	417. 9	51. 3	481	477. 4	58. 6	541	537. 0	65. 9
02	299. 7	36. 8	62	359. 3	44. 1	22	418. 9	51. 4	82	478. 4	58. 7	42	538. 0	66. 1
03	300. 7	36. 9	63	360. 3	44. 2	23	419. 8	51. 6	83	479. 4	58. 9	43	539. 0	66. 2
04	301. 7	37. 0	64	361. 3	44. 4	24	420. 8	51. 7	84	480. 4	59. 0	44	539. 9	66. 3
05	302. 7	37. 2	65	362. 3	44. 5	25	421. 8	51. 8	85	481. 4	59. 1	45	540. 9	66. 4
06	303. 7	37. 3	66	363. 3	44. 6	26	422. 8	51. 9	86	482. 4	59. 2	46	541. 9	66. 5
07	304. 7	37. 4	67	364. 3	44. 7	27	423. 8	52. 0	87	483. 4	59. 4	47	542. 9	66. 7
08	305. 7	37. 5	68	365. 3	44. 8	28	424. 8	52. 2	88	484. 4	59. 5	48	543. 9	66. 8
09	306. 7	37. 7	69	366. 2	45. 0	29	425. 8	52. 3	89	485. 4	59. 6	49	544. 9	66. 9
10	307. 7	37. 8	70	367. 2	45. 1	30	426. 8	52. 4	90	486. 3	59. 7	50	545. 9	67. 0
311	308. 7	37. 9	371	368. 2	45. 2	431	427. 8	52. 5	491	487. 3	59. 8	551	546. 9	67. 1
12	309. 7	38. 0	72	369. 2	45. 3	32	428. 8	52. 6	92	488. 3	60. 0	52	547. 9	67. 3
13	310. 7	38. 1	73	370. 2	45. 5	33	429. 8	52. 8	93	489. 3	60. 1	53	548. 9	67. 4
14	311. 7	38. 3	74	371. 2	45. 6	34	430. 8	52. 9	94	490. 3	60. 2	54	549. 9	67. 5
15	312. 7	38. 4	75	372. 2	45. 7	35	431. 8	53. 0	95	491. 3	60. 3	55	550. 9	67. 6
16	313. 6	38. 5	76	373. 2	45. 8	36	432. 8	53. 1	96	492. 3	60. 4	56	551. 9	67. 8
17	314. 6	38. 6	77	374. 2	45. 9	37	433. 7	53. 3	97	493. 3	60. 6	57	552. 8	67. 9
18	315. 6	38. 8	78	375. 2	46. 1	38	434. 7	53. 4	98	494. 3	60. 7	58	553. 8	68. 0
19	316. 6	38. 9	79	376. 2	46. 2	39	435. 7	53. 5	99	495. 3	60. 8	59	554. 8	68. 1
20	317. 6	39. 0	80	377. 2	46. 3	40	436. 7	53. 6	500	496. 3	60. 9	60	555. 8	68. 2
321	318. 6	39. 1	381	378. 2	46. 4	441	437. 7	53. 7	501	497. 3	61. 1	561	556. 8	68. 4
22	319. 6	39. 2	82	379. 2	46. 6	42	438. 7	53. 9	02	498. 3	61. 2	62	557. 8	68. 5
23	320. 6	39. 4	83	380. 1	46. 7	43	439. 7	54. 0	03	499. 3	61. 3	63	558. 8	68. 6
24	321. 6	39. 5	84	381. 1	46. 8	44	440. 7	54. 1	04	500. 2	61. 4	64	559. 8	68. 7
25	322. 6	39. 6	85	382. 1	46. 9	45	441. 7	54. 2	05	501. 2	61. 5	65	560. 8	68. 9
26	323. 6	39. 7	86	383. 1	47. 0	46	442. 7	54. 4	06	502. 2	61. 7	66	561. 8	69. 0
27	324. 6	39. 8	87	384. 1	47. 2	47	443. 7	54. 5	07	503. 2	61. 8	67	562. 8	69. 1
28	325. 6	40. 0	88	385. 1	47. 3	48	444. 7	54. 6	08	504. 2	61. 9	68	563. 8	69. 2
29	326. 5	40. 1	89	386. 1	47. 4	49	445. 7	54. 7	09	505. 2	62. 0	69	564. 8	69. 3
30	327. 5	40. 2	90	387. 1	47. 5	50	446. 6	54. 8	10	506. 2	62. 2	70	565. 8	69. 5
331	328. 5	40. 3	391	388. 1	47. 7	451	447. 6	55. 0	511	507. 2	62. 3	571	566. 7	69. 6
32	329. 5	40. 5	92	389. 1	47. 8	52	448. 6	55. 1	12	508. 2	62. 4	72	567. 7	69. 7
33	330. 5	40. 6	93	390. 1	47. 9	53	449. 6	55. 2	13	509. 2	62. 5	73	568. 7	69. 8
34	331. 5	40. 7	94	391. 1	48. 0	54	450. 6	55. 3	14	510. 2	62. 6	74	569. 7	70. 0
35	332. 5	40. 8	95	392. 1	48. 1	55	451. 6	55. 5	15	511. 2	62. 8	75	570. 7	70. 1
36	333. 5	40. 9	96	393. 0	48. 3	56	452. 6	55. 6	16	512. 2	62. 9	76	571. 7	70. 2
37	334. 5	41. 1	97	394. 0	48. 4	57	453. 6	55. 7	17	513. 1	63. 0	77	572. 7	70. 3
38	335. 5	41. 2	98	395. 0	48. 5	58	454. 6	55. 8	18	514. 1	63. 1	78	573. 7	70. 4
39	336. 5	41. 3	99	396. 0	48. 6	59	455. 6	55. 9	19	515. 1	63. 3	79	574. 7	70. 6
40	337. 5	41. 4	400	397. 0	48. 7	60	456. 6	56. 1	20	516. 1	63. 4	80	575. 7	70. 7
341	338. 5	41. 6	401	398. 0	48. 9	461	457. 6	56. 2	521	517. 1	63. 5	581	576. 7	70. 8
42	339. 5	41. 7	02	399. 0	49. 0	62	458. 6	56. 3	22	518. 1	63. 6	82	577. 7	70. 9
43	340. 4	41. 8	03	400. 0	49. 1	63	459. 5	56. 4	23	519. 1	63. 7	83	578. 7	71. 0
44	341. 4	41. 9	04	401. 0	49. 2	64	460. 5	56. 5	24	520. 1	63. 9	84	579. 6	71. 2
45	342. 4	42. 0	05	402. 0	49. 4	65	461. 5	56. 7	25	521. 1	64. 0	85	580. 6	71. 3
46	343. 4	42. 2	06	403. 0	49. 5	66	462. 5	56. 8	26	522. 1	64. 1	86	581. 6	71. 4
47	344. 4	42. 3	07	404. 0	49. 6	67	463. 5	56. 9	27	523. 1	64. 2	87	582. 6	71. 5
48	345. 4	42. 4	08	405. 0	49. 7	68	464. 5	57. 0	28	524. 1	64. 3	88	583. 6	71. 7
49	346. 4	42. 5	09	406. 0	49. 8	69	465. 5	57. 2	29	525. 1	64. 5	89	584. 6	71. 8
50	347. 4	42. 7	10	406. 9	50. 0	70	466. 5	57. 3	30	526. 0	64. 6	90	585. 6	71. 9
351	348. 4	42. 8	411	407. 9	50. 1	471	467. 5	57. 4	531	527. 0	64. 7	591	586. 6	72. 0
52	349. 4	42. 9	12	408. 9	50. 2	72	468. 5	57. 5	32	528. 0	64. 8	92	587. 6	72. 1
53	350. 4	43. 0	13	409. 9	50. 3	73	469. 5	57. 6	33	529. 0	65. 0	93	588. 6	72. 3
54	351. 4	43. 1	14	410. 9	50. 5	74	470. 5	57. 8	34	530. 0	65. 1	94	589. 6	72. 4
55	352. 4	43. 3	15	411. 9	50. 6	75	471. 5	57. 9	35	531. 0	65. 2	95	590. 6	72. 5
56	353. 3	43. 4	16	412. 9	50. 7	76	472. 5	58. 0	36	532. 0	65. 3	96	591. 6	72. 6
57	354. 3	43. 5	17	413. 9	50. 8	77	473. 4	58. 1	37	533. 0	65. 4	97	592. 6	72. 8
58	355. 3	43. 6	18	414. 9	50. 9	78	474. 4	58. 3	38	534. 0	65. 6	98	593. 5	72. 9
59	356. 3	43. 7	19	415. 9	51. 1	79	475. 4	58. 4	39	535. 0	65. 7	99	594. 5	73. 0
60	357. 3	43. 9	20	416. 9	51. 2	80	476. 4	58. 5	40	536. 0	65. 8	600	595. 5	73. 1
Dist.	Dep.	Lat.	Dist.	Dep.	Lat.	Dist.	Dep.	Lat.	Dist.	Dep.	Lat.	Dist.	Dep.	Lat.

83° (97°, 263°, 277°).

In **Plane Sailing.**	**Dist.**	**Lat.**	**Dep.**
For converting *Dep.* into *Diff. Long.* and *Diff. Long.* into *Dep.* In **Middle Latitude Sailing.**	Diff. Long.	Dep.	
For converting *Dep.* into *Diff. Long.* and *Diff. Long.* into *Dep.* In **Mercator Sailing.**		*m*	Diff. Long.
For multiplication of numbers by sines and by cosines, or solution of plane right-angled triangles.	N. Hypotenuse.	N×Cos. Side Adj.	N×Sin. Side Opp.

TABLE 3.

Difference of Latitude and Departure for 8° (172°, 188°, 352°).

Dist.	Lat.	Dep.	Dist.	Lat.	Dep.	Dist.	Lat.	Dep.	Dist.	Lat.	Dep.	Dist.	Lat.	Dep.
1	1.0	0.1	61	60.4	8.5	121	119.8	16.8	181	179.2	25.2	241	238.7	33.5
2	2.0	0.3	62	61.4	8.6	22	120.8	17.0	82	180.2	25.3	42	239.6	33.7
3	3.0	0.4	63	62.4	8.8	23	121.8	17.1	83	181.2	25.5	43	240.6	33.8
4	4.0	0.6	64	63.4	8.9	24	122.8	17.3	84	182.2	25.6	44	241.6	34.0
5	5.0	0.7	65	64.4	9.0	25	123.8	17.4	85	183.2	25.7	45	242.6	34.1
6	5.9	0.8	66	65.4	9.2	26	124.8	17.5	86	184.2	25.9	46	243.6	34.2
7	6.9	1.0	67	66.3	9.3	27	125.8	17.7	87	185.2	26.0	47	244.6	34.4
8	7.9	1.1	68	67.3	9.5	28	126.8	17.8	88	186.2	26.2	48	245.6	34.5
9	8.9	1.3	69	68.3	9.6	29	127.7	18.0	89	187.2	26.3	49	246.6	34.7
10	9.9	1.4	70	69.3	9.7	30	128.7	18.1	90	188.2	26.4	50	247.6	34.8
11	10.9	1.5	71	70.3	9.9	131	129.7	18.2	191	189.1	26.6	251	248.6	34.9
12	11.9	1.7	72	71.3	10.0	32	130.7	18.4	92	190.1	26.7	52	249.5	35.1
13	12.9	1.8	73	72.3	10.2	33	131.7	18.5	93	191.1	26.9	53	250.5	35.2
14	13.9	1.9	74	73.3	10.3	34	132.7	18.6	94	192.1	27.0	54	251.5	35.3
15	14.9	2.1	75	74.3	10.4	35	133.7	18.8	95	193.1	27.1	55	252.5	35.5
16	15.8	2.2	76	75.3	10.6	36	134.7	18.9	96	194.1	27.3	56	253.5	35.6
17	16.8	2.4	77	76.3	10.7	37	135.7	19.1	97	195.1	27.4	57	254.5	35.8
18	17.8	2.5	78	77.2	10.9	38	136.7	19.2	98	196.1	27.6	58	255.5	35.9
19	18.8	2.6	79	78.2	11.0	39	137.7	19.3	99	197.1	27.7	59	256.5	36.0
20	19.8	2.8	80	79.2	11.1	40	138.6	19.5	200	198.1	27.8	60	257.5	36.2
21	20.8	2.9	81	80.2	11.3	141	139.6	19.6	201	199.0	28.0	261	258.5	36.3
22	21.8	3.1	82	81.2	11.4	42	140.6	19.8	02	200.0	28.1	62	259.5	36.5
23	22.8	3.2	83	82.2	11.6	43	141.6	19.9	03	201.0	28.3	63	260.4	36.6
24	23.8	3.3	84	83.2	11.7	44	142.6	20.0	04	202.0	28.4	64	261.4	36.7
25	24.8	3.5	85	84.2	11.8	45	143.6	20.2	05	203.0	28.5	65	262.4	36.9
26	25.7	3.6	86	85.2	12.0	46	144.6	20.3	06	204.0	28.7	66	263.4	37.0
27	26.7	3.8	87	86.2	12.1	47	145.6	20.5	07	205.0	28.8	67	264.4	37.2
28	27.7	3.9	88	87.1	12.2	48	146.6	20.6	08	206.0	28.9	68	265.4	37.3
29	28.7	4.0	89	88.1	12.4	49	147.5	20.7	09	207.0	29.1	69	266.4	37.4
30	29.7	4.2	90	89.1	12.5	50	148.5	20.9	10	208.0	29.2	70	267.4	37.6
31	30.7	4.3	91	90.1	12.7	151	149.5	21.0	211	208.9	29.4	271	268.4	37.7
32	31.7	4.5	92	91.1	12.8	52	150.5	21.2	12	209.9	29.5	72	269.4	37.9
33	32.7	4.6	93	92.1	12.9	53	151.5	21.3	13	210.9	29.6	73	270.3	38.0
34	33.7	4.7	94	93.1	13.1	54	152.5	21.4	14	211.9	29.8	74	271.3	38.1
35	34.7	4.9	95	94.1	13.2	55	153.5	21.6	15	212.9	29.9	75	272.3	38.3
36	35.6	5.0	96	95.1	13.4	56	154.5	21.7	16	213.9	30.1	76	273.3	38.4
37	36.6	5.1	97	96.1	13.5	57	155.5	21.9	17	214.9	30.2	77	274.3	38.6
38	37.6	5.3	98	97.0	13.6	58	156.5	22.0	18	215.9	30.3	78	275.3	38.7
39	38.6	5.4	99	98.0	13.8	59	157.5	22.1	19	216.9	30.5	79	276.3	38.8
40	39.6	5.6	100	99.0	13.9	60	158.4	22.3	20	217.9	30.6	80	277.3	39.0
41	40.6	5.7	101	100.0	14.1	161	159.4	22.4	221	218.8	30.8	281	278.3	39.1
42	41.6	5.8	02	101.0	14.2	62	160.4	22.5	22	219.8	30.9	82	279.3	39.2
43	42.6	6.0	03	102.0	14.3	63	161.4	22.7	23	220.8	31.0	83	280.2	39.4
44	43.6	6.1	04	103.0	14.5	64	162.4	22.8	24	221.8	31.2	84	281.2	39.5
45	44.6	6.3	05	104.0	14.6	65	163.4	23.0	25	222.8	31.3	85	282.2	39.7
46	45.6	6.4	06	105.0	14.8	66	164.4	23.1	26	223.8	31.5	86	283.2	39.8
47	46.5	6.5	07	106.0	14.9	67	165.4	23.2	27	224.8	31.6	87	284.2	39.9
48	47.5	6.7	08	106.9	15.0	68	166.4	23.4	28	225.8	31.7	88	285.2	40.1
49	48.5	6.8	09	107.9	15.2	69	167.4	23.5	29	226.8	31.9	89	286.2	40.2
50	49.5	7.0	10	108.9	15.3	70	168.3	23.7	30	227.8	32.0	90	287.2	40.4
51	50.5	7.1	111	109.9	15.4	171	169.3	23.8	231	228.8	32.1	291	288.2	40.5
52	51.5	7.2	12	110.9	15.6	72	170.3	23.9	32	229.7	32.3	92	289.2	40.6
53	52.5	7.4	13	111.9	15.7	73	171.3	24.1	33	230.7	32.4	93	290.1	40.8
54	53.5	7.5	14	112.9	15.9	74	172.3	24.2	34	231.7	32.6	94	291.1	40.9
55	54.5	7.7	15	113.9	16.0	75	173.3	24.4	35	232.7	32.7	95	292.1	41.1
56	55.5	7.8	16	114.9	16.1	76	174.3	24.5	36	233.7	32.8	96	293.1	41.2
57	56.4	7.9	17	115.9	16.3	77	175.3	24.6	37	234.7	33.0	97	294.1	41.3
58	57.4	8.1	18	116.9	16.4	78	176.3	24.8	38	235.7	33.1	98	295.1	41.5
59	58.4	8.2	19	117.8	16.6	79	177.3	24.9	39	236.7	33.3	99	296.1	41.6
60	59.4	8.4	20	118.8	16.7	80	178.2	25.1	40	237.7	33.4	300	297.1	41.8
Dist.	Dep.	Lat.	Dist.	Dep.	Lat.	Dist.	Dep.	Lat	Dist.	Dep.	Lat.	Dist.	Dep.	Lat.

82° (98°, 262°, 278°).

In Plane Sailing.	Dist.	Lat.	Dep.
For converting *Dep.* into *Diff. Long.* and *Diff. Long.* into *Dep.* In Middle Latitude Sailing.	Diff. Long.	Dep.	
For converting *Dep.* into *Diff. Long.* and *Diff. Long.* into *Dep.* In Mercator Sailing.		*m*	Diff. Long.
For multiplication of numbers by sines and by cosines, or solution of plane right-angled triangles.	N. Hypotenuse.	N×Cos. Side Adj.	N×Sin. Side Opp.

TABLE 3.

Difference of Latitude and Departure for 8° (172°, 188°, 352°).

Dist.	Lat.	Dep.	Dist.	Lat.	Dep.	Dist.	Lat.	Dep.	Dist.	Lat.	Dep.	Dist.	Lat.	Dep.
301	298.1	41.9	361	357.5	50.2	421	416.9	58.6	481	476.3	66.9	541	535.7	75.3
02	299.1	42.0	62	358.5	50.4	22	417.9	58.7	82	477.3	67.1	42	536.7	75.4
03	300.1	42.2	63	359.5	50.5	23	418.9	58.9	83	478.3	67.2	43	537.7	75.6
04	301.0	42.3	64	360.5	50.7	24	419.9	59.0	84	479.3	67.4	44	538.7	75.7
05	302.0	42.4	65	361.4	50.8	25	420.9	59.1	85	480.3	67.5	45	539.7	75.8
06	303.0	42.6	66	362.4	50.9	26	421.9	59.3	86	481.3	67.6	46	540.7	76.0
07	304.0	42.7	67	363.4	51.1	27	422.8	59.4	87	482.3	67.8	47	541.7	76.1
08	305.0	42.9	68	364.4	51.2	28	423.8	59.6	88	483.3	67.9	48	542.7	76.3
09	306.0	43.0	69	365.4	51.4	29	424.8	59.7	89	484.2	68.1	49	543.7	73.4
10	307.0	43.1	70	366.4	51.5	30	425.8	59.8	90	485.2	68.2	50	544.6	76.5
311	308.0	43.3	371	367.4	51.6	431	426.8	60.0	491	486.2	68.3	551	545.6	76.7
12	309.0	43.4	72	368.4	51.8	32	427.8	60.1	92	487.2	68.5	52	546.6	76.8
13	310.0	43.6	73	369.4	51.9	33	428.8	60.3	93	488.2	68.6	53	547.6	77.0
14	310.9	43.7	74	370.4	52.1	34	429.8	60.4	94	489.2	68.8	54	548.6	77.1
15	311.9	43.8	75	371.4	52.2	35	430.8	60.5	95	490.2	68.9	55	549.6	77.2
16	312.9	44.0	76	372.3	52.3	36	431.8	60.7	96	491.2	69.0	56	550.6	77.4
17	313.9	44.1	77	373.3	52.5	37	432.7	60.8	97	492.2	69.2	57	551.6	77.5
18	314.9	44.3	78	374.3	52.6	38	433.7	61.0	98	493.2	69.3	58	552.6	77.7
19	315.9	44.4	79	375.3	52.7	39	434.7	61.1	99	494.1	69.6	59	553.6	77.8
20	316.9	44.5	80	376.3	52.9	40	435.7	61.2	500	495.1	69.6	60	554.6	77.9
321	317.9	44.7	381	377.3	53.0	441	436.7	61.4	501	496.1	69.7	561	555.5	78.1
22	318.9	44.8	82	378.3	53.2	42	437.7	61.5	02	497.1	69.9	62	556.5	78.2
23	319.9	45.0	83	379.3	53.3	43	438.7	61.7	03	498.1	70.0	63	557.5	78.4
24	320.8	45.1	84	380.3	53.4	44	439.7	61.8	04	499.1	70.2	64	558.5	78.5
25	321.8	45.2	85	381.3	53.6	45	440.7	61.9	05	500.1	70.3	65	559.5	78.6
26	322.8	45.4	86	382.2	53.7	46	441.7	62.1	06	501.1	70.4	66	560.5	78.8
27	323.8	45.5	87	383.2	53.9	47	442.6	62.2	07	502.1	70.6	67	561.5	78.9
28	324.8	45.6	88	384.2	54.0	48	443.6	62.3	08	503.1	70.7	68	562.5	79.1
29	325.8	45.8	89	385.2	54.1	49	444.6	62.5	09	504.0	70.8	69	563.5	79.2
30	326.8	45.9	90	386.2	54.3	50	445.6	62.6	10	505.0	71.0	70	564.5	79.3
331	327.8	46.1	391	387.2	54.4	451	446.6	62.8	511	506.0	71.1	571	565.4	79.5
32	328.8	46.2	92	388.2	54.6	52	447.6	62.9	12	507.0	71.3	72	566.4	79.6
33	329.8	46.3	93	389.1	54.7	53	448.6	63.0	13	508.0	71.4	73	567.4	79.7
34	330.7	46.5	94	390.1	54.8	54	449.6	63.2	14	509.0	71.5	74	568.4	79.9
35	331.7	46.6	95	391.1	55.0	55	450.6	63.3	15	510.0	71.7	75	569.4	80.0
36	332.7	46.8	96	392.1	55.1	56	451.6	63.5	16	511.0	71.8	76	570.4	80.2
37	333.7	46.9	97	393.1	55.3	57	452.6	63.6	17	512.0	72.0	77	571.4	80.3
38	334.7	47.0	98	394.1	55.4	58	453.5	63.7	18	513.0	72.1	78	572.4	80.4
39	335.7	47.2	99	395.1	55.5	59	454.5	63.9	19	513.9	72.2	79	573.4	80.6
40	336.7	47.3	400	396.1	55.7	60	455.5	64.0	20	514.9	72.4	80	574.4	80.7
341	337.7	47.5	401	397.1	55.8	461	456.5	64.2	521	515.9	72.5	581	575.3	80.9
42	338.7	47.6	02	398.1	55.9	62	457.5	64.3	22	516.9	72.6	82	576.3	81.0
43	339.7	47.7	03	399.1	56.1	63	458.5	64.4	23	517.9	72.8	83	577.3	81.1
44	340.7	47.9	04	400.1	56.2	64	459.5	64.6	24	518.9	72.9	84	578.3	81.3
45	341.6	48.0	05	401.1	56.4	65	460.5	64.7	25	519.9	73.1	85	579.3	81.4
46	342.6	48.2	06	402.0	56.5	66	461.5	64.9	26	520.9	73.2	86	580.3	81.6
47	343.6	48.3	07	403.0	56.6	67	462.5	65.0	27	521.9	73.3	87	581.3	81.7
48	344.6	48.4	08	404.0	56.8	68	463.4	65.1	28	522.9	73.5	88	582.3	81.8
49	345.6	48.6	09	405.0	56.9	69	464.4	65.3	29	523.9	73.6	89	583.3	82.0
50	346.6	48.7	10	406.0	57.1	70	465.4	65.4	30	524.8	73.8	90	584.3	82.1
351	347.6	48.8	411	407.0	57.2	471	466.4	65.6	531	525.8	73.9	591	585.2	82.3
52	348.6	49.0	12	408.0	57.3	72	467.4	65.7	32	526.8	74.0	92	586.2	82.4
53	349.6	49.1	13	409.0	57.5	73	468.4	65.8	33	527.8	74.2	93	587.2	82.5
54	350.6	49.3	14	410.0	57.6	74	469.4	66.0	34	528.8	74.3	94	588.2	82.7
55	351.5	49.4	15	411.0	57.8	75	470.4	66.1	35	529.8	74.5	95	589.2	82.8
56	352.5	49.5	16	411.9	57.9	76	471.4	66.2	36	530.8	74.6	96	590.2	82.9
57	353.5	49.7	17	412.9	58.0	77	472.4	66.4	37	531.8	74.7	97	591.2	83.1
58	354.5	49.8	18	413.9	58.2	78	473.3	66.5	38	532.8	74.9	98	592.2	83.2
59	355.5	50.0	19	414.9	58.3	79	474.3	66.7	39	533.8	75.0	99	593.2	83.4
60	356.5	50.1	20	415.9	58.5	80	475.3	66.8	40	534.7	75.2	600	594.2	83.5
Dist.	Dep.	Lat.	Dist.	Dep.	Lat.	Dist.	Dep.	Lat.	Dist.	Dep.	Lat.	Dist.	Dep.	Lat.

82° (98°, 262°, 278°).

In **Plane Sailing.**	**Dist.**	**Lat.**	**Dep.**
For converting *Dep.* into *Diff. Long.* and *Diff. Long.* into *Dep.* In **Middle Latitude Sailing.**	Diff. Long.	Dep.	
For converting *Dep.* into *Diff. Long.* and *Diff. Long.* into *Dep.* In **Mercator Sailing.**		*m*	Diff. Long.
For multiplication of numbers by sines and by cosines, or solution of plane right-angled triangles.	N. Hypotenuse.	N×Cos. Side Adj.	N×Sin. Side Opp.

TABLE 3.

Difference of Latitude and Departure for 9° (171°, 189°, 351°).

Dist.	Lat.	Dep.	Dist.	Lat.	Dep.	Dist.	Lat.	Dep.	Dist.	Lat.	Dep.	Dist.	Lat.	Dep.
1	1.0	0.2	61	60.2	9.5	121	119.5	18.9	181	178.8	28.3	241	238.0	37.7
2	2.0	0.3	62	61.2	9.7	22	120.5	19.1	82	179.8	28.5	42	239.0	37.9
3	3.0	0.5	63	62.2	9.9	23	121.5	19.2	83	180.7	28.6	43	240.0	38.0
4	4.0	0.6	64	63.2	10.0	24	122.5	19.4	84	181.7	28.8	44	241.0	38.2
5	4.9	0.8	65	64.2	10.2	25	123.5	19.6	85	182.7	28.9	45	242.0	38.3
6	5.9	0.9	66	65.2	10.3	26	124.4	19.7	86	183.7	29.1	46	243.0	38.5
7	6.9	1.1	67	66.2	10.5	27	125.4	19.9	87	184.7	29.3	47	244.0	38.6
8	7.9	1.3	68	67.2	10.6	28	126.4	20.0	88	185.7	29.4	48	244.9	38.8
9	8.9	1.4	69	68.2	10.8	29	127.4	20.2	89	186.7	29.6	49	245.9	39.0
10	9.9	1.6	70	69.1	11.0	30	128.4	20.3	90	187.7	29.7	50	246.9	39.1
11	10.9	1.7	71	70.1	11.1	131	129.4	20.5	191	188.6	29.9	251	247.9	39.3
12	11.9	1.9	72	71.1	11.3	32	130.4	20.6	92	189.6	30.0	52	248.9	39.4
13	12.8	2.0	73	72.1	11.4	33	131.4	20.8	93	190.6	30.2	53	249.9	39.6
14	13.8	2.2	74	73.1	11.6	34	132.4	21.0	94	191.6	30.3	54	250.9	39.7
15	14.8	2.3	75	74.1	11.7	35	133.3	21.1	95	192.6	30.5	55	251.9	39.9
16	15.8	2.5	76	75.1	11.9	36	134.3	21.3	96	193.6	30.7	56	252.8	40.0
17	16.8	2.7	77	76.1	12.0	37	135.3	21.4	97	194.6	30.8	57	253.8	40.2
18	17.8	2.8	78	77.0	12.2	38	136.3	21.6	98	195.6	31.0	58	254.8	40.4
19	18.8	3.0	79	78.0	12.4	39	137.3	21.7	99	196.5	31.1	59	255.8	40.5
20	19.8	3.1	80	79.0	12.5	40	138.3	21.9	200	197.5	31.3	60	256.8	40.7
21	20.7	3.3	81	80.0	12.7	141	139.3	22.1	201	198.5	31.4	261	257.8	40.8
22	21.7	3.4	82	81.0	12.8	42	140.3	22.2	02	199.5	31.6	62	258.8	41.0
23	22.7	3.6	83	82.0	13.0	43	141.2	22.4	03	200.5	31.8	63	259.8	41.1
24	23.7	3.8	84	83.0	13.1	44	142.2	22.5	04	201.5	31.9	64	260.7	41.3
25	24.7	3.9	85	84.0	13.3	45	143.2	22.7	05	202.5	32.1	65	261.7	41.5
26	25.7	4.1	86	84.9	13.5	46	144.2	22.8	06	203.5	32.2	66	262.7	41.6
27	26.7	4.2	87	85.9	13.6	47	145.2	23.0	07	204.5	32.4	67	263.7	41.8
28	27.7	4.4	88	86.9	13.8	48	146.2	23.2	08	205.4	32.5	68	264.7	41.9
29	28.6	4.5	89	87.9	13.9	49	147.2	23.3	09	206.4	32.7	69	265.7	42.1
30	29.6	4.7	90	88.9	14.1	50	148.2	23.5	10	207.4	32.9	70	266.7	42.2
31	30.6	4.8	91	89.9	14.2	151	149.1	23.6	211	208.4	33.0	271	267.7	42.4
32	31.6	5.0	92	90.9	14.4	52	150.1	23.8	12	209.4	33.2	72	268.7	42.6
33	32.6	5.2	93	91.9	14.5	53	151.1	23.9	13	210.4	33.3	73	269.6	42.7
34	33.6	5.3	94	92.8	14.7	54	152.1	24.1	14	211.4	33.5	74	270.6	42.9
35	34.6	5.5	95	93.8	14.9	55	153.1	24.2	15	212.4	33.6	75	271.6	43.0
36	35.6	5.6	96	94.8	15.0	56	154.1	24.4	16	213.3	33.8	76	272.6	43.2
37	36.5	5.8	97	95.8	15.2	57	155.1	24.6	17	214.3	33.9	77	273.6	43.3
38	37.5	5.9	98	96.8	15.3	58	156.1	24.7	18	215.3	34.1	78	274.6	43.5
39	38.5	6.1	99	97.8	15.5	59	157.0	24.9	19	216.3	34.3	79	275.6	43.6
40	39.5	6.3	100	98.8	15.6	60	158.0	25.0	20	217.3	34.4	80	276.6	43.8
41	40.5	6.4	101	99.8	15.8	161	159.0	25.2	221	218.3	34.6	281	277.5	44.0
42	41.5	6.6	02	100.7	16.0	62	160.0	25.3	22	219.3	34.7	82	278.5	44.1
43	42.5	6.7	03	101.7	16.1	63	161.0	25.5	23	220.3	34.9	83	279.5	44.3
44	43.5	6.9	04	102.7	16.3	64	162.0	25.7	24	221.2	35.0	84	280.5	44.4
45	44.4	7.0	05	103.7	16.4	65	163.0	25.8	25	222.2	35.2	85	281.5	44.6
46	45.4	7.2	06	104.7	16.6	66	164.0	26.0	26	223.2	35.4	86	282.5	44.7
47	46.4	7.4	07	105.7	16.7	67	164.9	26.1	27	224.2	35.5	87	283.5	44.9
48	47.4	7.5	08	106.7	16.9	68	165.9	26.3	28	225.2	35.7	88	284.5	45.1
49	48.4	7.7	09	107.7	17.1	69	166.9	26.4	29	226.2	35.8	89	285.4	45.2
50	49.4	7.8	10	108.6	17.2	70	167.9	26.6	30	227.2	36.0	90	286.4	45.4
51	50.4	8.0	111	109.6	17.4	171	168.9	26.8	231	228.2	36.1	291	287.4	45.5
52	51.4	8.1	12	110.6	17.5	72	169.9	26.9	32	229.1	36.3	92	288.4	45.7
53	52.3	8.3	13	111.6	17.7	73	170.9	27.1	33	230.1	36.4	93	289.4	45.8
54	53.3	8.4	14	112.6	17.8	74	171.9	27.2	34	231.1	36.6	94	290.4	46.0
55	54.3	8.6	15	113.6	18.0	75	172.8	27.4	35	232.1	36.8	95	291.4	46.1
56	55.3	8.8	16	114.6	18.1	76	173.8	27.5	36	233.1	36.9	96	292.4	46.3
57	56.3	8.9	17	115.6	18.3	77	174.8	27.7	37	234.1	37.1	97	293.3	46.5
58	57.3	9.1	18	116.5	18.5	78	175.8	27.8	38	235.1	37.2	98	294.3	46.6
59	58.3	9.2	19	117.5	18.6	79	176.8	28.0	39	236.1	37.4	99	295.3	46.8
60	59.3	9.4	20	118.5	18.8	80	177.8	28.2	40	237.0	37.5	300	296.3	46.9
Dist.	Dep.	Lat.	Dist.	Dep.	Lat.	Dist.	Dep.	Lat.	Dist.	Dep.	Lat.	Dist.	Dep.	Lat.

81° (99°, 261°, 279°).

In **Plane Sailing.**	**Dist.**	**Lat.**	**Dep.**
For converting *Dep.* into *Diff. Long.* and *Diff. Long.* into *Dep.* In **Middle Latitude Sailing.**	Diff. Long.	Dep.	
For converting *Dep.* into *Diff. Long.* and *Diff. Long.* into *Dep.* In **Mercator Sailing.**		*m*	Diff. Long.
For multiplication of numbers by sines and by cosines, or solution of plane right-angled triangles.	N. Hypotenuse.	N×Cos. Side. Adj.	N×Sin. Side Opp.

TABLE 3.

Difference of Latitude and Departure for 9° (171°, 189°, 351°).

Dist.	Lat.	Dep.	Dist.	Lat.	Dep.	Dist.	Lat.	Dep.	Dist.	Lat.	Dep.	Dist.	Lat.	Dep.
301	297.3	47.1	361	356.6	56.5	421	415.8	65.9	481	475.1	75.2	541	534.3	84.6
02	298.3	47.2	62	357.5	56.6	22	416.8	66.0	82	476.1	75.4	42	535.3	84.8
03	299.3	47.4	63	358.5	56.8	23	417.8	66.2	83	477.1	75.6	43	536.3	84.9
04	300.3	47.6	64	359.5	56.9	24	418.8	66.3	84	478.0	75.7	44	537.3	85.1
05	301.2	47.7	65	360.5	57.1	25	419.8	66.5	85	479.0	75.9	45	538.3	85.3
06	302.2	47.9	66	361.5	57.3	26	420.8	66.6	86	480.0	76.0	46	539.3	85.4
07	303.2	48.0	67	362.5	57.4	27	421.7	66.8	87	481.0	76.2	47	540.3	85.6
08	304.2	48.2	68	363.5	57.6	28	422.7	67.0	88	482.0	76.3	48	541.3	85.7
09	305.2	48.3	69	364.5	57.7	29	423.7	67.1	89	483.0	76.5	49	542.2	85.9
10	306.2	48.5	70	365.4	57.9	30	424.7	67.3	90	484.0	76.7	50	543.2	86.0
311	307.2	48.7	371	366.4	58.0	431	425.7	67.4	491	485.0	76.8	551	544.2	86.2
12	308.2	48.8	72	367.4	58.2	32	426.7	67.6	92	485.9	77.0	52	545.2	86.4
13	309.1	49.0	73	368.4	58.4	33	427.7	67.7	93	486.9	77.1	53	546.2	86.5
14	310.1	49.1	74	369.4	58.5	34	428.7	67.9	94	487.9	77.3	54	547.2	86.7
15	311.1	49.3	75	370.4	58.7	35	429.6	68.0	95	488.9	77.4	55	548.2	86.8
16	312.1	49.4	76	371.4	58.8	36	430.6	68.2	96	489.9	77.6	56	549.2	87.0
17	313.1	49.6	77	372.4	59.0	37	431.6	68.4	97	490.9	77.7	57	550.1	87.1
18	314.1	49.7	78	373.3	59.1	38	432.6	68.5	98	491.9	77.9	58	551.1	87.3
19	315.1	49.9	79	374.3	59.3	39	433.6	68.7	99	492.9	78.1	59	552.1	87.4
20	316.1	50.1	80	375.3	59.4	40	434.6	68.8	500	493.8	78.2	60	553.1	87.6
321	317.0	50.2	381	376.3	59.6	441	435.6	69.0	501	494.8	78.4	561	554.1	87.8
22	318.0	50.4	82	377.3	59.8	42	436.6	69.1	02	495.8	78.5	62	555.1	87.9
23	319.0	50.5	83	378.3	59.9	43	437.5	69.3	03	496.8	78.7	63	556.1	88.1
24	320.0	50.7	84	379.3	60.1	44	438.5	69.5	04	497.8	78.8	64	557.1	88.2
25	321.0	50.8	85	380.3	60.2	45	439.5	69.6	05	498.8	79.0	65	558.0	88.4
26	322.0	51.0	86	381.2	60.4	46	440.5	69.8	06	499.8	79.2	66	559.0	88.5
27	323.0	51.2	87	382.2	60.5	47	441.5	69.9	07	500.8	79.3	67	560.0	88.7
28	324.0	51.3	88	383.2	60.7	48	442.5	70.1	08	501.7	79.5	68	561.0	88.9
29	324.9	51.5	89	384.2	60.9	49	443.5	70.2	09	502.7	79.6	69	562.0	89.0
30	325.9	51.6	90	385.2	61.0	50	444.5	70.4	10	503.7	79.8	70	563.0	89.2
331	326.9	51.8	391	386.2	61.2	451	445.4	70.6	511	504.7	79.9	571	564.0	89.3
32	327.9	51.9	92	387.2	61.3	52	446.4	70.7	12	505.7	80.1	72	565.0	89.5
33	328.9	52.1	93	388.2	61.5	53	447.4	70.9	13	506.7	80.3	73	565.9	89.6
34	329.9	52.2	94	389.1	61.6	54	448.4	71.0	14	507.7	80.4	74	566.9	89.8
35	330.9	52.4	95	390.1	61.8	55	449.4	71.2	15	508.7	80.6	75	567.9	89.9
36	331.9	52.6	96	391.1	61.9	56	450.4	71.3	16	509.6	80.7	76	568.9	90.1
37	332.9	52.7	97	392.1	62.1	57	451.4	71.5	17	510.6	80.9	77	569.9	90.3
38	333.8	52.9	98	393.1	62.3	58	452.4	71.6	18	511.6	81.0	78	570.9	90.4
39	334.8	53.0	99	394.1	62.4	59	453.3	71.8	19	512.6	81.2	79	571.9	90.6
40	335.8	53.2	400	395.1	62.6	60	454.3	72.0	20	513.6	81.3	80	572.9	90.7
341	336.8	53.3	401	396.1	62.7	461	455.3	72.1	521	514.6	81.5	581	573.8	90.9
42	337.8	53.5	02	397.1	62.9	62	456.3	72.3	22	515.6	81.7	82	574.8	91.0
43	338.8	53.7	03	398.0	63.0	63	457.3	72.4	23	516.6	81.8	83	575.8	91.2
44	339.8	53.8	04	399.0	63.2	64	458.3	72.6	24	517.5	82.0	84	576.8	91.4
45	340.8	54.0	05	400.0	63.4	65	459.3	72.7	25	518.5	82.1	85	577.8	91.5
46	341.7	54.1	06	401.0	63.5	66	460.3	72.9	26	519.5	82.3	86	578.8	91.7
47	342.7	54.3	07	402.0	63.7	67	461.3	73.1	27	520.5	82.4	87	579.8	91.8
48	343.7	54.4	08	403.0	63.8	68	462.2	73.2	28	521.5	82.6	88	580.8	92.0
49	344.7	54.6	09	404.0	64.0	69	463.2	73.4	29	522.5	82.8	89	581.7	92.1
50	345.7	54.8	10	405.0	64.1	70	464.2	73.5	30	523.5	82.9	90	582.7	92.3
351	346.7	54.9	411	405.9	64.3	471	465.2	73.7	531	524.5	83.1	591	583.7	92.5
52	347.7	55.1	12	406.9	64.5	72	466.2	73.8	32	525.5	83.2	92	584.7	92.6
53	348.7	55.2	13	407.9	64.6	73	467.2	74.0	33	526.4	83.4	93	585.7	92.8
54	349.6	55.4	14	408.9	64.8	74	468.2	74.1	34	527.4	83.5	94	586.7	92.9
55	350.6	55.5	15	409.9	64.9	75	469.2	74.3	35	528.4	83.7	95	587.7	93.1
56	351.6	55.7	16	410.9	65.1	76	470.1	74.5	36	529.4	83.8	96	588.7	93.2
57	352.6	55.8	17	411.9	65.2	77	471.1	74.6	37	530.4	84.0	97	589.6	93.4
58	353.6	56.0	18	412.9	65.4	78	472.1	74.8	38	531.4	84.2	98	590.6	93.5
59	354.6	56.2	19	413.8	65.5	79	473.1	74.9	39	532.4	84.3	99	591.6	93.7
60	355.6	56.3	20	414.8	65.7	80	474.1	75.1	40	533.4	84.5	600	592.6	93.9
Dist.	Dep.	Lat.	Dist.	Dep.	Lat.	Dist.	Dep.	Lat.	Dist.	Dep.	Lat.	Dist.	Dep.	Lat.

81° (99°, 261°, 279°).

In **Plane Sailing.**	**Dist.**	**Lat.**	**Dep.**
For converting *Dep.* into *Diff. Long.* and *Diff. Long.* into *Dep.* in **Middle Latitude Sailing.**	Diff. Long.	Dep.	
For converting *Dep.* into *Diff. Long.* and *Diff. Long.* into *Dep.* In **Mercator Sailing.**		*m*	Diff. Long.
For multiplication of numbers by sines and by cosines, or solution of plane right-angled triangles.	N. Hypotenuse.	N×Cos. Side Adj.	N×Sin. Side Opp.

TABLE 3.

Difference of Latitude and Departure for 10° (170°, 190°, 350°).

Dist.	Lat.	Dep.	Dist.	Lat.	Dep.	Dist.	Lat.	Dep.	Dist.	Lat.	Dep.	Dist.	Lat.	Dep.
1	1.0	0.2	61	60.1	10.6	121	119.2	21.0	181	178.3	31.4	241	237.3	41.8
2	2.0	0.3	62	61.1	10.8	22	120.1	21.2	82	179.2	31.6	42	238.3	42.0
3	3.0	0.5	63	62.0	10.9	23	121.1	21.4	83	180.2	31.8	43	239.3	42.2
4	3.9	0.7	64	63.0	11.1	24	122.1	21.5	84	181.2	32.0	44	240.3	42.4
5	4.9	0.9	65	64.0	11.3	25	123.1	21.7	85	182.2	32.1	45	241.3	42.5
6	5.9	1.0	66	65.0	11.5	26	124.1	21.9	86	183.2	32.3	46	242.3	42.7
7	6.9	1.2	67	66.0	11.6	27	125.1	22.1	87	184.2	32.5	47	243.2	42.9
8	7.9	1.4	68	67.0	11.8	28	126.1	22.2	88	185.1	32.6	48	244.2	43.1
9	8.9	1.6	69	68.0	12.0	29	127.0	22.4	89	186.1	32.8	49	245.2	43.2
10	9.8	1.7	70	68.9	12.2	30	128.0	22.6	90	187.1	33.0	50	246.2	43.4
11	10.8	1.9	71	69.9	12.3	131	129.0	22.7	191	188.1	33.2	251	247.2	43.6
12	11.8	2.1	72	70.9	12.5	32	130.0	22.9	92	189.1	33.3	52	248.2	43.8
13	12.8	2.3	73	71.9	12.7	33	131.0	23.1	93	190.1	33.5	53	249.2	43.9
14	13.8	2.4	74	72.9	12.8	34	132.0	23.3	94	191.1	33.7	54	250.1	44.1
15	14.8	2.6	75	73.9	13.0	35	132.9	23.4	95	192.0	33.9	55	251.1	44.3
16	15.8	2.8	76	74.8	13.2	36	133.9	23.6	96	193.0	34.0	56	252.1	44.5
17	16.7	3.0	77	75.8	13.4	37	134.9	23.8	97	194.0	34.2	57	253.1	44.6
18	17.7	3.1	78	76.8	13.5	38	135.9	24.0	98	195.0	34.4	58	254.1	44.8
19	18.7	3.3	79	77.8	13.7	39	136.9	24.1	99	196.0	34.6	59	255.1	45.0
20	19.7	3.5	80	78.8	13.9	40	137.9	24.3	200	197.0	34.7	60	256.1	45.1
21	20.7	3.6	81	79.8	14.1	141	138.9	24.5	201	197.9	34.9	261	257.0	45.3
22	21.7	3.8	82	80.8	14.2	42	139.8	24.7	02	198.9	35.1	62	258.0	45.5
23	22.7	4.0	83	81.7	14.4	43	140.8	24.8	03	199.9	35.3	63	259.0	45.7
24	23.6	4.2	84	82.7	14.6	44	141.8	25.0	04	200.9	35.4	64	260.0	45.8
25	24.6	4.3	85	83.7	14.8	45	142.8	25.2	05	201.9	35.6	65	261.0	46.0
26	25.6	4.5	86	84.7	14.9	46	143.8	25.4	06	202.9	35.8	66	262.0	46.2
27	26.6	4.7	87	85.7	15.1	47	144.8	25.5	07	203.9	35.9	67	262.9	46.4
28	27.6	4.9	88	86.7	15.3	48	145.8	25.7	08	204.8	36.1	68	263.9	46.5
29	28.6	5.0	89	87.6	15.5	49	146.7	25.9	09	205.8	36.3	69	264.9	46.7
30	29.5	5.2	90	88.6	15.6	50	147.7	26.0	10	206.8	36.5	70	265.9	46.9
31	30.5	5.4	91	89.6	15.8	151	148.7	26.2	211	207.8	36.6	271	266.9	47.1
32	31.5	5.6	92	90.6	16.0	52	149.7	26.4	12	208.8	36.8	72	267.9	47.2
33	32.5	5.7	93	91.6	16.1	53	150.7	26.6	13	209.8	37.0	73	268.9	47.4
34	33.5	5.9	94	92.6	16.3	54	151.7	26.7	14	210.7	37.2	74	269.8	47.6
35	34.5	6.1	95	93.6	16.5	55	152.6	26.9	15	211.7	37.3	75	270.8	47.8
36	35.5	6.3	96	94.5	16.7	56	153.6	27.1	16	212.7	37.5	76	271.8	47.9
37	36.4	6.4	97	95.5	16.8	57	154.6	27.3	17	213.7	37.7	77	272.8	48.1
38	37.4	6.6	98	96.5	17.0	58	155.6	27.4	18	214.7	37.9	78	273.8	48.3
39	38.4	6.8	99	97.5	17.2	59	156.6	27.6	19	215.7	38.0	79	274.8	48.4
40	39.4	6.9	100	98.5	17.4	60	157.6	27.8	20	216.7	38.2	80	275.7	48.6
41	40.4	7.1	101	99.5	17.5	161	158.6	28.0	221	217.6	38.4	281	276.7	48.8
42	41.4	7.3	02	100.5	17.7	62	159.5	28.1	22	218.6	38.5	82	277.7	49.0
43	42.3	7.5	03	101.4	17.9	63	160.5	28.3	23	219.6	38.7	83	278.7	49.1
44	43.3	7.6	04	102.4	18.1	64	161.5	28.5	24	220.6	38.9	84	279.7	49.3
45	44.3	7.8	05	103.4	18.2	65	162.5	28.7	25	221.6	39.1	85	280.7	49.5
46	45.3	8.0	06	104.4	18.4	66	163.5	28.8	26	222.6	39.2	86	281.7	49.7
47	46.3	8.2	07	105.4	18.6	67	164.5	29.0	27	223.6	39.4	87	282.6	49.8
48	47.3	8.3	08	106.4	18.8	68	165.4	29.2	28	224.5	39.6	88	283.6	50.0
49	48.3	8.5	09	107.3	18.9	69	166.4	29.3	29	225.5	39.8	89	284.6	50.2
50	49.2	8.7	10	108.3	19.1	70	167.4	29.5	30	226.5	39.9	90	285.6	50.4
51	50.2	8.9	111	109.3	19.3	171	168.4	29.7	231	227.5	40.1	291	286.6	50.5
52	51.2	9.0	12	110.3	19.4	72	169.4	29.9	32	228.5	40.3	92	287.6	50.7
53	52.2	9.2	13	111.3	19.6	73	170.4	30.0	33	229.5	40.5	93	288.5	50.9
54	53.2	9.4	14	112.3	19.8	74	171.4	30.2	34	230.4	40.6	94	289.5	51.1
55	54.2	9.6	15	113.3	20.0	75	172.3	30.4	35	231.4	40.8	95	290.5	51.2
56	55.1	9.7	16	114.2	20.1	76	173.3	30.6	36	232.4	41.0	96	291.5	51.4
57	56.1	9.9	17	115.2	20.3	77	174.3	30.7	37	233.4	41.2	97	292.5	51.6
58	57.1	10.1	18	116.2	20.5	78	175.3	30.9	38	234.4	41.3	98	293.5	51.7
59	58.1	10.2	19	117.2	20.7	79	176.3	31.1	39	235.4	41.5	99	294.5	51.9
60	59.1	10.4	20	118.2	20.8	80	177.3	31.3	40	236.4	41.7	300	295.4	52.1
Dist.	Dep.	Lat.	Dist.	Dep.	Lat.	Dist.	Dep.	Lat.	Dist.	Dep.	Lat.	Dist.	Dep.	Lat.

80° (100°, 260°, 280°).

In Plane Sailing.	Dist.	Lat.	Dep.
For converting *Dep.* into *Diff. Long.* and *Diff. Long.* into *Dep.* In **Middle Latitude Sailing.**	Diff. Long.	Dep.	
For converting *Dep.* into *Diff. Long.* and *Diff. Long.* into *Dep.* In **Mercator Sailing.**		*m*	Diff Long.
For multiplication of numbers by sines and by cosines, or solution of plane right-angled triangles.	N. Hypotenuse.	N×Cos. Side Adj.	N×Sin. Side Opp.

TABLE 3.

Difference of Latitude and Departure for 10° (170°, 190°, 350°).

Dist.	Lat.	Dep.	Dist.	Lat.	Dep.	Dist.	Lat.	Dep.	Dist.	Lat.	Dep.	Dist.	Lat.	Dep.
301	296.4	52.3	361	355.5	62.7	421	414.6	73.1	481	473.7	83.5	541	532.8	93.9
02	297.4	52.4	62	356.5	62.9	22	415.6	73.3	82	474.7	83.7	42	533.8	94.1
03	298.4	52.6	63	357.5	63.0	23	416.6	73.5	83	475.7	83.9	43	534.8	94.3
04	299.4	52.8	64	358.5	63.2	24	417.6	73.6	84	476.6	84.0	44	535.7	94.5
05	300.4	53.0	65	359.5	63.4	25	418.5	73.8	85	477.6	84.2	45	536.7	94.6
06	301.4	53.1	66	360.4	63.6	26	419.5	74.0	86	478.6	84.4	46	537.7	94.8
07	302.3	53.3	67	361.4	63.7	27	420.5	74.1	87	479.6	84.6	47	538.7	95.0
08	303.3	53.5	68	362.4	63.9	28	421.5	74.3	88	480.6	84.7	48	539.7	95.2
09	304.3	53.7	69	363.4	64.1	29	422.5	74.5	89	481.6	84.9	49	540.7	95.3
10	305.3	53.8	70	364.4	64.2	30	423.5	74.7	90	482.6	85.1	50	541.6	95.5
311	306.3	54.0	371	365.4	64.4	431	424.5	74.8	491	483.5	85.3	551	542.6	95.7
12	307.3	54.2	72	366.4	64.6	32	425.4	75.0	92	484.5	85.4	52	543.6	95.9
13	308.2	54.4	73	367.3	64.8	33	426.4	75.2	93	485.5	85.6	53	544.6	96.0
14	309.2	54.5	74	368.3	64.9	34	427.4	75.4	94	486.5	85.8	54	545.6	96.2
15	310.2	54.7	75	369.3	65.1	35	428.4	75.5	95	487.5	86.0	55	546.6	96.4
16	311.2	54.9	76	370.3	65.3	36	429.4	75.7	96	488.5	86.1	56	547.6	96.5
17	312.2	55.0	77	371.3	65.5	37	430.4	75.9	97	489.4	86.3	57	548.5	96.7
18	313.2	55.2	78	372.3	65.6	38	431.3	76.1	98	490.4	86.5	58	549.5	96.9
19	314.2	55.4	79	373.2	65.8	39	432.3	76.2	99	491.4	86.7	59	550.5	97.1
20	315.1	55.6	80	374.2	66.0	40	433.3	76.4	500	492.4	86.8	60	551.5	97.2
321	316.1	55.7	381	375.2	66.2	441	434.3	76.6	501	493.4	87.0	561	552.5	97.4
22	317.1	55.9	82	376.2	66.3	42	435.3	76.8	02	494.4	87.2	62	553.5	97.6
23	318.1	56.1	83	377.2	66.5	43	436.3	76.9	03	495.4	87.3	63	554.4	97.8
24	319.1	56.3	84	378.2	66.7	44	437.3	77.1	04	496.3	87.5	64	555.4	97.9
25	320.1	56.4	85	379.2	66.9	45	438.2	77.3	05	497.3	87.7	65	556.4	98.1
26	321.0	56.6	86	380.1	67.0	46	439.2	77.4	06	498.3	87.9	66	557.4	98.3
27	322.0	56.8	87	381.1	67.2	47	440.2	77.6	07	499.3	88.0	67	558.4	98.5
28	323.0	57.0	88	382.1	67.4	48	441.2	77.8	08	500.3	88.2	68	559.4	98.6
29	324.0	57.1	89	383.1	67.5	49	442.2	78.0	09	501.3	88.4	69	560.4	98.8
30	325.0	57.3	90	384.1	67.7	50	443.2	78.1	10	502.3	88.6	70	561.3	99.0
331	326.0	57.5	391	385.1	67.9	451	444.1	78.3	511	503.2	88.7	571	562.3	99.2
32	327.0	57.7	92	386.0	68.1	52	445.1	78.5	12	504.2	88.9	72	563.3	99.3
33	327.9	57.8	93	387.0	68.2	53	446.1	78.7	13	505.2	89.1	73	564.3	99.5
34	328.9	58.0	94	388.0	68.4	54	447.1	78.8	14	506.2	89.3	74	565.3	99.7
35	329.9	58.2	95	389.0	68.6	55	448.1	79.0	15	507.2	89.4	75	566.3	99.8
36	330.9	58.3	96	390.0	68.8	56	449.1	79.2	16	508.2	89.6	76	567.2	100.0
37	331.9	58.5	97	391.0	68.9	57	450.1	79.4	17	509.1	89.8	77	568.2	100.2
38	332.9	58.7	98	392.0	69.1	58	451.0	79.5	18	510.1	89.9	78	569.2	100.4
39	333.9	58.9	99	392.9	69.3	59	452.0	79.7	19	511.1	90.1	79	570.2	100.5
40	334.8	59.0	400	393.9	69.5	60	453.0	79.9	20	512.1	90.3	80	571.2	100.7
341	335.8	59.2	401	394.9	69.6	461	454.0	80.1	521	513.1	90.5	581	572.2	100.9
42	336.8	59.4	02	395.9	69.8	62	455.0	80.2	22	514.1	90.6	82	573.2	101.1
43	337.8	59.6	03	396.9	70.0	63	456.0	80.4	23	515.1	90.8	83	574.1	101.2
44	338.8	59.7	04	397.9	70.2	64	457.0	80.6	24	516.0	91.0	84	575.1	101.4
45	339.8	59.9	05	398.9	70.3	65	457.9	80.7	25	517.0	91.2	85	576.1	101.6
46	340.7	60.1	06	399.8	70.5	66	458.9	80.9	26	518.0	91.3	86	577.1	101.8
47	341.7	60.3	07	400.8	70.7	67	459.9	81.1	27	519.0	91.5	87	578.1	101.9
48	342.7	60.4	08	401.8	70.8	68	460.9	81.3	28	520.0	91.7	88	579.1	102.1
49	343.7	60.6	09	402.8	71.0	69	461.9	81.4	29	521.0	91.9	89	580.1	102.3
50	344.7	60.8	10	403.8	71.2	70	462.9	81.6	30	521.9	92.0	90	581.0	102.5
351	345.7	61.0	411	404.8	71.4	471	463.8	81.8	531	522.9	92.2	591	582.0	102.6
52	346.7	61.1	12	405.7	71.5	72	464.8	82.0	32	523.9	92.4	92	583.0	102.8
53	347.6	61.3	13	406.7	71.7	73	465.8	82.1	33	524.9	92.6	93	584.0	103.0
54	348.6	61.5	14	407.7	71.9	74	466.8	82.3	34	525.9	92.7	94	585.0	103.1
55	349.6	61.6	15	408.7	72.1	75	467.8	82.5	35	526.9	92.9	95	586.0	103.3
56	350.6	61.8	16	409.7	72.2	76	468.8	82.7	36	527.9	93.1	96	586.9	103.5
57	351.6	62.0	17	410.7	72.4	77	469.8	82.8	37	528.8	93.2	97	587.9	103.7
58	352.6	62.2	18	411.6	72.6	78	470.7	83.0	38	529.8	93.4	98	588.9	103.8
59	353.5	62.3	19	412.6	72.8	79	471.7	83.2	39	530.8	93.6	99	589.9	104.0
60	354.5	62.5	20	413.6	72.9	80	472.7	83.4	40	531.8	93.8	600	590.9	104.2
Dist.	Dep.	Lat.	Dist.	Dep.	Lat.	Dist.	Dep.	Lat.	Dist.	Dep.	Lat.	Dist.	Dep.	Lat.

80° (100°, 260°, 280°).

In **Plane Sailing.**	**Dist.**	**Lat.**	**Dep.**
For converting *Dep.* into *Diff. Long.* and *Diff. Long.* into *Dep.* In **Middle Latitude Sailing.**	Diff. Long.	Dep.	
For converting *Dep.* into *Diff. Long.* and *Diff. Long.* into *Dep.* In **Mercator Sailing.**		*m*	Diff. Long.
For multiplication of numbers by sines and by cosines, or solution of plane right-angled triangles.	N. / Hypotenuse.	N×Cos. / Side Adj.	N×Sin. / Side Opp.

TABLE 3.

Difference of Latitude and Departure for 11° (169°, 191°, 349°).

Dist.	Lat.	Dep.	Dist.	Lat.	Dep.	Dist.	Lat.	Dep.	Dist.	Lat.	Dep.	Dist.	Lat.	Dep.
1	1.0	0.2	61	59.9	11.6	121	118.8	23.1	181	177.7	34.5	241	236.6	46.0
2	2.0	0.4	62	60.9	11.8	22	119.8	23.3	82	178.7	34.7	42	237.6	46.2
3	2.9	0.6	63	61.8	12.0	23	120.7	23.5	83	179.6	34.9	43	238.5	46.4
4	3.9	0.8	64	62.8	12.2	24	121.7	23.7	84	180.6	35.1	44	239.5	46.6
5	4.9	1.0	65	63.8	12.4	25	122.7	23.9	85	181.6	35.3	45	240.5	46.7
6	5.9	1.1	66	64.8	12.6	26	123.7	24.0	86	182.6	35.5	46	241.5	46.9
7	6.9	1.3	67	65.8	12.8	27	124.7	24.2	87	183.6	35.7	47	242.5	47.1
8	7.9	1.5	68	66.8	13.0	28	125.6	24.4	88	184.5	35.9	48	243.4	47.3
9	8.8	1.7	69	67.7	13.2	29	126.6	24.6	89	185.5	36.1	49	244.4	47.5
10	9.8	1.9	70	68.7	13.4	30	127.6	24.8	90	186.5	36.3	50	245.4	47.7
11	10.8	2.1	71	69.7	13.5	131	128.6	25.0	191	187.5	36.4	251	246.4	47.9
12	11.8	2.3	72	70.7	13.7	32	129.6	25.2	92	188.5	36.6	52	247.4	48.1
13	12.8	2.5	73	71.7	13.9	33	130.6	25.4	93	189.5	36.8	53	248.4	48.3
14	13.7	2.7	74	72.6	14.1	34	131.5	25.6	94	190.4	37.0	54	249.3	48.5
15	14.7	2.9	75	73.6	14.3	35	132.5	25.8	95	191.4	37.2	55	250.3	48.7
16	15.7	3.1	76	74.6	14.5	36	133.5	26.0	96	192.4	37.4	56	251.3	48.8
17	16.7	3.2	77	75.6	14.7	37	134.5	26.1	97	193.4	37.6	57	252.3	49.0
18	17.7	3.4	78	76.6	14.9	38	135.5	26.3	98	194.4	37.8	58	253.3	49.2
19	18.7	3.6	79	77.5	15.1	39	136.4	26.5	99	195.3	38.0	59	254.2	49.4
20	19.6	3.8	80	78.5	15.3	40	137.4	26.7	200	196.3	38.2	60	255.2	49.6
21	20.6	4.0	81	79.5	15.5	141	138.4	26.9	201	197.3	38.4	261	256.2	49.8
22	21.6	4.2	82	80.5	15.6	42	139.4	27.1	02	198.3	38.5	62	257.2	50.0
23	22.6	4.4	83	81.5	15.8	43	140.4	27.3	03	199.3	38.7	63	258.2	50.2
24	23.6	4.6	84	82.5	16.0	44	141.4	27.5	04	200.3	38.9	64	259.1	50.4
25	24.5	4.8	85	83.4	16.2	45	142.3	27.7	05	201.2	39.1	65	260.1	50.6
26	25.5	5.0	86	84.4	16.4	46	143.3	27.9	06	202.2	39.3	66	261.1	50.8
27	26.5	5.2	87	85.4	16.6	47	144.3	28.0	07	203.2	39.5	67	262.1	50.9
28	27.5	5.3	88	86.4	16.8	48	145.3	28.2	08	204.2	39.7	68	263.1	51.1
29	28.5	5.5	89	87.4	17.0	49	146.3	28.4	09	205.2	39.9	69	264.1	51.3
30	29.4	5.7	90	88.3	17.2	50	147.2	28.6	10	206.1	40.1	70	265.0	51.5
31	30.4	5.9	91	89.3	17.4	151	148.2	28.8	211	207.1	40.3	271	266.0	51.7
32	31.4	6.1	92	90.3	17.6	52	149.2	29.0	12	208.1	40.5	72	267.0	51.9
33	32.4	6.3	93	91.3	17.7	53	150.2	29.2	13	209.1	40.6	73	268.0	52.1
34	33.4	6.5	94	92.3	17.9	54	151.2	29.4	14	210.1	40.8	74	269.0	52.3
35	34.4	6.7	95	93.3	18.1	55	152.2	29.6	15	211.0	41.0	75	269.9	52.5
36	35.3	6.9	96	94.2	18.3	56	153.1	29.8	16	212.0	41.2	76	270.9	52.7
37	36.3	7.1	97	95.2	18.5	57	154.1	30.0	17	213.0	41.4	77	271.9	52.9
38	37.3	7.3	98	96.2	18.7	58	155.1	30.1	18	214.0	41.6	78	272.9	53.0
39	38.3	7.4	99	97.2	18.9	59	156.1	30.3	19	215.0	41.8	79	273.9	53.2
40	39.3	7.6	100	98.2	19.1	60	157.1	30.5	20	216.0	42.0	80	274.9	53.4
41	40.2	7.8	101	99.1	19.3	161	158.0	30.7	221	216.9	42.2	281	275.8	53.6
42	41.2	8.0	02	100.1	19.5	62	159.0	30.9	22	217.9	42.4	82	276.8	53.8
43	42.2	8.2	03	101.1	19.7	63	160.0	31.1	23	218.9	42.6	83	277.8	54.0
44	43.2	8.4	04	102.1	19.8	64	161.0	31.3	24	219.9	42.7	84	278.8	54.2
45	44.2	8.6	05	103.1	20.0	65	162.0	31.5	25	220.9	42.9	85	279.8	54.4
46	45.2	8.8	06	104.1	20.2	66	163.0	31.7	26	221.8	43.1	86	280.7	54.6
47	46.1	9.0	07	105.0	20.4	67	163.9	31.9	27	222.8	43.3	87	281.7	54.8
48	47.1	9.2	08	106.0	20.6	68	164.9	32.1	28	223.8	43.5	88	282.7	55.0
49	48.1	9.3	09	107.0	20.8	69	165.9	32.2	29	224.8	43.7	89	283.7	55.1
50	49.1	9.5	10	108.0	21.0	70	166.9	32.4	30	225.8	43.9	90	284.7	55.3
51	50.1	9.7	111	109.0	21.2	171	167.9	32.6	231	226.8	44.1	291	285.7	55.5
52	51.0	9.9	12	109.9	21.4	72	168.8	32.8	32	227.7	44.3	92	286.6	55.7
53	52.0	10.1	13	110.9	21.6	73	169.8	33.0	33	228.7	44.5	93	287.6	55.9
54	53.0	10.3	14	111.9	21.8	74	170.8	33.2	34	229.7	44.6	94	288.6	56.1
55	54.0	10.5	15	112.9	21.9	75	171.8	33.4	35	230.7	44.8	95	289.6	56.3
56	55.0	10.7	16	113.9	22.1	76	172.8	33.6	36	231.7	45.0	96	290.6	56.5
57	56.0	10.9	17	114.9	22.3	77	173.7	33.8	37	232.6	45.2	97	291.5	56.7
58	56.9	11.1	18	115.8	22.5	78	174.7	34.0	38	233.6	45.4	98	292.5	56.9
59	57.9	11.3	19	116.8	22.7	79	175.7	34.2	39	234.6	45.6	99	293.5	57.1
60	58.9	11.4	20	117.8	22.9	80	176.7	34.3	40	235.6	45.8	300	294.5	57.2
Dist.	Dep.	Lat.	Dist.	Dep.	Lat.	Dist.	Dep.	Lat.	Dist.	Dep.	Lat.	Dist.	Dep.	Lat.

79° (101°, 259°, 281°).

	Dist.	Lat.	Dep.
In **Plane Sailing.**			
For converting *Dep.* into *Diff. Long.* and *Diff. Long.* into *Dep.* **In Middle Latitude Sailing.**	Diff. Long.	Dep.	
For converting *Dep.* into *Diff. Long.* and *Diff. Long.* into *Dep.* **In Mercator Sailing.**		*m*	Diff. Long.
For multiplication of numbers by sines and by cosines, or solution of plane right-angled triangles.	N. Hypotenuse.	N×Cos. Side Adj.	N×Sin. Side Opp.

TABLE 3.

Difference of Latitude and Departure for 11° (169°, 191°, 349°).

Dist.	Lat.	Dep.	Dist.	Lat.	Dep.	Dist.	Lat.	Dep.	Dist.	Lat.	Dep.	Dist.	Lat.	Dep.
301	295.5	57.4	361	354.4	68.9	421	413.3	80.3	481	472.2	91.8	541	531.1	103.2
02	296.5	57.6	62	355.3	69.1	22	414.2	80.5	82	473.1	92.0	42	532.0	103.4
03	297.4	57.8	63	356.3	69.3	23	415.2	80.7	83	474.1	92.2	43	533.0	103.6
04	298.4	58.0	64	357.3	69.5	24	416.2	80.9	84	475.1	92.4	44	534.0	103.8
05	299.4	58.2	65	358.3	69.6	25	417.2	81.1	85	476.1	92.5	45	535.0	104.0
06	300.4	58.4	66	359.3	69.8	26	418.2	81.3	86	477.1	92.7	46	536.0	104.2
07	301.4	58.6	67	360.3	70.0	27	419.2	81.5	87	478.1	92.9	47	537.0	104.4
08	302.3	58.8	68	361.2	70.2	28	420.1	81.7	88	479.0	93.1	48	537.9	104.6
09	303.3	59.0	69	362.2	70.4	29	421.1	81.9	89	480.0	93.3	49	538.9	104.8
10	304.3	59.2	70	363.2	70.6	30	422.1	82.1	90	481.0	93.5	50	539.9	104.9
311	305.3	59.3	371	364.2	70.8	431	423.0	82.2	491	482.0	93.7	551	540.9	105.1
12	306.3	59.5	72	365.2	71.0	32	424.1	82.4	92	483.0	93.9	52	541.9	105.3
13	307.2	59.7	73	366.1	71.2	33	425.0	82.6	93	483.9	94.1	53	542.8	105.5
14	308.2	59.9	74	367.1	71.4	34	426.0	82.8	94	484.9	94.3	54	543.8	105.7
15	309.2	60.1	75	368.1	71.6	35	427.0	83.0	95	485.9	94.5	55	544.8	105.9
16	310.2	60.3	76	369.1	71.7	36	428.0	83.2	96	486.9	94.6	56	545.8	106.1
17	311.2	60.5	77	370.1	71.9	37	428.9	83.4	97	487.9	94.8	57	546.8	106.3
18	312.2	60.7	78	371.1	72.1	38	430.0	83.6	98	488.9	95.0	58	547.7	106.5
19	313.1	60.9	79	372.0	72.3	39	430.9	83.8	99	489.8	95.2	59	548.7	106.7
20	314.1	61.1	80	373.0	72.5	40	431.9	84.0	500	490.8	95.4	60	549.7	106.9
321	315.1	61.2	381	374.0	72.7	441	432.9	84.1	501	491.8	95.6	561	550.7	107.0
22	316.1	61.4	82	375.0	72.9	42	433.9	84.3	02	492.8	95.8	62	551.7	107.2
23	317.1	61.6	83	376.0	73.1	43	434.9	84.5	03	493.8	96.0	63	552.7	107.4
24	318.0	61.8	84	376.9	73.3	44	435.8	84.7	04	494.7	96.2	64	553.6	107.6
25	319.0	62.0	85	377.9	73.5	45	436.8	84.9	05	495.7	96.4	65	554.6	107.8
26	320.0	62.2	86	378.9	73.7	46	437.8	85.1	06	496.7	96.5	66	555.6	108.0
27	321.0	62.4	87	379.9	73.8	47	438.8	85.3	07	497.7	96.7	67	556.6	108.2
28	322.0	62.6	88	380.8	74.0	48	439.8	85.5	08	498.7	96.9	68	557.6	108.4
29	323.0	62.8	89	381.9	74.2	49	440.8	85.7	09	499.6	97.1	69	558.5	108.6
30	323.9	63.0	90	382.8	74.4	50	441.7	85.9	10	500.6	97.3	70	559.5	108.8
331	324.9	63.2	391	383.8	74.6	451	442.7	86.1	511	501.6	97.5	571	560.5	109.0
32	325.9	63.3	92	384.8	74.8	52	443.7	86.2	12	502.6	97.7	72	561.5	109.1
33	326.9	63.5	93	385.8	75.0	53	444.7	86.4	13	503.6	97.9	73	562.5	109.3
34	327.9	63.7	94	386.8	75.2	54	445.7	86.6	14	504.6	98.1	74	563.5	109.5
35	328.8	63.9	95	387.7	75.4	55	446.6	86.8	15	505.5	98.3	75	564.4	109.7
36	329.8	64.1	96	388.7	75.6	56	447.6	87.0	16	506.5	98.5	76	565.4	109.9
37	330.8	64.3	97	389.7	75.8	57	448.6	87.2	17	507.5	98.6	77	566.4	110.1
38	331.8	64.5	98	390.7	75.9	58	449.6	87.4	18	508.5	98.8	78	567.4	110.3
39	332.7	64.7	99	391.7	76.1	59	450.6	87.6	19	509.5	99.0	79	568.4	110.5
40	333.8	64.9	400	392.7	76.3	60	451.5	87.8	20	510.4	99.2	80	569.3	110.7
341	334.7	65.1	401	393.6	76.5	461	452.5	88.0	521	511.4	99.4	581	570.3	110.9
42	335.7	65.3	02	394.6	76.7	62	453.5	88.2	22	512.4	99.6	82	571.3	111.1
43	336.7	65.4	03	395.6	76.9	63	454.5	88.3	23	513.4	99.8	83	572.3	111.2
44	337.7	65.6	04	396.6	77.1	64	455.4	88.5	24	514.4	100.0	84	573.3	111.4
45	338.7	65.8	05	397.6	77.3	65	456.5	88.7	25	515.4	100.2	85	574.3	111.6
46	339.6	66.0	06	398.5	77.5	66	457.4	88.9	26	516.3	100.4	86	575.2	111.8
47	340.6	66.2	07	399.5	77.7	67	458.4	89.1	27	517.3	100.6	87	576.2	112.1
48	341.6	66.4	08	400.5	77.9	68	459.4	89.3	28	518.3	100.7	88	577.2	112.3
49	342.6	66.6	09	401.5	78.1	69	460.4	89.5	29	519.3	100.9	89	578.2	112.4
50	343.6	66.8	10	402.5	78.2	70	461.4	89.7	30	520.3	101.1	90	579.2	112.6
351	344.6	67.0	411	403.4	78.4	471	462.3	89.9	531	521.2	101.3	591	580.1	112.8
52	345.5	67.2	12	404.4	78.6	72	463.3	90.1	32	522.2	101.5	92	581.1	113.0
53	346.5	67.4	13	405.4	78.8	73	464.3	90.3	33	523.2	101.7	93	582.1	113.2
54	347.5	67.5	14	406.4	79.0	74	465.3	90.4	34	524.2	101.9	94	583.1	113.3
55	348.5	67.7	15	407.4	79.2	75	466.3	90.6	35	525.2	102.1	95	584.1	113.5
56	349.5	67.9	16	408.4	79.4	76	467.3	90.8	36	526.2	102.3	96	585.0	113.7
57	350.4	68.1	17	409.3	79.6	77	468.2	91.0	37	527.1	102.5	97	586.0	113.9
58	351.4	68.3	18	410.3	79.8	78	469.2	91.2	38	528.1	102.7	98	587.0	114.1
59	352.4	68.5	19	411.3	79.9	79	470.2	91.4	39	529.1	102.8	99	588.0	114.3
60	353.4	68.7	20	412.3	80.1	80	471.2	91.6	40	530.1	103.0	600	589.0	114.5
Dist.	Dep.	Lat.	Dist.	Dep.	Lat.	Dist.	Dep.	Lat.	Dist.	Dep.	Lat.	Dist.	Dep.	Lat.

79° (101°, 259°, 281°).

In **Plane Sailing.**	**Dist.**	**Lat.**	**Dep.**
For converting *Dep.* into *Diff. Long.* and *Diff. Long.* into *Dep.* In **Middle Latitude Sailing.**	Diff. Long.	Dep.	
For converting *Dep.* into *Diff. Long.* and *Diff. Long.* into *Dep.* In **Mercator Sailing.**		*m*	Diff. Long.
For multiplication of numbers by sines and by cosines, or solution of plane right-angled triangles.	N.	N×Cos.	N×Sin.
	Hypotenuse.	Side Adj.	Side Opp.

TABLE 3.

Difference of Latitude and Departure for 12° (168°, 192°, 348°).

Dist.	Lat.	Dep	Dist.	Lat.	Dep.	Dist.	Lat.	Dep.	Dist.	Lat.	Dep.	Dist.	Lat.	Dep.
1	1.0	0.2	61	59.7	12.7	121	118.4	25.2	181	177.0	37.6	241	235.7	50.1
2	2.0	0.4	62	60.6	12.9	22	119.3	25.4	82	178.0	37.8	42	236.7	50.3
3	2.9	0.6	63	61.6	13.1	23	120.3	25.6	83	179.0	38.0	43	237.7	50 5
4	3.9	0.8	64	62.6	13.3	24	121.3	25.8	84	180.0	38.3	44	238.7	50.7
5	4.9	1.0	65	63.6	13.5	25	122.3	26.0	85	181.0	38.5	45	239.6	50.9
6	5.9	1.2	66	64.6	13.7	26	123.2	26.2	86	181.9	38.7	46	240.6	51.1
7	6.8	1.5	67	65.5	13.9	27	124.2	26.4	87	182.9	38.9	47	241.6	51.4
8	7.8	1.7	68	66.5	14.1	28	125.2	26.6	88	183.9	39.1	48	242.6	51.6
9	8.8	1.9	69	67.5	14.3	29	126.2	26.8	89	184.9	39.3	49	243.6	51.8
10	9.8	2.1	70	68.5	14.6	30	127.2	27.0	90	185.8	39.5	50	244.5	52.0
11	10.8	2.3	71	69.4	14.8	131	128.1	27.2	191	186.8	39.7	251	245.5	52.2
12	11.7	2.5	72	70.4	15.0	32	129.1	27.4	92	187.8	39.9	52	246.5	52.4
13	12.7	2.7	73	71.4	15.2	33	130.1	27.7	93	188.8	40.1	53	247.5	52.6
14	13.7	2.9	74	72.4	15.4	34	131.1	27.9	94	189.8	40.3	54	248.4	52.8
15	14.7	3.1	75	73.4	15.6	35	132.0	28.1	95	190.7	40.5	55	249.4	53.0
16	15.7	3.3	76	74.3	15.8	36	133 0	28.3	96	191.7	40.8	56	250.4	53.2
17	16.6	3.5	77	75.3	16.0	37	134.0	28.5	97	192.7	41.0	57	251.4	53.4
18	17.6	3.7	78	76.3	16.2	38	135.0	28.7	98	193.7	41.2	58	252.4	53.6
19	18.6	4.0	79	77.3	16.4	39	136.0	28.9	99	194.7	41.4	59	253.3	53.8
20	19.6	4.2	80	78.3	16.6	40	136.9	29.1	200	195.6	41.6	60	254.3	54.1
21	20.5	4.4	81	79.2	16.8	141	137.9	29.3	201	196.6	41.8	261	255.3	54.3
22	21.5	4.6	82	80.2	17.0	42	138.9	29.5	02	197.6	42.0	62	256.3	54.5
23	22.5	4.8	83	81.2	17.3	43	139.9	29.7	03	198.6	42.2	63	257.3	54.7
24	23.5	5.0	84	82.2	17.5	44	140.9	29.9	04	199.5	42.4	64	258.2	54.9
25	24.5	5.2	85	83.1	17.7	45	141.8	30.1	05	200.5	42.6	65	259.2	55.1
26	25.4	5.4	86	84.1	17.9	46	142.8	30.4	06	201.5	42.8	66	260.2	55.3
27	26.4	5.6	87	85.1	18.1	47	143.8	30.6	07	202.5	43.0	67	261.2	55.5
28	27.4	5.8	88	86.1	18.3	48	144.8	30.8	08	203.5	43.2	68	262.1	55.7
29	28.4	6.0	89	87.1	18.5	49	145.7	31.0	09	204.4	43.5	69	263.1	55.9
30	29.3	6.2	90	88.0	18.7	50	146.7	31.2	10	205.4	43.7	70	264.1	56.1
31	30.3	6.4	91	89.0	18.9	151	147.7	31.4	211	206.4	43.9	271	265.1	56.3
32	31.3	6.7	92	90.0	19.1	52	148.7	31.6	12	207.4	44.1	72	266.1	56.6
33	32.3	6.9	93	91.0	19.3	53	149.7	31.8	13	208.3	44.3	73	267.0	56.8
34	33.3	7.1	94	91.9	19.5	54	150.6	32.0	14	209.3	44.5	74	268.0	57.0
35	34.2	7.3	95	92.9	19.8	55	151.6	32.2	15	210.3	44.7	75	269.0	57.2
36	35.2	7.5	96	93.9	20.0	56	152.6	32.4	16	211.3	44.9	76	270.0	57.4
37	36.2	7.7	97	94.9	20.2	57	153.6	32.6	17	212.3	45.1	77	270.9	57.6
38	37.2	7.9	98	95.9	20.4	58	154.5	32.9	18	213.2	45.3	78	271.9	57.8
39	38.1	8.1	99	96.8	20.6	59	155.5	33.1	19	214.2	45.5	79	272.9	58.0
40	39.1	8.3	100	97.8	20.8	60	156.5	33.3	20	215.2	45.7	80	273.9	58.2
41	40.1	8.5	101	98.8	21.0	161	157.5	33.5	221	216.2	45.9	281	274.9	58.4
42	41.1	8.7	02	99.8	21.2	62	158.5	33.7	22	217.1	46.2	82	275.8	58.6
43	42.1	8.9	03	100.7	21.4	63	159.4	33.9	23	218.1	46.4	83	276.8	58.8
44	43.0	9.1	04	101.7	21.6	64	160.4	34.1	24	219.1	46.6	84	277.8	59.0
45	44.0	9.4	05	102.7	21.8	65	161.4	34.3	25	220.1	46.8	85	278.8	59.3
46	45.0	9.6	06	103.7	22.0	66	162.4	34.5	26	221.1	47.0	86	279.8	59.5
47	46.0	9.8	07	104.7	22.2	67	163.4	34.7	27	222.0	47.2	87	280.7	59.7
48	47.0	10.0	08	105.7	22.5	68	164.3	34.9	28	223.0	47.4	88	281.7	59.9
49	47.9	10.2	09	106.6	22.7	69	165.3	35.1	29	224.0	47.6	89	282.7	60.1
50	48.9	10.4	10	107.6	22.9	70	166.3	35.3	30	225.0	47.8	90	283.7	60.3
51	49.9	10.6	111	108.6	23.1	171	167.3	35.6	231	226.0	48.0	291	284.6	60.5
52	50.9	10.8	12	109.6	23.3	72	168.2	35.8	32	226.9	48.2	92	285.6	60.7
53	51.8	11.0	13	110.5	23.5	73	169.2	36.0	33	227.9	48.4	93	286.6	60.9
54	52.8	11.2	14	111.5	23.7	74	170.2	36.2	34	228.9	48.7	94	287.6	61.1
55	53.8	11.4	15	112.5	23.9	75	171.2	36.4	35	229.9	48.9	95	288.6	61.3
56	54.8	11.6	16	113.5	24.1	76	172.2	36.6	36	230.8	49.1	96	289.5	61.5
57	55.8	11.9	17	114.4	24.3	77	173.1	36.8	37	231.8	49.3	97	290.5	61.7
58	56.7	12.1	18	115.4	24.5	78	174.1	37.0	38	232.8	49.5	98	291.5	62.0
59	57.7	12.3	19	116.4	24.7	79	175.1	37.2	39	233.8	49.7	99	292.5	62.2
60	58.7	12.5	20	117.4	24.9	80	176.1	37.4	40	234.8	49.9	300	293.4	62.4
Dist.	Dep.	Lat.	Dist.	Dep.	Lat.	Dist.	Dep.	Lat.	Dist.	Dep.	Lat.	Dist.	Dep.	Lat.

78° (102°, 258°, 282°).

In **Plane Sailing.**	**Dist.**	**Lat.**	**Dep.**
For converting *Dep.* into *Diff. Long.* and *Diff. Long.* into *Dep.* **In Middle Latitude Sailing.**	Diff. Long.	Dep.	
For converting *Dep.* into *Diff. Long.* and *Diff. Long.* into *Dep.* **In Mercator Sailing.**		*m*	Diff. Long.
For multiplication of numbers by sines and by cosines, or solution of plane right-angled triangles.	N. Hypotenuse.	N×Cos. Side Adj.	N×Sin. Side Opp.

TABLE 3.

Difference of Latitude and Departure for 12° (168°, 192°, 348°).

Dist.	Lat.	Dep.	Dist.	Lat.	Dep.	Dist.	Lat.	Dep.	Dist.	Lat.	Dep.	Dist.	Lat.	Dep.
301	294.4	62.6	361	353.1	75.0	421	411.8	87.5	481	470.5	100.0	541	529.2	112.5
02	295.4	62.8	62	354.1	75.2	22	412.8	87.7	82	471.5	100.2	42	530.2	112.7
03	296.4	63.0	63	355.1	75.4	23	413.8	87.9	83	472.4	100.4	43	531.1	112.9
04	297.4	63.2	64	356.0	75.7	24	414.7	88.1	84	473.4	100.6	44	532.1	113.1
05	298.3	63.4	65	357.0	75.9	25	415.7	88.3	85	474.4	100.8	45	533.1	113.3
06	299.3	63.6	66	358.0	76.1	26	416.7	88.6	86	475.4	101.0	46	534.1	113.5
07	300.3	63.8	67	359.0	76.3	27	417.7	88.8	87	476.4	101.3	47	535.0	113.7
08	301.3	64.0	68	360.0	76.5	28	418.6	89.0	88	477.3	101.5	48	536.0	113.9
09	302.2	64.2	69	360.9	76.7	29	419.6	89.2	89	478.3	101.7	49	537.0	114.1
10	303.2	64.5	70	361.9	76.9	30	420.6	89.4	90	479.3	101.9	50	538.0	114.4
311	304.2	64.7	371	362.9	77.1	431	421.6	89.6	491	480.3	102.1	551	539.0	114.6
12	305.2	64.9	72	363.9	77.3	32	422.6	89.8	92	481.2	102.3	52	539.9	114.8
13	306.2	65.1	73	364.8	77.6	33	423.5	90.0	93	482.2	102.5	53	540.9	115.0
14	307.1	65.3	74	365.8	77.8	34	424.5	90.2	94	483.2	102.7	54	541.9	115.2
15	308.1	65.5	75	366.8	78.0	35	425.5	90.4	95	484.2	102.9	55	542.9	115.4
16	309.1	65.7	76	367.8	78.2	36	426.5	90.6	96	485.2	103.1	56	543.9	115.6
17	310.1	65.9	77	368.8	78.4	37	427.5	90.9	97	486.1	103.3	57	544.8	115.8
18	311.1	66.1	78	369.7	78.6	38	428.4	91.1	98	487.1	103.5	58	545.8	116.0
19	312.0	66.3	79	370.7	78.8	39	429.4	91.3	99	488.1	103.7	59	546.8	116.2
20	313.0	66.5	80	371.7	79.0	40	430.4	91.5	500	489.1	104.0	60	547.8	116.4
321	314.0	66.7	381	372.7	79.2	441	431.4	91.7	501	490.1	104.2	561	548.7	116.6
22	315.0	66.9	82	373.7	79.4	42	432.3	91.9	02	491.0	104.4	62	549.7	116.8
23	315.9	67.2	83	374.6	79.6	43	433.3	92.1	03	492.0	104.6	63	550.7	117.1
24	316.9	67.4	84	375.6	79.8	44	434.3	92.3	04	493.0	104.8	64	551.7	117.3
25	317.9	67.6	85	376.6	80.0	45	435.3	92.5	05	494.0	105.0	65	552.7	117.5
26	318.9	67.8	86	377.6	80.3	46	436.3	92.7	06	494.9	105.2	66	553.6	117.7
27	319.9	68.0	87	378.5	80.5	47	437.2	92.9	07	495.9	105.4	67	554.6	117.9
28	320.8	68.2	88	379.5	80.7	48	438.2	93.1	08	496.9	105.6	68	555.6	118.1
29	321.8	68.4	89	380.5	80.9	49	439.2	93.4	09	497.9	105.8	69	556.6	118.3
30	322.8	68.6	90	381.5	81.1	50	440.2	93.6	10	498.9	106.0	70	557.5	118.5
331	323.8	68.8	391	382.5	81.3	451	441.1	93.8	511	499.8	106.2	571	558.5	118.7
32	324.7	69.0	92	383.4	81.5	52	442.1	94.0	12	500.8	106.5	72	559.5	118.9
33	325.7	69.2	93	384.4	81.7	53	443.1	94.2	13	501.8	106.7	73	560.5	119.1
34	326.7	69.4	94	385.4	81.9	54	444.1	94.4	14	502.8	106.9	74	561.5	119.3
35	327.7	69.7	95	386.4	82.1	55	445.1	94.6	15	503.7	107.1	75	562.4	119.5
36	328.7	69.9	96	387.3	82.3	56	446.0	94.8	16	504.7	107.3	76	563.4	119.8
37	329.6	70.1	97	388.3	82.5	57	447.0	95.0	17	505.7	107.5	77	564.4	120.0
38	330.6	70.3	98	389.3	82.7	58	448.0	95.2	18	506.7	107.7	78	565.4	120.2
39	331.6	70.5	99	390.3	83.0	59	449.0	95.4	19	507.7	107.9	79	566.3	120.4
40	332.6	70.7	400	391.3	83.2	60	449.9	95.6	20	508.7	108.1	80	567.3	120.6
341	333.5	70.9	401	392.2	83.4	461	450.9	95.8	521	509.6	108.3	581	568.3	120.8
42	334.5	71.1	02	393.2	83.6	62	451.9	96.1	22	510.6	108.5	82	569.3	121.0
43	335.5	71.3	03	394.2	83.8	63	452.9	96.3	23	511.6	108.7	83	570.3	121.2
44	336.5	71.5	04	395.2	84.0	64	453.9	96.5	24	512.5	108.9	84	571.2	121.4
45	337.5	71.7	05	396.2	84.2	65	454.8	96.7	25	513.5	109.2	85	572.2	121.6
46	338.4	71.9	06	397.1	84.4	66	455.8	96.9	26	514.5	109.4	86	573.2	121.8
47	339.4	72.1	07	398.1	84.6	67	456.8	97.1	27	515.5	109.6	87	574.2	122.0
48	340.4	72.4	08	399.1	84.8	68	457.8	97.3	28	516.5	109.8	88	575.2	122.3
49	341.4	72.6	09	400.1	85.0	69	458.8	97.5	29	517.4	110.0	89	576.1	122.5
50	342.4	72.8	10	401.0	85.2	70	459.7	97.7	30	518.4	110.2	90	577.1	122.7
351	343.3	73.0	411	402.0	85.5	471	460.7	97.9	531	519.4	110.4	591	578.1	122.9
52	344.3	73.2	12	403.0	85.7	72	461.7	98.1	32	520.4	110.6	92	579.1	123.1
53	345.3	73.4	13	404.0	85.9	73	462.7	98.3	33	521.4	110.8	93	580.0	123.3
54	346.3	73.6	14	405.0	86.1	74	463.6	98.6	34	522.3	111.0	94	581.0	123.5
55	347.2	73.8	15	405.9	86.3	75	464.6	98.8	35	523.3	111.2	95	582.0	123.7
56	348.2	74.0	16	406.9	86.5	76	465.6	99.0	36	524.3	111.4	96	583.0	123.9
57	349.2	74.2	17	407.9	86.7	77	466.6	99.2	37	525.3	111.6	97	584.0	124.1
58	350.2	74.4	18	408.9	86.9	78	467.6	99.4	38	526.2	111.9	98	584.9	124.3
59	351.2	74.6	19	409.8	87.1	79	468.5	99.6	39	527.2	112.1	99	585.9	124.5
60	352.1	74.8	20	410.8	87.3	80	469.5	99.8	40	528.2	112.3	600	586.9	124.7
Dist.	Dep.	Lat.	Dist.	Dep.	Lat.	Dist.	Dep.	Lat.	Dist.	Dep.	Lat.	Dist.	Dep.	Lat.

78° (102°, 258°, 282°).

In **Plane Sailing.**	**Dist.**	**Lat.**	**Dep.**
For converting *Dep.* into *Diff. Long.* and *Diff. Long.* into *Dep.* In **Middle Latitude Sailing.**	Diff. Long.	Dep.	
For converting *Dep.* into *Diff. Long.* and *Diff. Long.* into *Dep.* In **Mercator Sailing.**		*m*	Diff. Long.
For multiplication of numbers by sines and by cosines, or solution of plane right-angled triangles.	N. / Hypotenuse.	N×Cos / Side Adj.	N×Sin. / Side Opp.

TABLE 3.

Difference of Latitude and Departure for 13° (167°, 193°, 347°).

Dist.	Lat.	Dep.	Dist.	Lat.	Dep.	Dist.	Lat.	Dep.	Dist.	Lat.	Dep.	Dist.	Lat.	Dep.
1	1.0	0.2	61	59.4	13.7	121	117.9	27.2	181	176.4	40.7	241	234.8	54.2
2	1.9	0.4	62	60.4	13.9	22	118.9	27.4	82	177.3	40.9	42	235.8	54.4
3	2.9	0.7	63	61.4	14.2	23	119.8	27.7	83	178.3	41.2	43	236.8	54.7
4	3.9	0.9	64	62.4	14.4	24	120.8	27.9	84	179.3	41.4	44	237.7	54.9
5	4.9	1.1	65	63.3	14.6	25	121.8	28.1	85	180.3	41.6	45	238.7	55.1
6	5.8	1.3	66	64.3	14.8	26	122.8	28.3	86	181.2	41.8	46	239.7	55.3
7	6.8	1.6	67	65.3	15.1	27	123.7	28.6	87	182.2	42.1	47	240.7	55.6
8	7.8	1.8	68	66.3	15.3	28	124.7	28.8	88	183.2	42.3	48	241.6	55.8
9	8.8	2.0	69	67.2	15.5	29	125.7	29.0	89	184.2	42.5	49	242.6	56.0
10	9.7	2.2	70	68.2	15.7	30	126.7	29.2	90	185.1	42.7	50	243.6	56.2
11	10.7	2.5	71	69.2	16.0	131	127.6	29.5	191	186.1	43.0	251	244.6	56.5
12	11.7	2.7	72	70.2	16.2	32	128.6	29.7	92	187.1	43.2	52	245.5	56.7
13	12.7	2.9	73	71.1	16.4	33	129.6	29.9	93	188.1	43.4	53	246.5	56.9
14	13.6	3.1	74	72.1	16.6	34	130.6	30.1	94	189.0	43.6	54	247.5	57.1
15	14.6	3.4	75	73.1	16.9	35	131.5	30.4	95	190.0	43.9	55	248.5	57.4
16	15.6	3.6	76	74.1	17.1	36	132.5	30.6	96	191.0	44.1	56	249.4	57.6
17	16.6	3.8	77	75.0	17.3	37	133.5	30.8	97	192.0	44.3	57	250.4	57.8
18	17.5	4.0	78	76.0	17.5	38	134.5	31.0	98	192.9	44.5	58	251.4	58.0
19	18.5	4.3	79	77.0	17.8	39	135.4	31.3	99	193.9	44.8	59	252.4	58.3
20	19.5	4.5	80	77.9	18.0	40	136.4	31.5	200	194.9	45.0	60	253.3	58.5
21	20.5	4.7	81	78.9	18.2	141	137.4	31.7	201	195.8	45.2	261	254.3	58.7
22	21.4	4.9	82	79.9	18.4	42	138.4	31.9	02	196.8	45.4	62	255.3	58.9
23	22.4	5.2	83	80.9	18.7	43	139.3	32.2	03	197.8	45.7	63	256.3	59.2
24	23.4	5.4	84	81.8	18.9	44	140.3	32.4	04	198.8	45.9	64	257.2	59.4
25	24.4	5.6	85	82.8	19.1	45	141.3	32.6	05	199.7	46.1	65	258.2	59.6
26	25.3	5.8	86	83.8	19.3	46	142.3	32.8	06	200.7	46.3	66	259.2	59.8
27	26.3	6.1	87	84.8	19.6	47	143.2	33.1	07	201.7	46.6	67	260.2	60.1
28	27.3	6.3	88	85.7	19.8	48	144.2	33.3	08	202.7	46.8	68	261.1	60.3
29	28.3	6.5	89	86.7	20.0	49	145.2	33.5	09	203.6	47.0	69	262.1	60.5
30	29.2	6.7	90	87.7	20.2	50	146.2	33.7	10	204.6	47.2	70	263.1	60.7
31	30.2	7.0	91	88.7	20.5	151	147.1	34.0	211	205.6	47.5	271	264.1	61.0
32	31.2	7.2	92	89.6	20.7	52	148.1	34.2	12	206.6	47.7	72	265.0	61.2
33	32.2	7.4	93	90.6	20.9	53	149.1	34.4	13	207.5	47.9	73	266.0	61.4
34	33.1	7.6	94	91.6	21.1	54	150.1	34.6	14	208.5	48.1	74	267.0	61.6
35	34.1	7.9	95	92.6	21.4	55	151.0	34.9	15	209.5	48.4	75	268.0	61.9
36	35.1	8.1	96	93.5	21.6	56	152.0	35.1	16	210.5	48.6	76	268.9	62.1
37	36.1	8.3	97	94.5	21.8	57	153.0	35.3	17	211.4	48.8	77	269.9	62.3
38	37.0	8.5	98	95.5	22.0	58	154.0	35.5	18	212.4	49.0	78	270.9	62.5
39	38.0	8.8	99	96.5	22.3	59	154.9	35.8	19	213.4	49.3	79	271.8	62.8
40	39.0	9.0	100	97.4	22.5	60	155.9	36.0	20	214.4	49.5	80	272.8	63.0
41	39.9	9.2	101	98.4	22.7	161	156.9	36.2	221	215.3	49.7	281	273.8	63.2
42	40.9	9.4	02	99.4	22.9	62	157.8	36.4	22	216.3	49.9	82	274.8	63.4
43	41.9	9.7	03	100.4	23.2	63	158.8	36.7	23	217.3	50.2	83	275.7	63.7
44	42.9	9.9	04	101.3	23.4	64	159.8	36.9	24	218.3	50.4	84	276.7	63.9
45	43.8	10.1	05	102.3	23.6	65	160.8	37.1	25	219.2	50.6	85	277.7	64.1
46	44.8	10.3	06	103.3	23.8	66	161.7	37.3	26	220.2	50.8	86	278.7	64.3
47	45.8	10.6	07	104.3	24.1	67	162.7	37.6	27	221.2	51.1	87	279.6	64.6
48	46.8	10.8	08	105.2	24.3	68	163.7	37.8	28	222.2	51.3	88	280.6	64.8
49	47.7	11.0	09	106.2	24.5	69	164.7	38.0	29	223.1	51.5	89	281.6	65.0
50	48.7	11.2	10	107.2	24.7	70	165.6	38.2	30	224.1	51.7	90	282.6	65.2
51	49.7	11.5	111	108.2	25.0	171	166.6	38.5	231	225.1	52.0	291	283.5	65.5
52	50.7	11.7	12	109.1	25.2	72	167.6	38.7	32	226.1	52.2	92	284.5	65.7
53	51.6	11.9	13	110.1	25.4	73	168.6	38.9	33	227.0	52.4	93	285.5	65.9
54	52.6	12.1	14	111.1	25.6	74	169.5	39.1	34	228.0	52.6	94	286.5	66.1
55	53.6	12.4	15	112.1	25.9	75	170.5	39.4	35	229.0	52.9	95	287.4	66.4
56	54.6	12.6	16	113.0	26.1	76	171.5	39.6	36	230.0	53.1	96	288.4	66.6
57	55.5	12.8	17	114.0	26.3	77	172.5	39.8	37	230.9	53.3	97	289.4	66.8
58	56.5	13.0	18	115.0	26.5	78	173.4	40.0	38	231.9	53.5	98	290.4	67.0
59	57.5	13.3	19	116.0	26.8	79	174.4	40.3	39	232.9	53.8	99	291.3	67.3
60	58.5	13.5	20	116.9	27.0	80	175.4	40.5	40	233.8	54.0	300	292.3	67.5
Dist.	Dep.	Lat.	Dist.	Dep.	Lat.	Dist.	Dep.	Lat.	Dist.	Dep.	Lat.	Dist.	Dep.	Lat.

77° (103°, 257°, 283°).

In **Plane Sailing.**	**Dist.**	**Lat.**	**Dep.**
For converting *Dep.* into *Diff. Long.* and *Diff. Long.* into *Dep.* In **Middle Latitude Sailing.**	Diff. Long.	Dep.	
For converting *Dep.* into *Diff. Long.* and *Diff. Long.* into *Dep.* In **Mercator Sailing.**		*m*	Diff. Long.
For multiplication of numbers by sines and by cosines, or solution of plane right-angled triangles.	N. Hypote-nuse.	N×Cos. Side Adj.	N×Sin. Side Opp.

TABLE 3.

Difference of Latitude and Departure for 13° (167°, 193°, 347°).

Dist.	Lat.	Dep.	Dist.	Lat.	Dep.	Dist.	Lat.	Dep.	Dist.	Lat.	Dep.	Dist.	Lat.	Dep.
301	293.3	67.7	361	351.7	81.2	421	410.2	94.7	481	468.7	108.2	541	527.1	121.7
02	294.3	67.9	62	352.7	81.4	22	411.2	94.9	82	469.6	108.4	42	528.1	121.9
03	295.2	68.2	63	353.7	81.7	23	412.2	95.2	83	470.6	108.7	43	529.1	122.1
04	296.2	68.4	64	354.7	81.9	24	413.1	95.4	84	471.6	108.9	44	530.1	122.4
05	297.2	68.6	65	355.6	82.1	25	414.1	95.6	85	472.6	109.1	45	531.0	122.6
06	298.2	68.8	66	356.6	82.3	26	415.1	95.8	86	473.5	109.3	46	532.0	122.8
07	299.1	69.1	67	357.6	82.6	27	416.1	96.1	87	474.5	109.6	47	533.0	123.0
08	300.1	69.3	68	358.6	82.8	28	417.0	96.3	88	475.5	109.8	48	534.0	123.3
09	301.1	69.5	69	359.5	83.0	29	418.0	96.5	89	476.5	110.0	49	534.9	123.5
10	302.1	69.7	70	360.5	83.2	30	419.0	96.7	90	477.4	110.2	50	535.9	123.7
311	303.0	70.0	371	361.5	83.5	431	420.0	97.0	491	478.4	110.5	551	536.9	123.9
12	304.0	70.2	72	362.5	83.7	32	420.9	97.2	92	479.4	110.7	52	537.9	124.2
13	305.0	70.4	73	363.4	83.9	33	421.9	97.4	93	480.4	110.9	53	538.8	124.4
14	306.0	70.6	74	364.4	84.1	34	422.9	97.6	94	481.3	111.1	54	539.8	124.6
15	306.9	70.9	75	365.4	84.4	35	423.9	97.9	95	482.3	111.4	55	540.8	124.8
16	307.9	71.1	76	366.4	84.6	36	424.8	98.1	96	483.3	111.6	56	541.7	125.1
17	308.9	71.3	77	367.3	84.8	37	425.8	98.3	97	484.3	111.8	57	542.7	125.3
18	309.8	71.5	78	368.3	85.0	38	426.8	98.5	98	485.2	112.0	58	543.7	125.5
19	310.8	71.8	79	369.3	85.3	39	427.7	98.8	99	486.2	112.3	59	544.7	125.7
20	311.8	72.0	80	370.3	85.5	40	428.7	99.0	500	487.2	112.5	60	545.6	126.0
321	312.8	72.2	381	371.2	85.7	441	429.7	99.2	501	488.2	112.7	561	546.6	126.2
22	313.7	72.4	82	372.2	85.9	42	430.7	99.4	02	489.1	112.9	62	547.6	126.4
23	314.7	72.7	83	373.2	86.2	43	431.6	99.7	03	490.1	113.2	63	548.6	126.6
24	315.7	72.9	84	374.2	86.4	44	432.6	99.9	04	491.1	113.4	64	549.5	126.9
25	316.7	73.1	85	375.1	86.6	45	433.6	100.1	05	492.1	113.6	65	550.5	127.1
26	317.6	73.3	86	376.1	86.8	46	434.6	100.3	06	493.0	113.8	66	551.5	127.3
27	318.6	73.6	87	377.1	87.1	47	435.5	100.6	07	494.0	114.1	67	552.5	127.5
28	319.6	73.8	88	378.1	87.3	48	436.5	100.8	08	495.0	114.3	68	553.4	127.8
29	320.6	74.0	89	379.0	87.5	49	437.5	101.0	09	496.0	114.5	69	554.4	128.0
30	321.5	74.2	90	380.0	87.7	50	438.5	101.2	10	496.9	114.7	70	555.4	128.2
331	322.5	74.5	391	381.0	88.0	451	439.4	101.5	511	497.9	115.0	571	556.4	128.4
32	323.5	74.7	92	382.0	88.2	52	440.4	101.7	12	498.9	115.2	72	557.3	128.7
33	324.5	74.9	93	382.9	88.4	53	441.4	101.9	13	499.9	115.4	73	558.3	128.9
34	325.4	75.1	94	383.9	88.6	54	442.4	102.1	14	500.8	115.6	74	559.3	129.1
35	326.4	75.4	95	384.9	88.9	55	443.3	102.4	15	501.8	115.8	75	560.3	129.3
36	327.4	75.6	96	385.9	89.1	56	444.3	102.6	16	502.8	116.1	76	561.2	129.6
37	328.4	75.8	97	386.8	89.3	57	445.3	102.8	17	503.7	116.3	77	562.2	129.8
38	329.3	76.0	98	387.8	89.5	58	446.3	103.0	18	504.7	116.5	78	563.2	130.0
39	330.3	76.3	99	388.8	89.8	59	447.2	103.3	19	505.7	116.7	79	564.2	130.2
40	331.3	76.5	400	389.7	90.0	60	448.2	103.5	20	506.7	117.0	80	565.1	130.5
341	332.3	76.7	401	390.7	90.2	461	449.2	103.7	521	507.6	117.2	581	566.1	130.7
42	333.2	76.9	02	391.7	90.4	62	450.2	103.9	22	508.6	117.5	82	567.1	130.9
43	334.2	77.2	03	392.7	90.7	63	451.1	104.2	23	509.6	117.6	83	568.1	131.1
44	335.2	77.4	04	393.6	90.9	64	452.1	104.4	24	510.6	117.9	84	569.0	131.4
45	336.2	77.6	05	394.6	91.1	65	453.1	104.6	25	511.5	118.1	85	570.0	131.6
46	337.1	77.8	06	395.6	91.3	66	454.1	104.8	26	512.5	118.3	86	571.0	131.8
47	338.1	78.1	07	396.6	91.6	67	455.0	105.1	27	513.5	118.5	87	572.0	132.0
48	339.1	78.3	08	397.5	91.8	68	456.0	105.3	28	514.5	118.8	88	572.9	132.3
49	340.1	78.5	09	398.5	92.0	69	457.0	105.5	29	515.4	119.0	89	573.9	132.5
50	341.0	78.7	10	399.5	92.2	70	458.0	105.7	30	516.4	119.2	90	574.9	132.7
351	342.0	79.0	411	400.5	92.5	471	458.9	106.0	531	517.4	119.4	591	575.9	132.9
52	343.0	79.2	12	401.4	92.7	72	459.9	106.2	32	518.4	119.7	92	576.8	133.2
53	344.0	79.4	13	402.4	92.9	73	460.9	106.4	33	519.3	119.9	93	577.8	133.4
54	344.9	79.6	14	403.4	93.1	74	461.9	106.6	34	520.3	120.1	94	578.8	133.6
55	345.9	79.9	15	404.4	93.4	75	462.8	106.9	35	521.3	120.3	95	579.8	133.8
56	346.9	80.1	16	405.3	93.6	76	463.8	107.1	36	522.3	120.6	96	580.7	134.1
57	347.9	80.3	17	406.3	93.8	77	464.8	107.3	37	523.2	120.8	97	581.7	134.3
58	348.8	80.5	18	407.3	94.0	78	465.7	107.5	38	524.2	121.0	98	582.7	134.5
59	349.8	80.8	19	408.3	94.3	79	466.7	107.8	39	525.2	121.2	99	583.6	134.7
60	350.8	81.0	20	409.2	94.5	80	467.7	108.0	40	526.2	121.5	600	584.6	135.0
Dist.	Dep.	Lat.	Dist.	Dep.	Lat.	Dist.	Dep.	Lat.	Dist.	Dep.	Lat.	Dist.	Dep.	Lat.

77° (103°, 257°, 283°).

In Plane Sailing.	Dist.	Lat.	Dep.
For converting *Dep.* into *Diff. Long.* and *Diff. Long.* into *Dep.* **In Middle Latitude Sailing.**	Diff. Long.	Dep.	
For converting *Dep.* into *Diff. Long.* and *Diff. Long.* into *Dep.* **In Mercator Sailing.**		*m*	Diff. Long.
For multiplication of numbers by sines and by cosines, or solution of plane right-angled triangles.	N. Hypotenuse.	N×Cos. Side Adj.	N×Sin. Side Opp.

TABLE 3.

Difference of Latitude and Departure for 14° (166°, 194°, 346°).

Dist.	Lat.	Dep.	Dist.	Lat.	Dep.	Dist.	Lat.	Dep.	Dist.	Lat.	Dep.	Dist.	Lat.	Dep.
1	1.0	0.2	61	59.2	14.8	121	117.4	29.3	181	175.6	43.8	241	233.8	58.3
2	1.9	0.5	62	60.2	15.0	22	118.4	29.5	82	176.6	44.0	42	234.8	58.5
3	2.9	0.7	63	61.1	15.2	23	119.3	29.8	83	177.6	44.3	43	235.8	58.8
4	3.9	1.0	64	62.1	15.5	24	120.3	30.0	84	178.5	44.5	44	236.8	59.0
5	4.9	1.2	65	63.1	15.7	25	121.3	30.2	85	179.5	44.8	45	237.7	59.3
6	5.8	1.5	66	64.0	16.0	26	122.3	30.5	86	180.5	45.0	46	238.7	59.5
7	6.8	1.7	67	65.0	16.2	27	123.2	30.7	87	181.4	45.2	47	239.7	59 8
8	7.8	1.9	68	66.0	16.5	28	124.2	31.0	88	182.4	45.5	48	240.6	60.0
9	8.7	2.2	69	67.0	16.7	29	125.2	31.2	89	183.4	45.7	49	241.6	60.2
10	9.7	2.4	70	67 9	16.9	30	126.1	31.4	90	184.4	46.0	50	242.6	60.5
11	10.7	2.7	71	68.9	17.2	131	127.1	31.7	191	185.3	46.2	251	243.5	60.7
12	11.6	2.9	72	69.9	17.4	32	128.1	31.9	92	186.3	46.4	52	244.5	61.0
13	12.6	3.1	73	70.8	17.7	33	129.0	32.2	93	187.3	46.7	53	245.5	61.2
14	13.6	3.4	74	71.8	17.9	34	130.0	32.4	94	188.2	46.9	54	246.5	61.4
15	14.6	3.6	75	72.8	18.1	35	131.0	32.7	95	189.2	47.2	55	247.4	61.7
16	15.5	3.9	76	73.7	18.4	36	132.0	32.9	96	190.2	47.4	56	248.4	61.9
17	16.5	4.1	77	74.7	18.6	37	132.9	33.1	97	191.1	47.7	57	249.4	62.2
18	17.5	4.4	78	75.7	18.9	38	133.9	33.4	98	192.1	47.9	58	250.3	62.4
19	18.4	4.6	79	76.7	19.1	39	134.9	33.6	99	193.1	48.1	59	251.3	62.7
20	19.4	4.8	80	77.6	19.4	40	135.8	33.9	200	194.1	48.4	60	252.3	62.9
21	20.4	5.1	81	78.6	19.6	141	136.8	34.1	201	195.0	48.6	261	253.2	63.1
22	21.3	5.3	82	79.6	19.8	42	137.8	34.4	02	196.0	48.9	62	254.2	63.4
23	22.3	5.6	83	80.5	20.1	43	138.8	34.6	03	197.0	49.1	63	255.2	63.6
24	23.3	5.8	84	81.5	20.3	44	139.7	34.8	04	197.9	49.4	64	256.2	63.9
25	24.3	6.0	85	82.5	20.6	45	140.7	35.1	05	198.9	49.6	65	257.1	64.1
26	25.2	6.3	86	83.4	20.8	46	141.7	35.3	06	199.9	49.8	66	258.1	64.4
27	26.2	6.5	87	84.4	21.0	47	142.6	35.6	07	200.9	50.1	67	259.1	64.6
28	27.2	6.8	88	85.4	21.3	48	143.6	35.8	08	201.8	50.3	68	260.0	64.8
29	28.1	7.0	89	86.4	21.5	49	144.6	36.0	09	202.8	50.6	69	261.0	65.1
30	29.1	7.3	90	87.3	21.8	50	145.5	36.3	10	203.8	50.8	70	262.0	65.3
31	30.1	7.5	91	88.3	22.0	151	146.5	36.5	211	204.7	51.0	271	263.0	65.6
32	31.0	7.7	92	89.3	22.3	52	147.5	36.8	12	205.7	51.3	72	263.9	65.8
33	32.0	8.0	93	90.2	22.5	53	148.5	37.0	13	206.7	51.5	73	264.9	66.0
34	33.0	8.2	94	91.2	22.7	54	149.4	37.3	14	207.6	51.8	74	265.9	66.3
35	34.0	8.5	95	92.2	23.0	55	150.4	37.5	15	208.6	52.0	75	266.8	66.5
36	34.9	8.7	96	93.1	23.2	56	151.4	37.7	16	209.6	52.3	76	267.8	66.8
37	35.9	9.0	97	94.1	23.5	57	152.3	38.0	17	210.6	52.5	77	268.8	67.0
38	36.9	9.2	98	95.1	23.7	58	153.3	38.2	18	211.5	52.7	78	269.7	67.3
39	37.8	9.4	99	96.1	24.0	59	154.3	38.5	19	212.5	53.0	79	270.7	67.5
40	38.8	9.7	100	97.0	24.2	60	155.2	38.7	20	213.5	53.2	80	271.7	67.7
41	39.8	9.9	101	98.0	24.4	161	156.2	38.9	221	214.4	53.5	281	272.7	68.0
42	40.8	10.2	02	99.0	24.7	62	157.2	39.2	22	215.4	53.7	82	273.6	68.2
43	41.7	10.4	03	99.9	24.9	63	158.2	39.4	23	216.4	53.9	83	274.6	68.5
44	42.7	10.6	04	100.9	25.2	64	159.1	39.7	24	217.3	54.2	84	275.6	68.7
45	43.7	10.9	05	101.9	25.4	65	160.1	39.9	25	218.3	54.4	85	276.5	68.9
46	44.6	11.1	06	102.9	25.6	66	161.1	40.2	26	219.3	54.7	86	277.5	69.2
47	45.6	11.4	07	103.8	25.9	67	162.0	40.4	27	220.3	54.9	87	278.5	69.4
48	46.6	11.6	08	104.8	26.1	68	163.0	40.6	28	221.2	55.2	88	279.4	69.7
49	47.5	11.9	09	105.8	26.4	69	164.0	40.9	29	222.2	55.4	89	280.4	69.9
50	48.5	12.1	10	106.7	26.6	70	165.0	41.1	30	223.2	55.6	90	281.4	70.2
51	49.5	12.3	111	107.7	26.9	171	165.9	41.4	231	224.1	55.9	291	282.4	70.4
52	50.5	12.6	12	108.7	27.1	72	166.9	41.6	32	225.1	56.1	92	283.3	70.6
53	51.4	12.8	13	109.6	27.3	73	167.9	41.9	33	226.1	56.4	93	284.3	70.9
54	52.4	13.1	14	110.6	27.6	74	168.8	42.1	34	227.0	56.6	94	285.3	71.1
55	53.4	13.3	15	111.6	27.8	75	169.8	42.3	35	228.0	56.9	95	286.2	71.4
56	54.3	13.5	16	112.6	28.1	76	170.8	42.6	36	229.0	57.1	96	287.2	71.6
57	55.3	13.8	17	113.5	28.3	77	171.7	42.8	37	230.0	57.3	97	288.2	71.9
58	56.3	14.0	18	114.5	28.5	78	172.7	43.1	38	230.9	57.6	98	289.1	72.1
59	57.2	14.3	19	115.5	28.8	79	173.7	43.3	39	231.9	57.8	99	290.1	72.3
60	58.2	14.5	20	116.4	29.0	80	174.7	43.5	40	232.9	58.1	300	291.1	72.6
Dist.	Dep.	Lat.	Dist.	Dep.	Lat.	Dist.	Dep.	Lat.	Dist.	Dep.	Lat.	Dist.	Dep.	Lat.

76° (104°, 256°, 284°).

In **Plane Sailing.**	**Dist.**	**Lat.**	**Dep.**
For converting *Dep.* into *Diff. Long.* and *Diff. Long.* into *Dep.* In **Middle Latitude Sailing.**	Diff. Long.	Dep.	
For converting *Dep.* into *Diff. Long.* and *Diff. Long.* into *Dep.* In **Mercator Sailing.**		*m*	Diff. Long.
For multiplication of numbers by sines and by cosines, or solution of plane right-angled triangles.	N. / Hypotenuse.	N×Cos. / Side Adj.	N×Sin. / Side Opp.

TABLE 3.

Difference of Latitude and Departure for 14° (166°, 194°, 346°).

Dist.	Lat.	Dep.	Dist.	Lat.	Dep.	Dist.	Lat.	Dep.	Dist.	Lat.	Dep.	Dist.	Lat.	Dep.
301	292.1	72.8	361	350.3	87.3	421	408.5	101.8	481	466.7	116.4	541	524.9	130.9
02	293.0	73.1	62	351.2	87.6	22	409.5	102.1	82	467.7	116.6	42	525.9	131.1
03	294.0	73.3	63	352.2	87.8	23	410.4	102.3	83	468.7	116.8	43	526.9	131.4
04	295.0	73.5	64	353.2	88.1	24	411.4	102.6	84	469.6	117.1	44	527.8	131.6
05	295.9	73.8	65	354.2	88.3	25	412.4	102.8	85	470.6	117.3	45	528.8	131.8
06	296.9	74.0	66	355.1	88.5	26	413.3	103.1	86	471.6	117.6	46	529.8	132.1
07	297.9	74.3	67	356.1	88.8	27	414.3	103.3	87	472.5	117.8	47	530.8	132.3
08	298.9	74.5	68	357.1	89.0	28	415.3	103.5	88	473.5	118.1	48	531.7	132.6
09	299.8	74.8	69	358.0	89.3	29	416.3	103.8	89	474.5	118.3	49	532.7	132.8
10	300.8	75.0	70	359.0	89.5	30	417.2	104.0	90	475.4	118.5	50	533.7	133.1
311	301.8	75.2	371	360.0	89.8	431	418.2	104.3	491	476.4	118.8	551	534.6	133.3
12	302.7	75.5	72	361.0	90.0	32	419.2	104.5	92	477.4	119.0	52	535.6	133.5
13	303.7	75.7	73	361.9	90.2	33	420.1	104.8	93	478.4	119.3	53	536.6	133.8
14	304.6	76.0	74	362.9	90.5	34	421.1	105.0	94	479.3	119.5	54	537.5	134.0
15	305.6	76.2	75	363.9	90.7	35	422.0	105.2	95	480.3	119.8	55	538.5	134.3
16	306.6	76.4	76	364.8	91.0	36	423.0	105.5	96	481.3	120.0	56	539.5	134.5
17	307.6	76.7	77	365.8	91.2	37	424.0	105.7	97	482.2	120.2	57	540.5	134.8
18	308.6	76.9	78	366.8	91.4	38	425.0	106.0	98	483.2	120.5	58	541.4	135.0
19	309.5	77.2	79	367.7	91.7	39	426.0	106.2	99	484.2	120.7	59	542.4	135.2
20	310.5	77.4	80	368.7	91.9	40	426.9	106.4	500	485.1	121.0	60	543.4	135.5
321	311.5	77.7	381	369.7	92.2	441	427.9	106.7	501	486.1	121.2	561	544.3	135.7
22	312.4	77.9	82	370.7	92.4	42	428.9	106.9	02	487.1	121.4	62	545.3	136.0
23	313.4	78.1	83	371.6	92.7	43	429.8	107.2	03	488.1	121.7	63	546.3	136.2
24	314.4	78.4	84	372.6	92.9	44	430.8	107.4	04	489.0	121.9	64	547.2	136.4
25	315.3	78.6	85	373.6	93.1	45	431.8	107.7	05	490.0	122.2	65	548.2	136.7
26	316.3	78.9	86	374.5	93.4	46	432.8	107.9	06	491.0	122.4	66	549.2	136.9
27	317.3	79.1	87	375.5	93.6	47	433.7	108.1	07	491.9	122.7	67	550.2	137.2
28	318.3	79.4	88	376.4	93.9	48	434.7	108.4	08	492.9	122.9	68	551.1	137.4
29	319.2	79.6	89	377.4	94.1	49	435.7	108.6	09	493.9	123.1	69	552.1	137.7
30	320.2	79.8	90	378.4	94.3	50	436.6	108.9	10	494.9	123.4	70	553.1	137.9
331	321.2	80.1	391	379.4	94.6	451	437.6	109.1	511	495.8	123.6	571	554.0	138.1
32	322.1	80.3	92	380.4	94.8	52	438.6	109.3	12	496.8	123.9	72	555.0	138.4
33	323.1	80.6	93	381.3	95.1	53	439.5	109.6	13	497.8	124.1	73	556.0	138.6
34	324.1	80.8	94	382.3	95.3	54	440.5	109.8	14	498.7	124.3	74	556.9	138.9
35	325.0	81.0	95	383.3	95.6	55	441.5	110.1	15	499.7	124.6	75	557.9	139.1
36	326.0	81.3	96	384.2	95.8	56	442.5	110.3	16	500.7	124.8	76	558.9	139.3
37	327.0	81.5	97	385.2	96.0	57	443.4	110.6	17	501.6	125.1	77	559.9	139.6
38	328.0	81.8	98	386.2	96.3	58	444.4	110.8	18	502.6	125.3	78	560.8	139.8
39	328.9	82.0	99	387.1	96.5	59	445.4	111.0	19	503.6	125.6	79	561.8	140.1
40	329.9	82.3	400	388.1	96.8	60	446.3	111.3	20	504.6	125.8	80	562.8	140.3
341	330.8	82.5	401	389.1	97.0	461	447.3	111.5	521	505.5	126.0	581	563.7	140.6
42	331.8	82.7	02	390.1	97.3	62	448.3	111.8	22	506.5	126.3	82	564.7	140.8
43	332.8	83.0	03	391.0	97.5	63	449.2	112.0	23	507.5	126.5	83	565.7	141.0
44	333.8	83.2	04	392.0	97.7	64	450.2	112.3	24	508.4	126.8	84	566.7	141.3
45	334.8	83.5	05	393.0	98.0	65	451.2	112.5	25	509.4	127.0	85	567.6	141.5
46	335.7	83.7	06	393.9	98.2	66	452.2	112.7	26	510.4	127.3	86	568.6	141.8
47	336.7	83.9	07	394.9	98.5	67	453.1	113.0	27	511.3	127.5	87	569.6	142.0
48	337.7	84.2	08	395.9	98.7	68	454.1	113.2	28	512.3	127.7	88	570.5	142.3
49	338.6	84.4	09	396.9	98.9	69	455.1	113.5	29	513.3	128.0	89	571.5	142.5
50	339.6	84.7	10	397.8	99.2	70	456.0	113.7	30	514.3	128.2	90	572.5	142.7
351	340.6	84.9	411	398.8	99.4	471	457.0	113.9	531	515.2	128.5	591	573.4	143.0
52	341.5	85.2	12	399.8	99.7	72	458.0	114.2	32	516.2	128.7	92	574.4	143.2
53	342.5	85.4	13	400.7	99.9	73	458.9	114.4	33	517.2	128.9	93	575.4	143.5
54	343.5	85.6	14	401.7	100.2	74	459.9	114.7	34	518.1	129.2	94	576.4	143.7
55	344.5	85.9	15	402.7	100.4	75	460.9	114.9	35	519.1	129.4	95	577.3	143.9
56	345.4	86.1	16	403.6	100.6	76	461.9	115.2	36	520.1	129.7	96	578.3	144.2
57	346.4	86.4	17	404.6	100.9	77	462.8	115.4	37	521.0	129.9	97	579.3	144.4
58	347.4	86.6	18	405.6	101.1	78	463.8	115.6	38	522.0	130.2	98	580.2	144.7
59	348.3	86.8	19	406.6	101.4	79	464.8	115.9	39	523.0	130.4	99	581.2	144.9
60	349.3	87.1	20	407.5	101.6	80	465.7	116.1	40	524.0	130.6	600	582.2	145.2
Dist.	Dep.	Lat.	Dist.	Dep.	Lat.	Dist.	Dep.	Lat.	Dist.	Dep.	Lat.	Dist.	Dep.	Lat.

76° (104°, 256°, 284°).

In **Plane Sailing.**	**Dist.**	**Lat.**	**Dep.**
For converting *Dep.* into *Diff. Long.* and *Diff. Long.* into *Dep.* In **Middle Latitude Sailing.**	Diff. Long.	Dep.	
For converting *Dep.* into *Diff. Long.* and *Diff. Long.* into *Dep.* In **Mercator Sailing.**		*m*	Diff. Long.
For multiplication of numbers by sines and by cosines, or solution of plane right-angled triangles.	N. Hypotenuse.	N×Cos. Side Adj.	N×Sin. Side Opp.

541524°—43——29

TABLE 3.

Difference of Latitude and Departure for 15° (165°, 195°, 345°).

Dist.	Lat.	Dep.	Dist.	Lat.	Dep.	Dist.	Lat.	Dep.	Dist.	Lat.	Dep.	Dist.	Lat.	Dep.
1	1.0	0.3	61	58.9	15.8	121	116.9	31.3	181	174.8	46.8	241	232.8	62.4
2	1.9	0.5	62	59.9	16.0	22	117.8	31.6	82	175.8	47.1	42	233.8	62.6
3	2.9	0.8	63	60.9	16.3	23	118.8	31.8	83	176.8	47.4	43	234.7	62.9
4	3.9	1.0	64	61.8	16.6	24	119.8	32.1	84	177.7	47.6	44	235.7	63.2
5	4.8	1.3	65	62.8	16.8	25	120.7	32.4	85	178.7	47.9	45	236.7	63.4
6	5.8	1.6	66	63.8	17.1	26	121.7	32.6	86	179.7	48.1	46	237.6	63.7
7	6.8	1.8	67	64.7	17.3	27	122.7	32.9	87	180.6	48.4	47	238.6	63.9
8	7.7	2.1	68	65.7	17.6	28	123.6	33.1	88	181.6	48.7	48	239.5	64.2
9	8.7	2.3	69	66.6	17.9	29	124.6	33.4	89	182.6	48.9	49	240.5	64.4
10	9.7	2.6	70	67.6	18.1	30	125.6	33.6	90	183.5	49.2	50	241.5	64.7
11	10.6	2.8	71	68.6	18.4	131	126.5	33.9	191	184.5	49.4	251	242.4	65.0
12	11.6	3.1	72	69.5	18.6	32	127.5	34.2	92	185.5	49.7	52	243.4	65.2
13	12.6	3.4	73	70.5	18.9	33	128.5	34.4	93	186.4	50.0	53	244.4	65.5
14	13.5	3.6	74	71.5	19.2	34	129.4	34.7	94	187.4	50.2	54	245.3	65.7
15	14.5	3.9	75	72.4	19.4	35	130.4	34.9	95	188.4	50.5	55	246.3	66.0
16	15.5	4.1	76	73.4	19.7	36	131.4	35.2	96	189.3	50.7	56	247.3	66.3
17	16.4	4.4	77	74.4	19.9	37	132.3	35.5	97	190.3	51.0	57	248.2	66.5
18	17.4	4.7	78	75.3	20.2	38	133.3	35.7	98	191.3	51.2	58	249.2	66.8
19	18.4	4.9	79	76.3	20.4	39	134.3	36.0	99	192.2	51.5	59	250.2	67.0
20	19.3	5.2	80	77.3	20.7	40	135.2	36.2	200	193.2	51.8	60	251.1	67.3
21	20.3	5.4	81	78.2	21.0	141	136.2	36.5	201	194.2	52.0	261	252.1	67.6
22	21.3	5.7	82	79.2	21.2	42	137.2	36.8	02	195.1	52.3	62	253.1	67.8
23	22.2	6.0	83	80.2	21.5	43	138.1	37.0	03	196.1	52.5	63	254.0	68.1
24	23.2	6.2	84	81.1	21.7	44	139.1	37.3	04	197.0	52.8	64	255.0	68.3
25	24.1	6.5	85	82.1	22.0	45	140.1	37.5	05	198.0	53.1	65	256.0	68.6
26	25.1	6.7	86	83.1	22.3	46	141.0	37.8	06	199.0	53.3	66	256.9	68.8
27	26.1	7.0	87	84.0	22.5	47	142.0	38.0	07	199.9	53.6	67	257.9	69.1
28	27.0	7.2	88	85.0	22.8	48	143.0	38.3	08	200.9	53.8	68	258.9	69.4
29	28.0	7.5	89	86.0	23.0	49	143.9	38.6	09	201.9	54.1	69	259.8	69.6
30	29.0	7.8	90	86.9	23.3	50	144.9	38.8	10	202.8	54.4	70	260.8	69.9
31	29.9	8.0	91	87.9	23.6	151	145.9	39.1	211	203.8	54.6	271	261.8	70.1
32	30.9	8.3	92	88.9	23.8	52	146.8	39.3	12	204.8	54.9	72	262.7	70.4
33	31.9	8.5	93	89.8	24.1	53	147.8	39.6	13	205.7	55.1	73	263.7	70.7
34	32.8	8.8	94	90.8	24.3	54	148.8	39.9	14	206.7	55.4	74	264.7	70.9
35	33.8	9.1	95	91.8	24.6	55	149.7	40.1	15	207.7	55.6	75	265.6	71.2
36	34.8	9.3	96	92.7	24.8	56	150.7	40.4	16	208.6	55.9	76	266.6	71.4
37	35.7	9.6	97	93.7	25.1	57	151.7	40.6	17	209.6	56.2	77	267.6	71.7
38	36.7	9.8	98	94.7	25.4	58	152.6	40.9	18	210.6	56.4	78	268.5	72.0
39	37.7	10.1	99	95.6	25.6	59	153.6	41.2	19	211.5	56.7	79	269.5	72.2
40	38.6	10.4	100	96.6	25.9	60	154.5	41.4	20	212.5	56.9	80	270.5	72.5
41	39.6	10.6	101	97.6	26.1	161	155.5	41.7	221	213.5	57.2	281	271.4	72.7
42	40.6	10.9	02	98.5	26.4	62	156.5	41.9	22	214.4	57.5	82	272.4	73.0
43	41.5	11.1	03	99.5	26.7	63	157.4	42.2	23	215.4	57.7	83	273.4	73.2
44	42.5	11.4	04	100.5	26.9	64	158.4	42.4	24	216.4	58.0	84	274.3	73.5
45	43.5	11.6	05	101.4	27.2	65	159.4	42.7	25	217.3	58.2	85	275.3	73.8
46	44.4	11.9	06	102.4	27.4	66	160.3	43.0	26	218.3	58.5	86	276.3	74.0
47	45.4	12.2	07	103.4	27.7	67	161.3	43.2	27	219.3	58.8	87	277.2	74.3
48	46.4	12.4	08	104.3	28.0	68	162.3	43.5	28	220.2	59.0	88	278.2	74.5
49	47.3	12.7	09	105.3	28.2	69	163.2	43.7	29	221.2	59.3	89	279.2	74.8
50	48.3	12.9	10	106.3	28.5	70	164.2	44.0	30	222.2	59.5	90	280.1	75.1
51	49.3	13.2	111	107.2	28.7	171	165.2	44.3	231	223.1	59.8	291	281.1	75.3
52	50.2	13.5	12	108.2	29.0	72	166.1	44.5	32	224.1	60.0	92	282.1	75.6
53	51.2	13.7	13	109.1	29.2	73	167.1	44.8	33	225.1	60.3	93	283.0	75.8
54	52.2	14.0	14	110.1	29.5	74	168.1	45.0	34	226.0	60.6	94	284.0	76.1
55	53.1	14.2	15	111.1	29.8	75	169.0	45.3	35	227.0	60.8	95	284.9	76.4
56	54.1	14.5	16	112.0	30.0	76	170.0	45.6	36	228.0	61.1	96	285.9	76.6
57	55.1	14.8	17	113.0	30.3	77	171.0	45.8	37	228.9	61.3	97	286.9	76.9
58	56.0	15.0	18	114.0	30.5	78	171.9	46.1	38	229.9	61.6	98	287.8	77.1
59	57.0	15.3	19	114.9	30.8	79	172.9	46.3	39	230.9	61.9	99	288.8	77.4
60	58.0	15.5	20	115.9	31.1	80	173.9	46.6	40	231.8	62.1	300	289.8	77.6
Dist.	**Dep.**	**Lat.**	**Dist.**	**Dep.**	**Lat.**	**Dist.**	**Dep.**	**Lat.**	**Dist.**	**Dep.**	**Lat.**	**Dist.**	**Dep.**	**Lat.**

75° (105°, 255°, 285°).

In Plane Sailing.	Dist.	Lat.	Dep.
For converting *Dep.* into *Diff. Long.* and *Diff. Long.* into *Dep.* **In Middle Latitude Sailing.**	Diff. Long.	Dep.	
For converting *Dep.* into *Diff. Long.* and *Diff. Long.* into *Dep.* **In Mercator Sailing.**		*m*	Diff Long.
For multiplication of numbers by sines and by cosines, or solution of plane right-angled triangles.	N. Hypotenuse.	N×Cos. Side Adj.	N×Sin. Side Opp.

TABLE 3.

Difference of Latitude and Departure for 15° (165°, 195°, 345°).

Dist.	Lat.	Dep.	Dist.	Lat.	Dep.	Dist.	Lat.	Dep.	Dist.	Lat.	Dep.	Dist.	Lat.	Dep.
301	290.7	77.9	361	348.7	93.4	421	406.7	109.0	481	464.6	124.5	541	522.6	140.0
02	291.7	78.2	62	349.7	93.7	22	407.6	109.2	82	465.6	124.8	42	523.5	140.3
03	292.7	78.4	63	350.6	94.0	23	408.6	109.5	83	466.5	125.0	43	524.5	140.5
04	293.6	78.7	64	351.6	94.2	24	409.6	109.7	84	467.5	125.3	44	525.5	140.8
05	294.6	78.9	65	352.6	94.5	25	410.5	110.0	85	468.5	125.5	45	526.4	141.1
06	295.6	79.2	66	353.5	94.7	26	411.5	110.3	86	469.4	125.8	46	527.4	141.3
07	296.5	79.5	67	354.5	95.0	27	412.4	110.5	87	470.4	126.0	47	528.4	141.6
08	297.5	79.7	68	355.5	95.2	28	413.4	110.8	88	471.4	126.3	48	529.3	141.8
09	298.5	80.0	69	356.4	95.5	29	414.4	111.0	89	472.3	126.6	49	530.3	142.1
10	299.4	80.2	70	357.4	95.8	30	415.3	111.3	90	473.3	126.8	50	531.3	142.4
311	309.4	80.5	371	358.4	96.0	431	416.3	111.6	491	474.3	127.1	551	532.2	142.6
12	301.4	80.8	72	359.3	96.3	32	417.3	111.8	92	475.2	127.3	52	533.2	142.9
13	302.3	81.0	73	360.3	96.5	33	418.2	112.1	93	476.2	127.6	53	534.2	143.1
14	303.3	81.3	74	361.3	96.8	34	419.2	112.3	94	477.2	127.9	54	535.1	143.4
15	304.3	81.5	75	362.2	97.1	35	420.2	112.6	95	478.1	128.1	55	536.1	143.6
16	305.2	81.8	76	363.2	97.3	36	421.1	112.8	96	479.1	128.4	56	537.1	143.9
17	306.2	82.0	77	364.2	97.6	37	422.1	113.1	97	480.1	128.6	57	538.0	144.2
18	307.2	82.3	78	365.1	97.8	38	423.1	113.4	98	481.0	128.9	58	539.0	144.4
19	308.1	82.6	79	366.1	98.1	39	424.0	113.6	99	482.0	129.2	59	540.0	144.7
20	309.1	82.8	80	367.1	98.4	40	425.0	113.9	500	483.0	129.4	60	540.9	144.9
321	310.1	83.1	381	368.0	98.6	441	426.0	114.1	501	483.9	129.7	561	541.9	145.2
22	311.0	83.3	82	369.0	98.9	42	426.9	114.4	02	484.9	129.9	62	542.9	145.5
23	312.0	83.6	83	369.9	99.1	43	427.9	114.7	03	485.9	130.2	63	543.8	145.7
24	313.0	83.9	84	370.9	99.4	44	428.9	114.9	04	486.8	130.4	64	544.8	146.0
25	313.9	84.1	85	371.9	99.6	45	429.8	115.2	05	487.8	130.7	65	545.7	146.2
26	314.9	84.4	86	372.8	99.9	46	430.8	115.4	06	488.8	131.0	66	546.7	146.5
27	315.9	84.6	87	373.8	100.2	47	431.8	115.7	07	489.7	131.2	67	547.7	146.8
28	316.8	84.9	88	374.8	100.4	48	432.7	116.0	08	490.7	131.5	68	548.6	147.0
29	317.8	85.2	89	375.7	100.7	49	433.7	116.2	09	491.7	131.7	69	549.6	147.3
30	318.8	85.4	90	376.7	100.9	50	434.7	116.5	10	492.6	132.0	70	550.6	147.5
331	319.7	85.7	391	377.7	101.2	451	435.6	116.7	511	493.6	132.3	571	551.5	147.8
32	320.7	85.9	92	378.6	101.5	52	436.6	117.0	12	494.6	132.5	72	552.5	148.0
33	321.7	86.2	93	379.6	101.7	53	437.6	117.2	13	495.5	132.8	73	553.5	148.3
34	322.6	86.4	94	380.6	102.0	54	438.5	117.5	14	496.5	133.0	74	554.4	148.6
35	323.6	86.7	95	381.5	102.2	55	439.5	117.8	15	497.5	133.3	75	555.4	148.8
36	324.6	87.0	96	382.5	102.5	56	440.5	118.0	16	498.4	133.6	76	556.4	149.1
37	325.5	87.2	97	383.5	102.8	57	441.4	118.3	17	499.4	133.8	77	557.3	149.3
38	326.5	87.5	98	384.4	103.0	58	442.4	118.5	18	500.3	134.1	78	558.3	149.6
39	327.4	87.7	99	385.4	103.3	59	443.4	118.8	19	501.3	134.3	79	559.3	149.8
40	328.4	88.0	400	386.4	103.5	60	444.3	119.1	20	502.3	134.6	80	560.2	150.1
341	329.4	88.3	401	387.3	103.8	461	445.3	119.3	521	503.2	134.8	581	561.2	150.4
42	330.3	88.5	02	388.3	104.0	62	446.3	119.6	22	504.2	135.1	82	562.2	150.6
43	331.3	88.8	03	389.3	104.3	63	447.2	119.8	23	505.2	135.4	83	563.1	150.9
44	332.3	89.0	04	390.2	104.6	64	448.2	120.1	24	506.1	135.6	84	564.1	151.2
45	333.2	89.3	05	391.2	104.8	65	449.2	120.4	25	507.1	135.9	85	565.1	151.4
46	334.2	89.6	06	392.2	105.1	66	450.1	120.6	26	508.1	136.1	86	566.0	151.6
47	335.2	89.8	07	393.1	105.3	67	451.1	120.9	27	509.0	136.4	87	567.0	151.9
48	336.1	90.1	08	394.1	105.6	68	452.1	121.1	28	510.0	136.7	88	568.0	152.2
49	337.1	90.3	09	395.1	105.9	69	453.0	121.4	29	511.0	136.9	89	568.9	152.4
50	338.1	90.6	10	396.0	106.1	70	454.0	121.6	30	511.9	137.2	90	569.9	152.7
351	339.0	90.8	411	397.0	106.4	471	455.0	121.9	531	512.9	137.4	591	570.9	153.0
52	341.0	91.1	12	398.0	106.6	72	455.9	122.2	32	513.9	137.7	92	571.8	153.2
53	341.0	91.4	13	398.9	106.9	73	456.9	122.4	33	514.8	138.0	93	572.8	153.5
54	341.9	91.6	14	399.9	107.2	74	457.8	122.7	34	515.8	138.2	94	573.8	153.7
55	342.9	91.9	15	400.9	107.4	75	458.8	122.9	35	516.8	138.5	95	574.7	154.0
56	343.9	92.1	16	401.8	107.7	76	459.8	123.2	36	517.7	138.7	96	575.7	154.3
57	344.8	92.4	17	402.8	107.9	77	460.7	123.5	37	518.7	139.0	97	576.7	154.5
58	345.8	92.7	18	403.8	108.2	78	461.7	123.7	38	519.7	139.2	98	577.6	154.8
59	346.8	92.9	19	404.7	108.4	79	462.7	124.0	39	520.6	139.5	99	578.6	155.0
60	347.7	93.2	20	405.7	108.7	80	463.6	124.2	40	521.6	139.8	600	579.6	155.3
Dist.	Dep.	Lat.	Dist.	Dep.	Lat.	Dist.	Dep.	Lat.	Dist.	Dep.	Lat.	Dist.	Dep.	Lat.

75° (105°, 255°, 285°).

In **Plane Sailing.**	Dist.	Lat.	Dep.
For converting *Dep.* into *Diff. Long.* and *Diff. Long.* into *Dep.* In **Middle Latitude Sailing.**	Diff. Long.	Dep.	
For converting *Dep.* into *Diff. Long.* and *Diff. Long.* into *Dep.* In **Mercator Sailing.**		*m*	Diff. Long.
For multiplication of numbers by sines and by cosines, or solution of plane right-angled triangles.	N. Hypotenuse.	N×Cos. Side Adj.	N×Sin. Side Opp.

TABLE 3.

Difference of Latitude and Departure for 16° (164°, 196°, 344°).

Dist.	Lat.	Dep.	Dist.	Lat.	Dep.	Dist.	Lat.	Dep.	Dist.	Lat.	Dep.	Dist.	Lat.	Dep.
1	1.0	0.3	61	58.6	16.8	121	116.3	33.4	181	174.0	49.9	241	231.7	66.4
2	1.9	0.6	62	59.6	17.1	22	117.3	33.6	82	174.9	50.2	42	232.6	66.7
3	2.9	0.8	63	60.6	17.4	23	118.2	33.9	83	175.9	50.4	43	233.6	67.0
4	3.8	1.1	64	61.5	17.6	24	119.2	34.2	84	176.9	50.7	44	234.5	67.3
5	4.8	1.4	65	62.5	17.9	25	120.2	34.5	85	177.8	51.0	45	235.5	67.5
6	5.8	1.7	66	63.4	18.2	26	121.1	34.7	86	178.8	51.3	46	236.5	67.8
7	6.7	1.9	67	64.4	18.5	27	122.1	35.0	87	179.8	51.5	47	237.4	68.1
8	7.7	2.2	68	65.4	18.7	28	123.0	35.3	88	180.7	51.8	48	238.4	68.4
9	8.7	2.5	69	66.3	19.0	29	124.0	35.6	89	181.7	52.1	49	239.4	68.6
10	9.6	2.8	70	67.3	19.3	30	125.0	35.8	90	182.6	52.4	50	240.3	68.9
11	10.6	3.0	71	68.2	19.6	131	125.9	36.1	191	183.6	52.6	251	241.3	69.2
12	11.5	3.3	72	69.2	19.8	32	126.9	36.4	92	184.6	52.9	52	242.2	69.5
13	12.5	3.6	73	70.2	20.1	33	127.8	36.7	93	185.5	53.2	53	243.2	69.7
14	13.5	3.9	74	71.1	20.4	34	128.8	36.9	94	186.5	53.5	54	244.2	70.0
15	14.4	4.1	75	72.1	20.7	35	129.8	37.2	95	187.4	53.7	55	245.1	70.3
16	15.4	4.4	76	73.1	20.9	36	130.7	37.5	96	188.4	54.0	56	246.1	70.6
17	16.3	4.7	77	74.0	21.2	37	131.7	37.8	97	189.4	54.3	57	247.0	70.8
18	17.3	5.0	78	75.0	21.5	38	132.7	38.0	98	190.3	54.6	58	248.0	71.1
19	18.3	5.2	79	75.9	21.8	39	133.6	38.3	99	191.3	54.9	59	249.0	71.4
20	19.2	5.5	80	76.9	22.1	40	134.6	38.6	200	192.3	55.1	60	249.9	71.7
21	20.2	5.8	81	77.9	22.3	141	135.5	38.9	201	193.2	55.4	261	250.9	71.9
22	21.1	6.1	82	78.8	22.6	42	136.5	39.1	02	194.2	55.7	62	251.9	72.2
23	22.1	6.3	83	79.8	22.9	43	137.5	39.4	03	195.1	56.0	63	252.8	72.5
24	23.1	6.6	84	80.7	23.2	44	138.4	39.7	04	196.1	56.2	64	253.8	72.8
25	24.0	6.9	85	81.7	23.4	45	139.4	40.0	05	197.1	56.5	65	254.7	73.0
26	25.0	7.2	86	82.7	23.7	46	140.3	40.2	06	198.0	56.8	66	255.7	73.3
27	26.0	7.4	87	83.6	24.0	47	141.3	40.5	07	199.0	57.1	67	256.7	73.6
28	26.9	7.7	88	84.6	24.3	48	142.3	40.8	08	199.9	57.3	68	257.6	73.9
29	27.9	8.0	89	85.6	24.5	49	143.2	41.1	09	200.9	57.6	69	258.6	74.1
30	28.8	8.3	90	86.5	24.8	50	144.2	41.3	10	201.9	57.9	70	259.5	74.4
31	29.8	8.5	91	87.5	25.1	151	145.2	41.6	211	202.8	58.2	271	260.5	74.7
32	30.8	8.8	92	88.4	25.4	52	146.1	41.9	12	203.8	58.4	72	261.5	75.0
33	31.7	9.1	93	89.4	25.6	53	147.1	42.2	13	204.7	58.7	73	262.4	75.2
34	32.7	9.4	94	90.4	25.9	54	148.0	42.4	14	205.7	59.0	74	263.4	75.5
35	33.6	9.6	95	91.3	26.2	55	149.0	42.7	15	206.7	59.3	75	264.3	75.8
36	34.6	9.9	96	92.3	26.5	56	150.0	43.0	16	207.6	59.5	76	265.3	76.1
37	35.6	10.2	97	93.2	26.7	57	150.9	43.3	17	208.6	59.8	77	266.3	76.4
38	36.5	10.5	98	94.2	27.0	58	151.9	43.6	18	209.6	60.1	78	267.2	76.6
39	37.5	10.7	99	95.2	27.3	59	152.8	43.8	19	210.5	60.4	79	268.2	76.9
40	38.5	11.0	100	96.1	27.6	60	153.8	44.1	20	211.5	60.6	80	269.2	77.2
41	39.4	11.3	101	97.1	27.8	161	154.8	44.4	221	212.4	60.9	281	270.1	77.5
42	40.4	11.6	02	98.0	28.1	62	155.7	44.7	22	213.4	61.2	82	271.1	77.7
43	41.3	11.9	03	99.0	28.4	63	156.7	44.9	23	214.4	61.5	83	272.0	78.0
44	42.3	12.1	04	100.0	28.7	64	157.6	45.2	24	215.3	61.7	84	273.0	78.3
45	43.3	12.4	05	100.9	28.9	65	158.6	45.5	25	216.3	62.0	85	274.0	78.6
46	44.2	12.7	06	101.9	29.2	66	159.6	45.8	26	217.2	62.3	86	274.9	78.8
47	45.2	13.0	07	102.9	29.5	67	160.5	46.0	27	218.2	62.6	87	275.9	79.1
48	46.1	13.2	08	103.8	29.8	68	161.5	46.3	28	219.2	62.8	88	276.8	79.4
49	47.1	13.5	09	104.8	30.0	69	162.5	46.6	29	220.1	63.1	89	277.8	79.7
50	48.1	13.8	10	105.7	30.3	70	163.4	46.9	30	221.1	63.4	90	278.8	79.9
51	49.0	14.1	111	106.7	30.6	171	164.4	47.1	231	222.1	63.7	291	279.7	80.2
52	50.0	14.3	12	107.7	30.9	72	165.3	47.4	32	223.0	63.9	92	280.7	80.5
53	50.9	14.6	13	108.6	31.1	73	166.3	47.7	33	224.0	64.2	93	281.6	80.8
54	51.9	14.9	14	109.6	31.4	74	167.3	48.0	34	224.9	64.5	94	282.6	81.0
55	52.9	15.2	15	110.5	31.7	75	168.2	48.2	35	225.9	64.8	95	283.6	81.3
56	53.8	15.4	16	111.5	32.0	76	169.2	48.5	36	226.9	65.1	96	284.5	81.6
57	54.8	15.7	17	112.5	32.2	77	170.1	48.8	37	227.8	65.3	97	285.5	81.9
58	55.8	16.0	18	113.4	32.5	78	171.1	49.1	38	228.8	65.6	98	286.5	82.1
59	56.7	16.3	19	114.4	32.8	79	172.1	49.3	39	229.7	65.9	99	287.4	82.4
60	57.7	16.5	20	115.4	33.1	80	173.0	49.6	40	230.7	66.2	300	288.4	82.7
Dist.	Dep.	Lat.	Dist.	Dep.	Lat.	Dist.	Dep.	Lat.	Dist.	Dep.	Lat.	Dist.	Dep.	Lat.

74° (106°, 254°, 286°).

In **Plane Sailing.**	**Dist.**	**Lat.**	**Dep.**
For converting *Dep.* into *Diff. Long.* and *Diff. Long.* into *Dep.* In **Middle Latitude Sailing.**	Diff. Long.	Dep.	
For converting *Dep.* into *Diff. Long.* and *Diff. Long.* into *Dep.* In **Mercator Sailing.**		*m*	Diff. Long.
For multiplication of numbers by sines and by cosines, or solution of plane right-angled triangles.	N.	N×Cos.	N×Sin.
	Hypotenuse.	Side. Adj.	Side Opp.

TABLE 3.

Difference of Latitude and Departure for 16° (164°, 196°, 344°).

Dist.	Lat.	Dep.	Dist.	Lat.	Dep.	Dist.	Lat.	Dep.	Dist.	Lat.	Dep.	Dist.	Lat.	Dep.
301	289.3	83.0	361	347.0	99.5	421	404.7	116.0	481	462.4	132.6	541	520.0	149.1
02	290.3	83.2	62	348.0	99.8	22	405.7	116.3	82	463.3	132.9	42	521.0	149.4
03	291.3	83.5	63	348.9	100.1	23	406.6	116.6	83	464.3	133.1	43	522.0	149.7
04	292.2	83.8	64	349.9	100.3	24	407.6	116.9	84	465.3	133.4	44	522.9	149.9
05	293.2	84.1	65	350.9	100.6	25	408.5	117.1	85	466.2	133.7	45	523.9	150.2
06	294.1	84.3	66	351.8	100.9	26	409.5	117.4	86	467.2	134.0	46	524.8	150.5
07	295.1	84.6	67	352.8	101.2	27	410.5	117.7	87	468.1	134.2	47	525.8	150.8
08	296.1	84.9	68	353.7	101.4	28	411.4	118.0	88	469.1	134.5	48	526.8	151.0
09	297.0	85.2	69	354.7	101.7	29	412.4	118.2	89	470.1	134.8	49	527.7	151.3
10	298.0	85.4	70	355.7	102.0	30	413.3	118.5	90	471.0	135.1	50	528.7	151.6
311	299.0	85.7	371	356.6	102.3	431	414.3	118.8	491	472.0	135.3	551	529.7	151.9
12	299.9	86.0	72	357.6	102.5	32	415.3	119.1	92	472.9	135.6	52	530.6	152.2
13	300.9	86.3	73	358.6	102.8	33	416.2	119.4	93	473.9	135.9	53	531.6	152.4
14	301.8	86.6	74	359.5	103.1	34	417.2	119.6	94	474.9	136.2	54	532.5	152.7
15	302.8	86.8	75	360.5	103.4	35	418.1	119.9	95	475.8	136.4	55	533.5	153.0
16	303.8	87.1	76	361.4	103.6	36	419.1	120.2	96	476.8	136.7	56	534.5	153.3
17	304.7	87.4	77	362.4	103.9	37	420.1	120.5	97	477.7	137.0	57	535.4	153.5
18	305.7	87.7	78	363.4	104.2	38	421.0	120.7	98	478.7	137.3	58	536.4	153.8
19	306.6	87.9	79	364.3	104.5	39	422.0	121.0	99	479.7	137.5	59	537.3	154.1
20	307.6	88.2	80	365.3	104.7	40	423.0	121.3	500	480.6	137.8	60	538.3	154.4
321	308.6	88.5	381	366.2	105.0	441	423.9	121.6	501	481.6	138.1	561	539.3	154.6
22	309.5	88.8	82	367.2	105.3	42	424.9	121.8	02	482.6	138.4	62	540.2	154.9
23	310.5	89.0	83	368.2	105.6	43	425.8	122.1	03	483.5	138.6	63	541.2	155.2
24	311.4	89.3	84	369.1	105.8	44	426.8	122.4	04	484.5	138.9	64	542.2	155.5
25	312.4	89.6	85	370.1	106.1	45	427.8	122.7	05	485.4	139.2	65	543.1	155.7
26	313.4	89.9	86	371.0	106.4	46	428.7	122.9	06	486.4	139.5	66	544.1	156.0
27	314.3	90.1	87	372.0	106.7	47	429.7	123.2	07	487.4	139.7	67	545.0	156.3
28	315.3	90.4	88	373.0	106.9	48	430.6	123.5	08	488.3	140.0	68	546.0	156.6
29	316.3	90.7	89	373.9	107.2	49	431.6	123.8	09	489.3	140.3	69	547.0	156.8
30	317.2	91.0	90	374.9	107.5	50	432.6	124.0	10	490.2	140.5	70	547.9	157.1
331	318.2	91.2	391	375.9	107.8	451	433.5	124.3	511	491.2	140.9	571	548.9	157.4
32	319.1	91.5	92	376.8	108.0	52	434.5	124.6	12	492.2	141.1	72	549.8	157.7
33	320.1	91.8	93	377.8	108.3	53	435.5	124.9	13	493.1	141.4	73	550.8	157.9
34	321.1	92.1	94	378.7	108.6	54	436.4	125.1	14	494.1	141.7	74	551.8	158.2
35	322.0	92.3	95	379.7	108.9	55	437.4	125.4	15	495.0	142.0	75	552.7	158.5
36	323.0	92.6	96	380.7	109.2	56	438.3	125.7	16	496.0	142.2	76	553.7	158.8
37	323.9	92.9	97	381.6	109.4	57	439.3	126.0	17	497.0	142.5	77	554.6	159.0
38	324.9	93.2	98	382.6	109.7	58	440.3	126.2	18	497.9	142.8	78	555.6	159.3
39	325.8	93.4	99	383.5	110.0	59	441.2	126.5	19	498.9	143.1	79	556.6	159.6
40	326.8	93.7	400	384.5	110.3	60	442.2	126.8	20	499.9	143.3	80	557.5	159.9
341	327.8	94.0	401	385.5	110.5	461	443.1	127.1	521	500.8	143.6	581	558.5	160.1
42	328.8	94.3	02	386.4	110.8	62	444.1	127.3	22	501.8	143.9	82	559.5	160.4
43	329.7	94.5	03	387.4	111.1	63	445.1	127.6	23	502.7	144.2	83	560.4	160.6
44	330.7	94.8	04	388.3	111.4	64	446.0	127.9	24	503.7	144.4	84	561.4	161.0
45	331.6	95.1	05	389.3	111.6	65	447.0	128.2	25	504.7	144.7	85	562.3	161.2
46	332.6	95.4	06	390.3	111.9	66	447.9	128.4	26	505.6	145.0	86	563.3	161.5
47	333.6	95.6	07	391.2	112.2	67	448.9	128.7	27	506.6	145.3	87	564.3	161.8
48	334.5	95.9	08	392.2	112.5	68	449.9	129.0	28	507.5	145.5	88	565.2	162.1
49	335.5	96.2	09	393.2	112.7	69	450.8	129.3	29	508.5	145.8	89	566.2	162.4
50	336.4	96.5	10	394.1	113.0	70	451.8	129.5	30	509.5	146.1	90	567.1	162.6
351	337.4	96.7	411	395.1	113.3	471	452.8	129.8	531	510.4	146.4	591	568.1	162.9
52	338.4	97.0	12	396.0	113.6	72	453.7	130.1	32	511.4	146.6	92	569.1	163.2
53	339.3	97.3	13	397.0	113.8	73	454.7	130.4	33	512.4	146.9	93	570.0	163.5
54	340.3	97.6	14	398.0	114.1	74	455.6	130.7	34	513.3	147.2	94	571.0	163.7
55	341.2	97.9	15	398.9	114.4	75	456.6	130.9	35	514.3	147.5	95	572.0	164.0
56	342.2	98.1	16	399.9	114.7	76	457.6	131.2	36	515.2	147.7	96	572.9	164.3
57	343.2	98.4	17	400.8	114.9	77	458.5	131.6	37	516.2	148.0	97	573.9	164.6
58	344.1	98.7	18	401.8	115.2	78	459.5	131.8	38	517.2	148.3	98	574.8	164.8
59	345.1	99.0	19	402.8	115.5	79	460.4	132.0	39	518.1	148.6	99	575.8	165.1
60	346.1	99.2	20	403.7	115.8	80	461.4	132.3	40	519.1	148.8	600	576.8	165.4
Dist.	Dep.	Lat.	Dist.	Dep.	Lat.	Dist.	Dep.	Lat.	Dist.	Dep.	Lat.	Dist.	Dep.	Lat.

74° (106°, 254°, 286°).

In **Plane Sailing.**	**Dist.**	**Lat.**	**Dep.**
For converting *Dep.* into *Diff. Long.* and *Diff. Long.* into *Dep.* In **Middle Latitude Sailing.**	Diff. Long.	Dep.	
For converting *Dep.* into *Diff. Long.* and *Diff. Long.* into *Dep.* In **Mercator Sailing.**		*m*	Diff. Long.
For multiplication of numbers by sines and by cosines, or solution of plane right-angled triangles.	N. / Hypotenuse.	N×Cos. / Side Adj.	N×Sin. / Side Opp.

TABLE 3.

Difference of Latitude and Departure for 17° (163°, 197°, 343°).

Dist.	Lat.	Dep.	Dist.	Lat.	Dep.	Dist.	Lat.	Dep.	Dist.	Lat.	Dep.	Dist.	Lat.	Dep.
1	1.0	0.3	61	58.3	17.8	121	115.7	35.4	181	173.1	52.9	241	230.5	70.5
2	1.9	0.6	62	59.3	18.1	22	116.7	35.7	82	174.0	53.2	42	231.4	70.8
3	2.9	0.9	63	60.2	18.4	23	117.6	36.0	83	175.0	53.5	43	232.4	71.0
4	3.8	1.2	64	61.2	18.7	24	118.6	36.3	84	176.0	53.8	44	233.3	71.3
5	4.8	1.5	65	62.2	19.0	25	119.5	36.5	85	176.9	54.1	45	234.3	71.6
6	5.7	1.8	66	63.1	19.3	26	120.5	36.8	86	177.9	54.4	46	235.3	71.9
7	6.7	2.0	67	64.1	19.6	27	121.5	37.1	87	178.8	54.7	47	236.2	72.2
8	7.7	2.3	68	65.0	19.9	28	122.4	37.4	88	179.8	55.0	48	237.2	72.5
9	8.6	2.6	69	66.0	20.2	29	123.4	37.7	89	180.7	55.3	49	238.1	72.8
10	9.6	2.9	70	66.9	20.5	30	124.3	38.0	90	181.7	55.6	50	239.1	73.1
11	10.5	3.2	71	67.9	20.8	131	125.3	38.3	191	182.7	55.8	251	240.0	73.4
12	11.5	3.5	72	68.9	21.1	32	126.2	38.6	92	183.6	56.1	52	241.0	73.7
13	12.4	3.8	73	69.8	21.3	33	127.2	38.9	93	184.6	56.4	53	241.9	74.0
14	13.4	4.1	74	70.8	21.6	34	128.1	39.2	94	185.5	56.7	54	242.9	74.3
15	14.3	4.4	75	71.7	21.9	35	129.1	39.5	95	186.5	57.0	55	243.9	74.6
16	15.3	4.7	76	72.7	22.2	36	130.1	39.8	96	187.4	57.3	56	244.8	74.8
17	16.3	5.0	77	73.6	22.5	37	131.0	40.1	97	188.4	57.6	57	245.8	75.1
18	17.2	5.3	78	74.6	22.8	38	132.0	40.3	98	189.3	57.9	58	246.7	75.4
19	18.2	5.6	79	75.5	23.1	39	132.9	40.6	99	190.3	58.2	59	247.7	75.7
20	19.1	5.8	80	76.5	23.4	40	133.9	40.9	200	191.3	58.5	60	248.6	76.0
21	20.1	6.1	81	77.5	23.7	141	134.8	41.2	201	192.2	58.8	261	249.6	76.3
22	21.0	6.4	82	78.4	24.0	42	135.8	41.5	02	193.2	59.1	62	250.6	76.6
23	22.0	6.7	83	79.4	24.3	43	136.8	41.8	03	194.1	59.4	63	251.5	76.9
24	23.0	7.0	84	80.3	24.6	44	137.7	42.1	04	195.1	59.6	64	252.5	77.2
25	23.9	7.3	85	81.3	24.9	45	138.7	42.4	05	196.0	59.9	65	253.4	77.5
26	24.9	7.6	86	82.2	25.1	46	139.6	42.7	06	197.0	60.2	66	254.4	77.8
27	25.8	7.9	87	83.2	25.4	47	140.6	43.0	07	198.0	60.5	67	255.3	78.1
28	26.8	8.2	88	84.2	25.7	48	141.5	43.3	08	198.9	60.8	68	256.3	78.4
29	27.7	8.5	89	85.1	26.0	49	142.5	43.6	09	199.9	61.1	69	257.2	78.6
30	28.7	8.8	90	86.1	26.3	50	143.4	43.9	10	200.8	61.4	70	258.2	78.9
31	29.6	9.1	91	87.0	26.6	151	144.4	44.1	211	201.8	61.7	271	259.2	79.2
32	30.6	9.4	92	88.0	26.9	52	145.4	44.4	12	202.7	62.0	72	260.1	79.5
33	31.6	9.6	93	88.9	27.2	53	146.3	44.7	13	203.7	62.3	73	261.1	79.8
34	32.5	9.9	94	89.9	27.5	54	147.3	45.0	14	204.6	62.6	74	262.0	80.1
35	33.5	10.2	95	90.8	27.8	55	148.2	45.3	15	205.6	62.9	75	263.0	80.4
36	34.4	10.5	96	91.8	28.1	56	149.2	45.6	16	206.6	63.2	76	263.9	80.7
37	35.4	10.8	97	92.8	28.4	57	150.1	45.9	17	207.5	63.4	77	264.9	81.0
38	36.3	11.1	98	93.7	28.7	58	151.1	46.2	18	208.5	63.7	78	265.9	81.3
39	37.3	11.4	99	94.7	28.9	59	152.1	46.5	19	209.4	64.0	79	266.8	81.6
40	38.3	11.7	100	95.6	29.2	60	153.0	46.8	20	210.4	64.3	80	267.8	81.9
41	39.2	12.0	101	96.6	29.5	161	154.0	47.1	221	211.3	64.6	281	268.7	82.2
42	40.2	12.3	02	97.5	29.8	62	154.9	47.4	22	212.3	64.9	82	269.7	82.4
43	41.1	12.6	03	98.5	30.1	63	155.9	47.7	23	213.3	65.2	83	270.6	82.7
44	42.1	12.9	04	99.5	30.4	64	156.8	47.9	24	214.2	65.5	84	271.6	83.0
45	43.0	13.2	05	100.4	30.7	65	157.8	48.2	25	215.2	65.8	85	272.5	83.3
46	44.0	13.4	06	101.4	31.0	66	158.7	48.5	26	216.1	66.1	86	273.5	83.6
47	44.9	13.7	07	102.3	31.3	67	159.7	48.8	27	217.1	66.4	87	274.5	83.9
48	45.9	14.0	08	103.3	31.6	68	160.7	49.1	28	218.0	66.7	88	275.4	84.2
49	46.9	14.3	09	104.2	31.9	69	161.6	49.4	29	219.0	67.0	89	276.4	84.5
50	47.8	14.6	10	105.2	32.2	70	162.6	49.7	30	220.0	67.2	90	277.3	84.8
51	48.8	14.9	111	106.1	32.5	171	163.5	50.0	231	220.9	67.5	291	278.3	85.1
52	49.7	15.2	12	107.1	32.7	72	164.5	50.3	32	221.9	67.8	92	279.2	85.4
53	50.7	15.5	13	108.1	33.0	73	165.4	50.6	33	222.8	68.1	93	280.2	85.7
54	51.6	15.8	14	109.0	33.3	74	166.4	50.9	34	223.8	68.4	94	281.2	86.0
55	52.6	16.1	15	110.0	33.6	75	167.4	51.2	35	224.7	68.7	95	282.1	86.2
56	53.6	16.4	16	110.9	33.9	76	168.3	51.5	36	225.7	69.0	96	283.1	86.5
57	54.5	16.7	17	111.9	34.2	77	169.3	51.7	37	226.6	69.3	97	284.0	86.8
58	55.5	17.0	18	112.8	34.5	78	170.2	52.0	38	227.6	69.6	98	285.0	87.1
59	56.4	17.2	19	113.8	34.8	79	171.2	52.3	39	228.6	69.9	99	285.9	87.4
60	57.4	17.5	20	114.8	35.1	80	172.1	52.6	40	229.5	70.2	300	286.9	87.7
Dist.	Dep.	Lat.	Dist.	Dep.	Lat.	Dist.	Dep.	Lat.	Dist.	Dep.	Lat.	Dist.	Dep.	Lat.

73° (107°, 253°, 287°).

In **Plane Sailing.**	**Dist.**	**Lat.**	**Dep.**
For converting *Dep.* into *Diff. Long.* and *Diff. Long.* into *Dep.* In **Middle Latitude Sailing.**	Diff. Long.	Dep.	
For converting *Dep.* into *Diff. Long.* and *Diff. Long.* into *Dep.* In **Mercator Sailing.**		*m*	Diff Long.
For multiplication of numbers by sines and by cosines, or solution of plane right-angled triangles.	N. Hypotenuse.	N×Cos. Side Adj.	N×Sin. Side Opp.

Difference of Latitude and Departure for 17° (163°, 197°, 343°).

Dist.	Lat.	Dep.	Dist.	Lat.	Dep.	Dist.	Lat.	Dep.	Dist.	Lat.	Dep.	Dist.	Lat.	Dep.
301	287. 8	88. 0	361	345. 2	105. 5	421	402. 6	123. 1	481	460. 0	140. 6	541	517. 4	158. 2
02	288. 8	88. 3	62	346. 2	105. 8	22	403. 6	123. 4	82	460. 9	140. 9	42	518. 3	158. 5
03	289. 8	88. 6	63	347. 1	106. 1	23	404. 5	123. 7	83	461. 9	141. 2	43	519. 3	158. 8
04	290. 7	88. 9	64	348. 1	106. 4	24	405. 5	124. 0	84	462. 9	141. 5	44	520. 2	159. 1
05	291. 7	89. 2	65	349. 1	106. 7	25	406. 4	124. 3	85	463. 8	141. 8	45	521. 2	159. 3
06	292. 6	89. 5	66	350. 0	107. 0	26	407. 4	124. 6	86	464. 8	142. 1	46	522. 1	159. 6
07	293. 6	89. 8	67	351. 0	107. 3	27	408. 3	124. 8	87	465. 7	142. 4	47	523. 1	159. 9
08	294. 5	90. 1	68	351. 9	107. 6	28	409. 3	125. 1	88	466. 7	142. 7	48	524. 1	160. 2
09	295. 5	90. 3	69	352. 9	107. 9	29	410. 3	125. 4	89	467. 6	143. 0	49	525. 0	160. 5
10	296. 5	90. 6	70	353. 8	108. 2	30	411. 2	125. 7	90	468. 6	143. 3	50	526. 0	160. 8
311	297. 4	90. 9	371	354. 8	108. 5	431	412. 2	126. 0	491	469. 5	143. 6	551	526. 9	161. 1
12	298. 4	91. 2	72	355. 7	108. 8	32	413. 1	126. 3	92	470. 5	143. 8	52	527. 9	161. 4
13	299. 3	91. 5	73	356. 7	109. 1	33	414. 1	126. 6	93	471. 5	144. 1	53	528. 8	161. 7
14	300. 3	91. 8	74	357. 7	109. 3	34	415. 0	126. 9	94	472. 4	144. 4	54	529. 8	162. 0
15	301. 2	92. 1	75	358. 6	109. 6	35	416. 0	127. 2	95	473. 4	144. 7	55	530. 7	162. 3
16	302. 2	92. 4	76	359. 6	109. 9	36	416. 9	127. 5	96	474. 3	145. 0	56	531. 7	162. 6
17	303. 1	92. 7	77	360. 5	110. 2	37	417. 9	127. 8	97	475. 3	145. 3	57	532. 7	162. 9
18	304. 1	93. 0	78	361. 5	110. 5	38	418. 9	128. 1	98	476. 2	145. 6	58	533. 6	163. 1
19	305. 1	93. 3	79	362. 4	110. 8	39	419. 8	128. 4	99	477. 2	145. 9	59	534. 6	163. 4
20	306. 0	93. 6	80	363. 4	111. 1	40	420. 8	128. 6	500	478. 2	146. 2	60	535. 5	163. 7
321	307. 0	93. 9	381	364. 4	111. 4	441	421. 7	128. 9	501	479. 1	146. 5	561	536. 5	164. 0
22	307. 9	94. 1	82	365. 3	111. 7	42	422. 7	129. 2	02	480. 1	146. 8	62	537. 4	164. 3
23	308. 9	94. 4	83	366. 3	112. 0	43	423. 6	129. 5	03	481. 0	147. 1	63	538. 4	164. 6
24	309. 8	94. 7	84	367. 2	112. 3	44	424. 6	129. 8	04	482. 0	147. 4	64	539. 4	164. 9
25	310. 8	95. 0	85	368. 2	112. 6	45	425. 6	130. 1	05	482. 9	147. 6	65	540. 3	165. 2
26	311. 8	95. 3	86	369. 1	112. 9	46	426. 5	130. 4	06	483. 9	147. 9	66	541. 3	165. 5
27	312. 7	95. 6	87	370. 1	113. 1	47	427. 5	130. 7	07	484. 8	148. 2	67	542. 2	165. 8
28	313. 6	95. 9	88	371. 0	113. 4	48	428. 4	131. 0	08	485. 8	148. 5	68	543. 2	166. 1
29	314. 6	96. 2	89	372. 0	113. 7	49	429. 4	131. 3	09	486. 8	148. 8	69	544. 1	166. 4
30	315. 5	96. 5	90	373. 0	114. 0	50	430. 3	131. 6	10	487. 7	149. 1	70	545. 1	166. 7
331	316. 5	96. 8	391	373. 9	114. 3	451	431. 3	131. 9	511	488. 7	149. 4	571	546. 1	166. 9
32	317. 5	97. 1	92	374. 9	114. 6	52	432. 2	132. 2	12	489. 6	149. 7	72	547. 0	167. 2
33	318. 4	97. 4	93	375. 8	114. 9	53	433. 2	132. 4	13	490. 6	150. 0	73	548. 0	167. 5
34	319. 4	97. 7	94	376. 8	115. 2	54	434. 2	132. 7	14	491. 5	150. 3	74	548. 9	167. 8
35	320. 4	97. 9	95	377. 7	115. 5	55	435. 1	133. 0	15	492. 5	150. 6	75	549. 9	168. 1
36	321. 3	98. 2	96	378. 7	115. 8	56	436. 1	133. 3	16	493. 5	150. 9	76	550. 8	168. 4
37	322. 3	98. 5	97	379. 7	116. 1	57	437. 0	133. 6	17	494. 4	151. 2	77	551. 8	168. 7
38	323. 2	98. 8	98	380. 6	116. 4	58	438. 0	133. 9	18	495. 4	151. 4	78	552. 7	169. 0
39	324. 2	99. 1	99	381. 6	116. 7	59	438. 9	134. 2	19	496. 3	151. 7	79	553. 7	169. 3
40	325. 1	99. 4	400	382. 5	116. 9	60	439. 9	134. 5	20	497. 3	152. 0	80	554. 7	169. 6
341	326. 1	99. 7	401	383. 5	117. 2	461	440. 9	134. 8	521	498. 2	152. 3	581	555. 6	169. 9
42	327. 1	100. 0	02	384. 4	117. 5	62	441. 8	135. 1	22	499. 2	152. 6	82	556. 6	170. 2
43	328. 0	100. 3	03	385. 4	117. 8	63	442. 8	135. 4	23	500. 1	152. 9	83	557. 5	170. 5
44	329. 0	100. 6	04	386. 3	118. 1	64	443. 7	135. 7	24	501. 1	153. 2	84	558. 5	170. 7
45	329. 9	100. 9	05	387. 3	118. 4	65	444. 7	136. 0	25	502. 1	153. 5	85	559. 4	171. 0
46	330. 8	101. 2	06	388. 3	118. 7	66	445. 6	136. 2	26	503. 0	153. 8	86	560. 4	171. 3
47	331. 8	101. 5	07	389. 2	119. 0	67	446. 6	136. 5	27	504. 0	154. 1	87	561. 4	171. 6
48	332. 8	101. 7	08	390. 2	119. 3	68	447. 6	136. 8	28	504. 9	154. 4	88	562. 3	171. 9
49	333. 8	102. 0	09	391. 1	119. 6	69	448. 5	137. 1	29	505. 9	154. 7	89	563. 3	172. 2
50	334. 7	102. 3	10	392. 1	119. 9	70	449. 5	137. 4	30	506. 8	155. 0	90	564. 2	172. 5
351	335. 7	102. 6	411	393. 0	120. 2	471	450. 4	137. 7	531	507. 8	155. 2	591	565. 2	172. 8
52	336. 6	102. 9	12	394. 0	120. 5	72	451. 4	138. 0	32	508. 8	155. 5	92	566. 1	173. 1
53	337. 6	103. 2	13	395. 0	120. 7	73	452. 3	138. 3	33	509. 7	155. 8	93	567. 1	173. 4
54	338. 5	103. 5	14	395. 9	121. 0	74	453. 3	138. 6	34	510. 7	156. 1	94	568. 0	173. 7
55	339. 5	103. 8	15	396. 9	121. 3	75	454. 2	138. 9	35	511. 6	156. 4	95	569. 0	174. 0
56	340. 4	104. 1	16	397. 8	121. 6	76	455. 2	139. 2	36	512. 6	156. 7	96	570. 0	174. 3
57	341. 4	104. 4	17	398. 8	121. 9	77	456. 2	139. 5	37	513. 5	157. 0	97	570. 9	174. 5
58	342. 4	104. 7	18	399. 7	122. 2	78	457. 1	139. 8	38	514. 5	157. 3	98	571. 9	174. 8
59	343. 3	105. 0	19	400. 7	122. 5	79	458. 1	140. 0	39	515. 4	157. 6	99	572. 8	175. 1
60	344. 3	105. 3	20	401. 6	122. 8	80	459. 0	140. 3	40	516. 4	157. 9	600	573. 8	175. 4
Dist.	Dep.	Lat.	Dist.	Dep.	Lat.	Dist.	Dep.	Lat.	Dist.	Dep.	Lat.	Dist.	Dep.	Lat.

73° (107°, 253°, 287°).

In **Plane Sailing.**	**Dist.**	**Lat.**	**Dep.**
For converting *Dep.* into *Diff. Long.* and *Diff. Long.* into *Dep.* In **Middle Latitude Sailing.**	Diff. Long.	Dep.	
For converting *Dep.* into *Diff. Long.* and *Diff. Long.* into *Dep.* In **Mercator Sailing.**		*m*	Diff. Long.
For multiplication of numbers by sines and by cosines, or solution of plane right-angled triangles.	N.	N×Cos.	N×Sin.
	Hypotenuse.	Side Adj.	Side Opp.

TABLE 3.

Difference of Latitude and Departure for 18° (162°, 198°, 342°).

Dist.	Lat.	Dep.	Dist.	Lat.	Dep.	Dist.	Lat.	Dep.	Dist.	Lat.	Dep.	Dist.	Lat.	Dep.
1	1.0	0.3	61	58.0	18.9	121	115.1	37.4	181	172.1	55.9	241	229.2	74.5
2	1.9	0.6	62	59.0	19.2	22	116.0	37.7	82	173.1	56.2	42	230.2	74.8
3	2.9	0.9	63	59.9	19.5	23	117.0	38.0	83	174.0	56.6	43	231.1	75.1
4	3.8	1.2	64	60.9	19.8	24	117.9	38.3	84	175.0	56.9	44	232.1	75.4
5	4.8	1.5	65	61.8	20.1	25	118.9	38.6	85	175.9	57.2	45	233.0	75.7
6	5.7	1.9	66	62.8	20.4	26	119.8	38.9	86	176.9	57.5	46	234.0	76.0
7	6.7	2.2	67	63.7	20.7	27	120.8	39.2	87	177.8	57.8	47	234.9	76.3
8	7.6	2.5	68	64.7	21.0	28	121.7	39.6	88	178.8	58.1	48	235.9	76.6
9	8.6	2.8	69	65.6	21.3	29	122.7	39.9	89	179.7	58.4	49	236.8	76.9
10	9.5	3.1	70	66.6	21.6	30	123.6	40.2	90	180.7	58.7	50	237.8	77.3
11	10.5	3.4	71	67.5	21.9	131	124.6	40.5	191	181.7	59.0	251	238.7	77.6
12	11.4	3.7	72	68.5	22.2	32	125.5	40.8	92	182.6	59.3	52	239.7	77.9
13	12.4	4.0	73	69.4	22.6	33	126.5	41.1	93	183.6	59.6	53	240.6	78.2
14	13.3	4.3	74	70.4	22.9	34	127.4	41.4	94	184.5	59.9	54	241.6	78.5
15	14.3	4.6	75	71.3	23.2	35	128.4	41.7	95	185.5	60.3	55	242.5	78.8
16	15.2	4.9	76	72.3	23.5	36	129.3	42.0	96	186.4	60.6	56	243.5	79.1
17	16.2	5.3	77	73.2	23.8	37	130.3	42.3	97	187.4	60.9	57	244.4	79.4
18	17.1	5.6	78	74.2	24.1	38	131.2	42.6	98	188.3	61.2	58	245.4	79.7
19	18.1	5.9	79	75.1	24.4	39	132.2	43.0	99	189.3	61.5	59	246.3	80.0
20	19.0	6.2	80	76.1	24.7	40	133.1	43.3	200	190.2	61.8	60	247.3	80.3
21	20.0	6.5	81	77.0	25.0	141	134.1	43.6	201	191.2	62.1	261	248.2	80.7
22	20.9	6.8	82	78.0	25.3	42	135.1	43.9	02	192.1	62.4	62	249.2	81.0
23	21.9	7.1	83	78.9	25.6	43	136.0	44.2	03	193.1	62.7	63	250.1	81.3
24	22.8	7.4	84	79.9	26.0	44	137.0	44.5	04	194.0	63.0	64	251.1	81.6
25	23.8	7.7	85	80.8	26.3	45	137.9	44.8	05	195.0	63.3	65	252.0	81.9
26	24.7	8.0	86	81.8	26.6	46	138.9	45.1	06	195.9	63.7	66	253.0	82.2
27	25.7	8.3	87	82.7	26.9	47	139.8	45.4	07	196.9	64.0	67	253.9	82.5
28	26.6	8.7	88	83.7	27.2	48	140.8	45.7	08	197.8	64.3	68	254.9	82.8
29	27.6	9.0	89	84.6	27.5	49	141.7	46.0	09	198.8	64.6	69	255.8	83.1
30	28.5	9.3	90	85.6	27.8	50	142.7	46.4	10	199.7	64.9	70	256.8	83.4
31	29.5	9.6	91	86.5	28.1	151	143.6	46.7	211	200.7	65.2	271	257.7	83.7
32	30.4	9.9	92	87.5	28.4	52	144.6	47.0	12	201.6	65.5	72	258.7	84.1
33	31.4	10.2	93	88.4	28.7	53	145.5	47.3	13	202.6	65.8	73	259.6	84.4
34	32.3	10.5	94	89.4	29.0	54	146.5	47.6	14	203.5	66.1	74	260.6	84.7
35	33.3	10.8	95	90.4	29.4	55	147.4	47.9	15	204.5	66.4	75	261.5	85.0
36	34.2	11.1	96	91.3	29.7	56	148.4	48.2	16	205.4	66.7	76	262.5	85.3
37	35.2	11.4	97	92.3	30.0	57	149.3	48.5	17	206.4	67.1	77	263.4	85.6
38	36.1	11.7	98	93.2	30.3	58	150.3	48.8	18	207.3	67.4	78	264.4	85.9
39	37.1	12.1	99	94.2	30.6	59	151.2	49.1	19	208.3	67.7	79	265.3	86.2
40	38.0	12.4	100	95.1	30.9	60	152.2	49.4	20	209.2	68.0	80	266.3	86.5
41	39.0	12.7	101	96.1	31.2	161	153.1	49.8	221	210.2	68.3	281	267.2	86.8
42	39.9	13.0	02	97.0	31.5	62	154.1	50.1	22	211.1	68.6	82	268.2	87.1
43	40.9	13.3	03	98.0	31.8	63	155.0	50.4	23	212.1	68.9	83	269.1	87.5
44	41.8	13.6	04	98.9	32.1	64	156.0	50.7	24	213.0	69.2	84	270.1	87.8
45	42.8	13.9	05	99.9	32.4	65	156.9	51.0	25	214.0	69.5	85	271.1	88.1
46	43.7	14.2	06	100.8	32.8	66	157.9	51.3	26	214.9	69.8	86	272.0	88.4
47	44.7	14.5	07	101.8	33.1	67	158.8	51.6	27	215.9	70.1	87	273.0	88.7
48	45.7	14.8	08	102.7	33.4	68	159.8	51.9	28	216.8	70.5	88	273.9	89.0
49	46.6	15.1	09	103.7	33.7	69	160.7	52.2	29	217.8	70.8	89	274.9	89.3
50	47.6	15.5	10	104.6	34.0	70	161.7	52.5	30	218.7	71.1	90	275.8	89.6
51	48.5	15.8	111	105.6	34.3	171	162.6	52.8	231	219.7	71.4	291	276.8	89.9
52	49.5	16.1	12	106.5	34.6	72	163.6	53.2	32	220.6	71.7	92	277.7	90.2
53	50.4	16.4	13	107.5	34.9	73	164.5	53.5	33	221.6	72.0	93	278.7	90.5
54	51.4	16.7	14	108.4	35.2	74	165.5	53.8	34	222.5	72.3	94	279.6	90.9
55	52.3	17.0	15	109.4	35.5	75	166.4	54.1	35	223.5	72.6	95	280.6	91.2
56	53.3	17.3	16	110.3	35.8	76	167.4	54.4	36	224.4	72.9	96	281.5	91.5
57	54.2	17.6	17	111.3	36.2	77	168.3	54.7	37	225.4	73.2	97	282.5	91.8
58	55.2	17.9	18	112.2	36.5	78	169.3	55.0	38	226.4	73.5	98	283.4	92.1
59	56.1	18.2	19	113.2	36.8	79	170.2	55.3	39	227.3	73.9	99	284.4	92.4
60	57.1	18.5	20	114.1	37.1	80	171.2	55.6	40	228.3	74.2	300	285.3	92.7
Dist.	Dep.	Lat.	Dist.	Dep.	Lat.	Dist.	Dep.	Lat.	Dist.	Dep.	Lat.	Dist.	Dep.	Lat.

72° (108°, 252°, 288°).

In **Plane Sailing.**	**Dist.**	**Lat.**	**Dep.**
For converting *Dep.* into *Diff. Long.* and *Diff. Long.* into *Dep.* In **Middle Latitude Sailing.**	Diff. Long.	Dep.	
For converting *Dep.* into *Diff. Long.* and *Diff. Long.* into *Dep.* In **Mercator Sailing.**		*m*	Diff. Long.
For multiplication of numbers by sines and by cosines, or solution of plane right-angled triangles.	N. Hypotenuse.	N×Cos. Side. Adj.	N×Sin. Side Opp.

TABLE 3.

Difference of Latitude and Departure for 18° (162°, 198°, 342°).

Dist.	Lat.	Dep.	Dist.	Lat.	Dep.	Dist.	Lat.	Dep.	Dist.	Lat.	Dep.	Dist.	Lat.	Dep.
301	286.3	93.0	361	343.3	111.6	421	400.4	130.1	481	457.5	148.6	541	514.5	167.2
02	287.2	93.3	62	344.3	111.9	22	401.3	130.4	82	458.4	148.9	42	515.5	167.5
03	288.2	93.6	63	345.2	112.2	23	402.3	130.7	83	459.4	149.3	43	516.4	167.8
04	289.1	93.9	64	346.2	112.5	24	403.2	131.0	84	460.3	149.6	44	517.4	168.1
05	290.1	94.3	65	347.1	112.8	25	404.2	131.3	85	461.3	149.9	45	518.3	168.4
06	291.0	94.6	66	348.1	113.1	26	405.2	131.6	86	462.2	150.2	46	519.3	168.7
07	292.0	94.9	67	349.0	113.4	27	406.1	132.0	87	463.2	150.5	47	520.2	169.0
08	292.9	95.2	68	350.0	113.7	28	407.1	132.3	88	464.1	150.8	48	521.2	169.3
09	293.9	95.5	69	350.9	114.0	29	408.0	132.6	89	465.1	151.1	49	522.1	169.7
10	294.8	95.8	70	351.9	114.3	30	409.0	132.9	90	466.0	151.4	50	523.1	170.0
311	295.8	96.1	371	352.8	114.6	431	409.9	133.2	491	467.0	151.7	551	524.0	170.3
12	296.7	96.4	72	353.8	115.0	32	410.9	133.5	92	467.9	152.0	52	525.0	170.6
13	297.7	96.7	73	354.7	115.3	33	411.8	133.8	93	468.9	152.3	53	525.9	170.9
14	298.6	97.0	74	355.7	115.6	34	412.8	134.1	94	469.8	152.7	54	526.9	171.2
15	299.6	97.3	75	356.6	115.9	35	413.7	134.4	95	470.8	153.0	55	527.8	171.5
16	300.5	97.6	76	357.6	116.2	36	414.7	134.7	96	471.7	153.3	56	528.8	171.8
17	301.5	98.0	77	358.5	116.5	37	415.6	135.0	97	472.7	153.6	57	529.7	172.1
18	302.4	98.3	78	359.5	116.8	38	416.6	135.3	98	473.6	153.9	58	530.7	172.4
19	303.4	98.6	79	360.5	117.1	39	417.5	135.7	99	474.6	154.2	59	531.6	172.7
20	304.3	98.9	80	361.4	117.4	40	418.5	136.0	500	475.5	154.5	60	532.6	173.0
321	305.3	99.2	381	362.4	117.7	441	419.4	136.3	501	476.5	154.8	561	533.5	173.4
22	306.2	99.5	82	363.3	118.0	42	420.4	136.6	02	477.4	155.1	62	534.5	173.7
23	307.2	99.8	83	364.3	118.4	43	421.3	136.9	03	478.4	155.4	63	535.4	174.0
24	308.2	100.1	84	365.2	118.7	44	422.3	137.2	04	479.3	155.7	64	536.4	174.3
25	309.1	100.4	85	366.2	119.0	45	423.2	137.5	05	480.3	156.1	65	537.3	174.6
26	310.0	100.7	86	367.1	119.3	46	424.2	137.8	06	481.2	156.4	66	538.3	174.9
27	311.0	101.0	87	368.1	119.6	47	425.1	138.1	07	482.2	156.7	67	539.2	175.2
28	311.9	101.4	88	369.0	119.9	48	426.1	138.4	08	483.1	157.0	68	540.2	175.5
29	312.9	101.7	89	370.0	120.2	49	427.0	138.7	09	484.1	157.3	69	541.2	175.8
30	313.8	102.0	90	370.9	120.5	50	428.0	139.1	10	485.0	157.6	70	542.1	176.1
331	314.8	102.3	391	371.9	120.8	451	428.9	139.4	511	486.0	157.9	571	543.1	176.4
32	315.8	102.6	92	372.8	121.1	52	429.9	139.7	12	486.9	158.2	72	544.0	176.8
33	316.7	102.9	93	373.8	121.4	53	430.8	140.0	13	487.9	158.5	73	545.0	177.1
34	317.7	103.2	94	374.7	121.8	54	431.8	140.3	14	488.8	158.8	74	545.9	177.4
35	318.6	103.5	95	375.7	122.1	55	432.7	140.6	15	489.8	159.1	75	546.9	177.7
36	319.6	103.8	96	376.6	122.4	56	433.7	140.9	16	490.7	159.5	76	547.8	178.0
37	320.5	104.1	97	377.6	122.7	57	434.6	141.2	17	491.7	159.8	77	548.8	178.3
38	321.5	104.6	98	378.5	123.0	58	435.6	141.5	18	492.6	160.1	78	549.7	178.6
39	322.4	104.8	99	379.5	123.3	59	436.5	141.8	19	493.6	160.4	79	550.7	178.9
40	323.4	105.1	400	380.4	123.6	60	437.5	142.1	20	494.5	160.7	80	551.6	179.2
341	324.3	105.4	401	381.4	123.9	461	438.4	142.5	521	495.5	161.0	581	552.6	179.5
42	325.3	105.7	02	382.3	124.2	62	439.4	142.8	22	496.5	161.3	82	553.5	179.8
43	326.2	106.0	03	383.3	124.5	63	440.3	143.1	23	497.4	161.6	83	554.5	180.2
44	327.2	106.3	04	384.2	124.8	64	441.3	143.4	24	498.4	161.9	84	555.4	180.5
45	328.1	106.6	05	385.2	125.2	65	442.2	143.7	25	499.3	162.2	85	556.4	180.8
46	329.1	106.9	06	386.1	125.5	66	443.2	144.0	26	500.3	162.5	86	557.3	181.1
47	330.0	107.2	07	387.1	125.8	67	444.1	144.3	27	501.2	162.9	87	558.3	181.4
48	331.0	107.5	08	388.0	126.1	68	445.1	144.6	28	502.2	163.2	88	559.2	181.7
49	331.9	107.8	09	389.0	126.4	69	446.0	144.9	29	503.1	163.5	89	560.2	182.0
50	332.9	108.2	10	389.9	126.7	70	447.0	145.2	30	504.1	163.8	90	561.1	182.3
351	333.8	108.5	411	390.9	127.0	471	447.9	145.5	531	505.0	164.1	591	562.1	182.6
52	334.8	108.8	12	391.8	127.3	72	448.9	145.9	32	506.0	164.4	92	563.0	182.9
53	335.7	109.1	13	392.8	127.6	73	449.8	146.2	33	506.9	164.7	93	564.0	183.2
54	336.7	109.4	14	393.7	127.9	74	450.8	146.5	34	507.9	165.0	94	564.9	183.6
55	337.6	109.7	15	394.7	128.2	75	451.8	146.8	35	508.8	165.3	95	565.9	183.9
56	338.6	110.0	16	395.6	128.6	76	452.7	147.1	36	509.8	165.6	96	566.8	184.2
57	339.5	110.3	17	396.6	128.9	77	453.7	147.4	37	510.7	165.9	97	567.8	184.5
58	340.5	110.6	18	397.5	129.2	78	454.6	147.7	38	511.7	166.3	98	568.7	184.8
59	341.4	110.9	19	398.5	129.5	79	455.6	148.0	39	512.6	166.6	99	569.7	185.1
60	342.4	111.2	20	399.4	129.8	80	456.5	148.3	40	513.6	166.9	600	570.6	185.4
Dist.	Dep.	Lat.	Dist.	Dep.	Lat.	Dist.	Dep.	Lat.	Dist.	Dep.	Lat.	Dist.	Dep.	Lat.

72° (108°, 252°, 288°).

In **Plane Sailing.**	**Dist.**	**Lat.**	**Dep.**
For converting *Dep.* into *Diff. Long.* and *Diff. Long.* into *Dep.* In **Middle Latitude Sailing.**	Diff. Long.	Dep.	
For converting *Dep.* into *Diff. Long.* and *Diff. Long.* into *Dep.* In **Mercator Sailing.**		*m*	Diff. Long.
For multiplication of numbers by sines and by cosines, or solution of plane right-angled triangles.	N. Hypotenuse.	N×Cos. Side Adj.	N×Sin. Side Opp.

TABLE 3.

Difference of Latitude and Departure for 19° (161°, 199°, 341°).

Dist.	Lat.	Dep.	Dist.	Lat.	Dep.	Dist.	Lat.	Dep.	Dist.	Lat.	Dep.	Dist.	Lat.	Dep.
1	0.9	0.3	61	57.7	19.9	121	114.4	39.4	181	171.1	58.9	241	227.9	78.5
2	1.9	0.7	62	58.6	20.2	22	115.4	39.7	82	172.1	59.3	42	228.8	78.8
3	2.8	1.0	63	59.6	20.5	23	116.3	40.0	83	173.0	59.6	43	229.8	79.1
4	3.8	1.3	64	60.5	20.8	24	117.2	40.4	84	174.0	59.9	44	230.7	79.4
5	4.7	1.6	65	61.5	21.2	25	118.2	40.7	85	174.9	60.2	45	231.7	79.8
6	5.7	2.0	66	62.4	21.5	26	119.1	41.0	86	175.9	60.6	46	232.6	80.1
7	6.6	2.3	67	63.3	21.8	27	120.1	41.3	87	176.8	60.9	47	233.5	80.4
8	7.6	2.6	68	64.3	22.1	28	121.0	41.7	88	177.8	61.2	48	234.5	80.7
9	8.5	2.9	69	65.2	22.5	29	122.0	42.0	89	178.7	61.5	49	235.4	81.1
10	9.5	3.3	70	66.2	22.8	30	122.9	42.3	90	179.6	61.9	50	236.4	81.4
11	10.4	3.6	71	67.1	23.1	131	123.9	42.6	191	180.6	62.2	251	237.3	81.7
12	11.3	3.9	72	68.1	23.4	32	124.8	43.0	92	181.5	62.5	52	238.3	82.0
13	12.3	4.2	73	69.0	23.8	33	125.8	43.3	93	182.5	62.8	53	239.2	82.4
14	13.2	4.6	74	70.0	24.1	34	126.7	43.6	94	183.4	63.2	54	240.2	82.7
15	14.2	4.9	75	70.9	24.4	35	127.6	44.0	95	184.4	63.5	55	241.1	83.0
16	15.1	5.2	76	71.9	24.7	36	128.6	44.3	96	185.3	63.8	56	242.1	83.3
17	16.1	5.5	77	72.8	25.1	37	129.5	44.6	97	186.3	64.1	57	243.0	83.7
18	17.0	5.9	78	73.8	25.4	38	130.5	44.9	98	187.2	64.5	58	243.9	84.0
19	18.0	6.2	79	74.7	25.7	39	131.4	45.3	99	188.2	64.8	59	244.9	84.3
20	18.9	6.5	80	75.6	26.0	40	132.4	45.6	200	189.1	65.1	60	245.8	84.6
21	19.9	6.8	81	76.6	26.4	141	133.3	45.9	201	190.0	65.4	261	246.8	85.0
22	20.8	7.2	82	77.5	26.7	42	134.3	46.2	02	191.0	65.8	62	247.7	85.3
23	21.7	7.5	83	78.5	27.0	43	135.2	46.6	03	191.9	66.1	63	248.7	85.6
24	22.7	7.8	84	79.4	27.3	44	136.2	46.9	04	192.9	66.4	64	249.6	86.0
25	23.6	8.1	85	80.4	27.7	45	137.1	47.2	05	193.8	66.7	65	250.6	86.3
26	24.6	8.5	86	81.3	28.0	46	138.0	47.5	06	194.8	67.1	66	251.5	86.6
27	25.5	8.8	87	82.3	28.3	47	139.0	47.9	07	195.7	67.4	67	252.5	86.9
28	26.5	9.1	88	83.2	28.7	48	139.9	48.2	08	196.7	67.7	68	253.4	87.3
29	27.4	9.4	89	84.2	29.0	49	140.9	48.5	09	197.6	68.0	69	254.3	87.6
30	28.4	9.8	90	85.1	29.3	50	141.8	48.8	10	198.6	68.4	70	255.3	87.9
31	29.3	10.1	91	86.0	29.6	151	142.8	49.2	211	199.5	68.7	271	256.2	88.2
32	30.3	10.4	92	87.0	30.0	52	143.7	49.5	12	200.4	69.0	72	257.2	88.6
33	31.2	10.7	93	87.9	30.3	53	144.7	49.8	13	201.4	69.3	73	258.1	88.9
34	32.1	11.1	94	88.9	30.6	54	145.6	50.1	14	202.3	69.7	74	259.1	89.2
35	33.1	11.4	95	89.8	30.9	55	146.6	50.5	15	203.3	70.0	75	260.0	89.5
36	34.0	11.7	96	90.8	31.3	56	147.5	50.8	16	204.2	70.3	76	261.0	89.9
37	35.0	12.0	97	91.7	31.6	57	148.4	51.1	17	205.2	70.6	77	261.9	90.2
38	35.9	12.4	98	92.7	31.9	58	149.4	51.4	18	206.1	71.0	78	262.9	90.5
39	36.9	12.7	99	93.6	32.2	59	150.3	51.8	19	207.1	71.3	79	263.8	90.8
40	37.8	13.0	100	94.6	32.6	60	151.3	52.1	20	208.0	71.6	80	264.7	91.2
41	38.8	13.3	101	95.5	32.9	161	152.2	52.4	221	209.0	72.0	281	265.7	91.5
42	39.7	13.7	02	96.4	33.2	62	153.2	52.7	22	209.9	72.3	82	266.6	91.8
43	40.7	14.0	03	97.4	33.5	63	154.1	53.1	23	210.9	72.6	83	267.6	92.1
44	41.6	14.3	04	98.3	33.9	64	155.1	53.4	24	211.8	72.9	84	268.5	92.5
45	42.5	14.7	05	99.3	34.2	65	156.0	53.7	25	212.7	73.3	85	269.5	92.8
46	43.5	15.0	06	100.2	34.5	66	157.0	54.0	26	213.7	73.6	86	270.4	93.1
47	44.4	15.3	07	101.2	34.8	67	157.9	54.4	27	214.6	73.9	87	271.4	93.4
48	45.4	15.6	08	102.1	35.2	68	158.8	54.7	28	215.6	74.2	88	272.3	93.8
49	46.3	16.0	09	103.1	35.5	69	159.8	55.0	29	216.5	74.6	89	273.3	94.1
50	47.3	16.3	10	104.0	35.8	70	160.7	55.3	30	217.5	74.9	90	274.2	94.4
51	48.2	16.6	111	105.0	36.1	171	161.7	55.7	231	218.4	75.2	291	275.1	94.7
52	49.2	16.9	12	105.9	36.5	72	162.6	56.0	32	219.4	75.5	92	276.1	95.1
53	50.1	17.3	13	106.8	36.8	73	163.6	56.3	33	220.3	75.9	93	277.0	95.4
54	51.1	17.6	14	107.8	37.1	74	164.5	56.6	34	221.3	76.2	94	278.0	95.7
55	52.0	17.9	15	108.7	37.4	75	165.5	57.0	35	222.2	76.5	95	278.9	96.0
56	52.9	18.2	16	109.7	37.8	76	166.4	57.3	36	223.1	76.8	96	279.9	96.4
57	53.9	18.6	17	110.6	38.1	77	167.4	57.6	37	224.1	77.2	97	280.8	96.7
58	54.8	18.9	18	111.6	38.4	78	168.3	58.0	38	225.0	77.5	98	281.8	97.0
59	55.8	19.2	19	112.5	38.7	79	169.2	58.3	39	226.0	77.8	99	282.7	97.3
60	56.7	19.5	20	113.5	39.1	80	170.2	58.6	40	226.9	78.1	300	283.7	97.7
Dist.	Dep.	Lat.	Dist.	Dep.	Lat.	Dist.	Dep.	Lat.	Dist.	Dep.	Lat.	Dist.	Dep.	Lat.

71° (109°, 251°, 289°).

In Plane Sailing.	Dist.	Lat.	Dep.
For converting *Dep.* into *Diff. Long.* and *Diff. Long.* into *Dep.* In **Middle Latitude Sailing.**	Diff. Long.	Dep.	
For converting *Dep.* into *Diff. Long.* and *Diff. Long.* into *Dep.* In **Mercator Sailing.**		*m*	Diff Long.
For multiplication of numbers by sines and by cosines, or solution of plane right-angled triangles.	N. Hypotenuse.	N×Cos. Side Adj.	N×Sin. Side Opp.

TABLE 3.

Difference of Latitude and Departure for 19° (161°, 199°, 341°).

Dist.	Lat.	Dep.	Dist.	Lat.	Dep.	Dist.	Lat.	Dep.	Dist.	Lat.	Dep.	Dist.	Lat.	Dep.
301	284. 6	98. 0	361	341. 3	117. 5	421	398. 1	137. 1	481	454. 8	156. 6	541	511. 5	176. 1
02	285. 5	98. 3	62	342. 3	117. 9	22	399. 0	137. 4	82	455. 7	156. 9	42	512. 5	176. 5
03	286. 5	98. 6	63	343. 2	118. 2	23	400. 0	137. 7	83	456. 7	157. 2	43	513. 4	176. 8
04	287. 4	99. 0	64	344. 2	118. 5	24	400. 9	138. 0	84	457. 6	157. 6	44	514. 4	177. 1
05	288. 4	99. 3	65	345. 1	118. 8	25	401. 8	138. 4	85	458. 6	157. 9	45	515. 3	177. 4
06	289. 3	99. 6	66	346. 1	119. 2	26	402. 8	138. 7	86	459. 5	158. 2	46	516. 3	177. 8
07	290. 3	99. 9	67	347. 0	119 5	27	403. 7	139. 0	87	460. 5	158. 6	47	517. 2	178. 1
08	291. 2	100. 3	68	348. 0	119. 8	28	404. 7	139. 3	88	461. 4	158. 9	48	518. 1	178. 4
09	292. 2	100. 6	69	348. 9	120. 1	29	405. 6	139. 7	89	462. 4	159. 2	49	519. 1	178. 7
10	293. 1	100. 9	70	349. 8	120. 5	30	406. 6	140. 0	90	463. 3	159. 5	50	520. 0	179. 1
311	294 1	101. 3	371	350. 8	120. 8	431	407. 5	140. 3	491	464. 2	159. 9	551	521. 0	179. 4
12	295. 0	101. 6	72	351. 7	121. 1	32	408. 5	140. 6	92	465. 2	160. 2	52	521. 9	179. 7
13	295. 9	101. 9	73	352. 7	121. 4	33	409. 4	141. 0	93	466. 1	160. 5	53	522. 9	180. 0
14	296. 9	102. 2	74	353. 6	121. 8	34	410. 4	141. 3	94	467. 1	160. 8	54	523. 8	180. 4
15	297. 8	102. 6	75	354. 6	122. 1	35	411. 3	141. 6	95	468. 0	161. 2	55	524. 8	180. 7
16	298. 8	102. 9	76	355. 5	122. 4	36	412. 2	141. 9	96	469. 0	161. 5	56	525. 7	181. 0
17	299. 7	103. 2	77	356. 5	122. 7	37	413. 2	142. 3	97	469. 9	161. 8	57	526. 7	181. 3
18	300. 7	103. 5	78	357. 4	123. 1	38	414. 1	142. 6	98	470. 9	162. 1	58	527. 6	181. 7
19	301. 6	103. 8	79	358. 4	123. 4	39	415. 1	142. 9	99	471. 8	162. 5	59	528. 5	182. 0
20	302. 6	104. 2	80	359. 3	123. 7	40	416. 0	143. 3	500	472. 8	162. 8	60	529. 5	182. 3
321	303. 5	104. 5	381	360. 2	124. 0	441	417. 0	143. 6	501	473. 7	163. 1	561	530. 4	182. 6
22	304. 5	104. 8	82	361. 2	124. 4	42	417. 9	143. 9	02	474. 7	163. 4	62	531. 4	183. 0
23	305. 4	105. 2	83	362. 1	124. 7	43	418. 9	144. 2	03	475. 6	163. 8	63	532. 3	183. 3
24	306. 3	105 5	84	363. 1	125. 0	44	419. 8	144. 6	04	476. 5	164. 1	64	533. 3	183. 6
25	307. 3	105. 8	85	364 0	125. 3	45	420. 8	144. 9	05	477. 5	164. 4	65	534. 2	183. 9
26	308. 2	106. 1	86	365. 0	125. 7	46	421. 7	145. 2	06	478. 4	164. 7	66	535. 2	184. 3
27	309. 2	106. 5	87	365. 9	126. 0	47	422. 6	145. 5	07	479. 4	165. 1	67	536. 1	184. 6
28	310. 1	106. 8	88	366. 9	126. 3	48	423. 6	145. 9	08	480. 3	165. 4	68	537. 1	184. 9
29	311. 1	107. 1	89	367. 8	126. 6	49	424. 5	146. 2	09	481. 3	165. 7	69	538. 0	185. 2
30	312. 0	107. 4	90	368. 8	127. 0	50	425. 5	146. 5	10	482. 2	166. 0	70	538. 9	185. 6
331	313. 0	107. 8	391	369. 7	127. 3	451	426. 4	146. 8	511	483. 2	166. 4	571	539. 9	185. 9
32	313. 9	108. 1	92	370. 6	127. 6	52	427. 4	147. 2	12	484. 1	166. 7	72	540. 8	186. 2
33	314. 9	108. 4	93	371. 6	127. 9	53	428. 3	147. 5	13	485. 1	167. 0	73	541. 8	186. 6
34	315. 8	108. 7	94	372. 5	128. 3	54	429. 3	147. 8	14	486. 0	167. 3	74	542. 7	186. 9
35	316. 7	109. 1	95	373. 5	128. 6	55	430. 2	148. 1	15	486. 9	167. 7	75	543. 7	187. 2
36	317. 7	109. 4	96	374. 4	128. 9	56	431. 2	148. 5	16	487. 9	168. 0	76	544. 6	187. 5
37	318. 6	109. 7	97	375. 4	129. 3	57	432. 1	148. 8	17	488. 8	168. 3	77	545. 6	187. 9
38	319. 6	110. 0	98	376. 3	129. 6	58	433. 0	149. 1	18	489. 7	168. 6	78	546. 5	188. 2
39	320. 5	110. 4	99	377. 3	129. 9	59	434. 0	149. 4	19	490. 7	169. 0	79	547. 5	188. 5
40	321. 5	110. 7	400	378. 2	130. 2	60	434. 9	149. 8	20	491. 6	169. 3	80	548. 4	188. 8
341	322. 4	111. 0	401	379. 2	130. 6	461	435. 9	150. 1	521	492. 6	169. 6	581	549. 3	189. 2
42	323. 4	111. 3	02	380. 1	130. 9	62	436. 8	150. 4	22	493. 6	169. 9	82	550. 3	189. 5
43	324. 3	111. 7	03	381. 0	131. 2	63	437. 8	150. 7	23	494. 5	170. 3	83	551 2	189. 8
44	325. 3	112. 0	04	382. 0	131. 5	64	438. 7	151. 1	24	495. 5	170. 6	84	552. 2	190. 1
45	326. 2	112. 3	05	382. 9	131. 9	65	439. 7	151. 4	25	496. 4	170. 9	85	553. 1	190. 5
46	327. 1	112. 6	06	383. 9	132. 2	66	440. 6	151. 7	26	497. 3	171. 2	86	554. 1	190. 8
47	328. 1	113. 0	07	384. 8	132. 5	67	441. 6	152. 0	27	498. 3	171. 6	87	555. 0	191. 1
48	329. 0	113. 3	08	385. 8	132. 8	68	442. 5	152. 4	28	499. 2	171. 9	88	556. 0	191. 4
49	330. 0	113. 6	09	386. 7	133. 2	69	443. 4	152. 7	29	500. 2	172. 2	89	556. 9	191. 8
50	330. 9	113. 9	10	387. 7	133. 5	70	444. 4	153. 0	30	501. 1	172. 6	90	557. 9	192. 0
351	331. 9	114. 3	411	388. 6	133. 8	471	445. 3	153. 3	531	502. 1	172. 9	591	558. 8	192. 4
52	332. 8	114. 6	12	389. 6	134. 1	72	446. 3	153. 7	32	503. 0	173. 2	92	559. 7	192. 7
53	333. 8	114. 9	13	390. 5	134. 5	73	447. 2	154. 0	33	504. 0	173. 5	93	560. 7	193. 1
54	334. 7	115. 3	14	391. 4	134. 8	74	448. 2	154. 3	34	504. 9	173. 9	94	561. 6	193. 4
55	335. 7	115. 6	15	392. 4	135. 1	75	449. 1	154. 6	35	505. 9	174. 2	95	562. 6	193. 7
56	336. 6	115. 9	16	393. 3	135. 4	76	450. 1	155. 0	36	506. 8	174. 5	96	563. 5	194. 0
57	337. 6	116. 2	17	394. 3	135. 8	77	451. 0	155. 3	37	507. 7	174. 8	97	564. 5	194. 4
58	338. 5	116. 6	18	395. 2	136. 1	78	452. 0	155. 6	38	508. 7	175. 2	98	565. 4	194. 7
59	339. 4	116. 9	19	396. 2	136. 4	79	452. 9	155. 9	39	509. 6	175. 5	99	566. 4	195. 0
60	340. 4	117. 2	20	397. 1	136. 7	80	453. 8	156. 3	40	510. 6	175. 8	600	567. 3	195. 3
Dist.	Dep.	Lat.	Dist.	Dep.	Lat.	Dist.	Dep.	Lat.	Dist.	Dep.	Lat.	Dist.	Dep.	Lat.

71° (109°, 251°, 289°).

In **Plane Sailing.**	**Dist.**	**Lat.**	**Dep.**
For converting *Dep.* into *Diff. Long.* and *Diff. Long.* into *Dep.* In **Middle Latitude Sailing.**	Diff. Long.	Dep.	
For converting *Dep.* into *Diff. Long.* and *Diff. Long.* into *Dep.* In **Mercator Sailing.**		*m*	Diff. Long.
For multiplication of numbers by sines and by cosines, or solution of plane right-angled triangles.	N. Hypotenuse.	N×Cos. Side Adj.	N×Sin. Side Opp.

TABLE 3.

Difference of Latitude and Departure for 20° (160°, 200°, 340°).

Dist.	Lat.	Dep.	Dist.	Lat.	Dep.	Dist.	Lat.	Dep.	Dist.	Lat.	Dep.	Dist.	Lat.	Dep.
1	0.9	0.3	61	57.3	20.9	121	113.7	41.4	181	170.1	61.9	241	226.5	82.4
2	1.9	0.7	62	58.3	21.2	22	114.6	41.7	82	171.0	62.2	42	227.4	82.8
3	2.8	1.0	63	59.2	21.5	23	115.6	42.1	83	172.0	62.6	43	228.3	83.1
4	3.8	1.4	64	60.1	21.9	24	116.5	42.4	84	172.9	62.9	44	229.3	83.5
5	4.7	1.7	65	61.1	22.2	25	117.5	42.8	85	173.8	63.3	45	230.2	83.8
6	5.6	2.1	66	62.0	22.6	26	118.4	43.1	86	174.8	63.6	46	231.2	84.1
7	6 6	2.4	67	63.0	22.9	27	119.3	43.4	87	175.7	64.0	47	232.1	84.5
8	7.5	2.7	68	63.9	23.3	28	120.3	43.8	88	176.7	64.3	48	233.0	84.8
9	8.5	3.1	69	64.8	23.6	29	121.2	44.1	89	177.6	64.6	49	234.0	85.2
10	9.4	3.4	70	65.8	23.9	30	122.2	44.5	90	178.5	65.0	50	234.9	85.5
11	10.3	3.8	71	66.7	24.3	131	123.1	44.8	191	179.5	65.3	251	235.9	85.8
12	11.3	4.1	72	67.7	24.6	32	124.0	45.1	92	180.4	65.7	52	236.8	86.2
13	12.2	4.4	73	68.6	25.0	33	125.0	45.5	93	181.4	66.0	53	237.7	86.5
14	13.2	4.8	74	69.5	25.3	34	125.9	45.8	94	182.3	66.4	54	238.7	86.9
15	14.1	5.1	75	70.5	25.7	35	126.9	46.2	95	183.2	66.7	55	239.6	87.2
16	15.0	5.5	76	71.4	26.0	36	127.8	46.5	96	184.2	67.0	56	240.6	87.6
17	16.0	5.8	77	72.4	26.3	37	128.7	46.9	97	185.1	67.4	57	241.5	87.9
18	16.9	6.2	78	73.3	26.7	38	129.7	47.2	98	186.1	67.7	58	242.4	88.2
19	17.9	6.5	79	74.2	27.0	39	130.6	47.5	99	187.0	68.1	59	243.4	88.6
20	18.8	6.8	80	75.2	27.4	40	131.6	47.9	200	187.9	68.4	60	244.3	88.9
21	19.7	7.2	81	76.1	27.7	141	132.5	48.2	201	188.9	68.7	261	245.3	89.3
22	20.7	7.5	82	77.1	28.0	42	133.4	48.6	02	189.8	69.1	62	246.2	89.6
23	21.6	7.9	83	78.0	28.4	43	134.4	48.9	03	190.8	69.4	63	247.1	90.0
24	22.6	8.2	84	78.9	28.7	44	135.3	49.3	04	191.7	69.8	64	248.1	90.3
25	23.5	8.6	85	79.9	29.1	45	136.3	49.6	05	192.6	70.1	65	249.0	90.6
26	24.4	8.9	86	80.8	29.4	46	137.2	49.9	06	193.6	70.5	66	250.0	91.0
27	25.4	9.2	87	81.8	29.8	47	138.1	50.3	07	194.5	70.8	67	250.9	91.3
28	26.3	9.6	88	82.7	30.1	48	139.1	50.6	08	195.5	71.1	68	251.8	91.7
29	27.3	9.9	89	83.6	30.4	49	140.0	51.0	09	196.4	71.5	69	252.8	92.0
30	28.2	10.3	90	84.6	30.8	50	140.9	51.3	10	197.3	71.8	70	253.7	92.3
31	29.1	10.6	91	85.5	31.1	151	141.9	51.6	211	198.3	72.2	271	254.7	92.7
32	30.1	10.9	92	86.5	31.5	52	142.8	52.0	12	199.2	72.5	72	255.6	93.0
33	31.0	11.3	93	87.4	31.8	53	143.8	52.3	13	200.2	72.9	73	256.5	93.4
34	31.9	11.6	94	88.3	32.1	54	144.7	52.7	14	201.1	73.2	74	257.5	93.7
35	32.9	12.0	95	89.3	32.5	55	145.7	53.0	15	202.0	73.5	75	258.4	94.1
36	33.8	12.3	96	90.2	32.8	56	146.6	53.4	16	203.0	73.9	76	259.4	94.4
37	34.8	12.7	97	91.2	33.2	57	147.5	53.7	17	203.9	74.2	77	260.3	94.7
38	35.7	13.0	98	92.1	33.5	58	148.5	54.0	18	204.9	74.6	78	261.2	95.1
39	36.6	13.3	99	93.0	33.9	59	149.4	54.4	19	205.8	74.9	79	262.2	95.4
40	37.6	13.7	100	94.0	34.2	60	150.4	54.7	20	206.7	75.2	80	263.1	95.8
41	38.5	14.0	101	94.9	34.5	161	151.3	55.1	221	207.7	75.6	281	264.1	96.1
42	39.5	14.4	02	95.8	34.9	62	152.2	55.4	22	208.6	75.9	82	265.0	96.4
43	40.4	14.7	03	96.8	35.2	63	153.2	55.7	23	209.6	76.3	83	265.9	96.8
44	41.3	15.0	04	97.7	35.6	64	154.1	56.1	24	210.5	76.6	84	266.9	97.1
45	42.3	15.4	05	98.7	35.9	65	155.0	56.4	25	211.4	77.0	85	267.8	97.5
46	43.2	15.7	06	99.6	36.3	66	156.0	56.8	26	212.4	77.3	86	268.8	97.8
47	44.2	16.1	07	100.5	36.6	67	156.9	57.1	27	213.3	77.6	87	269.7	98.2
48	45.1	16.4	08	101.5	36.9	68	157.9	57.5	28	214.2	78.0	88	270.6	98.5
49	46.0	16.8	09	102.4	37.3	69	158.8	57.8	29	215.2	78.3	89	271.6	98.8
50	47.0	17.1	10	103.4	37.6	70	159.7	58.1	30	216.1	78.7	90	272.5	99.2
51	47.9	17.4	111	104.3	38.0	171	160.7	58.5	231	217.1	79.0	291	273.5	99.5
52	48.9	17.8	12	105.2	38.3	72	161.6	58.8	32	218.0	79.3	92	274.4	99.9
53	49.8	18.1	13	106.2	38.6	73	162.6	59.2	33	218.9	79.7	93	275.3	100.2
54	50.7	18.5	14	107.1	39.0	74	163.5	59.5	34	219.9	80.0	94	276.3	100.6
55	51.7	18.8	15	108.1	39.3	75	164.4	59.9	35	220.8	80.4	95	277.2	100.9
56	52.6	19.2	16	109.0	39.7	76	165.4	60.2	36	221.8	80.7	96	278.1	101.2
57	53.6	19.5	17	109.9	40.0	77	166.3	60.5	37	222.7	81.1	97	279.1	101.6
58	54.5	19.8	18	110.9	40.4	78	167.3	60.9	38	223.6	81.4	98	280.0	101.9
59	55.4	20.2	19	111.8	40.7	79	168.2	61.2	39	224.6	81.7	99	281.0	102.3
60	56.4	20.5	20	112.8	41.0	80	169.1	61.6	40	225.5	82.1	300	281.9	102.6
Dist.	Dep.	Lat.	Dist.	Dep.	Lat.	Dist.	Dep.	Lat.	Dist.	Dep.	Lat.	Dist.	Dep.	Lat.

70° (110°, 250°, 290°).

In Plane Sailing.	Dist.	Lat.	Dep.
For converting *Dep.* into *Diff. Long.* and *Diff. Long.* into *Dep.* **In Middle Latitude Sailing.**	Diff. Long.	Dep.	
For converting *Dep.* into *Diff. Long.* and *Diff. Long.* into *Dep.* **In Mercator Sailing.**		*m*	Diff. Long.
For multiplication of numbers by sines and by cosines, or solution of plane right-angled triangles.	N.	N×Cos.	N×Sin.
	Hypotenuse.	Side Adj.	Side Opp.

TABLE 3.

Difference of Latitude and Departure for 20° (160°, 200°, 340°).

Dist.	Lat.	Dep.	Dist.	Lat.	Dep.	Dist.	Lat.	Dep.	Dist.	Lat.	Dep.	Dist.	Lat.	Dep.
301	282.8	102.9	361	339.2	123.5	421	395.6	144.0	481	452.0	164.5	541	508.4	185.0
02	283.8	103.3	62	340.2	123.8	22	396.6	144.3	82	452.9	164.9	42	509.3	185.4
03	284.7	103.6	63	341.1	124.2	23	397.5	144.7	83	453.9	165.2	43	510.3	185.7
04	285.7	104.0	64	342.0	124.5	24	398.4	145.0	84	454.8	165.5	44	511.2	186.1
05	286.6	104.3	65	343.0	124.8	25	399.4	145.4	85	455.8	165.9	45	512.1	186.4
06	287.5	104.7	66	343.9	125.2	26	400.3	145.7	86	456.7	166.2	46	513.1	186.7
07	288.5	105.0	67	344.9	125.5	27	401.3	146.1	87	457.6	166.6	47	514.0	187.1
08	289.4	105.3	68	345.8	125.9	28	402.2	146.4	88	458.6	166.9	48	515.0	187.4
09	290.4	105.7	69	346.7	126.2	29	403.1	146.7	89	459.5	167.3	49	515.9	187.8
10	291.3	106.0	70	347.7	126.5	30	404.1	147.1	90	460.4	167.6	50	516.8	188.1
311	292.2	106.4	371	348.6	126.9	431	405.0	147.4	491	461.4	167.9	551	517.8	188.5
12	293.2	106.7	72	349.6	127.2	32	406.0	147.8	92	462.3	168.3	52	518.7	188.8
13	294.1	107.1	73	350.5	127.6	33	406.9	148.1	93	463.3	168.6	53	519.7	189.1
14	295.1	107.4	74	351.4	127.9	34	407.8	148.4	94	464.2	169.0	54	520.6	189.5
15	296.0	107.7	75	352.4	128.3	35	408.8	148.8	95	465.1	169.3	55	521.5	189.8
16	296.9	108.1	76	353.3	128.6	36	409.7	149.1	96	466.1	169.6	56	522.5	190.2
17	297.9	108.4	77	354.3	128.9	37	410.6	149.5	97	467.0	170.0	57	523.4	190.5
18	298.8	108.8	78	355.2	129.3	38	411.6	149.8	98	468.0	170.3	58	524.3	190.8
19	299.8	109.1	79	356.1	129.6	39	412.5	150.2	99	468.9	170.7	59	525.3	191.2
20	300.7	109.4	80	357.1	130.0	40	413.5	150.5	500	469.8	171.0	60	526.2	191.5
321	301.6	109.8	381	358.0	130.3	441	414.4	150.8	501	470.8	171.4	561	527.2	191.9
22	302.6	110.1	82	359.0	130.7	42	415.3	151.2	02	471.7	171.7	62	528.1	192.2
23	303.5	110.5	83	359.9	131.0	43	416.3	151.5	03	472.7	172.0	63	529.0	192.6
24	304.5	110.8	84	360.8	131.3	44	417.2	151.9	04	473.6	172.4	64	530.0	192.9
25	305.4	111.2	85	361.8	131.7	45	418.2	152.2	05	474.5	172.7	65	530.9	193.2
26	306.3	111.5	86	362.7	132.0	46	419.1	152.5	06	475.5	173.1	66	531.9	193.6
27	307.3	111.8	87	363.7	132.4	47	420.0	152.9	07	476.4	173.4	67	532.8	193.9
28	308.2	112.2	88	364.6	132.7	48	421.0	153.2	08	477.4	173.7	68	533.7	194.3
29	309.2	112.5	89	365.5	133.1	49	421.9	153.6	09	478.3	174.1	69	534.7	194.6
30	310.1	112.9	90	366.5	133.4	50	422.9	153.9	10	479.2	174.4	70	535.6	195.0
331	311.0	113.2	391	367.4	133.7	451	423.8	154.3	511	480.2	174.8	571	536.6	195.3
32	312.0	113.6	92	368.4	134.1	52	424.7	154.6	12	481.1	175.1	72	537.5	195.6
33	312.9	113.9	93	369.3	134.4	53	425.7	154.9	13	482.1	175.5	73	538.4	196.0
34	313.9	114.2	94	370.2	134.8	54	426.6	155.3	14	483.0	175.8	74	539.4	196.3
35	314.8	114.6	95	371.2	135.1	55	427.6	155.6	15	483.9	176.1	75	540.3	196.7
36	315.7	114.9	96	372.1	135.4	56	428.5	156.0	16	484.9	176.5	76	541.3	197.0
37	316.7	115.3	97	373.1	135.8	57	429.4	156.3	17	485.8	176.8	77	542.2	197.3
38	317.6	115.6	98	374.0	136.1	58	430.4	156.6	18	486.8	177.2	78	543.1	197.7
39	318.6	115.9	99	374.9	136.5	59	431.3	157.0	19	487.7	177.5	79	544.1	198.0
40	319.5	116.3	400	375.9	136.8	60	432.3	157.3	20	488.6	177.9	80	545.0	198.4
341	320.4	116.6	401	376.8	137.2	461	433.2	157.7	521	489.6	178.2	581	546.0	198.7
42	321.4	117.0	02	377.8	137.5	62	434.1	158.0	22	490.5	178.5	82	546.9	199.1
43	322.3	117.3	03	378.7	137.8	63	435.1	158.4	23	491.5	178.9	83	547.8	199.4
44	323.3	117.7	04	379.6	138.2	64	436.0	158.7	24	492.4	179.2	84	548.8	199.7
45	324.2	118.0	05	380.6	138.5	65	437.0	159.0	25	493.3	179.6	85	549.7	200.1
46	325.1	118.3	06	381.5	138.9	66	437.9	159.4	26	494.3	179.9	86	550.7	200.4
47	326.1	118.7	07	382.5	139.2	67	438.8	159.7	27	495.2	180.2	87	551.6	200.8
48	327.0	119.0	08	383.4	139.6	68	439.8	160.1	28	496.2	180.6	88	552.5	201.2
49	328.0	119.4	09	384.3	139.9	69	440.7	160.4	29	497.1	180.9	89	553.5	201.4
50	328.9	119.7	10	385.3	140.2	70	441.7	160.7	30	498.0	181.3	90	554.4	201.8
351	329.8	120.0	411	386.2	140.6	471	442.6	161.1	531	499.0	181.6	591	555.4	202.1
52	330.8	120.4	12	387.2	140.9	72	443.5	161.4	32	499.9	182.0	92	556.3	202.5
53	331.7	120.7	13	388.1	141.3	73	444.5	161.8	33	500.9	182.3	93	557.2	202.8
54	332.7	121.1	14	389.0	141.6	74	445.4	162.1	34	501.8	182.6	94	558.2	203.2
55	333.6	121.4	15	390.0	141.9	75	446.4	162.5	35	502.7	183.0	95	559.1	203.5
56	334.5	121.8	16	390.9	142.3	76	447.3	162.8	36	503.7	183.3	96	560.1	203.8
57	335.5	122.1	17	391.9	142.6	77	448.2	163.1	37	504.6	183.7	97	561.0	204.2
58	336.4	122.4	18	392.8	143.0	78	449.2	163.5	38	505.6	184.0	98	561.9	204.5
59	337.4	122.8	19	393.7	143.3	79	450.1	163.8	39	506.5	184.3	99	562.9	204.9
60	338.3	123.1	20	394.7	143.7	80	451.1	164.2	40	507.4	184.7	600	563.8	205.2
Dist.	Dep.	Lat.	Dist.	Dep.	Lat.	Dist.	Dep.	Lat.	Dist.	Dep.	Lat.	Dist.	Dep.	Lat.

70° (110°, 250°, 290°).

In **Plane Sailing.**	**Dist.**	**Lat.**	**Dep.**
For converting *Dep.* into *Diff. Long.* and *Diff. Long.* into *Dep.* In **Middle Latitude Sailing.**	Diff. Long.	Dep.	
For converting *Dep.* into *Diff. Long.* and *Diff. Long.* into *Dep.* In **Mercator Sailing.**		*m*	Diff. Long.
For multiplication of numbers by sines and by cosines, or solution of plane right-angled triangles.	N. / Hypotenuse.	N×Cos. / Side Adj.	N×Sin. / Side Opp.

TABLE 3.

Difference of Latitude and Departure for 21° (159°, 201°, 339°).

Dist	Lat.	Dep.	Dist.	Lat.	Dep.	Dist.	Lat.	Dep.	Dist.	Lat.	Dep.	Dist.	Lat.	Dep.
1	0.9	0.4	61	56.9	21.9	121	113.0	43.4	181	169.0	64.9	241	225.0	86.4
2	1.9	0.7	62	57.9	22.2	22	113.9	43.7	82	169.9	65.2	42	225.9	86.7
3	2.8	1.1	63	58.8	22.6	23	114.8	44.1	83	170.8	65.6	43	226.9	87.1
4	3.7	1.4	64	59.7	22.9	24	115.8	44.4	84	171.8	65.9	44	227.8	87.4
5	4.7	1.8	65	60.7	23.3	25	116.7	44.8	85	172.7	66.3	45	228.7	87.8
6	5.6	2.2	66	61.6	23.7	26	117.6	45.2	86	173.6	66.7	46	229.7	88.2
7	6.5	2.5	67	62.5	24.0	27	118.6	45.5	87	174.6	67.0	47	230.6	88.5
8	7.5	2.9	68	63.5	24.4	28	119.5	45.9	88	175.5	67.4	48	231.5	88.9
9	8.4	3.2	69	64.4	24.7	29	120.4	46.2	89	176.4	67.7	49	232.5	89.2
10	9.3	3.6	70	65.4	25.1	30	121.4	46.6	90	177.4	68.1	50	233.4	89.6
11	10.3	3.9	71	66.3	25.4	131	122.3	46.9	191	178.3	68.4	251	234.3	90.0
12	11.2	4.3	72	67.2	25.8	32	123.2	47.3	92	179.2	68.8	52	235.3	90.3
13	12.1	4.7	73	68.2	26.2	33	124.2	47.7	93	180.2	69.2	53	236.2	90.7
14	13.1	5.0	74	69.1	26.5	34	125.1	48.0	94	181.1	69.5	54	237.1	91.0
15	14.0	5.4	75	70.0	26.9	35	126.0	48.4	95	182.0	69.9	55	238.1	91.4
16	14.9	5.7	76	71.0	27.2	36	127.0	48.7	96	183.0	70.2	56	239.0	91.7
17	15.9	6.1	77	71.9	27.6	37	127.9	49.1	97	183.9	70.6	57	239.9	92.1
18	16.8	6.5	78	72.8	28.0	38	128.8	49.5	98	184.8	71.0	58	240.9	92.5
19	17.7	6.8	79	73.8	28.3	39	129.8	49.8	99	185.8	71.3	59	241.8	92.8
20	18.7	7.2	80	74.7	28.7	40	130.7	50.2	200	186.7	71.7	60	242.7	93.2
21	19.6	7.5	81	75.6	29.0	141	131.6	50.5	201	187.6	72.0	261	243.7	93.5
22	20.5	7.9	82	76.6	29.4	42	132.6	50.9	02	188.6	72.4	62	244.6	93.9
23	21.5	8.2	83	77.5	29.7	43	133.5	51.2	03	189.5	72.7	63	245.5	94.3
24	22.4	8.6	84	78.4	30.1	44	134.4	51.6	04	190.5	73.1	64	246.5	94.6
25	23.3	9.0	85	79.4	30.5	45	135.4	52.0	05	191.4	73.5	65	247.4	95.0
26	24.3	9.3	86	80.3	30.8	46	136.3	52.3	06	192.3	73.8	66	248.3	95.3
27	25.2	9.7	87	81.2	31.2	47	137.2	52.7	07	193.3	74.2	67	249.3	95.7
28	26.1	10.0	88	82.2	31.5	48	138.2	53.0	08	194.2	74.5	68	250.2	96.0
29	27.1	10.4	89	83.1	31.9	49	139.1	53.4	09	195.1	74.9	69	251.1	96.4
30	28.0	10.8	90	84.0	32.3	50	140.0	53.8	10	196.1	75.3	70	252.1	96.8
31	28.9	11.1	91	85.0	32.6	151	141.0	54.1	211	197.0	75.6	271	253.0	97.1
32	29.9	11.5	92	85.9	33.0	52	141.9	54.5	12	197.9	76.0	72	253.9	97.5
33	30.8	11.8	93	86.8	33.3	53	142.8	54.8	13	198.9	76.3	73	254.9	97.8
34	31.7	12.2	94	87.8	33.7	54	143.8	55.2	14	199.8	76.7	74	255.8	98.2
35	32.7	12.5	95	88.7	34.0	55	144.7	55.5	15	200.7	77.0	75	256.7	98.6
36	33.6	12.9	96	89.6	34.4	56	145.6	55.9	16	201.7	77.4	76	257.7	98.9
37	34.5	13.3	97	90.6	34.8	57	146.6	56.3	17	202.6	77.8	77	258.6	99.3
38	35.5	13.6	98	91.5	35.1	58	147.5	56.6	18	203.5	78.1	78	259.5	99.6
39	36.4	14.0	99	92.4	35.5	59	148.4	57.0	19	204.5	78.5	79	260.5	100.0
40	37.3	14.3	100	93.4	35.8	60	149.4	57.3	20	205.4	78.8	80	261.4	100.3
41	38.3	14.7	101	94.3	36.2	161	150.3	57.7	221	206.3	79.2	281	262.3	100.7
42	39.2	15.1	02	95.2	36.6	62	151.2	58.1	22	207.3	79.6	82	263.3	101.1
43	40.1	15.4	03	96.2	36.9	63	152.2	58.4	23	208.2	79.9	83	264.2	101.4
44	41.1	15.8	04	97.1	37.3	64	153.1	58.8	24	209.1	80.3	84	265.1	101.8
45	42.0	16.1	05	98.0	37.6	65	154.0	59.1	25	210.1	80.6	85	266.1	102.1
46	42.9	16.5	06	99.0	38.0	66	155.0	59.5	26	211.0	81.0	86	267.0	102.5
47	43.9	16.8	07	99.9	38.3	67	155.9	59.8	27	211.9	81.3	87	267.9	102.9
48	44.8	17.2	08	100.8	38.7	68	156.8	60.2	28	212.9	81.7	88	268.9	103.2
49	45.7	17.6	09	101.8	39.1	69	157.8	60.6	29	213.8	82.1	89	269.8	103.6
50	46.7	17.9	10	102.7	39.4	70	158.7	60.9	30	214.7	82.4	90	270.7	103.9
51	47.6	18.3	111	103.6	39.8	171	159.6	61.3	231	215.7	82.8	291	271.7	104.3
52	48.5	18.6	12	104.6	40.1	72	160.6	61.6	32	216.6	83.1	92	272.6	104.6
53	49.5	19.0	13	105.5	40.5	73	161.5	62.0	33	217.5	83.5	93	273.5	105.0
54	50.4	19.4	14	106.4	40.9	74	162.4	62.4	34	218.5	83.9	94	274.5	105.4
55	51.3	19.7	15	107.4	41.2	75	163.4	62.7	35	219.4	84.2	95	275.4	105.7
56	52.3	20.1	16	108.3	41.6	76	164.3	63.1	36	220.3	84.6	96	276.3	106.1
57	53.2	20.4	17	109.2	41.9	77	165.2	63.4	37	221.3	84.9	97	277.3	106.4
58	54.1	20.8	18	110.2	42.3	78	166.2	63.8	38	222.2	85.3	98	278.2	106.8
59	55.1	21.1	19	111.1	42.6	79	167.1	64.1	39	223.1	85.6	99	279.1	107.2
60	56.0	21.5	20	112.0	43.0	80	168.0	64.5	40	224.1	86.0	300	280.1	107.5
Dist.	Dep.	Lat.	Dist.	Dep.	Lat.	Dist.	Dep.	Lat.	Dist.	Dep.	Lat.	Dist.	Dep.	Lat.

69° (111°, 249°, 291°).

In **Plane Sailing.**	**Dist.**	**Lat.**	**Dep.**
For converting *Dep.* into *Diff. Long.* and *Diff. Long.* into *Dep.* In **Middle Latitude Sailing.**	Diff. Long.	Dep.	
For converting *Dep.* into *Diff. Long.* and *Diff. Long.* into *Dep.* In **Mercator Sailing.**		*m*	Diff Long.
For multiplication of numbers by sines and by cosines, or solution of plane right-angled triangles.	N. Hypotenuse.	N×Cos. Side Adj.	N×Sin. Side Opp.

TABLE 3.

Difference of Latitude and Departure for 21° (159°, 201°, 339°).

Dist.	Lat.	Dep.	Dist.	Lat.	Dep.	Dist.	Lat.	Dep.	Dist.	Lat.	Dep.	Dist.	Lat.	Dep.
301	281.0	107.9	361	337.0	129.4	421	393.0	150.9	481	449.1	172.4	541	505.1	193.9
02	281.9	108.2	62	338.0	129.7	22	394.0	151.2	82	450.0	172.7	42	506.0	194.2
03	282.9	108.6	63	338.9	130.1	23	394.9	151.6	83	450.9	173.1	43	506.9	194.6
04	283.8	108.9	64	339.8	130.4	24	395.8	151.9	84	451.9	173.5	44	507.9	195.0
05	284.7	109.3	65	340.8	130.8	25	396.8	152.3	85	452.8	173.8	45	508.8	195.3
06	285.7	109.7	66	341.7	131.2	26	397.7	152.7	86	453.7	174.2	46	509.7	195.7
07	286.6	110.0	67	342.6	131.5	27	398.6	153.0	87	454.7	174.5	47	510.7	196.0
08	287.5	110.4	68	343.6	131.9	28	399.6	153.4	88	455.6	174.9	48	511.6	196.4
09	288.5	110.7	69	344.5	132.2	29	400.5	153.7	89	456.5	175.2	49	512.5	196.7
10	289.4	111.1	70	345.4	132.6	30	401.4	154.1	90	457.5	175.6	50	513.5	197.1
311	290.3	111.5	371	346.4	133.0	431	402.4	154.5	491	458.4	176.0	551	514.4	197.5
12	291.3	111.8	72	347.3	133.3	32	403.3	154.8	92	459.3	176.3	52	515.3	197.8
13	292.2	112.2	73	348.2	133.7	33	404.2	155.2	93	460.5	176.7	53	516.3	198.2
14	293.1	112.5	74	349.1	134.0	34	405.2	155.5	94	461.2	177.0	54	517.2	198.5
15	294.1	112.9	75	350.1	134.4	35	406.1	155.9	95	462.1	177.4	55	518.1	198.9
16	295.0	113.2	76	351.0	134.7	36	407.0	156.2	96	463.1	177.8	56	519.1	199.3
17	295.9	113.6	77	352.0	135.1	37	408.0	156.6	97	464.0	178.1	57	520.0	199.6
18	296.9	114.0	78	352.9	135.5	38	408.9	157.0	98	464.9	178.5	58	520.9	200.0
19	297.8	114.3	79	353.8	135.8	39	409.8	157.3	99	465.9	178.8	59	521.9	200.3
20	298.7	114.7	80	354.8	136.2	40	410.8	157.7	500	466.8	179.2	60	522.8	200.7
321	299.7	115.0	381	355.7	136.5	441	411.7	158.0	501	467.7	179.5	561	523.7	201.0
22	300.6	115.4	82	356.6	136.9	42	412.6	158.4	02	468.7	179.9	62	524.7	201.4
23	301.5	115.8	83	357.6	137.3	43	413.6	158.8	03	469.6	180.3	63	525.6	201.8
24	302.5	116.1	84	358.5	137.6	44	414.5	159.1	04	470.5	180.6	64	526.5	202.1
25	303.4	116.5	85	359.4	138.0	45	415.4	159.5	05	471.5	181.0	65	527.5	202.5
26	304.3	116.8	86	360.4	138.3	46	416.4	159.8	06	472.4	181.3	66	528.4	202.8
27	305.3	117.2	87	361.3	138.7	47	417.3	160.2	07	473.3	181.7	67	529.3	203.2
28	306.2	117.5	88	362.2	139.0	48	418.2	160.5	08	474.3	182.1	68	530.3	203.6
29	307.1	117.9	89	363.2	139.4	49	419.2	160.9	09	475.2	182.4	69	531.2	203.9
30	308.1	118.3	90	364.1	139.8	50	420.1	161.3	10	476.1	182.8	70	532.1	204.3
331	309.0	118.6	391	365.0	140.1	451	421.0	161.6	511	477.1	183.1	571	533.1	204.6
32	309.9	119.0	92	365.9	140.5	52	422.0	162.0	12	478.0	183.5	72	534.0	205.0
33	310.9	119.3	93	366.9	140.8	53	422.9	162.3	13	478.9	183.8	73	534.9	205.3
34	311.8	119.7	94	367.8	141.2	54	423.8	162.7	14	479.9	184.2	74	535.9	205.7
35	312.7	120.1	95	368.8	141.6	55	424.8	163.1	15	480.8	184.6	75	536.8	206.1
36	313.7	120.4	96	369.7	141.9	56	425.7	163.4	16	481.7	184.9	76	537.7	206.4
37	314.6	120.8	97	370.6	142.3	57	426.6	163.8	17	482.7	185.3	77	538.7	206.8
38	315.6	121.1	98	371.6	142.6	58	427.6	164.1	18	483.6	185.6	78	539.6	207.1
39	316.5	121.5	99	372.5	143.0	59	428.5	164.5	19	484.5	186.0	79	540.5	207.5
40	317.4	121.8	400	373.4	143.3	60	429.4	164.8	20	485.5	186.4	80	541.5	207.9
341	318.4	122.2	401	374.4	143.7	461	430.4	165.2	521	486.4	186.7	581	542.4	208.2
42	319.3	122.6	02	375.3	144.1	62	431.3	165.6	22	487.3	187.1	82	543.3	208.6
43	320.2	122.9	03	376.2	144.4	63	432.2	165.9	23	488.3	187.4	83	544.3	208.9
44	321.2	123.2	04	377.1	144.8	64	433.2	166.3	24	489.2	187.8	84	545.2	209.3
45	322.1	123.6	05	378.1	145.1	65	434.1	166.6	25	490.1	188.1	85	546.1	209.6
46	323.0	124.0	06	379.0	145.5	66	435.0	167.0	26	491.1	188.5	86	547.1	210.0
47	324.0	124.4	07	379.9	145.9	67	436.0	167.4	27	492.0	188.9	87	548.0	210.4
48	324.9	124.7	08	380.9	146.2	68	436.9	167.7	28	492.9	189.2	88	548.9	210.7
49	325.8	125.1	09	381.8	146.6	69	437.8	168.1	29	493.9	189.6	89	549.9	211.1
50	326.8	125.4	10	382.8	146.9	70	438.8	168.4	30	494.8	189.9	90	550.8	211.4
351	327.7	125.8	411	383.7	147.3	471	439.7	168.8	531	495.7	190.3	591	551.7	211.8
52	328.6	126.1	12	384.6	147.6	72	440.6	169.1	32	496.7	190.7	92	552.7	212.2
53	329.6	126.5	13	385.6	148.0	73	441.6	169.5	33	497.6	191.0	93	553.6	212.5
54	330.5	126.9	14	386.5	148.4	74	442.5	169.9	34	498.5	191.4	94	554.5	212.9
55	331.4	127.2	15	387.4	148.7	75	443.5	170.2	35	499.5	191.7	95	555.5	213.2
56	332.4	127.6	16	388.4	149.1	76	444.4	170.6	36	500.4	192.1	96	556.4	213.6
57	333.3	127.9	17	389.3	149.4	77	445.3	170.9	37	501.3	192.4	97	557.3	213.9
58	334.2	128.3	18	390.2	149.8	78	446.3	171.3	38	502.3	192.8	98	558.2	214.3
59	335.2	128.7	19	391.2	150.2	79	447.2	171.7	39	503.2	193.2	99	559.2	214.7
60	336.1	129.0	20	392.1	150.5	80	448.1	172.0	40	504.1	193.5	600	560.1	215.0
Dist.	Dep.	Lat.	Dist.	Dep.	Lat.	Dist.	Dep.	Lat.	Dist.	Dep.	Lat.	Dist.	Dep.	Lat.

69° (111°, 249°, 291°).

In **Plane Sailing.**	Dist.	Lat.	Dep.
For converting *Dep.* into *Diff. Long.* and *Diff. Long.* into *Dep.* In **Middle Latitude Sailing.**	Diff. Long.	Dep.	
For converting *Dep.* into *Diff. Long.* and *Diff. Long.* into *Dep.* In **Mercator Sailing.**		*m*	Diff. Long.
For multiplication of numbers by sines and by cosines, or solution of plane right-angled triangles.	N.	N×Cos.	N×Sin.
	Hypotenuse.	Side Adj.	Side Opp.

TABLE 3.

Difference of Latitude and Departure for 22° (158°, 202, 338°).

Dist.	Lat.	Dep.	Dist.	Lat.	Dep.	Dist.	Lat.	Dep.	Dist.	Lat.	Dep.	Dist.	Lat.	Dep.
1	0.9	0.4	61	56.6	22.9	121	112.2	45.3	181	167.8	67.8	241	223.5	90.3
2	1.9	0.7	62	57.5	23.2	22	113.1	45.7	82	168.7	68.2	42	224.4	90.7
3	2.8	1.1	63	58.4	23.6	23	114.0	46.1	83	169.7	68.6	43	225.3	91.0
4	3.7	1.5	64	59.3	24.0	24	115.0	46.5	84	170.6	68.9	44	226.2	91.4
5	4.6	1.9	65	60.3	24.3	25	115.9	46.8	85	171.5	69.3	45	227.2	91.8
6	5.6	2.2	66	61.2	24.7	26	116.8	47.2	86	172.5	69.7	46	228.1	92.2
7	6.5	2.6	67	62.1	25.1	27	117.8	47.6	87	173.4	70.1	47	229.0	92.5
8	7.4	3.0	68	63.0	25.5	28	118.7	47.9	88	174.3	70.4	48	229.9	92.9
9	8.3	3.4	69	64.0	25.8	29	119.6	48.3	89	175.2	70.8	49	230.9	93.3
10	9.3	3.7	70	64.9	26.2	30	120.5	48.7	90	176.2	71.2	50	231.8	93.7
11	10.2	4.1	71	65.8	26.6	131	121.5	49.1	191	177.1	71.5	251	232.7	94.0
12	11.1	4.5	72	66.8	27.0	32	122.4	49.4	92	178.0	71.9	52	233.7	94.4
13	12.1	4.9	73	67.7	27.3	33	123.3	49.8	93	178.9	72.3	53	234.6	94.8
14	13.0	5.2	74	68.6	27.7	34	124.2	50.2	94	179.9	72.7	54	235.5	95.2
15	13.9	5.6	75	69.5	28.1	35	125.2	50.6	95	180.8	73.0	55	236.4	95.5
16	14.8	6.0	76	70.5	28.5	36	126.1	50.9	96	181.7	73.4	56	237.4	95.9
17	15.8	6.4	77	71.4	28.8	37	127.0	51.3	97	182.7	73.8	57	238.3	96.3
18	16.7	6.7	78	72.3	29.2	38	128.0	51.7	98	183.6	74.2	58	239.2	96.6
19	17.6	7.1	79	73.2	29.6	39	128.9	52.1	99	184.5	74.5	59	240.1	97.0
20	18.5	7.5	80	74.2	30.0	40	129.8	52.4	200	185.4	74.9	60	241.1	97.4
21	19.5	7.9	81	75.1	30.3	141	130.7	52.8	201	186.4	75.3	261	242.0	97.8
22	20.4	8.2	82	76.0	30.7	42	131.7	53.2	02	187.3	75.7	62	242.9	98.1
23	21.3	8.6	83	77.0	31.1	43	132.6	53.6	03	188.2	76.0	63	243.8	98.5
24	22.3	9.0	84	77.9	31.5	44	133.5	53.9	04	189.1	76.4	64	244.8	98.9
25	23.2	9.4	85	78.8	31.8	45	134.4	54.3	05	190.1	76.8	65	245.7	99.3
26	24.1	9.7	86	79.7	32.2	46	135.4	54.7	06	191.0	77.2	66	246.6	99.6
27	25.0	10.1	87	80.7	32.6	47	136.3	55.1	07	191.9	77.5	67	247.6	100.0
28	26.0	10.5	88	81.6	33.0	48	137.2	55.4	08	192.9	77.9	68	248.5	100.4
29	26.9	10.9	89	82.5	33.3	49	138.2	55.8	09	193.8	78.3	69	249.4	100.8
30	27.8	11.2	90	83.4	33.7	50	139.1	56.2	10	194.7	78.7	70	250.3	101.1
31	28.7	11.6	91	84.4	34.1	151	140.0	56.6	211	195.6	79.0	271	251.3	101.5
32	29.7	12.0	92	85.3	34.5	52	140.9	56.9	12	196.6	79.4	72	252.2	101.9
33	30.6	12.4	93	86.2	34.8	53	141.9	57.3	13	197.5	79.8	73	253.1	102.3
34	31.5	12.7	94	87.2	35.2	54	142.8	57.7	14	198.4	80.2	74	254.0	102.6
35	32.5	13.1	95	88.1	35.6	55	143.7	58.1	15	199.3	80.5	75	255.0	103.0
36	33.4	13.5	96	89.0	36.0	56	144.6	58.4	16	200.3	80.9	76	255.9	103.4
37	34.3	13.9	97	89.9	36.3	57	145.6	58.8	17	201.2	81.3	77	256.8	103.8
38	35.2	14.2	98	90.9	36.7	58	146.5	59.2	18	202.1	81.7	78	257.8	104.1
39	36.2	14.6	99	91.8	37.1	59	147.4	59.6	19	203.1	82.0	79	258.7	104.5
40	37.1	15.0	100	92.7	37.5	60	148.3	59.9	20	204.0	82.4	80	259.6	104.9
41	38.0	15.4	101	93.6	37.8	161	149.3	60.3	221	204.9	82.8	281	260.5	105.3
42	38.9	15.7	02	94.6	38.2	62	150.2	60.7	22	205.8	83.2	82	261.5	105.6
43	39.9	16.1	03	95.5	38.6	63	151.1	61.1	23	206.8	83.5	83	262.4	106.0
44	40.8	16.5	04	96.4	39.0	64	152.1	61.4	24	207.7	83.9	84	263.3	106.4
45	41.7	16.9	05	97.4	39.3	65	153.0	61.8	25	208.6	84.3	85	264.2	106.8
46	42.7	17.2	06	98.3	39.7	66	153.9	62.2	26	209.5	84.7	86	265.2	107.1
47	43.6	17.6	07	99.2	40.1	67	154.8	62.6	27	210.5	85.0	87	266.1	107.5
48	44.5	18.0	08	100.1	40.5	68	155.8	62.9	28	211.4	85.4	88	267.0	107.9
49	45.4	18.4	09	101.1	40.8	69	156.7	63.3	29	212.3	85.8	89	268.0	108.3
50	46.4	18.7	10	102.0	41.2	70	157.6	63.7	30	213.3	86.2	90	268.9	108.6
51	47.3	19.1	111	102.9	41.6	171	158.5	64.1	231	214.2	86.5	291	269.8	109.0
52	48.2	19.5	12	103.8	42.0	72	159.5	64.4	32	215.1	86.9	92	270.7	109.4
53	49.1	19.9	13	104.8	42.3	73	160.4	64.8	33	216.0	87.3	93	271.7	109.8
54	50.1	20.2	14	105.7	42.7	74	161.3	65.2	34	217.0	87.7	94	272.6	110.1
55	51.0	20.6	15	106.6	43.1	75	162.3	65.6	35	217.9	88.0	95	273.5	110.5
56	51.9	21.0	16	107.6	43.5	76	163.2	65.9	36	218.8	88.4	96	274.4	110.9
57	52.8	21.4	17	108.5	43.8	77	164.1	66.3	37	219.7	88.8	97	275.4	111.3
58	53.8	21.7	18	109.4	44.2	78	165.0	66.7	38	220.7	89.2	98	276.3	111.6
59	54.7	22.1	19	110.3	44.6	79	166.0	67.1	39	221.6	89.5	99	277.2	112.0
60	55.6	22.5	20	111.3	45.0	80	166.9	67.4	40	222.5	89.9	300	278.2	112.4
Dist.	Dep.	Lat.	Dist.	Dep.	Lat.	Dist.	Dep.	Lat.	Dist.	Dep.	Lat.	Dist.	Dep.	Lat.

68° (112°, 248°, 292°).

In **Plane Sailing.**	**Dist.**	**Lat.**	**Dep.**
For converting *Dep.* into *Diff. Long.* and *Diff. Long.* into *Dep.* In **Middle Latitude Sailing.**	Diff. Long.	Dep.	
For converting *Dep.* into *Diff. Long.* and *Diff. Long.* into *Dep.* In **Mercator Sailing.**		*m*	Diff. Long.
For multiplication of numbers by sines and by cosines, or solution of plane right-angled triangles.	N. Hypotenuse.	N×Cos. Side Adj.	N×Sin. Side Opp.

TABLE 3.

Difference of Latitude and Departure for 22° (158°, 202°, 338°).

Dist.	Lat.	Dep.	Dist.	Lat.	Dep.	Dist.	Lat.	Dep.	Dist.	Lat.	Dep.	Dist.	Lat.	Dep.
301	279.8	112.8	361	334.7	135.2	421	390.3	157.7	481	446.0	180.2	541	501.6	202.7
02	280.0	113.1	62	335.6	135.6	22	391.3	158.1	82	446.9	180.6	42	502.5	203.0
03	280.9	113.5	63	336.6	136.0	23	392.2	158.5	83	447.8	180.9	43	503.5	203.4
04	281.9	113.9	64	337.5	136.4	24	393.1	158.8	84	448.8	181.3	44	504.4	203.8
05	282.8	114.3	65	338.4	136.7	25	394.1	159.2	85	449.7	181.7	45	505.3	204.2
06	283.7	114.6	66	339.3	137.1	26	395.0	159.6	86	450.6	182.1	46	506.2	204.5
07	284.6	115.0	67	340.3	137.5	27	395.9	160.0	87	451.5	182.4	47	507.2	204.9
08	285.6	115.4	68	341.2	137.9	28	396.8	160.3	88	452.5	182.8	48	508.1	205.3
09	286.5	115.8	69	342.1	138.2	29	397.8	160.7	89	453.4	183.2	49	509.0	205.7
10	287.4	116.1	70	343.1	138.6	30	398.7	161.1	90	454.3	183.6	50	510.0	206.0
311	288.4	116.5	371	344.0	139.0	431	399.6	161.5	491	455.2	184.0	551	510.9	206.4
12	289.3	116.9	72	344.9	139.4	32	400.5	161.8	92	456.2	184.3	52	511.8	206.8
13	290.2	117.3	73	345.8	139.7	33	401.5	162.2	93	457.1	184.7	53	512.7	207.2
14	291.1	117.6	74	346.8	140.1	34	402.4	162.6	94	458.0	185.1	54	513.7	207.5
15	292.1	118.0	75	347.7	140.5	35	403.3	163.0	95	459.0	185.4	55	514.6	207.9
16	293.0	118.4	76	348.6	140.9	36	404.3	163.3	96	459.9	185.8	56	515.5	208.3
17	293.9	118.8	77	349.5	141.2	37	405.2	163.7	97	460.8	186.2	57	516.4	208.7
18	294.8	119.1	78	350.5	141.6	38	406.1	164.1	98	461.7	186.6	58	517.4	209.0
19	295.8	119.5	79	351.4	142.0	39	407.0	164.5	99	462.7	186.9	59	518.3	209.4
20	296.7	119.9	80	352.3	142.4	40	408.0	164.8	500	463.6	187.3	60	519.2	209.8
321	297.6	120.2	381	353.3	142.7	441	408.9	165.2	501	464.5	187.7	561	520.2	210.2
22	298.6	120.6	82	354.2	143.1	42	409.8	165.6	02	465.4	188.1	62	521.1	210.5
23	299.5	121.0	83	355.1	143.5	43	410.7	166.0	03	466.4	188.4	63	522.0	210.9
24	300.4	121.4	84	356.0	143.8	44	411.7	166.3	04	467.3	188.8	64	522.9	211.3
25	301.3	121.7	85	357.0	144.2	45	412.6	166.7	05	468.2	189.2	65	523.9	211.7
26	302.3	122.1	86	357.9	144.6	46	413.5	167.1	06	469.2	189.6	66	524.8	212.0
27	303.2	122.5	87	358.8	145.0	47	414.5	167.4	07	470.1	189.9	67	525.7	212.4
28	304.1	122.9	88	359.7	145.3	48	415.4	167.8	08	471.0	190.3	68	526.6	212.8
29	305.0	123.2	89	360.7	145.7	49	416.3	168.2	09	471.9	190.7	69	527.6	213.2
30	306.0	123.6	90	361.6	146.1	50	417.2	168.6	10	472.9	191.0	70	528.5	213.5
331	306.9	124.0	391	362.5	146.5	451	418.2	168.9	511	473.8	191.4	571	529.4	213.9
32	307.8	124.4	92	363.5	146.8	52	419.1	169.3	12	474.7	191.8	72	530.3	214.3
33	308.8	124.7	93	364.4	147.2	53	420.0	169.7	13	475.6	192.2	73	531.3	214.6
34	309.7	125.1	94	365.3	147.6	54	420.9	170.1	14	476.6	192.5	74	532.2	215.0
35	310.6	125.5	95	366.2	148.0	55	421.9	170.4	15	477.5	192.9	75	533.1	215.4
36	311.5	125.9	96	367.2	148.3	56	422.8	170.8	16	478.4	193.3	76	534.1	215.8
37	312.5	126.2	97	368.1	148.7	57	423.7	171.2	17	479.4	193.7	77	535.0	216.1
38	313.4	126.6	98	369.0	149.1	58	424.7	171.6	18	480.3	194.0	78	535.9	216.5
39	314.3	127.0	99	369.9	149.5	59	425.6	171.9	19	481.2	194.4	79	536.8	216.9
40	315.2	127.4	400	370.9	149.8	60	426.5	172.3	20	482.1	194.8	80	537.8	217.3
341	316.2	127.7	401	371.8	150.2	461	427.4	172.7	521	483.1	195.2	581	538.7	217.6
42	317.1	128.1	02	372.7	150.6	62	428.4	173.1	22	484.0	195.5	82	539.6	218.0
43	318.0	128.5	03	373.7	151.0	63	429.3	173.4	23	484.9	195.9	83	540.5	218.4
44	319.0	128.9	04	374.6	151.3	64	430.2	173.8	24	485.8	196.3	84	541.5	218.8
45	319.9	129.2	05	375.5	151.7	65	431.1	174.2	25	486.8	196.7	85	542.4	219.1
46	320.8	129.6	06	376.4	152.1	66	432.1	174.6	26	487.7	197.0	86	543.3	219.5
47	321.7	130.0	07	377.4	152.5	67	433.0	174.9	27	488.6	197.4	87	544.3	219.9
48	322.7	130.4	08	378.3	152.8	68	433.9	175.3	28	489.6	197.8	88	545.2	220.3
49	323.6	130.7	09	379.2	153.2	69	434.8	175.7	29	490.5	198.2	89	546.1	220.6
50	324.5	131.1	10	380.1	153.6	70	435.8	176.1	30	491.4	198.5	90	547.0	221.0
351	325.4	131.5	411	381.1	154.0	471	436.7	176.4	531	492.3	198.9	591	548.0	221.4
52	326.4	131.9	12	382.0	154.3	72	437.6	176.8	32	493.3	199.3	92	548.9	221.8
53	327.3	132.2	13	382.9	154.7	73	438.6	177.2	33	494.2	199.7	93	549.8	222.1
54	328.2	132.6	14	383.9	155.1	74	439.5	177.6	34	495.1	200.0	94	550.7	222.5
55	329.2	133.0	15	384.8	155.5	75	440.4	177.9	35	496.0	200.4	95	551.7	222.9
56	330.1	133.4	16	385.7	155.8	76	441.3	178.3	36	497.0	200.8	96	552.6	223.3
57	331.0	133.7	17	386.6	156.2	77	442.3	178.7	37	497.9	201.2	97	553.5	223.6
58	332.0	134.1	18	387.6	156.6	78	443.2	179.1	38	498.8	201.5	98	554.5	224.0
59	332.9	134.5	19	388.5	157.0	79	444.1	179.4	39	499.8	201.9	99	555.4	224.4
60	333.8	134.9	20	389.4	157.3	80	445.0	179.8	40	500.7	202.3	600	556.3	224.8
Dist.	Dep.	Lat.	Dist.	Dep.	Lat.	Dist.	Dep.	Lat.	Dist.	Dep.	Lat.	Dist.	Dep.	Lat.

68° (112°, 248°, 292°).

In **Plane Sailing.**	**Dist.**	**Lat.**	**Dep.**
For converting *Dep.* into *Diff. Long.* and *Diff. Long.* into *Dep.* In **Middle Latitude Sailing.**	Diff. Long.	Dep.	
For converting *Dep.* into *Diff. Long.* and *Diff. Long.* into *Dep.* In **Mercator Sailing.**		*m*	Diff. Long.
For multiplication of numbers by sines and by cosines, or solution of plane right-angled triangles.	N.	N×Cos.	N×Sin.
	Hypotenuse.	Side Adj.	Side Opp.

541524°—43——30

TABLE 3.

Difference of Latitude and Departure for 23° (157°, 203°, 337°).

Dist.	Lat.	Dep.	Dist.	Lat.	Dep.	Dist.	Lat.	Dep.	Dist.	Lat.	Dep.	Dist.	Lat.	Dep.
1	0.9	0.4	61	56.2	23.8	121	111.4	47.3	181	166.6	70.7	241	221.8	94.2
2	1.8	0.8	62	57.1	24.2	22	112.3	47.7	82	167.5	71.1	42	222.8	94.6
3	2.8	1.2	63	58.0	24.6	23	113.2	48.1	83	168.5	71.5	43	223.7	94.9
4	3.7	1.6	64	58.9	25.0	24	114.1	48.5	84	169.4	71.9	44	224.6	95.3
5	4.6	2.0	65	59.8	25.4	25	115.1	48.8	85	170.3	72.3	45	225.5	95.7
6	5.5	2.3	66	60.8	25.8	26	116.0	49.2	86	171.2	72.7	46	226.4	96.1
7	6.4	2.7	67	61.7	26.2	27	116.9	49.6	87	172.1	73.1	47	227.4	96.5
8	7.4	3.1	68	62.6	26.6	28	117.8	50.0	88	173.1	73.5	48	228.3	96.9
9	8.3	3.5	69	63.5	27.0	29	118.7	50.4	89	174.0	73.8	49	229.2	97.3
10	9.2	3.9	70	64.4	27.4	30	119.7	50.8	90	174.9	74.2	50	230.1	97.7
11	10.1	4.3	71	65.4	27.7	131	120.6	51.2	191	175.8	74.6	251	231.0	98.1
12	11.0	4.7	72	66.3	28.1	32	121.5	51.6	92	176.7	75.0	52	232.0	98.5
13	12.0	5.1	73	67.2	28.5	33	122.4	52.0	93	177.7	75.4	53	232.9	98.9
14	12.9	5.5	74	68.1	28.9	34	123.3	52.4	94	178.6	75.8	54	233.8	99.2
15	13.8	5.9	75	69.0	29.3	35	124.3	52.7	95	179.5	76.2	55	234.7	99.6
16	14.7	6.3	76	70.0	29.7	36	125.2	53.1	96	180.4	76.6	56	235.6	100.0
17	15.6	6.6	77	70.9	30.1	37	126.1	53.5	97	181.3	77.0	57	236.6	100.4
18	16.6	7.0	78	71.8	30.5	38	127.0	53.9	98	182.3	77.4	58	237.5	100.8
19	17.5	7.4	79	72.7	30.9	39	128.0	54.3	99	183.2	77.8	59	238.4	101.2
20	18.4	7.8	80	73.6	31.3	40	128.9	54.7	200	184.1	78.1	60	239.3	101.6
21	19.3	8.2	81	74.6	31.6	141	129.8	55.1	201	185.0	78.5	261	240.3	102.0
22	20.3	8.6	82	75.5	32.0	42	130.7	55.5	02	185.9	78.9	62	241.2	102.4
23	21.2	9.0	83	76.4	32.4	43	131.6	55.9	03	186.9	79.3	63	242.1	102.8
24	22.1	9.4	84	77.3	32.8	44	132.6	56.3	04	187.8	79.7	64	243.0	103.2
25	23.0	9.8	85	78.2	33.2	45	133.5	56.7	05	188.7	80.1	65	243.9	103.5
26	23.9	10.2	86	79.2	33.6	46	134.4	57.0	06	189.6	80.5	66	244.9	103.9
27	24.9	10.5	87	80.1	34.0	47	135.3	57.4	07	190.5	80.9	67	245.8	104.3
28	25.8	10.9	88	81.0	34.4	48	136.2	57.8	08	191.5	81.3	68	246.7	104.7
29	26.7	11.3	89	81.9	34.8	49	137.2	58.2	09	192.4	81.7	69	247.6	105.1
30	27.6	11.7	90	82.8	35.2	50	138.1	58.6	10	193.3	82.1	70	248.5	105.5
31	28.5	12.1	91	83.8	35.6	151	139.0	59.0	211	194.2	82.4	271	249.5	105.9
32	29.5	12.5	92	84.7	35.9	52	139.9	59.4	12	195.1	82.8	72	250.4	106.3
33	30.4	12.9	93	85.6	36.3	53	140.8	59.8	13	196.1	83.2	73	251.3	106.7
34	31.3	13.3	94	86.5	36.7	54	141.8	60.2	14	197.0	83.6	74	252.2	107.1
35	32.2	13.7	95	87.4	37.1	55	142.7	60.6	15	197.9	84.0	75	253.1	107.5
36	33.1	14.1	96	88.4	37.5	56	143.6	61.0	16	198.8	84.4	76	254.1	107.8
37	34.1	14.5	97	89.3	37.9	57	144.5	61.3	17	199.7	84.8	77	255.0	108.2
38	35.0	14.8	98	90.2	38.3	58	145.4	61.7	18	200.7	85.2	78	255.9	108.6
39	35.9	15.2	99	91.1	38.7	59	146.4	62.1	19	201.6	85.6	79	256.8	109.0
40	36.8	15.6	100	92.1	39.1	60	147.3	62.5	20	202.5	86.0	80	257.7	109.4
41	37.7	16.0	101	93.0	39.5	161	148.2	62.9	221	203.4	86.4	281	258.7	109.8
42	38.7	16.4	02	93.9	39.9	62	149.1	63.3	22	204.4	86.7	82	259.6	110.2
43	39.6	16.8	03	94.8	40.2	63	150.0	63.7	23	205.3	87.1	83	260.5	110.6
44	40.5	17.2	04	95.7	40.6	64	151.0	64.1	24	206.2	87.5	84	261.4	111.0
45	41.4	17.6	05	96.7	41.0	65	151.9	64.5	25	207.1	87.9	85	262.3	111.4
46	42.3	18.0	06	97.6	41.4	66	152.8	64.9	26	208.0	88.3	86	263.3	111.7
47	43.3	18.4	07	98.5	41.8	67	153.7	65.3	27	209.0	88.7	87	264.2	112.1
48	44.2	18.8	08	99.4	42.2	68	154.6	65.6	28	209.9	89.1	88	265.1	112.5
49	45.1	19.1	09	100.3	42.6	69	155.6	66.0	29	210.8	89.5	89	266.0	112.9
50	46.0	19.5	10	101.3	43.0	70	156.5	66.4	30	211.7	89.9	90	266.9	113.3
51	46.9	19.9	111	102.2	43.4	171	157.4	66.8	231	212.6	90.3	291	267.9	113.7
52	47.9	20.3	12	103.1	43.8	72	158.3	67.2	32	213.6	90.6	92	268.8	114.1
53	48.8	20.7	13	104.0	44.2	73	159.2	67.6	33	214.5	91.0	93	269.7	114.5
54	49.7	21.1	14	104.9	44.5	74	160.2	68.0	34	215.4	91.4	94	270.6	114.9
55	50.6	21.5	15	105.9	44.9	75	161.1	68.4	35	216.3	91.8	95	271.5	115.3
56	51.5	21.9	16	106.8	45.3	76	162.0	68.8	36	217.2	92.2	96	272.5	115.7
57	52.5	22.3	17	107.7	45.7	77	162.9	69.2	37	218.2	92.6	97	273.4	116.0
58	53.4	22.7	18	108.6	46.1	78	163.8	69.6	38	219.1	93.0	98	274.3	116.4
59	54.3	23.1	19	109.5	46.5	79	164.8	69.9	39	220.0	93.4	99	275.2	116.8
60	55.2	23.4	20	110.5	46.9	80	165.7	70.3	40	220.9	93.8	300	276.2	117.2
Dist.	Dep.	Lat.	Dist.	Dep.	Lat.	Dist.	Dep.	Lat.	Dist.	Dep.	Lat.	Dist.	Dep.	Lat.

67° (113°, 247°, 293°).

In **Plane Sailing.**	**Dist.**	**Lat.**	**Dep.**
For converting *Dep.* into *Diff. Long.* and *Diff. Long.* into *Dep.* In **Middle Latitude Sailing.**	Diff. Long.	Dep.	
For converting *Dep.* into *Diff. Long.* and *Diff. Long.* into *Dep.* In **Mercator Sailing.**		*m*	Diff Long.
For multiplication of numbers by sines and by cosines, or solution of plane right-angled triangles.	N. Hypotenuse.	N×Cos. Side Adj.	N×Sin. Side Opp.

TABLE 3.

Difference of Latitude and Departure for 23° (157°, 203°, 337°).

Dist.	Lat.	Dep.	Dist.	Lat.	Dep.	Dist.	Lat.	Dep.	Dist.	Lat.	Dep.	Dist.	Lat.	Dep.
301	277.1	117.6	361	332.3	141.1	421	387.5	164.5	481	442.8	187.9	541	498.0	211.4
02	278.0	118.0	62	333.2	141.4	22	388.5	164.9	82	443.7	188.3	42	498.9	211.8
03	278.9	118.4	63	334.1	141.8	23	389.4	165.3	83	444.6	188.7	43	499.8	212.2
04	279.8	118.8	64	335.1	142.2	24	390.3	165.7	84	445.5	189.1	44	500.8	212.6
05	280.8	119.2	65	336.0	142.6	25	391.2	166.1	85	446.4	189.5	45	501.7	212.9
06	281.7	119.6	66	336.9	143.0	26	392.1	166.5	86	447.4	189.9	46	502.6	213.3
07	282.6	120.0	67	337.8	143.4	27	393.1	166.8	87	448.3	190.3	47	503.5	213.7
08	283.5	120.3	68	338.7	143.8	28	394.0	167.2	88	449.2	190.7	48	504.4	214.1
09	284.4	120.7	69	339.7	144.2	29	394.9	167.6	89	450.1	191.1	49	505.4	214.5
10	285.4	121.1	70	340.6	144.6	30	395.8	168.0	90	451.0	191.5	50	506.3	214.9
311	286.3	121.5	371	341.5	145.0	431	396.7	168.4	491	452.0	191.8	551	507.2	215.3
12	287.2	121.9	72	342.4	145.4	32	397.7	168.8	92	452.9	192.2	52	508.1	215.7
13	288.1	122.3	73	343.3	145.7	33	398.6	169.2	93	453.8	192.6	53	509.0	216.1
14	289.0	122.7	74	344.3	146.1	34	399.5	169.6	94	454.7	193.0	54	510.0	216.5
15	290.0	123.1	75	345.2	146.5	35	400.4	170.0	95	455.6	193.4	55	510.9	216.9
16	290.9	123.5	76	346.1	146.9	36	401.3	170.4	96	456.6	193.8	56	511.8	217.2
17	291.8	123.9	77	347.0	147.3	37	402.3	170.7	97	457.5	194.2	57	512.7	217.6
18	292.7	124.3	78	348.0	147.7	38	403.2	171.1	98	458.4	194.6	58	513.6	218.0
19	293.6	124.6	79	348.9	148.1	39	404.1	171.5	99	459.3	195.0	59	514.6	218.4
20	294.6	125.0	80	349.8	148.5	40	405.0	171.9	500	460.3	195.4	60	515.5	218.8
321	295.5	125.4	381	350.7	148.9	441	405.9	172.3	501	461.2	195.8	561	516.4	219.2
22	296.4	125.8	82	351.6	149.3	42	406.9	172.7	02	462.1	196.1	62	517.3	219.6
23	297.3	126.2	83	352.6	149.7	43	407.8	173.1	03	463.0	196.5	63	518.2	220.0
24	298.2	126.6	84	353.5	150.0	44	408.7	173.5	04	463.9	196.9	64	519.2	220.4
25	299.2	127.0	85	354.4	150.4	45	409.6	173.9	05	464.9	197.3	65	520.1	220.8
26	300.1	127.4	86	355.3	150.8	46	410.5	174.3	06	465.8	197.7	66	521.0	221.2
27	301.0	127.8	87	356.2	151.2	47	411.5	174.7	07	466.7	198.1	67	521.9	221.5
28	301.9	128.2	88	357.2	151.6	48	412.4	175.0	08	467.6	198.5	68	522.8	221.9
29	302.8	128.6	89	358.1	152.0	49	413.3	175.4	09	468.5	198.9	69	523.8	222.3
30	303.8	128.9	90	359.0	152.4	50	414.2	175.8	10	469.5	199.3	70	524.7	222.7
331	304.7	129.3	391	359.9	152.8	451	415.1	176.2	511	470.4	199.7	571	525.6	223.1
32	305.6	129.7	92	360.8	153.2	52	416.1	176.6	12	471.3	200.1	72	526.5	223.5
33	306.5	130.1	93	361.8	153.6	53	417.0	177.0	13	472.2	200.4	73	527.4	223.9
34	307.4	130.5	94	362.7	153.9	54	417.9	177.4	14	473.1	200.8	74	528.4	224.3
35	308.4	130.9	95	363.6	154.3	55	418.8	177.8	15	474.1	201.2	75	529.3	224.7
36	309.3	131.3	96	364.5	154.7	56	419.8	178.2	16	475.0	201.6	76	530.2	225.1
37	310.2	131.7	97	365.4	155.1	57	420.7	178.6	17	475.9	202.0	77	531.1	225.5
38	311.1	132.1	98	366.4	155.5	58	421.6	179.0	18	476.8	202.4	78	532.1	225.8
39	312.1	132.5	99	367.3	155.9	59	422.5	179.3	19	477.7	202.8	79	533.0	226.2
40	313.0	132.8	400	368.2	156.3	60	423.4	179.7	20	478.7	203.2	80	533.9	226.6
341	313.9	133.2	401	369.1	156.7	461	424.4	180.1	521	479.6	203.6	581	534.8	227.0
42	314.8	133.6	02	370.0	157.1	62	425.3	180.5	22	480.5	204.0	82	535.7	227.4
43	315.7	134.0	03	371.0	157.5	63	426.2	180.9	23	481.4	204.4	83	536.7	227.8
44	316.7	134.4	04	371.9	157.9	64	427.1	181.3	24	482.3	204.7	84	537.6	228.2
45	317.6	134.8	05	372.8	158.2	65	428.0	181.7	25	483.3	205.1	85	538.5	228.6
46	318.5	135.2	06	373.7	158.6	66	429.0	182.1	26	484.2	205.5	86	539.4	229.0
47	319.4	135.6	07	374.6	159.0	67	429.9	182.5	27	485.1	205.9	87	540.3	229.4
48	320.3	136.0	08	375.6	159.4	68	430.8	182.9	28	486.0	206.3	88	541.3	229.7
49	321.3	136.4	09	376.5	159.8	69	431.7	183.3	29	486.9	206.7	89	542.2	230.1
50	322.2	136.8	10	377.4	160.2	70	432.6	183.6	30	487.9	207.1	90	543.1	230.5
351	323.1	137.1	411	378.3	160.6	471	433.6	184.0	531	488.8	207.5	591	544.0	230.9
52	324.0	137.5	12	379.2	161.0	72	434.5	184.4	32	489.7	207.9	92	544.9	231.3
53	324.9	137.9	13	380.2	161.4	73	435.4	184.8	33	490.6	208.3	93	545.9	231.7
54	325.9	138.3	14	381.1	161.8	74	436.3	185.2	34	491.5	208.7	94	546.8	232.1
55	326.8	138.7	15	382.0	162.2	75	437.2	185.6	35	492.5	209.0	95	547.7	232.5
56	327.7	139.1	16	382.9	162.5	76	438.2	186.0	36	493.4	209.4	96	548.6	232.9
57	328.6	139.5	17	383.9	162.9	77	439.1	186.4	37	494.3	209.8	97	549.5	233.3
58	329.5	139.9	18	384.8	163.3	78	440.0	186.8	38	495.2	210.2	98	550.5	233.7
59	330.5	140.3	19	385.7	163.7	79	440.9	187.2	39	496.2	210.6	99	551.4	234.0
60	331.4	140.7	20	386.6	164.1	80	441.8	187.6	40	497.1	211.0	600	552.3	234.4
Dist.	Dep.	Lat.	Dist.	Dep.	Lat.	Dist.	Dep.	Lat.	Dist.	Dep.	Lat.	Dist.	Dep.	Lat.

67° (113°, 247°, 293°).

In **Plane Sailing.**	Dist.	Lat.	Dep.
For converting *Dep.* into *Diff. Long.* and *Diff. Long.* into *Dep.* In **Middle Latitude Sailing.**	Diff. Long.	Dep.	
For converting *Dep.* into *Diff. Long.* and *Diff. Long.* into *Dep.* In **Mercator Sailing.**		*m*	Diff. Long.
For multiplication of numbers by sines and by cosines, or solution of plane right-angled triangles.	N. / Hypotenuse.	N×Cos. / Side Adj.	N×Sin. / Side Opp.

TABLE 3.

Difference of Latitude and Departure for 24° (156°, 204°, 336°).

Dist.	Lat.	Dep.	Dist.	Lat.	Dep.	Dist.	Lat.	Dep.	Dist.	Lat.	Dep.	Dist.	Lat.	Dep.
1	0.9	0.4	61	55.7	24.8	121	110.5	49.2	181	165.4	73.6	241	220.2	98.0
2	1.8	0.8	62	56.6	25.2	22	111.5	49.6	82	166.3	74.0	42	221.1	98.4
3	2.7	1.2	63	57.6	25.6	23	112.4	50.0	83	167.2	74.4	43	222.0	98.8
4	3.7	1.6	64	58.5	26.0	24	113.3	50.4	84	168.1	74.8	44	222.9	99.2
5	4.6	2.0	65	59.4	26.4	25	114.2	50.8	85	169.0	75.2	45	223.8	99.7
6	5.5	2.4	66	60.3	26.8	26	115.1	51.2	86	169.9	75.7	46	224.7	100.1
7	6.4	2.8	67	61.2	27.3	27	116.0	51.7	87	170.8	76.1	47	225.6	100.5
8	7.3	3.3	68	62.1	27.7	28	116.9	52.1	88	171.7	76.5	48	226.6	100.9
9	8.2	3.7	69	63.0	28.1	29	117.8	52.5	89	172.7	76.9	49	227.5	101.3
10	9.1	4.1	70	63.9	28.5	30	118.8	52.9	90	173.6	77.3	50	228.4	101.7
11	10.0	4.5	71	64.9	28.9	131	119.7	53.3	191	174.5	77.7	251	229.3	102.1
12	11.0	4.9	72	65.8	29.3	32	120.6	53.7	92	175.4	78.1	52	230.2	102.5
13	11.9	5.3	73	66.7	29.7	33	121.5	54.1	93	176.3	78.5	53	231.1	102.9
14	12.8	5.7	74	67.6	30.1	34	122.4	54.5	94	177.2	78.9	54	232.0	103.3
15	13.7	6.1	75	68.5	30.5	35	123.3	54.9	95	178.1	79.3	55	233.0	103.7
16	14.6	6.5	76	69.4	30.9	36	124.2	55.3	96	179.1	79.7	56	233.9	104.1
17	15.5	6.9	77	70.3	31.3	37	125.2	55.7	97	180.0	80.1	57	234.8	104.5
18	16.4	7.3	78	71.3	31.7	38	126.1	56.1	98	180.9	80.5	58	235.7	104.9
19	17.4	7.7	79	72.2	32.1	39	127.0	56.5	99	181.8	80.9	59	236.6	105.3
20	18.3	8.1	80	73.1	32.5	40	127.9	56.9	200	182.7	81.3	60	237.5	105.8
21	19.2	8.5	81	74.0	32.9	141	128.8	57.3	201	183.6	81.8	261	238.4	106.2
22	20.1	8.9	82	74.9	33.4	42	129.7	57.8	02	184.5	82.2	62	239.3	106.6
23	21.0	9.4	83	75.8	33.8	43	130.6	58.2	03	185.4	82.6	63	240.3	107.0
24	21.9	9.8	84	76.7	34.2	44	131.6	58.6	04	186.4	83.0	64	241.2	107.4
25	22.8	10.2	85	77.7	34.6	45	132.5	59.0	05	187.3	83.4	65	242.1	107.8
26	23.8	10.6	86	78.6	35.0	46	133.4	59.4	06	188.2	83.8	66	243.0	108.2
27	24.7	11.0	87	79.5	35.4	47	134.3	59.8	07	189.1	84.2	67	243.9	108.6
28	25.6	11.4	88	80.4	35.8	48	135.2	60.2	08	190.0	84.6	68	244.8	109.0
29	26.5	11.8	89	81.3	36.2	49	136.1	60.6	09	190.9	85.0	69	245.7	109.4
30	27.4	12.2	90	82.2	36.6	50	137.0	61.0	10	191.8	85.4	70	246.7	109.8
31	28.3	12.6	91	83.1	37.0	151	137.9	61.4	211	192.8	85.8	271	247.6	110.2
32	29.2	13.0	92	84.0	37.4	52	138.9	61.8	12	193.7	86.2	72	248.5	110.6
33	30.1	13.4	93	85.0	37.8	53	139.8	62.2	13	194.6	86.6	73	249.4	111.0
34	31.1	13.8	94	85.9	38.2	54	140.7	62.6	14	195.5	87.0	74	250.3	111.4
35	32.0	14.2	95	86.8	38.6	55	141.6	63.0	15	196.4	87.4	75	251.2	111.9
36	32.9	14.6	96	87.7	39.0	56	142.5	63.5	16	197.3	87.9	76	252.1	112.3
37	33.8	15.0	97	88.6	39.5	57	143.4	63.9	17	198.2	88.3	77	253.1	112.7
38	34.7	15.5	98	89.5	39.9	58	144.3	64.3	18	199.2	88.7	78	254.0	113.1
39	35.6	15.9	99	90.4	40.3	59	145.3	64.7	19	200.1	89.1	79	254.9	113.5
40	36.5	16.3	100	91.4	40.7	60	146.2	65.1	20	201.0	89.5	80	255.8	113.9
41	37.5	16.7	101	92.3	41.1	161	147.1	65.5	221	201.9	89.9	281	256.7	114.3
42	38.4	17.1	02	93.2	41.5	62	148.0	65.9	22	202.8	90.3	82	257.6	114.7
43	39.3	17.5	03	94.1	41.9	63	148.9	66.3	23	203.7	90.7	83	258.5	115.1
44	40.2	17.9	04	95.0	42.3	64	149.8	66.7	24	204.6	91.1	84	259.4	115.5
45	41.1	18.3	05	95.9	42.7	65	150.7	67.1	25	205.5	91.5	85	260.4	115.9
46	42.0	18.7	06	96.8	43.1	66	151.6	67.5	26	206.5	91.9	86	261.3	116.3
47	42.9	19.1	07	97.7	43.5	67	152.6	67.9	27	207.4	92.3	87	262.2	116.7
48	43.9	19.5	08	98.7	43.9	68	153.5	68.3	28	208.3	92.7	88	263.1	117.1
49	44.8	19.9	09	99.6	44.3	69	154.4	68.7	29	209.2	93.1	89	264.0	117.5
50	45.7	20.3	10	100.5	44.7	70	155.3	69.1	30	210.1	93.5	90	264.9	118.0
51	46.6	20.7	111	101.4	45.1	171	156.2	69.6	231	211.0	94.0	291	265.8	118.4
52	47.5	21.2	12	102.3	45.6	72	157.1	70.0	32	211.9	94.4	92	266.8	118.8
53	48.4	21.6	13	103.2	46.0	73	158.0	70.4	33	212.9	94.8	93	267.7	119.2
54	49.3	22.0	14	104.1	46.4	74	159.0	70.8	34	213.8	95.2	94	268.6	119.6
55	50.2	22.4	15	105.1	46.8	75	159.9	71.2	35	214.7	95.6	95	269.5	120.0
56	51.2	22.8	16	106.0	47.2	76	160.8	71.6	36	215.6	96.0	96	270.4	120.4
57	52.1	23.2	17	106.9	47.6	77	161.7	72.0	37	216.5	96.4	97	271.3	120.8
58	53.0	23.6	18	107.8	48.0	78	162.6	72.4	38	217.4	96.8	98	272.2	121.2
59	53.9	24.0	19	108.7	48.4	79	163.5	72.8	39	218.3	97.2	99	273.2	121.6
60	54.8	24.4	20	109.6	48.8	80	164.4	73.2	40	219.3	97.6	300	274.1	122.0
Dist.	Dep.	Lat.	Dist.	Dep.	Lat.	Dist.	Dep.	Lat.	Dist.	Dep.	Lat.	Dist.	Dep.	Lat.

66° (114°, 246°, 294°).

In Plane Sailing.	**Dist.**	**Lat.**	**Dep.**
For converting *Dep.* into *Diff. Long.* and *Diff. Long.* into *Dep.* **In Middle Latitude Sailing.**	Diff. Long.	Dep.	
For converting *Dep.* into *Diff. Long.* and *Diff. Long.* into *Dep.* **In Mercator Sailing.**		*m*	Diff. Long.
For multiplication of numbers by sines and by cosines, or solution of plane right-angled triangles.	N. / Hypotenuse.	N×Cos. / Side. Adj.	N×Sin. / Side Opp.

TABLE 3.

Difference of Latitude and Departure for 24° (156°, 204°, 336°).

Dist.	Lat.	Dep.	Dist.	Lat.	Dep.	Dist.	Lat.	Dep.	Dist.	Lat.	Dep.	Dist.	Lat.	Dep.
301	275.0	122.4	361	329.8	146.8	421	384.6	171.2	481	439.4	195.6	541	494.2	220.0
02	275.9	122.8	62	330.7	147.2	22	385.5	171.6	82	440.3	196.0	42	495.1	220.5
03	276.8	123.2	63	331.6	147.6	23	386.4	172 0	83	441.2	196.5	43	496.1	220.9
04	277.7	123.6	64	332.5	148.1	24	387.3	172.5	84	442.2	196.9	44	497.0	221.3
05	278.6	124.1	65	333.4	148.5	25	388.3	172.9	85	443.1	197.3	45	497.9	221.7
06	279.5	124.5	66	334.4	148.9	26	389.2	173.3	86	444.0	197.7	46	498.8	222.1
07	280.5	124.9	67	335.3	149.3	27	390.1	173.7	87	444.9	198.1	47	499.7	222.5
08	281.4	125.3	68	336.2	149.7	28	391.0	174.1	88	445.8	198.5	48	500.6	222.9
09	282.3	125.7	69	337.1	150.1	29	391.9	174.5	89	446.7	198.9	49	501.5	223.3
10	283.2	126.1	70	338.0	150.5	30	392.8	174.9	90	447.6	199.3	50	502.5	223.7
311	284.1	126.5	371	338.9	150.9	431	393.7	175.3	491	448.6	199.7	551	503.4	224.1
12	285.0	126.9	72	339.8	151.3	32	394.7	175.7	92	449.5	200.1	52	504.3	224.5
13	285.9	127.3	73	340.7	151.7	33	395.6	176.1	93	450.4	200.5	53	505.2	224.9
14	286.9	127.7	74	341.7	152.1	34	396.5	176.5	94	451.3	200.9	54	506.1	225.3
15	287.8	128.1	75	342.6	152.5	35	397.4	176.9	95	452.2	201.3	55	507.0	225.7
16	288.7	128.5	76	343.5	152.9	36	398.3	177.3	96	453.1	201.7	56	507.9	226.1
17	289.6	128.9	77	344.4	153.3	37	399.2	177.7	97	454.0	202.1	57	508.8	226.6
18	290.5	129.3	78	345.3	153.7	38	400.1	178.2	98	454.9	202.6	58	509.8	227.0
19	291.4	129.7	79	346.2	154.2	39	401.0	178.6	99	455.9	203.0	59	510.7	227.4
20	292.3	130.2	80	347.1	154.6	40	402.0	179.0	500	456.8	203.4	60	511.6	227.8
321	293.2	130.6	381	348.1	155.0	441	402.9	179.4	501	457.7	203.8	561	512.5	228.2
22	294.2	131.0	82	349.0	155.4	42	403.8	179.8	02	458.6	204.2	62	513.4	228.6
23	295.1	131.4	83	349.9	155.8	43	404.7	180.2	03	459.5	204.6	63	514.3	229.0
24	296.0	131.8	84	350.8	156.2	44	405.6	180.6	04	460.4	205.0	64	515.2	229.4
25	296.9	132.2	85	351.7	156.6	45	406.5	181.0	05	461.3	205.4	65	516.2	229.8
26	297.8	132.6	86	352.6	157.0	46	407.4	181.4	06	442.3	205.8	66	517.1	230.2
27	298.7	133.0	87	353.5	157.4	47	408.4	181.8	07	463.2	206.2	67	518.0	230.6
28	299.6	133.4	88	354.5	157.8	48	409.3	182.2	08	464.1	206.6	68	518.9	231.0
29	300.6	133.8	89	355.4	158.2	49	410.2	182.6	09	465.0	207.0	69	519.8	231.4
30	301.5	134.2	90	356.3	158.6	50	411.1	183.0	10	465.9	207.4	70	520.7	231.8
331	302.4	134.6	391	357.2	159.0	451	412.0	183.4	511	466.8	207.8	571	521.6	232.2
32	303.3	135.0	92	358.1	159.4	52	412.9	183.8	12	467.7	208.2	72	522.5	232.7
33	304.2	135.4	93	359.0	159.8	53	413.8	184.3	13	468.6	208.7	73	523.5	233.1
34	305.1	135.9	94	359.9	160.3	54	414.7	184.7	14	469.6	209.1	74	524.4	233.5
35	306.0	136.3	95	360.9	160.7	55	415.7	185.1	15	470.5	209.5	75	525.3	233.9
36	307.0	136.7	96	361.8	161.1	56	416.6	185.5	16	471.4	209.9	76	526.2	234.3
37	307.9	137.1	97	362.7	161.5	57	417.5	185.9	17	472.3	210.3	77	527.1	234.7
38	308.8	137.5	98	363.6	161.9	58	418.4	186.3	18	473.2	210.7	78	528.0	235.1
39	309.7	137.9	99	364.5	162.3	59	419.3	186.7	19	474.1	211.1	79	528.9	235.5
40	310.6	138.3	400	365.4	162.7	60	420.2	187.1	20	475.0	211.5	80	529.9	235.9
341	311.5	138.7	401	366.3	163.1	461	421.1	187.5	521	476.0	211.9	581	530.8	236.3
42	312.4	139.1	02	367.2	163.5	62	422.1	187.9	22	476.9	212.3	82	531.7	236.7
43	313.3	139.5	03	368.2	163.9	63	423.0	188.3	23	477.8	212.7	83	532.6	237.1
44	314.3	139.9	04	369.1	164.3	64	423.9	188.7	24	478.7	213.1	84	533.5	237.5
45	315.2	140.3	05	370.0	164.7	65	424.8	189.1	25	479.6	213.5	85	534.4	237.9
46	316.1	140.7	06	370.9	165.1	66	425.7	189.5	26	480.5	213.9	86	535.3	238.3
47	317.0	141.1	07	371.8	165.5	67	426.6	189.9	27	481.4	214.4	87	536.3	238.8
48	317.9	141.5	08	372.7	165.9	68	427.5	190.4	28	482.4	214.8	88	537.2	239.2
49	318.8	142.0	09	373.6	166.4	69	428.5	190.8	29	483.3	215.2	89	538.1	239.6
50	319.7	142.4	10	374.6	166.8	70	429.4	191.2	30	484.2	215.6	90	539.0	240.0
351	320.7	142.8	411	375.5	167.2	471	430.3	191.6	531	485.1	216.0	591	539.9	240.4
52	321.6	143.2	12	376.4	167.6	72	431.2	192.0	32	486.0	216.4	92	540.8	240.8
53	322.5	143.6	13	377.3	168.0	73	432.1	192.4	33	486.9	216.8	93	541.7	241.2
54	323.4	144.0	14	378.2	168.4	74	433.0	192.8	34	487.8	217.2	94	542.6	241.6
55	324.3	144.4	15	379.1	168.8	75	433.9	193.2	35	488.7	217.6	95	543.6	242.0
56	325.2	144.8	16	380.0	169.2	76	434.8	193.6	36	489.7	218.0	96	544.5	242.4
57	326.1	145.2	17	380.9	169.6	77	435.8	194.0	37	490.6	218.4	97	545.4	242.8
58	327.0	145.6	18	381.9	170.0	78	436.7	194.4	38	491.5	218.8	98	546.3	243.2
59	328.0	146.0	19	382.8	170.4	79	437.6	194.8	39	492.4	219.2	99	547.2	243.6
60	328.9	146.4	20	383.7	170.8	80	438.5	195.2	40	493.3	219.6	600	548.1	244.0
Dist.	Dep.	Lat.	Dist.	Dep.	Lat.	Dist.	Dep.	Lat.	Dist.	Dep.	Lat.	Dist.	Dep.	Lat.

66° (114°, 246°, 294°).

In **Plane Sailing.**	**Dist.**	**Lat.**	**Dep.**
For converting *Dep.* into *Diff. Long.* and *Diff. Long.* into *Dep.* In **Middle Latitude Sailing.**	Diff. Long.	Dep.	
For converting *Dep.* into *Diff. Long.* and *Diff. Long.* into *Dep.* In **Mercator Sailing.**		*m*	Diff. Long.
For multiplication of numbers by sines and by cosines, or solution of plane right-angled triangles.	N. Hypotenuse.	N×Cos. Side Adj.	N×Sin. Side Opp.

TABLE 3.

Difference of Latitude and Departure for 25° (155°, 205°, 335°).

Dist.	Lat.	Dep.	Dist.	Lat.	Dep.	Dist.	Lat.	Dep.	Dist.	Lat.	Dep.	Dist.	Lat.	Dep.
1	0.9	0.4	61	55.3	25.8	121	109.7	51.1	181	164.0	76.5	241	218.4	101.9
2	1.8	0.8	62	56.2	26.2	22	110.6	51.6	82	164.9	76.9	42	219.3	102.3
3	2.7	1.3	63	57.1	26.6	23	111.5	52.0	83	165.9	77.3	43	220.2	102.7
4	3.6	1.7	64	58.0	27.0	24	112.4	52.4	84	166.8	77.8	44	221.1	103.1
5	4.5	2.1	65	58.9	27.5	25	113.3	52.8	85	167.7	78.2	45	222.0	103.5
6	5.4	2.5	66	59.8	27.9	26	114.2	53.2	86	168.6	78.6	46	223.0	104.0
7	6.3	3.0	67	60.7	28.3	27	115.1	53.7	87	169.5	79.0	47	223.9	104.4
8	7.3	3.4	68	61.6	28.7	28	116.0	54.1	88	170.4	79.5	48	224.8	104.8
9	8.2	3.8	69	62.5	29.2	29	116.9	54.5	89	171.3	79.9	49	225.7	105.2
10	9.1	4.2	70	63.4	29.6	30	117.8	54.9	90	172.2	80.3	50	226.6	105.7
11	10.0	4.6	71	64.3	30.0	131	118.7	55.4	191	173.1	80.7	251	227.5	106.1
12	10.9	5.1	72	65.3	30.4	32	119.6	55.8	92	174.0	81.1	52	228.4	106.5
13	11.8	5.5	73	66.2	30.9	33	120.5	56.2	93	174.9	81.6	53	229.3	106.9
14	12.7	5.9	74	67.1	31.3	34	121.4	56.6	94	175.8	82.0	54	230.2	107.3
15	13.6	6.3	75	68.0	31.7	35	122.4	57.1	95	176.7	82.4	55	231.1	107.8
16	14.5	6.8	76	68.9	32.1	36	123.3	57.5	96	177.6	82.8	56	232.0	108.2
17	15.4	7.2	77	69.8	32.5	37	124.2	57.9	97	178.5	83.3	57	232.9	108.6
18	16.3	7.6	78	70.7	33.0	38	125.1	58.3	98	179.4	83.7	58	233.8	109.0
19	17.2	8.0	79	71.6	33.4	39	126.0	58.7	99	180.4	84.1	59	234.7	109.5
20	18.1	8.5	80	72.5	33.8	40	126.9	59.2	200	181.3	84.5	60	235.6	109.9
21	19.0	8.9	81	73.4	34.2	141	127.8	59.6	201	182.2	84.9	261	236.5	110.3
22	19.9	9.3	82	74.3	34.7	42	128.7	60.0	02	183.1	85.4	62	237.5	110.7
23	20.8	9.7	83	75.2	35.1	43	129.6	60.4	03	184.0	85.8	63	238.4	111.1
24	21.8	10.1	84	76.1	35.5	44	130.5	60.9	04	184.9	86.2	64	239.3	111.6
25	22.7	10.6	85	77.0	35.9	45	131.4	61.3	05	185.8	86.6	65	240.2	112.0
26	23.6	11.0	86	77.9	36.3	46	132.3	61.7	06	186.7	87.1	66	241.1	112.4
27	24.5	11.4	87	78.8	36.8	47	133.2	62.1	07	187.6	87.5	67	242.0	112.8
28	25.4	11.8	88	79.8	37.2	48	134.1	62.5	08	188.5	87.9	68	242.9	113.3
29	26.3	12.3	89	80.7	37.6	49	135.0	63.0	09	189.4	88.3	69	243.8	113.7
30	27.2	12.7	90	81.6	38.0	50	135.9	63.4	10	190.3	88.7	70	244.7	114.1
31	28.1	13.1	91	82.5	38.5	151	136.9	63.8	211	191.2	89.2	271	245.6	114.5
32	29.0	13.5	92	83.4	38.9	52	137.8	64.2	12	192.1	89.6	72	246.5	115.0
33	29.9	13.9	93	84.3	39.3	53	138.7	64.7	13	193.0	90.0	73	247.4	115.4
34	30.8	14.4	94	85.2	39.7	54	139.6	65.1	14	193.9	90.4	74	248.3	115.8
35	31.7	14.8	95	86.1	40.1	55	140.5	65.5	15	194.9	90.9	75	249.2	116.2
36	32.6	15.2	96	87.0	40.6	56	141.4	65.9	16	195.8	91.3	76	250.1	116.6
37	33.5	15.6	97	87.9	41.0	57	142.3	66.4	17	196.7	91.7	77	251.0	117.1
38	34.4	16.1	98	88.8	41.4	58	143.2	66.8	18	197.6	92.1	78	252.0	117.5
39	35.3	16.5	99	89.7	41.8	59	144.1	67.2	19	198.5	92.6	79	252.9	117.9
40	36.3	16.9	100	90.6	42.3	60	145.0	67.6	20	199.4	93.0	80	253.8	118.3
41	37.2	17.3	101	91.5	42.7	161	145.9	68.0	221	200.3	93.4	281	254.7	118.8
42	38.1	17.7	02	92.4	43.1	62	146.8	68.5	22	201.2	93.8	82	255.6	119.2
43	39.0	18.2	03	93.3	43.5	63	147.7	68.9	23	202.1	94.2	83	256.5	119.6
44	39.9	18.6	04	94.3	44.0	64	148.6	69.3	24	203.0	94.7	84	257.4	120.0
45	40.8	19.0	05	95.2	44.4	65	149.5	69.7	25	203.9	95.1	85	258.3	120.4
46	41.7	19.4	06	96.1	44.8	66	150.4	70.2	26	204.8	95.5	86	259.2	120.9
47	42.6	19.9	07	97.0	45.2	67	151.4	70.6	27	205.7	95.9	87	260.1	121.3
48	43.5	20.3	08	97.9	45.6	68	152.3	71.0	28	206.6	96.4	88	261.0	121.7
49	44.4	20.7	09	98.8	46.1	69	153.2	71.4	29	207.5	96.8	89	261.9	122.1
50	45.3	21.1	10	99.7	46.5	70	154.1	71.8	30	208.5	97.2	90	262.8	122.6
51	46.2	21.6	111	100.6	46.9	171	155.0	72.3	231	209.4	97.6	291	263.7	123.0
52	47.1	22.0	12	101.5	47.3	72	155.9	72.7	32	210.3	98.0	92	264.6	123.4
53	48.0	22.4	13	102.4	47.8	73	156.8	73.1	33	211.2	98.5	93	265.5	123.8
54	48.9	22.8	14	103.3	48.2	74	157.7	73.5	34	212.1	98.9	94	266.5	124.2
55	49.8	23.2	15	104.2	48.6	75	158.6	74.0	35	213.0	99.3	95	267.4	124.7
56	50.8	23.7	16	105.1	49.0	76	159.5	74.4	36	213.9	99.7	96	268.3	125.1
57	51.7	24.1	17	106.0	49.4	77	160.4	74.8	37	214.8	100.2	97	269.2	125.5
58	52.6	24.5	18	106.9	49.9	78	161.3	75.2	38	215.7	100.6	98	270.1	125.9
59	53.5	24.9	19	107.9	50.3	79	162.2	75.6	39	216.6	101.0	99	271.0	126.4
60	54.4	25.4	20	108.8	50.7	80	163.1	76.1	40	217.5	101.4	300	271.9	126.8
Dist.	Dep.	Lat.	Dist.	Dep.	Lat.	Dist.	Dep.	Lat.	Dist.	Dep.	Lat.	Dist.	Dep.	Lat.

65° (115°, 245°, 295°).

In **Plane Sailing.**	**Dist.**	**Lat.**	**Dep.**
For converting *Dep.* into *Diff. Long.* and *Diff. Long.* into *Dep.* In **Middle Latitude Sailing.**	Diff. Long.	Dep.	
For converting *Dep.* into *Diff. Long.* and *Diff. Long.* into *Dep.* In **Mercator Sailing.**		*m*	Diff Long.
For multiplication of numbers by sines and by cosines, or solution of plane right-angled triangles.	N. / Hypotenuse.	N×Cos. / Side Adj.	N×Sin. / Side Opp.

TABLE 3.

Difference of Latitude and Departure for 25° (155°, 205°, 335°).

Dist.	Lat.	Dep.	Dist.	Lat.	Dep.	Dist.	Lat.	Dep.	Dist.	Lat.	Dep.	Dist.	Lat.	Dep.
301	272.8	127.2	361	327.2	152.6	421	381.6	177.9	481	435.9	203.3	541	490.3	228.6
02	273.7	127.6	62	328.0	153.0	22	382.5	178.3	82	436.8	203.7	42	491.2	229.1
03	274.6	128.1	63	329.0	153.4	23	383.4	178.8	83	437.7	204.1	43	492.1	229.5
04	275.5	128.5	64	329.9	153.8	24	384.3	179.2	84	438.7	204.5	44	493.0	229.9
05	276.4	128.9	65	330.8	154.3	25	385.2	179.6	85	439.6	204.9	45	493.9	230.3
06	277.3	129.3	66	331.7	154.7	26	386.1	180.0	86	440.5	205.4	46	494.8	230.7
07	278.2	129.7	67	332.6	155.1	27	387.0	180.5	87	441.4	205.8	47	495.8	231.2
08	279.1	130.2	68	333.5	155.5	28	387.9	180.9	88	442.3	206.2	48	496.7	231.6
09	280.0	130.6	69	334.4	155.9	29	388.8	181.3	89	443.2	206.6	49	497.6	232.0
10	281.0	131.0	70	335.3	156.4	30	389.7	181.7	90	444.1	207.1	50	498.5	232.4
311	281.9	131.4	371	336.2	156.8	431	390.6	182.1	491	445.0	207.5	551	499.4	232.9
12	282.8	131.9	72	337.1	157.2	32	391.5	182.6	92	445.9	207.9	52	500.3	233.3
13	283.7	132.3	73	338.1	157.6	33	392.4	183.0	93	446.8	208.4	53	501.2	233.7
14	284.6	132.7	74	339.0	158.1	34	393.3	183.4	94	447.7	208.8	54	502.1	234.1
15	285.5	133.1	75	339.9	158.5	35	394.2	183.8	95	448.6	209.2	55	503.0	234.6
16	286.4	133.5	76	340.8	158.9	36	395.2	184.3	96	449.5	209.6	56	503.9	235.0
17	287.3	134.0	77	341.7	159.3	37	396.1	184.7	97	450.4	210.0	57	504.8	235.4
18	288.2	134.4	78	342.5	159.7	38	397.0	185.1	98	451.3	210.4	58	505.7	235.8
19	289.1	134.8	79	343.5	160.2	39	397.9	185.5	99	452.2	210.9	59	506.6	236.2
20	290.0	135.2	80	344.4	160.6	40	398.8	186.0	500	453.2	211.3	60	507.5	236.7
321	290.9	135.7	381	345.3	161.0	441	399.6	186.3	501	454.1	211.7	561	508.4	237.1
22	291.8	136.1	82	346.2	161.4	42	400.6	186.8	02	455.0	212.2	62	509.3	237.5
23	292.7	136.5	83	347.1	161.9	43	401.5	187.2	03	455.9	212.6	63	510.3	237.9
24	293.6	136.9	84	348.0	162.3	44	402.4	187.6	04	456.8	213.0	64	511.2	238.4
25	294.6	137.4	85	348.9	162.7	45	403.3	188.1	05	457.7	213.4	65	512.1	238.8
26	295.5	137.8	86	349.8	163.1	46	404.2	188.5	06	458.6	213.8	66	513.0	239.2
27	296.4	138.2	87	350.7	163.6	47	405.1	188.9	07	459.5	214.3	67	513.9	239.6
28	297.3	138.6	88	351.6	164.0	48	406.0	189.3	08	460.4	214.7	68	514.8	240.0
29	298.2	139.0	89	352.6	164.4	49	406.9	189.8	09	461.3	215.1	69	515.7	240.5
30	299.1	139.5	90	353.5	164.8	50	407.8	190.2	10	462.2	215.5	70	516.6	240.9
331	300.0	139.9	391	354.4	165.2	451	408.7	190.6	511	463.1	216.0	571	517.5	241.3
32	300.9	140.3	92	355.3	165.7	52	409.7	191.0	12	464.0	216.4	72	518.4	241.7
33	301.8	140.7	93	356.2	166.1	53	410.6	191.4	13	464.9	216.8	73	519.3	242.2
34	302.7	141.2	94	357.1	166.5	54	411.5	191.7	14	465.8	217.2	74	520.2	242.6
35	303.6	141.6	95	358.0	166.9	55	412.4	192.3	15	466.7	217.6	75	521.1	243.0
36	304.5	142.0	96	358.9	167.4	56	413.3	192.7	16	467.7	218.1	76	522.0	243.4
37	305.4	142.4	97	359.8	167.8	57	414.1	193.1	17	468.6	218.5	77	522.9	243.9
38	306.3	142.8	98	360.7	168.2	58	415.1	193.6	18	469.5	218.9	78	523.8	244.3
39	307.2	143.3	99	361.6	168.6	59	416.0	194.0	19	470.4	219.3	79	524.8	244.7
40	308.1	143.7	400	362.5	169.0	60	416.9	194.4	20	471.8	219.8	80	525.7	245.1
341	309.1	144.1	401	363.4	169.5	461	417.8	194.8	521	472.2	220.2	581	526.6	245.5
42	310.0	144.5	02	364.3	169.9	62	418.7	195.2	22	473.1	220.6	82	527.5	246.0
43	310.9	145.0	03	365.2	170.3	63	419.6	195.7	23	474.0	221.0	83	528.4	246.4
44	311.8	145.4	04	366.1	170.7	64	420.5	196.1	24	474.9	221.5	84	529.3	246.8
45	312.7	145.8	05	367.1	171.2	65	421.4	196.5	25	475.8	221.9	85	530.2	247.2
46	313.6	146.2	06	368.0	171.6	66	422.3	196.9	26	476.7	222.3	86	531.1	247.7
47	314.5	146.6	07	368.9	172.0	67	423.2	197.4	27	477.6	222.7	87	532.0	248.1
48	315.4	147.1	08	369.8	172.4	68	424.2	197.8	28	478.5	223.1	88	532.9	248.5
49	316.3	147.5	09	370.7	172.9	69	425.1	198.2	29	479.4	223.6	89	533.8	248.9
50	317.2	147.9	10	371.6	173.3	70	426.0	198.6	30	480.3	224.0	90	534.7	249.3
351	318.1	148.3	411	372.5	173.7	471	426.9	199.1	531	481.2	224.4	591	535.6	249.8
52	319.0	148.8	12	373.4	174.1	72	427.8	199.5	32	482.1	224.8	92	536.5	250.2
53	319.9	149.2	13	374.3	174.5	73	428.7	199.9	33	483.1	225.3	92	537.4	250.6
54	320.8	149.6	14	375.2	175.0	74	429.6	200.3	34	482.0	225.7	94	538.3	251.0
55	321.7	150.0	15	376.1	175.4	75	430.5	200.7	35	484.9	226.1	95	539.3	251.5
56	322.6	150.5	16	377.0	175.8	76	431.4	201.2	36	485.8	226.5	96	540.2	251.9
57	323.6	150.9	17	377.9	176.2	77	432.3	201.6	37	486.7	226.9	97	541.1	252.3
58	324.5	151.3	18	378.8	176.7	78	433.2	202.0	38	487.6	227.4	98	542.0	252.7
59	325.4	151.7	19	379.7	177.1	79	434.1	202.4	39	488.5	227.8	99	542.9	253.1
60	326.3	152.1	20	380.6	177.5	80	435.0	202.9	40	489.4	228.2	600	543.8	253.6
Dist.	Dep.	Lat.	Dist.	Dep.	Lat.	Dist.	Dep.	Lat.	Dist.	Dep.	Lat.	Dist.	Dep.	Lat.

65° (115°, 245°, 295°).

In **Plane Sailing.**	Dist.	Lat.	Dep.
For converting *Dep.* into *Diff. Long.* and *Diff. Long.* into *Dep.* In **Middle Latitude Sailing.**	Diff. Long.	Dep.	
For converting *Dep.* into *Diff. Long.* and *Diff. Long.* into *Dep.* In **Mercator Sailing.**		*m*	Diff. Long.
For multiplication of numbers by sines and by cosines, or solution of plane right-angled triangles.	N. Hypotenuse.	N×Cos. Side Adj.	N×Sin. Side Opp.

TABLE 3.

Difference of Latitude and Departure for 26° (154°, 206°, 334°).

Dist.	Lat.	Dep.	Dist.	Lat.	Dep.	Dist.	Lat.	Dep.	Dist.	Lat.	Dep.	Dist.	Lat.	Dep.
1	0.9	0.4	61	54.8	26.7	121	108.8	53.0	181	162.7	79.3	241	216.6	105.6
2	1.8	0.9	62	55.7	27.2	22	109.7	53.5	82	163.6	79.8	42	217.5	106.1
3	2.7	1.3	63	56.6	27.6	23	110.6	53.9	83	164.5	80.2	43	218.4	106.5
4	3.6	1.8	64	57.5	28.1	24	111.5	54.4	84	165.4	80.7	44	219.3	107.0
5	4.5	2.2	65	58.4	28.5	25	112.3	54.8	85	166.3	81.1	45	220.2	107.4
6	5.4	2.6	66	59.3	28.9	26	113.2	55.2	86	167.2	81.5	46	221.1	107.8
7	6.3	3.1	67	60.2	29.4	27	114.1	55.7	87	168.1	82.0	47	222.0	108.3
8	7.2	3.5	68	61.1	29.8	28	115.0	56.1	88	169.0	82.4	48	222.9	108.7
9	8.1	3.9	69	62.0	30.2	29	115.9	56.5	89	169.9	82.9	49	223.8	109.2
10	9.0	4.4	70	62.9	30.7	30	116.8	57.0	90	170.8	83.3	50	224.7	109.6
11	9.9	4.8	71	63.8	31.1	131	117.7	57.4	191	171.7	83.7	251	225.6	110.0
12	10.8	5.3	72	64.7	31.6	32	118.6	57.9	92	172.6	84.2	52	226.5	110.5
13	11.7	5.7	73	65.6	32.0	33	119.5	58.3	93	173.5	84.6	53	227.4	110.9
14	12.6	6.1	74	66.5	32.4	34	120.4	58.7	94	174.4	85.0	54	228.3	111.3
15	13.5	6.6	75	67.4	32.9	35	121.3	59.2	95	175.3	85.5	55	229.2	111.8
16	14.4	7.0	76	68.3	33.3	36	122.2	59.6	96	176.2	85.9	56	230.1	112.2
17	15.3	7.5	77	69.2	33.8	37	123.1	60.1	97	177.1	86.4	57	231.0	112.7
18	16.2	7.9	78	70.1	34.2	38	124.0	60.5	98	178.0	86.8	58	231.9	113.1
19	17.1	8.3	79	71.0	34.6	39	124.9	60.9	99	178.9	87.2	59	232.8	113.5
20	18.0	8.8	80	71.9	35.1	40	125.8	61.4	200	179.8	87.7	60	233.7	114.0
21	18.9	9.2	81	72.8	35.5	141	126.7	61.8	201	180.7	88.1	261	234.6	114.4
22	19.8	9.6	82	73.7	35.9	42	127.6	62.2	02	181.6	88.6	62	235.5	114.9
23	20.7	10.1	83	74.6	36.4	43	128.5	62.7	03	182.5	89.0	63	236.4	115.3
24	21.6	10.5	84	75.5	36.8	44	129.4	63.1	04	183.4	89.4	64	237.3	115.7
25	22.5	11.0	85	76.4	37.3	45	130.3	63.6	05	184.3	89.9	65	238.2	116.2
26	23.4	11.4	86	77.3	37.7	46	131.2	64.0	06	185.2	90.3	66	239.1	116.6
27	24.3	11.8	87	78.2	38.1	47	132.1	64.4	07	186.1	90.7	67	240.0	117.0
28	25.2	12.3	88	79.1	38.6	48	133.0	64.9	08	186.9	91.2	68	240.9	117.5
29	26.1	12.7	89	80.0	39.0	49	133.9	65.3	09	187.8	91.6	69	241.8	117.9
30	27.0	13.2	90	80.9	39.5	50	134.8	65.8	10	188.7	92.1	70	242.7	118.4
31	27.9	13.6	91	81.8	39.9	151	135.7	66.2	211	189.6	92.5	271	243.6	118.8
32	28.8	14.0	92	82.7	40.3	52	136.6	66.6	12	190.5	92.9	72	244.5	119.2
33	29.7	14.5	93	83.6	40.8	53	137.5	67.1	13	191.4	93.4	73	245.4	119.7
34	30.6	14.9	94	84.5	41.2	54	138.4	67.5	14	192.3	93.8	74	246.3	120.1
35	31.5	15.3	95	85.4	41.6	55	139.3	67.9	15	193.2	94.2	75	247.2	120.6
36	32.4	15.8	96	86.3	42.1	56	140.2	68.4	16	194.1	94.7	76	248.1	121.0
37	33.3	16.2	97	87.2	42.5	57	141.1	68.8	17	195.0	95.1	77	249.0	121.4
38	34.2	16.7	98	88.1	43.0	58	142.0	69.3	18	195.9	95.6	78	249.9	121.9
39	35.1	17.1	99	89.0	43.4	59	142.9	69.7	19	196.8	96.0	79	250.8	122.3
40	36.0	17.5	100	89.9	43.8	60	143.8	70.1	20	197.7	96.4	80	251.7	122.7
41	36.9	18.0	101	90.8	44.3	161	144.7	70.6	221	198.6	96.9	281	252.6	123.2
42	37.7	18.4	02	91.7	44.7	62	145.6	71.0	22	199.5	97.3	82	253.5	123.6
43	38.6	18.8	03	92.6	45.2	63	146.5	71.5	23	200.4	97.8	83	254.4	124.1
44	39.5	19.3	04	93.5	45.6	64	147.4	71.9	24	201.3	98.2	84	255.3	124.5
45	40.4	19.7	05	94.4	46.0	65	148.3	72.3	25	202.2	98.6	85	256.2	124.9
46	41.3	20.2	06	95.3	46.5	66	149.2	72.8	26	203.1	99.1	86	257.1	125.4
47	42.2	20.6	07	96.2	46.9	67	150.1	73.2	27	204.0	99.5	87	258.0	125.8
48	43.1	21.0	08	97.1	47.3	68	151.0	73.6	28	204.9	99.9	88	258.9	126.3
49	44.0	21.5	09	98.0	47.8	69	151.9	74.1	29	205.8	100.4	89	259.8	126.7
50	44.9	21.9	10	98.9	48.2	70	152.8	74.5	30	206.7	100.8	90	260.7	127.1
51	45.8	22.4	111	99.8	48.7	171	153.7	75.0	231	207.6	101.3	291	261.5	127.6
52	46.7	22.8	12	100.7	49.1	72	154.6	75.4	32	208.5	101.7	92	262.4	128.0
53	47.6	23.2	13	101.6	49.5	73	155.5	75.8	33	209.4	102.1	93	263.3	128.4
54	48.5	23.7	14	102.5	50.0	74	156.4	76.3	34	210.3	102.6	94	264.2	128.9
55	49.4	24.1	15	103.4	50.4	75	157.3	76.7	35	211.2	103.0	95	265.1	129.3
56	50.3	24.5	16	104.3	50.9	76	158.2	77.2	36	212.1	103.5	96	266.0	129.8
57	51.2	25.0	17	105.2	51.3	77	159.1	77.6	37	213.0	103.9	97	266.9	130.2
58	52.1	25.4	18	106.1	51.7	78	160.0	78.0	38	213.9	104.3	98	267.8	130.6
59	53.0	25.9	19	107.0	52.2	79	160.9	78.5	39	214.8	104.8	99	268.7	131.1
60	53.9	26.3	20	107.9	52.6	80	161.8	78.9	40	215.7	105.2	300	269.6	131.5
Dist.	Dep.	Lat.	Dist.	Dep.	Lat.	Dist.	Dep.	Lat.	Dist.	Dep.	Lat.	Dist.	Dep.	Lat.

64° (116°, 244°, 296°).

In **Plane Sailing.**	**Dist.**	**Lat.**	**Dep.**
For converting *Dep.* into *Diff. Long.* and *Diff. Long.* into *Dep.* **In Middle Latitude Sailing.**	Diff. Long.	Dep.	
For converting *Dep.* into *Diff. Long.* and *Diff. Long.* into *Dep.* **In Mercator Sailing.**		*m*	Diff. Long.
For multiplication of numbers by sines and by cosines, or solution of plane right-angled triangles.	N.	N×Cos.	N×Sin.
	Hypote-nuse.	Side. Adj.	Side Opp.

TABLE 3.

Difference of Latitude and Departure for 26° (154°, 206°, 334°).

Dist.	Lat.	Dep.	Dist.	Lat.	Dep.	Dist.	Lat.	Dep.	Dist.	Lat.	Dep.	Dist.	Lat.	Dep.
301	270.5	131.9	361	324.5	158.3	421	378.4	184.6	481	432.3	210.9	541	486.2	237.2
02	271.4	132.4	62	325.4	158.7	22	379.3	185.0	82	433.2	211.3	42	487.1	237.6
03	272.3	132.8	63	326.3	159.1	23	380.2	185.4	83	434.1	211.7	43	488.0	238.0
04	273.2	133.3	64	327.2	159.6	24	381.1	185.9	84	435.0	212.2	44	488.9	238.5
05	274.1	133.7	65	328.1	160.0	25	382.0	186.3	85	435.9	212.6	45	489.8	238.9
06	275.0	134.1	66	329.0	160.4	26	382.9	186.7	86	436.8	213.0	46	490.7	239.4
07	275.9	134.6	67	329.9	160.9	27	383.8	187.2	87	437.7	213.5	47	491.6	239.8
08	276.8	135.0	68	330.8	161.3	28	384.7	187.6	88	438.6	213.9	48	492.5	240.2
09	277.7	135.5	69	331.7	161.8	29	385.6	188.1	89	439.5	214.4	49	493.4	240.7
10	278.6	135.9	70	332.6	162.2	30	386.5	188.5	90	440.4	214.8	50	494.3	241.1
311	279.5	136.3	371	333.5	162.6	431	387.4	188.9	491	441.3	215.2	551	495.2	241.5
12	280.4	136.8	72	334.4	163.1	32	388.3	189.4	92	442.2	215.7	52	496.1	242.0
13	281.3	137.2	73	335.3	163.5	33	389.2	189.8	93	443.1	216.1	53	497.0	242.4
14	282.2	137.6	74	336.1	164.0	34	390.1	190.3	94	444.0	216.6	54	497.9	242.9
15	283.1	138.1	75	337.0	164.4	35	391.0	190.7	95	444.9	217.0	55	498.8	243.3
16	284.0	138.5	76	337.9	164.8	36	391.9	191.1	96	445.8	217.4	56	499.7	243.7
17	284.9	139.0	77	338.8	165.3	37	392.8	191.6	97	446.7	217.9	57	500.6	244.2
18	285.8	139.4	78	339.7	165.7	38	393.7	192.0	98	447.6	218.3	58	501.5	244.6
19	286.7	139.8	79	340.6	166.1	39	394.6	192.4	99	448.5	218.7	59	502.4	245.0
20	287.6	140.3	80	341.5	166.6	40	395.5	192.9	500	449.4	219.2	60	503.3	245.5
321	288.5	140.7	381	342.4	167.0	441	396.4	193.3	501	450.3	219.6	561	504.2	245.9
22	289.4	141.2	82	343.3	167.5	42	397.3	193.8	02	451.2	220.1	62	505.1	246.4
23	290.3	141.6	83	344.2	167.9	43	398.2	194.2	03	452.1	220.5	63	506.0	246.8
24	291.2	142.0	84	345.1	168.3	44	399.1	194.6	04	453.0	220.9	64	506.9	247.2
25	292.1	142.5	85	346.0	168.8	45	400.0	195.1	05	453.9	221.4	65	507.8	247.7
26	293.0	142.9	86	346.9	169.2	46	400.9	195.5	06	454.8	221.8	66	508.7	248.1
27	293.9	143.3	87	347.8	169.6	47	401.8	196.0	07	455.7	222.3	67	509.6	248.6
28	294.8	143.8	88	348.7	170.1	48	402.7	196.4	08	456.6	222.7	68	510.5	249.0
29	295.7	144.2	89	349.6	170.5	49	403.6	196.8	09	457.5	223.1	69	511.4	249.4
30	296.6	144.7	90	350.5	171.0	50	404.5	197.3	10	458.4	223.6	70	512.3	249.9
331	297.5	145.1	391	351.4	171.4	451	405.4	197.7	511	459.3	224.0	571	513.2	250.3
32	298.4	145.5	92	352.3	171.8	52	406.3	198.1	12	460.2	224.4	72	514.1	250.7
33	299.3	146.0	93	353.2	172.3	53	407.2	198.6	13	461.1	224.9	73	515.0	251.2
34	300.2	146.4	94	354.1	172.7	54	408.1	199.0	14	462.0	225.3	74	515.9	251.6
35	301.1	146.9	95	355.0	173.2	55	409.0	199.5	15	462.9	225.8	75	516.8	252.1
36	302.0	147.3	96	355.9	173.6	56	409.9	199.9	16	463.8	226.2	76	517.7	252.5
37	302.9	147.7	97	356.8	174.0	57	410.7	200.3	17	464.7	226.6	77	518.6	252.9
38	303.8	148.2	98	357.7	174.5	58	411.6	200.8	18	465.6	227.1	78	519.5	253.4
39	304.7	148.6	99	358.6	174.9	59	412.5	201.2	19	466.5	227.5	79	520.4	253.8
40	305.6	149.0	400	359.5	175.3	60	413.6	201.7	20	467.4	228.0	80	521.3	254.3
341	306.5	149.5	401	360.4	175.8	461	414.3	202.1	521	468.3	228.4	581	522.2	254.7
42	307.4	149.9	02	361.3	176.2	62	415.2	202.5	22	469.2	228.8	82	523.1	255.1
43	308.3	150.4	03	362.2	176.7	63	416.1	203.0	23	470.1	229.3	83	524.0	255.6
44	309.2	150.8	04	363.1	177.1	64	417.0	203.4	24	471.0	229.7	84	524.9	256.0
45	310.1	151.2	05	364.0	177.5	65	417.9	203.8	25	471.9	230.1	85	525.8	256.4
46	311.0	151.7	06	364.9	178.0	66	418.8	204.3	26	472.8	230.6	86	526.7	256.9
47	311.9	152.1	07	365.8	178.4	67	419.7	204.7	27	473.7	231.0	87	527.6	257.3
48	312.8	152.6	08	366.7	178.9	68	420.6	205.2	28	474.6	231.5	88	528.5	257.8
49	313.7	153.0	09	367.6	179.3	69	421.5	205.6	29	475.5	231.9	89	529.4	258.2
50	314.6	153.4	10	368.5	179.7	70	422.4	206.0	30	476.4	232.3	90	530.3	258.6
351	315.5	153.9	411	369.4	180.2	471	423.3	206.5	531	477.3	232.8	591	531.2	259.1
52	316.4	154.3	12	370.3	180.6	72	424.2	206.9	32	478.2	233.2	92	532.1	259.5
53	317.3	154.7	13	371.2	181.0	73	425.1	207.3	33	479.1	233.7	93	533.0	260.0
54	318.2	155.2	14	372.1	181.5	74	426.0	207.8	34	480.0	234.1	94	533.9	260.4
55	319.1	155.6	15	373.0	181.9	75	426.9	208.2	35	480.9	234.5	95	534.8	260.8
56	320.0	156.1	16	373.9	182.4	76	427.8	208.7	36	481.8	235.0	96	535.7	261.3
57	320.9	156.5	17	374.8	182.8	77	428.7	209.1	37	482.7	235.4	97	536.6	261.7
58	321.8	156.9	18	375.7	183.2	78	429.6	209.5	38	483.6	235.8	98	537.5	262.1
59	322.7	157.4	19	376.6	183.7	79	430.5	210.0	39	484.4	236.3	99	538.4	262.6
60	323.6	157.8	20	377.5	184.1	80	431.4	210.4	40	485.3	236.7	600	539.3	263.0
Dist.	Dep.	Lat.	Dist.	Dep.	Lat.	Dist.	Dep.	Lat.	Dist.	Dep.	Lat.	Dist.	Dep.	Lat.

64° (116°, 244°, 296°).

In **Plane Sailing.**	Dist.	Lat.	Dep.
For converting *Dep.* into *Diff. Long.* and *Diff. Long.* into *Dep.* In **Middle Latitude Sailing.**	Diff. Long.	Dep.	
For converting *Dep.* into *Diff. Long.* and *Diff. Long.* into *Dep.* In **Mercator Sailing.**		*m*	Diff. Long.
For multiplication of numbers by sines and by cosines, or solution of plane right-angled triangles.	N. / Hypotenuse.	N×Cos. / Side Adj.	N×Sin. / Side Opp.

TABLE 3.

Difference of Latitude and Departure for 27° (153°, 207°, 333°).

Dist.	Lat.	Dep.	Dist.	Lat.	Dep.	Dist.	Lat.	Dep.	Dist.	Lat.	Dep.	Dist.	Lat.	Dep.
1	0.9	0.5	61	54.4	27.7	121	107.8	54.9	181	161.3	82.2	241	214.7	109.4
2	1.8	0.9	62	55.2	28.1	22	108.7	55.4	82	162.2	82.6	42	215.6	109.9
3	2.7	1.4	63	56.1	28.6	23	109.6	55.8	83	163.1	83.1	43	216.5	110.3
4	3.6	1.8	64	57.0	29.1	24	110.5	56.3	84	163.9	83.5	44	217.4	110.8
5	4.5	2.3	65	57.9	29.5	25	111.4	56.7	85	164.8	84.0	45	218.3	111.2
6	5.3	2.7	66	58.8	30.0	26	112.3	57.2	86	165.7	84.4	46	219.2	111.7
7	6.2	3.2	67	59.7	30.4	27	113.2	57.7	87	166.6	84.9	47	220.1	112.1
8	7.1	3.6	68	60.6	30.9	28	114.0	58.1	88	167.5	85.4	48	221.0	112.6
9	8.0	4.1	69	61.5	31.3	29	114.9	58.6	89	168.4	85.8	49	221.9	113.0
10	8.9	4.5	70	62.4	31.8	30	115.8	59.0	90	169.3	86.3	50	222.8	113.5
11	9.8	5.0	71	63.3	32.2	131	116.7	59.5	191	170.2	86.7	251	223.6	114.0
12	10.7	5.4	72	64.2	32.7	32	117.6	59.9	92	171.1	87.2	52	224.5	114.4
13	11.6	5.9	73	65.0	33.1	33	118.5	60.4	93	172.0	87.6	53	225.4	114.9
14	12.5	6.4	74	65.9	33.6	34	119.4	60.8	94	172.9	88.1	54	226.3	115.3
15	13.4	6.8	75	66.8	34.0	35	120.3	61.3	95	173.7	88.5	55	227.2	115.8
16	14.3	7.3	76	67.7	34.5	36	121.2	61.7	96	174.6	89.0	56	228.1	116.2
17	15.1	7.7	77	68.6	35.0	37	122.1	62.2	97	175.5	89.4	57	229.0	116.7
18	16.0	8.2	78	69.5	35.4	38	123.0	62.7	98	176.4	89.9	58	229.9	117.1
19	16.9	8.6	79	70.4	35.9	39	123.8	63.1	99	177.3	90.3	59	230.8	117.6
20	17.8	9.1	80	71.3	36.3	40	124.7	63.6	200	178.2	90.8	60	231.7	118.0
21	18.7	9.5	81	72.2	36.8	141	125.6	64.0	201	179.1	91.3	261	232.6	118.5
22	19.6	10.0	82	73.1	37.2	42	126.5	64.5	02	180.0	91.7	62	233.4	118.9
23	20.5	10.4	83	74.0	37.7	43	127.4	64.9	03	180.9	92.2	63	234.3	119.4
24	21.4	10.9	84	74.8	38.1	44	128.3	65.4	04	181.8	92.6	64	235.2	119.9
25	22.3	11.3	85	75.7	38.6	45	129.2	65.8	05	182.7	93.1	65	236.1	120.3
26	23.2	11.8	86	76.6	39.0	46	130.1	66.3	06	183.5	93.5	66	237.0	120.8
27	24.1	12.3	87	77.5	39.5	47	131.0	66.7	07	184.4	94.0	67	237.9	121.2
28	24.9	12.7	88	78.4	40.0	48	131.9	67.2	08	185.3	94.4	68	238.8	121.7
29	25.8	13.2	89	79.3	40.4	49	132.8	67.6	09	186.2	94.9	69	239.7	122.1
30	26.7	13.6	90	80.2	40.9	50	133.7	68.1	10	187.1	95.3	70	240.6	122.6
31	27.6	14.1	91	81.1	41.3	151	134.5	68.6	211	188.0	95.8	271	241.5	123.0
32	28.5	14.5	92	82.0	41.8	52	135.4	69.0	12	188.9	96.2	72	242.4	123.5
33	29.4	15.0	93	82.9	42.2	53	136.3	69.5	13	189.8	96.7	73	243.2	123.9
34	30.3	15.4	94	83.8	42.7	54	137.2	69.9	14	190.7	97.2	74	244.1	124.4
35	31.2	15.9	95	84.6	43.1	55	138.1	70.4	15	191.6	97.6	75	245.0	124.8
36	32.1	16.3	96	85.5	43.6	56	139.0	70.8	16	192.5	98.1	76	245.9	125.3
37	33.0	16.8	97	86.4	44.0	57	139.9	71.3	17	193.3	98.5	77	246.8	125.8
38	33.9	17.3	98	87.3	44.5	58	140.8	71.7	18	194.2	99.0	78	247.7	126.2
39	34.7	17.7	99	88.2	44.9	59	141.7	72.2	19	195.1	99.4	79	248.6	126.7
40	35.6	18.2	100	89.1	45.4	60	142.6	72.6	20	196.0	99.9	80	249.5	127.1
41	36.5	18.6	101	90.0	45.9	161	143.5	73.1	221	196.9	100.3	281	250.4	127.6
42	37.4	19.1	02	90.9	46.3	62	144.3	73.5	22	197.8	100.8	82	251.3	128.0
43	38.3	19.5	03	91.8	46.8	63	145.2	74.0	23	198.7	101.2	83	252.2	128.5
44	39.2	20.0	04	92.7	47.2	64	146.1	74.5	24	199.6	101.7	84	253.0	128.9
45	40.1	20.4	05	93.6	47.7	65	147.0	74.9	25	200.5	102.1	85	253.9	129.4
46	41.0	20.9	06	94.4	48.1	66	147.9	75.4	26	201.4	102.6	86	254.8	129.8
47	41.9	21.3	07	95.3	48.6	67	148.8	75.8	27	202.3	103.1	87	255.7	130.3
48	42.8	21.8	08	96.2	49.0	68	149.7	76.3	28	203.1	103.5	88	256.6	130.7
49	43.7	22.2	09	97.1	49.5	69	150.6	76.7	29	204.0	104.0	89	257.5	131.2
50	44.6	22.7	10	98.0	49.9	70	151.5	77.2	30	204.9	104.4	90	258.4	131.7
51	45.4	23.2	111	98.9	50.4	171	152.4	77.6	231	205.8	104.9	291	259.3	132.1
52	46.3	23.6	12	99.8	50.8	72	153.3	78.1	32	206.7	105.3	92	260.2	132.6
53	47.2	24.1	13	100.7	51.3	73	154.1	78.5	33	207.6	105.8	93	261.1	133.0
54	48.1	24.5	14	101.6	51.8	74	155.0	79.0	34	208.5	106.2	94	262.0	133.5
55	49.0	25.0	15	102.5	52.2	75	155.9	79.4	35	209.4	106.7	95	262.8	133.9
56	49.9	25.4	16	103.4	52.7	76	156.8	79.9	36	210.3	107.1	96	263.7	134.4
57	50.8	25.9	17	104.2	53.1	77	157.7	80.4	37	211.2	107.6	97	264.6	134.8
58	51.7	26.3	18	105.1	53.6	78	158.6	80.8	38	212.1	108.0	98	265.5	135.3
59	52.6	26.8	19	106.0	54.0	79	159.5	81.3	39	213.0	108.5	99	266.4	135.7
60	53.5	27.2	20	106.9	54.5	80	160.4	81.7	40	213.8	109.0	300	267.3	136.2
Dist.	Dep.	Lat.	Dist.	Dep.	Lat.	Dist.	Dep.	Lat.	Dist.	Dep.	Lat.	Dist.	Dep.	Lat.

63° (117°, 243°, 297°).

In Plane Sailing.	Dist.	Lat.	Dep.
For converting *Dep.* into *Diff. Long.* and *Diff. Long.* into *Dep.* In **Middle Latitude Sailing.**	Diff. Long.	Dep.	
For converting *Dep.* into *Diff. Long.* and *Diff. Long.* into *Dep.* In **Mercator Sailing.**		*m*	Diff Long.
For multiplication of numbers by sines and by cosines, or solution of plane right-angled triangles.	N. Hypotenuse.	N×Cos. Side Adj.	N×Sin. Side Opp.

TABLE 3.

Difference of Latitude and Departure for 27° (153°, 207°, 333°).

Dist.	Lat.	Dep.	Dist.	Lat.	Dep.	Dist.	Lat.	Dep.	Dist.	Lat.	Dep.	Dist.	Lat.	Dep.
301	268.2	136.7	361	321.7	163.9	421	375.1	191.1	481	428.6	218.4	541	482.0	245.6
02	269.1	137.1	62	322.5	164.3	22	376.0	191.6	82	429.5	218.8	42	482.9	246.1
03	270.0	137.6	63	323.4	164.8	23	376.9	192.0	83	430.4	219.3	43	483.8	246.5
04	270.9	138.0	64	324.3	165.3	24	377.8	192.5	84	431.2	219.7	44	484.7	247.0
05	271.8	138.5	65	325.2	165.7	25	378.7	192.9	85	432.1	220.2	45	485.6	247.4
06	272.6	138.9	66	326.1	166.2	26	379.6	193.4	86	433.0	220.6	46	486.5	247.9
07	273.5	139.4	67	327.0	166.6	27	380.5	193.9	87	433.9	221.1	47	487.4	248.3
08	274.4	139.8	68	327.9	167.1	28	381.4	194.3	88	434.8	221.5	48	488.3	248.8
09	275.3	140.3	69	328.8	167.5	29	382.2	194.8	89	435.7	222.0	49	489.2	249.2
10	276.2	140.7	70	329.7	168.0	30	383.1	195.2	90	436.6	222.5	50	490.1	249.7
311	277.1	141.2	371	330.6	168.4	431	384.0	195.7	491	437.5	222.9	551	490.9	250.1
12	278.0	141.6	72	331.5	168.9	32	384.9	196.1	92	438.4	223.4	52	491.8	250.6
13	278.9	142.1	73	332.3	169.3	33	385.8	196.6	93	439.3	223.8	53	492.7	251.1
14	279.8	142.6	74	333.2	169.8	34	386.7	197.0	94	440.2	224.3	54	493.6	251.5
15	280.7	143.0	75	334.1	170.2	35	387.6	197.5	95	441.0	224.7	55	494.5	252.0
16	281.6	143.5	76	335.0	170.7	36	388.5	197.9	96	441.9	225.2	56	495.4	252.4
17	282.4	143.9	77	335.9	171.2	37	389.4	198.4	97	442.8	225.6	57	496.3	252.9
18	283.3	144.4	78	336.8	171.6	38	390.3	198.8	98	443.7	226.1	58	497.2	253.3
19	284.2	144.8	79	337.7	172.1	39	391.2	199.3	99	444.6	226.5	59	498.1	253.8
20	285.1	145.3	80	338.6	172.5	40	392.0	199.8	500	445.5	227.0	60	499.0	254.2
321	286.0	145.7	381	339.5	173.0	441	392.9	200.2	501	446.4	227.4	561	499.9	254.7
22	286.9	146.2	82	340.4	173.4	42	393.8	200.7	02	447.3	227.9	62	500.7	255.1
23	287.8	146.6	83	341.3	173.9	43	394.7	201.1	03	448.2	228.4	63	501.6	255.6
24	288.7	147.1	84	342.1	174.3	44	395.6	201.6	04	449.0	228.8	64	502.5	256.1
25	289.6	147.5	85	343.0	174.8	45	396.5	202.0	05	450.0	229.3	65	503.4	256.5
26	290.5	148.0	86	343.9	175.2	46	397.4	202.5	06	450.8	229.7	66	504.3	257.0
27	291.4	148.5	87	344.8	175.7	47	398.3	202.9	07	451.7	230.2	67	505.2	257.4
28	292.3	148.9	88	345.7	176.1	48	399.2	203.4	08	452.6	230.6	68	506.1	257.9
29	293.1	149.4	89	346.6	176.6	49	400.1	203.8	09	453.5	231.1	69	507.0	258.3
30	294.0	149.8	90	347.5	177.1	50	401.0	204.3	10	454.4	231.5	70	507.9	258.8
331	294.9	150.3	391	348.4	177.5	451	401.8	204.7	511	455.3	232.0	571	508.8	259.2
32	295.8	150.7	92	349.3	178.0	52	402.7	205.2	12	456.2	232.4	72	509.6	259.7
33	296.7	151.2	93	350.2	178.4	53	403.6	205.7	13	457.1	232.9	73	510.5	260.1
34	297.6	151.6	94	351.1	178.9	54	404.5	206.1	14	458.0	233.4	74	511.4	260.6
35	298.5	152.1	95	351.9	179.3	55	405.4	206.6	15	458.9	233.8	75	512.3	261.0
36	299.4	152.5	96	352.8	179.8	56	406.3	207.0	16	459.8	234.3	76	513.2	261.5
37	300.3	153.0	97	353.7	180.2	57	407.2	207.5	17	460.7	234.7	77	514.1	262.0
38	301.2	153.4	98	354.6	180.7	58	408.1	207.9	18	461.5	235.2	78	515.0	262.4
39	302.1	153.9	99	355.5	181.1	59	409.0	208.4	19	462.4	235.6	79	515.9	262.9
40	302.9	154.4	400	356.4	181.6	60	409.9	208.8	20	463.3	236.1	80	516.8	263.4
341	303.8	154.8	401	357.3	182.1	461	410.8	209.3	521	464.2	236.5	581	517.7	263.8
42	304.7	155.3	02	358.2	182.5	62	411.6	209.7	22	465.1	237.0	82	518.6	264.2
43	305.6	155.7	03	359.1	183.0	63	412.5	210.2	23	466.0	237.4	83	519.5	264.7
44	306.5	156.2	04	360.0	183.4	64	413.4	210.7	24	466.9	237.9	84	520.3	265.1
45	307.4	156.6	05	360.9	183.9	65	414.3	211.1	25	467.8	238.3	85	521.2	265.6
46	308.3	157.1	06	361.8	184.3	66	415.2	211.6	26	468.7	238.8	86	522.1	266.0
47	309.2	157.5	07	362.6	184.8	67	416.1	212.0	27	469.6	239.3	87	523.0	266.5
48	310.1	158.0	08	363.5	185.2	68	417.0	212.5	28	470.5	239.7	88	523.9	266.9
49	311.0	158.4	09	364.4	185.7	69	417.9	212.9	29	471.3	240.2	89	524.8	267.4
50	311.9	158.9	10	365.3	186.1	70	418.8	213.4	30	472.2	240.6	90	525.7	267.9
351	312.7	159.4	411	366.2	186.6	471	419.7	213.8	531	473.1	241.1	591	526.6	268.3
52	313.6	159.8	12	367.1	187.0	72	420.6	214.3	32	474.0	241.5	92	527.5	268.8
53	314.5	160.3	13	368.0	187.5	73	421.4	214.7	33	474.9	242.0	93	528.4	269.2
54	315.4	160.7	14	368.9	188.0	74	422.3	215.2	34	475.8	242.4	94	529.3	269.7
55	316.3	161.2	15	369.8	188.4	75	423.2	215.6	35	476.7	242.9	95	530.1	270.1
56	317.2	161.6	16	370.7	188.9	76	424.1	216.1	36	477.6	243.3	96	531.0	270.6
57	318.1	162.1	17	371.5	189.3	77	425.0	216.6	37	478.5	243.8	97	531.9	271.0
58	319.0	162.5	18	372.4	189.8	78	425.9	217.0	38	479.4	244.2	98	532.8	271.5
59	319.9	163.0	19	373.3	190.2	79	426.8	217.5	39	480.3	244.7	99	533.7	271.9
60	320.8	163.4	20	374.2	190.7	80	427.7	217.9	40	481.1	245.2	600	534.6	272.4
Dist.	Dep.	Lat.	Dist.	Dep.	Lat.	Dist.	Dep.	Lat.	Dist.	Dep.	Lat.	Dist.	Dep.	Lat.

63° (117°, 243°, 297°).

In **Plane Sailing.**	**Dist.**	**Lat.**	**Dep.**
For converting *Dep.* into *Diff. Long.* and *Diff. Long.* into *Dep.* In **Middle Latitude Sailing.**	Diff. Long.	Dep.	
For converting *Dep.* into *Diff. Long.* and *Diff. Long.* into *Dep.* In **Mercator Sailing.**		*m*	Diff. Long.
For multiplication of numbers by sines and by cosines, or solution of plane right-angled triangles.	N. Hypotenuse.	N×Cos. Side Adj.	N×Sin. Side Opp.

TABLE 3.

Difference of Latitude and Departure for 28° (152°, 208°, 332°).

Dist.	Lat.	Dep.	Dist.	Lat.	Dep.	Dist.	Lat.	Dep.	Dist.	Lat.	Dep.	Dist.	Lat.	Dep.
1	0.9	0.5	61	53.9	28.6	121	106.8	56.8	181	159.8	85.0	241	212.8	113.1
2	1.8	0.9	62	54.7	29.1	22	107.7	57.3	82	160.7	85.4	42	213.7	113.6
3	2.6	1.4	63	55.6	29.6	23	108.6	57.7	83	161.6	85.9	43	214.6	114.1
4	3.5	1.9	64	56.5	30.0	24	109.5	58.2	84	162.5	86.4	44	215.4	114.6
5	4.4	2.3	65	57.4	30.5	25	110.4	58.7	85	163.3	86.9	45	216.3	115.0
6	5.3	2.8	66	58.3	31.0	26	111.3	59.2	86	164.2	87.3	46	217.2	115.5
7	6.2	3.3	67	59.2	31.5	27	112.1	59.6	87	165.1	87.8	47	218.1	116.0
8	7.1	3.8	68	60.0	31.9	28	113.0	60.1	88	166.0	88.3	48	219.0	116.4
9	7.9	4.2	69	60.9	32.4	29	113.9	60.6	89	166.9	88.7	49	219.9	116.9
10	8.8	4.7	70	61.8	32.9	30	114.8	61.0	90	167.8	89.2	50	220.7	117.4
11	9.7	5.2	71	62.7	33.3	131	115.7	61.5	191	168.6	89.7	251	221.6	117.8
12	10.6	5.6	72	63.6	33.8	32	116.5	62.0	92	169.5	90.1	52	222.5	118.3
13	11.5	6.1	73	64.5	34.3	33	117.4	62.4	93	170.4	90.6	53	223.4	118.8
14	12.4	6.6	74	65.3	34.7	34	118.3	62.9	94	171.3	91.1	54	224.3	119.2
15	13.2	7.0	75	66.2	35.2	35	119.2	63.4	95	172.2	91.5	55	225.2	119.7
16	14.1	7.5	76	67.1	35.7	36	120.1	63.8	96	173.1	92.0	56	226.0	120.2
17	15.0	8.0	77	68.0	36.1	37	121.0	64.3	97	173.9	92.5	57	226.9	120.7
18	15.9	8.5	78	68.9	36.6	38	121.8	64.8	98	174.8	93.0	58	227.8	121.1
19	16.8	8.9	79	69.8	37.1	39	122.7	65.3	99	175.7	93.4	59	228.7	121.6
20	17.7	9.4	80	70.6	37.6	40	123.6	65.7	200	176.6	93.9	60	229.6	122.1
21	18.5	9.9	81	71.5	38.0	141	124.5	66.2	201	177.5	94.4	261	230.4	122.5
22	19.4	10.3	82	72.4	38.5	42	125.4	66.7	02	178.4	94.8	62	231.3	123.0
23	20.3	10.8	83	73.3	39.0	43	126.3	67.1	03	179.2	95.3	63	232.2	123.5
24	21.2	11.3	84	74.2	39.4	44	127.1	67.6	04	180.1	95.8	64	233.1	123.9
25	22.1	11.7	85	75.1	39.9	45	128.0	68.1	05	181.0	96.2	65	234.0	124.4
26	23.0	12.2	86	75.9	40.4	46	128.9	68.5	06	181.9	96.7	66	234.9	124.9
27	23.8	12.7	87	76.8	40.8	47	129.8	69.0	07	182.8	97.2	67	235.7	125.3
28	24.7	13.1	88	77.7	41.3	48	130.7	69.5	08	183.7	97.7	68	236.6	125.8
29	25.6	13.6	89	78.6	41.8	49	131.6	70.0	09	184.5	98.1	69	237.5	126.3
30	26.5	14.1	90	79.5	42.3	50	132.4	70.4	10	185.4	98.6	70	238.4	126.8
31	27.4	14.6	91	80.3	42.7	151	133.3	70.9	211	186.3	99.1	271	239.3	127.2
32	28.3	15.0	92	81.2	43.2	52	134.2	71.4	12	187.2	99.5	72	240.2	127.7
33	29.1	15.5	93	82.1	43.7	53	135.1	71.8	13	188.1	100.0	73	241.0	128.2
34	30.0	16.0	94	83.0	44.1	54	136.0	72.3	14	189.0	100.5	74	241.9	128.6
35	30.9	16.4	95	83.9	44.6	55	136.9	72.8	15	189.8	100.9	75	242.8	129.1
36	31.8	16.9	96	84.8	45.1	56	137.7	73.2	16	190.7	101.4	76	243.7	129.6
37	32.7	17.4	97	85.6	45.5	57	138.6	73.7	17	191.6	101.9	77	244.6	130.0
38	33.6	17.8	98	86.5	46.0	58	139.5	74.2	18	192.5	102.3	78	245.5	130.5
39	34.4	18.3	99	87.4	46.5	59	140.4	74.6	19	193.4	102.8	79	246.3	131.0
40	35.3	18.8	100	88.3	46.9	60	141.3	75.1	20	194.2	103.3	80	247.2	131.5
41	36.2	19.2	101	89.2	47.4	161	142.2	75.6	221	195.1	103.8	281	248.1	131.9
42	37.1	19.7	02	90.1	47.9	62	143.0	76.1	22	196.0	104.2	82	249.0	132.4
43	38.0	20.2	03	90.9	48.4	63	143.9	76.5	23	196.9	104.7	83	249.9	132.9
44	38.8	20.7	04	91.8	48.8	64	144.8	77.0	24	197.8	105.2	84	250.8	133.3
45	39.7	21.1	05	92.7	49.3	65	145.7	77.5	25	198.7	105.6	85	251.6	133.8
46	40.6	21.6	06	93.6	49.8	66	146.6	77.9	26	199.5	106.1	86	252.5	134.3
47	41.5	22.1	07	94.5	50.2	67	147.5	78.4	27	200.4	106.6	87	253.4	134.7
48	42.4	22.5	08	95.4	50.7	68	148.3	78.9	28	201.3	107.0	88	254.3	135.2
49	43.3	23.0	09	96.2	51.2	69	149.2	79.3	29	202.2	107.5	89	255.2	135.7
50	44.1	23.5	10	97.1	51.6	70	150.1	79.8	30	203.1	108.0	90	256.1	136.1
51	45.0	23.9	111	98.0	52.1	171	151.0	80.3	231	204.0	108.4	291	256.9	136.6
52	45.9	24.4	12	98.9	52.6	72	151.9	80.7	32	204.8	108.9	92	257.8	137.1
53	46.8	24.9	13	99.8	53.1	73	152.7	81.2	33	205.7	109.4	93	258.7	137.6
54	47.7	25.4	14	100.7	53.5	74	153.6	81.7	34	206.6	109.9	94	259.6	138.0
55	48.6	25.8	15	101.5	54.0	75	154.5	82.2	35	207.5	110.3	95	260.5	138.5
56	49.4	26.3	16	102.4	54.5	76	155.4	82.6	36	208.4	110.8	96	261.4	139.0
57	50.3	26.8	17	103.3	54.9	77	156.3	83.1	37	209.3	111.3	97	262.2	139.4
58	51.2	27.2	18	104.2	55.4	78	157.2	83.6	38	210.1	111.7	98	263.1	139.9
59	52.1	27.7	19	105.1	55.9	79	158.0	84.0	39	211.0	112.2	99	264.0	140.4
60	53.0	28.2	20	106.0	56.3	80	158.9	84.5	40	211.9	112.7	300	264.9	140.8
Dist.	Dep.	Lat.	Dist.	Dep.	Lat.	Dist.	Dep.	Lat.	Dist.	Dep.	Lat.	Dist.	Dep.	Lat.

62° (118°, 242°, 298°).

In Plane Sailing.	Dist.	Lat.	Dep.
For converting *Dep.* into *Diff. Long.* and *Diff. Long.* into *Dep.* **In Middle Latitude Sailing.**	Diff. Long.	Dep.	
For converting *Dep.* into *Diff. Long.* and *Diff. Long.* into *Dep.* **In Mercator Sailing.**		*m*	Diff. Long.
For multiplication of numbers by sines and by cosines, or solution of plane right-angled triangles.	N.	N×Cos.	N×Sin.
	Hypotenuse.	Side. Adj.	Side Opp.

TABLE 3.

Difference of Latitude and Departure for 28° (152°, 208°, 332°).

Dist.	Lat.	Dep.	Dist.	Lat.	Dep.	Dist.	Lat.	Dep.	Dist.	Lat.	Dep.	Dist.	Lat.	Dep.
301	265.8	141.3	361	318.7	169.5	421	371.7	197.6	481	424.7	225.8	541	477.7	254.0
02	266.7	141.8	62	319.6	169.9	22	372.6	198.1	82	425.6	226.3	42	478.6	254.5
03	267.5	142.2	63	320.5	170.4	23	373.5	198.6	83	426.5	226.8	43	479.4	254.9
04	268.4	142.7	64	321.4	170.9	24	374.4	199.1	84	427.3	227.2	44	480.3	255.4
05	269.3	143.2	65	322.3	171.4	25	375.3	199.5	85	428.2	227.7	45	481.2	255.9
06	270.2	143.7	66	323.2	171.8	26	376.1	200.0	86	429.1	228.2	46	482.1	256.3
07	271.1	144.1	67	324.0	172.3	27	377.0	200.5	87	430.0	228.6	47	483.0	256.8
08	271.9	144.6	68	324.9	172.8	28	377.9	200.9	88	430.9	229.1	48	483.9	257.3
09	272.8	145.1	69	325.8	173.2	29	378.8	201.4	89	431.8	229.6	49	484.7	257.7
10	273.7	145.5	70	326.7	173.7	30	379.7	201.9	90	432.6	230.0	50	485.6	258.2
311	274.6	146.0	371	327.6	174.2	431	380.6	202.3	491	433.5	230.5	551	486.5	258.7
12	275.5	146.5	72	328.5	174.6	32	381.4	202.8	92	434.4	231.0	52	487.4	259.1
13	276.4	146.9	73	329.3	175.1	33	382.3	203.3	93	435.3	231.4	53	488.3	259.6
14	277.2	147.4	74	330.2	175.6	34	383.2	203.8	94	436.2	231.9	54	489.2	260.1
15	278.1	147.9	75	331.1	176.1	35	384.1	204.2	95	437.1	232.4	55	490.0	260.6
16	279.0	148.4	76	332.0	176.5	36	385.0	204.7	96	437.9	232.9	56	490.9	261.0
17	279.9	148.8	77	332.9	177.0	37	385.8	205.2	97	438.8	233.3	57	491.8	261.5
18	280.8	149.3	78	333.8	177.5	38	386.7	205.6	98	439.7	233.8	58	492.7	262.0
19	281.7	149.8	79	334.6	177.9	39	387.6	206.1	99	440.6	234.3	59	493.6	262.4
20	282.5	150.2	80	335.5	178.4	40	388.5	206.6	500	441.5	234.7	60	494.5	262.9
321	283.4	150.7	381	336.4	178.9	441	389.4	207.0	501	442.4	235.2	561	495.3	263.4
22	284.3	151.2	82	337.3	179.3	42	390.3	207.5	02	443.2	235.7	62	496.2	263.8
23	285.2	151.6	83	338.2	179.8	43	391.1	208.0	03	444.1	236.1	63	497.1	264.3
24	286.1	152.1	84	339.1	180.3	44	392.0	208.4	04	445.0	236.6	64	498.0	264.8
25	287.0	152.6	85	339.9	180.7	45	392.9	208.9	05	445.9	237.1	65	498.9	265.3
26	287.8	153.0	86	340.8	181.2	46	393.8	209.4	06	446.8	237.6	66	499.7	265.7
27	288.7	153.5	87	341.7	181.7	47	394.7	209.9	07	447.7	238.0	67	500.6	266.2
28	289.6	154.0	88	342.6	182.2	48	395.6	210.3	08	448.5	238.5	68	501.5	266.7
29	290.5	154.5	89	343.5	182.6	49	396.4	210.8	09	449.4	239.0	69	502.4	267.1
30	291.4	154.9	90	344.3	183.1	50	397.3	211.3	10	450.3	239.4	70	503.3	267.6
331	292.3	155.4	391	345.2	183.6	451	398.2	211.7	511	451.2	239.9	571	504.2	268.1
32	293.1	155.9	92	346.1	184.0	52	399.1	212.2	12	452.1	240.4	72	505.0	268.5
33	294.0	156.3	93	347.0	184.5	53	400.0	212.7	13	453.0	240.8	73	505.9	269.0
34	294.9	156.8	94	347.9	185.0	54	400.9	213.1	14	453.8	241.3	74	506.8	269.5
35	295.8	157.3	95	348.8	185.4	55	401.7	213.6	15	454.7	241.8	75	507.7	269.9
36	296.7	157.7	96	349.6	185.9	56	402.6	214.1	16	455.6	242.2	76	508.6	270.4
37	297.6	158.2	97	350.5	186.4	57	403.5	214.5	17	456.5	242.7	77	509.5	270.9
38	298.4	158.7	98	351.4	186.8	58	404.4	215.0	18	457.4	243.2	78	510.3	271.4
39	299.3	159.2	99	352.3	187.3	59	405.3	215.5	19	458.2	243.7	79	511.2	271.8
40	300.2	159.6	400	353.2	187.8	60	406.2	216.0	20	459.1	244.1	80	512.1	272.3
341	301.1	160.1	401	354.1	188.3	461	407.0	216.4	521	460.0	244.6	581	513.0	272.8
42	302.0	160.6	02	354.9	188.7	62	407.9	216.9	22	460.9	245.1	82	513.9	273.2
43	302.9	161.0	03	355.8	189.2	63	408.8	217.4	23	461.8	245.5	83	514.8	273.7
44	303.7	161.5	04	356.7	189.7	64	409.7	217.8	24	462.7	246.0	84	515.6	274.2
45	304.6	162.0	05	357.6	190.1	65	410.6	218.3	25	463.5	246.5	85	516.5	274.6
46	305.5	162.4	06	358.5	190.6	66	411.5	218.8	26	464.4	246.9	86	517.4	275.1
47	306.4	162.9	07	359.4	191.1	67	412.3	219.2	27	465.3	247.4	87	518.3	275.4
48	307.3	163.4	08	360.2	191.5	68	413.2	219.7	28	466.2	247.9	88	519.2	276.0
49	308.1	163.8	09	361.1	192.0	69	414.1	220.2	29	467.1	248.4	89	520.1	276.5
50	309.0	164.3	10	362.0	192.5	70	415.0	220.7	30	468.0	248.8	90	520.9	277.0
351	309.9	164.8	411	362.9	193.0	471	415.9	221.1	531	468.8	249.3	591	521.8	277.5
52	310.8	165.3	12	363.8	193.4	72	416.8	221.6	32	469.7	249.8	92	522.7	277.9
53	311.7	165.7	13	364.7	193.9	73	417.6	222.1	33	470.7	250.2	93	523.6	278.4
54	312.6	166.2	14	365.5	194.4	74	418.5	222.5	34	471.5	250.7	94	524.5	278.9
55	313.4	166.7	15	366.4	194.8	75	419.4	223.0	35	472.4	251.2	95	525.4	279.3
56	314.3	167.1	16	367.3	195.3	76	420.3	223.5	36	473.3	251.6	96	526.2	279.8
57	315.2	167.6	17	368.2	195.8	77	421.2	223.9	37	474.1	252.1	97	527.1	280.3
58	316.1	168.1	18	369.1	196.2	78	422.0	224.4	38	475.0	252.6	98	528.0	280.7
59	317.0	168.5	19	370.0	196.7	79	422.9	224.9	39	475.9	253.0	99	528.9	281.2
60	317.9	169.0	20	370.8	197.2	80	423.8	225.3	40	476.8	253.5	600	529.8	281.7
Dist.	Dep.	Lat.	Dist.	Dep.	Lat.	Dist.	Dep.	Lat.	Dist.	Dep.	Lat.	Dist.	Dep.	Lat.

62° (118°, 242°, 298°).

In **Plane Sailing**.	Dist.	Lat.	Dep.
For converting *Dep.* into *Diff. Long.* and *Diff. Long.* into *Dep.* In **Middle Latitude Sailing.**	Diff. Long.	Dep.	
For converting *Dep.* into *Diff. Long.* and *Diff. Long.* into *Dep.* In **Mercator Sailing.**		*m*	Diff. Long.
For multiplication of numbers by sines and by cosines, or solution of plane right-angled triangles.	N. Hypotenuse.	N×Cos. Side Adj.	N×Sin. Side Opp.

TABLE 3.

Difference of Latitude and Departure for 29° (151°, 209°, 331°).

Dist.	Lat.	Dep.	Dist.	Lat.	Dep.	Dist.	Lat.	Dep.	Dist.	Lat.	Dep.	Dist.	Lat.	Dep.
1	0.9	0.5	61	53.4	29.6	121	105.8	58.7	181	158.3	87.8	241	210.8	116.8
2	1.7	1.0	62	54.2	30.1	22	106.7	59.1	82	159.2	88.2	42	211.7	117.3
3	2.6	1.5	63	55.1	30.5	23	107.6	59.6	83	160.1	88.7	43	212.5	117.8
4	3.5	1.9	64	56.0	31.0	24	108.5	60.1	84	160.9	89.2	44	213.4	118.3
5	4.4	2.4	65	56.9	31.5	25	109.3	60.6	85	161.8	89.7	45	214.3	118.8
6	5.2	2.9	66	57.7	32.0	26	110.2	61.1	86	162.7	90.2	46	215.2	119.3
7	6.1	3.4	67	58.6	32.5	27	111.1	61.6	87	163.6	90.7	47	216.0	119.7
8	7.0	3.9	68	59.5	33.0	28	112.0	62.1	88	164.4	91.1	48	216.9	120.2
9	7.9	4.4	69	60.3	33.5	29	112.8	62.5	89	165.3	91.6	49	217.8	120.7
10	8.7	4.8	70	61.2	33.9	30	113.7	63.0	90	166.2	92.1	50	218.7	121.2
11	9.6	5.3	71	62.1	34.4	131	114.6	63.5	191	167.1	92.6	251	219.5	121.7
12	10.5	5.8	72	63.0	34.9	32	115.4	64.0	92	167.9	93.1	52	220.4	122.2
13	11.4	6.3	73	63.8	35.4	33	116.3	64.5	93	168.8	93.6	53	221.3	122.7
14	12.2	6.8	74	64.7	35.9	34	117.2	65.0	94	169.7	94.1	54	222.2	123.1
15	13.1	7.3	75	65.6	36.4	35	118.1	65.4	95	170.6	94.5	55	223.0	123.6
16	14.0	7.8	76	66.5	36.8	36	118.9	65.9	96	171.4	95.0	56	223.9	124.1
17	14.9	8.2	77	67.3	37.3	37	119.8	66.4	97	172.3	95.5	57	224.8	124.6
18	15.7	8.7	78	68.2	37.8	38	120.7	66.9	98	173.2	96.0	58	225.7	125.1
19	16.6	9.2	79	69.1	38.3	39	121.6	67.4	99	174.0	96.5	59	226.5	125.6
20	17.5	9.7	80	70.0	38.8	40	122.4	67.9	200	174.9	97.0	60	227.4	126.1
21	18.4	10.2	81	70.8	39.3	141	123.3	68.4	201	175.8	97.4	261	228.3	126.5
22	19.2	10.7	82	71.7	39.8	42	124.2	68.8	02	176.7	97.9	62	229.2	127.0
23	20.1	11.2	83	72.6	40.2	43	125.1	69.3	03	177.5	98.4	63	230.0	127.5
24	21.0	11.6	84	73.5	40.7	44	125.9	69.8	04	178.4	98.9	64	230.9	128.0
25	21.9	12.1	85	74.3	41.2	45	126.8	70.3	05	179.3	99.4	65	231.8	128.5
26	22.7	12.6	86	75.2	41.7	46	127.7	70.8	06	180.2	99.9	66	232.6	129.0
27	23.6	13.1	87	76.1	42.2	47	128.6	71.3	07	181.0	100.4	67	233.5	129.4
28	24.5	13.6	88	77.0	42.7	48	129.4	71.8	08	181.9	100.8	68	234.4	129.9
29	25.4	14.1	89	77.8	43.1	49	130.3	72.2	09	182.8	101.3	69	235.3	130.4
30	26.2	14.5	90	78.7	43.6	50	131.2	72.7	10	183.7	101.8	70	236.1	130.9
31	27.1	15.0	91	79.6	44.1	151	132.1	73.2	211	184.5	102.3	271	237.0	131.4
32	28.0	15.5	92	80.5	44.6	52	132.9	73.7	12	185.4	102.8	72	237.9	131.9
33	28.9	16.0	93	81.3	45.1	53	133.8	74.2	13	186.3	103.3	73	238.8	132.4
34	29.7	16.5	94	82.2	45.6	54	134.7	74.7	14	187.2	103.7	74	239.6	132.8
35	30.6	17.0	95	83.1	46.1	55	135.6	75.1	15	188.0	104.2	75	240.5	133.3
36	31.5	17.5	96	84.0	46.5	56	136.4	75.6	16	188.9	104.7	76	241.4	133.8
37	32.4	17.9	97	84.8	47.0	57	137.3	76.1	17	189.8	105.2	77	242.3	134.3
38	33.2	18.4	98	85.7	47.5	58	138.2	76.6	18	190.7	105.7	78	243.1	134.8
39	34.1	18.9	99	86.6	48.0	59	139.1	77.1	19	191.5	106.2	79	244.0	135.3
40	35.0	19.4	100	87.5	48.5	60	139.9	77.6	20	192.4	106.7	80	244.9	135.7
41	35.9	19.9	101	88.3	49.0	161	140.8	78.1	221	193.3	107.1	281	245.8	136.2
42	36.7	20.4	02	89.2	49.5	62	141.7	78.5	22	194.2	107.6	82	246.6	136.7
43	37.6	20.8	03	90.1	49.9	63	142.6	79.0	23	195.0	108.1	83	247.5	137.2
44	38.5	21.3	04	91.0	50.4	64	143.4	79.5	24	195.9	108.6	84	248.4	137.7
45	39.4	21.8	05	91.8	50.9	65	144.3	80.0	25	196.8	109.1	85	249.3	138.2
46	40.2	22.3	06	92.7	51.4	66	145.2	80.5	26	197.7	109.6	86	250.1	138.7
47	41.1	22.8	07	93.6	51.9	67	146.1	81.0	27	198.5	110.1	87	251.0	139.1
48	42.0	23.3	08	94.5	52.4	68	146.9	81.4	28	199.4	110.5	88	251.9	139.6
49	42.9	23.8	09	95.3	52.8	69	147.8	81.9	29	200.3	111.0	89	252.8	140.1
50	43.7	24.2	10	96.2	53.3	70	148.7	82.4	30	201.2	111.5	90	253.6	140.6
51	44.6	24.7	111	97.1	53.8	171	149.6	82.9	231	202.0	112.0	291	254.5	141.1
52	45.5	25.2	12	98.0	54.3	72	150.4	83.4	32	202.9	112.5	92	255.4	141.6
53	46.4	25.7	13	98.8	54.8	73	151.3	83.9	33	203.8	113.0	93	256.3	142.0
54	47.2	26.2	14	99.7	55.3	74	152.2	84.4	34	204.7	113.4	94	257.1	142.5
55	48.1	26.7	15	100.6	55.8	75	153.1	84.8	35	205.5	113.9	95	258.0	143.0
56	49.0	27.1	16	101.5	56.2	76	153.9	85.3	36	206.4	114.4	96	258.9	143.5
57	49.9	27.6	17	102.3	56.7	77	154.8	85.8	37	207.3	114.9	97	259.8	144.0
58	50.7	28.1	18	103.2	57.2	78	155.7	86.3	38	208.2	115.4	98	260.6	144.5
59	51.6	28.6	19	104.1	57.7	79	156.6	86.8	39	209.0	115.9	99	261.5	145.0
60	52.5	29.1	20	105.0	58.2	80	157.4	87.3	40	209.9	116.4	300	262.4	145.4
Dist.	Dep.	Lat.	Dist.	Dep.	Lat.	Dist.	Dep.	Lat.	Dist.	Dep.	Lat.	Dist.	Dep.	Lat.

61° (119°, 241°, 299°).

In Plane Sailing.	Dist.	Lat.	Dep.
For converting *Dep.* into *Diff. Long.* and *Diff. Long.* into *Dep.* In Middle Latitude Sailing.	Diff. Long.	Dep.	
For converting *Dep.* into *Diff. Long.* and *Diff. Long.* into *Dep.* In Mercator Sailing.		*m*	Diff. Long.
For multiplication of numbers by sines and by cosines, or solution of plane right-angled triangles.	N. Hypotenuse.	N×Cos. Side Adj.	N×Sin. Side Opp.

Difference of Latitude and Departure for 29° (151°, 209°, 331°).

Dist.	Lat.	Dep.	Dist.	Lat.	Dep.	Dist.	Lat.	Dep.	Dist.	Lat.	Dep.	Dist.	Lat.	Dep.
301	263.3	145.9	361	315.7	175.0	421	368.2	204.1	481	420.7	233.2	541	473.2	262.3
02	264.1	146.4	62	316.6	175.5	22	369.1	204.6	82	421.6	233.7	42	474.0	262.8
03	265.0	146.9	63	317.5	176.0	23	370.0	205.1	83	422.4	234.2	43	474.9	263.3
04	265.9	147.4	64	318.4	176.5	24	370.8	205.6	84	423.3	234.6	44	475.8	263.7
05	266.8	147.9	65	319.2	177.0	25	371.7	206.0	85	424.2	235.1	45	476.7	264.2
06	267.6	148.4	66	320.1	177.4	26	372.6	206.5	86	425.1	235.6	46	477.5	264.7
07	268.5	148.8	67	321.0	177.9	27	373.5	207.0	87	425.9	236.1	47	478.4	265.2
08	269.4	149.3	68	321.9	178.4	28	374.3	207.5	88	426.8	236.6	48	479.3	265.7
09	270.3	149.8	69	322.7	178.9	29	375.2	208.0	89	427.7	237.1	49	480.2	266.2
10	271.1	150.3	70	323.6	179.4	30	376.1	208.5	90	428.6	237.6	50	481.0	266.6
311	272.0	150.8	371	324.5	179.9	431	377.0	209.0	491	429.4	238.0	551	481.9	267.1
12	272.9	151.3	72	325.4	180.3	32	377.8	209.4	92	430.3	238.5	52	482.8	267.6
13	273.8	151.7	73	326.2	180.8	33	378.7	209.9	93	431.2	239.0	53	483.7	268.1
14	274.6	152.2	74	327.1	181.3	34	379.6	210.4	94	432.1	239.5	54	484.5	268.6
15	275.5	152.7	75	328.0	181.8	35	380.5	210.9	95	432.9	240.0	55	485.4	269.1
16	276.4	153.2	76	328.9	182.3	36	381.3	211.4	96	433.8	240.5	56	486.3	269.6
17	277.3	153.7	77	329.7	182.8	37	382.2	211.9	97	434.7	241.0	57	487.2	270.0
18	278.1	154.2	78	330.6	183.3	38	383.1	212.3	98	435.6	241.4	58	488.0	270.5
19	279.0	154.7	79	331.5	183.7	39	384.0	212.8	99	436.4	241.9	59	488.9	271.0
20	279.9	155.1	80	332.4	184.2	40	384.8	213.3	500	437.3	242.4	60	489.8	271.5
321	280.8	155.6	381	333.2	184.7	441	385.7	213.8	501	438.2	242.9	561	490.7	272.0
22	281.6	156.1	82	334.1	185.2	42	386.6	214.3	02	439.1	243.4	62	491.5	272.5
23	282.5	156.6	83	335.0	185.7	43	387.5	214.8	03	439.9	243.9	63	492.4	272.9
24	283.4	157.1	84	335.9	186.2	44	388.3	215.3	04	440.8	244.3	64	493.3	273.4
25	284.3	157.6	85	336.7	186.7	45	389.2	215.7	05	441.7	244.8	65	494.2	273.9
26	285.1	158.0	86	337.6	187.1	46	390.0	216.2	06	442.6	245.3	66	495.0	274.4
27	286.0	158.5	87	338.5	187.6	47	391.0	216.7	07	443.4	245.8	67	495.9	274.9
28	286.9	159.0	88	339.4	188.1	48	391.8	217.2	08	444.3	246.3	68	496.8	275.4
29	287.7	159.5	89	340.2	188.6	49	392.7	217.7	09	445.2	246.8	69	497.7	275.9
30	288.6	160.0	90	341.1	189.1	50	393.6	218.2	10	446.1	247.3	70	498.5	276.3
331	289.5	160.5	391	342.0	189.6	451	394.5	218.6	511	446.9	247.7	571	499.4	276.8
32	290.4	161.0	92	342.9	190.0	52	395.3	219.1	12	447.8	248.2	72	500.3	277.3
33	291.2	161.4	93	343.7	190.5	53	396.2	219.6	13	448.7	248.7	73	501.2	277.8
34	292.1	161.9	94	344.6	191.0	54	397.1	220.1	14	449.6	249.2	74	502.0	278.3
35	293.0	162.4	95	345.5	191.5	55	398.0	220.6	15	450.4	249.7	75	502.9	278.8
36	293.9	162.9	96	346.3	192.0	56	398.8	221.1	16	451.3	250.2	76	503.8	279.3
37	294.7	163.4	97	347.2	192.5	57	399.7	221.6	17	452.2	250.6	77	504.7	279.7
38	295.6	163.9	98	348.1	193.0	58	400.6	222.0	18	453.1	251.1	78	505.5	280.2
39	296.5	164.4	99	349.0	193.4	59	401.5	222.5	19	453.9	251.6	79	506.4	280.7
40	297.4	164.8	400	349.8	193.9	60	402.3	223.0	20	454.8	252.1	80	507.3	281.2
341	298.2	165.3	401	350.7	194.4	461	403.2	223.5	521	455.7	252.6	581	508.2	281.7
42	299.1	165.8	02	351.6	194.9	62	404.0	224.0	22	456.6	253.1	82	509.0	282.2
43	300.0	166.3	03	352.5	195.4	63	404.9	224.5	23	457.4	253.6	83	509.9	282.6
44	300.9	166.8	04	353.3	195.9	64	405.8	225.0	24	458.3	254.0	84	510.7	283.1
45	301.7	167.3	05	354.2	196.3	65	406.7	225.4	25	459.2	254.5	85	511.7	283.6
46	302.6	167.7	06	355.1	196.8	66	407.5	225.9	26	460.0	255.0	86	512.5	284.1
47	303.5	168.2	07	356.0	197.3	67	408.4	226.4	27	460.9	255.5	87	513.4	284.6
48	304.4	168.7	08	356.8	197.8	68	409.3	226.9	28	461.8	256.0	88	514.3	285.1
49	305.2	169.2	09	357.7	198.3	69	410.2	227.4	29	462.7	256.5	89	515.2	285.6
50	306.1	169.7	10	358.6	198.8	70	411.0	227.9	30	463.5	256.9	90	516.0	286.0
351	307.0	170.2	411	359.5	199.3	471	411.9	228.3	531	464.4	257.4	591	516.9	286.5
52	307.9	170.7	12	360.3	199.7	72	412.8	228.8	32	465.3	257.9	92	517.8	287.0
53	308.7	171.1	13	361.2	200.2	73	413.7	229.3	33	466.2	258.4	93	518.6	287.5
54	309.6	171.6	14	362.1	200.7	74	414.5	229.8	34	467.0	258.9	94	519.5	288.0
55	310.5	172.1	15	363.0	201.2	75	415.4	230.3	35	467.9	259.4	95	520.4	288.5
56	311.4	172.6	16	363.8	201.7	76	416.3	230.8	36	468.8	259.9	96	521.3	288.9
57	312.2	173.1	17	364.7	202.2	77	417.2	231.3	37	469.6	260.3	97	522.1	289.4
58	313.1	173.6	18	365.6	202.7	78	418.0	231.7	38	470.5	260.8	98	523.0	289.9
59	314.0	174.0	19	366.5	203.1	79	418.9	232.2	39	471.4	261.3	99	523.9	290.4
60	314.9	174.5	20	367.3	203.6	80	419.8	232.7	40	472.3	261.8	600	524.8	290.9
Dist.	Dep.	Lat.	Dist.	Dep.	Lat.	Dist.	Dep.	Lat.	Dist.	Dep.	Lat.	Dist.	Dep.	Lat.

61° (119°, 241°, 299°).

In **Plane Sailing.**	Dist.	Lat.	Dep.
For converting *Dep.* into *Diff. Long.* and *Diff. Long.* into *Dep.* In **Middle Latitude Sailing.**	Diff. Long.	Dep.	
For converting *Dep.* into *Diff. Long.* and *Diff. Long.* into *Dep.* In **Mercator Sailing.**		*m*	Diff. Long.
For multiplication of numbers by sines and by cosines, or solution of plane right-angled triangles.	N. Hypotenuse.	N×Cos. Side Adj.	N×Sin. Side Opp.

TABLE 3.

Difference of Latitude and Departure for 30° (150°, 210°, 330°).

Dist.	Lat.	Dep.	Dist.	Lat.	Dep.	Dist.	Lat.	Dep.	Dist.	Lat.	Dep.	Dist.	Lat.	Dep.
1	0.9	0.5	61	52.8	30.5	121	104.8	60.5	181	156.8	90.5	241	208.7	120.5
2	1.7	1.0	62	53.7	31.0	22	105.7	61.0	82	157.6	91.0	42	209.6	121.0
3	2.6	1.5	63	54.6	31.5	23	106.5	61.5	83	158.5	91.5	43	210.4	121.5
4	3.5	2.0	64	55.4	32.0	24	107.4	62.0	84	159.3	92.0	44	211.3	122.0
5	4.3	2.5	65	56.3	32.5	25	108.3	62.5	85	160.2	92.5	45	212.2	122.5
6	5.2	3.0	66	57.2	33.0	26	109.1	63.0	86	161.1	93.0	46	213.0	123.0
7	6.1	3.5	67	58.0	33.5	27	110.0	63.5	87	161.9	93.5	47	213.9	123.5
8	6.9	4.0	68	58.9	34.0	28	110.9	64.0	88	162.8	94.0	48	214.8	124.0
9	7.8	4.5	69	59.8	34.5	29	111.7	64.5	89	163.7	94.5	49	215.6	124.5
10	8.7	5.0	70	60.6	35.0	30	112.6	65.0	90	164.5	95.0	50	216.5	125.0
11	9.5	5.5	71	61.5	35.5	131	113.4	65.5	191	165.4	95.5	251	217.4	125.5
12	10.4	6.0	72	62.4	36.0	32	114.3	66.0	92	166.3	96.0	52	218.2	126.0
13	11.3	6.5	73	63.2	36.5	33	115.2	66.5	93	167.1	96.5	53	219.1	126.5
14	12.1	7.0	74	64.1	37.0	34	116.0	67.0	94	168.0	97.0	54	220.0	127.0
15	13.0	7.5	75	65.0	37.5	35	116.9	67.5	95	168.9	97.5	55	220.8	127.5
16	13.9	8.0	76	65.8	38.0	36	117.8	68.0	96	169.7	98.0	56	221.7	128.0
17	14.7	8.5	77	66.7	38.5	37	118.6	68.5	97	170.6	98.5	57	222.6	128.5
18	15.6	9.0	78	67.5	39.0	38	119.5	69.0	98	171.5	99.0	58	223.4	129.0
19	16.5	9.5	79	68.4	39.5	39	120.4	69.5	99	172.3	99.5	59	224.3	129.5
20	17.3	10.0	80	69.3	40.0	40	121.2	70.0	200	173.2	100.0	60	225.2	130.0
21	18.2	10.5	81	70.1	40.5	141	122.1	70.5	201	174.1	100.5	261	226.0	130.5
22	19.1	11.0	82	71.0	41.0	42	123.0	71.0	02	174.9	101.0	62	226.9	131.0
23	19.9	11.5	83	71.9	41.5	43	123.8	71.5	03	175.8	101.5	63	227.8	131.5
24	20.8	12.0	84	72.7	42.0	44	124.7	72.0	04	176.7	102.0	64	228.6	132.0
25	21.7	12.5	85	73.6	42.5	45	125.6	72.5	05	177.5	102.5	65	229.5	132.5
26	22.5	13.0	86	74.5	43.0	46	126.4	73.0	06	178.4	103.0	66	230.4	133.0
27	23.4	13.5	87	75.3	43.5	47	127.3	73.5	07	179.3	103.5	67	231.2	133.5
28	24.2	14.0	88	76.2	44.0	48	128.2	74.0	08	180.1	104.0	68	232.1	134.0
29	25.1	14.5	89	77.1	44.5	49	129.0	74.5	09	181.0	104.5	69	233.0	134.5
30	26.0	15.0	90	77.9	45.0	50	129.9	75.0	10	181.9	105.0	70	233.8	135.0
31	26.8	15.5	91	78.8	45.5	151	130.8	75.5	211	182.7	105.5	271	234.7	135.5
32	27.7	16.0	92	79.7	46.0	52	131.6	76.0	12	183.6	106.0	72	235.6	136.0
33	28.6	16.5	93	80.5	46.5	53	132.5	76.5	13	184.5	106.5	73	236.4	136.5
34	29.4	17.0	94	81.4	47.0	54	133.4	77.0	14	185.3	107.0	74	237.3	137.0
35	30.3	17.5	95	82.3	47.5	55	134.2	77.5	15	186.2	107.5	75	238.2	137.5
36	31.2	18.0	96	83.1	48.0	56	135.1	78.0	16	187.1	108.0	76	239.0	138.0
37	32.0	18.5	97	84.0	48.5	57	136.0	78.5	17	187.9	108.5	77	239.9	138.5
38	32.9	19.0	98	84.9	49.0	58	136.8	79.0	18	188.8	109.0	78	240.8	139.0
39	33.8	19.5	99	85.7	49.5	59	137.7	79.5	19	189.7	109.5	79	241.6	139.5
40	34.6	20.0	100	86.6	50.0	60	138.6	80.0	20	190.5	110.0	80	242.5	140.0
41	35.5	20.5	101	87.5	50.5	161	139.4	80.5	221	191.4	110.5	281	243.4	140.5
42	36.4	21.0	02	88.3	51.0	62	140.3	81.0	22	192.3	111.0	82	244.2	141.0
43	37.2	21.5	03	89.2	51.5	63	141.2	81.5	23	193.1	111.5	83	245.1	141.5
44	38.1	22.0	04	90.1	52.0	64	142.0	82.0	24	194.0	112.0	84	246.0	142.0
45	39.0	22.5	05	90.9	52.5	65	142.9	82.5	25	194.9	112.5	85	246.8	142.5
46	39.8	23.0	06	91.8	53.0	66	143.8	83.0	26	195.7	113.0	86	247.7	143.0
47	40.7	23.5	07	92.7	53.5	67	144.6	83.5	27	196.6	113.5	87	248.5	143.5
48	41.6	24.0	08	93.5	54.0	68	145.5	84.0	28	197.5	114.0	88	249.4	144.0
49	42.4	24.5	09	94.4	54.5	69	146.4	84.5	29	198.3	114.5	89	250.3	144.5
50	43.3	25.0	10	95.3	55.0	70	147.2	85.0	30	199.2	115.0	90	251.1	145.0
51	44.2	25.5	111	96.1	55.5	171	148.1	85.5	231	200.1	115.5	291	252.0	145.5
52	45.0	26.0	12	97.0	56.0	72	149.0	86.0	32	200.9	116.0	92	252.9	146.0
53	45.9	26.5	13	97.9	56.5	73	149.8	86.5	33	201.8	116.5	93	253.7	146.5
54	46.8	27.0	14	98.7	57.0	74	150.7	87.0	34	202.6	117.0	94	254.6	147.0
55	47.6	27.5	15	99.6	57.5	75	151.6	87.5	35	203.5	117.5	95	255.5	147.5
56	48.5	28.0	16	100.5	58.0	76	152.4	88.0	36	204.4	118.0	96	256.3	148.0
57	49.4	28.5	17	101.3	58.5	77	153.3	88.5	37	205.2	118.5	97	257.2	148.5
58	50.2	29.0	18	102.2	59.0	78	154.2	89.0	38	206.1	119.0	98	258.1	149.0
59	51.1	29.5	19	103.1	59.5	79	155.0	89.5	39	207.0	119.5	99	258.9	149.5
60	52.0	30.0	20	103.9	60.0	80	155.9	90.0	40	207.8	120.0	300	259.8	150.0
Dist.	Dep.	Lat.	Dist.	Dep.	Lat.	Dist.	Dep.	Lat.	Dist.	Dep.	Lat.	Dist.	Dep.	Lat.

60° (120°, 240°, 300°).

In Plane Sailing.	Dist.	Lat.	Dep.
For converting *Dep.* into *Diff. Long.* and *Diff. Long.* into *Dep.* In Middle Latitude Sailing.	Diff. Long.	Dep.	
For converting *Dep.* into *Diff. Long.* and *Diff. Long.* into *Dep.* In Mercator Sailing.		*m*	Diff. Long.
For multiplication of numbers by sines and by cosines, or solution of plane right-angled triangles.	N. Hypotenuse.	N×Cos. Side Adj.	N×Sin. Side Opp.

TABLE 3.

Difference of Latitude and Departure for 30° (150°, 210°, 330°).

Dist.	Lat.	Dep.	Dist.	Lat.	Dep.	Dist.	Lat.	Dep.	Dist.	Lat.	Dep.	Dist.	Lat.	Dep.
301	260.7	150.5	361	312.6	180.5	421	364.6	210.5	481	416.6	240.5	541	468.5	270.5
02	261.5	151.0	62	313.5	181.0	22	365.5	211.0	82	417.4	241.0	42	469.4	271.0
03	262.4	151.5	63	314.4	181.5	23	366.3	211.5	83	418.3	241.5	43	470.3	271.5
04	263.3	152.0	64	315.2	182.0	24	367.2	212.0	84	419.2	242.0	44	471.1	272.0
05	264.1	152.5	65	316.1	182.5	25	368.1	212.5	85	420.0	242.5	45	472.0	272.5
06	265.0	153.0	66	317.0	183.0	26	368.9	213.0	86	420.9	243.0	46	472.8	273.0
07	265.9	153.5	67	317.8	183.5	27	369.8	213.5	87	421.8	243.5	47	473.7	273.5
08	266.6	154.0	68	318.7	184.0	28	370.7	214.0	88	422.6	244.0	48	474.6	274.0
09	267.6	154.5	69	319.6	184.5	29	371.5	214.5	89	423.5	244.5	49	475.4	274.5
10	268.5	155.0	70	320.4	185.0	30	372.4	215.0	90	424.4	245.0	50	476.3	275.0
311	269.3	155.5	371	321.3	185.5	431	373.3	215.5	491	425.2	245.5	551	477.2	275.5
12	270.2	156.0	72	322.2	186.0	32	374.1	216.0	92	426.1	246.0	52	478.0	276.0
13	271.1	156.5	73	323.0	186.5	33	375.0	216.5	93	427.0	246.5	53	478.9	276.5
14	271.9	157.0	74	323.9	187.0	34	375.9	217.0	94	427.8	247.0	54	479.8	277.0
15	272.8	157.5	75	324.8	187.5	35	376.7	217.5	95	428.7	247.5	55	480.6	277.5
16	273.7	158.0	76	325.6	188.0	36	377.6	218.0	96	429.5	248.0	56	481.5	278.0
17	274.5	158.5	77	326.5	188.5	37	378.5	218.5	97	430.4	248.5	57	482.4	278.5
18	275.4	159.0	78	327.4	189.0	38	379.3	219.0	98	431.3	249.0	58	483.2	279.0
19	276.3	159.5	79	328.2	189.5	39	380.2	219.5	99	432.1	249.5	59	484.1	279.5
20	277.1	160.0	80	329.1	190.0	40	381.1	220.0	500	433.0	250.0	60	485.0	280.0
321	278.0	160.5	381	330.0	190.5	441	381.9	220.5	501	433.9	250.5	561	485.8	280.5
22	278.9	161.0	82	330.8	191.0	42	382.8	221.0	02	434.7	251.0	62	486.7	281.0
23	279.7	161.5	83	331.7	191.5	43	383.6	221.5	03	435.6	251.5	63	487.6	281.5
24	280.6	162.0	84	332.6	192.0	44	384.5	222.0	04	436.5	252.0	64	488.4	282.0
25	281.5	162.5	85	333.4	192.5	45	385.4	222.5	05	437.3	252.5	65	489.3	282.5
26	282.3	163.0	86	334.3	193.0	46	386.3	223.0	06	438.2	253.0	66	490.2	283.0
27	283.2	163.5	87	335.2	193.5	47	387.1	223.5	07	439.1	253.5	67	491.0	283.5
28	284.1	164.0	88	336.0	194.0	48	388.0	224.0	08	439.9	254.0	68	491.9	284.0
29	284.9	164.5	89	336.9	194.5	49	388.8	224.5	09	440.8	254.5	69	492.8	284.5
30	285.8	165.0	90	337.7	195.0	50	389.7	225.0	10	441.7	255.0	70	493.6	285.0
331	286.7	165.5	391	338.6	195.5	451	390.6	225.5	511	442.5	255.5	571	494.5	285.5
32	287.5	166.0	92	339.5	196.0	52	391.4	226.0	12	443.4	256.0	72	495.4	286.0
33	288.4	166.5	93	340.3	196.5	53	392.3	226.5	13	444.3	256.5	73	496.2	286.5
34	289.3	167.0	94	341.2	197.0	54	393.2	227.0	14	445.1	257.0	74	497.1	287.0
35	290.1	167.5	95	342.1	197.5	55	394.0	227.5	15	446.0	257.5	75	498.0	287.5
36	291.0	168.0	96	342.9	198.0	56	394.9	228.0	16	446.9	258.0	76	498.8	288.0
37	291.9	168.5	97	343.8	198.5	57	395.8	228.5	17	447.7	258.5	77	499.7	288.5
38	292.7	169.0	98	344.7	199.0	58	396.6	229.0	18	448.6	259.0	78	500.6	289.0
39	293.6	169.5	99	345.5	199.5	59	397.5	229.5	19	449.5	259.5	79	501.3	289.5
40	294.5	170.0	400	346.4	200.0	60	398.4	230.0	20	450.3	260.0	80	502.3	290.0
341	295.3	170.5	401	347.3	200.5	461	399.2	230.5	521	451.2	260.5	581	503.2	290.5
42	296.2	171.0	02	348.1	201.0	62	400.1	231.0	22	452.1	261.0	82	504.0	291.0
43	297.0	171.5	03	349.0	201.5	63	401.0	231.5	23	452.9	261.5	83	504.9	291.5
44	297.9	172.0	04	349.9	202.0	64	401.8	232.0	24	453.8	262.0	84	505.8	292.0
45	298.8	172.5	05	350.7	202.5	65	402.7	232.7	25	454.7	262.5	85	506.6	292.5
46	299.6	173.0	06	351.6	203.0	66	403.6	233.0	26	455.5	263.0	86	507.5	293.0
47	300.5	173.5	07	352.5	203.5	67	404.4	233.5	27	456.4	263.5	87	508.4	293.5
48	301.4	174.0	08	353.3	204.0	68	405.3	234.0	28	457.3	264.0	88	509.2	294.0
49	302.2	174.5	09	354.2	204.5	69	406.2	234.5	29	458.1	264.5	89	510.1	294.5
50	303.1	175.0	10	355.1	205.0	70	407.0	235.0	30	459.0	265.0	90	511.0	295.0
351	304.0	175.5	411	355.9	205.5	471	407.9	235.5	531	459.9	265.5	591	511.8	295.5
52	304.8	176.0	12	356.8	206.0	72	408.8	236.0	32	460.7	266.0	92	512.7	296.0
53	305.7	176.5	13	357.7	206.5	73	409.6	236.5	33	461.6	266.5	93	513.6	296.5
54	306.6	177.0	14	358.5	207.0	74	410.5	237.0	34	462.5	267.0	94	514.4	297.0
55	307.4	177.5	15	359.4	207.5	75	411.4	237.5	35	463.3	267.5	95	515.3	297.5
56	308.3	178.0	16	360.3	208.0	76	412.2	238.0	36	464.2	268.0	96	516.2	298.0
57	309.2	178.5	17	361.1	208.5	77	413.1	238.5	37	465.1	268.5	97	517.0	298.5
58	310.0	179.0	18	362.0	209.0	78	414.0	239.0	38	465.9	269.0	98	517.9	299.0
59	310.9	179.5	19	362.9	209.5	79	414.8	239.5	39	466.8	269.5	99	518.7	299.5
60	311.8	180.0	20	363.7	210.0	80	415.7	240.0	40	467.7	270.0	600	519.6	300.0
Dist.	Dep.	Lat.	Dist.	Dep.	Lat.	Dist.	Dep.	Lat.	Dist.	Dep.	Lat.	Dist.	Dep.	Lat.

60° (120°, 240°, 300°).

In **Plane Sailing.**	**Dist.**	**Lat.**	**Dep.**
For converting *Dep.* into *Diff. Long.* and *Diff. Long.* into *Dep.* In **Middle Latitude Sailing.**	Diff. Long.	Dep.	
For converting *Dep.* into *Diff. Long* and *Diff. Long.* into *Dep.* In **Mercator Sailing.**		*m*	Diff. Long.
For multiplication of numbers by sines and by cosines, or solution of plane right-angled triangles.	N. Hypotenuse.	N×Cos. Side Adj.	N×Sin. Side Opp.

541524°—43——31

TABLE 3.

Difference of Latitude and Departure for 31° (149°, 211°, 329°).

Dist.	Lat.	Dep.	Dist.	Lat.	Dep.	Dist.	Lat.	Dep.	Dist.	Lat.	Dep.	Dist.	Lat.	Dep.
1	0.9	0.5	61	52.3	31.4	121	103.7	62.3	181	155.1	93.2	241	206.6	124.1
2	1.7	1.0	62	53.1	31.9	22	104.6	62.8	82	156.0	93.7	42	207.4	124.6
3	2.6	1.5	63	54.0	32.4	23	105.4	63.3	83	156.9	94.3	43	208.3	125.2
4	3.4	2.1	64	54.9	33.0	24	106.3	63.9	84	157.7	94.8	44	209.1	125.7
5	4.3	2.6	65	55.7	33.5	25	107.1	64.4	85	158.6	95.3	45	210.0	126.2
6	5.1	3.1	66	56.6	34.0	26	108.0	64.9	86	159.4	95.8	46	210.9	126.7
7	6.0	3.6	67	57.4	34.5	27	108.9	65.4	87	160.3	96.3	47	211.7	127.2
8	6.9	4.1	68	58.3	35.0	28	109.7	65.9	88	161.1	96.8	48	212.6	127.7
9	7.7	4.6	69	59.1	35.5	29	110.6	66.4	89	162.0	97.3	49	213.4	128.2
10	8.6	5.2	70	60.0	36.1	30	111.4	67.0	90	162.9	97.9	50	214.3	128.8
11	9.4	5.7	71	60.9	36.6	131	112.3	67.5	191	163.7	98.4	251	215.1	129.3
12	10.3	6.2	72	61.7	37.1	32	113.1	68.0	92	164.6	98.9	52	216.0	129.8
13	11.1	6.7	73	62.6	37.6	33	114.0	68.5	93	165.4	99.4	53	216.9	130.3
14	12.0	7.2	74	63.4	38.1	34	114.9	69.0	94	166.3	99.9	54	217.7	130.8
15	12.9	7.7	75	64.3	38.6	35	115.7	69.5	95	167.1	100.4	55	218.6	131.3
16	13.7	8.2	76	65.1	39.1	36	116.6	70.0	96	168.0	100.9	56	219.4	131.8
17	14.6	8.8	77	66.0	39.7	37	117.4	70.6	97	168.9	101.5	57	220.3	132.4
18	15.4	9.3	78	66.9	40.2	38	118.3	71.1	98	169.7	102.0	58	221.1	132.9
19	16.3	9.8	79	67.7	40.7	39	119.1	71.6	99	170.6	102.5	59	222.0	133.4
20	17.1	10.3	80	68.6	41.2	40	120.0	72.1	200	171.4	103.0	60	222.9	133.9
21	18.0	10.8	81	69.4	41.7	141	120.9	72.6	201	172.3	103.5	261	223.7	134.4
22	18.9	11.3	82	70.3	42.2	42	121.7	73.1	02	173.1	104.0	62	224.6	134.9
23	19.7	11.8	83	71.1	42.7	43	122.6	73.7	03	174.0	104.6	63	225.4	135.5
24	20.6	12.4	84	72.0	43.3	44	123.4	74.2	04	174.9	105.1	64	226.3	136.0
25	21.4	12.9	85	72.9	43.8	45	124.3	74.7	05	175.7	105.6	65	227.1	136.5
26	22.3	13.4	86	73.7	44.3	46	125.1	75.2	06	176.6	106.1	66	228.0	137.0
27	23.1	13.9	87	74.6	44.8	47	126.0	75.7	07	177.4	106.6	67	228.9	137.5
28	24.0	14.4	88	75.4	45.3	48	126.9	76.2	08	178.3	107.1	68	229.7	138.0
29	24.9	14.9	89	76.3	45.8	49	127.7	76.7	09	179.1	107.6	69	230.6	138.5
30	25.7	15.5	90	77.1	46.4	50	128.6	77.3	10	180.0	108.2	70	231.4	139.1
31	26.6	16.0	91	78.0	46.9	151	129.4	77.8	211	180.9	108.7	271	232.3	139.6
32	27.4	16.5	92	78.9	47.4	52	130.3	78.3	12	181.7	109.2	72	233.1	140.1
33	28.3	17.0	93	79.7	47.9	53	131.1	78.8	13	182.6	109.7	73	234.0	140.6
34	29.1	17.5	94	80.6	48.4	54	132.0	79.3	14	183.4	110.2	74	234.9	141.1
35	30.0	18.0	95	81.4	48.9	55	132.9	79.8	15	184.3	110.7	75	235.7	141.6
36	30.9	18.5	96	82.3	49.4	56	133.7	80.3	16	185.1	111.2	76	236.6	142.2
37	31.7	19.1	97	83.1	50.0	57	134.6	80.9	17	186.0	111.8	77	237.4	142.7
38	32.6	19.6	98	84.0	50.5	58	135.4	81.4	18	186.9	112.3	78	238.3	143.2
39	33.4	20.1	99	84.9	51.0	59	136.3	81.9	19	187.7	112.8	79	239.1	143.7
40	34.3	20.6	100	85.7	51.5	60	137.1	82.4	20	188.6	113.3	80	240.0	144.2
41	35.1	21.1	101	86.6	52.0	161	138.0	82.9	221	189.4	113.8	281	240.9	144.7
42	36.0	21.6	02	87.4	52.5	62	138.9	83.4	22	190.3	114.3	82	241.7	145.2
43	36.9	22.1	03	88.3	53.0	63	139.7	84.0	23	191.1	114.9	83	242.6	145.8
44	37.7	22.7	04	89.1	53.6	64	140.6	84.5	24	192.0	115.4	84	243.4	146.3
45	38.6	23.2	05	90.0	54.1	65	141.4	85.0	25	192.9	115.9	85	244.3	146.8
46	39.4	23.7	06	90.9	54.6	66	142.3	85.5	26	193.7	116.4	86	245.1	147.3
47	40.3	24.2	07	91.7	55.1	67	143.1	86.0	27	194.6	116.9	87	246.0	147.8
48	41.1	24.7	08	92.6	55.6	68	144.0	86.5	28	195.4	117.4	88	246.9	148.3
49	42.0	25.2	09	93.4	56.1	69	144.9	87.0	29	196.3	117.9	89	247.7	148.8
50	42.9	25.8	10	94.3	56.7	70	145.7	87.6	30	197.1	118.5	90	248.6	149.4
51	43.7	26.3	111	95.1	57.2	171	146.6	88.1	231	198.0	119.0	291	249.4	149.9
52	44.6	26.8	12	96.0	57.7	72	147.4	88.6	32	198.9	119.5	92	250.3	150.4
53	45.4	27.3	13	96.9	58.2	73	148.3	89.1	33	199.7	120.0	93	251.2	150.9
54	46.3	27.8	14	97.7	58.7	74	149.1	89.6	34	200.6	120.5	94	252.0	151.4
55	47.1	28.3	15	98.6	59.2	75	150.0	90.1	35	201.4	121.0	95	252.9	151.9
56	48.0	28.8	16	99.4	59.7	76	150.9	90.6	36	202.3	121.5	96	253.7	152.5
57	48.9	29.4	17	100.3	60.3	77	151.7	91.2	37	203.1	122.1	97	254.6	153.0
58	49.7	29.9	18	101.1	60.8	78	152.6	91.7	38	204.0	122.6	98	255.4	153.5
59	50.6	30.4	19	102.0	61.3	79	153.4	92.2	39	204.9	123.1	99	256.3	154.0
60	51.4	30.9	20	102.9	61.8	80	154.3	92.7	40	205.7	123.6	300	257.1	154.5
Dist.	Dep.	Lat.	Dist.	Dep.	Lat.	Dist.	Dep.	Lat.	Dist.	Dep.	Lat.	Dist.	Dep.	Lat.

59° (121°, 239°, 301°).

In Plane Sailing.	**Dist.**	**Lat.**	**Dep.**
For converting *Dep.* into *Diff. Long.* and *Diff. Long.* into *Dep.* **In Middle Latitude Sailing.**	Diff. Long.	Dep.	
For converting *Dep.* into *Diff. Long.* and *Diff. Long.* into *Dep.* **In Mercator Sailing.**		*m*	Diff Long.
For multiplication of numbers by sines and by cosines, or solution of plane right-angled triangles.	N. / Hypotenuse.	N×Cos. / Side Adj.	N×Sin. / Side Opp.

TABLE 3.

Difference of Latitude and Departure for 31° (149°, 211°, 329°).

Dist.	Lat.	Dep.	Dist.	Lat.	Dep.	Dist.	Lat.	Dep.	Dist.	Lat.	Dep.	Dist.	Lat.	Dep.
301	258.0	155.0	361	309.4	185.9	421	360.9	216.8	481	412.3	247.7	541	463.7	278.6
02	258.9	155.5	62	310.3	186.4	22	361.7	217.3	82	413.2	248.2	42	464.6	279.2
03	259.7	156.1	63	311.2	187.0	23	362.6	217.9	83	414.0	248.8	43	465.4	279.7
04	260.6	156.6	64	312.0	187.5	24	363.4	218.4	84	414.9	249.3	44	466.3	280.2
05	261.4	157.1	65	312.9	188.0	25	364.3	218.9	85	415.7	249.8	45	467.2	280.7
06	262.3	157.6	66	313.7	188.5	26	365.2	219.4	86	416.6	250.3	46	468.0	281.2
07	263.2	158.1	67	314.6	189.0	27	366.0	219.9	87	417.4	250.8	47	468.9	281.7
08	264.0	158.6	68	315.4	189.5	28	366.9	220.4	88	418.3	251.3	48	469.7	282.2
09	264.9	159.1	69	316.3	190.0	29	367.7	221.0	89	419.2	251.9	49	470.6	282.8
10	265.7	159.7	70	317.2	190.6	30	368.6	221.5	90	420.0	252.4	50	471.4	283.3
311	266.6	160.2	371	318.0	191.1	431	369.4	222.0	491	420.9	252.9	551	472.3	283.8
12	267.4	160.7	72	318.9	191.6	32	370.3	222.5	92	421.7	253.4	52	473.2	284.3
13	268.3	161.2	73	319.7	192.1	33	371.2	223.0	93	422.6	253.9	53	474.0	284.8
14	269.2	161.7	74	320.6	192.6	34	372.0	223.5	94	423.4	254.4	54	474.9	285.3
15	270.0	162.2	75	321.4	193.1	35	372.9	224.0	95	424.3	254.9	55	475.7	285.8
16	270.9	162.8	76	322.3	193.7	36	373.7	224.6	96	425.2	255.5	56	476.6	286.4
17	271.7	163.3	77	323.2	194.2	37	374.6	225.1	97	426.0	256.0	57	477.4	286.9
18	272.6	163.8	78	324.0	194.7	38	375.4	225.6	98	426.9	256.5	58	478.3	287.4
19	273.4	164.3	79	324.9	195.2	39	376.3	226.1	99	427.7	257.0	59	479.2	287.9
20	274.3	164.8	80	325.7	195.7	40	377.2	226.6	500	428.6	257.5	60	480.0	288.4
321	275.2	165.3	381	326.6	196.2	441	378.0	227.1	501	429.4	258.0	561	480.9	288.9
22	276.0	165.8	82	327.4	196.7	42	378.9	227.6	02	430.3	258.5	62	481.7	289.5
23	276.9	166.4	83	328.3	197.3	43	379.7	228.2	03	431.2	259.1	63	482.6	290.0
24	277.7	166.9	84	329.2	197.8	44	380.6	228.7	04	432.0	259.6	64	483.4	290.5
25	278.6	167.4	85	330.0	198.3	45	381.4	229.2	05	432.9	260.1	65	484.3	291.0
26	279.4	167.9	86	330.9	198.8	46	382.3	229.7	06	433.7	260.6	66	485.2	291.5
27	280.3	168.4	87	331.7	199.3	47	383.2	230.2	07	434.6	261.1	67	486.0	292.0
28	281.2	168.9	88	332.6	199.8	48	384.0	230.7	08	435.4	261.6	68	486.9	292.5
29	282.0	169.4	89	333.4	200.3	49	384.9	231.3	09	436.3	262.2	69	487.7	293.1
30	282.9	170.0	90	334.3	200.9	50	385.7	231.8	10	437.2	262.7	70	488.6	293.6
331	283.7	170.5	391	335.2	201.4	451	386.6	232.3	511	438.0	263.2	571	489.4	294.1
32	284.6	171.0	92	336.0	201.9	52	387.4	232.8	12	438.9	263.7	72	490.3	294.6
33	285.4	171.5	93	336.9	202.4	53	388.3	233.3	13	439.7	264.2	73	491.2	295.1
34	286.3	172.0	94	337.7	202.9	54	389.2	233.8	14	440.6	264.7	74	492.0	295.6
35	287.2	172.5	95	338.6	203.4	55	390.0	234.3	15	441.4	265.2	75	492.9	296.1
36	288.0	173.1	96	339.4	204.0	56	390.9	234.9	16	442.3	265.8	76	493.7	296.7
37	288.9	173.6	97	340.3	204.5	57	391.7	235.4	17	443.2	266.3	77	494.6	297.2
38	289.7	174.1	98	341.2	205.0	58	392.6	235.9	18	444.0	266.8	78	495.4	297.7
39	290.6	174.6	99	342.0	205.5	59	393.4	236.4	19	444.9	267.3	79	496.3	298.2
40	291.4	175.1	400	342.9	206.0	60	394.3	236.9	20	445.7	267.8	80	497.2	298.7
341	292.3	175.6	401	343.7	206.5	461	395.2	237.4	521	446.6	268.3	581	498.0	299.2
42	293.2	176.1	02	344.6	207.0	62	396.0	237.9	22	447.4	268.8	82	498.9	299.8
43	294.0	176.7	03	345.4	207.6	63	396.9	238.5	23	448.3	269.4	83	499.7	300.3
44	294.9	177.2	04	346.3	208.1	64	397.7	239.0	24	449.2	269.9	84	500.6	300.8
45	295.7	177.7	05	347.2	208.6	65	398.6	239.5	25	450.0	270.4	85	501.4	301.3
46	296.6	178.2	06	348.0	209.1	66	399.4	240.0	26	450.9	270.9	86	502.3	301.8
47	297.4	178.7	07	348.9	209.6	67	400.3	240.5	27	451.7	271.4	87	503.2	302.3
48	298.3	179.2	08	349.7	210.1	68	401.2	241.0	28	452.6	271.9	88	504.0	302.8
49	299.2	179.7	09	350.6	210.7	69	402.0	241.6	29	453.4	272.5	89	504.9	303.4
50	300.0	180.3	10	351.4	211.2	70	402.9	242.1	30	454.3	273.0	90	505.7	303.9
351	300.9	180.8	411	352.3	211.7	471	403.7	242.6	531	455.2	273.5	591	506.6	304.4
52	301.7	181.3	12	353.2	212.2	72	404.6	243.1	32	456.0	274.0	92	507.4	304.9
53	302.6	181.8	13	354.0	212.7	73	405.4	243.6	33	456.9	274.5	93	508.3	305.4
54	303.4	182.3	14	354.9	213.2	74	406.3	244.1	34	457.7	275.0	94	509.2	305.9
55	304.3	182.8	15	355.7	213.7	75	407.2	244.6	35	458.6	275.5	95	510.0	306.4
56	305.2	183.4	16	356.6	214.3	76	408.0	245.2	36	459.4	276.1	96	510.9	307.0
57	306.0	183.9	17	357.4	214.8	77	408.9	245.7	37	460.3	276.6	97	511.7	307.5
58	306.9	184.4	18	358.3	215.3	78	409.7	246.2	38	461.2	277.1	98	512.6	308.0
59	307.7	184.9	19	359.2	215.8	79	410.6	246.7	39	462.0	277.6	99	513.4	308.5
60	308.6	185.4	20	360.0	216.3	80	411.4	247.2	40	462.9	278.1	600	514.3	309.0
Dist.	Dep.	Lat.	Dist.	Dep.	Lat.	Dist.	Dep.	Lat.	Dist.	Dep.	Lat.	Dist.	Dep.	Lat.

59° (121°, 239°, 301°).

In **Plane Sailing.**	**Dist.**	**Lat.**	**Dep.**
For converting *Dep.* into *Diff. Long.* and *Diff. Long.* into *Dep.* In **Middle Latitude Sailing.**	Diff. Long.	Dep.	
For converting *Dep.* into *Diff. Long.* and *Diff. Long.* into *Dep.* In **Mercator Sailing.**		*m*	Diff. Long.
For multiplication of numbers by sines and by cosines, or solution of plane right-angled triangles.	N. / Hypotenuse.	N×Cos. / Side Adj.	N×Sin. / Side Opp.

TABLE 3.

Difference of Latitude and Departure for 32° (148°, 212°, 328°).

Dist.	Lat.	Dep.	Dist.	Lat.	Dep.	Dist.	Lat.	Dep.	Dist.	Lat.	Dep.	Dist.	Lat.	Dep.
1	0.8	0.5	61	51.7	32.3	121	102.6	64.1	181	153.5	95.9	241	204.4	127.7
2	1.7	1.1	62	52.6	32.9	22	103.5	64.7	82	154.3	96.4	42	205.2	128.2
3	2.5	1.6	63	53.4	33.4	23	104.3	65.2	83	155.2	97.0	43	206.1	128.8
4	3.4	2.1	64	54.3	33.9	24	105.2	65.7	84	156.0	97.5	44	206.9	129.3
5	4.2	2.6	65	55.1	34.4	25	106.0	66.2	85	156.9	98.0	45	207.8	129.8
6	5.1	3.2	66	56.0	35.0	26	106.9	66.8	86	157.7	98.6	46	208.6	130.4
7	5.9	3.7	67	56.8	35.5	27	107.7	67.3	87	158.6	99.1	47	209.5	130.9
8	6.8	4.2	68	57.7	36.0	28	108.6	67.8	88	159.4	99.6	48	210.3	131.4
9	7.6	4.8	69	58.5	36.6	29	109.4	68.4	89	160.3	100.2	49	211.2	131.9
10	8.5	5.3	70	59.4	37.1	30	110.2	68.9	90	161.1	100.7	50	212.0	132.5
11	9.3	5.8	71	60.2	37.6	131	111.1	69.4	191	162.0	101.2	251	212.9	133.0
12	10.2	6.4	72	61.1	38.2	32	111.9	69.9	92	162.8	101.7	52	213.7	133.5
13	11.0	6.9	73	61.9	38.7	33	112.8	70.5	93	163.7	102.3	53	214.6	134.1
14	11.9	7.4	74	62.8	39.2	34	113.6	71.0	94	164.5	102.8	54	215.4	134.6
15	12.7	7.9	75	63.6	39.7	35	114.5	71.5	95	165.4	103.3	55	216.3	135.1
16	13.6	8.5	76	64.5	40.3	36	115.3	72.1	96	166.2	103.9	56	217.1	135.7
17	14.4	9.0	77	65.3	40.8	37	116.2	72.6	97	167.1	104.4	57	217.9	136.2
18	15.3	9.5	78	66.1	41.3	38	117.0	73.1	98	167.9	104.9	58	218.8	136.7
19	16.1	10.1	79	67.0	41.9	39	117.9	73.7	99	168.8	105.5	59	219.6	137.2
20	17.0	10.6	80	67.8	42.4	40	118.7	74.2	200	169.6	106.0	60	220.5	137.8
21	17.8	11.1	81	68.7	42.9	141	119.6	74.7	201	170.5	106.5	261	221.3	138.3
22	18.7	11.7	82	69.5	43.5	42	120.4	75.2	02	171.3	107.0	62	222.2	138.8
23	19.5	12.2	83	70.4	44.0	43	121.3	75.8	03	172.2	107.6	63	223.0	139.4
24	20.4	12.7	84	71.2	44.5	44	122.1	76.3	04	173.0	108.1	64	223.9	139.9
25	21.2	13.2	85	72.1	45.0	45	123.0	76.8	05	173.8	108.6	65	224.7	140.4
26	22.0	13.8	86	72.9	45.6	46	123.8	77.4	06	174.7	109.2	66	225.6	141.0
27	22.9	14.3	87	73.8	46.1	47	124.7	77.9	07	175.5	109.7	67	226.4	141.5
28	23.7	14.8	88	74.6	46.6	48	125.5	78.4	08	176.4	110.2	68	227.3	142.0
29	24.6	15.4	89	75.5	47.2	49	126.4	79.0	09	177.2	110.8	69	228.1	142.5
30	25.4	15.9	90	76.3	47.7	50	127.2	79.5	10	178.1	111.3	70	229.0	143.1
31	26.3	16.4	91	77.2	48.2	151	128.1	80.0	211	178.9	111.8	271	229.8	143.6
32	27.1	17.0	92	78.0	48.8	52	128.9	80.5	12	179.8	112.3	72	230.7	144.1
33	28.0	17.5	93	78.9	49.3	53	129.8	81.1	13	180.6	112.9	73	231.5	144.7
34	28.8	18.0	94	79.7	49.8	54	130.6	81.6	14	181.5	113.4	74	232.4	145.2
35	29.7	18.5	95	80.6	50.3	55	131.4	82.1	15	182.3	113.9	75	233.2	145.7
36	30.5	19.1	96	81.4	50.9	56	132.3	82.7	16	183.2	114.5	76	234.1	146.3
37	31.4	19.6	97	82.3	51.4	57	133.1	83.2	17	184.0	115.0	77	234.9	146.8
38	32.2	20.1	98	83.1	51.9	58	134.0	83.7	18	184.9	115.5	78	235.8	147.3
39	33.1	20.7	99	84.0	52.5	59	134.8	84.3	19	185.7	116.1	79	236.6	147.8
40	33.9	21.2	100	84.8	53.0	60	135.7	84.8	20	186.6	116.6	80	237.5	148.4
41	34.8	21.7	101	85.7	53.5	161	136.5	85.3	221	187.4	117.1	281	238.3	148.9
42	35.6	22.3	02	86.5	54.1	62	137.4	85.8	22	188.3	117.6	82	239.1	149.4
43	36.5	22.8	03	87.3	54.6	63	138.2	86.4	23	189.1	118.2	83	240.0	150.0
44	37.3	23.3	04	88.2	55.1	64	139.1	86.9	24	190.0	118.7	84	240.8	150.5
45	38.2	23.8	05	89.0	55.6	65	139.9	87.4	25	190.8	119.2	85	241.7	151.0
46	39.0	24.4	06	89.9	56.2	66	140.8	88.0	26	191.7	119.8	86	242.5	151.6
47	39.9	24.9	07	90.7	56.7	67	141.6	88.5	27	192.5	120.3	87	243.4	152.1
48	40.7	25.4	08	91.6	57.2	68	142.5	89.0	28	193.4	120.8	88	244.2	152.6
49	41.6	26.0	09	92.4	57.8	69	143.3	89.6	29	194.2	121.4	89	245.1	153.1
50	42.4	26.5	10	93.3	58.3	70	144.2	90.1	30	195.1	121.9	90	245.9	153.7
51	43.3	27.0	111	94.1	58.8	171	145.0	90.6	231	195.9	122.4	291	246.8	154.2
52	44.1	27.6	12	95.0	59.4	72	145.9	91.1	32	196.7	122.9	92	247.6	154.7
53	44.9	28.1	13	95.8	59.9	73	146.7	91.7	33	197.6	123.5	93	248.5	155.3
54	45.3	28.6	14	96.7	60.4	74	147.6	92.2	34	198.4	124.0	94	249.3	155.8
55	46.6	29.1	15	97.5	60.9	75	148.4	92.7	35	199.3	124.5	95	250.2	156.3
56	47.5	29.7	16	98.4	61.5	76	149.3	93.3	36	200.1	125.1	96	251.0	156.9
57	48.3	30.2	17	99.2	62.0	77	150.1	93.8	37	201.0	125.6	97	251.9	157.4
58	49.2	30.7	18	100.1	62.5	78	151.0	94.3	38	201.8	126.1	98	252.7	157.9
59	50.0	31.3	19	100.9	63.1	79	151.8	94.9	39	202.7	126.7	99	253.6	158.4
60	50.9	31.8	20	101.8	63.6	80	152.6	95.4	40	203.5	127.2	300	254.4	159.0
Dist.	Dep.	Lat.	Dist.	Dep.	Lat.	Dist.	Dep.	Lat.	Dist.	Dep.	Lat.	Dist.	Dep.	Lat.

58° (122°, 238°, 302°).

In Plane Sailing.	Dist.	Lat.	Dep.
For converting *Dep.* into *Diff. Long.* and *Diff. Long.* into *Dep.* In Middle Latitude Sailing.	Diff. Long.	Dep.	
For converting *Dep.* into *Diff. Long.* and *Diff. Long.* into *Dep.* In Mercator Sailing.		*m*	Diff. Long.
For multiplication of numbers by sines and by cosines, or solution of plane right-angled triangles.	N. / Hypotenuse.	N×Cos. / Side. Adj.	N×Sin. / Side Opp.

TABLE 3.

Difference of Latitude and Departure for 32° (148°, 212°, 328°).

Dist.	Lat.	Dep.	Dist.	Lat.	Dep.	Dist.	Lat.	Dep.	Dist.	Lat.	Dep.	Dist.	Lat.	Dep.
301	255.3	159.5	361	306.1	191.3	421	357.0	223.1	481	407.9	254.9	541	458.8	286.7
02	256.1	160.0	62	307.0	191.8	22	357.9	223.6	82	408.8	255.4	42	459.6	287.2
03	257.0	160.6	63	307.8	192.4	23	358.7	224.2	83	409.6	256.0	43	460.5	287.7
04	257.8	161.1	64	308.7	192.9	24	359.6	224.7	84	410.5	256.5	44	461.3	288.3
05	258.7	161.6	65	309.5	193.4	25	360.4	225.2	85	411.3	257.0	45	462.2	288.8
06	259.5	162.2	66	310.4	194.0	26	361.3	225.7	86	412.2	257.5	46	463.0	289.3
07	260.4	162.7	67	311.2	194.5	27	362.1	226.3	87	413.0	258.1	47	463.9	289.9
08	261.2	163.2	68	312.1	195.0	28	363.0	226.8	88	413.8	258.6	48	464.7	290.4
09	262.0	163.7	69	312.9	195.5	29	363.8	227.3	89	414.7	259.1	49	465.6	290.9
10	262.9	164.3	70	313.8	196.1	30	364.7	227.9	90	415.5	259.7	50	466.4	291.5
311	263.7	164.8	371	314.6	196.6	431	365.5	228.4	491	416.4	260.2	551	467.3	292.0
12	264.6	165.3	72	315.5	197.1	32	366.4	228.9	92	417.2	260.7	52	468.1	292.5
13	265.4	165.9	73	316.3	197.7	33	367.2	229.5	93	418.1	261.3	53	469.0	293.0
14	266.3	166.4	74	317.2	198.2	34	368.1	230.0	94	418.9	261.8	54	469.8	293.6
15	267.1	166.9	75	318.0	198.7	35	368.9	230.5	95	419.8	262.3	55	470.7	294.1
16	268.0	167.5	76	318.9	199.2	36	369.7	231.0	96	420.6	262.8	56	471.5	294.6
17	268.8	168.0	77	319.7	199.8	37	370.6	231.6	97	421.5	263.4	57	472.4	295.2
18	269.7	168.5	78	320.6	200.3	38	371.4	232.1	98	422.3	263.9	58	473.2	295.7
19	270.5	169.0	79	321.4	200.8	39	372.3	232.6	99	423.2	264.4	59	474.1	296.2
20	271.4	169.6	80	322.3	201.4	40	373.1	233.2	500	424.0	265.0	60	474.9	296.8
321	272.2	170.1	381	323.1	201.9	441	374.0	233.7	501	424.9	265.5	561	475.8	297.3
22	273.1	170.6	82	324.0	202.4	42	374.8	234.2	02	425.7	266.0	62	476.6	297.8
23	273.9	171.2	83	324.8	203.0	43	375.7	234.8	03	426.6	266.5	63	477.5	298.3
24	274.8	171.7	84	325.7	203.5	44	376.5	235.3	04	427.4	267.1	64	478.3	298.9
25	275.6	172.2	85	326.5	204.0	45	377.4	235.8	05	428.3	267.6	65	479.1	299.4
26	276.5	172.8	86	327.3	204.5	46	378.2	236.3	06	429.1	268.1	66	480.0	299.9
27	277.3	173.3	87	328.2	205.1	47	379.1	236.9	07	430.0	268.7	67	480.8	300.5
28	278.2	173.8	88	329.0	205.6	48	379.9	237.4	08	430.8	269.2	68	481.7	301.0
29	279.0	174.3	89	329.9	206.1	49	380.8	237.9	09	431.7	269.7	69	482.5	301.5
30	279.9	174.9	90	330.7	206.7	50	381.6	238.5	10	432.5	270.3	70	483.4	302.1
331	280.7	175.4	391	331.6	207.2	451	382.5	239.0	511	433.4	270.8	571	484.2	302.6
32	281.6	175.9	92	332.4	207.7	52	383.3	239.5	12	434.2	271.3	72	485.1	303.1
33	282.4	176.5	93	333.3	208.3	53	384.2	240.1	13	435.0	271.9	73	485.9	303.6
34	283.2	177.0	94	334.1	208.8	54	385.0	240.6	14	435.9	272.4	74	486.8	304.2
35	284.1	177.5	95	335.0	209.3	55	385.9	241.1	15	436.7	272.9	75	487.6	304.7
36	284.9	178.1	96	335.8	209.8	56	386.7	241.6	16	437.6	273.4	76	488.5	305.2
37	285.8	178.6	97	336.7	210.4	57	387.6	242.2	17	438.4	274.0	77	489.3	305.8
38	286.6	179.1	98	337.5	210.9	58	388.4	242.7	18	439.3	274.5	78	490.2	306.3
39	287.5	179.6	99	338.4	211.4	59	389.3	243.2	19	440.1	275.0	79	491.0	306.8
40	288.3	180.2	400	339.2	212.0	60	390.1	243.8	20	441.0	275.6	80	491.9	307.4
341	289.2	180.7	401	340.1	212.5	461	391.0	244.3	521	441.8	276.1	581	492.7	307.9
42	290.0	181.2	02	340.9	213.0	62	391.8	244.8	22	442.7	276.6	82	493.6	308.4
43	290.9	181.8	03	341.8	213.6	63	392.6	245.4	23	443.5	277.1	83	494.4	308.9
44	291.7	182.3	04	342.6	214.1	64	393.5	245.9	24	444.4	277.7	84	495.3	309.5
45	292.6	182.8	05	343.5	214.6	65	394.3	246.4	25	445.2	278.2	85	496.1	310.0
46	293.4	183.4	06	344.3	215.1	66	395.2	246.9	26	446.1	278.7	86	497.0	310.5
47	294.3	183.9	07	345.2	215.7	67	396.0	247.5	27	446.9	279.3	87	497.8	311.1
48	295.1	184.4	08	346.0	216.2	68	396.9	248.0	28	447.8	279.8	88	498.7	311.6
49	296.0	184.9	09	346.9	216.7	69	397.7	248.5	29	448.6	280.3	89	499.5	312.1
50	296.8	185.5	10	347.7	217.3	70	398.6	249.1	30	449.5	280.9	90	500.3	312.7
351	297.7	186.0	411	348.5	217.8	471	399.4	249.6	531	450.3	281.4	591	501.2	313.2
52	298.5	186.5	12	349.4	218.3	72	400.3	250.1	32	451.2	281.9	92	502.0	313.7
53	299.4	187.1	13	350.2	218.9	73	401.1	250.7	33	452.0	282.4	93	502.9	314.2
54	300.2	187.6	14	351.1	219.4	74	402.0	251.2	34	452.9	283.0	94	503.7	314.8
55	301.1	188.1	15	351.9	219.9	75	402.8	251.7	35	453.7	283.5	95	504.6	315.3
56	301.9	188.7	16	352.8	220.4	76	403.7	252.2	36	454.6	284.0	96	505.4	315.8
57	302.8	189.2	17	353.6	221.0	77	404.5	252.8	37	455.4	284.6	97	506.3	316.4
58	303.6	189.7	18	354.5	221.5	78	405.4	253.3	38	456.2	285.1	98	507.1	316.9
59	304.4	190.2	19	355.3	222.0	79	406.2	253.8	39	457.1	285.6	99	508.0	317.4
60	305.3	190.8	20	356.2	222.6	80	407.1	254.4	40	457.9	286.2	600	508.8	318.0
Dist.	Dep.	Lat.	Dist.	Dep.	Lat.	Dist.	Dep.	Lat.	Dist.	Dep.	Lat.	Dist.	Dep.	Lat.

58° (122°, 238°, 302°).

In **Plane Sailing**.	Dist.	Lat.	Dep.
For converting *Dep.* into *Diff. Long.* and *Diff. Long.* into *Dep.* In **Middle Latitude Sailing**.	Diff. Long.	Dep.	
For converting *Dep.* into *Diff. Long.* and *Diff. Long.* into *Dep.* In **Mercator Sailing**.		*m*	Diff. Long.
For multiplication of numbers by sines and by cosines, or solution of plane right-angled triangles.	N. Hypotenuse.	N×Cos. Side Adj.	N×Sin. Side Opp.

TABLE 3.

Difference of Latitude and Departure for 33° (147°, 213°, 327°).

Dist.	Lat.	Dep.	Dist.	Lat.	Dep.	Dist.	Lat.	Dep.	Dist.	Lat.	Dep.	Dist.	Lat.	Dep.
1	0.8	0.5	61	51.2	33.2	121	101.5	65.9	181	151.8	98.6	241	202.1	131.3
2	1.7	1.1	62	52.0	33.8	22	102.3	66.4	82	152.6	99.1	42	203.0	131.8
3	2.5	1.6	63	52.8	34.3	23	103.2	67.0	83	153.5	99.7	43	203.8	132.3
4	3.4	2.2	64	53.7	34.9	24	104.0	67.5	84	154.3	100.2	44	204.6	132.9
5	4.2	2.7	65	54.5	35.4	25	104.8	68.1	85	155.2	100.8	45	205.5	133.4
6	5.0	3.3	66	55.4	35.9	26	105.7	68.6	86	156.0	101.3	46	206.3	134.0
7	5.9	3.8	67	56.2	36.5	27	106.5	69.2	87	156.8	101.8	47	207.2	134.5
8	6.7	4.4	68	57.0	37.0	28	107.3	69.7	88	157.7	102.4	48	208.0	135.1
9	7.5	4.9	69	57.9	37.6	29	108.2	70.3	89	158.5	102.9	49	208.8	135.6
10	8.4	5.4	70	58.7	38.1	30	109.0	70.8	90	159.3	103.5	50	209.7	136.2
11	9.2	6.0	71	59.5	38.7	131	109.9	71.3	191	160.2	104.0	251	210.5	136.7
12	10.1	6.5	72	60.4	39.2	32	110.7	71.9	92	161.0	104.6	52	211.3	137.2
13	10.9	7.1	73	61.2	39.8	33	111.5	72.4	93	161.9	105.1	53	212.2	137.8
14	11.7	7.6	74	62.1	40.3	34	112.4	73.0	94	162.7	105.7	54	213.0	138.3
15	12.6	8.2	75	62.9	40.8	35	113.2	73.5	95	163.5	106.2	55	213.9	138.9
16	13.4	8.7	76	63.7	41.4	36	114.1	74.1	96	164.4	106.7	56	214.7	139.4
17	14.3	9.3	77	64.6	41.9	37	114.9	74.6	97	165.2	107.3	57	215.5	140.0
18	15.1	9.8	78	65.4	42.5	38	115.7	75.2	98	166.1	107.8	58	216.4	140.5
19	15.9	10.3	79	66.3	43.0	39	116.6	75.7	99	166.9	108.4	59	217.2	141.1
20	16.8	10.9	80	67.1	43.6	40	117.4	76.2	200	167.7	108.9	60	218.1	141.6
21	17.6	11.4	81	67.9	44.1	141	118.3	76.8	201	168.6	109.5	261	218.9	142.2
22	18.5	12.0	82	68.8	44.7	42	119.1	77.3	02	169.4	110.0	62	219.7	142.7
23	19.3	12.5	83	69.6	45.2	43	119.9	77.9	03	170.3	110.6	63	220.6	143.2
24	20.1	13.1	84	70.4	45.7	44	120.8	78.4	04	171.1	111.1	64	221.4	143.8
25	21.0	13.6	85	71.3	46.3	45	121.6	79.0	05	171.9	111.7	65	222.2	144.3
26	21.8	14.2	86	72.1	46.8	46	122.4	79.5	06	172.8	112.2	66	223.1	144.9
27	22.6	14.7	87	73.0	47.4	47	123.3	80.1	07	173.6	112.7	67	223.9	145.4
28	23.5	15.2	88	73.8	47.9	48	124.1	80.6	08	174.4	113.3	68	224.8	146.0
29	24.3	15.8	89	74.6	48.5	49	125.0	81.2	09	175.3	113.8	69	225.6	146.5
30	25.2	16.3	90	75.5	49.0	50	125.8	81.7	10	176.1	114.4	70	226.4	147.1
31	26.0	16.9	91	76.3	49.6	151	126.6	82.2	211	177.0	114.9	271	227.3	147.6
32	26.8	17.4	92	77.2	50.1	52	127.5	82.8	12	177.8	115.5	72	228.1	148.1
33	27.7	18.0	93	78.0	50.7	53	128.3	83.3	13	178.6	116.0	73	229.0	148.7
34	28.5	18.5	94	78.8	51.2	54	129.2	83.9	14	179.5	116.6	74	229.8	149.2
35	29.4	19.1	95	79.7	51.7	55	130.0	84.4	15	180.3	117.1	75	230.6	149.8
36	30.2	19.6	96	80.5	52.3	56	130.8	85.0	16	181.2	117.6	76	231.5	150.3
37	31.0	20.2	97	81.4	52.8	57	131.7	85.5	17	182.0	118.2	77	232.3	150.9
38	31.9	20.7	98	82.2	53.4	58	132.5	86.1	18	182.8	118.7	78	233.2	151.4
39	32.7	21.2	99	83.0	53.9	59	133.3	86.6	19	183.7	119.3	79	234.0	152.0
40	33.5	21.8	100	83.9	54.5	60	134.2	87.1	20	184.5	119.8	80	234.8	152.5
41	34.4	22.3	101	84.7	55.0	161	135.0	87.7	221	185.3	120.4	281	235.7	153.0
42	35.2	22.9	02	85.5	55.6	62	135.9	88.2	22	186.2	120.9	82	236.5	153.6
43	36.1	23.4	03	86.4	56.1	63	136.7	88.8	23	187.0	121.5	83	237.3	154.1
44	36.9	24.0	04	87.2	56.6	64	137.5	89.3	24	187.9	122.0	84	238.2	154.7
45	37.7	24.5	05	88.1	57.2	65	138.4	89.9	25	188.7	122.5	85	239.0	155.2
46	38.6	25.1	06	88.9	57.7	66	139.2	90.4	26	189.5	123.1	86	239.9	155.8
47	39.4	25.6	07	89.7	58.3	67	140.1	91.0	27	190.4	123.6	87	240.7	156.3
48	40.3	26.1	08	90.6	58.8	68	140.9	91.5	28	191.2	124.2	88	241.5	156.9
49	41.1	26.7	09	91.4	59.4	69	141.7	92.0	29	192.1	124.7	89	242.4	157.4
50	41.9	27.2	10	92.3	59.9	70	142.6	92.6	30	192.9	125.3	90	243.2	157.9
51	42.8	27.8	111	93.1	60.5	171	143.4	93.1	231	193.7	125.8	291	244.1	158.5
52	43.6	28.3	12	93.9	61.0	72	144.3	93.7	32	194.6	126.4	92	244.9	159.0
53	44.4	28.9	13	94.8	61.5	73	145.1	94.2	33	195.4	126.9	93	245.7	159.6
54	45.3	29.4	14	95.6	62.1	74	145.9	94.8	34	196.2	127.4	94	246.6	160.1
55	46.1	30.0	15	96.4	62.6	75	146.8	95.3	35	197.1	128.0	95	247.4	160.7
56	47.0	30.5	16	97.3	63.2	76	147.6	95.9	36	197.9	128.5	96	248.2	161.2
57	47.8	31.0	17	98.1	63.7	77	148.4	96.4	37	198.8	129.1	97	249.1	161.8
58	48.6	31.6	18	99.0	64.3	78	149.3	96.9	38	199.6	129.6	98	249.9	162.3
59	49.5	32.1	19	99.8	64.8	79	150.1	97.5	39	200.4	130.2	99	250.8	162.8
60	50.3	32.7	20	100.6	65.4	80	151.0	98.0	40	201.3	130.7	300	251.6	163.4
Dist.	Dep.	Lat.	Dist.	Dep.	Lat.	Dist.	Dep.	Lat.	Dist.	Dep.	Lat.	Dist.	Dep.	Lat.

57° (123°, 237°, 303°).

In **Plane Sailing.**	**Dist.**	**Lat.**	**Dep.**
For converting *Dep.* into *Diff. Long.* and *Diff. Long.* into *Dep.* In **Middle Latitude Sailing.**	Diff. Long.	Dep.	
For converting *Dep.* into *Diff. Long.* and *Diff. Long.* into *Dep.* In **Mercator Sailing.**		*m*	Diff. Long.
For multiplication of numbers by sines and by cosines, or solution of plane right-angled triangles.	N.	N×Cos.	N×Sin.
	Hypotenuse.	Side Adj.	Side Opp.

TABLE 3.

Difference of Latitude and Departure for 33° (147°, 213°, 327°).

Dist.	Lat.	Dep.	Dist.	Lat.	Dep.	Dist.	Lat.	Dep.	Dist.	Lat.	Dep.	Dist.	Lat.	Dep.
301	252.4	163.9	361	302.8	196.6	421	353.1	229.3	481	403.4	262.0	541	453.7	294.6
02	253.3	164.5	62	303.6	197.2	22	353.9	229.8	82	404.2	262.5	42	454.6	295.2
03	254.1	165.0	63	304.4	197.7	23	354.8	230.4	83	405.1	263.1	43	455.4	295.7
04	255.0	165.6	64	305.3	198.2	24	355.6	230.9	84	405.9	263.6	44	456.2	296.3
05	255.8	166.1	65	306.1	198.8	25	356.4	231.5	85	406.8	264.1	45	457.1	296.8
06	256.6	166.7	66	307.0	199.3	26	357.3	232.0	86	407.6	264.7	46	457.9	297.4
07	257.5	167.2	67	307.8	199.9	27	358.1	232.6	87	408.4	265.2	47	458.8	297.9
08	258.3	167.7	68	308.6	200.4	28	359.0	233.1	88	409.3	265.8	48	459.6	298.5
09	259.1	168.3	69	309.5	201.0	29	359.8	233.7	89	410.1	266.3	49	460.4	299.0
10	260.0	168.8	70	310.3	201.5	30	360.6	234.2	90	410.9	266.9	50	461.3	299.6
311	260.8	169.4	371	311.1	202.1	431	361.5	234.7	491	411.8	267.4	551	462.1	300.1
12	261.7	169.9	72	312.0	202.6	32	362.3	235.3	92	412.6	268.0	52	462.9	300.6
13	262.5	170.5	73	312.8	203.2	33	363.1	235.8	93	413.5	268.5	53	463.8	301.2
14	263.3	171.0	74	313.7	203.7	34	364.0	236.4	94	414.3	269.0	54	464.6	301.7
15	264.2	171.6	75	314.5	204.2	35	364.8	236.9	95	415.1	269.6	55	465.5	302.3
16	265.0	172.1	76	315.3	204.7	36	365.7	237.5	96	416.0	270.1	56	466.3	302.8
17	265.9	172.7	77	316.2	205.3	37	366.5	238.0	97	416.8	270.7	57	467.1	303.4
18	266.7	173.2	78	317.0	205.9	38	367.3	238.6	98	417.7	271.2	58	468.0	303.9
19	267.5	173.7	79	317.9	206.4	39	368.2	239.1	99	418.5	271.8	59	468.8	304.5
20	268.4	174.3	80	318.7	207.0	40	369.0	239.6	500	419.3	272.3	60	469.7	305.0
321	269.2	174.8	381	319.5	207.5	441	369.9	240.2	501	420.2	272.9	561	470.5	305.5
22	270.1	175.4	82	320.4	208.1	42	370.7	240.7	02	421.0	273.4	62	471.3	306.1
23	270.9	175.9	83	321.2	208.6	43	371.5	241.3	03	421.9	274.0	63	472.2	306.6
24	271.7	176.5	84	322.0	209.1	44	372.4	241.8	04	422.7	274.5	64	473.0	307.2
25	272.6	177.0	85	322.9	209.7	45	373.2	242.4	05	423.5	275.0	65	473.8	307.7
26	273.4	177.6	86	323.7	210.2	46	374.0	242.9	06	424.4	275.6	66	474.7	308.3
27	274.2	178.1	87	324.6	210.8	47	374.9	243.5	07	425.2	276.1	67	475.5	308.8
28	275.1	178.6	88	325.4	211.3	48	375.7	244.0	08	426.0	276.7	68	476.4	309.4
29	275.9	179.2	89	326.2	211.9	49	376.6	244.5	09	426.9	277.2	69	477.2	309.9
30	276.8	179.7	90	327.1	212.4	50	377.4	245.1	10	427.7	277.8	70	478.0	310.4
331	277.6	180.3	391	327.9	213.0	451	378.2	245.6	511	428.6	278.3	571	478.9	311.0
32	278.4	180.8	92	328.8	213.5	52	379.1	246.2	12	429.4	278.9	72	479.7	311.5
33	279.3	181.4	93	329.6	214.0	53	379.9	246.7	13	430.2	279.4	73	480.6	312.1
34	280.1	181.9	94	330.4	214.6	54	380.8	247.3	14	431.1	279.9	74	481.4	312.6
35	281.0	182.5	95	331.3	215.1	55	381.6	247.8	15	431.9	280.5	75	482.2	313.2
36	281.8	183.0	96	332.1	215.7	56	382.4	248.4	16	432.8	281.0	76	483.1	313.7
37	282.6	183.5	97	333.0	216.2	57	383.3	248.9	17	433.6	281.6	77	483.9	314.3
38	283.5	184.1	98	333.8	216.8	58	384.1	249.4	18	434.4	282.1	78	484.8	314.8
39	284.3	184.6	99	334.6	217.3	59	384.9	250.0	19	435.3	282.7	79	485.6	315.3
40	285.1	185.2	400	335.5	217.9	60	385.8	250.5	20	436.1	283.2	80	486.4	315.9
341	286.0	185.7	401	336.3	218.4	461	386.6	251.1	521	436.9	283.8	581	487.3	316.4
42	286.8	186.3	02	337.1	218.9	62	387.5	251.6	22	437.8	284.3	82	488.1	317.0
43	287.7	186.8	03	338.0	219.5	63	388.3	252.2	23	438.6	284.8	83	488.9	317.5
44	288.5	187.4	04	338.8	220.0	64	389.1	252.7	24	439.5	285.4	84	489.8	318.1
45	289.3	187.9	05	339.7	220.6	65	390.0	253.3	25	440.3	285.9	85	490.6	318.6
46	290.2	188.4	06	340.5	221.1	66	390.8	253.8	26	441.1	286.5	86	491.5	319.2
47	291.0	189.0	07	341.3	221.7	67	391.7	254.3	27	442.0	287.0	87	492.3	319.7
48	291.9	189.5	08	342.2	222.2	68	392.5	254.9	28	442.8	287.6	88	493.1	320.2
49	292.7	190.1	09	343.0	222.8	69	393.3	255.4	29	443.7	288.1	89	494.0	320.8
50	293.5	190.6	10	343.9	223.3	70	394.2	256.0	30	444.5	288.7	90	494.8	321.3
351	294.4	191.2	411	344.7	223.8	471	395.0	256.5	531	445.3	289.2	591	495.7	321.9
52	295.2	191.7	12	345.5	224.4	72	395.9	257.1	32	446.2	289.7	92	496.5	322.4
53	296.1	192.3	13	346.4	224.9	73	396.7	257.6	33	447.0	290.3	93	497.3	323.0
54	296.9	192.8	14	347.2	225.5	74	397.5	258.2	34	447.9	290.8	94	498.2	323.5
55	297.7	193.3	15	348.0	226.0	75	398.4	258.7	35	448.7	291.4	95	499.0	324.1
56	298.6	193.9	16	348.9	226.6	76	399.2	259.2	36	449.5	291.9	96	499.8	324.6
57	299.4	194.4	17	349.7	227.1	77	400.0	259.8	37	450.4	292.5	97	500.7	325.1
58	300.2	195.0	18	350.6	227.7	78	400.9	260.3	38	451.2	293.0	98	501.5	325.7
59	301.1	195.5	19	351.4	228.2	79	401.7	260.9	39	452.0	293.6	99	502.4	326.2
60	301.9	196.1	20	352.2	228.7	80	402.6	261.4	40	452.9	294.1	600	503.2	326.8
Dist.	Dep.	Lat.	Dist.	Dep.	Lat.	Dist.	Dep.	Lat.	Dist.	Dep.	Lat.	Dist.	Dep.	Lat.

57° (123°, 237°, 303°).

In **Plane Sailing**.	Dist.	Lat.	Dep.
For converting *Dep.* into *Diff. Long.* and *Diff. Long.* into *Dep.* In **Middle Latitude Sailing**.	Diff. Long.	Dep.	
For converting *Dep.* into *Diff. Long.* and *Diff. Long.* into *Dep.* In **Mercator Sailing**.		*m*	Diff. Long.
For multiplication of numbers by sines and by cosines, or solution of plane right-angled triangles.	N. Hypotenuse.	N×Cos. Side Adj.	N×Sin. Side Opp.

TABLE 3.

Difference of Latitude and Departure for 34° (146°, 214°, 326°).

Dist.	Lat.	Dep.	Dist.	Lat.	Dep.	Dist.	Lat.	Dep.	Dist.	Lat.	Dep.	Dist.	Lat.	Dep.
1	0.8	0.6	61	50.6	34.1	121	100.3	67.7	181	150.1	101.2	241	199.8	134.8
2	1.7	1.1	62	51.4	34.7	22	101.1	68.2	82	150.9	101.8	42	200.6	135.3
3	2.5	1.7	63	52.2	35.2	23	102.0	68.8	83	151.7	102.3	43	201.5	135.9
4	3.3	2.2	64	53.1	35.8	24	102.8	69.3	84	152.5	102.9	44	202.3	136.4
5	4.1	2.8	65	53.9	36.3	25	103.6	69.9	85	153.4	103.5	45	203.1	137.0
6	5.0	3.4	66	54.7	36.9	26	104.5	70.5	86	154.2	104.0	46	203.9	137.6
7	5.8	3.9	67	55.5	37.5	27	105.3	71.0	87	155.0	104.6	47	204.8	138.1
8	6.6	4.5	68	56.4	38.0	28	106.1	71.6	88	155.9	105.1	48	205.6	138.7
9	7.5	5.0	69	57.2	38.6	29	106.9	72.1	89	156.7	105.7	49	206.4	139.2
10	8.3	5.6	70	58.0	39.1	30	107.8	72.7	90	157.5	106.2	50	207.3	139.8
11	9.1	6.2	71	58.9	39.7	131	108.6	73.3	191	158.3	106.8	251	208.1	140.4
12	9.9	6.7	72	59.7	40.3	32	109.4	73.8	92	159.2	107.4	52	208.9	140.9
13	10.8	7.3	73	60.5	40.8	33	110.3	74.4	93	160.0	107.9	53	209.7	141.5
14	11.6	7.8	74	61.3	41.4	34	111.1	74.9	94	160.8	108.5	54	210.6	142.0
15	12.4	8.4	75	62.2	41.9	35	111.9	75.5	95	161.7	109.0	55	211.4	142.6
16	13.3	8.9	76	63.0	42.5	36	112.7	76.1	96	162.5	109.6	56	212.2	143.2
17	14.1	9.5	77	63.8	43.1	37	113.6	76.6	97	163.3	110.2	57	213.1	143.7
18	14.9	10.1	78	64.7	43.6	38	114.4	77.2	98	164.1	110.7	58	213.9	144.3
19	15.8	10.6	79	65.5	44.2	39	115.2	77.7	99	165.0	111.3	59	214.7	144.8
20	16.6	11.2	80	66.3	44.7	40	116.1	78.3	200	165.8	111.8	60	215.5	145.4
21	17.4	11.7	81	67.2	45.3	141	116.9	78.8	201	166.6	112.4	261	216.4	145.9
22	18.2	12.3	82	68.0	45.9	42	117.7	79.4	02	167.5	113.0	62	217.2	146.5
23	19.1	12.9	83	68.8	46.4	43	118.6	80.0	03	168.3	113.5	63	218.0	147.1
24	19.9	13.4	84	69.6	47.0	44	119.4	80.5	04	169.1	114.1	64	218.9	147.6
25	20.7	14.0	85	70.5	47.5	45	120.2	81.1	05	170.0	114.6	65	219.7	148.2
26	21.6	14.5	86	71.3	48.1	46	121.0	81.6	06	170.8	115.2	66	220.5	148.7
27	22.4	15.1	87	72.1	48.6	47	121.9	82.2	07	171.6	115.8	67	221.4	149.3
28	23.2	15.7	88	73.0	49.2	48	122.7	82.8	08	172.4	116.3	68	222.2	149.9
29	24.0	16.2	89	73.8	49.8	49	123.5	83.3	09	173.3	116.9	69	223.0	150.4
30	24.9	16.8	90	74.6	50.3	50	124.4	83.9	10	174.1	117.4	70	223.8	151.0
31	25.7	17.3	91	75.4	50.9	151	125.2	84.4	211	174.9	118.0	271	224.7	151.5
32	26.5	17.9	92	76.3	51.4	52	126.0	85.0	12	175.8	118.5	72	225.5	152.1
33	27.4	18.5	93	77.1	52.0	53	126.8	85.6	13	176.6	119.1	73	226.3	152.7
34	28.2	19.0	94	77.9	52.6	54	127.7	86.1	14	177.4	119.7	74	227.2	153.2
35	29.0	19.6	95	78.8	53.1	55	128.5	86.7	15	178.2	120.2	75	228.0	153.8
36	29.8	20.1	96	79.6	53.7	56	129.3	87.2	16	179.1	120.8	76	228.8	154.3
37	30.7	20.7	97	80.4	54.2	57	130.2	87.8	17	179.9	121.3	77	229.6	154.9
38	31.5	21.2	98	81.2	54.8	58	131.0	88.4	18	180.7	121.9	78	230.5	155.5
39	32.3	21.8	99	82.1	55.4	59	131.8	88.9	19	181.6	122.5	79	231.3	156.0
40	33.2	22.4	100	82.9	55.9	60	132.3	89.5	20	182.4	123.0	80	232.1	156.6
41	34.0	22.9	101	83.7	56.5	161	133.5	90.0	221	183.2	123.6	281	233.0	157.1
42	34.8	23.5	02	84.6	57.0	62	134.3	90.6	22	184.0	124.1	82	233.8	157.7
43	35.6	24.0	03	85.4	57.6	63	135.1	91.1	23	184.9	124.7	83	234.6	158.3
44	36.5	24.6	04	86.2	58.2	64	136.0	91.7	24	185.7	125.3	84	235.4	158.8
45	37.3	25.2	05	87.0	58.7	65	136.8	92.3	25	186.5	125.8	85	236.3	159.4
46	38.1	25.7	06	87.9	59.3	66	137.6	92.8	26	187.4	126.4	86	237.1	159.9
47	39.0	26.3	07	88.7	59.8	67	138.4	93.4	27	188.2	126.9	87	237.9	160.5
48	39.8	26.8	08	89.5	60.4	68	139.3	93.9	28	189.0	127.5	88	238.8	161.0
49	40.3	27.4	09	90.4	61.0	69	140.1	94.5	29	189.8	128.1	89	239.6	161.6
50	41.5	28.0	10	91.2	61.5	70	140.9	95.1	30	190.7	128.6	90	240.4	162.2
51	42.3	28.5	111	92.0	62.1	171	141.8	95.6	231	191.5	129.2	291	241.2	162.7
52	43.1	29.1	12	92.9	62.6	72	142.6	96.2	32	192.3	129.7	92	242.1	163.3
53	43.9	29.6	13	93.7	63.2	73	143.4	96.7	33	193.2	130.3	93	242.9	163.8
54	44.8	30.2	14	94.5	63.7	74	144.3	97.3	34	194.0	130.9	94	243.7	164.4
55	45.6	30.8	15	95.3	64.3	75	145.1	97.9	35	194.8	131.4	95	244.6	165.0
56	46.4	31.3	16	96.2	64.9	76	145.9	98.4	36	195.7	132.0	96	245.4	165.5
57	47.3	31.9	17	97.0	65.4	77	146.7	99.0	37	196.5	132.5	97	246.2	166.1
58	48.1	32.4	18	97.8	66.0	78	147.6	99.5	38	197.3	133.1	98	247.1	166.6
59	48.9	33.0	19	98.7	66.5	79	148.4	100.1	39	198.1	133.6	99	247.9	167.2
60	49.7	33.6	20	99.5	67.1	80	149.2	100.7	40	199.0	134.2	300	248.7	167.8
Dist.	Dep.	Lat.	Dist.	Dep.	Lat.	Dist.	Dep.	Lat.	Dist.	Dep.	Lat.	Dist.	Dep.	Lat.

56° (124°, 236°, 304°).

In Plane Sailing.	Dist.	Lat.	Dep.
For converting *Dep.* into *Diff. Long.* and *Diff. Long.* into *Dep.* In **Middle Latitude Sailing.**	Diff. Long.	Dep.	
For converting *Dep.* into *Diff. Long.* and *Diff. Long.* into *Dep.* In **Mercator Sailing.**		*m*	Diff. Long.
For multiplication of numbers by sines and by cosines, or solution of plane right-angled triangles.	N. Hypotenuse.	N×Cos. Side. Adj.	N×Sin. Side Opp.

TABLE 3.

Difference of Latitude and Departure for 34° (146°, 214°, 326°).

Dist.	Lat.	Dep.	Dist.	Lat.	Dep.	Dist.	Lat.	Dep.	Dist.	Lat.	Dep.	Dist.	Lat.	Dep.
301	249.5	168.3	361	299.3	201.9	421	349.0	235.4	481	398.8	269.0	541	448.5	302.5
02	250.4	168.9	62	300.1	202.4	22	349.9	236.0	82	399.6	269.5	42	449.3	303.1
03	251.2	169.4	63	300.9	203.0	23	350.7	236.5	83	400.4	270.1	43	450.2	303.6
04	252.0	170.0	64	301.8	203.5	24	351.5	237.1	84	401.3	270.6	44	451.0	304.2
05	252.9	170.6	65	302.6	204.1	25	352.3	237.7	85	402.1	271.2	45	451.8	304.8
06	253.7	171.1	66	303.4	204.7	26	353.2	238.2	86	402.9	271.8	46	452.7	305.3
07	254.5	171.7	67	304.3	205.2	27	354.0	238.8	87	403.7	272.3	47	453.5	305.9
08	255.3	172.2	68	305.1	205.8	28	354.8	239.3	88	404.6	272.9	48	454.3	306.4
09	256.2	172.8	69	305.9	206.3	29	355.7	239.9	89	405.4	273.4	49	455.1	307.0
10	257.0	173.3	70	306.7	206.9	30	356.5	240.5	90	406.2	274.0	50	456.0	307.6
311	257.8	173.9	371	307.6	207.5	431	357.3	241.0	491	407.1	274.6	551	456.8	308.1
12	258.7	174.5	72	308.4	208.0	32	358.1	241.6	92	407.9	275.1	52	457.6	308.7
13	259.5	175.0	73	309.2	208.6	33	359.0	242.1	93	408.7	275.7	53	458.5	309.2
14	260.3	175.6	74	310.1	209.1	34	359.8	242.7	94	409.5	276.2	54	459.3	309.8
15	261.1	176.1	75	310.9	209.7	35	360.6	243.2	95	410.4	276.8	55	460.1	310.4
16	262.0	176.7	76	311.7	210.3	36	361.5	243.8	96	411.2	277.4	56	460.9	310.9
17	262.8	177.3	77	312.5	210.8	37	362.3	244.4	97	412.0	277.9	57	461.8	311.5
18	263.6	177.8	78	313.4	211.4	38	363.1	244.9	98	412.9	278.5	58	462.6	312.0
19	264.5	178.4	79	314.2	211.9	39	364.0	245.5	99	413.7	279.0	59	463.4	312.6
20	265.3	178.9	80	315.0	212.5	40	364.8	246.0	500	414.5	279.6	60	464.3	313.1
321	266.1	179.5	381	315.9	213.1	441	365.6	246.6	501	415.3	280.2	561	465.1	313.7
22	267.0	180.1	82	316.7	213.6	42	366.4	247.2	02	416.2	280.7	62	465.9	314.3
23	267.8	180.6	83	317.5	214.2	43	367.3	247.7	03	417.0	281.3	63	466.7	314.8
24	268.6	181.2	84	318.4	214.7	44	368.1	248.3	04	417.8	281.8	64	467.6	315.5
25	269.4	181.7	85	319.2	215.3	45	368.9	248.8	05	418.7	282.4	65	468.4	315.9
26	270.3	182.3	86	320.0	215.8	46	369.8	249.4	06	419.5	283.0	66	469.2	316.5
27	271.1	182.9	87	320.8	216.4	47	370.6	250.0	07	420.3	283.5	67	470.1	317.1
28	271.9	183.4	88	321.7	217.0	48	371.4	250.5	08	421.2	284.1	68	470.9	317.6
29	272.8	184.0	89	322.5	217.5	49	372.2	251.1	09	422.0	284.6	69	471.7	318.2
30	273.6	184.5	90	323.3	218.1	50	373.1	251.6	10	422.8	285.2	70	472.6	318.7
331	274.4	185.1	391	324.2	218.6	451	373.9	252.2	511	423.6	285.9	571	473.4	319.3
32	275.2	185.7	92	325.0	219.2	52	374.7	252.8	12	424.5	286.3	72	474.2	319.9
33	276.1	186.2	93	325.8	219.8	53	375.6	253.3	13	425.3	286.9	73	475.0	320.4
34	276.9	186.8	94	326.6	220.3	54	376.4	253.9	14	426.1	287.4	74	475.9	321.0
35	277.7	187.3	95	327.5	220.9	55	377.2	254.4	15	427.0	288.0	75	476.7	321.5
36	278.6	187.9	96	328.3	221.4	56	378.0	255.0	16	427.8	288.5	76	477.5	322.1
37	279.4	188.4	97	329.1	222.0	57	378.9	255.6	17	428.6	289.1	77	478.4	322.7
38	280.2	189.0	98	330.0	222.6	58	379.7	256.1	18	429.4	289.7	78	479.2	323.2
39	281.0	189.6	99	330.8	223.1	59	380.5	256.7	19	430.3	290.2	79	480.0	323.8
40	281.9	190.1	400	331.6	223.7	60	381.4	257.2	20	431.1	290.8	80	480.8	324.3
341	282.7	190.7	401	332.4	224.2	461	382.2	257.8	521	431.9	291.3	581	481.7	324.9
42	283.5	191.2	02	333.3	224.8	62	383.0	258.3	22	432.8	291.9	82	482.5	325.4
43	284.4	191.8	03	334.1	225.4	63	383.8	258.9	23	433.6	292.5	83	483.3	326.0
44	285.2	192.4	04	334.9	225.9	64	384.7	259.5	24	434.4	293.0	84	484.2	326.6
45	286.0	192.9	05	335.8	226.5	65	385.5	260.0	25	435.2	293.6	85	485.0	327.1
46	286.8	193.5	06	336.6	227.0	66	386.3	260.6	26	436.1	294.1	86	485.8	327.7
47	287.7	194.0	07	337.4	227.6	67	387.2	261.1	27	436.9	294.7	87	486.6	328.2
48	288.5	194.6	08	338.2	228.2	68	388.0	261.7	28	437.7	295.3	88	487.5	328.8
49	289.3	195.2	09	339.1	228.7	69	388.8	262.3	29	438.6	295.8	89	488.3	329.4
50	290.2	195.7	10	339.9	229.3	70	389.6	262.8	30	439.4	296.4	90	489.1	329.9
351	291.0	196.3	411	340.7	229.8	471	390.5	263.4	531	440.2	296.9	591	490.0	330.5
52	291.8	196.8	12	341.6	230.4	72	391.3	263.9	32	441.0	297.5	92	490.8	331.0
53	292.7	197.4	13	342.4	230.9	73	392.1	264.5	33	441.9	298.0	93	491.6	331.6
54	293.5	198.0	14	343.2	231.5	74	393.0	265.1	34	442.7	298.6	94	492.4	332.2
55	294.3	198.5	15	344.1	232.1	75	393.8	265.6	35	443.5	299.2	95	493.3	332.7
56	295.1	199.1	16	344.9	232.6	76	394.6	266.2	36	444.4	299.7	96	494.1	333.3
57	296.0	199.6	17	345.7	233.2	77	395.5	266.7	37	445.3	300.3	97	494.9	333.8
58	296.8	200.2	18	346.5	233.7	78	396.3	267.3	38	446.0	300.8	98	495.8	334.4
59	297.6	200.8	19	347.4	234.3	79	397.1	267.9	39	446.9	301.4	99	496.6	335.0
60	298.5	201.3	20	348.2	234.9	80	397.9	268.4	40	447.7	302.0	600	497.4	335.5
Dist.	Dep.	Lat.	Dist.	Dep.	Lat.	Dist.	Dep.	Lat.	Dist.	Dep.	Lat.	Dist.	Dep.	Lat.

56° (124°, 236°, 304°).

In Plane Sailing.	Dist.	Lat.	Dep.
For converting *Dep.* into *Diff. Long.* and *Diff. Long.* into *Dep.* **In Middle Latitude Sailing.**	Diff. Long.	Dep.	
For converting *Dep.* into *Diff. Long.* and *Diff. Long.* into *Dep.* **In Mercator Sailing.**		*m*	Diff. Long.
For multiplication of numbers by sines and by cosines, or solution of plane right-angled triangles.	N. / Hypotenuse.	N×Cos. / Side Adj.	N×Sin. / Side Opp.

TABLE 3.

Difference of Latitude and Departure for 35° (145°, 215°, 325°).

Dist.	Lat.	Dep.	Dist.	Lat.	Dep.	Dist.	Lat.	Dep.	Dist.	Lat.	Dep.	Dist.	Lat.	Dep.
1	0.8	0.6	61	50.0	35.0	121	99.1	69.4	181	148.3	103.8	241	197.4	138.2
2	1.6	1.1	62	50.8	35.6	22	99.9	70.0	82	149.1	104.4	42	198.2	138.8
3	2.5	1.7	63	51.6	36.1	23	100.8	70.5	83	149.9	105.0	43	199.1	139.4
4	3.3	2.3	64	52.4	36.7	24	101.6	71.1	84	150.7	105.5	44	199.9	140.0
5	4.1	2.9	65	53.2	37.3	25	102.4	71.7	85	151.5	106.1	45	200.7	140.5
6	4.9	3.4	66	54.1	37.9	26	103.2	72.3	86	152.4	106.7	46	201.5	141.1
7	5.7	4.0	67	54.9	38.4	27	104.0	72.8	87	153.2	107.3	47	202.3	141.7
8	6.6	4.6	68	55.7	39.0	28	104.9	73.4	88	154.0	107.8	48	203.1	142.2
9	7.4	5.2	69	56.5	39.6	29	105.7	74.0	89	154.8	108.4	49	204.0	142.8
10	8.2	5.7	70	57.3	40.2	30	106.5	74.6	90	155.6	109.0	50	204.8	143.4
11	9.0	6.3	71	58.2	40.7	131	107.3	75.1	191	156.5	109.6	251	205.6	144.0
12	9.8	6.9	72	59.0	41.3	32	108.1	75.7	92	157.3	110.1	52	206.4	144.5
13	10.6	7.5	73	59.8	41.9	33	108.9	76.3	93	158.1	110.7	53	207.2	145.1
14	11.5	8.0	74	60.6	42.4	34	109.8	76.9	94	158.9	111.3	54	208.1	145.7
15	12.3	8.6	75	61.4	43.0	35	110.6	77.4	95	159.7	111.8	55	208.9	146.3
16	13.1	9.2	76	62.3	43.6	36	111.4	78.0	96	160.6	112.4	56	209.7	146.8
17	13.9	9.8	77	63.1	44.2	37	112.2	78.6	97	161.4	113.0	57	210.5	147.4
18	14.7	10.3	78	63.9	44.7	38	113.0	79.2	98	162.2	113.6	58	211.3	148.0
19	15.6	10.9	79	64.7	45.3	39	113.9	79.7	99	163.0	114.1	59	212.2	148.6
20	16.4	11.5	80	65.5	45.9	40	114.7	80.3	200	163.8	114.7	60	213.0	149.1
21	17.2	12.0	81	66.4	46.5	141	115.5	80.9	201	164.6	115.3	261	213.8	149.7
22	18.0	12.6	82	67.2	47.0	42	116.3	81.4	02	165.5	115.9	62	214.6	150.3
23	18.8	13.2	83	68.0	47.6	43	117.1	82.0	03	166.3	116.4	63	215.4	150.9
24	19.7	13.8	84	68.8	48.2	44	118.0	82.6	04	167.1	117.0	64	216.3	151.4
25	20.5	14.3	85	69.6	48.8	45	118.8	83.2	05	167.9	117.6	65	217.1	152.0
26	21.3	14.9	86	70.4	49.3	46	119.6	83.7	06	168.7	118.2	66	217.9	152.6
27	22.1	15.5	87	71.3	49.9	47	120.4	84.3	07	169.6	118.7	67	218.7	153.1
28	22.9	16.1	88	72.1	50.5	48	121.2	84.9	08	170.4	119.3	68	219.5	153.7
29	23.8	16.6	89	72.9	51.0	49	122.1	85.5	09	171.2	119.9	69	220.4	154.3
30	24.6	17.2	90	73.7	51.6	50	122.9	86.0	10	172.0	120.5	70	221.2	154.9
31	25.4	17.8	91	74.5	52.2	151	123.7	86.6	211	172.8	121.0	271	222.0	155.4
32	26.2	18.4	92	75.4	52.8	52	124.5	87.2	12	173.7	121.6	72	222.8	156.0
33	27.0	18.9	93	76.2	53.3	53	125.3	87.8	13	174.5	122.2	73	223.6	156.6
34	27.9	19.5	94	77.0	53.9	54	126.1	88.3	14	175.3	122.7	74	224.4	157.2
35	28.7	20.1	95	77.8	54.5	55	127.0	88.9	15	176.1	123.3	75	225.3	157.7
36	29.5	20.6	96	78.6	55.1	56	127.8	89.5	16	176.9	123.9	76	226.1	158.3
37	30.3	21.2	97	79.5	55.6	57	128.6	90.1	17	177.8	124.5	77	226.9	158.9
38	31.1	21.8	98	80.3	56.2	58	129.4	90.6	18	178.6	125.0	78	227.7	159.5
39	31.9	22.4	99	81.1	56.8	59	130.2	91.2	19	179.4	125.6	79	228.5	160.0
40	32.8	22.9	100	81.9	57.4	60	131.1	91.8	20	180.2	126.2	80	229.4	160.6
41	33.6	23.5	101	82.7	57.9	161	131.9	92.3	221	181.0	126.8	281	230.2	161.2
42	34.4	24.1	02	83.6	58.5	62	132.7	92.9	22	181.9	127.3	82	231.0	161.7
43	35.2	24.7	03	84.4	59.1	63	133.5	93.5	23	182.7	127.9	83	231.8	162.3
44	36.0	25.2	04	85.2	59.7	64	134.3	94.1	24	183.5	128.5	84	232.6	162.9
45	36.9	25.8	05	86.0	60.2	65	135.2	94.6	25	184.3	129.1	85	233.5	163.5
46	37.7	26.4	06	86.8	60.8	66	136.0	95.2	26	185.1	129.6	86	234.3	164.0
47	38.5	27.0	07	87.6	61.4	67	136.8	95.8	27	185.9	130.2	87	235.1	164.6
48	39.3	27.5	08	88.5	61.9	68	137.6	96.4	28	186.8	130.8	88	235.9	165.2
49	40.1	28.1	09	89.3	62.5	69	138.4	96.9	29	187.6	131.3	89	236.7	165.8
50	41.0	28.7	10	90.1	63.1	70	139.3	97.5	30	188.4	131.9	90	237.6	166.3
51	41.8	29.3	111	90.9	63.7	171	140.1	98.1	231	189.2	132.5	291	238.4	166.9
52	42.6	29.8	12	91.7	64.2	72	140.9	98.7	32	190.0	133.1	92	239.2	167.5
53	43.4	30.4	13	92.6	64.8	73	141.7	99.2	33	190.9	133.6	93	240.0	168.1
54	44.2	31.0	14	93.4	65.4	74	142.5	99.8	34	191.7	134.2	94	240.8	168.6
55	45.1	31.5	15	94.2	66.0	75	143.4	100.4	35	192.5	134.8	95	241.6	169.2
56	45.9	32.1	16	95.0	66.5	76	144.2	100.9	36	193.3	135.4	96	242.5	169.8
57	46.7	32.7	17	95.8	67.1	77	145.0	101.5	37	194.1	135.9	97	243.3	170.4
58	47.5	33.3	18	96.7	67.7	78	145.8	102.1	38	195.0	136.5	98	244.1	170.9
59	48.3	33.8	19	97.5	68.3	79	146.6	102.7	39	195.8	137.1	99	244.9	171.5
60	49.1	34.4	20	98.3	68.8	80	147.4	103.2	40	196.6	137.7	300	245.7	172.1
Dist.	Dep.	Lat.	Dist.	Dep.	Lat.	Dist.	Dep.	Lat.	Dist.	Dep.	Lat.	Dist.	Dep.	Lat.

55° (125°, 235°, 305°).

In Plane Sailing.	**Dist.**	**Lat.**	**Dep.**
For converting *Dep.* into *Diff. Long.* and *Diff. Long.* into *Dep.* **In Middle Latitude Sailing.**	Diff. Long.	Dep.	
For converting *Dep.* into *Diff. Long.* and *Diff. Long.* into *Dep.* **In Mercator Sailing.**		*m*	Diff Long.
For multiplication of numbers by sines and by cosines, or solution of plane right-angled triangles.	N. Hypotenuse.	N×Cos. Side Adj.	N×Sin. Side Opp.

Difference of Latitude and Departure for 35° (145°, 215°, 325°).

Dist.	Lat.	Dep.	Dist.	Lat.	Dep.	Dist.	Lat.	Dep.	Dist.	Lat.	Dep.	Dist.	Lat.	Dep.
301	246. 6	172. 6	361	295. 7	207. 1	421	344. 9	241. 5	481	394. 0	275. 9	541	443. 2	310. 3
02	247. 4	173. 2	62	296. 5	207. 6	22	345. 7	242. 0	82	394. 8	276. 5	42	444. 0	310. 9
03	248. 2	173. 8	63	297. 4	208. 2	23	346. 5	242. 6	83	395. 7	277. 0	43	444. 8	311. 5
04	249. 0	174. 4	64	298. 2	208. 8	24	347. 3	243. 2	84	396. 5	277. 6	44	445. 6	312. 0
05	249. 8	174. 9	65	299. 0	209. 4	25	348. 1	243. 8	85	397. 3	278. 2	45	446. 4	312. 6
06	250. 7	175. 5	66	299. 8	209. 9	26	349. 0	244. 3	86	398. 1	278. 8	46	447. 3	313. 2
07	251. 5	176. 1	67	300. 6	210. 5	27	349. 8	244. 9	87	398. 9	279. 3	47	448. 1	313. 7
08	252. 3	176. 7	68	301. 4	211. 1	28	350. 6	245. 5	88	399. 7	279. 9	48	448. 9	314. 3
09	253. 1	177. 2	69	302. 3	211. 6	29	351. 4	246. 1	89	400. 6	280. 5	49	449. 7	314. 9
10	253. 9	177. 8	70	303. 1	212. 2	30	352. 2	246. 6	90	401. 4	281. 1	50	450. 5	315. 5
311	254. 8	178. 4	371	303. 9	212. 8	431	353. 1	247. 2	491	402. 2	281. 6	551	451. 4	316. 0
12	255. 6	179. 0	72	304. 7	213. 4	32	353. 9	247. 8	92	403. 0	282. 2	52	452. 2	316. 6
13	256. 4	179. 5	73	305. 5	213. 9	33	354. 7	248. 4	93	403. 8	282. 8	53	453. 0	317. 2
14	257. 2	180. 1	74	306. 4	214. 5	34	355. 5	248. 9	94	404. 7	283. 3	54	453. 8	317. 8
15	258. 0	180. 7	75	307. 2	215. 1	35	356. 3	249. 5	95	405. 5	283. 9	55	454. 6	318. 3
16	258. 9	181. 3	76	308. 0	215. 7	36	357. 2	250. 1	96	406. 3	284. 5	56	455. 4	318. 9
17	259. 7	181. 8	77	308. 8	216. 2	37	358. 0	250. 7	97	407. 1	285. 1	57	456. 3	319. 5
18	260. 5	182. 4	78	309. 6	216. 8	38	358. 8	251. 2	98	407. 9	285. 6	58	457. 1	320. 1
19	261. 3	183. 0	79	310. 5	217. 4	39	359. 6	251. 8	99	408. 8	286. 2	59	457. 9	320. 6
20	262. 1	183. 5	80	311. 3	218. 0	40	360. 4	252. 4	500	409. 6	286. 8	60	458. 7	321. 2
321	262. 9	184. 1	381	312. 1	218. 5	441	361. 2	252. 9	501	410. 4	287. 4	561	459. 5	321. 8
22	263. 8	184. 7	82	312. 9	219. 1	42	362. 1	253. 5	02	411. 2	287. 9	62	460. 4	322. 3
23	264. 6	185. 3	83	313. 7	219. 7	43	362. 9	254. 1	03	412. 0	288. 5	63	461. 2	322. 9
24	265. 4	185. 8	84	314. 6	220. 3	44	363. 7	254. 7	04	412. 9	289. 1	64	462. 0	323. 5
25	266. 2	186. 4	85	315. 4	220. 8	45	364. 5	255. 2	05	413. 7	289. 7	65	462. 8	324. 1
26	267. 0	187. 0	86	316. 2	221. 4	46	365. 3	255. 8	06	414. 5	290. 2	66	463. 6	324. 6
27	267. 9	187. 6	87	317. 0	222. 0	47	366. 2	256. 4	07	415. 3	290. 8	67	464. 5	325. 2
28	268. 7	188. 1	88	317. 8	222. 5	48	367. 0	257. 0	08	416. 1	291. 4	68	465. 3	325. 8
29	269. 5	188. 7	89	318. 7	223. 1	49	367. 8	257. 5	09	416. 9	292. 0	69	466. 1	326. 4
30	270. 3	189. 3	90	319. 5	223. 7	50	368. 6	258. 1	10	417. 8	292. 5	70	466. 9	326. 9
331	271. 1	189. 9	391	320. 3	224. 3	451	369. 4	258. 7	511	418. 6	293. 1	571	467. 7	327. 5
32	272. 0	190. 4	92	321. 1	224. 8	52	370. 3	259. 3	12	419. 4	293. 7	72	468. 6	328. 1
33	272. 8	191. 0	93	321. 9	225. 4	53	371. 1	259. 8	13	420. 2	294. 2	73	469. 4	328. 7
34	273. 6	191. 6	94	322. 7	226. 0	54	371. 9	260. 4	14	421. 0	294. 8	74	470. 2	329. 2
35	274. 4	192. 1	95	323. 6	226. 6	55	372. 7	261. 0	15	421. 9	295. 4	75	471. 0	329. 8
36	275. 2	192. 7	96	324. 4	227. 1	56	373. 5	261. 6	16	422. 7	296. 0	76	471. 8	330. 4
37	276. 1	193. 3	97	325. 2	227. 7	57	374. 4	262. 1	17	423. 5	296. 5	77	472. 7	331. 0
38	276. 9	193. 9	98	326. 0	228. 3	58	375. 2	262. 7	18	424. 3	297. 1	78	473. 5	331. 5
39	277. 7	194. 4	99	326. 8	228. 9	59	376. 0	263. 3	19	425. 1	297. 7	79	474. 3	332. 1
40	278. 5	195. 0	400	327. 7	229. 4	60	376. 8	263. 8	20	426. 0	298. 3	80	475. 1	332. 7
341	279. 3	195. 6	401	328. 5	230. 0	461	377. 6	264. 4	521	426. 8	298. 8	581	475. 9	333. 2
42	280. 1	196. 2	02	329. 3	230. 6	62	378. 4	265. 0	22	427. 6	299. 4	82	476. 7	333. 8
43	281. 0	196. 7	03	330. 1	231. 2	63	379. 3	265. 6	23	428. 4	300. 0	83	477. 6	334. 4
44	281. 8	197. 3	04	330. 9	231. 7	64	380. 1	266. 1	24	429. 2	300. 6	84	478. 4	335. 0
45	282. 6	197. 9	05	331. 8	232. 3	65	380. 9	266. 7	25	430. 1	301. 1	85	479. 2	335. 5
46	283. 4	198. 5	06	332. 6	232. 9	66	381. 7	267. 3	26	430. 9	301. 7	86	480. 0	336. 1
47	284. 2	199. 0	07	333. 4	233. 4	67	382. 5	267. 9	27	431. 7	302. 3	87	480. 8	336. 7
48	285. 1	199. 6	08	334. 2	234. 0	68	383. 4	268. 4	28	432. 5	302. 8	88	481. 7	337. 3
49	285. 9	200. 2	09	335. 0	234. 6	69	384. 2	269. 0	29	433. 3	303. 4	89	482. 5	337. 8
50	286. 7	200. 8	10	335. 9	235. 2	70	385. 0	269. 6	30	434. 2	304. 0	90	483. 3	338. 4
351	287. 5	201. 3	411	336. 7	235. 7	471	385. 8	270. 2	531	435. 0	304. 6	591	484. 1	339. 0
52	288. 3	201. 9	12	337. 5	236. 3	72	386. 6	270. 7	32	435. 8	305. 1	92	484. 9	339. 6
53	289. 2	202. 5	13	338. 3	236. 9	73	387. 5	271. 3	33	436. 6	305. 7	93	485. 8	340. 1
54	290. 0	203. 0	14	339. 1	237. 5	74	388. 3	271. 9	34	437. 4	306. 3	94	486. 6	340. 7
55	290. 8	203. 6	15	339. 9	238. 0	75	389. 1	272. 4	35	438. 2	306. 9	95	487. 4	341. 3
56	291. 6	204. 2	16	340. 8	238. 6	76	389. 9	273. 0	36	439. 1	307. 4	96	488. 2	341. 9
57	292. 4	204. 8	17	341. 6	239. 2	77	390. 7	273. 6	37	439. 9	308. 0	97	489. 0	342. 4
58	293. 3	205. 3	18	342. 4	239. 8	78	391. 6	274. 2	38	440. 7	308. 6	98	489. 9	343. 0
59	294. 1	205. 9	19	343. 2	240. 3	79	392. 4	274. 7	39	441. 5	309. 2	99	490. 7	343. 6
60	294. 9	206. 5	20	344. 1	240. 9	80	393. 2	275. 3	40	442. 3	309. 7	600	491. 5	344. 1
Dist.	Dep.	Lat.	Dist.	Dep.	Lat.	Dist.	Dep.	Lat.	Dist.	Dep.	Lat.	Dist.	Dep.	Lat.

55° (125°, 235°, 305°).

In **Plane Sailing.**	**Dist.**	**Lat.**	**Dep.**
For converting *Dep.* into *Diff. Long.* and *Diff. Long.* into *Dep.* In **Middle Latitude Sailing.**	Diff. Long.	Dep.	
For converting *Dep.* into *Diff. Long.* and *Diff. Long.* into *Dep.* In **Mercator Sailing.**		*m*	Diff. Long.
For multiplication of numbers by sines and by cosines, or solution of plane right-angled triangles.	N. Hypote-nuse.	N×Cos. Side Adj.	N×Sin. Side Opp.

TABLE 3.

Difference of Latitude and Departure for 36° (144°, 216°, 324°).

Dist.	Lat.	Dep.	Dist.	Lat.	Dep.	Dist.	Lat.	Dep.	Dist.	Lat.	Dep.	Dist.	Lat.	Dep.
1	0.8	0.6	61	49.4	35.9	121	97.9	71.1	181	146.4	106.4	241	195.0	141.7
2	1.6	1.2	62	50.2	36.4	22	98.7	71.7	82	147.2	107.0	42	195.8	142.2
3	2.4	1.8	63	51.0	37.0	23	99.5	72.3	83	148.1	107.6	43	196.6	142.8
4	3.2	2.4	64	51.8	37.6	24	100.3	72.9	84	148.9	108.2	44	197.4	143.4
5	4.0	2.9	65	52.6	38.2	25	101.1	73.5	85	149.7	108.7	45	198.2	144.0
6	4.9	3.5	66	53.4	38.8	26	101.9	74.1	86	150.5	109.3	46	199.0	144.6
7	5.7	4.1	67	54.2	39.4	27	102.7	74.6	87	151.3	109.9	47	199.8	145.2
8	6.5	4.7	68	55.0	40.0	28	103.6	75.2	88	152.1	110.5	48	200.6	145.8
9	7.3	5.3	69	55.8	40.6	29	104.4	75.8	89	152.9	111.1	49	201.4	146.4
10	8.1	5.9	70	56.6	41.1	30	105.2	76.4	90	153.7	111.7	50	202.3	146.9
11	8.9	6.5	71	57.4	41.7	131	106.0	77.0	191	154.5	112.3	251	203.1	147.5
12	9.7	7.1	72	58.2	42.3	32	106.8	77.6	92	155.3	112.9	52	203.9	148.1
13	10.5	7.6	73	59.1	42.9	33	107.6	78.2	93	156.1	113.4	53	204.7	148.7
14	11.3	8.2	74	59.9	43.5	34	108.4	78.8	94	156.9	114.0	54	205.5	149.3
15	12.1	8.8	75	60.7	44.1	35	109.2	79.4	95	157.8	114.6	55	206.3	149.9
16	12.9	9.4	76	61.5	44.7	36	110.0	79.9	96	158.6	115.2	56	207.1	150.5
17	13.8	10.0	77	62.3	45.3	37	110.8	80.5	97	159.4	115.8	57	207.9	151.1
18	14.6	10.6	78	63.1	45.8	38	111.6	81.1	98	160.2	116.4	58	208.7	151.6
19	15.4	11.2	79	63.9	46.4	39	112.5	81.7	99	161.0	117.0	59	209.5	152.2
20	16.2	11.8	80	64.7	47.0	40	113.3	82.3	200	161.8	117.6	60	210.3	152.8
21	17.0	12.3	81	65.5	47.6	141	114.1	82.9	201	162.6	118.1	261	211.2	153.4
22	17.8	12.9	82	66.3	48.2	42	114.9	83.5	02	163.4	118.7	62	212.0	154.0
23	18.6	13.5	83	67.1	48.8	43	115.7	84.1	03	164.2	119.3	63	212.8	154.6
24	19.4	14.1	84	68.0	49.4	44	116.5	84.6	04	165.0	119.9	64	213.6	155.2
25	20.2	14.7	85	68.8	50.0	45	117.3	85.2	05	165.8	120.5	65	214.4	155.8
26	21.0	15.3	86	69.6	50.5	46	118.1	85.8	06	166.7	121.1	66	215.2	156.4
27	21.8	15.9	87	70.4	51.1	47	118.9	86.4	07	167.5	121.7	67	216.0	156.9
28	22.7	16.5	88	71.2	51.7	48	119.7	87.0	08	168.3	122.3	68	216.8	157.5
29	23.5	17.0	89	72.0	52.3	49	120.5	87.6	09	169.1	122.8	69	217.6	158.1
30	24.3	17.6	90	72.8	52.9	50	121.4	88.2	10	169.9	123.4	70	218.4	158.7
31	25.1	18.2	91	73.6	53.5	151	122.2	88.8	211	170.7	124.0	271	219.2	159.3
32	25.9	18.8	92	74.4	54.1	52	123.0	89.3	12	171.5	124.6	72	220.1	159.9
33	26.7	19.4	93	75.2	54.7	53	123.8	89.9	13	172.3	125.2	73	220.9	160.5
34	27.5	20.0	94	76.0	55.3	54	124.6	90.5	14	173.1	125.8	74	221.7	161.1
35	28.3	20.6	95	76.9	55.8	55	125.4	91.1	15	173.9	126.4	75	222.5	161.6
36	29.1	21.2	96	77.7	56.4	56	126.2	91.7	16	174.7	127.0	76	223.3	162.2
37	29.9	21.7	97	78.5	57.0	57	127.0	92.3	17	175.6	127.5	77	224.1	162.8
38	30.7	22.3	98	79.3	57.6	58	127.8	92.9	18	176.4	128.1	78	224.9	163.4
39	31.6	22.9	99	80.1	58.2	59	128.6	93.5	19	177.2	128.7	79	225.7	164.0
40	32.4	23.5	100	80.9	58.8	60	129.4	94.0	20	178.0	129.3	80	226.5	164.6
41	33.2	24.1	101	81.7	59.4	161	130.3	94.6	221	178.8	129.9	281	227.3	165.2
42	34.0	24.7	02	82.5	60.0	62	131.1	95.2	22	179.6	130.5	82	228.1	165.8
43	34.8	25.3	03	83.3	60.5	63	131.9	95.8	23	180.4	131.1	83	229.0	166.3
44	35.6	25.9	04	84.1	61.1	64	132.7	96.4	24	181.2	131.7	84	229.8	166.9
45	36.4	26.5	05	84.9	61.7	65	133.5	97.0	25	182.0	132.3	85	230.6	167.5
46	37.2	27.0	06	85.8	62.3	66	134.3	97.6	26	182.8	132.8	86	231.4	168.1
47	38.0	27.6	07	86.6	62.9	67	135.1	98.2	27	183.6	133.4	87	232.2	168.7
48	38.8	28.2	08	87.4	63.5	68	135.9	98.7	28	184.5	134.0	88	233.0	169.3
49	39.6	28.8	09	88.2	64.1	69	136.7	99.3	29	185.3	134.6	89	233.8	169.9
50	40.5	29.4	10	89.0	64.7	70	137.5	99.9	30	186.1	135.2	90	234.6	170.5
51	41.3	30.0	111	89.8	65.2	171	138.3	100.5	231	186.9	135.8	291	235.4	171.0
52	42.1	30.6	12	90.6	65.8	72	139.2	101.1	32	187.7	136.4	92	236.2	171.6
53	42.9	31.2	13	91.4	66.4	73	140.0	101.7	33	188.5	137.0	93	237.0	172.2
54	43.7	31.7	14	92.2	67.0	74	140.8	102.3	34	189.3	137.5	94	237.9	172.8
55	44.5	32.3	15	93.0	67.6	75	141.6	102.9	35	190.1	138.1	95	238.7	173.4
56	45.3	32.9	16	93.8	68.2	76	142.4	103.5	36	190.9	138.7	96	239.5	174.0
57	46.1	33.5	17	94.7	68.8	77	143.2	104.0	37	191.7	139.3	97	240.3	174.6
58	46.9	34.1	18	95.5	69.4	78	144.0	104.6	38	192.5	139.9	98	241.1	175.2
59	47.7	34.7	19	96.3	69.9	79	144.8	105.2	39	193.4	140.5	99	241.9	175.7
60	48.5	35.3	20	97.1	70.5	80	145.6	105.8	40	194.2	141.1	300	242.7	176.3
Dist.	Dep.	Lat.	Dist.	Dep.	Lat.	Dist.	Dep.	Lat.	Dist.	Dep.	Lat.	Dist.	Dep.	Lat.

54° (126°, 234°, 306°).

In Plane Sailing.	**Dist.**	**Lat.**	**Dep.**
For converting *Dep.* into *Diff. Long.* and *Diff. Long.* into *Dep.* **In Middle Latitude Sailing.**	Diff. Long.	Dep.	
For converting *Dep.* into *Diff. Long.* and *Diff. Long.* into *Dep.* **In Mercator Sailing.**		*m*	Diff. Long.
For multiplication of numbers by sines and by cosines, or solution of plane right-angled triangles.	N.	N×Cos.	N×Sin.
	Hypotenuse.	Side. Adj.	Side Opp.

TABLE 3.

Difference of Latitude and Departure for 36° (144°, 216°, 324°).

Dist.	Lat.	Dep.	Dist.	Lat.	Dep.	Dist.	Lat.	Dep.	Dist.	Lat.	Dep.	Dist.	Lat.	Dep.
301	243.5	176.9	361	292.1	212.2	421	340.6	247.5	481	389.1	282.7	541	437.7	318.0
02	244.3	177.5	62	292.9	212.8	22	341.4	248.0	82	389.9	283.3	42	438.5	318.6
03	245.1	178.1	63	293.7	213.4	23	342.2	248.6	83	390.8	283.9	43	439.3	319.2
04	245.9	178.7	64	294.5	214.0	24	343.0	249.2	84	391.6	284.5	44	440.2	319.8
05	246.8	179.3	65	295.3	214.5	25	343.8	249.8	85	392.4	285.1	45	440.9	320.3
06	247.6	179.9	66	296.1	215.1	26	344.6	250.4	86	393.2	285.7	46	441.7	320.9
07	248.4	180.5	67	296.9	215.7	27	345.5	251.0	87	394.0	286.3	47	442.5	321.5
08	249.2	181.0	68	297.7	216.3	28	346.3	251.6	88	394.8	286.8	48	443.3	322.1
09	250.0	181.6	69	298.5	216.9	29	347.1	252.2	89	395.6	287.4	49	444.2	322.7
10	250.8	182.2	70	299.3	217.5	30	347.9	252.7	90	396.4	288.0	50	445.0	323.3
311	251.6	182.8	371	300.1	218.1	431	348.7	253.3	491	397.2	288.6	551	445.8	323.9
12	252.4	183.4	72	301.0	218.7	32	349.5	253.9	92	398.0	289.2	52	446.6	324.5
13	253.2	184.0	73	301.8	219.2	33	350.3	254.5	93	398.8	289.8	53	447.4	325.0
14	254.0	184.6	74	302.6	219.8	34	351.1	255.1	94	399.7	290.4	54	448.2	325.6
15	254.8	185.2	75	303.4	220.4	35	351.9	255.7	95	400.5	291.0	55	449.0	326.2
16	255.6	185.7	76	304.2	221.0	36	352.7	256.3	96	401.3	291.5	56	449.8	326.8
17	256.5	186.3	77	305.0	221.6	37	353.5	256.9	97	402.1	292.1	57	450.6	327.4
18	257.3	186.9	78	305.8	222.2	38	354.3	257.4	98	402.9	292.7	58	451.4	328.0
19	258.1	187.5	79	306.6	222.8	39	355.2	258.0	99	403.7	293.3	59	452.2	328.6
20	258.9	188.1	80	307.4	223.4	40	356.0	258.6	500	404.5	293.9	60	453.0	329.2
321	259.7	188.7	381	308.2	223.9	441	356.8	259.2	501	405.3	294.5	561	453.9	329.7
22	260.5	189.3	82	309.0	224.5	42	357.6	259.8	02	406.1	295.1	62	454.7	330.3
23	261.3	189.9	83	309.9	225.1	43	358.4	260.4	03	406.9	295.7	63	455.5	330.9
24	262.1	190.4	84	310.7	225.7	44	359.2	261.0	04	407.7	296.2	64	456.3	331.5
25	262.9	191.0	85	311.5	226.3	45	360.0	261.6	05	408.6	296.8	65	457.1	332.1
26	263.7	191.6	86	312.3	226.9	46	360.8	262.2	06	409.4	297.4	66	457.9	332.7
27	264.5	192.2	87	313.1	227.5	47	361.6	262.7	07	410.2	298.0	67	458.7	333.3
28	265.4	192.8	88	313.9	228.1	48	362.4	263.3	08	411.0	298.6	68	459.5	333.9
29	266.2	193.4	89	314.7	228.6	49	363.2	263.9	09	411.8	299.2	69	460.3	334.4
30	267.0	194.0	90	315.5	229.2	50	364.1	264.5	10	412.6	299.8	70	461.1	335.0
331	267.8	194.6	391	316.3	229.8	451	364.9	265.1	511	413.4	300.4	571	461.9	335.6
32	268.6	195.1	92	317.1	230.4	52	365.7	265.7	12	414.2	300.9	72	462.8	336.2
33	269.4	195.7	93	317.9	231.0	53	366.5	266.3	13	415.0	301.5	73	463.6	336.8
34	270.2	196.3	94	318.8	231.6	54	367.3	266.9	14	415.8	302.1	74	464.4	337.4
35	271.0	196.9	95	319.6	232.2	55	368.1	267.6	15	416.6	302.7	75	465.2	338.0
36	271.8	197.5	96	320.4	232.8	56	368.9	268.0	16	417.5	303.3	76	466.0	338.6
37	272.6	198.1	97	321.2	233.4	57	369.7	268.6	17	418.3	303.9	77	466.8	339.2
38	273.4	198.7	98	322.0	233.9	58	370.5	269.2	18	419.1	304.5	78	467.6	339.7
39	274.3	199.3	99	322.8	234.5	59	371.3	269.8	19	419.9	305.1	79	468.4	340.3
40	275.1	199.8	400	323.6	235.1	60	372.1	270.4	20	420.7	305.6	80	469.2	340.9
341	275.9	200.4	401	324.4	235.7	461	373.0	271.0	521	421.5	306.2	581	470.0	341.5
42	276.7	201.0	02	325.2	236.3	62	373.8	271.6	22	422.3	306.8	82	470.8	342.1
43	277.5	201.6	03	326.0	236.9	63	374.6	272.1	23	423.1	307.4	83	471.7	342.7
44	278.3	202.2	04	326.9	237.5	64	375.4	272.7	24	423.9	308.0	84	472.5	343.3
45	279.1	202.8	05	327.7	238.1	65	376.2	273.3	25	424.7	308.6	85	473.3	343.9
46	279.9	203.4	06	328.5	238.7	66	377.0	273.9	26	425.5	309.2	86	474.1	344.4
47	280.7	204.0	07	329.3	239.2	67	377.8	274.5	27	426.4	309.8	87	474.9	345.0
48	281.5	204.5	08	330.1	239.8	68	378.6	275.1	28	427.2	310.4	88	475.7	345.6
49	282.3	205.1	09	330.9	240.4	69	379.4	275.7	29	428.0	310.9	89	476.5	346.2
50	283.2	205.7	10	331.7	241.0	70	380.2	276.3	30	428.8	311.5	90	477.3	346.8
351	284.0	206.3	411	332.5	241.6	471	381.1	276.8	531	429.6	312.1	591	478.1	347.4
52	284.8	206.9	12	333.3	242.2	72	381.9	277.4	32	430.4	312.7	92	478.9	348.0
53	285.6	207.5	13	334.1	242.8	73	382.7	278.0	33	431.2	313.3	93	479.7	348.6
54	286.4	208.1	14	334.9	243.3	74	383.5	278.6	34	432.0	313.9	94	480.6	349.1
55	287.2	208.7	15	335.7	243.9	75	384.3	279.2	35	432.8	314.5	95	481.4	349.7
56	288.0	209.3	16	336.6	244.5	76	385.1	279.8	36	433.6	315.1	96	482.2	350.3
57	288.8	209.8	17	337.4	245.1	77	385.9	280.4	37	434.4	315.6	97	483.0	350.9
58	289.6	210.4	18	338.2	245.7	78	386.7	281.0	38	435.3	316.2	98	483.8	351.5
59	290.4	211.0	19	339.0	246.3	79	387.5	281.5	39	436.1	316.8	99	484.6	352.1
60	291.2	211.6	20	339.8	246.9	80	388.3	282.1	40	436.9	317.4	600	485.4	352.7
Dist.	Dep.	Lat.	Dist.	Dep.	Lat.	Dist.	Dep.	Lat.	Dist.	Dep.	Lat.	Dist.	Dep.	Lat.

54° (126°, 234°, 306°).

In **Plane Sailing.**	**Dist.**	**Lat.**	**Dep.**
For converting *Dep.* into *Diff. Long.* and *Diff. Long.* into *Dep.* In **Middle Latitude Sailing.**	Diff. Long.	Dep.	
For converting *Dep.* into *Diff. Long.* and *Diff. Long.* into *Dep.* In **Mercator Sailing.**		*m*	Diff. Long.
For multiplication of numbers by sines and by cosines, or solution of plane right-angled triangles.	N. Hypotenuse.	N×Cos. Side Adj.	N×Sin. Side Opp.

TABLE 3.

Difference of Latitude and Departure for 37° (143°, 217°, 323°).

Dist.	Lat.	Dep.	Dist.	Lat.	Dep.	Dist.	Lat.	Dep.	Dist.	Lat.	Dep.	Dist.	Lat.	Dep.
1	0.8	0.6	61	48.7	36.7	121	96.6	72.8	181	144.6	108.9	241	192.5	145.0
2	1.6	1.2	62	49.5	37.3	22	97.4	73.4	82	145.4	109.5	42	193.3	145.6
3	2.4	1.8	63	50.3	37.9	23	98.2	74.0	83	146.2	110.1	43	194.1	146.2
4	3.2	2.4	64	51.1	38.5	24	99.0	74.6	84	146.9	110.7	44	194.9	146.8
5	4.0	3.0	65	51.9	39.1	25	99.8	75.2	85	147.7	111.3	45	195.7	147.4
6	4.8	3.6	66	52.7	39.7	26	100.6	75.8	86	148.5	111.9	46	196.5	148.0
7	5.6	4.2	67	53.5	40.3	27	101.4	76.4	87	149.3	112.5	47	197.3	148.6
8	6.4	4.8	68	54.3	40.9	28	102.2	77.0	88	150.1	113.1	48	198.1	149.3
9	7.2	5.4	69	55.1	41.5	29	103.0	77.6	89	150.9	113.7	49	198.9	149.9
10	8.0	6.0	70	55.9	42.1	30	103.8	78.2	90	151.7	114.3	50	199.7	150.5
11	8.8	6.6	71	56.7	42.7	131	104.6	78.8	191	152.5	114.9	251	200.5	151.1
12	9.6	7.2	72	57.5	43.3	32	105.4	79.4	92	153.3	115.5	52	201.3	151.7
13	10.4	7.8	73	58.3	43.9	33	106.2	80.0	93	154.1	116.2	53	202.1	152.3
14	11.2	8.4	74	59.1	44.5	34	107.0	80.6	94	154.9	116.8	54	202.9	152.9
15	12.0	9.0	75	59.9	45.1	35	107.8	81.2	95	155.7	117.4	55	203.7	153.5
16	12.8	9.6	76	60.7	45.7	36	108.6	81.8	96	156.5	118.0	56	204.5	154.1
17	13.6	10.2	77	61.5	46.3	37	109.4	82.4	97	157.3	118.6	57	205.2	154.7
18	14.4	10.8	78	62.3	46.9	38	110.2	83.1	98	158.1	119.2	58	206.0	155.3
19	15.2	11.4	79	63.1	47.5	39	111.0	83.7	99	158.9	119.8	59	206.8	155.9
20	16.0	12.0	80	63.9	48.1	40	111.8	84.3	200	159.7	120.4	60	207.6	156.5
21	16.8	12.6	81	64.7	48.7	141	112.6	84.9	201	160.5	121.0	261	208.4	157.1
22	17.6	13.2	82	65.5	49.3	42	113.4	85.5	02	161.3	121.6	62	209.2	157.7
23	18.4	13.8	83	66.3	50.0	43	114.2	86.1	03	162.1	122.2	63	210.0	158.3
24	19.2	14.4	84	67.1	50.6	44	115.0	86.7	04	162.9	122.8	64	210.8	158.9
25	20.0	15.0	85	67.9	51.2	45	115.8	87.3	05	163.7	123.4	65	211.6	159.5
26	20.8	15.6	86	68.7	51.8	46	116.6	87.9	06	164.5	124.0	66	212.4	160.1
27	21.6	16.2	87	69.5	52.4	47	117.4	88.5	07	165.3	124.6	67	213.2	160.7
28	22.4	16.9	88	70.3	53.0	48	118.2	89.1	08	166.1	125.2	68	214.0	161.3
29	23.2	17.5	89	71.1	53.6	49	119.0	89.7	09	166.9	125.8	69	214.8	161.9
30	24.0	18.1	90	71.9	54.2	50	119.8	90.3	10	167.7	126.4	70	215.6	162.5
31	24.8	18.7	91	72.7	54.8	151	120.6	90.9	211	168.5	127.0	271	216.4	163.1
32	25.6	19.3	92	73.5	55.4	52	121.4	91.5	12	169.3	127.6	72	217.2	163.7
33	26.4	19.9	93	74.3	56.0	53	122.2	92.1	13	170.1	128.2	73	218.0	164.3
34	27.2	20.5	94	75.1	56.6	54	123.0	92.7	14	170.9	128.8	74	218.8	164.9
35	28.0	21.1	95	75.9	57.2	55	123.8	93.3	15	171.7	129.4	75	219.6	165.5
36	28.8	21.7	96	76.7	57.8	56	124.6	93.9	16	172.5	130.0	76	220.4	166.1
37	29.5	22.3	97	77.5	58.4	57	125.4	94.5	17	173.3	130.6	77	221.2	166.7
38	30.3	22.9	98	78.3	59.0	58	126.2	95.1	18	174.1	131.2	78	222.0	167.3
39	31.1	23.5	99	79.1	59.6	59	127.0	95.7	19	174.9	131.8	79	222.8	167.9
40	31.9	24.1	100	79.9	60.2	60	127.8	96.3	20	175.7	132.4	80	223.6	168.5
41	32.7	24.7	101	80.7	60.8	161	128.6	96.9	221	176.5	133.0	281	224.4	169.1
42	33.5	25.3	02	81.5	61.4	62	129.4	97.5	22	177.3	133.6	82	225.2	169.7
43	34.3	25.9	03	82.3	62.0	63	130.2	98.1	23	178.1	134.2	83	226.0	170.3
44	35.1	26.5	04	83.1	62.6	64	131.0	98.7	24	178.9	134.8	84	226.8	170.9
45	35.9	27.1	05	83.9	63.2	65	131.8	99.3	25	179.7	135.4	85	227.6	171.5
46	36.7	27.7	06	84.7	63.8	66	132.6	99.9	26	180.5	136.0	86	228.4	172.1
47	37.5	28.3	07	85.5	64.4	67	133.4	100.5	27	181.3	136.6	87	229.2	172.7
48	38.3	28.9	08	86.3	65.0	68	134.2	101.1	28	182.1	137.2	88	230.0	173.3
49	39.1	29.5	09	87.1	65.6	69	135.0	101.7	29	182.9	137.8	89	230.8	173.9
50	39.9	30.1	10	87.8	66.2	70	135.8	102.3	30	183.7	138.4	90	231.6	174.5
51	40.7	30.7	111	88.6	66.8	171	136.6	102.9	231	184.5	139.0	291	232.4	175.1
52	41.5	31.3	12	89.4	67.4	72	137.4	103.5	32	185.3	139.6	92	233.2	175.7
53	42.3	31.9	13	90.2	68.0	73	138.2	104.1	33	186.1	140.2	93	234.0	176.3
54	43.1	32.5	14	91.0	68.6	74	139.0	104.7	34	186.9	140.8	94	234.8	176.9
55	43.9	33.1	15	91.8	69.2	75	139.8	105.3	35	187.7	141.4	95	235.6	177.5
56	44.7	33.7	16	92.6	69.8	76	140.6	105.9	36	188.5	142.0	96	236.4	178.1
57	45.5	34.3	17	93.4	70.4	77	141.4	106.5	37	189.3	142.6	97	237.2	178.7
58	46.3	34.9	18	94.2	71.0	78	142.2	107.1	38	190.1	143.2	98	238.0	179.3
59	47.1	35.5	19	95.0	71.6	79	143.0	107.7	39	190.9	143.8	99	238.8	179.9
60	47.9	36.1	20	95.8	72.2	80	143.8	108.3	40	191.7	144.4	300	239.6	180.5
Dist.	Dep.	Lat.	Dist.	Dep.	Lat.	Dist.	Dep.	Lat.	Dist.	Dep.	Lat.	Dist.	Dep.	Lat.

53° (127°, 233°, 307°).

In **Plane Sailing.**	**Dist.**	**Lat.**	**Dep.**
For converting *Dep.* into *Diff. Long.* and *Diff. Long.* into *Dep.* In **Middle Latitude Sailing.**	Diff. Long.	Dep.	
For converting *Dep.* into *Diff. Long.* and *Diff. Long.* into *Dep.* In **Mercator Sailing.**		*m*	Diff. Long.
For multiplication of numbers by sines and by cosines, or solution of plane right-angled triangles.	N. / Hypotenuse.	N×Cos. / Side Adj.	N×Sin. / Side Opp.

TABLE 3.

Difference of Latitude and Departure for 37° (143°, 217°, 323°).

Dist.	Lat.	Dep.	Dist.	Lat.	Dep.	Dist.	Lat.	Dep.	Dist.	Lat.	Dep.	Dist.	Lat.	Dep.
301	240.4	181.1	361	288.3	217.3	421	336.2	253.4	481	384.1	289.5	541	432.1	325.6
02	241.2	181.7	62	289.1	217.9	22	337.0	254.0	82	384.9	290.1	42	432.9	326.2
03	242.0	182.4	63	289.9	218.5	23	337.8	254.6	83	385.7	290.7	43	433.7	326.8
04	242.7	183.0	64	290.7	219.1	24	338.6	255.2	84	386.5	291.3	44	434.5	327.4
05	243.6	183.6	65	291.5	219.7	25	339.4	255.8	85	387.3	291.9	45	435.3	328.0
06	244.4	184.2	66	292.3	220.3	26	340.2	256.4	86	388.1	292.5	46	436.1	328.6
07	245.2	184.8	67	293.1	220.9	27	341.0	257.0	87	388.9	293.1	47	436.9	329.2
08	246.0	185.4	68	293.9	221.5	28	341.8	257.6	88	389.7	293.7	48	437.7	329.8
09	246.8	186.0	69	294.7	222.1	29	342.6	258.2	89	390.5	294.3	49	438.5	330.4
10	247.6	186.6	70	295.5	222.7	30	343.4	258.8	90	391.3	294.9	50	439.2	331.0
311	248.4	187.2	371	296.3	223.3	431	344.2	259.4	491	392.1	295.5	551	440.0	331.6
12	249.2	187.8	72	297.1	223.9	32	345.0	260.0	92	392.9	296.1	52	440.8	332.2
13	250.0	188.4	73	297.9	224.5	33	345.8	260.6	93	393.7	296.7	53	441.6	332.8
14	250.8	189.0	74	298.7	225.1	34	346.6	261.2	94	394.5	297.3	54	442.4	333.4
15	251.6	189.6	75	299.5	225.7	35	347.4	261.8	95	395.3	297.9	55	443.2	334.0
16	252.4	190.2	76	300.3	226.3	36	348.2	262.4	96	396.1	298.5	56	444.0	334.6
17	253.2	190.8	77	301.1	226.9	37	349.0	263.0	97	396.9	299.1	57	444.8	335.2
18	254.0	191.4	78	301.9	227.5	38	349.8	263.6	98	397.7	299.7	58	445.6	335.8
19	254.8	192.0	79	302.7	228.1	39	350.6	264.2	99	398.5	300.3	59	446.4	336.4
20	255.6	192.6	80	303.5	228.7	40	351.4	264.8	500	399.3	300.9	60	447.2	337.0
321	256.4	193.2	381	304.3	229.3	441	352.2	265.4	501	400.1	301.5	561	448.0	337.6
22	257.2	193.8	82	305.1	229.9	42	353.0	266.0	02	400.9	302.1	62	448.8	338.2
23	258.0	194.4	83	305.9	230.5	43	353.8	266.6	03	401.7	302.7	63	449.6	338.8
24	258.8	195.0	84	306.7	231.1	44	354.6	267.2	04	402.5	303.3	64	450.4	339.4
25	259.6	195.6	85	307.5	231.7	45	355.4	267.8	05	403.3	303.9	65	451.2	340.0
26	260.4	196.2	86	308.3	232.3	46	356.2	268.4	06	404.1	304.5	66	452.0	340.6
27	261.2	196.8	87	309.1	232.9	47	357.0	269.0	07	404.9	305.1	67	452.8	341.2
28	262.0	197.4	88	309.9	233.5	48	357.8	269.6	08	405.7	305.7	68	453.6	341.8
29	262.8	198.0	89	310.7	234.1	49	358.6	270.2	09	406.5	306.3	69	454.4	342.4
30	263.5	198.6	90	311.5	234.7	50	359.4	270.8	10	407.3	306.9	70	455.2	343.0
331	264.3	199.2	391	312.3	235.3	451	360.2	271.4	511	408.1	307.5	571	456.0	343.6
32	265.1	199.8	92	313.1	235.9	52	361.0	272.0	12	408.9	308.1	72	456.8	344.2
33	265.9	200.4	93	313.9	236.5	53	361.8	272.6	13	409.7	308.7	73	457.6	344.8
34	266.7	201.0	94	314.7	237.1	54	362.6	273.2	14	410.5	309.3	74	458.4	345.4
35	267.5	201.6	95	315.5	237.7	55	363.4	273.8	15	411.3	309.9	75	459.2	346.0
36	268.3	202.2	96	316.3	238.3	56	364.2	274.4	16	412.1	310.5	76	460.0	346.6
37	269.1	202.8	97	317.1	238.9	57	365.0	275.0	17	412.9	311.1	77	460.8	347.2
38	269.9	203.4	98	317.9	239.5	58	365.8	275.6	18	413.7	311.7	78	461.6	347.8
39	270.7	204.0	99	318.7	240.1	59	366.6	276.2	19	414.5	312.3	79	462.4	348.5
40	271.5	204.6	400	319.5	240.7	60	367.4	276.8	20	415.3	312.1	80	463.2	349.1
341	272.3	205.2	401	320.3	241.3	461	368.2	277.4	521	416.1	313.5	581	464.0	349.7
42	273.1	205.8	02	321.1	241.9	62	369.0	278.0	22	416.9	314.1	82	464.8	350.3
43	273.9	206.4	03	321.9	242.5	63	369.8	278.6	23	417.7	314.7	83	465.6	350.9
44	274.7	207.0	04	322.6	243.1	64	370.6	279.2	24	418.5	315.4	84	466.4	351.5
45	275.5	207.6	05	323.4	243.7	65	371.4	279.8	25	419.3	316.0	85	467.2	352.1
46	276.3	208.2	06	324.2	244.3	66	372.2	280.4	26	420.1	316.6	86	468.0	352.7
47	277.1	208.8	07	325.0	244.9	67	373.0	281.0	27	420.9	317.2	87	468.8	353.3
48	277.9	209.4	08	325.8	245.5	68	373.8	281.6	28	421.7	317.8	88	469.6	353.9
49	278.7	210.0	09	326.6	246.1	69	374.6	282.3	29	422.5	318.4	89	470.4	354.5
50	279.5	210.6	10	327.4	246.7	70	375.4	282.9	30	423.3	319.0	90	471.2	355.1
351	280.3	211.2	411	328.2	247.3	471	376.2	283.5	531	424.1	319.6	591	472.0	355.7
52	281.1	211.8	12	329.0	247.9	72	377.0	284.1	32	424.9	320.2	92	472.8	356.3
53	281.9	212.4	13	329.8	248.5	73	377.8	284.7	33	425.7	320.8	93	473.6	356.9
54	282.7	213.0	14	330.6	249.2	74	378.6	285.3	34	426.5	321.4	94	474.4	357.5
55	283.5	213.6	15	331.4	249.8	75	379.4	285.9	35	427.3	322.0	95	475.2	358.1
56	284.3	214.2	16	332.2	250.4	76	380.2	286.5	36	428.1	322.6	96	476.0	358.7
57	285.1	214.8	17	333.0	251.0	77	380.9	287.1	37	428.9	323.2	97	476.8	359.3
58	285.9	215.4	18	333.8	251.6	78	381.7	287.7	38	429.7	323.8	98	477.6	359.9
59	286.7	216.1	19	334.6	252.2	79	382.5	288.3	39	430.5	324.4	99	478.4	360.5
60	287.5	216.7	20	335.4	252.8	80	383.3	288.9	40	431.3	325.0	600	479.2	361.1
Dist.	Dep.	Lat.	Dist.	Dep.	Lat.	Dist.	Dep.	Lat.	Dist.	Dep.	Lat.	Dist.	Dep.	Lat.

53° (127°, 233°, 307°).

In **Plane Sailing.**	**Dist.**	**Lat.**	**Dep.**
For converting *Dep.* into *Diff. Long.* and *Diff. Long.* into *Dep.* In **Middle Latitude Sailing.**	Diff. Long.	Dep.	
For converting *Dep.* into *Diff. Long.* and *Diff. Long.* into *Dep.* In **Mercator Sailing.**		*m*	Diff. Long.
For multiplication of numbers by sines and by cosines, or solution of plane right-angled triangles.	N. / Hypotenuse.	N×Cos. / Side Adj.	N×Sin. / Side Opp.

TABLE 3.

Difference of Latitude and Departure for 38° (142°, 218°, 322°).

Dist.	Lat.	Dep.	Dist.	Lat.	Dep.	Dist.	Lat.	Dep.	Dist.	Lat.	Dep.	Dist.	Lat.	Dep.
1	0.8	0.6	61	48.1	37.6	121	95.3	74.5	181	142.6	111.4	241	189.9	148.4
2	1.6	1.2	62	48.9	38.2	22	96.1	75.1	82	143.4	112.1	42	190.7	149.0
3	2.4	1.8	63	49.6	38.8	23	96.9	75.7	83	144.2	112.7	43	191.5	149.6
4	3.2	2.5	64	50.4	39.4	24	97.7	76.3	84	145.0	113.3	44	192.3	150.2
5	3.9	3.1	65	51.2	40.0	25	98.5	77.0	85	145.8	113.9	45	193.1	150.8
6	4.7	3.7	66	52.0	40.6	26	99.3	77.6	86	146.6	114.5	46	193.9	151.5
7	5.5	4.3	67	52.8	41.2	27	100.1	78.2	87	147.4	115.1	47	194.6	152.1
8	6.3	4.9	68	53.6	41.9	28	100.9	78.8	88	148.1	115.7	48	195.4	152.7
9	7.1	5.5	69	54.4	42.5	29	101.7	79.4	89	148.9	116.4	49	196.2	153.3
10	7.9	6.2	70	55.2	43.1	30	102.4	80.0	90	149.7	117.0	50	197.0	153.9
11	8.7	6.8	71	55.9	43.7	131	103.2	80.7	191	150.5	117.6	251	197.8	154.5
12	9.5	7.4	72	56.7	44.3	32	104.0	81.3	92	151.3	118.2	52	198.6	155.1
13	10.2	8.0	73	57.5	44.9	33	104.8	81.9	93	152.1	118.8	53	199.4	155.8
14	11.0	8.6	74	58.3	45.6	34	105.6	82.5	94	152.9	119.4	54	200.2	156.4
15	11.8	9.2	75	59.1	46.2	35	106.4	83.1	95	153.7	120.1	55	200.9	157.0
16	12.6	9.9	76	59.9	46.8	36	107.2	83.7	96	154.5	120.7	56	201.7	157.6
17	13.4	10.5	77	60.7	47.4	37	108.0	84.3	97	155.2	121.3	57	202.5	158.2
18	14.2	11.1	78	61.5	48.0	38	108.7	85.0	98	156.0	121.9	58	203.3	158.8
19	15.0	11.7	79	62.3	48.6	39	109.5	85.6	99	156.8	122.5	59	204.1	159.5
20	15.8	12.3	80	63.0	49.3	40	110.3	86.2	200	157.6	123.1	60	204.9	160.1
21	16.5	12.9	81	63.8	49.9	141	111.1	86.8	201	158.4	123.7	261	205.7	160.7
22	17.3	13.5	82	64.6	50.5	42	111.9	87.4	02	159.2	124.4	62	206.5	161.3
23	18.1	14.2	83	65.4	51.1	43	112.7	88.0	03	160.0	125.0	63	207.2	161.9
24	18.9	14.8	84	66.2	51.7	44	113.5	88.7	04	160.8	125.6	64	208.0	162.5
25	19.7	15.4	85	67.0	52.3	45	114.3	89.3	05	161.5	126.2	65	208.8	163.2
26	20.5	16.0	86	67.8	52.9	46	115.0	89.9	06	162.3	126.8	66	209.6	163.8
27	21.3	16.6	87	68.6	53.6	47	115.8	90.5	07	163.1	127.4	67	210.4	164.4
28	22.1	17.2	88	69.3	54.2	48	116.6	91.1	08	163.9	128.1	68	211.2	165.0
29	22.9	17.9	89	70.1	54.8	49	117.4	91.7	09	164.7	128.7	69	212.0	165.6
30	23.6	18.5	90	70.9	55.4	50	118.2	92.3	10	165.5	129.3	70	212.8	166.2
31	24.4	19.1	91	71.7	56.0	151	119.0	93.0	211	166.3	129.9	271	213.6	166.8
32	25.2	19.7	92	72.5	56.6	52	119.8	93.6	12	167.1	130.5	72	214.3	167.5
33	26.0	20.3	93	73.3	57.3	53	120.6	94.2	13	167.8	131.1	73	215.1	168.1
34	26.8	20.9	94	74.1	57.9	54	121.4	94.8	14	168.6	131.8	74	215.9	168.7
35	27.6	21.5	95	74.9	58.5	55	122.1	95.4	15	169.4	132.4	75	216.7	169.3
36	28.4	22.2	96	75.6	59.1	56	122.9	96.0	16	170.2	133.0	76	217.5	169.9
37	29.2	22.8	97	76.4	59.7	57	123.7	96.7	17	171.0	133.6	77	218.3	170.5
38	29.9	23.4	98	77.2	60.3	58	124.5	97.3	18	171.8	134.2	78	219.1	171.2
39	30.7	24.0	99	78.0	61.0	59	125.3	97.9	19	172.6	134.8	79	219.9	171.8
40	31.5	24.6	100	78.8	61.6	60	126.1	98.5	20	173.4	135.4	80	220.6	172.4
41	32.3	25.2	101	79.6	62.2	161	126.9	99.1	221	174.2	136.1	281	221.4	173.0
42	33.1	25.9	02	80.4	62.8	62	127.7	99.7	22	174.9	136.7	82	222.2	173.6
43	33.9	26.5	03	81.2	63.4	63	128.4	100.4	23	175.7	137.3	83	223.0	174.2
44	34.7	27.1	04	82.0	64.0	64	129.2	101.0	24	176.5	137.9	84	223.8	174.8
45	35.5	27.7	05	82.7	64.6	65	130.0	101.6	25	177.3	138.5	85	224.6	175.5
46	36.2	28.3	06	83.5	65.3	66	130.8	102.2	26	178.1	139.1	86	225.4	176.1
47	37.0	28.9	07	84.3	65.9	67	131.6	102.8	27	178.9	139.8	87	226.2	176.7
48	37.8	29.6	08	85.1	66.5	68	132.4	103.4	28	179.7	140.4	88	226.9	177.3
49	38.6	30.2	09	85.9	67.1	69	133.2	104.0	29	180.5	141.0	89	227.7	177.9
50	39.4	30.8	10	86.7	67.7	70	134.0	104.7	30	181.2	141.6	90	228.5	178.5
51	40.2	31.4	111	87.5	68.3	171	134.7	105.3	231	182.0	142.2	291	229.3	179.2
52	41.0	32.0	12	88.3	69.0	72	135.5	105.9	32	182.8	142.8	92	230.1	179.8
53	41.8	32.6	13	89.0	69.6	73	136.3	106.5	33	183.6	143.4	93	230.9	180.4
54	42.6	33.2	14	89.8	70.2	74	137.1	107.1	34	184.4	144.1	94	231.7	181.0
55	43.3	33.9	15	90.6	70.8	75	137.9	107.7	35	185.2	144.7	95	232.5	181.6
56	44.1	34.5	16	91.4	71.4	76	138.7	108.4	36	186.0	145.3	96	233.3	182.2
57	44.9	35.1	17	92.2	72.0	77	139.5	109.0	37	186.8	145.9	97	234.0	182.9
58	45.7	35.7	18	93.0	72.6	78	140.3	109.6	38	187.5	146.5	98	234.8	183.5
59	46.5	36.3	19	93.8	73.3	79	141.1	110.2	39	188.3	147.1	99	235.6	184.1
60	47.3	36.9	20	94.6	73.9	80	141.8	110.8	40	189.1	147.8	300	236.4	184.7
Dist.	Dep.	Lat.	Dist.	Dep.	Lat.	Dist.	Dep.	Lat.	Dist.	Dep.	Lat.	Dist.	Dep.	Lat.

52° (128°, 232°, 308°).

In Plane Sailing.	Dist.	Lat.	Dep.
For converting *Dep.* into *Diff. Long.* and *Diff. Long.* into *Dep.* In Middle Latitude Sailing.	Diff. Long.	Dep.	
For converting *Dep.* into *Diff. Long.* and *Diff. Long.* into *Dep.* In Mercator Sailing.		*m*	Diff. Long.
For multiplication of numbers by sines and by cosines, or solution of plane right-angled triangles.	N. Hypotenuse.	N×Cos. Side Adj.	N×Sin. Side Opp.

TABLE 3.

Difference of Latitude and Departure for 38° (142°, 218°, 322°).

Dist.	Lat.	Dep.	Dist.	Lat.	Dep.	Dist.	Lat.	Dep.	Dist.	Lat.	Dep.	Dist.	Lat.	Dep.
301	237.2	185.3	361	284.5	222.3	421	331.8	259.2	481	379.0	296.1	541	426.3	333.1
02	238.0	185.9	62	285.3	222.9	22	332.5	259.8	82	379.8	296.7	42	427.1	333.7
03	238.8	186.6	63	286.0	223.5	23	333.3	260.4	83	380.6	297.4	43	427.9	334.3
04	239.6	187.2	64	286.8	224.1	24	334.1	261.0	84	381.4	298.0	44	428.7	334.9
05	240.3	187.8	65	287.6	224.7	25	334.9	261.7	85	382.2	298.6	45	429.5	335.5
06	241.1	188.4	66	288.4	225.3	26	335.7	262.3	86	383.0	299.2	46	430.3	336.2
07	241.9	189.0	67	289.2	225.9	27	336.5	262.9	87	383.8	299.8	47	431.0	336.8
08	242.7	189.6	68	290.0	226.6	28	337.3	263.5	88	384.5	300.4	48	431.8	337.4
09	243.5	190.2	69	290.8	227.2	29	338.1	264.1	89	385.3	301.1	49	432.6	338.0
10	244.3	190.9	70	291.6	227.8	30	338.8	264.7	90	386.1	301.7	50	433.4	338.6
311	245.1	191.5	371	292.4	228.4	431	339.6	265.4	491	386.9	302.3	551	434.2	339.2
12	245.9	192.1	72	293.1	229.0	32	340.4	266.0	92	387.7	302.9	52	435.0	339.8
13	246.6	192.7	73	293.9	229.6	33	341.2	266.6	93	388.5	303.5	53	435.8	340.5
14	247.4	193.3	74	294.7	230.3	34	342.0	267.2	94	389.3	304.1	54	436.6	341.1
15	248.2	193.9	75	295.5	230.9	35	342.8	267.8	95	390.1	304.8	55	437.3	341.7
16	249.0	194.5	76	296.3	231.5	36	343.6	268.4	96	390.9	305.4	56	438.1	342.3
17	249.8	195.2	77	297.1	232.1	37	344.4	269.0	97	391.6	306.0	57	438.9	342.9
18	250.6	195.8	78	297.9	232.7	38	345.1	269.7	98	392.4	306.6	58	439.7	343.5
19	251.4	196.4	79	298.7	233.3	39	345.9	270.3	99	393.2	307.2	59	440.5	344.2
20	252.2	197.0	80	299.4	234.0	40	346.7	270.9	500	394.0	307.8	60	441.3	344.8
321	253.0	197.6	381	300.2	234.6	441	347.5	271.5	501	394.8	308.4	561	442.1	345.4
22	253.7	198.2	82	301.0	235.2	42	348.3	272.1	02	395.6	309.1	62	442.9	346.0
23	254.5	198.9	83	301.8	235.8	43	349.1	272.7	03	396.4	309.7	63	443.7	346.6
24	255.3	199.5	84	302.6	236.4	44	349.9	273.4	04	397.2	310.3	64	444.4	347.2
25	256.1	200.1	85	303.4	237.0	45	350.7	274.0	05	397.9	310.9	65	445.2	347.8
26	256.9	200.7	86	304.2	237.6	46	351.5	274.6	06	398.7	311.5	66	446.0	348.5
27	257.7	201.3	87	305.0	238.3	47	352.2	275.2	07	399.5	312.1	67	446.8	349.1
28	258.5	201.9	88	305.7	238.9	48	353.0	275.8	08	400.3	312.8	68	447.6	349.7
29	259.3	202.6	89	306.5	239.5	49	353.8	276.4	09	401.1	313.4	69	448.4	350.3
30	260.0	203.2	90	307.3	240.1	50	354.6	277.0	10	401.9	314.0	70	449.2	350.9
331	260.8	203.8	391	308.1	240.7	451	355.4	277.7	511	402.7	314.6	571	450.0	351.5
32	261.6	204.4	92	308.9	241.3	52	356.2	278.3	12	403.5	315.2	72	450.7	352.2
33	262.4	205.0	93	309.7	242.0	53	357.0	278.9	13	404.2	315.8	73	451.5	352.8
34	263.2	205.6	94	310.5	242.6	54	357.8	279.5	14	405.0	316.5	74	452.3	353.4
35	264.0	206.2	95	311.3	243.2	55	358.5	280.1	15	405.8	317.1	75	453.1	354.0
36	264.8	206.9	96	312.1	243.8	56	359.3	280.7	16	406.6	317.7	76	453.9	354.6
37	265.6	207.5	97	312.8	244.4	57	360.1	281.4	17	407.4	318.3	77	454.7	355.2
38	266.3	208.1	98	313.6	245.0	58	360.9	282.0	18	408.2	318.9	78	455.5	355.7
39	267.1	208.7	99	314.4	245.6	59	361.7	282.6	19	409.0	319.5	79	456.3	356.5
40	267.9	209.3	400	315.2	246.3	60	362.5	283.2	20	409.8	320.1	80	457.0	357.1
341	268.7	209.9	401	316.0	246.9	461	363.3	283.8	521	410.6	320.8	581	457.8	357.7
42	269.5	210.6	02	316.8	247.5	62	364.1	284.4	22	411.3	321.4	82	458.6	358.3
43	270.3	211.2	03	317.6	248.1	63	364.8	285.1	23	412.1	322.0	83	459.4	358.9
44	271.1	211.8	04	318.4	248.7	64	365.6	285.7	24	412.9	322.6	84	460.2	359.5
45	271.9	212.4	05	319.1	249.3	65	366.4	286.3	25	413.7	323.2	85	461.0	360.2
46	272.7	213.0	06	319.9	250.0	66	367.2	286.9	26	414.5	323.8	86	461.8	360.8
47	273.4	213.6	07	320.7	250.6	67	368.0	287.5	27	415.3	324.5	87	462.6	361.4
48	274.2	214.3	08	321.5	251.2	68	368.8	288.1	28	416.1	325.1	88	463.4	362.0
49	275.0	214.9	09	322.3	251.8	69	369.6	288.7	29	416.9	325.7	89	464.1	362.6
50	275.8	215.5	10	323.1	252.4	70	370.4	289.4	30	417.6	326.3	90	464.9	363.2
351	276.6	216.1	411	323.9	253.0	471	371.2	290.0	531	418.4	326.9	591	465.7	363.7
52	277.4	216.7	12	324.7	253.7	72	371.9	290.6	32	419.2	327.5	92	466.5	364.5
53	278.2	217.3	13	325.5	254.3	73	372.7	291.2	33	420.0	328.1	93	467.3	365.1
54	279.0	217.9	14	326.2	254.9	74	373.5	291.8	34	420.8	328.8	94	468.1	365.7
55	279.7	218.6	15	327.0	255.5	75	374.3	292.4	35	421.6	329.4	95	468.9	366.3
56	280.5	219.2	16	327.8	256.1	76	375.1	293.1	36	422.4	330.0	96	469.7	366.9
57	281.3	219.8	17	328.6	256.7	77	375.9	293.7	37	423.2	330.6	97	470.4	367.5
58	282.1	220.4	18	329.4	257.3	78	376.7	294.3	38	424.0	331.2	98	471.2	368.2
59	282.9	221.0	19	330.2	258.0	79	377.5	294.9	39	424.7	331.8	99	472.0	368.8
60	283.7	221.6	20	331.0	258.6	80	378.2	295.5	40	425.5	332.5	600	472.8	369.4
Dist.	Dep.	Lat.	Dist.	Dep.	Lat.	Dist.	Dep.	Lat.	Dist.	Dep.	Lat.	Dist.	Dep.	Lat.

52° (128°, 232°, 308°).

In **Plane Sailing.**	**Dist.**	**Lat.**	**Dep.**
For converting *Dep.* into *Diff. Long.* and *Diff. Long.* into *Dep.* In **Middle Latitude Sailing.**	Diff. Long.	Dep.	
For converting *Dep.* into *Diff. Long.* and *Diff. Long.* into *Dep.* In **Mercator Sailing.**		*m*	Diff. Long.
For multiplication of numbers by sines and by cosines, or solution of plane right-angled triangles.	N. Hypotenuse.	N×Cos. Side Adj.	N×Sin. Side Opp.

541524°—43——32

TABLE 3.

Difference of Latitude and Departure for 39° (141°, 219°, 321°).

Dist.	Lat.	Dep.	Dist.	Lat.	Dep.	Dist.	Lat.	Dep.	Dist.	Lat.	Dep.	Dist.	Lat.	Dep.
1	0.8	0.6	61	47.4	38.4	121	94.0	76.1	181	140.7	113.9	241	187.3	151.7
2	1.6	1.3	62	48.2	39.0	22	94.8	76.8	82	141.4	114.5	42	188.1	152.3
3	2.3	1.9	63	49.0	39.6	23	95.6	77.4	83	142.2	115.2	43	188.8	152.9
4	3.1	2.5	64	49.7	40.3	24	96.4	78.0	84	143.0	115.8	44	189.6	153.6
5	3.9	3.1	65	50.5	40.9	25	97.1	78.7	85	143.8	116.4	45	190.4	154.2
6	4.7	3.8	66	51.3	41.5	26	97.9	79.3	86	144.5	117.1	46	191.2	154.8
7	5.4	4.4	67	52.1	42.2	27	98.7	79.9	87	145.3	117.7	47	192.0	155.4
8	6.2	5.0	68	52.8	42.8	28	99.5	80.6	88	146.1	118.3	48	192.7	156.1
9	7.0	5.7	69	53.6	43.4	29	100.3	81.2	89	146.9	118.9	49	193.5	156.7
10	7.8	6.3	70	54.4	44.1	30	101.0	81.8	90	147.7	119.6	50	194.3	157.3
11	8.5	6.9	71	55.2	44.7	131	101.8	82.4	191	148.4	120.2	251	195.1	158.0
12	9.3	7.6	72	56.0	45.3	32	102.6	83.1	92	149.2	120.8	52	195.8	158.6
13	10.1	8.2	73	56.7	45.9	33	103.4	83.7	93	150.0	121.5	53	196.6	159.2
14	10.9	8.8	74	57.5	46.6	34	104.1	84.3	94	150.8	122.1	54	197.4	159.8
15	11.7	9.4	75	58.3	47.2	35	104.9	85.0	95	151.5	122.7	55	198.2	160.5
16	12.4	10.1	76	59.1	47.8	36	105.7	85.6	96	152.3	123.3	56	198.9	161.1
17	13.2	10.7	77	59.8	48.5	37	106.5	86.2	97	153.1	124.0	57	199.7	161.7
18	14.0	11.3	78	60.6	49.1	38	107.2	86.8	98	153.9	124.6	58	200.5	162.4
19	14.8	12.0	79	61.4	49.7	39	108.0	87.5	99	154.7	125.2	59	201.3	163.0
20	15.5	12.6	80	62.2	50.3	40	108.8	88.1	200	155.4	125.9	60	202.1	163.6
21	16.3	13.2	81	62.9	51.0	141	109.6	88.7	201	156.2	126.5	261	202.8	164.3
22	17.1	13.8	82	63.7	51.6	42	110.4	89.4	02	157.0	127.1	62	203.6	164.9
23	17.9	14.5	83	64.5	52.2	43	111.1	90.0	03	157.8	127.8	63	204.4	165.5
24	18.7	15.1	84	65.3	52.9	44	111.9	90.6	04	158.5	128.4	64	205.2	166.1
25	19.4	15.7	85	66.1	53.5	45	112.7	91.3	05	159.3	129.0	65	205.9	166.8
26	20.2	16.4	86	66.8	54.1	46	113.5	91.9	06	160.1	129.6	66	206.7	167.4
27	21.0	17.0	87	67.6	54.8	47	114.2	92.5	07	160.9	130.3	67	207.5	168.0
28	21.8	17.6	88	68.4	55.4	48	115.0	93.1	08	161.6	130.9	68	208.3	168.7
29	22.5	18.3	89	69.2	56.0	49	115.8	93.8	09	162.4	131.5	69	209.1	169.3
30	23.3	18.9	90	69.9	56.6	50	116.6	94.4	10	163.2	132.2	70	209.8	169.9
31	24.1	19.5	91	70.7	57.3	151	117.3	95.0	211	164.0	132.8	271	210.6	170.5
32	24.9	20.1	92	71.5	57.9	52	118.1	95.7	12	164.8	133.4	72	211.4	171.2
33	25.6	20.8	93	72.3	58.5	53	118.9	96.3	13	165.5	134.0	73	212.2	171.8
34	26.4	21.4	94	73.1	59.2	54	119.7	96.9	14	166.3	134.7	74	212.9	172.4
35	27.2	22.0	95	73.8	59.8	55	120.5	97.5	15	167.1	135.3	75	213.7	173.1
36	28.0	22.7	96	74.6	60.4	56	121.2	98.2	16	167.9	135.9	76	214.5	173.7
37	28.8	23.3	97	75.4	61.0	57	122.0	98.8	17	168.6	136.6	77	215.3	174.3
38	29.5	23.9	98	76.2	61.7	58	122.8	99.4	18	169.4	137.2	78	216.0	175.0
39	30.3	24.5	99	76.9	62.3	59	123.6	100.1	19	170.2	137.8	79	216.8	175.6
40	31.1	25.2	100	77.7	62.9	60	124.3	100.7	20	171.0	138.5	80	217.6	176.2
41	31.9	25.8	101	78.5	63.6	161	125.1	101.3	221	171.7	139.1	281	218.4	176.8
42	32.6	26.4	02	79.3	64.2	62	125.9	101.9	22	172.5	139.7	82	219.2	177.5
43	33.4	27.1	03	80.0	64.8	63	126.7	102.6	23	173.3	140.3	83	219.9	178.1
44	34.2	27.7	04	80.8	65.4	64	127.5	103.2	24	174.1	141.0	84	220.7	178.7
45	35.0	28.3	05	81.6	66.1	65	128.2	103.8	25	174.9	141.6	85	221.5	179.4
46	35.7	28.9	06	82.4	66.7	66	129.0	104.5	26	175.6	142.2	86	222.3	180.0
47	36.5	29.6	07	83.2	67.3	67	129.8	105.1	27	176.4	142.9	87	223.0	180.6
48	37.3	30.2	08	83.9	68.0	68	130.6	105.7	28	177.2	143.5	88	223.8	181.2
49	38.1	30.8	09	84.7	68.6	69	131.3	106.4	29	178.0	144.1	89	224.6	181.9
50	38.9	31.5	10	85.5	69.2	70	132.1	107.0	30	178.7	144.7	90	225.4	182.5
51	39.6	32.1	111	86.3	69.9	171	132.9	107.6	231	179.5	145.4	291	226.1	183.1
52	40.4	32.7	12	87.0	70.5	72	133.7	108.2	32	180.3	146.0	92	226.9	183.8
53	41.2	33.4	13	87.8	71.1	73	134.4	108.9	33	181.1	146.6	93	227.7	184.4
54	42.0	34.0	14	88.6	71.7	74	135.2	109.5	34	181.9	147.3	94	228.5	185.0
55	42.7	34.6	15	89.4	72.4	75	136.0	110.1	35	182.6	147.9	95	229.3	185.6
56	43.5	35.2	16	90.1	73.0	76	136.8	110.8	36	183.4	148.5	96	230.0	186.3
57	44.3	35.9	17	90.9	73.6	77	137.6	111.4	37	184.2	149.1	97	230.8	186.9
58	45.1	36.5	18	91.7	74.3	78	138.3	112.0	38	185.0	149.8	98	231.6	187.5
59	45.9	37.1	19	92.5	74.9	79	139.1	112.6	39	185.7	150.4	99	232.4	188.2
60	46.6	37.8	20	93.3	75.5	80	139.9	113.3	40	186.5	151.0	300	233.1	188.8
Dist.	Dep.	Lat.	Dist.	Dep.	Lat.	Dist.	Dep.	Lat.	Dist.	Dep.	Lat.	Dist.	Dep.	Lat.

51° (129°, 231°, 309°).

In Plane Sailing.	**Dist.**	**Lat.**	**Dep.**
For converting *Dep.* into *Diff. Long.* and *Diff. Long.* into *Dep.* In **Middle Latitude Sailing.**	Diff. Long.	Dep.	
For converting *Dep.* into *Diff. Long.* and *Diff. Long.* into *Dep.* In **Mercator Sailing.**		*m*	Diff Long.
For multiplication of numbers by sines and by cosines, or solution of plane right-angled triangles.	N. Hypotenuse.	N×Cos. Side Adj.	N×Sin. Side Opp.

TABLE 3.

Difference of Latitude and Departure for 39° (141°, 219°, 321°).

Dist.	Lat.	Dep.	Dist.	Lat.	Dep.	Dist.	Lat.	Dep.	Dist.	Lat.	Dep.	Dist.	Lat.	Dep.
301	233.9	189.4	361	280.5	227.2	421	327.2	264.9	481	373.8	302.7	541	420.4	340.5
02	234.7	190.1	62	281.3	227.8	22	328.0	265.6	82	374.6	303.3	42	421.2	341.1
03	235.5	190.7	63	282.1	228.4	23	328.7	266.2	83	375.4	304.0	43	422.0	341.7
04	236.3	191.3	64	282.9	229.1	24	329.5	266.8	84	376.1	304.6	44	422.8	342.2
05	237.0	191.9	65	283.7	229.7	25	330.3	267.5	85	376.9	305.2	45	423.5	343.0
06	237.8	192.6	66	284.4	230.3	26	331.1	268.1	86	377.7	305.8	46	424.3	343.6
07	238.6	193.2	67	285.2	231.0	27	331.8	268.7	87	378.5	306.5	47	425.1	344.2
08	239.4	193.8	68	286.0	231.5	28	332.6	269.3	88	379.2	307.1	48	425.9	344.9
09	240.1	194.5	69	286.8	232.2	29	333.4	270.0	89	380.0	307.7	49	426.7	345.5
10	240.9	195.1	70	287.5	232.8	30	334.2	270.6	90	380.8	308.4	50	427.4	346.1
311	241.7	195.7	371	288.3	233.5	431	334.9	271.2	491	381.6	309.0	551	428.2	346.8
12	242.5	196.3	72	289.1	234.1	32	335.7	271.9	92	382.4	309.6	52	429.0	347.4
13	243.2	197.0	73	289.9	234.7	33	336.5	272.5	93	383.1	310.3	53	429.8	348.0
14	244.0	197.6	74	290.7	235.4	34	337.3	273.1	94	383.9	310.9	54	430.5	348.6
15	244.8	198.2	75	291.4	236.0	35	338.1	273.8	95	384.7	311.5	55	431.3	349.3
16	245.6	198.9	76	292.2	236.6	36	338.8	274.4	96	385.5	312.1	56	432.1	349.9
17	246.4	199.5	77	293.0	237.3	37	339.6	275.0	97	386.2	312.8	57	432.9	350.5
18	247.1	200.1	78	293.8	237.9	38	340.4	275.6	98	387.0	313.4	58	433.6	351.2
19	247.9	200.8	79	294.5	238.5	39	341.2	276.3	99	387.8	314.0	59	434.4	351.8
20	248.7	201.4	80	295.3	239.1	40	341.9	276.9	500	388.6	314.7	60	435.2	352.4
321	249.5	202.0	381	296.1	239.8	441	342.7	277.5	501	389.4	315.3	561	436.0	353.0
22	250.2	202.6	82	296.9	240.4	42	343.5	278.2	02	390.1	315.9	62	436.8	353.7
23	251.0	203.3	83	297.6	241.0	43	344.3	278.8	03	390.9	316.5	63	437.5	354.3
24	251.8	203.9	84	298.4	241.7	44	345.1	279.4	04	391.7	317.2	64	438.3	354.9
25	252.6	204.5	85	299.2	242.3	45	345.8	280.0	05	392.5	317.8	65	439.1	355.6
26	253.3	205.2	86	300.0	242.9	46	346.6	280.7	06	393.2	318.4	66	439.9	356.2
27	254.1	205.8	87	300.8	243.5	47	347.4	281.3	07	394.0	319.1	67	440.6	356.8
28	254.9	206.4	88	301.5	244.2	48	348.2	281.9	08	394.8	319.7	68	441.4	357.5
29	255.7	207.0	89	302.3	244.8	49	348.9	282.6	09	395.6	320.3	69	442.2	358.1
30	256.5	207.7	90	303.1	245.4	50	349.7	283.2	10	396.3	321.0	70	443.0	358.7
331	257.2	208.3	391	303.9	246.1	451	350.5	283.8	511	397.1	321.6	571	443.8	359.3
32	258.0	208.9	92	304.6	246.7	52	351.3	284.5	12	397.9	322.2	72	444.5	360.0
33	258.8	209.6	93	305.4	247.3	53	352.0	285.1	13	398.7	322.8	73	445.3	360.6
34	259.6	210.2	94	306.2	248.0	54	352.8	285.7	14	399.5	323.5	74	446.1	361.2
35	260.3	210.8	95	307.0	248.6	55	353.6	286.3	15	400.2	324.1	75	446.9	361.9
36	261.1	211.5	96	307.7	249.2	56	354.4	287.0	16	401.0	324.7	76	447.7	362.5
37	261.9	212.1	97	308.5	249.8	57	355.2	287.6	17	401.8	325.4	77	448.4	363.1
38	262.7	212.7	98	309.3	250.5	58	355.9	288.2	18	402.6	326.0	78	449.2	363.7
39	263.5	213.3	99	310.1	251.1	59	356.7	288.9	19	403.3	326.6	79	450.0	364.4
40	264.2	214.0	400	310.9	251.7	60	357.5	289.5	20	404.1	327.2	80	450.7	365.0
341	265.0	214.6	401	311.6	252.4	461	358.3	290.1	521	404.9	327.9	581	451.5	365.6
42	265.8	215.2	02	312.4	253.0	62	359.0	290.7	22	405.7	328.5	82	452.3	366.3
43	266.6	215.9	03	313.2	253.6	63	359.8	291.4	23	406.4	329.1	83	453.1	366.9
44	267.3	216.5	04	314.0	254.2	64	360.6	292.0	24	407.2	329.8	84	453.9	367.5
45	268.1	217.1	05	314.7	254.9	65	361.4	292.6	25	408.0	330.4	85	454.6	368.2
46	268.9	217.7	06	315.5	255.5	66	362.2	293.3	26	408.8	331.0	86	455.4	368.8
47	269.7	218.4	07	316.3	256.1	67	362.9	293.9	27	409.6	331.7	87	456.2	369.4
48	270.4	219.0	08	317.1	256.8	68	363.7	294.5	28	410.3	332.3	88	457.0	370.0
49	271.2	219.6	09	317.9	257.4	69	364.5	295.2	29	411.1	332.9	89	457.8	370.7
50	272.0	220.3	10	318.6	258.0	70	365.3	295.8	30	411.9	333.5	90	458.5	371.3
351	272.8	220.9	411	319.4	258.7	471	366.0	296.4	531	412.7	334.2	591	459.3	371.9
52	273.6	221.5	12	320.2	259.3	72	366.8	297.0	32	413.4	334.8	92	460.1	372.6
53	274.3	222.2	13	321.0	259.9	73	367.6	297.7	33	414.2	335.4	93	460.8	373.2
54	275.1	222.7	14	321.7	260.5	74	368.4	298.3	34	415.0	336.1	94	461.6	373.8
55	275.9	223.4	15	322.5	261.2	75	369.1	298.9	35	415.8	336.7	95	462.4	374.4
56	276.7	224.0	16	323.3	261.8	76	369.9	299.6	36	416.6	337.3	96	463.2	375.1
57	277.4	224.7	17	324.1	262.4	77	370.7	300.2	37	417.3	337.9	97	464.0	375.7
58	278.2	225.3	18	324.8	263.1	78	371.5	300.8	38	418.1	338.6	98	464.7	376.3
59	279.0	225 9	19	325.6	263.7	79	372.3	301.4	39	418.9	339.2	99	465.5	377.0
60	279.8	226.6	20	326.4	264.3	80	373.0	302.1	40	419.7	339.8	600	466.3	377.6
Dist.	Dep.	Lat.	Dist.	Dep.	Lat.	Dist.	Dep.	Lat.	Dist.	Dep.	Lat.	Dist.	Dep.	Lat.

51° (129°, 231°, 309°).

In **Plane Sailing.**	Dist.	Lat.	Dep.
For converting *Dep.* into *Diff. Long.* and *Diff. Long.* into *Dep.* In **Middle Latitude Sailing.**	Diff. Long.	Dep.	
For converting *Dep.* into *Diff. Long.* and *Diff. Long.* into *Dep.* In **Mercator Sailing.**		*m*	Diff. Long.
For multiplication of numbers by sines and by cosines, or solution of plane right-angled triangles.	N. Hypotenuse.	N×Cos. Side Adj.	N×Sin. Side Opp.

TABLE 3.

Difference of Latitude and Departure for 40° (140°, 220°, 320°).

Dist.	Lat.	Dep.	Dist.	Lat.	Dep.	Dist.	Lat.	Dep.	Dist.	Lat.	Dep.	Dist.	Lat.	Dep.
1	0.8	0.6	61	46.7	39.2	121	92.7	77.8	181	138.7	116.3	241	184.6	154.9
2	1.5	1.3	62	47.5	39.9	22	93.5	78.4	82	139.4	117.0	42	185.4	155.6
3	2.3	1.9	63	48.3	40.5	23	94.2	79.1	83	140.2	117.6	43	186.1	156.2
4	3.1	2.6	64	49.0	41.1	24	95.0	79.7	84	141.0	118.3	44	186.9	156.8
5	3.8	3.2	65	49.8	41.8	25	95.8	80.3	85	141.7	118.9	45	187.7	157.5
6	4.6	3.9	66	50.6	42.4	26	96.5	81.0	86	142.5	119.6	46	188.4	158.1
7	5.4	4.5	67	51.3	43.1	27	97.3	81.6	87	143.3	120.2	47	189.2	158.8
8	6.1	5.1	68	52.1	43.7	28	98.1	82.3	88	144.0	120.8	48	190.0	159.4
9	6.9	5.8	69	52.9	44.4	29	98.8	82.9	89	144.8	121.5	49	190.7	160.1
10	7.7	6.4	70	53.6	45.0	30	99.6	83.6	90	145.5	122.1	50	191.5	160.7
11	8.4	7.1	71	54.4	45.6	131	100.4	84.2	191	146.3	122.8	251	192.3	161.3
12	9.2	7.7	72	55.2	46.3	32	101.1	84.8	92	147.1	123.4	52	193.0	162.0
13	10.0	8.4	73	55.9	46.9	33	101.9	85.5	93	147.8	124.1	53	193.8	162.6
14	10.7	9.0	74	56.7	47.6	34	102.6	86.1	94	148.6	124.7	54	194.6	163.3
15	11.5	9.6	75	57.5	48.2	35	103.4	86.8	95	149.4	125.3	55	195.3	163.9
16	12.3	10.3	76	58.2	48.9	36	104.2	87.4	96	150.1	126.0	56	196.1	164.6
17	13.0	10.9	77	59.0	49.5	37	104.9	88.1	97	150.9	126.6	57	196.9	165.2
18	13.8	11.6	78	59.8	50.1	38	105.7	88.7	98	151.7	127.3	58	197.6	165.8
19	14.6	12.2	79	60.5	50.8	39	106.5	89.3	99	152.4	127.9	59	198.4	166.5
20	15.3	12.9	80	61.3	51.4	40	107.2	90.0	200	153.2	128.6	60	199.2	167.1
21	16.1	13.5	81	62.0	52.1	141	108.0	90.6	201	154.0	129.2	261	199.9	167.8
22	16.9	14.1	82	62.8	52.7	42	108.8	91.3	02	154.7	129.8	62	200.7	168.4
23	17.6	14.8	83	63.6	53.4	43	109.5	91.9	03	155.5	130.5	63	201.5	169.1
24	18.4	15.4	84	64.3	54.0	44	110.3	92.6	04	156.3	131.1	64	202.2	169.7
25	19.2	16.1	85	65.1	54.6	45	111.1	93.2	05	157.0	131.8	65	203.0	170.3
26	19.9	16.7	86	65.9	55.3	46	111.8	93.8	06	157.8	132.4	66	203.8	171.0
27	20.7	17.4	87	66.6	55.9	47	112.6	94.5	07	158.6	133.1	67	204.5	171.6
28	21.4	18.0	88	67.4	56.6	48	113.4	95.1	08	159.3	133.7	68	205.3	172.3
29	22.2	18.6	89	68.2	57.2	49	114.1	95.8	09	160.1	134.3	69	206.1	172.9
30	23.0	19.3	90	68.9	57.9	50	114.9	96.4	10	160.9	135.0	70	206.8	173.6
31	23.7	19.9	91	69.7	58.5	151	115.7	97.1	211	161.6	135.6	271	207.6	174.2
32	24.5	20.6	92	70.5	59.1	52	116.4	97.7	12	162.4	136.3	72	208.4	174.8
33	25.3	21.2	93	71.2	59.8	53	117.2	98.3	13	163.2	136.9	73	209.1	175.5
34	26.0	21.9	94	72.0	60.4	54	118.0	99.0	14	163.9	137.6	74	209.9	176.1
35	26.8	22.5	95	72.8	61.1	55	118.7	99.6	15	164.7	138.2	75	210.7	176.8
36	27.6	23.1	96	73.5	61.7	56	119.5	100.3	16	165.5	138.8	76	211.4	177.4
37	28.3	23.8	97	74.3	62.4	57	120.3	100.9	17	166.2	139.5	77	212.2	178.1
38	29.1	24.4	98	75.1	63.0	58	121.0	101.6	18	167.0	140.1	78	213.0	178.7
39	29.9	25.1	99	75.8	63.6	59	121.8	102.2	19	167.8	140.8	79	213.7	179.3
40	30.6	25.7	100	76.6	64.3	60	122.6	102.8	20	168.5	141.4	80	214.5	180.0
41	31.4	26.4	101	77.4	64.9	161	123.3	103.5	221	169.3	142.1	281	215.3	180.6
42	32.2	27.0	02	78.1	65.6	62	124.1	104.1	22	170.1	142.7	82	216.0	181.3
43	32.9	27.6	03	78.9	66.2	63	124.9	104.8	23	170.8	143.3	83	216.8	181.9
44	33.7	28.3	04	79.7	66.8	64	125.6	105.4	24	171.6	144.0	84	217.6	182.6
45	34.5	28.9	05	80.4	67.5	65	126.4	106.1	25	172.4	144.6	85	218.3	183.2
46	35.2	29.6	06	81.2	68.1	66	127.2	106.7	26	173.1	145.3	86	219.1	183.8
47	36.0	30.2	07	82.0	68.8	67	127.9	107.3	27	173.9	145.9	87	219.9	184.5
48	36.8	30.9	08	82.7	69.4	68	128.7	108.0	28	174.7	146.6	88	220.6	185.1
49	37.5	31.5	09	83.5	70.1	69	129.5	108.6	29	175.4	147.2	89	221.4	185.8
50	38.3	32.1	10	84.3	70.7	70	130.2	109.3	30	176.2	147.8	90	222.2	186.4
51	39.1	32.8	111	85.0	71.3	171	131.0	109.9	231	177.0	148.5	291	222.9	187.1
52	39.8	33.4	12	85.8	72.0	72	131.8	110.6	32	177.7	149.1	92	223.7	187.7
53	40.6	34.1	13	86.6	72.6	73	132.5	111.2	33	178.5	149.8	93	224.5	188.3
54	41.4	34.7	14	87.3	73.3	74	133.3	111.8	34	179.3	150.4	94	225.2	189.0
55	42.1	35.4	15	88.1	73.9	75	134.1	112.5	35	180.0	151.1	95	226.0	189.6
56	42.9	36.0	16	88.9	74.6	76	134.8	113.1	36	180.8	151.7	96	226.7	190.3
57	43.7	36.6	17	89.6	75.2	77	135.6	113.8	37	181.6	152.3	97	227.5	190.9
58	44.4	37.3	18	90.4	75.8	78	136.4	114.4	38	182.3	153.0	98	228.3	191.6
59	45.2	37.9	19	91.2	76.5	79	137.1	115.1	39	183.1	153.6	99	229.0	192.2
60	46.0	38.6	20	91.9	77.1	80	137.9	115.7	40	183.9	154.3	300	229.8	192.8
Dist.	Dep.	Lat.	Dist.	Dep.	Lat.	Dist.	Dep.	Lat.	Dist.	Dep.	Lat.	Dist.	Dep.	Lat.

50° (130°, 230°, 310°).

In **Plane Sailing.**	Dist.	Lat.	Dep.
For converting *Dep.* into *Diff. Long.* and *Diff. Long.* into *Dep.* In **Middle Latitude Sailing.**	Diff. Long.	Dep.	
For converting *Dep.* into *Diff. Long.* and *Diff. Long.* into *Dep.* In **Mercator Sailing.**		*m*	Diff. Long.
For multiplication of numbers by sines and by cosines, or solution of plane right-angled triangles.	N. / Hypotenuse.	N×Cos. / Side. Adj.	N×Sin. / Side Opp.

TABLE 3.

Difference of Latitude and Departure for 40° (140°, 220°, 320°).

Dist.	Lat.	Dep.	Dist.	Lat.	Dep.	Dist.	Lat.	Dep.	Dist.	Lat.	Dep.	Dist.	Lat.	Dep.
301	230.6	193.5	361	276.5	232.1	421	322.5	270.6	481	368.5	309.2	541	414.4	347.7
02	231.3	194.1	62	277.3	232.7	22	323.3	271.3	82	369.2	309.8	42	415.2	348.4
03	232.1	194.8	63	278.1	233.3	23	324.0	271.9	83	370.0	310.5	43	416.0	349.0
04	232.9	195.4	64	278.8	234.0	24	324.8	272.5	84	370.8	311.1	44	416.7	349.7
05	233.6	196.1	65	279.6	234.6	25	325.6	273.2	85	371.5	311.8	45	417.5	350.3
06	234.4	196.7	66	280.4	235.3	26	326.3	273.8	86	372.3	312.4	46	418.3	351.0
07	235.2	197.3	67	281.1	235.9	27	327.1	274.5	87	373.1	313.0	47	419.0	351.6
08	235.9	198.0	68	281.9	236.5	28	327.9	275.1	88	373.8	313.7	48	419.8	352.2
09	236.7	198.6	69	282.7	237.2	29	328.6	275.8	89	374.6	314.3	49	420.6	352.9
10	237.5	199.3	70	283.4	237.8	30	329.4	276.4	90	375.4	315.0	50	421.3	353.5
311	238.2	199.9	371	284.2	238.5	431	330.2	277.0	491	376.1	315.6	551	422.1	354.2
12	239.0	200.5	72	285.0	239.1	32	330.9	277.7	92	376.9	316.3	52	422.9	354.8
13	239.8	201.2	73	285.7	239.8	33	331.7	278.3	93	377.7	316.9	53	423.6	355.5
14	240.5	201.8	74	286.5	240.4	34	332.5	279.0	94	378.4	317.5	54	424.4	356.1
15	241.3	202.5	75	287.3	241.0	35	333.2	279.6	95	379.2	318.2	55	425.2	356.7
16	242.1	203.1	76	288.0	241.7	36	334.0	280.3	96	380.0	318.8	56	425.9	357.4
17	242.8	203.8	77	288.8	242.3	37	334.8	280.9	97	380.7	319.5	57	426.7	358.0
18	243.6	204.4	78	289.6	243.0	38	335.5	281.5	98	381.5	320.1	58	427.5	358.7
19	244.4	205.0	79	290.3	243.6	39	336.3	282.2	99	382.3	320.8	59	428.2	359.3
20	245.1	205.7	80	291.1	244.3	40	337.1	282.8	500	383.0	321.4	60	429.0	360.0
321	245.9	206.3	381	291.9	244.9	441	337.8	283.5	501	383.8	322.0	561	429.8	360.6
22	246.7	207.0	82	292.6	245.5	42	338.6	284.1	02	384.6	322.7	62	430.5	361.2
23	247.4	207.6	83	293.4	246.2	43	339.4	284.8	03	385.3	323.3	63	431.3	361.9
24	248.2	208.3	84	294.2	246.8	44	340.1	285.4	04	386.1	324.0	64	432.0	362.5
25	249.0	208.9	85	294.9	247.5	45	340.9	286.0	05	386.9	324.6	65	432.8	363.2
26	249.7	209.5	86	295.7	248.1	46	341.7	286.7	06	387.6	325.3	66	433.6	363.8
27	250.5	210.2	87	296.5	248.8	47	342.4	287.3	07	388.4	325.9	67	434.3	364.5
28	251.3	210.8	88	297.2	249.4	48	343.2	288.0	08	389.2	326.5	68	435.1	365.1
29	252.0	211.5	89	298.0	250.0	49	344.0	288.6	09	389.9	327.2	69	435.9	365.7
30	252.8	212.1	90	298.8	250.7	50	344.7	289.3	10	390.7	327.8	70	436.6	366.4
331	253.6	212.8	391	299.5	251.3	451	345.5	289.9	511	391.4	328.5	571	437.4	367.0
32	254.3	213.4	92	300.3	252.0	52	346.3	290.5	12	392.2	329.1	72	438.2	367.7
33	255.1	214.0	93	301.1	252.6	53	347.0	291.2	13	393.0	329.8	73	438.9	368.3
34	255.9	214.7	94	301.8	253.3	54	347.8	291.8	14	393.7	330.4	74	439.7	369.0
35	256.6	215.3	95	302.6	253.9	55	348.6	292.5	15	394.5	331.0	75	440.5	369.6
36	257.4	216.0	96	303.4	254.5	56	349.3	293.1	16	395.3	331.7	76	441.2	370.2
37	258.2	216.6	97	304.1	255.2	57	350.1	293.8	17	396.0	332.3	77	442.0	370.9
38	258.9	217.3	98	304.9	255.8	58	350.8	294.4	18	396.8	333.0	78	442.8	371.5
39	259.7	217.9	99	305.7	256.5	59	351.6	295.0	19	397.6	333.6	79	443.5	372.2
40	260.5	218.5	400	306.4	257.1	60	352.4	295.7	20	398.3	334.2	80	444.3	372.8
341	261.2	219.2	401	307.2	257.8	461	353.1	296.3	521	399.1	334.9	581	445.1	373.5
42	262.0	219.8	02	307.9	258.4	62	353.9	297.0	22	399.9	335.5	82	445.8	374.1
43	262.8	220.5	03	308.7	259.0	63	354.7	297.6	23	400.6	336.2	83	446.6	374.7
44	263.5	221.1	04	309.5	259.7	64	355.4	298.3	24	401.4	336.8	84	447.4	375.4
45	264.3	221.8	05	310.2	260.3	65	356.2	298.9	25	402.2	337.5	85	448.1	376.0
46	265.1	222.4	06	311.0	261.0	66	357.0	299.5	26	402.9	338.1	86	448.9	376.7
47	265.8	223.0	07	311.8	261.6	67	357.7	300.2	27	403.7	338.7	87	449.7	377.3
48	266.6	223.7	08	312.5	262.3	68	358.5	300.8	28	404.5	339.4	88	450.4	378.0
49	267.3	224.3	09	313.3	262.9	69	359.3	301.5	29	405.2	340.0	89	451.2	378.6
50	268.1	225.0	10	314.1	263.5	70	360.0	302.1	30	406.0	340.7	90	452.0	379.2
351	268.9	225.6	411	314.8	264.2	471	360.8	302.8	531	406.8	341.3	591	452.7	379.9
52	269.6	226.3	12	315.6	264.8	72	361.6	303.4	32	407.5	342.0	92	453.5	380.5
53	270.4	226.9	13	316.4	265.5	73	362.3	304.0	33	408.3	342.6	93	454.3	381.2
54	271.2	227.5	14	317.1	266.1	74	363.1	304.7	34	409.1	343.2	94	455.0	381.8
55	271.9	228.2	15	317.9	266.8	75	363.9	305.3	35	409.8	343.9	95	455.8	382.5
56	272.7	228.8	16	318.7	267.4	76	364.6	306.0	36	410.6	344.5	96	456.6	383.1
57	273.5	229.5	17	319.4	268.0	77	365.4	306.6	37	411.4	345.2	97	457.3	383.7
58	274.2	230.1	18	320.2	268.7	78	366.2	307.3	38	412.1	345.8	98	458.1	384.4
59	275.0	230.8	19	321.0	269.3	79	366.9	307.9	39	412.9	346.5	99	458.9	385.0
60	275.8	231.4	20	321.7	270.0	80	367.7	308.5	40	413.7	347.1	600	459.6	385.7
Dist.	Dep.	Lat.	Dist.	Dep.	Lat.	Dist.	Dep.	Lat.	Dist.	Dep.	Lat.	Dist.	Dep.	Lat.

50° (130°, 230°, 310°).

In **Plane Sailing.**	Dist.	Lat.	Dep.
For converting *Dep.* into *Diff. Long.* and *Diff. Long.* into *Dep.* In **Middle Latitude Sailing.**	Diff. Long.	Dep.	
For converting *Dep.* into *Diff. Long.* and *Diff. Long.* into *Dep.* In **Mercator Sailing.**		*m*	Diff. Long.
For multiplication of numbers by sines and by cosines, or solution of plane right-angled triangles.	N. Hypotenuse.	N×Cos. Side Adj.	N×Sin. Side Opp.

TABLE 3.

Difference of Latitude and Departure for 41° (139°, 221°, 319°).

Dist.	Lat.	Dep.	Dist.	Lat.	Dep.	Dist.	Lat.	Dep.	Dist.	Lat.	Dep.	Dist.	Lat.	Dep.
1	0.8	0.7	61	46.0	40.0	121	91.3	79.4	181	136.6	118.7	241	181.9	158.1
2	1.5	1.3	62	46.8	40.7	22	92.1	80.0	82	137.4	119.4	42	182.6	158.8
3	2.3	2.0	63	47.5	41.3	23	92.8	80.7	83	138.1	120.1	43	183.4	159.4
4	3.0	2.6	64	48.3	42.0	24	93.6	81.4	84	138.9	120.7	44	184.1	160.1
5	3.8	3.3	65	49.1	42.6	25	94.3	82.0	85	139.6	121.4	45	184.9	160.7
6	4.5	3.9	66	49.8	43.3	26	95.1	82.7	86	140.4	122.0	46	185.7	161.4
7	5.3	4.6	67	50.6	44.0	27	95.8	83.3	87	141.1	122.7	47	186.4	162.0
8	6.0	5.2	68	51.3	44.6	28	96.6	84.0	88	141.9	123.3	48	187.2	162.7
9	6.8	5.9	69	52.1	45.3	29	97.4	84.6	89	142.6	124.0	49	187.9	163.4
10	7.5	6.6	70	52.8	45.9	30	98.1	85.3	90	143.4	124.7	50	188.7	164.0
11	8.3	7.2	71	53.6	46.6	131	98.9	85.9	191	144.1	125.3	251	189.4	164.7
12	9.1	7.9	72	54.3	47.2	32	99.6	86.6	92	144.9	126.0	52	190.2	165.3
13	9.8	8.5	73	55.1	47.9	33	100.4	87.3	93	145.7	126.6	53	190.9	166.0
14	10.6	9.2	74	55.8	48.5	34	101.1	87.9	94	146.4	127.3	54	191.7	166.6
15	11.3	9.8	75	56.6	49.2	35	101.9	88.6	95	147.2	127.9	55	192.5	167.3
16	12.1	10.5	76	57.4	49.9	36	102.6	89.2	96	147.9	128.6	56	193.2	168.0
17	12.8	11.2	77	58.1	50.5	37	103.4	89.9	97	148.7	129.2	57	194.0	168.6
18	13.6	11.8	78	58.9	51.2	38	104.1	90.5	98	149.4	129.9	58	194.7	169.3
19	14.3	12.5	79	59.6	51.8	39	104.9	91.2	99	150.2	130.6	59	195.5	169.9
20	15.1	13.1	80	60.4	52.5	40	105.7	91.8	200	150.9	131.2	60	196.2	170.6
21	15.8	13.8	81	61.1	53.1	141	106.4	92.5	201	151.7	131.9	261	197.0	171.2
22	16.6	14.4	82	61.9	53.8	42	107.2	93.2	02	152.5	132.5	62	197.7	171.9
23	17.4	15.1	83	62.6	54.5	43	107.9	93.8	03	153.2	133.2	63	198.5	172.5
24	18.1	15.7	84	63.4	55.1	44	108.7	94.5	04	154.0	133.8	64	199.2	173.2
25	18.9	16.4	85	64.2	55.8	45	109.4	95.1	05	154.7	134.5	65	200.0	173.9
26	19.6	17.1	86	64.9	56.4	46	110.2	95.8	06	155.5	135.1	66	200.8	174.5
27	20.4	17.7	87	65.7	57.1	47	110.9	96.4	07	156.2	135.8	67	201.5	175.2
28	21.1	18.4	88	66.4	57.7	48	111.7	97.1	08	157.0	136.5	68	202.3	175.8
29	21.9	19.0	89	67.2	58.4	49	112.5	97.8	09	157.7	137.1	69	203.0	176.5
30	22.6	19.7	90	67.9	59.0	50	113.2	98.4	10	158.5	137.8	70	203.8	177.1
31	23.4	20.3	91	68.7	59.7	151	114.0	99.1	211	159.2	138.4	271	204.5	177.8
32	24.2	21.0	92	69.4	60.4	52	114.7	99.7	12	160.0	139.1	72	205.3	178.4
33	24.9	21.6	93	70.2	61.0	53	115.5	100.4	13	160.8	139.7	73	206.0	179.1
34	25.7	22.3	94	70.9	61.7	54	116.2	101.0	14	161.5	140.4	74	206.8	179.8
35	26.4	23.0	95	71.7	62.3	55	117.0	101.7	15	162.3	141.1	75	207.5	180.4
36	27.2	23.6	96	72.5	63.0	56	117.7	102.3	16	163.0	141.7	76	208.3	181.1
37	27.9	24.3	97	73.2	63.6	57	118.5	103.0	17	163.8	142.4	77	209.1	181.7
38	28.7	24.9	98	74.0	64.3	58	119.2	103.7	18	164.5	143.0	78	209.8	182.4
39	29.4	25.6	99	74.7	64.9	59	120.0	104.3	19	165.3	143.7	79	210.6	183.0
40	30.2	26.2	100	75.5	65.6	60	120.8	105.0	20	166.0	144.3	80	211.3	183.7
41	30.9	26.9	101	76.2	66.3	161	121.5	105.6	221	166.8	145.0	281	212.1	184.4
42	31.7	27.6	02	77.0	66.9	62	122.3	106.3	22	167.5	145.6	82	212.8	185.0
43	32.5	28.2	03	77.7	67.6	63	123.0	106.9	23	168.3	146.3	83	213.6	185.7
44	33.2	28.9	04	78.5	68.2	64	123.8	107.6	24	169.1	147.0	84	214.3	186.3
45	34.0	29.5	05	79.2	68.9	65	124.5	108.2	25	169.8	147.6	85	215.1	187.0
46	34.7	30.2	06	80.0	69.5	66	125.3	108.9	26	170.6	148.3	86	215.8	187.6
47	35.5	30.8	07	80.8	70.2	67	126.0	109.6	27	171.3	148.9	87	216.6	188.3
48	36.2	31.5	08	81.5	70.9	68	126.8	110.2	28	172.1	149.6	88	217.4	188.9
49	37.0	32.1	09	82.3	71.5	69	127.5	110.9	29	172.8	150.2	89	218.1	189.6
50	37.7	32.8	10	83.0	72.2	70	128.3	111.5	30	173.6	150.9	90	218.9	190.3
51	38.5	33.5	111	83.8	72.8	171	129.1	112.2	231	174.3	151.5	291	219.6	190.9
52	39.2	34.1	12	84.5	73.5	72	129.8	112.8	32	175.1	152.2	92	220.4	191.6
53	40.0	34.8	13	85.3	74.1	73	130.6	113.5	33	175.8	152.9	93	221.1	192.2
54	40.8	35.4	14	86.0	74.8	74	131.3	114.2	34	176.6	153.5	94	221.9	192.9
55	41.5	36.1	15	86.8	75.4	75	132.1	114.8	35	177.4	154.2	95	222.6	193.5
56	42.3	36.7	16	87.5	76.1	76	132.8	115.5	36	178.1	154.8	96	223.4	194.2
57	43.0	37.4	17	88.3	76.8	77	133.6	116.1	37	178.9	155.5	97	224.1	194.8
58	43.8	38.1	18	89.1	77.4	78	134.3	116.8	38	179.6	156.1	98	224.9	195.5
59	44.5	38.7	19	89.8	78.1	79	135.1	117.4	39	180.4	156.8	99	225.7	196.2
60	45.3	39.4	20	90.6	78.7	80	135.8	118.1	40	181.1	157.5	300	226.4	196.8
Dist.	Dep.	Lat.	Dist.	Dep.	Lat.	Dist.	Dep.	Lat.	Dist.	Dep.	Lat.	Dist.	Dep.	Lat.

49° (131°, 229°, 311°).

In **Plane Sailing.**	Dist.	Lat.	Dep.
For converting *Dep.* into *Diff. Long.* and *Diff. Long.* into *Dep.* In **Middle Latitude Sailing.**	Diff. Long.	Dep.	
For converting *Dep.* into *Diff. Long.* and *Diff. Long.* into *Dep.* In **Mercator Sailing.**		*m*	Diff Long.
For multiplication of numbers by sines and by cosines, or solution of plane right-angled triangles.	N. Hypotenuse.	N×Cos. Side Adj.	N×Sin. Side Opp.

TABLE 3.

Difference of Latitude and Departure for 41° (139°, 221°, 319°).

Dist.	Lat.	Dep.	Dist.	Lat.	Dep.	Dist.	Lat.	Dep.	Dist.	Lat.	Dep.	Dist.	Lat.	Dep.
301	227.2	197.5	361	272.5	236.8	421	317.7	276.2	481	363.0	315.6	541	408.3	354.9
02	227.9	198.1	62	273.2	237.5	22	318.5	276.9	82	363.8	316.2	42	409.1	355.6
03	228.7	198.8	63	274.0	238.1	23	319.2	277.5	83	364.5	316.9	43	409.8	356.2
04	229.4	199.4	64	274.7	238.8	24	320.0	278.2	84	365.3	317.5	44	410.6	356.9
05	230.2	200.1	65	275.5	239.5	25	320.8	278.8	85	366.0	318.2	45	411.3	357.6
06	230.9	200.8	66	276.2	240.1	26	321.5	279.5	86	366.8	318.8	46	412.1	358.2
07	231.7	201.4	67	277.0	240.8	27	322.3	280.1	87	367.5	319.5	47	412.8	358.9
08	232.5	202.1	68	277.7	241.4	28	323.0	280.8	88	368.3	320.2	48	413.6	359.5
09	233.2	202.7	69	278.5	242.1	29	323.8	281.4	89	369.1	320.8	49	414.3	360.2
10	234.0	203.4	70	279.2	242.7	30	324.5	282.1	90	369.8	321.5	50	415.1	360.8
311	234.7	204.0	371	280.0	243.4	431	325.3	282.8	491	370.6	322.1	551	415.8	361.5
12	235.5	204.7	72	280.8	244.1	32	326.0	283.4	92	371.3	322.8	52	416.6	362.1
13	236.2	205.3	73	281.5	244.7	33	326.8	284.1	93	372.1	323.4	53	417.4	362.8
14	237.0	206.0	74	282.3	245.4	34	327.5	284.7	94	372.8	324.1	54	418.1	363.5
15	237.7	206.7	75	283.0	246.0	35	328.3	285.4	95	373.6	324.7	55	418.9	364.1
16	238.5	207.3	76	283.8	246.7	36	329.1	286.0	96	374.3	325.4	56	419.6	364.8
17	239.2	208.0	77	284.5	247.3	37	329.8	286.7	97	375.1	326.1	57	420.4	365.4
18	240.0	208.6	78	285.3	248.0	38	330.6	287.4	98	375.8	326.7	58	421.1	366.1
19	240.8	209.3	79	286.0	248.6	39	331.3	288.0	99	376.6	327.4	59	421.9	366.7
20	241.5	209.9	80	286.8	249.3	40	332.1	288.7	500	377.4	328.0	60	422.6	367.4
321	242.3	210.6	381	287.5	250.0	441	332.8	289.3	501	378.1	328.7	561	423.4	368.0
22	243.0	211.3	82	288.3	250.6	42	333.6	290.0	02	378.9	329.3	62	424.1	368.7
23	243.8	211.9	83	289.1	251.3	43	334.3	290.6	03	379.6	330.0	63	424.9	369.4
24	244.5	212.6	84	289.8	251.9	44	335.1	291.3	04	380.4	330.7	64	425.7	370.0
25	245.3	213.2	85	290.6	252.6	45	335.8	291.9	05	381.1	331.3	65	426.4	370.7
26	246.0	213.9	86	291.3	253.2	46	336.6	292.6	06	381.9	332.0	66	427.2	371.3
27	246.8	214.5	87	292.1	253.9	47	337.4	293.3	07	382.6	332.6	67	427.9	372.0
28	247.5	215.2	88	292.8	254.6	48	338.1	293.9	08	383.4	333.3	68	428.7	372.6
29	248.3	215.8	89	293.6	255.2	49	338.9	294.6	09	384.1	333.9	69	429.4	373.3
30	249.1	216.5	90	294.3	255.9	50	339.6	295.2	10	384.9	334.6	70	430.2	374.0
331	249.8	217.2	391	295.1	256.5	451	340.4	295.9	511	385.7	335.2	571	430.9	374.6
32	250.6	217.8	92	295.8	257.2	52	341.1	296.5	12	386.4	335.9	72	431.7	375.3
33	251.3	218.5	93	296.6	257.8	53	341.9	297.2	13	387.2	336.6	73	432.4	375.9
34	252.1	219.1	94	297.4	258.5	54	342.6	297.9	14	387.9	337.2	74	433.2	376.6
35	252.8	219.8	95	298.1	259.1	55	343.4	298.5	15	388.7	337.9	75	434.0	377.2
36	253.6	220.4	96	298.9	259.8	56	344.1	299.2	16	389.4	338.5	76	434.7	377.9
37	254.3	221.1	97	299.6	260.5	57	344.9	299.8	17	390.2	339.2	77	435.5	378.5
38	255.1	221.7	98	300.4	261.1	58	345.7	300.5	18	390.9	339.8	78	436.2	379.2
39	255.8	222.4	99	301.1	261.8	59	346.4	301.1	19	391.7	340.5	79	437.0	379.9
40	256.6	223.1	400	301.9	262.4	60	347.2	301.8	20	392.4	341.2	80	437.7	380.5
341	257.4	223.7	401	302.6	263.1	461	347.9	302.4	521	393.2	341.8	581	438.5	381.2
42	258.1	224.4	02	303.4	263.7	62	348.7	303.1	22	394.0	342.5	82	439.2	381.8
43	258.9	225.0	03	304.1	264.4	63	349.4	303.8	23	394.7	343.1	83	440.0	382.5
44	259.6	225.7	04	304.9	265.0	64	350.2	304.4	24	395.5	343.8	84	440.8	383.1
45	260.4	226.3	05	305.7	265.7	65	350.9	305.1	25	396.2	344.4	85	441.5	383.8
46	261.1	227.0	06	306.4	266.4	66	351.7	305.7	26	397.0	345.1	86	442.3	384.5
47	261.9	227.7	07	307.2	267.0	67	352.4	306.4	27	397.7	345.7	87	443.0	385.1
48	262.6	228.3	08	307.9	267.7	68	353.2	307.0	28	398.5	346.4	88	443.8	385.8
49	263.4	229.0	09	308.7	268.3	69	354.0	307.7	29	399.2	347.1	89	444.5	386.4
50	264.1	229.6	10	309.4	269.0	70	354.7	308.3	30	400.0	347.7	90	445.3	387.1
351	264.9	230.3	411	310.2	269.6	471	355.5	309.0	531	400.8	348.4	591	446.0	387.7
52	265.7	230.9	12	310.9	270.3	72	356.2	309.7	32	401.5	349.0	92	446.8	388.4
53	266.4	231.6	13	311.7	271.0	73	357.0	310.3	33	402.3	349.7	93	447.5	389.0
54	267.2	232.2	14	312.4	271.6	74	357.7	311.0	34	403.0	350.3	94	448.3	389.7
55	267.9	232.9	15	313.2	272.3	75	358.5	311.6	35	403.8	351.0	95	449.1	390.4
56	268.7	233.6	16	314.0	272.9	76	359.2	312.3	36	404.5	351.6	96	449.8	391.0
57	269.4	234.2	17	314.7	273.6	77	360.0	312.9	37	405.3	352.3	97	450.6	391.7
58	270.2	234.9	18	315.5	274.2	78	360.8	313.6	38	406.0	353.0	98	451.3	392.3
59	270.9	235.5	19	316.2	274.9	79	361.5	314.3	39	406.8	353.6	99	452.1	393.0
60	271.7	236.2	20	317.0	275.5	80	362.3	314.9	40	407.5	354.3	600	452.8	393.6
Dist.	Dep.	Lat.	Dist.	Dep.	Lat.	Dist.	Dep.	Lat.	Dist.	Dep.	Lat.	Dist.	Dep.	Lat.

49° (131°, 229°, 311°).

In **Plane Sailing.**	Dist.	Lat.	Dep.
For converting *Dep.* into *Diff. Long.* and *Diff. Long.* into *Dep.* In **Middle Latitude Sailing.**	Diff. Long.	Dep.	
For converting *Dep.* into *Diff. Long.* and *Diff. Long.* into *Dep.* In **Mercator Sailing.**		*m*	Diff. Long.
For multiplication of numbers by sines and by cosines, or solution of plane right-angled triangles.	N. Hypotenuse.	N×Cos. Side Adj.	N×Sin. Side Opp.

TABLE 3.

Difference of Latitude and Departure for 42° (138°, 222°, 318°).

Dist.	Lat.	Dep.	Dist.	Lat.	Dep.	Dist.	Lat.	Dep.	Dist.	Lat.	Dep.	Dist.	Lat.	Dep.
1	0.7	0.7	61	45.3	40.8	121	89.9	81.0	181	134.5	121.1	241	179.1	161.3
2	1.5	1.3	62	46.1	41.5	22	90.7	81.6	82	135.3	121.8	42	179.8	161.9
3	2.2	2.0	63	46.8	42.2	23	91.4	82.3	83	136.0	122.5	43	180.6	162.6
4	3.0	2.7	64	47.6	42.8	24	92.1	83.0	84	136.7	123.1	44	181.3	163.3
5	3.7	3.3	65	48.3	43.5	25	92.9	83.6	85	137.5	123.8	45	182.1	163.9
6	4.5	4.0	66	49.0	44.2	26	93.6	84.3	86	138.2	124.5	46	182.8	164.6
7	5.2	4.7	67	49.8	44.8	27	94.4	85.0	87	139.0	125.1	47	183.6	165.3
8	5.9	5.4	68	50.5	45.5	28	95.1	85.6	88	139.7	125.8	48	184.3	165.9
9	6.7	6.0	69	51.3	46.2	29	95.9	86.3	89	140.5	126.5	49	185.0	166.6
10	7.4	6.7	70	52.0	46.8	30	96.6	87.0	90	141.2	127.1	50	185.8	167.3
11	8.2	7.4	71	52.8	47.5	131	97.4	87.7	191	141.9	127.8	251	186.5	168.0
12	8.9	8.0	72	53.5	48.2	32	98.1	88.3	92	142.7	128.5	52	187.3	168.6
13	9.7	8.7	73	54.2	48.8	33	98.8	89.0	93	143.4	129.1	53	188.0	169.3
14	10.4	9.4	74	55.0	49.5	34	99.6	89.7	94	144.2	129.8	54	188.8	170.0
15	11.1	10.0	75	55.7	50.2	35	100.3	90.3	95	144.9	130.5	55	189.5	170.6
16	11.9	10.7	76	56.5	50.9	36	101.1	91.0	96	145.7	131.1	56	190.2	171.3
17	12.6	11.4	77	57.2	51.5	37	101.8	91.7	97	146.4	131.8	57	191.0	172.0
18	13.4	12.0	78	58.0	52.2	38	102.6	92.3	98	147.1	132.5	58	191.7	172.6
19	14.1	12.7	79	58.7	52.9	39	103.3	93.0	99	147.9	133.2	59	192.5	173.3
20	14.9	13.4	80	59.5	53.5	40	104.0	93.7	200	148.6	133.8	60	193.2	174.0
21	15.6	14.1	81	60.2	54.2	141	104.8	94.3	201	149.4	134.5	261	194.0	174.6
22	16.3	14.7	82	60.9	54.9	42	105.5	95.0	02	150.1	135.2	62	194.7	175.3
23	17.1	15.4	83	61.7	55.5	43	106.3	95.7	03	150.9	135.8	63	195.4	176.0
24	17.8	16.1	84	62.4	56.2	44	107.0	96.4	04	151.6	136.5	64	196.2	176.7
25	18.6	16.7	85	63.2	56.9	45	107.8	97.0	05	152.3	137.2	65	196.9	177.3
26	19.3	17.4	86	63.9	57.5	46	108.5	97.7	06	153.1	137.8	66	197.7	178.0
27	20.1	18.1	87	64.7	58.2	47	109.2	98.4	07	153.8	138.5	67	198.4	178.7
28	20.8	18.7	88	65.4	58.9	48	110.0	99.0	08	154.6	139.2	68	199.2	179.3
29	21.6	19.4	89	66.1	59.6	49	110.7	99.7	09	155.3	139.8	69	199.9	180.0
30	22.3	20.1	90	66.9	60.2	50	111.5	100.4	10	156.1	140.5	70	200.6	180.7
31	23.0	20.7	91	67.6	60.9	151	112.2	101.0	211	156.8	141.2	271	201.4	181.3
32	23.8	21.4	92	68.4	61.6	52	113.0	101.7	12	157.5	141.9	72	202.1	182.0
33	24.5	22.1	93	69.1	62.2	53	113.7	102.4	13	158.3	142.5	73	202.9	182.7
34	25.3	22.8	94	69.9	62.9	54	114.4	103.0	14	159.0	143.2	74	203.6	183.3
35	26.0	23.4	95	70.6	63.6	55	115.2	103.7	15	159.8	143.9	75	204.4	184.0
36	26.8	24.1	96	71.3	64.2	56	115.9	104.4	16	160.5	144.5	76	205.1	184.7
37	27.5	24.8	97	72.1	64.9	57	116.7	105.1	17	161.3	145.2	77	205.9	185.3
38	28.2	25.4	98	72.8	65.6	58	117.4	105.7	18	162.0	145.9	78	206.6	186.0
39	29.0	26.1	99	73.6	66.2	59	118.2	106.4	19	162.7	146.5	79	207.3	186.7
40	29.7	26.8	100	74.3	66.9	60	118.9	107.1	20	163.5	147.2	80	208.1	187.4
41	30.5	27.4	101	75.1	67.6	161	119.6	107.7	221	164.2	147.9	281	208.8	188.0
42	31.2	28.1	02	75.8	68.3	62	120.4	108.4	22	165.0	148.5	82	209.6	188.7
43	32.0	28.8	03	76.5	68.9	63	121.1	109.1	23	165.7	149.2	83	210.3	189.4
44	32.7	29.4	04	77.3	69.6	64	121.9	109.7	24	166.5	149.9	84	211.1	190.0
45	33.4	30.1	05	78.0	70.3	65	122.6	110.4	25	167.2	150.6	85	211.8	190.7
46	34.2	30.8	06	78.8	70.9	66	123.4	111.1	26	168.0	151.2	86	212.5	191.4
47	34.9	31.4	07	79.5	71.6	67	124.1	111.7	27	168.7	151.9	87	213.3	192.0
48	35.7	32.1	08	80.3	72.3	68	124.8	112.4	28	169.4	152.6	88	214.0	192.7
49	36.4	32.8	09	81.0	72.9	69	125.6	113.1	29	170.2	153.2	89	214.8	193.4
50	37.2	33.5	10	81.7	73.6	70	126.3	113.8	30	170.9	153.9	90	215.5	194.0
51	37.9	34.1	111	82.5	74.3	171	127.1	114.4	231	171.7	154.6	291	216.3	194.7
52	38.6	34.8	12	83.2	74.9	72	127.8	115.1	32	172.4	155.2	92	217.0	195.4
53	39.4	35.5	13	84.0	75.6	73	128.6	115.8	33	173.2	155.9	93	217.7	196.1
54	40.1	36.1	14	84.7	76.3	74	129.3	116.4	34	173.9	156.6	94	218.5	196.7
55	40.9	36.8	15	85.5	77.0	75	130.1	117.1	35	174.6	157.2	95	219.2	197.4
56	41.6	37.5	16	86.2	77.6	76	130.8	117.8	36	175.4	157.9	96	220.0	198.1
57	42.4	38.1	17	86.9	78.3	77	131.5	118.4	37	176.1	158.6	97	220.7	198.7
58	43.1	38.8	18	87.7	79.0	78	132.3	119.1	38	176.9	159.3	98	221.5	199.4
59	43.8	39.5	19	88.4	79.6	79	133.0	119.8	39	177.6	159.9	99	222.2	200.1
60	44.6	40.1	20	89.2	80.3	80	133.8	120.4	40	178.4	160.6	300	222.9	200.7
Dist.	Dep.	Lat.	Dist.	Dep.	Lat.	Dist.	Dep.	Lat.	Dist.	Dep.	Lat.	Dist.	Dep.	Lat.

48° (132°, 228°, 312).

In **Plane Sailing.**	**Dist.**	**Lat.**	**Dep.**
For converting *Dep.* into *Diff. Long.* and *Diff. Long.* into *Dep.* In **Middle Latitude Sailing.**	Diff. Long.	Dep.	
For converting *Dep.* into *Diff. Long.* and *Diff. Long.* into *Dep.* In **Mercator Sailing.**		*m*	Diff. Long.
For multiplication of numbers by sines and by cosines, or solution of plane right-angled triangles.	N. Hypotenuse.	N×Cos. Side Adj.	N×Sin. Side Opp.

TABLE 3.

Difference of Latitude and Departure for 42° (138°, 222°, 318°).

Dist.	Lat.	Dep.	Dist.	Lat.	Dep.	Dist.	Lat.	Dep.	Dist.	Lat.	Dep.	Dist.	Lat.	Dep.
301	223.7	201.4	361	268.3	241.6	421	312.9	281.7	481	357.5	321.9	541	402.0	362.0
02	224.4	202.1	62	269.0	242.2	22	313.6	282.4	82	358.2	322.5	42	402.8	362.7
03	225.2	202.7	63	269.8	242.9	23	314.4	283.0	83	358.9	323.2	43	403.5	363.3
04	225.9	203.4	64	270.5	243.6	24	315.1	283.7	84	359.7	323.9	44	404.3	364.0
05	226.7	204.1	65	271.2	244.2	25	315.8	284.4	85	360.4	324.5	45	405.0	364.7
06	227.4	204.8	66	272.0	244.9	26	316.6	285.1	86	361.2	325.2	46	405.8	365.3
07	228.1	205.4	67	272.7	245.6	27	317.3	285.7	87	361.9	325.9	47	406.5	366.0
08	228.9	206.1	68	273.5	246.2	28	318.1	286.4	88	362.7	326.5	48	407.2	366.7
09	229.6	206.8	69	274.2	246.9	29	318.8	287.1	89	363.4	327.2	49	408.0	367.4
10	230.4	207.4	70	275.0	247.6	30	319.6	287.7	90	364.1	327.9	50	408.7	368.0
311	231.1	208.1	371	275.7	248.2	431	320.3	288.4	491	364.9	328.5	551	409.5	368.7
12	231.9	208.8	72	276.4	248.9	32	321.0	289.1	92	365.6	329.2	52	410.2	369.4
13	232.6	209.4	73	277.2	249.6	33	321.8	289.7	93	366.4	329.9	53	411.0	370.0
14	233.3	210.1	74	277.9	250.3	34	322.5	290.4	94	367.1	330.6	54	411.7	370.7
15	234.1	210.8	75	278.7	250.9	35	323.3	291.1	95	367.9	331.2	55	412.4	371.4
16	234.8	211.4	76	279.4	251.6	36	324.0	291.7	96	368.6	331.9	56	413.2	372.0
17	235.6	212.1	77	280.2	252.3	37	324.8	292.4	97	369.3	332.6	57	413.9	372.7
18	236.3	212.8	78	280.9	252.9	38	325.5	293.1	98	370.1	333.2	58	414.7	373.4
19	237.1	213.5	79	281.7	253.6	39	326.2	293.7	99	370.8	333.9	59	415.4	374.0
20	237.8	214.1	80	282.4	254.3	40	327.0	294.4	500	371.6	334.6	60	416.2	374.7
321	238.5	214.8	381	283.1	254.9	441	327.7	295.1	501	372.3	335.2	561	416.9	375.4
22	239.3	215.5	82	283.9	255.6	42	328.5	295.8	02	373.1	335.9	62	417.6	376.1
23	240.0	216.1	83	284.6	256.3	43	329.2	296.4	03	373.8	336.6	63	418.4	376.7
24	240.8	216.8	84	285.4	256.9	44	330.0	297.1	04	374.5	337.2	64	419.1	377.4
25	241.5	217.5	85	286.1	257.6	45	330.7	297.8	05	375.3	337.9	65	419.9	378.1
26	242.3	218.1	86	286.9	258.3	46	331.4	298.4	06	376.0	338.6	66	420.6	378.7
27	243.0	218.8	87	287.6	259.0	47	332.2	299.1	07	376.8	339.2	67	421.4	379.4
28	243.8	219.5	88	288.3	259.6	48	332.9	299.8	08	377.5	339.9	68	422.1	380.1
29	244.5	220.1	89	289.1	260.3	49	333.7	300.4	09	378.3	340.6	69	422.8	380.7
30	245.2	220.8	90	289.8	261.0	50	334.4	301.1	10	379.0	341.3	70	423.6	381.4
331	246.0	221.5	391	290.6	261.6	451	335.2	301.8	511	379.7	341.9	571	424.3	382.1
32	246.7	222.2	92	291.3	262.3	52	335.9	302.4	12	380.5	342.6	72	425.1	382.7
33	247.5	222.8	93	292.1	263.0	53	336.6	303.1	13	381.2	343.3	73	425.8	383.4
34	248.2	223.5	94	292.8	263.6	54	337.4	303.8	14	382.0	343.9	74	426.6	384.1
35	249.0	224.2	95	293.5	264.3	55	338.1	304.5	15	382.7	344.6	75	427.3	384.8
36	249.7	224.8	96	294.3	265.0	56	338.9	305.1	16	383.5	345.3	76	428.1	385.4
37	250.4	225.5	97	295.0	265.6	57	339.6	305.8	17	384.2	345.9	77	428.8	386.1
38	251.2	226.2	98	295.8	266.3	58	340.4	306.5	18	384.9	346.6	78	429.5	386.8
39	251.9	226.8	99	296.5	267.0	59	341.1	307.1	19	385.7	347.3	79	430.3	387.4
40	252.7	227.5	400	297.3	267.7	60	341.8	307.8	20	386.4	347.9	80	431.0	388.1
341	253.4	228.2	401	298.0	268.3	461	342.6	308.5	521	387.2	348.6	581	431.8	388.8
42	254.2	228.8	02	298.7	269.0	62	343.3	309.1	22	387.9	349.3	82	432.5	389.4
43	254.9	229.5	03	299.5	269.7	63	344.1	309.8	23	388.7	350.0	83	433.3	390.1
44	255.6	230.2	04	300.2	270.3	64	344.8	310.5	24	389.4	350.6	84	434.0	390.8
45	256.4	230.9	05	301.0	271.0	65	345.6	311.1	25	390.2	351.3	85	434.7	391.4
46	257.1	231.5	06	301.7	271.7	66	346.3	311.8	26	390.9	352.0	86	435.5	392.1
47	257.9	232.2	07	302.5	272.3	67	347.0	312.5	27	391.6	352.6	87	436.2	392.8
48	258.6	232.9	08	303.2	273.0	68	347.8	313.2	28	392.4	353.3	88	437.0	393.4
49	259.4	233.5	09	303.9	273.7	69	348.5	313.8	29	393.1	354.0	89	437.7	394.1
50	260.1	234.2	10	304.7	274.3	70	349.3	314.5	30	393.9	354.6	90	438.5	394.8
351	260.8	234.9	411	305.4	275.0	471	350.0	315.2	531	394.6	355.3	591	439.2	395.5
52	261.6	235.5	12	306.2	275.7	72	350.8	315.8	32	395.4	356.0	92	439.9	396.1
53	262.3	236.2	13	306.9	276.4	73	351.5	316.5	33	396.1	356.6	93	440.7	396.8
54	263.1	236.9	14	307.7	277.0	74	352.3	317.2	34	396.8	357.3	94	441.4	397.5
55	263.8	237.5	15	308.4	277.7	75	353.0	317.8	35	397.6	358.0	95	442.2	398.1
56	264.6	238.2	16	309.1	278.4	76	353.7	318.5	36	398.3	358.7	96	442.9	398.8
57	265.3	238.9	17	309.9	279.0	77	354.5	319.2	37	399.1	359.3	97	443.7	399.5
58	266.0	239.5	18	310.6	279.7	78	355.2	319.8	38	399.8	360.0	98	444.4	400.1
59	266.8	240.2	19	311.4	280.4	79	356.0	320.5	39	400.6	360.7	99	445.1	400.8
60	267.5	240.9	20	312.1	281.0	80	356.7	321.2	40	401.3	361.3	600	445.9	401.5
Dist.	Dep.	Lat.	Dist.	Dep.	Lat.	Dist.	Dep.	Lat.	Dist.	Dep.	Lat.	Dist.	Dep.	Lat.

48° (132°, 228°, 312°).

In **Plane Sailing.**	Dist.	Lat.	Dep.
For converting *Dep.* into *Diff. Long.* and *Diff. Long.* into *Dep.* In **Middle Latitude Sailing.**	Diff. Long.	Dep.	
For converting *Dep.* into *Diff. Long.* and *Diff. Long.* into *Dep.* In **Mercator Sailing.**		*m*	Diff. Long.
For multiplication of numbers by sines and by cosines, or solution of plane right-angled triangles.	N. Hypotenuse.	N×Cos. Side Adj.	N×Sin. Side Opp.

TABLE 3.

Difference of Latitude and Departure for 43° (137°, 223°, 317°).

Dist.	Lat.	Dep.	Dist.	Lat.	Dep.	Dist.	Lat.	Dep.	Dist.	Lat.	Dep.	Dist.	Lat.	Dep.
1	0.7	0.7	61	44.6	41.6	121	88.5	82.5	181	132.4	123.4	241	176.3	164.4
2	1.5	1.4	62	45.3	42.3	22	89.2	83.2	82	133.1	124.1	42	177.0	165.0
3	2.2	2.0	63	46.1	43.0	23	90.0	83.9	83	133.8	124.8	43	177.7	165.7
4	2.9	2.7	64	46.8	43.6	24	90.7	84.6	84	134.6	125.5	44	178.5	166.4
5	3.7	3.4	65	47.5	44.3	25	91.4	85.2	85	135.3	126.2	45	179.2	167.1
6	4.4	4.1	66	48.3	45.0	26	92.2	85.9	86	136.0	126.9	46	179.9	167.8
7	5.1	4.8	67	49.0	45.7	27	92.9	86.6	87	136.8	127.5	47	180.6	168.5
8	5.9	5.5	68	49.7	46.4	28	93.6	87.3	88	137.5	128.2	48	181.4	169.1
9	6.6	6.1	69	50.5	47.1	29	94.3	88.0	89	138.2	128.9	49	182.1	169.8
10	7.3	6.8	70	51.2	47.7	30	95.1	88.7	90	139.0	129.6	50	182.8	170.5
11	8.0	7.5	71	51.9	48.4	131	95.8	89.3	191	139.7	130.3	251	183.6	171.2
12	8.8	8.2	72	52.7	49.1	32	96.5	90.0	92	140.4	130.9	52	184.3	171.9
13	9.5	8.9	73	53.4	49.8	33	97.3	90.7	93	141.2	131.6	53	185.0	172.5
14	10.2	9.5	74	54.1	50.5	34	98.0	91.4	94	141.9	132.3	54	185.8	173.2
15	11.0	10.2	75	54.9	51.1	35	98.7	92.1	95	142.6	133.0	55	186.5	173.9
16	11.7	10.9	76	55.6	51.8	36	99.5	92.8	96	143.3	133.7	56	187.2	174.6
17	12.4	11.6	77	56.3	52.5	37	100.2	93.4	97	144.1	134.4	57	188.0	175.3
18	13.2	12.3	78	57.0	53.2	38	100.9	94.1	98	144.8	135.0	58	188.7	176.0
19	13.9	13.0	79	57.8	53.9	39	101.7	94.8	99	145.5	135.7	59	189.4	176.6
20	14.6	13.6	80	58.5	54.6	40	102.4	95.5	200	146.3	136.4	60	190.2	177.3
21	15.4	14.3	81	59.2	55.2	141	103.1	96.2	201	147.0	137.1	261	190.9	178.0
22	16.1	15.0	82	60.0	55.9	42	103.9	96.8	02	147.7	137.8	62	191.6	178.7
23	16.8	15.7	83	60.7	56.6	43	104.6	97.5	03	148.5	138.4	63	192.3	179.4
24	17.6	16.4	84	61.4	57.3	44	105.3	98.2	04	149.2	139.1	64	193.1	180.0
25	18.3	17.0	85	62.2	58.0	45	106.0	98.9	05	149.9	139.8	65	193.8	180.7
26	19.0	17.7	86	62.9	58.7	46	106.8	99.6	06	150.7	140.5	66	194.5	181.4
27	19.7	18.4	87	63.6	59.3	47	107.5	100.3	07	151.4	141.2	67	195.3	182.1
28	20.5	19.1	88	64.4	60.0	48	108.2	100.9	08	152.1	141.9	68	196.0	182.8
29	21.2	19.8	89	65.1	60.7	49	109.0	101.6	09	152.9	142.5	69	196.7	183.5
30	21.9	20.5	90	65.8	61.4	50	109.7	102.3	10	153.6	143.2	70	197.5	184.1
31	22.7	21.1	91	66.6	62.1	151	110.4	103.0	211	154.3	143.9	271	198.2	184.8
32	23.4	21.8	92	67.3	62.7	52	111.2	103.7	12	155.0	144.6	72	198.9	185.5
33	24.1	22.5	93	68.0	63.4	53	111.9	104.3	13	155.8	145.3	73	199.7	186.2
34	24.9	23.2	94	68.7	64.1	54	112.6	105.0	14	156.5	145.9	74	200.4	186.9
35	25.6	23.9	95	69.5	64.8	55	113.4	105.7	15	157.2	146.6	75	201.1	187.5
36	26.3	24.6	96	70.2	65.5	56	114.1	106.4	16	158.0	147.3	76	201.9	188.2
37	27.1	25.2	97	70.9	66.2	57	114.8	107.1	17	158.7	148.0	77	202.6	188.9
38	27.8	25.9	98	71.7	66.8	58	115.6	107.8	18	159.4	148.7	78	203.3	189.6
39	28.5	26.6	99	72.4	67.5	59	116.3	108.4	19	160.2	149.4	79	204.0	190.3
40	29.3	27.3	100	73.1	68.2	60	117.0	109.1	20	160.9	150.0	80	204.8	191.0
41	30.0	28.0	101	73.9	68.9	161	117.7	109.8	221	161.6	150.7	281	205.5	191.6
42	30.7	28.6	02	74.6	69.6	62	118.5	110.5	22	162.4	151.4	82	206.2	192.3
43	31.4	29.3	03	75.3	70.2	63	119.2	111.2	23	163.1	152.1	83	207.0	193.0
44	32.2	30.0	04	76.1	70.9	64	119.9	111.8	24	163.8	152.8	84	207.7	193.7
45	32.9	30.7	05	76.8	71.6	65	120.7	112.5	25	164.6	153.4	85	208.4	194.4
46	33.6	31.4	06	77.5	72.3	66	121.4	113.2	26	165.3	154.1	86	209.2	195.1
47	34.4	32.1	07	78.3	73.0	67	122.1	113.9	27	166.0	154.8	87	209.9	195.7
48	35.1	32.7	08	79.0	73.7	68	122.9	114.6	28	166.7	155.5	88	210.6	196.4
49	35.8	33.4	09	79.7	74.3	69	123.6	115.3	29	167.5	156.2	89	211.4	197.1
50	36.6	34.1	10	80.4	75.0	70	124.3	115.9	30	168.2	156.9	90	212.1	197.8
51	37.3	34.8	111	81.2	75.7	171	125.1	116.6	231	168.9	157.5	291	212.8	198.5
52	38.0	35.5	12	81.9	76.4	72	125.8	117.3	32	169.7	158.2	92	213.6	199.1
53	38.8	36.1	13	82.6	77.1	73	126.5	118.0	33	170.4	158.9	93	214.3	199.8
54	39.5	36.8	14	83.4	77.7	74	127.3	118.7	34	171.1	159.6	94	215.0	200.5
55	40.2	37.5	15	84.1	78.4	75	128.0	119.3	35	171.9	160.3	95	215.7	201.2
56	41.0	38.2	16	84.8	79.1	76	128.7	120.0	36	172.6	161.0	96	216.5	201.9
57	41.7	38.9	17	85.6	79.8	77	129.4	120.7	37	173.3	161.6	97	217.2	202.6
58	42.4	39.6	18	86.3	80.5	78	130.2	121.4	38	174.1	162.3	98	217.9	203.2
59	43.1	40.2	19	87.0	81.2	79	130.9	122.1	39	174.8	163.0	99	218.7	203.9
60	43.9	40.9	20	87.8	81.8	80	131.6	122.8	40	175.5	163.7	300	219.4	204.6
Dist.	Dep.	Lat.	Dist.	Dep.	Lat.	Dist.	Dep.	Lat.	Dist.	Dep.	Lat.	Dist.	Dep.	Lat.

47° (133°, 227°, 313°).

In **Plane Sailing.**	**Dist.**	**Lat.**	**Dep.**
For converting *Dep.* into *Diff. Long.* and *Diff. Long.* into *Dep.* In **Middle Latitude Sailing.**	Diff. Long.	Dep.	
For converting *Dep.* into *Diff. Long.* and *Diff. Long.* into *Dep.* In **Mercator Sailing.**		*m*	Diff. Long.
For multiplication of numbers by sines and by cosines, or solution of plane right-angled triangles.	N. Hypotenuse.	N×Cos. Side Adj.	N×Sin. Side Opp.

TABLE 3.

Difference of Latitude and Departure for 43° (137°, 223°, 317°).

Dist.	Lat.	Dep.	Dist.	Lat.	Dep.	Dist.	Lat.	Dep.	Dist.	Lat.	Dep.	Dist.	Lat.	Dep.
301	220.1	205.3	361	264.0	246.2	421	307.9	287.1	481	351.8	328.1	541	395.7	369.0
02	220.9	206.0	62	264.8	246.9	22	308.6	287.8	82	352.5	328.7	42	396.4	369.6
03	221.6	206.6	63	265.5	247.6	23	309.4	288.5	83	353.2	329.4	43	397.1	370.3
04	222.3	207.3	64	266.2	248.2	24	310.1	289.2	84	354.0	330.1	44	397.9	371.0
05	223.1	208.0	65	266.9	248.9	25	310.8	289.8	85	354.7	330.8	45	398.6	371.7
06	223.8	208.7	66	267.7	249.6	26	311.6	290.5	86	355.4	331.5	46	399.3	372.4
07	224.5	209.4	67	268.4	250.3	27	312.3	291.2	87	356.2	332.1	47	400.1	373.1
08	225.3	210.1	68	269.1	251.0	28	313.0	291.9	88	356.9	332.8	48	400.8	373.7
09	226.0	210.7	69	269.9	251.7	29	313.8	292.6	89	357.6	333.5	49	401.5	374.4
10	226.7	211.4	70	270.6	252.3	30	314.5	293.3	90	358.4	334.2	50	402.2	375.1
311	227.5	212.1	371	271.3	253.0	431	315.2	293.9	491	359.1	334.9	551	403.0	375.8
12	228.2	212.8	72	272.1	253.7	32	315.9	294.6	92	359.8	335.5	52	403.7	376.5
13	228.9	213.5	73	272.8	254.4	33	316.7	295.3	93	360.6	336.2	53	404.4	377.1
14	229.6	214.1	74	273.5	255.1	34	317.4	296.0	94	361.3	336.9	54	405.2	377.8
15	230.4	214.8	75	274.3	255.7	35	318.1	296.7	95	362.0	337.6	55	405.9	378.5
16	231.1	215.5	76	275.0	256.4	36	318.9	297.4	96	362.8	338.3	56	406.6	379.2
17	231.8	216.2	77	275.7	257.1	37	319.6	298.0	97	363.5	339.0	57	407.4	379.9
18	232.6	216.9	78	276.5	257.8	38	320.3	298.7	98	364.2	339.6	58	408.1	380.6
19	233.3	217.6	79	277.2	258.5	39	321.1	299.4	99	364.9	340.3	59	408.8	381.2
20	234.0	218.2	80	277.9	259.2	40	321.8	300.1	500	365.7	341.0	60	409.6	381.9
321	234.8	218.9	381	278.6	259.8	441	322.5	300.8	501	366.4	341.7	561	410.3	382.6
22	235.5	219.6	82	279.4	260.5	42	323.3	301.4	02	367.1	342.4	62	411.0	383.3
23	236.2	220.3	83	280.1	261.2	43	324.0	302.1	03	367.9	343.0	63	411.8	384.0
24	237.0	221.0	84	280.8	261.9	44	324.7	302.8	04	368.6	343.7	64	412.5	384.6
25	237.7	221.6	85	281.6	262.6	45	325.5	303.5	05	369.3	344.4	65	413.2	385.3
26	238.4	222.3	86	282.3	263.3	46	326.2	304.2	06	370.1	345.1	66	413.9	386.0
27	239.2	223.0	87	283.0	263.9	47	326.9	304.9	07	370.8	345.8	67	414.7	386.7
28	239.9	223.7	88	283.8	264.6	48	327.6	305.5	08	371.5	346.5	68	415.4	387.4
29	240.6	224.4	89	284.5	265.3	49	328.4	306.2	09	372.3	347.1	69	416.1	388.1
30	241.3	225.1	90	285.2	266.0	50	329.1	306.9	10	373.0	347.8	70	416.9	388.7
331	242.1	225.7	391	286.0	266.7	451	329.9	307.6	511	373.7	348.5	571	417.6	389.4
32	242.8	226.4	92	286.7	267.3	52	330.6	308.3	12	374.5	349.2	72	418.3	390.1
33	243.5	227.1	93	287.4	268.0	53	331.3	308.9	13	375.2	349.9	73	419.1	390.8
34	244.3	227.8	94	288.2	268.7	54	332.0	309.6	14	375.9	350.5	74	419.8	391.5
35	245.0	228.5	95	288.9	269.4	55	332.8	310.3	15	376.6	351.2	75	420.5	392.1
36	245.7	229.2	96	289.6	270.1	56	333.5	311.0	16	377.4	351.9	76	421.3	392.8
37	246.5	229.8	97	290.3	270.8	57	334.2	311.7	17	378.1	352.6	77	422.0	393.5
38	247.2	230.5	98	291.1	271.4	58	335.0	312.4	18	378.8	353.3	78	422.7	394.2
39	247.9	231.2	99	291.8	272.1	59	335.7	313.0	19	379.6	354.0	79	423.5	394.9
40	248.7	231.9	400	292.5	272.8	60	336.4	313.7	20	380.3	354.6	80	424.2	395.6
341	249.4	232.6	401	293.3	273.5	461	337.2	314.4	521	381.0	355.3	581	424.9	396.2
42	250.1	233.2	02	294.0	274.2	62	337.9	315.1	22	381.8	356.0	82	425.6	396.9
43	250.9	233.9	03	294.7	274.8	63	338.6	315.8	23	382.5	356.7	83	426.4	397.6
44	251.6	234.6	04	295.5	275.5	64	339.3	316.4	24	383.2	357.4	84	427.1	398.3
45	252.3	235.3	05	296.2	276.2	65	340.1	317.1	25	384.0	358.0	85	427.8	399.0
46	253.0	236.0	06	296.9	276.9	66	340.8	317.8	26	384.7	358.7	86	428.6	399.7
47	253.8	236.7	07	297.7	277.6	67	341.5	318.5	27	385.4	359.4	87	429.3	400.3
48	254.5	237.3	08	298.4	278.3	68	342.3	319.2	28	386.2	360.1	88	430.0	401.0
49	255.2	238.0	09	299.1	278.9	69	343.0	319.9	29	386.9	360.8	89	430.8	401.7
50	256.0	238.7	10	299.9	279.6	70	343.7	320.5	30	387.6	361.5	90	431.5	402.4
351	256.7	239.4	411	300.6	280.3	471	344.5	321.2	531	388.3	362.1	591	432.2	403.1
52	257.4	240.1	12	301.3	281.0	72	345.2	321.9	32	389.1	362.8	92	433.0	403.7
53	258.2	240.9	13	302.0	281.7	73	345.9	322.6	33	389.8	363.5	93	433.7	404.4
54	258.9	241.4	14	302.8	282.3	74	346.7	323.3	34	390.5	364.2	94	434.4	405.1
55	259.6	242.1	15	303.5	283.0	75	347.4	323.9	35	391.3	364.9	95	435.2	405.8
56	260.4	242.8	16	304.3	283.7	76	348.1	324.6	36	392.0	365.6	96	435.9	406.5
57	261.1	243.5	17	305.0	284.4	77	348.9	325.3	37	392.7	366.2	97	436.6	407.2
58	261.8	244.2	18	305.7	285.1	78	349.6	326.0	38	393.5	366.9	98	437.3	407.8
59	262.6	244.8	19	306.4	285.8	79	350.3	326.7	39	394.2	367.6	99	438.1	408.5
60	263.3	245.5	20	307.2	286.4	80	351.0	327.4	40	394.9	368.3	600	438.8	409.2
Dist.	Dep.	Lat.	Dist.	Dep.	Lat.	Dist.	Dep.	Lat.	Dist.	Dep.	Lat.	Dist.	Dep.	Lat.

47° (133°, 227°, 313°).

	Dist.	Lat.	Dep.
In **Plane Sailing.**			
For converting *Dep.* into *Diff. Long.* and *Diff. Long.* into *Dep.* In **Middle Latitude Sailing.**	Diff. Long.	Dep.	
For converting *Dep.* into *Diff. Long.* and *Diff. Long.* into *Dep.* In **Mercator Sailing.**		*m*	Diff. Long.
	N.	N×Cos.	N×Sin.
For multiplication of numbers by sines and by cosines, or solution of plane right-angled triangles.	Hypotenuse.	Side Adj.	Side Opp.

TABLE 3.

Difference of Latitude and Departure for 44° (136°, 224°, 316°).

Dist.	Lat.	Dep.	Dist.	Lat.	Dep.	Dist.	Lat.	Dep.	Dist.	Lat.	Dep.	Dist.	Lat.	Dep.
1	0.7	0.7	61	43.9	42.4	121	87.0	84.1	181	130.2	125.7	241	173.4	167.4
2	1.4	1.4	62	44.6	43.1	22	87.8	84.7	82	130.9	126.4	42	174.1	168.1
3	2.2	2.1	63	45.3	43.8	23	88.5	85.4	83	131.6	127.1	43	174.8	168.8
4	2.9	2.8	64	46.0	44.5	24	89.2	86.1	84	132.4	127.8	44	175.5	169.5
5	3.6	3.5	65	46.8	45.2	25	89.9	86.8	85	133.1	128.5	45	176.2	170.2
6	4.3	4.2	66	47.5	45.8	26	90.6	87.5	86	133.8	129.2	46	177.0	170.9
7	5.0	4.9	67	48.2	46.5	27	91.4	88.2	87	134.5	129.9	47	177.7	171.6
8	5.8	5.6	68	48.9	47.2	28	92.1	88.9	88	135.2	130.6	48	178.4	172.3
9	6.5	6.3	69	49.6	47.9	29	92.8	89.6	89	136.0	131.3	49	179.1	173.0
10	7.2	6.9	70	50.4	48.6	30	93.5	90.3	90	136.7	132.0	50	179.8	173.7
11	7.9	7.6	71	51.1	49.3	131	94.2	91.0	191	137.4	132.7	251	180.6	174.4
12	8.6	8.3	72	51.8	50.0	32	95.0	91.7	92	138.1	133.4	52	181.3	175.1
13	9.4	9.0	73	52.5	50.7	33	95.7	92.4	93	138.8	134.1	53	182.0	175.7
14	10.1	9.7	74	53.2	51.4	34	96.4	93.1	94	139.6	134.8	54	182.7	176.4
15	10.8	10.4	75	54.0	52.1	35	97.1	93.8	95	140.3	135.5	55	183.4	177.1
16	11.5	11.1	76	54.7	52.8	36	97.8	94.5	96	141.0	136.2	56	184.2	177.8
17	12.2	11.8	77	55.4	53.5	37	98.5	95.2	97	141.7	136.8	57	184.9	178.5
18	12.9	12.5	78	56.1	54.2	38	99.3	95.9	98	142.4	137.5	58	185.6	179.2
19	13.7	13.2	79	56.8	54.9	39	100.0	96.6	99	143.1	138.2	59	186.3	179.9
20	14.4	13.9	80	57.5	55.6	40	100.7	97.3	200	143.9	138.9	60	187.0	180.6
21	15.1	14.6	81	58.3	56.3	141	101.4	97.9	201	144.6	139.6	261	187.7	181.3
22	15.8	15.3	82	59.0	57.0	42	102.1	98.6	02	145.3	140.3	62	188.5	182.0
23	16.5	16.0	83	59.7	57.7	43	102.9	99.3	03	146.0	141.0	63	189.2	182.7
24	17.3	16.7	84	60.4	58.4	44	103.6	100.0	04	146.7	141.7	64	189.9	183.4
25	18.0	17.4	85	61.1	59.0	45	104.3	100.7	05	147.5	142.4	65	190.6	184.1
26	18.7	18 1	86	61.9	59.7	46	105.0	101.4	06	148.2	143.1	66	191.3	184.8
27	19.4	18.8	87	62.6	60.4	47	105.7	102.1	07	148.9	143.8	67	192.1	185.5
28	20.1	19.5	88	63.3	61.1	48	106.5	102.8	08	149.6	144.5	68	192.8	186.2
29	20.9	20.1	89	64.0	61.8	49	107.2	103.5	09	150.3	145.2	69	193.5	186.9
30	21.6	20.8	90	64.7	62.5	50	107.9	104.2	10	151.1	145.9	70	194.2	187.6
31	22.3	21.5	91	65.5	63.2	151	108.6	104.9	211	151.8	146.6	271	194.9	188.3
32	23.0	22.2	92	66.2	63.9	52	109.3	105.6	12	152.5	147.3	72	195.7	188.9
33	23.7	22.9	93	66.9	64.6	53	110.1	106.3	13	153.2	148.0	73	196.4	189.6
34	24.5	23.6	94	67.6	65.3	54	110.8	107.0	14	153.9	148.7	74	197.1	190.3
35	25.2	24.3	95	68.3	66.0	55	111.5	107.7	15	154.7	149.4	75	197.8	191.0
36	25.9	25.0	96	69.1	66.7	56	112.2	108.4	16	155.4	150.0	76	198.5	191.7
37	26.6	25.7	97	69.8	67.4	57	112.9	109.1	17	156.1	150.7	77	199.3	192.4
38	27.3	26.4	98	70.5	68.1	58	113.7	109.8	18	156.8	151.4	78	200.0	193.1
39	28.1	27.1	99	71.2	68.8	59	114.4	110.5	19	157.5	152.1	79	200.7	193.8
40	28.8	27.8	100	71.9	69.5	60	115.1	111.1	20	158.3	152.8	80	201.4	194.5
41	29.5	28.5	101	72.7	70.2	161	115.8	111.8	221	159.0	153.5	281	202.1	195.2
42	30.2	29.2	02	73.4	70.9	62	116.5	112.5	22	159.7	154.2	82	202.9	195.9
43	30.9	29.9	03	74.1	71.5	63	117.3	113.2	23	160.4	154.9	83	203.6	196.6
44	31.7	30.6	04	74.8	72.2	64	118.0	113.9	24	161.1	155.6	84	204.3	197.3
45	32.4	31.3	05	75.5	72.9	65	118.7	114.6	25	161.9	156.3	85	205.0	198.0
46	33.1	32.0	06	76.3	73.6	66	119.4	115.3	26	162.6	157.0	86	205.7	198.7
47	33.8	32.6	07	77.0	74.3	67	120.1	116.0	27	163.3	157.7	87	206.5	199.4
48	34.5	33.3	08	77.7	75.0	68	120.8	116.7	28	164.0	158.4	88	207.2	200.1
49	35.2	34.0	09	78.4	75.7	69	121.6	117.4	29	164.7	159.1	89	207.9	200.8
50	36.0	34.7	10	79.1	76.4	70	122.3	118.1	30	165.4	159.8	90	208.6	201.5
51	36.7	35.4	111	79.8	77.1	171	123.0	118.8	231	166.2	160.5	291	209.3	202.1
52	37.4	36.1	12	80.6	77.8	72	123.7	119.5	32	166.9	161.2	92	210.0	202.8
53	38.1	36.8	13	81.3	78.5	73	124.4	120.2	33	167.6	161.9	93	210.8	203.5
54	38.8	37.5	14	82.0	79.2	74	125.2	120.9	34	168.3	162.6	94	211.5	204.2
55	39.6	38.2	15	82.7	79.9	75	125.9	121.6	35	169.0	163.2	95	212.2	204.9
56	40.3	38.9	16	83.4	80.6	76	126.6	122.3	36	169.8	163.9	96	212.9	205.6
57	41.0	39.6	17	84.2	81.3	77	127.3	123.0	37	170.5	164.6	97	213.6	206.3
58	41.7	40.3	18	84.9	82.0	78	128.0	123.6	38	171.2	165.3	98	214.4	207.0
59	42.4	41.0	19	85.6	82.7	79	128.8	124.3	39	171.9	166.0	99	215.1	207.7
60	43.2	41.7	20	86.3	83.4	80	129.5	125.0	40	172.6	166.7	300	215.8	208.4
Dist.	Dep.	Lat.	Dist.	Dep.	Lat.	Dist.	Dep.	Lat.	Dist.	Dep.	Lat.	Dist.	Dep.	Lat.

46° (134°, 226°, 314°).

In **Plane Sailing.**	**Dist.**	**Lat.**	**Dep.**
For converting *Dep.* into *Diff. Long.* and *Diff. Long.* into *Dep.* In **Middle Latitude Sailing.**	Diff. Long.	Dep.	
For converting *Dep.* into *Diff. Long.* and *Diff. Long.* into *Dep.* In **Mercator Sailing.**		*m*	Diff Long.
For multiplication of numbers by sines and by cosines, or solution of plane right-angled triangles.	N. Hypotenuse.	N×Cos. Side Adj.	N×Sin. Side Opp.

TABLE 3.

Difference of Latitude and Departure for 44° (136°, 224°, 316°).

Dist.	Lat.	Dep.	Dist.	Lat.	Dep.	Dist.	Lat.	Dep.	Dist.	Lat.	Dep.	Dist.	Lat.	Dep.
301	216.5	209.1	361	259.7	250.8	421	302.8	292.5	481	346.0	334.1	541	389.2	375.8
02	217.2	209.8	62	260.4	251.5	22	303.6	293.1	82	346.7	334.8	42	389.9	376.5
03	218.0	210.5	63	261.1	252.2	23	304.3	293.8	83	347.4	335.5	43	390.6	377.2
04	218.7	211.2	64	261.8	252.9	24	305.0	294.5	84	348.2	336.2	44	391.3	377.9
05	219.4	211.9	65	262.6	253.6	25	305.7	295.2	85	348.9	336.9	45	392.0	378.6
06	220.1	212.6	66	263.3	254.2	26	306.4	295.9	86	349.6	337.6	46	392.8	379.3
07	220.8	213.3	67	264.0	254.9	27	307.2	296.6	87	350.3	338.3	47	393.5	380.0
08	221.6	214.0	68	264.7	255.6	28	307.9	297.3	88	351.0	339.0	48	394.2	380.7
09	222.3	214.6	69	265.4	256.3	29	308.6	298.0	89	351.7	339.7	49	394.9	381.4
10	223.0	215.3	70	266.2	257.0	30	309.3	298.7	90	352.5	340.4	50	395.6	382.1
311	223.7	216.0	371	266.9	257.7	431	310.0	299.4	491	353.2	341.1	551	396.4	382.8
12	224.4	216.7	72	267.6	258.4	32	310.8	300.1	92	353.9	341.8	52	397.1	383.5
13	225.2	217.4	73	268.3	259.1	33	311.5	300.8	93	354.6	342.5	53	397.8	384.1
14	225.9	218.1	74	269.0	259.8	34	312.2	301.5	94	355.4	343.2	54	398.5	384.8
15	226.6	218.8	75	269.8	260.5	35	312.9	302.2	95	356.1	343.9	55	399.2	385.5
16	227.3	219.5	76	270.5	261.2	36	313.6	302.9	96	356.8	344.6	56	400.0	386.2
17	228.0	220.2	77	271.2	261.9	37	314.4	303.6	97	357.5	345.2	57	400.7	386.9
18	228.8	220.9	78	271.9	262.6	38	315.1	304.3	98	358.2	345.9	58	401.4	387.6
19	229.5	221.6	79	272.6	263.3	39	315.8	305.0	99	359.0	346.6	59	402.1	388.3
20	230.2	222.3	80	273.3	264.0	40	316.6	305.6	500	359.7	347.3	60	402.8	389.0
321	230.9	223.0	381	274.1	264.7	441	317.2	306.3	501	360.4	348.0	561	403.5	389.7
22	231.6	223.7	82	274.8	265.4	42	317.9	307.0	02	361.1	348.7	62	404.3	390.4
23	232.3	224.4	83	275.5	266.1	43	318.7	307.7	03	361.8	349.4	63	405.0	391.1
24	233.1	225.1	84	276.2	266.7	44	319.4	308.4	04	362.5	350.1	64	405.7	391.8
25	233.8	225.8	85	276.9	267.4	45	320.1	309.1	05	363.3	350.8	65	406.4	392.5
26	234.5	226.5	86	277.7	268.1	46	320.8	309.8	06	364.0	351.5	66	407.1	393.2
27	235.2	227.2	87	278.4	268.8	47	321.5	310.5	07	364.7	352.2	67	407.9	393.9
28	235.9	227.8	88	279.1	269.5	48	322.3	311.2	08	365.4	352.9	68	408.6	394.6
29	236.7	228.5	89	279.8	270.2	49	323.0	311.9	09	366.1	353.6	69	409.3	395.3
30	237.4	229.2	90	280.5	270.9	50	323.7	312.6	10	366.9	354.3	70	410.0	396.0
331	238.1	229.9	391	281.3	271.6	451	324.4	313.3	511	367.6	355.0	571	410.7	396.6
32	238.8	230.6	92	282.0	272.3	52	325.1	314.0	12	368.3	355.7	72	411.5	397.3
33	239.5	231.3	93	282.7	273.0	53	325.9	314.7	13	369.0	356.4	73	412.2	398.0
34	240.3	232.0	94	283.4	273.7	54	326.6	315.4	14	369.7	357.1	74	412.9	398.7
35	241.0	232.7	95	284.1	274.4	55	327.3	316.1	15	370.5	357.7	75	413.6	399.4
36	241.7	233.4	96	284.9	275.1	56	328.0	316.8	16	371.2	358.4	76	414.3	400.1
37	242.4	234.1	97	285.6	275.8	57	328.7	317.5	17	371.9	359.1	77	415.1	400.8
38	243.1	234.8	98	286.3	276.5	58	329.5	318.2	18	372.6	359.8	78	415.8	401.5
39	243.9	235.5	99	287.0	277.2	59	330.2	318.8	19	373.3	360.5	79	416.5	402.2
40	244.6	236.2	400	287.7	277.9	60	330.9	319.5	20	374.1	361.2	80	417.2	402.9
341	245.3	236.9	401	288.5	278.6	461	331.6	320.2	521	374.8	361.9	581	417.9	403.6
42	246.0	237.6	02	289.2	279.3	62	332.3	320.9	22	375.5	362.6	82	418.7	404.3
43	246.7	238.3	03	289.9	279.9	63	333.1	321.6	23	376.2	363.3	83	419.4	405.0
44	247.5	239.0	04	290.6	280.6	64	333.8	322.3	24	376.9	364.0	84	420.1	405.7
45	248.2	239.7	05	291.3	281.3	65	334.5	323.0	25	377.7	364.7	85	420.8	406.4
46	248.9	240.4	06	292.1	282.0	66	335.2	323.7	26	378.4	365.4	86	421.5	407.1
47	249.6	241.0	07	292.8	282.7	67	335.9	324.4	27	379.1	366.1	87	422.3	407.8
48	250.3	241.7	08	293.5	283.4	68	336.7	325.1	28	379.8	366.8	88	423.0	408.5
49	251.0	242.4	09	294.2	284.1	69	337.4	325.8	29	380.5	367.5	89	423.7	409.2
50	251.8	243.1	10	294.9	284.8	70	338.1	326.5	30	381.3	368.2	90	424.4	409.8
351	252.5	243.8	411	295.6	285.5	471	338.8	327.2	531	382.0	368.9	591	425.1	410.5
52	253.2	244.5	12	296.4	286.2	72	339.5	327.9	32	382.7	369.6	92	425.8	411.2
53	253.9	245.2	13	297.1	286.9	73	340.2	328.6	33	383.4	370.3	93	426.6	411.9
54	254.6	245.9	14	297.8	287.6	74	341.0	329.3	34	384.1	370.9	94	427.3	412.6
55	255.4	246.6	15	298.5	288.3	75	341.7	330.0	35	384.8	371.6	95	428.0	413.3
56	256.1	247.3	16	299.2	289.0	76	342.4	330.7	36	385.6	372.3	96	428.7	414.0
57	256.8	248.0	17	300.0	289.7	77	343.1	331.4	37	386.3	373.0	97	429.4	414.7
58	257.5	248.7	18	300.7	290.4	78	343.8	332.0	38	387.0	373.7	98	430.2	415.4
59	258.2	249.4	19	301.4	291.1	79	344.6	332.7	39	387.7	374.4	99	430.9	416.1
60	259.0	250.1	20	302.1	291.8	80	345.3	333.4	40	388.4	375.1	600	431.6	416.8
Dist.	Dep.	Lat.	Dist.	Dep.	Lat.	Dist.	Dep.	Lat.	Dist.	Dep.	Lat.	Dist.	Dep.	Lat.

46° (134°, 226°, 314°).

In **Plane Sailing.**	Dist.	Lat.	Dep.
For converting *Dep.* into *Diff. Long.* and *Diff. Long.* into *Dep.* In **Middle Latitude Sailing.**	Diff. Long.	Dep.	
For converting *Dep.* into *Diff. Long.* and *Diff. Long.* into *Dep.* In **Mercator Sailing.**		*m*	Diff. Long.
	N.	N×Cos.	N×Sin.
For multiplication of numbers by sines and by cosines, or solution of plane right-angled triangles.	Hypotenuse.	Side Adj.	Side Opp.

TABLE 3.

Difference of Latitude and Departure for 45° (135°, 225°, 315°).

Dist.	Lat.	Dep.	Dist.	Lat.	Dep.	Dist.	Lat.	Dep.	Dist.	Lat.	Dep.	Dist.	Lat.	Dep.
1	0.7	0.7	61	43.1	43.1	121	85.6	85.6	181	128.0	128.0	241	170.4	170.4
2	1.4	1.4	62	43.8	43.8	22	86.3	86.3	82	128.7	128.7	42	171.1	171.1
3	2.1	2.1	63	44.5	44.5	23	87.0	87.0	83	129.4	129.4	43	171.8	171.8
4	2.8	2.8	64	45.3	45.3	24	87.7	87.7	84	130.1	130.1	44	172.5	172.5
5	3.5	3.5	65	46.0	46.0	25	88.4	88.4	85	130.8	130.8	45	173.2	173.2
6	4.2	4.2	66	46.7	46.7	26	89.1	89.1	86	131.5	131.5	46	173.9	173.9
7	4.9	4.9	67	47.4	47.4	27	89.8	89.8	87	132.2	132.2	47	174.7	174.7
8	5.7	5.7	68	48.1	48.1	28	90.5	90.5	88	132.9	132.9	48	175.4	175.4
9	6.4	6.4	69	48.8	48.8	29	91.2	91.2	89	133.6	133.6	49	176.1	176.1
10	7.1	7.1	70	49.5	49.5	30	91.9	91.9	90	134.4	134.4	50	176.8	176.8
11	7.8	7.8	71	50.2	50.2	131	92.6	92.6	191	135.1	135.1	251	177.5	177.5
12	8.5	8.5	72	50.9	50.9	32	93.3	93.3	92	135.8	135.8	52	178.2	178.2
13	9.2	9.2	73	51.6	51.6	33	94.0	94.0	93	136.5	136.5	53	178.9	178.9
14	9.9	9.9	74	52.3	52.3	34	94.8	94.8	94	137.2	137.2	54	179.6	179.6
15	10.6	10.6	75	53.0	53.0	35	95.5	95.5	95	137.9	137.9	55	180.3	180.3
16	11.3	11.3	76	53.7	53.7	36	96.2	96.2	96	138.6	138.6	56	181.0	181.0
17	12.0	12.0	77	54.4	54.4	37	96.9	96.9	97	139.3	139.3	57	181.7	181.7
18	12.7	12.7	78	55.2	55.2	38	97.6	97.6	98	140.0	140.0	58	182.4	182.4
19	13.4	13.4	79	55.9	55.9	39	98.3	98.3	99	140.7	140.7	59	183.1	183.1
20	14.1	14.1	80	56.6	56.6	40	99.0	99.0	200	141.4	141.4	60	183.8	183.8
21	14.8	14.8	81	57.3	57.3	141	99.7	99.7	201	142.1	142.1	261	184.6	184.6
22	15.6	15.6	82	58.0	58.0	42	100.4	100.4	02	142.8	142.8	62	185.3	185.3
23	16.3	16.3	83	58.7	58.7	43	101.1	101.1	03	143.5	143.5	63	186.0	186.0
24	17.0	17.0	84	59.4	59.4	44	101.8	101.8	04	144.2	144.2	64	186.7	186.7
25	17.7	17.7	85	60.1	60.1	45	102.5	102.5	05	145.0	145.0	65	187.4	187.4
26	18.4	18.4	86	60.8	60.8	46	103.2	103.2	06	145.7	145.7	66	188.1	188.1
27	19.1	19.1	87	61.5	61.5	47	103.9	103.9	07	146.4	146.4	67	188.8	188.8
28	19.8	19.8	88	62.2	62.2	48	104.7	104.7	08	147.1	147.1	68	189.5	189.5
29	20.5	20.5	89	62.9	62.9	49	105.4	105.4	09	147.8	147.8	69	190.2	190.2
30	21.2	21.2	90	63.6	63.6	50	106.1	106.1	10	148.5	148.5	70	190.9	190.9
31	21.9	21.9	91	64.3	64.3	151	106.8	106.8	211	149.2	149.2	271	191.6	191.6
32	22.6	22.6	92	65.1	65.1	52	107.5	107.5	12	149.9	149.9	72	192.3	192.3
33	23.3	23.3	93	65.8	65.8	53	108.2	108.2	13	150.6	150.6	73	193.0	193.0
34	24.0	24.0	94	66.5	66.5	54	108.9	108.9	14	151.3	151.3	74	193.7	193.7
35	24.7	24.7	95	67.2	67.2	55	109.6	109.6	15	152.0	152.0	75	194.5	194.5
36	25.5	25.5	96	67.9	67.9	56	110.3	110.3	16	152.7	152.7	76	195.2	195.2
37	26.2	26.2	97	68.6	68.6	57	111.0	111.0	17	153.4	153.4	77	195.9	195.9
38	26.9	26.9	98	69.3	69.3	58	111.7	111.7	18	154.1	154.1	78	196.6	196.6
39	27.6	27.6	99	70.0	70.0	59	112.4	112.4	19	154.9	154.9	79	197.3	197.3
40	28.3	28.3	100	70.7	70.7	60	113.1	113.1	20	155.6	155.6	80	198.0	198.0
41	29.0	29.0	101	71.4	71.4	161	113.8	113.8	221	156.3	156.3	281	198.7	198.7
42	29.7	29.7	02	72.1	72.1	62	114.6	114.6	22	157.0	157.0	82	199.4	199.4
43	30.4	30.4	03	72.8	72.8	63	115.3	115.3	23	157.7	157.7	83	200.1	200.1
44	31.1	31.1	04	73.5	73.5	64	116.0	116.0	24	158.4	158.4	84	200.8	200.8
45	31.8	31.8	05	74.2	74.2	65	116.7	116.7	25	159.1	159.1	85	201.5	201.5
46	32.5	32.5	06	75.0	75.0	66	117.4	117.4	26	159.8	159.8	86	202.2	202.2
47	33.2	33.2	07	75.7	75.7	67	118.1	118.1	27	160.5	160.5	87	202.9	202.9
48	33.9	33.9	08	76.4	76.4	68	118.8	118.8	28	161.2	161.2	88	203.6	203.6
49	34.6	34.6	09	77.1	77.1	69	119.5	119.5	29	161.9	161.9	89	204.4	204.4
50	35.4	35.4	10	77.8	77.8	70	120.2	120.2	30	162.6	162.6	90	205.1	205.1
51	36.1	36.1	111	78.5	78.5	171	120.9	120.9	231	163.3	163.3	291	205.8	205.8
52	36.8	36.8	12	79.2	79.2	72	121.6	121.6	32	164.0	164.0	92	206.5	206.5
53	37.5	37.5	13	79.9	79.9	73	122.3	122.3	33	164.8	164.8	93	207.2	207.2
54	38.2	38.2	14	80.6	80.6	74	123.0	123.0	34	165.5	165.5	94	207.9	207.9
55	38.9	38.9	15	81.3	81.3	75	123.7	123.7	35	166.2	166.2	95	208.6	208.6
56	39.6	39.6	16	82.0	82.0	76	124.5	124.5	36	166.9	166.9	96	209.3	209.3
57	40.3	40.3	17	82.7	82.7	77	125.2	125.2	37	167.6	167.6	97	210.0	210.0
58	41.0	41.0	18	83.4	83.4	78	125.9	125.9	38	168.3	168.3	98	210.7	210.7
59	41.7	41.7	19	84.1	84.1	79	126.6	126.6	39	169.0	169.0	99	211.4	211.4
60	42.4	42.4	20	84.9	84.9	80	127.3	127.3	40	169.7	169.7	300	212.1	212.1
Dist.	Dep.	Lat.	Dist.	Dep.	Lat.	Dist.	Dep.	Lat.	Dist.	Dep.	Lat.	Dist.	Dep.	Lat.

45° (135°, 225°, 315°).

In **Plane Sailing.**	**Dist.**	**Lat.**	**Dep.**
For converting *Dep.* into *Diff. Long.* and *Diff. Long.* into *Dep.* In **Middle Latitude Sailing.**	Diff. Long.	Dep.	
For converting *Dep.* into *Diff. Long.* and *Diff. Long.* into *Dep.* In **Mercator Sailing.**		*m*	Diff. Long.
For multiplication of numbers by sines and by cosines, or solution of plane right-angled triangles.	N.	N×Cos.	N×Sin.
	Hypotenuse.	Side Adj.	Side Opp.

TABLE 3.

Difference of Latitude and Departure for 45° (135°, 225°, 315°).

Dist.	Lat.	Dep.	Dist.	Lat.	Dep.	Dist.	Lat.	Dep.	Dist.	Lat.	Dep.	Dist.	Lat.	Dep.
301	212.8	212.8	361	255.3	255.3	421	297.7	297.7	481	340.1	340.1	541	382.5	382.5
02	213.5	213.5	62	256.0	256.0	22	298.4	298.4	82	340.8	340.8	42	383.2	383.3
03	214.3	214.3	63	256.7	256.7	23	299.1	299.1	83	341.5	341.5	43	383.9	384.0
04	215.0	215.0	64	257.4	257.4	24	299.8	299.8	84	342.2	342.2	44	384.7	384.7
05	215.7	215.7	65	258.1	258.1	25	300.5	300.5	85	342.9	342.9	45	385.4	385.4
06	216.4	216.4	66	258.8	258.8	26	301.2	301.2	86	343.7	343.6	46	386.1	386.1
07	217.1	217.1	67	259.5	259.5	27	301.9	301.9	87	344.4	344.3	47	386.8	386.8
08	217.8	217.8	68	260.2	260.2	28	302.6	302.6	88	345.1	345.1	48	387.5	387.5
09	218.5	218.5	69	260.9	260.9	29	303.4	303.3	89	345.8	345.8	49	388.2	388.2
10	219.2	219.2	70	261.6	261.6	30	304.1	304.1	90	346.5	346.5	50	388.9	388.9
311	219.9	219.9	371	262.3	262.3	431	304.8	304.8	491	347.2	347.2	551	389.6	389.6
12	220.6	220.6	72	263.0	263.0	32	305.5	305.5	92	347.9	347.9	52	390.3	390.3
13	221.3	221.3	73	263.8	263.8	33	306.2	306.2	93	348.6	348.6	53	391.0	391.0
14	222.0	222.0	74	264.5	264.5	34	306.9	306.9	94	349.3	349.3	54	391.7	391.7
15	222.7	222.7	75	265.2	265.2	35	307.6	307.6	95	350.0	350.0	55	392.4	392.4
16	223.4	223.4	76	265.9	265.9	36	308.3	308.3	96	350.7	350.7	56	393.1	393.2
17	224.2	224.2	77	266.6	266.6	37	309.0	309.0	97	351.4	351.4	57	393.9	393.9
18	224.9	224.9	78	267.3	267.3	38	309.7	309.7	98	352.1	352.1	58	394.6	394.6
19	225.6	225.6	79	268.0	268.0	39	310.4	310.4	99	352.8	352.8	59	395.3	395.3
20	226.3	226.3	80	268.7	268.7	40	311.1	311.1	500	353.6	353.6	60	396.0	396.0
321	227.0	227.0	381	269.4	269.4	441	311.8	311.8	501	354.3	354.3	561	396.7	396.7
22	227.7	227.7	82	270.1	270.1	42	312.5	312.5	02	355.0	355.0	62	397.4	397.4
23	228.4	228.4	83	270.8	270.8	43	313.3	313.2	03	355.7	355.7	63	398.1	398.1
24	229.1	229.1	84	271.5	271.5	44	314.0	314.0	04	356.4	356.4	64	398.8	398.8
25	229.8	229.8	85	272.2	272.2	45	314.7	314.7	05	357.1	357.1	65	399.5	399.5
26	230.5	230.5	86	272.9	272.9	46	315.4	315.4	06	357.8	357.8	66	400.2	400.2
27	231.2	231.2	87	273.7	273.7	47	316.1	316.1	07	358.5	358.5	67	400.9	400.9
28	231.9	231.9	88	274.4	274.4	48	316.8	316.8	08	359.2	359.2	68	401.6	401.6
29	232.6	232.6	89	275.1	275.1	49	317.5	317.5	09	359.9	359.9	69	402.3	402.3
30	233.3	233.3	90	275.8	275.8	50	318.2	318.2	10	360.6	360.6	70	403.0	403.1
331	234.1	234.1	391	276.5	276.5	451	318.9	318.9	511	361.3	361.3	571	403.8	403.8
32	234.8	234.8	92	277.2	277.2	52	319.6	319.6	12	362.0	362.0	72	404.5	404.5
33	235.5	235.5	93	277.9	277.9	53	320.3	320.3	13	362.7	362.7	73	405.2	405.2
34	236.2	236.2	94	278.6	278.6	54	321.0	321.0	14	363.5	363.5	74	405.9	405.9
35	236.9	236.9	95	279.3	279.3	55	321.7	321.7	15	364.2	364.2	75	406.6	406.6
36	237.6	237.6	96	280.0	280.0	56	322.4	322.4	16	364.9	364.9	76	407.3	407.3
37	238.3	238.3	97	280.7	280.7	57	323.2	323.1	17	365.6	365.6	77	408.0	408.0
38	239.0	239.0	98	281.4	281.4	58	323.9	323.9	18	366.3	366.3	78	408.7	408.7
39	239.7	239.7	99	282.1	282.1	59	324.6	324.6	19	367.0	367.0	79	409.4	409.4
40	240.4	240.4	400	282.8	282.8	60	325.3	325.3	20	367.7	367.7	80	410.1	410.1
341	241.1	241.1	401	283.6	283.5	461	326.0	326.0	521	368.4	368.4	581	410.8	410.8
42	241.8	241.8	02	284.3	284.3	62	326.7	326.7	22	369.1	369.1	82	411.5	411.5
43	242.5	242.5	03	285.0	285.0	63	327.4	327.4	23	369.8	369.8	83	412.2	412.2
44	243.2	243.2	04	285.7	285.7	64	328.1	328.1	24	370.5	370.5	84	412.9	413.0
45	244.0	244.0	05	286.4	286.4	65	328.8	328.8	25	371.2	371.2	85	413.7	413.7
46	244.7	244.7	06	287.1	287.1	66	329.5	329.5	26	371.9	371.9	86	414.4	414.4
47	245.4	245.4	07	287.8	287.8	67	330.2	330.2	27	372.6	372.6	87	415.1	415.1
48	246.1	246.1	08	288.5	288.5	68	330.9	330.9	28	373.4	373.4	88	415.8	415.8
49	246.8	246.8	09	289.2	289.2	69	331.6	331.6	29	374.1	374.1	89	416.5	416.5
50	247.5	247.5	10	289.9	289.9	70	332.3	332.3	30	374,8	374.8	90	417.2	417.2
351	248.2	248.2	411	290.6	290.6	471	333.1	333.0	531	375.5	375.5	591	417.9	417.9
52	248.9	248.9	12	291.3	291.3	72	333.8	333.8	32	376.2	376.2	92	418.6	418.6
53	249.6	249.6	13	292.0	292.0	73	334.5	334.5	33	376.9	376.9	93	419.3	419.3
54	250.3	250.3	14	292.7	292.7	74	335.2	335.2	34	377.6	377.6	94	420.0	420.0
55	251.0	251.0	15	293.5	293.4	75	335.9	335.9	35	378.3	378.3	95	420.7	420.7
56	251.7	251.7	16	294.2	294.2	76	336.6	336.6	36	379.0	379.0	96	421.4	421.4
57	252.4	252.4	17	294.9	294.9	77	337.3	337.3	37	379.7	379.7	97	422.1	422.1
58	253.1	253.1	18	295.6	295.6	78	338.0	338.0	38	380.4	380.4	98	422.8	422.8
59	253.9	253.9	19	296.3	296.3	79	338.7	338.7	39	381.1	381.1	99	423.6	423.6
60	254.6	254.6	20	297.0	297.0	80	339.4	339.4	40	381.8	381.8	600	424.3	424.3
Dist.	Dep.	Lat.	Dist.	Dep.	Lat.	Dist.	Dep.	Lat.	Dist.	Dep.	Lat.	Dist.	Dep.	Lat.

45° (135°, 225°, 315°).

In **Plane Sailing.**	**Dist.**	**Lat.**	**Dep.**
For converting *Dep.* into *Diff. Long.* and *Diff. Long.* into *Dep.* In **Middle Latitude Sailing.**	Diff. Long.	Dep.	
For converting *Dep.* into *Diff. Long.* and *Diff. Long.* into *Dep.* In **Mercator Sailing.**		*m*	Diff. Long.
For multiplication of numbers by sines and by cosines, or solution of plane right-angled triangles.	N. Hypotenuse.	N×Cos. Side Adj.	N×Sin. Side Opp.

TABLE 4.

Conversion of Departure into Difference of Longitude.

Dep.	Middle Latitude													Dep.
	4°	6°	8°	10°	11°	12°	13°	14°	15°	16°	17°	18°	19°	
	D. Lo.	D. Lo.	D. Lo.	D. Lo.	D. Lo.	D. Lo.	D. Lo.	D. Lo.	D. Lo.	D. Lo.	D. Lo.	D. Lo.	D. Lo.	
1	1.0	1.0	1.0	1.0	1.0	1.0	1.0	1.0	1.0	1.0	1.0	1.1	1.1	1
2	2.0	2.0	2.0	2.0	2.0	2.0	2.1	2.1	2.1	2.1	2.1	2.1	2.1	2
3	3.0	3.0	3.0	3.1	3.1	3.1	3.1	3.1	3.1	3.1	3.1	3.2	3.2	3
4	4.0	4.0	4.0	4.1	4.1	4.1	4.1	4.1	4.1	4.2	4.2	4.2	4.2	4
5	5.0	5.0	5.0	5.1	5.1	5.1	5.1	5.2	5.2	5.2	5.2	5.3	5.3	5
6	6.0	6.0	6.1	6.1	6.1	6.1	6.2	6.2	6.2	6.2	6.3	6.3	6.3	6
7	7.0	7.0	7.1	7.1	7.1	7.2	7.2	7.2	7.2	7.3	7.3	7.4	7.4	7
8	8.0	8.0	8.1	8.1	8.2	8.2	8.2	8.2	8.3	8.3	8.4	8.4	8.5	8
9	9.0	9.0	9.1	9.1	9.2	9.2	9.2	9.3	9.3	9.4	9.4	9.5	9.5	9
10	10.0	10.1	10.1	10.2	10.2	10.2	10.3	10.3	10.4	10.4	10.5	10.5	10.6	10
11	11.0	11.1	11.1	11.2	11.2	11.2	11.3	11.3	11.4	11.4	11.5	11.6	11.6	11
12	12.0	12.1	12.1	12.2	12.2	12.3	12.3	12.4	12.4	12.5	12.5	12.6	12.7	12
13	13.0	13.1	13.1	13.2	13.2	13.3	13.3	13.4	13.5	13.5	13.6	13.7	13.7	13
14	14.0	14.1	14.1	14.2	14.3	14.3	14.4	14.4	14 5	14.6	14.6	14.7	14.8	14
15	15.0	15.1	15.1	15.2	15.3	15.3	15.4	15.5	15.5	15.6	15.7	15.8	15.9	15
16	16.0	16.1	16.2	16.2	16.3	16.4	16.4	16.5	16.6	16.6	16.7	16.8	16.9	16
17	17.0	17.1	17.2	17.3	17.3	17.4	17.4	17.5	17.6	17.7	17.8	17.9	18.0	17
18	18.0	18.1	18.2	18.3	18.3	18.4	18.5	18.6	18.6	18.7	18.8	18.9	19.0	18
19	19.0	19.1	19.2	19.3	19.4	19.4	19.5	19.6	19.7	19.8	19.9	20.0	20.1	19
20	20.0	20.1	20.2	20.3	20.4	20.4	20.5	20.6	20.7	20.8	20.9	21.0	21.2	20
21	21.1	21.1	21.2	21.3	21.4	21.5	21.6	21.6	21.7	21.8	22.0	22.1	22.2	21
22	22.1	22.1	22.2	22.3	22.4	22.5	22.6	22.7	22.8	22.9	23.0	23.1	23.3	22
23	23.1	23.1	23.2	23.4	23.4	23.5	23.6	23.7	23.8	24.0	24.1	24.2	24.3	23
24	24.1	24.1	24.2	24.4	24.4	24.5	24.6	24.7	24.8	25.0	25.1	25.2	25.4	24
25	25.1	25.1	25.2	25.4	25.5	25.6	25.7	25.8	25.9	26.0	26.1	26.3	26.4	25
26	26.1	26.1	26.3	26.4	26.5	26.6	26.7	26.8	26.9	27.1	27.2	27.3	27.5	26
27	27.1	27.1	27.3	27.4	27.5	27.6	27.7	27.8	28.0	28.1	28.2	28.4	28.6	27
28	28.1	28.2	28.3	28.4	28.5	28.6	28.7	28.9	29.0	29.2	29.3	29.4	29.6	28
29	29.1	29.2	29.3	29.4	29.5	29.6	29.8	29.9	30.0	30.2	30.3	30.5	30.7	29
30	30.1	30.2	30.3	30.5	30.6	30.7	30.8	30.9	31.1	31.2	31.4	31.5	31.7	30
31	31.1	31.2	31.3	31.5	31.6	31.7	31.8	31.9	32.1	32.2	32.4	32.6	32.8	31
32	32.1	32.2	32.3	32.5	32.6	32.7	32.8	33.0	33.1	33.3	33.4	33.6	33.8	32
33	33.1	33.2	33.3	33.5	33.6	33.7	33.9	34.0	34.2	34.3	34.5	34.7	34.9	33
34	34.1	34.2	34.3	34.5	34.6	34.8	34.9	35.0	35.2	35.4	35.6	35.7	36.0	34
35	35.1	35.2	35.3	35.5	35.7	35.8	35.9	36.1	36.2	36.4	36.6	36.8	37.0	35
36	36.1	36.2	36.4	36.6	36.7	36.8	36.9	37.1	37.3	37.5	37.6	37.9	38.1	36
37	37.1	37.2	37.4	37.6	37.7	37.8	38.0	38.1	38.3	38.5	38.7	38.9	39.1	37
38	38.1	38.2	38.4	38.6	38.7	38.8	39.0	39.2	39.3	39.5	39.7	40.0	40.2	38
39	39.1	39.2	39.4	39.6	39.7	39.9	40.0	40.2	40.4	40.6	40.8	41.0	41.2	39
40	40.1	40.2	40.4	40.6	40.7	40.9	41.1	41.2	41.4	41.6	41.8	42.1	42.3	40
41	41.1	41.2	41.4	41.6	41.8	41.9	42.1	42.3	42.4	42.7	42.9	43.1	43.4	41
42	42.1	42.2	42.4	42.6	42.8	42.9	43.1	43.3	43.5	43.7	43.9	44.2	44.4	42
43	43.1	43.2	43.4	43.7	43.8	44.0	44.1	44.3	44.5	44.7	45.0	45.2	45.5	43
44	44.1	44.2	44.4	44.7	44.8	45.0	45.2	45.3	45.6	45.8	46.0	46.3	46.5	44
45	45.1	45.2	45.4	45.7	45.8	46.0	46.2	46.4	46.6	46.8	47.1	47.3	47.6	45
46	46.1	46.3	46.5	46.7	46.9	47.0	47.2	47.4	47.6	47.9	48.1	48.4	48.7	46
47	47.1	47.3	47.5	47.7	47.9	48.1	48.2	48.4	48.7	48.9	49.1	49.4	49.7	47
48	48.1	48.3	48.5	48.7	48.9	49.1	49.3	49.5	49.7	49.9	50.2	50.5	50.8	48
49	49.1	49.3	49.5	49.8	49.9	50.1	50.3	50.5	50.7	51.0	51.2	51.5	51.8	49
50	50.1	50.3	50.5	50.8	50.9	51.1	51.3	51.5	51.8	52.0	52.3	52.6	52.9	50
51	51.1	51.3	51.5	51.8	52.0	52.1	52.3	52.6	52.8	53.1	53.3	53.6	53.9	51
52	52.1	52.3	52.5	52.8	53.0	53.2	53.4	53.6	53.8	54.1	54.4	54.7	55.0	52
53	53.1	53.3	53.5	53.8	54.0	54.2	54.4	54.6	54.9	55.1	55.4	55.7	56.1	53
54	54.1	54.3	54.5	54.8	55.0	55.2	55.4	55.7	55.9	56.2	56.5	56.8	57.1	54
55	55.1	55.3	55.5	55.8	56.0	56.2	56.4	56.7	56.9	57.2	57.5	57.8	58.2	55
56	56.1	56.3	56.6	56.9	57.1	57.2	57.5	57.7	58.0	58.3	58.6	58.9	59.2	56
57	57.1	57.3	57.6	57.9	58.1	58.3	58.5	58.7	59.0	59.3	59.6	59.9	60.3	57
58	58.1	58.3	58.6	58.9	59.1	59.3	59.5	59.8	60.0	60.3	60.7	61.0	61.3	58
59	59.1	59.3	59.6	59.9	60.1	60.3	60.6	60.8	61.1	61.4	61.7	62.0	62.4	59
60	60.1	60.3	60.6	60.9	61.1	61.3	61.6	61.8	62.1	62.4	62.7	63.1	63.5	60

TABLE 4.

Conversion of Departure into Difference of Longitude.

Dep.	Middle Latitude.													Dep.
	20°	21°	22°	23°	24°	25°	26°	27°	28°	29°	30°	31°	32°	
	D. Lo.	D. Lo.	D. Lo.	D. Lo.	D. Lo.	D. Lo.	D. Lo.	D. Lo.	D. Lo.	D. Lo.	D. Lo.	D. Lo.	D. Lo.	
1	1.1	1.1	1.1	1.1	1.1	1.1	1.1	1.1	1.1	1.1	1.2	1.2	1.2	1
2	2.1	2.1	2.2	2.2	2.2	2.2	2.2	2.2	2.3	2.3	2.3	2.3	2.4	2
3	3.2	3.2	3.2	3.3	3.3	3.3	3.3	3.4	3.4	3.4	3.5	3.5	3.5	3
4	4.3	4.3	4.3	4.3	4.4	4.4	4.5	4.5	4.5	4.6	4.6	4.7	4.7	4
5	5.3	5.4	5.4	5.4	5.5	5.5	5.6	5.6	5.7	5.7	5.8	5.8	5.9	5
6	6.4	6.4	6.5	6.5	6.6	6.6	6.7	6.7	6.8	6.9	6.9	7.0	7.1	6
7	7.4	7.5	7.5	7.6	7.7	7.7	7.8	7.9	7.9	8.0	8.1	8.2	8.3	7
8	8.5	8.6	8.6	8.7	8.8	8.8	8.9	9.0	9.1	9.1	9.2	9.3	9.4	8
9	9.6	9.6	9.7	9.8	9.9	9.9	10.0	10.1	10.2	10.3	10.4	10.5	10.6	9
10	10.6	10.7	10.8	10.9	10.9	11.0	11.1	11.2	11.3	11.4	11.5	11.7	11.8	10
11	11.7	11.8	11.9	12.0	12.0	12.1	12.2	12.3	12.5	12.6	12.7	12.8	13.0	11
12	12.8	12.9	12.9	13.0	13.1	13.2	13.4	13.5	13.6	13.7	13.9	14.0	14.2	12
13	13.8	13.9	14.0	14.1	14.2	14.3	14.5	14.6	14.7	14.9	15.0	15.2	15.3	13
14	14.9	15.0	15.1	15.2	15.3	15.4	15.6	15.7	15.9	16.0	16.2	16.3	16.5	14
15	16.0	16.1	16.2	16.3	16.4	16.6	16.7	16.8	17.0	17.1	17.3	17.5	17.7	15
16	17.0	17.1	17.3	17.4	17.5	17.7	17.8	18.0	18.1	18.3	18.5	18.7	18.9	16
17	18.1	18.2	18.3	18.5	18.6	18.8	18.9	19.1	19.3	19.4	19.6	19.8	20.0	17
18	19.2	19.3	19.4	19.6	19.7	19.9	20.0	20.2	20.4	20.6	20.8	21.0	21.2	18
19	20.2	20.4	20.5	20.6	20.8	21.0	21.1	21.3	21.5	21.7	21.9	22.2	22.4	19
20	21.3	21.4	21.6	21.7	21.9	22.1	22.3	22.5	22.7	22.9	23.1	23.3	23.6	20
21	22.3	22.5	22.7	22.8	23.0	23.2	23.4	23.6	23.8	24.0	24.2	24.5	24.8	21
22	23.4	23.6	23.7	23.9	24.1	24.3	24.5	24.7	24.9	25.2	25.4	25.7	25.9	22
23	24.5	24.6	24.8	25.0	25.2	25.4	25.6	25.8	26.0	26.3	26.6	26.8	27.1	23
24	25.5	25.7	25.9	26.1	26.3	26.5	26.7	26.9	27.2	27.4	27.7	28.0	28.3	24
25	26.6	26.8	26.9	27.2	27.4	27.6	27.8	28.0	28.3	28.6	28.9	29.2	29.5	25
26	27.7	27.8	28.0	28.2	28.5	28.7	28.9	29.1	29.4	29.7	30.0	30.3	30.7	26
27	28.7	28.9	29.1	29.3	29.6	29.8	30.0	30.3	30.6	30.9	31.2	31.5	31.8	27
28	29.8	30.0	30.2	30.4	30.6	30.9	31.2	31.4	31.7	32.0	32.3	32.7	33.0	28
29	30.9	31.1	31.3	31.5	31.7	32.0	32.3	32.5	32.8	33.2	33.5	33.8	34.2	29
30	31.9	32.1	32.4	32.6	32.8	33.1	33.4	33.7	34.0	34.3	34.6	35.0	35.4	30
31	33.0	33.2	33.4	33.7	33.9	34.2	34.5	34.8	35.1	35.4	35.8	36.2	36.6	31
32	34.1	34.3	34.5	34.8	35.1	35.3	35.6	35.9	36.2	36.6	37.0	37.3	37.7	32
33	35.1	35.3	35.6	35.9	36.2	36.4	36.7	37.0	37.4	37.7	38.1	38.5	38.9	33
34	36.2	36.4	36.7	36.9	37.3	37.5	37.8	38.1	38.5	38.9	39.3	39.7	40.1	34
35	37.2	37.5	37.7	38.0	38.4	38.6	38.9	39.2	39.6	40.0	40.4	40.8	41.3	35
36	38.3	38.6	38.8	39.1	39.5	39.7	40.1	40.4	40.8	41.2	41.6	42.0	42.5	36
37	39.4	39.6	39.9	40.2	40.6	40.8	41.2	41.5	41.9	42.3	42.7	43.2	43.6	37
38	40.4	40.7	41.0	41.3	41.7	41.9	42.3	42.6	43.0	43.4	43.9	44.3	44.8	38
39	41.5	41.8	42.1	42.4	42.8	43.0	43.4	43.8	44.2	44.6	45.0	45.5	46.0	39
40	42.6	42.8	43.1	43.5	43.8	44.1	44.5	44.9	45.3	45.7	46.2	46.7	47.2	40
41	43.6	43.9	44.2	44.5	44.9	45.2	45.6	46.0	46.4	46.9	47.3	47.8	48.3	41
42	44.7	45.0	45.3	45.6	46.0	46.3	46.7	47.1	47.6	48.0	48.5	49.0	49.5	42
43	45.8	46.1	46.4	46.7	47.1	47.4	47.8	48.3	48.7	49.2	49.7	50.2	50.7	43
44	46.8	47.1	47.5	47.8	48.2	48.5	49.0	49.4	49.8	50.3	50.8	51.3	51.9	44
45	47.9	48.2	48.5	48.9	49.3	49.7	50.1	50.5	51.0	51.5	52.0	52.5	53.1	45
46	49.0	49.3	49.6	50.0	50.4	50.8	51.2	51.6	52.1	52.6	53.1	53.7	54.2	46
47	50.0	50.3	50.7	51.1	51.4	51.9	52.3	52.7	53.2	53.7	54.3	54.8	55.4	47
48	51.1	51.4	51.8	52.1	52.5	52.9	53.4	53.9	54.4	54.9	55.4	56.0	56.6	48
49	52.1	52.5	52.8	53.2	53.6	54.0	54.5	55.0	55.5	56.0	56.6	57.2	57.8	49
50	53.2	53.6	53.9	54.3	54.7	55.2	55.6	56.1	56.6	57.2	57.7	58.3	59.0	50
51	54.3	54.6	55.0	55.4	55.8	56.3	56.7	57.2	57.8	58.3	58.9	59.5	60.1	51
52	55.3	55.7	56.1	56.5	56.9	57.4	57.9	58.4	58.9	59.5	60.0	60.7	61.3	52
53	56.4	56.8	57.2	57.6	58.0	58.5	59.0	59.5	60.0	60.6	61.2	61.8	62.5	53
54	57.5	57.8	58.2	58.7	59.1	59.6	60.1	60.6	61.2	61.8	62.4	63.0	63.7	54
55	58.5	58.9	59.3	59.8	60.2	60.7	61.2	61.7	62.3	62.9	63.5	64.2	64.9	55
56	59.6	60.0	60.4	60.8	61.3	61.8	62.3	62.9	63.4	64.0	64.7	65.3	66.0	56
57	60.7	61.1	61.5	61.9	62.4	62.9	63.4	64.0	64.6	65.2	65.8	66.5	67.2	57
58	61.7	62.1	62.6	63.0	63.5	64.0	64.5	65.1	65.7	66.3	67.0	67.7	68.4	58
59	62.8	63.2	63.6	64.1	64.6	65.1	65.6	66.2	66.8	67.5	68.1	68.8	69.6	59
60	63.9	64.3	64.7	65.2	65.7	66.2	66.8	67.3	68.0	68.6	69.3	70.0	70.8	60

541524°—43——33

TABLE 4.

Conversion of Departure into Difference of Longitude.

Dep.	Middle Latitude.												Dep.
	33°	34°	35°	36°	37°	38°	39°	39° 30′	40°	40° 30′	41°	41° 30′	
	D. Lo.	D. Lo.	D. Lo.	D. Lo.	D. Lo.	D. Lo.	D. Lo.	D. Lo.	D. Lo.	D. Lo.	D. Lo.	D. Lo.	
1	1.2	1.2	1.2	1.2	1.3	1.3	1.3	1.3	1.3	1.3	1.3	1.3	1
2	2.4	2.4	2.4	2.5	2.5	2.5	2.6	2.6	2.6	2.6	2.7	2.7	2
3	3.6	3.6	3.7	3.7	3.8	3.8	3.9	3.9	3.9	3.9	4.0	4.0	3
4	4.8	4.8	4.9	4.9	5.0	5.1	5.1	5.2	5.2	5.2	5.3	5.3	4
5	6.0	6.0	6.1	6.2	6.3	6.3	6.4	6.4	6.5	6.5	6.6	6.6	5
6	7.2	7.2	7.3	7.4	7.5	7.6	7.7	7.8	7.8	7.9	8.0	8.0	6
7	8.3	8.4	8.5	8.7	8.8	8.9	9.0	9.0	9.1	9.2	9.3	9.3	7
8	9.5	9.6	9.8	9.9	10.0	10.2	10.3	10.4	10.4	10.5	10.6	10.7	8
9	10.7	10.9	11.0	11.1	11.3	11.4	11.6	11.7	11.7	11.8	11.9	12.0	9
10	11.9	12.1	12.2	12.4	12.5	12.7	12.9	13.0	13.1	13.2	13.3	13.4	10
11	13.1	13.3	13.4	13.6	13.8	14.0	14.2	14.3	14.4	14.5	14.6	14.7	11
12	14.3	14.5	14.6	14.8	15.0	15.2	15.4	15.6	15.7	15.8	15.9	16.0	12
13	15.5	15.7	15.9	16.1	16.3	16.5	16.7	16.9	17.0	17.1	17.2	17.3	13
14	16.7	16.9	17.1	17.3	17.5	17.8	18.0	18.2	18.3	18.4	18.6	18.7	14
15	17.9	18.1	18.3	18.5	18.8	19.0	19.3	19.5	19.6	19.7	19.9	20.1	15
16	19.1	19.3	19.5	19.8	20.0	20.3	20.6	20.8	20.9	21.0	21.2	21.3	16
17	20.3	20.5	20.8	21.0	21.3	21.6	21.9	22.1	22.2	22.4	22.5	22.7	17
18	21.5	21.7	22.0	22.2	22.5	22.8	23.2	23.4	23.5	23.7	23.9	24.1	18
19	22.6	22.9	23.2	23.5	23.8	24.1	24.4	24.6	24.8	25.0	25.2	25.4	19
20	23.8	24.1	24.4	24.7	25.0	25.4	25.7	25.9	26.1	26.3	26.5	26.7	20
21	25.0	25.3	25.6	26.0	26.3	26.6	27.0	27.2	27.4	27.6	27.8	28.1	21
22	26.2	26.5	26.9	27.2	27.5	27.9	28.3	28.5	28.7	29.0	29.2	29.4	22
23	27.4	27.7	28.1	28.4	28.8	29.2	29.6	29.8	30.0	30.2	30.5	30.7	23
24	28.6	28.9	29.3	29.7	30.1	30.5	30.9	31.1	31.3	31.6	31.8	32.1	24
25	29.8	30.2	30.5	30.9	31.3	31.7	32.2	32.4	32.6	32.9	33.1	33.4	25
26	31.0	31.4	31.7	32.1	32.6	33.0	33.5	33.7	33.9	34.2	34.5	34.8	26
27	32.2	32.6	33.0	33.4	33.8	34.3	34.7	34.9	35.2	35.5	35.8	36.1	27
28	33.4	33.8	34.2	34.6	35.1	35.5	36.0	36.3	36.6	36.9	37.1	37.4	28
29	34.6	35.0	35.4	35.8	36.3	36.8	37.3	37.6	37.9	38.2	38.4	38.7	29
30	35.8	36.2	36.6	37.1	37.6	38.1	38.6	38.9	39.2	39.5	39.8	40.1	30
31	37.0	37.4	37.8	38.3	38.8	39.3	39.9	40.2	40.5	40.8	41.1	41.4	31
32	38.2	38.6	39.1	39.6	40.1	40.6	41.2	41.5	41.8	42.1	42.4	42.8	32
33	39.3	39.8	40.3	40.8	41.3	41.9	42.5	42.8	43.1	43.4	43.7	44.1	33
34	40.5	41.0	41.5	42.0	42.6	43.1	43.8	44.1	44.4	44.7	45.1	45.5	34
35	41.7	42.2	42.7	43.3	43.8	44.4	45.0	45.4	45.7	46.1	46.4	46.5	35
36	42.9	43.4	43.9	44.5	45.1	45.7	46.3	46.7	47.0	47.4	47.7	48.1	36
37	44.1	44.6	45.2	45.7	46.3	47.0	47.6	47.9	48.3	48.7	49.0	49.4	37
38	45.3	45.8	46.4	47.0	47.6	48.2	48.9	49.3	49.6	50.0	50.4	50.8	38
39	46.5	47.0	47.6	48.2	48.8	49.5	50.2	50.6	50.9	51.3	51.7	52.1	39
40	47.7	48.2	48.8	49.4	50.1	50.8	51.5	51.9	52.2	52.6	53.0	53.4	40
41	48.9	49.5	50.1	50.7	51.3	52.0	52.8	53.2	53.5	53.9	54.3	54.7	41
42	50.1	50.7	51.3	51.9	52.6	53.3	54.0	54.4	54.8	55.2	55.7	56.1	42
43	51.3	51.9	52.5	53.2	53.8	54.6	55.3	55.7	56.1	56.5	57.0	57.5	43
44	52.5	53.1	53.7	54.4	55.1	55.8	56.6	57.0	57.4	57.9	58.3	58.8	44
45	53.7	54.3	54.9	55.6	56.3	57.1	57.9	58.3	58.7	59.1	59.6	60.1	45
46	54.8	55.5	56.2	56.9	57.6	58.4	59.2	59.6	60.0	60.5	61.0	61.5	46
47	56.0	56.7	57.4	58.1	58.9	59.6	60.5	61.0	61.4	61.9	62.3	62.8	47
48	57.2	57.9	58.6	59.3	60.1	60.9	61.8	62.3	62.7	63.1	63.6	64.1	48
49	58.4	59.1	59.8	60.6	61.4	62.2	63.1	63.6	64.0	64.5	64.9	65.4	49
50	59.6	60.3	61.0	61.8	62.6	63.5	64.3	64.8	65.3	65.8	66.3	66.8	50
51	60.8	61.5	62.3	63.0	63.9	64.7	65.6	66.1	66.6	67.1	67.6	68.1	51
52	62.0	62.7	63.5	64.3	65.1	66.0	66.9	67.4	67.9	68.4	69.0	69.5	52
53	63.2	63.9	64.7	65.5	66.4	67.3	68.2	68.7	69.2	69.7	70.2	70.8	53
54	64.4	65.1	65.9	66.7	67.6	68.5	69.5	69.9	70.5	71.0	71.6	72.1	54
55	65.6	66.3	67.1	68.0	68.9	69.8	70.8	71.3	71.8	72.3	72.9	73.5	55
56	66.8	67.5	68.3	69.2	70.1	71.1	72.1	72.6	73.1	73.6	74.2	74.8	56
57	68.0	68.7	69.5	70.5	71.4	72.3	73.3	73.8	74.4	74.9	75.5	76.1	57
58	69.2	70.0	70.7	71.7	72.6	73.6	74.6	75.2	75.7	76.3	76.9	77.5	58
59	70.4	71.2	72.0	72.9	73.9	74.9	75.9	76.5	77.0	77.6	78.2	78.8	59
60	71.5	72.4	73.2	74.2	75.1	76.1	77.2	77.8	78.3	78.9	79.5	80.1	60

Conversion of Departure into Difference of Longitude.

Middle Latitude.

Dep.	42°	42°30′	43°	43°30′	44°	44°30′	45°	45°30′	46°	46°30′	47°	47°30′	Dep.
	D. Lo.	D. Lo.	D. Lo.	D. Lo.	D. Lo.	D. Lo.	D. Lo.	D. Lo.	D. Lo.	D. Lo.	D. Lo.	D. Lo.	
1	1. 3	1. 3	1. 4	1. 4	1. 4	1. 4	1. 4	1. 4	1. 4	1. 4	1. 5	1. 5	1
2	2. 7	2. 7	2. 7	2. 7	2. 8	2. 8	2. 8	2. 8	2. 9	2. 9	2. 9	2. 9	2
3	4. 0	4. 0	4. 1	4. 1	4. 2	4. 2	4. 2	4. 2	4. 3	4. 3	4. 4	4. 4	3
4	5. 4	5. 4	5. 5	5. 5	5. 6	5. 6	5. 7	5. 7	5. 8	5. 8	5. 9	5. 9	4
5	6. 7	6. 7	6. 8	6. 9	7. 0	7. 0	7. 1	7. 1	7. 2	7. 2	7. 3	7. 4	5
6	8. 1	8. 1	8. 2	8. 2	8. 3	8. 4	8. 5	8. 5	8. 6	8. 7	8. 8	8. 9	6
7	9. 4	9. 5	9. 6	9. 6	9. 7	9. 8	9. 9	10. 0	10. 1	10. 2	10. 3	10. 4	7
8	10. 8	10. 8	10. 9	11. 0	11. 1	11. 2	11. 3	11. 4	11. 5	11. 6	11. 7	11. 9	8
9	12. 1	12. 2	12. 3	12. 4	12. 5	12. 6	12. 7	12. 8	13. 0	13. 1	13. 2	13. 3	9
10	13. 5	13. 6	13. 7	13. 8	13. 9	14. 0	14. 1	14. 3	14. 4	14. 5	14. 7	14. 8	10
11	14. 8	14. 9	15. 0	15. 2	15. 3	15. 4	15. 6	15. 7	15. 8	16. 0	16. 1	16. 3	11
12	16. 1	16. 3	16. 4	16. 6	16. 7	16. 9	17. 0	17. 1	17. 3	17. 5	17. 6	17. 8	12
13	17. 5	17. 6	17. 8	18. 0	18. 1	18. 3	18. 4	18. 6	18. 7	18. 9	19. 1	19. 3	13
14	18. 8	19. 0	19. 1	19. 3	19. 5	19. 7	19. 8	20. 0	20. 2	20. 4	20. 5	20. 7	14
15	20. 2	20. 4	20. 5	20. 7	20. 9	21. 1	21. 2	21. 4	21. 6	21. 8	22. 0	22. 2	15
16	21. 5	21. 7	21. 9	22. 1	22. 2	22. 4	22. 6	22. 8	23. 0	23. 3	23. 5	23. 7	16
17	22. 9	23. 1	23. 2	23. 4	23. 6	23. 8	24. 0	24. 3	24. 5	24. 7	24. 9	25. 2	17
18	24. 2	24. 4	24. 6	24. 8	25. 0	25. 3	25. 5	25. 7	25. 9	26. 2	26. 4	26. 7	18
19	25. 6	25. 8	26. 0	26. 2	26. 4	26. 7	26. 9	27. 2	27. 4	27. 7	27. 9	28. 2	19
20	26. 9	27. 1	27. 3	27. 6	27. 8	28. 2	28. 3	28. 6	28. 8	29. 1	29. 3	29. 6	20
21	28. 3	28. 5	28. 7	29. 0	29. 2	29. 5	29. 7	30. 0	30. 2	30. 5	30. 8	31. 1	21
22	29. 6	29. 9	30. 1	30. 3	30. 6	30. 9	31. 1	31. 4	31. 7	32. 0	32. 3	32. 6	22
23	30. 9	31. 2	31. 4	31. 7	32. 0	32. 3	32. 5	32. 8	33. 1	33. 4	33. 7	34. 1	23
24	32. 3	32. 6	32. 8	33. 1	33. 4	33. 7	33. 9	34. 2	34. 5	34. 9	35. 2	35. 6	24
25	33. 6	33. 9	34. 2	34. 5	34. 8	35. 1	35. 4	35. 7	36. 0	36. 4	36. 7	37. 1	25
26	35. 0	35. 3	35. 6	35. 9	36. 1	36. 5	36. 8	37. 1	37. 4	37. 8	38. 1	38. 5	26
27	36. 3	36. 6	36. 9	37. 2	37. 5	37. 9	38. 2	38. 5	38. 9	39. 4	39. 6	40. 0	27
28	37. 7	38. 0	38. 3	38. 6	38. 9	39. 3	39. 6	40. 0	40. 3	40. 7	41. 1	41. 5	28
29	39. 0	39. 4	39. 7	40. 0	40. 3	40. 7	41. 0	41. 4	41. 7	42. 1	42. 5	42. 9	29
30	40. 4	40. 7	41. 0	41. 4	41. 7	42. 1	42. 4	42. 8	43. 2	43. 6	44. 0	44. 4	30
31	41. 7	42. 1	42. 4	42. 8	43. 1	43. 5	43. 8	44. 2	44. 6	45. 1	45. 5	45. 9	31
32	43. 1	43. 5	43. 8	44. 1	44. 4	44. 9	45. 3	45. 7	46. 1	46. 5	46. 9	47. 4	32
33	44. 4	44. 8	45. 1	45. 5	45. 8	46. 3	46. 7	47. 1	47. 5	48. 0	48. 4	48. 9	33
34	45. 8	46. 2	46. 5	46. 9	47. 2	47. 7	48. 1	48. 5	48. 9	49. 4	49. 9	50. 4	34
35	47. 1	47. 5	47. 9	48. 3	48. 6	49. 1	49. 5	50. 0	50. 4	50. 9	51. 3	51. 8	35
36	48. 4	48. 8	49. 2	49. 6	50. 0	50. 5	50. 9	51. 4	51. 8	52. 3	52. 8	53. 3	36
37	49. 8	50. 2	50. 6	51. 0	51. 4	51. 9	52. 3	52. 8	53. 3	53. 8	54. 2	54. 8	37
38	51. 1	51. 6	52. 0	52. 4	52. 8	53. 3	53. 7	54. 2	54. 7	55. 2	55. 7	56. 3	38
39	52. 5	52. 9	53. 3	53. 8	54. 2	54. 7	55. 2	55. 7	56. 1	56. 7	57. 2	57. 8	39
40	53. 8	54. 2	54. 7	55. 2	55. 6	56. 1	56. 6	57. 1	57. 6	58. 2	58. 7	59. 3	40
41	55. 2	55. 7	56. 1	56. 6	57. 0	57. 5	58. 0	58. 5	59. 0	59. 6	60. 1	60. 7	41
42	56. 5	57. 0	57. 4	57. 9	58. 4	59. 0	59. 4	59. 9	60. 5	61. 1	61. 6	62. 2	42
43	57. 9	58. 4	58. 8	59. 3	59. 8	60. 4	60. 8	61. 4	61. 9	62. 5	63. 0	63. 7	43
44	59. 2	59. 7	60. 2	60. 7	61. 2	61. 8	62. 2	62. 8	63. 3	63. 9	64. 5	65. 2	44
45	60. 6	61. 1	61. 5	62. 1	62. 6	63. 1	63. 6	64. 2	64. 8	65. 4	66. 0	66. 7	45
46	61. 9	62. 5	62. 9	63. 5	64. 0	64. 6	65. 1	65. 7	66. 2	66. 8	67. 4	68. 1	46
47	63. 3	63. 8	64. 3	64. 9	65. 4	66. 0	66. 5	67. 2	67. 7	68. 3	68. 9	69. 6	47
48	64. 6	65. 1	65. 6	66. 2	66. 7	67. 3	67. 9	68. 5	69. 1	69. 8	70. 4	71. 1	48
49	65. 9	66. 6	67. 0	67. 6	68. 1	68. 7	69. 3	69. 9	70. 5	71. 2	71. 8	72. 5	49
50	67. 3	67. 9	68. 4	69. 0	69. 5	70. 1	70. 7	71. 4	72. 0	72. 7	73. 3	74. 0	50
51	68. 6	69. 2	69. 7	70. 3	70. 9	71. 5	72. 1	72. 8	73. 4	74. 1	74. 8	75. 5	51
52	70. 0	70. 6	71. 1	71. 7	72. 3	72. 9	73. 5	74. 2	74. 9	75. 4	76. 2	77. 0	52
53	71. 3	71. 9	72. 5	73. 1	73. 7	74. 4	75. 0	75. 7	76. 3	77. 0	77. 7	78. 5	53
54	72. 7	73. 3	73. 8	74. 4	75. 1	75. 8	76. 4	77. 1	77. 8	78. 5	79. 2	80. 0	54
55	74. 0	74. 6	75. 2	75. 8	76. 5	77. 2	77. 8	78. 5	79. 3	80. 0	80. 6	81. 4	55
56	75. 4	76. 0	76. 6	77. 2	77. 8	78. 5	79. 2	80. 0	80. 7	81. 4	82. 1	82. 9	56
57	76. 7	77. 3	77. 9	78. 6	79. 2	79. 9	80. 6	81. 4	82. 2	82. 9	83. 6	84. 4	57
58	78. 0	78. 7	79. 3	80. 0	80. 6	81. 3	82. 0	82. 8	83. 6	84. 3	85. 0	85. 9	58
59	79. 4	80. 0	80. 7	81. 4	82. 0	82. 7	83. 4	84. 2	85. 0	85. 8	86. 5	87. 4	59
60	80. 7	81. 4	82. 0	82. 7	83. 4	84. 1	84. 9	85. 7	86. 4	87. 2	88. 0	88. 9	60

TABLE 4.

Conversion of Departure into Difference of Longitude.

Dep.	48°	48° 30′	49°	49° 30′	50°	50° 30′	51°	51° 30′	52°	52° 30′	53°	53° 30′	Dep.
	Middle Latitude.												
	D. Lo.	D. Lo.	D. Lo.	D. Lo.	D. Lo.	D. Lo.	D. Lo.	D. Lo.	D. Lo.	D. Lo.	D. Lo.	D. Lo.	
1	1. 5	1. 5	1. 5	1. 5	1. 6	1. 6	1. 6	1. 6	1. 6	1. 6	1. 7	1. 7	1
2	3. 0	3. 0	3. 0	3. 0	3. 1	3. 1	3. 2	3. 2	3. 2	3. 2	3. 3	3. 3	2
3	4. 5	4. 6	4. 6	4. 6	4. 7	4. 7	4. 8	4. 8	4. 9	4. 9	5. 0	5. 0	3
4	6. 0	6. 0	6. 1	6. 1	6. 2	6. 3	6. 4	6. 4	6. 5	6. 5	6. 6	6. 7	4
5	7. 5	7. 5	7. 6	7. 7	7. 8	7. 8	7. 9	8. 0	8. 1	8. 2	8. 3	8. 4	5
6	9. 0	9. 0	9. 1	9. 2	9. 3	9. 4	9. 5	9. 6	9. 7	9. 8	10. 0	10. 1	6
7	10. 5	10. 6	10. 7	10. 8	10. 9	11. 0	11. 1	11. 2	11. 4	11. 5	11. 6	11. 7	7
8	12. 0	12. 1	12. 2	12. 3	12. 4	12. 5	12. 7	12. 8	13. 0	13. 1	13. 3	13. 4	8
9	13. 4	13. 6	13. 7	13. 8	14. 0	14. 1	14. 3	14. 4	14. 6	14. 8	15. 0	15. 1	9
10	14. 9	15. 1	15. 2	15. 4	15. 6	15. 7	15. 9	16. 0	16. 2	16. 4	16. 6	16. 8	10
11	16. 4	16. 6	16. 8	16. 9	17. 1	17. 3	17. 5	17. 7	17. 9	18. 1	18. 3	18. 5	11
12	17. 9	18. 1	18. 3	18. 5	18. 7	18. 9	19. 1	19. 3	19. 5	19. 7	19. 9	20. 1	12
13	19. 4	19. 6	19. 8	20. 0	20. 2	20. 4	20. 7	20. 9	21. 1	21. 3	21. 6	21. 8	13
14	20. 9	21. 1	21. 3	21. 5	21. 8	22. 0	22. 2	22. 4	22. 7	23. 0	23. 3	23. 5	14
15	22. 4	22. 6	22. 9	23. 1	23. 3	23. 5	23. 8	24. 1	24. 4	24. 6	24. 9	25. 2	15
16	23. 9	24. 2	24. 4	24. 6	24. 9	25. 1	25. 4	25. 7	26. 0	26. 3	26. 6	26. 9	16
17	25. 4	25. 7	25. 9	26. 2	26. 4	26. 7	27. 0	27. 3	27. 6	27. 9	28. 2	28. 5	17
18	26. 9	27. 2	27. 4	27. 7	28. 0	28. 3	28. 6	28. 9	29. 2	29. 5	29. 9	30. 2	18
19	28. 4	28. 7	29. 0	29. 3	29. 6	29. 9	30. 2	30. 5	30. 9	31. 2	31. 6	31. 9	19
20	29. 9	30. 2	30. 5	30. 8	31. 1	31. 4	31. 8	32. 1	32. 5	32. 8	33. 2	33. 6	20
21	31. 4	31. 7	32. 0	32. 3	32. 7	33. 0	33. 4	33. 7	34. 1	34. 5	34. 9	35. 3	21
22	32. 9	33. 2	33. 5	33. 8	34. 2	34. 6	35. 0	35. 3	35. 7	36. 1	36. 6	37. 0	22
23	34. 4	34. 7	35. 1	35. 4	35. 8	36. 1	36. 5	36. 9	37. 4	37. 8	38. 2	38. 6	23
24	35. 9	36. 3	36. 6	36. 9	37. 3	37. 7	38. 1	38. 5	39. 0	39. 4	39. 9	40. 3	24
25	37. 4	37. 7	38. 1	38. 5	38. 9	39. 3	39. 7	40. 1	40. 6	41. 0	41. 5	42. 0	25
26	38. 9	39. 2	39. 6	40. 0	40. 4	40. 8	41. 3	41. 7	42. 2	42. 7	43. 2	43. 7	26
27	40. 4	40. 8	41. 2	41. 6	42. 0	42. 4	42. 9	43. 4	43. 9	44. 4	44. 9	45. 4	27
28	41. 8	42. 2	42. 7	43. 1	43. 6	44. 0	44. 5	45. 0	45. 5	46. 0	46. 5	47. 0	28
29	43. 3	43. 7	44. 2	44. 6	45. 1	45. 6	46. 1	46. 6	47. 1	47. 6	48. 2	48. 7	29
30	44. 8	45. 2	45. 7	46. 2	46. 7	47. 2	47. 7	48. 2	48. 7	49. 2	49. 8	50. 4	30
31	46. 3	46. 8	47. 3	47. 7	48. 2	48. 7	49. 3	49. 8	50. 4	50. 9	51. 5	52. 1	31
32	47. 8	48. 3	48. 8	49. 3	49. 8	50. 3	50. 8	51. 4	52. 0	52. 6	53. 2	53. 8	32
33	49. 3	49. 8	50. 3	50. 8	51. 3	51. 8	52. 4	53. 0	53. 6	54. 2	54. 8	55. 4	33
34	50. 8	51. 3	51. 8	52. 3	52. 9	53. 4	54. 0	54. 6	55. 2	55. 8	56. 5	57. 1	34
35	52. 3	52. 8	53. 3	53. 8	54. 4	55. 0	55. 6	56. 2	56. 8	57. 5	58. 2	58. 8	35
36	53. 8	54. 3	54. 9	55. 5	56. 0	56. 6	57. 2	57. 8	58. 5	59. 1	59. 8	60. 4	36
37	55. 3	55. 8	56. 4	57. 0	57. 6	58. 2	58. 8	59. 4	60. 1	60. 7	61. 5	62. 2	37
38	56. 8	57. 3	57. 9	58. 5	59. 1	59. 7	60. 4	61. 0	61. 7	62. 4	63. 1	63. 8	38
39	58. 3	58. 8	59. 4	59. 9	60. 7	61. 3	62. 0	62. 6	63. 3	64. 0	64. 8	65. 5	39
40	59. 8	60. 4	61. 0	61. 6	62. 2	62. 9	63. 6	64. 3	65. 0	65. 7	66. 5	67. 3	40
41	61. 3	61. 9	62. 5	63. 1	63. 8	64. 5	65. 2	65. 9	66. 6	67. 3	68. 1	68. 9	41
42	62. 8	63. 4	64. 0	64. 6	65. 3	66. 0	66. 7	67. 4	68. 2	69. 0	69. 8	70. 4	42
43	64. 3	64. 9	65. 5	66. 2	66. 9	67. 6	68. 3	69. 0	69. 8	70. 6	71. 5	72. 3	43
44	65. 8	66. 4	67. 1	67. 8	68. 5	69. 2	69. 9	70. 7	71. 5	72. 3	73. 1	74. 0	44
45	67. 3	68. 0	68. 6	69. 3	70. 0	70. 7	71. 5	72. 3	73. 1	73. 9	74. 8	75. 7	45
46	68. 7	69. 4	70. 1	70. 8	71. 6	72. 3	73. 1	73. 8	74. 7	75. 5	76. 4	77. 3	46
47	70. 2	70. 9	71. 6	72. 3	73. 1	73. 8	74. 7	75. 5	76. 3	77. 2	78. 1	79. 0	47
48	71. 7	72. 4	73. 2	73. 9	74. 7	75. 5	76. 3	77. 1	78. 0	78. 9	79. 8	80. 7	48
49	73. 2	74. 0	74. 7	75. 4	76. 2	77. 0	77. 9	78. 7	79. 6	80. 5	81. 4	82. 4	49
50	74. 7	75. 5	76. 2	77. 0	77. 8	78. 6	79. 5	80. 3	81. 2	82. 1	83. 1	84. 1	50
51	76. 2	76. 9	77. 7	78. 5	79. 3	80. 1	81. 0	81. 9	82. 8	83. 7	84. 7	85. 7	51
52	77. 7	78. 5	79. 3	80. 1	80. 9	81. 7	82. 6	83. 5	84. 5	85. 4	86. 4	87. 4	52
53	79. 2	80. 0	80. 8	81. 6	82. 4	83. 2	84. 2	85. 1	86. 1	87. 1	88. 1	89. 1	53
54	80. 7	81. 5	82. 3	83. 1	84. 0	84. 9	85. 8	86. 7	87. 7	88. 7	89. 7	90. 8	54
55	82. 2	83. 0	83. 8	84. 7	85. 6	86. 4	87. 4	88. 3	89. 3	90. 3	91. 4	92. 5	55
56	83. 7	84. 5	85. 4	86. 2	87. 1	88. 0	89. 0	90. 0	91. 0	92. 0	93. 1	94. 2	56
57	85. 2	86. 0	86. 9	87. 8	88. 7	89. 6	90. 6	91. 6	92. 6	93. 6	94. 7	95. 8	57
58	86. 7	87. 5	88. 4	89. 3	90. 2	91. 2	92. 2	93. 2	94. 2	95. 2	96. 3	97. 5	58
59	88. 2	89. 0	89. 9	90. 8	91. 8	92. 8	93. 8	94. 8	95. 8	96. 9	98. 0	99. 2	59
60	89. 7	90. 6	91. 5	92. 4	93. 3	94. 3	95. 3	96. 2	97. 5	98. 4	99. 7	100. 9	60

TABLE 4.

Conversion of Departure into Difference Longitude.

Dep.	Middle Latitude.												Dep.
	54°	54°30′	55°	55°30′	56°	56°30′	57°	57°30′	58°	58°30′	59°	59°30′	
	D. Lo.	D. Lo.	D. Lo.	D. Lo.	D. Lo.	D. Lo.	D. Lo.	D. Lo.	D. Lo.	D. Lo.	D. Lo.	D. Lo.	
1	1.7	1.7	1.7	1.7	1.8	1.8	1.8	1.8	1.9	1.9	1.9	2.0	1
2	3.4	3.4	3.5	3.5	3.6	3.6	3.7	3.7	3.8	3.8	3.9	3.9	2
3	5.1	5.1	5.2	5.3	5.4	5.4	5.5	5.6	5.7	5.7	5.8	5.9	3
4	6.8	6.9	7.0	7.1	7.2	7.2	7.3	7.4	7.5	7.6	7.8	7.9	4
5	8.5	8.6	8.7	8.8	8.9	9.0	9.2	9.3	9.4	9.5	9.7	9.8	5
6	10.2	10.3	10.5	10.6	10.7	10.8	11.0	11.1	11.3	11.4	11.6	11.8	6
7	11.9	12.0	12.2	12.3	12.5	12.7	12.9	13.0	13.2	13.4	13.6	13.8	7
8	13.6	13.7	13.9	14.1	14.3	14.5	14.7	14.9	15.1	15.3	15.5	15.8	8
9	15.3	15.5	15.7	15.9	16.1	16.3	16.5	16.7	17.0	17.2	17.5	17.7	9
10	17.0	17.2	17.4	17.6	17.9	18.1	18.4	18.7	18.9	19.1	19.4	19.7	10
11	18.7	18.9	19.2	19.4	19.7	20.0	20.2	20.5	20.8	21.1	21.4	21.6	11
12	20.4	20.6	20.9	21.2	21.5	21.8	22.0	22.3	22.6	22.9	23.3	23.7	12
13	22.1	22.4	22.7	22.9	23.2	23.5	23.9	24.2	24.5	24.9	25.2	25.6	13
14	23.8	24.1	24.4	24.7	25.0	25.3	25.7	26.0	26.4	26.8	27.2	27.6	14
15	25.5	25.8	26.2	26.5	26.8	27.1	27.5	27.9	28.3	28.7	29.1	29.6	15
16	27.2	27.5	27.9	28.2	28.6	29.0	29.4	29.8	30.2	30.6	31.1	31.5	16
17	28.9	29.2	29.6	30.0	30.4	30.8	31.2	31.6	32.1	32.6	33.0	33.5	17
18	30.6	31.0	31.4	31.8	32.2	32.6	33.0	33.5	34.0	34.5	34.9	35.5	18
19	32.3	32.7	33.1	33.5	34.0	34.4	34.9	35.4	35.9	36.4	36.9	37.4	19
20	34.0	34.4	34.9	35.3	35.8	36.2	36.7	37.2	37.7	38.2	38.8	39.4	20
21	35.7	36.1	36.6	37.1	37.6	38.1	38.6	39.1	39.6	40.2	40.8	41.4	21
22	37.4	37.9	38.4	38.9	39.3	39.8	40.4	40.9	41.5	42.1	42.7	43.3	22
23	39.1	39.6	40.1	40.6	41.1	41.6	42.2	42.8	43.4	44.0	44.7	45.3	23
24	40.8	41.3	41.8	42.3	42.9	43.5	44.1	44.7	45.3	45.9	46.6	47.3	24
25	42.5	43.0	43.6	44.1	44.7	45.3	45.9	46.5	47.2	47.8	48.5	49.3	25
26	44.2	44.7	45.3	45.9	46.5	47.1	47.7	48.4	49.1	49.8	50.5	51.2	26
27	45.9	46.4	47.1	47.7	48.3	48.9	49.6	50.3	51.0	51.7	52.4	53.2	27
28	47.6	48.2	48.8	49.4	50.1	50.7	51.4	52.1	52.8	53.4	54.4	55.2	28
29	49 3	49.9	50.6	51.2	51.9	52.5	53.2	53.9	54.7	55.5	56.3	57.1	29
30	51.0	51.6	52.3	52.9	53.6	54.3	55.1	55.8	56.6	57.4	58.2	59.1	30
31	52.7	53.3	54.0	54.7	55.4	56.1	56.9	57.7	58.5	59.3	60.2	61.0	31
32	54.4	55.2	55.8	56.5	57.2	58.0	58.8	59.6	60.4	61.2	62.1	63 0	32
33	56.1	56.8	57.5	58.2	59.0	59.8	60.6	61.4	62.3	63.2	64.1	65.0	33
34	57.8	58.5	59.3	60.0	60.8	61.4	62.4	63.3	64.2	65.1	66.0	67.0	34
35	59.5	60.2	61.0	61.8	62.6	63.4	64.3	65.1	66.0	67.0	68.0	69.0	35
36	61.2	62.0	62.8	63.6	64.4	65.2	66.1	67.0	67.9	68.9	69.9	70.9	36
37	62.9	63.7	64.5	65.3	66.2	67.0	67.9	68.8	69.8	70.8	71.8	72.9	37
38	64.6	65.4	66.3	67.1	68.0	68.9	69.8	70.7	71.7	72.7	73.8	74.9	38
39	66.3	67.1	68.0	68.8	69.7	70.6	71.6	72.6	73.6	74.6	75.7	76.8	39
40	68.1	68.9	69.7	70.4	71.5	72.4	73.4	74.4	75.5	76.6	77.7	78.8	40
41	69.8	70.6	71.5	72.4	73.3	74.3	75.3	76.3	77.4	78.5	79.6	80.8	41
42	71.5	72.3	73.2	74.1	75.1	76.1	77.1	78.2	79.3	80.4	81.5	82.8	42
43	73.2	74.1	75.0	75.9	76.9	77.9	79.0	80.0	81.1	82.3	83.5	84.7	43
44	74.9	75.8	76.7	77.7	78.7	79.7	80.8	81.9	83.0	84.2	85.4	86.7	44
45	76.6	77.5	78.5	79.5	80.5	81.5	82.6	83.7	84.9	86.1	87.4	88.7	45
46	78.3	79.2	80.2	81.2	82.3	83.4	84.5	85.6	86.8	88.0	89.3	90.6	46
47	80.0	80.9	81.9	82.9	84.0	85.1	86.3	87.5	88.7	90.0	91.3	92.6	47
48	81.7	82.7	83.7	84.7	85.8	86.9	88.1	89.3	90.6	91.9	93.2	94.6	48
49	83.4	84.4	85.4	86.5	87.6	88.8	90.0	91.2	92.5	93.8	95.1	96.5	49
50	85.1	86.1	87.2	88.4	89.4	90.6	91.8	93.1	94.4	95.7	97.1	98.5	50
51	86.8	87.8	88.9	90.0	91.2	92.4	93.6	94.9	96.2	97.6	99.0	100.5	51
52	88.5	89.6	90.7	91.8	93.0	94.2	95.5	96.8	98.1	99.6	101.0	102.5	52
53	90.2	91.3	92.5	93.6	94.8	96.0	97.3	98.6	100.0	101.5	102.9	104.4	53
54	91.9	93.0	94.2	95.4	96.6	97.9	99.1	100.5	101.9	103.4	104.8	106.4	54
55	93.6	94.8	96.0	97.2	98.4	99.7	101.0	102.4	103.8	105.1	106.7	108.3	55
56	95.3	96.5	97.7	98.9	100.1	101.4	102.8	104.2	105.7	107.2	108.6	110.3	56
57	97.0	98.2	99.5	100.7	101.9	103.3	104.7	106.1	107.6	109.1	110.6	112.3	57
58	98.7	99.9	101.2	102.4	103.7	105.1	106.5	108.0	109.5	111.0	112.5	114.2	58
59	100.4	101.6	102.9	104.2	105.5	106.9	108.3	109.8	111.3	112.9	114.5	116.2	59
60	102.1	103.3	104.6	106.0	107.3	108.8	110.2	111.7	113.2	114.8	116.5	118.2	60

TABLE 5.

Meridional Parts, or Increased Latitudes.

Comp. $\frac{1}{293.465}$

M.	0°	1°	2°	3°	4°	5°	6°	7°	8°	9°	M.
0	0.0	59.6	119.2	178.9	238.6	298.3	358.2	418.2	478.3	538.6	0
1	1.0	60.6	20.2	79.9	39.6	99.3	59.2	19.2	79.3	39.6	1
2	2.0	61.6	21.2	80.8	40.6	300.3	60.2	20.2	80.3	40.6	2
3	3.0	62.6	22.2	81.8	41.6	01.3	61.2	21.2	81.3	41.6	3
4	4.0	63.6	23.2	82.8	42.5	02.3	62.2	22.2	82.3	42.6	4
5	5.0	64.6	124.2	183.8	243.5	303.3	363.2	423.2	483.3	543.6	5
6	6.0	65.6	25.2	84.8	44.5	04.3	64.2	24.2	84.3	44.6	6
7	7.0	66.5	26.2	85.8	45.5	05.3	65.2	25.2	85.3	45.6	7
8	7.9	67.5	27.2	86.8	46.5	06.3	66.2	26.2	86.3	46.6	8
9	8.9	68.5	28.2	87.8	47.5	07.3	67.2	27.2	87.3	47.6	9
10	9.9	69.5	129.1	188.8	248.5	308.3	368.2	428.2	488.3	548.6	10
11	10.9	70.5	30.1	89.8	49.5	09.3	69.2	29.2	89.3	49.6	11
12	11.9	71.5	31.1	90.8	50.5	10.3	70.2	30.2	90.4	50.6	12
13	12.9	72.5	32.1	91.8	51.5	11.3	71.2	31.2	91.4	51.7	13
14	13.9	73.5	33.1	92.8	52.5	12.3	72.2	32.2	92.4	52.7	14
15	14.9	74.5	134.1	193.8	253.5	313.3	373.2	433.2	493.4	553.7	15
16	15.9	75.5	35.1	94.8	54.5	14.3	74.2	34.2	94.4	54.7	16
17	16.9	76.5	36.1	95.8	55.5	15.3	75.2	35.2	95.4	55.7	17
18	17.9	77.5	37.1	96.8	56.5	16.3	76.2	36.2	96.4	56.7	18
19	18.9	78.5	38.1	97.8	57.5	17.3	77.2	37.2	97.4	57.7	19
20	19.9	79.5	139.1	198.8	258.5	318.3	378.2	438.2	498.4	558.7	20
21	20.9	80.5	40.1	99.7	59.5	19.3	79.2	39.2	99.4	59.7	21
22	21.9	81.5	41.1	200.7	60.5	20.3	80.2	40.2	500.4	60.7	22
23	22.8	82.4	42.1	01.7	61.5	21.3	81.2	41.2	01.4	61.7	23
24	23.8	83.4	43.1	02.7	62.5	22.3	82.2	42.2	02.4	62.7	24
25	24.8	84.4	144.1	203.7	263.5	323.3	383.2	443.2	503.4	563.7	25
26	25.8	85.4	45.1	04.7	64.5	24.3	84.2	44.2	04.4	64.7	26
27	26.8	86.4	46.0	05.7	65.5	25.3	85.2	45.2	05.4	65.7	27
28	27.8	87.4	47.0	06.7	66.5	26.3	86.2	46.2	06.4	66.8	28
29	28.8	88.4	48.0	07.7	67.4	27.3	87.2	47.2	07.4	67.8	29
30	29.8	89.4	149.0	208.7	268.4	328.3	388.2	448.2	508.4	568.8	30
31	30.8	90.4	50.0	09.7	69.4	29.3	89.2	49.2	09.4	69.8	31
32	31.8	91.4	51.0	10.7	70.4	30.3	90.2	50.2	10.4	70.8	32
33	32.8	92.4	52.0	11.7	71.4	31.3	91.2	51.2	11.4	71.8	33
34	33.8	93.4	53.0	12.7	72.4	32.3	92.2	52.2	12.4	72.8	34
35	34.8	94.4	154.0	213.7	273.4	333.3	393.2	453.2	513.4	573.8	35
36	35.8	95.4	55.0	14.7	74.4	34.3	94.2	54.3	14.5	74.8	36
37	36.7	96.4	56.0	15.7	75.4	35.3	95.2	55.3	15.5	75.8	37
38	37.7	97.3	57.0	16.7	76.4	36.2	96.2	56.3	16.5	76.8	38
39	38.7	98.3	58.0	17.7	77.4	37.2	97.2	57.3	17.5	77.8	39
40	39.7	99.3	159.0	218.7	278.4	338.2	398.2	458.3	518.5	578.8	40
41	40.7	100.3	60.0	19.7	79.4	39.2	99.2	59.3	19.5	79.9	41
42	41.7	01.3	61.0	20.6	80.4	40.2	400.2	60.3	20.5	80.9	42
43	42.7	02.3	62.0	21.6	81.4	41.2	01.2	61.3	21.5	81.9	43
44	43.7	03.3	63.0	22.6	82.4	42.2	02.2	62.3	22.5	82.9	44
45	44.7	104.3	164.0	223.6	283.4	343.2	403.2	463.3	523.5	583.9	45
46	45.7	05.3	65.0	24.6	84.4	44.2	04.2	64.3	24.5	84.9	46
47	46.7	06.3	66.0	25.6	85.4	45.2	05.2	65.3	25.5	85.9	47
48	47.7	07.3	67.0	26.6	86.4	46.2	06.2	66.3	26.5	86.9	48
49	48.7	08.3	68.0	27.6	87.4	47.2	07.2	67.3	27.5	87.9	49
50	49.7	109.3	168.9	228.6	288.4	348.2	408.2	468.3	528.5	588.9	50
51	50.7	10.3	69.9	29.6	89.4	49.2	09.2	69.3	29.5	89.9	51
52	51.6	11.3	70.9	30.6	90.4	50.2	10.2	70.3	30.5	90.9	52
53	52.6	12.3	71.9	31.6	91.4	51.2	11.2	71.3	31.5	91.9	53
54	53.6	13.2	72.9	32.6	92.4	52.2	12.2	72.3	32.5	93.0	54
55	54.6	114.2	173.9	233.6	293.4	353.2	413.2	473.3	533.5	594.0	55
56	55.6	15.2	74.9	34.6	94.4	54.2	14.2	74.3	34.6	95.0	56
57	56.6	16.2	75.9	35.6	95.4	55.2	15.2	75.3	35.6	96.0	57
58	57.6	17.2	76.9	36.6	96.3	56.2	16.2	76.3	36.6	97.0	58
59	58.6	18.2	77.9	37.6	97.3	57.2	17.2	77.3	37.6	98.0	59
M.	0°	1°	2°	3°	4°	5°	6°	7°	8°	9°	M.

TABLE 5.

Meridional Parts, or Increased Latitudes.

Comp. $\frac{1}{293.465}$

M.	10°	11°	12°	13°	14°	15°	16°	17°	18°	19°	M.
0	599.0	659.6	720.5	781.5	842.8	904.4	966.3	1028.5	1091.0	1153.9	0
1	600.0	60.6	21.5	82.5	43.9	05.4	67.3	29.5	92.0	54.9	1
2	01.0	61.7	22.5	83.6	44.9	06.5	68.3	30.5	93.1	56.0	2
3	02.0	62.7	23.5	84.6	45.9	07.5	69.4	31.6	94.1	57.0	3
4	03.0	63.7	24.5	85.6	46.9	08.5	70.4	32.6	95.2	58.1	4
5	604.1	664.7	725.5	786.6	847.9	909.6	971.4	1033.7	1096.2	1159.1	5
6	05.1	65.7	26.6	87.6	49.0	10.6	72.5	34.7	97.3	60.2	6
7	06.1	66.7	27.6	88.7	50.0	11.6	73.5	35.7	98.3	61.2	7
8	07.1	67.7	28.6	89.7	51.0	12.6	74.6	36.8	99.4	62.3	8
9	08.1	68.7	29.6	90.7	52.0	13.7	75.6	37.8	1100.4	63.3	9
10	609.1	669.8	730.6	791.7	853.1	914.7	976.6	1038.9	1101.4	1164.4	10
11	10.1	70.8	31.6	92.7	54.1	15.7	77.7	39.9	02.5	65.4	11
12	11.1	71.8	32.7	93.8	55.1	16.8	78.7	40.9	03.5	66.5	12
13	12.1	72.8	33.7	94.8	56.1	17.8	79.7	42.0	04.6	67.5	13
14	13.1	73.8	34.7	95.8	57.2	18.8	80.8	43.0	05.6	68.6	14
15	614.1	674.8	735.7	796.8	858.2	919.8	981.8	1044.1	1106.7	1169.7	15
16	15.2	75.8	36.7	97.8	59.2	20.9	82.8	45.1	07.7	70.7	16
17	16.2	76.8	37.7	98.9	60.2	21.9	83.9	46.1	08.8	71.8	17
18	17.2	77.9	38.8	99.9	61.3	22.9	84.9	47.2	09.8	72.8	18
19	18.2	78.9	39.8	800.9	62.3	24.0	85.9	48.2	10.9	73.9	19
20	619.2	679.9	740.8	801.9	863.3	925.0	987.0	1049.3	1111.9	1174.9	20
21	20.2	80.9	41.8	02.9	64.3	26.0	88.0	50.3	13.0	76.0	21
22	21.2	81.9	42.8	04.0	65.4	27.1	89.0	51.3	14.0	77.0	22
23	22.2	82.9	43.8	05.0	66.4	28.1	90.1	52.4	15.0	78.1	23
24	23.2	83.9	44.9	06.0	67.4	29.1	91.1	53.4	16.1	79.1	24
25	624.2	684.9	745.9	807.0	868.5	930.1	992.1	1054.5	1117.1	1180.2	25
26	25.3	86.0	46.9	08.1	69.5	31.2	93.2	55.5	18.2	81.2	26
27	26.3	87.0	47.9	09.1	70.5	32.2	94.2	56.6	19.2	82.3	27
28	27.3	88.0	48.9	10.1	71.5	33.2	95.3	57.6	20.3	83.3	28
29	28.3	89.0	49.9	11.1	72.6	34.3	96.3	58.6	21.3	84.4	29
30	629.3	690.0	751.0	812.1	873.6	935.3	997.3	1059.7	1122.4	1185.5	30
31	30.3	91.0	52.0	13.2	74.6	36.3	98.4	60.7	23.4	86.5	31
32	31.3	92.0	53.0	14.2	75.6	37.4	99.4	61.8	24.5	87.6	32
33	32.3	93.1	54.0	15.2	76.7	38.4	1000.4	62.8	25.5	88.6	33
34	33.3	94.1	55.0	16.2	77.7	39.4	01.5	63.9	26.6	89.7	34
35	634.3	695.1	756.0	817.3	878.7	940.5	1002.5	1064.9	1127.6	1190.7	35
36	35.4	96.1	57.1	18.3	79.7	41.5	03.6	65.9	28.7	91.8	36
37	36.4	97.1	58.1	19.3	80.8	42.5	04.6	67.0	29.7	92.8	37
38	37.4	98.1	59.1	20.3	81.8	43.6	05.6	68.0	30.8	93.9	38
39	38.4	99.1	60.1	21.3	82.8	44.6	06.7	69.1	31.8	95.0	39
40	639.4	700.2	761.1	822.4	883.8	945.6	1007.7	1070.1	1132.9	1196.0	40
41	40.4	01.2	62.2	23.4	84.9	46.7	08.7	71.2	33.9	97.1	41
42	41.4	02.2	63.2	24.4	85.9	47.7	09.8	72.2	35.0	98.1	42
43	42.4	03.2	64.2	25.4	86.9	48.7	10.8	73.2	36.0	99.2	43
44	43.4	04.2	65.2	26.5	88.0	49.7	11.8	74.3	37.1	1200.2	44
45	644.5	705.2	766.2	827.5	889.0	950.8	1012.9	1075.3	1138.1	1201.3	45
46	45.5	06.2	67.3	28.5	90.0	51.8	13.9	76.4	39.2	02.3	46
47	46.5	07.3	68.3	29.5	91.0	52.8	15.0	77.4	40.2	03.4	47
48	47.5	08.3	69.3	30.5	92.1	53.9	16.0	78.5	41.3	04.5	48
49	48.5	09.3	70.3	31.6	93.1	54.9	17.0	79.5	42.3	05.5	49
50	649.5	710.3	771.3	832.6	894.1	955.9	1018.1	1080.5	1143.4	1206.6	50
51	50.5	11.3	72.3	33.6	95.2	57.0	19.1	81.6	44.4	07.6	51
52	51.5	12.3	73.4	34.6	96.2	58.0	20.2	82.6	45.5	08.7	52
53	52.5	13.4	74.4	35.7	97.2	59.0	21.2	83.7	46.5	09.7	53
54	53.6	14.4	75.4	36.7	98.2	60.1	22.2	84.7	47.6	10.8	54
55	654.6	715.4	776.4	837.7	899.3	961.1	1023.3	1085.8	1148.6	1211.8	55
56	55.6	16.4	77.4	38.7	900.3	62.1	24.3	86.8	49.7	12.9	56
57	56.6	17.4	78.5	39.8	01.3	63.2	25.3	87.9	50.7	14.0	57
58	57.6	18.4	79.5	40.8	02.3	64.2	26.4	88.9	51.8	15.0	58
59	58.6	19.4	80.5	41.8	03.4	65.2	27.4	89.9	52.8	16.1	59
M.	10°	11°	12°	13°	14°	15°	16°	17°	18°	19°	M.

TABLE 5.

Meridional Parts, or Increased Latitudes.

Comp. $\frac{1}{293.465}$

M.	20°	21°	22°	23°	24°	25°	26°	27°	28°	29°	M.
0	1217.1	1280.8	1344.9	1409.5	1474.5	1540.1	1606.2	1672.9	1740.2	1808.1	0
1	18.2	81.9	46.0	10.6	75.6	41.2	07.3	74.0	41.3	09.2	1
2	19.3	82.9	47.1	11.6	76.7	42.3	08.4	75.1	42.4	10.4	2
3	20.3	84.0	48.1	12.7	77.8	43.4	09.5	76.2	43.6	11.5	3
4	21.4	85.1	49.2	13.8	78.9	44.5	10.6	77.4	44.7	12.6	4
5	1222.4	1286.1	1350.3	1414.9	1480.0	1545.6	1611.7	1678.5	1745.8	1813.8	5
6	23.5	87.2	51.4	16.0	81.1	46.7	12.9	79.6	46.9	14.9	6
7	24.5	88.3	52.4	17.1	82.2	47.8	14.0	80.7	48.1	16.1	7
8	25.6	89.3	53.5	18.1	83.3	48.9	15.1	81.8	49.2	17.2	8
9	26.7	90.4	54.6	19.2	84.3	50.0	16.2	82.9	50.3	18.3	9
10	1227.7	1291.5	1355.7	1420.3	1485.4	1551.1	1617.3	1684.1	1751.5	1819.5	10
11	28.8	92.5	56.7	21.4	86.5	52.2	18.4	85.2	52.6	20.6	11
12	29.8	93.6	57.8	22.5	87.6	53.3	19.5	86.3	53.7	21.8	12
13	30.9	94.7	58.9	23.5	88.7	54.4	20.6	87.4	54.8	22.9	13
14	32.0	95.7	59.9	24.6	89.8	55.5	21.7	88.5	56.0	24.0	14
15	1233.0	1296.8	1361.0	1425.7	1490.9	1556.6	1622.8	1689.7	1757.1	1825.2	15
16	34.1	97.9	62.1	26.8	92.0	57.7	23.9	90.8	58.2	26.3	16
17	35.1	98.9	63.2	27.9	93.1	58.8	25.0	91.9	59.4	27.5	17
18	36.2	1300.0	64.2	29.0	94.2	59.9	26.2	93.0	60.5	28.6	18
19	37.3	01.1	65.3	30.0	95.2	61.0	27.3	94.1	61.6	29.7	19
20	1238.3	1302.1	1366.4	1431.1	1496.3	1562.1	1628.4	1695.3	1762.7	1830.9	20
21	39.4	03.2	67.5	32.2	97.4	63.2	29.5	96.4	63.9	32.0	21
22	40.4	04.3	68.5	33.3	98.5	64.3	30.6	97.5	65.0	33.2	22
23	41.5	05.3	69.6	34.4	99.6	65.4	31.7	98.6	66.1	34.3	23
24	42.6	06.4	70.7	35.4	1500.7	66.5	32.8	99.7	67.3	35.4	24
25	1243.6	1307.5	1371.8	1436.5	1501.8	1567.6	1633.9	1700.9	1768.4	1836.6	25
26	44.7	08.5	72.8	37.6	02.9	68.7	35.0	02.0	69.5	37.7	26
27	45.7	09.6	73.9	38.7	04.0	69.8	36.1	03.1	70.7	38.9	27
28	46.8	10.7	75.0	39.8	05.1	70.9	37.3	04.2	71.8	40.0	28
29	47.9	11.7	76.1	40.9	06.2	72.0	38.4	05.3	72.9	41.2	29
30	1248.9	1312.8	1377.1	1442.0	1507.3	1573.1	1639.5	1706.5	1774.1	1842.3	30
31	50.0	13.9	78.2	43.0	08.4	74.2	40.6	07.6	75.2	43.4	31
32	51.0	14.9	79.3	44.1	09.4	75.3	41.7	08.7	76.3	44.6	32
33	52.1	16.0	80.4	45.2	10.5	76.4	42.8	09.8	77.4	45.7	33
34	53.2	17.1	81.5	46.3	11.6	77.5	43.9	10.9	78.6	46.9	34
35	1254.2	1318.2	1382.5	1447.4	1512.7	1578.6	1645.0	1712.1	1779.7	1848.0	35
36	55.3	19.2	83.6	48.5	13.8	79.7	46.2	13.2	80.8	49.2	36
37	56.4	20.3	84.7	49.5	14.9	80.8	47.3	14.3	82.0	50.3	37
38	57.4	21.4	85.8	50.6	16.0	81.9	48.4	15.4	83.1	51.4	38
39	58.5	22.4	86.8	51.7	17.1	83.0	49.5	16.6	84.2	52.6	39
40	1259.5	1323.5	1387.9	1452.8	1518.2	1584.1	1650.6	1717.7	1785.4	1853.7	40
41	60.6	24.6	89.0	53.9	19.3	85.2	51.7	18.8	86.5	54.9	41
42	61.7	25.6	90.1	55.0	20.4	86.3	52.8	19.9	87.6	56.0	42
43	62.7	26.7	91.1	56.1	21.5	87.4	53.9	21.1	88.8	57.2	43
44	63.8	27.8	92.2	57.1	22.6	88.5	55.1	22.2	89.9	58.3	44
45	1264.9	1328.9	1393.3	1458.2	1523.7	1589.6	1656.2	1723.3	1791.1	1859.5	45
46	65.9	29.9	94.4	59.3	24.8	90.7	57.3	24.4	92.2	60.6	46
47	67.0	31.0	95.5	60.4	25.9	91.8	58.4	25.5	93.3	61.8	47
48	68.0	32.1	96.5	61.5	27.0	92.9	59.5	26.7	94.5	62.9	48
49	69.1	33.1	97.6	62.6	28.0	94.1	60.6	27.8	95.6	64.0	49
50	1270.2	1334.2	1398.7	1463.7	1529.1	1595.2	1661.7	1728.9	1796.7	1865.2	50
51	71.2	35.3	99.8	64.8	30.2	96.3	62.9	30.0	97.9	66.3	51
52	72.3	36.3	1400.9	65.8	31.3	97.4	64.0	31.2	99.0	67.5	52
53	73.4	37.4	01.9	66.9	32.4	98.5	65.1	32.3	1800.1	68.6	53
54	74.4	38.5	03.0	68.0	33.5	99.6	66.2	33.4	01.3	69.8	54
55	1275.5	1339.6	1404.1	1469.1	1534.6	1600.7	1667.3	1734.5	1802.4	1870.9	55
56	76.6	40.6	05.2	70.2	35.7	01.8	68.4	35.7	03.5	72.1	56
57	77.6	41.7	06.2	71.3	36.8	02.9	69.5	36.8	04.7	73.2	57
58	78.7	42.8	07.3	72.4	37.9	04.0	70.7	37.9	05.8	74.4	58
59	79.7	43.8	08.4	73.5	39.0	05.1	71.8	39.1	07.0	75.5	59
M.	20°	21°	22°	23°	24°	25°	26°	27°	28°	29°	M.

TABLE 5.

Meridional Parts, or Increased Latitudes.

Comp. $\frac{1}{293.465}$

M.	30°	31°	32°	33°	34°	35°	36°	37°	38°	39°	M.
0	1876.7	1946.0	2016.0	2086.8	2158.4	2230.9	2304.2	2378.5	2453.8	2530.2	0
1	77.8	47.1	17.2	88.0	59.6	32.1	05.5	79.8	55.1	31.5	1
2	79.0	48.3	18.3	89.2	60.8	33.3	06.7	81.0	56.4	32.8	2
3	80.1	49.4	19.5	90.3	62.0	34.5	07.9	82.3	57.6	34.0	3
4	81.3	50.6	20.7	91.5	63.2	35.7	09.2	83.5	58.9	35.3	4
5	1882.4	1951.8	2021.9	2092.7	2164.4	2236.9	2310.4	2384.8	2460.2	2536.6	5
6	83.6	52.9	23.0	93.9	65.6	38.2	11.6	86.0	61.4	37.9	6
7	84.7	54.1	24.2	95.1	66.8	39.4	12.9	87.3	62.7	39.2	7
8	85.9	55.3	25.4	96.3	68.0	40.6	14.1	88.5	64.0	40.5	8
9	87.0	56.4	26.6	97.5	69.2	41.8	15.3	89.8	65.2	41.7	9
10	1888.2	1957.6	2027.7	2098.7	2170.4	2243.0	2316.5	2391.0	2466.5	2543.0	10
11	89.3	58.7	28.9	99.8	71.6	44.2	17.8	92.3	67.8	44.3	11
12	90.5	59.9	30.1	2101.0	72.8	45.5	19.0	93.5	69.0	45.6	12
13	91.6	61.1	31.3	02.2	74.0	46.7	20.3	94.8	70.3	46.9	13
14	92.8	62.2	32.4	03.4	75.2	47.9	21.5	96.0	71.6	48.2	14
15	1893.9	1963.4	2033.6	2104.6	2176.4	2249.1	2322.7	2397.3	2472.8	2549.5	15
16	95.1	64.6	34.8	05.8	77.6	50.3	24.0	98.5	74.1	50.7	16
17	96.2	65.7	36.0	07.0	78.8	51.6	25.2	99.8	75.4	52.0	17
18	97.4	66.9	37.1	08.2	80.0	52.8	26.4	2401.0	76.6	53.3	18
19	98.5	68.1	38.3	09.4	81.2	54.0	27.7	02.3	77.9	54.6	19
20	1899.7	1969.2	2039.5	2110.6	2182.5	2255.2	2328.9	2403.5	2479.2	2555.9	20
21	1900.8	70.4	40.7	11.8	83.7	56.4	30.1	04.8	80.4	57.2	21
22	02.0	71.5	41.8	12.9	84.9	57.7	31.4	06.0	81.7	58.5	22
23	03.1	72.7	43.0	14.1	86.1	58.9	32.6	07.3	83.0	59.8	23
24	04.3	73.9	44.2	15.3	87.3	60.1	33.8	08.5	84.3	61.0	24
25	1905.5	1975.0	2045.1	2116.5	2188.5	2261.3	2335.1	2409.8	2485.5	2562.3	25
26	06.6	76.2	46.6	17.7	89.7	62.5	36.3	11.1	86.8	63.6	26
27	07.8	77.4	47.7	18.9	90.9	63.8	37.6	12.3	88.1	64.9	27
28	08.9	78.5	48.9	20.1	92.1	65.0	38.8	13.6	89.3	66.2	28
29	10.1	79.7	50.1	21.3	93.3	66.2	40.0	14.8	90.6	67.5	29
30	1911.2	1980.9	2051.3	2122.5	2194.5	2267.4	2341.3	2416.1	2491.9	2568.8	30
31	12.4	82.0	52.5	23.7	95.7	68.7	42.5	17.3	93.2	70.1	31
32	13.5	83.2	53.6	24.9	96.9	69.9	43.7	18.6	94.4	71.4	32
33	14.7	84.4	54.8	26.1	98.1	71.1	45.0	19.8	95.7	72.7	33
34	15.8	85.5	56.0	27.3	99.4	72.3	46.2	21.1	97.0	73.9	34
35	1917.0	1986.7	2057.2	2128.5	2200.6	2273.5	2347.5	2422.3	2498.3	2575.2	35
36	18.2	87.9	58.4	29.6	01.8	74.8	48.7	23.6	99.5	76.5	36
37	19.3	89.1	59.5	30.8	03.0	76.0	49.9	24.9	2500.8	77.8	37
38	20.5	90.2	60.7	32.0	04.2	77.2	51.2	26.1	02.1	79.1	38
39	21.6	91.4	61.9	33.2	05.4	78.4	52.4	27.4	03.4	80.4	39
40	1922.8	1992.6	2063.1	2134.4	2206.6	2279.7	2353.7	2428.6	2504.6	2581.7	40
41	23.9	93.7	64.3	35.6	07.8	80.9	54.9	29.9	05.9	83.0	41
42	25.1	94.9	65.5	36.8	09.0	82.1	56.1	31.2	07.2	84.3	42
43	26.3	96.1	66.6	38.0	10.2	83.3	57.4	32.4	08.5	85.6	43
44	27.4	97.2	67.8	39.2	11.5	84.6	58.6	33.7	09.7	86.9	44
45	1928.6	1998.4	2069.0	2140.4	2212.7	2285.8	2359.9	2434.9	2511.0	2588.2	45
46	29.7	99.6	70.2	41.6	13.9	87.0	61.1	36.2	12.3	89.5	46
47	30.9	2000.7	71.4	42.8	15.1	88.3	62.4	37.4	13.6	90.8	47
48	32.0	01.9	72.6	44.0	16.3	89.5	63.6	38.7	14.8	92.1	48
49	33.2	03.1	73.7	45.2	17.5	90.7	64.8	40.0	16.1	93.4	49
50	1934.4	2004.3	2074.9	2146.4	2218.7	2291.9	2366.1	2441.2	2517.4	2594.7	50
51	35.5	05.4	76.1	47.6	19.9	93.2	67.3	42.5	18.7	96.0	51
52	36.7	06.6	77.3	48.8	21.1	94.4	68.6	43.7	20.0	97.3	52
53	37.8	07.8	78.5	50.0	22.4	95.6	69.8	45.0	21.2	98.5	53
54	39.0	08.9	79.7	51.2	23.6	96.9	71.1	46.3	22.5	99.8	54
55	1940.2	2010.1	2080.8	2152.4	2224.8	2298.1	2372.3	2447.5	2523.8	2601.1	55
56	41.3	11.3	82.0	53.6	26.0	99.3	73.6	48.8	25.1	02.4	56
57	42.5	12.5	83.2	54.8	27.2	2300.5	74.8	50.1	26.4	03.7	57
58	43.6	13.6	84.4	56.0	28.4	01.8	76.1	51.3	27.6	05.0	58
59	44.8	14.8	85.6	57.2	29.6	03.0	77.3	52.6	28.9	06.3	59
M.	30°	31°	32°	33°	34°	35°	36°	37°	38°	39°	M.

TABLE 5.

Meridional Parts, or Increased Latitudes.

Comp. $\frac{1}{293.465}$

M.	40°	41°	42°	43°	44°	45°	46°	47°	48°	49°	M.
0	2607.6	2686.2	2766.0	2847.1	2929.5	3013.4	3098.7	3185.6	3274.1	3364.4	0
1	08.9	87.6	67.4	48.5	30.9	14.8	3100.1	87.1	75.6	65.9	1
2	10.2	88.9	68.7	49.9	32.3	16.2	01.6	88.5	77.1	67.4	2
3	11.5	90.2	70.1	51.2	33.7	17.6	03.0	90.0	78.6	69.0	3
4	12.8	91.5	71.4	52.6	35.1	19.0	04.4	91.4	80.1	70.5	4
5	2614.1	2692.8	2772.8	2853.9	2936.5	3020.4	3105.9	3192.9	3281.6	3372.0	5
6	15.4	94.2	74.1	55.3	37.9	21.8	07.3	94.4	83.1	73.5	6
7	16.8	95.5	75.4	56.7	39.3	23.3	08.8	95.8	84.6	75.1	7
8	18.1	96.8	76.8	58.0	40.6	24.7	10.2	97.3	86.1	76.6	8
9	19.4	98.1	78.1	59.4	42.0	26.1	11.6	98.8	87.6	78.1	9
10	2620.7	2699.5	2779.5	2860.8	2943.4	3027.5	3113.1	3200.2	3289.0	3379.6	10
11	22.0	2700.8	80.8	62.1	44.8	28.9	14.5	01.7	90.5	81.2	11
12	23.3	02.1	82.2	63.5	46.2	30.3	16.0	03.2	92.0	82.7	12
13	24.6	03.4	83.5	64.9	47.6	31.7	17.4	04.6	93.5	84.2	13
14	25.9	04.8	84.8	66.2	49.0	33.2	18.8	06.1	95.0	85.7	14
15	2627.2	2706.1	2786.2	2867.6	2950.4	3034.6	3120.3	3207.6	3296.5	3387.3	15
16	28.5	07.4	87.5	69.0	51.8	36.0	21.7	09.0	98.0	88.8	16
17	29.8	08.7	88.9	70.3	53.2	37.4	23.2	10.5	99.5	90.3	17
18	31.1	10.1	90.2	71.7	54.5	38.8	24.6	12.0	3301.0	91.8	18
19	32.4	11.4	91.6	73.1	55.9	40.2	26.0	13.4	02.5	93.4	19
20	2633.7	2712.7	2792.9	2874.4	2957.3	3041.7	3127.5	3214.9	3304.0	3394.9	20
21	35.0	14.0	94.3	75.8	58.7	43.1	28.9	16.4	05.5	96.4	21
22	36.3	15.4	95.6	77.2	60.1	44.5	30.4	17.9	07.0	98.0	22
23	37.6	16.7	97.0	78.6	61.5	45.9	31.8	19.3	08.5	99.5	23
24	38.9	18.0	98.3	79.9	62.9	47.3	33.3	20.8	10.0	3401.0	24
25	2640.2	2719.3	2799.7	2881.3	2964.3	3048.7	3134.7	3222.3	3311.5	3402.6	25
26	41.6	20.7	2801.0	82.7	65.7	50.2	36.2	23.7	13.0	04.1	26
27	42.9	22.0	02.4	84.0	67.1	51.6	37.6	25.2	14.5	05.6	27
28	44.2	23.3	03.7	85.4	68.5	53.0	39.0	26.7	16.0	07.2	28
29	45.5	24.7	05.1	86.8	69.9	54.4	40.5	28.2	17.5	08.7	29
30	2646.8	2726.0	2806.4	2888.2	2971.3	3055.9	3141.9	3229.6	3319.0	3410.2	30
31	48.1	27.3	07.8	89.5	72.7	57.3	43.4	31.1	20.5	11.8	31
32	49.4	28.6	09.1	90.9	74.1	58.7	44.8	32.6	22.1	13.3	32
33	50.7	30.0	10.5	92.3	75.5	60.1	46.3	34.1	23.6	14.8	33
34	52.0	31.3	11.8	93.7	76.9	61.5	47.7	35.6	25.1	16.4	34
35	2653.3	2732.6	2813.2	2895.0	2978.3	3063.0	3149.2	3237.0	3326.6	3417.9	35
36	54.7	34.0	14.5	96.4	79.7	64.4	50.6	38.5	28.1	19.5	36
37	56.0	35.3	15.9	97.8	81.1	65.8	52.1	40.0	29.6	21.0	37
38	57.3	36.6	17.2	99.2	82.5	67.2	53.5	41.5	31.1	22.5	38
39	58.6	38.0	18.6	2900.5	83.9	68.7	55.0	42.9	32.6	24.1	39
40	2659.9	2739.3	2820.0	2901.9	2985.3	3070.1	3156.4	3244.4	3334.1	3425.6	40
41	61.2	40.6	21.3	03.3	86.7	71.5	57.9	45.9	35.6	27.2	41
42	62.5	42.0	22.7	04.7	88.1	72.9	59.4	47.4	37.1	28.7	42
43	63.9	43.3	24.0	06.1	89.5	74.4	60.8	48.9	38.6	30.2	43
44	65.2	44.6	25.4	07.4	90.9	75.8	62.3	50.3	40.2	31.8	44
45	2666.5	2746.0	2826.7	2908.8	2992.3	3077.2	3163.7	3251.8	3341.7	3433.3	45
46	67.8	47.3	28.1	10.2	93.7	78.7	65.2	53.3	43.2	34.9	46
47	69.1	48.6	29.4	11.6	95.1	80.1	66.6	54.8	44.7	36.4	47
48	70.4	50.0	30.8	13.0	96.5	81.5	68.1	56.3	46.2	38.0	48
49	71.7	51.3	32.2	14.3	97.9	82.9	69.5	57.8	47.7	39.5	49
50	2673.1	2752.7	2833.5	2915.7	2999.3	3084.4	3171.0	3259.3	3349.2	3441.0	50
51	74.4	54.0	34.9	17.1	3000.7	85.8	72.5	60.7	50.8	42.6	51
52	75.7	55.3	36.2	18.5	02.1	87.2	73.9	62.2	52.3	44.1	52
53	77.0	56.7	37.6	19.9	03.5	88.7	75.4	63.7	53.8	45.7	53
54	78.3	58.0	39.0	21.2	04.9	90.1	76.8	65.2	55.3	47.2	54
55	2679.6	2759.3	2840.3	2922.6	3006.3	3091.5	3178.3	3266.7	3356.8	3448.8	55
56	81.0	60.7	41.7	24.0	07.7	93.0	79.7	68.2	58.3	50.3	56
57	82.3	62.0	43.0	25.4	09.2	94.4	81.2	69.7	59.9	51.9	57
58	83.6	63.4	44.4	26.8	10.6	95.8	82.7	71.1	61.4	53.4	58
59	84.9	64.7	45.8	28.2	12.0	97.3	84.1	72.6	62.9	55.0	59
M.	40°	41°	42°	43°	44°	45°	46°	47°	48°	49°	M.

TABLE 5.

Meridional Parts, or Increased Latitudes.

Comp. $\frac{1}{293.465}$

M.	50°	51°	52°	53°	54°	55°	56°	57°	58°	59°	M.
0	3456.5	3550.6	3646.7	3745.1	3845.7	3948.8	4054.5	4163.0	4274.4	4389.1	0
1	58.1	52.2	48.4	46.7	47.4	50.5	56.3	64.8	76.3	91.0	1
2	59.6	53.8	50.0	48.4	49.1	52.3	58.1	66.6	78.2	92.9	2
3	61.2	55.4	51.6	50.0	50.8	54.0	59.8	68.5	80.1	94.9	3
4	62.7	56.9	53.2	51.7	52.5	55.7	61.6	70.3	82.0	96.8	4
5	3464.3	3558.5	3654.8	3753.4	3854.2	3957.5	4063.4	4172.1	4283.9	4398.8	5
6	65.9	60.1	56.5	55.0	55.9	59.2	65.2	74.0	85.7	4400.7	6
7	67.4	61.7	58.1	56.7	57.6	61.0	67.0	75.8	87.6	02.6	7
8	69.0	63.3	59.7	58.3	59.3	62.7	68.8	77.7	89.5	04.6	8
9	70.5	64.9	61.3	60.0	61.0	64.5	70.6	79.5	91.4	06.5	9
10	3472.1	3566.5	3663.0	3761.7	3862.7	3966.2	4072.4	4181.3	4293.3	4408.5	10
11	73.6	68.1	64.6	63.3	64.4	68.0	74.2	83.2	95.2	10.4	11
12	75.2	69.7	66.2	65.0	66.1	69.7	76.0	85.0	97.1	12.4	12
13	76.7	71.3	67.9	66.7	67.8	71.5	77.7	86.9	99.0	14.3	13
14	78.3	72.8	69.5	68.3	69.5	73.2	79.5	88.7	4300.9	16.3	14
15	3479.9	3574.4	3671.1	3770.0	3871.2	3975.0	4081.3	4190.6	4302.8	4418.2	15
16	81.4	76.0	72.7	71.7	72.9	76.7	83.1	92.4	04.7	20.2	16
17	83.0	77.6	74.4	73.3	74.6	78.5	84.9	94.2	06.6	22.1	17
18	84.5	79.2	76.0	75.0	76.3	80.2	86.7	96.1	08.5	24.1	18
19	86.1	80.8	77.6	76.7	78.1	82.0	88.5	97.9	10.4	26.1	19
20	3487.7	3582.4	3679.3	3778.3	3879.8	3983.7	4090.3	4199.8	4312.3	4428.0	20
21	89.2	84.0	80.9	80.0	81.5	85.5	92.1	4201.6	14.2	30.0	21
22	90.8	85.6	82.5	81.7	83.2	87.2	93.9	03.5	16.1	31.9	22
23	92.4	87.2	84.2	83.3	84.9	89.0	95.7	05.3	18.0	33.9	23
24	93.9	88.8	85.8	85.0	86.6	90.7	97.5	07.2	19.9	35.8	24
25	3495.5	3590.4	3687.4	3786.7	3888.3	3992.5	4099.3	4209.0	4321.8	4437.8	25
26	97.1	92.0	89.1	88.4	90.0	94.3	4101.1	10.9	23.7	39.8	26
27	98.6	93.6	90.7	90.0	91.8	96.0	02.9	12.8	25.6	41.7	27
28	3500.2	95.2	92.3	91.7	93.5	97.8	04.8	14.6	27.5	43.7	28
29	01.8	96.8	94.0	93.4	95.2	99.5	06.6	16.5	29.4	45.7	29
30	3503.3	3598.4	3695.6	3795.1	3896.9	4001.3	4108.4	4218.3	4331.3	4447.6	30
31	04.9	3600.0	97.3	96.8	98.6	03.1	10.2	20.2	33.2	49.6	31
32	06.5	01.6	98.9	98.4	3900.4	04.8	12.0	22.0	35.2	51.6	32
33	08.0	03.2	3700.5	3800.1	02.1	06.6	13.8	23.9	37.1	53.5	33
34	09.6	04.8	02.2	01.8	03.8	08.3	15.6	25.8	39.0	55.5	34
35	3511.2	3606.4	3703.8	3803.5	3905.5	4010.1	4117.4	4227.6	4340.9	4457.5	35
36	12.7	08.0	05.5	05.1	07.2	11.9	19.2	29.5	42.8	59.4	36
37	14.3	09.6	07.1	06.8	09.0	13.6	21.0	31.3	44.7	61.4	37
38	15.9	11.2	08.7	08.5	10.7	15.4	22.9	33.2	46.6	63.4	38
39	17.5	12.8	10.4	10.2	12.4	17.2	24.7	35.1	48.6	65.4	39
40	3519.0	3614.5	3712.0	3811.9	3914.1	4018.9	4126.5	4236.9	4350.5	4467.3	40
41	20.6	16.1	13.7	13.6	15.9	20.7	28.3	38.8	52.4	69.3	41
42	22.2	17.7	15.3	15.2	17.6	22.5	30.1	40.7	54.3	71.3	42
43	23.7	19.3	17.0	17.0	19.3	24.3	31.9	42.5	56.2	73.3	43
44	25.3	20.9	18.6	18.6	21.0	26.0	33.8	44.4	58.2	75.3	44
45	3526.9	3622.5	3720.3	3820.3	3922.8	4027.8	4135.6	4246.3	4360.1	4477.2	45
46	28.5	24.1	21.9	22.0	24.5	29.6	37.4	48.1	62.0	79.2	46
47	30.1	25.7	23.6	23.7	26.2	31.4	39.2	50.0	63.9	81.2	47
48	31.6	27.3	25.2	25.4	28.0	33.1	41.0	51.9	65.9	83.2	48
49	33.2	29.0	26.9	27.1	29.7	34.9	42.9	53.8	67.8	85.2	49
50	3534.8	3630.6	3728.5	3828.7	3931.4	4036.7	4144.7	4255.6	4369.7	4487.2	50
51	36.4	32.2	30.2	30.4	33.2	38.5	46.5	57.5	71.7	89.1	51
52	37.9	33.8	31.8	32.1	34.9	40.2	48.3	59.4	73.6	91.1	52
53	39.5	35.4	33.5	33.8	36.6	42.0	50.2	61.3	75.5	93.1	53
54	41.1	37.0	35.1	35.5	38.4	43.8	52.0	63.1	77.4	95.1	54
55	3542.7	3638.6	3736.8	3837.2	3940.1	4045.6	4153.8	4265.0	4379.4	4497.1	55
56	44.3	40.3	38.4	38.9	41.8	47.4	55.7	66.9	81.3	99.1	56
57	45.9	41.9	40.1	40.6	43.6	49.1	57.5	68.8	83.2	4501.1	57
58	47.4	43.5	41.7	42.3	45.3	50.9	59.3	70.7	85.2	03.1	58
59	49.0	45.1	43.4	45.0	47.0	52.7	61.1	72.5	87.1	05.1	59
M.	50°	51°	52°	53°	54°	55°	56°	57°	58°	59°	M.

TABLE 5.

Meridional Parts, or Increased Latitudes.

Comp. $\frac{1}{293.465}$

M.	60°	61°	62°	63°	64°	65°	66°	67°	68°	69°	M.
0	4507.1	4628.7	4754.3	4884.1	5018.4	5157.6	5302.1	5452.4	5609.1	5772.7	0
1	09.1	30.8	56.4	86.3	20.6	59.9	04.6	55.0	11.8	75.5	1
2	11.1	32.9	58.6	88.5	22.9	62.3	07.0	57.6	14.4	78.3	2
3	13.1	34.9	60.7	90.7	25.2	64.7	09.5	60.1	17.1	81.1	3
4	15.1	37.0	62.8	92.9	27.5	67.0	11.9	62.7	19.8	83.8	4
5	4517.1	4639.0	4764.9	4895.1	5029.8	5169.4	5314.4	5465.2	5622.4	5786.6	5
6	19.1	41.1	67.1	97.3	32.1	71.8	16.9	67.8	25.1	89.4	6
7	21.1	43.2	69.2	99.5	34.3	74.2	19.3	70.4	27.8	92.2	7
8	23.1	45.2	71.3	4901.7	36.6	76.5	21.8	72.9	30.5	95.1	8
9	25.1	47.3	73.5	03.9	38.9	78.9	24.3	75.5	33.2	97.9	9
10	4527.1	4649.4	4775.6	4906.1	5041.2	5181.3	5326.7	5477.1	5635.9	5800.7	10
11	29.1	51.5	77.8	08.3	43.5	83.7	29.2	80.7	38.5	03.5	11
12	31.1	53.5	79.9	10.5	45.8	86.0	31.7	83.2	41.2	06.3	12
13	33.1	55.6	82.0	12.8	48.1	88.4	34.2	85.8	43.9	09.1	13
14	35.1	57.7	84.2	15.0	50.4	90.8	36.6	88.4	46.6	11.9	14
15	4537.1	4659.7	4786.3	4917.2	5052.7	5193.2	5339.1	5491.0	5649.3	5814.7	15
16	39.2	61.8	88.5	19.4	55.0	95.6	41.6	93.6	52.0	17.6	16
17	41.2	63.9	90.6	21.6	57.3	98.0	44.1	96.2	54.7	20.4	17
18	43.2	66.0	92.8	23.9	59.6	5200.4	46.6	98.7	57.4	23.2	18
19	45.2	68.1	94.9	26.1	61.9	02.7	49.1	5501.3	60.1	26.0	19
20	4547.2	4670.1	4797.1	4928.3	5064.2	5205.1	5351.5	5503.9	5662.8	5828.9	20
21	49.2	72.2	99.2	30.5	66.5	07.5	54.0	06.5	65.5	31.7	21
22	51.3	74.3	4801.4	32.8	68.8	09.9	56.5	09.1	68.2	34.5	22
23	53.3	76.4	03.5	35.0	71.1	12.3	59.0	11.7	70.9	37.4	23
24	55.3	78.5	05.7	37.2	73.4	14.7	61.5	14.3	73.7	40.2	24
25	4557.3	4680.6	4807.8	4939.4	5075.7	5217.1	5364.0	5516.9	5676.4	5843.0	25
26	59.3	82.6	10.0	41.7	78.1	19.5	66.5	19.5	79.1	45.9	26
27	61.4	84.7	12.1	43.9	80.4	21.9	69.0	22.1	81.8	48.7	27
28	63.4	86.8	14.3	46.1	82.7	24.3	71.5	24.7	84.5	51.6	28
29	65.4	88.9	16.5	48.4	85.0	26.7	74.0	27.3	87.3	54.4	29
30	4567.4	4691.0	4818.6	4950.6	5087.3	5229.1	5376.5	5529.9	5690.0	5857.3	30
31	69.5	93.1	20.8	52.9	89.6	31.6	79.0	32.5	92.7	60.1	31
32	71.5	95.2	23.0	55.1	92.0	34.0	81.5	35.2	95.4	63.0	32
33	73.5	97.3	25.1	57.3	94.3	36.4	84.0	37.8	98.2	65.9	33
34	75.6	99.4	27.3	59.6	96.6	38.8	86.5	40.4	5700.9	68.7	34
35	4577.6	4701.5	4829.5	4961.8	5098.9	5241.2	5389.1	5543.0	5703.6	5871.6	35
36	79.6	03.6	31.6	64.1	5101.3	43.6	91.6	45.6	06.4	74.4	36
37	81.7	05.7	33.8	66.3	03.6	46.0	94.1	48.3	09.1	77.3	37
38	83.7	07.8	36.0	68.6	05.9	48.5	96.6	50.9	11.9	80.2	38
39	85.7	09.9	38.1	70.8	08.3	50.9	99.1	53.5	14.6	83.1	39
40	4587.8	4712.0	4840.3	4973.1	5110.6	5253.3	5401.6	5556.1	5717.3	5885.9	40
41	89.8	14.1	42.5	75.3	12.9	55.7	04.2	58.8	20.1	88.8	41
42	91.8	16.2	44.7	77.6	15.3	58.2	06.7	61.4	22.8	91.7	42
43	93.9	18.3	46.8	79.8	17.6	60.6	09.2	64.0	25.6	94.6	43
44	95.9	20.4	49.0	82.1	19.9	63.0	11.8	66.7	28.3	97.4	44
45	4598.0	4722.5	4851.2	4984.3	5122.3	5265.4	5414.3	5569.3	5731.1	5900.3	45
46	4600.0	24.6	53.4	86.6	24.6	67.9	16.8	71.9	33.9	03.2	46
47	02.1	26.7	55.6	88.9	27.0	70.3	19.3	74.6	36.6	06.1	47
48	04.1	28.9	57.8	91.1	29.3	72.8	21.9	77.2	39.4	09.0	48
49	06.1	31.0	59.9	93.4	31.7	75.2	24.4	79.9	42.1	11.9	49
50	4608.2	4733.1	4862.1	4995.6	5134.0	5277.6	5427.0	5582.5	5744.9	5914.8	50
51	10.2	35.2	64.3	97.9	36.4	80.1	29.5	85.2	47.7	17.7	51
52	12.3	37.3	66.5	5000.2	38.7	82.5	32.0	87.8	50.4	20.6	52
53	14.3	39.4	68.7	02.4	41.1	85.0	34.6	90.5	53.2	23.5	53
54	16.4	41.6	70.9	04.7	43.4	87.4	37.1	93.1	56.0	26.4	54
55	4618.5	4743.7	4873.1	5007.0	5145.8	5289.8	5439.7	5595.8	5758.8	5929.3	55
56	20.5	45.8	75.3	09.3	48.1	92.3	42.2	98.4	61.5	32.2	56
57	22.6	47.9	77.5	11.5	50.5	94.7	44.8	5601.1	64.3	35.1	57
58	24.6	50.0	79.7	13.8	52.8	97.2	47.3	03.8	67.1	38.1	58
59	26.7	52.2	81.9	16.1	55.2	99.7	49.9	06.4	69.9	41.0	59
M.	60°	61°	62°	63°	64°	65°	66°	67°	68°	69°	M.

TABLE 5.

Meridional Parts, or Increased Latitudes.

Comp. $\frac{1}{293.465}$

M.	70°	71°	72°	73°	74°	75°	76°	77°	78°	79°	M.
0	5943. 9	6123. 5	6312. 5	6512. 0	6723. 2	6947. 7	7187. 3	7444. 4	7721. 6	8022. 7	0
1	46. 8	26. 6	15. 8	15. 4	26. 8	51. 6	91. 5	48. 8	26. 4	27. 9	1
2	49. 7	29. 7	19. 0	18. 9	30. 5	55. 4	95. 6	53. 3	31. 3	33. 2	2
3	52. 7	32. 8	22. 3	22. 3	34. 1	59. 3	99. 7	57. 7	36. 1	38. 5	3
4	55. 6	35. 8	25. 5	25. 7	37. 7	63. 2	7203. 9	62. 2	40. 9	43. 7	4
5	5958. 5	6138. 9	6328. 8	6529. 1	6741. 4	6967. 1	7208. 0	7466. 7	7745. 8	8049. 0	5
6	61. 5	42. 0	32. 0	32. 6	45. 0	70. 9	12. 2	71. 1	50. 6	54. 3	6
7	64. 4	45. 1	35. 3	36. 0	48. 7	74. 8	16. 4	75. 6	55. 5	59. 6	7
8	67. 3	48. 2	38. 5	39. 5	52. 3	78. 7	20. 5	80. 1	60. 3	64. 9	8
9	70. 3	51. 3	41. 8	42. 9	56. 0	82. 6	24. 7	84. 6	65. 2	70. 2	9
10	5973. 2	6154. 4	6345. 0	6546. 4	6759. 7	6986. 5	7228. 9	7489. 1	7770. 1	8075. 5	10
11	76. 2	57. 5	48. 3	49. 8	63. 3	90. 4	33. 1	93. 6	74. 9	80. 8	11
12	79. 1	60. 6	51. 6	53. 3	67. 0	94. 3	37. 3	98. 1	79. 8	86. 1	12
13	82. 1	63. 7	54. 8	56. 7	70. 7	98. 3	41. 5	7502. 6	84. 7	91. 5	13
14	85. 0	66. 8	58. 1	60. 2	74. 3	7002. 2	45. 7	07. 1	89. 6	96. 8	14
15	5988. 0	6169. 9	6361. 4	6563. 7	6778. 0	7006. 1	7249. 9	7511. 7	7794. 5	8102. 2	15
16	90. 9	73. 0	64. 7	67. 1	81. 7	10. 0	54. 1	16. 2	99. 4	07. 5	16
17	93. 9	76. 1	67. 9	70. 6	85. 4	14. 0	58. 3	20. 7	7804. 3	12. 9	17
18	96. 9	79. 2	71. 2	74. 1	89. 1	17. 9	62. 5	25. 3	09. 3	18. 3	18
19	99. 8	82. 3	74. 5	77. 6	92. 8	21. 8	66. 7	29. 8	14. 2	23. 7	19
20	6002. 8	6185. 5	6377. 8	6581. 0	6796. 5	7025. 8	7270. 9	7534. 4	7819. 1	8129. 1	20
21	05. 8	88. 6	81. 1	84. 5	6800. 2	29. 7	75. 2	38. 9	24. 1	34. 5	21
22	08. 7	91. 7	84. 4	88. 0	03. 9	33. 7	79. 4	43. 5	29. 0	39. 9	22
23	11. 7	94. 8	87. 7	91. 5	07. 6	37. 7	83. 7	48. 1	34. 0	45. 3	23
24	14. 7	98. 0	91. 0	95. 0	11. 3	41. 6	87. 9	52. 7	39. 0	50. 8	24
25	6017. 7	6201. 1	6394. 3	6598. 5	6815. 0	7045. 6	7292. 2	7557. 3	7844. 0	8156. 2	25
26	20. 7	04. 2	97. 6	6602. 0	18. 8	49. 6	96. 4	61. 8	48. 9	61. 6	26
27	23. 6	07. 4	6400. 9	05. 5	22. 5	53. 5	7300. 7	66. 4	53. 9	67. 1	27
28	26. 6	10. 5	04. 3	09. 0	26. 2	57. 5	05. 0	71. 0	58. 9	72. 6	28
29	29. 6	13. 7	07. 6	12. 5	30. 0	61. 5	09. 2	75. 7	63. 9	78. 0	29
30	6032. 6	6216. 8	6410. 9	6616. 1	6833. 7	7065. 5	7313. 5	7580. 3	7868. 9	8183. 5	30
31	35. 6	20. 0	14. 2	19. 6	37. 4	69. 5	17. 8	84. 9	74. 0	89. 0	31
32	38. 6	23. 1	17. 6	23. 1	41. 2	73. 5	22. 1	89. 5	79. 0	94. 5	32
33	41. 6	26. 3	20. 9	26. 6	44. 9	77. 5	26. 4	94. 2	84. 0	8200. 0	33
34	44. 6	29. 4	24. 2	30. 2	48. 7	81. 5	30. 7	98. 8	89. 1	05. 5	34
35	6047. 6	6232. 6	6427. 6	6633. 7	6852. 4	7085. 5	7335. 0	7603. 4	7894. 1	8211. 1	35
36	50. 6	35. 8	30. 9	37. 2	56. 2	89. 5	39. 3	08. 1	99. 2	16. 6	36
37	53. 6	38. 9	34. 2	40. 8	60. 0	93. 5	43. 6	12. 8	7904. 2	22. 1	37
38	56. 6	42. 1	37. 6	44. 3	63. 7	97. 6	47. 9	17. 4	09. 3	27. 7	38
39	59. 7	45. 3	40. 9	47. 9	67. 5	7101. 6	52. 3	22. 1	14. 4	33. 3	39
40	6062. 7	6248. 4	6444. 3	6651. 4	6871. 3	7105. 6	7356. 6	7626. 8	7919. 4	8238. 8	40
41	65. 7	51. 6	47. 6	55. 0	75. 1	09. 7	60. 9	31. 4	24. 5	44. 4	41
42	68. 7	54. 8	51. 0	58. 5	78. 9	13. 7	65. 3	36. 1	29. 6	50. 0	42
43	71. 7	58. 0	54. 4	62. 1	82. 6	17. 8	69. 6	40. 8	34. 7	55. 6	43
44	74. 8	61. 2	57. 7	65. 7	86. 4	21. 8	74. 0	45. 5	39. 9	61. 2	44
45	6077. 8	6264. 4	6461. 1	6669. 2	6890. 2	7125. 9	7378. 3	7650. 2	7945. 0	8266. 8	45
46	80. 8	67. 6	64. 5	72. 8	94. 0	29. 9	82. 7	55. 0	50. 1	72. 4	46
47	83. 9	70. 8	67. 8	76. 4	97. 8	34. 0	87. 1	59. 7	55. 2	78. 1	47
48	86. 9	74. 0	71. 2	80. 0	6901. 7	38. 1	91. 4	64. 4	60. 4	83. 7	48
49	89. 9	77. 2	74. 6	83. 5	05. 5	42. 2	95. 8	69. 1	65. 5	89. 3	49
50	6093. 0	6280. 4	6478. 0	6687. 1	6909. 3	7146. 2	7400. 2	7673. 9	7970. 7	8295. 0	50
51	96. 0	83. 6	81. 4	90. 7	13. 1	50. 3	04. 6	78. 6	75. 9	8300. 7	51
52	99. 1	86. 8	84. 8	94. 3	16. 9	54. 4	09. 0	83. 4	81. 0	06. 4	52
53	6102. 1	90. 0	88. 2	97. 9	20. 8	58. 5	13. 4	88. 1	86. 2	12. 0	53
54	05. 2	93. 2	91. 6	6701. 5	24. 6	62. 6	17. 8	92. 9	91. 4	17. 7	54
55	6108. 2	6296. 4	6495. 0	6705. 1	6928. 4	7166. 7	7422. 2	7697. 7	7996. 6	8323. 4	55
56	11. 3	99. 6	98. 4	08. 7	32. 3	70. 8	26. 6	7702. 5	8001. 8	29. 2	56
57	14. 3	6302. 9	6501. 8	12. 4	36. 1	75. 0	31. 1	07. 2	07. 0	34. 9	57
58	17. 4	06. 1	05. 2	16. 0	40. 0	79. 1	35. 5	12. 0	12. 2	40. 6	58
59	20. 5	09. 3	08. 6	19. 6	43. 8	83. 2	39. 9	16. 8	17. 5	46. 4	59
M.	70°	71°	72°	73°	74°	75°	76°	77°	78°	79°	M.

TABLE 6.

Length of a Degree in Latitude and Longitude.

Lat.	Degree of Long.			Degree of Lat.			Lat.
	Naut. miles.	Statute miles.	Meters.	Naut. miles.	Statute miles.	Meters.	
°							°
0	60.068	69.172	111 321	59.661	68.704	110 567	0
1	0.059	9.162	1 304	.661	.704	568	1
2	0.031	9.130	1 253	.662	.705	569	2
3	59.986	9.078	1 169	.663	.706	570	3
4	9.922	9.005	1 051	.664	.708	573	4
5	59.840	68.911	110 900	59.666	68.710	110 576	5
6	9.741	8.795	0 715	.668	.712	580	6
7	9.622	8.660	0 497	.670	.715	584	7
8	9.487	8.504	0 245	.673	.718	589	8
9	9.333	8.326	109 959	.676	.721	595	9
10	59.161	68.129	109 641	59.680	68.725	110 601	10
11	8.971	7.910	9 289	.684	.730	608	11
12	8.764	7.670	8 904	.687	.734	616	12
13	8.538	7.410	8 486	.692	.739	624	13
14	8.295	7.131	8 036	.697	.744	633	14
15	58.034	66.830	107 553	59.702	68.751	110 643	15
16	7.756	6.510	7 036	.707	.757	653	16
17	7.459	6.169	6 487	.713	.764	663	17
18	7.146	5.808	5 906	.719	.771	675	18
19	6.816	5.427	5 294	.725	.778	686	19
20	56.468	65.026	104 649	59.732	68.786	110 699	20
21	6.102	4.606	3 972	.739	.794	712	21
22	5.720	4.166	3 264	.746	.802	725	22
23	5.321	3.706	2 524	.754	.811	739	23
24	4.905	3.228	1 754	.761	.820	753	24
25	54.473	62.729	100 952	59.769	68.829	110 768	25
26	4.024	2.212	0 119	.777	.839	783	26
27	3.558	1.676	99 257	.786	.848	799	27
28	3.076	1.122	8 364	.795	.858	815	28
29	2.578	0.548	7 441	.804	.869	832	29
30	52.064	59.956	96 488	59.813	68.879	110 849	30
31	1.534	9.345	5 506	.822	.890	866	31
32	0.989	8.716	4 495	.831	.901	883	32
33	0.428	8.071	3 455	.841	.912	901	33
34	49.851	7.407	2 387	.851	.923	919	34
35	49.259	56.725	91 290	59.861	68.935	110 938	35
36	8.653	6.027	0 166	.871	.946	956	36
37	8.031	5.311	89 014	.881	.958	975	37
38	7.395	4.579	7 835	.891	.969	994	38
39	6.744	3.829	6 629	.902	.981	111 013	39
40	46.079	53.063	85 396	59.912	68.993	111 033	40
41	5.399	2.281	4 137	.923	69.006	052	41
42	4.706	1.483	2 853	.933	.018	072	42
43	4.000	0.669	1 543	.944	.030	091	43
44	3.280	49.840	0 208	.954	.042	111	44
45	2.546	8.995	78 849	.965	.054	131	45

TABLE 6.

Length of a Degree in Latitude and Longitude.

Lat.	Degree of Long.			Degree of Lat.			Lat.
	Naut. miles.	Statute miles.	Meters.	Naut. miles.	Statute miles.	Meters.	
°							°
45	42.546	48.995	78 849	59.965	69.054	111 131	45
46	1.801	8.136	7 466	.976	.066	151	46
47	1.041	7.261	6 058	.987	.079	170	47
48	0.268	6.372	4 628	.997	.091	190	48
49	39.484	5.469	3 174	60.008	.103	210	49
50	38.688	44.552	71 698	60.019	69.115	111 229	50
51	7.880	3.621	0 200	.029	.127	249	51
52	7.060	2.676	68 680	.039	.139	268	52
53	6.229	1.719	7 140	.050	.151	287	53
54	5.386	0.749	5 578	.060	.163	306	54
55	34.532	39.766	63 996	60.070	69.175	111 325	55
56	3.668	8.771	2 395	.080	.186	343	56
57	2.794	7.764	0 774	.090	.197	362	57
58	1.909	6.745	59 135	.100	.209	380	58
59	1.015	5.716	7 478	.109	.220	397	59
60	30.110	34.674	55 802	60.118	69.230	111 415	60
61	29.197	3.623	4 110	.128	.241	432	61
62	8.275	2.560	2 400	.137	.251	448	62
63	7.344	1.488	0 675	.145	.261	464	63
64	6.404	0.406	48 934	.154	.271	480	64
65	25.456	29.315	47 177	60.162	69.281	111 496	65
66	4.501	8.215	5 407	.170	.290	511	66
67	3.538	7.106	3 622	.178	.299	525	67
68	2.567	5.988	1 823	.186	.308	539	68
69	1.590	4.862	0 012	.193	.316	553	69
70	20.606	23.729	38 188	60.200	69.324	111 566	70
71	19.616	2.589	6 353	.207	.332	578	71
72	8.619	1.441	4 506	.213	.340	590	72
73	7.617	0.287	2 648	.220	.347	602	73
74	6.609	19.127	0 781	.225	.354	613	74
75	15.596	17.960	28 903	60.231	69.360	111 623	75
76	4.578	6.788	7 017	.236	.366	633	76
77	3.556	5.611	5 123	.241	.372	642	77
78	2.529	4.428	3 220	.246	.377	650	78
79	1.499	3.242	1 311	.250	.382	658	79
80	10.465	12.051	19 394	60.254	69.386	111 665	80
81	9.428	10.857	7 472	.257	.390	671	81
82	8.388	9.659	5 545	.260	.394	677	82
83	7.345	8.458	3 612	.263	.397	682	83
84	6.300	7.255	1 675	.265	.400	687	84
85	5.253	6.049	9 735	60.268	69.402	111 691	85
86	4.205	4.842	7 792	.269	.404	694	86
87	3.154	3.632	5 846	.270	.405	696	87
88	2.103	2.422	3 898	.271	.407	698	88
89	1.052	1.211	1 949	.272	.407	699	89
90	0	0	0	.272	.407	699	90

TABLE 7.

Distance of an Object by Two Bearings.

Difference between the course and second bearing.	Difference between the course and first bearing.													
	20°		22°		24°		26°		28°		30°		32°	
30°	1.97	0.98												
32	1.64	0.87	2.16	1.14										
34	1.41	0.79	1.80	1.01	2.34	1.31								
36	1.24	0.73	1.55	0.91	1.96	1.15	2.52	1.48						
38	1.11	0.68	1.36	0.84	1.68	1.04	2.11	1.30	2.70	1.66				
40	1.00	0.64	1.21	0.78	1.48	0.95	1.81	1.16	2.26	1.45	2.88	1.85		
42	0.91	0.61	1.10	0.73	1.32	0.88	1.59	1.06	1.94	1.30	2.40	1.61	3.05	2.04
44	0.84	0.58	1.00	0.69	1.19	0.83	1.42	0.98	1.70	1.18	2.07	1.44	2.55	1.77
46	0.78	0.56	0.92	0.66	1.09	0.78	1.28	0.92	1.52	1.09	1.81	1.30	2.19	1.58
48	0.73	0.54	0.85	0.64	1.00	0.74	1.17	0.87	1.37	1.02	1.62	1.20	1.92	1.43
50	0.68	0.52	0.80	0.61	0.93	0.71	1.08	0.83	1.25	0.96	1.46	1.12	1.71	1.31
52	0.65	0.51	0.75	0.59	0.87	0.68	1.00	0.79	1.15	0.91	1.33	1.05	1.55	1.22
54	0.61	0.49	0.71	0.57	0.81	0.66	0.93	0.76	1.07	0.87	1.23	0.99	1.41	1.14
56	0.58	0.48	0.67	0.56	0.77	0.64	0.88	0.73	1.00	0.83	1.14	0.95	1.30	1.08
58	0.56	0.47	0.64	0.54	0.73	0.62	0.83	0.70	0.94	0.80	1.07	0.90	1.21	1.03
60	0.53	0.46	0.61	0.53	0.69	0.60	0.78	0.68	0.89	0.77	1.00	0.87	1.13	0.98
62	0.51	0.45	0.58	0.51	0.66	0.58	0.75	0.66	0.84	0.74	0.94	0.83	1.06	0.94
64	0.49	0.44	0.56	0.50	0.63	0.57	0.71	0.64	0.80	0.72	0.89	0.80	1.00	0.90
66	0.48	0.43	0.54	0.49	0.61	0.56	0.68	0.62	0.76	0.70	0.85	0.78	0.95	0.87
68	0.46	0.43	0.52	0.48	0.59	0.54	0.66	0.61	0.73	0.68	0.81	0.75	0.90	0.84
70	0.45	0.42	0.50	0.47	0.57	0.53	0.63	0.59	0.70	0.66	0.78	0.73	0.86	0.81
72	0.43	0.41	0.49	0.47	0.55	0.52	0.61	0.58	0.68	0.64	0.75	0.71	0.82	0.78
74	0.42	0.41	0.48	0.46	0.53	0.51	0.59	0.57	0.65	0.63	0.72	0.69	0.79	0.76
76	0.41	0.40	0.46	0.45	0.52	0.50	0.57	0.56	0.63	0.61	0.70	0.67	0.76	0.74
78	0.40	0.39	0.45	0.44	0.50	0.49	0.56	0.54	0.61	0.60	0.67	0.66	0.74	0.72
80	0.39	0.39	0.44	0.44	0.49	0.48	0.54	0.53	0.60	0.59	0.65	0.64	0.71	0.70
82	0.39	0.38	0.43	0.43	0.48	0.47	0.53	0.52	0.58	0.57	0.63	0.63	0.69	0.69
84	0.38	0.38	0.42	0.42	0.47	0.47	0.52	0.51	0.57	0.56	0.62	0.61	0.67	0.67
86	0.37	0.37	0.42	0.42	0.46	0.46	0.51	0.51	0.55	0.55	0.60	0.60	0.66	0.65
88	0.37	0.37	0.41	0.41	0.45	0.45	0.50	0.50	0.54	0.54	0.59	0.59	0.64	0.64
90	0.36	0.36	0.40	0.40	0.45	0.45	0.49	0.49	0.53	0.53	0.58	0.58	0.62	0.62
92	0.36	0.36	0.40	0.40	0.44	0.44	0.48	0.48	0.52	0.52	0.57	0.57	0.61	0.61
94	0.36	0.35	0.39	0.39	0.43	0.43	0.47	0.47	0.51	0.51	0.56	0.55	0.60	0.60
96	0.35	0.35	0.39	0.39	0.43	0.43	0.47	0.46	0.51	0.50	0.55	0.54	0.59	0.59
98	0.35	0.35	0.39	0.38	0.42	0.42	0.46	0.46	0.50	0.50	0.54	0.53	0.58	0.57
100	0.35	0.34	0.38	0.38	0.42	0.41	0.46	0.45	0.49	0.49	0.53	0.52	0.57	0.56
102	0.35	0.34	0.38	0.37	0.42	0.41	0.45	0.44	0.49	0.48	0.53	0.51	0.56	0.55
104	0.34	0.33	0.38	0.37	0.41	0.40	0.45	0.43	0.48	0.47	0.52	0.50	0.56	0.54
106	0.34	0.33	0.38	0.36	0.41	0.39	0.45	0.43	0.48	0.46	0.52	0.50	0.55	0.53
108	0.34	0.32	0.38	0.36	0.41	0.39	0.44	0.42	0.48	0.45	0.51	0.49	0.55	0.52
110	0.34	0.32	0.37	0.35	0.41	0.38	0.44	0.41	0.47	0.44	0.51	0.48	0.54	0.51
112	0.34	0.32	0.37	0.35	0.41	0.38	0.44	0.41	0.47	0.44	0.50	0.47	0.54	0.50
114	0.34	0.31	0.37	0.34	0.41	0.37	0.44	0.40	0.47	0.43	0.50	0.46	0.54	0.49
116	0.34	0.31	0.38	0.34	0.41	0.37	0.44	0.39	0.47	0.42	0.50	0.45	0.53	0.48
118	0.35	0.31	0.38	0.33	0.41	0.36	0.44	0.39	0.47	0.41	0.50	0.44	0.53	0.47
120	0.35	0.30	0.38	0.33	0.41	0.36	0.44	0.38	0.47	0.41	0.50	0.43	0.53	0.46
122	0.35	0.30	0.38	0.32	0.41	0.35	0.44	0.37	0.47	0.40	0.50	0.42	0.53	0.45
124	0.35	0.29	0.38	0.32	0.41	0.34	0.44	0.37	0.47	0.39	0.50	0.42	0.53	0.44
126	0.36	0.29	0.39	0.31	0.42	0.34	0.45	0.36	0.47	0.38	0.50	0.41	0.53	0.43
128	0.36	0.28	0.39	0.31	0.42	0.33	0.45	0.35	0.48	0.38	0.50	0.40	0.53	0.42
130	0.36	0.28	0.39	0.30	0.42	0.32	0.45	0.35	0.48	0.37	0.51	0.39	0.54	0.41
132	0.37	0.27	0.40	0.30	0.43	0.32	0.46	0.34	0.48	0.36	0.51	0.38	0.54	0.40
134	0.37	0.27	0.40	0.29	0.43	0.31	0.46	0.33	0.49	0.35	0.52	0.37	0.54	0.39
136	0.38	0.26	0.41	0.28	0.44	0.30	0.47	0.32	0.49	0.34	0.52	0.36	0.55	0.38
138	0.39	0.26	0.42	0.28	0.45	0.30	0.47	0.32	0.50	0.33	0.53	0.35	0.55	0.37
140	0.39	0.25	0.42	0.27	0.45	0.29	0.48	0.31	0.51	0.33	0.53	0.34	0.56	0.36
142	0.40	0.25	0.43	0.27	0.46	0.28	0.49	0.30	0.51	0.32	0.54	0.33	0.56	0.35
144	0.41	0.24	0.44	0.26	0.47	0.28	0.50	0.29	0.52	0.31	0.55	0.32	0.57	0.34
146	0.42	0.24	0.45	0.25	0.48	0.27	0.51	0.28	0.53	0.30	0.56	0.31	0.58	0.32
148	0.43	0.23	0.46	0.25	0.49	0.26	0.52	0.27	0.54	0.29	0.57	0.30	0.59	0.31
150	0.45	0.22	0.48	0.24	0.50	0.25	0.53	0.26	0.55	0.28	0.58	0.29	0.60	0.30
152	0.46	0.22	0.49	0.23	0.52	0.24	0.54	0.25	0.57	0.27	0.59	0.28	0.61	0.29
154	0.48	0.21	0.50	0.22	0.53	0.23	0.56	0.24	0.58	0.25	0.60	0.26	0.62	0.27
156	0.49	0.20	0.52	0.21	0.55	0.22	0.57	0.23	0.60	0.24	0.62	0.25	0.64	0.26
158	0.51	0.19	0.54	0.20	0.57	0.21	0.59	0.22	0.61	0.23	0.63	0.24	0.66	0.25
160	0.53	0.18	0.56	0.19	0.59	0.20	0.61	0.21	0.63	0.22	0.65	0.22	0.67	0.23

TABLE 7.

Distance of an Object by Two Bearings.

Difference between the course and second bearing.	Difference between the course and first bearing.													
	34°		36°		38°		40°		42°		44°		46°	
44°	3.22	2.24												
46	2.69	1.93	3.39	2.43										
48	2.31	1.72	2.83	2.10	3.55	2.63								
50	2.03	1.55	2.43	1.86	2.96	2.27	3.70	2.84						
52	1.81	1.43	2.13	1.68	2.54	2.01	3.09	2.44	3.85	3.04				
54	1.63	1.32	1.90	1.54	2.23	1.81	2.66	2.15	3.22	2.60	4.00	3.24		
56	1.49	1.24	1.72	1.42	1.99	1.65	2.33	1.93	2.77	2.29	3.34	2.77	4.14	3.43
58	1.37	1.17	1.57	1.33	1.80	1.53	2.08	1.76	2.43	2.06	2.87	2.44	3.46	2.93
60	1.28	1.10	1.45	1.25	1.64	1.42	1.88	1.63	2.17	1.88	2.52	2.18	2.97	2.57
62	1.19	1.05	1.34	1.18	1.51	1.34	1.72	1.52	1.96	1.73	2.25	1.98	2.61	2.30
64	1.12	1.01	1.25	1.13	1.40	1.26	1.58	1.42	1.79	1.61	2.03	1.83	2.33	2.09
66	1.06	0.96	1.18	1.07	1.31	1.20	1.47	1.34	1.65	1.51	1.85	1.69	2.10	1.92
68	1.00	0.93	1.11	1.03	1.23	1.14	1.37	1.27	1.53	1.42	1.71	1.58	1.92	1.78
70	0.95	0.89	1.05	0.99	1.16	1.09	1.29	1.21	1.43	1.34	1.58	1.49	1.77	1.66
72	0.91	0.86	1.00	0.95	1.10	1.05	1.21	1.15	1.34	1.27	1.48	1.41	1.64	1.56
74	0.87	0.84	0.95	0.92	1.05	1.01	1.15	1.10	1.26	1.21	1.39	1.34	1.53	1.47
76	0.84	0.81	0.91	0.89	1.00	0.97	1.09	1.06	1.20	1.16	1.31	1.27	1.44	1.40
78	0.80	0.79	0.88	0.86	0.96	0.94	1.04	1.02	1.14	1.11	1.24	1.22	1.36	1.33
80	0.78	0.77	0.85	0.83	0.92	0.91	1.00	0.98	1.09	1.07	1.18	1.16	1.28	1.27
82	0.75	0.75	0.82	0.81	0.89	0.88	0.96	0.95	1.04	1.03	1.13	1.12	1.22	1.21
84	0.73	0.73	0.79	0.79	0.86	0.85	0.93	0.92	1.00	0.99	1.08	1.07	1.17	1.16
86	0.71	0.71	0.77	0.77	0.83	0.83	0.89	0.89	0.96	0.96	1.04	1.04	1.12	1.12
88	0.69	0.69	0.75	0.75	0.80	0.80	0.86	0.86	0.93	0.93	1.00	1.00	1.08	1.07
90	0.67	0.67	0.73	0.73	0.78	0.78	0.84	0.84	0.90	0.90	0.97	0.97	1.04	1.04
92	0.66	0.66	0.71	0.71	0.76	0.76	0.82	0.82	0.87	0.87	0.93	0.93	1.00	1.00
94	0.65	0.64	0.69	0.69	0.74	0.74	0.79	0.79	0.85	0.85	0.91	0.90	0.97	0.97
96	0.63	0.63	0.68	0.67	0.73	0.72	0.78	0.77	0.83	0.82	0.88	0.88	0.94	0.93
98	0.62	0.62	0.67	0.66	0.71	0.70	0.76	0.75	0.81	0.80	0.86	0.85	0.91	0.90
100	0.61	0.60	0.65	0.64	0.70	0.69	0.74	0.73	0.79	0.78	0.84	0.83	0.89	0.88
102	0.60	0.59	0.64	0.63	0.68	0.67	0.73	0.71	0.77	0.76	0.82	0.80	0.87	0.85
104	0.60	0.58	0.63	0.61	0.67	0.65	0.72	0.69	0.76	0.74	0.80	0.78	0.85	0.82
106	0.59	0.57	0.63	0.60	0.66	0.64	0.70	0.68	0.74	0.72	0.79	0.76	0.83	0.80
108	0.58	0.55	0.62	0.59	0.66	0.62	0.69	0.66	0.73	0.70	0.77	0.74	0.81	0.77
110	0.58	0.54	0.61	0.57	0.65	0.61	0.68	0.64	0.72	0.68	0.76	0.71	0.80	0.75
112	0.57	0.53	0.61	0.56	0.64	0.59	0.68	0.63	0.71	0.66	0.75	0.69	0.79	0.73
114	0.57	0.52	0.60	0.55	0.63	0.58	0.67	0.61	0.70	0.64	0.74	0.68	0.78	0.71
116	0.56	0.51	0.60	0.54	0.63	0.57	0.66	0.60	0.70	0.63	0.73	0.66	0.77	0.69
118	0.56	0.50	0.59	0.52	0.63	0.55	0.66	0.58	0.69	0.61	0.72	0.64	0.76	0.67
120	0.56	0.49	0.59	0.51	0.62	0.54	0.65	0.57	0.68	0.59	0.72	0.62	0.75	0.65
122	0.56	0.47	0.59	0.50	0.62	0.53	0.65	0.55	0.68	0.58	0.71	0.60	0.74	0.63
124	0.56	0.46	0.59	0.49	0.62	0.51	0.65	0.54	0.68	0.56	0.71	0.58	0.74	0.61
126	0.56	0.45	0.59	0.48	0.62	0.50	0.64	0.52	0.67	0.54	0.70	0.57	0.73	0.59
128	0.56	0.44	0.59	0.46	0.62	0.49	0.64	0.51	0.67	0.53	0.70	0.55	0.73	0.57
130	0.56	0.43	0.59	0.45	0.62	0.47	0.64	0.49	0.67	0.51	0.70	0.53	0.72	0.55
132	0.56	0.42	0.59	0.44	0.62	0.46	0.64	0.48	0.67	0.50	0.70	0.52	0.72	0.54
134	0.57	0.41	0.59	0.43	0.62	0.45	0.64	0.46	0.67	0.48	0.69	0.50	0.72	0.52
136	0.57	0.40	0.60	0.41	0.62	0.43	0.65	0.45	0.67	0.47	0.70	0.48	0.72	0.50
138	0.58	0.39	0.60	0.40	0.63	0.42	0.65	0.43	0.67	0.45	0.70	0.47	0.72	0.48
140	0.58	0.37	0.61	0.39	0.63	0.40	0.65	0.42	0.68	0.43	0.70	0.45	0.72	0.46
142	0.59	0.36	0.61	0.38	0.63	0.39	0.66	0.41	0.68	0.42	0.70	0.43	0.72	0.45
144	0.60	0.35	0.62	0.36	0.64	0.38	0.66	0.39	0.68	0.40	0.71	0.41	0.73	0.43
146	0.60	0.34	0.63	0.35	0.65	0.36	0.67	0.37	0.69	0.39	0.71	0.40	0.73	0.41
148	0.61	0.32	0.63	0.34	0.66	0.35	0.68	0.36	0.70	0.37	0.72	0.38	0.74	0.39
150	0.62	0.31	0.64	0.32	0.66	0.33	0.68	0.34	0.70	0.35	0.72	0.36	0.74	0.37
152	0.63	0.30	0.65	0.31	0.67	0.32	0.69	0.33	0.71	0.33	0.73	0.34	0.75	0.35
154	0.65	0.28	0.67	0.29	0.68	0.30	0.70	0.31	0.72	0.32	0.74	0.32	0.76	0.33
156	0.66	0.27	0.68	0.28	0.70	0.28	0.72	0.29	0.73	0.30	0.75	0.30	0.77	0.31
158	0.67	0.25	0.69	0.26	0.71	0.27	0.73	0.27	0.74	0.28	0.76	0.28	0.78	0.29
160	0.69	0.24	0.71	0.24	0.73	0.25	0.74	0.25	0.76	0.26	0.77	0.26	0.79	0.27

541524°—43——34

TABLE 7.

Distance of an Object by Two Bearings.

Difference between the course and second bearing.	Difference between the course and first bearing.													
	48°		50°		52°		54°		56°		58°		60°	
58°	4.28	3.63												
60	3.57	3.10	4.41	3.82										
62	3.07	2.71	3.68	3.25	4.54	4.01								
64	2.70	2.42	3.17	2.85	3.79	3.41	4.66	4.19						
66	2.40	2.20	2.78	2.54	3.26	2.98	3.89	3.55	4.77	4.36				
68	2.17	2.01	2.48	2.30	2.86	2.65	3.34	3.10	3.99	3.71	4.88	4.53		
70	1.98	1.86	2.24	2.10	2.55	2.39	2.94	2.76	3.43	3.22	4.08	3.83	4.99	4.69
72	1.83	1.74	2.04	1.94	2.30	2.19	2.62	2.49	3.01	2.86	3.51	3.33	4.17	3.96
74	1.70	1.63	1.88	1.81	2.10	2.02	2.37	2.27	2.68	2.58	3.08	2.96	3.58	3.44
76	1.58	1.54	1.75	1.70	1.94	1.88	2.16	2.10	2.42	2.35	2.74	2.66	3.14	3.05
78	1.49	1.45	1.63	1.60	1.80	1.76	1.99	1.95	2.21	2.16	2.48	2.43	2.80	2.74
80	1.40	1.38	1.53	1.51	1.68	1.65	1.85	1.82	2.04	2.01	2.26	2.23	2.53	2.49
82	1.33	1.32	1.45	1.43	1.58	1.56	1.72	1.71	1.89	1.87	2.08	2.06	2.31	2.29
84	1.26	1.26	1.37	1.36	1.49	1.48	1.62	1.61	1.77	1.76	1.93	1.92	2.13	2.12
86	1.21	1.20	1.30	1.30	1.41	1.41	1.53	1.52	1.66	1.65	1.81	1.80	1.98	1.97
88	1.16	1.16	1.24	1.24	1.34	1.34	1.45	1.45	1.56	1.56	1.70	1.70	1.84	1.84
90	1.11	1.11	1.19	1.19	1.28	1.28	1.38	1.38	1.48	1.48	1.60	1.60	1.73	1.73
92	1.07	1.07	1.14	1.14	1.23	1.23	1.31	1.31	1.41	1.41	1.52	1.52	1.63	1.63
94	1.03	1.03	1.10	1.10	1.18	1.17	1.26	1.26	1.35	1.34	1.44	1.44	1.55	1.54
96	1.00	0.99	1.06	1.06	1.13	1.13	1.21	1.20	1.29	1.28	1.38	1.37	1.47	1.47
98	0.97	0.96	1.03	1.02	1.10	1.08	1.16	1.15	1.24	1.23	1.32	1.31	1.41	1.39
100	0.94	0.93	1.00	0.98	1.06	1.04	1.12	1.11	1.19	1.18	1.27	1.25	1.35	1.33
102	0.92	0.90	0.97	0.95	1.03	1.01	1.09	1.06	1.15	1.13	1.22	1.19	1.29	1.27
104	0.90	0.87	0.95	0.92	1.00	0.97	1.06	1.02	1.12	1.08	1.18	1.14	1.25	1.21
106	0.88	0.84	0.92	0.89	0.97	0.94	1.03	0.99	1.09	1.04	1.14	1.10	1.20	1.16
108	0.86	0.82	0.90	0.86	0.95	0.90	1.00	0.95	1.05	1.00	1.11	1.05	1.17	1.11
110	0.84	0.79	0.88	0.83	0.93	0.87	0.98	0.92	1.02	0.96	1.08	1.01	1.13	1.06
112	0.83	0.77	0.87	0.80	0.91	0.84	0.95	0.88	1.00	0.93	1.05	0.97	1.10	1.02
114	0.81	0.74	0.85	0.78	0.89	0.82	0.93	0.85	0.98	0.89	1.02	0.93	1.07	0.98
116	0.80	0.72	0.84	0.75	0.88	0.79	0.92	0.82	0.96	0.85	1.00	0.90	1.04	0.94
118	0.79	0.70	0.83	0.73	0.86	0.76	0.90	0.79	0.94	0.83	0.98	0.86	1.02	0.90
120	0.78	0.68	0.82	0.71	0.85	0.74	0.89	0.77	0.91	0.80	0.96	0.83	1.00	0.87
122	0.77	0.66	0.81	0.68	0.84	0.71	0.87	0.74	0.90	0.77	0.95	0.80	0.98	0.83
124	0.77	0.63	0.80	0.66	0.83	0.69	0.86	0.71	0.90	0.74	0.93	0.77	0.96	0.80
126	0.76	0.61	0.79	0.64	0.82	0.66	0.85	0.69	0.88	0.71	0.91	0.74	0.95	0.77
128	0.75	0.59	0.78	0.62	0.81	0.64	0.84	0.66	0.87	0.69	0.90	0.71	0.93	0.74
130	0.75	0.57	0.78	0.60	0.81	0.62	0.83	0.64	0.86	0.66	0.89	0.68	0.92	0.71
132	0.75	0.56	0.77	0.57	0.80	0.59	0.83	0.61	0.85	0.64	0.88	0.66	0.91	0.68
134	0.74	0.54	0.77	0.55	0.80	0.57	0.82	0.59	0.85	0.61	0.87	0.63	0.90	0.65
136	0.74	0.52	0.77	0.53	0.80	0.55	0.82	0.57	0.84	0.58	0.87	0.60	0.89	0.62
138	0.74	0.50	0.77	0.51	0.79	0.53	0.81	0.54	0.84	0.56	0.86	0.58	0.89	0.59
140	0.74	0.48	0.77	0.49	0.79	0.51	0.81	0.52	0.83	0.54	0.86	0.55	0.88	0.57
142	0.74	0.46	0.77	0.47	0.79	0.49	0.81	0.50	0.83	0.51	0.85	0.52	0.87	0.54
144	0.75	0.44	0.77	0.45	0.79	0.46	0.81	0.48	0.83	0.49	0.85	0.50	0.87	0.51
146	0.75	0.42	0.77	0.43	0.79	0.44	0.81	0.45	0.83	0.46	0.85	0.47	0.87	0.49
148	0.76	0.40	0.77	0.41	0.79	0.42	0.81	0.43	0.83	0.44	0.85	0.45	0.87	0.46
150	0.76	0.38	0.78	0.39	0.80	0.40	0.81	0.41	0.83	0.42	0.85	0.42	0.87	0.43
152	0.77	0.36	0.78	0.37	0.80	0.38	0.82	0.38	0.83	0.39	0.85	0.40	0.87	0.41
154	0.77	0.34	0.79	0.35	0.81	0.35	0.82	0.36	0.84	0.37	0.85	0.37	0.87	0.38
156	0.78	0.32	0.80	0.32	0.81	0.33	0.83	0.34	0.84	0.34	0.86	0.35	0.87	0.35
158	0.79	0.30	0.81	0.30	0.82	0.31	0.83	0.31	0.85	0.32	0.86	0.32	0.87	0.33
160	0.80	0.27	0.82	0.28	0.83	0.28	0.84	0.29	0.85	0.29	0.86	0.30	0.88	0.30

TABLE 7.

Distance of an Object by Two Bearings.

Difference between the course and second bearing.	Difference between the course and first bearing.															
	62°		64°		66°		68°		70°		72°		74°		76°	
72°	5.08	4.84														
74	4.25	4.08	5.18	4.98												
76	3.65	3.54	4.32	4.19	5.26	5.10										
78	3.20	3.13	3.72	3.63	4.39	4.30	5.34	5.22								
80	2.86	2.81	3.26	3.21	3.78	3.72	4.46	4.39	5.41	5.33						
82	2.58	2.56	2.91	2.88	3.31	3.28	3.83	3.80	4.52	4.48	5.48	5.42				
84	2.36	2.34	2.63	2.61	2.96	2.94	3.36	3.35	3.88	3.86	4.57	4.55	5.54	5.51		
86	2.17	2.17	2.40	2.39	2.67	2.66	3.00	2.99	3.41	3.40	3.93	3.92	4.62	4.61	5.59	5.57
88	2.01	2.01	2.21	2.21	2.44	2.44	2.71	2.71	3.04	3.04	3.45	3.45	3.97	3.97	4.67	4.66
90	1.88	1.88	2.05	2.05	2.25	2.25	2.48	2.48	2.75	2.75	3.08	3.08	3.49	3.49	4.01	4.01
92	1.77	1.76	1.91	1.91	2.08	2.08	2.28	2.28	2.51	2.51	2.78	2.78	3.11	3.11	3.52	3.52
94	1.67	1.66	1.80	1.79	1.95	1.94	2.12	2.11	2.31	2.30	2.54	2.53	2.81	2.80	3.14	3.13
96	1.58	1.57	1.70	1.69	1.83	1.82	1.97	1.96	2.14	2.13	2.34	2.33	2.57	2.55	2.84	2.82
98	1.50	1.49	1.61	1.59	1.72	1.71	1.85	1.84	2.00	1.98	2.17	2.15	2.36	2.34	2.59	2.56
100	1.43	1.41	1.53	1.51	1.63	1.61	1.75	1.72	1.88	1.85	2.03	2.00	2.19	2.16	2.39	2.35
102	1.37	1.34	1.46	1.43	1.55	1.52	1.66	1.62	1.77	1.73	1.90	1.86	2.05	2.00	2.21	2.16
104	1.32	1.28	1.40	1.36	1.48	1.44	1.58	1.53	1.68	1.63	1.79	1.74	1.92	1.87	2.07	2.01
106	1.27	1.22	1.34	1.29	1.42	1.37	1.51	1.45	1.60	1.54	1.70	1.63	1.81	1.74	1.94	1.87
108	1.23	1.17	1.29	1.23	1.37	1.30	1.44	1.37	1.53	1.45	1.62	1.54	1.72	1.63	1.83	1.74
110	1.19	1.12	1.25	1.17	1.32	1.24	1.39	1.30	1.46	1.37	1.54	1.45	1.64	1.54	1.74	1.63
112	1.15	1.07	1.21	1.12	1.27	1.18	1.33	1.24	1.40	1.30	1.48	1.37	1.56	1.45	1.65	1.53
114	1.12	1.02	1.17	1.07	1.23	1.12	1.29	1.18	1.35	1.24	1.42	1.30	1.50	1.37	1.58	1.44
116	1.09	0.98	1.14	1.03	1.19	1.07	1.25	1.12	1.31	1.17	1.37	1.23	1.44	1.29	1.51	1.36
118	1.07	0.94	1.11	0.98	1.16	1.02	1.21	1.07	1.26	1.12	1.32	1.17	1.38	1.22	1.45	1.28
120	1.04	0.90	1.08	0.94	1.13	0.98	1.18	1.02	1.23	1.06	1.28	1.11	1.34	1.16	1.40	1.21
122	1.02	0.86	1.06	0.90	1.10	0.93	1.15	0.97	1.19	1.01	1.24	1.05	1.29	1.10	1.35	1.14
124	1.00	0.83	1.04	0.86	1.08	0.89	1.12	0.93	1.16	0.96	1.21	1.00	1.25	1.04	1.31	1.08
126	0.98	0.79	1.02	0.82	1.05	0.85	1.09	0.88	1.13	0.92	1.18	0.95	1.22	0.99	1.27	1.02
128	0.97	0.76	1.00	0.79	1.03	0.82	1.07	0.84	1.11	0.87	1.15	0.90	1.19	0.94	1.23	0.97
130	0.95	0.73	0.98	0.75	1.02	0.78	1.05	0.80	1.09	0.83	1.12	0.86	1.16	0.89	1.20	0.92
132	0.94	0.70	0.97	0.72	1.00	0.74	1.03	0.77	1.06	0.79	1.10	0.82	1.13	0.84	1.17	0.87
134	0.93	0.67	0.96	0.69	0.99	0.71	1.01	0.73	1.04	0.75	1.08	0.77	1.11	0.80	1.14	0.82
136	0.92	0.64	0.95	0.66	0.97	0.68	1.00	0.69	1.03	0.71	1.06	0.74	1.09	0.76	1.12	0.78
138	0.91	0.61	0.94	0.63	0.96	0.64	0.99	0.66	1.01	0.68	1.04	0.70	1.07	0.72	1.10	0.74
140	0.90	0.58	0.93	0.60	0.95	0.61	0.97	0.63	1.00	0.64	1.03	0.66	1.05	0.68	1.08	0.70
142	0.90	0.55	0.92	0.57	0.94	0.58	0.96	0.59	0.99	0.61	1.01	0.62	1.04	0.64	1.06	0.65
144	0.89	0.52	0.91	0.54	0.93	0.55	0.96	0.56	0.98	0.57	1.00	0.59	1.02	0.60	1.05	0.62
146	0.89	0.50	0.91	0.51	0.93	0.52	0.95	0.53	0.97	0.54	0.99	0.55	1.01	0.57	1.03	0.58
148	0.89	0.47	0.90	0.48	0.92	0.49	0.94	0.50	0.96	0.51	0.98	0.52	1.00	0.53	1.02	0.54
150	0.88	0.44	0.90	0.45	0.92	0.46	0.94	0.47	0.95	0.48	0.97	0.49	0.99	0.50	1.01	0.50
152	0.88	0.41	0.90	0.42	0.92	0.43	0.93	0.44	0.95	0.45	0.97	0.45	0.98	0.46	1.00	0.47
154	0.88	0.39	0.90	0.39	0.91	0.40	0.93	0.41	0.94	0.41	0.96	0.42	0.98	0.43	0.99	0.43
156	0.89	0.36	0.90	0.37	0.91	0.37	0.93	0.38	0.94	0.38	0.96	0.39	0.97	0.39	0.99	0.40
158	0.89	0.33	0.90	0.34	0.91	0.34	0.93	0.35	0.94	0.35	0.95	0.36	0.97	0.36	0.98	0.37
160	0.89	0.30	0.90	0.31	0.91	0.31	0.93	0.32	0.94	0.32	0.95	0.33	0.96	0.33	0.98	0.33

TABLE 7.

Distance of an Object by Two Bearings.

Difference between the course and second bearing.	Difference between the course and first bearing.															
	78°		80°		82°		84°		86°		88°		90°		92°	
88°	5.63	5.63														
90	4.70	4.70	5.67	5.67												
92	4.04	4.04	4.74	4.73	5.70	5.70										
94	3.55	3.54	4.07	4.06	4.76	4.75	5.73	5.71								
96	3.17	3.15	3.57	3.55	4.09	4.07	4.78	4.76	5.74	5.71						
98	2.86	2.83	3.19	3.16	3.59	3.56	4.11	4.07	4.80	4.75	5.78	5.70				
100	2.61	2.57	2.88	2.84	3.20	3.16	3.61	3.55	4.12	4.06	4.81	4.73	5.76	5.67		
102	2.40	2.35	2.63	2.57	2.90	2.83	3.22	3.15	3.62	3.54	4.13	4.04	4.81	4.70	5.76	5.63
104	2.23	2.16	2.42	2.35	2.64	2.56	2.91	2.82	3.23	3.13	3.63	3.52	4.13	4.01	4.81	4.66
106	2.08	2.00	2.25	2.16	2.43	2.34	2.65	2.55	2.92	2.80	3.23	3.11	3.63	3.49	4.13	3.97
108	1.96	1.86	2.10	2.00	2.26	2.15	2.45	2.33	2.66	2.53	2.92	2.78	3.24	3.08	3.63	3.45
110	1.85	1.73	1.97	1.85	2.11	1.98	2.27	2.13	2.45	2.31	2.67	2.51	2.92	2.75	3.23	3.04
112	1.75	1.62	1.86	1.72	1.98	1.83	2.12	1.96	2.28	2.11	2.46	2.28	2.67	2.48	2.92	2.71
114	1.66	1.52	1.76	1.61	1.87	1.71	1.99	1.82	2.12	1.94	2.28	2.08	2.46	2.25	2.67	2.44
116	1.59	1.43	1.68	1.51	1.77	1.59	1.88	1.69	2.00	1.79	2.13	1.91	2.28	2.05	2.46	2.21
118	1.52	1.34	1.60	1.41	1.68	1.49	1.78	1.57	1.88	1.66	2.00	1.76	2.13	1.88	2.28	2.01
120	1.46	1.27	1.53	1.33	1.61	1.39	1.69	1.47	1.78	1.54	1.89	1.63	2.00	1.73	2.13	1.84
122	1.41	1.19	1.47	1.25	1.54	1.31	1.62	1.37	1.70	1.44	1.79	1.52	1.89	1.60	2.00	1.70
124	1.36	1.13	1.42	1.18	1.48	1.23	1.55	1.28	1.62	1.34	1.70	1.41	1.79	1.48	1.89	1.56
126	1.32	1.06	1.37	1.11	1.43	1.15	1.48	1.20	1.55	1.26	1.62	1.31	1.70	1.38	1.79	1.45
128	1.28	1.01	1.33	1.04	1.38	1.08	1.43	1.13	1.49	1.17	1.55	1.23	1.62	1.28	1.70	1.34
130	1.24	0.95	1.29	0.98	1.33	1.02	1.38	1.06	1.44	1.10	1.49	1.14	1.56	1.19	1.62	1.24
132	1.21	0.90	1.25	0.93	1.29	0.96	1.34	0.99	1.39	1.03	1.44	1.07	1.49	1.11	1.55	1.16
134	1.18	0.85	1.22	0.88	1.26	0.90	1.30	0.93	1.34	0.97	1.39	1.00	1.44	1.04	1.49	1.07
136	1.15	0.80	1.19	0.83	1.22	0.85	1.26	0.88	1.30	0.90	1.34	0.93	1.39	0.97	1.44	1.00
138	1.13	0.76	1.16	0.78	1.19	0.80	1.23	0.82	1.27	0.85	1.30	0.87	1.35	0.90	1.39	0.93
140	1.11	0.71	1.14	0.73	1.17	0.75	1.20	0.77	1.23	0.79	1.27	0.82	1.31	0.84	1.34	0.86
142	1.09	0.67	1.12	0.69	1.14	0.70	1.17	0.72	1.20	0.74	1.24	0.76	1.27	0.78	1.30	0.80
144	1.07	0.63	1.10	0.64	1.12	0.66	1.15	0.67	1.18	0.69	1.21	0.71	1.24	0.73	1.27	0.75
146	1.05	0.59	1.08	0.60	1.10	0.62	1.13	0.63	1.15	0.64	1.18	0.66	1.21	0.67	1.24	0.69
148	1.04	0.55	1.06	0.56	1.08	0.57	1.11	0.59	1.13	0.60	1.15	0.61	1.18	0.62	1.21	0.64
150	1.03	0.51	1.05	0.52	1.07	0.53	1.09	0.54	1.11	0.55	1.13	0.57	1.15	0.58	1.18	0.59
152	1.02	0.48	1.04	0.49	1.05	0.49	1.07	0.50	1.09	0.51	1.11	0.52	1.13	0.53	1.15	0.54
154	1.01	0.44	1.02	0.45	1.04	0.46	1.06	0.46	1.08	0.47	1.09	0.48	1.11	0.49	1.13	0.50
156	1.00	0.41	1.01	0.41	1.03	0.42	1.05	0.43	1.06	0.43	1.08	0.44	1.09	0.45	1.11	0.45
158	0.99	0.37	1.01	0.38	1.02	0.38	1.03	0.39	1.05	0.39	1.06	0.40	1.08	0.40	1.09	0.41
160	0.99	0.34	1.00	0.34	1.01	0.35	1.02	0.35	1.04	0.35	1.05	0.36	1.06	0.36	1.08	0.37

	94°		96°		98°		100°		102°		104°		106°		108°	
104°	5.74	5.57														
106	4.80	4.61	5.78	5.51												
108	4.12	3.92	4.78	4.55	5.70	5.42										
110	3.62	3.40	4.11	3.86	4.76	4.48	5.67	5.33								
112	3.23	2.99	3.61	3.35	4.09	3.80	4.74	4.40	5.63	5.22						
114	2.92	2.66	3.22	2.94	3.59	3.28	4.07	3.72	4.70	4.30	5.59	5.10				
116	2.66	2.39	2.91	2.61	3.20	2.88	3.57	3.21	4.04	3.63	4.67	4.19	5.54	4.98		
118	2.45	2.17	2.65	2.34	2.90	2.56	3.19	2.81	3.55	3.13	4.01	3.54	4.62	4.08	5.48	4.84
120	2.28	1.97	2.45	2.12	2.64	2.29	2.88	2.49	3.17	2.74	3.52	3.05	3.97	3.44	4.57	3.96
122	2.12	1.80	2.27	1.92	2.43	2.06	2.63	2.23	2.86	2.43	3.14	2.66	3.49	2.96	3.93	3.33
124	2.00	1.65	2.12	1.76	2.26	1.87	2.42	2.01	2.61	2.16	2.84	2.35	3.11	2.58	3.45	2.86
126	1.88	1.52	1.99	1.61	2.11	1.71	2.25	1.82	2.40	1.95	2.59	2.10	2.81	2.27	3.08	2.49
128	1.78	1.41	1.88	1.48	1.98	1.56	2.10	1.65	2.23	1.76	2.39	1.88	2.57	2.02	2.78	2.19
130	1.70	1.30	1.78	1.36	1.87	1.43	1.97	1.51	2.08	1.60	2.21	1.70	2.36	1.81	2.54	1.94
132	1.62	1.20	1.69	1.26	1.77	1.32	1.86	1.38	1.96	1.45	2.07	1.54	2.19	1.63	2.34	1.74
134	1.55	1.12	1.62	1.16	1.68	1.21	1.76	1.27	1.85	1.33	1.94	1.40	2.05	1.47	2.17	1.56
136	1.49	1.04	1.55	1.07	1.61	1.12	1.68	1.16	1.75	1.22	1.83	1.27	1.92	1.34	2.03	1.41
138	1.44	0.96	1.49	0.99	1.54	1.03	1.60	1.07	1.66	1.11	1.74	1.16	1.81	1.21	1.90	1.27
140	1.39	0.89	1.43	0.92	1.48	0.95	1.53	0.98	1.59	1.02	1.65	1.06	1.72	1.10	1.79	1.15
142	1.34	0.83	1.38	0.85	1.43	0.88	1.47	0.91	1.52	0.94	1.58	0.97	1.64	1.01	1.70	1.05
144	1.30	0.77	1.34	0.79	1.38	0.81	1.42	0.83	1.46	0.86	1.51	0.89	1.56	0.92	1.62	0.95
146	1.27	0.71	1.30	0.73	1.33	0.75	1.37	0.77	1.41	0.79	1.45	0.81	1.50	0.84	1.54	0.86
148	1.23	0.65	1.26	0.67	1.29	0.69	1.33	0.70	1.36	0.72	1.40	0.74	1.44	0.76	1.48	0.78
150	1.20	0.60	1.23	0.61	1.26	0.63	1.29	0.64	1.32	0.66	1.35	0.67	1.38	0.69	1.42	0.71
152	1.18	0.55	1.20	0.56	1.22	0.57	1.25	0.59	1.28	0.60	1.31	0.61	1.34	0.63	1.37	0.64
154	1.15	0.50	1.17	0.51	1.19	0.52	1.22	0.53	1.24	0.54	1.27	0.56	1.29	0.57	1.32	0.58
156	1.13	0.46	1.15	0.47	1.17	0.47	1.19	0.48	1.21	0.49	1.23	0.50	1.25	0.51	1.28	0.52
158	1.11	0.42	1.13	0.42	1.14	0.43	1.16	0.44	1.18	0.44	1.20	0.45	1.22	0.46	1.24	0.47
160	1.09	0.37	1.11	0.38	1.12	0.38	1.14	0.39	1.15	0.39	1.17	0.40	1.19	0.41	1.21	0.41

TABLE 7.

Distance of an Object by Two Bearings.

Difference between the course and second bearing.	Difference between the course and first bearing.													
	110°		112°		114°		116°		118°		120°		122°	
120°	5.41	4.69												
122	4.52	3.83	5.34	4.53										
124	3.88	3.22	4.46	3.70	5.26	4.36								
126	3.41	2.76	3.83	3.10	4.39	3.55	5.18	4.19						
128	3.04	2.40	3.36	2.65	3.78	2.98	4.32	3.41	5.08	4.01				
130	2.75	2.10	3.00	2.30	3.31	2.54	3.72	2.85	4.25	3.25	4.99	3.82		
132	2.51	1.86	2.71	2.01	2.96	2.20	3.26	2.42	3.65	2.71	4.17	3.10	4.88	3.63
134	2.31	1.66	2.48	1.78	2.67	1.92	2.91	2.09	3.20	2.30	3.58	2.57	4.08	2.93
136	2.14	1.49	2.28	1.58	2.44	1.69	2.63	1.83	2.86	1.98	3.14	2.18	3.51	2.44
138	2.00	1.34	2.12	1.42	2.25	1.50	2.40	1.61	2.58	1.73	2.80	1.88	3.08	2.06
140	1.88	1.21	1.97	1.27	2.08	1.34	2.21	1.42	2.36	1.52	2.53	1.63	2.74	1.76
142	1.77	1.09	1.85	1.14	1.95	1.20	2.05	1.26	2.17	1.34	2.31	1.42	2.48	1.53
144	1.68	0.99	1.75	1.03	1.83	1.07	1.91	1.13	2.01	1.18	2.13	1.25	2.26	1.33
146	1.60	0.89	1.66	0.93	1.72	0.96	1.80	1.01	1.88	1.05	1.98	1.10	2.08	1.17
148	1.53	0.81	1.58	0.84	1.63	0.87	1.70	0.90	1.77	0.94	1.84	0.98	1.93	1.03
150	1.46	0.73	1.51	0.75	1.55	0.78	1.61	0.80	1.67	0.83	1.73	0.87	1.81	0.90
152	1.40	0.66	1.44	0.68	1.48	0.70	1.53	0.72	1.58	0.74	1.63	0.77	1.70	0.80
154	1.35	0.59	1.39	0.61	1.42	0.62	1.46	0.64	1.50	0.66	1.55	0.68	1.60	0.70
156	1.31	0.53	1.33	0.54	1.37	0.56	1.40	0.57	1.43	0.58	1.47	0.60	1.52	0.62
158	1.26	0.47	1.29	0.48	1.32	0.49	1.34	0.50	1.37	0.51	1.41	0.53	1.44	0.54
160	1.23	0.42	1.25	0.43	1.27	0.43	1.29	0.44	1.32	0.45	1.35	0.46	1.38	0.47

	124°		126°		128°		130°		132°		134°		136°	
134°	4.77	3.43												
136	3.99	2.77	4.66	3.23										
138	3.43	2.29	3.89	2.60	4.54	3.04								
140	3.01	1.93	3.34	2.15	3.79	2.44	4.41	2.84						
142	2.68	1.65	2.94	1.81	3.26	2.01	3.63	2.27	4.28	2.63				
144	2.42	1.42	2.62	1.54	2.86	1.68	3.17	1.86	3.57	2.10	4.14	2.43		
146	2.21	1.24	2.37	1.32	2.55	1.43	2.78	1.55	3.07	1.72	3.46	1.93	4.00	2.24
148	2.04	1.08	2.16	1.14	2.30	1.22	2.48	1.31	2.70	1.43	2.97	1.58	3.34	1.77
150	1.89	0.95	1.99	0.99	2.10	1.05	2.24	1.12	2.40	1.20	2.61	1.30	2.87	1.44
152	1.77	0.83	1.85	0.87	1.94	0.91	2.04	0.96	2.17	1.02	2.33	1.09	2.52	1.18
154	1.66	0.73	1.72	0.76	1.80	0.79	1.88	0.83	1.98	0.87	2.10	0.92	2.25	0.99
156	1.56	0.64	1.62	0.66	1.68	0.68	1.75	0.71	1.83	0.74	1.92	0.78	2.03	0.83
158	1.48	0.56	1.53	0.57	1.58	0.59	1.63	0.61	1.70	0.64	1.77	0.66	1.85	0.69
160	1.41	0.48	1.45	0.49	1.49	0.51	1.53	0.52	1.58	0.54	1.64	0.56	1.71	0.58

	138°		140°		142°		144°		146°		148°		150°	
148°	3.85	2.04												
150	3.22	1.61	3.70	1.85										
152	2.77	1.30	3.09	1.45	3.55	1.66								
154	2.43	1.06	2.66	1.16	2.96	1.30	3.38	1.48						
156	2.17	0.88	2.33	0.95	2.54	1.04	2.83	1.15	3.22	1.31				
158	1.96	0.73	2.08	0.78	2.23	0.84	2.43	0.91	2.69	1.01	3.05	1.14		
160	1.79	0.61	1.88	0.64	1.99	0.68	2.13	0.73	2.31	0.79	2.55	0.87	2.88	0.98

TABLE 8.

Distance of Visibility of Objects at Sea.

Height, feet.	Nautical miles.	Statute miles.	Height, feet.	Nautical miles.	Statute miles.	Height, feet.	Nautical miles.	Statute miles.
1	1.1	1.3	100	11.5	13.2	760	31.6	36.4
2	1.7	1.9	105	11.7	13.5	780	32.0	36.9
3	2.0	2.3	110	12.0	13.8	800	32.4	37.3
4	2.3	2.6	115	12.3	14.1	820	32.8	37.8
5	2.5	2.9	120	12.6	14.5	840	33.2	38.3
6	2.8	3.2	125	12.9	14.8	860	33.6	38.7
7	2.9	3.5	130	13.1	15.1	880	34.0	39.2
8	3.1	3.7	135	13.3	15.3	900	34.4	39.6
9	3.5	4.0	140	13.6	15.6	920	34.7	40.0
10	3.6	4.2	145	13.8	15.9	940	35.2	40.5
11	3.8	4.4	150	14.1	16.2	960	35.5	40.9
12	4.0	4.6	160	14.5	16.7	980	35.9	41.3
13	4.2	4.8	170	14.9	17.2	1,000	36.2	41.7
14	4.3	4.9	180	15.4	17.7	1,100	38.0	43.8
15	4.4	5.1	190	15.8	18.2	1,200	39.6	45.6
16	4.6	5.3	200	16.2	18.7	1,300	41.3	47.6
17	4.7	5.4	210	16.6	19.1	1,400	42.9	49.4
18	4.9	5.6	220	17.0	19.6	1,500	44.4	51.1
19	5.0	5.8	230	17.4	20.0	1,600	45.8	52.8
20	5.1	5.9	240	17.7	20.4	1,700	47.2	54.4
21	5.3	6.1	250	18.2	20.9	1,800	48.6	56.0
22	5.4	6.2	260	18.5	21.3	1,900	49.9	57.5
23	5.5	6.3	270	18.9	21.7	2,000	51.2	59.0
24	5.6	6.5	280	19.2	22.1	2,100	52.5	60.5
25	5.7	6.6	290	19.6	22.5	2,200	53.8	61.9
26	5.8	6.7	300	19.9	22.9	2,300	55.0	63.3
27	6.0	6.9	310	20.1	23.2	2,400	56.2	64.7
28	6.1	7.0	320	20.5	23.6	2,500	57.3	66.0
29	6.2	7.1	330	20.8	24.0	2,600	58.5	67.3
30	6.3	7.2	340	21.1	24.3	2,700	59.6	68.6
31	6.4	7.3	350	21.5	24.7	2,800	60.6	69.8
32	6.5	7.5	360	21.7	25.0	2,900	61.8	71.1
33	6.6	7.6	370	22.1	25.4	3,000	62.8	72.3
34	6.7	7.7	380	22.3	25.7	3,100	63.8	73.5
35	6.8	7.8	390	22.7	26.1	3,200	64.9	74.7
36	6.9	7.9	400	22.9	26.4	3,300	65.9	75.9
37	6.9	8.0	410	23.2	26.7	3,400	66.9	77.0
38	7.0	8.1	420	23.5	27.1	3,500	67.8	78.1
39	7.1	8.2	430	23.8	27.4	3,600	68.8	79.2
40	7.2	8.3	440	24.1	27.7	3,700	69.7	80.3
41	7.3	8.4	450	24.3	28.0	3,800	70.7	81.4
42	7.4	8.5	460	24.6	28.3	3,900	71.6	82.4
43	7.5	8.7	470	24.8	28.6	4,000	72.5	83.5
44	7.6	8.8	480	25.1	28.9	4,100	73.4	84.5
45	7.7	8.9	490	25.4	29.2	4,200	74.3	85.6
46	7.8	9.0	500	25.6	29.5	4,300	75.2	86.6
47	7.9	9.0	520	26.1	30.1	4,400	76.1	87.6
48	7.9	9.1	540	26.7	30.7	4,500	76.9	88.5
49	8.0	9.2	560	27.1	31.2	4,600	77.7	89.5
50	8.1	9.3	580	27.6	31.8	4,700	78.6	90.5
55	8.5	9.8	600	28.0	32.3	4,800	79.4	91.4
60	8.9	10.2	620	28.6	32.9	4,900	80.2	92.4
65	9.2	10.6	640	29.0	33.4	5,000	81.0	93.3
70	9.6	11.0	660	29.4	33.9	6,000	88.8	102.2
75	9.9	11.4	680	29.9	34.4	7,000	96.0	110.5
80	10.3	11.8	700	30.3	34.9	8,000	102.6	118.1
85	10.6	12.2	720	30.7	35.4	9,000	108.7	125.2
90	10.9	12.5	740	31.1	35.9	10,000	114.6	132.0
95	11.2	12.9						

TABLE 9.

Distance by Vertical Angle (Distance less than 5 miles).

Dist., nautical miles.	Heights in feet.																	
	40	45	50	55	60	65	70	75	80	85	90	95	100	110	120	130	140	150
	° ′	° ′	° ′	° ′	° ′	° ′	° ′	° ′	° ′	° ′	° ′	° ′	° ′	° ′	° ′	° ′	° ′	° ′
0.1	3 46	4 14	4 42	5 10	5 38	6 06	6 34	7 02	7 30	7 58	8 25	8 53	9 20	10 15	11 10	12 04	12 58	13 52
.2	1 53	2 07	2 21	2 35	2 49	3 04	3 18	3 32	3 46	4 00	4 14	4 28	4 42	5 10	5 38	6 06	6 34	7 02
.3	1 15	1 25	1 34	1 44	1 53	2 02	2 12	2 21	2 31	2 40	2 49	2 59	3 08	3 27	3 46	4 05	4 23	4 42
.4	0 57	1 04	1 11	1 18	1 25	1 32	1 39	1 46	1 53	2 00	2 07	2 14	2 21	2 35	2 49	3 04	3 18	3 32
0.5	0 45	0 51	0 57	1 02	1 08	1 14	1 19	1 25	1 30	1 36	1 42	1 47	1 53	2 04	2 16	2 27	2 38	2 49
.6	0 38	0 42	0 47	0 52	0 57	1 01	1 06	1 11	1 15	1 20	1 25	1 30	1 34	1 44	1 53	2 02	2 12	2 21
.7	0 32	0 36	0 40	0 44	0 48	0 53	0 57	1 01	1 05	1 09	1 13	1 17	1 21	1 29	1 37	1 45	1 53	2 01
.8	0 28	0 32	0 35	0 39	0 42	0 46	0 49	0 53	0 57	1 00	1 04	1 07	1 11	1 18	1 25	1 32	1 39	1 46
.9	0 25	0 28	0 31	0 35	0 38	0 41	0 44	0 47	0 50	0 53	0 57	1 00	1 03	1 09	1 15	1 22	1 28	1 34
1.0	0 23	0 25	0 28	0 31	0 34	0 37	0 40	0 42	0 45	0 48	0 51	0 54	0 57	1 02	1 08	1 14	1 19	1 25
.1	0 21	0 23	0 26	0 28	0 31	0 33	0 36	0 39	0 41	0 44	0 46	0 49	0 51	0 57	1 02	1 07	1 12	1 17
.2	0 19	0 21	0 24	0 26	0 28	0 31	0 33	0 35	0 38	0 40	0 42	0 45	0 47	0 52	0 57	1 01	1 06	1 11
.3	0 17	0 20	0 22	0 24	0 26	0 28	0 30	0 33	0 35	0 37	0 39	0 41	0 44	0 48	0 52	0 57	1 01	1 05
.4	0 16	0 18	0 20	0 22	0 24	0 26	0 28	0 30	0 32	0 34	0 36	0 38	0 40	0 44	0 48	0 53	0 57	1 01
1.5	0 15	0 17	0 19	0 21	0 23	0 25	0 26	0 28	0 30	0 32	0 34	0 36	0 38	0 41	0 45	0 49	0 53	0 57
.6	0 14	0 16	0 18	0 19	0 21	0 23	0 25	0 27	0 28	0 30	0 32	0 34	0 35	0 39	0 42	0 46	0 49	0 53
.7	0 13	0 15	0 17	0 18	0 20	0 22	0 23	0 25	0 27	0 28	0 30	0 32	0 33	0 37	0 40	0 43	0 47	0 50
.8	0 13	0 14	0 16	0 17	0 19	0 20	0 22	0 24	0 25	0 27	0 28	0 30	0 31	0 35	0 38	0 41	0 44	0 47
.9	0 12	0 13	0 15	0 16	0 18	0 19	0 21	0 22	0 24	0 25	0 27	0 28	0 30	0 33	0 36	0 39	0 42	0 45
2.0	0 11	0 13	0 14	0 16	0 17	0 18	0 20	0 21	0 23	0 24	0 25	0 27	0 28	0 31	0 34	0 37	0 40	0 42
.1	0 11	0 13	0 14	0 15	0 16	0 18	0 19	0 20	0 22	0 23	0 24	0 26	0 27	0 30	0 32	0 35	0 38	0 40
.2	0 10	0 12	0 13	0 14	0 15	0 17	0 18	0 19	0 21	0 22	0 23	0 24	0 26	0 28	0 31	0 33	0 36	0 39
.3	0 10	0 12	0 12	0 14	0 14	0 16	0 17	0 18	0 20	0 21	0 22	0 23	0 25	0 27	0 30	0 32	0 34	0 37
.4	0 10	0 11	0 12	0 13	0 14	0 15	0 17	0 18	0 19	0 20	0 21	0 22	0 24	0 26	0 28	0 31	0 33	0 35
2.5	0 9	0 11	0 11	0 12	0 13	0 15	0 16	0 17	0 18	0 19	0 20	0 21	0 23	0 25	0 27	0 29	0 32	0 34
.6	0 9	0 10	0 11	0 12	0 13	0 14	0 15	0 16	0 17	0 18	0 20	0 21	0 22	0 24	0 26	0 28	0 30	0 33
.7	0 9	0 10	0 10	0 11	0 12	0 14	0 15	0 16	0 17	0 18	0 19	0 20	0 21	0 23	0 25	0 27	0 29	0 31
.8	0 8	0 9	0 10	0 11	0 12	0 13	0 14	0 15	0 16	0 17	0 18	0 19	0 20	0 22	0 24	0 26	0 28	0 30
.9	0 8	0 9	0 10	0 10	0 11	0 13	0 14	0 15	0 16	0 17	0 18	0 19	0 20	0 21	0 23	0 25	0 27	0 29
3.0	0 8	0 9	0 9	0 10	0 10	0 12	0 13	0 14	0 15	0 16	0 17	0 18	0 19	0 21	0 23	0 25	0 26	0 28
.2							0 12	0 13	0 14	0 15	0 16	0 17	0 18	0 19	0 21	0 23	0 25	0 27
.4							0 12	0 12	0 13	0 14	0 15	0 16	0 17	0 18	0 20	0 22	0 23	0 25
.6							0 11	0 12	0 13	0 13	0 14	0 15	0 16	0 17	0 19	0 20	0 22	0 24
.8							0 10	0 11	0 12	0 13	0 13	0 14	0 15	0 16	0 18	0 19	0 21	0 22
4.0							0 10	0 11	0 11	0 12	0 13	0 13	0 14	0 16	0 17	0 18	0 20	0 21
.2										0 11	0 12	0 13	0 14	0 15	0 16	0 17	0 19	0 20
.4										0 11	0 12	0 12	0 13	0 14	0 15	0 17	0 18	0 19
.6										0 10	0 11	0 12	0 13	0 14	0 15	0 16	0 17	0 18
.8										0 10	0 11	0 11	0 12	0 13	0 14	0 15	0 16	0 18
5.0										0 10	0 10	0 11	0 11	0 12	0 14	0 15	0 16	0 17

TABLE 9.

Distance by Vertical Angle (Distance less than 5 miles).

Dist., nautical miles.	Heights in feet.																	
	160	170	180	190	200	300	400	500	600	700	800	900	1,000	1,200	1,400	1,600	1,800	2,000
	° ′	° ′	° ′	° ′	° ′	° ′	° ′	° ′	° ′	° ′	° ′	° ′	° ′	° ′	° ′	° ′	° ′	° ′
0.1	14 45	15 37	16 29	17 21	18 13	26 16												
.2	7 30	7 58	8 25	8 53	9 20	13 52	18 13	22 21	26 16	29 56								
.3	5 01	5 19	5 38	5 57	6 15	9 20	12 22	15 20	18 13	21 00	23 41	26 16	28 44					
.4	3 46	4 00	4 14	4 28	4 42	7 02	9 20	11 37	13 52	16 03	18 13	20 18	22 21	26 16	29 56			
0.5	3 01	3 12	3 23	3 35	3 46	5 38	7 30	9 20	11 10	12 58	14 45	16 30	18 13	21 32	24 44	27 46	30 38	
.6	2 31	2 40	2 49	2 59	3 08	4 42	6 15	7 48	9 20	10 52	12 22	13 52	15 20	18 13	21 00	23 41	26 16	28 44
.7	2 09	2 17	2 25	2 33	2 41	4 02	5 22	6 42	8 01	9 20	10 39	11 56	13 13	15 45	18 13	20 36	22 56	25 10
.8	1 53	2 00	2 07	2 14	2 21	3 32	4 42	5 52	7 02	8 11	9 20	10 29	11 37	13 52	16 03	18 13	20 18	22 21
.9	1 40	1 47	1 53	1 59	2 06	3 08	4 11	5 13	6 15	7 17	8 19	9 20	10 21	12 22	14 21	16 18	18 13	20 05
1.0	1 30	1 36	1 42	1 47	1 53	2 49	3 46	4 42	5 38	6 34	7 30	8 25	9 20	11 10	12 58	14 45	16 29	18 13
.1	1 22	1 27	1 33	1 38	1 43	2 34	3 25	4 17	5 08	5 59	6 49	7 40	8 30	10 10	11 49	13 27	15 04	16 39
.2	1 15	1 20	1 25	1 30	1 34	2 21	3 08	3 55	4 42	5 29	6 15	7 02	7 48	9 20	10 52	12 22	13 52	15 20
.3	1 10	1 14	1 18	1 23	1 27	2 10	2 54	3 37	4 20	5 04	5 47	6 30	7 13	8 38	10 03	11 27	12 50	14 12
.4	1 05	1 09	1 13	1 17	1 21	2 01	2 41	3 22	4 02	4 42	5 22	6 02	6 42	8 01	9 20	10 39	11 56	13 13
1.5	1 00	1 04	1 08	1 12	1 15	1 53	2 31	3 08	3 46	4 23	5 01	5 38	6 15	7 30	8 44	9 57	11 10	12 22
.6	0 57	1 00	1 04	1 07	1 11	1 46	2 21	2 57	3 32	4 07	4 42	5 17	5 52	7 02	8 11	9 20	10 29	11 37
.7	0 53	0 57	1 00	1 03	1 07	1 40	2 13	2 46	3 19	3 52	4 26	4 59	5 32	6 38	7 43	8 48	9 53	10 57
.8	0 50	0 53	0 57	1 00	1 03	1 34	2 06	2 37	3 08	3 40	4 11	4 42	5 13	6 15	7 17	8 19	9 20	10 21
.9	0 48	0 51	0 54	0 57	1 00	1 29	1 59	2 29	2 58	3 28	3 58	4 27	4 57	5 56	6 55	7 54	8 52	9 50
2.0	0 45	0 48	0 51	0 54	0 57	1 25	1 53	2 21	2 49	3 18	3 46	4 14	4 42	5 38	6 34	7 30	8 25	9 20
.1	0 43	0 46	0 48	0 51	0 54	1 21	1 48	2 15	2 41	3 08	3 35	4 02	4 29	5 22	6 15	7 08	8 01	8 53
.2	0 41	0 44	0 46	0 49	0 51	1 17	1 43	2 08	2 34	3 00	3 25	3 51	4 17	5 08	5 59	6 49	7 40	8 30
.3	0 39	0 42	0 44	0 47	0 49	1 14	1 38	2 03	2 27	2 52	3 16	3 41	4 05	4 55	5 44	6 32	7 21	8 09
.4	0 38	0 40	0 42	0 45	0 47	1 11	1 34	1 58	2 21	2 45	3 08	3 32	3 55	4 42	5 29	6 15	7 02	7 48
2.5	0 36	0 38	0 41	0 43	0 45	1 08	1 30	1 53	2 16	2 38	3 01	3 23	3 46	4 31	5 16	6 01	6 45	7 30
.6	0 35	0 37	0 39	0 41	0 44	1 05	1 27	1 49	2 10	2 32	2 54	3 16	3 37	4 20	5 04	5 47	6 30	7 13
.7	0 34	0 36	0 38	0 40	0 42	1 03	1 24	1 45	2 06	2 27	2 47	3 08	3 29	4 11	4 53	5 34	6 15	6 57
.8	0 32	0 34	0 36	0 38	0 40	1 01	1 21	1 41	2 01	2 21	2 41	3 02	3 22	4 02	4 42	5 22	6 02	6 42
.9	0 31	0 33	0 35	0 37	0 39	0 58	1 18	1 37	1 57	2 16	2 36	2 55	3 15	3 54	4 32	5 11	5 50	6 28
3.0	0 30	0 32	0 34	0 36	0 38	0 57	1 15	1 34	1 53	2 12	2 31	2 49	3 08	3 46	4 23	5 01	5 38	6 15
.2	0 28	0 30	0 32	0 34	0 35	0 53	1 11	1 28	1 46	2 04	2 21	2 39	2 57	3 32	4 07	4 42	5 17	5 52
.4	0 27	0 28	0 30	0 32	0 33	0 50	1 07	1 23	1 40	1 56	2 13	2 30	2 46	3 19	3 52	4 26	4 59	5 32
.6	0 25	0 27	0 28	0 30	0 31	0 47	1 03	1 19	1 34	1 50	2 06	2 21	2 37	3 08	3 40	4 11	4 42	5 13
.8	0 24	0 25	0 27	0 28	0 30	0 45	1 00	1 14	1 29	1 44	1 59	2 14	2 29	2 58	3 28	3 58	4 27	4 57
4.0	0 23	0 24	0 25	0 27	0 28	0 42	0 57	1 11	1 25	1 39	1 53	2 07	2 21	2 49	3 18	3 46	4 14	4 42
.2	0 22	0 23	0 24	0 26	0 27	0 40	0 54	1 07	1 21	1 34	1 48	2 01	2 15	2 41	3 08	3 35	4 02	4 29
.4	0 21	0 22	0 23	0 24	0 26	0 39	0 51	1 04	1 17	1 30	1 43	1 56	2 08	2 34	3 00	3 25	3 51	4 17
.6	0 20	0 21	0 22	0 23	0 25	0 37	0 49	1 01	1 14	1 26	1 38	1 51	2 03	2 27	2 52	3 16	3 41	4 05
.8	0 19	0 20	0 21	0 22	0 24	0 35	0 47	0 59	1 11	1 22	1 34	1 46	1 58	2 21	2 45	3 08	3 32	3 55
5.0	0 18	0 19	0 20	0 21	0 23	0 34	0 45	0 57	1 08	1 19	1 30	1 42	1 53	2 16	2 38	3 01	3 23	3 46

TABLE 10.

Distance by Vertical Angle (Distance greater than 5 miles).

(1) Surface craft correct observed vertical angle for Refraction and Dip.
(2) Aircraft (using bubble sextant) correct observed vertical angle for Refraction only.

Correction for Refraction.

Est. Dist.	Corr.	Est. Dist.	Corr.
	′		′
5	−0. 4	55	−4. 0
10	−0. 8	60	−4. 4
15	−1. 1	65	−4. 7
20	−1. 5	70	−5. 1
25	−1. 9	75	−5. 5
30	−2. 2	80	−5. 8
35	−2. 5	85	−6. 2
40	−2. 9	90	−6. 6
45	−3. 3	95	−7. 0
50	−3. 6	100	−7. 5

Correction for Dip.

Ht. of eye	Corr.	Ht. of eye	Corr.
	′		′
10	−3. 1	60	−7. 6
15	−3. 8	65	−7. 9
20	−4. 4	70	−8. 2
25	−4. 9	75	−8. 5
30	−5. 4	80	−8. 8
35	−5. 8	85	−9. 0
40	−6. 2	90	−9. 3
45	−6. 6	95	−9. 5
50	−6. 9	100	−9. 8
55	−7. 3	105	−10. 1

Distance in nautical miles	Difference in feet between height of object and height of eye.												Distance in nautical miles
	400	600	800	1,000	1,200	1,400	1,600	1,800	2,000	2,200	2,400	2,600	
	° ′	° ′	° ′	° ′	° ′	° ′	° ′	° ′	° ′	° ′	° ′	° ′	
6	0 35	0 54	1 12	1 31	1 50	2 09	2 28	2 46	3 05	3 23	3 42	4 00	6
7	0 29	0 45	1 01	1 17	1 34	1 50	2 06	2 22	2 38	2 54	3 10	3 26	7
8	0 24	0 39	0 53	1 07	1 21	1 35	1 49	2 03	2 18	2 32	2 46	3 00	8
9	0 21	0 33	0 46	0 58	1 11	1 24	1 36	1 48	2 01	2 14	2 26	2 39	9
10	0 18	0 29	0 40	0 52	1 03	1 14	1 26	1 37	1 48	1 59	2 11	2 22	10
11	0 15	0 25	0 36	0 46	0 56	1 06	1 17	1 27	1 37	1 48	1 58	2 08	11
12	0 13	0 22	0 32	0 41	0 51	1 00	1 09	1 19	1 28	1 38	1 47	1 56	12
13	0 11	0 20	0 28	0 37	0 46	0 54	1 03	1 12	1 21	1 29	1 38	1 47	13
14		0 17	0 25	0 33	0 41	0 49	0 57	1 06	1 14	1 22	1 30	1 38	14
15		0 15	0 22	0 30	0 38	0 45	0 53	1 00	1 08	1 15	1 23	1 30	15
16		0 13	0 20	0 27	0 34	0 41	0 48	0 56	1 03	1 10	1 17	1 24	16
17		0 11	0 18	0 25	0 31	0 38	0 45	0 52	0 58	1 04	1 11	1 18	17
18		0 10	0 16	0 22	0 29	0 35	0 41	0 48	0 54	1 00	1 06	1 12	18
19			0 14	0 20	0 26	0 32	0 38	0 44	0 50	0 56	1 02	1 08	19
20			0 12	0 18	0 24	0 29	0 35	0 41	0 46	0 52	0 58	1 04	20
21			0 11	0 16	0 22	0 27	0 32	0 38	0 43	0 49	0 54	1 00	21
22			0 10	0 15	0 20	0 25	0 30	0 35	0 41	0 46	0 51	0 56	22
23				0 13	0 18	0 23	0 28	0 33	0 38	0 43	0 47	0 52	23
24				0 11	0 16	0 21	0 26	0 30	0 35	0 40	0 45	0 49	24
25				0 10	0 15	0 19	0 24	0 28	0 33	0 37	0 42	0 46	25
26					0 13	0 17	0 22	0 26	0 30	0 35	0 39	0 44	26
27					0 11	0 16	0 20	0 24	0 28	0 33	0 37	0 41	27
28					0 10	0 14	0 18	0 22	0 26	0 30	0 35	0 39	28
29						0 13	0 17	0 21	0 25	0 28	0 32	0 36	29
30						0 11	0 15	0 19	0 23	0 26	0 30	0 34	30
31						0 10	0 14	0 17	0 21	0 25	0 28	0 32	31
32							0 12	0 16	0 19	0 23	0 26	0 30	32
33							0 11	0 14	0 18	0 21	0 25	0 28	33
34							0 10	0 13	0 16	0 20	0 23	0 26	34
35								0 12	0 15	0 18	0 21	0 25	35
36								0 10	0 13	0 17	0 20	0 23	36
37									0 12	0 15	0 18	0 21	37
38									0 11	0 14	0 17	0 20	38
39									0 10	0 12	0 15	0 18	39
40										0 11	0 14	0 17	40
41										0 10	0 12	0 15	41
42											0 11	0 14	42
43											0 10	0 13	43
44												0 11	44
45												0 10	45

TABLE 10.

Distance by Vertical Angle (Distance greater than 5 miles).

Distance in nautical miles.	Difference in feet between height of object and height of eye.												Distance in nautical miles.
	2,800	3,000	3,200	3,400	3,600	3,800	4,000	4,200	4,400	4,600	4,800	5,000	
	° ′	° ′	° ′	° ′	° ′	° ′	° ′	° ′	° ′	° ′	° ′	° ′	
6	4 20	4 39	4 48	5 17	5 35	5 54	6 13	6 31	6 50	7 08	7 27	7 46	6
7	3 42	3 59	4 15	4 31	4 46	5 02	5 19	5 35	5 50	6 06	6 22	6 38	7
8	3 14	3 28	3 42	3 56	4 10	4 24	4 38	4 52	5 06	5 20	5 34	5 47	8
9	2 51	3 04	3 16	3 29	3 41	3 54	4 07	4 19	4 32	4 44	4 56	5 08	9
10	2 33	2 45	2 56	3 07	3 18	3 29	3 40	3 52	4 03	4 15	4 26	4 37	10
11	2 18	2 29	2 39	2 49	2 59	3 10	3 20	3 30	3 40	3 51	4 01	4 11	11
12	2 06	2 15	2 25	2 34	2 44	2 53	3 02	3 12	3 21	3 30	3 40	3 49	12
13	1 55	2 04	2 12	2 22	2 30	2 39	2 48	2 56	3 05	3 14	3 22	3 30	13
14	1 46	1 54	2 02	2 10	2 18	2 26	2 35	2 43	2 51	2 59	3 07	3 15	14
15	1 38	1 45	1 53	2 01	2 08	2 16	2 23	2 31	2 38	2 46	2 53	3 01	15
16	1 31	1 38	1 45	1 52	1 59	2 06	2 13	2 20	2 27	2 34	2 42	2 49	16
17	1 25	1 31	1 38	1 44	1 51	1 58	2 04	2 11	2 18	2 24	2 31	2 38	17
18	1 19	1 25	1 31	1 38	1 44	1 50	1 56	2 03	2 09	2 15	2 22	2 28	18
19	1 14	1 20	1 26	1 32	1 37	1 43	1 49	1 55	2 01	2 07	2 13	2 19	19
20	1 09	1 15	1 20	1 26	1 32	1 37	1 43	1 49	1 55	2 00	2 05	2 11	20
21	1 05	1 10	1 16	1 21	1 26	1 32	1 37	1 43	1 48	1 53	1 59	2 04	21
22	1 01	1 06	1 11	1 16	1 22	1 27	1 32	1 37	1 42	1 47	1 52	1 57	22
23	0 57	1 02	1 07	1 12	1 17	1 22	1 27	1 32	1 36	1 41	1 46	1 51	23
24	0 54	0 59	1 03	1 08	1 13	1 18	1 22	1 27	1 32	1 36	1 41	1 46	24
25	0 51	0 55	1 00	1 04	1 09	1 13	1 18	1 22	1 27	1 32	1 36	1 40	25
26	0 48	0 52	0 57	1 01	1 05	1 10	1 14	1 18	1 23	1 27	1 32	1 36	26
27	0 45	0 49	0 54	0 58	1 02	1 06	1 10	1 14	1 18	1 23	1 27	1 32	27
28	0 43	0 47	0 51	0 55	0 59	1 03	1 07	1 11	1 15	1 19	1 23	1 27	28
29	0 40	0 44	0 48	0 52	0 56	0 59	1 03	1 07	1 11	1 15	1 19	1 23	29
30	0 38	0 41	0 45	0 49	0 53	0 57	1 00	1 04	1 08	1 12	1 16	1 19	30
31	0 36	0 39	0 43	0 46	0 50	0 54	0 57	1 01	1 05	1 08	1 12	1 16	31
32	0 34	0 37	0 40	0 44	0 47	0 51	0 55	0 58	1 02	1 05	1 09	1 12	32
33	0 31	0 35	0 38	0 42	0 45	0 49	0 52	0 55	0 59	1 02	1 06	1 09	33
34	0 29	0 33	0 36	0 39	0 43	0 46	0 49	0 53	0 56	0 59	1 03	1 06	34
35	0 28	0 31	0 34	0 37	0 41	0 44	0 47	0 50	0 53	0 57	1 00	1 04	35
36	0 26	0 29	0 32	0 35	0 39	0 42	0 45	0 48	0 51	0 54	0 57	1 01	36
37	0 24	0 27	0 30	0 33	0 37	0 40	0 43	0 46	0 49	0 52	0 55	0 58	37
38	0 23	0 26	0 29	0 32	0 35	0 38	0 40	0 43	0 46	0 49	0 53	0 55	38
39	0 21	0 24	0 27	0 30	0 33	0 36	0 38	0 41	0 44	0 47	0 50	0 53	39
40	0 20	0 22	0 25	0 28	0 31	0 34	0 36	0 39	0 42	0 45	0 48	0 51	40
41	0 18	0 21	0 24	0 26	0 29	0 32	0 35	0 37	0 40	0 43	0 46	0 49	41
42	0 17	0 19	0 22	0 25	0 27	0 30	0 33	0 35	0 38	0 41	0 44	0 46	42
43	0 15	0 18	0 21	0 23	0 26	0 28	0 31	0 34	0 36	0 39	0 42	0 44	43
44	0 14	0 17	0 19	0 22	0 24	0 27	0 29	0 32	0 34	0 37	0 40	0 42	44
45	0 13	0 15	0 18	0 20	0 23	0 25	0 28	0 30	0 33	0 35	0 38	0 40	45
46	0 11	0 13	0 16	0 19	0 21	0 24	0 26	0 29	0 31	0 33	0 36	0 38	46
47	0 10	0 12	0 15	0 17	0 20	0 22	0 25	0 27	0 29	0 32	0 34	0 37	47
48		0 11	0 14	0 16	0 18	0 21	0 23	0 25	0 28	0 30	0 32	0 35	48
49		0 10	0 12	0 15	0 17	0 19	0 22	0 24	0 26	0 29	0 31	0 33	49
50			0 11	0 13	0 16	0 18	0 20	0 22	0 25	0 27	0 29	0 31	50
51			0 10	0 12	0 14	0 17	0 19	0 21	0 23	0 26	0 28	0 30	51
52				0 11	0 13	0 15	0 17	0 20	0 22	0 24	0 26	0 28	52
53				0 10	0 12	0 14	0 16	0 18	0 20	0 23	0 25	0 27	53
54					0 11	0 13	0 15	0 17	0 19	0 21	0 23	0 25	54
55					0 10	0 12	0 14	0 16	0 18	0 20	0 22	0 24	55
56						0 10	0 12	0 14	0 16	0 18	0 20	0 22	56
57							0 11	0 13	0 15	0 17	0 19	0 21	57
58							0 10	0 12	0 14	0 16	0 18	0 20	58
59								0 11	0 13	0 14	0 17	0 18	59
60								0 10	0 11	0 13	0 16	0 17	60
61									0 10	0 12	0 14	0 16	61
62										0 11	0 13	0 15	62
63										0 10	0 12	0 13	63
64											0 10	0 12	64
65												0 11	65

TABLE 10.

Distance by Vertical Angle (Distance greater than 5 miles).

Distance in nautical miles.	Difference in feet between height of object and height of eye.												Distance in nautical miles.
	5,200	5,400	5,600	5,800	6,000	6,200	6,400	6,600	6,800	7,000	7,200	7,400	
	° ′	° ′	° ′	° ′	° ′	° ′	° ′	° ′	° ′	° ′	° ′	° ′	
11	4 22	4 32	4 42	4 53	5 03	5 13	5 23	5 33	5 43	5 53	6 03	6 13	11
12	3 59	4 08	4 17	4 27	4 36	4 45	4 55	5 05	5 14	5 23	5 33	5 42	12
13	3 39	3 48	3 57	4 05	4 14	4 23	4 31	4 40	4 48	4 57	5 06	5 15	13
14	3 23	3 31	3 39	3 47	3 55	4 03	4 11	4 19	4 27	4 35	4 43	4 51	14
15	3 08	3 16	3 23	3 31	3 38	3 46	3 54	4 01	4 08	4 16	4 23	4 31	15
16	2 56	3 03	3 10	3 17	3 24	3 31	3 38	3 45	3 52	3 59	4 06	4 13	16
17	2 44	2 51	2 58	3 04	3 11	3 17	3 24	3 31	3 38	3 44	3 51	3 57	17
18	2 34	2 41	2 47	2 53	2 59	3 06	3 12	3 18	3 24	3 31	3 37	3 43	18
19	2 25	2 31	2 37	2 43	2 49	2 55	3 01	3 07	3 13	3 19	3 25	3 30	19
20	2 17	2 23	2 29	2 34	2 40	2 45	2 51	2 57	3 02	3 08	3 13	3 19	20
21	2 09	2 15	2 20	2 25	2 31	2 36	2 42	2 47	2 52	2 58	3 03	3 09	21
22	2 03	2 08	2 13	2 18	2 23	2 28	2 33	2 38	2 44	2 49	2 54	2 59	22
23	1 56	2 01	2 06	2 11	2 16	2 21	2 26	2 31	2 36	2 41	2 46	2 50	23
24	1 50	1 55	2 00	2 05	2 09	2 14	2 19	2 23	2 28	2 33	2 38	2 42	24
25	1 45	1 50	1 54	1 58	2 03	2 08	2 12	2 17	2 21	2 26	2 31	2 35	25
26	1 40	1 44	1 48	1 53	1 57	2 02	2 06	2 11	2 15	2 19	2 24	2 28	26
27	1 36	1 40	1 44	1 48	1 52	1 56	2 00	2 04	2 09	2 13	2 17	2 21	27
28	1 31	1 35	1 39	1 43	1 47	1 51	1 55	1 59	2 03	2 07	2 11	2 15	28
29	1 27	1 31	1 34	1 38	1 42	1 46	1 50	1 54	1 58	2 02	2 06	2 10	29
30	1 23	1 27	1 30	1 34	1 38	1 42	1 46	1 49	1 53	1 57	2 01	2 04	30
31	1 20	1 23	1 27	1 30	1 34	1 38	1 41	1 45	1 48	1 52	1 56	2 00	31
32	1 16	1 19	1 23	1 26	1 30	1 34	1 37	1 40	1 44	1 48	1 51	1 54	32
33	1 12	1 16	1 19	1 23	1 26	1 30	1 33	1 36	1 40	1 43	1 47	1 50	33
34	1 09	1 13	1 16	1 19	1 23	1 26	1 29	1 33	1 36	1 39	1 42	1 46	34
35	1 07	1 10	1 13	1 16	1 19	1 23	1 26	1 29	1 32	1 36	1 39	1 42	35
36	1 04	1 07	1 10	1 13	1 16	1 19	1 23	1 26	1 29	1 32	1 35	1 38	36
37	1 01	1 04	1 07	1 10	1 13	1 16	1 19	1 22	1 25	1 29	1 31	1 34	37
38	0 58	1 01	1 04	1 07	1 10	1 13	1 16	1 19	1 22	1 25	1 28	1 31	38
39	0 56	0 59	1 02	1 05	1 08	1 10	1 13	1 16	1 19	1 22	1 25	1 28	39
40	0 54	0 56	0 59	1 02	1 05	1 08	1 11	1 13	1 16	1 19	1 22	1 25	40
41	0 51	0 54	0 57	1 00	1 02	1 05	1 08	1 11	1 13	1 16	1 19	1 21	41
42	0 49	0 52	0 54	0 57	1 00	1 03	1 05	1 08	1 10	1 13	1 16	1 19	42
43	0 47	0 49	0 52	0 55	0 57	1 00	1 03	1 05	1 08	1 10	1 13	1 16	43
44	0 45	0 47	0 50	0 53	0 55	0 58	1 00	1 03	1 05	1 08	1 10	1 13	44
45	0 43	0 45	0 48	0 50	0 53	0 55	0 58	1 00	1 03	1 05	1 08	1 10	45
46	0 41	0 43	0 46	0 48	0 51	0 53	0 56	0 58	1 01	1 03	1 05	1 08	46
47	0 39	0 42	0 44	0 46	0 49	0 51	0 53	0 56	0 58	1 01	1 03	1 05	47
48	0 37	0 40	0 42	0 44	0 47	0 49	0 51	0 54	0 56	0 58	1 01	1 03	48
49	0 36	0 38	0 40	0 42	0 45	0 47	0 49	0 52	0 54	0 56	0 59	1 01	49
50	0 34	0 36	0 38	0 40	0 43	0 45	0 47	0 50	0 52	0 54	0 56	0 59	50
51	0 32	0 34	0 37	0 39	0 41	0 43	0 45	0 48	0 50	0 52	0 54	0 56	51
52	0 31	0 33	0 35	0 37	0 39	0 41	0 43	0 46	0 48	0 50	0 52	0 54	52
53	0 29	0 31	0 33	0 35	0 37	0 40	0 42	0 44	0 46	0 48	0 50	0 52	53
54	0 27	0 30	0 32	0 34	0 36	0 38	0 40	0 42	0 44	0 46	0 48	0 50	54
55	0 26	0 28	0 30	0 32	0 34	0 36	0 38	0 40	0 42	0 44	0 46	0 49	55
56	0 24	0 26	0 28	0 31	0 33	0 35	0 37	0 39	0 41	0 43	0 45	0 47	56
57	0 23	0 25	0 27	0 29	0 31	0 33	0 35	0 37	0 39	0 41	0 43	0 45	57
58	0 22	0 24	0 26	0 28	0 29	0 31	0 33	0 35	0 37	0 39	0 41	0 43	58
59	0 20	0 22	0 24	0 26	0 28	0 30	0 32	0 34	0 36	0 38	0 39	0 41	59
60	0 19	0 21	0 23	0 25	0 27	0 28	0 30	0 32	0 34	0 36	0 38	0 40	60
61	0 18	0 19	0 21	0 23	0 25	0 27	0 29	0 31	0 32	0 34	0 36	0 38	61
62	0 16	0 18	0 20	0 22	0 24	0 25	0 27	0 29	0 31	0 33	0 35	0 36	62
63	0 15	0 17	0 19	0 21	0 22	0 24	0 26	0 28	0 29	0 31	0 33	0 35	63
64	0 14	0 16	0 17	0 19	0 21	0 23	0 25	0 26	0 28	0 30	0 32	0 33	64
65	0 13	0 14	0 16	0 18	0 20	0 21	0 23	0 25	0 27	0 28	0 30	0 32	65
66	0 12	0 13	0 15	0 17	0 18	0 20	0 22	0 23	0 25	0 27	0 29	0 30	66
67	0 10	0 12	0 14	0 15	0 17	0 19	0 21	0 22	0 24	0 25	0 27	0 29	67
68		0 11	0 13	0 14	0 16	0 17	0 19	0 21	0 22	0 24	0 26	0 27	68
69		0 10	0 11	0 13	0 15	0 16	0 18	0 20	0 21	0 23	0 24	0 26	69
70			0 10	0 12	0 13	0 15	0 17	0 18	0 20	0 22	0 23	0 25	70

TABLE 10.

Distance by Vertical Angle (Distance greater than 5 miles)

Distance in nautical miles	Difference in feet between height of object and height of eye												Distance in nautical miles
	7.600	7,800	8,000	8,200	8,400	8,600	8,800	9,000	9,200	9,400	9,600	9,800	
	° ′	° ′	° ′	° ′	° ′	° ′	° ′	°	° ′	° ′	° ′	° ′	
16	4 20	4 27	4 34	4 41	4 48	4 55	5 02	5 09	5 16	5 23	5 30	5 37	16
17	4 04	4 11	4 17	4 24	4 30	4 37	4 44	4 50	4 57	5 03	5 10	5 16	17
18	3 49	3 56	4 02	4 08	4 15	4 21	4 27	4 33	4 39	4 46	4 52	4 58	18
19	3 36	3 42	3 48	3 54	4 00	4 06	4 12	4 18	4 24	4 30	4 36	4 42	19
20	3 25	3 30	3 36	3 41	3 47	3 53	3 58	4 04	4 09	4 15	4 20	4 26	20
21	3 14	3 19	3 25	3 30	3 35	3 41	3 46	3 51	3 57	4 02	4 08	4 13	21
22	3 04	3 09	3 14	3 20	3 25	3 30	3 35	3 40	3 45	3 50	3 56	4 01	22
23	2 55	3 00	3 05	3 10	3 15	3 20	3 25	3 30	3 34	3 39	3 44	3 49	23
24	2 48	2 52	2 56	3 01	3 06	3 10	3 15	3 20	3 25	3 29	3 34	3 39	24
25	2 40	2 44	2 49	2 53	2 57	3 02	3 06	3 11	3 15	3 20	3 24	3 29	25
26	2 32	2 36	2 41	2 45	2 49	2 54	2 58	3 02	3 07	3 11	3 16	3 20	26
27	2 26	2 30	2 34	2 38	2 42	2 46	2 51	2 55	2 59	3 03	3 07	3 12	27
28	2 20	2 24	2 27	2 31	2 35	2 39	2 43	2 47	2 51	2 55	2 59	3 03	28
29	2 14	2 18	2 21	2 25	2 29	2 33	2 37	2 41	2 45	2 49	2 53	2 56	29
30	2 08	2 12	2 16	2 19	2 23	2 27	2 31	2 34	2 38	2 42	2 46	2 49	30
31	2 03	2 06	2 10	2 14	2 18	2 21	2 25	2 28	2 32	2 36	2 40	2 43	31
32	1 58	2 02	2 05	2 08	2 12	2 16	2 20	2 23	2 27	2 30	2 33	2 37	32
33	1 54	1 57	2 00	2 04	2 07	2 11	2 14	2 18	2 21	2 24	2 28	2 31	33
34	1 49	1 53	1 56	1 59	2 02	2 06	2 10	2 13	2 16	2 19	2 23	2 26	34
35	1 45	1 48	1 52	1 55	1 58	2 01	2 05	2 08	2 11	2 14	2 17	2 20	35
36	1 41	1 44	1 48	1 51	1 54	1 57	2 00	2 03	2 06	2 10	2 13	2 16	36
37	1 38	1 41	1 44	1 47	1 50	1 53	1 56	1 59	2 02	2 05	2 08	2 11	37
38	1 34	1 37	1 40	1 43	1 46	1 49	1 52	1 55	1 58	2 01	2 04	2 07	38
39	1 31	1 34	1 36	1 39	1 42	1 45	1 48	1 51	1 54	1 57	2 00	2 02	39
40	1 27	1 30	1 33	1 36	1 39	1 41	1 44	1 47	1 50	1 53	1 56	1 58	40
41	1 24	1 27	1 30	1 32	1 35	1 38	1 41	1 43	1 46	1 49	1 52	1 54	41
42	1 21	1 24	1 27	1 29	1 32	1 35	1 37	1 40	1 43	1 45	1 48	1 51	42
43	1 19	1 21	1 24	1 26	1 29	1 31	1 34	1 37	1 39	1 42	1 45	1 47	43
44	1 16	1 18	1 21	1 23	1 26	1 28	1 31	1 33	1 36	1 39	1 41	1 44	44
45	1 13	1 15	1 18	1 21	1 23	1 25	1 28	1 30	1 33	1 35	1 38	1 40	45
46	1 10	1 13	1 15	1 18	1 20	1 23	1 25	1 27	1 30	1 32	1 35	1 37	46
47	1 08	1 10	1 13	1 15	1 18	1 20	1 22	1 25	1 27	1 29	1 32	1 34	47
48	1 05	1 08	1 10	1 12	1 15	1 17	1 19	1 22	1 24	1 26	1 29	1 31	48
49	1 03	1 05	1 08	1 10	1 12	1 15	1 17	1 19	1 21	1 24	1 26	1 29	49
50	1 01	1 03	1 05	1 08	1 10	1 12	1 14	1 17	1 19	1 21	1 23	1 26	50
51	0 59	1 01	1 03	1 05	1 08	1 10	1 12	1 14	1 16	1 19	1 21	1 23	51
52	0 57	0 59	1 01	1 03	1 05	1 08	1 09	1 12	1 14	1 16	1 18	1 20	52
53	0 54	0 57	0 59	1 01	1 03	1 05	1 07	1 09	1 12	1 14	1 16	1 18	53
54	0 52	0 55	0 57	0 59	1 01	1 03	1 05	1 07	1 10	1 11	1 13	1 15	54
55	0 51	0 53	0 55	0 57	0 59	1 01	1 03	1 05	1 07	1 09	1 11	1 13	55
56	0 49	0 51	0 53	0 55	0 57	0 59	1 01	1 03	1 05	1 07	1 09	1 11	56
57	0 47	0 49	0 51	0 53	0 55	0 57	0 59	1 01	1 03	1 05	1 07	1 09	57
58	0 45	0 47	0 49	0 51	0 53	0 55	0 57	0 59	1 01	1 03	1 05	1 06	58
59	0 43	0 45	0 47	0 49	0 51	0 53	0 55	0 57	0 59	1 01	1 03	1 04	59
60	0 42	0 43	0 45	0 47	0 49	0 51	0 53	0 55	0 57	0 59	1 00	1 02	60
61	0 40	0 42	0 43	0 45	0 47	0 49	0 51	0 53	0 55	0 57	0 58	1 00	61
62	0 38	0 40	0 42	0 44	0 45	0 47	0 49	0 51	0 53	0 55	0 56	0 58	62
63	0 37	0 38	0 40	0 42	0 44	0 46	0 47	0 49	0 51	0 53	0 55	0 56	63
64	0 35	0 37	0 38	0 40	0 42	0 44	0 46	0 47	0 49	0 51	0 53	0 55	64
65	0 33	0 35	0 37	0 39	0 40	0 42	0 44	0 46	0 47	0 49	0 51	0 53	65
66	0 32	0 34	0 35	0 37	0 39	0 41	0 42	0 44	0 46	0 47	0 49	0 51	66
67	0 31	0 32	0 34	0 36	0 37	0 39	0 41	0 42	0 44	0 46	0 47	0 49	67
68	0 29	0 31	0 32	0 34	0 36	0 37	0 39	0 41	0 42	0 44	0 46	0 47	68
69	0 28	0 29	0 31	0 33	0 34	0 36	0 37	0 39	0 41	0 42	0 44	0 46	69
70	0 26	0 28	0 30	0 31	0 33	0 34	0 36	0 38	0 39	0 41	0 42	0 44	70
71	0 25	0 27	0 28	0 30	0 31	0 33	0 34	0 36	0 38	0 39	0 41	0 42	71
72	0 24	0 25	0 27	0 28	0 30	0 31	0 33	0 35	0 36	0 38	0 39	0 41	72
73	0 22	0 24	0 25	0 27	0 28	0 30	0 32	0 33	0 35	0 36	0 38	0 39	73
74	0 21	0 23	0 24	0 26	0 27	0 29	0 30	0 32	0 33	0 35	0 36	0 38	74
75	0 20	0 21	0 23	0 24	0 26	0 27	0 29	0 30	0 32	0 33	0 35	0 36	75

TABLE 10.

Distance by Vertical Angle (Distance Greater than 5 miles).

Distance in nautical miles	Difference in feet between height of object and height of eye.												Distance in nautical miles
	10, 000	10, 500	11, 000	11, 500	12, 000	12, 500	13, 000	13, 500	14, 000	14, 500	15, 000	15, 500	
	° ′	° ′	° ′	° ′	° ′	° ′	° ′	° ′	° ′	° ′	° ′	° ′	
21	4 18	4 32	4 45	4 58	5 12	5 25	5 38	5 52	6 05	6 18	6 32	6 45	21
22	4 06	4 18	4 31	4 44	4 57	5 09	5 22	5 35	5 47	6 00	6 13	6 26	22
23	3 54	4 06	4 19	4 31	4 43	4 55	5 07	5 19	5 31	5 43	5 56	6 08	23
24	3 43	3 55	4 07	4 19	4 30	4 42	4 54	5 05	5 17	5 29	5 40	5 52	24
25	3 33	3 45	3 56	4 07	4 18	4 30	4 41	4 52	5 03	5 15	5 26	5 37	25
26	3 24	3 35	3 46	3 57	4 08	4 18	4 29	4 40	4 51	5 01	5 12	5 23	26
27	3 16	3 26	3 37	3 47	3 57	4 08	4 18	4 29	4 39	4 49	5 00	5 10	27
28	3 08	3 18	3 28	3 38	3 48	3 58	4 08	4 18	4 28	4 38	4 48	4 58	28
29	3 00	3 10	3 20	3 30	3 39	3 49	3 59	4 08	4 18	4 28	4 37	4 47	29
30	2 53	3 03	3 12	3 22	3 31	3 40	3 50	3 59	4 08	4 17	4 27	4 37	30
31	2 47	2 56	3 05	3 14	3 23	3 32	3 41	3 50	3 59	4 08	4 18	4 27	31
32	2 41	2 50	2 58	3 07	3 16	3 25	3 33	3 42	3 51	4 00	4 09	4 17	32
33	2 35	2 44	2 52	3 00	3 09	3 17	3 26	3 34	3 43	3 51	4 00	4 09	33
34	2 29	2 38	2 46	2 54	3 02	3 10	3 19	3 27	3 35	3 43	3 52	4 00	34
35	2 24	2 32	2 40	2 48	2 56	3 04	3 12	3 20	3 28	3 36	3 44	3 53	35
36	2 19	2 27	2 34	2 42	2 50	2 58	3 06	3 13	3 21	3 29	3 37	3 45	36
37	2 14	2 22	2 29	2 37	2 45	2 52	3 00	3 07	3 15	3 22	3 30	3 38	37
38	2 10	2 17	2 24	2 32	2 40	2 47	2 54	3 01	3 09	3 16	3 24	3 31	38
39	2 05	2 13	2 20	2 27	2 35	2 42	2 49	2 56	3 03	3 10	3 17	3 25	39
40	2 01	2 08	2 15	2 22	2 29	2 36	2 43	2 50	2 57	3 05	3 12	3 19	40
41	1 57	2 04	2 11	2 18	2 25	2 32	2 38	2 45	2 52	2 59	3 06	3 13	41
42	1 53	2 00	2 07	2 14	2 20	2 27	2 34	2 40	2 47	2 54	3 00	3 07	42
43	1 50	1 57	2 03	2 10	2 16	2 22	2 29	2 36	2 42	2 49	2 55	3 02	43
44	1 46	1 53	1 59	2 06	2 12	2 18	2 24	2 31	2 38	2 44	2 50	2 56	44
45	1 43	1 49	1 56	2 02	2 08	2 14	2 20	2 27	2 33	2 39	2 46	2 52	45
46	1 40	1 46	1 52	1 58	2 04	2 10	2 16	2 23	2 29	2 35	2 41	2 47	46
47	1 37	1 43	1 49	1 55	2 01	2 07	2 13	2 19	2 24	2 30	2 36	2 42	47
48	1 34	1 40	1 45	1 51	1 57	2 03	2 09	2 15	2 20	2 26	2 32	2 38	48
49	1 31	1 37	1 42	1 48	1 54	1 59	2 05	2 11	2 17	2 23	2 28	2 34	49
50	1 28	1 34	1 39	1 45	1 50	1 56	2 02	2 07	2 13	2 19	2 24	2 30	50
51	1 25	1 31	1 36	1 42	1 48	1 53	1 58	2 04	2 09	2 15	2 20	2 26	51
52	1 23	1 28	1 33	1 39	1 44	1 50	1 55	2 01	2 06	2 11	2 17	2 22	52
53	1 20	1 25	1 31	1 36	1 41	1 47	1 52	1 57	2 03	2 08	2 13	2 18	53
54	1 17	1 23	1 28	1 33	1 38	1 44	1 49	1 54	1 59	2 05	2 10	2 15	54
55	1 15	1 20	1 25	1 30	1 36	1 41	1 46	1 51	1 56	2 01	2 06	2 12	55
56	1 13	1 18	1 23	1 28	1 33	1 38	1 43	1 48	1 53	1 58	2 03	2 08	56
57	1 11	1 16	1 20	1 25	1 30	1 35	1 40	1 45	1 50	1 55	2 00	2 05	57
58	1 08	1 13	1 18	1 23	1 28	1 32	1 37	1 42	1 47	1 52	1 57	2 02	58
59	1 06	1 11	1 16	1 21	1 25	1 30	1 35	1 39	1 44	1 49	1 54	1 59	59
60	1 04	1 09	1 14	1 18	1 23	1 28	1 32	1 37	1 42	1 47	1 51	1 56	60
61	1 02	1 07	1 11	1 16	1 21	1 25	1 30	1 34	1 39	1 44	1 48	1 53	61
62	1 00	1 05	1 09	1 14	1 18	1 23	1 27	1 32	1 36	1 41	1 45	1 50	62
63	0 58	1 03	1 07	1 12	1 16	1 20	1 25	1 29	1 34	1 38	1 43	1 47	63
64	0 56	1 01	1 05	1 10	1 14	1 18	1 23	1 27	1 31	1 36	1 40	1 45	64
65	0 54	0 59	1 03	1 07	1 12	1 16	1 20	1 25	1 29	1 34	1 38	1 42	65
66	0 53	0 57	1 01	1 05	1 10	1 14	1 18	1 22	1 27	1 31	1 35	1 40	66
67	0 51	0 55	0 59	1 03	1 08	1 12	1 16	1 20	1 24	1 29	1 33	1 37	67
68	0 49	0 53	0 57	1 01	1 06	1 10	1 14	1 18	1 22	1 26	1 30	1 34	68
69	0 47	0 51	0 56	1 00	1 04	1 08	1 12	1 16	1 20	1 24	1 28	1 32	69
70	0 46	0 50	0 54	0 58	1 02	1 06	1 10	1 14	1 18	1 22	1 26	1 30	70
71	0 44	0 48	0 52	0 56	1 00	1 04	1 08	1 12	1 16	1 20	1 24	1 28	71
72	0 42	0 46	0 50	0 54	0 58	1 02	1 06	1 10	1 14	1 18	1 22	1 26	72
73	0 41	0 45	0 49	0 52	0 56	1 00	1 04	1 08	1 12	1 16	1 20	1 24	73
74	0 39	0 43	0 47	0 51	0 55	0 58	1 02	1 06	1 10	1 14	1 18	1 22	74
75	0 38	0 42	0 45	0 49	0 53	0 56	1 00	1 04	1 08	1 12	1 16	1 19	75
76	0 36	0 40	0 44	0 47	0 51	0 55	0 58	1 02	1 06	1 10	1 14	1 17	76
77	0 35	0 39	0 42	0 46	0 49	0 53	0 57	1 00	1 04	1 08	1 12	1 15	77
78	0 33	0 37	0 41	0 44	0 48	0 51	0 55	0 59	1 02	1 06	1 10	1 13	78
79	0 32	0 36	0 39	0 43	0 46	0 50	0 53	0 57	1 00	1 04	1 07	1 11	79
80	0 31	0 34	0 38	0 41	0 45	0 48	0 52	0 55	0 59	1 02	1 06	1 09	80
81	0 29	0 33	0 36	0 40	0 43	0 47	0 50	0 54	0 57	1 01	1 04	1 07	81
82	0 28	0 31	0 35	0 38	0 42	0 45	0 49	0 52	0 55	0 59	1 02	1 06	82
83	0 27	0 30	0 33	0 37	0 40	0 43	0 47	0 50	0 54	0 57	1 00	1 04	83
84	0 25	0 29	0 32	0 35	0 39	0 42	0 45	0 49	0 52	0 56	0 59	1 02	84
85	0 24	0 27	0 31	0 34	0 37	0 41	0 44	0 47	0 50	0 54	0 57	1 00	85

TABLE 11.

For finding the distance of an object by an angle, measured from an elevated position, between the object and the horizon beyond.

Dist., yards.	Height of the Eye Above the Level of the Sea, in Feet.											Dist., yards.
	20	30	40	50	60	70	80	90	100	110	120	
	° ′	° ′	° ′	° ′	° ′	° ′	° ′	° ′	° ′	° ′	° ′	
100	3 44	5 37	7 29	9 21	11 11	13 00	14 47	16 34	18 16	19 58	21 37	100
200	1 50	2 46	3 43	4 39	5 35	6 31	7 27	8 23	9 18	10 13	11 08	200
300	1 12	1 49	2 26	3 04	3 41	4 19	4 56	5 33	6 11	6 48	7 25	300
400	52	1 21	1 48	2 16	2 44	3 12	3 40	4 08	4 36	5 04	5 32	400
500	41	1 03	1 25	1 48	2 10	2 32	2 54	3 17	3 39	4 01	4 24	500
600	34	52	1 10	1 29	1 47	2 05	2 24	2 42	3 01	3 20	3 38	600
700	28	44	1 01	1 15	1 31	1 46	2 01	2 18	2 34	2 50	3 05	700
800	24	38	51	1 05	1 18	1 32	1 46	2 00	2 13	2 27	2 41	800
900	21	33	45	57	1 09	1 22	1 33	1 45	1 57	2 10	2 22	900
1,000	18	29	40	50	1 01	1 12	1 23	1 34	1 45	1 56	2 07	1,000
1,100	16	26	35	45	55	1 05	1 15	1 24	1 34	1 44	1 54	1,100
1,200	15	23	32	41	50	59	1 08	1 17	1 26	1 35	1 44	1,200
1,300	13	21	29	37	45	53	1 02	1 10	1 18	1 27	1 35	1,300
1,400	12	19	27	34	41	49	57	1 04	1 12	1 20	1 27	1,400
1,500	11	18	24	31	38	45	52	59	1 07	1 14	1 21	1,500
1,600	10	16	22	29	35	42	48	55	1 02	1 08	1 15	1,600
1,700		15	21	27	33	39	45	51	58	1 04	1 10	1,700
1,800		14	19	25	31	36	42	48	54	1 00	1 06	1,800
1,900		13	18	23	29	34	39	45	50	56	1 02	1,900
2,000		12	17	22	27	32	37	42	47	53	58	2,000
2,100		11	16	20	25	30	35	40	45	50	55	2,100
2,200		10	15	19	24	28	33	38	42	47	52	2,200
2,300			14	18	22	27	31	36	40	45	49	2,300
2,400			13	17	21	25	29	34	38	42	47	2,400
2,500			12	16	20	24	28	32	36	40	44	2,500
2,600			11	15	19	23	26	30	34	38	42	2,600
2,700			11	14	18	22	25	29	33	36	40	2,700
2,800			10	14	17	20	24	28	31	35	38	2,800
2,900				13	16	19	23	26	30	33	37	2,900
3,000				12	15	19	22	25	28	32	35	3,000
3,100				12	15	18	21	24	27	30	34	3,100
3,200				11	14	17	20	23	26	29	32	3,200
3,300				10	13	16	19	22	25	28	31	3,300
3,400					13	15	18	21	24	27	30	3,400
3,500					12	15	17	20	23	26	29	3,500
3,600					12	14	17	19	22	25	27	3,600
3,700					11	13	16	19	21	24	26	3,700
3,800					11	13	15	18	20	23	25	3,800
3,900					10	12	15	17	20	22	25	3,900
4,000						12	14	16	19	21	24	4,000
4,100						11	14	16	18	20	23	4,100
4,200						11	13	15	17	20	22	4,200
4,300						10	13	15	17	19	21	4,300
4,400							12	14	16	18	21	4,400
4,500							12	14	16	18	20	4,500
4,600							11	13	15	17	19	4,600
4,700							11	13	15	17	19	4,700
4,800							10	12	14	16	18	4,800
4,900								12	14	15	17	4,900
5,000								11	13	15	17	5,000

TABLE 12.

Speed in knots developed by a vessel traversing a measured nautical mile in any given number of minutes and seconds.

Sec.	Number of minutes.												Sec.
	1	2	3	4	5	6	7	8	9	10	11	12	
	Knots.	*Knots.*	*Knots.*	*Knots.*	*Knots.*	*Knots.*	*Knots.*	*Knots.*	*Knots.*	*Knots.*	*Knots.*	*Knots.*	
0	60.000	30.000	20.000	15.000	12.000	10.000	8.571	7.500	6.666	6.000	5.455	5.000	0
1	59.016	29.752	19.890	14.938	11.960	9.972	8.551	7.484	6.654	5.990	5.446	4.993	1
2	58.065	29.508	19.780	14.876	11.920	9.944	8.530	7.468	6.642	5.980	5.438	4.986	2
3	57.143	29.268	19.672	14.815	11.880	9.917	8.510	7.453	6.629	5.970	5.429	4.979	3
4	56.250	29.032	19.565	14.754	11.841	9.890	8.490	7.438	6.617	5.960	5.421	4.972	4
5	55.385	28.800	19.460	14.694	11.803	9.863	8.470	7.422	6.605	5.950	5.413	4.965	5
6	54.545	28.571	19.355	14.634	11.764	9.836	8.450	7.407	6.593	5.940	5.405	4.958	6
7	53.731	28.346	19.251	14.575	11.726	9.809	8.430	7.392	6.581	5.930	5.397	4.951	7
8	52.941	28.125	19.149	14.516	11.688	9.783	8.411	7.377	6.569	5.921	5.389	4.945	8
9	52.174	27.907	19.048	14.458	11.650	9.756	8.392	7.362	6.557	5.911	5.381	4.938	9
10	51.429	27.692	18.947	14.400	11.613	9.729	8.372	7.346	6.545	5.902	5.373	4.932	10
11	50.704	27.481	18.848	14.342	11.575	9.703	8.353	7.331	6.533	5.892	5.365	4.924	11
12	50.000	27.273	18.750	14.286	11.538	9.677	8.334	7.317	6.521	5.882	5.357	4.918	12
13	49.315	27.068	18.652	14.229	11.501	9.651	8.315	7.302	6.509	5.872	5.349	4.911	13
14	48.649	26.866	18.556	14.173	11.465	9.625	8.295	7.287	6.498	5.863	5.341	4.904	14
15	48.000	26.667	18.461	14.118	11.428	9.600	8.276	7.272	6.486	5.853	5.333	4.897	15
16	47.368	26.471	18.367	14.063	11.392	9.574	8.257	7.258	6.474	5.844	5.325	4.891	16
17	46.753	26.277	18.274	14.008	11.356	9.549	8.238	7.243	6.463	5.834	5.317	4.884	17
18	46.154	26.087	18.182	13.953	11.321	9.524	8.219	7.229	6.451	5.825	5.309	4.878	18
19	45.570	25.899	18.090	13.900	11.285	9.499	8.200	7.214	6.440	5.815	5.301	4.871	19
20	45.000	25.714	18.000	13.846	11.250	9.473	8.181	7.200	6.428	5.806	5.294	4.865	20
21	44.444	25.532	17.910	13.793	11.214	9.448	8.163	7.185	6.417	5.797	5.286	4.858	21
22	43.902	25.352	17.822	13.740	11.180	9.424	8.144	7.171	6.405	5.787	5.278	4.851	22
23	43.373	25.175	17.734	13.688	11.146	9.399	8.126	7.157	6.394	5.778	5.270	4.845	23
24	42.857	25.000	17.647	13.636	11.111	9.375	8.108	7.142	6.383	5.769	5.263	4.838	24
25	42.353	24.828	17.560	13.584	11.077	9.350	8.090	7.128	6.371	5.760	5.255	4.832	25
26	41.860	24.658	17.475	13.533	11.043	9.326	8.071	7.114	6.360	5.750	5.247	4.825	26
27	41.379	24.490	17.391	13.483	11.009	9.302	8.053	7.100	6.349	5.741	5.240	4.819	27
28	40.909	24.324	17.307	13.433	10.975	9.278	8.035	7.086	6.338	5.732	5.232	4.812	28
29	40.449	24.161	17.225	13.383	10.942	9.254	8.017	7.072	6.327	5.723	5.224	4.806	29
30	40.000	24.000	17.143	13.333	10.909	9.230	8.000	7.059	6.315	5.714	5.217	4.800	30
31	39.560	23.841	17.061	13.284	10.876	9.207	7.982	7.045	6.304	5.705	5.210	4.793	31
32	39.130	23.684	16.981	13.235	10.843	9.183	7.964	7.031	6.293	5.696	5.202	4.787	32
33	38.710	23.529	16.901	13.186	10.810	9.160	7.947	7.017	6.282	5.687	5.195	4.780	33
34	38.298	23.377	16.822	13.138	10.778	9.137	7.929	7.004	6.271	5.678	5.187	4.774	34
35	37.895	23.226	16.744	13.091	10.746	9.113	7.912	6.990	6.260	5.669	5.179	4.768	35
36	37.500	23.077	16.667	13.043	10.714	9.090	7.895	6.977	6.250	5.660	5.172	4.761	36
37	37.113	22.930	16.590	12.996	10.682	9.068	7.877	6.963	6.239	5.651	5.164	4.755	37
38	36.735	22.785	16.514	12.950	10.651	9.045	7.860	6.950	6.228	5.642	5.157	4.749	38
39	36.364	22.642	16.438	12.903	10.619	9.022	7.843	6.936	6.217	5.633	5.150	4.743	39
40	36.000	22.500	16.363	12.857	10.588	9.000	7.826	6.923	6.207	5.625	5.143	4.737	40
41	35.644	22.360	16.289	12.811	10.557	8.977	7.809	6.909	6.196	5.616	5.135	4.731	41
42	35.294	22.222	16.216	12.766	10.526	8.955	7.792	6.896	6.185	5.607	5.128	4.724	42
43	34.951	22.086	16.143	12.721	10.495	8.933	7.775	6.883	6.174	5.598	5.121	4.718	43
44	34.615	21.951	16.071	12.676	10.465	8.911	7.758	6.870	6.164	5.590	5.114	4.712	44
45	34.286	21.818	16.000	12.631	10.434	8.889	7.741	6.857	6.153	5.581	5.106	4.706	45
46	33.962	21.687	15.929	12.587	10.404	8.867	7.725	6.844	6.143	5.572	5.099	4.700	46
47	33.645	21.557	15.859	12.543	10.375	8.845	7.708	6.831	6.132	5.564	5.091	4.693	47
48	33.333	21.429	15.789	12.500	10.345	8.823	7.692	6.818	6.122	5.555	5.084	4.687	48
49	33.028	21.302	15.721	12.456	10.315	8.801	7.675	6.805	6.112	5.547	5.077	4.681	49
50	32.727	21.176	15.652	12.413	10.286	8.780	7.659	6.792	6.101	5.538	5.070	4.675	50
51	32.432	21.053	15.584	12.371	10.256	8.759	7.643	6.779	6.091	5.530	5.063	4.669	51
52	32.143	20.930	15.517	12.329	10.227	8.737	7.627	6.766	6.081	5.521	5.056	4.663	52
53	31.858	20.809	15.450	12.287	10.198	8.716	7.611	6.754	6.071	5.513	5.049	4.657	53
54	31.579	20.690	15.384	12.245	10.169	8.695	7.595	6.741	6.060	5.504	5.042	4.651	54
55	31.304	20.571	15.319	12.203	10.140	8.675	7.579	6.739	6.050	5.496	5.035	4.645	55
56	31.034	20.455	15.254	12.162	10.112	8.654	7.563	6.716	6.040	5.487	5.028	4.639	56
57	30.769	20.339	15.190	12.121	10.084	8.633	7.547	6.704	6.030	5.479	5.020	4.633	57
58	30.508	20.225	15.126	12.080	10.055	8.612	7.531	6.691	6.020	5.471	5.013	4.627	58
59	30.252	20.112	15.062	12.040	10.027	8.591	7.515	6.679	6.010	5.463	5.006	4.621	59
Sec.	1	2	3	4	5	6	7	8	9	10	11	12	Sec.

TABLE 13.

Time Speed and Distance.

Minutes.	Speed in knots.															
	5	**5.5**	**6**	**6.5**	**7**	**7.5**	**8**	**8.5**	**9**	**9.5**	**10**	**10.5**	**11**	**11.5**	**12**	**12.5**
1	0.1	0.1	0.1	0.1	0.1	0.1	0.1	0.1	0.2	0.2	0.2	0.2	0.2	0.2	0.2	0.2
2	.2	.2	.2	.2	.2	.3	.3	.3	.3	.3	.3	.4	.4	.4	.4	.4
3	.3	.3	.3	.3	.4	.4	.4	.4	.5	.5	.5	.5	.6	.6	.6	.6
4	.3	.4	.4	.4	.5	.5	.5	.6	.6	.6	.7	.7	.7	.8	.8	.8
5	.4	.5	.5	.5	.6	.6	.7	.7	.8	.8	.8	.9	.9	1.0	1.0	1.0
6	.5	.6	.6	.7	.7	.8	.8	.9	.9	1.0	1.0	1.1	1.1	1.2	1.2	1.3
7	.6	.6	.7	.8	.8	.9	.9	1.0	1.1	1.1	1.2	1.2	1.3	1.3	1.4	1.5
8	.7	.7	.8	.9	.9	1.0	1.1	1.1	1.2	1.3	1.3	1.4	1.5	1.5	1.6	1.7
9	.8	.8	.9	1.0	1.1	1.1	1.2	1.3	1.4	1.4	1.5	1.6	1.7	1.7	1.8	1.9
10	.8	.9	1.0	1.1	1.2	1.3	1.3	1.4	1.5	1.6	1.7	1.8	1.8	1.9	2.0	2.1
11	.9	1.0	1.1	1.2	1.3	1.4	1.5	1.6	1.7	1.7	1.8	1.9	2.0	2.1	2.2	2.3
12	1.0	1.1	1.2	1.3	1.4	1.5	1.6	1.7	1.8	1.9	2.0	2.1	2.2	2.3	2.4	2.5
13	1.1	1.2	1.3	1.4	1.5	1.6	1.7	1.8	2.0	2.1	2.2	2.3	2.4	2.5	2.6	2.7
14	1.2	1.3	1.4	1.5	1.6	1.8	1.9	2.0	2.1	2.2	2.3	2.5	2.6	2.7	2.8	2.9
15	1.3	1.4	1.5	1.6	1.8	1.9	2.0	2.1	2.3	2.4	2.5	2.6	2.8	2.9	3.0	3.1
16	1.3	1.5	1.6	1.7	1.9	2.0	2.1	2.3	2.4	2.5	2.7	2.8	2.9	3.1	3.2	3.3
17	1.4	1.6	1.7	1.8	2.0	2.1	2.3	2.4	2.6	2.7	2.8	3.0	3.1	3.3	3.4	3.5
18	1.5	1.7	1.8	2.0	2.1	2.3	2.4	2.6	2.7	2.9	3.0	3.2	3.3	3.5	3.6	3.8
19	1.6	1.8	1.9	2.1	2.2	2.4	2.5	2.7	2.9	3.0	3.2	3.3	3.5	3.6	3.8	4.0
20	1.7	1.8	2.0	2.2	2.3	2.5	2.7	2.8	3.0	3.2	3.3	3.5	3.7	3.8	4.0	4.2
21	1.8	1.9	2.1	2.3	2.5	2.6	2.8	3.0	3.2	3.3	3.5	3.7	3.9	4.0	4.2	4.4
22	1.8	2.0	2.2	2.4	2.6	2.8	2.9	3.1	3.3	3.5	3.7	3.9	4.0	4.2	4.4	4.6
23	1.9	2.1	2.3	2.5	2.7	2.9	3.1	3.3	3.5	3.6	3.8	4.0	4.2	4.4	4.6	4.8
24	2.0	2.2	2.4	2.6	2.8	3.0	3.2	3.4	3.6	3.8	4.0	4.2	4.4	4.6	4.8	5.0
25	2.1	2.3	2.5	2.7	2.9	3.1	3.3	3.5	3.8	4.0	4.2	4.4	4.6	4.8	5.0	5.2
26	2.2	2.4	2.6	2.8	3.0	3.3	3.5	3.7	3.9	4.1	4.3	4.6	4.8	5.0	5.2	5.4
27	2.3	2.5	2.7	2.9	3.2	3.4	3.6	3.8	4.1	4.3	4.5	4.7	5.0	5.2	5.4	5.6
28	2.3	2.6	2.8	3.0	3.3	3.5	3.7	4.0	4.2	4.4	4.7	4.9	5.1	5.4	5.6	5.8
29	2.4	2.7	2.9	3.1	3.4	3.6	3.9	4.1	4.4	4.6	4.8	5.1	5.3	5.6	5.8	6.0
30	2.5	2.8	3.0	3.3	3.5	3.8	4.0	4.3	4.5	4.8	5.0	5.3	5.5	5.8	6.0	6.3
31	2.6	2.8	3.1	3.4	3.6	3.9	4.1	4.4	4.7	4.9	5.2	5.4	5.7	5.9	6.2	6.5
32	2.7	2.9	3.2	3.5	3.7	4.0	4.3	4.5	4.8	5.1	5.3	5.6	5.9	6.1	6.4	6.7
33	2.8	3.0	3.3	3.6	3.9	4.1	4.4	4.7	5.0	5.2	5.5	5.8	6.1	6.3	6.6	6.9
34	2.8	3.1	3.4	3.7	4.0	4.3	4.5	4.8	5.1	5.4	5.7	6.0	6.2	6.5	6.8	7.1
35	2.9	3.2	3.5	3.8	4.1	4.4	4.7	5.0	5.3	5.5	5.8	6.1	6.4	6.7	7.0	7.3
36	3.0	3.3	3.6	3.9	4.2	4.5	4.8	5.1	5.4	5.7	6.0	6.3	6.6	6.9	7.2	7.5
37	3.1	3.4	3.7	4.0	4.3	4.6	4.9	5.2	5.6	5.9	6.2	6.5	6.8	7.1	7.4	7.7
38	3.2	3.5	3.8	4.1	4.4	4.8	5.1	5.4	5.7	6.0	6.3	6.7	7.0	7.3	7.6	7.9
39	3.3	3.6	3.9	4.2	4.6	4.9	5.2	5.5	5.9	6.2	6.5	6.8	7.2	7.5	7.8	8.1
40	3.3	3.7	4.0	4.3	4.7	5.0	5.3	5.7	6.0	6.3	6.7	7.0	7.3	7.7	8.0	8.3
41	3.4	3.8	4.1	4.4	4.8	5.1	5.5	5.8	6.2	6.5	6.8	7.2	7.5	7.9	8.2	8.5
42	3.5	3.9	4.2	4.6	4.9	5.3	5.6	6.0	6.3	6.7	7.0	7.4	7.7	8.1	8.4	8.8
43	3.6	3.9	4.3	4.7	5.0	5.4	5.7	6.1	6.5	6.8	7.2	7.5	7.9	8.2	8.6	9.0
44	3.7	4.0	4.4	4.8	5.1	5.5	5.9	6.2	6.6	7.0	7.3	7.7	8.1	8.4	8.8	9.2
45	3.8	4.1	4.5	4.9	5.3	5.6	6.0	6.4	6.8	7.1	7.5	7.9	8.3	8.6	9.0	9.4
46	3.8	4.2	4.6	5.0	5.4	5.8	6.1	6.5	6.9	7.3	7.7	8.1	8.4	8.8	9.2	9.6
47	3.9	4.3	4.7	5.1	5.5	5.9	6.3	6.7	7.1	7.4	7.8	8.2	8.6	9.0	9.4	9.8
48	4.0	4.4	4.8	5.2	5.6	6.0	6.4	6.8	7.2	7.6	8.0	8.4	8.8	9.2	9.6	10.0
49	4.1	4.5	4.9	5.3	5.7	6.1	6.5	6.9	7.4	7.8	8.2	8.6	9.0	9.4	9.8	10.2
50	4.2	4.6	5.0	5.4	5.8	6.3	6.7	7.1	7.5	7.9	8.3	8.8	9.2	9.6	10.0	10.4
51	4.3	4.7	5.1	5.5	6.0	6.4	6.8	7.2	7.7	8.1	8.5	8.9	9.4	9.8	10.2	10.6
52	4.3	4.8	5.2	5.6	6.1	6.5	6.9	7.4	7.8	8.2	8.7	9.1	9.5	10.0	10.4	10.8
53	4.4	4.9	5.3	5.7	6.2	6.6	7.1	7.5	8.0	8.4	8.8	9.3	9.7	10.2	10.6	11.0
54	4.5	5.0	5.4	5.9	6.3	6.8	7.2	7.7	8.1	8.6	9.0	9.5	9.9	10.4	10.8	11.3
55	4.6	5.0	5.5	6.0	6.4	6.9	7.3	7.8	8.3	8.7	9.2	9.6	10.1	10.5	11.0	11.5
56	4.7	5.1	5.6	6.1	6.5	7.0	7.5	7.9	8.4	8.9	9.3	9.8	10.3	10.7	11.2	11.7
57	4.8	5.2	5.7	6.2	6.7	7.1	7.6	8.1	8.6	9.0	9.5	10.0	10.5	10.9	11.4	11.9
58	4.8	5.3	5.8	6.3	6.8	7.3	7.7	8.2	8.7	9.2	9.7	10.2	10.6	11.1	11.6	12.1
59	4.9	5.4	5.9	6.4	6.9	7.4	7.9	8.4	8.9	9.3	9.8	10.3	10.8	11.3	11.8	12.3
60	5.0	5.5	6.0	6.5	7.0	7.5	8.0	8.5	9.0	9.5	10.0	10.5	11.0	11.5	12.0	12.5

Special Instructions for Midshipmen

1. This sheet should be brought to class each day that work on dead reckoning is being done.

2. Place your name at the designated place below.

3. Each day at the end of the period place your chart on the instructor's desk. On top of the lower left corner of the chart place your "voyage" sheet for the day.

4. Each midshipman will bring his copy of Bowditch to class each day that we study dead reckoning. He will also bring the necessary tools for his work on the charts.

Name J. W. Bower

... to Pelee Island FR Buoy using 2 ship headings. Fill in the following:

At 1300 change course to 89° (T) and instruct helmsman to steer course 94° (psc).

At 1350 change course to 17° (T) and instruct helmsman to steer course 21° (psc).

1 hr 2½ mi

2.5

1 / 2½

2°W
3°W
5°W

1°W
3°W
4°W

2 hr. 3 mi

1½

2 / 3

Name J. W. Bower

Third Cruise of the Fiction (on Erie)

At 1200 the Fiction takes her departure from an anchorage one-half mile due north of the light in North Bay of Pelee Island. She steams on course ~~265~~ 266° (psc) at 12 knots until 1240. At this time course is changed to ~~221~~ 220 (psc).

At 1300 the black spar buoy (lat. approximately 41°44'30") bears ~~291~~ 290° (psc) while the black spar buoy almost dead ahead bears ~~226~~ 225° (psc).

1. What is the latitude of the 1300 fix? 41°43'50"

2. What is the longitude of the 1300 fix? 82°55'40"

3. What is the set (DIR.) of the current since 1200? 217°

4. What is the drift (SPEED) of the current since 1200? 2.5 knts.

If conditions have changed so that no current can be counted on

Third Cruise of the Fiction (on Erie)

Name________________

At 1200 the Fiction takes her departure from an anchorage one-half mile due north of the light in North Bay of Pelee Island. She steams on course 265° (psc) at 12 knots until 1240. At this time course is changed to 221 (psc).

At 1300 the black spar buoy (lat. approximately 41°44'30") bears 291°(psc) while the black spar buoy almost dead ahead bears 226° (psc).

1. What is the latitude of the 1300 fix? ________

2. What is the longitude of the 1300 fix? ________

3. What is the set of the current since 1200? ________

4. What is the drift of the current since 1200? ________

If conditions have changed so that no current can be

DATA SHEET FOR THE FICTION

Length over-all	70 ft.
Beam	13 ft.
Draft (maximum)	10 ft.
Maximum speed	25 knots
Most economical speed	10 knots
Steam radius	800 miles
Power	Diesel
Height of eye (wheel house)	15 ft.

Deviation Table

0°	0°	180	1°E
15	1°W	195	1°E
30	2°W	210	2°E
45	3°W	225	2°E
60	3°W	240	3°E
75	3°W	255	3°E
90	2°W	270	4°E
105	2°W	285	5°E
120	1°W	300	4°E
135	1°W	315	3°E

TABLE 13.

Time Speed and Distance.

Minutes.	Speed in knots.															
	13	13.5	14	14.5	15	15.5	16	16.5	17	17.5	18	18.5	19	19.5	20	20.5
1	0.2	0.2	0.2	0.2	0.3	0.3	0.3	0.3	0.3	0.3	0.3	0.3	0.3	0.3	0.3	0.3
2	.4	.5	.5	.5	.5	.5	.5	.6	.6	.6	.6	.6	.6	.7	.7	.7
3	.7	.7	.7	.7	.8	.8	.8	.8	.9	.9	.9	.9	1.0	1.0	1.0	1.0
4	.9	.9	.9	1.0	1.0	1.0	1.1	1.1	1.1	1.2	1.2	1.2	1.3	1.3	1.3	1.4
5	1.1	1.1	1.2	1.2	1.3	1.3	1.3	1.4	1.4	1.5	1.5	1.5	1.6	1.6	1.7	1.7
6	1.3	1.4	1.4	1.5	1.5	1.6	1.6	1.7	1.7	1.8	1.8	1.9	1.9	2.0	2.0	2.1
7	1.5	1.6	1.6	1.7	1.8	1.8	1.9	1.9	2.0	2.0	2.1	2.2	2.2	2.3	2.3	2.4
8	1.7	1.8	1.9	1.9	2.0	2.1	2.1	2.2	2.3	2.3	2.4	2.5	2.5	2.6	2.7	2.7
9	2.0	2.0	2.1	2.2	2.3	2.3	2.4	2.5	2.6	2.6	2.7	2.8	2.9	2.9	3.0	3.1
10	2.2	2.3	2.3	2.4	2.5	2.6	2.7	2.8	2.8	2.9	3.0	3.1	3.2	3.3	3.3	3.4
11	2.4	2.5	2.6	2.7	2.8	2.8	2.9	3.0	3.1	3.2	3.3	3.4	3.5	3.6	3.7	3.8
12	2.6	2.7	2.8	2.9	3.0	3.1	3.2	3.3	3.4	3.5	3.6	3.7	3.8	3.9	4.0	4.1
13	2.8	2.9	3.0	3.1	3.3	3.4	3.5	3.6	3.7	3.8	3.9	4.0	4.1	4.2	4.3	4.4
14	3.0	3.2	3.3	3.4	3.5	3.6	3.7	3.9	4.0	4.1	4.2	4.3	4.4	4.6	4.7	4.8
15	3.3	3.4	3.5	3.6	3.8	3.9	4.0	4.1	4.3	4.4	4.5	4.6	4.8	4.9	5.0	5.1
16	3.5	3.6	3.7	3.9	4.0	4.1	4.3	4.4	4.5	4.7	4.8	4.9	5.1	5.2	5.3	5.5
17	3.7	3.8	4.0	4.1	4.3	4.4	4.5	4.7	4.8	5.0	5.1	5.2	5.4	5.5	5.7	5.8
18	3.9	4.1	4.2	4.4	4.5	4.7	4.8	5.0	5.1	5.3	5.4	5.6	5.7	5.9	6.0	6.2
19	4.1	4.3	4.4	4.6	4.8	4.9	5.1	5.2	5.4	5.5	5.7	5.9	6.0	6.2	6.3	6.5
20	4.3	4.5	4.7	4.8	5.0	5.2	5.3	5.5	5.7	5.8	6.0	6.2	6.3	6.5	6.7	6.8
21	4.6	4.7	4.9	5.1	5.3	5.4	5.6	5.8	6.0	6.1	6.3	6.5	6.7	6.8	7.0	7.2
22	4.8	5.0	5.1	5.3	5.5	5.7	5.9	6.1	6.2	6.4	6.6	6.8	7.0	7.2	7.3	7.5
23	5.0	5.2	5.4	5.6	5.8	5.9	6.1	6.3	6.5	6.7	6.9	7.1	7.3	7.5	7.7	7.9
24	5.2	5.4	5.6	5.8	6.0	6.2	6.4	6.6	6.8	7.0	7.2	7.4	7.6	7.8	8.0	8.2
25	5.4	5.6	5.8	6.0	6.3	6.5	6.7	6.9	7.1	7.3	7.5	7.7	7.9	8.1	8.3	8.5
26	5.6	5.9	6.1	6.3	6.5	6.7	6.9	7.2	7.4	7.6	7.8	8.0	8.2	8.5	8.7	8.9
27	5.9	6.1	6.3	6.5	6.8	7.0	7.2	7.4	7.7	7.9	8.1	8.3	8.6	8.8	9.0	9.2
28	6.1	6.3	6.5	6.8	7.0	7.2	7.5	7.7	7.9	8.2	8.4	8.6	8.9	9.1	9.3	9.6
29	6.3	6.5	6.8	7.0	7.3	7.5	7.7	8.0	8.2	8.5	8.7	8.9	9.2	9.4	9.7	9.9
30	6.5	6.8	7.0	7.3	7.5	7.8	8.0	8.3	8.5	8.8	9.0	9.3	9.5	9.8	10.0	10.3
31	6.7	7.0	7.2	7.5	7.8	8.0	8.3	8.5	8.8	9.0	9.3	9.6	9.8	10.1	10.3	10.6
32	6.9	7.2	7.5	7.7	8.0	8.3	8.5	8.8	9.1	9.3	9.6	9.9	10.1	10.4	10.7	10.9
33	7.2	7.4	7.7	8.0	8.3	8.5	8.8	9.1	9.4	9.6	9.9	10.2	10.5	10.7	11.0	11.3
34	7.4	7.7	7.9	8.2	8.5	8.8	9.1	9.4	9.6	9.9	10.2	10.5	10.8	11.1	11.3	11.6
35	7.6	7.9	8.2	8.5	8.8	9.0	9.3	9.6	9.9	10.2	10.5	10.8	11.1	11.4	11.7	12.0
36	7.8	8.1	8.4	8.7	9.0	9.3	9.6	9.9	10.2	10.5	10.8	11.1	11.4	11.7	12.0	12.3
37	8.0	8.3	8.6	8.9	9.3	9.6	9.9	10.2	10.5	10.8	11.1	11.4	11.7	12.0	12.3	12.6
38	8.2	8.6	8.9	9.2	9.5	9.8	10.1	10.5	10.8	11.1	11.4	11.7	12.0	12.4	12.7	13.0
39	8.5	8.8	9.1	9.4	9.8	10.1	10.4	10.7	11.1	11.4	11.7	12.0	12.4	12.7	13.0	13.3
40	8.7	9.0	9.3	9.7	10.0	10.3	10.7	11.0	11.3	11.7	12.0	12.3	12.7	13.0	13.3	13.7
41	8.9	9.2	9.6	9.9	10.3	10.6	10.9	11.3	11.6	12.0	12.3	12.6	13.0	13.3	13.7	14.0
42	9.1	9.5	9.8	10.2	10.5	10.9	11.2	11.6	11.9	12.3	12.6	13.0	13.3	13.7	14.0	14.4
43	9.3	9.7	10.0	10.4	10.8	11.1	11.5	11.8	12.2	12.5	12.9	13.3	13.6	14.0	14.3	14.7
44	9.5	9.9	10.3	10.6	11.0	11.4	11.7	12.1	12.5	12.8	13.2	13.6	13.9	14.3	14.7	15.0
45	9.8	10.1	10.5	10.9	11.3	11.6	12.0	12.4	12.8	13.1	13.5	13.9	14.3	14.6	15.0	15.4
46	10.0	10.4	10.7	11.1	11.5	11.9	12.3	12.7	13.0	13.4	13.8	14.2	14.6	15.0	15.3	15.7
47	10.2	10.6	11.0	11.4	11.8	12.1	12.5	12.9	13.3	13.7	14.1	14.5	14.9	15.3	15.7	16.1
48	10.4	10.8	11.2	11.6	12.0	12.4	12.8	13.2	13.6	14.0	14.4	14.8	15.2	15.6	16.0	16.4
49	10.6	11.0	11.4	11.8	12.3	12.7	13.1	13.5	13.9	14.3	14.7	15.1	15.5	15.9	16.3	16.7
50	10.8	11.3	11.7	12.1	12.5	12.9	13.3	13.8	14.2	14.6	15.0	15.4	15.8	16.3	16.7	17.1
51	11.1	11.5	11.9	12.3	12.8	13.2	13.6	14.0	14.5	14.9	15.3	15.7	16.2	16.6	17.0	17.4
52	11.3	11.7	12.1	12.6	13.0	13.4	13.9	14.3	14.7	15.2	15.6	16.0	16.5	16.9	17.3	17.8
53	11.5	11.9	12.4	12.8	13.3	13.7	14.1	14.6	15.0	15.5	15.9	16.3	16.8	17.2	17.7	18.1
54	11.7	12.2	12.6	13.1	13.5	14.0	14.4	14.9	15.3	15.8	16.2	16.7	17.1	17.6	18.0	18.5
55	11.9	12.4	12.8	13.3	13.8	14.2	14.7	15.1	15.6	16.0	16.5	17.0	17.4	17.9	18.3	18.8
56	12.1	12.6	13.1	13.5	14.0	14.5	14.9	15.4	15.9	16.3	16.8	17.3	17.7	18.2	18.7	19.1
57	12.4	12.8	13.3	13.8	14.3	14.7	15.2	15.7	16.2	16.6	17.1	17.6	18.1	18.5	19.0	19.5
58	12.6	13.1	13.5	14.0	14.5	15.0	15.5	16.0	16.4	16.9	17.4	17.9	18.4	18.9	19.3	19.8
59	12.8	13.3	13.8	14.3	14.8	15.2	15.7	16.2	16.7	17.2	17.7	18.2	18.7	19.2	19.7	20.2
60	13.0	13.5	14.0	14.5	15.0	15.5	16.0	16.5	17.0	17.5	18.0	18.5	19.0	19.5	20.0	20.5

541524°—43——35

TABLE 13.

Time Speed and Distance.

Minutes.	Speed in knots.															
	21	21.5	22	22.5	23	23.5	24	24.5	25	25.5	26	26.5	27	27.5	28	28.5
1	0.4	0.4	0.4	0.4	0.4	0.4	0.4	0.4	0.4	0.4	0.4	0.4	0.5	0.5	0.5	0.5
2	.7	.7	.7	.8	.8	.8	.8	.8	.8	.9	.9	.9	.9	.9	.9	1.0
3	1.1	1.1	1.1	1.1	1.2	1.2	1.2	1.2	1.3	1.3	1.3	1.3	1.4	1.4	1.4	1.4
4	1.4	1.4	1.5	1.5	1.5	1.6	1.6	1.6	1.7	1.7	1.7	1.8	1.8	1.8	1.9	1.9
5	1.8	1.8	1.8	1.9	1.9	2.0	2.0	2.0	2.1	2.1	2.2	2.2	2.3	2.3	2.3	2.4
6	2.1	2.2	2.2	2.3	2.3	2.4	2.4	2.5	2.5	2.6	2.6	2.7	2.7	2.8	2.8	2.9
7	2.5	2.5	2.6	2.6	2.7	2.7	2.8	2.9	2.9	3.0	3.0	3.1	3.2	3.2	3.3	3.3
8	2.8	2.9	2.9	3.0	3.1	3.1	3.2	3.3	3.3	3.4	3.5	3.5	3.6	3.7	3.7	3.8
9	3.2	3.2	3.3	3.4	3.5	3.5	3.6	3.7	3.8	3.8	3.9	4.0	4.1	4.1	4.2	4.3
10	3.5	3.6	3.7	3.8	3.8	3.9	4.0	4.1	4.2	4.3	4.3	4.4	4.5	4.6	4.7	4.8
11	3.9	3.9	4.0	4 1	4.2	4.3	4.4	4.5	4.6	4.7	4.8	4.9	5.0	5.0	5.1	5.2
12	4.2	4.3	4.4	4.5	4.6	4.7	4.8	4.9	5.0	5.1	5.2	5.3	5.4	5.5	5.6	5.7
13	4.6	4.7	4.8	4.9	5.0	5.1	5.2	5.3	5.4	5.5	5.6	5.7	5.9	6.0	6.1	6.2
14	4.9	5.0	5.1	5.3	5.4	5.5	5.6	5.7	5.8	6.0	6.1	6.2	6.3	6.4	6.5	6.7
15	5.3	5.4	5.5	5.6	5.8	5.9	6.0	6.1	6.3	6.4	6.5	6.6	6.8	6.9	7.0	7.1
16	5.6	5.7	5.9	6.0	6.1	6.3	6.4	6.5	6.7	6.8	6.9	7.1	7.2	7.3	7.5	7.6
17	6.0	6.1	6.2	6.4	6.5	6.7	6.8	6.9	7.1	7.2	7.4	7.5	7.7	7.8	7.9	8.1
18	6.3	6.5	6.6	6.8	6.9	7.1	7.2	7.4	7.5	7.7	7.8	8.0	8.1	8.3	8.4	8.6
19	6.7	6.8	7.0	7.1	7.3	7.4	7.6	7.8	7.9	8.1	8.2	8.4	8.6	8.7	8.9	9.0
20	7.0	7.2	7.3	7.5	7.7	7.8	8.0	8.2	8.3	8.5	8.7	8.8	9.0	9.2	9.3	9.5
21	7.4	7.5	7.7	7.9	8.1	8.2	8.4	8.6	8.8	8.9	9.1	9.3	9.5	9.6	9.8	10.0
22	7.7	7.9	8.1	8.3	8.4	8.6	8.8	9.0	9.2	9.4	9.5	9.7	9.9	10.1	10.3	10.5
23	8.1	8.2	8.4	8.6	8.8	9.0	9.2	9.4	9.6	9.8	10.0	10.2	10.4	10.5	10.7	10.9
24	8.4	8.6	8.8	9.0	9.2	9.4	9.6	9.8	10.0	10.2	10.4	10.6	10.8	11.0	11.2	11.4
25	8.8	9.0	9.2	9.4	9.6	9.8	10.0	10.2	10.4	10.6	10.8	11.0	11.3	11.5	11.7	11.9
26	9.1	9.3	9.5	9.8	10.0	10.2	10.4	10.6	10.8	11.1	11.3	11.5	11.7	11.9	12.1	12.4
27	9.5	9.7	9.9	10.1	10.4	10.6	10.8	11.0	11.3	11.5	11.7	11.9	12.2	12.4	12.6	12.8
28	9.8	10.0	10.3	10.5	10.7	11.0	11.2	11.4	11.7	11.9	12.1	12.4	12.6	12.8	13.1	13.3
29	10.2	10.4	10.6	10.9	11.1	11.4	11.6	11.8	12.1	12.3	12.6	12.8	13.1	13.3	13.5	13.8
30	10.5	10.8	11.0	11.3	11.5	11.8	12.0	12.3	12.5	12.8	13.0	13.3	13.5	13.8	14.0	14.3
31	10.9	11.1	11.4	11.6	11.9	12.1	12.4	12.7	12.9	13.2	13.4	13.7	14.0	14.2	14.5	14.7
32	11.2	11.5	11.7	12.0	12.3	12.5	12.8	13.1	13.3	13.6	13.9	14.1	14.4	14.7	14.9	15.2
33	11.6	11.8	12.1	12.4	12.7	12.9	13.2	13.5	13.8	14.0	14.3	14.6	14.9	15.1	15.4	15.7
34	11.9	12.2	12.5	12.8	13.0	13.3	13.6	13.9	14.2	14.5	14.7	15.0	15.3	15.6	15.9	16.2
35	12.3	12.5	12.8	13.1	13.4	13.7	14.0	14.3	14.6	14.9	15.2	15.5	15.8	16.0	16.3	16.6
36	12.6	12.9	13.2	13.5	13.8	14.1	14.4	14.7	15.0	15.3	15.6	15.9	16.2	16.5	16.8	17.1
37	13.0	13.3	13.6	13.9	14.2	14.5	14.8	15.1	15.4	15.7	16.0	16.3	16.7	17.0	17.3	17.6
38	13.3	13.6	13.9	14.3	14.6	14.9	15.2	15.5	15.8	16.2	16.5	16.8	17.1	17.4	17.7	18.1
39	13.7	14.0	14.3	14.6	15.0	15.3	15.6	15.9	16.3	16.6	16.9	17.2	17.6	17.9	18.2	18.5
40	14.0	14.3	14.7	15.0	15.3	15.7	16.0	16.3	16.7	17.0	17.3	17.7	18.0	18.3	18.7	19.0
41	14.4	14.7	15.0	15.4	15.7	16.1	16.4	16.7	17.1	17.4	17.8	18.1	18.5	18.8	19.1	19.5
42	14.7	15.1	15.4	15.8	16.1	16.5	16.8	17.2	17.5	17.9	18.2	18.6	18.9	19.3	19.6	20.0
43	15.1	15.4	15.8	16.1	16.5	16.8	17.2	17.6	17.9	18.3	18.6	19.0	19.4	19.7	20.1	20.4
44	15.4	15.8	16.1	16.5	16.9	17 2	17.6	18.0	18.3	18.7	19.1	19.4	19.8	20.2	20.5	20.9
45	15.8	16.1	16.5	16.9	17.3	17.6	18.0	18.4	18.8	19.1	19.5	19.9	20.3	20.6	21.0	21.4
46	16.1	16.5	16.9	17 3	17.6	18.0	18.4	18.8	19.2	19.6	19.9	20.3	20.7	21.1	21.5	21.9
47	16.5	16.8	17.2	17.6	18.0	18.4	18.8	19.2	19.6	20.0	20.4	20.8	21.2	21.5	21.9	22.3
48	16.8	17.2	17.6	18.0	18.4	18.8	19.2	19.6	20.0	20.4	20.8	21.2	21.6	22.0	22.4	22.8
49	17.2	17.6	18.0	18.4	18.8	19.2	19.6	20.0	20.4	20.8	21.2	21.6	22.1	22.5	22.9	23.3
50	17.5	17.9	18.3	18.8	19.2	19.6	20.0	20.4	20.8	21.3	21.7	22.1	22.5	22.9	23.3	23.8
51	17.9	18.3	18.7	19.1	19.6	20.0	20.4	20.8	21.3	21.7	22.1	22.5	23.0	23.4	23.8	24.2
52	18.2	18.6	19.1	19.5	19.9	20.4	20.8	21.2	21.7	22.1	22.5	23.0	23.4	23.8	24.3	24.7
53	18.6	19.0	19.4	19.9	20.3	20.8	21.2	21.6	22.1	22.5	23.0	23.4	23.9	24.3	24.7	25.2
54	18.9	19.4	19.8	20.3	20.7	21.2	21.6	22.1	22.5	23.0	23.4	23.9	24.3	24.8	25.2	25.7
55	19.3	19.7	20.2	20.6	21.1	21.5	22.0	22.5	22.9	23.4	23.8	24.3	24.8	25.2	25.7	26.1
56	19.6	20.1	20.5	21.0	21.5	21.9	22.4	22.9	23.3	23.8	24.3	24.7	25.2	25.7	26.1	26.6
57	20.0	20.4	20.9	21.4	21.9	22.3	22.8	23.3	23.8	24.2	24.7	25.2	25.7	26.1	26.6	27.1
58	20.3	20.8	21.3	21.8	22.2	22.7	23.2	23.7	24.2	24.7	25.1	25.6	26.1	26.6	27.1	27.6
59	20.7	21.1	21.6	22.1	22.6	23.1	23.6	24.1	24.6	25.1	25.6	26.1	26.6	27.0	27.5	28.0
60	21.0	21.5	22.0	22.5	23.0	23.5	24.0	24.5	25.0	25.5	26.0	26.5	27.0	27.5	28.0	28.5

TABLE 13.

Time Speed and Distance.

Minutes.	Speed in knots.															
	29	**29.5**	**30**	**30.5**	**31**	**31.5**	**32**	**32.5**	**33**	**33.5**	**34**	**34.5**	**35**	**35.5**	**36**	**36.5**
1	.5	.5	.5	.5	.5	.5	.5	.5	.6	.6	.6	.6	.6	.6	.6	.6
2	1.0	1.0	1.0	1.0	1.0	1.1	1.1	1.1	1.1	1.1	1.1	1.2	1.2	1.2	1.2	1.2
3	1.5	1.5	1.5	1.5	1.6	1.6	1.6	1.6	1.7	1.7	1.7	1.7	1.8	1.8	1.8	1.8
4	1.9	2.0	2.0	2.0	2.1	2.1	2.1	2.2	2.2	2.2	2.3	2.3	2.3	2.4	2.4	2.4
5	2.4	2.5	2.5	2.5	2.6	2.6	2.7	2.7	2.8	2.8	2.8	2.9	2.9	3.0	3.0	3.0
6	2.9	3.0	3.0	3.1	3.1	3.2	3.2	3.3	3.3	3.4	3.4	3.5	3.5	3.6	3.6	3.7
7	3.4	3.4	3.5	3.6	3.6	3.7	3.7	3.8	3.9	3.9	4.0	4.0	4.1	4.1	4.2	4.3
8	3.9	3.9	4.0	4.1	4.1	4.2	4.3	4.3	4.4	4.5	4.5	4.6	4.7	4.7	4.8	4.9
9	4.4	4.4	4.5	4.6	4.7	4.7	4.8	4.9	5.0	5.0	5.1	5.2	5.3	5.3	5.4	5.5
10	4.8	4.9	5.0	5.1	5.2	5.3	5.3	5.4	5.5	5.6	5.7	5.8	5.8	5.9	6.0	6.1
11	5.3	5.4	5.5	5.6	5.7	5.8	5.9	6.0	6.1	6.1	6.2	6.3	6.4	6.5	6.6	6.7
12	5.8	5.9	6.0	6.1	6.2	6.3	6.4	6.5	6.6	6.7	6.8	6.9	7.0	7.1	7.2	7.3
13	6.3	6.4	6.5	6.6	6.7	6.8	6.9	7.0	7.2	7.3	7.4	7.5	7.6	7.7	7.8	7.9
14	6.8	6.9	7.0	7.1	7.2	7.4	7.5	7.6	7.7	7.8	7.9	8.1	8.2	8.3	8.4	8.5
15	7.3	7.4	7.5	7.6	7.8	7.9	8.0	8.1	8.3	8.4	8.5	8.6	8.8	8.9	9.0	9.1
16	7.7	7.9	8.0	8.1	8.3	8.4	8.5	8.7	8.8	8.9	9.1	9.2	9.3	9.5	9.6	9.7
17	8.2	8.4	8.5	8.6	8.8	8.9	9.1	9.2	9.4	9.5	9.6	9.8	9.9	10.1	10.2	10.3
18	8.7	8.9	9.0	9.2	9.3	9.5	9.6	9.8	9.9	10.1	10.2	10.4	10.5	10.7	10.8	11.0
19	9.2	9.3	9.5	9.7	9.8	10.0	10.1	10.3	10.5	10.6	10.8	10.9	11.1	11.2	11.4	11.6
20	9.7	9.8	10.0	10 2	10.3	10.5	10.7	10.8	11.0	11.2	11.3	11.5	11.7	11.8	12.0	12.2
21	10.2	10.3	10.5	10.7	10.9	11.0	11.2	11.4	11.6	11.7	11.9	12.1	12.3	12.4	12.6	12.8
22	10.6	10.8	11.0	11.2	11.4	11.6	11.7	11.9	12.1	12.3	12.5	12.7	12.8	13.0	13.2	13.4
23	11.1	11.3	11.5	11.7	11.9	12.1	12.3	12.5	12.7	12.8	13.0	13.2	13.4	13.6	13.8	14.0
24	11.6	11.8	12.0	12.2	12.4	12.6	12.8	13.0	13.2	13.4	13.6	13.8	14.0	14.2	14.4	14.6
25	12.1	12.3	12.5	12.7	12.9	13.1	13.3	13.5	13.8	14.0	14.2	14.4	14.6	14.8	15.0	15.2
26	12.6	12.8	13.0	13.2	13.4	13.7	13.9	14.1	14.3	14.5	14.7	15.0	15.2	15.4	15.6	15.8
27	13.1	13.3	13.5	13.7	14.0	14.2	14.4	14.6	14.9	15.1	15.3	15.5	15.8	16.0	16.2	16.4
28	13.5	13.8	14.0	14.2	14.5	14.7	14.9	15.2	15.4	15.6	15.9	16.1	16.3	16.6	16.8	17.0
29	14.0	14.3	14.5	14.7	15.0	15.2	15.5	15.7	16.0	16.2	16.4	16.7	16.9	17.2	17.4	17.6
30	14.5	14.8	15.0	15.3	15.5	15.8	16.0	16.3	16.5	16.8	17.0	17.3	17.5	17.8	18.0	18.3
31	15.0	15.2	15.5	15.8	16.0	16.3	16.5	16.8	17.1	17.3	17.6	17.8	18.1	18.3	18.6	18.9
32	15.5	15.7	16.0	16.3	16.5	16.8	17.1	17.3	17.6	17.9	18 1	18.4	18.7	18.9	19.2	19.5
33	16.0	16.2	16.5	16.8	17.1	17.3	17.6	17.9	18.2	18.4	18.7	19.0	19.3	19.5	19.8	20.1
34	16.4	16.7	17.0	17.3	17.6	17.9	18.1	18.4	18.7	19.0	19.3	19.6	19.8	20.1	20.4	20.7
35	16.9	17.2	17.5	17.8	18.1	18.4	18.7	19.0	19.3	19.5	19.8	20.1	20.4	20.7	21.0	21.3
36	17.4	17.7	18.0	18.3	18.6	18.9	19.2	19.5	19.8	20.1	20.4	20.7	21.0	21.3	21.6	21.9
37	17.9	18.2	18.5	18.8	19.1	19.4	19.7	20.0	20.4	20.7	21.0	21.3	21.6	21.9	22.2	22.5
38	18.4	18.7	19.0	19.3	19.6	20.0	20.3	20.6	20.9	21.2	21.5	21.9	22.2	22.5	22 8	23.1
39	18.9	19 2	19.5	19.8	20.2	20.5	20.8	21.1	21.5	21.8	22.1	22.4	22.8	23.1	23.4	23.7
40	19.3	19.7	20.0	20.3	20.7	21.0	21.3	21.7	22.0	22.3	22.7	23.0	23.3	23.7	24.0	24.3
41	19.8	20.2	20.5	20.8	21.2	21.5	21.9	22.2	22.6	22.9	23.2	23.6	23.9	24.3	24.6	24.9
42	20.3	20.7	21.0	21.4	21.7	22.1	22.4	22.8	23.1	23.5	23.8	24.2	24.5	24.9	25.2	25.6
43	20.8	21.1	21.5	21.9	22.2	22.6	22.9	23.3	23.7	24.0	24.4	24.7	25.1	25.4	25.8	26.2
44	21.3	21.6	22.0	22.4	22.7	23.1	23.5	23.8	24.2	24.6	24.9	25.3	25.7	26.0	26.4	26.8
45	21.8	22.1	22.5	22.9	23.3	23.6	24.0	24.4	24.8	25.1	25.5	25.9	26.3	26.6	27.0	27,4
46	22.2	22.6	23.0	23.4	23.8	24.2	24.5	24.9	25.3	25.7	26.1	26.5	26.8	27.2	27.6	28.0
47	22.7	23.1	23.5	23.9	24.3	24.7	25.1	25.5	25.9	26.2	26.6	27.0	27.4	27.8	28.2	28.6
48	23.2	23.6	24.0	24.4	24.8	25.2	25.6	26.0	26.4	26.8	27.2	27.6	28.0	28.4	28.8	29.2
49	23.7	24.1	24.5	24.9	25.3	25.7	26.1	26.5	27.0	27.4	27.8	28.2	28.6	29.0	29.4	29.8
50	24.2	24.6	25.0	25.4	25.8	26.3	26.7	27.1	27.5	27.9	28.3	28.8	29.2	29.6	30.0	30.4
51	24.7	25.1	25.5	25.9	26.4	26.8	27.2	27.6	28.1	28 5	28.9	29.3	29.8	30.2	30.6	31.0
52	25.1	25.6	26.0	26.4	26.9	27.3	27.7	28.2	28.6	29.0	29.5	29.9	30.3	30.8	31.2	31.6
53	25.6	26.1	26.5	26.9	27.4	27.8	28.3	28.7	29.2	29.6	30.0	30.5	30.9	31.4	31.8	32.2
54	26.1	26.6	27.0	27.5	27.9	28.4	28.8	29.3	29.7	30.2	30.6	31.1	31.5	32.0	32.4	32.9
55	26.6	27.0	27.5	28.0	28.4	28.9	29.3	29.8	30.3	30.7	31.2	31.6	32.1	32.5	33.0	33.5
56	27.1	27.5	28.0	28.5	28.9	29.4	29.9	30.3	30.8	31.3	31.7	32.2	32.7	33.1	33.6	34.1
57	27.6	28.0	28.5	29.0	29.5	29.9	30.4	30.9	31.4	31.8	32.3	32.8	33.3	33.7	34.2	34.7
58	28.0	28.5	29.0	29.5	30.0	30.5	30.9	31.4	31.9	32.4	32.9	33.4	33.8	34.3	34.8	35.3
59	28.5	29.0	29 5	30.0	30.5	31.0	31.5	32.0	32.5	32.9	33.4	33.9	34.4	34.9	35.4	35.9
60	29.0	29.5	30.0	30.5	31.0	31.5	32.0	32.5	33.0	33.5	34.0	34.5	35.0	35.5	36.0	36.5

TABLE 14.

Conversion Tables for Nautical and Statute Miles.

Nautical miles into statute miles.

1 nautical mile or knot=6,080.20 feet.
1 statute mile =5,280 feet.

Nautical miles.	Statute miles.	Nautical miles.	Statute miles.
1	1.15	51	58.729
2	2.30	52	59.881
3	3.45	53	61.032
4	4.61	54	62.184
5	5.76	55	63.335
6	6.91	56	64.487
7	8.06	57	65.639
8	9.21	58	66.790
9	10.36	59	67.942
10	11.52	60	69.093
11	12.667	61	70.245
12	13.819	62	71.396
13	14.970	63	72.548
14	16.122	64	73.699
15	17.273	65	74.851
16	18.425	66	76.003
17	19.576	67	77.154
18	20.728	68	78.306
19	21.880	69	79.457
20	23.031	70	80.609
21	24.183	71	81.760
22	25.334	72	82.912
23	26.486	73	84.063
24	27.637	74	85.215
25	28.789	75	86.366
26	29.940	76	87.518
27	31.092	77	88.670
28	32.243	78	89.821
29	33.395	79	90.973
30	34.547	80	92.124
31	35.698	81	93.276
32	36.850	82	94.427
33	38.001	83	95.579
34	39.153	84	96.730
35	40.304	85	97.882
36	41.456	86	99.034
37	42.607	87	100.185
38	43.759	88	101.337
39	44.911	89	102.488
40	46.062	90	103.640
41	47.214	91	104.791
42	48.365	92	105.942
43	49.517	93	107.094
44	50.668	94	108.246
45	51.820	95	109.397
46	52.971	96	110.549
47	54.123	97	111.701
48	55.275	98	112.852
49	56.426	99	114.004
50	57.578	100	115.155

Statute miles into nautical miles.

1 statute mile =5,280 feet
1 nautical mile or knot=6,080.20 feet.

Statute miles.	Nautical miles.	Statute miles.	Nautical miles.
1	0.87	51	44.288
2	1.74	52	45.156
3	2.61	53	46.025
4	3.47	54	46.893
5	4.34	55	47.762
6	5.21	56	48.630
7	6.08	57	49.498
8	6.95	58	50.367
9	7.82	59	51.235
10	8.68	60	52.104
11	9.552	61	52.972
12	10.421	62	53.840
13	11.289	63	54.709
14	12.158	64	55.577
15	13.026	65	56.445
16	13.894	66	57.314
17	14.763	67	58.182
18	15.631	68	59.051
19	16.499	69	59.919
20	17.368	70	60.787
21	18.236	71	61.656
22	19.105	72	62.524
23	19.973	73	63.393
24	20.841	74	64.261
25	21.710	75	65.129
26	22.578	76	65.998
27	23.447	77	66.866
28	24.315	78	67.735
29	25.183	79	68.603
30	26.052	80	69.471
31	26.920	81	70.340
32	27.789	82	71.208
33	28.657	83	72.077
34	29.525	84	72.945
35	30.394	85	73.813
36	31.262	86	74.682
37	32.131	87	75.550
38	32.999	88	76.419
39	33.867	89	77.287
40	34.736	90	78.155
41	35.604	91	79.024
42	36.473	92	79.892
43	37.341	93	80.760
44	38.209	94	81.629
45	39.078	95	82.497
46	39.946	96	83.366
47	40.814	97	84.234
48	41.683	98	85.102
49	42.551	99	85.971
50	43.420	100	86.839

TABLE 15.

Conversion Tables for Metric and English Linear Measure.

Metric to English.

Meters.	Feet.	Yards.	Statute miles.	Nautical miles.
1	3.280 833 3	1.093 611 1	0.000 621 370	0.000 539 593
2	6.561 666 7	2.187 222 2	.001 242 740	.001 079 185
3	9.842 500 0	3.280 833 3	.001 864 110	.001 618 778
4	13.123 333 3	4.374 444 4	.002 485 480	.002 158 370
5	16.404 166 7	5.468 055 6	.003 106 850	.002 697 963
6	19.685 000 0	6.561 666 7	.003 728 220	.003 237 556
7	22.965 833 3	7.655 277 8	.004 349 590	.003 777 148
8	26.246 666 7	8.748 888 9	.004 970 960	.004 316 741
9	29.527 500 0	9.842 500 0	.005 592 330	.004 856 333

English to metric.

No.	Feet to meters.	Yards to meters.	Statute miles to meters.	Nautical miles to meters.
1	0.304 800 6	0.914 401 8	1,609.35	1,853.25
2	0.609 601 2	1.828 803 7	3,218.69	3,706.50
3	0.914 401 8	2.743 205 5	4,828.04	5,559.75
4	1.219 202 4	3.657 607 3	6,437.39	7,413.00
5	1.524 003 0	4.572 009 1	8,046.74	9,266.25
6	1.828 803 7	5.486 411 0	9,656.08	11,119.50
7	2.133 604 3	6.400 812 8	11,265.43	12,972.75
8	2.438 404 9	7.315 214 6	12,874.78	14,826.00
9	2.743 205 5	8.229 616 5	14,484.13	16,679.25

Millimeters.	Inches
1	0.03937
2	.07874
3	.11811
4	.15748
5	.19685
6	.23622
7	.27559
8	.31496
9	.35433

Statute miles.	Kilometers
1	1.60935
2	3.21869
3	4.82804
4	6.43739
5	8.04674
6	9.65608
7	11.26543
8	12.87478
9	14.48413

Inches.	Centimeters.	Meters
1	2.54001	0.02540
2	5.08002	.05080
3	7.62003	.07620
4	10.16004	.10160
5	12.70005	.12700
6	15.24006	.15240
7	17.78007	.17780
8	20.32008	.20320
9	22.86009	.22860

TABLE 16.

Conversion Tables for Thermometer Scales.

[F°=Fahrenheit temperature; C°=Centigrade temperature; R°=Réaumur temperature.]

Equivalent temperatures—Fahr., Cent., Réau

$R° = \frac{4}{5} C° = \frac{4}{9} (F° - 32°)$.
$C° = \frac{5}{4} R° = \frac{5}{9} (F° - 32°)$.

F°.	C°.	R°.	F°.	C°.	R°.
1	−17.2	−13.8	51	+10.6	+ 8.4
2	16.7	13.3	52	11.1	8.9
3	16.1	12.9	53	11.7	9.3
4	15.6	12.4	54	12.2	9.8
5	15.0	12.0	55	12.8	10.2
6	14.4	11.6	56	13.3	10.7
7	13.9	11.1	57	13.9	11.1
8	13.3	10.7	58	14.4	11.6
9	12.8	10.2	59	15.0	12.0
10	12.2	9.8	60	15.6	12.4
11	11.7	9.3	61	16.1	12.9
12	11.1	8.9	62	16.7	13.3
13	10.6	8.4	63	17.2	13.8
14	10.0	8.0	64	17.8	14.2
15	9.4	7.6	65	18.3	14.7
16	8.9	7.1	66	18.9	15.1
17	8.3	6.7	67	19.4	15.6
18	7.8	6.2	68	20.0	16.0
19	7.2	5.8	69	20.6	16.4
20	6.7	5.3	70	21.1	16.9
21	6.1	4.9	71	21.7	17.3
22	5.6	4.4	72	22.2	17.8
23	5.0	4.0	73	22.8	18.2
24	4.4	3.6	74	23.3	18.7
25	3.9	3.1	75	23.9	19.1
26	3.3	2.7	76	24.4	19.6
27	2.8	2.2	77	25.0	20.0
28	2.2	1.8	78	25.6	20.4
29	1.7	1.3	79	26.1	20.9
30	1.1	0.9	80	26.7	21.3
31	− 0.6	− 0.4	81	27.2	21.8
32	0.0	0.0	82	27.8	22.2
33	+ 0.6	+ 0.4	83	28.3	22.7
34	1.1	0.9	84	28.9	23.1
35	1.7	1.3	85	29.4	23.6
36	2.2	1.8	86	30.0	24.0
37	2.8	2.2	87	30.6	24.4
38	3.3	2.7	88	31.1	24.9
39	3.9	3.1	89	31.7	25.3
40	4.4	3.6	90	32.2	25.8
41	5.0	4.0	91	32.8	26.2
42	5.6	4.4	92	33.3	26.7
43	6.1	4.9	93	33.9	27.1
44	6.7	5.3	94	34.4	27.6
45	7.2	5.8	95	35.0	28.0
46	7.8	6.2	96	35.6	28.4
47	8.3	6.7	97	36.1	28.9
48	8.9	7.1	98	36.7	29.3
49	9.4	7.6	99	37.2	29.8
50	+10.0	+ 8.0	100	+37.8	+30.2

Equivalent temperatures—Centigrade and Fahrenheit.

$F° = \frac{9}{5} C° + 32°$.

C°.	F°.	C°.	F°.	C°.	F°.	C°.	F°.	C°.	F°.
−10	14.0	0	32.0	10	50.0	20	68.0	30	86.0
− 9	15.8	1	33.8	11	51.8	21	69.8	31	87.8
− 8	17.6	2	35.6	12	53.6	22	71.6	32	89.6
− 7	19.4	3	37.4	13	55.4	23	73.4	33	91.4
− 6	21.2	4	39.2	14	57.2	24	75.2	34	93.2
− 5	23.0	5	41.0	15	59.0	25	77.0	35	95.0
− 4	24.8	6	42.8	16	60.8	26	78.8	36	96.8
− 3	26.6	7	44.6	17	62.6	27	80.6	37	98.6
− 2	28.4	8	46.4	18	64.4	28	82.4	38	100.4
− 1	30.2	9	48.2	19	66.2	29	84.2	39	102.2

Equivalent temperatures—Réaumur and Fahrenheit.

$F° = \frac{9}{4} R° + 32°$.

R°.	F°.	R°.	F°.	R°.	F°.	R°.	F°.
−10	9.5	0	32.0	10	54.5	20	77.0
− 9	11.8	1	34.2	11	56.8	21	79.2
− 8	14.0	2	36.5	12	59.0	22	81.5
− 7	16.2	3	38.8	13	61.2	23	83.8
− 6	18.5	4	41.0	14	63.5	24	86.0
− 5	20.8	5	43.2	15	65.8	25	88.2
− 4	23.0	6	45.5	16	68.0	26	90.5
− 3	25.2	7	47.8	17	70.2	27	92.8
− 2	27.5	8	50.0	18	72.5	28	95.0
− 1	29.8	9	52.2	19	74.8	29	97.2

TABLE 17.

Reduction of Local Civil Time to Standard Meridian Time, and the reverse.

[If local meridian is east of standard meridian, subtract from local civil time, or add to standard meridian time. If local meridian is west of standard meridian, add to local civil time, or subtract from standard meridian time.]

Difference of longitude between local meridian and standard meridian.	Reduction to be applied to local civil time	Difference of longitude between local meridian and standard meridian.	Reduction to be applied to local civil time.
° ′ ° ′	*Minutes.*	° ′ ° ′	*Minutes.*
0 00 to 0 07	0	7 23 to 7 37	30
0 08 to 0 22	1	7 38 to 7 52	31
0 23 to 0 37	2	7 53 to 8 07	32
0 38 to 0 52	3	8 08 to 8 22	33
0 53 to 1 07	4	8 23 to 8 37	34
1 08 to 1 22	5	8 38 to 8 52	35
1 23 to 1 37	6	8 53 to 9 07	36
1 38 to 1 52	7	9 08 to 9 22	37
1 53 to 2 07	8	9 23 to 9 37	38
2 08 to 2 22	9	9 38 to 9 52	39
2 23 to 2 37	10	9 53 to 10 07	40
2 38 to 2 52	11	10 08 to 10 22	41
2 53 to 3 07	12	10 23 to 10 37	42
3 08 to 3 22	13	10 38 to 10 52	43
3 23 to 3 37	14	10 53 to 11 07	44
3 38 to 3 52	15	11 08 to 11 22	45
3 53 to 4 07	16	11 23 to 11 37	46
4 08 to 4 22	17	11 38 to 11 52	47
4 23 to 4 37	18	11 53 to 12 07	48
4 38 to 4 52	19	12 08 to 12 22	49
4 53 to 5 07	20	12 23 to 12 37	50
5 08 to 5 22	21	12 38 to 12 52	51
5 23 to 5 37	22	12 53 to 13 07	52
5 38 to 5 52	23	13 08 to 13 22	53
5 53 to 6 07	24	13 23 to 13 37	54
6 08 to 6 22	25	13 38 to 13 52	55
6 23 to 6 37	26	13 53 to 14 07	56
6 38 to 6 52	27	14 08 to 14 22	57
6 53 to 7 07	28	14 23 to 14 37	58
7 08 to 7 22	29	14 38 to 14 52	59

TABLE 18, 19, 20.

TABLE 18

Dip of the Sea Horizon.

Height of the Eye.	Dip of the Horizon.
Feet.	′ ″
1	0 59
2	1 23
3	1 42
4	1 58
5	2 11
6	2 24
7	2 36
8	2 46
9	2 56
10	3 06
11	3 15
12	3 24
13	3 32
14	3 40
15	3 48
16	3 55
17	4 02
18	4 09
19	4 16
20	4 23
21	4 29
22	4 36
23	4 42
24	4 48
25	4 54
26	5 00
27	5 06
28	5 11
29	5 17
30	5 22
31	5 27
32	5 33
33	5 38
34	5 43
35	5 48
36	5 53
37	5 58
38	6 02
39	6 07
40	6 12
45	6 36
50	6 56
55	7 16
60	7 35
65	7 54
70	8 12
75	8 29
80	8 46
85	9 02
90	9 18
95	9 33
100	9 48

Height of Eye	Dip of Horizon
	′
50	6.9
100	9.8
150	12.1
200	13.9
250	15.5
300	17.0
400	19.6
500	21.9
600	24.0
700	25.9
800	27.7
900	29.4
1000	31.0
1100	32.5
1200	34.0
1300	35.3
1400	36.7
1500	38.0
1600	39.2
1700	40.4
1800	41.6
1900	42.7
2000	43.8
2100	44.9
2200	46.0
2300	47.0
2400	48.0
2500	49.0
2600	50.0
2700	50.9

TABLE 19.

Dip of the Sea at different Distances from the Observer.

Dist. of Land in Sea Miles.	Height of the Eye above the Sea in Feet.							
	5	10	15	20	25	30	35	40
	′	′	′	′	′	′	′	′
¼	11	23	34	45	57	68	79	91
½	6	12	17	23	28	34	40	45
¾	4	8	12	15	19	23	27	30
1	3	6	9	12	15	17	20	23
1¼	3	5	7	10	12	14	16	19
1½	3	4	6	8	10	12	14	16
2	2	4	5	7	8	9	11	12
2½	2	3	4	6	7	8	9	10
3	2	3	4	5	6	7	8	9
3½	2	3	4	5	6	6	7	8
4	2	3	4	5	5	6	7	7
5	2	3	4	4	5	6	6	7
6	2	3	4	4	5	5	6	6

NOTE TO TABLE 19.—The numbers of this Table below the black lines are the same as are given in Table 18, the visible horizon corresponding to those heights not being so far distant as the land.

TABLE 20.

The Sun's Parallax in Altitude.

Altitude.	Parallax.
°	″
0	9
10	9
20	8
30	8
40	7
50	6
55	5
60	4
65	4
70	3
75	2
80	2
85	1
90	0

TABLE 21.

Parallax in Altitude of a Planet.

Altitude.	1″	2″	3″	4″	5″	6″	7″	8″	9″	10″	11″	12″	13″	14″	15″	16″	17″	18″	19″	20″	21″	22″	23″	24″	25″	26″	27″	28″	30″	35″	Altitude.
	Horizontal parallax of planet.																														
°																															°
0	1	2	3	4	5	6	7	8	9	10	11	12	13	14	15	16	17	18	19	20	21	22	23	24	25	26	27	28	30	35	0
10	1	2	3	4	5	6	7	8	9	10	11	12	13	14	15	16	17	18	19	20	21	22	23	24	25	26	27	28	30	35	10
20	1	2	3	4	5	6	7	8	8	9	10	11	12	13	14	15	16	17	18	19	20	21	22	23	23	24	25	26	28	33	20
30	1	2	3	3	4	5	6	7	8	9	10	10	11	12	13	14	15	16	16	17	18	19	20	21	22	23	23	24	26	30	30
35	1	2	2	3	4	5	6	7	7	8	9	10	11	11	12	13	14	15	16	16	17	18	19	20	20	21	22	23	25	29	35
40	1	2	2	3	4	5	5	6	7	8	8	9	10	11	11	12	13	14	15	15	16	17	18	18	19	20	21	21	23	27	40
43	1	1	2	3	4	4	5	6	7	7	8	9	10	10	11	12	12	13	14	15	15	16	17	18	18	19	20	20	22	26	43
46	1	1	2	3	3	4	5	6	6	7	8	8	9	10	10	11	12	13	13	14	15	15	16	17	17	18	19	19	21	24	46
49	1	1	2	3	3	4	5	5	6	7	7	8	9	9	10	10	11	12	12	13	14	14	15	16	16	17	18	18	20	23	49
52	1	1	2	2	3	4	4	5	6	6	7	7	8	9	9	10	10	11	12	12	13	14	14	15	15	16	17	17	18	22	52
55	1	1	2	2	3	3	4	5	5	6	6	7	7	8	9	9	10	10	11	11	12	13	13	14	14	15	15	16	17	20	55
58	1	1	2	2	3	3	4	4	5	5	6	6	7	7	8	8	9	10	10	11	11	12	12	13	13	14	14	15	16	19	58
61	0	1	1	2	2	3	3	4	4	5	5	6	6	7	7	8	8	9	9	10	10	11	11	12	12	13	13	14	15	17	61
64	0	1	1	2	2	3	3	4	4	4	5	5	6	6	7	7	7	8	8	9	9	10	10	11	11	11	12	12	13	15	64
67	0	1	1	2	2	2	3	3	4	4	4	5	5	5	6	6	7	7	7	8	8	9	9	9	10	10	11	11	12	14	67
70	0	1	1	1	2	2	2	3	3	3	4	4	4	5	5	5	6	6	6	7	7	8	8	8	9	9	9	10	10	12	70
72	0	1	1	1	2	2	2	2	3	3	3	4	4	4	5	5	5	6	6	6	6	7	7	7	8	8	8	9	9	11	72
74	0	1	1	1	1	2	2	2	2	3	3	3	4	4	4	4	5	5	5	6	6	6	6	7	7	7	7	8	8	10	74
76	0	0	1	1	1	1	2	2	2	2	3	3	3	3	4	4	4	4	5	5	5	5	6	6	6	6	7	7	7	8	76
78	0	0	1	1	1	1	1	2	2	2	2	2	3	3	3	3	4	4	4	4	4	5	5	5	5	5	6	6	6	7	78
80	0	0	1	1	1	1	1	1	2	2	2	2	2	2	3	3	3	3	3	3	4	4	4	4	4	5	5	5	5	6	80
82	0	0	0	1	1	1	1	1	1	1	2	2	2	2	2	2	2	3	3	3	3	3	3	3	3	4	4	4	4	5	82
84	0	0	0	0	1	1	1	1	1	1	1	1	1	1	2	2	2	2	2	2	2	2	2	3	3	3	3	3	3	4	84
86	0	0	0	0	0	0	0	1	1	1	1	1	1	1	1	1	1	1	1	1	1	2	2	2	2	2	2	2	2	2	86
88	0	0	0	0	0	0	0	0	0	0	0	0	0	0	1	1	1	1	1	1	1	1	1	1	1	1	1	1	1	1	88
90	0	0	0	0	0	0	0	0	0	0	0	0	0	0	0	0	0	0	0	0	0	0	0	0	0	0	0	0	0	0	90

TABLE 22.

Mean Refraction.

[Barometer, 30 inches. Fahrenheit's Thermometer, 50°.]

Apparent Altitude.	Mean Refraction.	Apparent Altitude.	Mean Refraction.	Apparent Altitude.	Mean Refraction.	Apparent Altitude.	Mean Refraction.	Apparent Altitude.	Mean Refraction.
° ′	′ ″	° ′	′ ″	° ′	′ ″	° ′	′ ″	° ′	′ ″
		9 30	5 35.1	15 00	3 34.1	25 00	2 4.4	42 00	1 04.7
0 00	36 29.4	35	5 32.4	10	3 31.7	10	2 3.4	20	1 03.9
1 00	24 53.6	40	5 29.6	20	3 29.4	20	2 2.5	40	1 03.2
2 00	18 25.5	45	5 27.0	30	3 27.1	30	2 1.6	43 00	1 02.4
3 00	14 25.1	50	5 24.3	40	3 24.8	40	2 0.7	20	1 01.7
4 00	11 44.4	55	5 21.7	50	3 22.6	50	1 59.8	40	1 01.0
5 00	9 52.0	10 00	5 19.2	16 00	3 20.5	26 00	1 58.9	44 00	1 00.3
05	9 44.0	05	5 16.7	10	3 18.4	10	1 58.1	20	0 59.6
10	9 36.2	10	5 14.2	20	3 16.3	20	1 57.2	40	0 58.9
15	9 28.6	15	5 11.7	30	3 14.2	30	1 56.4	45 00	0 58.2
20	9 21.2	20	5 9.3	40	3 12.2	40	1 55.5	20	0 57.6
25	9 14.0	25	5 6.9	50	3 10.3	50	1 54.7	40	0 56.9
5 30	9 7.0	10 30	5 4.6	17 00	3 8.3	27 00	1 53.9	46 00	0 56.2
35	9 0.1	35	5 2.3	10	3 6.4	10	1 53.1	20	0 55.6
40	8 53.4	40	5 0.0	20	3 4.6	20	1 52.3	40	0 55.0
45	8 46.8	45	4 57.8	30	3 2.8	30	1 51.5	47 00	0 54.3
50	8 40.4	50	4 55.6	40	3 1.0	40	1 50.7	20	0 53.7
55	8 34.2	55	4 53.4	50	2 59.2	50	1 50.0	40	0 53.1
6 00	8 28.0	11 00	4 51.2	18 00	2 57.5	28 00	1 49.2	48 00	0 52.5
05	8 22.1	05	4 49.1	10	2 55.8	20	1 47.7	49 00	0 50.6
10	8 16.2	10	4 47.0	20	2 54.1	40	1 46.2	50 00	0 48.9
15	8 10.5	15	4 44.9	30	2 52.4	29 00	1 44.8	51 00	0 47.2
20	8 4.8	20	4 42.9	40	2 50.8	20	1 43.4	52 00	0 45.5
25	7 59.3	25	4 40.9	50	2 49.2	40	1 42.0	53 00	0 43.9
6 30	7 53.9	11 30	4 38.9	19 00	2 47.7	30 00	1 40.6	54 00	0 42.3
35	7 48.7	35	4 36.9	10	2 46.1	20	1 39.3	55 00	0 40.8
40	7 43.5	40	4 35.0	20	2 44.6	40	1 38.0	56 00	0 39.3
45	7 38.4	45	4 33.1	30	2 43.1	31 00	1 36.7	57 00	0 37.8
50	7 33.5	50	4 31.2	40	2 41.6	20	1 35.5	58 00	0 36.4
55	7 28.6	55	4 29.4	50	2 40.2	40	1 34.2	59 00	0 35.0
7 00	7 23.8	12 00	4 27.5	20 00	2 38.8	32 00	1 33.0	60 00	0 33.6
05	7 19.2	05	4 25.7	10	2 37.4	20	1 31.8	61 00	0 32.3
10	7 14.6	10	4 23.9	20	2 36.0	40	1 30.7	62 00	0 31.0
15	7 10.1	15	4 22.2	30	2 34.6	33 00	1 29.5	63 00	0 29.7
20	7 5.7	20	4 20.4	40	2 33.3	20	1 28.4	64 00	0 28.4
25	7 1.4	25	4 18.7	50	2 32.0	40	1 27.3	65 00	0 27.2
7 30	6 57.1	12 30	4 17.0	21 00	2 30.7	34 00	1 26.2	66 00	0 25.9
35	6 53.0	35	4 15.3	10	2 29.4	20	1 25.1	67 00	0 24.7
40	6 48.9	40	4 13.6	20	2 28.1	40	1 24.1	68 00	0 23.6
45	6 44.9	45	4 12.0	30	2 26.9	35 00	1 23.1	69 00	0 22.4
50	6 41.0	50	4 10.4	40	2 25.7	20	1 22.0	70 00	0 21.2
55	6 37.1	55	4 8.8	50	2 24.5	40	1 21.0	71 00	0 20.1
8 00	6 33.3	13 00	4 7.2	22 00	2 23.3	36 00	1 20.1	72 00	0 18.9
05	6 29.6	05	4 5.6	10	2 22.1	20	1 19.1	73 00	0 17.8
10	6 25.9	10	4 4.1	20	2 20.9	40	1 18.2	74 00	0 16.7
15	6 22.3	15	4 2.6	30	2 19.8	37 00	1 17.2	75 00	0 15.6
20	6 18.8	20	4 1.0	40	2 18.7	20	1 16.3	76 00	0 14.5
25	6 15.3	25	3 59.6	50	2 17.5	40	1 15.4	77 00	0 13.5
8 30	6 11.9	13 30	3 58.1	23 00	2 16.4	38 00	1 14.5	78 00	0 12.4
35	6 8.5	35	3 56.6	10	2 15.4	20	1 13.6	79 00	0 11.3
40	6 5.2	40	3 55.2	20	2 14.3	40	1 12.7	80 00	0 10.3
45	6 2.0	45	3 53.7	30	2 13.3	39 00	1 11.9	81 00	0 9.2
50	5 58.8	50	3 52.3	40	2 12.2	20	1 11.0	82 00	0 8.2
55	5 55.7	55	3 50.9	50	2 11.2	40	1 10.2	83 00	0 7.2
9 00	5 52.6	14 00	3 49.5	24 00	2 10.2	40 00	1 9.4	84 00	0 6.1
05	5 49.6	10	3 46.8	10	2 9.2	20	1 8.6	85 00	0 5.1
10	5 46.6	20	3 44.2	20	2 8.2	40	1 7.8	86 00	0 4.1
15	5 43.6	30	3 41.6	30	2 7.2	41 00	1 7.0	87 00	0 3.1
20	5 40.7	40	3 39.0	40	2 6.2	20	1 6.2	88 00	0 2.0
25	5 37.9	50	3 36.5	50	2 5.3	40	1 5.4	89 00	0 1.0
9 30	5 35.1	15 00	3 34.1	25 00	2 4.4	42 00	1 4.7	90 00	0 0.0

TABLE 23.

Correction of the Sun's Apparent Altitude for Refraction and Parallax.

[Barometer, 30 inches. Fahrenheit's Thermometer, 50°.]

Apparent Altitude.	Mean Refraction and Parallax ⊙.	Apparent Altitude.	Mean Refraction and Parallax ⊙.	Apparent Altitude.	Mean Refraction and Parallax ⊙.	Apparent Altitude.	Mean Refraction and Parallax ⊙.	Apparent Altitude.	Mean Refraction and Parallax ⊙.
° ′	′ ″	° ′	′ ″	° ′	′ ″	° ′	′ ″	° ′	′ ″
		9 30	5 26	15 00	3 25	25 00	1 56	42 00	0 58
0 00	36 20	35	5 23	10	3 24	10	1 55	20	0 57
1 00	24 45	40	5 21	20	3 21	20	1 55	40	0 56
2 00	18 17	45	5 18	30	3 19	30	1 54	43 00	0 55
3 00	14 16	50	5 15	40	3 17	40	1 53	29	0 55
4 00	11 35	55	5 13	50	3 15	50	1 52	40	0 54
5 00	9 43	10 00	5 10	16 00	3 13	26 00	1 51	44 00	0 53
05	9 35	05	5 8	10	3 10	10	1 50	20	0 53
10	9 27	10	5 5	20	3 8	20	1 49	40	0 52
15	9 20	15	5 3	30	3 6	30	1 48	45 00	0 52
20	9 12	20	5 0	40	3 4	40	1 48	20	0 52
25	9 5	25	4 58	50	3 2	50	1 47	40	0 51
5 30	8 58	10 30	4 56	17 00	3 0	27 00	1 46	46 00	0 50
35	8 51	35	4 53	10	2 58	10	1 45	20	0 50
40	8 44	40	4 51	20	2 57	20	1 44	40	0 49
45	8 38	45	4 49	30	2 55	30	1 44	47 00	0 48
50	8 31	50	4 47	40	2 53	40	1 43	20	0 48
55	8 25	55	4 44	50	2 51	50	1 42	40	0 47
6 00	8 19	11 00	4 42	18 00	2 50	28 00	1 41	48 00	0 47
05	8 13	05	4 40	10	2 48	20	1 40	49 00	0 45
10	8 7	10	4 38	20	2 46	40	1 38	50 00	0 43
15	8 2	15	4 36	30	2 44	29 00	1 37	51 00	0 41
20	7 56	20	4 34	40	2 43	20	1 35	52 00	0 40
25	7 50	25	4 32	50	2 41	40	1 34	53 00	0 39
6 30	7 45	11 30	4 30	19 00	2 40	30 00	1 33	54 00	0 37
35	7 40	35	4 28	10	2 38	20	1 31	55 00	0 36
40	7 35	40	4 26	20	2 37	40	1 30	56 00	0 34
45	7 29	45	4 24	30	2 35	31 00	1 29	57 00	0 33
50	7 25	50	4 22	40	2 34	20	1 28	58 00	0 32
55	7 20	55	4 20	50	2 32	40	1 26	59 00	0 31
7 00	7 15	12 00	4 19	20 00	2 31	32 00	1 25	60 00	0 30
05	7 10	05	4 17	10	2 29	20	1 24	61 00	0 28
10	7 6	10	4 15	20	2 28	40	1 23	62 00	0 27
15	7 1	15	4 13	30	2 27	33 00	1 22	63 00	0 26
20	6 57	20	4 11	40	2 25	20	1 20	64 00	0 24
25	6 52	25	4 10	50	2 24	40	1 19	65 00	0 23
7 30	6 48	12 30	4 8	21 00	2 23	34 00	1 18	66 00	0 22
35	6 44	35	4 6	10	2 21	20	1 17	67 00	0 21
40	6 40	40	4 5	20	2 20	40	1 16	68 00	0 21
45	6 36	45	4 3	30	2 19	35 00	1 15	69 00	0 19
50	6 32	50	4 1	40	2 18	20	1 15	70 00	0 18
55	6 28	55	4 0	50	2 17	40	1 14	71 00	0 17
8 00	6 24	13 00	3 58	22 00	2 15	36 00	1 13	72 00	0 16
05	6 21	05	3 57	10	2 14	20	1 12	73 00	0 16
10	6 17	10	3 55	20	2 13	40	1 11	74 00	0 15
15	6 13	15	3 54	30	2 12	37 00	1 10	75 00	0 14
20	6 10	20	3 52	40	2 11	20	1 9	76 00	0 13
25	6 6	25	3 51	50	2 10	40	1 8	77 00	0 12
8 30	6 3	13 30	3 49	23 00	2 8	38 00	1 8	78 00	0 10
35	6 0	35	3 48	10	2 7	20	1 7	79 00	0 9
40	5 56	40	3 46	20	2 6	40	1 6	80 00	0 8
45	5 53	45	3 45	30	2 5	39 00	1 5	81 00	0 7
50	5 50	50	3 43	40	2 4	20	1 4	82 00	0 6
55	5 47	55	3 42	50	2 3	40	1 3	83 00	0 6
9 00	5 44	14 00	3 41	24 00	2 2	40 00	1 2	84 00	0 5
05	5 41	10	3 38	10	2 1	20	1 2	85 00	0 4
10	5 38	20	3 35	20	2 0	40	1 1	86 00	0 3
15	5 35	30	3 33	30	1 59	41 00	1 0	87 00	0 2
20	5 32	40	3 30	40	1 58	20	0 59	88 00	0 2
25	5 29	50	3 28	50	1 57	40	0 58	89 00	0 1
9 30	5 26	15 00	3 25	25 00	1 56	42 00	0 58	90 00	0 0

TABLE 24.

Correction of the Mean Refraction for the Height of the Barometer.

Barom. Subtract.	Mean refraction. 0′ 0″	0′ 30″	1′ 0″	1′ 30″	2′ 0″	2′ 30″	3′ 0″	3′ 30″	4′ 0″	4′ 30″	5′ 0″	5′ 30″	6′ 0″	6′ 30″	7′ 0″	7′ 30″	8′ 0″	8′ 30″	9′ 0″	9′ 30″	10′ 0″	Barom. Add.
	″	″	″	″	″	″	″	″	″	″	″	″	″	″	″	″	″	″	″	″	″	
27.50	0	2	5	7	10	12	15	17	20	23	25	28	30	33	35	38	40	43	45	48	51	
27.55	0	2	5	7	10	12	15	17	20	22	25	27	30	32	35	37	40	42	45	47	50	
27.60	0	2	5	7	10	12	14	17	19	22	24	27	29	31	34	36	39	41	44	46	49	
27.65	0	2	5	7	9	12	14	16	19	21	24	26	28	31	33	36	38	40	43	45	48	
27.70	0	2	5	7	9	11	14	16	18	21	23	25	28	30	32	35	37	39	42	44	47	
27.75	0	2	4	7	9	11	13	16	18	20	23	25	27	29	32	34	36	39	41	43	46	
27.80	0	2	4	7	9	11	13	15	18	20	22	24	27	29	31	33	35	38	40	42	45	
27.85	0	2	4	6	9	11	13	15	17	19	22	24	26	28	30	32	35	37	39	41	44	
27.90	0	2	4	6	8	10	13	15	17	19	21	23	25	27	30	32	34	36	38	40	43	
27.95	0	2	4	6	8	10	12	14	16	18	21	23	25	27	29	31	33	35	37	39	42	
28.00	0	2	4	6	8	10	12	14	16	18	20	22	24	26	28	30	32	34	36	38	41	
28.05	0	2	4	6	8	10	12	14	16	18	20	22	24	25	27	29	31	33	35	37	39	
28.10	0	2	4	6	8	9	11	13	15	17	19	21	23	25	27	29	31	33	34	36	38	
28.15	0	2	4	6	7	9	11	13	15	17	19	20	22	24	26	28	30	32	34	36	37	
28.20	0	2	4	5	7	9	11	13	14	16	18	20	22	24	25	27	29	31	33	35	36	
28.25	0	2	3	5	7	9	10	12	14	16	18	19	21	23	25	26	28	30	32	34	35	
28.30	0	2	3	5	7	8	10	12	14	15	17	19	21	22	24	26	27	29	31	33	34	
28.35	0	2	3	5	7	8	10	12	13	15	17	18	20	22	23	25	27	28	30	32	33	
28.40	0	2	3	5	6	8	10	11	13	14	16	18	19	21	23	24	26	27	29	31	32	
28.45	0	2	3	5	6	8	9	11	12	14	16	17	19	20	22	23	25	27	28	30	31	
28.50	0	1	3	4	6	7	9	10	12	14	15	17	18	20	21	23	24	26	27	29	30	31.50
28.55	0	1	3	4	6	7	9	10	12	13	15	16	17	19	20	22	23	25	26	28	29	31.45
28.60	0	1	3	4	6	7	8	10	11	13	14	15	17	18	20	21	23	24	25	27	28	31.40
28.65	0	1	3	4	5	7	8	9	11	12	14	15	16	18	19	20	22	23	25	26	27	31.35
28.70	0	1	3	4	5	6	8	9	10	12	13	14	16	17	18	20	21	22	24	25	26	31.30
28.75	0	1	2	4	5	6	7	9	10	11	13	14	15	16	18	19	20	21	23	24	25	31.25
28.80	0	1	2	4	5	6	7	8	10	11	12	13	14	16	17	18	19	21	22	23	24	31.20
28.85	0	1	2	3	5	6	7	8	9	10	12	13	14	15	16	17	19	20	21	22	23	31.15
28.90	0	1	2	3	4	5	7	8	9	10	11	12	13	14	16	17	18	19	20	21	22	31.10
28.95	0	1	2	3	4	5	6	7	8	9	11	12	13	14	15	16	17	18	19	20	21	31.05
29.00	0	1	2	3	4	5	6	7	8	9	10	11	12	13	14	15	16	17	18	19	20	31.00
29.05	0	1	2	3	4	5	6	7	8	9	10	11	11	12	13	14	15	16	17	18	19	30.95
29.10	0	1	2	3	4	4	5	6	7	8	9	10	11	12	13	14	15	15	16	17	18	30.90
29.15	0	1	2	3	3	4	5	6	7	8	9	9	10	11	12	13	14	15	15	16	17	30.85
29.20	0	1	2	2	3	4	5	6	6	7	8	9	10	10	11	12	13	14	15	15	16	30.80
29.25	0	1	1	2	3	4	4	5	6	7	8	8	9	10	11	11	12	13	14	14	15	30.75
29.30	0	1	1	2	3	3	4	5	6	6	7	8	8	9	10	11	11	12	13	13	14	30.70
29.35	0	1	1	2	3	3	4	5	5	6	7	7	8	9	9	10	10	11	12	13	13	30.65
29.40	0	1	1	2	2	3	4	4	5	5	6	7	7	8	8	9	10	10	11	12	12	30.60
29.45	0	1	1	2	2	3	3	4	4	5	6	6	7	7	8	8	9	9	10	11	11	30.55
29.50	0	0	1	1	2	2	3	3	4	5	5	6	6	7	7	8	8	9	9	10	10	30.50
29.55	0	0	1	1	2	2	3	3	4	4	5	5	5	6	6	7	7	8	8	9	9	30.45
29.60	0	0	1	1	2	2	2	3	3	4	4	4	5	5	6	6	6	7	7	8	8	30.40
29.65	0	0	1	1	1	2	2	2	3	3	4	4	4	5	5	5	6	6	6	7	7	30.35
29.70	0	0	1	1	1	1	2	2	2	3	3	3	4	4	4	5	5	5	5	6	6	30.30
29.75	0	0	0	1	1	1	1	2	2	2	3	3	3	3	4	4	4	4	5	5	5	30.25
29.80	0	0	0	1	1	1	1	1	2	2	2	2	2	3	3	3	3	3	4	4	4	30.20
29.85	0	0	0	0	1	1	1	1	1	1	2	2	2	2	2	2	2	3	3	3	3	30.15
29.90	0	0	0	0	0	0	1	1	1	1	1	1	1	1	1	2	2	2	2	2	2	30.10
29.95	0	0	0	0	0	0	0	0	0	0	1	1	1	1	1	1	1	1	1	1	1	30.05
30.00	0	0	0	0	0	0	0	0	0	0	0	0	0	0	0	0	0	0	0	0	0	30.00
Subtract.	0″	30″	0″	30″	0″	30″	0″	30″	0″	30″	0″	30″	0″	30″	0″	30″	0″	30″	0″	30″	0″	Add.
Barom.	0′		1′		2′		3′		4′		5′		6′		7′		8′		9′		10′	Barom.
	Mean refraction.																					

TABLE 25.

Correction of the Mean Refraction for the Height of the Thermometer.

Ther. Add.	Mean refraction. 0'		1'		2'		3'		4'		5'		6'		7'		8'		9'		10'	Ther. Add.
	0"	30"	0"	30"	0"	30"	0"	30"	0"	30"	0"	30"	0'	30"	0"	30"	0"	30'	0"	30"	0"	
°	"	"	"	"	"	"	"	"	"	"	"	"	"	"	"	"	"	"	"	"	"	°
—10	0	4	8	12	16	20	24	28	33	37	41	46	50	55	60	65	70	75	80	85	90	—10
— 8	0	4	8	12	15	19	23	27	31	36	40	44	48	53	58	62	67	72	77	82	87	— 8
— 6	0	4	7	11	15	19	22	26	30	34	38	42	47	51	55	60	64	69	74	79	84	— 6
— 4	0	4	7	11	14	18	22	25	29	33	37	41	45	49	53	57	62	66	71	76	80	— 4
— 2	0	3	7	10	14	17	21	24	28	31	35	39	43	47	51	55	59	64	68	72	77	— 2
0	0	3	7	10	13	16	20	23	27	30	34	37	41	45	49	53	57	61	65	69	74	0
2	0	3	6	9	12	16	19	22	25	29	32	36	39	43	47	50	54	58	62	66	70	2
4	0	3	6	9	12	15	18	21	24	28	31	34	37	41	44	48	52	55	59	63	67	4
6	0	3	6	8	11	14	17	20	23	26	29	32	36	39	42	46	49	53	56	60	64	6
8	0	3	5	8	11	14	16	19	22	25	28	31	34	37	40	43	47	50	54	57	61	8
10	0	3	5	8	10	13	15	18	21	24	26	29	32	35	38	41	44	48	51	54	58	10
11	0	2	5	7	10	13	15	18	20	23	26	28	31	34	37	40	43	46	49	53	56	11
12	0	2	5	7	10	12	15	17	20	22	25	28	30	33	36	39	42	45	48	51	54	12
13	0	2	5	7	9	12	14	17	19	22	24	27	30	32	35	38	41	44	47	50	53	13
14	0	2	5	7	9	11	14	16	19	21	24	26	29	31	34	37	40	42	45	48	51	14
15	0	2	4	7	9	11	13	16	18	20	23	25	28	30	33	36	38	41	44	47	50	15
16	0	2	4	6	9	11	13	15	18	20	22	25	27	29	32	35	37	40	43	45	48	16
17	0	2	4	6	8	10	13	15	17	19	21	24	26	29	31	33	36	39	41	44	47	17
18	0	2	4	6	8	10	12	14	16	19	21	23	25	28	30	32	35	37	40	43	45	18
19	0	2	4	6	8	10	12	14	16	18	20	22	24	27	29	31	34	36	39	41	44	19
20	0	2	4	6	8	9	11	13	15	17	19	22	24	26	28	30	33	35	37	40	42	20
21	0	2	4	5	7	9	11	13	15	17	19	21	23	25	27	29	31	34	36	38	41	21
22	0	2	3	5	7	9	11	12	14	16	18	20	22	24	26	28	30	32	35	37	39	22
23	0	2	3	5	7	8	10	12	14	15	17	19	21	23	25	27	29	31	33	36	38	23
24	0	2	3	5	6	8	10	11	13	15	17	18	20	22	24	26	28	30	32	34	36	24
25	0	2	3	5	6	8	9	11	13	14	16	18	19	21	23	25	27	29	31	33	35	25
26	0	1	3	4	6	7	9	11	12	14	15	17	19	20	22	24	26	28	29	31	33	26
27	0	1	3	4	6	7	9	10	12	13	15	16	18	19	21	23	25	26	28	30	32	27
28	0	1	3	4	5	7	8	10	11	12	14	15	17	19	20	22	23	25	27	29	30	28
29	0	1	3	4	5	6	8	9	11	12	13	15	16	18	19	21	22	24	26	27	29	29
30	0	1	2	4	5	6	7	9	10	11	13	14	15	17	18	20	21	23	24	26	28	30
31	0	1	2	3	5	6	7	8	9	11	12	13	15	16	17	19	20	22	23	25	26	31
32	0	1	2	3	4	6	7	8	9	10	11	13	14	15	16	18	19	20	22	23	25	32
33	0	1	2	3	4	5	6	7	8	10	11	12	13	14	15	17	18	19	21	22	23	33
34	0	1	2	3	4	5	6	7	8	9	10	11	12	13	14	16	17	18	19	21	22	34
35	0	1	2	3	4	5	6	6	7	8	9	10	11	13	14	15	16	17	18	19	20	35
36	0	1	2	3	3	4	5	6	7	8	9	10	11	12	13	14	15	16	17	18	19	36
37	0	1	2	2	3	4	5	6	6	7	8	9	10	11	12	13	14	15	16	17	18	37
38	0	1	1	2	3	4	4	5	6	7	7	8	9	10	11	12	13	13	14	15	16	38
39	0	1	1	2	3	3	4	5	5	6	7	8	8	9	10	11	11	12	13	14	15	39
40	0	1	1	2	2	3	4	4	5	6	6	7	8	8	9	10	10	11	12	13	13	40
41	0	1	1	2	2	3	3	4	4	5	6	6	7	7	8	9	9	10	11	11	12	41
42	0	0	1	1	2	2	3	3	4	4	5	5	6	7	7	8	8	9	9	10	11	42
43	0	0	1	1	2	2	3	3	3	4	4	5	5	6	6	7	7	8	8	9	9	43
44	0	0	1	1	1	2	2	3	3	3	4	4	4	5	5	6	6	7	7	8	8	44
45	0	0	1	1	1	1	2	2	2	3	3	3	4	4	4	5	5	6	6	6	7	45
46	0	0	0	1	1	1	1	2	2	2	2	2	3	3	4	4	4	4	5	5	5	46
47	0	0	0	1	1	1	1	1	1	2	2	2	2	2	3	3	3	3	4	4	4	47
48	0	0	0	0	0	1	1	1	1	1	1	1	1	2	2	2	2	2	2	2	3	48
49	0	0	0	0	0	0	0	0	0	1	1	1	1	1	1	1	1	1	1	1	1	49
50	0	0	0	0	0	0	0	0	0	0	0	0	0	0	0	0	0	0	0	0	0	50
Add.	0"	30"	0"	30"	0"	30"	0"	30"	0"	30"	0"	30"	0"	30"	0"	30"	0"	30"	0"	30"	0"	Add.
Ther.	0'		1'		2'		3'		4'		5'		6'		7'		8'		9'		10'	Ther.
	Mean refraction.																					

TABLE 25.

Correction of the Mean Refraction for the Height of the Thermometer.

Ther. Subt.	Mean refraction. 0′ 0″	0′ 30″	1′ 0″	1′ 30″	2′ 0″	2′ 30″	3′ 0″	3′ 30″	4′ 0″	4′ 30″	5′ 0″	5′ 30″	6′ 0″	6′ 30″	7′ 0″	7′ 30″	8′ 0″	8′ 30″	9′ 0″	9′ 30″	10′ 0″	Ther. Subt.
°	″	″	″	″	″	″	″	″	″	″	″	″	″	″	″	″	″	″	″	″	″	°
50	0	0	0	0	0	0	0	0	0	0	0	0	0	0	0	0	0	0	0	0	0	50
51	0	0	0	0	0	0	0	0	0	1	1	1	1	1	1	1	1	1	1	1	1	51
52	0	0	0	0	0	1	1	1	1	1	1	1	1	2	2	2	2	2	2	2	3	52
53	0	0	0	1	1	1	1	1	1	2	2	2	2	2	2	3	3	3	3	4	4	53
54	0	0	0	1	1	1	1	2	2	2	2	3	3	3	3	4	4	4	5	5	5	54
55	0	0	1	1	1	1	2	2	2	3	3	3	4	4	4	5	5	5	6	6	6	55
56	0	0	1	1	1	2	2	2	3	3	4	4	4	5	5	6	6	6	7	7	8	56
57	0	0	1	1	2	2	2	3	3	4	4	5	5	6	6	6	7	8	8	8	9	57
58	0	0	1	1	2	2	3	3	4	4	5	5	6	6	7	7	8	9	9	10	10	58
59	0	1	1	2	2	3	3	4	4	5	5	6	6	7	8	8	9	10	10	11	12	59
60	0	1	1	2	2	3	3	4	5	5	6	7	7	8	9	9	10	11	11	12	13	60
61	0	1	1	2	3	3	4	4	5	6	7	7	8	9	9	10	11	12	12	13	14	61
62	0	1	1	2	3	3	4	5	6	6	7	8	9	9	10	11	12	13	14	15	15	62
63	0	1	1	2	3	4	5	5	6	7	8	8	9	10	11	12	13	14	15	16	17	63
64	0	1	2	2	3	4	5	6	7	7	8	9	10	11	12	13	14	15	16	17	18	64
65	0	1	2	3	3	4	5	6	7	8	9	10	11	12	13	14	15	16	17	18	19	65
66	0	1	2	3	4	5	6	6	7	8	9	10	11	12	14	15	16	17	18	19	20	66
67	0	1	2	3	4	5	6	7	8	9	10	11	12	13	14	16	17	18	19	20	22	67
68	0	1	2	3	4	5	6	7	8	9	11	11	13	14	15	16	18	19	20	22	23	68
69	0	1	2	3	4	5	7	8	9	10	11	12	13	15	16	17	19	20	21	23	24	69
70	0	1	2	3	5	6	7	8	9	10	12	12	14	16	17	18	20	21	22	24	25	70
71	0	1	2	4	5	6	7	8	10	11	12	13	15	16	18	19	20	22	23	25	27	71
72	0	1	2	4	5	6	8	9	10	11	13	14	16	17	18	20	21	23	25	26	28	72
73	0	1	3	4	5	7	8	9	11	12	13	14	16	18	19	21	22	24	26	27	29	73
74	0	1	3	4	5	7	8	10	11	12	14	15	17	18	20	22	23	25	27	28	30	74
75	0	1	3	4	6	7	8	10	11	13	14	16	18	19	21	22	24	26	28	29	31	75
76	0	1	3	4	6	7	9	10	12	13	15	16	18	20	22	23	25	27	29	31	32	76
77	0	1	3	5	6	8	9	11	12	14	16	17	19	21	22	24	26	28	30	32	34	77
78	0	2	3	5	6	8	9	11	13	14	16	18	20	21	23	25	27	29	31	33	35	78
79	0	2	3	5	6	8	10	11	13	15	17	18	20	22	24	26	28	30	32	34	36	79
80	0	2	3	5	7	8	10	12	14	15	17	19	21	23	25	27	29	31	33	35	37	80
81	0	2	3	5	7	9	10	12	14	16	18	20	21	24	26	28	30	32	34	36	38	81
82	0	2	4	5	7	9	11	13	14	16	18	20	22	24	26	28	31	33	35	37	40	82
83	0	2	4	5	7	9	11	13	15	17	19	21	23	25	27	29	31	34	36	38	41	83
84	0	2	4	6	8	9	11	13	15	17	19	21	23	26	28	30	32	35	37	39	42	84
85	0	2	4	6	8	10	12	14	16	18	20	22	24	26	29	31	33	36	38	40	43	85
86	0	2	4	6	8	10	12	14	16	18	20	23	25	27	29	32	34	37	39	42	44	86
87	0	2	4	6	8	10	12	14	17	19	21	23	25	28	30	32	35	38	40	43	45	87
88	0	2	4	6	8	10	13	15	17	19	21	24	26	28	31	33	36	38	41	44	46	88
89	0	2	4	6	9	11	13	15	17	20	22	24	27	29	32	34	37	39	42	45	48	89
90	0	2	4	7	9	11	13	16	18	20	23	25	27	30	32	35	38	40	43	46	49	90
91	0	2	4	7	9	11	14	16	18	21	23	25	28	31	33	36	39	41	44	47	50	91
92	0	2	5	7	9	11	14	16	19	21	24	26	29	31	34	37	39	42	45	48	51	92
93	0	2	5	7	9	12	14	17	19	22	24	27	29	32	35	37	40	43	46	49	52	93
94	0	2	5	7	10	12	14	17	19	22	25	27	30	33	35	38	41	44	47	50	53	94
95	0	2	5	7	10	12	15	17	20	22	25	28	30	33	36	39	42	45	48	51	54	95
96	0	2	5	7	10	12	15	18	20	23	26	28	31	34	37	40	43	46	49	52	55	96
97	0	3	5	8	10	13	15	18	21	23	26	29	32	35	38	41	44	47	50	53	56	97
98	0	3	5	8	10	13	16	18	21	24	27	29	32	35	38	41	44	48	51	54	58	98
99	0	3	5	8	11	13	16	19	21	24	27	30	33	36	39	42	45	49	52	55	59	99
100	0	3	5	8	11	13	16	19	22	25	28	31	34	37	40	43	46	50	53	56	60	100
Subt.	0″	30″	0″	30″	0″	30″	0″	30″	0″	30″	0″	30″	0″	30″	0″	30″	0″	30″	0″	30″	0″	Subt.
	0′		1′		2′		3′		4′		5′		6′		7′		8′		9′		10′	
Ther.	Mean refraction.																					Ther.

TABLE 26.

For reducing the Time of the Moon's passage over the Meridian of Greenwich to the Time of its passage over any other Meridian. The numbers taken from this Table are to be added to the Time at Greenwich in West Longitude, subtracted in East Longitude.

Longitude.	Daily variation of the moon's passing the meridian.														Longitude.
	40m	42m	44m	46m	48m	50m	52m	54m	56m	58m	60m	62m	64m	66m	
°	m.	m.	m.	m.	m.	m.	m.	m.	m.	m.	m.	m.	m.	m.	°
0	0	0	0	0	0	0	0	0	0	0	0	0	0	0	0
5	1	1	1	1	1	1	1	1	1	1	1	1	1	1	5
10	1	1	1	1	1	1	1	1	2	2	2	2	2	2	10
15	2	2	2	2	2	2	2	2	2	2	2	3	3	3	15
20	2	2	2	3	3	3	3	3	3	3	3	3	4	4	20
25	3	3	3	3	3	3	4	4	4	4	4	4	4	5	25
30	3	3	4	4	4	4	4	4	5	5	5	5	5	5	30
35	4	4	4	4	5	5	5	5	5	6	6	6	6	6	35
40	4	5	5	5	5	6	6	6	6	6	7	7	7	7	40
45	5	5	5	6	6	6	6	7	7	7	7	8	8	8	45
50	6	6	6	6	7	7	7	7	8	8	8	9	9	9	50
55	6	6	7	7	7	8	8	8	9	9	9	9	10	10	55
60	7	7	7	8	8	8	9	9	9	10	10	10	11	11	60
65	7	8	8	8	9	9	9	10	10	10	11	11	12	12	65
70	8	8	9	9	9	10	10	10	11	11	12	12	12	13	70
75	8	9	9	10	10	10	11	11	12	12	12	13	13	14	75
80	9	9	10	10	11	11	12	12	12	13	13	14	14	15	80
85	9	10	10	11	11	12	12	13	13	14	14	15	15	16	85
90	10	10	11	11	12	12	13	13	14	14	15	15	16	16	90
95	11	11	12	12	13	13	14	14	15	15	16	16	17	17	95
100	11	12	12	13	13	14	14	15	16	16	17	17	18	18	100
105	12	12	13	13	14	15	15	16	16	17	17	18	19	19	105
110	12	13	13	14	15	15	16	16	17	18	18	19	20	20	110
115	13	13	14	15	15	16	17	17	18	19	19	20	20	21	115
120	13	14	15	15	16	17	17	18	19	19	20	21	21	22	120
125	14	15	15	16	17	17	18	19	19	20	21	22	22	23	125
130	14	15	16	17	17	18	19	19	20	21	22	22	23	24	130
135	15	16	16	17	18	19	19	20	21	22	22	23	24	25	135
140	16	16	17	18	19	19	20	21	22	23	23	24	25	26	140
145	16	17	18	19	19	20	21	22	23	23	24	25	26	27	145
150	17	17	18	19	20	21	22	22	23	24	25	26	27	27	150
155	17	18	19	20	21	22	22	23	24	25	26	27	28	28	155
160	18	19	20	20	21	22	23	24	25	26	27	28	28	29	160
165	18	19	20	21	22	23	24	25	26	27	27	28	29	30	165
170	19	20	21	22	23	24	25	25	26	27	28	29	30	31	170
175	19	20	21	22	23	24	25	26	27	28	29	30	31	32	175
180	20	21	22	23	24	25	26	27	28	29	30	31	32	33	180
	40m	42m	44m	46m	48m	50m	52m	54m	56m	58m	60m	62m	64m	66m	

TABLE 27.

Amplitudes.

Latitude.	Declination. 0°.0	0°.5	1°.0	1°.5	2°.0	2°.5	3°.0	3°.5	4°.0	4°.5	5°.0	5°.5	6°.0	Latitude.
°	°	°	°	°	°	°	°	°	°	°	°	°	°	°
0	0.0	0.5	1.0	1.5	2.0	2.5	3.0	3.5	4.0	4.5	5.0	5.5	6.0	0
10	0.0	0.5	1.0	1.5	2.0	2.5	3.0	3.5	4.1	4.6	5.1	5.6	6.1	10
15	0.0	0.5	1.0	1.5	2.1	2.6	3.1	3.6	4.2	4.7	5.2	5.7	6.2	15
20	0.0	0.5	1.1	1.6	2.1	2.7	3.2	3.7	4.3	4.8	5.3	5.8	6.4	20
25	0.0	0.5	1.1	1.6	2.2	2.8	3.3	3.8	4.4	5.0	5.5	6.0	6.6	25
30	0.0	0.6	1.2	1.7	2.3	2.9	3.4	4.0	4.6	5.2	5.8	6.3	6.9	30
32	0.0	0.6	1.2	1.8	2.4	2.9	3.5	4.1	4.7	5.3	5.9	6.5	7.0	32
34	0.0	0.6	1.2	1.8	2.4	3.0	3.6	4.2	4.8	5.4	6.0	6.6	7.2	34
36	0.0	0.6	1.2	1.8	2.5	3.1	3.7	4.3	4.9	5.6	6.1	6.8	7.4	36
38	0.0	0.6	1.3	1.9	2.5	3.2	3.8	4.4	5.1	5.7	6.3	7.0	7.6	38
40	0.0	0.7	1.3	2.0	2.6	3.3	3.9	4.6	5.2	5.9	6.5	7.2	7.8	40
42	0.0	0.7	1.3	2.0	2.7	3.4	4.0	4.7	5.4	6.1	6.7	7.4	8.0	42
44	0.0	0.7	1.4	2.1	2.8	3.5	4.2	4.9	5.6	6.3	6.9	7.6	8.3	44
46	0.0	0.7	1.4	2.2	2.9	3.6	4.3	5.0	5.8	6.5	7.2	7.9	8.6	46
48	0.0	0.7	1.5	2.2	3.0	3.7	4.5	5.2	6.0	6.7	7.5	8.2	9.0	48
50	0.0	0.8	1.5	2.3	3.1	3.9	4.7	5.4	6.2	7.0	7.8	8.6	9.3	50
51	0.0	0.8	1.6	2.4	3.2	4.0	4.8	5.6	6.4	7.2	8.0	8.8	9.5	51
52	0.0	0.8	1.6	2.4	3.3	4.1	4.9	5.7	6.5	7.3	8.1	9.0	9.7	52
53	0.0	0.8	1.6	2.5	3.3	4.2	5.0	5.8	6.7	7.5	8.3	9.2	10.0	53
54	0.0	0.9	1.7	2.5	3.4	4.3	5.1	6.0	6.8	7.7	8.5	9.4	0.2	54
55	0.0	0.9	1.7	2.6	3.5	4.4	5.2	6.1	7.0	7.9	8.7	9.6	10.5	55
56	0.0	0.9	1.8	2.7	3.6	4.5	5.4	6.3	7.2	8.1	9.0	9.9	0.8	56
57	0.0	0.9	1.8	2.7	3.7	4.6	5.5	6.4	7.4	8.3	9.2	10.1	1.1	57
58	0.0	0.9	1.9	2.8	3.8	4.7	5.7	6.6	7.6	8.5	9.5	0.4	1.4	58
59	0.0	1.0	1.9	2.9	3.9	4.9	5.8	6.8	7.8	8.8	9.7	0.7	1.7	59
60	0.0	1.0	2.0	3.0	4.0	5.0	6.0	7.0	8.0	9.0	10.0	11.0	12.1	60
61	0.0	1.0	2.1	3.1	4.1	5.2	6.2	7.2	8.3	9.3	0.3	1.4	2.5	61
62	0.0	1.1	2.1	3.2	4.3	5.3	6.4	7.5	8.5	9.6	0.7	1.8	2.9	62
63	0.0	1.1	2.2	3.3	4.5	5.5	6.6	7.7	8.8	9.9	1.1	2.2	3.4	63
64	0.0	1.1	2.3	3.4	4.6	5.7	6.9	8.0	9.2	10.3	1.5	2.6	3.9	64
65.0	0.0	1.2	2.4	3.5	4.8	5.9	7.1	8.3	9.5	10.7	11.9	13.1	14.4	65.0
5.5	0.0	1.2	2.4	3.6	4.8	6.0	7.2	8.5	9.7	0.9	2.1	3.4	4.6	5.5
6.0	0.0	1.2	2.5	3.7	4.9	6.1	7.4	8.6	9.9	1.1	2.4	3.6	4.9	6.0
6.5	0.0	1.2	2.5	3.8	5.0	6.3	7.5	8.8	10.1	1.3	2.6	3.9	5.2	6.5
7.0	0.0	1.3	2.6	3.8	5.1	6.4	7.7	9.0	0.3	1.6	2.9	4.2	5.5	7.0
67.5	0.0	1.3	2.6	3.9	5.2	6.5	7.9	9.2	10.5	11.8	13.2	14.5	15.9	67.5
8.0	0.0	1.3	2.7	4.0	5.3	6.7	8.0	9.4	0.7	2.1	3.5	4.8	6.2	8.0
8.5	0.0	1.4	2.7	4.1	5.4	6.8	8.2	9.6	1.0	2.4	3.8	5.2	6.6	8.5
9.0	0.0	1.4	2.8	4.2	5.5	7.0	8.4	9.8	1.2	2.6	4.1	5.5	7.0	9.0
9.5	0.0	1.4	2.9	4.3	5.7	7.2	8.6	10.0	1.5	2.9	4.4	5.9	7.4	9.5
70.0	0.0	1.5	2.9	4.4	5.8	7.3	8.8	10.3	11.8	13.3	14.8	16.3	17.8	70.0
0.5	0.0	1.5	3.0	4.5	6.0	7.5	9.0	0.5	2.1	3.6	5.1	6.7	8.2	0.5
1.0	0.0	1.5	3.1	4.6	6.2	7.7	9.3	0.8	2.4	3.9	5.5	7.1	8.7	1.0
1.5	0.0	1.6	3.2	4.7	6.3	7.9	9.5	1.1	2.7	4.3	5.9	7.8	9.2	1.5
2.0	0.0	1.6	3.2	4.9	6.5	8.1	9.8	1.4	3.0	4.7	6.4	8.1	9.8	2.0
72.5	0.0	1.7	3.3	5.0	6.7	8.3	10.0	11.7	13.4	15.1	16.9	18.6	20.3	72.5
3.0	0.0	1.7	3.4	5.1	6.9	8.6	0.3	2.0	3.8	5.5	7.4	9.1	0.9	3.0
3.5	0.0	1.8	3.5	5.2	7.1	8.8	0.6	2.4	4.2	6.0	7.9	9.7	1.6	3.5
4.0	0.0	1.8	3.6	5.4	7.3	9.1	0.9	2.8	4.6	6.5	8.4	20.3	2.3	4.0
4.5	0.0	1.9	3.7	5.6	7.5	9.4	1.3	3.2	5.1	7.1	9.0	1.0	3.0	4.5
75.0	0.0	1.9	3.8	5.8	7.7	9.7	11.7	13.6	15.6	17.7	19.7	21.7	23.8	75.0
5.5	0.0	2.0	3.9	6.0	8.0	10.0	2.1	4.1	6.2	8.3	20.4	2.5	4.7	5.5
6.0	0.0	2.1	4.0	6.2	8.3	0.4	2.5	4.6	6.8	8.9	1.1	3.3	5.6	6.0
6.5	0.0	2.1	4.2	6.4	8.6	0.8	3.0	5.2	7.4	9.6	1.9	4.2	6.6	6.5
7.0	0.0	2.2	4.4	6.6	8.9	1.2	3.5	5.8	8.1	20.4	2.8	5.2	7.7	7.0

TABLE 27.

Amplitudes.

Latitude.	Declination. 6°.0	6°.5	7°.0	7°.5	8°.0	8°.5	9°.0	9°.5	10°.0	10°.5	11°.0	11°.5	12°.0	Latitude.
°	°	°	°	°	°	°	°	°	°	°	°	°	°	°
0	6.0	6.5	7.0	7.5	8.0	8.5	9.0	9.5	10.0	10.5	11.0	11.5	12.0	0
10	6.1	6.6	7.1	7.6	8.1	8.6	9.1	9.7	0.1	0.7	1.2	1.7	2.2	10
15	6.2	6.7	7.2	7.8	8.3	8.8	9.3	9.8	0.4	0.9	1.4	1.9	2.5	15
20	6.4	6.9	7.4	8.0	8.5	9.1	9.6	10.1	0.7	1.2	1.7	2.3	2.8	20
25	6.6	7.1	7.7	8.3	8.8	9.4	9.9	0.5	1.1	1.6	2.2	2.8	3.3	25
30	6.9	7.5	8.1	8.7	9.3	9.8	10.4	11.0	11.5	12.1	12.7	13.3	13.9	30
32	7.0	7.7	8.3	8.8	9.5	10.0	0.6	1.2	1.8	2.4	3.0	3.6	4.2	32
34	7.2	7.8	8.5	9.0	9.7	0.3	0.8	1.5	2.1	2.7	3.3	3.9	4.5	34
36	7.4	8.0	8.7	9.3	9.9	0.5	1.1	1.8	2.4	3.0	3.6	4.3	4.9	36
38	7.6	8.2	8.9	9.5	10.2	0.8	1.4	2.1	2.7	3.4	4.0	4.7	5.3	38
40	7.8	8.5	9.1	9.8	10.5	11.1	11.7	12.4	13.1	13.8	14.4	15.1	15.7	40
42	8.0	8.8	9.4	10.1	0.8	1.5	2.1	2.8	3.5	4.2	4.8	5.6	6.2	42
44	8.3	9.1	9.7	0.5	1.1	1.9	2.5	3.3	4.0	4.7	5.3	6.1	6.8	44
46	8.6	9.4	10.1	0.8	1.5	2.3	3.0	3.8	4.5	5.2	5.9	6.7	7.4	46
48	9.0	9.7	0.5	1.2	2.0	2.8	3.5	4.3	5.0	5.8	6.6	7.3	8.1	48
50	9.3	10.1	10.9	11.7	12.5	13.3	14.1	14.9	15.7	16.5	17.3	18.1	18.9	50
51	9.5	0.4	1.2	2.0	2.8	3.6	4.4	5.2	6.0	6.8	7.7	8.5	9.3	51
52	9.7	0.6	1.4	2.2	3.1	3.9	4.7	5.6	6.4	7.2	8.1	8.9	9.7	52
53	10.0	0.8	1.7	2.5	3.4	4.2	5.1	5.9	6.8	7.6	8.5	9.4	20.2	53
54	0.2	1.1	2.0	2.8	3.7	4.6	5.4	6.3	7.2	8.1	8.9	9.8	0.7	54
55	10.5	11.4	12.3	13.1	14.0	14.9	15.8	16.7	17.6	18.5	19.4	20.3	21.2	55
56	0.8	1.7	2.6	3.5	4.4	5.3	6.2	7.2	8.1	9.0	9.9	0.9	1.8	56
57	1.1	2.0	2.9	3.9	4.8	5.8	6.7	7.7	8.6	9.6	20.5	1.5	2.4	57
58	1.4	2.3	3.3	4.3	5.2	6.2	7.2	8.2	9.1	20.1	1.1	2.1	3.1	58
59	1.7	2.7	3.7	4.7	5.7	6.7	7.7	8.7	9.7	0.7	1.7	2.8	3.8	59
60	12.1	13.1	14.1	15.1	16.2	17.2	18.2	19.3	20.3	21.4	22.4	23.5	24.6	60
61	2.5	3.5	4.6	5.6	6.7	7.8	8.8	9.9	1.0	2.1	3.1	4.3	5.4	61
62	2.9	3.9	5.1	6.1	7.3	8.4	9.4	20.6	1.7	2.9	3.9	5.2	6.3	62
63	3.4	4.4	5.6	6.7	7.9	9.0	20.1	1.3	2.5	3.7	4.8	6.1	7.2	63
64	3.9	5.0	6.2	7.3	8.5	9.7	0.9	2.1	3.3	4.6	5.7	7.1	8.3	64
65.0	14.4	15.5	16.8	18.0	19.3	20.5	21.7	23.0	24.2	25.6	26.8	28.2	29.5	65.0
5.5	4.6	5.8	7.1	8.3	9.6	0.9	2.2	3.5	4.7	6.1	7.4	8.7	30.1	5.5
6.0	4.9	6.2	7.4	8.7	20.0	1.3	2.6	3.9	5.3	6.6	8.0	9.3	0.7	6.0
6.5	5.2	6.5	7.8	9.1	0.4	1.8	3.1	4.4	5.8	7.2	8.6	30.0	1.4	6.5
7.0	5.5	6.8	8.2	9.5	0.9	2.2	3.6	5.0	6.4	7.8	9.2	0.7	2.1	7.0
67.5	15.9	17.2	18.6	19.9	21.3	22.7	24.1	25.5	27.0	28.4	29.9	31.4	32.9	67.5
8.0	6.2	7.6	9.0	20.4	1.8	3.2	4.7	6.1	7.6	9.1	30.6	2.2	3.7	8.0
8.5	6.6	8.0	9.4	0.9	2.3	3.8	5.3	6.8	8.3	9.8	1.4	3.0	4.6	8.5
9.0	7.0	8.4	9.9	1.4	2.8	4.4	5.9	7.4	9.0	30.6	2.2	3.8	5.5	9.0
9.5	7.4	8.9	20.4	1.9	3.4	5.0	6.5	8.1	9.7	1.4	3.0	4.7	6.4	9.5
70.0	17.8	19.3	20.9	22.4	24.0	25.6	27.2	28.8	30.5	32.2	33.9	35.7	37.4	70.0
0.5	8.2	9.8	1.4	3.0	4.6	6.3	7.9	9.6	1.3	3.1	4.9	6.7	8.5	0.5
1.0	8.7	20.3	2.0	3.6	5.3	7.0	8.7	30.5	2.2	4.0	5.9	7.8	9.7	1.0
1.5	9.2	0.9	2.6	4.3	6.0	7.8	9.5	1.4	3.2	5.0	7.0	8.9	40.9	1.5
2.0	9.8	1.5	3.2	5.0	6.8	8.6	30.4	2.3	4.2	6.1	8.1	40.2	2.3	2.0
72.5	20.3	22.1	23.9	25.7	27.6	29.5	31.4	33.3	35.3	37.3	39.4	41.5	43.7	72.5
3.0	0.9	2.8	4.6	6.5	8.4	30.4	2.4	4.4	6.5	8.6	40.8	3.0	5.3	3.0
3.5	1.6	3.5	5.4	7.4	9.3	1.4	3.4	5.5	7.7	9.9	2.2	4.6	7.0	3.5
4.0	2.3	4.3	6.2	8.3	30.3	2.5	4.6	6.8	9.1	41.4	3.8	6.3	8.9	4.0
4.5	3.0	5.1	7.1	9.3	1.4	3.6	5.8	8.2	40.5	3.0	5.6	8.2	51.1	4.5
75.0	23.8	26.0	28.1	30.3	32.5	34.8	37.2	39.6	42.1	44.8	47.5	50.4	53.5	75.0
5.5	4.7	6.9	9.1	1.4	3.8	6.2	8.7	41.2	3.9	6.7	9.6	2.8	6.2	5.5
6.0	5.6	7.9	30.2	2.6	5.1	7.7	40.3	3.0	5.9	8.9	52.1	5.5	9.3	6.0
6.5	6.6	9.0	1.4	4.0	6.6	9.3	2.1	5.0	8.1	51.3	4.8	8.7	63.0	6.5
7.0	7.7	30.2	2.8	5.5	8.2	41.1	4.1	7.2	50.5	4.1	8.0	62.4	7.6	7.0

541524°—43——36

TABLE 27.

Amplitudes.

Latitude.	Declination.													Latitude.
	12°.0	12°.5	13°.0	13°.5	14°.0	14°.5	15°.0	15°.5	16°.0	16°.5	17°.0	17°.5	18°.0	
°	°	°	°	°	°	°	°	°	°	°	°	°	°	°
0	12.0	12.5	13.0	13.5	14.0	14.5	15.0	15.5	16.0	16.5	17.0	17.5	18.0	0
10	2.2	2.7	3.2	3.7	4.2	4.7	5.3	5.8	6.3	6.8	7.3	7.9	8.3	10
15	2.5	2.9	3.5	4.0	4.5	5.0	5.6	6.1	6.6	7.1	7.7	8.2	8.7	15
20	2.8	3.3	3.8	4.4	4.9	5.5	6.0	6.5	7.1	7.6	8.1	8.7	9.2	20
25	3.3	3.8	4.4	4.9	5.5	6.1	6.6	7.1	7.7	8.3	8.8	9.4	9.9	25
30	13.9	14.5	15.0	15.6	16.2	16.8	17.4	18.0	18.6	19.2	19.7	20.3	20.9	30
32	4.2	4.8	5.3	6.0	6.6	7.2	7.8	8.4	9.0	9.6	20.2	0.8	1.4	32
34	4.5	5.1	5.7	6.4	7.0	7.6	8.2	8.8	9.5	20.0	0.7	1.3	1.9	34
36	4.9	5.5	6.1	6.8	7.4	8.0	8.7	9.3	20.0	0.5	1.2	1.8	2.5	36
38	5.3	6.0	6.6	7.2	7.9	8.5	9.2	9.8	0.5	1.1	1.8	2.4	3.1	38
40	15.7	16.4	17.1	17.8	18.4	19.1	19.7	20.4	21.1	21.8	22.4	23.1	23.8	40
41	6.0	6.7	7.3	8.0	8.7	9.4	20.0	0.8	1.4	2.1	2.8	3.5	4.2	41
42	6.2	6.9	7.6	8.3	9.0	9.7	0.4	1.1	1.8	2.5	3.2	3.9	4.6	42
43	6.5	7.2	7.9	8.6	9.3	20.0	0.7	1.4	2.2	2.9	3.6	4.3	5.0	43
44	6.8	7.5	8.2	8.9	9.6	0.4	1.1	1.8	2.6	3.3	4.0	4.7	5.4	44
45	17.1	17.8	18.5	19.3	20.0	20.7	21.5	22.2	23.0	23.7	24.4	25.2	25.9	45
46	7.4	8.2	8.9	9.6	0.4	1.1	1.9	2.6	3.4	4.1	4.9	5.7	6.4	46
47	7.7	8.5	9.3	20.0	0.8	1.5	2.3	3.1	3.8	4.6	5.4	6.2	6.9	47
48	8.1	8.9	9.7	0.4	1.2	2.0	2.8	3.6	4.3	5.1	5.9	6.7	7.5	48
49	8.5	9.3	20.1	0.8	1.6	2.4	3.2	4.1	4.9	5.7	6.5	7.3	8.1	49
50	18.9	19.7	20.5	21.3	22.1	22.9	23.7	24.6	25.4	26.2	27.0	27.9	28.7	50
51	9.3	20.1	0.9	1.8	2.6	3.5	4.3	5.1	6.0	6.8	7.6	8.5	9.4	51
52	9.7	0.6	1.4	2.3	3.1	4.0	4.9	5.7	6.6	7.5	8.3	9.2	30.1	52
53	20.2	1.1	1.9	2.8	3.7	4.6	5.5	6.4	7.3	8.2	9.0	30.0	0.9	53
54	0.7	1.6	2.5	3.4	4.3	5.2	6.1	7.1	8.0	8.9	9.8	0.8	1.7	54
55	21.2	22.2	23.1	24.0	24.9	25.9	26.8	27.8	28.7	29.7	30.6	31.6	32.6	55
56	1.8	2.8	3.7	4.7	5.6	6.6	7.6	8.6	9.5	30.5	1.5	2.5	3.6	56
57	2.4	3.4	4.4	5.4	6.4	7.4	8.4	9.4	30.4	1.4	2.5	3.5	4.6	57
58	3.1	4.1	5.1	6.1	7.2	8.2	9.2	30.3	1.3	2.4	3.5	4.6	5.7	58
59	3.8	4.8	5.9	6.9	8.0	9.1	30.2	1.3	2.3	3.5	4.6	5.7	6.9	59
60	24.6	25.6	26.7	27.8	28.9	30.1	31.2	32.3	33.4	34.6	35.8	36.9	38.2	60
61	5.4	6.5	7.6	8.8	9.9	1.1	2.2	3.5	4.6	5.8	7.1	8.3	9.6	61
62	6.3	7.5	8.6	9.8	31.0	2.2	3.4	4.7	5.9	7.2	8.5	9.8	41.2	62
63	7.2	8.5	9.7	31.0	2.2	3.5	4.7	6.1	7.4	8.7	40.1	41.5	2.9	63
64	8.3	9.6	30.9	2.2	3.5	4.8	6.2	7.6	9.0	40.4	1.8	3.3	4.8	64
65.0	29.5	30.8	32.2	33.5	34.9	36.3	37.8	39.2	40.7	42.2	43.8	45.4	47.0	65.0
5.5	30.1	1.5	2.9	4.3	5.7	7.1	8.6	40.1	1.6	3.2	4.8	6.5	8.2	5.5
6.0	0.7	2.2	3.6	5.0	6.5	8.0	9.5	1.1	2.7	4.3	5.9	7.7	9.4	6.0
6.5	1.4	2.9	4.3	5.8	7.3	8.9	40.5	2.1	3.8	5.4	7.1	8.9	50.8	6.5
7.0	2.1	3.6	5.1	6.7	8.2	9.8	1.5	3.2	4.9	6.6	8.4	50.3	2.3	7.0
67.5	32.9	34.4	36.0	37.6	39.2	40.8	42.6	44.3	46.1	47.9	49.8	51.8	53.9	67.5
8.0	3.7	5.3	6.9	8.6	40.2	1.9	3.7	5.5	7.4	9.3	51.3	3.4	5.6	8.0
8.5	4.6	6.2	7.9	9.6	1.3	3.1	4.9	6.8	8.8	50.8	2.9	5.1	7.5	8.5
9.0	5.5	7.2	8.9	40.7	2.5	4.3	6.2	8.2	50.3	2.4	4.6	7.0	9.6	9.0
9.5	6.4	8.2	40.0	1.8	3.7	5.6	7.6	9.7	1.9	4.2	6.5	9.1	61.9	9.5
70.0	37.4	39.3	41.1	43.0	45.0	47.0	49.2	51.4	53.7	56.1	58.7	61.5	64.6	70.0
0.5	8.5	40.4	2.4	4.4	6.4	8.6	50.8	3.2	5.7	8.3	61.1	4.3	7.8	0.5
1.0	9.7	1.7	3.7	5.8	8.0	50.3	2.6	5.2	7.9	60.7	3.9	7.5	71.7	1.0
1.5	40.9	3.0	5.1	7.4	9.7	2.1	4.6	7.4	60.3	3.5	7.1	71.4	6.9	1.5
2.0	2.3	4.4	6.7	9.1	51.5	4.1	6.9	9.9	3.1	6.8	71.1	6.7	90.0	2.0
72.5	43.7	46.0	48.4	50.9	53.6	56.4	59.4	62.7	66.4	70.9	76.5	90.0		72.5
3.0	5.3	7.7	50.3	3.0	5.9	8.9	62.2	6.1	70.6	6.3	90.0			3.0
3.5	7.0	9.6	2.3	5.3	8.4	61.8	5.6	70.3	6.1	90.0				3.5
4.0	8.9	51.7	4.7	7.9	61.4	5.3	9.8	75.9	90.0					4.0
4.5	51.1	4.1	7.3	60.9	4.9	9.5	75.5	90.0						4.5

TABLE 27.

Amplitudes.

Latitude.	Declination. 18°.0	18°.5	19°.0	19°.5	20°.0	20°.5	21°.0	21°.5	22°.0	22°.5	23°.0	23°.5	24°.0	Latitude.
°	°	°	°	°	°	°	°	°	°	°	°	°	°	°
0	18.0	18.5	19.0	19.5	20.0	20.5	21.0	21.5	22.0	22.5	23.0	23.5	24.0	0
10	8.3	8.8	9.3	9.8	0.3	0.8	1.3	1.8	2.3	2.9	3.4	3.9	4.4	10
15	8.7	9.2	9.7	20.2	0.7	1.3	1.8	2.3	2.8	3.3	3.9	4.4	4.9	15
20	9.2	9.7	20.3	0.8	1.4	1.9	2.4	3.0	3.5	4.0	4.6	5.1	5.7	20
25	9.9	20.5	1.1	1.6	2.2	2.7	3.3	3.9	4.4	5.0	5.5	6.1	6.7	25
30	20.9	21.5	22.1	22.7	23.3	23.8	24.4	25.0	25.6	26.2	26.8	27.4	28.0	30
32	1.4	2.0	2.6	3.2	3.8	4.4	5.0	5.6	6.2	6.8	7.4	8.0	8.7	32
34	1.9	2.5	3.1	3.8	4.4	5.0	5.6	6.2	6.9	7.5	8.1	8.7	9.4	34
36	2.5	3.1	3.7	4.4	5.0	5.7	6.3	6.9	7.6	8.2	8.9	9.5	30.2	36
38	3.1	3.8	4.4	5.1	5.7	6.4	7.0	7.7	8.4	9.1	9.7	30.4	1.1	38
40	23.9	24.4	25.1	25.8	26.5	27.2	27.9	28.6	29.3	30.0	30.7	31.3	32.1	40
41	4.2	4.8	5.5	6.2	6.9	7.7	8.3	9.1	9.8	0.5	1.2	1.8	2.6	41
42	4.6	5.3	6.0	6.7	7.4	8.1	8.8	9.6	30.3	1.0	1.7	2.4	3.2	42
43	5.0	5.7	6.4	7.2	7.9	8.6	9.3	30.1	0.8	1.6	2.3	3.0	3.8	43
44	5.4	6.2	6.9	7.7	8.4	9.1	9.8	0.6	1.4	2.2	2.9	3.6	4.4	44
45	25.9	26.7	27.4	28.2	28.9	29.7	30.4	31.2	32.0	32.8	33.5	34.3	35.1	45
46	6.4	7.2	7.9	8.7	9.5	30.3	1.0	1.8	2.6	3.4	4.2	5.0	5.8	46
47	6.9	7.7	8.5	9.3	30.1	0.9	1.7	2.5	3.3	4.1	4.9	5.7	6.6	47
48	7.5	8.3	9.1	9.9	0.7	1.6	2.4	3.2	4.0	4.9	5.7	6.5	7.4	48
49	8.1	8.9	9.7	30.6	1.4	2.3	3.1	4.0	4.8	5.7	6.5	7.4	8.3	49
50	28.7	29.6	30.4	31.3	32.1	33.0	33.9	34.8	35.6	36.5	37.4	38.3	39.2	50
51	9.4	30.3	1.1	2.0	2.9	3.8	4.7	5.6	6.5	7.4	8.4	9.3	40.2	51
52	30.1	1.0	1.9	2.8	3.7	4.7	5.6	6.5	7.5	8.4	9.4	40.3	1.3	52
53	0.9	1.8	2.7	3.7	4.6	5.6	6.6	7.5	8.5	9.5	40.5	1.4	2.5	53
54	1.7	2.7	3.6	4.6	5.6	6.6	7.6	8.6	9.6	40.6	1.7	2.6	3.8	54
55	32.6	33.6	34.6	35.6	36.6	37.6	38.7	39.7	40.8	41.9	42.9	44.0	45.2	55
56	3.6	4.6	5.6	6.7	7.7	8.8	9.8	41.0	2.1	3.2	4.3	5.4	6.7	56
57	4.6	5.6	6.7	7.8	8.9	40.0	41.1	2.3	3.5	4.6	5.8	7.0	8.3	57
58	5.7	6.8	7.9	9.1	40.2	1.4	2.5	3.8	5.0	6.2	7.5	8.8	50.1	58
59	6.9	8.0	9.2	40.4	1.6	2.8	4.1	5.4	6.7	8.0	9.3	50.7	2.2	59
60.0	38.2	39.4	40.6	41.9	43.2	44.5	45.8	47.2	48.6	49.9	51.4	52.9	54.4	60.0
0.5	8.9	40.1	1.4	2.7	4.0	5.4	6.7	8.1	9.6	51.0	2.5	4.1	5.7	0.5
1.0	9.6	0.9	2.2	3.5	4.9	6.3	7.7	9.1	50.6	2.1	3.7	5.3	7.0	1.0
1.5	40.4	1.7	3.0	4.4	5.8	7.3	8.7	50.2	1.7	3.3	5.0	6.7	8.5	1.5
2.0	1.2	2.5	3.9	5.3	6.8	8.3	9.8	1.3	2.9	4.6	6.3	8.1	60.0	2.0
62.5	42.0	43.4	44.9	46.3	47.8	49.4	51.0	52.6	54.2	56.0	57.8	59.7	61.7	62.5
3.0	2.9	4.3	5.9	7.4	8.9	50.5	2.2	3.9	5.6	7.5	9.4	61.4	3.6	3.0
3.5	3.8	5.3	6.9	8.5	50.1	1.7	3.5	5.3	7.1	9.1	61.1	3.4	5.7	3.5
4.0	4.8	6.4	8.0	9.7	1.3	3.0	4.9	6.7	8.7	60.7	3.0	5.5	8.1	4.0
4.5	5.9	7.5	9.2	50.9	2.6	4.5	6.4	8.4	60.5	2.8	5.2	7.8	70.9	4.5
65.0	47.0	48.7	50.4	52.2	54.0	56.0	58.0	60.2	62.5	64.9	67.6	70.6	74.4	65.0
5.5	8.2	50.0	1.8	3.6	5.6	7.6	9.8	2.2	4.7	7.3	70.4	4.1	8.9	5.5
6.0	9.4	1.3	3.2	5.1	7.3	9.4	61.8	4.4	7.1	70.2	3.8	8.6	90.0	6.0
6.5	50.8	2.7	4.7	6.8	9.1	61.4	4.0	6.8	70.0	3.7	8.4	90.0		6.5
7.0	2.3	4.3	6.4	8.7	61.1	3.7	6.5	9.8	3.5	8.3	90.0			7.0
67.5	53.9	56.0	58.3	60.7	63.4	66.2	69.5	73.3	78.2	90.0				67.5
8.0	5.6	7.9	60.3	3.0	5.9	9.2	73.0	8.1	90.0					8.0
8.5	7.5	60.0	2.6	5.6	8.9	72.8	7.9	90.0						8.5
9.0	9.6	2.3	5.3	8.7	72.7	7.7	90.0							9.0
9.5	61.9	5.0	8.4	72.4	7.6	90.0								9.5
70.0	64.6	69.1	72.2	77.4	90.0									70.0
0.5	7.8	71.9	7.2	90.0										0.5
1.0	71.7	7.1	90.0											1.0
1.5	6.9	90.0												1.5
2.0	90.0													2.0

TABLE 27.

Amplitudes.

Latitude.	Declination.													Latitude.
	24°.0	24°.5	25°.0	25°.5	26°.0	26°.5	27°.0	27°.5	28°.0	28°.5	29°.0	29°.5	30°.0	
°	°	°	°	°	°	°	°	°	°	°	°	°	°	°
0	24.0	24.5	25.0	25.5	26.0	26.5	27.0	27.5	28.0	28.5	29.0	29.5	30.0	0
4	4.1	4.6	5.1	5.6	6.1	6.6	7.1	7.6	8.1	8.6	9.1	9.6	0.1	4
8	4.3	4.8	5.3	5.8	6.3	6.8	7.3	7.8	8.3	8.8	9.3	9.8	0.3	8
12	4.6	5.1	5.6	6.1	6.6	7.1	7.6	8.1	8.7	9.2	9.7	30.2	0.7	12
16	5.0	5.6	6.1	6.6	7.1	7.6	8.2	8.7	9.2	9.8	30.3	0.8	1.3	16
20	25.7	26.2	26.7	27.3	27.8	28.3	28.9	29.4	30.0	30.5	31.1	31.6	32.1	20
22	6.0	6.6	7.1	7.7	8.2	8.8	9.3	9.9	0.4	1.0	1.5	2.1	2.6	22
24	6.4	7.0	7.6	8.1	8.7	9.2	9.8	30.4	0.9	1.5	2.0	2.6	3.2	24
26	6.9	7.5	8.1	8.6	9.2	9.7	30.3	0.9	1.5	2.1	2.6	3.2	3.8	26
28	7.4	8.0	8.6	9.2	9.8	30.3	0.9	1.5	2.1	2.7	3.3	3.9	4.5	28
30	28.0	28.6	29.2	29.8	30.4	31.0	31.6	32.2	32.8	33.4	34.0	34.7	35.3	30
31	8.3	8.9	9.5	30.1	0.8	1.4	2.0	2.6	3.2	3.8	4.5	5.1	5.7	31
32	8.7	9.3	9.9	0.5	1.1	1.7	2.4	3.0	3.6	4.2	4.9	5.5	6.1	32
33	9.0	9.6	30.2	0.9	1.5	2.1	2.8	3.4	4.0	4.7	5.3	6.0	6.6	33
34	9.4	30.0	0.6	31.3	1.9	2.6	3.2	3.8	4.5	5.1	5.8	6.4	7.1	34
35	29.8	30.4	31.1	31.7	32.3	33.0	33.6	34.3	35.0	35.6	36.3	36.9	37.6	35
36	30.2	0.8	1.5	2.1	2.8	3.5	4.1	4.8	5.5	6.1	6.8	7.5	8.2	36
37	0.6	1.3	1.9	2.6	3.3	4.0	4.6	5.3	6.0	6.7	7.4	8.1	8.8	37
38	1.1	1.7	2.4	3.1	3.8	4.5	5.2	5.9	6.6	7.3	8.0	8.7	9.4	38
39	1.6	2.2	2.9	3.6	4.3	5.0	5.7	6.5	7.2	7.9	8.6	9.3	40.0	39
40	32.1	32.8	33.5	34.2	34.9	35.6	36.3	37.1	37.8	38.5	39.3	40.0	40.7	40
41	2.6	3.3	4.1	4.8	5.5	6.2	7.0	7.7	8.5	9.2	40.0	0.7	1.5	41
42	3.2	3.9	4.7	5.4	6.1	6.9	7.7	8.4	9.2	9.9	0.7	1.5	2.3	42
43	3.8	4.5	5.3	6.1	6.8	7.6	8.4	9.2	9.9	40.7	1.5	2.3	3.1	43
44	4.4	5.2	6.0	6.8	7.5	8.3	9.1	40.0	40.7	1.6	2.4	3.2	4.0	44
45	35.1	35.9	36.7	37.5	38.3	39.1	39.9	40.8	41.6	42.5	43.3	44.1	45.0	45
46	5.8	6.6	7.5	8.3	9.1	40.0	40.8	1.7	2.5	3.4	4.3	5.1	6.0	46
47	6.6	7.4	8.3	9.1	40.0	0.9	1.7	2.6	3.5	4.4	5.3	6.2	7.1	47
48	7.4	8.3	9.2	40.0	0.9	1.8	2.7	3.6	4.6	5.5	6.4	7.4	8.3	48
49	8.3	9.2	40.1	1.0	1.9	2.8	3.8	4.7	5.7	6.7	7.6	8.6	9.6	49
50	39.2	40.2	41.1	42.0	43.0	43.9	44.9	45.9	46.9	47.9	48.9	50.0	51.1	50
51	40.2	1.2	2.2	3.2	4.1	5.1	6.2	7.2	8.2	9.3	50.4	1.5	2.6	51
52	1.3	2.3	3.3	4.4	5.4	6.4	7.5	8.6	9.7	50.8	2.0	3.1	4.3	52
53	2.5	3.5	4.6	5.7	6.7	7.8	9.0	50.1	51.3	2.5	3.7	4.9	6.2	53
54	3.8	4.9	6.0	7.1	8.2	9.4	50.6	1.8	3.0	4.3	5.6	6.9	8.3	54
55.0	45.2	46.3	47.5	48.6	49.8	51.1	52.3	53.6	54.9	56.3	57.7	59.1	60.7	55.0
5.5	5.9	7.1	8.3	9.5	50.7	2.0	3.3	4.6	6.0	7.4	8.9	60.4	2.0	5.5
6.0	6.7	7.9	9.1	50.4	1.6	2.9	4.3	5.7	7.1	8.6	60.1	1.7	3.4	6.0
6.5	7.5	8.8	50.0	1.3	2.6	3.9	5.4	6.8	8.3	9.9	1.5	3.2	5.0	6.5
7.0	8.3	9.6	0.9	2.2	3.6	5.0	6.5	8.0	9.5	61.2	2.9	4.7	6.6	7.0
57.5	49.2	50.5	51.9	53.2	54.7	56.2	57.7	59.3	60.9	62.6	64.5	66.4	68.5	57.5
8.0	50.1	1.5	2.9	4.3	5.8	7.4	8.9	60.6	2.4	4.2	6.2	8.3	70.7	8.0
8.5	1.1	2.5	4.0	5.5	7.0	8.6	60.3	2.1	3.9	6.0	8.1	70.4	3.1	8.5
9.0	2.2	3.6	5.1	6.7	8.3	60.0	1.8	3.7	5.7	7.9	70.3	3.0	6.2	9.0
9.5	3.3	4.8	6.4	8.0	9.7	1.5	3.4	5.5	7.7	70.1	2.8	5.9	80.1	9.5
60.0	54.4	56.0	57.7	59.4	61.2	63.2	65.2	67.4	69.9	72.6	75.8	80.0	90.0	60.0
0.5	5.7	7.4	9.1	61.0	2.9	5.0	7.2	9.6	72.4	5.8	9.9	90.0		0.5
1.0	7.0	8.8	60.7	2.6	4.7	7.0	9.5	72.3	5.5	9.8	90.0			1.0
1.5	8.5	60.3	2.3	4.4	6.7	9.2	72.0	5.4	9.7	90.0				1.5
2.0	60.0	2.0	4.2	6.5	9.0	71.9	5.2	9.6	90.0					2.0
62.5	61.7	63.9	66.2	68.8	71.7	75.1	9.5	90.0						62.5
3.0	3.6	6.0	8.6	71.5	4.9	9.4	90.0							3.0
3.5	5.7	8.3	71.3	4.8	9.3	90.0								3.5
4.0	8.1	71.1	4.6	9.2	90.0									4.0
4.5	70.9	4.4	9.0	90.0										4.5

TABLE 28.

Correction of the Amplitude as observed on the Apparent Horizon.

Latitude.	Declination.													Latitude.
	0°	5°	10°	12°	14°	16°	18°	20°	22°	24°	26°	28°	30°	
°	°	°	°	°	°	°	°	°	°	°	°	°	°	°
0	0.0	0.0	0.0	0.0	0.0	0.0	0.0	0.0	0.0	0.0	0.0	0.0	0.0	0
5	.1	.1	.1	.1	.1	.1	.1	.1	.1	.1	.1	.1	.1	5
10	.1	.1	.1	.1	.1	.1	.1	.1	.1	.1	.1	.1	.1	10
15	.2	.2	.2	.2	.2	.2	.2	.2	.2	.2	.2	.2	.2	15
20	.2	.2	.2	.2	.2	.2	.3	.3	.3	.3	.3	.3	.3	20
24	0.3	0.3	0.3	0.3	0.3	0.3	0.3	0.3	0.3	0.3	0.3	0.4	0.4	24
28	.3	.4	.4	.4	.4	.4	.4	.4	.4	.4	.4	.4	.4	28
32	.4	.4	.4	.4	.4	.4	.4	.5	.5	.5	.5	.5	.5	32
36	.5	.5	.5	.5	.5	.5	.5	.5	.6	.6	.6	.6	.6	36
38	.5	.5	.5	.5	.6	.6	.6	.6	.6	.6	.6	.7	.7	38
40	0.6	0.6	0.6	0.6	0.6	0.6	0.6	0.6	0.6	0.7	0.7	0.7	0.7	40
42	.6	.6	.6	.6	.6	.7	.7	.7	.7	.7	.8	.8	.8	42
44	.6	.6	.7	.7	.7	.7	.7	.7	.8	.8	.8	.9	.9	44
46	.7	.7	.7	.7	.7	.8	.8	.8	.8	.9	.9	.9	1.0	46
48	.7	.8	.8	.8	.8	.8	.8	.9	.9	1.0	1.0	1.0	.1	48
50	0.8	0.8	0.8	0.8	0.9	0.9	0.9	0.9	1.0	1.1	1.1	1.1	1.3	50
52	.8	.9	.9	.9	.9	1.0	1.0	1.0	.1	.2	.2	.3	.5	52
54	.9	.9	1.0	1.0	1.0	.1	.1	.1	.2	.3	.4	.5	.8	54
56	1.0	1.0	.1	.1	.1	.2	.2	.2	.3	.5	.6	.8	2.2	56
58	.1	.1	.2	.2	.2	.3	.3	.4	.5	.7	.9	2.3	3.2	58
60	1.2	1.2	1.3	1.3	1.3	1.4	1.5	1.6	1.7	2.0	2.4	3.4		60
62	.3	.3	.4	.4	.4	.6	.7	.8	2.1	.5	3.5			62
64	.4	.4	.5	.5	.6	.8	.9	2.2	.6	3.7				64
66	.5	.5	.7	.7	.9	2.0	2.3	.8	3.8					66
68	.6	.7	.9	2.0	2.2	.4	.9	4.0						68
70	1.8	1.9	2.1	2.3	2.6	3.1	4.3							70
72	2.0	2.1	.5	.8	3.3	4.6								72
74	.2	.5	3.0	3.5	4.8									74
76	.6	3.0	.8	5.2										76
78	3.1	.6	5.7											78
80	3.8	4.4												80

TABLE 29.

Variation of Altitude in one minute from meridian passage.

Latitude.	Declination of the same name as the latitude; upper transit; reduction additive.												Latitude.
	0°	1°	2°	3°	4°	5°	6°	7°	8°	9°	10°	11°	
°	″	″	″	″	″	″	″	″	″	″	″	″	°
0					28.1	22.4	18.7	16.0	14.0	12.4	11.1	10.1	0
1						28.0	22.4	18.6	16.0	13.9	12.4	11.1	1
2							28.0	22.3	18.6	15.9	13.9	12.3	2
3								27.9	22.3	18.5	15.8	13.8	3
4	28.1								27.8	22.2	18.5	15.8	4
5	22.4	28.0								27.7	22.1	18.4	5
6	18.7	22.4	28.0								27.6	22.0	6
7	16.0	18.6	22.3	27.9								27.4	7
8	14.0	16.0	18.6	22.3	27.8								8
9	12.4	13.9	15.9	18.5	22.2	27.7							9
10	11.1	12.4	13.9	15.8	18.5	22.1	27.6						10
11	10.1	11.1	12.3	13.8	15.8	18.4	22.0	27.4					11
12	9.2	10.1	11.1	12.3	13.8	15.7	18.3	21.9	27.3				12
13	8.5	9.2	10.0	11.0	12.2	13.7	15.6	18.2	21.7	27.1			13
14	7.9	8.5	9.2	10.0	10.9	12.1	13.6	15.5	18.0	21.6	26.9		14
15	7.3	7.8	8.4	9.1	9.9	10.9	12.1	13.5	15.4	17.9	21.4	26.7	15
16	6.8	7.3	7.8	8.4	9.1	9.8	10.8	12.0	13.4	15.3	17.8	21.3	16
17	6.4	6.8	7.2	7.8	8.3	9.0	9.8	10.7	11.9	13.3	15.2	17.6	17
18	6.0	6.4	6.8	7.2	7.7	8.3	8.9	9.7	10.6	11.8	13.2	15.0	18
19	5.7	6.0	6.3	6.7	7.2	7.6	8.2	8.9	9.6	10.6	11.7	13.1	19
20	5.4	5.7	6.0	6.3	6.7	7.1	7.6	8.1	8.8	9.5	10.5	11.6	20
21	5.1	5.4	5.6	5.9	6.3	6.6	7.0	7.5	8.1	8.7	9.5	10.4	21
22	4.9	5.1	5.3	5.6	5.9	6.2	6.6	7.0	7.5	8.0	8.6	9.4	22
23	4.6	4.8	5.0	5.3	5.5	5.8	6.1	6.5	6.9	7.4	7.9	8.5	23
24	4.4	4.6	4.8	5.0	5.2	5.5	5.8	6.1	6.4	6.8	7.3	7.8	24
25	4.2	4.4	4.6	4.7	5.0	5.2	5.4	5.7	6.0	6.4	6.8	7.2	25
26	4.0	4.2	4.3	4.5	4.7	4.9	5.1	5.4	5.7	6.0	6.3	6.7	26
27	3.9	4.0	4.1	4.3	4.5	4.7	4.9	5.1	5.3	5.6	5.9	6.2	27
28	3.7	3.8	4.0	4.1	4.3	4.4	4.6	4.8	5.0	5.3	5.5	5.8	28
29	3.5	3.7	3.8	3.9	4.1	4.2	4.4	4.6	4.7	5.0	5.2	5.5	29
30	3.4	3.5	3.6	3.7	3.9	4.0	4.2	4.3	4.5	4.7	4.9	5.1	30
31	3.3	3.4	3.5	3.6	3.7	3.8	4.0	4.1	4.3	4.4	4.6	4.8	31
32	3.1	3.2	3.3	3.4	3.5	3.7	3.8	3.9	4.1	4.2	4.4	4.6	32
33	3.0	3.1	3.2	3.3	3.4	3.5	3.6	3.7	3.9	4.0	4.2	4.3	33
34	2.9	3.0	3.1	3.2	3.2	3.3	3.4	3.6	3.7	3.8	3.9	4.1	34
35	2.8	2.9	3.0	3.0	3.1	3.2	3.3	3.4	3.5	3.6	3.7	3.9	35
36	2.7	2.8	2.8	2.9	3.0	3.1	3.2	3.3	3.4	3.5	3.6	3.7	36
37	2.6	2.7	2.7	2.8	2.9	2.9	3.0	3.1	3.2	3.3	3.4	3.5	37
38	2.5	2.6	2.6	2.7	2.8	2.8	2.9	3.0	3.0	3.2	3.2	3.3	38
39	2.4	2.5	2.5	2.6	2.7	2.7	2.8	2.9	2.9	3.0	3.1	3.2	39
40	2.3	2.4	2.4	2.5	2.6	2.6	2.7	2.7	2.8	2.9	3.0	3.0	40
41	2.3	2.3	2.4	2.4	2.5	2.5	2.6	2.6	2.7	2.8	2.8	2.9	41
42	2.2	2.2	2.3	2.3	2.4	2.4	2.5	2.5	2.6	2.6	2.7	2.8	42
43	2.1	2.1	2.2	2.2	2.3	2.3	2.4	2.4	2.5	2.5	2.6	2.7	43
44	2.0	2.1	2.1	2.1	2.2	2.2	2.3	2.3	2.4	2.4	2.5	2.5	44
45	2.0	2.0	2.0	2.1	2.1	2.2	2.2	2.2	2.3	2.3	2.4	2.4	45
46	1.9	1.9	2.0	2.0	2.0	2.1	2.1	2.2	2.2	2.2	2.3	2.3	46
47	1.8	1.9	1.9	1.9	2.0	2.0	2.0	2.1	2.1	2.1	2.2	2.2	47
48	1.8	1.8	1.8	1.9	1.9	1.9	2.0	2.0	2.0	2.1	2.1	2.1	48
49	1.7	1.7	1.8	1.8	1.8	1.8	1.9	1.9	1.9	2.0	2.0	2.1	49
50	1.6	1.7	1.7	1.7	1.8	1.8	1.8	1.8	1.9	1.9	1.9	2.0	50
51	1.6	1.6	1.6	1.7	1.7	1.7	1.7	1.8	1.8	1.8	1.9	1.9	51
52	1.5	1.6	1.6	1.6	1.6	1.6	1.7	1.7	1.7	1.8	1.8	1.8	52
53	1.5	1.5	1.5	1.5	1.6	1.6	1.6	1.6	1.7	1.7	1.7	1.7	53
54	1.4	1.4	1.5	1.5	1.5	1.5	1.5	1.6	1.6	1.6	1.6	1.7	54
55	1.4	1.4	1.4	1.4	1.5	1.5	1.5	1.5	1.5	1.6	1.6	1.6	55
56	1.3	1.3	1.4	1.4	1.4	1.4	1.4	1.4	1.5	1.5	1.5	1.5	56
57	1.3	1.3	1.3	1.3	1.3	1.4	1.4	1.4	1.4	1.4	1.4	1.5	57
58	1.2	1.2	1.3	1.3	1.3	1.3	1.3	1.3	1.3	1.4	1.4	1.4	58
59	1.2	1.2	1.2	1.2	1.2	1.3	1.3	1.3	1.3	1.3	1.3	1.3	59
60	1.1	1.1	1.2	1.2	1.2	1.2	1.2	1.2	1.2	1.2	1.3	1.3	60
	0°	1°	2°	3°	4°	5°	6°	7°	8°	9°	10°	11°	
	Declination of the same name as the latitude; upper transit; reduction additive.												

TABLE 29.

Variation of Altitude in one minute from meridian passage.

Latitude.	Declination of the **same** name as the latitude; **upper** transit; reduction **additive.**													Latitude.
	12°	**13°**	**14°**	**15°**	**16°**	**17°**	**18°**	**19°**	**20°**	**21°**	**22°**	**23°**	**24°**	
°	′	′	′	′	′	′	′	′	′	′	′	′	′	°
0	9.2	8.5	7.9	7.3	6.8	6.4	6.0	5.7	5.4	5.1	4.9	4.6	4.4	0
1	10.1	9.2	8.5	7.8	7.3	6.8	6.4	6.0	5.7	5.4	5.1	4.8	4.6	1
2	11.1	10.0	9.2	8.4	7.8	7.2	6.8	6.3	6.0	5.6	5.3	5.0	4.8	2
3	12.3	11.0	10.0	9.1	8.4	7.8	7.2	6.7	6.3	5.9	5.6	5.3	5.0	3
4	13.8	12.2	10.9	9.9	9.1	8.3	7.7	7.2	6.7	6.3	5.9	5.5	5.2	4
5	15.7	13.7	12.1	10.9	9.8	9.0	8.3	7.6	7.1	6.6	6.2	5.8	5.5	5
6	18.3	15.6	13.6	12.1	10.8	9.8	8.9	8.2	7.6	7.0	6.6	6.1	5.8	6
7	21.9	18.2	15.5	13.5	12.0	10.7	9.7	8.9	8.1	7.5	7.0	6.5	6.1	7
8	27.3	21.7	18.0	15.4	13.4	11.9	10.6	9.6	8.8	8.1	7.5	6.9	6.4	8
9		27.1	21.6	17.9	15.3	13.3	11.8	10.6	9.5	8.7	8.0	7.4	6.8	9
10			26.9	21.4	17.8	15.2	13.2	11.7	10.5	9.5	8.6	7.9	7.3	10
11				26.7	21.3	17.6	15.0	13.1	11.6	10.4	9.4	8.5	7.8	11
12					26.5	21.1	17.5	14.9	13.0	11.5	10.3	9.3	8.4	12
13						26.2	20.9	17.3	14.8	12.8	11.3	10.1	9.2	13
14							26.0	20.7	17.1	14.6	12.7	11.2	10.0	14
15								25.7	20.4	16.9	14.4	12.5	11.1	15
16	26.5								25.4	20.2	16.7	14.3	12.4	16
17	21.1	26.2								25.1	20.0	16.5	14.1	17
18	17.5	20.9	26.0								24.8	19.7	16.3	18
19	14.9	17.3	20.7	25.7								24.5	19.5	19
20	13.0	14.8	17.1	20.4	25.4								24.2	20
21	11.5	12.8	14.6	16.9	20.2	25.1								21
22	10.3	11.3	12.7	14.4	16.7	20.0	24.8							22
23	9.3	10.1	11.2	12.5	14.3	16.5	19.7	24.5						23
24	8.4	9.2	10.0	11.1	12.4	14.1	16.3	19.5	24.2					24
25	7.7	8.3	9.0	9.9	10.9	12.2	13.9	16.1	19.2	23.8				25
26	7.1	7.6	8.2	8.9	9.8	10.8	12.1	13.7	15.9	18.9	23.5			26
27	6.6	7.0	7.5	8.1	8.8	9.6	10.6	11.9	13.5	15.6	18.6	23.1		27
28	6.2	6.5	7.0	7.4	8.0	8.7	9.5	10.5	11.7	13.3	15.4	18.3	22.7	28
29	5.7	6.1	6.4	6.9	7.3	7.9	8.6	9.4	10.3	11.5	13.1	15.1	18.0	29
30	5.4	5.7	6.0	6.4	6.8	7.2	7.8	8.4	9.2	10.1	11.3	12.8	14.9	30
31	5.1	5.3	5.6	5.9	6.3	6.7	7.1	7.7	8.3	9.0	10.0	11.1	12.6	31
32	4.8	5.0	5.2	5.5	5.8	6.2	6.5	7.0	7.5	8.1	8.9	9.8	10.9	32
33	4.5	4.7	4.9	5.1	5.4	5.7	6.1	6.4	6.9	7.4	8.0	8.7	9.6	33
34	4.3	4.4	4.6	4.8	5.1	5.3	5.6	5.9	6.3	6.8	7.3	7.8	8.6	34
35	4.0	4.2	4.4	4.5	4.7	5.0	5.2	5.5	5.8	6.2	6.6	7.1	7.7	35
36	3.8	4.0	4.1	4.3	4.5	4.7	4.9	5.1	5.4	5.7	6.1	6.5	7.0	36
37	3.6	3.8	3.9	4.0	4.2	4.4	4.6	4.8	5.0	5.3	5.6	6.0	6.4	37
38	3.4	3.6	3.7	3.8	4.0	4.1	4.3	4.5	4.7	4.9	5.2	5.5	5.8	38
39	3.3	3.4	3.5	3.6	3.8	3.9	4.0	4.2	4.4	4.6	4.8	5.1	5.4	39
40	3.1	3.2	3.3	3.4	3.6	3.7	3.8	4.0	4.1	4.3	4.5	4.7	5.0	40
41	3.0	3.1	3.2	3.3	3.4	3.5	3.6	3.7	3.9	4.0	4.2	4.4	4.6	41
42	2.9	2.9	3.0	3.1	3.2	3.3	3.4	3.5	3.7	3.8	4.0	4.1	4.3	42
43	2.7	2.8	2.9	3.0	3.0	3.1	3.2	3.3	3.5	3.6	3.7	3.9	4.0	43
44	2.6	2.7	2.7	2.8	2.9	3.0	3.1	3.2	3.3	3.4	3.5	3.6	3.8	44
45	2.5	2.6	2.6	2.7	2.8	2.8	2.9	3.0	3.1	3.2	3.3	3.4	3.5	45
46	2.4	2.4	2.5	2.6	2.6	2.7	2.8	2.8	2.9	3.0	3.1	3.2	3.3	46
47	2.3	2.3	2.4	2.4	2.5	2.6	2.6	2.7	2.8	2.9	2.9	3.0	3.1	47
48	2.2	2.2	2.3	2.3	2.4	2.4	2.5	2.6	2.6	2.7	2.8	2.9	3.0	48
49	2.1	2.1	2.2	2.2	2.3	2.3	2.4	2.4	2.5	2.6	2.6	2.7	2.8	49
50	2.0	2.0	2.1	2.1	2.2	2.2	2.3	2.3	2.4	2.4	2.5	2.6	2.6	50
51	1.9	2.0	2.0	2.0	2.1	2.1	2.2	2.2	2.3	2.3	2.4	2.4	2.5	51
52	1.8	1.9	1.9	1.9	2.0	2.0	2.1	2.1	2.1	2.2	2.2	2.3	2.4	52
53	1.8	1.8	1.8	1.9	1.9	1.9	2.0	2.0	2.0	2.1	2.1	2.2	2.2	53
54	1.7	1.7	1.7	1.8	1.8	1.8	1.9	1.9	1.9	2.0	2.0	2.1	2.1	54
55	1.6	1.6	1.7	1.7	1.7	1.8	1.8	1.8	1.9	1.9	1.9	2.0	2.0	55
56	1.5	1.6	1.6	1.6	1.6	1.7	1.7	1.7	1.8	1.8	1.8	1.9	1.9	56
57	1.5	1.5	1.5	1.5	1.6	1.6	1.6	1.6	1.7	1.7	1.7	1.8	1.8	57
58	1.4	1.4	1.5	1.5	1.5	1.5	1.5	1.6	1.6	1.6	1.6	1.7	1.7	58
59	1.4	1.4	1.4	1.4	1.4	1.5	1.5	1.5	1.5	1.5	1.6	1.6	1.6	59
60	1.3	1.3	1.3	1.3	1.4	1.4	1.4	1.4	1.4	1.5	1.5	1.5	1.5	60
	12°	**13°**	**14°**	**15°**	**16°**	**17°**	**18°**	**19°**	**20°**	**21°**	**22°**	**23°**	**24°**	
	Declination of the **same** name as the latitude; **upper** transit; reduction **additive.**													

TABLE 29.

Variation of Altitude in one minute from meridian passage.

Latitude.	25°	26°	27°	28°	29°	30°	31°	32°	33°	34°	35°	36°	37°	Latitude.
	Declination of the same name as the latitude; upper transit; reduction additive.													
°	"	"	"	"	"	"	"	"	"	"	"	"	"	°
0	4.2	4.0	3.9	3.7	3.5	3.4	3.3	3.1	3.0	2.9	2.8	2.7	2.6	0
1	4.4	4.2	4.0	3.8	3.7	3.5	3.4	3.2	3.1	3.0	2.9	2.8	2.7	1
2	4.6	4.3	4.1	4.0	3.8	3.6	3.5	3.3	3.2	3.1	3.0	2.8	2.7	2
3	4.7	4.5	4.3	4.1	3.9	3.7	3.6	3.4	3.3	3.2	3.0	2.9	2.8	3
4	5.0	4.7	4.5	4.3	4.1	3.9	3.7	3.5	3.4	3.3	3.1	3.0	2.9	4
5	5.2	4.9	4.7	4.4	4.2	4.0	3.8	3.7	3.5	3.3	3.2	3.1	3.0	5
6	5.4	5.1	4.9	4.6	4.4	4.2	4.0	3.8	3.6	3.5	3.3	3.2	3.0	6
7	5.7	5.4	5.1	4.8	4.6	4.3	4.1	3.9	3.7	3.6	3.4	3.3	3.1	7
8	6.0	5.7	5.3	5.0	4.8	4.5	4.3	4.1	3.9	3.7	3.5	3.4	3.2	8
9	6.4	6.0	5.6	5.3	5.0	4.7	4.4	4.2	4.0	3.8	3.6	3.5	3.3	9
10	6.8	6.3	5.9	5.5	5.2	4.9	4.6	4.4	4.2	3.9	3.8	3.6	3.4	10
11	7.2	6.7	6.2	5.8	5.5	5.1	4.8	4.6	4.3	4.1	3.9	3.7	3.5	11
12	7.7	7.1	6.6	6.2	5.8	5.4	5.1	4.8	4.5	4.3	4.0	3.8	3.6	12
13	8.3	7.6	7.1	6.5	6.1	5.7	5.3	5.0	4.7	4.4	4.2	4.0	3.8	13
14	9.1	8.2	7.6	7.0	6.4	6.0	5.6	5.2	4.9	4.6	4.4	4.1	3.9	14
15	9.9	8.9	8.1	7.4	6.9	6.4	5.9	5.5	5.2	4.8	4.5	4.3	4.0	15
16	10.9	9.8	8.8	8.0	7.3	6.8	6.3	5.8	5.4	5.1	4.8	4.5	4.2	16
17	12.2	10.8	9.6	8.7	7.9	7.2	6.7	6.2	5.7	5.3	5.0	4.7	4.4	17
18	13.9	12.1	10.6	9.5	8.6	7.8	7.1	6.6	6.1	5.6	5.2	4.9	4.6	18
19	16.1	13.7	11.9	10.5	9.4	8.4	7.7	7.0	6.4	6.0	5.5	5.1	4.8	19
20	19.2	15.9	13.5	11.7	10.3	9.2	8.3	7.5	6.9	6.3	5.8	5.4	5.0	20
21	23.8	18.9	15.6	13.3	11.5	10.2	9.1	8.2	7.4	6.8	6.2	5.7	5.3	21
22		23.5	18.6	15.4	13.1	11.3	10.0	8.9	8.0	7.3	6.6	6.1	5.6	22
23			23.1	18.3	15.1	12.8	11.1	9.8	8.7	7.9	7.1	6.5	6.0	23
24				22.7	18.0	14.9	12.6	10.9	9.6	8.6	7.7	7.0	6.4	24
25					22.3	17.7	14.6	12.4	10.7	9.4	8.4	7.5	6.8	25
26						21.9	17.4	14.3	12.1	10.5	9.2	8.2	7.4	26
27							21.5	17.0	14.0	11.9	10.3	9.1	8.1	27
28								21.1	16.7	13.8	11.7	10.1	8.9	28
29	22.3								20.6	16.3	13.5	11.4	9.9	29
30	17.7	21.9								20.2	16.0	13.2	11.1	30
31	14.6	17.4	21.5								19.8	15.6	12.9	31
32	12.4	14.3	17.0	21.1								19.3	15.3	32
33	10.7	12.1	14.0	16.7	20.6								18.9	33
34	9.4	10.5	11.9	13.8	16.3	20.2								34
35	8.4	9.2	10.3	11.7	13.5	16.0	19.8							35
36	7.5	8.2	9.1	10.1	11.4	13.2	15.6	19.3						36
37	6.8	7.4	8.1	8.9	9.9	11.1	12.9	15.3	18.9					37
38	6.2	6.7	7.2	7.9	8.7	9.6	10.9	12.6	14.9	18.4				38
39	5.7	6.1	6.5	7.1	7.7	8.5	9.4	10.6	12.2	14.5	17.9			39
40	5.3	5.6	6.0	6.4	6.9	7.5	8.2	9.2	10.4	11.9	14.1	17.4		40
41	4.9	5.2	5.5	5.8	6.2	6.7	7.3	8.0	8.9	10.1	11.6	13.8	17.0	41
42	4.5	4.8	5.0	5.3	5.7	6.1	6.6	7.1	7.8	8.7	9.8	11.3	13.4	42
43	4.2	4.4	4.6	4.9	5.2	5.5	5.9	6.4	6.9	7.6	8.5	9.5	11.0	43
44	3.9	4.1	4.3	4.5	4.8	5.1	5.4	5.8	6.2	6.7	7.4	8.2	9.3	44
45	3.7	3.8	4.0	4.2	4.4	4.7	4.9	5.2	5.6	6.0	6.6	7.2	8.0	45
46	3.5	3.6	3.7	3.9	4.1	4.3	4.5	4.8	5.1	5.4	5.9	6.4	7.0	46
47	3.3	3.4	3.5	3.6	3.8	4.0	4.2	4.4	4.6	4.9	5.3	5.7	6.2	47
48	3.1	3.2	3.3	3.4	3.5	3.7	3.9	4.0	4.3	4.5	4.8	5.1	5.5	48
49	2.9	3.0	3.1	3.2	3.3	3.4	3.6	3.7	3.9	4.1	4.4	4.6	5.0	49
50	2.7	2.8	2.9	3.0	3.1	3.2	3.3	3.5	3.6	3.8	4.0	4.2	4.5	50
51	2.6	2.6	2.7	2.8	2.9	3.0	3.1	3.2	3.4	3.5	3.7	3.9	4.1	51
52	2.4	2.5	2.6	2.6	2.7	2.8	2.9	3.0	3.1	3.2	3.4	3.6	3.7	52
53	2.3	2.3	2.4	2.5	2.5	2.6	2.7	2.8	2.9	3.0	3.1	3.3	3.4	53
54	2.2	2.2	2.3	2.3	2.4	2.5	2.5	2.6	2.7	2.8	2.9	3.0	3.2	54
55	2.0	2.1	2.1	2.2	2.3	2.3	2.4	2.4	2.5	2.6	2.7	2.8	2.9	55
56	1.9	2.0	2.0	2.1	2.1	2.2	2.2	2.3	2.4	2.4	2.5	2.6	2.7	56
57	1.8	1.9	1.9	2.0	2.0	2.0	2.1	2.2	2.2	2.3	2.3	2.4	2.5	57
58	1.7	1.8	1.8	1.8	1.9	1.9	2.0	2.0	2.1	2.1	2.2	2.3	2.3	58
59	1.6	1.7	1.7	1.7	1.8	1.8	1.9	1.9	1.9	2.0	2.0	2.1	2.2	59
60	1.6	1.6	1.6	1.6	1.7	1.7	1.7	1.8	1.8	1.9	1.9	2.0	2.0	60
	25°	26°	27°	28°	29°	30°	31°	32°	33°	34°	35°	36°	37°	
	Declination of the same name as the latitude; upper transit; reduction additive.													

TABLE 29.

Variation of Altitude in one minute from meridian passage.

Latitude.	Declination of the **same** name as the latitude; **upper transit**; reduction **additive.**													Latitude.
	38°	39°	40°	41°	42°	43°	44°	45°	46°	47°	48°	49°	50°	
°	"	"	"	"	"	"	"	"	"	"	"	"	"	°
0	2.5	2.4	2.3	2.3	2.2	2.1	2.0	2.0	1.9	1.8	1.8	1.7	1.7	0
1	2.6	2.5	2.4	2.3	2.2	2.2	2.1	2.0	1.9	1.9	1.8	1.7	1.7	1
2	2.6	2.5	2.4	2.4	2.3	2.2	2.1	2.0	2.0	1.9	1.8	1.8	1.7	2
3	2.7	2.6	2.5	2.4	2.3	2.2	2.2	2.1	2.0	1.9	1.9	1.8	1.7	3
4	2.8	2.7	2.6	2.5	2.4	2.3	2.2	2.1	2.0	2.0	1.9	1.8	1.8	4
5	2.8	2.7	2.6	2.5	2.4	2.3	2.2	2.2	2.1	2.0	1.9	1.9	1.8	5
6	2.9	2.8	2.7	2.6	2.5	2.4	2.3	2.2	2.1	2.0	2.0	1.9	1.8	6
7	3.0	2.9	2.7	2.6	2.5	2.4	2.3	2.2	2.2	2.1	2.0	1.9	1.8	7
8	3.1	2.9	2.8	2.7	2.6	2.5	2.4	2.3	2.2	2.1	2.0	1.9	1.9	8
9	3.2	3.0	2.9	2.8	2.7	2.5	2.4	2.3	2.2	2.2	2.1	2.0	1.9	9
10	3.3	3.1	3.0	2.8	2.7	2.6	2.5	2.4	2.3	2.2	2.1	2.0	1.9	10
11	3.4	3.2	3.1	2.9	2.8	2.7	2.6	2.4	2.3	2.2	2.1	2.1	2.0	11
12	3.5	3.3	3.1	3.0	2.9	2.7	2.6	2.5	2.4	2.3	2.2	2.1	2.0	12
13	3.6	3.4	3.2	3.1	2.9	2.8	2.7	2.6	2.4	2.3	2.2	2.1	2.0	13
14	3.7	3.5	3.3	3.2	3.0	2.9	2.7	2.6	2.5	2.4	2.3	2.2	2.1	14
15	3.8	3.6	3.4	3.3	3.1	3.0	2.8	2.7	2.6	2.4	2.3	2.2	2.1	15
16	4.0	3.8	3.6	3.4	3.2	3.0	2.9	2.8	2.6	2.5	2.4	2.3	2.2	16
17	4.1	3.9	3.7	3.5	3.3	3.1	3.0	2.8	2.7	2.6	2.4	2.3	2.2	17
18	4.3	4.1	3.8	3.6	3.4	3.2	3.1	2.9	2.8	2.6	2.5	2.4	2.3	18
19	4.5	4.2	4.0	3.7	3.5	3.3	3.2	3.0	2.8	2.7	2.6	2.4	2.3	19
20	4.7	4.4	4.1	3.9	3.7	3.5	3.3	3.1	2.9	2.8	2.6	2.5	2.4	20
21	4.9	4.6	4.3	4.0	3.8	3.6	3.4	3.2	3.0	2.9	2.7	2.6	2.4	21
22	5.2	4.8	4.5	4.2	4.0	3.7	3.5	3.3	3.1	2.9	2.8	2.6	2.5	22
23	5.5	5.1	4.7	4.4	4.1	3.9	3.6	3.4	3.2	3.0	2.9	2.7	2.6	23
24	5.8	5.4	5.0	4.6	4.3	4.0	3.8	3.5	3.3	3.1	3.0	2.8	2.6	24
25	6.2	5.7	5.3	4.9	4.5	4.2	3.9	3.7	3.5	3.3	3.1	2.9	2.7	25
26	6.7	6.1	5.6	5.2	4.8	4.4	4.1	3.8	3.6	3.4	3.2	3.0	2.8	26
27	7.2	6.5	6.0	5.5	5.0	4.6	4.3	4.0	3.7	3.5	3.3	3.1	2.9	27
28	7.9	7.1	6.4	5.8	5.3	4.9	4.5	4.2	3.9	3.6	3.4	3.2	3.0	28
29	8.7	7.7	6.9	6.2	5.7	5.2	4.8	4.4	4.1	3.8	3.5	3.3	3.1	29
30	9.6	8.5	7.5	6.7	6.1	5.5	5.1	4.7	4.3	4.0	3.7	3.4	3.2	30
31	10.9	9.4	8.2	7.3	6.6	5.9	5.4	4.9	4.5	4.2	3.9	3.6	3.3	31
32	12.6	10.6	9.2	8.0	7.1	6.4	5.8	5.2	4.8	4.4	4.0	3.7	3.5	32
33	14.9	12.2	10.4	8.9	7.8	6.9	6.2	5.6	5.1	4.6	4.3	3.9	3.6	33
34	18.4	14.5	11.9	10.1	8.7	7.6	6.7	6.0	5.4	4.9	4.5	4.1	3.8	34
35		17.9	14.1	11.6	9.8	8.5	7.4	6.6	5.9	5.3	4.8	4.4	4.0	35
36			17.4	13.8	11.3	9.5	8.2	7.2	6.4	5.7	5.1	4.6	4.2	36
37				17.0	13.4	11.0	9.3	8.0	7.0	6.2	5.5	5.0	4.5	37
38					16.5	13.0	10.7	9.0	7.7	6.8	6.0	5.3	4.8	38
39						16.0	12.6	10.3	8.7	7.5	6.5	5.8	5.1	39
40							15.5	12.2	10.0	8.4	7.2	6.3	5.6	40
41								15.0	11.8	9.7	8.1	7.0	6.1	41
42	16.5								14.5	11.4	9.3	7.9	6.7	42
43	13.0	16.0								14.0	11.0	9.0	7.6	43
44	10.7	12.6	15.5								13.6	10.6	8.7	44
45	9.0	10.3	12.2	15.0								13.1	10.2	45
46	7.7	8.7	10.0	11.8	14.5								12.6	46
47	6.8	7.5	8.4	9.7	11.4	14.0								47
48	6.0	6.5	7.2	8.1	9.3	11.0	13.6							48
49	5.3	5.8	6.3	7.0	7.9	9.0	10.6	13.1						49
50	4.8	5.1	5.6	6.1	6.7	7.6	8.7	10.2	12.6					50
51	4.3	4.6	5.0	5.4	5.9	6.5	7.3	8.4	9.9	12.1				51
52	3.9	4.2	4.5	4.8	5.2	5.7	6.3	7.0	8.0	9.5	11.6			52
53	3.6	3.8	4.0	4.3	4.6	5.0	5.4	6.0	6.7	7.7	9.1	11.1		53
54	3.3	3.5	3.7	3.9	4.1	4.4	4.8	5.2	5.8	6.5	7.4	8.7	10.6	54
55	3.0	3.2	3.3	3.5	3.7	4.0	4.3	4.6	5.0	5.5	6.2	7.1	8.3	55
56	2.8	2.9	3.1	3.2	3.4	3.6	3.8	4.1	4.4	4.8	5.3	5.9	6.8	56
57	2.6	2.7	2.8	2.9	3.1	3.2	3.4	3.6	3.9	4.2	4.6	5.0	5.6	57
58	2.4	2.5	2.6	2.7	2.8	2.9	3.1	3.3	3.5	3.7	4.0	4.4	4.8	58
59	2.2	2.3	2.4	2.5	2.6	2.7	2.8	3.0	3.1	3.3	3.6	3.8	4.2	59
60	2.1	2.1	2.2	2.3	2.4	2.5	2.6	2.7	2.8	3.0	3.2	3.4	3.6	60
	38°	39°	40°	41°	42°	43°	44°	45°	46°	47°	48°	49°	50°	
	Declination of the **same** name as the latitude; **upper transit**; reduction **additive.**													

TABLE 29.

Variation of Altitude in one minute from meridian passage.

Latitude.	Declination of the **same** name as the latitude; **upper** transit; reduction **additive.**													Latitude.
	51°	52°	53°	54°	55°	56°	57°	58°	59°	60°	61°	62°	63°	
°	"	"	"	"	"	"	"	"	"	"	"	"	"	°
0	1.6	1.5	1.5	1.4	1.4	1.3	1.3	1.2	1.2	1.1	1.1	1.0	1.0	0
1	1.6	1.6	1.5	1.4	1.4	1.3	1.3	1.2	1.2	1.2	1.1	1.1	1.0	1
2	1.6	1.6	1.5	1.5	1.4	1.4	1.3	1.3	1.2	1.2	1.1	1.1	1.0	2
3	1.7	1.6	1.5	1.5	1.4	1.4	1.3	1.3	1.2	1.2	1.1	1.1	1.0	3
4	1.7	1.6	1.6	1.5	1.5	1.4	1.3	1.3	1.2	1.2	1.1	1.1	1.0	4
5	1.7	1.7	1.6	1.5	1.5	1.4	1.4	1.3	1.3	1.2	1.1	1.1	1.1	5
6	1.7	1.7	1.6	1.5	1.5	1.4	1.4	1.3	1.3	1.2	1.2	1.1	1.1	6
7	1.8	1.7	1.6	1.6	1.5	1.4	1.4	1.3	1.3	1.2	1.2	1.1	1.1	7
8	1.8	1.7	1.7	1.6	1.5	1.5	1.4	1.4	1.3	1.2	1.2	1.1	1.1	8
9	1.8	1.8	1.7	1.6	1.6	1.5	1.4	1.4	1.3	1.3	1.2	1.1	1.1	9
10	1.9	1.8	1.7	1.6	1.6	1.5	1.4	1.4	1.3	1.3	1.2	1.2	1.1	10
11	1.9	1.8	1.7	1.7	1.6	1.5	1.5	1.4	1.3	1.3	1.2	1.2	1.1	11
12	1.9	1.8	1.8	1.7	1.6	1.6	1.5	1.4	1.4	1.3	1.2	1.2	1.1	12
13	2.0	1.9	1.8	1.7	1.6	1.6	1.5	1.4	1.4	1.3	1.3	1.2	1.1	13
14	2.0	1.9	1.8	1.7	1.7	1.6	1.5	1.5	1.4	1.3	1.3	1.2	1.2	14
15	2.0	1.9	1.9	1.8	1.7	1.6	1.5	1.5	1.4	1.3	1.3	1.2	1.2	15
16	2.1	2.0	1.9	1.8	1.7	1.6	1.6	1.5	1.4	1.4	1.3	1.2	1.2	16
17	2.1	2.0	1.9	1.8	1.8	1.7	1.6	1.5	1.5	1.4	1.3	1.3	1.2	17
18	2.2	2.1	2.0	1.9	1.8	1.7	1.6	1.5	1.5	1.4	1.3	1.3	1.2	18
19	2.2	2.1	2.0	1.9	1.8	1.7	1.6	1.6	1.5	1.4	1.4	1.3	1.2	19
20	2.3	2.1	2.0	1.9	1.9	1.8	1.7	1.6	1.5	1.4	1.4	1.3	1.2	20
21	2.3	2.2	2.1	2.0	1.9	1.8	1.7	1.6	1.5	1.5	1.4	1.3	1.2	21
22	2.4	2.2	2.1	2.0	1.9	1.8	1.7	1.6	1.6	1.5	1.4	1.3	1.3	22
23	2.4	2.3	2.2	2.1	2.0	1.9	1.8	1.7	1.6	1.5	1.4	1.4	1.3	23
24	2.5	2.4	2.2	2.1	2.0	1.9	1.8	1.7	1.6	1.5	1.5	1.4	1.3	24
25	2.6	2.4	2.3	2.2	2.0	1.9	1.8	1.7	1.6	1.6	1.5	1.4	1.3	25
26	2.6	2.5	2.3	2.2	2.1	2.0	1.9	1.8	1.7	1.6	1.5	1.4	1.3	26
27	2.7	2.6	2.4	2.3	2.1	2.0	1.9	1.8	1.7	1.6	1.5	1.4	1.4	27
28	2.8	2.6	2.5	2.3	2.2	2.1	2.0	1.8	1.7	1.6	1.5	1.5	1.4	28
29	2.9	2.7	2.5	2.4	2.3	2.1	2.0	1.9	1.8	1.7	1.6	1.5	1.4	29
30	3.0	2.8	2.6	2.5	2.3	2.2	2.0	1.9	1.8	1.7	1.6	1.5	1.4	30
31	3.1	2.9	2.7	2.5	2.4	2.2	2.1	2.0	1.9	1.7	1.6	1.5	1.4	31
32	3.2	3.0	2.8	2.6	2.4	2.3	2.2	2.0	1.9	1.8	1.7	1.6	1.5	32
33	3.4	3.1	2.9	2.7	2.5	2.4	2.2	2.1	1.9	1.8	1.7	1.6	1.5	33
34	3.5	3.2	3.0	2.8	2.6	2.4	2.3	2.1	2.0	1.9	1.7	1.6	1.5	34
35	3.7	3.4	3.1	2.9	2.7	2.5	2.3	2.2	2.0	1.9	1.8	1.7	1.6	35
36	3.9	3.6	3.3	3.0	2.8	2.6	2.4	2.3	2.1	2.0	1.8	1.7	1.6	36
37	4.1	3.7	3.4	3.2	2.9	2.7	2.5	2.3	2.2	2.0	1.9	1.7	1.6	37
38	4.3	3.9	3.6	3.3	3.0	2.8	2.6	2.4	2.2	2.1	1.9	1.8	1.7	38
39	4.6	4.2	3.8	3.5	3.2	2.9	2.7	2.5	2.3	2.1	2.0	1.8	1.7	39
40	5.0	4.5	4.0	3.7	3.3	3.1	2.8	2.6	2.4	2.2	2.0	1.9	1.8	40
41	5.4	4.8	4.3	3.9	3.5	3.2	2.9	2.7	2.5	2.3	2.1	1.9	1.8	41
42	5.9	5.2	4.6	4.1	3.7	3.4	3.1	2.8	2.6	2.4	2.2	2.0	1.9	42
43	6.5	5.7	5.0	4.4	4.0	3.6	3.2	2.9	2.7	2.5	2.3	2.1	1.9	43
44	7.3	6.3	5.4	4.8	4.3	3.8	3.4	3.1	2.8	2.6	2.3	2.2	2.0	44
45	8.4	7.0	6.0	5.2	4.6	4.1	3.6	3.3	3.0	2.7	2.4	2.2	2.0	45
46	9.9	8.0	6.7	5.8	5.0	4.4	3.9	3.5	3.1	2.8	2.6	2.3	2.1	46
47	12.1	9.5	7.7	6.5	5.5	4.8	4.2	3.7	3.3	3.0	2.7	2.4	2.2	47
48		11.6	9.1	7.4	6.2	5.3	4.6	4.0	3.6	3.2	2.8	2.6	2.3	48
49			11.1	8.7	7.1	5.9	5.0	4.4	3.8	3.4	3.0	2.7	2.4	49
50				10.6	8.3	6.8	5.6	4.8	4.2	3.6	3.2	2.9	2.6	50
51					10.2	7.9	6.4	5.4	4.6	4.0	3.5	3.0	2.7	51
52						9.7	7.6	6.1	5.1	4.3	3.8	3.3	2.9	52
53							9.2	7.2	5.9	4.9	4.1	3.6	3.1	53
54								8.8	6.8	5.5	4.6	3.9	3.4	54
55	10.2								8.3	6.5	5.3	4.3	3.7	55
56	7.9	9.7								7.9	6.1	5.0	4.1	56
57	6.4	7.6	9.2								7.4	5.8	4.7	57
58	5.4	6.1	7.2	8.8								7.0	5.4	58
59	4.6	5.1	5.9	6.8	8.3								6.6	59
60	4.0	4.3	4.9	5.5	6.5	7.9								60
	51°	52°	53°	54°	55°	56°	57°	58°	59°	60°	61°	62°	63°	
	Declination of the **same** name as the latitude; **upper** transit; reduction **additive.**													

TABLE 29.

Variation of Altitude in one minute from meridian passage.

Latitude.	0°	1°	2°	3°	4°	5°	6°	7°	8°	9°	10°	11°	Latitude.
	Declination of a different name from the latitude; upper transit; reduction additive.												
°	"	"	"	"	"	"	"	"	"	"	"	"	°
0					28.1	22.4	18.7	16.0	14.0	12.4	11.1	10.1	0
1				28.1	22.4	18.7	16.0	14.0	12.4	11.2	10.1	9.3	1
2			28.1	22.4	18.7	16.0	14.0	12.5	11.2	10.2	9.3	8.6	2
3		28.1	22.4	18.7	16.0	14.0	12.5	11.2	10.2	9.3	8.6	8.0	3
4	28.1	22.4	18.7	16.0	14.0	12.5	11.2	10.2	9.3	8.6	8.0	7.4	4
5	22.4	18.7	16.0	14.0	12.5	11.2	10.2	9.3	8.6	8.0	7.4	7.0	5
6	18.7	16.0	14.0	12.5	11.2	10.2	9.3	8.6	8.0	7.5	7.0	6.6	6
7	16.0	14.0	12.4	11.2	10.2	9.3	8.6	8.0	7.5	7.0	6.6	6.2	7
8	14.0	12.4	11.2	10.2	9.3	8.6	8.0	7.5	7.0	6.6	6.2	5.9	8
9	12.4	11.2	10.2	9.3	8.6	8.0	7.5	7.0	6.6	6.2	5.9	5.6	9
10	11.1	10.1	9.3	8.6	8.0	7.4	7.0	6.6	6.2	5.9	5.6	5.3	10
11	10.1	9.3	8.6	8.0	7.4	7.0	6.6	6.2	5.9	5.6	5.3	5.1	11
12	9.2	8.5	7.9	7.4	7.0	6.5	6.2	5.9	5.6	5.3	5.0	4.8	12
13	8.5	7.9	7.4	6.9	6.5	6.2	5.8	5.6	5.3	5.0	4.8	4.6	13
14	7.9	7.4	6.9	6.5	6.2	5.8	5.5	5.3	5.0	4.8	4.6	4.4	14
15	7.3	6.9	6.5	6.1	5.8	5.5	5.3	5.0	4.8	4.6	4.4	4.2	15
16	6.8	6.5	6.1	5.8	5.5	5.2	5.0	4.8	4.6	4.4	4.2	4.1	16
17	6.4	6.1	5.8	5.5	5.2	5.0	4.8	4.6	4.4	4.2	4.1	3.9	17
18	6.0	5.7	5.5	5.2	5.0	4.8	4.6	4.4	4.2	4.1	3.9	3.8	18
19	5.7	5.4	5.2	4.9	4.7	4.5	4.4	4.2	4.0	3.9	3.8	3.6	19
20	5.4	5.1	4.9	4.7	4.5	4.3	4.2	4.0	3.9	3.8	3.6	3.5	20
21	5.1	4.9	4.7	4.5	4.3	4.2	4.0	3.9	3.7	3.6	3.5	3.4	21
22	4.9	4.7	4.5	4.3	4.1	4.0	3.9	3.7	3.6	3.5	3.4	3.3	22
23	4.6	4.4	4.3	4.1	4.0	3.8	3.7	3.6	3.5	3.4	3.3	3.2	23
24	4.4	4.2	4.1	3.9	3.8	3.7	3.6	3.5	3.4	3.3	3.2	3.1	24
25	4.2	4.1	3.9	3.8	3.7	3.5	3.4	3.3	3.2	3.1	3.1	3.0	25
26	4.0	3.9	3.8	3.6	3.5	3.4	3.3	3.2	3.1	3.0	3.0	2.9	26
27	3.9	3.7	3.6	3.5	3.4	3.3	3.2	3.1	3.0	2.9	2.9	2.8	27
28	3.7	3.6	3.5	3.4	3.3	3.2	3.1	3.0	2.9	2.8	2.8	2.7	28
29	3.5	3.4	3.3	3.2	3.1	3.1	3.0	2.9	2.8	2.8	2.7	2.6	29
30	3.4	3.3	3.2	3.1	3.0	3.0	2.9	2.8	2.7	2.7	2.6	2.5	30
31	3.3	3.2	3.1	3.0	2.9	2.9	2.8	2.7	2.6	2.6	2.5	2.5	31
32	3.2	3.1	3.0	2.9	2.8	2.8	2.7	2.6	2.6	2.5	2.5	2.4	32
33	3.0	2.9	2.9	2.8	2.7	2.7	2.6	2.5	2.5	2.4	2.4	2.3	33
34	2.9	2.8	2.8	2.7	2.6	2.6	2.5	2.5	2.4	2.4	2.3	2.3	34
35	2.8	2.7	2.7	2.6	2.5	2.5	2.4	2.4	2.3	2.3	2.2	2.2	35
36	2.7	2.6	2.6	2.5	2.5	2.4	2.4	2.3	2.3	2.2	2.2	2.1	36
37	2.6	2.5	2.5	2.4	2.4	2.3	2.3	2.2	2.2	2.2	2.1	2.1	37
38	2.5	2.5	2.4	2.4	2.3	2.3	2.2	2.2	2.1	2.1	2.1	2.0	38
39	2.4	2.4	2.3	2.3	2.2	2.2	2.1	2.1	2.1	2.0	2.0	2.0	39
40	2.3	2.3	2.2	2.2	2.2	2.1	2.1	2.0	2.0	2.0	1.9	1.9	40
41	2.3	2.2	2.2	2.1	2.1	2.1	2.0	2.0	1.9	1.9	1.9	1.8	41
42	2.2	2.1	2.1	2.1	2.0	2.0	2.0	1.9	1.9	1.9	1.8	1.8	42
43	2.1	2.1	2.0	2.0	2.0	1.9	1.9	1.9	1.8	1.8	1.8	1.7	43
44	2.0	2.0	2.0	1.9	1.9	1.9	1.8	1.8	1.8	1.7	1.7	1.7	44
45	2.0	1.9	1.9	1.9	1.8	1.8	1.8	1.7	1.7	1.7	1.7	1.6	45
46	1.9	1.9	1.8	1.8	1.8	1.7	1.7	1.7	1.7	1.6	1.6	1.6	46
47	1.8	1.8	1.8	1.7	1.7	1.7	1.7	1.6	1.6	1.6	1.6	1.6	47
48	1.8	1.7	1.7	1.7	1.7	1.6	1.6	1.6	1.6	1.6	1.5	1.5	48
49	1.7	1.7	1.7	1.6	1.6	1.6	1.6	1.5	1.5	1.5	1.5	1.5	49
50	1.6	1.6	1.6	1.6	1.6	1.5	1.5	1.5	1.5	1.5	1.4	1.4	50
51	1.6	1.6	1.6	1.5	1.5	1.5	1.5	1.5	1.4	1.4	1.4	1.4	51
52	1.5	1.5	1.5	1.5	1.5	1.4	1.4	1.4	1.4	1.4	1.4	1.3	52
53	1.5	1.5	1.4	1.4	1.4	1.4	1.4	1.4	1.3	1.3	1.3	1.3	53
54	1.4	1.4	1.4	1.4	1.4	1.3	1.3	1.3	1.3	1.3	1.3	1.3	54
55	1.4	1.4	1.3	1.3	1.3	1.3	1.3	1.3	1.3	1.2	1.2	1.2	55
56	1.3	1.3	1.3	1.3	1.3	1.3	1.2	1.2	1.2	1.2	1.2	1.2	56
57	1.3	1.3	1.3	1.2	1.2	1.2	1.2	1.2	1.2	1.2	1.1	1.1	57
58	1.2	1.2	1.2	1.2	1.2	1.2	1.2	1.1	1.1	1.1	1.1	1.1	58
59	1.2	1.2	1.2	1.2	1.1	1.1	1.1	1.1	1.1	1.1	1.1	1.1	59
60	1.1	1.1	1.1	1.1	1.1	1.1	1.1	1.1	1.0	1 0	1.0	1.0	60
	0°	1°	2°	3°	4°	5°	6°	7°	8°	9°	10°	11°	
	Declination of a different name from the latitude; upper transit; reduction additive.												

TABLE 29.

Variation of Altitude in one minute from meridian passage.

Latitude.	Declination of a **different** name from the latitude; **upper** transit; reduction **additive.**													Latitude.
	12°	13°	14°	15°	16°	17°	18°	19°	20°	21°	22°	23°	24°	
°	″	″	″	″	″	″	″	″	″	″	″	″	″	°
0	9.2	8.5	7.9	7.3	6.8	6.4	6.0	5.7	5.4	5.1	4.9	4.6	4.4	0
1	8.5	7.9	7.4	6.9	6.5	6.1	5.7	5.4	5.1	4.9	4.7	4.4	4.2	1
2	7.9	7.4	6.9	6.5	6.1	5.8	5.5	5.2	4.9	4.7	4.5	4.3	4.1	2
3	7.4	6.9	6.5	6.1	5.8	5.5	5.2	4.9	4.7	4.5	4.3	4.1	3.9	3
4	7.0	6.5	6.2	5.8	5.5	5.2	5.0	4.7	4.5	4.3	4.1	4.0	3.8	4
5	6.5	6.2	5.8	5.5	5.2	5.0	4.8	4.5	4.3	4.2	4.0	3.8	3.7	5
6	6.2	5.8	5.5	5.3	5.0	4.8	4.6	4.4	4.2	4.0	3.9	3.7	3.6	6
7	5.9	5.6	5.3	5.0	4.8	4.6	4.4	4.2	4.0	3.9	3.7	3.6	3.5	7
8	5.6	5.3	5.0	4.8	4.6	4.4	4.2	4.0	3.9	3.7	3.6	3.5	3.4	8
9	5.3	5.0	4.8	4.6	4.4	4.2	4.1	3.9	3.8	3.6	3.5	3.4	3.3	9
10	5.0	4.8	4.6	4.4	4.2	4.1	3.9	3.8	3.6	3.5	3.4	3.3	3.2	10
11	4.8	4.6	4.4	4.2	4.1	3.9	3.8	3.6	3.5	3.4	3.3	3.2	3.1	11
12	4.6	4.4	4.3	4.1	3.9	3.8	3.7	3.5	3.4	3.3	3.2	3.1	3.0	12
13	4.4	4.3	4.1	3.9	3.8	3.7	3.5	3.4	3.3	3.2	3.1	3.0	2.9	13
14	4.2	4.1	3.9	3.8	3.7	3.5	3.4	3.3	3.2	3.1	3.0	2.9	2.8	14
15	4.1	3.9	3.8	3.7	3.5	3.4	3.3	3.2	3.1	3.0	2.9	2.8	2.8	15
16	3.9	3.8	3.7	3.5	3.4	3.3	3.2	3.1	3.0	2.9	2.8	2.8	2.7	16
17	3.8	3.7	3.5	3.4	3.3	3.2	3.1	3.0	2.9	2.8	2.8	2.7	2.6	17
18	3.7	3.5	3.4	3.3	3.2	3.1	3.0	2.9	2.9	2.8	2.7	2.6	2.5	18
19	3.5	3.4	3.3	3.2	3.1	3.0	2.9	2.9	2.8	2.7	2.6	2.6	2.5	19
20	3.4	3.3	3.2	3.1	3.0	2.9	2.9	2.8	2.7	2.6	2.6	2.5	2.4	20
21	3.3	3.2	3.1	3.0	2.9	2.8	2.8	2.7	2.6	2.6	2.5	2.4	2.4	21
22	3.2	3.1	3.0	2.9	2.8	2.8	2.7	2.6	2.6	2.5	2.4	2.4	2.3	22
23	3.1	3.0	2.9	2.8	2.8	2.7	2.6	2.6	2.5	2.4	2.4	2.3	2.3	23
24	3.0	2.9	2.8	2.8	2.7	2.6	2.5	2.5	2.4	2.4	2.3	2.3	2.2	24
25	2.9	2.8	2.7	2.7	2.6	2.5	2.5	2.4	2.4	2.3	2.3	2.2	2.2	25
26	2.8	2.7	2.7	2.6	2.5	2.5	2.4	2.4	2.3	2.3	2.2	2.1	2.1	26
27	2.7	2.7	2.6	2.5	2.5	2.4	2.4	2.3	2.2	2.2	2.1	2.1	2.1	27
28	2.6	2.6	2.5	2.5	2.4	2.3	2.3	2.2	2.2	2.1	2.1	2.1	2.0	28
29	2.6	2.5	2.4	2.4	2.3	2.3	2.2	2.2	2.1	2.1	2.0	2.0	2.0	29
30	2.5	2.4	2.4	2.3	2.3	2.2	2.2	2.1	2.1	2.0	2.0	2.0	1.9	30
31	2.4	2.4	2.3	2.3	2.2	2.2	2.1	2.1	2.0	2.0	2.0	1.9	1.9	31
32	2.3	2.3	2.2	2.2	2.2	2.1	2.1	2.0	2.0	1.9	1.9	1.9	1.8	32
33	2.3	2.2	2.2	2.1	2.1	2.1	2.0	2.0	1.9	1.9	1.9	1.8	1.8	33
34	2.2	2.2	2.1	2.1	2.0	2.0	2.0	1.9	1.9	1.9	1.8	1.8	1.8	34
35	2.2	2.1	2.1	2.0	2.0	2.0	1.9	1.9	1.8	1.8	1.8	1.7	1.7	35
36	2.1	2.1	2.0	2.0	1.9	1.9	1.9	1.8	1.8	1.8	1.7	1.7	1.7	36
37	2.0	2.0	2.0	1.9	1.9	1.9	1.8	1.8	1.8	1.7	1.7	1.7	1.6	37
38	2.0	1.9	1.9	1.9	1.8	1.8	1.8	1.8	1.7	1.7	1.7	1.6	1.6	38
39	1.9	1.9	1.9	1.8	1.8	1.8	1.7	1.7	1.7	1.6	1.6	1.6	1.6	39
40	1.9	1.8	1.8	1.8	1.7	1.7	1.7	1.7	1.6	1.6	1.6	1.6	1.5	40
41	1.8	1.8	1.8	1.7	1.7	1.7	1.6	1.6	1.6	1.6	1.5	1.5	1.5	41
42	1.8	1.7	1.7	1.7	1.7	1.6	1.6	1.6	1.6	1.5	1.5	1.5	1.5	42
43	1.7	1.7	1.7	1.6	1.6	1.6	1.6	1.5	1.5	1.5	1.5	1.4	1.4	43
44	1.7	1.6	1.6	1.6	1.6	1.5	1.5	1.5	1.5	1.5	1.4	1.4	1.4	44
45	1.6	1.6	1.6	1.5	1.5	1.5	1.5	1.5	1.4	1.4	1.4	1.4	1.4	45
46	1.6	1.6	1.5	1.5	1.5	1.5	1.4	1.4	1.4	1.4	1.4	1.3	1.3	46
47	1.5	1.5	1.5	1.5	1.4	1.4	1.4	1.4	1.4	1.3	1.3	1.3	1.3	47
48	1.5	1.5	1.4	1.4	1.4	1.4	1.4	1.4	1.3	1.3	1.3	1.3	1.3	48
49	1.4	1.4	1.4	1.4	1.4	1.3	1.3	1.3	1.3	1.3	1.3	1.2	1.2	49
50	1.4	1.4	1.4	1.3	1.3	1.3	1.3	1.3	1.3	1.3	1.2	1.2	1.2	50
51	1.4	1.3	1.3	1.3	1.3	1.3	1.3	1.2	1.2	1.2	1.2	1.2	1.2	51
52	1.3	1.3	1.3	1.3	1.3	1.3	1.2	1.2	1.2	1.2	1.2	1.1	1.1	52
53	1.3	1.3	1.3	1.2	1.2	1.2	1.2	1.2	1.2	1.2	1.1	1.1	1.1	53
54	1.2	1.2	1.2	1.2	1.2	1.2	1.2	1.1	1.1	1.1	1.1	1.1	1.1	54
55	1.2	1.2	1.2	1.2	1.1	1.1	1.1	1.1	1.1	1.1	1.1	1.1	1.1	55
56	1.2	1.1	1.1	1.1	1.1	1.1	1.1	1.1	1.1	1.1	1.0	1.0	1.0	56
57	1.1	1.1	1.1	1.1	1.1	1.1	1.1	1.0	1.0	1.0	1.0	1.0	1.0	57
58	1.1	1.1	1.1	1.1	1.0	1.0	1.0	1.0	1.0	1.0	1.0	1.0	1.0	58
59	1.1	1.0	1.0	1.0	1.0	1.0	1.0	1.0	1.0	1.0	1.0	0.9	0.9	59
60	1.0	1.0	1.0	1.0	1.0	1.0	1.0	0.9	0.9	0.9	0.9	0.9	0.9	60
	12°	13°	14°	15°	16°	17°	18°	19°	20°	21°	22°	23°	24°	
	Declination of a **different** name from the latitude; **upper** transit; reduction **additive.**													

TABLE 29.

Variation of Altitude in one minute from meridian passage.

Declination of a **different** name from the latitude; **upper** transit; reduction **additive.**

Lati-tude.	25°	26°	27°	28°	29°	30°	31°	32°	33°	34°	35°	36°	37°	Lati-tude.
°	″	″	″	″	″	″	″	″	″	″	″	″	″	°
0	4.2	4.0	3.9	3.7	3.5	3.4	3.3	3.1	3.0	2.9	2.8	2.7	2.6	0
1	4.1	3.9	3.7	3.6	3.4	3.3	3.2	3.1	2.9	2.8	2.7	2.6	2.6	1
2	3.9	3.8	3.6	3.5	3.3	3.2	3.1	3.0	2.9	2.8	2.7	2.6	2.5	2
3	3.8	3.6	3.5	3.4	3.2	3.1	3.0	2.9	2.8	2.7	2.6	2.5	2.4	3
4	3.7	3.5	3.4	3.3	3.2	3.0	2.9	2.8	2.7	2.6	2.6	2.5	2.4	4
5	3.6	3.4	3.3	3.2	3.1	3.0	2.9	2.8	2.7	2.6	2.5	2.4	2.3	5
6	3.4	3.3	3.2	3.1	3.0	2.9	2.8	2.7	2.6	2.5	2.4	2.4	2.3	6
7	3.3	3.2	3.1	3.0	2.9	2.8	2.7	2.6	2.5	2.5	2.4	2.3	2.2	7
8	3.2	3.1	3.0	2.9	2.8	2.7	2.7	2.6	2.5	2.4	2.3	2.3	2.2	8
9	3.1	3.0	2.9	2.9	2.8	2.7	2.6	2.5	2.4	2.4	2.3	2.2	2.2	9
10	3.1	3.0	2.9	2.8	2.7	2.6	2.5	2.5	2.4	2.3	2.2	2.2	2.1	10
11	3.0	2.9	2.8	2.7	2.6	2.5	2.5	2.4	2.3	2.3	2.2	2.1	2.1	11
12	2.9	2.8	2.7	2.6	2.6	2.5	2.4	2.3	2.3	2.2	2.2	2.1	2.0	12
13	2.8	2.7	2.7	2.6	2.5	2.4	2.4	2.3	2.2	2.2	2.1	2.1	2.0	13
14	2.7	2.7	2.6	2.5	2.4	2.4	2.3	2.3	2.2	2.1	2.1	2.0	2.0	14
15	2.7	2.6	2.5	2.5	2.4	2.3	2.3	2.2	2.1	2.1	2.0	2.0	1.9	15
16	2.6	2.5	2.5	2.4	2.3	2.3	2.2	2.2	2.1	2.0	2.0	1.9	1.9	16
17	2.5	2.5	2.4	2.3	2.3	2.2	2.2	2.1	2.1	2.0	2.0	1.9	1.9	17
18	2.5	2.4	2.4	2.3	2.2	2.2	2.1	2.1	2.0	2.0	1.9	1.9	1.8	18
19	2.4	2.4	2.3	2.2	2.2	2.1	2.1	2.0	2.0	1.9	1.9	1.8	1.8	19
20	2.4	2.3	2.3	2.2	2.1	2.1	2.0	2.0	1.9	1.9	1.9	1.8	1.8	20
21	2.3	2.3	2.2	2.1	2.1	2.0	2.0	2.0	1.9	1.9	1.8	1.8	1.7	21
22	2.3	2.2	2.2	2.1	2.1	2.0	2.0	1.9	1.9	1.8	1.8	1.7	1.7	22
23	2.2	2.2	2.1	2.1	2.0	2.0	1.9	1.9	1.8	1.8	1.8	1.7	1.7	23
24	2.2	2.1	2.1	2.0	2.0	1.9	1.9	1.8	1.8	1.8	1.7	1.7	1.6	24
25	2.1	2.1	2.0	2.0	1.9	1.9	1.8	1.8	1.8	1.7	1.7	1.6	1.6	25
26	2.1	2.0	2.0	1.9	1.9	1.9	1.8	1.8	1.7	1.7	1.7	1.6	1.6	26
27	2.0	2.0	1.9	1.9	1.9	1.8	1.8	1.7	1.7	1.7	1.6	1.6	1.6	27
28	2.0	1.9	1.9	1.9	1.8	1.8	1.7	1.7	1.7	1.6	1.6	1.6	1.5	28
29	1.9	1.9	1.9	1.8	1.8	1.7	1.7	1.7	1.6	1.6	1.6	1.5	1.5	29
30	1.9	1.8	1.8	1.8	1.7	1.7	1.7	1.6	1.6	1.6	1.5	1.5	1.5	30
31	1.8	1.8	1.8	1.7	1.7	1.7	1.6	1.6	1.6	1.5	1.5	1.5	1.5	31
32	1.8	1.8	1.7	1.7	1.7	1.6	1.6	1.6	1.5	1.5	1.5	1.5	1.4	32
33	1.8	1.7	1.7	1.7	1.6	1.6	1.6	1.5	1.5	1.5	1.5	1.4	1.4	33
34	1.7	1.7	1.7	1.6	1.6	1.6	1.5	1.5	1.5	1.5	1.4	1.4	1.4	34
35	1.7	1.7	1.6	1.6	1.6	1.5	1.5	1.5	1.5	1.4	1.4	1.4	1.4	35
36	1.6	1.6	1.6	1.6	1.5	1.5	1.5	1.5	1.4	1.4	1.4	1.4	1.3	36
37	1.6	1.6	1.6	1.5	1.5	1.5	1.5	1.4	1.4	1.4	1.4	1.3	1.3	37
38	1.6	1.5	1.5	1.5	1.5	1.5	1.4	1.4	1.4	1.4	1.3	1.3	1.3	38
39	1.5	1.5	1.5	1.5	1.4	1.4	1.4	1.4	1.4	1.3	1.3	1.3	1.3	39
40	1.5	1.5	1.5	1.4	1.4	1.4	1.4	1.3	1.3	1.3	1.3	1.3	1.2	40
41	1.5	1.4	1.4	1.4	1.4	1.4	1.3	1.3	1.3	1.3	1.3	1.2	1.2	41
42	1.4	1.4	1.4	1.4	1.4	1.3	1.3	1.3	1.3	1.2	1.2	1.2	1.2	42
43	1.4	1.4	1.4	1.3	1.3	1.3	1.3	1.3	1.2	1.2	1.2	1.2	1.2	43
44	1.4	1.4	1.3	1.3	1.3	1.3	1.3	1.2	1.2	1.2	1.2	1.2	1.2	44
45	1.3	1.3	1.3	1.3	1.3	1.2	1.2	1.2	1.2	1.2	1.2	1.1	1.1	45
46	1.3	1.3	1.3	1.3	1.2	1.2	1.2	1.2	1.2	1.2	1.1	1.1	1.1	46
47	1.3	1.3	1.2	1.2	1.2	1.2	1.2	1.2	1.1	1.1	1.1	1.1	1.1	47
48	1.2	1.2	1.2	1.2	1.2	1.2	1.1	1.1	1.1	1.1	1.1	1.1		48
49	1.2	1.2	1.2	1.2	1.2	1.1	1.1	1.1	1.1	1.1	1.1			49
50	1.2	1.2	1.2	1.1	1.1	1.1	1.1	1.1	1.1	1.1				50
51	1.2	1.1	1.1	1.1	1.1	1.1	1.1	1.1	1.0					51
52	1.1	1.1	1.1	1.1	1.1	1.1	1.0	1.0						52
53	1.1	1.1	1.1	1.1	1.0	1.0	1.0							53
54	1.1	1.0	1.0	1.0	1.0	1.0								54
55	1.0	1.0	1.0	1.0	1.0									55
56	1.0	1.0	1.0	1.0										56
57	1.0	1.0	1.0											57
58	1.0	0.9												58
59	0.9												0.8	59
60												0.8	0.8	60
	25°	26°	27°	28°	29°	30°	31°	32°	33°	34°	35°	36°	37°	

Declination of the **same** name as the latitude; **lower** transit; reduction **subtractive.**

TABLE 29.

Variation of Altitude in one minute from meridian passage.

Latitude.	38°	39°	40°	41°	42°	43°	44°	45°	46°	47°	48°	49°	50°	Latitude.
	Declination of a **different** name from the latitude; **upper** transit; reduction **additive.**													
°	″	″	″	″	″	″	″	″	″	″	″	″	″	°
0	2.5	2.4	2.3	2.3	2.2	2.1	2.0	2.0	1.9	1.8	1.8	1.7	1.7	0
1	2.5	2.4	2.3	2.2	2.1	2.1	2.0	1.9	1.9	1.8	1.7	1.7	1.6	1
2	2.4	2.3	2.3	2.2	2.1	2.0	2.0	1.9	1.8	1.8	1.7	1.7	1.6	2
3	2.4	2.3	2.2	2.1	2.1	2.0	1.9	1.9	1.8	1.8	1.7	1.6	1.6	3
4	2.3	2.2	2.2	2.1	2.0	2.0	1.9	1.8	1.8	1.7	1.7	1.6	1.6	4
5	2.3	2.2	2.1	2.1	2.0	1.9	1.9	1.8	1.8	1.7	1.6	1.6	1.5	5
6	2.2	2.2	2.1	2.0	2.0	1.9	1.8	1.8	1.7	1.7	1.6	1.6	1.5	6
7	2.2	2.1	2.0	2.0	1.9	1.9	1.8	1.8	1.7	1.6	1.6	1.5	1.5	7
8	2.1	2.1	2.0	1.9	1.9	1.8	1.8	1.7	1.7	1.6	1.6	1.5	1.5	8
9	2.1	2.0	2.0	1.9	1.9	1.8	1.8	1.7	1.6	1.6	1.6	1.5	1.5	9
10	2.1	2.0	1.9	1.9	1.8	1.8	1.7	1.7	1.6	1.6	1.5	1.5	1.4	10
11	2.0	2.0	1.9	1.8	1.8	1.7	1.7	1.6	1.6	1.6	1.5	1.5	1.4	11
12	2.0	1.9	1.9	1.8	1.8	1.7	1.7	1.6	1.6	1.5	1.5	1.4	1.4	12
13	1.9	1.9	1.8	1.8	1.7	1.7	1.6	1.6	1.6	1.5	1.5	1.4	1.4	13
14	1.9	1.9	1.8	1.8	1.7	1.7	1.6	1.6	1.5	1.5	1.4	1.4	1.4	14
15	1.9	1.8	1.8	1.7	1.7	1.6	1.6	1.6	1.5	1.5	1.4	1.4	1.4	15
16	1.8	1.8	1.7	1.7	1.7	1.6	1.6	1.5	1.5	1.4	1.4	1.4	1.3	16
17	1.8	1.8	1.7	1.7	1.6	1.6	1.5	1.5	1.5	1.4	1.4	1.4	1.3	17
18	1.8	1.7	1.7	1.6	1.6	1.6	1.5	1.5	1.4	1.4	1.4	1.3	1.3	18
19	1.7	1.7	1.7	1.6	1.6	1.5	1.5	1.5	1.4	1.4	1.4	1.3	1.3	19
20	1.7	1.7	1.6	1.6	1.6	1.5	1.5	1.4	1.4	1.4	1.3	1.3	1.3	20
21	1.7	1.6	1.6	1.6	1.5	1.5	1.5	1.4	1.4	1.4	1.3	1.3	1.3	21
22	1.7	1.6	1.6	1.5	1.5	1.5	1.4	1.4	1.4	1.3	1.3	1.3	1.2	22
23	1.6	1.6	1.6	1.5	1.5	1.4	1.4	1.4	1.3	1.3	1.3	1.3	1.2	23
24	1.6	1.6	1.5	1.5	1.5	1.4	1.4	1.4	1.3	1.3	1.3	1.2	1.2	24
25	1.6	1.5	1.5	1.5	1.4	1.4	1.4	1.3	1.3	1.3	1.2	1.2	1.2	25
26	1.6	1.5	1.5	1.5	1.4	1.4	1.4	1.3	1.3	1.3	1.2	1.2	1.2	26
27	1.5	1.5	1.5	1.4	1.4	1.4	1.3	1.3	1.3	1.2	1.2	1.2	1.2	27
28	1.5	1.5	1.4	1.4	1.4	1.3	1.3	1.3	1.3	1.2	1.2	1.2	1.1	28
29	1.5	1.4	1.4	1.4	1.4	1.3	1.3	1.3	1.2	1.2	1.2	1.2	1.1	29
30	1.5	1.4	1.4	1.4	1.3	1.3	1.3	1.2	1.2	1.2	1.2	1.1	1.1	30
31	1.4	1.4	1.4	1.3	1.3	1.3	1.3	1.2	1.2	1.2	1.2	1.1	1.1	31
32	1.4	1.4	1.3	1.3	1.3	1.3	1.2	1.2	1.2	1.2	1.1	1.1	1.1	32
33	1.4	1.4	1.3	1.3	1.3	1.2	1.2	1.2	1.2	1.1	1.1	1.1	1.1	33
34	1.4	1.3	1.3	1.3	1.3	1.2	1.2	1.2	1.2	1.1	1.1	1.1	1.1	34
35	1.3	1.3	1.3	1.3	1.2	1.2	1.2	1.2	1.1	1.1	1.1	1.1		35
36	1.3	1.3	1.3	1.2	1.2	1.2	1.2	1.1	1.1	1.1	1.1			36
37	1.3	1.3	1.2	1.2	1.2	1.2	1.2	1.1	1.1	1.1				37
38	1.3	1.2	1.2	1.2	1.2	1.2	1.1	1.1	1.1					38
39	1.2	1.2	1.2	1.2	1.2	1.1	1.1	1.1						39
40	1.2	1.2	1.2	1.2	1.1	1.1	1.1							40
41	1.2	1.2	1.2	1.1	1.1	1.1								41
42	1.2	1.2	1.1	1.1	1.1									42
43	1.2	1.1	1.1	1.1										43
44	1.1	1.1	1.1											44
45	1.1	1.1												45
46	1.1												0.9	46
47												0.9	0.9	47
48											0.9	0.9	0.9	48
49										0.9	0.9	0.9	0.8	49
50									0.9	0.9	0.8	0.8	0.8	50
51								0.9	0.9	0.9	0.8	0.8	0.8	51
52							0.9	0.9	0.9	0.8	0.8	0.8	0.8	52
53						0.9	0.9	0.8	0.8	0.8	0.8	0.8	0.8	53
54					0.9	0.9	0.8	0.8	0.8	0.8	0.8	0.8	0.8	54
55				0.9	0.8	0.8	0.8	0.8	0.8	0.8	0.8	0.8	0.7	55
56			0.8	0.8	0.8	0.8	0.8	0.8	0.8	0.8	0.8	0.7	0.7	56
57		0.8	0.8	0.8	0.8	0.8	0.8	0.8	0.8	0.8	0.7	0.7	0.7	57
58	0.8	0.8	0.8	0.8	0.8	0.8	0.8	0.8	0.8	0.7	0.7	0.7	0.7	58
59	0.8	0.8	0.8	0.8	0.8	0.8	0.8	0.7	0.7	0.7	0.7	0.7	0.7	59
60	0.8	0.8	0.8	0.8	0.8	0.7	0.7	0.7	0.7	0.7	0.7	0.7	0.7	60
	38°	39°	40°	41°	42°	43°	44°	45°	46°	47°	48°	49°	50°	
	Declination of the **same** name as the latitude; **lower** transit; reduction **subtractive.**													

TABLE 29.

Variation of Altitude in one minute from meridian passage.

Latitude.	51°	52°	53°	54°	55°	56°	57°	58°	59°	60°	61°	62°	63°	Latitude.
	Declination of a **different** name from the latitude; **upper** transit; reduction **additive.**													
°	″	″	″	″	″	″	″	″	″	″	″	″	″	°
0	1.6	1.5	1.5	1.4	1.4	1.3	1.3	1.2	1.2	1.1	1.1	1.0	1.0	0
1	1.6	1.5	1.5	1.4	1.4	1.3	1.3	1.2	1.2	1.1	1.1	1.0	1.0	1
2	1.5	1.5	1.4	1.4	1.3	1.3	1.3	1.2	1.2	1.1	1.1	1.0	1.0	2
3	1.5	1.5	1.4	1.4	1.3	1.3	1.2	1.2	1.1	1.1	1.1	1.0	1.0	3
4	1.5	1.5	1.4	1.4	1.3	1.3	1.2	1.2	1.1	1.1	1.1	1.0	1.0	4
5	1.5	1.4	1.4	1.3	1.3	1.3	1.2	1.2	1.1	1.1	1.0	1.0	1.0	5
6	1.5	1.4	1.4	1.3	1.3	1.2	1.2	1.2	1.1	1.1	1.0	1.0	1.0	6
7	1.4	1.4	1.4	1.3	1.3	1.2	1.2	1.1	1.1	1.1	1.0	1.0	0.9	7
8	1.4	1.4	1.3	1.3	1.3	1.2	1.2	1.1	1.1	1.1	1.0	1.0	0.9	8
9	1.4	1.4	1.3	1.3	1.2	1.2	1.2	1.1	1.1	1.0	1.0	1.0	0.9	9
10	1.4	1.4	1.3	1.3	1.2	1.2	1.1	1.1	1.1	1.0	1.0	1.0	0.9	10
11	1.4	1.3	1.3	1.3	1.2	1.2	1.1	1.1	1.1	1.0	1.0	1.0	0.9	11
12	1.4	1.3	1.3	1.2	1.2	1.2	1.1	1.1	1.1	1.0	1.0	0.9	0.9	12
13	1.3	1.3	1.3	1.2	1.2	1.2	1.1	1.1	1.0	1.0	1.0	0.9	0.9	13
14	1.3	1.3	1.3	1.2	1.2	1.1	1.1	1.1	1.0	1.0	1.0	0.9	0.9	14
15	1.3	1.3	1.2	1.2	1.2	1.1	1.1	1.1	1.0	1.0	1.0	0.9	0.9	15
16	1.3	1.3	1.2	1.2	1.1	1.1	1.1	1.0	1.0	1.0	0.9	0.9	0.9	16
17	1.3	1.2	1.2	1.2	1.1	1.1	1.1	1.0	1.0	1.0	0.9	0.9	0.9	17
18	1.3	1.2	1.2	1.2	1.1	1.1	1.1	1.0	1.0	1.0	0.9	0.9	0.9	18
19	1.2	1.2	1.2	1.1	1.1	1.1	1.0	1.0	1.0	1.0	0.9	0.9	0.9	19
20	1.2	1.2	1.2	1.1	1.1	1.1	1.0	1.0	1.0	0.9	0.9	0.9	0.8	20
21	1.2	1.2	1.2	1.1	1.1	1.1	1.0	1.0	1.0	0.9	0.9	0.9	0.8	21
22	1.2	1.2	1.1	1.1	1.1	1.0	1.0	1.0	1.0	0.9	0.9	0.9		22
23	1.2	1.2	1.1	1.1	1.1	1.0	1.0	1.0	0.9	0.9	0.9			23
24	1.2	1.1	1.1	1.1	1.1	1.0	1.0	1.0	0.9	0.9				24
25	1.2	1.1	1.1	1.1	1.0	1.0	1.0	1.0	0.9					25
26	1.1	1.1	1.1	1.1	1.0	1.0	1.0	0.9						26
27	1.1	1.1	1.1	1.0	1.0	1.0	1.0							27
28	1.1	1.1	1.1	1.0	1.0	1.0								28
29	1.1	1.1	1.0	1.0	1.0									29
30	1.1	1.1	1.0	1.0										30
31	1.1	1.0	1.0											31
32	1.1	1.0												32
33	1.1												0.8	33
34												0.8	0.7	34
35											0.8	0.8	0.7	35
36										0.8	0.8	0.8	0.7	36
37									0.8	0.8	0.8	0.7	0.7	37
38								0.8	0.8	0.8	0.8	0.7	0.7	38
39							0.8	0.8	0.8	0.8	0.8	0.7	0.7	39
40						0.8	0.8	0.8	0.8	0.8	0.8	0.7	0.7	40
41					0.9	0.8	0.8	0.8	0.8	0.8	0.7	0.7	0.7	41
42				0.9	0.8	0.8	0.8	0.8	0.8	0.8	0.7	0.7	0.7	42
43			0.9	0.9	0.8	0.8	0.8	0.8	0.8	0.7	0.7	0.7	0.7	43
44		0.9	0.9	0.8	0.8	0.8	0.8	0.8	0.8	0.7	0.7	0.7	0.7	44
45	0.9	0.9	0.8	0.8	0.8	0.8	0.8	0.8	0.7	0.7	0.7	0.7	0.7	45
46	0.9	0.9	0.8	0.8	0.8	0.8	0.8	0.8	0.7	0.7	0.7	0.7	0.7	46
47	0.9	0.8	0.8	0.8	0.8	0.8	0.8	0.7	0.7	0.7	0.7	0.7	0.6	47
48	0.8	0.8	0.8	0.8	0.8	0.8	0.7	0.7	0.7	0.7	0.7	0.7	0.6	48
49	0.8	0.8	0.8	0.8	0.8	0.7	0.7	0.7	0.7	0.7	0.7	0.6	0.6	49
50	0.8	0.8	0.8	0.8	0.7	0.7	0.7	0.7	0.7	0.7	0.7	0.6	0.6	50
51	0.8	0.8	0.8	0.8	0.7	0.7	0.7	0.7	0.7	0.7	0.7	0.6	0.6	51
52	0.8	0.8	0.8	0.7	0.7	0.7	0.7	0.7	0.7	0.7	0.6	0.6	0.6	52
53	0.8	0.8	0.7	0.7	0.7	0.7	0.7	0.7	0.7	0.6	0.6	0.6	0.6	53
54	0.8	0.7	0.7	0.7	0.7	0.7	0.7	0.7	0.6	0.6	0.6	0.6	0.6	54
55	0.7	0.7	0.7	0.7	0.7	0.7	0.7	0.7	0.6	0.6	0.6	0.6	0.6	55
56	0.7	0.7	0.7	0.7	0.7	0.7	0.7	0.6	0.6	0.6	0.6	0.6	0.6	56
57	0.7	0.7	0.7	0.7	0.7	0.7	0.6	0.6	0.6	0.6	0.6	0.6	0.6	57
58	0.7	0.7	0.7	0.7	0.7	0.6	0.6	0.6	0.6	0.6	0.6	0.6	0.6	58
59	0.7	0.7	0.7	0.6	0.6	0.6	0.6	0.6	0.6	0.6	0.6	0.6	0.5	59
60	0.7	0.7	0.6	0.6	0.6	0.6	0.6	0.6	0.6	0.6	0.6	0.6	0.5	60
	51°	52°	53°	54°	55°	56°	57°	58°	59°	60°	61°	62°	63°	
	Declination of the **same** name as the latitude; **lower** transit; reduction **subtractive.**													

TABLE 30.

Reduction to be Applied to Altitudes Near the Meridian.

Var. 1 min. (table 29).	Arc or Time from Meridian Passage														Var. 1 min. (table 29).
	5′	10′	15′	20′	25′	30′	35′	40′	45′	50′	55′	1°00′	1°05′	1°10′	
	m s 0 20	m s 0 40	m s 1 00	m s 1 20	m s 1 40	m s 2 00	m s 2 20	m s 2 40	m s 3 00	m s 3 20	m s 3 40	m s 4 00	m s 4 20	m s 4 40	
″	′	′	′	′	′	′	′	′	′	′	′	′	′	′	″
. 1	0. 0	0. 0	0. 0	0. 0	0. 0	0. 0	0. 0	0. 0	0. 0	0. 0	0. 0	0. 0	0. 0	0. 0	. 1
. 2									0. 0	0. 0	0. 0	0. 1	0. 1	0. 1	. 2
. 3									0. 1	0. 1	0. 1	0. 1	0. 1	0. 1	. 3
. 4								0. 1	0. 1	0. 1	0. 1	0. 1	0. 1	0. 1	. 4
. 5							0. 1	0. 1	0. 1	0. 1	0. 1	0. 1	0. 2	0. 2	. 5
. 6							0. 1	0. 1	0. 1	0. 1	0. 1	0. 2	0. 2	0. 2	. 6
. 7						0. 1	0. 1	0. 1	0. 1	0. 1	0. 2	0. 2	0. 2	0. 3	. 7
. 8						0. 1	0. 1	0. 1	0. 1	0. 2	0. 2	0. 2	0. 3	0. 3	. 8
. 9	0. 0	0. 0	0. 0	0. 0	0. 0	0. 1	0. 1	0. 1	0. 1	0. 2	0. 2	0. 2	0. 3	0. 3	. 9
1. 0	0. 0	0. 0	0. 0	0. 0	0. 0	0. 1	0. 1	0. 1	0. 2	0. 2	0. 2	0. 3	0. 3	0. 4	1. 0
2. 0	0. 0	0. 0	0. 0	0. 1	0. 1	0. 1	0. 2	0. 2	0. 3	0. 4	0. 4	0. 5	0. 6	0. 7	2. 0
3. 0	0. 0	0. 0	0. 1	0. 1	0. 1	0. 2	0. 3	0. 4	0. 5	0. 6	0. 7	0. 8	0. 9	1. 1	3. 0
4. 0	0. 0	0. 0	0. 1	0. 1	0. 2	0. 3	0. 4	0. 5	0. 6	0. 7	0. 9	1. 1	1. 2	1. 4	4. 0
5. 0	0. 0	0. 0	0. 1	0. 1	0. 2	0. 3	0. 5	0. 6	0. 8	0. 9	1. 1	1. 3	1. 6	1. 8	5. 0
6. 0	0. 0	0. 0	0. 1	0. 2	0. 3	0. 4	0. 5	0. 7	0. 9	1. 1	1. 3	1. 6	1. 9	2. 2	6. 0
7. 0	0. 0	0. 1	0. 1	0. 2	0. 3	0. 5	0. 6	0. 8	1. 1	1. 3	1. 6	1. 9	2. 2	2. 5	7. 0
8. 0	0. 0	0. 1	0. 1	0. 2	0. 4	0. 5	0. 7	0. 9	1. 2	1. 5	1. 8	2. 1	2. 5	2. 9	8. 0
9. 0	0. 0	0. 1	0. 2	0. 3	0. 4	0. 6	0. 8	1. 1	1. 4	1. 7	2. 0	2. 4	2. 8	3. 3	9. 0
10. 0	0. 0	0. 1	0. 2	0. 3	0. 5	0. 7	0. 9	1. 2	1. 5	1. 9	2. 2	2. 7	3. 1	3. 6	10. 0
11. 0	0. 0	0. 1	0. 2	0. 3	0. 5	0. 7	1. 0	1. 3	1. 7	2. 0	2. 5	2. 9	3. 4	4. 0	11. 0
12. 0	0. 0	0. 1	0. 2	0. 4	0. 6	0. 8	1. 1	1. 4	1. 8	2. 2	2. 7	3. 2	3. 8	4. 4	12. 0
13. 0	0. 0	0. 1	0. 2	0. 4	0. 6	0. 9	1. 2	1. 5	2. 0	2. 4	2. 9	3. 5	4. 1	4. 7	13. 0
14. 0	0. 0	0. 1	0. 2	0. 4	0. 6	0. 9	1. 3	1. 7	2. 1	2. 6	3. 1	3. 7	4. 4	5. 1	14. 0
15. 0	0. 0	0. 1	0. 3	0. 5	0. 7	1. 0	1. 4	1. 8	2. 3	2. 8	3. 4	4. 0	4. 7	5. 4	15. 0
16. 0	0. 0	0. 1	0. 3	0. 5	0. 7	1. 1	1. 5	1. 9	2. 4	3. 0	3. 6	4. 3	5. 0	5. 8	16. 0
17. 0	0. 0	0. 1	0. 3	0. 5	0. 8	1. 1	1. 5	2. 0	2. 6	3. 1	3. 8	4. 5	5. 3	6. 2	17. 0
18. 0	0. 0	0. 2	0. 3	0. 6	0. 8	1. 2	1. 6	2. 1	2. 7	3. 3	4. 0	4. 8	5. 6	6. 5	18. 0
19. 0	0. 1	0. 2	0. 3	0. 6	0. 9	1. 2	1. 7	2. 3	2. 9	3. 5	4. 3	5. 1	5. 9	6. 9	19. 0
20. 0	0. 1	0. 2	0. 3	0. 6	0. 9	1. 3	1. 8	2. 4	3. 0	3. 7	4. 5	5. 3	6. 3	7. 3	20. 0
21. 0	0. 1	0. 2	0. 4	0. 7	1. 0	1. 4	1. 9	2. 5	3. 1	3. 9	4. 7	5. 6	6. 6	7. 6	21. 0
22. 0	0. 1	0. 2	0. 4	0. 7	1. 0	1. 5	2. 0	2. 6	3. 3	4. 1	4. 9	5. 9	6. 9	8. 0	22. 0
23. 0	0. 1	0. 2	0. 4	0. 7	1. 1	1. 5	2. 1	2. 7	3. 5	4. 3	5. 2	6. 1	7. 2	8. 3	23. 0
24. 0	0. 1	0. 2	0. 4	0. 8	1. 1	1. 6	2. 2	2. 8	3. 6	4. 4	5. 4	6. 4	7. 5	8. 7	24. 0
25. 0	0. 1	0. 2	0. 4	0. 8	1. 2	1. 7	2. 3	3. 0	3. 8	4. 6	5. 6	6. 7	7. 8	9. 1	25. 0
26. 0	0. 1	0. 2	0. 4	0. 8	1. 2	1. 7	2. 4	3. 1	3. 9	4. 8	5. 8	6. 9	8. 1	9. 4	26. 0
27. 0	0. 1	0. 2	0. 5	0. 8	1. 2	1. 8	2. 4	3. 2	4. 1	5. 0	6. 0	7. 2	8. 4	9. 8	27. 0
28. 0	0. 1	0. 2	0. 5	0. 9	1. 3	1. 9	2. 5	3. 3	4. 2	5. 2	6. 3	7. 5	8. 8	10. 2	28. 0

TABLE 30.

Reduction to be Applied to Altitudes Near the Meridian.

Var. 1 min. (Table 29).	Arc or Time from Meridian Passage.														Var. 1 min. (Table 29).
	1°15′	1°20′	1°25′	1°30′	1°35′	1°40′	1°45′	1°50′	1°55′	2°00′	2°05′	2°10′	2°15′	2°20′	
	m s 5 00	m s 5 20	m s 5 40	m s 6 00	m s 6 20	m s 6 40	m s 7 00	m s 7 20	m s 7 40	m s 8 00	m s 8 20	m s 8 40	m s 9 00	m s 9 20	
″	′	′	′	′	′	′	′	′	′	′	′	′	′	′	″
.1	0.0	0.1	0.1	0.1	0.1	0.1	0.1	0.1	0.1	0.1	0.1	0.1	0.1	0.2	.1
.2	0.1	0.1	0.1	0.1	0.1	0.2	0.2	0.2	0.2	0.2	0.2	0.3	0.3	0.3	.2
.3	0.1	0.1	0.2	0.2	0.2	0.2	0.3	0.3	0.3	0.3	0.4	0.4	0.4	0.4	.3
.4	0.1	0.2	0.2	0.2	0.3	0.3	0.3	0.4	0.4	0.4	0.5	0.5	0.5	0.6	.4
.5	0.2	0.2	0.3	0.3	0.3	0.4	0.4	0.5	0.5	0.5	0.6	0.6	0.7	0.7	.5
.6	0.3	0.3	0.3	0.4	0.4	0.4	0.5	0.5	0.6	0.6	0.7	0.8	0.8	0.9	.6
.7	0.3	0.3	0.4	0.4	0.5	0.5	0.6	0.6	0.7	0.8	0.8	0.9	1.0	1.0	.7
.8	0.3	0.4	0.4	0.5	0.5	0.6	0.7	0.7	0.8	0.9	0.9	1.0	1.1	1.2	.8
.9	0.4	0.4	0.5	0.6	0.6	0.7	0.7	0.8	0.9	1.0	1.0	1.1	1.2	1.3	.9
1.0	0.4	0.5	0.5	0.6	0.7	0.7	0.8	0.9	1.0	1.1	1.2	1.3	1.4	1.5	1.0
2.0	0.8	0.9	1.1	1.2	1.3	1.5	1.6	1.8	2.0	2.1	2.3	2.5	2.7	2.9	2.0
3.0	1.3	1.4	1.6	1.8	2.0	2.2	2.5	2.7	2.9	3.2	3.5	3.8	4.1	4.4	3.0
4.0	1.7	1.9	2.1	2.4	2.7	3.0	3.3	3.6	3.9	4.3	4.7	5.0	5.4	5.8	4.0
5.0	2.1	2.4	2.7	3.0	3.3	3.7	4.1	4.5	4.9	5.3	5.8	6.3	6.8	7.3	5.0
6.0	2.5	2.8	3.2	3.6	4.0	4.4	4.9	5.4	5.9	6.4	6.9	7.5	8.1	8.7	6.0
7.0	2.9	3.3	3.7	4.2	4.7	5.2	5.7	6.3	6.9	7.5	8.1	8.8	9.5	10.2	7.0
8.0	3.3	3.8	4.3	4.8	5.3	5.9	6.5	7.2	7.8	8.5	9.2	10.0	10.8	11.6	8.0
9.0	3.8	4.3	4.8	5.4	6.0	6.7	7.4	8.1	8.8	9.6	10.4	11.3	12.2	13.1	9.0
10.0	4.2	4.7	5.4	6.0	6.7	7.4	8.2	9.0	9.8	10.7	11.6	12.5	13.5	14.5	10.0
11.0	4.6	5.2	5.9	6.6	7.4	8.1	9.0	9.9	10.8	11.7	12.7	13.8	14.9	16.0	11.0
12.0	5.0	5.7	6.4	7.2	8.0	8.9	9.8	10.8	11.8	12.8	13.9	15.0	16.2	17.4	12.0
13.0	5.4	6.2	7.0	7.8	8.7	9.6	10.6	11.7	12.7	13.9	15.0	16.3	17.6	18.9	13.0
14.0	5.8	6.6	7.5	8.4	9.4	10.4	11.4	12.5	13.7	14.9	16.2	17.5	18.9	20.3	14.0
15.0	6.3	7.1	8.0	9.0	10.0	11.1	12.3	13.4	14.7	16.0	17.4	18.8	20.3	21.8	15.0
16.0	6.7	7.6	8.6	9.6	10.7	11.9	13.1	14.3	15.7	17.1	18.5	20.0	21.6	23.2	16.0
17.0	7.1	8.1	9.1	10.2	11.4	12.6	13.9	15.2	16.7	18.1	19.7	21.3	23.0	24.7	17.0
18.0	7.5	8.5	9.6	10.8	12.0	13.3	14.7	16.1	17.6	19.2	20.8	22.5	24.3	26.1	18.0
19.0	7.9	9.0	10.2	11.4	12.7	14.1	15.5	17.0	18.6	20.3	22.0	23.8			19.0
20.0	8.3	9.5	10.7	12.0	13.4	14.8	16.3	17.9	19.6	21.4	23.1				20.0
21.0	8.8	10.0	11.2	12.6	14.0	15.6	17.2	18.8	20.6						21.0
22.0	9.2	10.4	11.8	13.2	14.7	16.3	18.0	19.7	21.6						22.0
23.0	9.6	10.9	12.3	13.8	15.4	17.0	18.8	20.6							23.0
24.0	10.0	11.4	12.8	14.4	16.0	17.8	19.6	21.5							24.0
25.0	10.4	11.9	13.4	15.0	16.7	18.5	20.4								25.0
26.0	10.8	12.3	13.9	15.6	17.4	19.3									26.0
27.0	11.3	12.8	14.5	16.2	18.1	20.0									27.0

541524°—43——37

TABLE 30.

Reduction to be applied to Altitudes near the Meridian.

Var. 1 min. (Table 29).	Arc or Time from Meridian Passage.														Var. 1 min. (Table 29).
	2°25′	2°30′	2°35′	2°40′	2°45′	2°50′	2°55′	3°00′	3°05′	3°10′	3°15′	3°20′	3°25′	3°30′	
	m s 9 40	m s 10 00	m s 10 20	m s 10 40	m s 11 00	m s 11 20	m s 11 40	m s 12 00	m s 12 20	m s 12 40	m s 13 00	m s 13 20	m s 13 40	m s 14 00	
″	′	′	′	′	′	′	′	′	′	′	′	′	′	′	″
.1	0.2	0.2	0.2	0.2	0.2	0.2	0.2	0.2	0.3	0.3	0.3	0.3	0.3	0.3	.1
.2	0.3	0.3	0.4	0.4	0.4	0.4	0.5	0.5	0.5	0.5	0.6	0.6	0.6	0.7	.2
.3	0.5	0.5	0.5	0.6	0.6	0.7	0.8	0.7	0.8	0.8	0.9	0.9	0.9	1.0	.3
.4	0.6	0.7	0.7	0.8	0.8	0.9	0.9	1.0	1.0	1.1	1.1	1.2	1.3	1.3	.4
.5	0.8	0.8	0.9	1.0	1.0	1.1	1.1	1.2	1.3	1.3	1.4	1.5	1.6	1.6	.5
.6	0.9	1.0	1.1	1.1	1.2	1.3	1.4	1.4	1.5	1.6	1.7	1.8	1.9	2.0	.6
.7	1.1	1.2	1.3	1.3	1.4	1.5	1.6	1.7	1.8	1.9	2.0	2.1	2.2	2.3	.7
.8	1.3	1.3	1.4	1.5	1.6	1.7	1.8	1.9	2.0	2.1	2.3	2.4	2.5	2.6	.8
.9	1.4	1.5	1.6	1.7	1.8	1.9	2.1	2.2	2.3	2.4	2.5	2.7	2.8	2.9	.9
1.0	1.6	1.7	1.8	1.9	2.0	2.1	2.3	2.4	2.5	2.7	2.8	2.9	3.1	3.3	1.0
2.0	3.1	3.3	3.5	3.8	4.0	4.2	4.5	4.8	5.1	5.3	5.6	5.9	6.2	6.5	2.0
3.0	4.7	5.0	5.3	5.7	6.1	6.5	6.9	7.2	7.6	8.0	8.5	8.9	9.4	9.8	3.0
4.0	6.2	6.7	7.1	7.6	8.1	8.6	9.1	9.6	10.1	10.7	11.3	11.9	12.5	13.2	4.0
5.0	7.8	8.3	8.9	9.5	10.1	10.7	11.4	12.0	12.7	13.4	14.1	14.8	15.6	16.3	5.0
6.0	9.3	10.0	10.7	11.4	12.1	12.8	13.6	14.4	15.2	16.0	16.9	17.8	18.7	19.6	6.0
7.0	10.9	11.7	12.5	13.3	14.1	14.9	15.8	16.8	17.7	18.7	19.7	20.7	21.8	22.9	7.0
8.0	12.5	13.3	14.2	15.1	16.1	17.1	18.1	19.2	20.3	21.4	22.5	23.7	24.9	26.1	8.0
9.0	14.1	15.0	16.0	17.1	18.2	19.3	20.5	21.6	22.8	24.1	25.3	26.7	28.0	29.4	9.0
10.0	15.6	16.7	17.8	19.0	20.2	21.4	22.7	24.0	25.4	26.8	28.2	29.7			10.0
11.0	17.1	18.3	19.6	20.9	22.2	23.5	25.0	26.4	28.0	29.5					11.0
12.0	18.7	20.0	21.4	22.8	24.2	25.7	27.2	28.8							12.0
13.0	20.2	21.7	23.1	24.7	26.2	27.8	29.5								13.0
14.0	21.8	23.3	24.9	26.5	28.2	30.0									14.0
15.0	23.4	25.0	26.7	28.4	30.2										15.0
16.0	24.9	26.7	28.5	30.3											16.0
17.0	26.5	27.4	30.3												17.0

Var. 1 min. (Table 29).	Arc or Time from Meridian Passage.														Var. 1 min. (Table 29).
	3°35′	3°40′	3°45′	3°50′	3°55′	4°00′	4°05′	4°10′	4°15′	4°20′	4°25′	4°30′	4°35′	4°40′	
	m s 14 20	m s 14 40	m s 15 00	m s 15 20	m s 15 40	m s 16 00	m s 16 20	m s 16 40	m s 17 00	m s 17 20	m s 17 40	m s 18 00	m s 18 20	m s 18 40	
″	′	′	′	′	′	′	′	′	′	′	′	′	′	′	″
.1	0.4	0.4	0.4	0.4	0.4	0.4	0.5	0.5	0.5	0.5	0.5	0.5	0.6	0.6	.1
.2	0.7	0.7	0.8	0.8	0.8	0.9	0.9	0.9	1.0	1.0	1.0	1.1	1.1	1.2	.2
.3	1.0	1.1	1.1	1.2	1.2	1.3	1.3	1.4	1.5	1.5	1.6	1.6	1.7	1.7	.3
.4	1.4	1.4	1.5	1.6	1.6	1.7	1.8	1.9	1.9	2.0	2.1	2.2	2.2	2.3	.4
.5	1.7	1.8	1.9	2.0	2.1	2.1	2.2	2.3	2.4	2.5	2.6	2.7	2.8	2.9	.5
.6	2.1	2.2	2.3	2.4	2.5	2.6	2.7	2.8	2.9	3.0	3.1	3.2	3.4	3.5	.6
.7	2.4	2.5	2.6	2.8	2.9	3.0	3.1	3.2	3.4	3.5	3.6	3.8	3.9	4.1	.7
.8	2.7	2.9	3.0	3.1	3.3	3.4	3.6	3.7	3.9	4.0	4.2	4.3	4.5	4.7	.8
.9	3.1	3.2	3.4	3.5	3.7	3.8	4.0	4.2	4.3	4.5	4.7	4.9	5.0	5.2	.9
1.0	3.5	3.6	3.8	4.0	4.1	4.3	4.5	4.7	4.8	5.0	5.2	5.4	5.6	5.8	1.0
2.0	6.8	7.1	7.5	7.8	8.2	8.5	8.9	9.2	9.6	10.0	10.4	10.8	11.2	11.6	2.0
3.0	10.3	10.8	11.3	11.8	12.3	12.8	13.3	13.9	14.5	15.1	15.7	16.2	16.8	17.4	3.0
4.0	13.7	14.4	15.0	15.7	16.4	17.1	17.8	18.5	19.3	20.1	20.8	21.6	22.4	23.2	4.0
5.0	17.1	17.9	18.8	19.6	20.5	21.3	22.2	23.1	24.1	25.1	26.0	27.0	28.0	29.0	5.0
6.0	20.5	21.5	22.5	23.5	24.5	25.6	26.7	27.8							6.0
7.0	24.0	25.1	26.3	27.5											7.0
8.0	27.4	28.7	30.0												8.0

TABLE 30.

Reduction to be Applied to Altitudes near the Meridian.

Arc or **Time** from Meridian Passage.

Var. 1 min. (Table 29).	4°45′	4°50′	4°55′	5°00′	5°05′	5°10′	5°15′	5°20′	5°25′	5°30′	5°35′	5°40′	5°45′	5°50′	Var. 1 min. (Table 29).
	m s 19 00	*m s* 19 20	*m s* 19 40	*m s* 20 00	*m s* 20 20	*m s* 20 40	*m s* 21 00	*m s* 21 20	*m s* 21 40	*m s* 22 00	*m s* 22 20	*m s* 22 40	*m s* 23 00	*m s* 23 20	
″	′	′	′	′	′	′	′	′	′	′	′	′	′	′	″
.1	0.6	0.6	0.6	0.7	0.7	0.7	0.7	0.8	0.8	0.8	0.8	0.9	0.9	0.9	.1
.2	1.2	1.2	1.3	1.3	1.4	1.4	1.5	1.5	1.6	1.6	1.7	1.7	1.8	1.8	.2
.3	1.8	1.9	1.9	2.0	2.1	2.1	2.2	2.3	2.4	2.4	2.5	2.6	2.7	2.7	.3
.4	2.4	2.5	2.6	2.7	2.8	2.9	2.9	3.0	3.1	3.2	3.3	3.4	3.5	3.6	.4
.5	3.0	3.1	3.2	3.3	3.4	3.6	3.7	3.8	3.9	4.0	4.2	4.3	4.4	4.5	.5
.6	3.6	3.7	3.9	4.0	4.1	4.3	4.4	4.6	4.7	4.8	5.0	5.1	5.3	5.4	.6
.7	4.2	4.4	4.5	4.7	4.8	5.0	5.2	5.3	5.5	5.7	5.8	6.0	6.2	6.4	.7
.8	4.8	5.0	5.2	5.3	5.5	5.7	5.9	6.1	6.3	6.5	6.7	6.9	7.1	7.3	.8
.9	5.4	5.6	5.8	6.0	6.2	6.4	6.6	6.8	7.1	7.3	7.5	7.7	7.9	8.2	.9
1.0	6.0	6.2	6.4	6.7	6.9	7.2	7.4	7.6	7.9	8.1	8.3	8.6	8.8	9.1	1.0
2.0	12.0	12.4	12.9	13.3	13.7	14.2	14.7	15.2	15.6	16.1	16.6	17.1	17.6	18.1	2.0
3.0	18.1	18.7	19.4	20.0	20.7	21.4	22.1	22.8	23.5	24.2	24.9	25.7	26.5	27.3	3.0
4.0	24.1	24.9	25.7	26.7	27.6	28.5	29.4	30.3	31.3						4.0

Arc or **Time** from Meridian Passage.

Var. 1 min. (Table 29).	5°55′	6°00′	6°05′	6°10′	6°15′	6°20′	6°25′	6°30′	6°35′	6°40′	6°45′	6°50′	6°55′	7°00′	Var. 1 min. (Table 29).
	m s 23 40	*m s* 24 00	*m s* 24 20	*m s* 24 40	*m s* 25 00	*m s* 25 20	*m s* 25 40	*m s* 26 00	*m s* 26 20	*m s* 26 40	*m s* 27 00	*m s* 27 20	*m s* 27 40	*m s* 28 00	
″	′	′	′	′	′	′	′	′	′	′	′	′	′	′	″
.1	0.9	0.9	1.0	1.0	1.0	1.1	1.1	1.1	1.2	1.2	1.2	1.3	1.3	1.3	.1
.2	1.9	1.9	2.0	2.0	2.1	2.1	2.2	2.3	2.3	2.4	2.4	2.5	2.6	2.6	.2
.3	2.8	2.9	3.0	3.0	3.1	3.2	3.3	3.4	3.5	3.6	3.7	3.7	3.8	3.9	.3
.4	3.7	3.8	4.0	4.1	4.2	4.3	4.4	4.5	4.6	4.7	4.9	5.0	5.1	5.2	.4
.5	4.7	4.8	4.9	5.1	5.2	5.4	5.5	5.6	5.8	5.9	6.1	6.2	6.4	6.5	.5
.6	5.6	5.8	5.9	6.1	6.3	6.4	6.6	6.8	6.9	7.1	7.3	7.5	7.7	7.8	.6
.7	6.5	6.7	6.9	7.1	7.3	7.5	7.7	7.9	8.1	8.3	8.5	8.7	8.9	9.2	.7
.8	7.5	7.7	7.9	8.1	8.3	8.6	8.8	9.0	9.2	9.5	9.7	10.0	10.2	10.5	.8
.9	8.4	8.6	8.9	9.1	9.4	9.6	9.9	10.1	10.4	10.7	10.9	11.2	11.5	11.8	.9
1.0	9.3	9.6	9.9	10.1	10.4	10.7	11.0	11.3	11.6	11.9	12.2	12.5	12.8	13.1	1.0
2.0	18.6	19.2	19.7	20.3	20.8	21.4	21.9	22.5	23.1	23.7	24.3	24.9	25.5	26.1	2.0
3.0	28.1	28.8	29.6	30.4											3.0

TABLE 31.

Natural Trigonometric Functions.

0°

′	sin	tan	cot	cos	
0	.00000	.00000	∞	1.0000	60
1	029	029	3437.7	000	59
2	058	058	1718.9	000	58
3	087	087	1145.9	000	57
4	116	116	859.44	000	56
5	145	145	687.55	000	55
6	175	175	572.96	000	54
7	204	204	491.11	000	53
8	.00233	.00233	429.72	000	52
9	262	262	381.97	000	51
10	291	291	343.77	1.0000	50
11	320	320	312.52	.99999	49
12	349	349	286.48	999	48
13	378	378	264.44	999	47
14	407	407	245.55	999	46
15	436	436	229.18	999	45
16	465	465	214.86	999	44
17	.00495	.00495	202.22	999	43
18	524	524	190.98	999	42
19	553	553	180.93	998	41
20	582	582	171.89	.99998	40
21	611	611	163.70	998	39
22	640	640	156.26	998	38
23	669	669	149.47	998	37
24	698	698	143.24	998	36
25	.00727	.00727	137.51	997	35
26	756	756	132.22	997	34
27	785	785	127.32	997	33
28	814	815	122.77	997	32
29	844	844	118.54	996	31
30	873	873	114.59	.99996	30
31	902	902	110.89	996	29
32	931	931	107.43	996	28
33	960	960	104.17	995	27
34	.00989	.00989	101.11	995	26
35	.01018	.01018	98.218	995	25
36	047	047	95.489	995	24
37	076	076	92.908	994	23
38	105	105	90.463	994	22
39	134	135	88.144	994	21
40	164	164	85.940	.99993	20
41	193	193	83.844	993	19
42	222	222	81.847	993	18
43	.01251	251	79.943	992	17
44	280	.01280	78.126	992	16
45	309	309	76.390	991	15
46	338	338	74.729	991	14
47	367	367	73.139	991	13
48	396	396	71.615	990	12
49	425	425	70.153	990	11
50	454	455	68.750	.99989	10
51	483	484	67.402	989	9
52	.01513	.01513	66.105	989	8
53	542	542	64.858	988	7
54	571	571	63.657	988	6
55	600	600	62.499	987	5
56	629	629	61.383	987	4
57	658	658	60.306	986	3
58	687	687	59.266	986	2
59	716	716	58.261	985	1
60	.01745	.01746	57.290	.99985	0
	cos	cot	tan	sin	′

89°

1°

′	sin	tan	cot	cos	
0	.01745	.01746	57.290	.99985	60
1	774	775	56.351	984	59
2	803	804	55.442	984	58
3	832	833	54.561	983	57
4	862	862	53.709	983	56
5	891	891	52.882	982	55
6	920	920	52.081	982	54
7	949	949	51.303	981	53
8	.01978	.01978	50.549	980	52
9	.02007	.02007	49.816	980	51
10	036	036	49.104	.99979	50
11	065	066	48.412	979	49
12	094	095	47.740	978	48
13	123	124	47.085	977	47
14	152	153	46.449	977	46
15	181	182	45.829	976	45
16	211	211	45.226	976	44
17	240	.02240	44.639	975	43
18	269	269	44.066	974	42
19	298	298	43.508	974	41
20	.02327	328	42.964	.99973	40
21	356	357	42.433	972	39
22	385	386	41.916	972	38
23	414	415	41.411	971	37
24	443	444	40.917	970	36
25	472	473	40.436	969	35
26	501	.02502	39.965	969	34
27	530	531	39.506	968	33
28	560	560	39.057	967	32
29	589	589	38.618	966	31
30	.02618	619	38.188	.99966	30
31	647	648	37.769	965	29
32	676	677	37.358	964	28
33	705	706	36.956	963	27
34	734	735	36.563	963	26
35	763	.02764	36.178	962	25
36	792	793	35.801	961	24
37	.02821	822	35.431	960	23
38	850	851	35.070	959	22
39	879	881	34.715	959	21
40	908	910	34.368	.99958	20
41	938	939	34.027	957	19
42	967	968	33.694	956	18
43	.02996	.02997	33.366	955	17
44	.03025	.03026	33.045	954	16
45	054	055	32.730	953	15
46	083	084	32.421	952	14
47	112	114	32.118	952	13
48	141	143	31.821	951	12
49	170	172	31.528	950	11
50	199	201	31.242	.99949	10
51	228	230	30.960	948	9
52	.03257	.03259	30.683	947	8
53	286	288	30.412	946	7
54	316	317	30.145	945	6
55	345	346	29.882	944	5
56	374	376	29.624	943	4
57	403	405	29.371	942	3
58	432	434	29.122	941	2
59	461	463	28.877	940	1
60	.03490	.03492	28.636	.99939	0
	cos	cot	tan	sin	′

88°

TABLE 31.

Natural Trigonometric Functions.

2°

′	sin	tan	cot	cos	
0	.03490	.03492	28.636	.99939	60
1	519	521	.399	938	59
2	548	550	28.166	937	58
3	577	579	27.937	936	57
4	606	609	.712	935	56
5	635	638	.490	934	55
6	664	667	.271	933	54
7	693	696	27.057	932	53
8	723	.03725	26.845	931	52
9	.03752	754	.637	930	51
10	781	783	.432	.99929	50
11	810	812	.230	927	49
12	839	842	26.031	926	48
13	868	871	25.835	925	47
14	897	900	.642	924	46
15	926	929	.452	923	45
16	955	958	.264	922	44
17	.03984	.03987	25.080	921	43
18	.04013	.04016	24.898	919	42
19	042	046	.719	918	41
20	071	075	.542	.99917	40
21	100	104	.368	916	39
22	129	133	.196	915	38
23	159	162	24.026	913	37
24	188	191	23.859	912	36
25	217	220	.695	911	35
26	246	.04250	.532	910	34
27	.04275	279	.372	909	33
28	304	308	.214	907	32
29	333	337	23.058	906	31
30	362	366	22.904	.99905	30
31	391	395	.752	904	29
32	420	424	.602	902	28
33	449	454	.454	901	27
34	478	.04483	.308	900	26
35	.04507	512	.164	898	25
36	536	541	22.022	897	24
37	565	570	21.881	896	23
38	594	599	.743	894	22
39	623	628	.606	893	21
40	653	658	.470	.99892	20
41	682	687	.337	890	19
42	.04711	.04716	.205	889	18
43	740	745	21.075	888	17
44	769	774	20.946	886	16
45	798	803	.819	885	15
46	827	833	.693	883	14
47	856	862	.569	882	13
48	885	891	.446	881	12
49	914	920	.325	879	11
50	943	949	.206	.99878	10
51	.04972	.04978	20.087	876	9
52	.05001	.05007	19.970	875	8
53	030	037	.855	873	7
54	059	066	.740	872	6
55	088	095	.627	870	5
56	117	124	.516	869	4
57	146	153	.405	867	3
58	175	182	.296	866	2
59	205	212	.188	864	1
60	.05234	.05241	19.081	.99863	0
	cos	cot	tan	sin	′

87°

3°

′	sin	tan	cot	cos	
0	.05234	.05241	19.081	.99863	60
1	263	270	18.976	861	59
2	292	299	.871	860	58
3	321	328	.768	858	57
4	350	357	.666	857	56
5	379	387	.564	855	55
6	408	416	.464	854	54
7	437	445	.366	852	53
8	466	474	.268	851	52
9	.05495	.05503	.171	849	51
10	524	533	18.075	.99847	50
11	553	562	17.980	846	49
12	582	591	.886	844	48
13	611	620	.793	842	47
14	640	649	.702	841	46
15	669	678	.611	839	45
16	698	708	.521	838	44
17	.05727	737	.431	836	43
18	756	.05766	.343	834	42
19	785	795	.256	833	41
20	814	824	.169	.99831	40
21	844	854	17.084	829	39
22	873	883	16.999	827	38
23	902	912	.915	826	37
24	931	941	.832	824	36
25	960	970	.750	822	35
26	.05989	.05999	.668	821	34
27	.06018	.06029	.587	819	33
28	047	058	16.507	817	32
29	076	087	.428	815	31
30	105	116	.350	.99813	30
31	134	145	.272	812	29
32	163	175	.195	810	28
33	192	204	.119	808	27
34	221	233	16.043	806	26
35	.06250	262	15.969	804	25
36	279	.06291	.895	803	24
37	308	321	.821	801	23
38	337	350	.748	799	22
39	366	379	.676	797	21
40	395	408	.605	.99795	20
41	424	438	.534	793	19
42	453	467	15.464	792	18
43	.06482	496	.394	790	17
44	511	.06525	.325	788	16
45	540	554	.257	786	15
46	569	584	.189	784	14
47	598	613	.122	782	13
48	627	642	15.056	780	12
49	656	671	14.990	778	11
50	685	700	.924	.99776	10
51	.06714	730	.860	774	9
52	743	.06759	.795	772	8
53	773	788	.732	770	7
54	802	817	.669	768	6
55	831	847	.606	766	5
56	860	876	.544	764	4
57	889	905	.482	762	3
58	918	934	.421	760	2
59	947	963	.361	758	1
60	.06976	.06993	14.301	.99756	0
	cos	cot	tan	sin	′

86°

TABLE 31.

Natural Trigonometric Functions.

4°

′	sin	tan	cot	cos	
0	.06976	.06993	**14.** 301	.99756	**60**
1	.07005	.07022	.241	754	59
2	034	051	.182	752	58
3	063	080	.124	750	57
4	092	110	.065	748	56
5	121	139	**14.** 008	746	55
6	150	168	**13.** 951	744	54
7	179	197	.894	742	53
8	208	227	.838	740	52
9	237	.07256	.782	738	51
10	.07266	285	.727	.99736	**50**
11	295	314	.672	734	49
12	324	344	.617	731	48
13	353	373	.563	729	47
14	382	402	13. 510	727	46
15	411	431	.457	725	45
16	440	461	.404	723	44
17	469	490	.352	721	43
18	.07498	.07519	.300	719	42
19	527	548	.248	716	41
20	556	578	.197	.99714	**40**
21	585	607	.146	712	39
22	614	636	.096	710	38
23	643	665	**13.** 046	708	37
24	672	695	**12.** 996	705	36
25	701	724	.947	703	35
26	.07730	.07753	.898	701	34
27	759	782	.850	699	33
28	788	812	.801	696	32
29	817	841	.754	694	31
30	846	870	.706	.99692	**30**
31	875	899	.659	689	29
32	904	929	12. 612	687	28
33	933	958	.566	685	27
34	962	.07987	.520	683	26
35	.07991	.08017	.474	680	25
36	.08020	046	.429	678	24
37	049	075	.384	676	23
38	078	104	12. 339	673	22
39	107	134	.295	671	21
40	136	163	.251	.99668	**20**
41	165	192	.207	666	19
42	194	221	.163	664	18
43	223	.08251	.120	661	17
44	.08252	280	.077	659	16
45	281	309	**12.** 035	657	15
46	310	339	**11.** 992	654	14
47	339	368	.950	652	13
48	368	397	.909	649	12
49	397	427	.867	647	11
50	426	456	.826	.99644	**10**
51	455	485	.785	642	9
52	.08484	.08514	.745	639	8
53	513	544	.705	637	7
54	542	573	11. 664	635	6
55	571	602	.625	632	5
56	600	632	.585	630	4
57	629	661	.546	627	3
58	658	690	.507	625	2
59	687	720	.468	622	1
60	.08716	.08749	11. 430	.99619	**0**
	cos	cot	tan	sin	′

85°

5°

′	sin	tan	cot	cos	
0	.08716	.08749	**11.** 430	.**99**619	**60**
1	745	778	.392	617	59
2	774	807	.354	614	58
3	803	837	.316	612	57
4	831	866	.279	609	56
5	860	895	.242	607	55
6	889	925	.205	604	54
7	918	954	.168	602	53
8	947	.08983	.132	599	52
9	.08976	.**09**013	.095	596	51
10	.**09**005	042	.059	.99594	**50**
11	034	071	**11.** 024	591	49
12	063	101	**10.** 988	588	48
13	092	130	.953	586	47
14	121	159	.918	583	46
15	150	189	.883	580	45
16	179	218	.848	578	44
17	208	.09247	.814	575	43
18	.09237	277	.780	572	42
19	266	306	.746	570	41
20	295	335	.712	.99567	**40**
21	324	365	.678	564	39
22	353	394	10. 645	562	38
23	382	423	.612	559	37
24	411	453	.579	556	36
25	440	.09482	.546	553	35
26	.09469	511	.514	551	34
27	498	541	.481	548	33
28	527	570	.449	545	32
29	556	600	.417	542	31
30	585	629	.385	.99540	**30**
31	614	658	.354	537	29
32	642	688	10. 322	534	28
33	671	.09717	.291	531	27
34	700	746	.260	528	26
35	.09729	776	.229	526	25
36	758	805	.199	523	24
37	787	834	.168	520	23
38	816	864	.138	517	22
39	845	893	.108	514	21
40	874	923	.078	.99511	**20**
41	903	952	.048	508	19
42	932	.**09**981	**10.** 019	506	18
43	961	.**10**011	**9.** 9893	503	17
44	.**09**990	040	.9601	500	16
45	.**10**019	069	.9310	497	15
46	048	099	.9021	494	14
47	077	128	.8734	491	13
48	106	158	.8448	488	12
49	135	187	.8164	485	11
50	164	216	.7882	.99482	**10**
51	192	.10246	.7601	479	9
52	221	275	9. 7322	476	8
53	.10250	305	.7044	473	7
54	279	334	.6768	470	6
55	308	363	.6493	467	5
56	337	393	.6220	464	4
57	366	422	.5949	461	3
58	395	452	.5679	458	2
59	424	481	.5411	455	1
60	.10453	.10510	9. 5144	.99452	**0**
	cos	cot	tan	sin	′

84°

TABLE 31.

Natural Trigonometric Functions.

6°

′	sin	tan	cot	cos	
0	.10453	.10510	9.5144	.99452	60
1	482	540	.4878	449	59
2	511	569	.4614	446	58
3	540	599	.4352	443	57
4	569	628	.4090	440	56
5	597	657	.3831	437	55
6	626	687	.3572	434	54
7	655	716	.3315	431	53
8	684	.10746	.3060	428	52
9	.10713	775	.2806	424	51
10	742	805	9.2553	.99421	50
11	771	834	.2302	418	49
12	800	863	.2052	415	48
13	829	893	.1803	412	47
14	858	922	.1555	409	46
15	887	952	.1309	406	45
16	916	.10981	.1065	402	44
17	945	.11011	.0821	399	43
18	.10973	040	.0579	396	42
19	.11002	070	.0338	393	41
20	031	099	9.0098	.99390	40
21	060	128	8.9860	386	39
22	089	158	.9623	383	38
23	118	187	.9387	380	37
24	147	217	.9152	377	36
25	176	.11246	.8919	374	35
26	205	276	.8686	370	34
27	234	305	.8455	367	33
28	.11263	335	.8225	364	32
29	291	364	.7996	360	31
30	320	394	.7769	.99357	30
31	349	423	8.7542	354	29
32	378	452	.7317	351	28
33	407	.11482	.7093	347	27
34	436	511	.6870	344	26
35	465	541	.6648	341	25
36	494	570	.6427	337	24
37	.11523	600	.6208	334	23
38	552	629	.5989	331	22
39	580	659	.5772	327	21
40	609	688	.5555	.99324	20
41	638	.11718	8.5340	320	19
42	667	747	.5126	317	18
43	696	777	.4913	314	17
44	725	806	.4701	310	16
45	.11754	836	.4490	307	15
46	783	865	.4280	303	14
47	812	895	.4071	300	13
48	840	924	.3863	297	12
49	869	954	.3656	293	11
50	898	.11983	.3450	.99290	10
51	927	.12013	8.3245	286	9
52	956	042	.3041	283	8
53	.11985	072	.2838	279	7
54	.12014	101	.2636	276	6
55	043	131	.2434	272	5
56	071	160	.2234	269	4
57	100	190	.2035	265	3
58	129	219	.1837	262	2
59	158	249	.1640	258	1
60	.12187	.12278	8.1443	.99255	0
	cos	cot	tan	sin	′

83°

7°

′	sin	tan	cot	cos	
0	.12187	.12278	8.1443	.99255	60
1	216	308	.1248	251	59
2	245	338	.1054	248	58
3	274	367	.0860	244	57
4	302	397	.0667	240	56
5	331	426	.0476	237	55
6	360	456	.0285	233	54
7	389	485	8.0095	230	53
8	418	.12515	7.9906	226	52
9	.12447	544	.9718	222	51
10	476	574	.9530	.99219	50
11	504	603	.9344	215	49
12	533	633	.9158	211	48
13	562	662	.8973	208	47
14	591	692	.8789	204	46
15	620	722	.8606	200	45
16	649	.12751	7.8424	197	44
17	678	781	.8243	193	43
18	.12706	810	.8062	189	42
19	735	840	.7882	186	41
20	764	869	.7704	.99182	40
21	793	899	.7525	178	39
22	822	929	.7348	175	38
23	851	958	.7171	171	37
24	880	.12988	.6996	167	36
25	908	.13017	7.6821	163	35
26	937	047	.6647	160	34
27	966	076	.6473	156	33
28	.12995	106	.6301	152	32
29	.13024	136	.6129	148	31
30	053	165	.5958	.99144	30
31	081	195	.5787	141	29
32	110	224	.5618	137	28
33	139	.13254	.5449	133	27
34	168	284	7.5281	129	26
35	197	313	.5113	125	25
36	.13226	343	.4947	122	24
37	254	372	.4781	118	23
38	283	402	.4615	114	22
39	312	432	.4451	110	21
40	341	461	.4287	.99106	20
41	370	.13491	.4124	102	19
42	399	521	.3962	098	18
43	427	550	7.3800	094	17
44	.13456	580	.3639	091	16
45	485	609	.3479	087	15
46	514	639	.3319	083	14
47	543	669	.3160	079	13
48	572	698	.3002	075	12
49	600	.13728	.2844	071	11
50	629	758	.2687	.99067	10
51	658	787	7.2531	063	9
52	.13687	817	.2375	059	8
53	716	846	.2220	055	7
54	744	876	.2066	051	6
55	773	906	.1912	047	5
56	802	935	.1759	043	4
57	831	965	.1607	039	3
58	860	.13995	.1455	035	2
59	889	.14024	.1304	031	1
60	.13917	.14054	7.1154	.99027	0
	cos	cot	tan	sin	′

82°

TABLE 31.

Natural Trigonometric Functions.

8°

′	sin	tan	cot	cos	
0	.13917	.14054	7.1154	.99027	60
1	946	084	.1004	023	59
2	.13975	113	.0855	019	58
3	.14004	143	.0706	015	57
4	033	173	.0558	011	56
5	061	202	.0410	006	55
6	090	232	.0264	.99002	54
7	119	262	7.0117	.98998	53
8	148	.14291	6.9972	994	52
9	177	321	.9827	990	51
10	205	351	.9682	986	50
11	.14234	381	.9538	982	49
12	263	410	.9395	978	48
13	292	440	.9252	973	47
14	320	470	.9110	969	46
15	349	499	.8969	965	45
16	378	.14529	.8828	961	44
17	407	559	6.8687	.98957	43
18	436	588	.8548	953	42
19	464	618	.8408	948	41
20	.14493	648	.8269	944	40
21	522	678	.8131	940	39
22	551	707	.7994	936	38
23	580	737	.7856	931	37
24	608	.14767	.7720	927	36
25	637	796	6.7584	.98923	35
26	666	826	.7448	919	34
27	695	856	.7313	914	33
28	.14723	886	.7179	910	32
29	752	915	.7045	906	31
30	781	945	.6912	902	30
31	810	.14975	.6779	897	29
32	838	.15005	.6646	893	28
33	867	034	.6514	889	27
34	896	064	6.6383	.98884	26
35	925	094	.6252	880	25
36	954	124	.6122	876	24
37	.14982	153	.5992	871	23
38	.15011	183	.5863	867	22
39	040	213	.5734	863	21
40	069	243	.5606	858	20
41	097	.15272	.5478	854	19
42	126	302	.5350	849	18
43	155	332	6.5223	.98845	17
44	184	362	.5097	841	16
45	.15212	391	.4971	836	15
46	241	421	.4846	832	14
47	270	451	.4721	827	13
48	299	481	.4596	823	12
49	327	511	.4472	818	11
50	356	.15540	.4348	814	10
51	385	570	.4225	809	9
52	.15414	600	6.4103	.98805	8
53	442	630	.3980	800	7
54	471	660	.3859	796	6
55	500	689	.3737	791	5
56	529	719	.3617	787	4
57	557	749	.3496	782	3
58	586	779	.3376	778	2
59	615	809	.3257	773	1
60	.15643	.15838	6.3138	.98769	0
	cos	cot	tan	sin	′

81°

9°

′	sin	tan	cot	cos	
0	.15643	.15838	6.3138	.98769	60
1	672	868	.3019	764	59
2	701	898	.2901	760	58
3	730	928	.2783	755	57
4	758	958	.2666	751	56
5	787	.15988	.2549	746	55
6	.15816	.16017	.2432	741	54
7	845	047	.2316	737	53
8	873	077	.2200	732	52
9	902	107	6.2085	728	51
10	931	137	.1970	.98723	50
11	959	167	.1856	718	49
12	.15988	196	.1742	714	48
13	.16017	226	.1628	709	47
14	046	.16256	.1515	704	46
15	074	286	.1402	700	45
16	103	316	.1290	695	44
17	132	346	.1178	690	43
18	160	376	6.1066	686	42
19	189	405	.0955	681	41
20	218	435	.0844	.98676	40
21	246	465	.0734	671	39
22	.16275	.16495	.0624	667	38
23	304	525	.0514	662	37
24	333	555	.0405	657	36
25	361	585	.0296	652	35
26	390	615	.0188	648	34
27	419	645	6.0080	643	33
28	447	674	5.9972	638	32
29	476	704	.9865	633	31
30	505	.16734	.9758	.98629	30
31	.16533	764	.9651	624	29
32	562	794	.9545	619	28
33	591	824	.9439	614	27
34	620	854	.9333	609	26
35	648	884	.9228	604	25
36	677	914	5.9124	600	24
37	706	944	.9019	595	23
38	734	.16974	.8915	590	22
39	.16763	.17004	.8811	585	21
40	792	033	.8708	.98580	20
41	820	063	.8605	575	19
42	849	093	.8502	570	18
43	878	123	.8400	565	17
44	906	153	5.8298	561	16
45	935	183	.8197	556	15
46	964	.17213	.8095	551	14
47	.16992	243	.7994	546	13
48	.17021	273	.7894	541	12
49	050	303	.7794	536	11
50	078	333	.7694	.98531	10
51	107	363	.7594	526	9
52	136	393	5.7495	521	8
53	164	.17423	.7396	516	7
54	.17193	453	.7297	511	6
55	222	483	.7199	506	5
56	250	513	.7101	501	4
57	279	543	.7004	496	3
58	308	573	.6906	491	2
59	336	603	.6809	486	1
60	.17365	.17633	5.6713	.98481	0
	cos	cot	tan	sin	′

80°

TABLE 31.

Natural Trigonometric Functions.

10°

′	sin	tan	cot	cos	
0	**.17365**	**.17633**	**5.** 6713	**.98481**	**60**
1	393	663	.6617	476	59
2	422	693	.6521	471	58
3	451	723	.6425	466	57
4	479	753	.6329	461	56
5	508	783	.6234	455	55
6	537	.17813	.6140	450	54
7	.17565	843	.6045	445	53
8	594	873	.5951	440	52
9	623	903	.5857	435	51
10	651	933	5. 5764	.98430	**50**
11	680	963	.5671	425	49
12	708	**.17993**	.5578	420	48
13	737	**.18023**	.5485	414	47
14	766	053	.5393	409	46
15	.17794	083	.5301	404	45
16	823	113	.5209	399	44
17	852	143	.5118	394	43
18	880	173	.5026	389	42
19	909	203	.4936	383	41
20	937	233	5. 4845	.98378	**40**
21	966	.18263	.4755	373	39
22	**.17995**	293	.4665	368	38
23	**.18023**	323	.4575	362	37
24	052	353	.4486	357	36
25	081	384	.4397	352	35
26	109	414	.4308	347	34
27	138	444	.4219	341	33
28	166	474	.4131	336	32
29	195	.18504	.4043	331	31
30	224	534	5. 3955	.98325	**30**
31	252	564	.3868	320	29
32	.18281	594	.3781	315	28
33	309	624	.3694	310	27
34	338	654	.3607	304	26
35	367	684	.3521	299	25
36	395	714	.3435	294	24
37	424	.18745	.3349	288	23
38	452	775	.3263	283	22
39	481	805	.3178	277	21
40	.18509	835	5. 3093	.98272	**20**
41	538	865	.3008	267	19
42	567	895	.2924	261	18
43	595	925	.2839	256	17
44	624	955	.2755	250	16
45	652	**.18986**	.2672	245	15
46	681	**.19016**	.2588	240	14
47	710	046	.2505	234	13
48	738	076	.2422	229	12
49	.18767	106	.2339	223	11
50	795	136	5. 2257	.98218	**10**
51	824	166	.2174	212	9
52	852	197	.2092	207	8
53	881	.19227	.2011	201	7
54	910	257	.1929	196	6
55	938	287	.1848	190	5
56	967	317	.1767	185	4
57	**.18995**	347	.1686	179	3
58	**.19024**	378	.1606	174	2
59	052	408	.1526	168	1
60	.19081	.19438	**5.** 1446	.98163	**0**
	cos	cot	tan	sin	′

79°

11°

′	sin	tan	cot	cos	
0	.19081	**.19438**	**5.** 1446	**.98163**	**60**
1	109	468	.1366	157	59
2	138	498	.1286	152	58
3	167	529	.1207	146	57
4	195	559	.1128	140	56
5	224	589	.1049	135	55
6	252	619	.0970	129	54
7	281	649	.0892	124	53
8	.19309	680	.0814	118	52
9	338	.19710	5. 0736	.98112	51
10	366	740	.0658	107	**50**
11	395	770	.0581	101	49
12	423	801	.0504	096	48
13	452	831	.0427	090	47
14	481	861	.0350	084	46
15	509	891	.0273	079	45
16	.19538	921	.0197	073	44
17	566	952	.0121	067	43
18	595	**.19982**	**5.** 0045	061	42
19	623	**.20012**	4. 9969	.98056	41
20	652	042	.9894	050	**40**
21	680	073	.9819	044	39
22	709	103	.9744	039	38
23	737	133	.9669	033	37
24	.19766	164	.9594	027	36
25	794	194	.9520	021	35
26	823	.20224	.9446	016	34
27	851	254	4. 9372	010	33
28	880	285	.9298	**.98004**	32
29	908	315	.9225	**.97998**	31
30	937	345	.9152	992	**30**
31	965	376	.9078	987	29
32	**.19994**	406	.9006	981	28
33	**.20022**	436	.8933	975	27
34	051	.20466	.8860	969	26
35	079	497	4. 8788	963	25
36	108	527	.8716	958	24
37	136	557	.8644	.97952	23
38	165	588	.8573	946	22
39	193	618	.8501	940	21
40	222	648	.8430	934	**20**
41	250	679	.8359	928	19
42	.20279	709	.8288	922	18
43	307	.20739	.8218	916	17
44	336	770	4. 8147	.97910	16
45	364	800	.8077	905	15
46	393	830	.8007	899	14
47	421	861	.7937	893	13
48	450	891	.7867	887	12
49	478	921	.7798	881	11
50	507	952	.7729	875	**10**
51	.20535	.20982	.7659	869	9
52	563	.21013	4. 7591	.97863	8
53	592	043	.7522	857	7
54	620	073	.7453	851	6
55	649	104	.7385	845	5
56	677	134	.7317	839	4
57	706	164	.7249	833	3
58	734	195	.7181	827	2
59	763	225	.7114	821	1
60	.20791	.21256	4. 7046	**.97815**	**0**
	cos	cot	tan	sin	′

78°

TABLE 31.

Natural Trigonometric Functions.

12°

′	sin	tan	cot	cos	
0	.20791	.21256	4.7046	.97815	60
1	820	286	4.6979	809	59
2	848	316	912	803	58
3	877	347	845	797	57
4	905	377	779	791	56
5	933	408	712	784	55
6	962	438	646	778	54
7	.20990	469	580	772	53
8	.21019	.21499	4.6514	766	52
9	047	529	448	760	51
10	076	560	382	.97754	50
11	104	590	317	748	49
12	132	621	252	742	48
13	161	651	187	735	47
14	189	682	122	729	46
15	218	712	4.6057	723	45
16	.21246	.21743	4.5993	717	44
17	275	773	928	711	43
18	303	804	864	705	42
19	331	834	800	698	41
20	360	864	736	.97692	40
21	388	895	673	686	39
22	417	925	609	680	38
23	445	956	4.5546	673	37
24	474	.21986	483	667	36
25	.21502	.22017	420	661	35
26	530	047	357	655	34
27	559	078	294	648	33
28	587	108	232	642	32
29	616	139	169	636	31
30	644	169	107	.97630	30
31	672	200	4.5045	623	29
32	701	231	4.4983	617	28
33	729	.22261	922	611	27
34	.21758	292	860	604	26
35	786	322	799	598	25
36	814	353	737	592	24
37	843	383	676	585	23
38	871	414	615	579	22
39	899	444	555	573	21
40	928	475	4.4494	.97566	20
41	956	.22505	434	560	19
42	.21985	536	373	553	18
43	.22013	567	313	547	17
44	041	597	253	541	16
45	070	628	194	534	15
46	098	658	134	528	14
47	126	689	075	521	13
48	155	719	4.4015	515	12
49	183	.22750	4.3956	508	11
50	212	781	897	.97502	10
51	240	811	838	496	9
52	.22268	842	779	489	8
53	297	872	721	483	7
54	325	903	662	476	6
55	353	934	604	470	5
56	382	964	546	463	4
57	410	.22995	488	457	3
58	438	.23026	430	450	2
59	467	056	372	444	1
60	.22495	.23087	4.3315	.97437	0
	cos	cot	tan	sin	′

77°

13°

′	sin	tan	cot	cos	
0	.22495	.23087	4.3315	.97437	60
1	523	117	257	430	59
2	552	148	200	424	58
3	580	179	143	417	57
4	608	209	086	411	56
5	637	240	4.3029	404	55
6	665	271	4.2972	398	54
7	693	23301	916	391	53
8	.22722	332	859	384	52
9	750	363	803	378	51
10	778	393	747	.97371	50
11	807	424	691	365	49
12	835	455	635	358	48
13	863	485	580	351	47
14	892	516	4.2524	345	46
15	920	.23547	468	338	45
16	948	578	413	331	44
17	.22977	608	358	325	43
18	.23005	639	303	318	42
19	033	670	248	311	41
20	062	700	193	.97304	40
21	090	731	139	298	39
22	118	.23762	084	291	38
23	146	793	4.2030	284	37
24	175	823	4.1976	278	36
25	203	854	922	271	35
26	231	885	868	264	34
27	.23260	916	814	257	33
28	288	946	760	251	32
29	316	.23977	706	244	31
30	345	.24008	653	.97237	30
31	373	039	600	230	29
32	401	069	547	223	28
33	429	100	4.1493	217	27
34	458	131	441	210	26
35	.23486	162	388	203	25
36	514	193	335	196	24
37	542	223	282	189	23
38	571	.24254	230	182	22
39	599	285	178	176	21
40	627	316	126	.97169	20
41	656	347	074	162	19
42	684	377	4.1022	155	18
43	712	408	4.0970	148	17
44	.23740	439	918	141	16
45	769	.24470	867	134	15
46	797	501	815	127	14
47	825	532	764	120	13
48	853	562	713	113	12
49	882	593	662	106	11
50	910	624	611	.97100	10
51	938	655	560	093	9
52	966	.24686	4.0509	086	8
53	.23995	717	459	079	7
54	.24023	747	408	072	6
55	051	778	358	065	5
56	079	809	308	058	4
57	108	840	257	051	3
58	136	871	207	044	2
59	164	902	158	037	1
60	.24192	.24933	4.0108	.97030	0
	cos	cot	tan	sin	′

76°

TABLE 31.

Natural Trigonometric Functions.

14°

′	sin	tan	cot	cos	
0	.24192	.24933	4.0108	.97030	60
1	220	964	058	023	59
2	249	.24995	4.0009	015	58
3	277	.25026	3.9959	008	57
4	305	056	910	.97001	56
5	333	087	861	.96994	55
6	362	118	812	987	54
7	390	149	763	980	53
8	418	180	714	973	52
9	.24446	211	665	966	51
10	474	242	617	959	50
11	503	.25273	568	952	49
12	531	304	3.9520	945	48
13	559	335	471	.96937	47
14	587	366	423	930	46
15	615	397	375	923	45
16	644	428	327	916	44
17	672	459	279	909	43
18	700	.25490	232	902	42
19	.24728	521	184	894	41
20	756	552	136	887	40
21	784	583	089	.96880	39
22	813	614	3.9042	873	38
23	841	645	3.8995	866	37
24	869	676	947	858	36
25	897	707	900	851	35
26	925	.25738	854	844	34
27	954	769	807	837	33
28	.24982	800	760	829	32
29	.25010	831	714	.96822	31
30	038	862	3.8667	815	30
31	066	893	621	807	29
32	094	924	575	800	28
33	122	955	528	793	27
34	151	.25986	482	786	26
35	179	.26017	436	778	25
36	207	048	391	771	24
37	.25235	079	3.8345	.96764	23
38	263	110	299	756	22
39	291	141	254	749	21
40	320	172	208	742	20
41	348	203	163	734	19
42	376	235	118	727	18
43	404	.26266	073	719	17
44	.25432	297	3.8028	712	16
45	460	328	3.7983	.96705	15
46	488	359	938	697	14
47	516	390	893	690	13
48	545	421	848	682	12
49	573	452	804	675	11
50	601	483	760	667	10
51	629	515	715	660	9
52	.25657	.26546	3.7671	653	8
53	685	577	627	.96645	7
54	713	608	583	638	6
55	741	639	539	630	5
56	769	670	495	623	4
57	798	701	451	615	3
58	826	733	408	608	2
59	854	764	364	600	1
60	.25882	.26795	3.7321	.96593	0
	cos	cot	tan	sin	′

75°

15°

′	sin	tan	cot	cos	
0	.25882	.26795	3.7321	.96593	60
1	910	826	277	585	59
2	938	857	234	578	58
3	966	888	191	570	57
4	.25994	920	148	562	56
5	.26022	951	105	555	55
6	050	.26982	062	547	54
7	079	.27013	3.7019	540	53
8	107	044	3.6976	532	52
9	135	076	933	524	51
10	163	107	891	.96517	50
11	191	138	848	509	49
12	219	169	806	502	48
13	.26247	201	764	494	47
14	275	232	722	486	46
15	303	.27263	680	479	45
16	331	294	3.6638	471	44
17	359	326	596	463	43
18	387	357	554	456	42
19	415	388	512	448	41
20	443	419	470	.96440	40
21	.26471	451	429	433	39
22	500	.27482	387	425	38
23	528	513	346	417	37
24	556	545	3.6305	410	36
25	584	576	264	402	35
26	612	607	222	394	34
27	640	638	181	386	33
28	668	670	140	379	32
29	696	701	100	371	31
30	.26724	.27732	059	.96363	30
31	752	764	3.6018	355	29
32	780	795	3.5978	347	28
33	808	826	937	340	27
34	836	858	897	332	26
35	864	889	856	324	25
36	892	921	816	316	24
37	920	952	776	308	23
38	948	.27983	736	301	22
39	.26976	.28015	696	293	21
40	.27004	046	3.5656	.96285	20
41	032	077	616	277	19
42	060	109	576	269	18
43	088	140	536	261	17
44	116	172	497	253	16
45	144	203	457	246	15
46	172	.28234	418	238	14
47	200	266	379	230	13
48	228	297	3.5339	222	12
49	256	329	300	214	11
50	.27284	360	261	.96206	10
51	312	391	222	198	9
52	340	423	183	190	8
53	368	.28454	144	182	7
54	396	486	105	174	6
55	424	517	067	166	5
56	452	549	3.5028	158	4
57	480	580	3.4989	150	3
58	508	612	951	142	2
59	536	643	912	134	1
60	.27564	.28675	3.4874	.96126	0
	cos	cot	tan	sin	′

74°

TABLE 31.

Natural Trigonometric Functions.

16°

′	sin	tan	cot	cos	
0	.27564	.28675	3.4874	.96126	60
1	592	706	836	118	59
2	620	738	798	110	58
3	648	769	760	102	57
4	676	801	722	094	56
5	704	832	684	086	55
6	731	864	646	078	54
7	.27759	895	608	.96070	53
8	787	927	3.4570	062	52
9	815	958	533	054	51
10	843	.28990	495	046	50
11	871	.29021	458	037	49
12	899	053	420	029	48
13	927	084	383	021	47
14	955	116	346	013	46
15	.27983	147	3.4308	.96005	45
16	.28011	179	271	.95997	44
17	039	210	234	989	43
18	067	.29242	197	981	42
19	095	274	160	972	41
20	123	305	124	964	40
21	150	337	087	956	39
22	178	368	050	948	38
23	206	400	3.4014	940	37
24	.28234	432	3.3977	931	36
25	262	.29463	941	.95923	35
26	290	495	904	915	34
27	318	526	868	907	33
28	346	558	832	898	32
29	374	590	796	890	31
30	402	621	759	882	30
31	429	653	723	874	29
32	457	685	687	865	28
33	.28485	.29716	3.3652	.95857	27
34	513	748	616	849	26
35	541	780	580	841	25
36	569	811	544	832	24
37	597	843	509	824	23
38	625	875	473	816	22
39	652	906	438	807	21
40	680	938	402	799	20
41	708	.29970	367	791	19
42	.28736	.30001	3.3332	.95782	18
43	764	033	297	774	17
44	792	065	261	766	16
45	820	097	226	757	15
46	847	128	191	749	14
47	875	160	156	740	13
48	903	192	122	732	12
49	931	224	087	724	11
50	959	255	052	715	10
51	.28987	.30287	3.3017	.95707	9
52	.29015	319	3.2983	698	8
53	042	351	948	690	7
54	070	382	914	681	6
55	098	414	879	673	5
56	126	446	845	664	4
57	154	478	811	656	3
58	182	509	777	647	2
59	209	541	743	639	1
60	.29237	.30573	3.2709	.95630	0
	cos	cot	tan	sin	′

73°

17°

′	sin	tan	cot	cos	
0	.29237	.30573	3.2709	.95630	60
1	265	605	675	622	59
2	293	637	641	613	58
3	321	669	607	605	57
4	348	700	573	596	56
5	376	732	539	588	55
6	404	764	506	579	54
7	432	.30796	3.2472	571	53
8	460	828	438	562	52
9	.29487	860	405	554	51
10	515	891	371	.95545	50
11	543	923	338	536	49
12	571	955	305	528	48
13	599	.30987	272	519	47
14	626	.31019	3.2238	511	46
15	654	051	205	502	45
16	682	083	172	493	44
17	710	115	139	485	43
18	.29737	147	106	476	42
19	765	178	073	467	41
20	793	210	041	.95459	40
21	821	242	3.2008	450	39
22	849	.31274	3.1975	441	38
23	876	306	943	433	37
24	904	338	910	424	36
25	932	370	878	415	35
26	960	402	845	407	34
27	.29987	434	813	398	33
28	.30015	466	780	389	32
29	043	.31498	3.1748	380	31
30	071	530	716	.95372	30
31	098	562	684	363	29
32	126	594	652	354	28
33	154	626	620	345	27
34	182	658	588	337	26
35	209	690	556	328	25
36	237	722	524	319	24
37	.30265	.31754	3.1492	310	23
38	292	786	460	301	22
39	320	818	429	293	21
40	348	850	397	.95284	20
41	376	882	366	275	19
42	403	914	334	260	18
43	431	946	303	257	17
44	459	.31978	3.1271	248	16
45	.30486	.32010	240	240	15
46	514	042	209	231	14
47	542	074	178	222	13
48	570	106	146	213	12
49	597	139	115	204	11
50	625	171	084	.95195	10
51	653	203	053	186	9
52	680	235	3.1022	177	8
53	.30708	.32267	3.0991	168	7
54	736	299	961	159	6
55	763	331	930	150	5
56	791	363	899	142	4
57	819	396	868	133	3
58	846	428	838	124	2
59	874	460	807	115	1
60	.30902	.32492	3.0777	.95106	0
	cos	cot	tan	sin	′

72°

Natural Trigonometric Functions.

18°

′	sin	tan	cot	cos	
0	.30902	.32492	3.0777	.95106	60
1	929	524	746	097	59
2	957	556	716	088	58
3	.30985	588	686	079	57
4	.31012	621	655	070	56
5	040	653	625	061	55
6	068	685	595	.95052	54
7	095	717	565	043	53
8	123	.32749	535	033	52
9	151	782	3.0505	024	51
10	178	814	475	015	50
11	206	846	445	.95006	49
12	233	878	415	.94997	48
13	261	911	385	988	47
14	.31289	943	356	979	46
15	316	.32975	326	970	45
16	344	.33007	296	961	44
17	372	040	3.0267	952	43
18	399	072	237	943	42
19	427	104	208	933	41
20	454	136	178	.94924	40
21	482	169	149	915	39
22	.31510	201	120	906	38
23	537	233	090	897	37
24	565	.33266	061	888	36
25	593	298	032	878	35
26	620	330	3.0003	869	34
27	648	363	2.9974	860	33
28	675	395	945	.94851	32
29	703	427	916	842	31
30	730	460	887	832	30
31	.31758	.33492	858	823	29
32	786	524	829	814	28
33	813	557	800	805	27
34	841	589	772	795	26
35	868	621	2.9743	786	25
36	896	654	714	.94777	24
37	923	686	686	768	23
38	951	.33718	657	758	22
39	.31979	751	629	749	21
40	.32006	783	600	740	20
41	034	816	572	730	19
42	061	848	544	721	18
43	089	881	515	712	17
44	116	913	2.9487	.94702	16
45	144	945	459	693	15
46	171	.33978	431	684	14
47	199	.34010	403	674	13
48	227	043	375	665	12
49	254	075	347	656	11
50	.32282	108	319	646	10
51	309	140	2.9291	637	9
52	337	173	263	.94627	8
53	364	205	235	618	7
54	392	.34238	208	609	6
55	419	270	180	599	5
56	447	303	152	590	4
57	474	335	125	580	3
58	502	368	097	571	2
59	529	400	070	561	1
60	.32557	.34433	2.9042	.94552	0
	cos	cot	tan	sin	′

71°

19°

′	sin	tan	cot	cos	
0	.32557	.34433	2.9042	.94552	60
1	584	465	2.9015	542	59
2	612	498	2.8987	533	58
3	639	530	960	523	57
4	667	563	933	514	56
5	694	596	905	504	55
6	722	628	878	495	54
7	749	661	851	485	53
8	.32777	693	824	476	52
9	804	.34726	797	466	51
10	832	758	770	.94457	50
11	859	791	2.8743	447	49
12	887	824	716	438	48
13	914	856	689	428	47
14	942	889	662	418	46
15	969	922	636	409	45
16	.32997	954	609	399	44
17	.33024	.34987	582	390	43
18	051	.35020	556	380	42
19	079	052	529	370	41
20	106	085	2.8502	.94361	40
21	134	118	476	351	39
22	161	150	449	342	38
23	189	183	423	332	37
24	.33216	216	397	322	36
25	244	.35248	370	313	35
26	271	281	344	303	34
27	298	314	318	293	33
28	326	346	291	284	32
29	353	379	2.8265	274	31
30	381	412	239	.94264	30
31	.33408	.35445	213	254	29
32	436	477	187	245	28
33	463	510	161	235	27
34	490	543	135	225	26
35	518	576	109	215	25
36	545	608	083	206	24
37	573	641	057	196	23
38	.33600	674	032	186	22
39	627	.35707	2.8006	176	21
40	655	740	2.7980	.94167	20
41	682	772	955	157	19
42	710	805	929	147	18
43	737	838	903	137	17
44	764	871	878	127	16
45	.33792	904	852	118	15
46	819	937	2.7827	108	14
47	846	.35969	801	098	13
48	874	.36002	776	.94088	12
49	901	035	751	078	11
50	929	068	725	068	10
51	956	101	700	058	9
52	.33983	134	675	049	8
53	.34011	167	2.7650	039	7
54	038	.36199	625	029	6
55	065	232	600	019	5
56	093	265	575	.94009	4
57	120	298	550	.93999	3
58	147	331	525	989	2
59	175	364	500	979	1
60	.34202	.36397	2.7475	.93969	0
	cos	cot	tan	sin	′

70°

TABLE 31.

Natural Trigonometric Functions.

20°

′	sin	tan	cot	cos	
0	.34202	.36397	2.7475	.93969	60
1	229	430	450	959	59
2	257	463	425	949	58
3	284	496	400	939	57
4	311	529	376	929	56
5	339	562	351	919	55
6	366	595	326	909	54
7	.34393	628	302	899	53
8	421	661	277	889	52
9	448	.36694	2.7253	879	51
10	475	727	228	.93869	50
11	503	760	204	859	49
12	530	793	179	849	48
13	557	826	155	839	47
14	.34584	859	130	829	46
15	612	892	106	819	45
16	639	925	082	809	44
17	666	958	058	799	43
18	694	.36991	034	789	42
19	721	.37024	2.7009	779	41
20	748	057	2.6985	.93769	40
21	.34775	090	961	759	39
22	803	123	937	748	38
23	830	157	913	738	37
24	857	190	889	728	36
25	884	223	865	718	35
26	912	.37256	841	708	34
27	939	289	818	698	33
28	966	322	2.6794	688	32
29	.34993	355	770	677	31
30	.35021	388	746	.93667	30
31	048	422	723	657	29
32	075	455	699	647	28
33	102	.37488	675	637	27
34	130	521	652	626	26
35	157	554	628	616	25
36	184	588	2.6605	606	24
37	.35211	621	581	596	23
38	239	654	558	585	22
39	266	687	534	575	21
40	293	.37720	511	.93565	20
41	320	754	488	555	19
42	347	787	464	544	18
43	375	820	441	534	17
44	.35402	853	2.6418	524	16
45	429	887	395	514	15
46	456	920	371	503	14
47	484	953	348	493	13
48	511	.37986	325	483	12
49	538	.38020	302	472	11
50	565	053	279	.93462	10
51	.35592	086	256	452	9
52	619	120	2.6233	441	8
53	647	153	210	431	7
54	674	186	187	420	6
55	701	220	165	410	5
56	728	253	142	400	4
57	755	286	119	389	3
58	782	320	096	379	2
59	810	353	074	368	1
60	.35837	.38386	2.6051	.93358	0
	cos	cot	tan	sin	′

69°

21°

′	sin	tan	cot	cos	
0	.35837	.38386	2.6051	.93358	60
1	864	420	028	348	59
2	891	453	2.6006	337	58
3	918	487	2.5983	327	57
4	945	520	961	316	56
5	.35973	553	938	306	55
6	.36000	587	916	295	54
7	027	620	893	285	53
8	054	654	871	.93274	52
9	081	.38687	848	264	51
10	108	721	826	253	50
11	135	754	2.5804	243	49
12	162	787	782	232	48
13	190	821	759	222	47
14	217	854	737	211	46
15	.36244	888	715	201	45
16	271	921	693	.93190	44
17	298	955	671	180	43
18	325	.38988	2.5649	169	42
19	352	.39022	627	159	41
20	379	055	605	148	40
21	406	089	583	137	39
22	434	122	561	127	38
23	461	156	539	116	37
24	.36488	190	517	106	36
25	515	223	2.5495	.93095	35
26	542	.39257	473	084	34
27	569	290	452	074	33
28	596	324	430	063	32
29	623	357	408	052	31
30	650	391	386	042	30
31	677	425	365	031	29
32	704	458	2.5343	020	28
33	.36731	.39492	322	.93010	27
34	758	526	300	.92999	26
35	785	559	279	988	25
36	812	593	257	978	24
37	839	626	236	967	23
38	867	660	214	956	22
39	894	694	193	945	21
40	921	.39727	2.5172	935	20
41	948	761	150	924	19
42	.36975	795	129	913	18
43	.37002	829	108	.92902	17
44	029	862	086	892	16
45	056	896	065	881	15
46	083	930	044	870	14
47	110	963	023	859	13
48	137	.39997	2.5002	849	12
49	164	.40031	2.4981	838	11
50	191	065	960	827	10
51	218	098	939	816	9
52	.37245	132	918	.92805	8
53	272	166	897	794	7
54	299	200	876	784	6
55	326	234	2.4855	773	5
56	353	267	834	762	4
57	380	301	813	751	3
58	407	335	792	740	2
59	434	369	772	729	1
60	.37461	.40403	2.4751	.92718	0
	cos	cot	tan	sin	′

68°

TABLE 31.

Natural Trigonometric Functions.

22°

′	sin	tan	cot	cos	
0	.37461	.40403	2.4751	.92718	60
1	488	436	730	707	59
2	515	470	709	697	58
3	542	504	689	686	57
4	569	538	668	675	56
5	595	572	648	664	55
6	622	606	627	653	54
7	649	640	606	642	53
8	676	674	586	631	52
9	703	.40707	2.4566	620	51
10	.37730	741	545	.92609	50
11	757	775	525	598	49
12	784	809	504	587	48
13	811	843	484	576	47
14	838	877	464	565	46
15	865	911	443	554	45
16	892	945	423	543	44
17	919	.40979	403	532	43
18	946	.41013	2.4383	521	42
19	973	047	362	510	41
20	.37999	081	342	.92499	40
21	.38026	115	322	488	39
22	053	149	302	477	38
23	080	183	282	466	37
24	107	217	262	455	36
25	134	.41251	242	444	35
26	161	285	222	432	34
27	188	319	2.4202	421	33
28	215	353	182	410	32
29	241	387	162	399	31
30	.38268	421	142	.92388	30
31	295	455	122	377	29
32	322	.41490	102	366	28
33	349	524	083	355	27
34	376	558	063	343	26
35	403	592	043	332	25
36	430	626	023	321	24
37	456	660	2.4004	310	23
38	483	694	2.3984	299	22
39	.38510	.41728	964	287	21
40	537	763	945	.92276	20
41	564	797	925	265	19
42	591	831	906	254	18
43	617	865	886	243	17
44	644	899	867	231	16
45	671	933	2.3847	220	15
46	698	.41968	828	209	14
47	725	.42002	808	198	13
48	.38752	036	789	186	12
49	778	070	770	175	11
50	805	105	750	.92164	10
51	832	139	731	152	9
52	859	173	2.3712	141	8
53	886	207	693	130	7
54	912	.42242	673	119	6
55	939	276	654	107	5
56	966	310	635	096	4
57	.38993	345	616	085	3
58	.39020	379	597	073	2
59	046	413	578	062	1
60	.39073	.42447	2.3559	.92050	0
	cos	cot	tan	sin	′

67°

23°

′	sin	tan	cot	cos	
0	.39073	.42447	2.3559	.92050	60
1	100	482	539	039	59
2	127	516	520	028	58
3	153	551	501	016	57
4	180	585	483	.92005	56
5	207	619	464	.91994	55
6	234	654	445	982	54
7	260	688	2.3426	971	53
8	287	.42722	407	959	52
9	.39314	757	388	948	51
10	341	791	369	936	50
11	367	826	351	925	49
12	394	860	332	914	48
13	421	894	313	.91902	47
14	448	929	2.3294	891	46
15	474	963	276	879	45
16	501	.42998	257	868	44
17	528	.43032	238	856	43
18	.39555	067	220	845	42
19	581	101	201	833	41
20	608	136	183	822	40
21	635	170	2.3164	.91810	39
22	661	205	146	799	38
23	688	239	127	787	37
24	715	274	109	775	36
25	741	308	090	764	35
26	.39768	.43343	072	752	34
27	795	378	053	741	33
28	822	412	035	729	32
29	848	447	2.3017	.91718	31
30	875	481	2.2998	706	30
31	902	516	980	694	29
32	928	550	962	683	28
33	955	585	944	671	27
34	.39982	620	925	660	26
35	.40008	.43654	907	648	25
36	035	689	889	636	24
37	062	724	2.2871	.91625	23
38	088	758	853	613	22
39	115	793	835	601	21
40	141	828	817	590	20
41	168	862	799	578	19
42	195	897	781	566	18
43	.40221	932	763	555	17
44	248	.43966	745	543	16
45	275	.44001	2.2727	.91531	15
46	301	036	709	519	14
47	328	071	691	508	13
48	355	105	673	496	12
49	381	140	655	484	11
50	408	175	637	472	10
51	.40434	210	620	461	9
52	461	.44244	2.2602	.91449	8
53	488	279	584	437	7
54	514	314	566	425	6
55	541	349	549	414	5
56	567	384	531	402	4
57	594	418	513	390	3
58	621	453	496	378	2
59	647	488	478	366	1
60	.40674	.44523	2.2460	.91355	0
	cos	cot	tan	sin	′

66°

TABLE 31.

Natural Trigonometric Functions.

24°

′	sin	tan	cot	cos	
0	.40674	.44523	2.2460	.91355	60
1	700	558	443	343	59
2	727	593	425	331	58
3	753	627	408	319	57
4	780	662	390	307	56
5	806	697	373	295	55
6	.40833	732	355	283	54
7	860	.44767	338	.91272	53
8	886	802	320	260	52
9	913	837	2.2303	248	51
10	939	872	286	236	50
11	966	907	268	224	49
12	.40992	942	251	212	48
13	.41019	.44977	234	200	47
14	045	.45012	216	188	46
15	072	047	199	.91176	45
16	098	082	182	164	44
17	125	117	2.2165	152	43
18	151	152	148	140	42
19	178	187	130	128	41
20	204	222	113	116	40
21	231	.45257	096	104	39
22	.41257	292	079	.91092	38
23	284	327	062	080	37
24	310	362	045	068	36
25	337	397	028	056	35
26	363	432	2.2011	044	34
27	390	467	2.1994	032	33
28	416	.45502	977	020	32
29	443	538	960	.91008	31
30	469	573	943	.90996	30
31	.41496	608	926	984	29
32	522	643	909	972	28
33	549	678	892	960	27
34	575	713	876	948	26
35	602	.45748	2.1859	936	25
36	628	784	842	924	24
37	655	819	825	.90911	23
38	681	854	808	899	22
39	707	889	792	887	21
40	.41734	924	775	875	20
41	760	960	758	863	19
42	787	.45995	742	851	18
43	813	.46030	2.1725	839	17
44	840	065	708	826	16
45	866	101	692	814	15
46	892	136	675	.90802	14
47	919	171	659	790	13
48	945	206	642	778	12
49	972	242	625	766	11
50	.41998	277	609	753	10
51	.42024	312	592	741	9
52	051	.46348	2.1576	729	8
53	077	383	560	.90717	7
54	104	418	543	704	6
55	130	454	527	692	5
56	156	489	510	680	4
57	183	525	494	668	3
58	209	560	478	655	2
59	235	595	461	643	1
60	.42262	.46631	2.1445	.90631	0
	cos	cot	tan	sin	′

65°

25°

′	sin	tan	cot	cos	
0	.42262	.46631	2.1445	.90631	60
1	288	666	429	618	59
2	315	702	413	606	58
3	341	737	396	594	57
4	367	772	380	582	56
5	394	808	364	569	55
6	420	843	348	557	54
7	.42446	879	332	545	53
8	473	914	315	532	52
9	499	950	2.1299	520	51
10	525	.46985	283	.90507	50
11	552	.47021	267	495	49
12	578	056	251	483	48
13	604	092	235	470	47
14	.42631	128	219	458	46
15	657	163	203	446	45
16	683	199	187	433	44
17	709	234	171	421	43
18	736	270	2.1155	408	42
19	762	305	139	396	41
20	788	.47341	123	.90383	40
21	.42815	377	107	371	39
22	841	412	092	358	38
23	867	448	076	346	37
24	894	483	060	334	36
25	920	519	044	321	35
26	946	555	028	309	34
27	972	590	2.1013	296	33
28	.42999	626	2.0997	284	32
29	.43025	.47662	981	271	31
30	051	698	965	.90259	30
31	077	733	950	246	29
32	104	769	934	233	28
33	130	805	918	221	27
34	156	840	903	208	26
35	182	876	887	196	25
36	209	912	2.0872	183	24
37	.43235	948	856	171	23
38	261	.47984	840	158	22
39	287	.48019	825	146	21
40	313	055	809	.90133	20
41	340	091	794	120	19
42	366	127	778	108	18
43	392	163	763	095	17
44	.43418	198	2.0748	082	16
45	445	234	732	070	15
46	471	.48270	717	057	14
47	497	306	701	045	13
48	523	342	686	032	12
49	549	378	671	019	11
50	575	414	655	.90007	10
51	602	450	640	.89994	9
52	.43628	486	2.0625	981	8
53	654	.48521	609	968	7
54	680	557	594	956	6
55	706	593	579	943	5
56	733	629	564	930	4
57	759	665	549	918	3
58	785	701	533	905	2
59	811	737	518	892	1
60	.43837	.48773	2.0503	.89879	0
	cos	cot	tan	sin	′

64°

TABLE 31.

Natural Trigonometric Functions.

26°

′	sin	tan	cot	cos	
0	.43837	.48773	2.0503	.89879	**60**
1	863	809	488	867	59
2	889	845	473	854	58
3	916	881	458	841	57
4	942	917	443	828	56
5	968	953	428	816	55
6	.43994	.48989	413	803	54
7	.44020	.49026	398	790	53
8	046	062	2.0383	777	52
9	072	098	368	764	51
10	098	134	353	.89752	**50**
11	124	170	338	739	49
12	151	206	323	726	48
13	177	242	308	713	47
14	203	278	293	700	46
15	.44229	.49315	2.0278	687	45
16	255	351	263	674	44
17	281	387	248	662	43
18	307	423	233	649	42
19	333	459	219	636	41
20	359	495	204	.89623	**40**
21	385	532	189	610	39
22	.44411	568	174	597	38
23	437	604	160	584	37
24	464	.49640	2.0145	571	36
25	490	677	130	558	35
26	516	713	115	545	34
27	542	749	101	532	33
28	568	786	086	519	32
29	.44594	822	072	506	31
30	620	858	057	.89493	**30**
31	646	894	042	480	29
32	672	931	028	467	28
33	698	.49967	2.0013	454	27
34	724	.50004	1.9999	441	26
35	750	040	984	428	25
36	.44776	076	970	415	24
37	802	113	955	402	23
38	828	149	941	389	22
39	854	185	926	376	21
40	880	222	912	.89363	**20**
41	906	258	897	350	19
42	932	295	883	337	18
43	958	.50331	1.9868	324	17
44	.44984	368	854	311	16
45	.45010	404	840	298	15
46	036	441	825	285	14
47	062	477	811	272	13
48	088	514	797	259	12
49	114	550	782	245	11
50	140	587	768	.89232	**10**
51	166	623	754	219	9
52	.45192	.50660	1.9740	206	8
53	218	696	725	193	7
54	243	733	711	180	6
55	269	769	697	167	5
56	295	806	683	153	4
57	321	843	669	140	3
58	347	879	654	127	2
59	373	916	640	114	1
60	.45399	.50953	1.9626	.89101	**0**
	cos	cot	tan	sin	′

63°

27°

′	sin	tan	cot	cos	
0	.45399	.50953	1.9626	.89101	**60**
1	425	.50989	612	087	59
2	451	.51026	598	074	58
3	477	063	584	061	57
4	503	099	570	048	56
5	529	136	556	035	55
6	554	173	542	021	54
7	.45580	209	528	.89008	53
8	606	246	1.9514	.88995	52
9	632	283	500	981	51
10	658	319	486	968	**50**
11	684	.51356	472	955	49
12	710	393	458	942	48
13	736	430	444	928	47
14	762	467	430	915	46
15	.45787	503	1.9416	902	45
16	813	540	402	.88888	44
17	839	577	388	875	43
18	865	614	375	862	42
19	891	651	361	848	41
20	917	.51688	347	835	**40**
21	942	724	333	822	39
22	968	761	1.9319	808	38
23	.45994	798	306	795	37
24	.46020	835	292	.88782	36
25	046	872	278	768	35
26	072	909	265	755	34
27	097	946	251	741	33
28	123	.51983	237	728	32
29	149	.52020	1.9223	715	31
30	175	057	210	701	**30**
31	201	094	196	.88688	29
32	226	131	183	674	28
33	.46252	168	169	661	27
34	278	205	155	647	26
35	304	242	142	634	25
36	330	279	128	620	24
37	355	316	1.9115	607	23
38	381	.52353	101	.88593	22
39	407	390	088	580	21
40	433	427	074	566	**20**
41	458	464	061	553	19
42	.46484	501	047	539	18
43	510	538	034	526	17
44	536	575	020	512	16
45	561	613	1.9007	.88499	15
46	587	650	1.8993	485	14
47	613	.52687	980	472	13
48	639	724	967	458	12
49	664	761	953	445	11
50	690	798	940	431	**10**
51	.46716	836	927	417	9
52	742	873	913	404	8
53	767	910	1.8900	.88390	7
54	793	947	887	377	6
55	819	.52985	873	363	5
56	844	.53022	860	349	4
57	870	059	847	336	3
58	896	096	834	322	2
59	921	134	820	308	1
60	.46947	.53171	1.8807	.88295	**0**
	cos	cot	tan	sin	′

62°

541524°—43——38

TABLE 31.

Natural Trigonometric Functions.

28°

′	sin	tan	cot	cos	
0	.46947	.53171	1.8807	.88295	**60**
1	973	208	794	281	59
2	.46999	246	781	267	58
3	.47024	283	768	254	57
4	050	320	755	240	56
5	076	358	741	226	55
6	101	395	728	213	54
7	127	.53432	715	.88199	53
8	153	470	702	185	52
9	178	507	689	172	51
10	.47204	545	1.8676	158	**50**
11	229	582	663	144	49
12	255	620	650	130	48
13	281	657	637	117	47
14	306	694	624	.88103	46
15	332	.53732	611	089	45
16	358	769	598	075	44
17	383	807	585	062	43
18	.47409	844	572	048	42
19	434	882	559	034	41
20	460	920	1.8546	020	**40**
21	486	957	533	.88006	39
22	511	.53995	520	.87993	38
23	537	.54032	507	979	37
24	562	070	495	965	36
25	588	107	482	951	35
26	.47614	145	469	937	34
27	639	183	456	923	33
28	665	220	443	909	32
29	690	258	430	896	31
30	716	296	1.8418	.87882	**30**
31	741	.54333	405	868	29
32	767	371	392	854	28
33	793	409	379	840	27
34	.47818	446	367	826	26
35	844	484	354	812	25
36	869	522	341	798	24
37	895	560	329	.87784	23
38	920	597	316	770	22
39	946	635	303	756	21
40	971	.54673	1.8291	743	**20**
41	.47997	711	278	729	19
42	.48022	748	265	715	18
43	048	786	253	701	17
44	073	824	240	687	16
45	099	862	228	.87673	15
46	124	900	215	659	14
47	150	938	202	645	13
48	175	.54975	190	631	12
49	201	.55013	177	617	11
50	226	051	1.8165	603	**10**
51	.48252	089	152	589	9
52	277	127	140	.87575	8
53	303	165	127	561	7
54	328	203	115	546	6
55	354	241	103	532	5
56	379	279	090	518	4
57	405	317	078	504	3
58	430	355	065	490	2
59	456	393	053	476	1
60	.48481	.55431	1.8040	.87462	**0**
	cos	cot	tan	sin	′

61°

29°

′	sin	tan	cot	cos	
0	.48481	.55431	1.8040	.87462	**60**
1	506	469	028	448	59
2	532	507	016	434	58
3	557	545	1.8003	420	57
4	583	583	1.7991	406	56
5	608	621	979	391	55
6	634	659	966	377	54
7	659	.55697	954	363	53
8	684	736	942	.87349	52
9	710	774	930	335	51
10	.48735	812	917	321	**50**
11	761	850	905	306	49
12	786	888	1.7893	292	48
13	811	926	881	278	47
14	837	.55964	868	264	46
15	862	.56003	856	250	45
16	888	041	844	.87235	44
17	913	079	832	221	43
18	938	117	820	207	42
19	964	156	808	193	41
20	.48989	194	1.7796	178	**40**
21	.49014	232	783	164	39
22	040	270	771	150	38
23	065	.56309	759	136	37
24	090	347	747	.87121	36
25	116	385	735	107	35
26	141	424	723	093	34
27	166	462	711	079	33
28	.49192	501	1.7699	064	32
29	217	539	687	050	31
30	242	.56577	675	036	**30**
31	268	616	663	021	29
32	293	654	651	.87007	28
33	318	693	639	.86993	27
34	344	731	627	978	26
35	369	769	615	964	25
36	.49394	808	1.7603	949	24
37	419	846	591	935	23
38	445	885	579	921	22
39	470	923	567	906	21
40	495	.56962	556	892	**20**
41	521	.57000	544	878	19
42	546	039	532	.86863	18
43	571	078	520	849	17
44	.49596	116	1.7508	834	16
45	622	155	496	820	15
46	647	193	485	805	14
47	672	232	473	791	13
48	697	271	461	777	12
49	723	309	449	762	11
50	748	.57348	437	748	**10**
51	773	386	426	.86733	9
52	.49798	425	1.7414	719	8
53	824	464	402	704	7
54	849	503	391	690	6
55	874	541	379	675	5
56	899	580	367	661	4
57	924	619	355	646	3
58	950	657	344	632	2
59	.49975	696	332	617	1
60	.50000	.57735	1.7321	.86603	**0**
	cos	cot	tan	sin	′

60°

TABLE 31.

Natural Trigonometric Functions.

30°

′	sin	tan	cot	cos	
0	.50000	.57735	1.7321	.86603	60
1	025	774	309	588	59
2	050	813	297	573	58
3	076	851	286	559	57
4	101	890	274	544	56
5	126	929	262	530	55
6	151	.57968	251	515	54
7	176	.58007	239	501	53
8	201	046	228	.86486	52
9	227	085	1.7216	471	51
10	.50252	124	205	457	50
11	277	162	193	442	49
12	302	201	182	427	48
13	327	240	170	413	47
14	352	279	159	398	46
15	377	.58318	147	384	45
16	403	357	136	.86369	44
17	428	396	124	354	43
18	453	435	1.7113	340	42
19	478	474	102	325	41
20	.50503	513	090	310	40
21	528	552	079	295	39
22	553	591	067	281	38
23	578	631	056	266	37
24	603	.58670	045	.86251	36
25	628	709	033	237	35
26	654	748	022	222	34
27	679	787	1.7011	207	33
28	704	826	1.6999	192	32
29	729	865	988	178	31
30	.50754	905	977	163	30
31	779	944	965	148	29
32	804	.58983	954	.86133	28
33	829	.59022	943	119	27
34	854	061	932	104	26
35	879	101	920	089	25
36	904	140	1.6909	074	24
37	929	179	898	059	23
38	954	218	887	045	22
39	.50979	258	875	030	21
40	.51004	297	864	015	20
41	029	.59336	853	.86000	19
42	054	376	842	.85985	18
43	079	415	831	970	17
44	104	454	1.6820	956	16
45	129	494	808	941	15
46	154	533	797	926	14
47	179	573	786	911	13
48	204	612	775	896	12
49	229	.59651	764	881	11
50	.51254	691	753	866	10
51	279	730	742	.85851	9
52	304	770	1.6731	836	8
53	329	809	720	821	7
54	354	849	709	806	6
55	379	888	698	792	5
56	404	928	687	777	4
57	429	.59967	676	762	3
58	454	.60007	665	747	2
59	479	046	654	732	1
60	.51504	.60086	1.6643	.85717	0
	cos	cot	tan	sin	′

59°

31°

′	sin	tan	cot	cos	
0	.51504	.60086	1.6643	.85717	60
1	529	126	632	702	59
2	554	165	621	687	58
3	579	205	610	672	57
4	604	245	599	657	56
5	628	284	588	642	55
6	653	324	577	627	54
7	678	.60364	566	.85612	53
8	703	403	555	597	52
9	.51728	443	545	582	51
10	753	483	1.6534	567	50
11	778	522	523	551	49
12	803	562	512	536	48
13	828	602	501	521	47
14	852	642	490	506	46
15	877	.60681	479	.85491	45
16	902	721	469	476	44
17	927	761	458	461	43
18	952	801	447	446	42
19	.51977	841	436	431	41
20	.52002	881	1.6426	416	40
21	026	921	415	401	39
22	051	.60960	404	385	38
23	076	.61000	393	.85370	37
24	101	040	383	355	36
25	126	080	372	340	35
26	151	120	361	325	34
27	175	160	351	310	33
28	.52200	200	340	294	32
29	225	240	329	279	31
30	250	280	1.6319	264	30
31	275	.61320	308	.85249	29
32	299	360	297	234	28
33	324	400	287	218	27
34	349	440	276	203	26
35	374	480	265	188	25
36	.52399	520	255	173	24
37	423	561	244	157	23
38	448	601	234	142	22
39	473	.61641	223	.85127	21
40	498	681	1.6212	112	20
41	522	721	202	096	19
42	547	761	191	081	18
43	572	801	181	066	17
44	.52597	842	170	051	16
45	621	882	160	035	15
46	646	922	149	020	14
47	671	.61962	139	.85005	13
48	696	.62003	128	.84989	12
49	720	043	118	974	11
50	745	083	1.6107	959	10
51	.52770	124	097	943	9
52	794	164	087	928	8
53	819	204	076	913	7
54	844	.62245	066	.84897	6
55	869	285	055	882	5
56	893	325	045	866	4
57	918	366	034	851	3
58	943	406	024	836	2
59	967	446	014	820	1
60	.52992	.62487	1.6003	.84805	0
	cos	cot	tan	sin	′

58°

TABLE 31.

Natural Trigonometric Functions.

32°

′	sin	tan	cot	cos	
0	.52992	.62487	1.6003	.84805	60
1	.53017	527	1.5993	789	59
2	041	568	983	774	58
3	066	608	972	759	57
4	091	649	962	743	56
5	115	689	952	728	55
6	140	.62730	941	712	54
7	164	770	931	697	53
8	189	811	921	.84681	52
9	.53214	852	911	666	51
10	238	892	1.5900	650	50
11	263	933	890	635	49
12	288	.62973	880	619	48
13	312	.63014	869	604	47
14	337	055	859	588	46
15	361	095	849	.84573	45
16	.53386	136	839	557	44
17	411	177	829	542	43
18	435	217	818	526	42
19	460	258	808	511	41
20	484	299	1.5798	495	40
21	509	.63340	788	480	39
22	534	380	778	464	38
23	558	421	768	.84448	37
24	.53583	462	757	433	36
25	607	503	747	417	35
26	632	544	737	402	34
27	656	584	727	386	33
28	681	625	717	370	32
29	705	.63666	707	355	31
30	730	707	1.5697	.84339	30
31	754	748	687	324	29
32	.53779	789	677	308	28
33	804	830	667	292	27
34	828	871	657	277	26
35	853	912	647	261	25
36	877	953	637	245	24
37	902	.63994	627	230	23
38	926	.64035	617	.84214	22
39	951	076	607	198	21
40	.53975	117	1.5597	182	20
41	.54000	158	587	167	19
42	024	199	577	151	18
43	049	240	567	135	17
44	073	281	557	120	16
45	097	.64322	547	.84104	15
46	122	363	537	088	14
47	146	404	527	072	13
48	171	446	517	057	12
49	195	487	507	041	11
50	.54220	528	1.5497	025	10
51	244	569	487	.84009	9
52	269	.64610	477	.83994	8
53	293	652	468	978	7
54	317	693	458	962	6
55	342	734	448	946	5
56	366	775	438	930	4
57	391	817	428	915	3
58	415	858	418	899	2
59	440	899	408	883	1
60	.54464	.64941	1.5399	.83867	0
	cos	cot	tan	sin	′

57°

33°

′	sin	tan	cot	cos	
0	.54464	.64941	1.5399	.83867	60
1	488	.64982	389	851	59
2	513	.65024	379	835	58
3	537	065	369	819	57
4	561	106	359	804	56
5	586	148	350	788	55
6	610	189	340	772	54
7	.54635	231	330	.83756	53
8	659	272	1.5320	740	52
9	683	.65314	311	724	51
10	708	355	301	708	50
11	732	397	291	692	49
12	756	438	282	676	48
13	781	480	272	660	47
14	805	521	262	645	46
15	.54829	563	253	.83629	45
16	854	604	1.5243	613	44
17	878	.65646	233	597	43
18	902	688	224	581	42
19	927	729	214	565	41
20	951	771	204	549	40
21	975	813	195	533	39
22	.54999	854	185	517	38
23	.55024	896	175	.83501	37
24	048	938	1.5166	485	36
25	072	.65980	156	469	35
26	097	.66021	147	453	34
27	121	063	137	437	33
28	145	105	127	421	32
29	169	147	118	405	31
30	.55194	189	108	389	30
31	218	230	099	.83373	29
32	242	272	1.5089	356	28
33	266	314	080	340	27
34	291	.66356	070	324	26
35	315	398	061	308	25
36	339	440	051	292	24
37	.55363	482	042	276	23
38	388	524	032	260	22
39	412	566	023	.83244	21
40	436	608	013	228	20
41	460	.66650	1.5004	212	19
42	484	692	1.4994	195	18
43	509	734	985	179	17
44	533	776	975	163	16
45	.55557	818	966	147	15
46	581	860	957	131	14
47	605	902	947	.83115	13
48	630	944	938	098	12
49	654	.66986	928	082	11
50	678	.67028	919	066	10
51	702	071	1.4910	050	9
52	.55726	113	900	034	8
53	750	155	891	017	7
54	775	197	882	.83001	6
55	799	239	872	.82985	5
56	823	282	863	969	4
57	847	324	854	953	3
58	871	366	844	936	2
59	895	409	835	920	1
60	.55919	.67451	1.4826	.82904	0
	cos	cot	tan	sin	′

56°

Natural Trigonometric Functions.

34°

′	sin	tan	cot	cos	
0	.55919	.67451	1.4826	.82904	60
1	943	493	816	887	59
2	968	536	807	871	58
3	.55992	578	798	855	57
4	.56016	620	788	839	56
5	040	663	779	822	55
6	064	.67705	770	806	54
7	088	748	761	790	53
8	112	790	751	773	52
9	136	832	742	.82757	51
10	160	875	1.4733	741	50
11	184	917	724	724	49
12	.56208	.67960	715	708	48
13	232	.68002	705	692	47
14	256	045	696	675	46
15	280	088	687	659	45
16	305	130	678	643	44
17	329	173	669	626	43
18	353	215	659	.82610	42
19	377	258	650	593	41
20	.56401	301	1.4641	577	40
21	425	.68343	632	561	39
22	449	386	623	544	38
23	473	429	614	528	37
24	497	471	605	511	36
25	521	514	596	495	35
26	545	557	586	478	34
27	569	600	577	.82462	33
28	.56593	.68642	568	446	32
29	617	685	559	429	31
30	641	728	1.4550	413	30
31	665	771	541	396	29
32	689	814	532	380	28
33	713	857	523	363	27
34	736	900	514	347	26
35	760	942	505	330	25
36	.56784	.68985	496	.82314	24
37	808	.69028	487	297	23
38	832	071	478	281	22
39	856	114	469	264	21
40	880	157	1.4460	248	20
41	904	200	451	231	19
42	928	243	442	214	18
43	952	286	433	198	17
44	.56976	.69329	424	181	16
45	.57000	372	415	165	15
46	024	416	406	.82148	14
47	047	459	397	132	13
48	071	502	388	115	12
49	095	545	379	098	11
50	119	588	1.4370	082	10
51	143	631	361	065	9
52	167	.69675	352	048	8
53	.57191	718	344	032	7
54	215	761	335	.82015	6
55	238	804	326	.81999	5
56	262	847	317	982	4
57	286	891	308	965	3
58	310	934	299	949	2
59	334	.69977	290	932	1
60	.57358	.70021	1.4281	.81915	0
	cos	cot	tan	sin	′

55°

35°

′	sin	tan	cot	cos	
0	.57358	.70021	1.4281	.81915	60
1	381	064	273	899	59
2	405	107	264	882	58
3	429	151	255	865	57
4	453	194	246	848	56
5	477	238	237	832	55
6	501	281	229	815	54
7	524	.70325	220	.81798	53
8	548	368	1.4211	782	52
9	.57572	412	202	765	51
10	596	455	193	748	50
11	619	499	185	731	49
12	643	542	176	714	48
13	667	586	167	698	47
14	691	629	158	681	46
15	715	.70673	150	.81664	45
16	738	717	1.4141	647	44
17	762	760	132	631	43
18	.57786	804	124	614	42
19	810	848	115	597	41
20	833	891	106	580	40
21	857	935	097	563	39
22	881	.70979	089	546	38
23	904	.71023	080	.81530	37
24	928	066	1.4071	513	36
25	952	110	063	496	35
26	976	154	054	479	34
27	.57999	198	045	462	33
28	.58023	242	037	445	32
29	047	285	028	428	31
30	070	.71329	019	412	30
31	094	373	011	.81395	29
32	118	417	1.4002	378	28
33	141	461	1.3994	361	27
34	165	505	985	344	26
35	189	549	976	327	25
36	.58212	593	968	310	24
37	236	637	959	293	23
38	260	.71681	951	276	22
39	283	725	942	.81259	21
40	307	769	934	242	20
41	330	813	925	225	19
42	354	857	1.3916	208	18
43	378	901	908	191	17
44	.58401	946	899	174	16
45	425	.71990	891	157	15
46	449	.72034	882	140	14
47	472	078	874	.81123	13
48	496	122	865	106	12
49	519	167	857	089	11
50	543	211	848	072	10
51	567	255	1.3840	055	9
52	.58590	299	831	038	8
53	614	.72344	823	021	7
54	637	388	814	.81004	6
55	661	432	806	.80987	5
56	684	477	798	970	4
57	708	521	789	953	3
58	731	565	781	936	2
59	755	610	772	919	1
60	.58779	.72654	1.3764	.80902	0
	cos	cot	tan	sin	′

54°

TABLE 31.

Natural Trigonometric Functions.

36°

′	sin	tan	cot	cos	
0	.58779	.72654	1.3764	.80902	**60**
1	802	699	755	885	59
2	826	743	747	867	58
3	849	788	739	850	57
4	873	832	730	833	56
5	896	877	722	816	55
6	920	921	713	799	54
7	943	.72966	705	.80782	53
8	967	.73010	697	765	52
9	.58990	055	688	748	51
10	.59014	100	1.3680	730	**50**
11	037	144	672	713	49
12	061	189	663	696	48
13	084	234	655	679	47
14	108	278	647	662	46
15	131	.73323	638	.80644	45
16	154	368	630	627	44
17	178	413	622	610	43
18	201	457	613	593	42
19	.59225	502	605	576	41
20	248	547	1.3597	558	**40**
21	272	592	588	541	39
22	295	.73637	580	.80524	38
23	318	681	572	507	37
24	342	726	564	489	36
25	365	771	555	472	35
26	389	816	547	455	34
27	.59412	861	539	438	33
28	436	906	531	420	32
29	459	951	522	403	31
30	482	.73996	1.3514	.80386	**30**
31	506	.74041	506	368	29
32	529	086	498	351	28
33	552	131	490	334	27
34	576	176	481	316	26
35	.59599	221	473	299	25
36	622	267	465	282	24
37	646	312	457	.80264	23
38	669	.74357	449	247	22
39	693	402	440	230	21
40	716	447	1.3432	212	**20**
41	739	492	424	195	19
42	763	538	416	178	18
43	.59786	583	408	160	17
44	809	628	400	143	16
45	832	.74674	392	.80125	15
46	856	719	384	108	14
47	879	764	375	091	13
48	902	810	367	073	12
49	926	855	359	056	11
50	949	900	1.3351	038	**10**
51	972	946	343	021	9
52	.59995	.74991	335	.80003	8
53	.60019	.75037	327	.79986	7
54	042	082	319	968	6
55	065	128	311	951	5
56	089	173	303	934	4
57	112	219	295	916	3
58	135	264	287	899	2
59	158	310	278	881	1
60	.60182	.75355	1.3270	.79864	**0**
	cos	cot	tan	sin	′

53°

37°

′	sin	tan	cot	cos	
0	.60182	.75355	1.3270	.79864	**60**
1	205	401	262	846	59
2	228	447	254	829	58
3	251	492	246	811	57
4	274	538	238	793	56
5	298	584	230	776	55
6	321	629	222	758	54
7	344	.75675	214	741	53
8	367	721	206	723	52
9	.60390	767	1.3198	706	51
10	414	812	190	.79688	**50**
11	437	858	182	671	49
12	460	904	175	653	48
13	483	950	167	635	47
14	506	.75996	159	618	46
15	529	.76042	151	600	45
16	553	088	143	583	44
17	.60576	134	1.3135	565	43
18	599	180	127	547	42
19	622	226	119	530	41
20	645	272	111	.79512	**40**
21	668	318	103	494	39
22	691	364	095	477	38
23	714	410	087	459	37
24	738	456	079	441	36
25	761	.76502	072	424	35
26	.60784	548	1.3064	406	34
27	807	594	056	388	33
28	830	640	048	371	32
29	853	686	040	353	31
30	876	733	032	.79335	**30**
31	899	779	024	318	29
32	922	825	017	300	28
33	945	871	009	282	27
34	968	918	1.3001	264	26
35	.60991	.76964	1.2993	247	25
36	.61015	.77010	985	229	24
37	038	057	977	211	23
38	061	103	970	193	22
39	084	149	962	176	21
40	107	196	954	.79158	**20**
41	130	242	946	140	19
42	153	289	938	122	18
43	176	.77335	1.2931	105	17
44	.61199	382	923	087	16
45	222	428	915	069	15
46	245	475	907	051	14
47	268	521	900	033	13
48	291	568	892	.79016	12
49	314	615	884	.78998	11
50	337	.77661	876	980	**10**
51	360	708	869	962	9
52	.61383	754	1.2861	944	8
53	406	801	853	926	7
54	429	848	846	908	6
55	451	895	838	891	5
56	474	941	830	873	4
57	497	.77988	822	855	3
58	520	.78035	815	837	2
59	543	082	807	819	1
60	.61566	.78129	1.2799	.78801	**0**
	cos	cot	tan	sin	′

52°

TABLE 31.

Natural Trigonometric Functions.

38°

′	sin	tan	cot	cos	
0	.61566	.78129	1.2799	.78801	60
1	589	175	792	783	59
2	612	222	784	765	58
3	635	269	776	747	57
4	658	316	769	729	56
5	681	363	761	711	55
6	704	410	753	694	54
7	726	457	746	676	53
8	749	504	738	.78658	52
9	.61772	.78551	731	640	51
10	795	598	1.2723	622	50
11	818	645	715	604	49
12	841	692	708	586	48
13	864	739	700	568	47
14	887	786	693	550	46
15	909	834	685	.78532	45
16	932	881	677	514	44
17	955	928	670	496	43
18	.61978	.78975	662	478	42
19	.62001	.79022	655	460	41
20	024	070	1.2647	442	40
21	046	117	640	424	39
22	069	164	632	.78405	38
23	092	212	624	387	37
24	115	259	617	369	36
25	138	306	609	351	35
26	160	354	602	333	34
27	.62183	401	594	315	33
28	206	449	587	297	32
29	229	.79496	579	.78279	31
30	251	544	1.2572	261	30
31	274	591	564	243	29
32	297	639	557	225	28
33	320	686	549	206	27
34	342	734	542	188	26
35	.62365	781	534	170	25
36	388	829	527	.78152	24
37	411	877	519	134	23
38	433	924	512	116	22
39	456	.79972	504	098	21
40	479	.80020	1.2497	079	20
41	502	067	489	061	19
42	524	115	482	043	18
43	547	163	475	025	17
44	.62570	211	467	.78007	16
45	592	258	460	.77988	15
46	615	306	452	970	14
47	638	354	445	952	13
48	660	402	437	934	12
49	683	450	430	916	11
50	706	.80498	1.2423	897	10
51	728	546	415	879	9
52	.62751	594	408	.77861	8
53	774	642	401	843	7
54	796	690	393	824	6
55	819	738	386	806	5
56	842	786	378	788	4
57	864	834	371	769	3
58	887	882	364	751	2
59	909	930	356	733	1
60	.62932	.80978	1.2349	.77715	0
	cos	cot	tan	sin	′

51°

39°

′	sin	tan	cot	cos	
0	.62932	.80978	1.2349	.77715	60
1	955	.81027	342	696	59
2	.62977	075	334	678	58
3	.63000	123	327	660	57
4	022	171	320	641	56
5	045	220	312	623	55
6	068	268	305	605	54
7	090	316	298	586	53
8	113	364	290	.77568	52
9	135	413	283	550	51
10	.63158	461	1.2276	531	50
11	180	.81510	268	513	49
12	203	558	261	494	48
13	225	606	254	476	47
14	248	655	247	458	46
15	271	703	239	439	45
16	293	752	232	.77421	44
17	.63316	800	225	402	43
18	338	849	218	384	42
19	361	898	210	366	41
20	383	946	1.2203	347	40
21	406	.81995	196	329	39
22	428	.82044	189	310	38
23	451	092	181	.77292	37
24	.63473	141	174	273	36
25	496	190	167	255	35
26	518	238	160	236	34
27	540	287	153	218	33
28	563	336	145	199	32
29	585	385	138	181	31
30	608	434	1.2131	.77162	30
31	.63630	.82483	124	144	29
32	653	531	117	125	28
33	675	580	109	107	27
34	698	629	102	088	26
35	720	678	095	070	25
36	742	727	088	051	24
37	765	776	081	033	23
38	787	825	074	.77014	22
39	.63810	874	066	.76996	21
40	832	923	1.2059	977	20
41	854	.82972	052	959	19
42	877	.83022	045	940	18
43	899	071	038	921	17
44	922	120	031	903	16
45	944	169	024	884	15
46	966	218	017	.76866	14
47	.63989	268	009	847	13
48	.64011	317	1.2002	828	12
49	033	366	1.1995	810	11
50	056	415	988	791	10
51	078	.83465	981	772	9
52	100	514	974	754	8
53	123	564	967	.76735	7
54	.64145	613	960	717	6
55	167	662	953	698	5
56	190	712	946	679	4
57	212	761	939	661	3
58	234	811	932	642	2
59	256	860	925	623	1
60	.64279	.83910	1.1918	.76604	0
	cos	cot	tan	sin	′

50°

TABLE 31.

Natural Trigonometric Functions.

40°

′	sin	tan	cot	cos	
0	.64279	.83910	1.1918	.76604	60
1	301	.83960	910	586	59
2	323	.84009	903	567	58
3	346	059	896	548	57
4	368	108	889	530	56
5	390	158	882	511	55
6	412	208	875	492	54
7	435	258	868	473	53
8	.64457	307	861	.76455	52
9	479	357	854	436	51
10	501	407	1.1847	417	50
11	524	.84457	840	398	49
12	546	507	833	380	48
13	568	556	826	361	47
14	590	606	819	342	46
15	612	656	812	323	45
16	.64635	706	806	.76304	44
17	657	756	799	286	43
18	679	806	792	267	42
19	701	856	785	248	41
20	723	906	1.1778	229	40
21	746	.84956	771	210	39
22	768	.85006	764	192	38
23	790	057	757	173	37
24	.64812	107	750	.76154	36
25	834	157	743	135	35
26	856	207	736	116	34
27	878	257	729	097	33
28	901	308	722	078	32
29	923	358	715	059	31
30	945	408	1.1708	041	30
31	967	.85458	702	022	29
32	.64989	509	695	.76003	28
33	.65011	559	688	.75984	27
34	033	609	681	965	26
35	055	660	674	946	25
36	077	710	667	927	24
37	100	761	660	908	23
38	122	811	653	889	22
39	144	862	647	870	21
40	166	912	1.1640	851	20
41	188	.85963	633	832	19
42	.65210	.86014	626	.75813	18
43	232	064	619	794	17
44	254	115	612	775	16
45	276	166	606	756	15
46	298	216	599	738	14
47	320	267	592	719	13
48	342	318	585	700	12
49	364	368	578	680	11
50	.65386	419	1.1571	661	10
51	408	.86470	565	.75642	9
52	430	521	558	623	8
53	452	572	551	604	7
54	474	623	544	585	6
55	496	674	538	566	5
56	518	725	531	547	4
57	540	776	524	528	3
58	562	827	517	509	2
59	584	878	510	490	1
60	.65606	.86929	1.1504	.75471	0
	cos	cot	tan	sin	′

49°

41°

′	sin	tan	cot	cos	
0	.65606	.86929	1.1504	.75471	60
1	628	.86980	497	452	59
2	650	.87031	490	433	58
3	672	082	483	414	57
4	694	133	477	395	56
5	716	184	470	375	55
6	738	236	463	356	54
7	759	287	456	337	53
8	781	338	450	.75318	52
9	.65803	389	443	299	51
10	825	441	1.1436	280	50
11	847	.87492	430	261	49
12	869	543	423	241	48
13	891	595	416	222	47
14	913	646	410	203	46
15	935	698	403	184	45
16	956	749	396	.75165	44
17	.65978	801	389	146	43
18	.66000	852	383	126	42
19	022	904	376	107	41
20	044	.87955	1.1369	088	40
21	066	.88007	363	069	39
22	088	059	356	050	38
23	109	110	349	030	37
24	131	162	343	.75011	36
25	.66153	214	336	.74992	35
26	175	265	329	973	34
27	197	317	323	953	33
28	218	369	316	934	32
29	240	421	310	915	31
30	262	.88473	1.1303	896	30
31	284	524	296	876	29
32	.66306	576	290	857	28
33	327	628	283	838	27
34	349	680	276	.74818	26
35	371	732	270	799	25
36	393	784	263	780	24
37	414	836	257	760	23
38	436	888	250	741	22
39	.66458	940	243	722	21
40	480	.88992	1.1237	703	20
41	501	.89045	230	683	19
42	523	097	224	664	18
43	545	149	217	.74644	17
44	566	201	211	625	16
45	588	253	204	606	15
46	.66610	306	197	586	14
47	632	358	191	567	13
48	653	410	184	548	12
49	675	463	178	528	11
50	697	.89515	1.1171	509	10
51	718	567	165	.74489	9
52	740	620	158	470	8
53	.66762	672	152	451	7
54	783	725	145	431	6
55	805	777	139	412	5
56	827	830	132	392	4
57	848	883	126	373	3
58	870	935	119	353	2
59	891	.89988	113	334	1
60	.66913	.90040	1.1106	.74314	0
	cos	cot	tan	sin	′

48°

Natural Trigonometric Functions.

42°

′	sin	tan	cot	cos	
0	.66913	.90040	1.1106	.74314	60
1	935	093	100	295	59
2	956	146	093	276	58
3	978	199	087	256	57
4	.66999	251	080	237	56
5	.67021	304	074	217	55
6	043	357	067	198	54
7	064	410	061	178	53
8	086	463	1.1054	.74159	52
9	107	.90516	048	139	51
10	129	569	041	120	50
11	151	621	035	100	49
12	172	674	028	080	48
13	.67194	727	022	061	47
14	215	781	016	041	46
15	237	834	009	022	45
16	258	887	1.1003	.74002	44
17	280	940	1.0996	.73983	43
18	301	.90993	990	963	42
19	323	.91046	983	944	41
20	.67344	099	977	924	40
21	366	153	971	904	39
22	387	206	964	885	38
23	409	259	958	865	37
24	430	313	951	846	36
25	452	366	1.0945	.73826	35
26	473	419	939	806	34
27	495	473	932	787	33
28	.67516	.91526	926	767	32
29	538	580	919	747	31
30	559	633	913	728	30
31	580	687	907	708	29
32	602	740	900	688	28
33	623	794	894	669	27
34	645	847	1.0888	.73649	26
35	.67666	901	881	629	25
36	688	.91955	875	610	24
37	709	.92008	869	590	23
38	730	062	862	570	22
39	752	116	856	551	21
40	773	170	850	531	20
41	795	224	843	511	19
42	816	277	1.0837	.73491	18
43	.67837	331	831	472	17
44	859	385	824	452	16
45	880	439	818	432	15
46	901	.92493	812	413	14
47	923	547	805	393	13
48	944	601	799	373	12
49	965	655	793	353	11
50	.67987	709	786	333	10
51	.68008	763	1.0780	.73314	9
52	029	817	774	294	8
53	051	872	768	274	7
54	072	926	761	254	6
55	093	.92980	755	234	5
56	115	.93034	749	215	4
57	136	088	742	195	3
58	157	143	736	175	2
59	179	197	730	155	1
60	.68200	.93252	1.0724	.73135	0
	cos	cot	tan	sin	′

47°

43°

′	sin	tan	cot	cos	
0	.68200	.93252	1.0724	.73135	60
1	221	306	717	116	59
2	242	360	711	096	58
3	264	415	705	076	57
4	285	469	699	056	56
5	306	524	692	036	55
6	327	.93578	686	.73016	54
7	349	633	680	.72996	53
8	370	688	674	976	52
9	.68391	742	668	957	51
10	412	797	1.0661	937	50
11	434	852	655	917	49
12	455	906	649	897	48
13	476	.93961	643	877	47
14	497	.94016	637	857	46
15	518	071	630	.72837	45
16	539	125	624	817	44
17	561	180	618	797	43
18	.68582	235	612	777	42
19	603	290	606	757	41
20	624	345	1.0599	737	40
21	645	400	593	717	39
22	666	455	587	697	38
23	688	.94510	581	.72677	37
24	709	565	575	657	36
25	730	620	569	637	35
26	751	676	562	617	34
27	.68772	731	556	597	33
28	793	786	550	577	32
29	814	841	544	557	31
30	835	896	1.0538	537	30
31	857	.94952	532	517	29
32	878	.95007	526	.72497	28
33	899	062	519	477	27
34	920	118	513	457	26
35	941	173	507	437	25
36	962	229	501	417	24
37	.68983	284	495	397	23
38	.69004	340	489	377	22
39	025	395	483	357	21
40	046	451	1.0477	337	20
41	067	.95506	470	.72317	19
42	088	562	464	297	18
43	109	618	458	277	17
44	130	673	452	257	16
45	.69151	729	446	236	15
46	172	785	440	216	14
47	193	841	434	196	13
48	214	897	428	.72176	12
49	235	.95952	422	156	11
50	256	.96008	1.0416	136	10
51	277	064	410	116	9
52	.69298	120	404	095	8
53	319	176	398	075	7
54	340	232	392	055	6
55	361	288	385	035	5
56	382	344	379	.72015	4
57	403	400	373	.71995	3
58	424	457	367	974	2
59	445	513	361	954	1
60	.69466	.96569	1.0355	.71934	0
	cos	cot	tan	sin	′

46°

 TABLE 31.

Natural Trigonometric Functions.

44°

′	sin	tan	cot	cos	
0	.69466	.96569	1.0355	.71934	60
1	487	625	349	914	59
2	508	681	343	894	58
3	529	738	337	873	57
4	549	794	331	853	56
5	570	850	325	833	55
6	591	907	319	813	54
7	.69612	.96963	313	792	53
8	633	.97020	307	772	52
9	654	076	301	.71752	51
10	675	133	1.0295	732	50
11	696	189	289	711	49
12	717	246	283	691	48
13	737	302	277	671	47
14	758	359	271	650	46
15	779	416	265	630	45
16	.69800	.97472	259	610	44
17	821	529	253	590	43
18	842	586	247	.71569	42
19	862	643	241	549	41
20	883	700	1.0235	529	40
21	904	756	230	508	39
22	925	813	224	488	38
23	946	870	218	468	37
24	966	927	212	447	36
25	.69987	.97984	206	427	35
26	.70008	.98041	200	407	34
27	029	098	194	.71386	33
28	049	155	188	366	32
29	070	213	182	345	31
30	091	270	1.0176	325	30
31	112	327	170	305	29
32	132	384	164	284	28
33	153	441	158	264	27
34	.70174	.98499	152	243	26
35	195	556	147	223	25
36	215	613	141	.71203	24
37	236	671	135	182	23
38	257	728	129	162	22
39	277	786	123	141	21
40	298	843	1.0117	121	20
41	319	901	111	100	19
42	.70339	.98958	105	080	18
43	360	.99016	099	059	17
44	381	073	094	039	16
45	401	131	088	.71019	15
46	422	189	082	.70998	14
47	443	247	076	978	13
48	463	304	070	957	12
49	484	362	064	937	11
50	505	420	1.0058	916	10
51	.70525	.99478	052	896	9
52	546	536	047	875	8
53	567	594	041	.70855	7
54	587	652	035	834	6
55	608	710	029	813	5
56	628	768	023	793	4
57	649	826	017	772	3
58	670	884	012	752	2
59	690	.99942	006	731	1
60	.70711	1.0000	1.0000	.70711	0
	cos	cot	tan	sin	′

45°

TABLE 32.

Logarithms of Numbers.

100

No.	0	d	1	d	2	d	3	d	4	d	5	d	6	d	7	d	8	d	9	d
100	00000	43	00043	44	00087	43	00130	43	00173	44	00217	43	00260	43	00303	43	00346	43	00389	43
101	432	43	475	43	518	43	561	43	00604	43	00647	42	00689	43	00732	43	00775	42	00817	43
102	00860	43	00903	42	00945	43	00988	42	01030	42	01072	43	01115	42	01157	42	01199	43	01242	42
103	01284	42	01326	42	01368	42	01410	42	452	42	494	42	536	42	578	42	01620	42	01662	41
104	01703	42	01745	42	01787	41	01828	42	01870	42	01912	41	01953	42	01995	41	02036	42	02078	41
105	02119	41	02160	42	02202	41	02243	41	02284	41	02325	41	02366	41	02407	42	449	41	490	41
106	531	41	572	40	02612	41	02653	41	02694	41	02735	41	02776	40	02816	41	02857	41	02898	40
107	02938	41	02979	40	03019	41	03060	40	03100	41	03141	40	03181	41	03222	40	03262	40	03302	40
108	03342	41	03383	40	423	40	463	40	503	40	543	40	583	40	03623	40	03663	40	03703	40
109	03743	39	03782	40	03822	40	03862	40	03902	39	03941	40	03981	40	04021	39	04060	40	04100	39
110	04139	40	04179	39	04218	40	04258	39	04297	39	04336	40	04376	39	415	39	454	39	493	39
111	532	39	571	39	610	40	04650	39	04689	38	04727	39	04766	39	04805	39	04844	39	04883	39
112	04922	39	04961	38	04999	39	05038	39	05077	38	05115	39	05154	38	05192	39	05231	38	05269	39
113	05308	38	05346	39	05385	38	423	38	461	39	500	38	538	38	576	38	614	38	05652	38
114	05690	39	05729	38	05767	38	05805	38	05843	38	05881	37	05918	38	05956	38	05994	38	06032	38
115	06070	38	06108	37	06145	38	06183	38	06221	37	06258	38	06296	37	06333	38	06371	37	408	38
116	446	37	483	38	521	37	558	37	595	38	06633	37	06670	37	06707	37	06744	37	06781	38
117	06819	37	06856	37	06893	37	06930	37	06967	37	07004	37	07041	37	07078	37	07115	36	07151	37
118	07188	37	07225	37	07262	36	07298	37	07335	37	372	36	408	37	445	37	482	36	518	37
119	555	36	591	37	628	36	07664	36	07700	37	07737	36	07773	36	07809	37	07846	36	07882	36
120	07918	36	07954	36	07990	37	08027	36	08063	36	08099	36	08135	36	08171	36	08207	36	08243	36
121	08279	35	08314	36	08350	36	386	36	422	36	458	35	493	36	529	36	565	35	600	36
122	636	36	08672	35	08707	36	08743	35	08778	36	08814	35	08849	35	08884	36	08920	35	08955	36
123	08991	35	09026	35	09061	35	09096	36	09132	35	09167	35	09202	35	09237	35	09272	35	09307	35
124	09342	35	377	35	412	35	447	35	482	35	517	35	552	35	587	34	621	35	09656	35
125	09691	35	09726	34	09760	35	09795	35	09830	34	09864	35	09899	35	09934	34	09968	35	10003	34
126	10037	35	10072	34	10106	34	10140	35	10175	34	10209	34	10243	35	10278	34	10312	34	346	34
127	380	35	415	34	449	34	483	34	517	34	551	34	585	34	619	34	653	34	10687	34
128	10721	34	10755	34	10789	34	10823	34	10857	33	10890	34	10924	34	10958	34	10992	33	11025	34
129	11059	34	11093	33	11126	34	11160	33	11193	34	11227	34	11261	33	11294	33	11327	34	361	33
130	394	34	428	33	461	33	494	34	528	33	561	33	594	34	628	33	661	33	11694	33
131	11727	33	11760	33	11793	33	11826	34	11860	33	11893	33	11926	33	11959	33	11992	32	12024	33
132	12057	33	12090	33	12123	33	12156	33	12189	33	12222	32	12254	33	12287	33	12320	32	352	33
133	385	33	418	32	450	33	483	33	516	32	548	33	581	32	613	33	646	32	12678	32
134	12710	33	12743	32	12775	33	12808	32	12840	32	12872	33	12905	32	12937	32	12969	32	13001	32
135	13033	33	13066	32	13098	32	13130	32	13162	32	13194	32	13226	32	13258	32	13290	32	322	32
136	354	32	386	32	418	32	450	31	481	32	513	32	545	32	577	32	609	31	640	32
137	672	32	13704	31	13735	32	13767	32	13799	31	13830	32	13862	31	13893	32	13925	31	13956	32
138	13988	31	14019	32	14051	31	14082	32	14114	31	14145	31	14176	32	14208	31	14239	31	14270	31
139	14301	32	333	31	364	31	395	31	426	31	457	32	489	31	520	31	551	31	582	31
140	613	31	644	31	675	31	14706	31	14737	31	14768	31	14799	30	14829	31	14860	31	14891	31
141	14922	31	14953	30	14983	31	15014	31	15045	31	15076	30	15106	31	15137	31	15168	30	15198	31
142	15229	30	15259	31	15290	30	320	31	351	30	381	31	412	30	442	31	473	30	503	31
143	534	30	564	30	594	31	625	30	655	30	685	30	15715	31	15746	30	15776	30	15806	30
144	15836	30	15866	31	15897	30	15927	30	15957	30	15987	30	16017	30	16047	30	16077	30	16107	30
145	16137	30	16167	30	16197	30	16227	29	16256	30	16286	30	316	30	346	30	376	30	406	29
146	435	30	465	30	495	29	524	30	554	30	584	29	613	30	643	30	673	29	702	30
147	16732	29	16761	30	16791	29	16820	30	16850	29	16879	30	16909	29	16938	29	16967	30	16997	29
148	17026	30	17056	29	17085	29	17114	29	17143	30	17173	29	17202	29	17231	29	17260	29	17289	30
149	319	29	348	29	377	29	406	29	435	29	464	29	493	29	522	29	551	29	580	29
150	17609	29	17638	29	17667	29	17696	29	17725	29	17754	28	17782	29	17811	29	17840	29	17869	29
No.	0		1		2		3		4		5		6		7		8		9	

Prop. Parts

	43	42
0	0	0
1	4	4
2	9	8
3	13	13
4	17	17
5	22	21
6	26	25
7	30	29
8	34	34
9	39	38
10	43	42
	41	40
0	0	0
1	4	4
2	8	8
3	12	12
4	16	16
5	21	20
6	25	24
7	29	28
8	33	32
9	37	36
10	41	40
	39	38
0	0	0
1	4	4
2	8	8
3	12	11
4	16	15
5	20	19
6	23	23
7	27	27
8	31	30
9	35	34
10	39	38
	37	36
0	0	0
1	4	4
2	7	7
3	11	11
4	15	14
5	19	18
6	22	22
7	26	25
8	30	29
9	33	32
10	37	36
	35	34
0	0	0
1	4	3
2	7	7
3	11	10
4	14	14
5	18	17
6	21	20
7	25	24
8	28	27
9	32	31
10	35	34
	33	32
0	0	0
1	3	3
2	7	6
3	10	10
4	13	13
5	17	16
6	20	19
7	23	22
8	26	26
9	30	29
10	33	32

TABLE 32.

Logarithms of Numbers.

150

No.	0	d	1	d	2	d	3	d	4	d	5	d	6	d	7	d	8	d	9	d
150	17609	29	17638	29	17667	29	17696	29	17725	29	17754	28	17782	29	17811	29	17840	29	17869	29
151	17898	28	17926	29	17955	29	17984	29	18013	28	18041	29	18070	29	18099	28	18127	29	18156	28
152	18184	29	18213	28	18241	29	18270	28	298	29	327	28	355	29	384	28	412	29	441	28
153	469	29	498	28	526	28	554	29	583	28	611	28	639	28	667	29	696	28	18724	28
154	18752	28	18780	28	18808	29	18837	28	18865	28	18893	28	18921	28	18949	28	18977	28	19005	28
155	19033	28	19061	28	19089	28	19117	28	19145	28	19173	28	19201	28	19229	28	19257	28	285	27
156	312	28	340	28	368	28	396	28	424	27	451	28	479	28	507	28	535	27	562	28
157	590	28	618	27	645	28	673	27	700	28	19728	28	19756	27	19783	28	19811	27	19838	28
158	19866	27	19893	28	19921	27	19948	28	19976	27	20003	27	20030	28	20058	27	20085	27	20112	28
159	20140	27	20167	27	20194	28	20222	27	20249	27	276	27	303	27	330	28	358	27	385	27
160	412	27	439	27	466	27	493	27	520	28	548	27	575	27	602	27	629	27	656	27
161	683	27	710	27	20737	26	20763	27	20790	27	20817	27	20844	27	20871	27	20898	27	20925	27
162	20952	26	20978	27	21005	27	21032	27	21059	26	21085	27	21112	27	21139	26	21165	27	21192	27
163	21219	26	21245	27	272	27	299	26	325	27	352	26	378	27	405	26	431	27	458	26
164	484	27	511	26	537	27	564	26	590	27	617	26	643	26	669	27	696	26	722	26
165	21748	27	21775	26	21801	26	21827	27	21854	26	21880	26	21906	26	21932	26	21958	27	21985	26
166	22011	26	22037	26	22063	26	22089	26	22115	26	22141	26	22167	27	22194	26	22220	26	22246	26
167	272	26	298	26	324	26	350	26	376	25	401	26	427	26	453	26	479	26	505	26
168	531	26	557	26	583	25	608	26	634	26	660	26	686	26	712	25	737	26	22763	26
169	22789	25	22814	26	22840	26	22866	25	22891	26	22917	26	22943	25	22968	26	22994	25	23019	26
170	23045	25	23070	26	23096	25	23121	26	23147	25	23172	26	23198	25	23223	26	23249	25	274	26
171	300	25	325	25	350	26	376	25	401	25	426	26	452	25	477	25	502	26	528	25
172	553	25	578	25	603	26	629	25	654	25	679	25	704	25	729	25	23754	25	23779	26
173	23805	25	23830	25	23855	25	23880	25	23905	25	23930	25	23955	25	23980	25	24005	25	24030	25
174	24055	25	24080	25	24105	25	24130	25	24155	25	24180	24	24204	25	24229	25	254	25	279	25
175	304	25	329	24	353	25	378	25	403	25	428	24	452	25	477	25	502	25	527	24
176	551	25	576	25	601	24	625	25	650	24	674	25	699	25	724	24	748	25	24773	24
177	24797	25	24822	24	24846	25	24871	24	24895	25	24920	24	24944	25	24969	24	24993	25	25018	24
178	25042	24	25066	25	25091	24	25115	24	25139	25	25164	24	25188	24	25212	25	25237	24	261	24
179	285	25	310	24	334	24	358	24	382	24	406	25	431	24	455	24	479	24	503	24
180	527	24	551	24	575	25	600	24	624	24	648	24	672	24	696	24	720	24	744	24
181	25768	24	25792	24	25816	24	25840	24	25864	24	25888	24	25912	23	25935	24	25959	24	25983	24
182	26007	24	26031	24	26055	24	26079	23	26102	24	26126	24	26150	24	26174	24	26198	23	26221	24
183	245	24	269	24	293	23	316	24	340	24	364	23	387	24	411	24	435	23	458	24
184	482	23	505	24	529	24	553	23	576	24	600	23	623	24	647	23	670	24	694	23
185	717	24	741	23	764	24	26788	23	26811	23	26834	24	26858	23	26881	24	26905	23	26928	23
186	26951	24	26975	23	26998	23	27021	24	27045	23	27068	23	27091	23	27114	24	27138	23	27161	23
187	27184	23	27207	24	27231	23	254	23	277	23	300	23	323	23	346	24	370	23	393	23
188	416	23	439	23	462	23	485	23	508	23	531	23	554	23	577	23	600	23	623	23
189	646	23	669	23	692	23	715	23	738	23	761	23	27784	23	27807	23	27830	22	27852	23
190	27875	23	27898	23	27921	23	27944	23	27967	22	27989	23	28012	23	28035	23	28058	23	28081	22
191	28103	23	28126	23	28149	22	28171	23	28194	23	28217	23	240	22	262	23	285	22	307	23
192	330	23	353	22	375	23	398	23	421	22	443	23	466	22	488	23	511	22	533	23
193	556	22	578	23	601	22	623	23	646	22	668	23	691	22	713	22	735	23	758	22
194	28780	23	28803	22	28825	22	28847	23	28870	22	28892	22	28914	23	28937	22	28959	22	28981	22
195	29003	23	29026	22	29048	22	29070	22	29092	23	29115	22	29137	22	29159	22	29181	22	29203	23
196	226	22	248	22	270	22	292	22	314	22	336	22	358	22	380	23	403	22	425	22
197	447	22	469	22	491	22	513	22	535	22	557	22	579	22	601	22	623	22	645	22
198	667	21	688	22	710	22	732	22	754	22	776	22	29798	22	29820	22	29842	21	29863	22
199	29885	22	29907	22	29929	22	29951	22	29973	21	29994	22	30016	22	30038	22	30060	21	30081	22
200	30103	22	30125	21	30146	22	30168	22	30190	21	30211	22	30233	22	30255	21	30276	22	30298	22
No.	0		1		2		3		4		5		6		7		8		9	

Prop. Parts

	31	30
0	0	0
1	3	3
2	6	6
3	9	9
4	12	12
5	16	15
6	19	18
7	22	21
8	25	24
9	28	27
10	31	30

	29	28
0	0	0
1	3	3
2	6	6
3	9	8
4	12	11
5	15	14
6	17	17
7	20	20
8	23	22
9	26	25
10	29	28

	27	26
0	0	0
1	3	3
2	5	5
3	8	8
4	11	10
5	14	13
6	16	16
7	19	18
8	22	21
9	24	23
10	27	26

	25	24
0	0	0
1	3	2
2	5	5
3	8	7
4	10	10
5	13	12
6	15	14
7	18	17
8	20	19
9	23	22
10	25	24

	23	22
0	0	0
1	2	2
2	5	4
3	7	7
4	9	9
5	12	11
6	14	13
7	16	15
8	18	18
9	21	20
10	23	22

	21
0	0
1	2
2	4
3	6
4	8
5	11
6	13
7	15
8	17
9	19
10	21

Logarithms of Numbers.

200

No.	0	d	1	d	2	d	3	d	4	d	5	d	6	d	7	d	8	d	9	d
200	30103	22	30125	21	30146	22	30168	22	30190	21	30211	22	30233	22	30255	21	30276	22	30298	22
201	320	21	341	22	363	21	384	22	406	22	428	21	449	22	471	21	492	22	514	21
202	535	22	557	21	578	22	600	21	621	22	643	21	664	21	685	22	707	21	728	22
203	750	21	771	21	30792	22	30814	21	30835	21	30856	22	30878	21	30899	21	30920	22	30942	21
204	30963	21	30984	22	31006	21	31027	21	31048	21	31069	22	31091	21	31112	21	31133	21	31154	21
205	31175	22	31197	21	218	21	239	21	260	21	281	21	302	21	323	22	345	21	366	21
206	387	21	408	21	429	21	450	21	471	21	492	21	513	21	534	21	555	21	576	21
207	597	21	618	21	639	21	660	21	681	21	702	21	723	21	744	21	765	20	785	21
208	31806	21	31827	21	31848	21	31869	21	31890	21	31911	20	31931	21	31952	21	31973	21	31994	21
209	32015	20	32035	21	32056	21	32077	21	32098	20	32118	21	32139	21	32160	21	32181	20	32201	21
210	222	21	243	20	263	21	284	21	305	20	325	21	346	20	366	21	387	21	408	20
211	428	21	449	20	469	21	490	20	510	21	531	21	552	20	572	21	593	20	613	21
212	634	20	654	21	675	20	695	20	715	21	736	20	756	21	777	20	32797	21	32818	20
213	32838	20	32858	21	32879	20	32899	20	32919	21	32940	20	32960	20	32980	21	33001	20	33021	20
214	33041	21	33062	20	33082	20	33102	20	33122	21	33143	20	33163	20	33183	20	203	21	224	20
215	244	20	264	20	284	20	304	21	325	20	345	20	365	20	385	20	405	20	425	20
216	445	20	465	21	486	20	506	20	526	20	546	20	566	20	586	20	606	20	626	20
217	646	20	666	20	686	20	706	20	726	20	746	20	766	20	786	20	33806	20	33826	20
218	33846	20	33866	19	33885	20	33905	20	33925	20	33945	20	33965	20	33985	20	34005	20	34025	19
219	34044	20	34064	20	34084	20	34104	20	34124	19	34143	20	34163	20	34183	20	203	20	223	19
220	242	20	262	20	282	19	301	20	321	20	341	20	361	19	380	20	400	20	420	19
221	439	20	459	20	479	19	498	20	518	19	537	20	557	20	577	19	596	20	616	19
222	635	20	655	19	674	20	694	19	713	20	733	20	753	19	772	20	792	19	34811	19
223	34830	20	34850	19	34869	20	34889	19	34908	20	34928	19	34947	20	34967	19	34986	19	35005	20
224	35025	19	35044	20	35064	19	35083	19	35102	20	35122	19	35141	19	35160	20	35180	19	199	19
225	218	20	238	19	257	19	276	19	295	20	315	19	334	19	353	19	372	20	392	19
226	411	19	430	19	449	19	468	20	488	19	507	19	526	19	545	19	564	19	583	20
227	603	19	622	19	641	19	660	19	679	19	698	19	717	19	736	19	755	19	774	19
228	793	20	35813	19	35832	19	35851	19	35870	19	35889	19	35908	19	35927	19	35946	19	35965	19
229	35984	19	36003	18	36021	19	36040	19	36059	19	36078	19	36097	19	36116	19	36135	19	36154	19
230	36173	19	192	19	211	18	229	19	248	19	267	19	286	19	305	19	324	18	342	19
231	361	19	380	19	399	19	418	18	436	19	455	19	474	19	493	18	511	19	530	19
232	549	19	568	18	586	19	605	19	624	18	642	19	661	19	680	18	698	19	717	19
233	736	18	754	19	773	18	791	19	810	19	36829	18	36847	19	36866	18	36884	19	36903	19
234	36922	18	36940	19	36959	18	36977	19	36996	18	37014	19	37033	18	37051	19	37070	18	37088	19
235	37107	18	37125	19	37144	18	37162	19	37181	18	199	19	218	18	236	18	254	19	273	18
236	291	19	310	18	328	18	346	19	365	18	383	18	401	19	420	18	438	19	457	18
237	475	18	493	18	511	19	530	18	548	18	566	19	585	18	603	18	621	18	639	19
238	658	18	676	18	694	18	712	19	731	18	749	18	767	18	785	18	803	19	37822	18
239	37840	18	37858	18	37876	18	37894	18	37912	19	37931	18	37949	18	37967	18	37985	18	38003	18
240	38021	18	38039	18	38057	18	38075	18	38093	19	38112	18	38130	18	38148	18	38166	18	184	18
241	202	18	220	18	238	18	256	18	274	18	292	18	310	18	328	18	346	18	364	18
242	382	17	399	18	417	18	435	18	453	18	471	18	489	18	507	18	525	18	543	18
243	561	17	578	18	596	18	614	18	632	18	650	18	668	18	686	17	703	18	721	18
244	739	18	757	18	775	17	792	18	810	18	38828	18	38846	17	38863	18	38881	18	38899	18
245	38917	17	38934	18	38952	18	38970	17	38987	18	39005	18	39023	18	39041	17	39058	18	39076	18
246	39094	17	39111	18	39129	17	39146	18	39164	18	182	17	199	18	217	18	235	17	252	18
247	270	17	287	18	305	17	322	18	340	18	358	17	375	18	393	17	410	18	428	17
248	445	18	463	17	480	18	498	17	515	18	533	17	550	18	568	17	585	17	602	18
249	620	17	637	18	655	17	672	18	690	17	707	17	724	18	742	17	759	18	777	17
250	39794	17	39811	18	39829	17	39846	17	39863	18	39881	17	39898	17	39915	18	39933	17	39950	17
No.	0		1		2		3		4		5		6		7		8		9	

Prop. Parts

	22	21	20	19	18	17
0	0	0	0	0	0	0
1	2	2	2	2	2	2
2	4	4	4	4	4	3
3	7	6	6	6	5	5
4	9	8	8	8	7	7
5	11	11	10	10	9	9
6	13	13	12	11	11	10
7	15	15	14	13	13	12
8	18	17	16	15	14	14
9	20	19	18	17	16	15
10	22	21	20	19	18	17

TABLE 32.

Logarithms of Numbers.

250

No.	0	d	1	d	2	d	3	d	4	d	5	d	6	d	7	d	8	d	9	d
250	39794	17	39811	18	39829	17	39846	17	39863	18	39881	17	39898	17	39915	18	39933	17	39950	17
251	39967	18	39985	17	40002	17	40019	18	40037	17	40054	17	40071	17	40088	18	40106	17	40123	17
252	40140	17	40157	18	175	17	192	17	209	17	226	17	243	18	261	17	278	17	295	17
253	312	17	329	17	346	18	364	17	381	17	398	17	415	17	432	17	449	17	466	17
254	483	17	500	18	518	17	535	17	552	17	569	17	586	17	603	17	620	17	637	17
255	654	17	671	17	688	17	705	17	722	17	739	17	756	17	773	17	790	17	807	17
256	824	17	40841	17	40858	17	40875	17	40892	17	40909	17	40926	17	40943	17	40960	16	40976	17
257	40993	17	41010	17	41027	17	41044	17	41061	17	41078	17	41095	16	41111	17	41128	17	41145	17
258	41162	17	179	17	196	16	212	17	229	17	246	17	263	17	280	16	296	17	313	17
259	330	17	347	16	363	17	380	17	397	17	414	16	430	17	447	17	464	17	481	16
260	497	17	514	17	531	16	547	17	564	17	581	16	597	17	614	17	631	16	647	17
261	664	17	681	16	697	17	714	17	731	16	747	17	764	16	780	17	797	17	814	16
262	830	17	41847	16	41863	17	41880	16	41896	17	41913	16	41929	17	41946	17	41963	16	41979	17
263	41996	16	42012	17	42029	16	42045	17	42062	16	42078	17	42095	16	42111	16	42127	17	42144	16
264	42160	17	177	16	193	17	210	16	226	17	243	16	259	16	275	17	292	16	308	17
265	325	16	341	16	357	17	374	16	390	16	406	17	423	16	439	16	455	17	472	16
266	488	16	504	17	521	16	537	16	553	17	570	16	586	16	602	17	619	16	635	16
267	651	16	667	17	684	16	700	16	716	16	732	17	749	16	765	16	781	16	797	16
268	813	17	830	16	42846	16	42862	16	42878	16	42894	17	42911	16	42927	16	42943	16	42959	16
269	42975	16	42991	17	43008	16	43024	16	43040	16	43056	16	43072	16	43088	16	43104	16	43120	16
270	43136	16	43152	17	169	16	185	16	201	16	217	16	233	16	249	16	265	16	281	16
271	297	16	313	16	329	16	345	16	361	16	377	16	393	16	409	16	425	16	441	16
272	457	16	473	16	489	16	505	16	521	16	537	16	553	16	569	15	584	16	600	16
273	616	16	632	16	648	16	664	16	680	16	696	16	712	15	727	16	743	16	759	16
274	775	16	791	16	807	16	823	15	838	16	43854	16	43870	16	43886	16	43902	15	43917	16
275	43933	16	43949	16	43965	16	43981	15	43996	16	44012	16	44028	16	44044	15	44059	16	44075	16
276	44091	16	44107	15	44122	16	44138	16	44154	16	170	15	185	16	201	16	217	15	232	16
277	248	16	264	15	279	16	295	16	311	15	326	16	342	16	358	15	373	16	389	15
278	404	16	420	16	436	15	451	16	467	16	483	15	498	16	514	15	529	16	545	15
279	560	16	576	16	592	15	607	16	623	15	638	16	654	15	669	16	685	15	700	16
280	716	15	731	16	747	15	762	16	778	15	793	16	809	15	824	16	840	15	44855	16
281	44871	15	44886	16	44902	15	44917	15	44932	16	44948	15	44963	16	44979	15	44994	16	45010	15
282	45025	15	45040	16	45056	15	45071	15	45086	16	45102	15	45117	16	45133	15	45148	15	163	16
283	179	15	194	15	209	16	225	15	240	15	255	16	271	15	286	15	301	16	317	15
284	332	15	347	15	362	16	378	15	393	15	408	15	423	16	439	15	454	15	469	15
285	484	16	500	15	515	15	530	15	545	16	561	15	576	15	591	15	606	15	621	16
286	637	15	652	15	667	15	682	15	697	15	712	16	728	15	743	15	758	15	773	15
287	788	15	803	15	818	16	834	15	45849	15	45864	15	45879	15	45894	15	45909	15	45924	15
288	45939	15	45954	15	45969	15	45984	16	46000	15	46015	15	46030	15	46045	15	46060	15	46075	15
289	46090	15	46105	15	46120	15	46135	15	150	15	165	15	180	15	195	15	210	15	225	15
290	240	15	255	15	270	15	285	15	300	15	315	15	330	15	345	14	359	15	374	15
291	389	15	404	15	419	15	434	15	449	15	464	15	479	15	494	15	509	14	523	15
292	538	15	553	15	568	15	583	15	598	15	613	14	627	15	642	15	657	15	672	15
293	687	15	702	14	716	15	731	15	746	15	761	15	776	14	790	15	805	15	820	15
294	835	15	850	14	46864	15	46879	15	46894	15	46909	14	46923	15	46938	15	46953	14	46967	15
295	46982	15	46997	15	47012	14	47026	15	47041	15	47056	14	47070	15	47085	15	47100	14	47114	15
296	47129	15	47144	15	159	14	173	15	188	14	202	15	217	15	232	14	246	15	261	15
297	276	14	290	15	305	14	319	15	334	15	349	14	363	15	378	14	392	15	407	15
298	422	14	436	15	451	14	465	15	480	14	494	15	509	15	524	14	538	15	553	14
299	567	15	582	14	596	15	611	14	625	15	640	14	654	15	669	14	683	15	698	14
300	47712	15	47727	14	47741	15	47756	14	47770	14	47784	15	47799	14	47813	15	47828	14	47842	15
No.	0		1		2		3		4		5		6		7		8		9	

Prop. Parts

	18
0	0
1	2
2	4
3	5
4	7
5	9
6	11
7	13
8	14
9	16
10	18

	17
0	0
1	2
2	3
3	5
4	7
5	9
6	10
7	12
8	14
9	15
10	17

	16
0	0
1	2
2	3
3	5
4	6
5	8
6	10
7	11
8	13
9	14
10	16

	15
0	0
1	2
2	3
3	5
4	6
5	8
6	9
7	11
8	12
9	14

	14
1	1
2	3
3	4
4	6
5	7
6	8
7	10
8	11
9	13

TABLE 32.

Logarithms of Numbers.

300

No.	0	d	1	d	2	d	3	d	4	d	5	d	6	d	7	d	8	d	9	d
300	47712	15	47727	14	47741	15	47756	14	47770	14	47784	15	47799	14	47813	15	47828	14	47842	15
301	47857	14	47871	14	47885	15	47900	14	47914	15	47929	14	47943	15	47958	14	47972	14	47986	15
302	48001	14	48015	14	48029	15	48044	14	48058	15	48073	14	48087	14	48101	15	48116	14	48130	14
303	144	15	159	14	173	14	187	15	202	14	216	14	230	14	244	15	259	14	273	14
304	287	15	302	14	316	14	330	14	344	15	359	14	373	14	387	14	401	15	416	14
305	430	14	444	14	458	15	473	14	487	14	501	14	515	15	530	14	544	14	558	14
306	572	14	586	15	601	14	615	14	629	14	643	14	657	14	671	15	686	14	700	14
307	714	14	728	14	742	14	756	14	770	15	785	14	799	14	813	14	827	14	841	14
308	855	14	48869	14	48883	14	48897	14	48911	15	48926	14	48940	14	48954	14	48968	14	48982	14
309	48996	14	49010	14	49024	14	49038	14	49052	14	49066	14	49080	14	49094	14	49108	14	49122	14
310	49136	14	150	14	164	14	178	14	192	14	206	14	220	14	234	14	248	14	262	14
311	276	14	290	14	304	14	318	14	332	14	346	14	360	14	374	14	388	14	402	13
312	415	14	429	14	443	14	457	14	471	14	485	14	499	14	513	14	527	14	541	13
313	554	14	568	14	582	14	596	14	610	14	624	14	638	13	651	14	665	14	679	14
314	693	14	707	14	721	13	734	14	748	14	762	14	776	14	790	13	803	14	817	14
315	831	14	845	14	859	13	49872	14	49886	14	49900	14	49914	13	49927	14	49941	14	49955	14
316	49969	13	49982	14	49996	14	50010	14	50024	13	50037	14	50051	14	50065	14	50079	13	50092	14
317	50106	14	50120	13	50133	14	147	14	161	13	174	14	188	14	202	13	215	14	229	14
318	243	13	256	14	270	14	284	13	297	14	311	14	325	13	338	14	352	13	365	14
319	379	14	393	13	406	14	420	13	433	14	447	14	461	13	474	14	488	13	501	14
320	515	14	529	13	542	14	556	13	569	14	583	13	596	14	610	13	623	14	637	14
321	651	13	664	14	678	13	691	14	705	13	718	14	732	13	745	14	759	13	772	14
322	786	13	799	14	813	13	826	14	840	13	853	14	50866	14	50880	13	50893	14	50907	13
323	50920	14	50934	13	50947	14	50961	13	50974	13	50987	14	51001	13	51014	14	51028	13	51041	14
324	51055	13	51068	13	51081	14	51095	13	51108	13	51121	14	135	13	148	14	162	13	175	13
325	188	14	202	13	215	13	228	14	242	13	255	13	268	14	282	13	295	13	308	14
326	322	13	335	13	348	14	362	13	375	13	388	14	402	13	415	13	428	13	441	14
327	455	13	468	13	481	14	495	13	508	13	521	13	534	14	548	13	561	13	574	13
328	587	14	601	13	614	13	627	13	640	14	654	13	667	13	680	13	693	13	706	14
329	720	13	733	13	746	13	759	13	772	14	786	13	799	13	812	13	825	13	838	13
330	851	14	865	13	51878	13	51891	13	51904	13	51917	13	51930	13	51943	14	51957	13	51970	13
331	51983	13	51996	13	52009	13	52022	13	52035	13	52048	13	52061	14	52075	13	52088	13	52101	13
332	52114	13	52127	13	140	13	153	13	166	13	179	13	192	13	205	13	218	13	231	13
333	244	13	257	13	270	14	284	13	297	13	310	13	323	13	336	13	349	13	362	13
334	375	13	388	13	401	13	414	13	427	13	440	13	453	13	466	13	479	13	492	12
335	504	13	517	13	530	13	543	13	556	13	569	13	582	13	595	13	608	13	621	13
336	634	13	647	13	660	13	673	13	686	13	699	12	711	13	724	13	737	13	750	13
337	763	13	776	13	789	13	802	13	815	12	827	13	840	13	853	13	866	13	52879	13
338	52892	13	52905	12	52917	13	52930	13	52943	13	52956	13	52969	13	52982	12	52994	13	53007	13
339	53020	13	53033	13	53046	12	53058	13	53071	13	53084	13	53097	13	53110	12	53122	13	135	13
340	148	13	161	12	173	13	186	13	199	13	212	12	224	13	237	13	250	13	263	12
341	275	13	288	13	301	13	314	12	326	13	339	13	352	12	364	13	377	13	390	13
342	403	12	415	13	428	13	441	12	453	13	466	13	479	12	491	13	504	13	517	12
343	529	13	542	13	555	12	567	13	580	13	593	12	605	13	618	13	631	12	643	13
344	656	12	668	13	681	13	694	12	706	13	719	13	732	12	744	13	757	12	769	13
345	782	12	794	13	807	13	820	12	832	13	845	12	857	13	870	12	53882	13	53895	13
346	53908	12	53920	13	53933	12	53945	13	53958	12	53970	13	53983	12	53995	13	54008	12	54020	13
347	54033	12	54045	13	54058	12	54070	13	54083	12	54095	13	54108	12	54120	13	133	12	145	13
348	158	12	170	13	183	12	195	13	208	12	220	13	233	12	245	13	258	12	270	13
349	283	12	295	12	307	13	320	12	332	13	345	12	357	13	370	12	382	12	394	13
350	54407	12	54419	13	54432	12	54444	12	54456	13	54469	12	54481	13	54494	12	54506	12	54518	13
No.	0		1		2		3		4		5		6		7		8		9	

Prop. Parts

	15
0	0
1	2
2	3
3	5
4	6
5	8
6	9
7	11
8	12
9	14

	14
1	1
2	3
3	4
4	6
5	7
6	8
7	10
8	11
9	13

	13
1	1
2	3
3	4
4	5
5	7
6	8
7	9
8	10
9	12

	12
1	1
2	2
3	4
4	5
5	6
6	7
7	8
8	10
9	11

TABLE 32.

Logarithms of Numbers.

350

No.	0	d	1	d	2	d	3	d	4	d	5	d	6	d	7	d	8	d	9	d
350	54407	12	54419	13	54432	12	54444	12	54456	13	54469	12	54481	13	54494	12	54506	12	54518	13
351	531	12	543	12	555	13	568	12	580	13	593	12	605	12	617	13	630	12	642	12
352	654	13	667	12	679	12	691	13	704	12	716	12	728	13	741	12	753	12	765	12
353	777	13	790	12	802	12	814	13	827	12	839	12	851	13	864	12	876	12	54888	12
354	54900	13	54913	12	54925	12	54937	12	54949	13	54962	12	54974	12	54986	12	54998	13	55011	12
355	55023	12	55035	12	55047	13	55060	12	55072	12	55084	12	55096	12	55108	13	55121	12	133	12
356	145	12	157	12	169	13	182	12	194	12	206	12	218	12	230	12	242	13	255	12
357	267	12	279	12	291	12	303	12	315	13	328	12	340	12	352	12	364	12	376	12
358	388	12	400	13	413	12	425	12	437	12	449	12	461	12	473	12	485	12	497	12
359	509	13	522	12	534	12	546	12	558	12	570	12	582	12	594	12	606	12	618	12
360	630	12	642	12	654	12	666	12	678	13	691	12	703	12	715	12	727	12	739	12
361	751	12	763	12	775	12	787	12	799	12	811	12	823	12	835	12	847	12	859	12
362	871	12	55883	12	55895	12	55907	12	55919	12	55931	12	55943	12	55955	12	55967	12	55979	12
363	55991	12	56003	12	56015	12	56027	11	56038	12	56050	12	56062	12	56074	12	56086	12	56098	12
364	56110	12	122	12	134	12	146	12	158	12	170	12	182	12	194	11	205	12	217	12
365	229	12	241	12	253	12	265	12	277	12	289	12	301	11	312	12	324	12	336	12
366	348	12	360	12	372	12	384	12	396	11	407	12	419	12	431	12	443	12	455	12
367	467	11	478	12	490	12	502	12	514	12	526	12	538	11	549	12	561	12	573	12
368	585	12	597	11	608	12	620	12	632	12	644	12	656	11	667	12	679	12	691	12
369	703	11	714	12	726	12	738	12	750	11	761	12	773	12	785	12	797	11	808	12
370	820	12	832	12	844	11	855	12	867	12	879	12	56891	11	56902	12	56914	12	56926	11
371	56937	12	56949	12	56961	11	56972	12	56984	12	56996	12	57008	11	57019	12	57031	12	57043	11
372	57054	12	57066	12	57078	11	57089	12	57101	12	57113	11	124	12	136	12	148	11	159	12
373	171	12	183	11	194	12	206	11	217	12	229	12	241	11	252	12	264	12	276	11
374	287	12	299	11	310	12	322	12	334	11	345	12	357	11	368	12	380	12	392	11
375	403	12	415	11	426	12	438	11	449	12	461	12	473	11	484	12	496	11	507	12
376	519	11	530	12	542	11	553	12	565	11	576	12	588	12	600	11	611	12	623	11
377	634	12	646	11	657	12	669	11	680	12	692	11	703	12	715	11	726	12	738	11
378	749	12	761	11	772	12	784	11	795	12	807	11	818	12	830	11	841	11	852	12
379	864	11	875	12	57887	11	57898	12	57910	11	57921	12	57933	11	57944	11	57955	12	57967	11
380	57978	12	57990	11	58001	12	58013	11	58024	11	58035	12	58047	11	58058	12	58070	11	58081	11
381	58092	12	58104	11	115	12	127	11	138	11	149	12	161	11	172	12	184	11	195	11
382	206	12	218	11	229	11	240	12	252	11	263	11	274	12	286	11	297	12	309	11
383	320	11	331	12	343	11	354	11	365	12	377	11	388	11	399	11	410	12	422	11
384	433	11	444	12	456	11	467	11	478	12	490	11	501	11	512	12	524	11	535	11
385	546	11	557	12	569	11	580	11	591	11	602	12	614	11	625	11	636	11	647	12
386	659	11	670	11	681	11	692	12	704	11	715	11	726	11	737	12	749	11	760	11
387	771	11	782	12	794	11	805	11	816	11	827	11	838	12	850	11	861	11	872	11
388	883	11	58894	12	58906	11	58917	11	58928	11	58939	11	58950	11	58961	12	58973	11	58984	11
389	58995	11	59006	11	59017	11	59028	12	59040	11	59051	11	59062	11	59073	11	59084	11	59095	11
390	59106	12	118	11	129	11	140	11	151	11	162	11	173	11	184	11	195	12	207	11
391	218	11	229	11	240	11	251	11	262	11	273	11	284	11	295	11	306	12	318	11
392	329	11	340	11	351	11	362	11	373	11	384	11	395	11	406	11	417	11	428	11
393	439	11	450	11	461	11	472	11	483	11	494	12	506	11	517	11	528	11	539	11
394	550	11	561	11	572	11	583	11	594	11	605	11	616	11	627	11	638	11	649	11
395	660	11	671	11	682	11	693	11	704	11	715	11	726	11	737	11	748	11	759	11
396	770	10	780	11	791	11	802	11	813	11	824	11	835	11	846	11	857	11	868	11
397	879	11	890	11	59901	11	59912	11	59923	11	59934	11	59945	11	59956	10	59966	11	59977	11
398	59988	11	59999	11	60010	11	60021	11	60032	11	60043	11	60054	11	60065	11	60076	10	60086	11
399	60097	11	60108	11	119	11	130	11	141	11	152	11	163	10	173	11	184	11	195	11
400	60206	11	60217	11	60228	11	60239	10	60249	11	60260	11	60271	11	60282	11	60293	11	60304	10
No.	0		1		2		3		4		5		6		7		8		9	

Prop. Parts

	13	12	11	10
1	1	1	1	1
2	3	2	2	2
3	4	4	3	3
4	5	5	4	4
5	7	6	6	5
6	8	7	7	6
7	9	8	8	7
8	10	10	9	8
9	12	11	10	9

TABLE 32.

Logarithms of Numbers.

400

No.	0	d	1	d	2	d	3	d	4	d	5	d	6	d	7	d	8	d	9	d
400	60206	11	60217	11	60228	11	60239	10	60249	11	60260	11	60271	11	60282	11	60293	11	60304	10
401	314	11	325	11	336	11	347	11	358	11	369	10	379	11	390	11	401	11	412	11
402	423	10	433	11	444	11	455	11	466	11	477	10	487	11	498	11	509	11	520	11
403	531	10	541	11	552	11	563	11	574	10	584	11	595	11	606	11	617	10	627	11
404	638	11	649	11	660	10	670	11	681	11	692	11	703	10	713	11	724	11	735	11
405	746	10	756	11	767	11	778	10	788	11	799	11	810	11	821	10	831	11	842	11
406	853	10	863	11	874	11	885	10	60895	11	60906	11	60917	10	60927	11	60938	11	60949	10
407	60959	11	60970	11	60981	10	60991	11	61002	11	61013	10	61023	11	61034	11	61045	10	61055	11
408	61066	11	61077	10	61087	11	61098	11	109	10	119	11	130	10	140	11	151	11	162	10
409	172	11	183	11	194	10	204	11	215	10	225	11	236	11	247	10	257	11	268	10
410	278	11	289	11	300	10	310	11	321	10	331	11	342	10	352	11	363	11	374	10
411	384	11	395	10	405	11	416	10	426	11	437	11	448	10	458	11	469	10	479	11
412	490	10	500	11	511	10	521	11	532	10	542	11	553	10	563	11	574	10	584	11
413	595	11	606	10	616	11	627	10	637	11	648	10	658	11	669	10	679	11	690	10
414	700	11	711	10	721	10	731	11	742	10	752	11	763	10	773	11	784	10	794	11
415	805	10	815	11	826	10	836	11	847	10	857	11	868	10	878	10	888	11	61899	10
416	61909	11	61920	10	61930	11	61941	10	61951	11	61962	10	61972	10	61982	11	61993	10	62003	11
417	62014	10	62024	10	62034	11	62045	10	62055	11	62066	10	62076	10	62086	11	62097	10	107	11
418	118	10	128	10	138	11	149	10	159	11	170	10	180	10	190	11	201	10	211	10
419	221	11	232	10	242	10	252	11	263	10	273	11	284	10	294	10	304	11	315	10
420	325	10	335	11	346	10	356	10	366	11	377	10	387	10	397	11	408	10	418	10
421	428	11	439	10	449	10	459	10	469	11	480	10	490	10	500	11	511	10	521	10
422	531	11	542	10	552	10	562	10	572	11	583	10	593	10	603	10	613	11	624	10
423	634	10	644	11	655	10	665	10	675	10	685	11	696	10	706	10	716	10	726	11
424	737	10	747	10	757	10	767	11	778	10	788	10	798	10	808	10	818	11	829	10
425	839	10	849	10	859	11	870	10	880	10	890	10	62900	10	62910	11	62921	10	62931	10
426	62941	10	62951	10	62961	11	62972	10	62982	10	62992	10	63002	10	63012	10	63022	11	63033	10
427	63043	10	63053	10	63063	10	63073	10	63083	11	63094	10	104	10	114	10	124	10	134	10
428	144	11	155	10	165	10	175	10	185	10	195	10	205	10	215	10	225	11	236	10
429	246	10	256	10	266	10	276	10	286	10	296	10	306	11	317	10	327	10	337	10
430	347	10	357	10	367	10	377	10	387	10	397	10	407	10	417	11	428	10	438	10
431	448	10	458	10	468	10	478	10	488	10	498	10	508	10	518	10	528	10	538	10
432	548	10	558	10	568	11	579	10	589	10	599	10	609	10	619	10	629	10	639	10
433	649	10	659	10	669	10	679	10	689	10	699	10	709	10	719	10	729	10	739	10
434	749	10	759	10	769	10	779	10	789	10	799	10	809	10	819	10	829	10	839	10
435	849	10	859	10	869	10	879	10	889	10	899	10	63909	10	63919	10	63929	10	63939	10
436	63949	10	63959	10	63969	10	63979	9	63988	10	63998	10	64008	10	64018	10	64028	10	64038	10
437	64048	10	64058	10	64068	10	64078	10	64088	10	64098	10	108	10	118	10	128	9	137	10
438	147	10	157	10	167	10	177	10	187	10	197	10	207	10	217	10	227	10	237	9
439	246	10	256	10	266	10	276	10	286	10	296	10	306	10	316	10	326	9	335	10
440	345	10	355	10	365	10	375	10	385	10	395	9	404	10	414	10	424	10	434	10
441	444	10	454	10	464	9	473	10	483	10	493	10	503	10	513	10	523	9	532	10
442	542	10	552	10	562	10	572	10	582	9	591	10	601	10	611	10	621	10	631	9
443	640	10	650	10	660	10	670	10	680	9	689	10	699	10	709	10	719	10	729	9
444	738	10	748	10	758	10	768	9	777	10	787	10	797	10	807	9	816	10	826	10
445	836	10	846	10	856	9	865	10	875	10	885	10	895	9	64904	10	64914	10	64924	9
446	64933	10	64943	10	64953	10	64963	9	64972	10	64982	10	64992	10	65002	9	65011	10	65021	10
447	65031	9	65040	10	65050	10	65060	10	65070	9	65079	10	65089	10	099	9	108	10	118	10
448	128	9	137	10	147	10	157	10	167	9	176	10	186	10	196	9	205	10	215	10
449	225	9	234	10	244	10	254	9	263	10	273	10	283	9	292	10	302	10	312	9
450	65321	10	65331	10	65341	9	65350	10	65360	9	65369	10	65379	10	65389	9	65398	10	65408	10
No.	**0**		**1**		**2**		**3**		**4**		**5**		**6**		**7**		**8**		**9**	

Prop. Parts

	11
1	1
2	2
3	3
4	4
5	6
6	7
7	8
8	9
9	10

	10
1	1
2	2
3	3
4	4
5	5
6	6
7	7
8	8
9	9

	9
1	1
2	2
3	3
4	4
5	5
6	5
7	6
8	7
9	8

541524°—43——39

TABLE 32.

Logarithms of Numbers.

450

No.	0	d	1	d	2	d	3	d	4	d	5	d	6	d	7	d	8	d	9	d
450	65321	10	65331	10	65341	9	65350	10	65360	9	65369	10	65379	10	65389	9	65398	10	65408	10
451	418	9	427	10	437	10	447	9	456	10	466	9	475	10	485	10	495	9	504	10
452	514	9	523	10	533	10	543	9	552	10	562	9	571	10	581	10	591	9	600	10
453	610	9	619	10	629	10	639	9	648	10	658	9	667	10	677	9	686	10	696	10
454	706	9	715	10	725	9	734	10	744	9	753	10	763	9	772	10	782	10	792	9
455	801	10	811	9	820	10	830	9	839	10	849	9	858	10	868	9	877	10	887	9
456	896	10	65906	10	65916	9	65925	10	65935	9	65944	10	65954	9	65963	10	65973	9	65982	10
457	65992	9	66001	10	66011	9	66020	10	66030	9	66039	10	66049	9	66058	10	66068	9	66077	10
458	66087	9	096	10	106	9	115	9	124	10	134	9	143	10	153	9	162	10	172	9
459	181	10	191	9	200	10	210	9	219	10	229	9	238	9	247	10	257	9	266	10
460	276	9	285	10	295	9	304	10	314	9	323	9	332	10	342	9	351	10	361	9
461	370	10	380	9	389	9	398	10	408	9	417	10	427	9	436	9	445	10	455	9
462	464	10	474	9	483	9	492	10	502	9	511	10	521	9	530	9	539	10	549	9
463	558	9	567	10	577	9	586	10	596	9	605	9	614	10	624	9	633	9	642	10
464	652	9	661	10	671	9	680	9	689	10	699	9	708	9	717	10	727	9	736	9
465	745	10	755	9	764	9	773	10	783	9	792	9	801	10	811	9	820	9	829	10
466	839	9	848	9	857	10	867	9	876	9	885	9	894	10	904	9	66913	9	66922	10
467	66932	9	66941	9	66950	10	66960	9	66969	9	66978	9	66987	10	66997	9	67006	9	67015	10
468	67025	9	67034	9	67043	9	67052	10	67062	9	67071	9	67080	9	67089	10	099	9	108	9
469	117	10	127	9	136	9	145	9	154	10	164	9	173	9	182	9	191	10	201	9
470	210	9	219	9	228	9	237	10	247	9	256	9	265	9	274	10	284	9	293	9
471	302	9	311	10	321	9	330	9	339	9	348	9	357	10	367	9	376	9	385	9
472	394	9	403	10	413	9	422	9	431	9	440	9	449	10	67459	9	67468	9	67477	9
473	67486	9	67495	9	67504	10	67514	9	67523	9	67532	9	67541	9	550	10	560	9	569	9
474	578	9	587	9	596	9	605	9	614	10	624	9	633	9	642	9	651	9	660	9
475	669	10	679	9	688	9	697	9	706	9	715	9	724	9	733	9	742	10	752	9
476	761	9	770	9	779	9	788	9	797	9	806	9	815	10	825	9	834	9	843	9
477	852	9	861	9	870	9	879	9	888	9	897	9	906	10	67916	9	67925	9	67934	9
478	67943	9	67952	9	67961	9	67970	9	67979	9	67988	9	67997	9	68006	9	68015	9	68024	10
479	68034	9	68043	9	68052	9	68061	9	68070	9	68079	9	68088	9	097	9	106	9	115	9
480	124	9	133	9	142	9	151	9	160	9	169	9	178	9	187	9	196	9	205	10
481	215	9	224	9	233	9	242	9	251	9	260	9	269	9	278	9	287	9	296	9
482	305	9	314	9	323	9	332	9	341	9	350	9	359	9	368	9	377	9	386	9
483	395	9	404	9	413	9	422	9	431	9	440	9	449	9	458	9	68467	9	68476	9
484	68485	9	68494	8	68502	9	68511	9	68520	9	68529	9	68538	9	68547	9	556	9	565	9
485	574	9	583	9	592	9	601	9	610	9	619	9	628	9	637	9	646	9	655	9
486	664	9	673	8	681	9	690	9	699	9	708	9	717	9	726	9	735	9	744	9
487	753	9	762	9	771	9	780	9	789	8	797	9	806	9	815	9	824	9	833	9
488	842	9	851	9	860	9	869	9	878	8	886	9	895	9	904	9	68913	9	68922	9
489	68931	9	68940	9	68949	9	68958	8	68966	9	68975	9	68984	9	68993	9	69002	9	69011	9
490	69020	8	69028	9	69037	9	69046	9	69055	9	69064	9	69073	9	69082	8	090	9	099	9
491	108	9	117	9	126	9	135	9	144	8	152	9	161	9	170	9	179	9	188	9
492	197	8	205	9	214	9	223	9	232	9	241	8	249	9	258	9	267	9	276	9
493	285	9	294	8	302	9	311	9	320	9	329	9	338	8	346	9	355	9	364	9
494	373	8	381	9	390	9	399	9	408	9	417	8	425	9	434	9	443	9	452	9
495	461	8	469	9	478	9	487	9	496	8	504	9	513	9	522	9	531	8	539	9
496	548	9	557	9	566	8	574	9	583	9	592	9	601	8	609	9	618	9	627	9
497	636	8	644	9	653	9	662	9	671	8	679	9	688	9	697	8	705	9	714	9
498	723	9	732	8	740	9	749	9	758	9	767	8	775	9	784	9	793	8	801	9
499	810	9	819	8	827	9	836	9	845	9	854	8	862	9	871	9	880	8	888	9
500	69897	9	69906	8	69914	9	69923	9	69932	8	69940	9	69949	9	69958	8	69966	9	69975	9
No.	0		1		2		3		4		5		6		7		8		9	

Prop. Parts

	10
1	1
2	2
3	3
4	4
5	5
6	6
7	7
8	8
9	9

	9
1	1
2	2
3	3
4	4
5	5
6	5
7	6
8	7
9	8

	8
1	1
2	2
3	2
4	3
5	4
6	5
7	6
8	6
9	7

TABLE 32.

Logarithms of Numbers.

500

No.	0	d	1	d	2	d	3	d	4	d	5	d	6	d	7	d	8	d	9	d
500	69897	9	69906	8	69914	9	69923	9	69932	8	69940	9	69949	9	69958	8	69966	9	69975	9
501	69984	8	69992	9	70001	9	70010	8	70018	9	70027	9	70036	8	70044	9	70053	9	70062	8
502	70070	9	70079	9	088	8	096	9	105	9	114	8	122	9	131	9	140	8	148	9
503	157	8	165	9	174	9	183	8	191	9	200	9	209	8	217	9	226	8	234	9
504	243	9	252	8	260	9	269	9	278	8	286	9	295	8	303	9	312	9	321	8
505	329	9	338	8	346	9	355	9	364	8	372	9	381	8	389	9	398	8	406	9
506	415	9	424	8	70432	9	70441	8	70449	9	70458	9	70467	8	70475	9	70484	8	70492	9
507	70501	8	70509	9	518	8	526	9	535	9	544	8	552	9	561	8	569	9	578	8
508	586	9	595	8	603	9	612	9	621	8	629	9	638	8	646	9	655	8	663	9
509	672	8	680	9	689	8	697	9	706	8	714	9	723	8	731	9	740	9	749	8
510	757	9	766	8	774	9	783	8	791	9	800	8	808	9	817	8	825	9	834	8
511	842	9	851	8	859	9	868	8	876	9	885	8	893	9	902	8	910	9	70919	8
512	70927	8	70935	9	70944	8	70952	9	70961	8	70969	9	70978	8	70986	9	70995	8	71003	9
513	71012	8	71020	9	71029	8	71037	9	71046	8	71054	9	71063	8	71071	8	71079	9	088	8
514	096	9	105	8	113	9	122	8	130	9	139	8	147	8	155	9	164	8	172	9
515	181	8	189	9	198	8	206	8	214	9	223	8	231	9	240	8	248	9	257	8
516	265	8	273	9	282	8	290	9	299	8	307	8	315	9	324	8	332	9	341	8
517	349	8	357	9	366	8	374	9	383	8	391	8	399	9	408	8	416	9	425	8
518	433	8	441	9	450	8	458	8	466	9	475	8	483	9	492	8	500	8	508	9
519	517	8	525	8	533	9	542	8	550	9	559	8	567	8	575	9	584	8	592	8
520	600	9	609	8	617	8	625	9	634	8	642	8	650	9	659	8	667	8	675	9
521	684	8	692	8	700	9	709	8	717	8	725	9	734	8	742	8	750	9	759	8
522	767	8	775	9	784	8	792	8	800	9	809	8	817	8	825	9	834	8	842	8
523	850	8	858	9	867	8	875	8	883	9	892	8	900	8	908	9	917	8	71925	8
524	71933	8	71941	9	71950	8	71958	8	71966	9	71975	8	71983	8	71991	8	71999	9	72008	8
525	72016	8	72024	8	72032	9	72041	8	72049	8	72057	9	72066	8	72074	8	72082	8	090	9
526	099	8	107	8	115	8	123	9	132	8	140	8	148	8	156	9	165	8	173	8
527	181	8	189	9	198	8	206	8	214	8	222	8	230	9	239	8	247	8	255	8
528	263	9	272	8	280	8	288	8	296	8	304	9	313	8	321	8	329	8	337	9
529	346	8	354	8	362	8	370	8	378	9	387	8	395	8	403	8	411	8	419	9
530	428	8	72436	8	72444	8	72452	8	72460	9	72469	8	72477	8	72485	8	72493	8	72501	8
531	72509	9	518	8	526	8	534	8	542	8	550	8	558	9	567	8	575	8	583	8
532	591	8	599	8	607	9	616	8	624	8	632	8	640	8	648	8	656	9	665	8
533	673	8	681	8	689	8	697	8	705	8	713	9	722	8	730	8	738	8	746	8
534	754	8	762	8	770	9	779	8	787	8	795	8	803	8	811	8	819	8	827	8
535	835	8	843	9	852	8	860	8	868	8	876	8	884	8	892	8	900	8	908	8
536	916	9	72925	8	72933	8	72941	8	72949	8	72957	8	72965	8	72973	8	72981	8	72989	8
537	72997	9	73006	8	73014	8	73022	8	73030	8	73038	8	73046	8	73054	8	73062	8	73070	8
538	73078	8	086	8	094	8	102	9	111	8	119	8	127	8	135	8	143	8	151	8
539	159	8	167	8	175	8	183	8	191	8	199	8	207	8	215	8	223	8	231	8
540	239	8	247	8	255	8	263	9	272	8	280	8	288	8	296	8	304	8	312	8
541	320	8	328	8	336	8	344	8	352	8	360	8	368	8	376	8	384	8	392	8
542	400	8	408	8	416	8	424	8	432	8	440	8	448	8	456	8	464	8	472	8
543	73480	8	73488	8	73496	8	73504	8	73512	8	73520	8	73528	8	73536	8	73544	8	73552	8
544	560	8	568	8	576	8	584	8	592	8	600	8	608	8	616	8	624	8	632	8
545	640	8	648	8	656	8	664	8	672	7	679	8	687	8	695	8	703	8	711	8
546	719	8	727	8	735	8	743	8	751	8	759	8	767	8	775	8	783	8	791	8
547	799	8	807	8	815	8	823	7	830	8	838	8	846	8	854	8	862	8	870	8
548	878	8	886	8	894	8	902	8	910	8	918	8	73926	7	73933	8	73941	8	73949	8
549	73957	8	73965	8	73973	8	73981	8	73989	8	73997	8	74005	8	74013	7	74020	8	74028	8
550	74036	8	74044	8	74052	8	74060	8	74068	8	74076	8	74084	8	74092	7	74099	8	74107	8
No.	0		1		2		3		4		5		6		7		8		9	

Prop. Parts

	9
1	1
2	2
3	3
4	4
5	5
6	5
7	6
8	7
9	8

	8
1	1
2	2
3	2
4	3
5	4
6	5
7	6
8	6
9	7

	7
1	1
2	1
3	2
4	3
5	4
6	4
7	5
8	6
9	6

TABLE 32.

Logarithms of Numbers.

550

No.	0	d	1	d	2	d	3	d	4	d	5	d	6	d	7	d	8	d	9	d
550	74036	8	74044	8	74052	8	74060	8	74068	8	74076	8	74084	8	74092	7	74099	8	74107	8
551	115	8	123	8	131	8	139	8	147	8	155	7	162	8	170	8	178	8	186	8
552	194	8	202	8	210	8	218	7	225	8	233	8	241	8	249	8	257	8	265	8
553	273	7	280	8	288	8	296	8	304	8	312	8	320	7	327	8	335	8	343	8
554	351	8	359	8	367	7	374	8	382	8	390	8	398	8	406	8	414	7	421	8
555	429	8	437	8	445	8	453	8	74461	7	74468	8	74476	8	74484	8	74492	8	74500	7
556	74507	8	74515	8	74523	8	74531	8	539	8	547	7	554	8	562	8	570	8	578	8
557	586	7	593	8	601	8	609	8	617	7	624	8	632	8	640	8	648	8	656	7
558	663	8	671	8	679	8	687	8	695	7	702	8	710	8	718	8	726	7	733	8
559	741	8	749	8	757	7	764	8	772	8	780	8	788	8	796	7	803	8	811	8
560	819	8	827	7	834	8	842	8	850	8	858	7	865	8	873	8	881	8	889	7
561	896	8	904	8	912	8	920	7	74927	8	74935	8	74943	7	74950	8	74958	8	74966	8
562	74974	7	74981	8	74989	8	74997	8	75005	7	75012	8	75020	8	75028	7	75035	8	75043	8
563	75051	8	75059	7	75066	8	75074	8	082	7	089	8	097	8	105	8	113	7	120	8
564	128	8	136	7	143	8	151	8	159	7	166	8	174	8	182	7	189	8	197	8
565	205	8	213	7	220	8	228	8	236	7	243	8	251	8	259	7	266	8	274	8
566	282	7	289	8	297	8	305	7	312	8	320	8	328	7	335	8	343	8	351	7
567	358	8	366	8	374	7	381	8	389	8	397	7	404	8	412	8	420	7	427	8
568	435	7	442	8	450	8	458	7	465	8	75473	8	75481	7	75488	8	75496	8	75504	7
569	75511	8	75519	7	75526	8	75534	8	75542	7	549	8	557	8	565	7	572	8	580	7
570	587	8	595	8	603	7	610	8	618	8	626	7	633	8	641	7	648	8	656	8
571	664	7	671	8	679	7	686	8	694	8	702	7	709	8	717	7	724	8	732	8
572	740	7	747	8	755	7	762	8	770	8	778	7	785	8	793	7	800	8	808	7
573	815	8	823	8	831	7	838	8	846	7	853	8	861	7	868	8	876	8	884	7
574	891	8	899	7	906	8	914	7	921	8	75929	8	75937	7	75944	8	75952	7	75959	8
575	75967	7	75974	8	75982	7	75989	8	75997	8	76005	7	76012	8	76020	7	76027	8	76035	7
576	76042	8	76050	7	76057	8	76065	7	76072	8	080	7	087	8	095	8	103	7	110	8
577	118	7	125	8	133	7	140	8	148	7	155	8	163	7	170	8	178	7	185	8
578	193	7	200	8	208	7	215	8	223	7	230	8	238	7	245	8	253	7	260	8
579	268	7	275	8	283	7	290	8	298	7	305	8	313	7	320	8	328	7	335	8
580	343	7	350	8	358	7	365	8	373	7	380	8	388	7	395	8	403	7	410	8
581	418	7	425	8	433	7	440	8	448	7	76455	7	76462	8	76470	7	76477	8	76485	7
582	76492	8	76500	7	76507	8	76515	7	76522	8	530	7	537	8	545	7	552	7	559	8
583	567	7	574	8	582	7	589	8	597	7	604	8	612	7	619	7	626	8	634	7
584	641	8	649	7	656	8	664	7	671	7	678	8	686	7	693	8	701	7	708	8
585	716	7	723	7	730	8	738	7	745	8	753	7	760	8	768	7	775	7	782	8
586	790	7	797	8	805	7	812	7	819	8	827	7	834	8	842	7	849	7	856	8
587	864	7	871	8	879	7	886	7	893	8	901	7	908	8	916	7	923	7	76930	8
588	76938	7	76945	8	76953	7	76960	7	76967	8	76975	7	76982	7	76989	8	76997	7	77004	8
589	77012	7	77019	7	77026	8	77034	7	77041	7	77048	8	77056	7	77063	7	77070	8	078	7
590	085	8	093	7	100	7	107	8	115	7	122	7	129	8	137	7	144	7	151	8
591	159	7	166	7	173	8	181	7	188	7	195	8	203	7	210	7	217	8	225	7
592	232	8	240	7	247	7	254	8	262	7	269	7	276	7	283	8	291	7	298	7
593	305	8	313	7	320	7	327	8	335	7	342	7	349	8	357	7	364	7	371	8
594	379	7	386	7	393	8	401	7	408	7	415	7	422	8	430	7	437	7	77444	8
595	77452	7	77459	7	77466	8	77474	7	77481	7	77488	7	77495	8	77503	7	77510	7	517	8
596	525	7	532	7	539	7	546	8	554	7	561	7	568	8	576	7	583	7	590	7
597	597	8	605	7	612	7	619	8	627	7	634	7	641	7	648	8	656	7	663	7
598	670	7	677	8	685	7	692	7	699	7	706	8	714	7	721	7	728	7	735	8
599	743	7	750	7	757	7	764	8	772	7	779	7	786	7	793	8	801	7	808	7
600	77815	7	77822	8	77830	7	77837	7	77844	7	77851	8	77859	7	77866	7	77873	7	77880	7
No.	0		1		2		3		4		5		6		7		8		9	

Prop. Parts

	8
1	1
2	2
3	2
4	3
5	4
6	5
7	6
8	6
9	7

	7
1	1
2	1
3	2
4	3
5	4
6	4
7	5
8	6
9	6

TABLE 32.

Logarithms of Numbers.

600

No.	0	d	1	d	2	d	3	d	4	d	5	d	6	d	7	d	8	d	9	d
600	77815	7	77822	8	77830	7	77837	7	77844	7	77851	8	77859	7	77866	7	77873	7	77880	7
601	887	8	895	7	902	7	909	7	916	8	924	7	77931	7	77938	7	77945	7	77952	8
602	77960	7	77967	7	77974	7	77981	7	77988	8	77996	7	78003	7	78010	7	78017	8	78025	7
603	78032	7	78039	7	78046	7	78053	8	78061	7	78068	7	075	7	082	7	089	8	097	7
604	104	7	111	7	118	7	125	7	132	8	140	7	147	7	154	7	161	7	168	8
605	176	7	183	7	190	7	197	7	204	7	211	8	219	7	226	7	233	7	240	7
606	247	7	254	8	262	7	269	7	276	7	283	7	290	7	297	8	305	7	312	7
607	319	7	326	7	333	7	340	7	347	8	355	7	362	7	369	7	376	7	383	7
608	390	8	398	7	405	7	412	7	419	7	426	7	78433	7	78440	7	78447	8	78455	7
609	78462	7	78469	7	78476	7	78483	7	78490	7	78497	7	504	8	512	7	519	7	526	7
610	533	7	540	7	547	7	554	7	561	8	569	7	576	7	583	7	590	7	597	7
611	604	7	611	7	618	7	625	8	633	7	640	7	647	7	654	7	661	7	668	7
612	675	7	682	7	689	7	696	8	704	7	711	7	718	7	725	7	732	7	739	7
613	746	7	753	7	760	7	767	7	774	7	781	8	789	7	796	7	803	7	810	7
614	817	7	824	7	831	7	838	7	845	7	852	7	859	7	866	7	873	7	880	8
615	888	7	895	7	902	7	909	7	916	7	923	7	78930	7	78937	7	78944	7	78951	7
616	78958	7	78965	7	78972	7	78979	7	78986	7	78993	7	79000	7	79007	7	79014	7	79021	8
617	79029	7	79036	7	79043	7	79050	7	79057	7	79064	7	071	7	078	7	085	7	092	7
618	099	7	106	7	113	7	120	7	127	7	134	7	141	7	148	7	155	7	162	7
619	169	7	176	7	183	7	190	7	197	7	204	7	211	7	218	7	225	7	232	7
620	239	7	246	7	253	7	260	7	267	7	274	7	281	7	288	7	295	7	302	7
621	309	7	316	7	323	7	330	7	337	7	344	7	351	7	358	7	365	7	372	7
622	379	7	386	7	393	7	400	7	407	7	414	7	421	7	428	7	435	7	442	7
623	449	7	456	7	463	7	470	7	477	7	484	7	79491	7	79498	7	79505	6	79511	7
624	79518	7	79525	7	79532	7	79539	7	79546	7	79553	7	560	7	567	7	574	7	581	7
625	588	7	595	7	602	7	609	7	616	7	623	7	630	7	637	7	644	6	650	7
626	657	7	664	7	671	7	678	7	685	7	692	7	699	7	706	7	713	7	720	7
627	727	7	734	7	741	7	748	6	754	7	761	7	768	7	775	7	782	7	789	7
628	796	7	803	7	810	7	817	7	824	7	831	6	837	7	844	7	851	7	858	7
629	865	7	872	7	879	7	886	7	893	7	900	6	906	7	913	7	920	7	927	7
630	79934	7	79941	7	79948	7	79955	7	79962	7	79969	6	79975	7	79982	7	79989	7	79996	7
631	80003	7	80010	7	80017	7	80024	6	80030	7	80037	7	80044	7	80051	7	80058	7	80065	7
632	072	7	079	6	085	7	092	7	099	7	106	7	113	7	120	7	127	7	134	6
633	140	7	147	7	154	7	161	7	168	7	175	7	182	6	188	7	195	7	202	7
634	209	7	216	7	223	6	229	7	236	7	243	7	250	7	257	7	264	7	271	6
635	277	7	284	7	291	7	298	7	305	7	312	6	318	7	325	7	332	7	339	7
636	346	7	353	6	359	7	366	7	373	7	380	7	387	6	393	7	400	7	407	7
637	414	7	421	7	428	6	434	7	441	7	448	7	455	7	462	6	468	7	475	7
638	80482	7	80489	7	80496	6	80502	7	80509	7	80516	7	80523	7	80530	6	80536	7	80543	7
639	550	7	557	7	564	6	570	7	577	7	584	7	591	7	598	6	604	7	611	7
640	618	7	625	7	632	6	638	7	645	7	652	7	659	6	665	7	672	7	679	7
641	686	7	693	6	699	7	706	7	713	7	720	6	726	7	733	7	740	7	747	7
642	754	6	760	7	767	7	774	7	781	6	787	7	794	7	801	7	808	6	814	7
643	821	7	828	7	835	6	841	7	848	7	855	7	862	6	868	7	875	7	882	7
644	889	6	895	7	902	7	909	7	916	6	922	7	929	7	80936	7	80943	6	80949	7
645	80956	7	80963	6	80969	7	80976	7	80983	7	80990	6	80996	7	81003	7	81010	7	81017	6
646	81023	7	81030	7	81037	6	81043	7	81050	7	81057	7	81064	6	070	7	077	7	084	6
647	090	7	097	7	104	7	111	6	117	7	124	7	131	6	137	7	144	7	151	7
648	158	6	164	7	171	7	178	6	184	7	191	7	198	6	204	7	211	7	218	6
649	224	7	231	7	238	7	245	6	251	7	258	7	265	6	271	7	278	7	285	6
650	81291	7	81298	7	81305	6	81311	7	81318	7	81325	6	81331	7	81338	7	81345	6	81351	7
No.	0		1		2		3		4		5		6		7		8		9	

Prop. Parts

	8
1	1
2	2
3	2
4	3
5	4
6	5
7	6
8	6
9	7

	7
1	1
2	1
3	2
4	3
5	4
6	4
7	5
8	6
9	6

	6
1	1
2	1
3	2
4	2
5	3
6	4
7	4
8	5
9	5

TABLE 32.

Logarithms of Numbers.

650

No.	0	d	1	d	2	d	3	d	4	d	5	d	6	d	7	d	8	d	9	d
650	81291	7	81298	7	81305	6	81311	7	81318	7	81325	6	81331	7	81338	7	81345	6	81351	7
651	358	7	365	6	371	7	378	7	385	6	391	7	398	7	405	6	411	7	418	7
652	425	6	431	7	438	7	445	6	451	7	458	7	465	6	471	7	478	7	485	6
653	491	7	498	7	505	6	511	7	518	7	525	6	531	7	538	6	544	7	551	7
654	558	6	564	7	571	7	578	6	584	7	591	7	598	6	604	7	611	6	617	7
655	624	7	631	6	637	7	644	7	651	6	657	7	664	7	671	6	677	7	684	6
656	690	7	697	7	704	6	710	7	717	6	723	7	730	7	737	6	743	7	750	7
657	757	6	763	7	770	6	776	7	783	7	790	6	796	7	803	6	809	7	816	7
658	823	6	829	7	836	6	842	7	849	7	856	6	862	7	869	6	875	7	882	7
659	889	6	895	7	902	6	908	7	915	6	921	7	928	7	81935	6	81941	7	81948	6
660	81954	7	81961	7	81968	6	81974	7	81981	6	81987	7	81994	6	82000	7	82007	7	82014	6
661	82020	7	82027	6	82033	7	82040	6	82046	7	82053	7	82060	6	066	7	073	6	079	7
662	086	6	092	7	099	6	105	7	112	7	119	6	125	7	132	6	138	7	145	6
663	151	7	158	6	164	7	171	7	178	6	184	7	191	6	197	7	204	6	210	7
664	217	6	223	7	230	6	236	7	243	6	249	7	256	7	263	6	269	7	276	6
665	282	7	289	6	295	7	302	6	308	7	315	6	321	7	328	6	334	7	341	6
666	347	7	354	6	360	7	367	6	373	7	380	7	387	6	393	7	400	6	406	7
667	413	6	419	7	426	6	432	7	439	6	445	7	452	6	458	7	465	6	471	7
668	82478	6	82484	7	82491	6	82497	7	82504	6	82510	7	82517	6	82523	7	82530	6	82536	7
669	543	6	549	7	556	6	562	7	569	6	575	7	582	6	588	7	595	6	601	6
670	607	7	614	6	620	7	627	6	633	7	640	6	646	7	653	6	659	7	666	6
671	672	7	679	6	685	7	692	6	698	7	705	6	711	7	718	6	724	6	730	7
672	737	6	743	7	750	6	756	7	763	6	769	7	776	6	782	7	789	6	795	7
673	802	6	808	6	814	7	821	6	827	7	834	6	840	7	847	6	853	7	860	6
674	866	6	872	7	879	6	885	7	892	6	898	7	905	6	911	7	918	6	924	6
675	930	7	82937	6	82943	7	82950	6	82956	7	82963	6	82969	6	82975	7	82982	6	82988	7
676	82995	6	83001	7	83008	6	83014	6	83020	7	83027	6	83033	7	83040	6	83046	6	83052	7
677	83059	6	065	7	072	6	078	7	085	6	091	6	097	7	104	6	110	7	117	6
678	123	6	129	7	136	6	142	7	149	6	155	6	161	7	168	6	174	7	181	6
679	187	6	193	7	200	6	206	7	213	6	219	6	225	7	232	6	238	7	245	6
680	251	6	257	7	264	6	270	6	276	7	283	6	289	7	296	6	302	6	308	7
681	315	6	321	6	327	7	334	6	340	7	347	6	353	6	359	7	366	6	372	6
682	378	7	385	6	391	7	398	6	404	6	410	7	417	6	423	6	429	7	436	6
683	442	6	448	7	455	6	461	6	467	7	474	6	480	7	487	6	493	6	83499	7
684	83506	6	83512	6	83518	7	83525	6	83531	6	83537	7	83544	6	83550	6	83556	7	563	6
685	569	6	575	7	582	6	588	6	594	7	601	6	607	6	613	7	620	6	626	6
686	632	7	639	6	645	6	651	7	658	6	664	6	670	7	677	6	683	6	689	7
687	696	6	702	6	708	7	715	6	721	6	727	7	734	6	740	6	746	7	753	6
688	759	6	765	6	771	7	778	6	784	6	790	7	797	6	803	6	809	7	816	6
689	822	6	828	7	835	6	841	6	847	6	853	7	860	6	866	6	872	7	879	6
690	885	6	891	6	897	7	904	6	910	6	916	7	923	6	929	6	935	7	83942	6
691	83948	6	83954	6	83960	7	83967	6	83973	6	83979	6	83985	7	83992	6	83998	6	84004	7
692	84011	6	84017	6	84023	6	84029	7	84036	6	84042	6	84048	7	84055	6	84061	6	067	6
693	073	7	080	6	086	6	092	6	098	7	105	6	111	6	117	6	123	7	130	6
694	136	6	142	6	148	7	155	6	161	6	167	6	173	7	180	6	186	6	192	6
695	198	7	205	6	211	6	217	6	223	7	230	6	236	6	242	6	248	7	255	6
696	261	6	267	6	273	7	280	6	286	6	292	6	298	7	305	6	311	6	317	6
697	323	7	330	6	336	6	342	6	348	6	354	7	361	6	367	6	373	6	379	7
698	386	6	392	6	398	6	404	6	410	7	417	6	423	6	429	6	435	7	442	6
699	448	6	454	6	460	6	466	7	473	6	479	6	485	6	491	6	497	7	504	6
700	84510	6	84516	6	84522	6	84528	7	84535	6	84541	6	84547	6	84553	6	84559	7	84566	6
No.	0		1		2		3		4		5		6		7		8		9	

Prop. Parts

	7
1	1
2	1
3	2
4	3
5	4
6	4
7	5
8	6
9	6

	6
1	1
2	1
3	2
4	2
5	3
6	4
7	4
8	5
9	5

TABLE 32.

Logarithms of Numbers

700

No.	0	d	1	d	2	d	3	d	4	d	5	d	6	d	7	d	8	d	9	d
700	84510	6	84516	6	84522	6	84528	7	84535	6	84541	6	84547	6	84553	6	84559	7	84566	6
701	572	6	578	6	584	6	590	7	597	6	603	6	609	6	615	6	621	7	628	6
702	634	6	640	6	646	6	652	6	658	7	665	6	671	6	677	6	683	6	689	7
703	696	6	702	6	708	6	714	6	720	6	726	7	733	6	739	6	745	6	751	6
704	757	6	763	7	770	6	776	6	782	6	788	6	794	6	800	7	807	6	813	6
705	819	6	825	6	831	6	837	7	844	6	850	6	856	6	862	6	868	6	874	6
706	880	7	887	6	893	6	899	6	905	6	911	6	917	7	924	6	930	6	936	6
707	84942	6	84948	6	84954	6	84960	7	84967	6	84973	6	84979	6	84985	6	84991	6	84997	6
708	85003	6	85009	7	85016	6	85022	6	85028	6	85034	6	85040	6	85046	6	85052	6	85058	7
709	065	6	071	6	077	6	083	6	089	6	095	6	101	6	107	7	114	6	120	6
710	126	6	132	6	138	6	144	6	150	6	156	7	163	6	169	6	175	6	181	6
711	187	6	193	6	199	6	205	6	211	6	217	7	224	6	230	6	236	6	242	6
712	248	6	254	6	260	6	266	6	272	6	278	7	285	6	291	6	297	6	303	6
713	309	6	315	6	321	6	327	6	333	6	339	6	345	7	352	6	358	6	364	6
714	370	6	376	6	382	6	388	6	394	6	400	6	406	6	412	6	418	7	425	6
715	431	6	437	6	443	6	449	6	455	6	461	6	467	6	473	6	479	6	485	6
716	85491	6	85497	6	85503	6	85509	7	85516	6	85522	6	85528	6	85534	6	85540	6	85546	6
717	552	6	558	6	564	6	570	6	576	6	582	6	588	6	594	6	600	6	606	6
718	612	6	618	7	625	6	631	6	637	6	643	6	649	6	655	6	661	6	667	6
719	673	6	679	6	685	6	691	6	697	6	703	6	709	6	715	6	721	6	727	6
720	733	6	739	6	745	6	751	6	757	6	763	6	769	6	775	6	781	7	788	6
721	794	6	800	6	806	6	812	6	818	6	824	6	830	6	836	6	842	6	848	6
722	854	6	860	6	866	6	872	6	878	6	884	6	890	6	896	6	902	6	908	6
723	914	6	920	6	926	6	932	6	938	6	85944	6	85950	6	85956	6	85962	6	85968	6
724	85974	6	85980	6	85986	6	85992	6	85998	6	86004	6	86010	6	86016	6	86022	6	86028	6
725	86034	6	86040	6	86046	6	86052	6	86058	6	064	6	070	6	076	6	082	6	088	6
726	094	6	100	6	106	6	112	6	118	6	124	6	130	6	136	5	141	6	147	6
727	153	6	159	6	165	6	171	6	177	6	183	6	189	6	195	6	201	6	207	6
728	213	6	219	6	225	6	231	6	237	6	243	6	249	6	255	6	261	6	267	6
729	273	6	279	6	285	6	291	6	297	6	303	5	308	6	314	6	320	6	326	6
730	332	6	338	6	344	6	350	6	356	6	362	6	368	6	374	6	380	6	386	6
731	392	6	398	6	404	6	410	5	415	6	421	6	427	6	433	6	439	6	445	6
732	86451	6	86457	6	86463	6	86469	6	86475	6	86481	6	86487	6	86493	6	86499	5	86504	6
733	510	6	516	6	522	6	528	6	534	6	540	6	546	6	552	6	558	6	564	6
734	570	6	576	5	581	6	587	6	593	6	599	6	605	6	611	6	617	6	623	6
735	629	6	635	6	641	5	646	6	652	6	658	6	664	6	670	6	676	6	682	6
736	688	6	694	6	700	5	705	6	711	6	717	6	723	6	729	6	735	6	741	6
737	747	6	753	6	759	5	764	6	770	6	776	6	782	6	788	6	794	6	800	6
738	806	6	812	5	817	6	823	6	829	6	835	6	841	6	847	6	853	6	859	5
739	864	6	870	6	876	6	882	6	888	6	894	6	900	6	906	5	911	6	917	6
740	923	6	929	6	935	6	941	6	86947	6	86953	5	86958	6	86964	6	86970	6	86976	6
741	86982	6	86988	6	86994	5	86999	6	87005	6	87011	6	87017	6	87023	6	87029	6	87035	5
742	87040	6	87046	6	87052	6	87058	6	064	6	070	5	075	6	081	6	087	6	093	6
743	099	6	105	6	111	5	116	6	122	6	128	6	134	6	140	6	146	5	151	6
744	157	6	163	6	169	6	175	6	181	5	186	6	192	6	198	6	204	6	210	6
745	216	5	221	6	227	6	233	6	239	6	245	6	251	5	256	6	262	6	268	6
746	274	6	280	6	286	5	291	6	297	6	303	6	309	6	315	5	320	6	326	6
747	332	6	338	6	344	5	349	6	355	6	361	6	367	6	373	6	379	5	384	6
748	390	6	396	6	402	6	408	5	413	6	419	6	425	6	431	6	437	5	442	6
749	448	6	454	6	460	6	466	5	471	6	477	6	483	6	489	6	495	5	500	6
750	87506	6	87512	6	87518	5	87523	6	87529	6	87535	6	87541	6	87547	5	87552	6	87558	6
No.	0		1		2		3		4		5		6		7		8		9	

Prop. Parts

	7
1	1
2	1
3	2
4	3
5	4
6	4
7	5
8	6
9	6

	6
1	1
2	1
3	2
4	2
5	3
6	4
7	4
8	5
9	5

	5
1	1
2	1
3	2
4	2
5	3
6	3
7	4
8	4
9	5
10	5

TABLE 32.

Logarithms of Numbers.

750

No.	0	d	1	d	2	d	3	d	4	d	5	d	6	d	7	d	8	d	9	d
750	87506	6	87512	6	87518	5	87523	6	87529	6	87535	6	87541	6	87547	5	87552	6	87558	6
751	564	6	570	6	576	5	581	6	587	6	593	6	599	5	604	6	610	6	616	6
752	622	6	628	5	633	6	639	6	645	6	651	5	656	6	662	6	668	6	674	5
753	679	6	685	6	691	6	697	6	703	5	708	6	714	6	720	6	726	5	731	6
754	737	6	743	6	749	5	754	6	760	6	766	6	772	5	777	6	783	6	789	6
755	795	5	800	6	806	6	812	6	818	5	823	6	829	6	835	6	841	5	846	6
756	852	6	858	6	864	5	869	6	875	6	881	6	887	5	892	6	898	6	904	6
757	910	5	915	6	921	6	927	6	933	5	938	6	87944	6	87950	5	87955	6	87961	6
758	87967	6	87973	5	87978	6	87984	6	87990	6	87996	5	88001	6	88007	6	88013	5	88018	6
759	88024	6	88030	6	88036	5	88041	6	88047	6	88053	5	058	6	064	6	070	6	076	5
760	081	6	087	6	093	5	098	6	104	6	110	6	116	5	121	6	127	6	133	5
761	138	6	144	6	150	6	156	5	161	6	167	6	173	5	178	6	184	6	190	5
762	195	6	201	6	207	6	213	5	218	6	224	6	230	5	235	6	241	6	247	5
763	252	6	258	6	264	6	270	5	275	6	281	6	287	5	292	6	298	6	304	5
764	309	6	315	6	321	5	326	6	332	6	338	5	343	6	349	6	355	5	360	6
765	366	6	372	5	377	6	383	6	389	6	395	5	400	6	406	6	412	5	417	6
766	423	6	429	5	434	6	440	6	446	5	451	6	457	6	463	5	468	6	474	6
767	480	5	485	6	491	6	88497	5	88502	6	88508	5	88513	6	88519	6	88525	5	88530	6
768	88536	6	88542	5	88547	6	553	6	559	5	564	6	570	6	576	5	581	6	587	6
769	593	5	598	6	604	6	610	5	615	6	621	6	627	5	632	6	638	5	643	6
770	649	6	655	5	660	6	666	6	672	5	677	6	683	6	689	5	694	6	700	5
771	705	6	711	6	717	5	722	6	728	6	734	5	739	6	745	5	750	6	756	6
772	762	5	767	6	773	6	779	5	784	6	790	5	795	6	801	6	807	5	812	6
773	818	6	824	5	829	6	835	5	840	6	846	6	852	5	857	6	863	5	868	6
774	874	6	880	5	885	6	891	6	897	5	902	6	908	5	913	6	919	6	925	5
775	930	6	936	5	941	6	88947	6	88953	5	88958	6	88964	5	88969	6	88975	6	88981	5
776	88986	6	88992	5	88997	6	89003	6	89009	5	89014	6	89020	5	89025	6	89031	6	89037	5
777	89042	6	89048	5	89053	6	059	5	064	6	070	6	076	5	081	6	087	5	092	6
778	098	6	104	5	109	6	115	5	120	6	126	5	131	6	137	6	143	5	148	6
779	154	5	159	6	165	5	170	6	176	6	182	5	187	6	193	5	198	6	204	5
780	209	6	215	6	221	5	226	6	232	5	237	6	243	5	248	6	254	6	260	5
781	265	6	271	5	276	6	282	5	287	6	293	5	298	6	304	6	310	5	315	6
782	321	5	326	6	332	5	337	6	343	5	348	6	354	6	360	5	365	6	371	5
783	376	6	382	5	387	6	393	5	398	6	404	5	409	6	415	6	421	5	426	6
784	432	5	437	6	443	5	448	6	89454	5	89459	6	89465	5	89470	6	89476	5	89481	6
785	89487	5	89492	6	89498	6	89504	5	509	6	515	5	520	6	526	5	531	6	537	5
786	542	6	548	5	553	6	559	5	564	6	570	5	575	6	581	5	586	6	592	5
787	597	6	603	6	609	5	614	6	620	5	625	6	631	5	636	6	642	5	647	6
788	653	5	658	6	664	5	669	6	675	5	680	6	686	5	691	6	697	5	702	6
789	708	5	713	6	719	5	724	6	730	5	735	6	741	5	746	6	752	5	757	6
790	763	5	768	6	774	5	779	6	785	5	790	6	796	5	801	6	807	5	812	6
791	818	5	823	6	829	5	834	6	840	5	845	6	851	5	856	6	862	5	867	6
792	873	5	878	5	883	6	889	5	894	6	900	5	905	6	911	5	916	6	922	5
793	927	6	933	5	938	6	944	5	89949	6	89955	5	89960	6	89966	5	89971	6	89977	5
794	89982	6	89988	5	89993	5	89998	6	90004	5	90009	6	90015	5	90020	6	90026	5	90031	6
795	90037	5	90042	6	90048	5	90053	6	059	5	064	5	069	6	075	5	080	6	086	5
796	091	6	097	5	102	6	108	5	113	6	119	5	124	5	129	6	135	5	140	6
797	146	5	151	6	157	5	162	6	168	5	173	6	179	5	184	5	189	6	195	5
798	200	6	206	5	211	6	217	5	222	5	227	6	233	5	238	6	244	5	249	6
799	255	5	260	6	266	5	271	5	276	6	282	5	287	6	293	5	298	6	304	5
800	90309	5	90314	6	90320	5	90325	6	90331	5	90336	6	90342	5	90347	5	90352	6	90358	5
No.	0		1		2		3		4		5		6		7		8		9	

Prop. Parts

	6
1	1
2	1
3	2
4	2
5	3
6	4
7	4
8	5
9	5

	5
1	1
2	1
3	2
4	2
5	3
6	3
7	4
8	4
9	5
10	5

TABLE 32.

Logarithms of Numbers.

800

No.	0	d	1	d	2	d	3	d	4	d	5	d	6	d	7	d	8	d	9	d
800	**90309**	5	**90314**	6	**90320**	5	**90325**	6	**90331**	5	**90336**	6	**90342**	5	**90347**	5	**90352**	6	**90358**	5
801	363	6	369	5	374	6	380	5	385	5	390	6	396	5	401	6	407	5	412	5
802	417	6	423	5	428	6	434	5	439	6	445	5	450	5	455	6	461	5	466	6
803	472	5	477	5	482	6	488	5	493	6	90499	5	504	5	509	6	515	5	520	6
804	526	5	531	5	536	6	542	5	547	6	553	5	558	5	563	6	569	5	574	6
805	580	5	585	5	590	6	596	5	601	6	607	5	612	5	617	6	623	5	90628	6
806	90634	5	90639	5	90644	6	90650	5	90655	5	90660	6	90666	5	90671	6	90677	5	682	5
807	687	6	693	5	698	5	703	6	709	5	714	6	720	5	725	5	730	6	736	5
808	741	6	747	5	752	5	757	6	763	5	768	5	773	6	779	5	784	5	789	6
809	795	5	800	6	806	5	811	5	816	6	822	5	827	5	832	6	838	5	843	6
810	849	5	854	5	859	6	865	5	870	5	875	6	881	5	886	5	891	6	897	5
811	902	5	907	6	913	5	918	6	924	5	929	5	934	6	940	5	945	5	90950	6
812	**90956**	5	**90961**	5	**90966**	6	**90972**	5	**90977**	5	**90982**	6	**90988**	5	**90993**	5	**90998**	6	**91004**	5
813	**91009**	5	**91014**	6	**91020**	5	**91025**	5	**91030**	6	**91036**	5	**91041**	5	**91046**	6	**91052**	5	057	5
814	062	6	068	5	073	5	078	6	084	5	089	5	094	6	100	5	105	5	110	6
815	116	5	121	5	126	6	132	5	137	5	142	6	148	5	153	5	158	6	164	5
816	169	5	174	6	180	5	185	5	190	6	196	5	201	5	206	6	212	5	217	5
817	222	6	228	5	233	5	238	5	243	6	249	5	254	5	259	6	265	5	270	5
818	275	6	281	5	286	5	291	6	297	5	302	5	307	5	312	6	318	5	91323	5
819	91328	6	91334	5	91339	5	91344	6	91350	5	91355	5	91360	5	91365	6	91371	5	376	5
820	381	6	387	5	392	5	397	6	403	5	408	5	413	5	418	6	424	5	429	5
821	434	6	440	5	445	5	450	5	455	6	461	5	466	5	471	6	477	5	482	5
822	487	5	492	6	498	5	503	5	508	6	514	5	519	5	524	5	529	6	535	5
823	540	5	545	6	551	5	556	5	561	5	566	6	572	5	577	5	582	5	587	6
824	593	5	598	5	603	6	609	5	614	5	619	5	624	6	630	5	635	5	91640	5
825	91645	6	91651	5	91656	5	91661	5	91666	6	91672	5	91677	5	91682	5	91687	6	693	5
826	698	5	703	6	709	5	714	5	719	5	724	6	730	5	735	5	740	5	745	6
827	751	5	756	5	761	5	766	6	772	5	777	5	782	5	787	6	793	5	798	5
828	803	5	808	6	814	5	819	5	824	5	829	5	834	6	840	5	845	5	850	5
829	855	6	861	5	866	5	871	5	876	6	882	5	887	5	892	5	897	6	903	5
830	908	5	913	5	918	6	924	5	929	5	934	5	939	5	944	6	**91950**	5	**91955**	5
831	**91960**	5	**91965**	6	**91971**	5	**91976**	5	**91981**	5	**91986**	5	**91991**	6	**91997**	5	**92002**	5	**92007**	5
832	**92012**	6	**92018**	5	**92023**	5	**92028**	5	**92033**	5	**92038**	6	**92044**	5	**92049**	5	054	5	059	6
833	065	5	070	5	075	5	080	5	085	6	091	5	096	5	101	5	106	5	111	6
834	117	5	122	5	127	5	132	5	137	6	143	5	148	5	153	5	158	5	163	6
835	169	5	174	5	179	5	184	5	189	6	195	5	200	5	205	5	210	5	215	6
836	221	5	226	5	231	5	236	5	241	6	247	5	252	5	257	5	262	5	267	6
837	273	5	278	5	283	5	288	5	293	5	298	6	304	5	309	5	314	5	319	5
838	324	6	330	5	335	5	340	5	345	5	350	5	355	6	361	5	366	5	371	5
839	376	5	381	6	387	5	392	5	397	5	402	5	407	5	412	6	418	5	423	5
840	428	5	433	5	438	5	443	6	449	5	454	5	459	5	464	5	92469	5	92474	6
841	92480	5	92485	5	92490	5	92495	5	92500	5	92505	6	92511	5	92516	5	521	5	526	5
842	531	5	536	6	542	5	547	5	552	5	557	5	562	5	567	5	572	6	578	5
843	583	5	588	5	593	5	598	5	603	6	609	5	614	5	619	5	624	5	629	5
844	634	5	639	6	645	5	650	5	655	5	660	5	665	5	670	5	675	6	681	5
845	686	5	691	5	696	5	701	5	706	5	711	5	716	6	722	5	727	5	732	5
846	737	5	742	5	747	5	752	6	758	5	763	5	768	5	773	5	778	5	783	5
847	788	5	793	6	799	5	804	5	809	5	814	5	819	5	824	5	829	5	834	6
848	840	5	845	5	850	5	855	5	860	5	865	5	870	5	875	6	881	5	886	5
849	891	5	896	5	901	5	906	5	911	5	916	5	921	6	927	5	932	5	937	5
850	92942	5	92947	5	92952	5	92957	5	92962	5	92967	6	92973	5	92978	5	92983	5	92988	5
No.	0		1		2		3		4		5		6		7		8		9	

Prop. Parts

	6
1	1
2	1
3	2
4	2
5	3
6	4
7	4
8	5
9	5

	5
1	1
2	1
3	2
4	2
5	3
6	3
7	4
8	4
9	5
10	5

TABLE 32.

Logarithms of Numbers.

850

No.	0	d	1	d	2	d	3	d	4	d	5	d	6	d	7	d	8	d	9	d
850	92942	5	92947	5	92952	5	92957	5	92962	5	92967	6	92973	5	92978	5	92983	5	92988	5
851	92993	5	92998	5	93003	5	93008	5	93013	5	93018	6	93024	5	93029	5	93034	5	93039	5
852	93044	5	93049	5	054	5	059	5	064	5	069	6	075	5	080	5	085	5	090	5
853	095	5	100	5	105	5	110	5	115	5	120	5	125	6	131	5	136	5	141	5
854	146	5	151	5	156	5	161	5	166	5	171	5	176	5	181	5	186	6	192	5
855	197	5	202	5	207	5	212	5	217	5	222	5	227	5	232	5	237	5	242	5
856	247	5	252	6	258	5	263	5	268	5	273	5	278	5	283	5	288	5	293	5
857	298	5	303	5	93308	5	93313	5	93318	5	93323	5	93328	6	93334	5	93339	5	93344	5
858	93349	5	93354	5	359	5	364	5	369	5	374	5	379	5	384	5	389	5	394	5
859	399	5	404	5	409	5	414	6	420	5	425	5	430	5	435	5	440	5	445	5
860	450	5	455	5	460	5	465	5	470	5	475	5	480	5	485	5	490	5	495	5
861	500	5	505	5	510	5	515	5	520	6	526	5	531	5	536	5	541	5	546	5
862	551	5	556	5	561	5	566	5	571	5	576	5	581	5	586	5	591	5	596	5
863	601	5	606	5	611	5	616	5	621	5	626	5	631	5	636	5	641	5	646	5
864	93651	5	93656	5	93661	5	93666	5	93671	5	93676	6	93682	5	93687	5	93692	5	93697	5
865	702	5	707	5	712	5	717	5	722	5	727	5	732	5	737	5	742	5	747	5
866	752	5	757	5	762	5	767	5	772	5	777	5	782	5	787	5	792	5	797	5
867	802	5	807	5	812	5	817	5	822	5	827	5	832	5	837	5	842	5	847	5
868	852	5	857	5	862	5	867	5	872	5	877	5	882	5	887	5	892	5	897	5
869	902	5	907	5	912	5	917	5	922	5	927	5	932	5	937	5	942	5	947	5
870	93952	5	93957	5	93962	5	93967	5	93972	5	93977	5	93982	5	93987	5	93992	5	93997	5
871	94002	5	94007	5	94012	5	94017	5	94022	5	94027	5	94032	5	94037	5	94042	5	94047	5
872	052	5	057	5	062	5	067	5	072	5	077	5	082	4	086	5	091	5	096	5
873	101	5	106	5	111	5	116	5	121	5	126	5	131	5	136	5	141	5	146	5
874	151	5	156	5	161	5	166	5	171	5	176	5	181	5	186	5	191	5	196	5
875	201	5	206	5	211	5	216	5	221	5	226	5	231	5	236	4	240	5	245	5
876	250	5	255	5	260	5	265	5	270	5	275	5	280	5	285	5	290	5	295	5
877	300	5	305	5	310	5	315	5	320	5	325	5	330	5	335	5	340	5	345	4
878	349	5	354	5	359	5	364	5	369	5	374	5	379	5	384	5	389	5	394	5
879	399	5	404	5	409	5	414	5	419	5	424	5	429	4	433	5	438	5	443	5
880	94448	5	94453	5	94458	5	94463	5	94468	5	94473	5	94478	5	94483	5	94488	5	94493	5
881	498	5	503	4	507	5	512	5	517	5	522	5	527	5	532	5	537	5	542	5
882	547	5	552	5	557	5	562	5	567	4	571	5	576	5	581	5	586	5	591	5
883	596	5	601	5	606	5	611	5	616	5	621	5	626	4	630	5	635	5	640	5
884	645	5	650	5	655	5	660	5	665	5	670	5	675	5	680	5	685	4	689	5
885	694	5	699	5	704	5	709	5	714	5	719	5	724	5	729	5	734	4	738	5
886	743	5	748	5	753	5	758	5	763	5	768	5	773	5	778	5	783	4	787	5
887	792	5	797	5	802	5	807	5	812	5	817	5	822	5	827	5	832	4	836	5
888	841	5	846	5	851	5	856	5	861	5	866	5	871	5	876	4	880	5	885	5
889	890	5	895	5	900	5	905	5	910	5	915	4	919	5	924	5	929	5	934	5
890	939	5	944	5	949	5	94954	5	94959	4	94963	5	94968	5	94973	5	94978	5	94983	5
891	94988	5	94993	5	94998	4	95002	5	95007	5	95012	5	95017	5	95022	5	95027	5	95032	4
892	95036	5	95041	5	95046	5	051	5	056	5	061	5	066	5	071	4	075	5	080	5
893	085	5	090	5	095	5	100	5	105	4	109	5	114	5	119	5	124	5	129	5
894	134	5	139	4	143	5	148	5	153	5	158	5	163	5	168	5	173	4	177	5
895	182	5	187	5	192	5	197	5	202	5	207	4	211	5	216	5	221	5	226	5
896	231	5	236	4	240	5	245	5	250	5	255	5	260	5	265	5	270	4	274	5
897	279	5	284	5	289	5	294	5	299	4	303	5	308	5	313	5	318	5	323	5
898	328	4	332	5	337	5	342	5	347	5	352	5	357	4	361	5	366	5	371	5
899	376	5	381	5	386	4	390	5	395	5	400	5	405	5	410	5	415	4	419	5
900	95424	5	95429	5	95434	5	95439	5	95444	4	95448	5	95453	5	95458	5	95463	5	95468	4
No.	0		1		2		3		4		5		6		7		8		9	

Prop. Parts

	6
1	1
2	1
3	2
4	2
5	3
6	4
7	4
8	5
9	5

	5
1	1
2	1
3	2
4	2
5	3
6	3
7	4
8	4
9	5
10	5

	4
1	0
2	1
3	1
4	2
5	2
6	2
7	3
8	3
9	4
10	4

TABLE 32.

Logarithms of Numbers.

900

No.	0	d	1	d	2	d	3	d	4	d	5	d	6	d	7	d	8	d	9	d
900	95424	5	95429	5	95434	5	95439	5	95444	4	95448	5	95453	5	95458	5	95463	5	95468	4
901	472	5	477	5	482	5	487	5	492	5	497	4	501	5	506	5	511	5	516	5
902	521	4	525	5	530	5	535	5	540	5	545	5	550	4	554	5	559	5	564	5
903	569	5	574	4	578	5	583	5	588	5	593	5	598	4	602	5	607	5	612	5
904	617	5	622	4	626	5	631	5	636	5	641	5	646	4	650	5	655	5	660	5
905	665	5	95670	4	95674	5	95679	5	95684	5	95689	5	95694	4	95698	5	95703	5	95708	5
906	95713	5	718	4	722	5	727	5	732	5	737	5	742	4	746	5	751	5	756	5
907	761	5	766	4	770	5	775	5	780	5	785	4	789	5	794	5	799	5	804	5
908	809	4	813	5	818	5	823	5	828	4	832	5	837	5	842	5	847	5	852	4
909	856	5	861	5	866	5	871	4	875	5	880	5	885	5	890	5	895	4	899	5
910	904	5	909	5	914	4	918	5	923	5	928	5	933	5	938	4	942	5	947	5
911	952	5	95957	4	95961	5	95966	5	95971	5	95976	4	95980	5	95985	5	95990	5	95995	4
912	95999	5	96004	5	96009	5	96014	5	96019	4	96023	5	96028	5	96033	5	96038	4	96042	5
913	96047	5	052	5	057	4	061	5	066	5	071	5	076	4	080	5	085	5	090	5
914	095	4	099	5	104	5	109	5	114	4	118	5	123	5	128	5	133	4	137	5
915	142	5	147	5	152	4	156	5	161	5	166	5	171	4	175	5	180	5	185	5
916	190	4	194	5	199	5	204	5	209	4	213	5	218	5	223	4	227	5	232	5
917	237	5	242	4	246	5	251	5	256	5	261	4	265	5	270	5	275	5	280	4
918	284	5	289	5	294	4	298	5	303	5	308	5	313	4	317	5	322	5	327	5
919	332	4	96336	5	96341	5	96346	4	96350	5	96355	5	96360	5	96365	4	96369	5	96374	5
920	96379	5	384	4	388	5	393	5	398	4	402	5	407	5	412	5	417	4	421	5
921	426	5	431	4	435	5	440	5	445	5	450	4	454	5	459	5	464	4	468	5
922	473	5	478	5	483	4	487	5	492	5	497	4	501	5	506	5	511	4	515	5
923	520	5	525	5	530	4	534	5	539	5	544	4	548	5	553	5	558	4	562	5
924	567	5	572	5	577	4	581	5	586	5	591	4	595	5	600	5	605	4	609	5
925	614	5	619	5	624	4	96628	5	96633	5	96638	4	96642	5	96647	5	96652	4	96656	5
926	96661	5	96666	4	96670	5	675	5	680	5	685	4	689	5	694	5	699	4	703	5
927	708	5	713	4	717	5	722	5	727	4	731	5	736	5	741	4	745	5	750	5
928	755	4	759	5	764	5	769	5	774	4	778	5	783	5	788	4	792	5	797	5
929	802	4	806	5	811	5	816	4	820	5	825	5	830	4	834	5	839	5	844	4
930	848	5	853	5	858	4	862	5	867	5	872	4	876	5	881	5	886	4	890	5
931	895	5	900	4	904	5	909	5	914	4	918	5	923	5	928	4	932	5	937	5
932	942	4	946	5	951	5	96956	4	96960	5	96965	5	96970	4	96974	5	96979	5	96984	4
933	96988	5	96993	4	96997	5	97002	5	97007	4	97011	5	97016	5	97021	4	97025	5	97030	5
934	97035	4	97039	5	97044	5	049	4	053	5	058	5	063	4	067	5	072	5	077	4
935	081	5	086	4	090	5	095	5	100	4	104	5	109	5	114	4	118	5	123	5
936	128	4	132	5	137	5	142	4	146	5	151	4	155	5	160	5	165	4	169	5
937	174	5	179	4	183	5	188	4	192	5	197	5	202	4	206	5	211	5	216	4
938	220	5	225	5	230	4	234	5	239	4	243	5	248	5	253	4	257	5	262	5
939	267	4	271	5	276	4	280	5	285	5	290	4	294	5	299	5	304	4	308	5
940	313	4	317	5	322	5	327	4	331	5	336	4	340	5	345	5	350	4	354	5
941	359	5	364	4	368	5	373	4	377	5	382	5	387	4	391	5	396	4	400	5
942	97405	5	97410	4	97414	5	97419	5	97424	4	97428	5	97433	4	97437	5	97442	5	97447	4
943	451	5	456	4	460	5	465	5	470	4	474	5	479	4	483	5	488	5	493	4
944	497	5	502	4	506	5	511	5	516	4	520	5	525	4	529	5	534	5	539	4
945	543	5	548	4	552	5	557	5	562	4	566	5	571	4	575	5	580	5	585	4
946	589	5	594	4	598	5	603	4	607	5	612	5	617	4	621	5	626	4	630	5
947	635	5	640	4	644	5	649	4	653	5	658	5	663	4	667	5	672	4	676	5
948	681	4	685	5	690	5	695	4	699	5	704	4	708	5	713	4	717	5	722	5
949	727	4	731	5	736	4	740	5	745	4	749	5	754	5	759	4	763	5	97768	4
950	97772	5	97777	5	97782	4	97786	5	97791	4	97795	5	97800	4	97804	5	97809	4	97813	5
No.	0		1		2		3		4		5		6		7		8		9	

Prop. Parts

	5
1	1
2	1
3	2
4	2
5	3
6	3
7	4
8	4
9	5
10	5

	4
1	0
2	1
3	1
4	2
5	2
6	2
7	3
8	3
9	4
10	4

TABLE 32.

Logarithms of Numbers.

950

No.	0	d	1	d	2	d	3	d	4	d	5	d	6	d	7	d	8	d	9	d
950	97772	5	97777	5	97782	4	97786	5	97791	4	97795	5	97800	4	97804	5	97809	4	97813	5
951	818	5	823	4	827	5	832	4	836	5	841	4	845	5	850	5	855	4	859	5
952	864	4	868	5	873	4	877	5	882	4	886	5	891	5	896	4	900	5	905	4
953	909	5	914	4	918	5	923	5	928	4	932	5	937	4	941	5	946	4	950	5
954	97955	4	97959	5	97964	4	97968	5	97973	5	97978	4	97982	5	97987	4	97991	5	97996	4
955	98000	5	98005	4	98009	5	98014	5	98019	4	98023	5	98028	4	98032	5	98037	4	98041	5
956	046	4	050	5	055	4	059	5	064	4	068	5	073	5	078	4	082	5	087	4
957	091	5	096	4	100	5	105	4	109	5	114	4	118	5	123	4	127	5	132	5
958	137	4	141	5	146	4	150	5	155	4	159	5	164	4	168	5	173	4	177	5
959	182	4	186	5	191	4	195	5	200	4	204	5	209	5	214	4	218	5	223	4
960	227	5	232	4	236	5	241	4	245	5	250	4	254	5	259	4	263	5	268	4
961	272	5	277	4	281	5	286	4	290	5	295	4	299	5	304	4	308	5	313	5
962	98318	4	98322	5	98327	4	98331	5	98336	4	98340	5	98345	4	98349	5	98354	4	98358	5
963	363	4	367	5	372	4	376	5	381	4	385	5	390	4	394	5	399	4	403	5
964	408	4	412	5	417	4	421	5	426	4	430	5	435	4	439	5	444	4	448	5
965	453	4	457	5	462	4	466	5	471	4	475	5	480	4	484	5	489	4	493	5
966	498	4	502	5	507	4	511	5	516	4	520	5	525	4	529	5	534	4	538	5
967	543	4	547	5	552	4	556	5	561	4	565	5	570	4	574	5	579	4	583	5
968	588	4	592	5	597	4	601	4	605	5	610	4	614	5	619	4	623	5	628	4
969	632	5	637	4	641	5	98646	4	98650	5	98655	4	98659	5	98664	4	98668	5	98673	4
970	98677	5	98682	4	98686	5	691	4	695	5	700	4	704	5	709	4	713	4	717	5
971	722	4	726	5	731	4	735	5	740	4	744	5	749	4	753	5	758	4	762	5
972	767	4	771	5	776	4	780	4	784	5	789	4	793	5	798	4	802	5	807	4
973	811	5	816	4	820	5	825	4	829	5	834	4	838	5	843	4	847	4	851	5
974	856	4	860	5	865	4	869	5	874	4	878	5	883	4	887	5	892	4	896	4
975	900	5	905	4	909	5	914	4	918	5	923	4	927	5	932	4	936	5	941	4
976	945	4	949	5	954	4	98958	5	98963	4	98967	5	98972	4	98976	5	98981	4	98985	4
977	98989	5	98994	4	98998	5	99003	4	99007	5	99012	4	99016	5	99021	4	99025	4	99029	5
978	99034	4	99038	5	99043	4	047	5	052	4	056	5	061	4	065	4	069	5	074	4
979	078	5	083	4	087	5	092	4	096	4	100	5	105	4	109	5	114	4	118	5
980	123	4	127	4	131	5	136	4	140	5	145	4	149	5	154	4	158	4	162	5
981	167	4	171	5	176	4	180	5	185	4	189	4	193	5	198	4	202	5	207	4
982	211	5	216	4	220	4	224	5	229	4	233	5	238	4	242	5	247	4	251	4
983	255	5	260	4	264	5	269	4	273	4	277	5	282	4	286	5	291	4	295	5
984	300	4	304	4	308	5	99313	4	99317	5	99322	4	99326	4	99330	5	99335	4	99339	5
985	99344	4	99348	4	99352	5	357	4	361	5	366	4	370	4	374	5	379	4	383	5
986	388	4	392	4	396	5	401	4	405	5	410	4	414	5	419	4	423	4	427	5
987	432	4	436	5	441	4	445	4	449	5	454	4	458	5	463	4	467	4	471	5
988	476	4	480	4	484	5	489	4	493	5	498	4	502	4	506	5	511	4	515	5
989	520	4	524	4	528	5	533	4	537	5	542	4	546	4	550	5	555	4	559	5
990	564	4	568	4	572	5	577	4	581	4	585	5	590	4	594	5	599	4	603	4
991	607	5	612	4	616	5	621	4	625	4	629	5	634	4	638	4	642	5	647	4
992	99651	5	99656	4	99660	4	99664	5	99669	4	99673	4	99677	5	99682	4	99686	5	99691	4
993	695	4	699	5	704	4	708	4	712	5	717	4	721	5	726	4	730	4	734	5
994	739	4	743	4	747	5	752	4	756	4	760	5	765	4	769	5	774	4	778	4
995	782	5	787	4	791	4	795	5	800	4	804	4	808	5	813	4	817	5	822	4
996	826	4	830	5	835	4	839	4	843	5	848	4	852	4	856	5	861	4	865	5
997	870	4	874	4	878	5	883	4	887	4	891	5	896	4	900	4	904	5	909	4
998	913	4	917	5	922	4	926	4	930	5	935	4	939	5	944	4	948	4	952	5
999	99957	4	99961	4	99965	5	99970	4	99974	4	99978	5	99983	4	99987	4	99991	5	99996	4
1000	00000	4	00004	5	00009	4	00013	4	00017	5	00022	4	00026	4	00030	5	00035	4	00039	
No.	0		1		2		3		4		5		6		7		8		9	

Prop. Parts

	5
1	1
2	1
3	2
4	2
5	3
6	3
7	4
8	4
9	5
10	5

	4
1	0
2	1
3	1
4	2
5	2
6	2
7	3
8	3
9	4
10	4

TABLE 33.

Logarithms of Trigonometric Functions.

0° → ′	sin	Diff. 1′.	csc	tan	Diff. 1′.	cot	sec	cos ← 179°	′
0	Inf. neg.		Infinite.	Inf. neg.		Infinite.	10. 00000	10. 00000	60
1	**6.** 46373	30103	**13.** 53627	**6.** 46373	30103	**13.** 53627	000	000	59
2	76476	17609	23524	76476	17609	23524	000	000	58
3	**6.** 94085	12494	**13.** 05915	**6.** 94085	12494	**13.** 05915	000	000	57
4	**7.** 06579	9691	**12.** 93421	**7.** 06579	9691	**12.** 93421	000	000	56
5	16270	7918	83730	. 16270	7918	83730	000	000	55
6	24188	6694	75812	24188	6694	75812	000	000	54
7	30882	5800	69118	30882	5800	69118	000	000	53
8	36682	5115	63318	36682	5115	63318	000	000	52
9	41797	4576	58203	41797	4576	58203	000	000	51
10	7. 46373	4139	12. 53627	7. 46373	4139	12. 53627	10. 00000	10. 00000	**50**
11	50512	3779	49488	50512	3779	49488	000	000	49
12	54291	3476	45709	54291	3476	45709	000	000	48
13	57767	3218	42233	57767	3219	42233	000	000	47
14	60985	2997	39015	60986	2996	39014	000	000	46
15	7. 63982	2802	12. 36018	7. 63982	2803	12. 36018	000	000	45
16	66784	2633	33216	66785	2633	33215	000	**10.** 00000	44
17	69417	2483	30583	69418	2482	30582	001	**9.** 99999	43
18	71900	2348	28100	71900	2348	28100	001	999	42
19	74248	2227	25752	74248	2228	25752	001	999	41
20	7. 76475	2119	12. 23525	7. 76476	2119	12. 23524	10. 00001	9. 99999	**40**
21	78594	2021	21406	78595	2020	21405	001	999	39
22	80615	1930	19385	80615	1931	19385	001	999	38
23	82545	1848	17455	82546	1848	17454	001	999	37
24	84393	1773	15607	84394	1773	15606	001	999	36
25	7. 86166	1704	12. 13834	7. 86167	1704	12. 13833	001	999	35
26	87870	1639	12130	87871	1639	12129	001	999	34
27	7. 89509	1579	10491	89510	1579	10490	001	999	33
28	91088	1524	08912	91089	1524	08911	001	999	32
29	92612	1472	07388	92613	1473	07387	002	998	31
30	7. 94084	1424	12. 05916	7. 94086	1424	12. 05914	10. 00002	9. 99998	**30**
31	95508	1379	04492	95510	1379	04490	002	998	29
32	96887	1336	03113	96889	1336	03111	002	998	28
33	98223	1297	01777	98225	1297	01775	002	998	27
34	**7.** 99520	1259	**12.** 00480	**7.** 99522	1259	**12.** 00478	002	998	26
35	**8.** 00779	1223	**11.** 99221	**8.** 00781	1223	**11.** 99219	002	998	25
36	02002	1190	97998	02004	1190	97996	002	998	24
37	03192	1158	96808	03194	1159	96806	003	997	23
38	04350	1128	95650	04353	1128	95647	003	997	22
39	05478	1100	94522	05481	1100	94519	003	997	21
40	8. 06578	1072	11. 93422	8. 06581	1072	11. 93419	10. 00003	9. 99997	**20**
41	07650	1046	92350	07653	1047	92347	003	997	19
42	08696	1022	91304	08700	1022	91300	003	997	18
43	09718	999	90282	09722	998	90278	003	997	17
44	10717	976	89283	10720	976	89280	004	996	16
45	8. 11693	954	11. 88307	8. 11696	955	11. 88304	004	996	15
46	12647	934	87353	12651	934	87349	004	996	14
47	13581	914	86419	13585	915	86415	004	996	13
48	14495	896	85505	14500	895	85500	004	996	12
49	15391	877	84609	15395	878	84605	004	996	11
50	8. 16268	860	11. 83732	8. 16273	860	11. 83727	10. 00005	9. 99995	**10**
51	17128	843	82872	17133	843	82867	005	995	9
52	17971	827	82029	17976	828	82024	005	995	8
53	18798	812	81202	18804	812	81196	005	995	7
54	19610	797	80390	19616	797	80384	005	995	6
55	8. 20407	782	11. 79593	8. 20413	782	11. 79587	006	994	5
56	21189	769	78811	21195	769	78805	006	994	4
57	21958	755	78042	21964	756	78036	006	994	3
58	22713	743	77287	22720	742	77280	006	994	2
59	23456	730	76544	23462	730	76538	006	994	1
60	**8.** 24186	717	**11.** 75814	8. 24192	718	**11.** 75808	10. 00007	9. 99993	0
′ 90° →	cos	Diff. 1′.	sec	cot	Diff. 1′.	tan	csc	sin ← 89°	′

TABLE 33.

Logarithms of Trigonometric Functions.

1°→ ↓ ′	sin	Diff. 1′.	csc	tan	Diff. 1′.	cot	sec	cos ←178° ↓ ′	
0	8. 24186	717	**11. 75814**	8. 24192	718	**11. 75808**	10. 00007	9. 99993	**60**
1	4903	706	5097	4910	706	5090	007	993	59
2	5609	695	4391	5616	696	4384	007	993	58
3	6304	684	3696	6312	684	3688	007	993	57
4	6988	673	3012	6996	673	3004	008	992	56
5	7661	663	2339	7669	663	2331	008	992	55
6	8324	653	1676	8332	654	1668	008	992	54
7	8977	644	1023	8986	643	1014	008	992	53
8	8. 29621	634	11. 70379	8. 29629	634	11. 70371	008	992	52
9	8. 30255	624	11. 69745	8. 30263	625	11. 69737	009	991	51
10	0879	616	9121	0888	617	9112	10. 00009	9. 99991	**50**
11	1495	608	8505	1505	607	8495	009	991	49
12	2103	599	7897	2112	599	7888	010	990	48
13	2702	590	7298	2711	591	7289	010	990	47
14	3292	583	6708	3302	584	6698	010	990	46
15	3875	575	6125	8. 33886	575	11. 66114	010	990	45
16	4450	568	5550	4461	568	5539	011	989	44
17	8. 35018	560	11. 64982	5029	561	4971	011	989	43
18	5578	553	4422	5590	553	4410	011	989	42
19	6131	547	3869	6143	546	3857	011	989	41
20	6678	539	3322	8. 36689	540	11. 63311	10. 00012	9. 99988	**40**
21	7217	533	2783	7229	533	2771	012	988	39
22	7750	526	2250	7762	527	2238	012	988	38
23	8276	520	1724	8289	520	1711	013	987	37
24	8796	514	1204	8809	514	1191	013	987	36
25	9310	508	0690	9323	509	0677	013	987	35
26	8. 39818	502	11. 60182	8. 39832	502	11. 60168	014	986	34
27	8. 40320	496	11. 59680	8. 40334	496	11. 59666	014	986	33
28	0816	491	9184	0830	491	9170	014	986	32
29	1307	485	8693	1321	486	8679	015	985	31
30	1792	480	8208	1807	480	8193	10. 00015	9. 99985	**30**
31	2272	474	7728	2287	475	7713	015	985	29
32	2746	470	7254	2762	470	7238	016	984	28
33	3216	464	6784	3232	464	6768	016	984	27
34	8. 43680	459	11. 56320	8. 43696	460	11. 56304	016	984	26
35	4139	455	5861	4156	455	5844	017	983	25
36	4594	450	5406	4611	450	5389	017	983	24
37	5044	445	4956	5061	446	4939	017	983	23
38	5489	441	4511	5507	441	4493	018	982	22
39	5930	436	4070	5948	437	4052	018	982	21
40	6366	433	3634	6385	432	3615	10. 00018	9. 99982	**20**
41	8. 46799	427	11. 53201	6817	428	3183	019	981	19
42	7226	424	2774	8. 47245	424	11. 52755	019	981	18
43	7650	419	2350	7669	420	2331	019	981	17
44	8069	416	1931	8089	416	1911	020	980	16
45	8485	411	1515	8505	412	1495	020	980	15
46	8896	408	1104	8917	408	1083	021	979	14
47	9304	404	0696	9325	404	0675	021	979	13
48	8. 49708	400	11. 50292	8. 49729	401	11. 50271	021	979	12
49	8. 50108	396	11. 49892	8. 50130	397	11. 49870	022	978	11
50	0504	393	9496	0527	393	9473	10. 00022	9. 99978	**10**
51	0897	390	9103	0920	390	9080	023	977	9
52	1287	386	8713	1310	386	8690	023	977	8
53	1673	382	8327	1696	383	8304	023	977	7
54	2055	379	7945	2079	380	7921	024	976	6
55	8. 52434	376	11. 47566	8. 52459	376	11. 47541	024	976	5
56	2810	373	7190	2835	373	7165	025	975	4
57	3183	369	6817	3208	370	6792	025	975	3
58	3552	367	6448	3578	367	6422	026	974	2
59	3919	363	6081	3945	363	6055	026	974	1
60	**8. 54282**	360	**11. 45718**	8. 54308	361	**11. 45692**	10. 00026	9. 99974	**0**
′ ↑ 91°→	cos	Diff. 1′.	sec	cot	Diff. 1′.	tan	csc	sin ←88°	′ ↑

Logarithms of Trigonometric Functions.

2° → ′	sin	Diff.1′.	csc	tan	Diff.1′.	cot	sec	cos ← 177°	′
0	8. 54282	360	11. 45718	8. 54308	361	11. 45692	10. 00026	9. 99974	60
1	4642	357	5358	4669	358	5331	027	973	59
2	4999	355	5001	5027	355	4973	027	973	58
3	5354	351	4646	5382	352	4618	028	972	57
4	5705	349	4295	5734	349	4266	028	972	56
5	6054	346	3946	6083	346	3917	029	971	55
6	6400	343	3600	6429	344	3571	029	971	54
7	6743	341	3257	6773	341	3227	030	970	53
8	8. 57084	337	11. 42916	8. 57114	338	11. 42886	030	970	52
9	7421	336	2579	7452	336	2548	031	969	51
10	7757	332	2243	7788	333	2212	10. 00031	9. 99969	50
11	8089	330	1911	8121	330	1879	032	968	49
12	8419	328	1581	8451	328	1549	032	968	48
13	8747	325	1253	8779	326	1221	033	967	47
14	9072	323	0928	9105	323	0895	033	967	46
15	9395	320	0605	9428	321	0572	033	967	45
16	8. 59715	318	11. 40285	8. 59749	319	11. 40251	034	966	44
17	8. 60033	316	11. 39967	8. 60068	316	11. 39932	034	966	43
18	0349	313	9651	0384	314	9616	035	965	42
19	0662	311	9338	0698	311	9302	036	964	41
20	0973	309	9027	1009	310	8991	10. 00036	9. 99964	40
21	1282	307	8718	1319	307	8681	037	963	39
22	1589	305	8411	1626	305	8374	037	963	38
23	1894	302	8106	1931	303	8069	038	962	37
24	2196	301	7804	2234	301	7766	038	962	36
25	2497	298	7503	2535	299	7465	039	961	35
26	8. 62795	296	11. 37205	8. 62834	297	11. 37166	039	961	34
27	3091	294	6909	3131	295	6869	040	960	33
28	3385	293	6615	3426	292	6574	040	960	32
29	3678	290	6322	3718	291	6282	041	959	31
30	3968	288	6032	4009	289	5991	10. 00041	9. 99959	30
31	4256	287	5744	4298	287	5702	042	958	29
32	4543	284	5457	4585	285	5415	042	958	28
33	4827	283	5173	4870	284	5130	043	957	27
34	5110	281	4890	5154	281	4846	044	956	26
35	8. 65391	279	11. 34609	8. 65435	280	11. 34565	044	956	25
36	5670	277	4330	5715	278	4285	045	955	24
37	5947	276	4053	5993	276	4007	045	955	23
38	6223	274	3777	6269	274	3731	046	954	22
39	6497	272	3503	6543	273	3457	046	954	21
40	6769	270	3231	6816	271	3184	10. 00047	9. 99953	20
41	7039	269	2961	7087	269	2913	048	952	19
42	7308	267	2692	7356	268	2644	048	952	18
43	7575	266	2425	7624	266	2376	049	951	17
44	7841	263	2159	7890	264	2110	049	951	16
45	8. 68104	263	11. 31896	8. 68154	263	11. 31846	050	950	15
46	8367	260	1633	8417	261	1583	051	949	14
47	8627	259	1373	8678	260	1322	051	949	13
48	8886	258	1114	8938	258	1062	052	948	12
49	9144	256	0856	9196	257	0804	052	948	11
50	9400	254	0600	9453	255	0547	10. 00053	9. 99947	10
51	9654	253	0346	9708	254	0292	054	946	9
52	8. 69907	252	11. 30093	8. 69962	252	11. 30038	054	946	8
53	8. 70159	250	11. 29841	8. 70214	251	11. 29786	055	945	7
54	0409	249	9591	0465	249	9535	056	944	6
55	0658	247	9342	0714	248	9286	056	944	5
56	0905	246	9095	0962	246	9038	057	943	4
57	1151	244	8849	1208	245	8792	058	942	3
58	1395	243	8605	1453	244	8547	058	942	2
59	1638	242	8362	1697	243	8303	059	941	1
60	8. 71880	240	11. 28120	8. 71940	241	11. 28060	10. 00060	9. 99940	0
′ 92° →	cos	Diff.1′.	sec	cot	Diff.1′.	tan	csc	sin ← 87°	′

TABLE 33.

Logarithms of Trigonometric Functions.

3° → ↓ ′	sin	Diff. 1′.	csc	tan	Diff. 1′.	cot	sec	cos	← 176° ↓ ′
0	8. 71880	240	11. 28120	8. 71940	241	11. 28060	10. 00060	9. 99940	60
1	8. 72120	239	11. 27880	8. 72181	239	11. 27819	060	940	59
2	359	238	641	420	239	580	061	939	58
3	597	237	403	659	237	341	062	938	57
4	8. 72834	235	11. 27166	8. 72896	236	11. 27104	062	938	56
5	8. 73069	234	11. 26931	8. 73132	234	11. 26868	063	937	55
6	303	232	697	366	234	634	064	936	54
7	535	232	465	600	232	400	064	936	53
8	767	230	233	8. 73832	231	11. 26168	065	935	52
9	8. 73997	229	11. 26003	8. 74063	229	11. 25937	066	934	51
10	8. 74226	228	11. 25774	292	229	708	10. 00066	9. 99934	50
11	454	226	546	521	227	479	067	933	49
12	680	226	320	748	226	252	068	932	48
13	8. 74906	224	11. 25094	8. 74974	225	11. 25026	068	932	47
14	8. 75130	223	11. 24870	8. 75199	224	11. 24801	069	931	46
15	353	222	647	423	222	577	070	930	45
16	575	220	425	645	222	355	071	929	44
17	8. 75795	220	11. 24205	8. 75867	220	11. 24133	071	929	43
18	8. 76015	219	11. 23985	8. 76087	219	11. 23913	072	928	42
19	234	217	766	306	219	694	073	927	41
20	451	216	549	525	217	475	10. 00074	9. 99926	40
21	667	216	333	742	216	258	074	926	39
22	8. 76883	214	11. 23117	8. 76958	215	11. 23042	075	925	38
23	8. 77097	213	11. 22903	8. 77173	214	11. 22827	076	924	37
24	310	212	690	387	213	613	077	923	36
25	522	211	478	600	211	400	077	923	35
26	733	210	267	8. 77811	211	11. 22189	078	922	34
27	8. 77943	209	11. 22057	8. 78022	210	11. 21978	079	921	33
28	8. 78152	208	11. 21848	232	209	768	080	920	32
29	360	208	640	441	208	559	080	920	31
30	568	206	432	649	206	351	10. 00081	9. 99919	30
31	774	205	226	8. 78855	206	11. 21145	082	918	29
32	8. 78979	204	11. 21021	8. 79061	205	11. 20939	083	917	28
33	8. 79183	203	11. 20817	266	204	734	083	917	27
34	386	202	614	470	203	530	084	916	26
35	588	201	412	673	202	327	085	915	25
36	789	201	211	8. 79875	201	11. 20125	086	914	24
37	8. 79990	199	11. 20010	8. 80076	201	11. 19924	087	913	23
38	8. 80189	199	11. 19811	277	199	723	087	913	22
39	388	197	612	476	198	524	088	912	21
40	585	197	415	674	198	326	10. 00089	9. 99911	20
41	782	196	218	8. 80872	196	11. 19128	090	910	19
42	8. 80978	195	11. 19022	8. 81068	196	11. 18932	091	909	18
43	8. 81173	194	11. 18827	264	195	736	091	909	17
44	367	193	633	459	194	541	092	908	16
45	560	192	440	653	193	347	093	907	15
46	752	192	248	8. 81846	192	11. 18154	094	906	14
47	8. 81944	190	11. 18056	8. 82038	192	11. 17962	095	905	13
48	8. 82134	190	11. 17866	230	190	770	096	904	12
49	324	189	676	420	190	580	096	904	11
50	513	188	487	610	189	390	10. 00097	9. 99903	10
51	701	187	299	799	188	201	098	902	9
52	8. 82888	187	11. 17112	8. 82987	188	11. 17013	099	901	8
53	8. 83075	186	11. 16925	8. 83175	186	11. 16825	100	900	7
54	261	185	739	361	186	639	101	899	6
55	446	184	554	547	185	453	102	898	5
56	630	183	370	732	184	268	102	898	4
57	813	183	187	8. 83916	184	11. 16084	103	897	3
58	8. 83996	181	11. 16004	8. 84100	182	11. 15900	104	896	2
59	8. 84177	181	11. 15823	282	182	718	105	895	1
60	8. 84358	181	11. 15642	8. 84464	182	11. 15536	10. 00106	9. 99894	0
′ ↑ 93° →	cos	Diff. 1′.	sec	cot	Diff. 1′.	tan	csc	sin	′ ↑ ← 86°

Logarithms of Trigonometric Functions.

4° → ↓ ′	sin	Diff. 1′.	csc	tan	Diff. 1′.	cot	sec	cos	← 175° ↓ ′
0	8. 84358	181	11. 15642	8. 84464	182	11. 15536	10. 00106	9. 99894	60
1	539	179	461	646	180	354	107	893	59
2	718	179	282	8. 84826	180	11. 15174	108	892	58
3	8. 84897	178	11. 15103	8. 85006	179	11. 14994	109	891	57
4	8. 85075	177	11. 14925	185	178	815	109	891	56
5	252	177	748	363	177	637	110	890	55
6	429	176	571	540	177	460	111	889	54
7	605	175	395	717	176	283	112	888	53
8	780	175	220	8. 85893	176	11. 14107	113	887	52
9	8. 85955	173	11. 14045	8. 86069	174	11. 13931	114	886	51
10	8. 86128	173	11. 13872	243	174	757	10. 00115	9. 99885	50
11	301	173	699	417	174	583	116	884	49
12	474	171	526	591	172	409	117	883	48
13	645	171	355	763	172	237	118	882	47
14	816	171	184	8. 86935	171	11. 13065	119	881	46
15	8. 86987	169	11. 13013	8. 87106	171	11. 12894	120	880	45
16	8. 87156	169	11. 12844	277	170	723	121	879	44
17	325	169	675	447	169	553	121	879	43
18	494	167	506	616	169	384	122	878	42
19	661	168	339	785	168	215	123	877	41
20	829	166	171	8. 87953	167	11. 12047	10. 00124	9. 99876	40
21	8. 87995	166	11. 12005	8. 88120	167	11. 11880	125	875	39
22	8. 88161	165	11. 11839	287	166	713	126	874	38
23	326	164	674	453	165	547	127	873	37
24	490	164	510	618	165	382	128	872	36
25	654	163	346	783	165	217	129	871	35
26	817	163	183	8. 88948	163	11. 11052	130	870	34
27	8. 88980	162	11. 11020	8. 89111	163	11. 10889	131	869	33
28	8. 89142	162	11. 10858	274	163	726	132	868	32
29	304	160	696	437	161	563	133	867	31
30	464	161	536	598	162	402	10. 00134	9. 99866	30
31	625	159	375	760	160	240	135	865	29
32	784	159	216	8. 89920	160	11. 10080	136	864	28
33	8. 89943	159	11. 10057	8. 90080	160	11. 09920	137	863	27
34	8. 90102	158	11. 09898	240	159	760	138	862	26
35	260	157	740	399	158	601	139	861	25
36	417	157	583	557	158	443	140	860	24
37	574	156	426	715	157	285	141	859	23
38	730	155	270	8. 90872	157	11. 09128	142	858	22
39	8. 90885	155	11. 09115	8. 91029	156	11. 08971	143	857	21
40	8. 91040	155	11. 08960	185	155	815	10. 00144	9. 99856	20
41	195	154	805	340	155	660	145	855	19
42	349	153	651	495	155	505	146	854	18
43	502	153	498	650	153	350	147	853	17
44	655	152	345	803	154	197	148	852	16
45	807	152	193	8. 91957	153	11. 08043	149	851	15
46	8. 91959	151	11. 08041	8. 92110	152	11. 07890	150	850	14
47	8. 92110	151	11. 07890	262	152	738	152	848	13
48	261	150	739	414	151	586	153	847	12
49	411	150	589	565	151	435	154	846	11
50	561	149	439	716	150	284	10. 00155	9. 99845	10
51	710	149	290	8. 92866	150	11. 07134	156	844	9
52	8. 92859	148	11. 07141	8. 93016	149	11. 06984	157	843	8
53	8. 93007	147	11. 06993	165	148	835	158	842	7
54	154	147	846	313	149	687	159	841	6
55	301	147	699	462	147	538	160	840	5
56	448	146	552	609	147	391	161	839	4
57	594	146	406	756	147	244	162	838	3
58	740	145	260	8. 93903	146	11. 06097	163	837	2
59	8. 93885	145	11. 06115	8. 94049	146	11. 05951	164	836	1
60	8. 94030	144	11. 05970	8. 94195	145	11. 05805	10. 00166	9. 99834	0
′ ↑ 94° →	cos	Diff. 1′.	sec	cot	Diff. 1′.	tan	csc	sin	′ ↑ ← 85°

541524°—43——40

TABLE 33.

Logarithms of Trigonometric Functions.

5° → '	sin	"	Diff.	csc	tan	"	Diff.	cot	sec	"	Diff.	cos ← 174°	'
0	8.94030	0	0	11.05970	8.94195	0	0	11.05805	10.00166	0	0	9.99834	60
1	174	1	2	826	340	1	2	660	167	1	0	833	59
2	317	2	4	683	485	2	4	515	168	2	0	832	58
3	461	3	7	539	630	3	7	370	169	3	0	831	57
4	603	4	9	397	773	4	9	227	170	4	0	830	56
5	746	5	11	254	8.94917	5	11	11.05083	171	5	0	829	55
6	8.94887	6	13	11.05113	8.95060	6	13	11.04940	172	6	0	828	54
7	8.95029	7	15	11.04971	202	7	15	798	173	7	0	827	53
8	170	8	18	830	344	8	18	656	175	8	0	825	52
9	310	9	20	690	486	9	20	514	176	9	0	824	51
10	450	10	22	550	627	10	22	373	10.00177	10	0	9.99823	50
11	589	11	24	411	767	11	24	233	178	11	0	822	49
12	728	12	26	272	8.95908	12	27	11.04092	179	12	0	821	48
13	8.95867	13	29	11.04133	8.96047	13	29	11.03953	180	13	0	820	47
14	8.96005	14	31	11.03995	187	14	31	813	181	14	0	819	46
15	143	15	33	857	325	15	33	675	183	15	0	817	45
16	280	16	35	720	464	16	35	536	184	16	0	816	44
17	417	17	37	583	602	17	38	398	185	17	0	815	43
18	553	18	39	447	739	18	40	261	186	18	0	814	42
19	689	19	42	311	8.96877	19	42	11.03123	187	19	0	813	41
20	825	20	44	175	8.97013	20	44	11.02987	10.00188	20	0	9.99812	40
21	8.96960	21	46	11.03040	150	21	46	850	190	21	0	810	39
22	8.97095	22	48	11.02905	285	22	49	715	191	22	0	809	38
23	229	23	50	771	421	23	51	579	192	23	0	808	37
24	363	24	53	637	556	24	53	444	193	24	0	807	36
25	496	25	55	504	691	25	55	309	194	25	1	806	35
26	629	26	57	371	825	26	58	175	196	26	1	804	34
27	762	27	59	238	8.97959	27	60	11.02041	197	27	1	803	33
28	8.97894	28	61	11.02106	8.98092	28	62	11.01908	198	28	1	802	32
29	8.98026	29	64	11.01974	225	29	64	775	199	29	1	801	31
30	157	30	66	843	358	30	66	642	10.00200	30	1	9.99800	30
31	288	31	68	712	490	31	69	510	202	31	1	798	29
32	419	32	70	581	622	32	71	378	203	32	1	797	28
33	549	33	72	451	753	33	73	247	204	33	1	796	27
34	679	34	75	321	8.98884	34	75	11.01116	205	34	1	795	26
35	808	35	77	192	8.99015	35	77	11.00985	207	35	1	793	25
36	8.98937	36	79	11.01063	145	36	80	855	208	36	1	792	24
37	8.99066	37	81	11.00934	275	37	82	725	209	37	1	791	23
38	194	38	83	806	405	38	84	595	210	38	1	790	22
39	322	39	86	678	534	39	86	466	212	39	1	788	21
40	450	40	88	550	662	40	89	338	10.00213	40	1	9.99787	20
41	577	41	90	423	791	41	91	209	214	41	1	786	19
42	704	42	92	296	8.99919	42	93	11.00081	215	42	1	785	18
43	830	43	94	170	9.00046	43	95	10.99954	217	43	1	783	17
44	8.99956	44	96	11.00044	174	44	97	826	218	44	1	782	16
45	9.00082	45	99	10.99918	301	45	100	699	219	45	1	781	15
46	207	46	101	793	427	46	102	573	220	46	1	780	14
47	332	47	103	668	553	47	104	447	222	47	1	778	13
48	456	48	105	544	679	48	106	321	223	48	1	777	12
49	581	49	107	419	805	49	108	195	224	49	1	776	11
50	704	50	110	296	9.00930	50	111	10.99070	10.00225	50	1	9.99775	10
51	828	51	112	172	9.01055	51	113	10.98945	227	51	1	773	9
52	9.00951	52	114	10.99049	179	52	115	821	228	52	1	772	8
53	9.01074	53	116	10.98926	303	53	117	697	229	53	1	771	7
54	196	54	118	804	427	54	120	573	231	54	1	769	6
55	318	55	121	682	550	55	122	450	232	55	1	768	5
56	440	56	123	560	673	56	124	327	233	56	1	767	4
57	561	57	125	439	796	57	126	204	235	57	1	765	3
58	682	58	127	318	9.01918	58	128	10.98082	236	58	1	764	2
59	803	59	129	197	9.02040	59	131	10.97960	237	59	1	763	1
60	9.01923	60	132	10.98077	9.02162	60	133	10.97838	10.00239	60	1	9.99761	0
' 95° →	cos	"	Diff.	sec	cot	"	Diff.	tan	csc	"	Diff.	sin ← 84°	'

TABLE 33.

Logarithms of Trigonometric Functions.

6° → ′	sin	″	Diff.	csc	tan	″	Diff.	cot	sec	″	Diff.	cos	← 173° ′
0	9.01923	0	0	10.98077	9.02162	0	0	10.97838	10.00239	0	0	9.99761	60
1	9.02043	1	2	10.97957	283	1	2	717	240	1	0	760	59
2	163	2	4	837	404	2	4	596	241	2	0	759	58
3	283	3	6	717	525	3	6	475	243	3	0	757	57
4	402	4	7	598	645	4	8	355	244	4	0	756	56
5	520	5	9	480	766	5	9	234	245	5	0	755	55
6	639	6	11	361	9.02885	6	11	10.97115	247	6	0	753	54
7	757	7	13	243	9.03005	7	13	10.96995	248	7	0	752	53
8	874	8	15	126	124	8	15	876	249	8	0	751	52
9	9.02992	9	17	10.97008	242	9	17	758	251	9	0	749	51
10	9.03109	10	19	10.96891	361	10	19	639	10.00252	10	0	9.99748	50
11	226	11	20	774	479	11	21	521	253	11	0	747	49
12	342	12	22	658	597	12	23	403	255	12	0	745	48
13	458	13	24	542	714	13	24	286	256	13	0	744	47
14	574	14	26	426	832	14	26	168	258	14	0	742	46
15	690	15	28	310	9.03948	15	28	10.96052	259	15	0	741	45
16	805	16	30	195	9.04065	16	30	10.95935	260	16	0	740	44
17	9.03920	17	31	10.96080	181	17	32	819	262	17	0	738	43
18	9.04034	18	33	10.95966	297	18	34	703	263	18	0	737	42
19	149	19	35	851	413	19	36	587	264	19	0	736	41
20	262	20	37	738	528	20	38	472	10.00266	20	0	9.99734	40
21	376	21	39	624	643	21	39	357	267	21	1	733	39
22	490	22	41	510	758	22	41	242	269	22	1	731	38
23	603	23	43	397	873	23	43	127	270	23	1	730	37
24	715	24	44	285	9.04987	24	45	10.95013	272	24	1	728	36
25	828	25	46	172	9.05101	25	47	10.94899	273	25	1	727	35
26	9.04940	26	48	10.95060	214	26	49	786	274	26	1	726	34
27	9.05052	27	50	10.94948	328	27	51	672	276	27	1	724	33
28	164	28	52	836	441	28	53	559	277	28	1	723	32
29	275	29	54	725	553	29	54	447	279	29	1	721	31
30	386	30	56	614	666	30	56	334	10.00280	30	1	9.99720	30
31	497	31	57	503	778	31	58	222	282	31	1	718	29
32	607	32	59	393	9.05890	32	60	10.94110	283	32	1	717	28
33	717	33	61	283	9.06002	33	62	10.93998	284	33	1	716	27
34	827	34	63	173	113	34	64	887	286	34	1	714	26
35	9.05937	35	65	10.94063	224	35	66	776	287	35	1	713	25
36	9.06046	36	67	10.93954	335	36	68	665	289	36	1	711	24
37	155	37	69	845	445	37	69	555	290	37	1	710	23
38	264	38	70	736	556	38	71	444	292	38	1	708	22
39	372	39	72	628	666	39	73	334	293	39	1	707	21
40	481	40	74	519	775	40	75	225	10.00295	40	1	9.99705	20
41	589	41	76	411	885	41	77	115	296	41	1	704	19
42	696	42	78	304	9.06994	42	79	10.93006	298	42	1	702	18
43	804	43	80	196	9.07103	43	81	10.92897	299	43	1	701	17
44	9.06911	44	81	10.93089	211	44	83	789	301	44	1	699	16
45	9.07018	45	83	10.92982	320	45	84	680	302	45	1	698	15
46	124	46	85	876	428	46	86	572	304	46	1	696	14
47	231	47	87	769	536	47	88	464	305	47	1	695	13
48	337	48	89	663	643	48	90	357	307	48	1	693	12
49	442	49	91	558	751	49	92	249	308	49	1	692	11
50	548	50	93	452	858	50	94	142	10.00310	50	1	9.99690	10
51	653	51	94	347	9.07964	51	96	10.92036	311	51	1	689	9
52	758	52	96	242	9.08071	52	98	10.91929	313	52	1	687	8
53	863	53	98	137	177	53	99	823	314	53	1	686	7
54	9.07968	54	100	10.92032	283	54	101	717	316	54	1	684	6
55	9.08072	55	102	10.91928	389	55	103	611	317	55	1	683	5
56	176	56	104	824	495	56	105	505	319	56	1	681	4
57	280	57	106	720	600	57	107	400	320	57	1	680	3
58	383	58	107	617	705	58	109	295	322	58	1	678	2
59	486	59	109	514	810	59	111	190	323	59	1	677	1
60	9.08589	60	111	10.91411	9.08914	60	113	10.91086	10.00325	60	1	9.99675	0
′ 96° →	cos	″	Diff.	sec	cot	″	Diff.	tan	csc	″	Diff.	sin	← 83° ′

TABLE 33.

Logarithms of Trigonometric Functions.

7° → ↓ '	sin	"	Diff.	csc	tan	"	Diff.	cot	sec	"	Diff.	cos	← 172° ↓ '
0	9. 08589	*0*	0	10. 91411	9. 08914	*0*	0	10. 91086	10. 00325	*0*	0	9. 99675	60
1	692	*1*	2	308	9. 09019	*1*	2	10. 90981	326	*1*	0	674	59
2	795	*2*	3	205	123	*2*	3	877	328	*2*	0	672	58
3	897	*3*	5	103	227	*3*	5	773	330	*3*	0	670	57
4	9. 08999	*4*	6	10. 91001	330	*4*	7	670	331	*4*	0	669	56
5	9. 09101	*5*	8	10. 90899	434	*5*	8	566	333	*5*	0	667	55
6	202	*6*	10	798	537	*6*	10	463	334	*6*	0	666	54
7	304	*7*	11	696	640	*7*	11	360	336	*7*	0	664	53
8	405	*8*	13	595	742	*8*	13	258	337	*8*	0	663	52
9	506	*9*	14	494	845	*9*	15	155	339	*9*	0	661	51
10	606	*10*	16	394	9. 09947	*10*	16	10. 90053	10. 00341	*10*	0	9. 99659	50
11	707	*11*	18	293	9. 10049	*11*	18	10. 89951	342	*11*	0	658	49
12	807	*12*	19	193	150	*12*	20	850	344	*12*	0	656	48
13	9. 09907	*13*	21	10. 90093	252	*13*	21	748	345	*13*	0	655	47
14	9. 10006	*14*	22	10. 89994	353	*14*	23	647	347	*14*	0	653	46
15	106	*15*	24	894	454	*15*	24	546	349	*15*	0	651	45
16	205	*16*	26	795	555	*16*	26	445	350	*16*	0	650	44
17	304	*17*	27	696	656	*17*	28	344	352	*17*	0	648	43
18	402	*18*	29	598	756	*18*	29	244	353	*18*	1	647	42
19	501	*19*	30	499	856	*19*	31	144	355	*19*	1	645	41
20	599	*20*	32	401	9. 10956	*20*	33	10. 89044	10. 00357	*20*	1	9. 99643	40
21	697	*21*	34	303	9. 11056	*21*	34	10. 88944	358	*21*	1	642	39
22	795	*22*	35	205	155	*22*	36	845	360	*22*	1	640	38
23	893	*23*	37	107	254	*23*	37	746	362	*23*	1	638	37
24	9. 10990	*24*	38	10. 89010	353	*24*	39	647	363	*24*	1	637	36
25	9. 11087	*25*	40	10. 88913	452	*25*	41	548	365	*25*	1	635	35
26	184	*26*	42	816	551	*26*	42	449	367	*26*	1	633	34
27	281	*27*	43	719	649	*27*	44	351	368	*27*	1	632	33
28	377	*28*	45	623	747	*28*	46	253	370	*28*	1	630	32
29	474	*29*	46	526	845	*29*	47	155	371	*29*	1	629	31
30	570	*30*	48	430	9. 11943	*30*	49	10. 88057	10. 00373	*30*	1	9. 99627	30
31	666	*31*	50	334	9. 12040	*31*	51	10. 87960	375	*31*	1	625	29
32	761	*32*	51	239	138	*32*	52	862	376	*32*	1	624	28
33	857	*33*	53	143	235	*33*	54	765	378	*33*	1	622	27
34	9. 11952	*34*	54	10. 88048	332	*34*	55	668	380	*34*	1	620	26
35	9. 12047	*35*	56	10. 87953	428	*35*	57	572	382	*35*	1	618	25
36	142	*36*	58	858	525	*36*	59	475	383	*36*	1	617	24
37	236	*37*	59	764	621	*37*	60	379	385	*37*	1	615	23
38	331	*38*	61	669	717	*38*	62	283	387	*38*	1	613	22
39	425	*39*	62	575	813	*39*	64	187	388	*39*	1	612	21
40	519	*40*	64	481	9. 12909	*40*	65	10. 87091	10. 00390	*40*	1	9. 99610	20
41	612	*41*	66	388	9. 13004	*41*	67	10. 86996	392	*41*	1	608	19
42	706	*42*	67	294	099	*42*	68	901	393	*42*	1	607	18
43	799	*43*	69	201	194	*43*	70	806	395	*43*	1	605	17
44	892	*44*	70	108	289	*44*	72	711	397	*44*	1	603	16
45	9. 12985	*45*	72	10. 87015	384	*45*	73	616	399	*45*	1	601	15
46	9. 13078	*46*	74	10. 86922	478	*46*	75	522	400	*46*	1	600	14
47	171	*47*	75	829	573	*47*	77	427	402	*47*	1	598	13
48	263	*48*	77	737	667	*48*	78	333	404	*48*	1	596	12
49	355	*49*	78	645	761	*49*	80	239	405	*49*	1	595	11
50	447	*50*	80	553	854	*50*	81	146	10. 00407	*50*	1	9. 99593	10
51	539	*51*	82	461	9. 13948	*51*	83	10. 86052	409	*51*	1	591	9
52	630	*52*	83	370	9. 14041	*52*	85	10. 85959	411	*52*	1	589	8
53	722	*53*	85	278	134	*53*	86	866	412	*53*	1	588	7
54	813	*54*	87	187	227	*54*	88	773	414	*54*	2	586	6
55	904	*55*	88	096	320	*55*	90	680	416	*55*	2	584	5
56	9. 13994	*56*	90	10. 86006	412	*56*	91	588	418	*56*	2	582	4
57	9. 14085	*57*	91	10. 85915	504	*57*	93	496	419	*57*	2	581	3
58	175	*58*	93	825	597	*58*	95	403	421	*58*	2	579	2
59	266	*59*	95	734	688	*59*	96	312	423	*59*	2	577	1
60	9. 14356	*60*	96	10. 85644	9. 14780	*60*	98	10. 85220	10. 00425	*60*	2	9. 99575	0
' ↑ 97° →	cos	"	Diff.	sec	cot	"	Diff.	tan	csc	"	Diff.	sin	' ↑ ← 82°

TABLE 33.

Logarithms of Trigonometric Functions.

8°→ ↓ ′	sin	″	Diff.	csc	tan	″	Diff.	cot	sec	″	Diff.	cos	←171° ↓ ′
0	9.14356	0	0	10.85644	9.14780	0	0	10.85220	10.00425	0	0	9.99575	60
1	445	1	1	555	872	1	1	128	426	1	0	574	59
2	535	2	3	465	9.14963	2	3	10.85037	428	2	0	572	58
3	624	3	4	376	9.15054	3	4	10.84946	430	3	0	570	57
4	714	4	6	286	145	4	6	855	432	4	0	568	56
5	803	5	7	197	236	5	7	764	434	5	0	566	55
6	891	6	8	109	327	6	9	673	435	6	0	565	54
7	9.14980	7	10	10.85020	417	7	10	583	437	7	0	563	53
8	9.15069	8	11	10.84931	508	8	12	492	439	8	0	561	52
9	157	9	13	843	598	9	13	402	441	9	0	559	51
10	245	10	14	755	688	10	14	312	10.00443	10	0	9.99557	50
11	333	11	16	667	777	11	16	223	444	11	0	556	49
12	421	12	17	579	867	12	17	133	446	12	0	554	48
13	508	13	18	492	9.15956	13	19	10.84044	448	13	0	552	47
14	596	14	20	404	9.16046	14	20	10.83954	450	14	0	550	46
15	683	15	21	317	135	15	22	865	452	15	0	548	45
16	770	16	23	230	224	16	23	776	454	16	1	546	44
17	857	17	24	143	312	17	25	688	455	17	1	545	43
18	9.15944	18	25	10.84056	401	18	26	599	457	18	1	543	42
19	9.16030	19	27	10.83970	489	19	27	511	459	19	1	541	41
20	116	20	28	884	577	20	29	423	10.00461	20	1	9.99539	40
21	203	21	30	797	665	21	30	335	463	21	1	537	39
22	289	22	31	711	753	22	32	247	465	22	1	535	38
23	374	23	32	626	841	23	33	159	467	23	1	533	37
24	460	24	34	540	9.16928	24	35	10.83072	468	24	1	532	36
25	545	25	35	455	9.17016	25	36	10.82984	470	25	1	530	35
26	631	26	37	369	103	26	37	897	472	26	1	528	34
27	716	27	38	284	190	27	39	810	474	27	1	526	33
28	801	28	39	199	277	28	40	723	476	28	1	524	32
29	886	29	41	114	363	29	42	637	478	29	1	522	31
30	9.16970	30	42	10.83030	450	30	43	550	10.00480	30	1	9.99520	30
31	9.17055	31	44	10.82945	536	31	45	464	482	31	1	518	29
32	139	32	45	861	622	32	46	378	483	32	1	517	28
33	223	33	47	777	708	33	48	292	485	33	1	515	27
34	307	34	48	693	794	34	49	206	487	34	1	513	26
35	391	35	49	609	880	35	50	120	489	35	1	511	25
36	474	36	51	526	9.17965	36	52	10.82035	491	36	1	509	24
37	558	37	52	442	9.18051	37	53	10.81949	493	37	1	507	23
38	641	38	54	359	136	38	55	864	495	38	1	505	22
39	724	39	55	276	221	39	56	779	497	39	1	503	21
40	807	40	56	193	306	40	58	694	10.00499	40	1	9.99501	20
41	890	41	58	110	391	41	59	609	501	41	1	499	19
42	9.17973	42	59	10.82027	475	42	61	525	503	42	1	497	18
43	9.18055	43	61	10.81945	560	43	62	440	505	43	1	495	17
44	137	44	62	863	644	44	63	356	506	44	1	494	16
45	220	45	63	780	728	45	65	272	508	45	1	492	15
46	302	46	65	698	812	46	66	188	510	46	1	490	14
47	383	47	66	617	896	47	68	104	512	47	1	488	13
48	465	48	68	535	9.18979	48	69	10.81021	514	48	2	486	12
49	547	49	69	453	9.19063	49	71	10.80937	516	49	2	484	11
50	628	50	71	372	146	50	72	854	10.00518	50	2	9.99482	10
51	709	51	72	291	229	51	74	771	520	51	2	480	9
52	790	52	73	210	312	52	75	688	522	52	2	478	8
53	871	53	75	129	395	53	76	605	524	53	2	476	7
54	9.18952	54	76	10.81048	478	54	78	522	526	54	2	474	6
55	9.19033	55	78	10.80967	561	55	79	439	528	55	2	472	5
56	113	56	79	887	643	56	81	357	530	56	2	470	4
57	193	57	80	807	725	57	82	275	532	57	2	468	3
58	273	58	82	727	807	58	84	193	534	58	2	466	2
59	353	59	83	647	889	59	85	111	536	59	2	464	1
60	9.19433	60	85	10.80567	9.19971	60	87	10.80029	10.00538	60	2	9.99462	0
′ ↑ 98°→	cos	″	Diff.	sec	cot	″	Diff.	tan	csc	″	Diff.	sin	′ ↑ ←81°

TABLE 33.

Logarithms of Trigonometric Functions.

9°→ ↓ ′	sin	″	Diff.	csc	tan	″	Diff.	cot	sec	″	Diff.	cos	←170° ↓ ′
0	9.19433	*0*	0	10.80567	9.19971	*0*	0	10.80029	10.00538	*0*	0	9.99462	60
1	513	*1*	1	487	9.20053	*1*	1	10.79947	540	*1*	0	460	59
2	592	*2*	3	408	134	*2*	3	866	542	*2*	0	458	58
3	672	*3*	4	328	216	*3*	4	784	544	*3*	0	456	57
4	751	*4*	5	249	297	*4*	5	703	546	*4*	0	454	56
5	830	*5*	6	170	378	*5*	6	622	548	*5*	0	452	55
6	909	*6*	8	091	459	*6*	8	541	550	*6*	0	450	54
7	9.19988	*7*	9	10.80012	540	*7*	9	460	552	*7*	0	448	53
8	9.20067	*8*	10	10.79933	621	*8*	10	379	554	*8*	0	446	52
9	145	*9*	11	855	701	*9*	12	299	556	*9*	0	444	51
10	223	*10*	13	777	782	*10*	13	218	10.00558	*10*	0	9.99442	50
11	302	*11*	14	698	862	*11*	14	138	560	*11*	0	440	49
12	380	*12*	15	620	9.20942	*12*	16	10.79058	562	*12*	0	438	48
13	458	*13*	16	542	9.21022	*13*	17	10.78978	564	*13*	0	436	47
14	9.20535	*14*	18	10.79465	102	*14*	18	898	566	*14*	0	434	46
15	613	*15*	19	387	182	*15*	19	818	568	*15*	1	432	45
16	691	*16*	20	309	261	*16*	21	739	571	*16*	1	429	44
17	768	*17*	21	232	341	*17*	22	659	573	*17*	1	427	43
18	845	*18*	23	155	420	*18*	23	580	575	*18*	1	425	42
19	922	*19*	24	078	9.21499	*19*	25	10.78501	577	*19*	1	423	41
20	9.20999	*20*	25	10.79001	578	*20*	26	422	10.00579	*20*	1	9.99421	40
21	9.21076	*21*	26	10.78924	657	*21*	27	343	581	*21*	1	419	39
22	153	*22*	28	847	736	*22*	28	264	583	*22*	1	417	38
23	229	*23*	29	771	814	*23*	30	186	585	*23*	1	415	37
24	306	*24*	30	694	893	*24*	31	107	587	*24*	1	413	36
25	382	*25*	31	618	9.21971	*25*	32	10.78029	589	*25*	1	411	35
26	458	*26*	33	542	9.22049	*26*	34	10 77951	591	*26*	1	409	34
27	9.21534	*27*	34	10 78466	127	*27*	35	873	593	*27*	1	407	33
28	610	*28*	35	390	205	*28*	36	795	596	*28*	1	404	32
29	685	*29*	37	315	283	*29*	38	717	598	*29*	1	402	31
30	761	*30*	38	239	361	*30*	39	639	10.00600	*30*	1	9.99400	30
31	836	*31*	39	164	438	*31*	40	562	602	*31*	1	398	29
32	912	*32*	40	088	9.22516	*32*	41	10.77484	604	*32*	1	396	28
33	9.21987	*33*	42	10.78013	593	*33*	43	407	606	*33*	1	394	27
34	9.22062	*34*	43	10.77938	670	*34*	44	330	608	*34*	1	392	26
35	137	*35*	44	863	747	*35*	45	253	610	*35*	1	390	25
36	211	*36*	45	789	824	*36*	47	176	612	*36*	1	388	24
37	286	*37*	47	714	901	*37*	48	099	615	*37*	1	385	23
38	361	*38*	48	639	9.22977	*38*	49	10.77023	617	*38*	1	383	22
39	435	*39*	49	565	9.23054	*39*	50	10.76946	619	*39*	1	381	21
40	9.22509	*40*	50	10.77491	130	*40*	52	870	10.00621	*40*	1	9.99379	20
41	583	*41*	52	417	206	*41*	53	794	623	*41*	1	377	19
42	657	*42*	53	343	283	*42*	54	717	625	*42*	1	375	18
43	731	*43*	54	269	359	*43*	56	641	628	*43*	2	372	17
44	805	*44*	55	195	435	*44*	57	565	630	*44*	2	370	16
45	878	*45*	57	122	9.23510	*45*	58	10.76490	632	*45*	2	368	15
46	9.22952	*46*	58	10.77048	586	*46*	60	414	634	*46*	2	366	14
47	9.23025	*47*	59	10.76975	661	*47*	61	339	636	*47*	2	364	13
48	098	*48*	60	902	737	*48*	62	263	638	*48*	2	362	12
49	171	*49*	62	829	812	*49*	63	188	641	*49*	2	359	11
50	244	*50*	63	756	887	*50*	65	113	10.00643	*50*	2	9.99357	10
51	317	*51*	64	683	9.23962	*51*	66	10.76038	645	*51*	2	355	9
52	390	*52*	65	610	9.24037	*52*	67	10.75963	647	*52*	2	353	8
53	462	*53*	67	538	112	*53*	69	888	649	*53*	2	351	7
54	9.23535	*54*	68	10.76465	186	*54*	70	814	652	*54*	2	348	6
55	607	*55*	69	393	261	*55*	71	739	654	*55*	2	346	5
56	679	*56*	71	321	335	*56*	73	665	656	*56*	2	344	4
57	752	*57*	72	248	410	*57*	74	590	658	*57*	2	342	3
58	823	*58*	73	177	484	*58*	75	516	660	*58*	2	340	2
59	895	*59*	74	105	558	*59*	76	442	663	*59*	2	337	1
60	9.23967	*60*	76	10.76033	9.24632	*60*	78	10.75368	10.00665	*60*	2	9.99335	0
′ ↑ 99°→	cos	″	Diff.	sec	cot	″	Diff.	tan	csc	″	Diff.	sin	′ ↑ ←80°

Logarithms of Trigonometric Functions.

10°→ ↓ '	sin	"	Diff.	csc	tan	"	Diff.	cot	sec	"	Diff.	cos	←169° ↓ '
0	9. 23967	*0*	0	10. 76033	**9. 24632**	*0*	0	**10. 75368**	10. 00665	*0*	0	**9. 99335**	60
1	9. 24039	*1*	1	10. 75961	706	*1*	1	294	667	*1*	0	333	59
2	110	*2*	2	890	779	*2*	**2**	221	669	*2*	0	331	58
3	181	*3*	3	819	853	*3*	4	147	672	*3*	0	328	57
4	253	*4*	**5**	747	9. 24926	*4*	5	074	674	*4*	0	326	56
5	324	*5*	6	676	9. 25000	*5*	6	10. 75000	676	*5*	0	324	55
6	395	*6*	7	605	073	*6*	7	10. 74927	678	*6*	0	322	54
7	9. 24466	*7*	8	10. 75534	146	*7*	8	854	681	*7*	0	319	53
8	536	*8*	9	464	219	*8*	**9**	781	683	*8*	0	317	52
9	607	*9*	10	393	292	*9*	11	708	685	*9*	0	315	51
10	677	*10*	**11**	323	365	*10*	12	635	10. 00687	*10*	0	9. 99313	**50**
11	748	*11*	13	252	9. 25437	*11*	13	563	690	*11*	0	310	49
12	818	*12*	14	182	510	*12*	14	10. 74490	692	*12*	0	308	48
13	888	*13*	15	112	582	*13*	15	418	694	*13*	1	306	47
14	**9. 24958**	*14*	16	**10. 75042**	655	*14*	**16**	345	696	*14*	1	304	46
15	**9. 25028**	*15*	17	**10. 74972**	727	*15*	18	273	699	*15*	1	301	45
16	098	*16*	18	902	799	*16*	19	201	701	*16*	1	299	44
17	168	*17*	19	832	871	*17*	20	129	703	*17*	1	297	43
18	237	*18*	**20**	763	9. 25943	*18*	21	10. 74057	706	*18*	1	294	42
19	307	*19*	22	693	9. 26015	*19*	22	10. 73985	708	*19*	1	292	41
20	376	*20*	23	624	086	*20*	**24**	914	10. 00710	*20*	1	9. 99290	**40**
21	445	*21*	24	555	158	*21*	25	842	712	*21*	1	288	39
22	9. 25514	*22*	25	10. 74486	229	*22*	26	771	715	*22*	1	285	38
23	583	*23*	26	417	301	*23*	27	699	717	*23*	1	283	37
24	652	*24*	27	348	372	*24*	28	628	719	*24*	1	281	36
25	721	*25*	28	279	9. 26443	*25*	29	10. 73557	722	*25*	1	278	35
26	790	*26*	**30**	210	514	*26*	**31**	486	724	*26*	**1**	276	34
27	858	*27*	31	142	585	*27*	32	415	726	*27*	1	274	33
28	927	*28*	32	073	655	*28*	33	345	729	*28*	1	271	32
29	9. 25995	*29*	33	10. 74005	726	*29*	34	274	731	*29*	1	269	31
30	**9. 26063**	*30*	34	**10. 73937**	797	*30*	35	203	10 00733	*30*	1	9. 99267	**30**
31	131	*31*	35	869	867	*31*	36	133	736	*31*	1	264	29
32	199	*32*	**36**	801	9. 26937	*32*	**38**	10. 73063	738	*32*	1	262	28
33	267	*33*	38	733	9. 27008	*33*	39	10. 72992	740	*33*	1	260	27
34	335	*34*	39	665	078	*34*	40	922	743	*34*	1	257	26
35	403	*35*	40	597	148	*35*	41	852	745	*35*	1	255	25
36	9. 26470	*36*	41	10. 73530	218	*36*	**42**	782	748	*36*	1	252	24
37	538	*37*	42	462	288	*37*	44	712	750	*37*	1	250	23
38	605	*38*	43	395	357	*38*	45	643	752	*38*	1	248	22
39	672	*39*	44	328	427	*39*	46	573	755	*39*	2	245	21
40	739	*40*	**45**	261	9. 27496	*40*	47	10. 72504	10. 00757	*40*	2	9. 99243	**20**
41	806	*41*	47	194	566	*41*	48	434	759	*41*	2	241	19
42	873	*42*	48	127	635	*42*	**49**	365	762	*42*	2	238	18
43	9. 26940	*43*	49	10. 73060	704	*43*	51	296	764	*43*	2	236	17
44	9. 27007	*44*	50	10. 72993	773	*44*	52	227	767	*44*	2	233	16
45	073	*45*	51	927	842	*45*	53	158	769	*45*	2	231	15
46	140	*46*	52	860	911	*46*	54	089	771	*46*	2	229	14
47	206	*47*	53	794	9. 27980	*47*	55	10. 72020	774	*47*	2	226	13
48	273	*48*	**55**	727	9. 28049	*48*	**56**	10. 71951	776	*48*	2	224	12
49	339	*49*	56	661	117	*49*	58	883	779	*49*	2	221	11
50	405	*50*	57	595	186	*50*	59	814	10. 00781	*50*	2	9. 99219	**10**
51	471	*51*	58	529	254	*51*	60	746	783	*51*	2	217	9
52	9. 27537	*52*	59	10. 72463	323	*52*	61	677	786	*52*	2	214	8
53	602	*53*	60	398	391	*53*	62	609	788	*53*	2	212	7
54	668	*54*	**61**	332	9. 28459	*54*	**63**	10. 71541	791	*54*	2	209	6
55	734	*55*	63	266	527	*55*	65	473	793	*55*	2	207	5
56	799	*56*	64	201	595	*56*	66	405	796	*56*	2	204	4
57	864	*57*	65	136	662	*57*	67	338	798	*57*	2	202	3
58	930	*58*	66	070	730	*58*	68	270	800	*58*	2	200	2
59	9. 27995	*59*	67	10. 72005	798	*59*	69	202	803	*59*	2	197	1
60	9. 28060	*60*	68	10. 71940	9. 28865	*60*	**71**	10. 71135	10. 00805	*60*	2	9. 99195	0
' ↑ 100°→	cos	"	Diff.	sec	cot	"	Diff.	tan	csc	"	Diff.	sin	' ↑ ←79°

TABLE 33.

Logarithms of Trigonometric Functions.

11° → ↓ ′	sin	″	Diff.	csc	tan	″	Diff.	cot	sec	″	Diff.	cos	← 168° ↓ ′
0	9.28060	*0*	0	10.71940	9.28865	*0*	0	10.71135	10.00805	*0*	0	9.99195	60
1	125	*1*	1	875	9.28933	*1*	1	067	808	*1*	0	192	59
2	190	*2*	2	810	9.29000	*2*	2	10.71000	810	*2*	0	190	58
3	254	*3*	3	746	067	*3*	3	10.70933	813	*3*	0	187	57
4	319	*4*	4	681	134	*4*	4	866	815	*4*	0	185	56
5	384	*5*	5	616	201	*5*	5	799	818	*5*	0	182	55
6	448	*6*	6	552	268	*6*	6	732	820	*6*	0	180	54
7	9.28512	*7*	7	10.71488	335	*7*	8	665	823	*7*	0	177	53
8	577	*8*	8	423	402	*8*	9	598	825	*8*	0	175	52
9	641	*9*	9	359	468	*9*	10	532	828	*9*	0	172	51
10	705	*10*	10	295	9.29535	*10*	11	10.70465	10.00830	*10*	0	9.99170	50
11	769	*11*	11	231	601	*11*	12	399	833	*11*	0	167	49
12	833	*12*	12	167	668	*12*	13	332	835	*12*	1	165	48
13	896	*13*	13	104	734	*13*	14	266	838	*13*	1	162	47
14	9.28960	*14*	14	10.71040	800	*14*	15	200	840	*14*	1	160	46
15	9.29024	*15*	16	10.70976	866	*15*	16	134	843	*15*	1	157	45
16	087	*16*	17	913	932	*16*	17	068	845	*16*	1	155	44
17	150	*17*	18	850	9.29998	*17*	18	10.70002	848	*17*	1	152	43
18	214	*18*	19	786	9.30064	*18*	19	10.69936	850	*18*	1	150	42
19	277	*19*	20	723	130	*19*	20	870	853	*19*	1	147	41
20	340	*20*	21	660	195	*20*	22	805	10.00855	*20*	1	9.99145	40
21	403	*21*	22	597	261	*21*	23	739	858	*21*	1	142	39
22	9.29466	*22*	23	10.70534	326	*22*	24	674	860	*22*	1	140	38
23	529	*23*	24	471	391	*23*	25	609	863	*23*	1	137	37
24	591	*24*	25	409	457	*24*	26	543	865	*24*	1	135	36
25	654	*25*	26	346	9.30522	*25*	27	10.69478	868	*25*	1	132	35
26	716	*26*	27	284	587	*26*	28	413	870	*26*	1	130	34
27	779	*27*	28	221	652	*27*	29	348	873	*27*	1	127	33
28	841	*28*	29	159	717	*28*	30	283	876	*28*	1	124	32
29	903	*29*	30	097	782	*29*	31	218	878	*29*	1	122	31
30	9.29966	*30*	31	10.70034	846	*30*	32	154	10.00881	*30*	1	9.99119	30
31	9.30028	*31*	32	10.69972	911	*31*	33	089	883	*31*	1	117	29
32	090	*32*	33	910	9.30975	*32*	35	10.69025	886	*32*	1	114	28
33	151	*33*	34	849	9.31040	*33*	36	10.68960	888	*33*	1	112	27
34	213	*34*	35	787	104	*34*	37	896	891	*34*	1	109	26
35	275	*35*	36	725	168	*35*	38	832	894	*35*	2	106	25
36	336	*36*	37	664	233	*36*	39	767	896	*36*	2	104	24
37	398	*37*	38	602	297	*37*	40	703	899	*37*	2	101	23
38	9.30459	*38*	39	10.69541	361	*38*	41	639	901	*38*	2	099	22
39	521	*39*	40	479	425	*39*	42	575	904	*39*	2	096	21
40	582	*40*	41	418	9.31489	*40*	43	10.68511	10.00907	*40*	2	9.99093	20
41	643	*41*	42	357	552	*41*	44	448	909	*41*	2	091	19
42	704	*42*	43	296	616	*42*	45	384	912	*42*	2	088	18
43	765	*43*	45	235	679	*43*	46	321	914	*43*	2	086	17
44	826	*44*	46	174	743	*44*	47	257	917	*44*	2	083	16
45	887	*45*	47	113	806	*45*	49	194	920	*45*	2	080	15
46	9.30947	*46*	48	10.69053	870	*46*	50	130	922	*46*	2	078	14
47	9.31008	*47*	49	10.68992	933	*47*	51	067	925	*47*	2	075	13
48	068	*48*	50	932	9.31996	*48*	52	10.68004	928	*48*	2	072	12
49	129	*49*	51	871	9.32059	*49*	53	10.67941	930	*49*	2	070	11
50	189	*50*	52	811	122	*50*	54	878	10.00933	*50*	2	9.99067	10
51	250	*51*	53	750	185	*51*	55	815	936	*51*	2	064	9
52	310	*52*	54	690	248	*52*	56	752	938	*52*	2	062	8
53	370	*53*	55	630	311	*53*	57	689	941	*53*	2	059	7
54	9.31430	*54*	56	10.68570	373	*54*	58	627	944	*54*	2	056	6
55	490	*55*	57	510	9.32436	*55*	59	10.67564	946	*55*	2	054	5
56	549	*56*	58	451	498	*56*	60	502	949	*56*	2	051	4
57	609	*57*	59	391	561	*57*	61	439	952	*57*	2	048	3
58	669	*58*	60	331	623	*58*	63	377	954	*58*	2	046	2
59	728	*59*	61	272	685	*59*	64	315	957	*59*	3	043	1
60	9.31788	*60*	62	10.68212	9.32747	*60*	65	10.67253	10.00960	*60*	3	9.99040	0
′ ↑ 101° →	cos	″	Diff.	sec	cot	″	Diff.	tan	csc	″	Diff.	sin	′ ↑ ← 78°

Logarithms of Trigonometric Functions.

12°→ ↓ ′	sin	″	Diff.	csc	tan	″	Diff.	cot	sec	″	Diff.	cos	←167° ↓ ′
0	9. **31788**	*0*	0	10. 68212	**9. 32747**	*0*	0	**10. 67253**	10. **00960**	*0*	0	9. **99040**	**60**
1	847	*1*	1	153	810	*1*	1	190	962	*1*	0	038	59
2	907	*2*	2	093	872	*2*	2	128	965	*2*	0	035	58
3	9. **31966**	*3*	3	10. **68034**	933	*3*	3	067	968	*3*	0	032	57
4	9. 32025	*4*	4	10. **67975**	9. 32995	*4*	4	10. 67005	970	*4*	0	030	56
5	084	*5*	5	916	9. **33057**	*5*	5	10. **66943**	973	*5*	0	027	55
6	143	*6*	6	857	119	*6*	6	881	976	*6*	0	024	54
7	202	*7*	7	798	180	*7*	7	820	10. 00978	*7*	0	9. 99022	53
8	261	*8*	8	739	242	*8*	8	758	981	*8*	0	019	52
9	319	*9*	9	681	303	*9*	9	697	984	*9*	0	016	51
10	378	*10*	**10**	622	365	*10*	10	635	987	*10*	0	013	**50**
11	437	*11*	10	563	426	*11*	11	574	989	*11*	1	011	49
12	9. 32495	*12*	11	10. 67505	9. 33487	*12*	12	10. 66513	992	*12*	1	008	48
13	553	*13*	12	447	548	*13*	13	452	995	*13*	1	005	47
14	612	*14*	13	388	609	*14*	14	391	10. **00998**	*14*	1	002	46
15	670	*15*	14	330	670	*15*	15	330	10. **01000**	*15*	1	9. **99000**	45
16	728	*16*	15	272	731	*16*	16	269	003	*16*	1	9. **98997**	44
17	786	*17*	16	214	792	*17*	17	208	006	*17*	1	994	43
18	844	*18*	17	156	853	*18*	18	147	009	*18*	1	991	42
19	902	*19*	18	098	913	*19*	19	087	011	*19*	1	989	41
20	9. 32960	*20*	19	10. **67040**	9. 33974	*20*	20	10. 66026	014	*20*	1	986	**40**
21	9. **33018**	*21*	20	10. **66982**	9. **34034**	*21*	21	10. **65966**	017	*21*	1	983	39
22	075	*22*	21	925	095	*22*	22	905	020	*22*	1	980	38
23	133	*23*	22	867	155	*23*	23	845	022	*23*	1	978	37
24	190	*24*	23	810	215	*24*	24	785	10. 01025	*24*	1	9. 98975	36
25	248	*25*	24	752	276	*25*	25	724	028	*25*	1	972	35
26	305	*26*	25	695	336	*26*	26	664	031	*26*	1	969	34
27	362	*27*	26	638	396	*27*	27	604	033	*27*	1	967	33
28	420	*28*	27	580	456	*28*	28	544	036	*28*	1	964	32
29	477	*29*	28	523	9. 34516	*29*	29	10. 65484	039	*29*	1	961	31
30	9. 33534	*30*	**29**	10. 66466	576	*30*	30	424	042	*30*	1	958	**30**
31	591	*31*	29	409	635	*31*	31	365	045	*31*	1	9. 98955	29
32	647	*32*	30	353	695	*32*	32	305	10. 01047	*32*	1	953	28
33	704	*33*	31	296	755	*33*	33	245	050	*33*	2	950	27
34	761	*34*	32	239	814	*34*	34	186	053	*34*	2	947	26
35	818	*35*	33	182	874	*35*	35	126	056	*35*	2	944	25
36	874	*36*	34	126	933	*36*	36	067	059	*36*	2	941	24
37	931	*37*	35	069	9. 34992	*37*	37	10. **65008**	062	*37*	2	938	23
38	9. **33987**	*38*	36	10. **66013**	9. **35051**	*38*	38	10. **64949**	10. 01064	*38*	2	9. 98936	22
39	9. **34043**	*39*	37	10. **65957**	111	*39*	39	889	067	*39*	2	933	21
40	100	*40*	38	900	170	*40*	40	830	070	*40*	2	930	**20**
41	156	*41*	39	844	229	*41*	41	771	073	*41*	2	927	19
42	212	*42*	40	788	288	*42*	42	712	076	*42*	2	924	18
43	268	*43*	41	732	347	*43*	43	653	079	*43*	2	921	17
44	324	*44*	42	676	405	*44*	44	595	081	*44*	2	919	16
45	380	*45*	43	620	464	*45*	45	536	10. 01084	*45*	2	9. 98916	15
46	436	*46*	44	564	9. 35523	*46*	46	10. 64477	087	*46*	2	913	14
47	491	*47*	45	509	581	*47*	47	419	090	*47*	2	910	13
48	9. 34547	*48*	46	10. 65453	640	*48*	48	360	093	*48*	2	907	12
49	602	*49*	47	398	698	*49*	49	302	096	*49*	2	904	11
50	658	*50*	**48**	342	757	*50*	50	243	099	*50*	2	901	**10**
51	713	*51*	48	287	815	*51*	51	185	102	*51*	2	898	9
52	769	*52*	49	231	873	*52*	52	127	10. 01104	*52*	2	9. 98896	8
53	824	*53*	50	176	931	*53*	53	069	107	*53*	2	893	7
54	879	*54*	51	121	9. **35989**	*54*	54	10. **64011**	110	*54*	3	890	6
55	934	*55*	52	066	9. **36047**	*55*	55	10. **63953**	113	*55*	3	887	5
56	9. **34989**	*56*	53	10. **65011**	105	*56*	56	895	116	*56*	3	884	4
57	9. **35044**	*57*	54	10. **64956**	163	*57*	57	837	119	*57*	3	881	3
58	099	*58*	55	901	221	*58*	58	779	122	*58*	3	878	2
59	154	*59*	56	846	279	*59*	59	721	125	*59*	3	875	1
60	9. 35209	*60*	57	10. 64791	9. 36336	*60*	60	10. 63664	10. **01128**	*60*	3	9. 98872	**0**
′ ↑ 102°→	cos	″	Diff.	sec	cot	″	Diff.	tan	csc	″	Diff.	sin	′ ↑ ←77°

TABLE 33.

Logarithms of Trigonometric Functions.

13°→ ↓ ′	sin	″	Diff.	csc	tan	″	Diff.	cot	sec	″	Diff.	cos	←166° ↓ ′
0	9. 35209	0	0	10. 64791	9. 36336	0	0	10. 63664	10. 01128	0	0	9. 98872	60
1	263	1	1	737	394	1	1	606	131	1	0	869	59
2	318	2	2	682	452	2	2	548	133	2	0	867	58
3	373	3	3	627	509	3	3	491	136	3	0	864	57
4	427	4	4	573	566	4	4	434	139	4	0	861	56
5	481	5	4	519	9. 36624	5	5	10. 63376	142	5	0	858	55
6	536	6	5	464	681	6	6	319	145	6	0	855	54
7	9. 35590	7	6	10. 64410	738	7	6	262	148	7	0	852	53
8	644	8	7	356	795	8	7	205	151	8	0	849	52
9	698	9	8	302	852	9	8	148	154	9	0	846	51
10	752	10	9	248	909	10	9	091	10. 01157	10	1	9. 98843	50
11	806	11	10	194	9. 36966	11	10	10. 63034	160	11	1	840	49
12	860	12	11	140	9. 37023	12	11	10. 62977	163	12	1	837	48
13	914	13	11	086	080	13	12	920	166	13	1	834	47
14	9. 35968	14	12	10. 64032	137	14	13	863	169	14	1	831	46
15	9. 36022	15	13	10. 63978	193	15	14	807	172	15	1	828	45
16	075	16	14	925	250	16	15	750	175	16	1	825	44
17	129	17	15	871	306	17	16	694	178	17	1	822	43
18	182	18	16	818	363	18	17	637	181	18	1	819	42
19	236	19	17	764	419	19	18	581	184	19	1	816	41
20	289	20	18	711	9. 37476	20	19	10. 62524	10. 01187	20	1	9. 98813	40
21	342	21	18	658	532	21	19	468	190	21	1	810	39
22	395	22	19	605	588	22	20	412	193	22	1	807	38
23	449	23	20	551	644	23	21	356	196	23	1	804	37
24	9. 36502	24	21	10. 63498	700	24	22	300	199	24	1	801	36
25	555	25	22	445	756	25	23	244	202	25	1	798	35
26	608	26	23	392	812	26	24	188	205	26	1	795	34
27	660	27	24	340	868	27	25	132	208	27	1	792	33
28	713	28	25	287	924	28	26	076	211	28	1	789	32
29	766	29	25	234	9. 37980	29	27	10. 62020	214	29	1	786	31
30	819	30	26	181	9. 38035	30	28	10. 61965	10. 01217	30	2	9. 98783	30
31	871	31	27	129	091	31	29	909	220	31	2	780	29
32	924	32	28	076	147	32	30	853	223	32	2	777	28
33	9. 36976	33	29	10. 63024	202	33	31	798	226	33	2	774	27
34	9. 37028	34	30	10. 62972	257	34	32	743	229	34	2	771	26
35	081	35	31	919	313	35	32	687	232	35	2	768	25
36	133	36	32	867	368	36	33	632	235	36	2	765	24
37	185	37	32	815	423	37	34	577	238	37	2	762	23
38	237	38	33	763	479	38	35	521	241	38	2	759	22
39	289	39	34	711	9. 38534	39	36	10. 61466	244	39	2	756	21
40	341	40	35	659	589	40	37	411	10. 01247	40	2	9. 98753	20
41	393	41	36	607	644	41	38	356	250	41	2	750	19
42	445	42	37	555	699	42	39	301	254	42	2	746	18
43	9. 37497	43	38	10. 62503	754	43	40	246	257	43	2	743	17
44	549	44	39	451	808	44	41	192	260	44	2	740	16
45	600	45	39	400	863	45	42	137	263	45	2	737	15
46	652	46	40	348	918	46	43	082	266	46	2	734	14
47	703	47	41	297	9. 38972	47	44	10. 61028	269	47	2	731	13
48	755	48	42	245	9. 39027	48	45	10. 60973	272	48	2	728	12
49	806	49	43	194	082	49	45	918	275	49	2	725	11
50	858	50	44	142	136	50	46	864	10. 01278	50	3	9. 98722	10
51	909	51	45	091	190	51	47	810	281	51	3	719	9
52	9. 37960	52	46	10. 62040	245	52	48	755	285	52	3	715	8
53	9. 38011	53	47	10. 61989	299	53	49	701	288	53	3	712	7
54	062	54	47	938	9. 39353	54	50	10. 60647	291	54	3	709	6
55	113	55	48	887	407	55	51	593	294	55	3	706	5
56	164	56	49	836	461	56	52	539	297	56	3	703	4
57	215	57	50	785	515	57	53	485	300	57	3	700	3
58	266	58	51	734	569	58	54	431	303	58	3	697	2
59	317	59	52	683	623	59	55	377	306	59	3	694	1
60	9. 38368	60	53	10. 61632	9. 39677	60	56	10. 60323	10. 01310	60	3	9. 98690	0
′ ↑ 103°→	cos	″	Diff.	sec	cot	″	Diff.	tan	csc	″	Diff.	sin	′ ↑ ←76°

TABLE 33.

Logarithms of Trigonometric Functions.

14°→ ′	sin	″	Diff.	csc	tan	″	Diff.	cot	sec	″	Diff.	cos ←165° ′
0	9. 38368	0	0	10. 61632	9. 39677	0	0	10. 60323	10. 01310	0	0	9. 98690	60
1	418	1	1	582	731	1	1	269	313	1	0	687	59
2	469	2	2	531	785	2	2	215	316	2	0	684	58
3	519	3	2	481	838	3	3	162	319	3	0	681	57
4	570	4	3	430	892	4	3	108	322	4	0	678	56
5	620	5	4	380	945	5	4	055	325	5	0	675	55
6	9. 38670	6	5	10. 61330	9. 39999	6	5	10. 60001	329	6	0	671	54
7	721	7	6	279	9. 40052	7	6	10. 59948	332	7	0	668	53
8	771	8	7	229	106	8	7	894	335	8	0	665	52
9	821	9	7	179	159	9	8	841	338	9	0	662	51
10	871	10	8	129	212	10	9	788	10. 01341	10	1	9. 98659	50
11	921	11	9	079	266	11	10	734	344	11	1	656	49
12	9. 38971	12	10	10. 61029	319	12	10	681	348	12	1	652	48
13	9. 39021	13	11	10. 60979	372	13	11	628	351	13	1	649	47
14	071	14	11	929	425	14	12	575	354	14	1	646	46
15	121	15	12	879	9. 40478	15	13	10. 59522	357	15	1	643	45
16	170	16	13	830	531	16	14	469	360	16	1	640	44
17	220	17	14	780	584	17	15	416	364	17	1	636	43
18	270	18	15	730	636	18	16	364	367	18	1	633	42
19	319	19	15	681	689	19	17	311	370	19	1	630	41
20	369	20	16	631	742	20	17	258	10. 01373	20	1	9. 98627	40
21	418	21	17	582	795	21	18	205	377	21	1	623	39
22	9. 39467	22	18	10. 60533	847	22	19	153	380	22	1	620	38
23	517	23	19	483	900	23	20	100	383	23	1	617	37
24	566	24	20	434	9. 40952	24	21	10. 59048	386	24	1	614	36
25	615	25	20	385	9. 41005	25	22	10. 58995	390	25	1	610	35
26	664	26	21	336	057	26	23	943	393	26	1	607	34
27	713	27	22	287	109	27	23	891	396	27	1	604	33
28	762	28	23	238	161	28	24	839	399	28	2	601	32
29	811	29	24	189	214	29	25	786	403	29	2	597	31
30	860	30	24	140	266	30	26	734	10. 01406	30	2	9. 98594	30
31	909	31	25	091	318	31	27	682	409	31	2	591	29
32	9. 39958	32	26	10. 60042	370	32	28	630	412	32	2	588	28
33	9. 40006	33	27	10. 59994	422	33	29	578	416	33	2	584	27
34	055	34	28	945	474	34	30	526	419	34	2	581	26
35	103	35	29	897	9. 41526	35	30	10. 58474	422	35	2	578	25
36	152	36	29	848	578	36	31	422	426	36	2	574	24
37	200	37	30	800	629	37	32	371	429	37	2	571	23
38	249	38	31	751	681	38	33	319	432	38	2	568	22
39	297	39	32	703	733	39	34	267	435	39	2	565	21
40	346	40	33	654	784	40	35	216	10. 01439	40	2	9. 98561	20
41	394	41	33	606	836	41	36	164	442	41	2	558	19
42	442	42	34	558	887	42	36	113	445	42	2	555	18
43	9. 40490	43	35	10. 59510	939	43	37	061	449	43	2	551	17
44	538	44	36	462	9. 41990	44	38	10. 58010	452	44	2	548	16
45	586	45	37	414	9. 42041	45	39	10. 57959	455	45	2	545	15
46	634	46	37	366	093	46	40	907	459	46	3	541	14
47	682	47	38	318	144	47	41	856	462	47	3	538	13
48	730	48	39	270	195	48	42	805	465	48	3	535	12
49	778	49	40	222	246	49	43	754	469	49	3	531	11
50	825	50	41	175	297	50	43	703	10. 01472	50	3	9. 98528	10
51	873	51	42	127	348	51	44	652	475	51	3	525	9
52	921	52	42	079	399	52	45	601	479	52	3	521	8
53	9. 40968	53	43	10. 59032	9. 42450	53	46	10. 57550	482	53	3	518	7
54	9. 41016	54	44	10. 58984	501	54	47	499	485	54	3	515	6
55	063	55	45	937	552	55	48	448	489	55	3	511	5
56	111	56	46	889	603	56	49	397	492	56	3	508	4
57	158	57	46	842	653	57	50	347	495	57	3	505	3
58	205	58	47	795	704	58	50	296	499	58	3	501	2
59	252	59	48	748	755	59	51	245	502	59	3	498	1
60	9. 41300	60	49	10. 58700	9. 42805	60	52	10. 57195	10. 01506	60	3	9. 98494	0
′ 104°→	cos	″	Diff.	sec	cot	″	Diff.	tan	csc	″	Diff.	sin	←75° ′

TABLE 33.

Logarithms of Trigonometric Functions.

15°→ ↓ ′	sin	″	Diff.	csc	tan	″	Diff.	cot	sec	″	Diff.	cos ←164°	↓ ′
0	9. 41300	0	0	10. 58700	9. 42805	0	0	10. 57195	10. 01506	0	0	9. 98494	60
1	347	1	1	653	856	1	1	144	509	1	0	491	59
2	394	2	2	606	906	2	2	094	512	2	0	488	58
3	441	3	2	559	9. 42957	3	2	10. 57043	516	3	0	484	57
4	488	4	3	512	9. 43007	4	3	10. 56993	519	4	0	481	56
5	535	5	4	465	057	5	4	943	523	5	0	477	55
6	582	6	5	418	108	6	5	892	526	6	0	474	54
7	9. 41628	7	5	10. 58372	158	7	6	842	529	7	0	471	53
8	675	8	6	325	208	8	7	792	533	8	0	467	52
9	722	9	7	278	258	9	7	742	536	9	1	464	51
10	768	10	8	232	308	10	8	692	10. 01540	10	1	9. 98460	50
11	815	11	8	185	358	11	9	642	543	11	1	457	49
12	861	12	9	139	408	12	10	592	547	12	1	453	48
13	908	13	10	092	458	13	11	542	550	13	1	450	47
14	9. 41954	14	11	10. 58046	9. 43508	14	11	10. 56492	553	14	1	447	46
15	9. 42001	15	11	10. 57999	558	15	12	442	557	15	1	443	45
16	047	16	12	953	607	16	13	393	560	16	1	440	44
17	093	17	13	907	657	17	14	343	564	17	1	436	43
18	140	18	14	860	707	18	15	293	567	18	1	433	42
19	186	19	14	814	756	19	16	244	571	19	1	429	41
20	232	20	15	768	806	20	16	194	10. 01574	20	1	9. 98426	40
21	278	21	16	722	855	21	17	145	578	21	1	422	39
22	324	22	17	676	905	22	18	095	581	22	1	419	38
23	370	23	17	630	9. 43954	23	19	10. 56046	585	23	1	415	37
24	416	24	18	584	9. 44004	24	20	10. 55996	588	24	1	412	36
25	9 42461	25	19	10. 57539	053	25	20	947	591	25	1	409	35
26	507	26	20	493	102	26	21	898	595	26	2	405	34
27	553	27	21	447	151	27	22	849	598	27	2	402	33
28	599	28	21	401	201	28	23	799	602	28	2	398	32
29	644	29	22	356	250	29	24	750	605	29	2	395	31
30	690	30	23	310	299	30	25	701	10. 01609	30	2	9. 98391	30
31	735	31	24	265	348	31	25	652	612	31	2	388	29
32	781	32	24	219	397	32	26	603	616	32	2	384	28
33	826	33	25	174	446	33	27	554	619	33	2	381	27
34	872	34	26	128	9. 44495	34	28	10. 55505	623	34	2	377	26
35	917	35	27	083	544	35	29	456	627	35	2	373	25
36	9. 42962	36	27	10. 57038	592	36	29	408	630	36	2	370	24
37	9. 43008	37	28	10 56992	641	37	30	359	634	37	2	366	23
38	053	38	29	947	690	38	31	310	637	38	2	363	22
39	098	39	30	902	738	39	32	262	641	39	2	359	21
40	143	40	30	857	787	40	33	213	10. 01644	40	2	9. 98356	20
41	188	41	31	812	836	41	34	164	648	41	2	352	19
42	233	42	32	767	884	42	34	116	651	42	2	349	18
43	278	43	33	722	933	43	35	067	655	43	3	345	17
44	323	44	33	677	9. 44981	44	36	10. 55019	658	44	3	342	16
45	367	45	34	633	9. 45029	45	37	10. 54971	662	45	3	338	15
46	412	46	35	588	078	46	38	922	666	46	3	334	14
47	457	47	36	543	126	47	38	874	669	47	3	331	13
48	9. 43502	48	36	10. 56498	174	48	39	826	673	48	3	327	12
49	546	49	37	454	222	49	40	778	676	49	3	324	11
50	591	50	38	409	271	50	41	729	10. 01680	50	3	9. 98320	10
51	635	51	39	365	319	51	42	681	683	51	3	317	9
52	680	52	39	320	367	52	43	633	687	52	3	313	8
53	724	53	40	276	9. 45415	53	43	10. 54585	691	53	3	309	7
54	769	54	41	231	463	54	44	537	694	54	3	306	6
55	813	55	42	187	511	55	45	489	698	55	3	302	5
56	857	56	43	143	559	56	46	441	701	56	3	299	4
57	901	57	43	099	606	57	47	394	705	57	3	295	3
58	946	58	44	054	654	58	47	346	709	58	3	291	2
59	9. 43990	59	45	10. 56010	702	59	48	298	712	59	3	288	1
60	9. 44034	60	46	10. 55966	9. 45750	60	49	10. 54250	10. 01716	60	4	9. 98284	0
′ ↑ 105°→	cos	″	Diff.	sec	cot	″	Diff.	tan	csc	″	Diff.	sin ←74°	′ ↑

TABLE 33.

Logarithms of Trigonometric Functions.

16°→ ↓ ′	sin	″	Diff.	csc	tan	″	Diff.	cot	sec	″	Diff.	cos	←163° ↓ ′
0	9. 44034	0	0	10. 55966	9. 45750	0	0	10. 54250	10. 01716	0	0	9. 98284	60
1	078	1	1	922	797	1	1	203	719	1	0	281	59
2	122	2	1	878	845	2	2	155	723	2	0	277	58
3	166	3	2	834	892	3	2	108	727	3	0	273	57
4	210	4	3	790	940	4	3	060	730	4	0	270	56
5	253	5	4	747	9. 45987	5	4	10. 54013	734	5	0	266	55
6	297	6	4	703	9. 46035	6	5	10. 53965	738	6	0	262	54
7	9. 44341	7	5	10. 55659	082	7	5	918	741	7	0	259	53
8	385	8	6	615	130	8	6	870	745	8	0	255	52
9	428	9	6	572	177	9	7	823	749	9	1	251	51
10	472	10	7	528	224	10	8	776	10. 01752	10	1	9. 98248	50
11	516	11	8	484	271	11	9	729	756	11	1	244	49
12	559	12	9	441	319	12	9	681	760	12	1	240	48
13	602	13	9	398	366	13	10	634	763	13	1	237	47
14	646	14	10	354	413	14	11	587	767	14	1	233	46
15	9. 44689	15	11	10. 55311	460	15	12	540	771	15	1	229	45
16	733	16	11	267	9. 46507	16	12	10. 53493	774	16	1	226	44
17	776	17	12	224	554	17	13	446	778	17	1	222	43
18	819	18	13	181	601	18	14	399	782	18	1	218	42
19	862	19	14	138	648	19	15	352	785	19	1	215	41
20	905	20	14	095	694	20	15	306	10. 01789	20	1	9. 98211	40
21	948	21	15	052	741	21	16	259	793	21	1	207	39
22	9. 44992	22	16	10. 55008	788	22	17	212	796	22	1	204	38
23	9. 45035	23	16	10. 54965	835	23	18	165	800	23	1	200	37
24	077	24	17	923	881	24	19	119	804	24	1	196	36
25	120	25	18	880	928	25	19	072	808	25	2	192	35
26	163	26	18	837	9. 46975	26	20	10. 53025	811	26	2	189	34
27	206	27	19	794	9. 47021	27	21	10. 52979	815	27	2	185	33
28	249	28	20	751	068	28	22	932	819	28	2	181	32
29	292	29	21	708	114	29	22	886	823	29	2	177	31
30	9. 45334	30	21	10. 54666	160	30	23	840	10. 01826	30	2	9. 98174	30
31	377	31	22	623	207	31	24	793	830	31	2	170	29
32	419	32	23	581	253	32	25	747	834	32	2	166	28
33	462	33	23	538	299	33	26	701	838	33	2	162	27
34	504	34	24	496	346	34	26	654	841	34	2	159	26
35	547	35	25	453	392	35	27	608	845	35	2	155	25
36	589	36	26	411	438	36	28	562	849	36	2	151	24
37	632	37	26	368	484	37	29	516	853	37	2	147	23
38	9. 45674	38	27	10. 54326	9. 47530	38	29	10. 52470	856	38	2	144	22
39	716	39	28	284	576	39	30	424	860	39	2	140	21
40	758	40	28	242	622	40	31	378	10. 01864	40	2	9. 98136	20
41	801	41	29	199	668	41	32	332	868	41	3	132	19
42	843	42	30	157	714	42	32	286	871	42	3	129	18
43	885	43	31	115	760	43	33	240	875	43	3	125	17
44	927	44	31	073	806	44	34	194	879	44	3	121	16
45	9. 45969	45	32	10. 54031	852	45	35	148	883	45	3	117	15
46	9. 46011	46	33	10. 53989	897	46	36	103	887	46	3	113	14
47	053	47	33	947	943	47	36	057	890	47	3	110	13
48	095	48	34	905	9. 47989	48	37	10. 52011	894	48	3	106	12
49	136	49	35	864	9. 48035	49	38	10. 51965	898	49	3	102	11
50	178	50	36	822	080	50	39	920	10. 01902	50	3	9. 98098	10
51	220	51	36	780	126	51	39	874	906	51	3	094	9
52	262	52	37	738	171	52	40	829	910	52	3	090	8
53	9. 46303	53	38	10. 53697	217	53	41	783	913	53	3	087	7
54	345	54	38	655	262	54	42	738	917	54	3	083	6
55	386	55	39	614	307	55	43	693	921	55	3	079	5
56	428	56	40	572	353	56	43	647	925	56	3	075	4
57	469	57	41	531	398	57	44	602	929	57	4	071	3
58	511	58	41	489	443	58	45	557	933	58	4	067	2
59	552	59	42	448	489	59	46	511	937	59	4	063	1
60	9. 46594	60	43	10. 53406	9. 48534	60	46	10. 51466	10. 01940	60	4	9. 98060	0
′ ↑ 106°→	cos	″	Diff.	sec	cot	″	Diff.	tan	csc	″	Diff.	sin	′ ↑ ←73°

TABLE 33.

Logarithms of Trigonometric Functions.

17°→ ↓ ′	sin	″	Diff.	csc	tan	″	Diff.	cot	sec	″	Diff.	cos ←162°	↓ ′
0	9. 46594	0	0	10. 53406	9. 48534	0	0	10. 51466	10. 01940	0	0	9. 98060	60
1	635	1	1	365	579	1	1	421	944	1	0	056	59
2	676	2	1	324	624	2	1	376	948	2	0	052	58
3	717	3	2	283	669	3	2	331	952	3	0	048	57
4	758	4	3	242	714	4	3	286	956	4	0	044	56
5	800	5	3	200	759	5	4	241	960	5	0	040	55
6	841	6	4	159	804	6	4	196	964	6	0	036	54
7	882	7	5	118	849	7	5	151	10. 01968	7	0	9. 98032	53
8	923	8	5	077	894	8	6	106	971	8	1	029	52
9	9. 46964	9	6	10. 53036	939	9	7	061	975	9	1	025	51
10	9. 47005	10	7	10. 52995	9. 48984	10	7	10. 51016	979	10	1	021	50
11	045	11	7	955	9. 49029	11	8	10. 50971	983	11	1	017	49
12	086	12	8	914	073	12	9	927	987	12	1	013	48
13	127	13	9	873	118	13	10	882	991	13	1	009	47
14	168	14	9	832	163	14	10	837	995	14	1	005	46
15	209	15	10	791	207	15	11	793	10. 01999	15	1	9. 98001	45
16	249	16	11	751	252	16	12	748	10. 02003	16	1	9. 97997	44
17	290	17	11	710	296	17	12	704	007	17	1	993	43
18	9. 47330	18	12	10. 52670	341	18	13	659	011	18	1	989	42
19	371	19	13	629	385	19	14	615	014	19	1	986	41
20	411	20	13	589	430	20	15	570	018	20	1	982	40
21	452	21	14	548	9. 49474	21	15	10. 50526	022	21	1	978	39
22	492	22	15	508	519	22	16	481	026	22	1	974	38
23	533	23	15	467	563	23	17	437	030	23	2	970	37
24	573	24	16	427	607	24	18	393	10. 02034	24	2	9. 97966	36
25	613	25	17	387	652	25	18	348	038	25	2	962	35
26	9. 47654	26	17	10. 52346	696	26	19	304	042	26	2	958	34
27	694	27	18	306	740	27	20	260	046	27	2	954	33
28	734	28	19	266	784	28	21	216	050	28	2	950	32
29	774	29	19	226	828	29	21	172	054	29	2	946	31
30	814	30	20	186	872	30	22	128	058	30	2	942	30
31	854	31	21	146	916	31	23	084	062	31	2	938	29
32	894	32	21	106	9. 49960	32	24	10. 50040	066	32	2	934	28
33	934	33	22	066	9. 50004	33	24	10. 49996	10. 02070	33	2	9. 97930	27
34	9. 47974	34	23	10. 52026	048	34	25	952	074	34	2	926	26
35	9. 48014	35	23	10. 51986	092	35	26	908	078	35	2	922	25
36	054	36	24	946	136	36	26	864	082	36	2	918	24
37	094	37	25	906	180	37	27	820	086	37	2	914	23
38	133	38	25	867	223	38	28	777	090	38	3	910	22
39	173	39	26	827	267	39	29	733	094	39	3	906	21
40	213	40	27	787	311	40	29	689	098	40	3	902	20
41	252	41	27	748	355	41	30	645	102	41	3	898	19
42	292	42	28	708	398	42	31	602	10. 02106	42	3	9. 97894	18
43	9. 48332	43	29	10. 51668	442	43	32	558	110	43	3	890	17
44	371	44	29	629	9. 50485	44	32	10. 49515	114	44	3	886	16
45	411	45	30	589	529	45	33	471	118	45	3	882	15
46	450	46	31	550	572	46	34	428	122	46	3	878	14
47	490	47	31	510	616	47	35	384	126	47	3	874	13
48	529	48	32	471	659	48	35	341	130	48	3	870	12
49	568	49	33	432	703	49	36	297	134	49	3	866	11
50	607	50	33	393	746	50	37	254	139	50	3	861	10
51	9. 48647	51	34	10. 51353	789	51	37	211	10. 02143	51	3	9. 97857	9
52	686	52	35	314	833	52	38	167	147	52	3	853	8
53	725	53	35	275	876	53	39	124	151	53	4	849	7
54	764	54	36	236	919	54	40	081	155	54	4	845	6
55	803	55	37	197	9. 50962	55	40	10. 49038	159	55	4	841	5
56	842	56	37	158	9. 51005	56	41	10. 48995	163	56	4	837	4
57	881	57	38	119	048	57	42	952	167	57	4	833	3
58	920	58	39	080	092	58	43	908	171	58	4	829	2
59	959	59	39	041	135	59	43	865	175	59	4	825	1
60	9. 48998	60	40	10. 51002	9. 51178	60	44	10. 48822	10. 02179	60	4	9. 97821	0
′ ↑ 107°→	cos	″	Diff.	sec	cot	″	Diff.	tan	csc	″	Diff.	sin ←72°	′ ↑

TABLE 33.

Logarithms of Trigonometric Functions.

18°→ ↓ ′	sin	″	Diff.	csc	tan	″	Diff.	cot	sec	″	Diff.	cos	←161° ↓ ′
0	9. 48998	0	0	10. 51002	9. 51178	0	0	10. 48822	10. 02179	0	0	9. 97821	60
1	9. 49037	1	1	10. 50963	221	1	1	779	183	1	0	817	59
2	076	2	1	924	264	2	1	736	188	2	0	812	58
3	115	3	2	885	306	3	2	694	192	3	0	808	57
4	153	4	3	847	349	4	3	651	196	4	0	804	56
5	192	5	3	808	392	5	3	608	200	5	0	800	55
6	231	6	4	769	435	6	4	565	204	6	0	796	54
7	269	7	4	731	478	7	5	522	208	7	0	792	53
8	308	8	5	692	520	8	6	480	212	8	1	788	52
9	347	9	6	653	563	9	6	437	216	9	1	784	51
10	9. 49385	10	6	10. 50615	9. 51606	10	7	10. 48394	10. 02221	10	1	9. 97779	50
11	424	11	7	576	648	11	8	352	225	11	1	775	49
12	462	12	8	538	691	12	8	309	229	12	1	771	48
13	500	13	8	500	734	13	9	266	233	13	1	767	47
14	539	14	9	461	776	14	10	224	237	14	1	763	46
15	577	15	9	423	819	15	10	181	241	15	1	759	45
16	615	16	10	385	861	16	11	139	246	16	1	754	44
17	654	17	11	346	903	17	12	097	250	17	1	750	43
18	9. 49692	18	11	10. 50308	946	18	13	054	254	18	1	746	42
19	730	19	12	270	9. 51988	19	13	10. 48012	258	19	1	742	41
20	768	20	13	232	9. 52031	20	14	10. 47969	10. 02262	20	1	9. 97738	40
21	806	21	13	194	073	21	15	927	266	21	1	734	39
22	844	22	14	156	115	22	15	885	271	22	2	729	38
23	882	23	14	118	157	23	16	843	275	23	2	725	37
24	920	24	15	080	200	24	17	800	279	24	2	721	36
25	958	25	16	042	242	25	17	758	283	25	2	717	35
26	9. 49996	26	16	10. 50004	284	26	18	716	287	26	2	713	34
27	9. 50034	27	17	10. 49966	9. 52326	27	19	10. 47674	292	27	2	708	33
28	072	28	18	928	368	28	20	632	296	28	2	704	32
29	110	29	18	890	410	29	20	590	300	29	2	700	31
30	148	30	19	852	452	30	21	548	10. 02304	30	2	9. 97696	30
31	185	31	20	815	494	31	22	506	309	31	2	691	29
32	223	32	20	777	536	32	22	464	313	32	2	687	28
33	261	33	21	739	578	33	23	422	317	33	2	683	27
34	298	34	21	702	620	34	24	380	321	34	2	679	26
35	9. 50336	35	22	10. 49664	9. 52661	35	24	10. 47339	326	35	2	674	25
36	374	36	23	626	703	36	25	297	330	36	3	670	24
37	411	37	23	589	745	37	26	255	334	37	3	666	23
38	449	38	24	551	787	38	27	213	338	38	3	662	22
39	486	39	25	514	829	39	27	171	343	39	3	657	21
40	523	40	25	477	870	40	28	130	10. 02347	40	3	9. 97653	20
41	561	41	26	439	912	41	29	088	351	41	3	649	19
42	598	42	26	402	953	42	29	047	355	42	3	645	18
43	635	43	27	365	9. 52995	43	30	10. 47005	360	43	3	640	17
44	9. 50673	44	28	10. 49327	9. 53037	44	31	10. 46963	364	44	3	636	16
45	710	45	28	290	078	45	31	922	368	45	3	632	15
46	747	46	29	253	120	46	32	880	372	46	3	628	14
47	784	47	30	216	161	47	33	839	377	47	3	623	13
48	821	48	30	179	202	48	34	798	381	48	3	619	12
49	858	49	31	142	244	49	34	756	385	49	3	615	11
50	896	50	31	104	285	50	35	715	10. 02390	50	4	9. 97610	10
51	933	51	32	067	327	51	36	673	394	51	4	606	9
52	9. 50970	52	33	10. 49030	9. 53368	52	36	10. 46632	398	52	4	602	8
53	9. 51007	53	33	10. 48993	409	53	37	591	403	53	4	597	7
54	043	54	34	957	450	54	38	550	407	54	4	593	6
55	080	55	35	920	492	55	38	508	411	55	4	589	5
56	117	56	35	883	533	56	39	467	416	56	4	584	4
57	154	57	36	846	574	57	40	426	420	57	4	580	3
58	191	58	37	809	615	58	41	385	424	58	4	576	2
59	227	59	37	773	656	59	41	344	429	59	4	571	1
60	9. 51264	60	38	10. 48736	9. 53697	60	42	10. 46303	10. 02433	60	4	9. 97567	0
′ ↑ 108°→	cos	″	Diff.	sec	cot	″	Diff.	tan	csc	″	Diff.	sin	←71° ↑ ′

TABLE 33.

Logarithms of Trigonometric Functions.

19° → ↓ ′	sin	″	Diff.	csc	tan	″	Diff.	cot	sec	″	Diff.	cos	← 160° ↓ ′
0	9. 51264	0	0	10. 48736	9. 53697	0	0	10. 46303	10. 02433	0	0	9. 97567	60
1	301	1	1	699	738	1	1	262	437	1	0	563	59
2	338	2	1	662	779	2	1	221	442	2	0	558	58
3	374	3	2	626	820	3	2	180	446	3	0	554	57
4	411	4	2	589	861	4	3	139	450	4	0	550	56
5	447	5	3	553	902	5	3	098	455	5	0	545	55
6	484	6	4	516	943	6	4	057	459	6	0	541	54
7	520	7	4	480	9. 53984	7	5	10. 46016	464	7	1	536	53
8	557	8	5	443	9. 54025	8	5	10. 45975	468	8	1	532	52
9	593	9	5	407	065	9	6	935	472	9	1	528	51
10	9. 51629	10	6	10. 48371	106	10	7	894	10. 02477	10	1	9. 97523	50
11	666	11	7	334	147	11	7	853	481	11	1	519	49
12	702	12	7	298	187	12	8	813	485	12	1	515	48
13	738	13	8	262	228	13	9	772	490	13	1	510	47
14	774	14	8	226	269	14	9	731	494	14	1	506	46
15	811	15	9	189	309	15	10	691	499	15	1	501	45
16	847	16	10	153	9. 54350	16	11	10. 45650	503	16	1	497	44
17	883	17	10	117	390	17	11	610	508	17	1	492	43
18	919	18	11	081	431	18	12	569	512	18	1	488	42
19	955	19	11	045	471	19	13	529	516	19	1	484	41
20	9. 51991	20	12	10. 48009	512	20	13	488	10. 02521	20	1	9. 97479	40
21	9. 52027	21	12	10. 47973	552	21	14	448	525	21	2	475	39
22	063	22	13	937	593	22	15	407	530	22	2	470	38
23	099	23	14	901	633	23	15	367	534	23	2	466	37
24	135	24	14	865	9. 54673	24	16	10. 45327	539	24	2	461	36
25	171	25	15	829	714	25	17	286	543	25	2	457	35
26	207	26	15	793	754	26	17	246	547	26	2	453	34
27	242	27	16	758	794	27	18	206	552	27	2	448	33
28	278	28	17	722	835	28	19	165	556	28	2	444	32
29	314	29	17	686	875	29	19	125	561	29	2	439	31
30	9. 52350	30	18	10. 47650	915	30	20	085	10. 02565	30	2	9. 97435	30
31	385	31	18	615	955	31	21	045	570	31	2	430	29
32	421	32	19	579	9. 54995	32	21	10. 45005	574	32	2	426	28
33	456	33	20	544	9. 55035	33	22	10. 44965	579	33	2	421	27
34	492	34	20	508	075	34	23	925	583	34	3	417	26
35	527	35	21	473	115	35	23	885	588	35	3	412	25
36	563	36	21	437	155	36	24	845	592	36	3	408	24
37	598	37	22	402	195	37	25	805	597	37	3	403	23
38	634	38	23	366	235	38	25	765	601	38	3	399	22
39	9. 52669	39	23	10. 47331	275	39	26	725	606	39	3	394	21
40	705	40	24	295	315	40	27	685	10. 02610	40	3	9. 97390	20
41	740	41	24	260	9. 55355	41	27	10. 44645	615	41	3	385	19
42	775	42	25	225	395	42	28	605	619	42	3	381	18
43	811	43	26	189	434	43	29	566	624	43	3	376	17
44	846	44	26	154	474	44	29	526	628	44	3	372	16
45	881	45	27	119	514	45	30	486	633	45	3	367	15
46	916	46	27	084	554	46	31	446	637	46	3	363	14
47	951	47	28	049	593	47	31	407	642	47	3	358	13
48	9. 52986	48	29	10. 47014	633	48	32	367	647	48	4	353	12
49	9. 53021	49	29	10. 46979	9. 55673	49	33	10. 44327	651	49	4	349	11
50	056	50	30	944	712	50	33	288	10. 02656	50	4	9. 97344	10
51	092	51	30	908	752	51	34	248	660	51	4	340	9
52	126	52	31	874	791	52	35	209	665	52	4	335	8
53	161	53	32	839	831	53	35	169	669	53	4	331	7
54	196	54	32	804	870	54	36	130	674	54	4	326	6
55	231	55	33	769	910	55	37	090	678	55	4	322	5
56	266	56	33	734	949	56	37	051	683	56	4	317	4
57	301	57	34	699	9. 55989	57	38	10. 44011	688	57	4	312	3
58	336	58	34	664	9. 56028	58	39	10. 43972	692	58	4	308	2
59	370	59	35	630	067	59	39	933	697	59	4	303	1
60	9. 53405	60	36	10. 46595	9. 56107	60	40	10. 43893	10. 02701	60	4	9. 97299	0
′ ↑ 109° →	cos	″	Diff.	sec	cot	″	Diff.	tan	csc	″	Diff.	sin	′ ↑ ← 70°

TABLE 33.

Logarithms of Trigonometric Functions.

20°→ ↓ ′	sin	″ Diff.		csc	tan	″ Diff.		cot	sec	″ Diff.		cos ←159°	↓ ′
0	9.53405	0	0	10.46595	9.56107	0	0	10.43893	10.02701	0	0	9.97299	60
1	440	1	1	560	146	1	1	854	706	1	0	294	59
2	475	2	1	525	185	2	1	815	711	2	0	289	58
3	509	3	2	491	224	3	2	776	715	3	0	285	57
4	544	4	2	456	264	4	3	736	720	4	0	280	56
5	578	5	3	422	303	5	3	697	724	5	0	276	55
6	613	6	3	387	342	6	4	658	729	6	0	271	54
7	647	7	4	353	9.56381	7	4	10.43619	734	7	1	266	53
8	682	8	5	318	420	8	5	580	738	8	1	262	52
9	9.53716	9	5	10.46284	459	9	6	541	743	9	1	257	51
10	751	10	6	249	498	10	6	502	10.02748	10	1	9.97252	50
11	785	11	6	215	537	11	7	463	752	11	1	248	49
12	819	12	7	181	576	12	8	424	757	12	1	243	48
13	854	13	7	146	615	13	8	385	762	13	1	238	47
14	888	14	8	112	654	14	9	346	766	14	1	234	46
15	922	15	8	078	9.56693	15	10	10.43307	771	15	1	229	45
16	957	16	9	043	732	16	10	268	776	16	1	224	44
17	9.53991	17	10	10.46009	771	17	11	229	780	17	1	220	43
18	9.54025	18	10	10.45975	810	18	12	190	785	18	1	215	42
19	059	19	11	941	849	19	12	151	790	19	1	210	41
20	093	20	11	907	887	20	13	113	10.02794	20	2	9.97206	40
21	127	21	12	873	926	21	13	074	799	21	2	201	39
22	161	22	12	839	9.56965	22	14	10.43035	804	22	2	196	38
23	195	23	13	805	9.57004	23	15	10.42996	808	23	2	192	37
24	229	24	14	771	042	24	15	958	813	24	2	187	36
25	263	25	14	737	081	25	16	919	818	25	2	182	35
26	9.54297	26	15	10.45703	120	26	17	880	822	26	2	178	34
27	331	27	15	669	158	27	17	842	827	27	2	173	33
28	365	28	16	635	197	28	18	803	832	28	2	168	32
29	399	29	16	601	235	29	19	765	837	29	2	163	31
30	433	30	17	567	274	30	19	726	10.02841	30	2	9.97159	30
31	466	31	17	534	312	31	20	688	846	31	2	154	29
32	9.54500	32	18	10.45500	9.57351	32	21	10.42649	851	32	3	149	28
33	534	33	19	466	389	33	21	611	855	33	3	145	27
34	567	34	19	433	428	34	22	572	860	34	3	140	26
35	601	35	20	399	466	35	22	534	865	35	3	135	25
36	635	36	20	365	504	36	23	496	870	36	3	130	24
37	668	37	21	332	543	37	24	457	874	37	3	126	23
38	702	38	21	298	581	38	24	419	879	38	3	121	22
39	735	39	22	265	619	39	25	381	884	39	3	116	21
40	9.54769	40	23	10.45231	9.57658	40	26	10.42342	10.02889	40	3	9.97111	20
41	802	41	23	198	696	41	26	304	893	41	3	107	19
42	836	42	24	164	734	42	27	266	898	42	3	102	18
43	869	43	24	131	772	43	28	228	903	43	3	097	17
44	903	44	25	097	810	44	28	190	908	44	3	092	16
45	936	45	25	064	849	45	29	151	913	45	4	087	15
46	9.54969	46	26	10.45031	887	46	30	113	917	46	4	083	14
47	9.55003	47	26	10.44997	925	47	30	075	922	47	4	078	13
48	036	48	27	964	9.57963	48	31	10.42037	927	48	4	073	12
49	069	49	28	931	9.58001	49	31	10.41999	932	49	4	068	11
50	102	50	28	898	039	50	32	961	10.02937	50	4	9.97063	10
51	136	51	29	864	077	51	33	923	941	51	4	059	9
52	169	52	29	831	115	52	33	885	946	52	4	054	8
53	9.55202	53	30	798	153	53	34	847	951	53	4	049	7
54	235	54	30	10.44765	191	54	35	809	956	54	4	044	6
55	268	55	31	732	9.58229	55	35	10.41771	961	55	4	039	5
56	301	56	32	699	267	56	36	733	965	56	4	035	4
57	334	57	32	666	304	57	37	696	970	57	4	030	3
58	367	58	33	633	342	58	37	658	975	58	5	025	2
59	400	59	33	600	380	59	38	620	980	59	5	020	1
60	9.55433	60	34	10.44567	9.58418	60	39	10.41582	10.02985	60	5	9.97015	0
′ ↑ 110°→	cos	″ Diff.		sec	cot	″ Diff.		tan	csc	″ Diff.		sin ←69°	′ ↑

541524°—43——41

TABLE 33.

Logarithms of Trigonometric Functions.

21°→ ↓ ′	sin	″	Diff.	csc	tan	″	Diff.	cot	sec	″	Diff.	cos ←158° ↓	′
0	9. 55433	0	0	10. 44567	9. 58418	0	0	10. 41582	10. 02985	0	0	9. 97015	60
1	466	1	1	534	455	1	1	545	990	1	0	010	59
2	499	2	1	501	493	2	1	507	995	2	0	005	58
3	532	3	2	468	531	3	2	469	10. 02999	3	0	9. 97001	57
4	564	4	2	436	569	4	2	431	10. 03004	4	0	9. 96996	56
5	597	5	3	403	606	5	3	394	009	5	0	991	55
6	630	6	3	370	644	6	4	356	014	6	0	986	54
7	663	7	4	337	681	7	4	319	019	7	1	981	53
8	695	8	4	305	9. 58719	8	5	10. 41281	024	8	1	976	52
9	9. 55728	9	5	10. 44272	757	9	6	243	029	9	1	971	51
10	761	10	5	239	794	10	6	206	034	10	1	966	50
11	793	11	6	207	832	11	7	168	038	11	1	962	49
12	826	12	6	174	869	12	7	131	043	12	1	957	48
13	858	13	7	142	907	13	8	093	10. 03048	13	1	9. 96952	47
14	891	14	7	109	944	14	9	056	053	14	1	947	46
15	923	15	8	077	9. 58981	15	9	10. 41019	058	15	1	942	45
16	956	16	9	044	9. 59019	16	10	10. 40981	063	16	1	937	44
17	9. 55988	17	9	10. 44012	056	17	10	944	068	17	1	932	43
18	9. 56021	18	10	10. 43979	094	18	11	906	073	18	1	927	42
19	053	19	10	947	131	19	12	869	078	19	2	922	41
20	085	20	11	915	168	20	12	832	083	20	2	917	40
21	118	21	11	882	205	21	13	795	088	21	2	912	39
22	150	22	12	850	243	22	14	757	10. 03093	22	2	9. 96907	38
23	182	23	12	818	280	23	14	720	097	23	2	903	37
24	215	24	13	785	317	24	15	683	102	24	2	898	36
25	247	25	13	753	9. 59354	25	15	10. 40646	107	25	2	893	35
26	279	26	14	721	391	26	16	609	112	26	2	888	34
27	311	27	14	689	429	27	17	571	117	27	2	883	33
28	9. 56343	28	15	10. 43657	466	28	17	534	122	28	2	878	32
29	375	29	16	625	503	29	18	497	127	29	2	873	31
30	408	30	16	592	540	30	19	460	132	30	2	868	30
31	440	31	17	560	577	31	19	423	10. 03137	31	3	9. 96863	29
32	472	32	17	528	614	32	20	386	142	32	3	858	28
33	504	33	18	496	9. 59651	33	20	10. 40349	147	33	3	853	27
34	536	34	18	464	688	34	21	312	152	34	3	848	26
35	568	35	19	432	725	35	22	275	157	35	3	843	25
36	599	36	19	401	762	36	22	238	162	36	3	838	24
37	631	37	20	369	799	37	23	201	167	37	3	833	23
38	9. 56663	38	20	10. 43337	835	38	23	165	172	38	3	828	22
39	695	39	21	305	872	39	24	128	177	39	3	823	21
40	727	40	21	273	909	40	25	091	10. 03182	40	3	9. 96818	20
41	759	41	22	241	946	41	25	054	187	41	3	813	19
42	790	42	22	210	9. 59983	42	26	10. 40017	192	42	3	808	18
43	822	43	23	178	9. 60019	43	27	10. 39981	197	43	4	803	17
44	854	44	24	146	056	44	27	944	202	44	4	798	16
45	886	45	24	114	093	45	28	907	207	45	4	793	15
46	917	46	25	083	130	46	28	870	212	46	4	788	14
47	949	47	25	051	166	47	29	834	217	47	4	783	13
48	9. 56980	48	26	10. 43020	203	48	30	797	222	48	4	778	12
49	9. 57012	49	26	10. 42988	240	49	30	760	228	49	4	772	11
50	044	50	27	956	276	50	31	724	10. 03233	50	4	9. 96767	10
51	075	51	27	925	9. 60313	51	31	10. 39687	238	51	4	762	9
52	107	52	28	893	349	52	32	651	243	52	4	757	8
53	138	53	28	862	386	53	33	614	248	53	4	752	7
54	169	54	29	831	422	54	33	578	253	54	4	747	6
55	201	55	29	799	459	55	34	541	258	55	5	742	5
56	232	56	30	768	495	56	35	505	263	56	5	737	4
57	264	57	30	736	532	57	35	468	268	57	5	732	3
58	295	58	31	705	568	58	36	432	273	58	5	727	2
59	326	59	32	674	605	59	36	395	278	59	5	722	1
60	9. 57358	60	32	10. 42642	9. 60641	60	37	10. 39359	10. 03283	60	5	9. 96717	0
′ ↑ 111°→	cos	″	Diff.	sec	cot	″	Diff.	tan	csc	″	Diff.	sin ←68° ↑	′

TABLE 33.

Logarithms of Trigonometric Functions.

22°→ ↓ ′	sin	″ Diff.		csc	tan	″ Diff.		cot	sec	″ Diff.		cos	←157° ↓ ′
0	9. 57358	0	0	10. 42642	9. 60641	0	0	10. 39359	10. 03283	0	0	9. 96717	60
1	389	1	1	611	677	1	1	323	289	1	0	711	59
2	420	2	1	580	714	2	1	286	294	2	0	706	58
3	451	3	2	549	750	3	2	250	299	3	0	701	57
4	482	4	2	518	786	4	2	214	304	4	0	696	56
5	514	5	3	486	823	5	3	177	309	5	0	691	55
6	545	6	3	455	859	6	4	141	314	6	1	686	54
7	576	7	4	424	895	7	4	105	319	7	1	681	53
8	607	8	4	393	931	8	5	069	324	8	1	676	52
9	638	9	5	362	9. 60967	9	5	10. 39033	330	9	1	670	51
10	9. 57669	10	5	10. 42331	9. 61004	10	6	10. 38996	10. 03335	10	1	9. 96665	50
11	700	11	6	300	040	11	7	960	340	11	1	660	49
12	731	12	6	269	076	12	7	924	345	12	1	655	48
13	762	13	7	238	112	13	8	888	350	13	1	650	47
14	793	14	7	207	148	14	8	852	355	14	1	645	46
15	824	15	8	176	184	15	9	816	360	15	1	640	45
16	855	16	8	145	220	16	10	780	366	16	1	634	44
17	885	17	9	115	9. 61256	17	10	10. 38744	371	17	1	629	43
18	916	18	9	084	292	18	11	708	376	18	2	624	42
19	947	19	10	053	328	19	11	672	381	19	2	619	41
20	9. 57978	20	10	10. 42022	364	20	12	636	10. 03386	20	2	9. 96614	40
21	9. 58008	21	11	10. 41992	400	21	13	600	392	21	2	608	39
22	039	22	11	961	436	22	13	564	397	22	2	603	38
23	070	23	12	930	472	23	14	528	402	23	2	598	37
24	101	24	12	899	9. 61508	24	14	10. 38492	407	24	2	593	36
25	131	25	13	869	544	25	15	456	412	25	2	588	35
26	162	26	13	838	579	26	15	421	418	26	2	582	34
27	192	27	14	808	615	27	16	385	423	27	2	577	33
28	223	28	14	777	651	28	17	349	428	28	2	572	32
29	9. 58253	29	15	10. 41747	687	29	17	313	433	29	3	567	31
30	284	30	15	716	722	30	18	278	10. 03438	30	3	9. 96562	30
31	314	31	16	686	9. 61758	31	18	10. 38242	444	31	3	556	29
32	345	32	16	655	794	32	19	206	449	32	3	551	28
33	375	33	17	625	830	33	20	170	454	33	3	546	27
34	406	34	17	594	865	34	20	135	459	34	3	541	26
35	436	35	18	564	901	35	21	099	465	35	3	535	25
36	467	36	18	533	936	36	21	064	470	36	3	530	24
37	9. 58497	37	19	10. 41503	9. 61972	37	22	10. 38028	475	37	3	525	23
38	527	38	19	473	9. 62008	38	23	10. 37992	480	38	3	520	22
39	557	39	20	443	043	39	23	957	486	39	3	514	21
40	588	40	20	412	079	40	24	921	10. 03491	40	3	9. 96509	20
41	618	41	21	382	114	41	24	886	496	41	4	504	19
42	648	42	21	352	150	42	25	850	502	42	4	498	18
43	678	43	22	322	185	43	26	815	507	43	4	493	17
44	709	44	22	291	221	44	26	779	512	44	4	488	16
45	9. 58739	45	23	10. 41261	9. 62256	45	27	10. 37744	517	45	4	483	15
46	769	46	23	231	292	46	27	708	523	46	4	477	14
47	799	47	24	201	327	47	28	673	528	47	4	472	13
48	829	48	24	171	362	48	29	638	533	48	4	467	12
49	859	49	25	141	398	49	29	602	539	49	4	461	11
50	889	50	25	111	433	50	30	567	10. 03544	50	4	9. 96456	10
51	919	51	26	081	468	51	30	532	549	51	4	451	9
52	949	52	26	051	9. 62504	52	31	10. 37496	555	52	5	445	8
53	9. 58979	53	27	10. 41021	539	53	32	461	560	53	5	440	7
54	9. 59009	54	27	10. 40991	574	54	32	426	565	54	5	435	6
55	039	55	28	961	609	55	33	391	571	55	5	429	5
56	069	56	28	931	645	56	33	355	576	56	5	424	4
57	098	57	29	902	680	57	34	320	581	57	5	419	3
58	128	58	29	872	715	58	35	285	587	58	5	413	2
59	158	59	30	842	750	59	35	250	592	59	5	408	1
60	9. 59188	60	31	10. 40812	9. 62785	60	36	10. 37215	10. 03597	60	5	9. 96403	0
′ ↑ 112°→	cos	″ Diff.		sec	cot	″ Diff.		tan	csc	″ Diff.		sin	′ ↑ ←67°

TABLE 33.

Logarithms of Trigonometric Functions.

23°→ ↓ ′	sin	″	Diff.	csc	tan	″	Diff.	cot	sec	″	Diff.	cos ←156°	↓ ′
0	9.59188	*0*	0	10.40812	9.62785	*0*	0	10.37215	10.03597	*0*	0	9.96403	60
1	218	*1*	0	782	820	*1*	1	180	603	*1*	0	397	59
2	247	*2*	1	753	855	*2*	1	145	608	*2*	0	392	58
3	277	*3*	1	723	890	*3*	2	110	613	*3*	0	387	57
4	307	*4*	2	693	926	*4*	2	074	619	*4*	0	381	56
5	336	*5*	2	664	961	*5*	3	039	624	*5*	0	376	55
6	366	*6*	3	634	9.62996	*6*	3	10.37004	630	*6*	1	370	54
7	396	*7*	3	604	9.63031	*7*	4	10.36969	635	*7*	1	365	53
8	425	*8*	4	575	066	*8*	5	934	640	*8*	1	360	52
9	9.59455	*9*	4	10.40545	101	*9*	5	899	646	*9*	1	354	51
10	484	*10*	5	516	135	*10*	6	865	10.03651	*10*	1	9.96349	50
11	514	*11*	5	486	170	*11*	6	830	657	*11*	1	343	49
12	543	*12*	6	457	205	*12*	7	795	662	*12*	1	338	48
13	573	*13*	6	427	240	*13*	7	760	667	*13*	1	333	47
14	602	*14*	7	398	275	*14*	8	725	673	*14*	1	327	46
15	632	*15*	7	368	310	*15*	9	690	678	*15*	1	322	45
16	661	*16*	8	339	9.63345	*16*	9	10.36655	684	*16*	1	316	44
17	690	*17*	8	310	379	*17*	10	621	689	*17*	2	311	43
18	9.59720	*18*	9	10.40280	414	*18*	10	586	695	*18*	2	305	42
19	749	*19*	9	251	449	*19*	11	551	700	*19*	2	300	41
20	778	*20*	10	222	484	*20*	12	516	10.03706	*20*	2	9.96294	40
21	808	*21*	10	192	519	*21*	12	481	711	*21*	2	289	39
22	837	*22*	11	163	553	*22*	13	447	716	*22*	2	284	38
23	866	*23*	11	134	588	*23*	13	412	722	*23*	2	278	37
24	895	*24*	12	105	623	*24*	14	377	727	*24*	2	273	36
25	924	*25*	12	076	9.63657	*25*	14	10.36343	733	*25*	2	267	35
26	954	*26*	13	046	692	*26*	15	308	738	*26*	2	262	34
27	9.59983	*27*	13	10.40017	726	*27*	16	274	744	*27*	2	256	33
28	9.60012	*28*	14	10.39988	761	*28*	16	239	749	*28*	3	251	32
29	041	*29*	14	959	796	*29*	17	204	755	*29*	3	245	31
30	070	*30*	15	930	830	*30*	17	170	10.03760	*30*	3	9.96240	30
31	099	*31*	15	901	865	*31*	18	135	766	*31*	3	234	29
32	128	*32*	15	872	899	*32*	18	101	771	*32*	3	229	28
33	157	*33*	16	843	934	*33*	19	066	777	*33*	3	223	27
34	186	*34*	16	814	9.63968	*34*	20	10.36032	782	*34*	3	218	26
35	215	*35*	17	785	9.64003	*35*	20	10.35997	788	*35*	3	212	25
36	244	*36*	17	756	037	*36*	21	963	793	*36*	3	207	24
37	273	*37*	18	727	072	*37*	21	928	799	*37*	3	201	23
38	302	*38*	18	698	106	*38*	22	894	804	*38*	3	196	22
39	9.60331	*39*	19	10.39669	140	*39*	22	860	810	*39*	4	190	21
40	359	*40*	19	641	175	*40*	23	825	10.03815	*40*	4	9.96185	20
41	388	*41*	20	612	209	*41*	24	791	821	*41*	4	179	19
42	417	*42*	20	583	243	*42*	24	757	826	*42*	4	174	18
43	446	*43*	21	554	9.64278	*43*	25	10.35722	832	*43*	4	168	17
44	474	*44*	21	526	312	*44*	25	688	838	*44*	4	162	16
45	503	*45*	22	497	346	*45*	26	654	843	*45*	4	157	15
46	532	*46*	22	468	381	*46*	26	619	849	*46*	4	151	14
47	561	*47*	23	439	415	*47*	27	585	854	*47*	4	146	13
48	589	*48*	23	411	449	*48*	28	551	860	*48*	4	140	12
49	9.60618	*49*	24	10.39382	483	*49*	28	517	865	*49*	4	135	11
50	646	*50*	24	354	517	*50*	29	483	10.03871	*50*	5	9.96129	10
51	675	*51*	25	325	9.64552	*51*	29	10.35448	877	*51*	5	123	9
52	704	*52*	25	296	586	*52*	30	414	882	*52*	5	118	8
53	732	*53*	26	268	620	*53*	31	380	888	*53*	5	112	7
54	761	*54*	26	239	654	*54*	31	346	893	*54*	5	107	6
55	789	*55*	27	211	688	*55*	32	312	899	*55*	5	101	5
56	818	*56*	27	182	722	*56*	32	278	905	*56*	5	095	4
57	846	*57*	28	154	756	*57*	33	244	910	*57*	5	090	3
58	875	*58*	28	125	790	*58*	33	210	916	*58*	5	084	2
59	903	*59*	29	097	824	*59*	34	176	921	*59*	5	079	1
60	9.60931	*60*	29	10.39069	9.64858	*60*	35	10.35142	10.03927	*60*	6	9.96073	0
′ ↑ 113°→	cos	″	Diff.	sec	cot	″	Diff.	tan	csc	″	Diff.	sin ←66°	′ ↑

TABLE 33.

Logarithms of Trigonometric Functions.

24° → ↓ ′	sin	″	Diff.	csc	tan	″	Diff.	cot	sec	″	Diff.	cos	← 155° ↓ ′
0	9.60931	*0*	0	10.39069	9.64858	*0*	0	10.35142	10.03927	*0*	0	9.96073	60
1	960	*1*	0	040	892	*1*	1	108	933	*1*	0	067	59
2	9.60988	*2*	1	10.39012	926	*2*	1	074	938	*2*	0	062	58
3	9.61016	*3*	1	10.38984	960	*3*	2	040	944	*3*	0	056	57
4	045	*4*	2	955	9.64994	*4*	2	10.35006	950	*4*	0	050	56
5	073	*5*	2	927	9.65028	*5*	3	10.34972	955	*5*	0	045	55
6	101	*6*	3	899	062	*6*	3	938	10.03961	*6*	1	9.96039	54
7	129	*7*	3	871	096	*7*	4	904	966	*7*	1	034	53
8	158	*8*	4	842	130	*8*	4	870	972	*8*	1	028	52
9	186	*9*	4	814	164	*9*	5	836	978	*9*	1	022	51
10	214	*10*	5	786	197	*10*	6	803	983	*10*	1	017	50
11	242	*11*	5	758	231	*11*	6	769	989	*11*	1	011	49
12	9.61270	*12*	6	10.38730	265	*12*	7	735	10.03995	*12*	1	005	48
13	298	*13*	6	702	299	*13*	7	701	10.04000	*13*	1	9.96000	47
14	326	*14*	6	674	9.65333	*14*	8	10.34667	.006	*14*	1	9.95994	46
15	354	*15*	7	646	366	*15*	8	634	012	*15*	1	988	45
16	382	*16*	7	618	400	*16*	9	600	018	*16*	2	982	44
17	411	*17*	8	589	434	*17*	9	566	023	*17*	2	977	43
18	438	*18*	8	562	467	*18*	10	533	029	*18*	2	971	42
19	466	*19*	9	534	501	*19*	11	499	035	*19*	2	965	41
20	494	*20*	9	506	535	*20*	11	465	040	*20*	2	960	40
21	9.61522	*21*	10	10.38478	568	*21*	12	432	046	*21*	2	954	39
22	550	*22*	10	450	602	*22*	12	398	10.04052	*22*	2	9.95948	38
23	578	*23*	11	422	636	*23*	13	364	058	*23*	2	942	37
24	606	*24*	11	394	9.65669	*24*	13	10.34331	063	*24*	2	937	36
25	634	*25*	12	366	703	*25*	14	297	069	*25*	2	931	35
26	662	*26*	12	338	736	*26*	15	264	075	*26*	2	925	34
27	689	*27*	12	311	770	*27*	15	230	080	*27*	3	920	33
28	717	*28*	13	283	803	*28*	16	197	086	*28*	3	914	32
29	9.61745	*29*	13	10.38255	837	*29*	16	163	092	*29*	3	908	31
30	773	*30*	14	227	870	*30*	17	130	098	*30*	3	902	30
31	800	*31*	14	200	904	*31*	17	096	10.04103	*31*	3	9.95897	29
32	828	*32*	15	172	937	*32*	18	063	109	*32*	3	891	28
33	856	*33*	15	144	9.65971	*33*	18	10.34029	115	*33*	3	885	27
34	883	*34*	16	117	9.66004	*34*	19	10.33996	121	*34*	3	879	26
35	911	*35*	16	089	038	*35*	20	962	127	*35*	3	873	25
36	939	*36*	17	061	071	*36*	20	929	132	*36*	3	868	24
37	966	*37*	17	034	104	*37*	21	896	138	*37*	4	862	23
38	9.61994	*38*	18	10.38006	138	*38*	21	862	144	*38*	4	856	22
39	9.62021	*39*	18	10.37979	171	*39*	22	829	150	*39*	4	850	21
40	049	*40*	18	951	204	*40*	22	796	10.04156	*40*	4	9.95844	20
41	076	*41*	19	924	238	*41*	23	762	161	*41*	4	839	19
42	104	*42*	19	896	271	*42*	23	729	167	*42*	4	833	18
43	131	*43*	20	869	9.66304	*43*	24	10.33696	173	*43*	4	827	17
44	159	*44*	20	841	337	*44*	25	663	179	*44*	4	821	16
45	186	*45*	21	814	371	*45*	25	629	185	*45*	4	815	15
46	214	*46*	21	786	404	*46*	26	596	190	*46*	4	810	14
47	241	*47*	22	759	437	*47*	26	563	196	*47*	5	804	13
48	268	*48*	22	732	470	*48*	27	530	202	*48*	5	798	12
49	296	*49*	23	704	503	*49*	27	497	208	*49*	5	792	11
50	9.62323	*50*	23	10.37677	537	*50*	28	463	10.04214	*50*	5	9.95786	10
51	350	*51*	24	650	570	*51*	28	430	220	*51*	5	780	9
52	377	*52*	24	623	9.66603	*52*	29	10.33397	225	*52*	5	775	8
53	405	*53*	24	595	636	*53*	30	364	231	*53*	5	769	7
54	432	*54*	25	568	669	*54*	30	331	237	*54*	5	763	6
55	459	*55*	25	541	702	*55*	31	298	243	*55*	5	757	5
56	486	*56*	26	514	735	*56*	31	265	249	*56*	5	751	4
57	513	*57*	26	487	768	*57*	32	232	255	*57*	5	745	3
58	541	*58*	27	459	801	*58*	32	199	261	*58*	6	739	2
59	568	*59*	27	432	834	*59*	33	166	267	*59*	6	733	1
60	9.62595	*60*	28	10.37405	9.66867	*60*	33	10.33133	10.04272	*60*	6	9.95728	0
′ ↑ 114° →	cos	″	Diff.	sec	cot	″	Diff.	tan	csc	″	Diff.	sin	′ ↑ ← 65°

TABLE 33.

Logarithms of Trigonometric Functions.

25° → ↓ ′	sin	″	Diff.	csc	tan	″	Diff.	cot	sec	″	Diff.	cos	← 154° ↓ ′
0	9. 62595	0	0	10. 37405	9. 66867	0	0	10. 33133	10. 04272	0	0	9. 95728	60
1	622	1	0	378	900	1	1	100	278	1	0	722	59
2	649	2	1	351	933	2	1	067	284	2	0	716	58
3	676	3	1	324	966	3	2	034	290	3	0	710	57
4	703	4	2	297	9. 66999	4	2	10. 33001	296	4	0	704	56
5	730	5	2	270	9. 67032	5	3	10. 32968	302	5	1	698	55
6	757	6	3	243	065	6	3	935	308	6	1	692	54
7	9. 62784	7	3	10. 37216	098	7	4	902	314	7	1	686	53
8	811	8	4	189	131	8	4	869	320	8	1	680	52
9	838	9	4	162	163	9	5	837	326	9	1	674	51
10	865	10	4	135	196	10	5	804	10. 04332	10	1	9. 95668	50
11	892	11	5	108	229	11	6	771	337	11	1	663	49
12	918	12	5	082	262	12	7	738	343	12	1	657	48
13	945	13	6	055	295	13	7	705	349	13	1	651	47
14	972	14	6	028	327	14	8	673	355	14	1	645	46
15	9. 62999	15	7	10. 37001	9. 67360	15	8	10. 32640	361	15	2	639	45
16	9. 63026	16	7	10. 36974	393	16	9	607	367	16	2	633	44
17	052	17	8	948	426	17	9	574	373	17	2	627	43
18	079	18	8	921	458	18	10	542	379	18	2	621	42
19	106	19	8	894	491	19	10	509	385	19	2	615	41
20	133	20	9	867	524	20	11	476	10. 04391	20	2	9. 95609	40
21	159	21	9	841	556	21	11	444	397	21	2	603	39
22	186	22	10	814	589	22	12	411	403	22	2	597	38
23	213	23	10	787	622	23	12	378	409	23	2	591	37
24	239	24	11	761	654	24	13	346	415	24	2	585	36
25	9. 63266	25	11	10. 36734	9. 67687	25	14	10. 32313	421	25	3	579	35
26	292	26	11	708	719	26	14	281	427	26	3	573	34
27	319	27	12	681	752	27	15	248	433	27	3	567	33
28	345	28	12	655	785	28	15	215	439	28	3	561	32
29	372	29	13	628	817	29	16	183	445	29	3	555	31
30	398	30	13	602	850	30	16	150	10. 04451	30	3	9. 95549	30
31	425	31	14	575	882	31	17	118	457	31	3	543	29
32	451	32	14	549	915	32	17	085	463	32	3	537	28
33	478	33	15	522	947	33	18	053	469	33	3	531	27
34	9. 63504	34	15	10. 36496	9. 67980	34	18	10. 32020	475	34	3	525	26
35	531	35	15	469	9. 68012	35	19	10. 31988	481	35	4	519	25
36	557	36	16	443	044	36	20	956	487	36	4	513	24
37	583	37	16	417	077	37	20	923	493	37	4	507	23
38	610	38	17	390	109	38	21	891	500	38	4	500	22
39	636	39	17	364	142	39	21	858	506	39	4	494	21
40	662	40	18	338	9. 68174	40	22	826	10. 04512	40	4	9. 95488	20
41	689	41	18	311	206	41	22	794	518	41	4	482	19
42	715	42	19	285	239	42	23	761	524	42	4	476	18
43	9. 63741	43	19	10. 36259	271	43	23	729	530	43	4	470	17
44	767	44	19	233	9. 68303	44	24	10. 31697	536	44	4	464	16
45	794	45	20	206	336	45	24	664	542	45	5	458	15
46	820	46	20	180	368	46	25	632	548	46	5	452	14
47	846	47	21	154	400	47	25	600	554	47	5	446	13
48	872	48	21	128	432	48	26	568	560	48	5	440	12
49	898	49	22	102	465	49	27	535	566	49	5	434	11
50	924	50	22	076	497	50	27	503	10. 04573	50	5	9. 95427	10
51	950	51	23	050	529	51	28	471	579	51	5	421	9
52	9. 63976	52	23	10. 36024	9. 68561	52	28	10. 31439	585	52	5	415	8
53	9. 64002	53	23	10. 35998	593	53	29	407	591	53	5	409	7
54	028	54	24	972	626	54	29	374	597	54	5	403	6
55	054	55	24	946	658	55	30	342	603	55	6	397	5
56	080	56	25	920	690	56	30	310	609	56	6	391	4
57	106	57	25	894	722	57	31	278	616	57	6	384	3
58	132	58	26	868	754	58	31	246	622	58	6	378	2
59	158	59	26	842	786	59	32	214	628	59	6	372	1
60	9. 64184	60	26	10. 35816	9. 68818	60	33	10. 31182	10. 04634	60	6	9. 95366	0
′ ↑ 115° →	cos	″	Diff.	sec	cot	″	Diff.	tan	csc	″	Diff.	sin	′ ↑ ← 64°

TABLE 33.

Logarithms of Trigonometric Functions.

26°→ ↓ '	sin	''	Diff.	csc	tan	''	Diff.	cot	sec	''	Diff.	cos ←153° ↓	'
0	9.64184	0	0	10.35816	9.68818	0	0	10.31182	10.04634	0	0	9.95366	60
1	210	1	0	790	850	1	1	150	640	1	0	360	59
2	236	2	1	764	882	2	1	118	646	2	0	354	58
3	262	3	1	738	914	3	2	086	652	3	0	348	57
4	288	4	2	712	946	4	2	054	659	4	0	341	56
5	313	5	2	687	9.68978	5	3	10.31022	665	5	1	335	55
6	339	6	3	661	9.69010	6	3	10.30990	671	6	1	329	54
7	365	7	3	635	042	7	4	958	677	7	1	323	53
8	9.64391	8	3	10.35609	074	8	4	926	683	8	1	317	52
9	417	9	4	583	106	9	5	894	690	9	1	310	51
10	442	10	4	558	138	10	5	862	10.04696	10	1	9.95304	50
11	468	11	5	532	170	11	6	830	702	11	1	298	49
12	494	12	5	506	202	12	6	798	708	12	1	292	48
13	519	13	5	481	234	13	7	766	714	13	1	286	47
14	545	14	6	455	9.69266	14	7	10.30734	721	14	1	279	46
15	9.64571	15	6	10.35429	298	15	8	702	727	15	2	273	45
16	596	16	7	404	329	16	8	671	733	16	2	267	44
17	622	17	7	378	361	17	9	639	739	17	2	261	43
18	647	18	8	353	393	18	9	607	746	18	2	254	42
19	673	19	8	327	425	19	10	575	752	19	2	248	41
20	698	20	8	302	457	20	11	543	10.04758	20	2	9.95242	40
21	724	21	9	276	488	21	11	512	764	21	2	236	39
22	749	22	9	251	9.69520	22	12	10.30480	771	22	2	229	38
23	9.64775	23	10	10.35225	552	23	12	448	777	23	2	223	37
24	800	24	10	200	584	24	13	416	783	24	3	217	36
25	826	25	11	174	615	25	13	385	789	25	3	211	35
26	851	26	11	149	647	26	14	353	796	26	3	204	34
27	877	27	11	123	679	27	14	321	802	27	3	198	33
28	902	28	12	098	710	28	15	290	808	28	3	192	32
29	927	29	12	073	742	29	15	258	815	29	3	185	31
30	953	30	13	047	9.69774	30	16	10.30226	10.04821	30	3	9.95179	30
31	9.64978	31	13	10.35022	805	31	16	195	827	31	3	173	29
32	9.65003	32	14	10.34997	837	32	17	163	833	32	3	167	28
33	029	33	14	971	868	33	17	132	840	33	3	160	27
34	054	34	14	946	900	34	18	100	846	34	4	154	26
35	079	35	15	921	932	35	18	068	852	35	4	148	25
36	104	36	15	896	963	36	19	037	859	36	4	141	24
37	130	37	16	870	9.69995	37	20	10.30005	865	37	4	135	23
38	155	38	16	845	9.70026	38	20	10.29974	871	38	4	129	22
39	9.65180	39	16	10.34820	058	39	21	942	878	39	4	122	21
40	205	40	17	795	089	40	21	911	10.04884	40	4	9.95116	20
41	230	41	17	770	121	41	22	879	890	41	4	110	19
42	255	42	18	745	152	42	22	848	897	42	4	103	18
43	281	43	18	719	184	43	23	816	903	43	5	097	17
44	306	44	19	694	215	44	23	785	910	44	5	090	16
45	331	45	19	669	9.70247	45	24	10.29753	916	45	5	084	15
46	9.65356	46	19	10.34644	278	46	24	722	922	46	5	078	14
47	381	47	20	619	309	47	25	691	929	47	5	071	13
48	406	48	20	594	341	48	25	659	935	48	5	065	12
49	431	49	21	569	372	49	26	628	10.04941	49	5	9.95059	11
50	456	50	21	544	404	50	26	596	948	50	5	052	10
51	481	51	22	519	435	51	27	565	954	51	5	046	9
52	506	52	22	494	466	52	27	534	961	52	5	039	8
53	9.65531	53	22	10.34469	9.70498	53	28	10.29502	967	53	6	033	7
54	556	54	23	444	529	54	28	471	973	54	6	027	6
55	580	55	23	420	560	55	29	440	980	55	6	020	5
56	605	56	24	395	592	56	30	408	986	56	6	014	4
57	630	57	24	370	623	57	30	377	993	57	6	007	3
58	655	58	25	345	654	58	31	346	10.04999	58	6	9.95001	2
59	680	59	25	320	685	59	31	315	10.05005	59	6	9.94995	1
60	9.65705	60	25	10.34295	9.70717	60	32	10.29283	10.05012	60	6	9.94988	0
' ↑ 116°→	cos	''	Diff.	sec	cot	''	Diff.	tan	csc	''	Diff.	sin	' ↑ ←63°

TABLE 33.

Logarithms of Trigonometric Functions.

27°→ ↓ ′	sin	″	Diff.	csc	tan	″	Diff.	cot	sec	″	Diff.	cos	←152° ↓ ′
0	9. 65705	0	0	10. 34295	9. 70717	0	0	10. 29283	10. 05012	0	0	9. 94988	60
1	729	1	0	271	748	1	1	252	018	1	0	982	59
2	754	2	1	246	779	2	1	221	025	2	0	975	58
3	779	3	1	221	810	3	2	190	031	3	0	969	57
4	804	4	2	196	841	4	2	159	038	4	0	962	56
5	9. 65828	5	2	172	873	5	3	127	044	5	1	956	55
6	853	6	2	147	904	6	3	096	051	6	1	949	54
7	878	7	3	122	935	7	4	065	057	7	1	943	53
8	902	8	3	098	966	8	4	034	064	8	1	936	52
9	927	9	4	073	9. 70997	9	5	10. 29003	070	9	1	930	51
10	952	10	4	048	9. 71028	10	5	10. 28972	10. 05077	10	1	9. 94923	50
11	9. 65976	11	4	10. 34024	059	11	6	941	083	11	1	917	49
12	9. 66001	12	5	10. 33999	090	12	6	910	089	12	1	911	48
13	025	13	5	975	121	13	7	879	096	13	1	904	47
14	050	14	6	950	153	14	7	847	102	14	2	898	46
15	075	15	6	925	184	15	8	816	109	15	2	891	45
16	099	16	6	901	215	16	8	785	115	16	2	885	44
17	124	17	7	876	246	17	9	754	122	17	2	878	43
18	148	18	7	852	277	18	9	723	129	18	2	871	42
19	173	19	8	827	308	19	10	692	135	19	2	865	41
20	197	20	8	803	9. 71339	20	10	10. 28661	10. 05142	20	2	9. 94858	40
21	221	21	8	779	370	21	11	630	148	21	2	852	39
22	9. 66246	22	9	10. 33754	401	22	11	599	155	22	2	845	38
23	270	23	9	730	431	23	12	569	161	23	3	839	37
24	295	24	10	705	462	24	12	538	168	24	3	832	36
25	319	25	10	681	493	25	13	507	174	25	3	826	35
26	343	26	11	657	524	26	13	476	181	26	3	819	34
27	368	27	11	632	555	27	14	445	187	27	3	813	33
28	392	28	11	608	586	28	14	414	194	28	3	806	32
29	416	29	12	584	617	29	15	383	201	29	3	799	31
30	441	30	12	559	9. 71648	30	15	10. 28352	10. 05207	30	3	9. 94793	30
31	465	31	13	535	679	31	16	321	214	31	3	786	29
32	9. 66489	32	13	10. 33511	709	32	16	291	220	32	4	780	28
33	513	33	13	487	740	33	17	260	227	33	4	773	27
34	537	34	14	463	771	34	17	229	233	34	4	767	26
35	562	35	14	438	802	35	18	198	240	35	4	760	25
36	586	36	15	414	833	36	19	167	247	36	4	753	24
37	610	37	15	390	863	37	19	137	253	37	4	747	23
38	634	38	15	366	894	38	20	106	260	38	4	740	22
39	658	39	16	342	925	39	20	075	266	39	4	734	21
40	682	40	16	318	955	40	21	045	10. 05273	40	4	9. 94727	20
41	706	41	17	294	9. 71986	41	21	10. 28014	280	41	4	720	19
42	9. 66731	42	17	10. 33269	9. 72017	42	22	10. 27983	286	42	5	714	18
43	755	43	17	245	048	43	22	952	293	43	5	707	17
44	779	44	18	221	078	44	23	922	300	44	5	700	16
45	803	45	18	197	109	45	23	891	306	45	5	694	15
46	827	46	19	173	140	46	24	860	313	46	5	687	14
47	851	47	19	149	170	47	24	830	320	47	5	680	13
48	875	48	19	125	201	48	25	799	326	48	5	674	12
49	899	49	20	101	231	49	25	769	333	49	5	667	11
50	922	50	20	078	262	50	26	738	10. 05340	50	5	9. 94660	10
51	946	51	21	054	9. 72293	51	26	10. 27707	346	51	6	654	9
52	970	52	21	030	323	52	27	677	353	52	6	647	8
53	9. 66994	53	21	10. 33006	354	53	27	646	360	53	6	640	7
54	9. 67018	54	22	10. 32982	384	54	28	616	366	54	6	634	6
55	042	55	22	958	415	55	28	585	373	55	6	627	5
56	066	56	23	934	445	56	29	555	380	56	6	620	4
57	090	57	23	910	476	57	29	524	386	57	6	614	3
58	113	58	23	887	506	58	30	494	393	58	6	607	2
59	137	59	24	863	537	59	30	463	400	59	6	600	1
60	9. 67161	60	24	10. 32839	9. 72567	60	31	10. 27433	10. 05407	60	7	9. 94593	0
′ ↑ 117°→	cos	″	Diff.	sec	cot	″	Diff.	tan	csc	″	Diff.	sin	′ ↑ ←62°

TABLE 33.

Logarithms of Trigonometric Functions.

28°→ ↓ ′	sin	″	Diff.	csc	tan	″	Diff.	cot	sec	″	Diff.	cos	←151° ↓ ′
0	9.67161	0	0	10.32839	9.72567	0	0	10.27433	10.05407	0	0	9.94593	60
1	185	1	0	815	598	1	1	402	413	1	0	587	59
2	208	2	1	792	628	2	1	372	420	2	0	580	58
3	232	3	1	768	659	3	2	341	427	3	0	573	57
4	256	4	2	744	689	4	2	311	433	4	0	567	56
5	280	5	2	720	720	5	3	280	440	5	1	560	55
6	303	6	2	697	750	6	3	250	447	6	1	553	54
7	9.67327	7	3	10.32673	9.72780	7	4	10.27220	454	7	1	546	53
8	350	8	3	650	811	8	4	189	460	8	1	540	52
9	374	9	3	626	841	9	5	159	467	9	1	533	51
10	398	10	4	602	872	10	5	128	10.05474	10	1	9.94526	50
11	421	11	4	579	902	11	6	098	481	11	1	519	49
12	445	12	5	555	932	12	6	068	487	12	1	513	48
13	468	13	5	532	963	13	7	037	494	13	1	506	47
14	9.67492	14	5	10.32508	9.72993	14	7	10.27007	501	14	2	499	46
15	515	15	6	485	9.73023	15	8	10.26977	508	15	2	492	45
16	539	16	6	461	054	16	8	946	515	16	2	485	44
17	562	17	7	438	084	17	9	916	521	17	2	479	43
18	586	18	7	414	114	18	9	886	528	18	2	472	42
19	609	19	7	391	144	19	10	856	535	19	2	465	41
20	633	20	8	367	175	20	10	825	10.05542	20	2	9.94458	40
21	9.67656	21	8	10.32344	205	21	11	795	549	21	2	451	39
22	680	22	9	320	235	22	11	765	555	22	3	445	38
23	703	23	9	297	9.73265	23	12	10.26735	562	23	3	438	37
24	726	24	9	274	295	24	12	705	569	24	3	431	36
25	750	25	10	250	326	25	13	674	576	25	3	424	35
26	773	26	10	227	356	26	13	644	583	26	3	417	34
27	796	27	10	204	386	27	14	614	590	27	3	410	33
28	9.67820	28	11	10.32180	416	28	14	584	596	28	3	404	32
29	843	29	11	157	446	29	15	554	603	29	3	397	31
30	866	30	12	134	476	30	15	524	10.05610	30	3	9.94390	30
31	890	31	12	110	507	31	16	493	617	31	4	383	29
32	913	32	12	087	9.73537	32	16	10.26463	624	32	4	376	28
33	936	33	13	064	567	33	17	433	631	33	4	369	27
34	959	34	13	041	597	34	17	403	638	34	4	362	26
35	9.67982	35	14	10.32018	627	35	18	373	645	35	4	355	25
36	9.68006	36	14	10.31994	657	36	18	343	651	36	4	349	24
37	029	37	14	971	687	37	19	313	658	37	4	342	23
38	052	38	15	948	717	38	19	283	665	38	4	335	22
39	075	39	15	925	747	39	20	253	672	39	4	328	21
40	098	40	16	902	9.73777	40	20	10.26223	10.05679	40	5	9.94321	20
41	121	41	16	879	807	41	21	193	686	41	5	314	19
42	144	42	16	856	837	42	21	163	693	42	5	307	18
43	167	43	17	833	867	43	22	133	700	43	5	300	17
44	9.68190	44	17	10.31810	897	44	22	103	707	44	5	293	16
45	213	45	17	787	927	45	23	073	714	45	5	286	15
46	237	46	18	763	957	46	23	043	721	46	5	279	14
47	260	47	18	740	9.73987	47	24	10.26013	727	47	5	273	13
48	283	48	19	717	9.74017	48	24	10.25983	734	48	5	266	12
49	305	49	19	695	047	49	25	953	741	49	6	259	11
50	328	50	19	672	077	50	25	923	10.05748	50	6	9.94252	10
51	351	51	20	649	107	51	26	893	755	51	6	245	9
52	9.68374	52	20	10.31626	137	52	26	863	762	52	6	238	8
53	397	53	21	603	166	53	27	834	769	53	6	231	7
54	420	54	21	580	196	54	27	10.25804	776	54	6	224	6
55	443	55	21	557	9.74226	55	28	774	783	55	6	217	5
56	466	56	22	534	256	56	28	744	790	56	6	210	4
57	489	57	22	511	286	57	29	714	797	57	7	203	3
58	512	58	22	488	316	58	29	684	804	58	7	196	2
59	534	59	23	466	345	59	30	655	811	59	7	189	1
60	9.68557	60	23	10.31443	9.74375	60	30	10.25625	10.05818	60	7	9.94182	0
′ ↑ 118°→	cos	″	Diff.	sec	cot	″	Diff.	tan	csc	″	Diff.	sin	′ ↑ ←61°

TABLE 33.

Logarithms of Trigonometric Functions.

29° → '	sin	"	Diff.	csc	tan	"	Diff.	cot	sec	"	Diff.	cos	← 150° '
0	9. 68557	*0*	0	10. 31443	9. 74375	*0*	0	10. 25625	10. 05818	*0*	0	9. 94182	60
1	580	*1*	0	420	405	*1*	0	595	825	*1*	0	175	59
2	603	*2*	1	397	435	*2*	1	565	832	*2*	0	168	58
3	625	*3*	1	375	465	*3*	1	535	839	*3*	0	161	57
4	648	*4*	1	352	494	*4*	2	506	846	*4*	0	154	56
5	671	*5*	2	329	524	*5*	2	476	853	*5*	1	147	55
6	694	*6*	2	306	554	*6*	3	446	860	*6*	1	140	54
7	716	*7*	3	284	583	*7*	3	417	867	*7*	1	133	53
8	739	*8*	3	261	613	*8*	4	387	10. 05874	*8*	1	9. 94126	52
9	762	*9*	3	238	643	*9*	4	357	881	*9*	1	119	51
10	9. 68784	*10*	4	10. 31216	9. 74673	*10*	5	10. 25327	888	*10*	1	112	50
11	807	*11*	4	193	702	*11*	5	298	895	*11*	1	105	49
12	829	*12*	4	171	732	*12*	6	268	902	*12*	1	098	48
13	852	*13*	5	148	762	*13*	6	238	910	*13*	2	090	47
14	875	*14*	5	125	791	*14*	7	209	917	*14*	2	083	46
15	897	*15*	6	103	821	*15*	7	179	924	*15*	2	076	45
16	920	*16*	6	080	851	*16*	8	149	10. 05931	*16*	2	9. 94069	44
17	942	*17*	6	058	880	*17*	8	120	938	*17*	2	062	43
18	965	*18*	7	035	910	*18*	9	090	945	*18*	2	055	42
19	9. 68987	*19*	7	10. 31013	939	*19*	9	061	952	*19*	2	048	41
20	9. 69010	*20*	7	10. 30990	969	*20*	10	031	959	*20*	2	041	40
21	032	*21*	8	968	9. 74998	*21*	10	10. 25002	966	*21*	3	034	39
22	055	*22*	8	945	9. 75028	*22*	11	10. 24972	973	*22*	3	027	38
23	077	*23*	9	923	058	*23*	11	942	980	*23*	3	020	37
24	100	*24*	9	900	087	*24*	12	913	988	*24*	3	012	36
25	122	*25*	9	878	117	*25*	12	883	10. 05995	*25*	3	9. 94005	35
26	144	*26*	10	856	146	*26*	13	854	10. 06002	*26*	3	9. 93998	34
27	167	*27*	10	833	176	*27*	13	824	009	*27*	3	991	33
28	189	*28*	10	811	205	*28*	14	795	016	*28*	3	984	32
29	212	*29*	11	788	235	*29*	14	765	023	*29*	3	977	31
30	9. 69234	*30*	11	10. 30766	9. 75264	*30*	15	10. 24736	030	*30*	4	970	30
31	256	*31*	12	744	294	*31*	15	706	037	*31*	4	963	29
32	279	*32*	12	721	323	*32*	16	677	045	*32*	4	955	28
33	301	*33*	12	699	353	*33*	16	647	052	*33*	4	948	27
34	323	*34*	13	677	382	*34*	17	618	059	*34*	4	941	26
35	345	*35*	13	655	411	*35*	17	589	10. 06066	*35*	4	9. 93934	25
36	368	*36*	13	632	441	*36*	18	559	073	*36*	4	927	24
37	390	*37*	14	610	470	*37*	18	530	080	*37*	4	920	23
38	412	*38*	14	588	9. 75500	*38*	19	10. 24500	088	*38*	5	912	22
39	434	*39*	15	566	529	*39*	19	471	095	*39*	5	905	21
40	9. 69456	*40*	15	10. 30544	558	*40*	20	442	102	*40*	5	898	20
41	479	*41*	15	521	588	*41*	20	412	109	*41*	5	891	19
42	501	*42*	16	499	617	*42*	21	383	116	*42*	5	884	18
43	523	*43*	16	477	647	*43*	21	353	10. 06124	*43*	5	9. 93876	17
44	545	*44*	16	455	676	*44*	22	324	131	*44*	5	869	16
45	567	*45*	17	433	705	*45*	22	295	138	*45*	5	862	15
46	589	*46*	17	411	9. 75735	*46*	23	10. 24265	145	*46*	5	855	14
47	611	*47*	17	389	764	*47*	23	236	153	*47*	6	847	13
48	633	*48*	18	367	793	*48*	24	207	160	*48*	6	840	12
49	655	*49*	18	345	822	*49*	24	178	167	*49*	6	833	11
50	9. 69677	*50*	19	10. 30323	852	*50*	25	148	174	*50*	6	826	10
51	699	*51*	19	301	881	*51*	25	119	10. 06181	*51*	6	9. 93819	9
52	721	*52*	19	279	910	*52*	26	090	189	*52*	6	811	8
53	743	*53*	20	257	939	*53*	26	061	196	*53*	6	804	7
54	765	*54*	20	235	969	*54*	27	031	203	*54*	6	797	6
55	787	*55*	20	213	9. 75998	*55*	27	10. 24002	211	*55*	7	789	5
56	809	*56*	21	191	9. 76027	*56*	28	10. 23973	218	*56*	7	782	4
57	831	*57*	21	169	056	*57*	28	944	225	*57*	7	775	3
58	853	*58*	22	147	086	*58*	29	914	232	*58*	7	768	2
59	875	*59*	22	125	115	*59*	29	885	240	*59*	7	760	1
60	9. 69897	*60*	22	10. 30103	9. 76144	*60*	29	10. 23856	10. 06247	*60*	7	9. 93753	0
' 119° →	cos	"	Diff.	sec	cot	"	Diff.	tan	csc	"	Diff.	sin	← 60° '

Logarithms of Trigonometric Functions.

30° → ′	sin	″	Diff.	csc	tan	″	Diff.	cot	sec	″	Diff.	cos	← 149° ′
0	9.69897	0	0	10.30103	9.76144	0	0	10.23856	10.06247	0	0	9.93753	60
1	919	1	0	081	173	1	0	827	254	1	0	746	59
2	941	2	1	059	202	2	1	798	262	2	0	738	58
3	963	3	1	037	231	3	1	769	269	3	0	731	57
4	9.69984	4	1	10.30016	261	4	2	739	276	4	0	724	56
5	9.70006	5	2	10.29994	290	5	2	710	283	5	1	717	55
6	028	6	2	972	319	6	3	681	291	6	1	709	54
7	050	7	3	950	348	7	3	652	298	7	1	702	53
8	072	8	3	928	377	8	4	623	305	8	1	695	52
9	093	9	3	907	406	9	4	594	313	9	1	687	51
10	115	10	4	885	9.76435	10	5	10.23565	10.06320	10	1	9.93680	50
11	137	11	4	863	464	11	5	536	327	11	1	673	49
12	159	12	4	841	493	12	6	507	335	12	1	665	48
13	9.70180	13	5	10.29820	522	13	6	478	342	13	2	658	47
14	202	14	5	798	551	14	7	449	350	14	2	650	46
15	224	15	5	776	580	15	7	420	357	15	2	643	45
16	245	16	6	755	609	16	8	391	364	16	2	636	44
17	267	17	6	733	639	17	8	361	372	17	2	628	43
18	288	18	6	712	668	18	9	332	379	18	2	621	42
19	310	19	7	690	697	19	9	303	386	19	2	614	41
20	332	20	7	668	9.76725	20	10	10.23275	10.06394	20	2	9.93606	40
21	9.70353	21	8	10.29647	754	21	10	246	401	21	3	599	39
22	375	22	8	625	783	22	11	217	409	22	3	591	38
23	396	23	8	604	812	23	11	188	416	23	3	584	37
24	418	24	9	582	841	24	12	159	423	24	3	577	36
25	439	25	9	561	870	25	12	130	431	25	3	569	35
26	461	26	9	539	899	26	13	101	438	26	3	562	34
27	482	27	10	518	928	27	13	072	446	27	3	554	33
28	9.70504	28	10	10.29496	957	28	13	043	453	28	3	547	32
29	525	29	10	475	9.76986	29	14	10.23014	461	29	4	539	31
30	547	30	11	453	9.77015	30	14	10.22985	10.06468	30	4	9.93532	30
31	568	31	11	432	044	31	15	956	475	31	4	525	29
32	590	32	11	410	073	32	15	927	483	32	4	517	28
33	611	33	12	389	101	33	16	899	490	33	4	510	27
34	633	34	12	367	130	34	16	870	498	34	4	502	26
35	654	35	13	346	159	35	17	841	505	35	4	495	25
36	9.70675	36	13	10.29325	188	36	17	812	513	36	4	487	24
37	697	37	13	303	217	37	18	783	520	37	5	480	23
38	718	38	14	282	246	38	18	754	528	38	5	472	22
39	739	39	14	261	274	39	19	726	535	39	5	465	21
40	761	40	14	239	9.77303	40	19	10.22697	10.06543	40	5	9.93457	20
41	782	41	15	218	332	41	20	668	550	41	5	450	19
42	803	42	15	197	361	42	20	639	558	42	5	442	18
43	9.70824	43	15	10.29176	390	43	21	610	565	43	5	435	17
44	846	44	16	154	418	44	21	582	573	44	5	427	16
45	867	45	16	133	447	45	22	553	580	45	6	420	15
46	888	46	16	112	476	46	22	524	588	46	6	412	14
47	909	47	17	091	505	47	23	495	595	47	6	405	13
48	931	48	17	069	533	48	23	467	603	48	6	397	12
49	952	49	18	048	562	49	24	438	610	49	6	390	11
50	973	50	18	027	9.77591	50	24	10.22409	10.06618	50	6	9.93382	10
51	9.70994	51	18	10.29006	619	51	25	381	625	51	6	375	9
52	9.71015	52	19	10.28985	648	52	25	352	633	52	6	367	8
53	036	53	19	964	677	53	26	323	640	53	7	360	7
54	058	54	19	942	706	54	26	294	648	54	7	352	6
55	079	55	20	921	734	55	26	266	656	55	7	344	5
56	100	56	20	900	763	56	27	237	663	56	7	337	4
57	121	57	20	879	791	57	27	209	671	57	7	329	3
58	142	58	21	858	820	58	28	180	678	58	7	322	2
59	163	59	21	837	849	59	28	151	686	59	7	314	1
60	9.71184	60	21	10.28816	9.77877	60	29	10.22123	10.06693	60	7	9.93307	0
′ 120° →	cos	″	Diff.	sec	cot	″	Diff.	tan	csc	″	Diff.	sin	← 59° ′

TABLE 33.

Logarithms of Trigonometric Functions.

31° → ↓ ′	sin	″	Diff.	csc	tan	″	Diff.	cot	sec	″	Diff.	cos	← 148° ↓ ′
0	9.71184	0	0	10.28816	9.77877	0	0	10.22123	10.06693	0	0	9.93307	60
1	205	1	0	795	906	1	0	094	701	1	0	299	59
2	226	2	1	774	935	2	1	065	709	2	0	291	58
3	247	3	1	753	963	3	1	037	716	3	0	284	57
4	268	4	1	732	9.77992	4	2	10.22008	724	4	1	276	56
5	289	5	2	711	9.78020	5	2	10.21980	731	5	1	269	55
6	310	6	2	690	049	6	3	951	739	6	1	261	54
7	331	7	2	669	077	7	3	923	747	7	1	253	53
8	352	8	3	648	106	8	4	894	754	8	1	246	52
9	373	9	3	627	135	9	4	865	762	9	1	238	51
10	9.71393	10	3	10.28607	163	10	5	837	10.06770	10	1	9.93230	50
11	414	11	4	586	192	11	5	808	777	11	1	223	49
12	435	12	4	565	220	12	6	780	785	12	2	215	48
13	456	13	4	544	249	13	6	751	793	13	2	207	47
14	477	14	5	523	9.78277	14	7	10.21723	800	14	2	200	46
15	498	15	5	502	306	15	7	694	808	15	2	192	45
16	519	16	5	481	334	16	8	666	816	16	2	184	44
17	539	17	6	461	363	17	8	637	823	17	2	177	43
18	560	18	6	440	391	18	9	609	831	18	2	169	42
19	581	19	7	419	419	19	9	581	839	19	2	161	41
20	9.71602	20	7	10.28398	448	20	9	552	10.06846	20	3	9.93154	40
21	622	21	7	378	476	21	10	524	854	21	3	146	39
22	643	22	8	357	9.78505	22	10	10.21495	862	22	3	138	38
23	664	23	8	336	533	23	11	467	869	23	3	131	37
24	685	24	8	315	562	24	11	438	877	24	3	123	36
25	705	25	9	295	590	25	12	410	885	25	3	115	35
26	726	26	9	274	618	26	12	382	892	26	3	108	34
27	747	27	9	253	647	27	13	353	900	27	3	100	33
28	767	28	10	233	675	28	13	325	908	28	4	092	32
29	788	29	10	212	704	29	14	296	916	29	4	084	31
30	9.71809	30	10	10.28191	9.78732	30	14	10.21268	10.06923	30	4	9.93077	30
31	829	31	11	171	760	31	15	240	931	31	4	069	29
32	850	32	11	150	789	32	15	211	939	32	4	061	28
33	870	33	11	130	817	33	16	183	947	33	4	053	27
34	891	34	12	109	845	34	16	155	954	34	4	046	26
35	911	35	12	089	874	35	17	126	962	35	5	038	25
36	932	36	12	068	902	36	17	098	970	36	5	030	24
37	952	37	13	048	930	37	17	070	978	37	5	022	23
38	973	38	13	027	959	38	18	041	986	38	5	014	22
39	9.71994	39	13	10.28006	9.78987	39	18	10.21013	10.06993	39	5	9.93007	21
40	9.72014	40	14	10.27986	9.79015	40	19	10.20985	10.07001	40	5	9.92999	20
41	034	41	14	966	043	41	19	957	009	41	5	991	19
42	055	42	14	945	072	42	20	928	017	42	5	983	18
43	075	43	15	925	100	43	20	900	024	43	6	976	17
44	096	44	15	904	128	44	21	872	032	44	6	968	16
45	116	45	15	884	156	45	21	844	040	45	6	960	15
46	137	46	16	863	185	46	22	815	048	46	6	952	14
47	157	47	16	843	213	47	22	787	056	47	6	944	13
48	177	48	16	823	241	48	23	759	064	48	6	936	12
49	198	49	17	802	269	49	23	731	071	49	6	929	11
50	9.72218	50	17	10.27782	9.79297	50	24	10.20703	10.07079	50	6	9.92921	10
51	238	51	18	762	326	51	24	674	087	51	7	913	9
52	259	52	18	741	354	52	25	646	095	52	7	905	8
53	279	53	18	721	382	53	25	618	103	53	7	897	7
54	299	54	19	701	410	54	26	590	111	54	7	889	6
55	320	55	19	680	438	55	26	562	119	55	7	881	5
56	340	56	19	660	466	56	26	534	126	56	7	874	4
57	360	57	20	640	495	57	27	505	134	57	7	866	3
58	381	58	20	619	523	58	27	477	142	58	7	858	2
59	401	59	20	599	551	59	28	449	150	59	8	850	1
60	9.72421	60	21	10.27579	9.79579	60	28	10.20421	10.07158	60	8	9.92842	0
′ ↑ 121° →	cos	″	Diff.	sec	cot	″	Diff.	tan	csc	″	Diff.	sin	′ ↑ ← 58°

TABLE 33.

Logarithms of Trigonometric Functions.

32°→ ′	sin	″	Diff.	csc	tan	″	Diff.	cot	sec	″	Diff.	cos	←147° ′
0	9. 72421	*0*	0	10. 27579	9. 79579	*0*	0	10. 20421	10. 07158	*0*	0	9. 92842	60
1	441	*1*	0	559	607	*1*	0	393	166	*1*	0	834	59
2	461	*2*	1	539	635	*2*	1	365	174	*2*	0	826	58
3	482	*3*	1	518	663	*3*	1	337	182	*3*	0	818	57
4	502	*4*	1	498	691	*4*	2	309	190	*4*	1	810	56
5	522	*5*	2	478	719	*5*	2	281	197	*5*	1	803	55
6	542	*6*	2	458	747	*6*	3	253	205	*6*	1	795	54
7	9. 72562	*7*	2	10. 27438	9. 79776	*7*	3	10. 20224	213	*7*	1	787	53
8	582	*8*	3	418	804	*8*	4	196	221	*8*	1	779	52
9	602	*9*	3	398	832	*9*	4	168	229	*9*	1	771	51
10	622	*10*	3	378	860	*10*	5	140	10. 07237	*10*	1	9. 92763	50
11	643	*11*	4	357	888	*11*	5	112	245	*11*	1	755	49
12	663	*12*	4	337	916	*12*	6	084	253	*12*	2	747	48
13	683	*13*	4	317	944	*13*	6	056	261	*13*	2	739	47
14	9. 72703	*14*	5	10. 27297	9. 79972	*14*	7	028	269	*14*	2	731	46
15	723	*15*	5	277	9. 80000	*15*	7	10. 20000	277	*15*	2	723	45
16	743	*16*	5	257	028	*16*	7	10. 19972	285	*16*	2	715	44
17	763	*17*	6	237	056	*17*	8	944	293	*17*	2	707	43
18	783	*18*	6	217	084	*18*	8	916	301	*18*	2	699	42
19	803	*19*	6	197	112	*19*	9	888	309	*19*	3	691	41
20	823	*20*	7	177	140	*20*	9	860	10. 07317	*20*	3	9. 92683	40
21	9. 72843	*21*	7	10. 27157	168	*21*	10	832	325	*21*	3	675	39
22	863	*22*	7	137	9. 80195	*22*	10	10. 19805	333	*22*	3	667	38
23	883	*23*	8	117	223	*23*	11	777	341	*23*	3	659	37
24	902	*24*	8	098	251	*24*	11	749	349	*24*	3	651	36
25	922	*25*	8	078	279	*25*	12	721	357	*25*	3	643	35
26	942	*26*	9	058	307	*26*	12	693	365	*26*	3	635	34
27	962	*27*	9	038	335	*27*	13	665	373	*27*	4	627	33
28	9. 72982	*28*	9	10. 27018	363	*28*	13	637	381	*28*	4	619	32
29	9. 73002	*29*	10	10. 26998	9. 80391	*29*	13	10. 19609	389	*29*	4	611	31
30	022	*30*	10	978	419	*30*	14	581	10. 07397	*30*	4	9. 92603	30
31	041	*31*	10	959	447	*31*	14	553	405	*31*	4	595	29
32	061	*32*	11	939	474	*32*	15	526	413	*32*	4	587	28
33	081	*33*	11	919	502	*33*	15	498	421	*33*	4	579	27
34	101	*34*	11	899	530	*34*	16	470	429	*34*	5	571	26
35	121	*35*	12	879	558	*35*	16	442	437	*35*	5	563	25
36	140	*36*	12	860	9. 80586	*36*	17	10. 19414	445	*36*	5	555	24
37	160	*37*	12	840	614	*37*	17	386	454	*37*	5	546	23
38	180	*38*	13	820	642	*38*	18	358	462	*38*	5	538	22
39	200	*39*	13	800	669	*39*	18	331	470	*39*	5	530	21
40	9. 73219	*40*	13	10. 26781	697	*40*	19	303	10. 07478	*40*	5	9. 92522	20
41	239	*41*	14	761	725	*41*	19	275	486	*41*	6	514	19
42	259	*42*	14	741	753	*42*	20	247	494	*42*	6	506	18
43	278	*43*	14	722	9. 80781	*43*	20	10. 19219	502	*43*	6	498	17
44	298	*44*	15	702	808	*44*	20	192	510	*44*	6	490	16
45	318	*45*	15	682	836	*45*	21	164	518	*45*	6	482	15
46	337	*46*	15	663	864	*46*	21	136	527	*46*	6	473	14
47	357	*47*	16	643	892	*47*	22	108	535	*47*	6	465	13
48	377	*48*	16	623	919	*48*	22	081	543	*48*	6	457	12
49	396	*49*	16	604	947	*49*	23	053	551	*49*	7	449	11
50	9. 73416	*50*	17	10. 26584	9. 80975	*50*	23	10. 19025	10. 07559	*50*	7	9. 92441	10
51	435	*51*	17	565	9. 81003	*51*	24	10. 18997	567	*51*	7	433	9
52	455	*52*	17	545	030	*52*	24	970	575	*52*	7	425	8
53	474	*53*	18	526	058	*53*	25	942	584	*53*	7	416	7
54	494	*54*	18	506	086	*54*	25	914	592	*54*	7	408	6
55	513	*55*	18	487	113	*55*	26	887	600	*55*	7	400	5
56	533	*56*	19	467	141	*56*	26	859	608	*56*	8	392	4
57	552	*57*	19	448	169	*57*	26	831	616	*57*	8	384	3
58	572	*58*	19	428	196	*58*	27	804	624	*58*	8	376	2
59	591	*59*	20	409	224	*59*	27	776	633	*59*	8	367	1
60	9. 73611	*60*	20	10. 26389	9. 81252	*60*	28	10. 18748	10. 07641	*60*	8	9. 92359	0
′ ↑ 122°→	cos	″	Diff.	sec	cot	″	Diff.	tan	csc	″	Diff.	sin	′ ↑ ←57°

TABLE 33.

Logarithms of Trigonometric Functions.

33°→ ↓ ′	sin	″	Diff.	csc	tan	″	Diff.	cot	sec	″	Diff.	cos ←146° ↓	′
0	9. 73611	0	0	10. 26389	9. 81252	0	0	10. 18748	10. 07641	0	0	9. 92359	60
1	630	1	0	370	279	1	0	721	649	1	0	351	59
2	650	2	1	350	307	2	1	693	657	2	0	343	58
3	669	3	1	331	335	3	1	665	665	3	0	335	57
4	689	4	1	311	362	4	2	638	674	4	1	326	56
5	708	5	2	292	390	5	2	610	682	5	1	318	55
6	727	6	2	273	418	6	3	582	690	6	1	310	54
7	747	7	2	253	445	7	3	555	698	7	1	302	53
8	766	8	3	234	473	8	4	527	10. 07707	8	1	9. 92293	52
9	785	9	3	215	9. 81500	9	4	10. 18500	715	9	1	285	51
10	9. 73805	10	3	10. 26195	528	10	5	472	723	10	1	277	50
11	824	11	3	176	556	11	5	444	731	11	2	269	49
12	843	12	4	157	583	12	5	417	740	12	2	260	48
13	863	13	4	137	611	13	6	389	748	13	2	252	47
14	882	14	4	118	638	14	6	362	756	14	2	244	46
15	901	15	5	099	666	15	7	334	765	15	2	235	45
16	921	16	5	079	693	16	7	307	773	16	2	227	44
17	940	17	5	060	721	17	8	279	10. 07781	17	2	9. 92219	43
18	959	18	6	041	9. 81748	18	8	10. 18252	789	18	3	211	42
19	978	19	6	022	776	19	9	224	798	19	3	202	41
20	9. 73997	20	6	10. 26003	803	20	9	197	806	20	3	194	40
21	9. 74017	21	7	10. 25983	831	21	10	169	814	21	3	186	39
22	036	22	7	964	858	22	10	142	823	22	3	177	38
23	055	23	7	945	886	23	11	114	831	23	3	169	37
24	074	24	8	926	913	24	11	087	839	24	3	161	36
25	093	25	8	907	941	25	11	059	848	25	3	152	35
26	113	26	8	887	968	26	12	032	10. 07856	26	4	9. 92144	34
27	132	27	9	868	9. 81996	27	12	10. 18004	864	27	4	136	33
28	151	28	9	849	9. 82023	28	13	10. 17977	873	28	4	127	32
29	170	29	9	830	051	29	13	949	881	29	4	119	31
30	9. 74189	30	10	10. 25811	078	30	14	922	889	30	4	111	30
31	208	31	10	792	106	31	14	894	898	31	4	102	29
32	227	32	10	773	133	32	15	867	906	32	4	094	28
33	246	33	10	754	161	33	15	839	914	33	5	086	27
34	265	34	11	735	188	34	16	812	923	34	5	077	26
35	284	35	11	716	215	35	16	785	10. 07931	35	5	9. 92069	25
36	303	36	11	697	243	36	16	757	940	36	5	060	24
37	322	37	12	678	270	37	17	730	948	37	5	052	23
38	341	38	12	659	298	38	17	702	956	38	5	044	22
39	360	39	12	640	9. 82325	39	18	10. 17675	965	39	5	035	21
40	9. 74379	40	13	10. 25621	352	40	18	648	973	40	6	027	20
41	398	41	13	602	380	41	19	620	982	41	6	018	19
42	417	42	13	583	407	42	19	593	990	42	6	010	18
43	436	43	14	564	435	43	20	565	10. 07998	43	6	9. 92002	17
44	455	44	14	545	462	44	20	538	10. 08007	44	6	9. 91993	16
45	474	45	14	526	489	45	21	511	015	45	6	985	15
46	493	46	15	507	517	46	21	483	024	46	6	976	14
47	512	47	15	488	544	47	22	456	032	47	7	968	13
48	531	48	15	469	571	48	22	429	041	48	7	959	12
49	549	49	16	451	9. 82599	49	22	10. 17401	049	49	7	951	11
50	9. 74568	50	16	10. 25432	626	50	23	374	058	50	7	942	10
51	587	51	16	413	653	51	23	347	066	51	7	934	9
52	606	52	17	394	681	52	24	319	10. 08075	52	7	9. 91925	8
53	625	53	17	375	708	53	24	292	083	53	7	917	7
54	644	54	17	356	735	54	25	265	092	54	8	908	6
55	662	55	17	338	762	55	25	238	100	55	8	900	5
56	681	56	18	319	790	56	26	210	109	56	8	891	4
57	700	57	18	300	817	57	26	183	117	57	8	883	3
58	719	58	18	281	844	58	27	156	126	58	8	874	2
59	737	59	19	263	871	59	27	129	134	59	8	866	1
60	9. 74756	60	19	10. 25244	9. 82899	60	27	10. 17101	10. 08143	60	8	9. 91857	0
′ ↑ 123°→	cos	″	Diff.	sec	cot	″	Diff.	tan	csc	″	Diff.	sin ←56° ↑	′

Logarithms of Trigonometric Functions.

34° → ′ ↓	sin	″	Diff.	csc	tan	″	Diff.	cot	sec	″	Diff.	cos	← 145° ′ ↓
0	9.74756	0	0	10.25244	9.82899	0	0	10.17101	10.08143	0	0	9.91857	60
1	775	1	0	225	926	1	0	074	151	1	0	849	59
2	794	2	1	206	953	2	1	047	160	2	0	840	58
3	812	3	1	188	9.82980	3	1	10.17020	168	3	0	832	57
4	831	4	1	169	9.83008	4	2	10.16992	177	4	1	823	56
5	850	5	2	150	035	5	2	965	185	5	1	815	55
6	9.74868	6	2	10.25132	062	6	3	938	194	6	1	806	54
7	887	7	2	113	089	7	3	911	202	7	1	798	53
8	906	8	2	094	117	8	4	883	211	8	1	789	52
9	924	9	3	076	144	9	4	856	219	9	1	781	51
10	943	10	3	057	171	10	5	829	10.08228	10	1	9.91772	50
11	961	11	3	039	9.83198	11	5	10.16802	237	11	2	763	49
12	980	12	4	020	225	12	5	775	245	12	2	755	48
13	9.74999	13	4	10.25001	252	13	6	748	254	13	2	746	47
14	9.75017	14	4	10.24983	280	14	6	720	262	14	2	738	46
15	036	15	5	964	307	15	7	693	271	15	2	729	45
16	054	16	5	946	334	16	7	666	280	16	2	720	44
17	073	17	5	927	361	17	8	639	288	17	2	712	43
18	091	18	6	909	9.83388	18	8	10.16612	297	18	3	703	42
19	110	19	6	890	415	19	9	585	305	19	3	695	41
20	128	20	6	872	442	20	9	558	10.08314	20	3	9.91686	40
21	147	21	6	853	470	21	9	530	323	21	3	677	39
22	9.75165	22	7	10.24835	497	22	10	503	331	22	3	669	38
23	184	23	7	816	524	23	10	476	340	23	3	660	37
24	202	24	7	798	551	24	11	449	349	24	3	651	36
25	221	25	8	779	578	25	11	422	357	25	4	643	35
26	239	26	8	761	9.83605	26	12	10.16395	366	26	4	634	34
27	258	27	8	742	632	27	12	368	375	27	4	625	33
28	276	28	9	724	659	28	13	341	383	28	4	617	32
29	294	29	9	706	686	29	13	314	392	29	4	608	31
30	9.75313	30	9	10.24687	713	30	14	287	10.08401	30	4	9.91599	30
31	331	31	9	669	740	31	14	260	409	31	4	591	29
32	350	32	10	650	768	32	14	232	418	32	5	582	28
33	368	33	10	632	9.83795	33	15	10.16205	427	33	5	573	27
34	386	34	10	614	822	34	15	178	435	34	5	565	26
35	405	35	11	595	849	35	16	151	444	35	5	556	25
36	423	36	11	577	876	36	16	124	453	36	5	547	24
37	9.75441	37	11	10.24559	903	37	17	097	462	37	5	538	23
38	459	38	12	541	930	38	17	070	470	38	5	530	22
39	478	39	12	522	957	39	18	043	479	39	6	521	21
40	496	40	12	504	9.83984	40	18	10.16016	10.08488	40	6	9.91512	20
41	514	41	13	486	9.84011	41	18	10.15989	496	41	6	504	19
42	533	42	13	467	038	42	19	962	505	42	6	495	18
43	551	43	13	449	065	43	19	935	514	43	6	486	17
44	9.75569	44	13	10.24431	092	44	20	908	523	44	6	477	16
45	587	45	14	413	119	45	20	881	531	45	7	469	15
46	605	46	14	395	146	46	21	854	540	46	7	460	14
47	624	47	14	376	173	47	21	827	549	47	7	451	13
48	642	48	15	358	200	48	22	800	558	48	7	442	12
49	660	49	15	340	227	49	22	773	567	49	7	433	11
50	678	50	15	322	9.84254	50	23	10.15746	10.08575	50	7	9.91425	10
51	696	51	16	304	280	51	23	720	584	51	7	416	9
52	9.75714	52	16	10.24286	307	52	23	693	593	52	8	407	8
53	733	53	16	267	334	53	24	666	602	53	8	398	7
54	751	54	17	249	361	54	24	639	611	54	8	389	6
55	769	55	17	231	388	55	25	612	619	55	8	381	5
56	787	56	17	213	415	56	25	585	628	56	8	372	4
57	805	57	17	195	442	57	26	558	637	57	8	363	3
58	823	58	18	177	469	58	26	531	646	58	8	354	2
59	841	59	18	159	496	59	27	504	655	59	9	345	1
60	9.75859	60	18	10.24141	9.84523	60	27	10.15477	10.08664	60	9	9.91336	0
′ ↑ 124° →	cos	″	Diff.	sec	cot	″	Diff.	tan	csc	″	Diff.	sin	′ ↑ ← 55°

TABLE 33.

Logarithms of Trigonometric Functions.

35°→ ↓ ′	sin	″	Diff.	csc	tan	″	Diff.	cot	sec	″	Diff.	cos	←144° ↓ ′
0	9. 75859	0	0	10. 24141	9. 84523	0	0	10. 15477	10. 08664	0	0	9. 91336	60
1	877	1	0	123	550	1	0	450	672	1	0	328	59
2	895	2	1	105	576	2	1	424	681	2	0	319	58
3	913	3	1	087	603	3	1	397	690	3	0	310	57
4	931	4	1	069	630	4	2	370	699	4	1	301	56
5	949	5	1	051	657	5	2	343	708	5	1	292	55
6	967	6	2	033	9. 84684	6	3	10. 15316	717	6	1	283	54
7	9. 75985	7	2	10. 24015	711	7	3	289	726	7	1	274	53
8	9. 76003	8	2	10. 23997	738	8	4	262	10. 08734	8	1	9. 91266	52
9	021	9	3	979	764	9	4	236	743	9	1	257	51
10	039	10	3	961	791	10	4	209	752	10	2	248	50
11	057	11	3	943	9. 84818	11	5	10. 15182	761	11	2	239	49
12	075	12	4	925	845	12	5	155	770	12	2	230	48
13	093	13	4	907	872	13	6	128	779	13	2	221	47
14	111	14	4	889	899	14	6	101	788	14	2	212	46
15	129	15	4	871	925	15	7	075	10. 08797	15	2	9. 91203	45
16	146	16	5	854	952	16	7	048	806	16	2	194	44
17	164	17	5	836	9. 84979	17	8	10. 15021	815	17	3	185	43
18	182	18	5	818	9. 85006	18	8	10. 14994	824	18	3	176	42
19	9. 76200	19	6	10. 23800	033	19	8	967	833	19	3	167	41
20	218	20	6	782	059	20	9	941	842	20	3	158	40
21	236	21	6	764	086	21	9	914	851	21	3	149	39
22	253	22	6	747	113	22	10	887	10. 08859	22	3	9. 91141	38
23	271	23	7	729	140	23	10	860	868	23	3	132	37
24	289	24	7	711	166	24	11	834	877	24	4	123	36
25	307	25	7	693	193	25	11	807	886	25	4	114	35
26	324	26	8	676	9. 85220	26	12	10. 14780	895	26	4	105	34
27	342	27	8	658	247	27	12	753	904	27	4	096	33
28	360	28	8	640	273	28	12	727	913	28	4	087	32
29	378	29	9	622	300	29	13	700	10. 08922	29	4	9. 91078	31
30	9. 76395	30	9	10. 23605	327	30	13	673	931	30	5	069	30
31	413	31	9	587	354	31	14	646	940	31	5	060	29
32	431	32	9	569	380	32	14	620	949	32	5	051	28
33	448	33	10	552	9. 85407	33	15	10. 14593	958	33	5	042	27
34	466	34	10	534	434	34	15	566	967	34	5	033	26
35	484	35	10	516	460	35	16	540	977	35	5	023	25
36	501	36	11	499	487	36	16	513	986	36	5	014	24
37	519	37	11	481	514	37	16	486	10. 08995	37	6	9. 91005	23
38	537	38	11	463	540	38	17	460	10. 09004	38	6	9. 90996	22
39	554	39	12	446	567	39	17	433	013	39	6	987	21
40	9. 76572	40	12	10. 23428	594	40	18	406	022	40	6	978	20
41	590	41	12	410	9. 85620	41	18	10. 14380	031	41	6	969	19
42	607	42	12	393	647	42	19	353	040	42	6	960	18
43	625	43	13	375	674	43	19	326	049	43	6	951	17
44	642	44	13	358	700	44	20	300	058	44	7	942	16
45	660	45	13	340	727	45	20	273	10. 09067	45	7	9. 90933	15
46	677	46	14	323	754	46	20	246	076	46	7	924	14
47	695	47	14	305	780	47	21	220	085	47	7	915	13
48	712	48	14	288	9. 85807	48	21	10. 14193	094	48	7	906	12
49	730	49	14	270	834	49	22	166	104	49	7	896	11
50	9. 76747	50	15	10. 23253	860	50	22	140	113	50	8	887	10
51	765	51	15	235	887	51	23	113	122	51	8	878	9
52	782	52	15	218	913	52	23	087	131	52	8	869	8
53	800	53	16	200	940	53	24	060	10. 09140	53	8	9. 90860	7
54	817	54	16	183	967	54	24	033	149	54	8	851	6
55	835	55	16	165	9. 85993	55	24	10. 14007	158	55	8	842	5
56	852	56	17	148	9. 86020	56	25	10. 13980	168	56	8	832	4
57	870	57	17	130	046	57	25	954	177	57	9	823	3
58	887	58	17	113	073	58	26	927	186	58	9	814	2
59	904	59	17	096	100	59	26	900	195	59	9	805	1
60	9. 76922	60	18	10. 23078	9. 86126	60	27	10. 13874	10. 09204	60	9	9. 90796	0
′ ↑ 125°→	cos	″	Diff.	sec	cot	″	Diff.	tan	csc	″	Diff.	sin	′ ↑ ←54°

TABLE 33.

Logarithms of Trigonometric Functions.

36°→ ↓ ′	sin	″	Diff.	csc	tan	″	Diff.	cot	sec	″	Diff.	cos ←143° ↓ ′	
0	9. 76922	0	0	10. 23078	9. 86126	0	0	10. 13874	10. 09204	0	0	9. 90796	60
1	939	1	0	061	153	1	0	847	213	1	0	787	59
2	957	2	1	043	179	2	1	821	223	2	0	777	58
3	974	3	1	026	206	3	1	794	232	3	0	768	57
4	9. 76991	4	1	10. 23009	232	4	2	768	241	4	1	759	56
5	9. 77009	5	1	10. 22991	259	5	2	741	250	5	1	750	55
6	026	6	2	974	285	6	3	715	259	6	1	741	54
7	043	7	2	957	312	7	3	688	269	7	1	731	53
8	061	8	2	939	338	8	4	662	278	8	1	722	52
9	078	9	3	922	365	9	4	635	287	9	1	713	51
10	095	10	3	905	392	10	4	608	10. 09296	10	2	9. 90704	50
11	112	11	3	888	9. 86418	11	5	10. 13582	306	11	2	694	49
12	130	12	3	870	445	12	5	555	315	12	2	685	48
13	147	13	4	853	471	13	6	529	324	13	2	676	47
14	9. 77164	14	4	10. 22836	498	14	6	502	333	14	2	667	46
15	181	15	4	819	524	15	7	476	343	15	2	657	45
16	199	16	5	801	551	16	7	449	352	16	2	648	44
17	216	17	5	784	577	17	7	423	361	17	3	639	43
18	233	18	5	767	603	18	8	397	370	18	3	630	42
19	250	19	5	750	630	19	8	370	380	19	3	620	41
20	268	20	6	732	656	20	9	344	10. 09389	20	3	9. 90611	40
21	285	21	6	715	9. 86683	21	9	317	398	21	3	602	39
22	302	22	6	698	709	22	10	10. 13291	408	22	3	592	38
23	9. 77319	23	7	10. 22681	736	23	10	264	417	23	4	583	37
24	336	24	7	664	762	24	11	238	426	24	4	574	36
25	353	25	7	647	789	25	11	211	435	25	4	565	35
26	370	26	7	630	815	26	11	185	445	26	4	555	34
27	387	27	8	613	842	27	12	158	454	27	4	546	33
28	405	28	8	595	868	28	12	132	463	28	4	537	32
29	422	29	8	578	894	29	13	106	473	29	5	527	31
30	439	30	9	561	921	30	13	079	10. 09482	30	5	9. 90518	30
31	456	31	9	544	947	31	14	053	491	31	5	509	29
32	473	32	9	527	9. 86974	32	14	026	501	32	5	499	28
33	9. 77490	33	9	10. 22510	9. 87000	33	15	10. 13000	510	33	5	490	27
34	507	34	10	493	027	34	15	10. 12973	520	34	5	480	26
35	524	35	10	476	053	35	15	947	529	35	5	471	25
36	541	36	10	459	079	36	16	921	538	36	6	462	24
37	558	37	11	442	106	37	16	894	548	37	6	452	23
38	575	38	11	425	132	38	17	868	557	38	6	443	22
39	592	39	11	408	158	39	17	842	566	39	6	434	21
40	609	40	11	391	185	40	18	815	10. 09576	40	6	9. 90424	20
41	626	41	12	374	211	41	18	789	585	41	6	415	19
42	9. 77643	42	12	10. 22357	9. 87238	42	18	762	595	42	7	405	18
43	660	43	12	340	264	43	19	10. 12736	604	43	7	396	17
44	677	44	13	323	290	44	19	710	614	44	7	386	16
45	694	45	13	306	317	45	20	683	623	45	7	377	15
46	711	46	13	289	343	46	20	657	632	46	7	368	14
47	728	47	13	272	369	47	21	631	642	47	7	358	13
48	744	48	14	256	396	48	21	604	651	48	7	349	12
49	761	49	14	239	422	49	22	578	661	49	8	339	11
50	778	50	14	222	448	50	22	552	10. 09670	50	8	9. 90330	10
51	9. 77795	51	15	10. 22205	9. 87475	51	22	10. 12525	680	51	8	320	9
52	812	52	15	188	501	52	23	499	689	52	8	311	8
53	829	53	15	171	527	53	23	473	699	53	8	301	7
54	846	54	15	154	554	54	24	446	708	54	8	292	6
55	862	55	16	138	580	55	24	420	718	55	9	282	5
56	879	56	16	121	606	56	25	394	727	56	9	273	4
57	896	57	16	104	633	57	25	367	737	57	9	263	3
58	913	58	16	087	659	58	26	341	746	58	9	254	2
59	930	59	17	070	685	59	26	315	756	59	9	244	1
60	9. 77946	60	17	10. 22054	9. 87711	60	26	10. 12289	10. 09785	60	9	9. 90235	0
′ ↑ 126°→	cos	″	Diff.	sec	cot	″	Diff.	tan	csc	″	Diff.	sin ←53°	′ ↑

541524°—43——42

TABLE 33.

Logarithms of Trigonometric Functions.

37° → ↓ ′	sin	″	Diff.	csc	tan	″	Diff.	cot	sec	″	Diff.	cos	← 142° ↓ ′
0	9. 77946	0	0	10. 22054	9. 87711	0	0	10. 12289	10. 09765	0	0	9. 90235	60
1	963	1	0	037	738	1	0	262	775	1	0	225	59
2	980	2	1	020	764	2	1	236	784	2	0	216	58
3	9. 77997	3	1	10. 22003	790	3	1	210	794	3	0	206	57
4	9. 78013	4	1	10. 21987	817	4	2	183	803	4	1	197	56
5	030	5	1	970	843	5	2	157	813	5	1	187	55
6	047	6	2	953	869	6	3	131	822	6	1	178	54
7	063	7	2	937	895	7	3	105	832	7	1	168	53
8	080	8	2	920	922	8	3	078	10. 09841	8	1	9. 90159	52
9	097	9	2	903	948	9	4	052	851	9	1	149	51
10	113	10	3	887	9. 87974	10	4	026	861	10	2	139	50
11	130	11	3	870	9. 88000	11	5	10. 12000	870	11	2	130	49
12	9. 78147	12	3	10. 21853	027	12	5	10. 11973	880	12	2	120	48
13	163	13	4	837	053	13	6	947	889	13	2	111	47
14	180	14	4	820	079	14	6	921	899	14	2	101	46
15	197	15	4	803	105	15	7	895	909	15	2	091	45
16	213	16	4	787	131	16	7	869	10. 09918	16	3	9. 90082	44
17	230	17	5	770	158	17	7	842	928	17	3	072	43
18	246	18	5	754	184	18	8	816	937	18	3	063	42
19	263	19	5	737	210	19	8	790	947	19	3	053	41
20	9. 78280	20	5	10. 21720	236	20	9	764	957	20	3	043	40
21	296	21	6	704	9. 88262	21	9	10. 11738	966	21	3	034	39
22	313	22	6	687	289	22	10	711	976	22	4	024	38
23	329	23	6	671	315	23	10	685	986	23	4	014	37
24	346	24	7	654	341	24	10	659	10. 09995	24	4	9. 90005	36
25	362	25	7	638	367	25	11	633	10. 10005	25	4	9. 89995	35
26	379	26	7	621	393	26	11	607	015	26	4	985	34
27	395	27	7	605	420	27	12	580	024	27	4	976	33
28	9. 78412	28	8	10. 21588	446	28	12	554	034	28	5	966	32
29	428	29	8	572	472	29	13	528	044	29	5	956	31
30	445	30	8	555	9. 88498	30	13	10. 11502	053	30	5	947	30
31	461	31	9	539	524	31	14	476	063	31	5	937	29
32	478	32	9	522	550	32	14	450	10. 10073	32	5	9. 89927	28
33	494	33	9	506	577	33	14	423	082	33	5	918	27
34	510	34	9	490	603	34	15	397	092	34	5	908	26
35	527	35	10	473	629	35	15	371	102	35	6	898	25
36	9. 78543	36	10	10. 21457	655	36	16	345	112	36	6	888	24
37	560	37	10	440	681	37	16	319	121	37	6	879	23
38	576	38	10	424	707	38	17	293	131	38	6	869	22
39	592	39	11	408	733	39	17	267	10. 10141	39	6	9. 89859	21
40	609	40	11	391	9. 88759	40	17	10. 11241	151	40	6	849	20
41	625	41	11	375	786	41	18	214	160	41	7	840	19
42	642	42	12	358	812	42	18	188	170	42	7	830	18
43	658	43	12	342	838	43	19	162	180	43	7	820	17
44	9. 78674	44	12	10. 21326	864	44	19	136	190	44	7	810	16
45	691	45	12	309	890	45	20	110	199	45	7	801	15
46	707	46	13	293	916	46	20	084	10. 10209	46	7	9. 89791	14
47	723	47	13	277	942	47	20	058	219	47	8	781	13
48	739	48	13	261	968	48	21	032	229	48	8	771	12
49	756	49	13	244	9. 88994	49	21	10. 11006	239	49	8	761	11
50	772	50	14	228	9. 89020	50	22	10. 10980	248	50	8	752	10
51	788	51	14	212	046	51	22	954	258	51	8	742	9
52	9. 78805	52	14	10. 21195	073	52	23	927	268	52	8	732	8
53	821	53	15	179	099	53	23	901	10. 10278	53	9	9. 89722	7
54	837	54	15	163	125	54	24	875	288	54	9	712	6
55	853	55	15	147	151	55	24	849	298	55	9	702	5
56	869	56	15	131	177	56	24	823	307	56	9	693	4
57	886	57	16	114	203	57	25	797	317	57	9	683	3
58	902	58	16	098	229	58	25	771	327	58	9	673	2
59	918	59	16	082	255	59	26	745	337	59	10	663	1
60	9. 78934	60	16	10. 21066	9. 89281	60	26	10. 10719	10. 10347	60	10	9. 89653	0
′ ↑ 127° →	cos	″	Diff.	sec	cot	″	Diff.	tan	csc	″	Diff.	sin	′ ↑ ← 52°

TABLE 33.

Logarithms of Trigonometric Functions.

38°→ ↓ ′	sin	″	Diff.	csc	tan	″	Diff.	cot	sec	″	Diff.	cos ←141°	↓ ′
0	9. 78934	*0*	0	10. 21066	9. 89281	*0*	0	10. 10719	10. 10347	*0*	0	9. 89653	60
1	950	*1*	0	050	307	*1*	0	693	357	*1*	0	643	59
2	967	*2*	1	033	333	*2*	1	667	367	*2*	0	633	58
3	983	*3*	1	017	359	*3*	1	641	376	*3*	1	624	57
4	9. 78999	*4*	1	10. 21001	385	*4*	2	615	386	*4*	1	614	56
5	9. 79015	*5*	1	10. 20985	411	*5*	2	589	396	*5*	1	604	55
6	031	*6*	2	969	437	*6*	3	563	406	*6*	1	594	54
7	047	*7*	2	953	9. 89463	*7*	3	10. 10537	416	*7*	1	584	53
8	063	*8*	2	937	489	*8*	3	511	426	*8*	1	574	52
9	079	*9*	2	921	515	*9*	4	485	436	*9*	2	564	51
10	095	*10*	3	905	541	*10*	4	459	10. 10446	*10*	2	9. 89554	50
11	111	*11*	3	889	567	*11*	5	433	456	*11*	2	544	49
12	128	*12*	3	872	593	*12*	5	407	466	*12*	2	534	48
13	9. 79144	*13*	3	10. 20856	619	*13*	6	381	476	*13*	2	524	47
14	160	*14*	4	840	9. 89645	*14*	6	10. 10355	486	*14*	2	514	46
15	176	*15*	4	824	671	*15*	6	329	496	*15*	3	504	45
16	192	*16*	4	808	697	*16*	7	303	505	*16*	3	495	44
17	208	*17*	5	792	723	*17*	7	277	515	*17*	3	485	43
18	224	*18*	5	776	749	*18*	8	251	525	*18*	3	475	42
19	240	*19*	5	760	775	*19*	8	225	535	*19*	3	465	41
20	256	*20*	5	744	801	*20*	9	199	10. 10545	*20*	3	9. 89455	40
21	9. 79272	*21*	6	10. 20728	9. 89827	*21*	9	10. 10173	555	*21*	4	445	39
22	288	*22*	6	712	853	*22*	10	147	565	*22*	4	435	38
23	304	*23*	6	696	879	*23*	10	121	575	*23*	4	425	37
24	319	*24*	6	681	905	*24*	10	095	585	*24*	4	415	36
25	335	*25*	7	665	931	*25*	11	069	595	*25*	4	405	35
26	351	*26*	7	649	957	*26*	11	043	605	*26*	4	395	34
27	367	*27*	7	633	9. 89983	*27*	12	10. 10017	615	*27*	5	385	33
28	383	*28*	7	617	9. 90009	*28*	12	10. 09991	625	*28*	5	375	32
29	9. 79399	*29*	8	10. 20601	035	*29*	13	965	636	*29*	5	364	31
30	415	*30*	8	585	061	*30*	13	939	10. 10646	*30*	5	9. 89354	30
31	431	*31*	8	569	086	*31*	13	914	656	*31*	5	344	29
32	447	*32*	8	553	112	*32*	14	888	666	*32*	5	334	28
33	463	*33*	9	537	138	*33*	14	862	676	*33*	6	324	27
34	478	*34*	9	522	164	*34*	15	836	686	*34*	6	314	26
35	494	*35*	9	506	190	*35*	15	810	696	*35*	6	304	25
36	9. 79510	*36*	10	10. 20490	9. 90216	*36*	16	10. 09784	706	*36*	6	294	24
37	526	*37*	10	474	242	*37*	16	758	716	*37*	6	284	23
38	542	*38*	10	458	268	*38*	16	732	726	*38*	6	274	22
39	558	*39*	10	442	294	*39*	17	706	736	*39*	7	264	21
40	573	*40*	11	427	320	*40*	17	680	10. 10746	*40*	7	9. 89254	20
41	589	*41*	11	411	346	*41*	18	654	756	*41*	7	244	19
42	605	*42*	11	395	371	*42*	18	629	767	*42*	7	233	18
43	621	*43*	11	379	397	*43*	19	603	777	*43*	7	223	17
44	9. 79636	*44*	12	10. 20364	9. 90423	*44*	19	10. 09577	787	*44*	7	213	16
45	652	*45*	12	348	449	*45*	19	551	797	*45*	8	203	15
46	668	*46*	12	332	475	*46*	20	525	807	*46*	8	193	14
47	684	*47*	12	316	501	*47*	20	499	817	*47*	8	183	13
48	699	*48*	13	301	527	*48*	21	473	827	*48*	8	173	12
49	715	*49*	13	285	553	*49*	21	447	838	*49*	8	162	11
50	731	*50*	13	269	578	*50*	22	422	10. 10848	*50*	8	9. 89152	10
51	746	*51*	14	254	604	*51*	22	396	858	*51*	9	142	9
52	9. 79762	*52*	14	10. 20238	630	*52*	22	370	868	*52*	9	132	8
53	778	*53*	14	222	9. 90656	*53*	23	10. 09344	878	*53*	9	122	7
54	793	*54*	14	207	682	*54*	23	318	888	*54*	9	112	6
55	809	*55*	15	191	708	*55*	24	292	899	*55*	9	101	5
56	825	*56*	15	175	734	*56*	24	266	909	*56*	9	091	4
57	840	*57*	15	160	759	*57*	25	241	919	*57*	10	081	3
58	856	*58*	15	144	785	*58*	25	215	929	*58*	10	071	2
59	872	*59*	16	128	811	*59*	26	189	940	*59*	10	060	1
60	9. 79887	*60*	16	10. 20113	9. 90837	*60*	26	10. 09163	10. 10950	*60*	10	9. 89050	0
′ ↑ 128°→	cos	″	Diff.	sec	cot	″	Diff.	tan	csc	″	Diff.	sin ←51°	′ ↑

TABLE 33.

Logarithms of Trigonometric Functions.

39°→ ↓ ′	sin	″ Diff.		csc	tan	″ Diff.		cot	sec	″ Diff.		cos ←140° ↓	′
0	9.79887	0	0	10.20113	9.90837	0	0	10.09163	10.10950	0	0	9.89050	60
1	903	1	0	097	863	1	0	137	960	1	0	040	59
2	918	2	1	082	889	2	1	111	970	2	0	030	58
3	934	3	1	066	914	3	1	086	980	3	1	020	57
4	950	4	1	050	940	4	2	060	10.10991	4	1	9.89009	56
5	965	5	1	035	966	5	2	034	10.11001	5	1	9.88999	55
6	981	6	2	019	9.90992	6	3	10.09008	011	6	1	989	54
7	9.79996	7	2	10.20004	9.91018	7	3	10.08982	022	7	1	978	53
8	9.80012	8	2	10.19988	043	8	3	957	032	8	1	968	52
9	027	9	2	973	069	9	4	931	042	9	2	958	51
10	043	10	3	957	095	10	4	905	052	10	2	948	50
11	058	11	3	942	121	11	5	879	063	11	2	937	49
12	074	12	3	926	147	12	5	853	073	12	2	927	48
13	089	13	3	911	172	13	6	828	083	13	2	917	47
14	105	14	4	895	198	14	6	802	10.11094	14	2	9.88906	46
15	120	15	4	880	9.91224	15	6	10.08776	104	15	3	896	45
16	136	16	4	864	250	16	7	750	114	16	3	886	44
17	151	17	4	849	276	17	7	724	125	17	3	875	43
18	166	18	5	834	301	18	8	699	135	18	3	865	42
19	9.80182	19	5	10.19818	327	19	8	673	145	19	3	855	41
20	197	20	5	803	353	20	9	647	156	20	3	844	40
21	213	21	5	787	379	21	9	621	166	21	4	834	39
22	228	22	6	772	404	22	9	596	176	22	4	824	38
23	244	23	6	756	430	23	10	570	10.11187	23	4	9.88813	37
24	259	24	6	741	456	24	10	544	197	24	4	803	36
25	274	25	6	726	9.91482	25	11	10.08518	207	25	4	793	35
26	290	26	7	710	507	26	11	493	218	26	5	782	34
27	305	27	7	695	533	27	12	467	228	27	5	772	33
28	320	28	7	680	559	28	12	441	239	28	5	761	32
29	336	29	7	664	585	29	12	415	249	29	5	751	31
30	9.80351	30	8	10.19649	610	30	13	390	259	30	5	741	30
31	366	31	8	634	636	31	13	364	270	31	5	730	29
32	382	32	8	618	662	32	14	338	10.11280	32	6	9.88720	28
33	397	33	8	603	688	33	14	312	291	33	6	709	27
34	412	34	9	588	713	34	15	287	301	34	6	699	26
35	428	35	9	572	9.91739	35	15	10.08261	312	35	6	688	25
36	443	36	9	557	765	36	15	235	322	36	6	678	24
37	458	37	9	542	791	37	16	209	332	37	6	668	23
38	473	38	10	527	816	38	16	184	343	38	7	657	22
39	489	39	10	511	842	39	17	158	353	39	7	647	21
40	9.80504	40	10	10.19496	868	40	17	132	364	40	7	636	20
41	519	41	10	481	893	41	18	107	10.11374	41	7	9.88626	19
42	534	42	11	466	919	42	18	081	385	42	7	615	18
43	550	43	11	450	945	43	18	055	395	43	7	605	17
44	565	44	11	435	971	44	19	029	406	44	8	594	16
45	580	45	12	420	9.91996	45	19	10.08004	416	45	8	584	15
46	595	46	12	405	9.92022	46	20	10.07978	427	46	8	573	14
47	610	47	12	390	048	47	20	952	437	47	8	563	13
48	625	48	12	375	073	48	21	927	448	48	8	552	12
49	641	49	13	359	099	49	21	901	458	49	9	542	11
50	9.80656	50	13	10.19344	125	50	21	875	10.11469	50	9	9.88531	10
51	671	51	13	329	150	51	22	850	479	51	9	521	9
52	686	52	13	314	176	52	22	824	490	52	9	510	8
53	701	53	14	299	9.92202	53	23	10.07798	501	53	9	499	7
54	716	54	14	284	227	54	23	773	511	54	9	489	6
55	731	55	14	269	253	55	24	747	522	55	10	478	5
56	746	56	14	254	279	56	24	721	532	56	10	468	4
57	762	57	15	238	304	57	24	696	543	57	10	457	3
58	777	58	15	223	330	58	25	670	553	58	10	447	2
59	792	59	15	208	356	59	25	644	564	59	10	436	1
60	9.80807	60	15	10.19193	9.92381	60	26	10.07619	10.11575	60	10	9.88425	0
′ ↑ 129°	→cos	″ Diff.		sec	cot	″ Diff.		tan	csc	″ Diff.		sin ←50° ↑	′

TABLE 33.

Logarithms of Trigonometric Functions.

40°→ ↓ ′	sin	″	Diff.	csc	tan	″	Diff.	cot	sec	″	Diff.	cos ←139°	↓ ′
0	9. 80807	0	0	10. 19193	9. 92381	0	0	10. 07619	10. 11575	0	0	9. 88425	60
1	822	1	0	178	407	1	0	593	585	1	0	415	59
2	837	2	0	163	433	2	1	567	596	2	0	404	58
3	852	3	1	148	458	3	1	542	606	3	1	394	57
4	867	4	1	133	484	4	2	516	617	4	1	383	56
5	882	5	1	118	510	5	2	490	628	5	1	372	55
6	9. 80897	6	1	10. 19103	9. 92535	6	3	10. 07465	638	6	1	362	54
7	912	7	2	088	561	7	3	439	649	7	1	351	53
8	927	8	2	073	587	8	3	413	660	8	1	340	52
9	942	9	2	058	612	9	4	388	670	9	2	330	51
10	957	10	2	043	638	10	4	362	10. 11681	10	2	9. 88319	50
11	972	11	3	028	663	11	5	337	692	11	2	308	49
12	9. 80987	12	3	10. 19013	9. 92689	12	5	10. 07311	702	12	2	298	48
13	9. 81002	13	3	10. 18998	715	13	6	285	713	13	2	287	47
14	017	14	3	983	740	14	6	260	724	14	3	276	46
15	032	15	4	968	766	15	6	234	734	15	3	266	45
16	047	16	4	953	792	16	7	208	745	16	3	255	44
17	061	17	4	939	817	17	7	183	756	17	3	244	43
18	076	18	4	924	9. 92843	18	8	10. 07157	766	18	3	234	42
19	091	19	5	909	868	19	8	132	777	19	3	223	41
20	106	20	5	894	894	20	9	106	10. 11788	20	4	9. 88212	40
21	9. 81121	21	5	10. 18879	920	21	9	080	799	21	4	201	39
22	136	22	5	864	945	22	9	055	809	22	4	191	38
23	151	23	6	849	971	23	10	029	820	23	4	180	37
24	166	24	6	834	9. 92996	24	10	10. 07004	831	24	4	169	36
25	180	25	6	820	9. 93022	25	11	10. 06978	842	25	4	158	35
26	195	26	6	805	048	26	11	952	852	26	5	148	34
27	210	27	7	790	073	27	12	927	863	27	5	137	33
28	225	28	7	775	099	28	12	901	874	28	5	126	32
29	9. 81240	29	7	10. 18760	124	29	12	876	885	29	5	115	31
30	254	30	7	746	150	30	13	850	10. 11895	30	5	9. 88105	30
31	269	31	8	731	175	31	13	825	906	31	6	094	29
32	284	32	8	716	9. 93201	32	14	10. 06799	917	32	6	083	28
33	299	33	8	701	227	33	14	773	928	33	6	072	27
34	314	34	8	686	252	34	14	748	939	34	6	061	26
35	328	35	9	672	278	35	15	722	949	35	6	051	25
36	343	36	9	657	303	36	15	697	960	36	6	040	24
37	9. 81358	37	9	10. 18642	329	37	16	671	971	37	7	029	23
38	372	38	9	628	354	38	16	646	982	38	7	018	22
39	387	39	10	613	9. 93380	39	17	10. 06620	10. 11993	39	7	9. 88007	21
40	402	40	10	598	406	40	17	594	10. 12004	40	7	9. 87996	20
41	417	41	10	583	431	41	17	569	015	41	7	985	19
42	431	42	10	569	457	42	18	543	025	42	8	975	18
43	446	43	11	554	482	43	18	518	036	43	8	964	17
44	9. 81461	44	11	10. 18539	508	44	19	492	047	44	8	953	16
45	475	45	11	525	533	45	19	467	058	45	8	942	15
46	490	46	11	510	9. 93559	46	20	10. 06441	069	46	8	931	14
47	505	47	12	495	584	47	20	416	080	47	8	920	13
48	519	48	12	481	610	48	20	390	091	48	9	909	12
49	534	49	12	466	636	49	21	364	102	49	9	898	11
50	549	50	12	451	661	50	21	339	10. 12113	50	9	9. 87887	10
51	563	51	13	437	687	51	22	313	123	51	9	877	9
52	9. 81578	52	13	10. 18422	712	52	22	288	134	52	9	866	8
53	592	53	13	408	9. 93738	53	23	10. 06262	145	53	10	855	7
54	607	54	13	393	763	54	23	237	156	54	10	844	6
55	622	55	14	378	789	55	23	211	167	55	10	833	5
56	636	56	14	364	814	56	24	186	178	56	10	822	4
57	651	57	14	349	840	57	24	160	189	57	10	811	3
58	665	58	14	335	865	58	25	135	200	58	10	800	2
59	680	59	15	320	891	59	25	109	211	59	11	789	1
60	9. 81694	60	15	10. 18306	9. 93916	60	26	10. 06084	10. 12222	60	11	9. 87778	0
′ ↑ 130°→	cos	″	Diff.	sec	cot	″	Diff.	tan	csc	″	Diff.	sin ←49°	′ ↑

TABLE 33.

Logarithms of Trigonometric Functions.

41°→ ↓ ′	sin	″	Diff.	csc	tan	″	Diff.	cot	sec	″	Diff.	cos ←138°	↓ ′
0	9.81694	*0*	0	10.18306	9.93916	*0*	0	10.06084	10.12222	*0*	0	9.87778	60
1	709	*1*	0	291	942	*1*	0	058	233	*1*	0	767	59
2	723	*2*	0	277	967	*2*	1	033	244	*2*	0	756	58
3	738	*3*	1	262	9.93993	*3*	1	10.06007	255	*3*	1	745	57
4	752	*4*	1	248	9.94018	*4*	2	10.05982	266	*4*	1	734	56
5	767	*5*	1	233	044	*5*	2	956	277	*5*	1	723	55
6	781	*6*	1	219	069	*6*	3	931	288	*6*	1	712	54
7	9.81796	*7*	2	10.18204	095	*7*	3	905	299	*7*	1	701	53
8	810	*8*	2	190	120	*8*	3	880	310	*8*	1	690	52
9	825	*9*	2	175	146	*9*	4	854	321	*9*	2	679	51
10	839	*10*	2	161	171	*10*	4	829	10.12332	*10*	2	9.87668	50
11	854	*11*	3	146	197	*11*	5	803	343	*11*	2	657	49
12	868	*12*	3	132	9.94222	*12*	5	10.05778	354	*12*	2	646	48
13	882	*13*	3	118	248	*13*	6	752	365	*13*	2	635	47
14	9.81897	*14*	3	10.18103	273	*14*	6	727	376	*14*	3	624	46
15	911	*15*	4	089	299	*15*	6	701	387	*15*	3	613	45
16	926	*16*	4	074	324	*16*	7	676	399	*16*	3	601	44
17	940	*17*	4	060	350	*17*	7	650	410	*17*	3	590	43
18	955	*18*	4	045	375	*18*	8	625	421	*18*	3	579	42
19	969	*19*	5	031	9.94401	*19*	8	10.05599	432	*19*	4	568	41
20	983	*20*	5	017	426	*20*	8	574	10.12443	*20*	4	9.87557	40
21	9.81998	*21*	5	10.18002	452	*21*	9	548	454	*21*	4	546	39
22	9.82012	*22*	5	10.17988	477	*22*	9	523	465	*22*	4	535	38
23	026	*23*	5	974	503	*23*	10	497	476	*23*	4	524	37
24	041	*24*	6	959	528	*24*	10	472	487	*24*	4	513	36
25	055	*25*	6	945	554	*25*	11	446	499	*25*	5	501	35
26	069	*26*	6	931	579	*26*	11	421	510	*26*	5	490	34
27	084	*27*	6	916	9.94604	*27*	11	10.05396	521	*27*	5	479	33
28	098	*28*	7	902	630	*28*	12	370	532	*28*	5	468	32
29	112	*29*	7	888	655	*29*	12	345	543	*29*	5	457	31
30	9.82126	*30*	7	10.17874	681	*30*	13	319	10.12554	*30*	6	9.87446	30
31	141	*31*	7	859	706	*31*	13	294	566	*31*	6	434	29
32	155	*32*	8	845	732	*32*	14	268	577	*32*	6	423	28
33	169	*33*	8	831	757	*33*	14	243	588	*33*	6	412	27
34	184	*34*	8	816	9.94783	*34*	14	10.05217	599	*34*	6	401	26
35	198	*35*	8	802	808	*35*	15	192	610	*35*	7	390	25
36	212	*36*	9	788	834	*36*	15	166	622	*36*	7	378	24
37	226	*37*	9	774	859	*37*	16	141	633	*37*	7	367	23
38	9.82240	*38*	9	10.17760	884	*38*	16	116	644	*38*	7	356	22
39	255	*39*	9	745	910	*39*	17	090	655	*39*	7	345	21
40	269	*40*	10	731	935	*40*	17	065	10.12666	*40*	7	9.87334	20
41	283	*41*	10	717	961	*41*	17	039	678	*41*	8	322	19
42	297	*42*	10	703	9.94986	*42*	18	10.05014	689	*42*	8	311	18
43	311	*43*	10	689	9.95012	*43*	18	10.04988	700	*43*	8	300	17
44	326	*44*	10	674	037	*44*	19	963	712	*44*	8	288	16
45	9.82340	*45*	11	10.17660	062	*45*	19	938	723	*45*	8	277	15
46	354	*46*	11	646	088	*46*	20	912	734	*46*	9	266	14
47	368	*47*	11	632	113	*47*	20	887	745	*47*	9	255	13
48	382	*48*	11	618	139	*48*	20	861	757	*48*	9	243	12
49	396	*49*	12	604	164	*49*	21	836	768	*49*	9	232	11
50	410	*50*	12	590	190	*50*	21	810	10.12779	*50*	9	9.87221	10
51	424	*51*	12	576	9.95215	*51*	22	10.04785	791	*51*	10	209	9
52	9.82439	*52*	12	10.17561	240	*52*	22	760	802	*52*	10	198	8
53	453	*53*	13	547	266	*53*	22	734	813	*53*	10	187	7
54	467	*54*	13	533	291	*54*	23	709	825	*54*	10	175	6
55	481	*55*	13	519	317	*55*	23	683	836	*55*	10	164	5
56	495	*56*	13	505	342	*56*	24	658	847	*56*	10	153	4
57	509	*57*	14	491	368	*57*	24	632	859	*57*	11	141	3
58	523	*58*	14	477	393	*58*	25	607	870	*58*	11	130	2
59	537	*59*	14	463	418	*59*	25	582	881	*59*	11	119	1
60	9.82551	*60*	14	10.17449	9.95444	*60*	25	10.04556	10.12893	*60*	11	9.87107	0
′ ↑ 131°→	cos	″	Diff.	sec	cot	″	Diff.	tan	csc	″	Diff.	sin ←48°	′ ↑

TABLE 33.

Logarithms of Trigonometric Functions.

42°→ ↓ ′	sin	″	Diff.	csc	tan	″	Diff.	cot	sec	″	Diff.	cos ←137°	↓ ′
0	9. 82551	0	0	10. 17449	9. 95444	0	0	10. 04556	10. 12893	0	0	9. 87107	60
1	565	1	0	435	469	1	0	531	904	1	0	096	59
2	579	2	0	421	495	2	1	505	915	2	0	085	58
3	593	3	1	407	520	3	1	480	927	3	1	073	57
4	607	4	1	393	545	4	2	455	938	4	1	062	56
5	621	5	1	379	571	5	2	429	950	5	1	050	55
6	635	6	1	365	596	6	3	404	961	6	1	039	54
7	9. 82649	7	2	10. 17351	9. 95622	7	3	10. 04378	972	7	1	028	53
8	663	8	2	337	647	8	3	353	984	8	2	016	52
9	677	9	2	323	672	9	4	328	10. 12995	9	2	9. 87005	51
10	691	10	2	309	698	10	4	302	10. 13007	10	2	9. 86993	50
11	705	11	3	295	723	11	5	277	018	11	2	982	49
12	719	12	3	281	748	12	5	252	030	12	2	970	48
13	9. 82733	13	3	10. 17267	774	13	5	226	041	13	3	959	47
14	747	14	3	253	9. 95799	14	6	10. 04201	053	14	3	947	46
15	761	15	3	239	825	15	6	175	064	15	3	936	45
16	775	16	4	225	850	16	7	150	076	16	3	924	44
17	788	17	4	212	875	17	7	125	087	17	3	913	43
18	802	18	4	198	901	18	8	099	098	18	3	902	42
19	9. 82816	19	4	10. 17184	926	19	8	074	110	19	4	890	41
20	830	20	5	170	952	20	8	048	10. 13121	20	4	9. 86879	40
21	844	21	5	156	9. 95977	21	9	10. 04023	133	21	4	867	39
22	858	22	5	142	9. 96002	22	9	10. 03998	145	22	4	855	38
23	872	23	5	128	028	23	10	972	156	23	4	844	37
24	885	24	6	115	053	24	10	947	168	24	5	832	36
25	9. 82899	25	6	10. 17101	078	25	11	922	179	25	5	821	35
26	913	26	6	087	104	26	11	896	191	26	5	809	34
27	927	27	6	073	129	27	11	871	202	27	5	798	33
28	941	28	6	059	155	28	12	845	214	28	5	786	32
29	955	29	7	045	180	29	12	820	225	29	6	775	31
30	968	30	7	032	205	30	13	795	10. 13237	30	6	9. 86763	30
31	982	31	7	018	231	31	13	769	248	31	6	752	29
32	9. 82996	32	7	10. 17004	9. 96256	32	14	10. 03744	260	32	6	740	28
33	9. 83010	33	8	10. 16990	281	33	14	719	272	33	6	728	27
34	023	34	8	977	307	34	14	693	283	34	7	717	26
35	037	35	8	963	332	35	15	668	295	35	7	705	25
36	051	36	8	949	357	36	15	643	306	36	7	694	24
37	065	37	8	935	383	37	16	617	318	37	7	682	23
38	078	38	9	922	408	38	16	592	330	38	7	670	22
39	092	39	9	908	433	39	16	567	341	39	8	659	21
40	9. 83106	40	9	10. 16894	459	40	17	541	10. 13353	40	8	9. 86647	20
41	120	41	9	880	484	41	17	516	365	41	8	635	19
42	133	42	10	867	9. 96510	42	18	10. 03490	376	42	8	624	18
43	147	43	10	853	535	43	18	465	388	43	8	612	17
44	161	44	10	839	560	44	19	440	400	44	8	600	16
45	174	45	10	826	586	45	19	414	411	45	9	589	15
46	188	46	11	812	611	46	19	389	423	46	9	577	14
47	9. 83202	47	11	10. 16798	636	47	20	364	435	47	9	565	13
48	215	48	11	785	662	48	20	338	446	48	9	554	12
49	229	49	11	771	687	49	21	313	458	49	9	542	11
50	242	50	11	758	712	50	21	288	10. 13470	50	10	9. 86530	10
51	256	51	12	744	9. 96738	51	22	10. 03262	482	51	10	518	9
52	270	52	12	730	763	52	22	237	493	52	10	507	8
53	9. 83283	53	12	10. 16717	788	53	22	212	505	53	10	495	7
54	297	54	12	703	814	54	23	186	517	54	10	483	6
55	310	55	13	690	839	55	23	161	528	55	11	472	5
56	324	56	13	676	864	56	24	136	540	56	11	460	4
57	338	57	13	662	890	57	24	110	552	57	11	448	3
58	351	58	13	649	915	58	25	085	564	58	11	436	2
59	365	59	14	635	940	59	25	060	575	59	11	425	1
60	9. 83378	60	14	10. 16622	9. 96966	60	25	10. 03034	10. 13587	60	12	9. 86413	0
′ ↑ 132°→	cos	″	Diff.	sec	cot	″	Diff.	tan	csc	″	Diff.	sin ←47°	′ ↑

TABLE 33.

Logarithms of Trigonometric Functions.

43°→ ↓ ′	sin	″	Diff.	csc	tan	″	Diff.	cot	sec	″	Diff.	cos	←136° ↓ ′
0	9. 83378	0	0	10. 16622	9. 96966	0	0	10. 03034	10. 13587	0	0	9. 86413	60
1	392	1	0	608	9. 96991	1	0	10. 03009	599	1	0	401	59
2	405	2	0	595	9. 97016	2	1	10. 02984	611	2	0	389	58
3	419	3	1	581	042	3	1	958	623	3	1	377	57
4	432	4	1	568	067	4	2	933	634	4	1	366	56
5	446	5	1	554	092	5	2	908	646	5	1	354	55
6	459	6	1	541	118	6	3	882	658	6	1	342	54
7	473	7	2	527	143	7	3	857	670	7	1	330	53
8	9. 83486	8	2	10. 16514	168	8	3	832	682	8	2	318	52
9	500	9	2	500	9. 97193	9	4	10. 02807	10. 13694	9	2	9. 86306	51
10	513	10	2	487	219	10	4	781	705	10	2	295	50
11	527	11	2	473	244	11	5	756	717	11	2	283	49
12	540	12	3	460	269	12	5	731	729	12	2	271	48
13	554	13	3	446	295	13	5	705	741	13	3	259	47
14	567	14	3	433	320	14	6	680	753	14	3	247	46
15	9. 83581	15	3	10. 16419	345	15	6	655	765	15	3	235	45
16	594	16	4	406	9. 97371	16	7	10. 02629	777	16	3	223	44
17	608	17	4	392	396	17	7	604	10. 13789	17	3	9. 86211	43
18	621	18	4	379	421	18	8	579	800	18	4	200	42
19	634	19	4	366	447	19	8	553	812	19	4	188	41
20	648	20	4	352	472	20	8	528	824	20	4	176	40
21	661	21	5	339	497	21	9	503	836	21	4	164	39
22	674	22	5	326	523	22	9	477	848	22	4	152	38
23	9. 83688	23	5	10. 16312	548	23	10	452	860	23	5	140	37
24	701	24	5	299	9. 97573	24	10	10. 02427	872	24	5	128	36
25	715	25	6	285	598	25	11	402	10. 13884	25	5	9. 86116	35
26	728	26	6	272	624	26	11	376	896	26	5	104	34
27	741	27	6	259	649	27	11	351	908	27	5	092	33
28	755	28	6	245	674	28	12	326	920	28	6	080	32
29	768	29	6	232	700	29	12	300	932	29	6	068	31
30	9. 83781	30	7	10. 16219	725	30	13	275	944	30	6	056	30
31	795	31	7	205	750	31	13	250	956	31	6	044	29
32	808	32	7	192	9. 97776	32	13	10. 02224	968	32	6	032	28
33	821	33	7	179	801	33	14	199	980	33	7	020	27
34	834	34	8	166	826	34	14	174	10. 13992	34	7	9. 86008	26
35	848	35	8	152	851	35	15	149	10. 14004	35	7	9. 85996	25
36	861	36	8	139	877	36	15	123	016	36	7	984	24
37	874	37	8	126	902	37	16	098	028	37	7	972	23
38	9. 83887	38	8	10. 16113	927	38	16	073	040	38	8	960	22
39	901	39	9	099	953	39	16	047	052	39	8	948	21
40	914	40	9	086	9. 97978	40	17	10. 02022	064	40	8	936	20
41	927	41	9	073	9. 98003	41	17	10. 01997	076	41	8	924	19
42	940	42	9	060	029	42	18	971	088	42	8	912	18
43	954	43	10	046	054	43	18	946	10. 14100	43	9	9. 85900	17
44	967	44	10	033	079	44	19	921	112	44	9	888	16
45	980	45	10	020	104	45	19	896	124	45	9	876	15
46	9. 83993	46	10	10. 16007	130	46	19	870	136	46	9	864	14
47	9. 84006	47	10	10. 15994	155	47	20	845	149	47	9	851	13
48	020	48	11	980	9. 98180	48	20	10. 01820	161	48	10	839	12
49	033	49	11	967	206	49	21	794	173	49	10	827	11
50	046	50	11	954	231	50	21	769	185	50	10	815	10
51	059	51	11	941	256	51	22	744	197	51	10	803	9
52	072	52	12	928	281	52	22	719	10. 14209	52	10	9. 85791	8
53	9. 84085	53	12	10. 15915	307	53	22	693	221	53	11	779	7
54	098	54	12	902	9. 98332	54	23	10. 01668	234	54	11	766	6
55	112	55	12	888	357	55	23	643	246	55	11	754	5
56	125	56	12	875	383	56	24	617	258	56	11	742	4
57	138	57	13	862	408	57	24	592	270	57	11	730	3
58	151	58	13	849	433	58	24	567	282	58	12	718	2
59	164	59	13	836	458	59	25	542	294	59	12	706	1
60	9. 84177	60	13	10. 15823	9. 98484	60	25	10. 01516	10. 14307	60	12	9. 85693	0
′ ↑ 133°→	cos	″	Diff.	sec	cot	″	Diff.	tan	csc	″	Diff.	sin	′ ↑ ←46°

TABLE 33.

Logarithms of Trigonometric Functions.

44°→ ′	sin	″	Diff.	csc	tan	″	Diff.	cot	sec	″	Diff.	cos	←135° ′
0	9.84177	0	0	10.15823	9.98484	0	0	10.01516	10.14307	0	0	9.85693	60
1	190	1	0	810	509	1	0	491	319	1	0	681	59
2	203	2	0	797	534	2	1	466	331	2	0	669	58
3	216	3	1	784	560	3	1	440	343	3	1	657	57
4	229	4	1	771	585	4	2	415	355	4	1	645	56
5	242	5	1	758	610	5	2	390	368	5	1	632	55
6	255	6	1	745	635	6	3	365	380	6	1	620	54
7	269	7	2	731	661	7	3	339	392	7	1	608	53
8	282	8	2	718	686	8	3	314	404	8	2	596	52
9	295	9	2	705	711	9	4	289	10.14417	9	2	9.85583	51
10	9.84308	10	2	10.15692	9.98737	10	4	10.01263	429	10	2	571	50
11	321	11	2	679	762	11	5	238	441	11	2	559	49
12	334	12	3	666	787	12	5	213	453	12	2	547	48
13	347	13	3	653	812	13	5	188	466	13	3	534	47
14	360	14	3	640	838	14	6	162	478	14	3	522	46
15	373	15	3	627	863	15	6	137	490	15	3	510	45
16	385	16	3	615	888	16	7	112	503	16	3	497	44
17	398	17	4	602	913	17	7	087	515	17	4	485	43
18	411	18	4	589	939	18	8	061	10.14527	18	4	9.85473	42
19	424	19	4	576	964	19	8	036	540	19	4	460	41
20	9.84437	20	4	10.15563	9.98989	20	8	10.01011	552	20	4	448	40
21	450	21	5	550	9.99015	21	9	10.00985	564	21	4	436	39
22	463	22	5	537	040	22	9	960	577	22	5	423	38
23	476	23	5	524	065	23	10	935	589	23	5	411	37
24	489	24	5	511	090	24	10	910	601	24	5	399	36
25	502	25	5	498	116	25	11	884	10.14614	25	5	9.85386	35
26	515	26	6	485	141	26	11	859	626	26	5	374	34
27	528	27	6	472	166	27	11	834	639	27	6	361	33
28	540	28	6	460	191	28	12	809	651	28	6	349	32
29	553	29	6	447	217	29	12	783	663	29	6	337	31
30	9.84566	30	6	10.15434	9.99242	30	13	10.00758	676	30	6	324	30
31	579	31	7	421	267	31	13	733	10.14688	31	6	9.85312	29
32	592	32	7	408	293	32	13	707	701	32	7	299	28
33	605	33	7	395	318	33	14	682	713	33	7	287	27
34	618	34	7	382	343	34	14	657	726	34	7	274	26
35	630	35	8	370	368	35	15	632	738	35	7	262	25
36	643	36	8	357	394	36	15	606	750	36	7	250	24
37	656	37	8	344	419	37	16	581	10.14763	37	8	9.85237	23
38	669	38	8	331	444	38	16	556	775	38	8	225	22
39	682	39	8	318	469	39	16	531	788	39	8	212	21
40	9.84694	40	9	10.15306	9.99495	40	17	10.00505	800	40	8	200	20
41	707	41	9	293	520	41	17	480	813	41	8	187	19
42	720	42	9	280	545	42	18	455	825	42	9	175	18
43	733	43	9	267	570	43	18	430	838	43	9	162	17
44	745	44	9	255	596	44	19	404	850	44	9	150	16
45	758	45	10	242	621	45	19	379	863	45	9	137	15
46	771	46	10	229	646	46	19	354	10.14875	46	10	9.85125	14
47	784	47	10	216	672	47	20	328	888	47	10	112	13
48	796	48	10	204	697	48	20	303	900	48	10	100	12
49	809	49	11	191	722	49	21	278	913	49	10	087	11
50	9.84822	50	11	10.15178	9.99747	50	21	10.00253	926	50	10	074	10
51	835	51	11	165	773	51	21	227	938	51	11	062	9
52	847	52	11	153	798	52	22	202	951	52	11	049	8
53	860	53	11	140	823	53	22	177	963	53	11	037	7
54	873	54	12	127	848	54	23	152	976	54	11	024	6
55	885	55	12	115	874	55	23	126	10.14988	55	11	9.85012	5
56	898	56	12	102	899	56	24	101	10.15001	56	12	9.84999	4
57	911	57	12	089	924	57	24	076	014	57	12	986	3
58	923	58	12	077	949	58	24	051	026	58	12	974	2
59	936	59	13	064	9.99975	59	25	025	039	59	12	961	1
60	9.84949	60	13	10.15051	10.00000	60	25	10.00000	10.15051	60	12	9.84949	0
′ 134°→	cos	″	Diff.	sec	cot	″	Diff.	tan	csc	″	Diff.	sin	←45° ′

TABLE 34.

Haversines.

s ′	0h 0m 0° 0′		0h 2m 0° 30′		0h 4m 1° 0′		0h 6m 1° 30′		0h 8m 2° 0′		s
	Log. Hav.	Nat. Hav.	Log. Hav.	Nat. Hav.	Log. Hav.	Nat. Hav.	Log. Hav.	Nat. Hav.	Log. Hav.	Nat. Hav.	
0 0	—00	0.00000	5.27963	0.00002	5.88168	0.00008	6.23385	0.00017	6.48371	0.00030	60
2	1.72333	.00000	.29399	.00002	.88889	.00008	.23866	.00017	.48732	.00031	58
4+ 1	2.32539	.00000	.30811	.00002	.89604	.00008	.24345	.00018	.49092	.00031	56
6	2.67757	.00000	.32201	.00002	.90313	.00008	.24821	.00018	.49450	.00031	54
8+ 2	2.92745	0.00000	5.33569	0.00002	5.91016	0.00008	6.25294	0.00018	6.49807	0.00031	52
10	3.12127	.00000	.34916	.00002	.91714	.00008	.25765	.00018	.50162	.00032	50
12+ 3	3.27963	.00000	.36242	.00002	.92406	.00008	.26233	.00018	.50516	.00032	48
14	3.41353	.00000	.37548	.00002	.93093	.00009	.26699	.00018	.50868	.00032	46
16+ 4	3.52951	0.00000	5.38835	0.00002	5.93774	0.00009	6.27162	0.00019	6.51219	0.00033	44
18	3.63182	.00000	.40103	.00003	.94450	.00009	.27623	.00019	.51568	.00033	42
20+ 5	3.72333	.00000	.41352	.00003	.95121	.00009	.28081	.00019	.51916	.00033	40
22	3.80612	.00000	.42585	.00003	.95786	.00009	.28537	.00019	.52263	.00033	38
24+ 6	3.88169	0.00000	5.43799	0.00003	5.96447	0.00009	6.28991	0.00019	6.52608	0.00034	36
26	3.95122	.00000	.44997	.00003	.97102	.00009	29442	.00020	.52952	.00034	34
28+ 7	4.01559	.00000	.46179	.00003	.97753	.00010	.29891	.00020	.53295	.00034	32
30	4.07551	.00000	.47345	.00003	.98399	.00010	.30337	.00020	.53636	.00034	30
32+ 8	4.13157	0.00000	5.48496	0.00003	5.99040	0.00010	6.30781	0.00020	6.53976	0.00035	28
34	.18423	.00000	.49631	.00003	5.99676	.00010	.31223	.00021	.54315	.00035	26
36+ 9	.23388	.00000	.50752	.00003	6.00308	.00010	.31663	.00021	.54652	.00035	24
38	.28084	.00000	.51858	.00003	.00935	.00010	.32101	.00021	.54988	.00035	22
40+10	4.32539	0.00000	5.52951	0.00003	6.01557	0.00010	6.32536	0.00021	6.55323	0.00036	20
42	.36777	.00000	.54030	.00003	.02176	.00011	.32969	.00021	.55656	.00036	18
44+11	.40818	.00000	.55095	.00004	.02789	.00011	.33400	.00022	.55988	.00036	16
46	.44679	.00000	.56148	.00004	.03399	.00011	.33829	.00022	.56319	.00037	14
48+12	4.48375	0.00000	5.57189	0.00004	6.04004	0.00011	6.34256	0.00022	6.56649	0.00037	12
50	.51921	.00000	.58216	.00004	.04605	.00011	.34681	.00022	.56977	.00037	10
52+13	.55328	.00000	.59232	.00004	.05202	.00011	.35103	.00022	.57304	.00037	8
54	.58606	.00000	.60236	.00004	.05795	.00011	.35524	.00023	.57630	.00038	6
56+14	4.61765	0.00000	5.61229	0.00004	6.06384	0.00012	6.35943	0.00023	6.57955	0.00038	4
58	4.64813	0.00000	5.62211	0.00004	6.06969	0.00012	6.36359	0.00023	6.58278	0.00038	2
	23h 59m		23h 57m		23h 55m		23h 53m		23h 51m		

s ′	0h 1m 0° 0′		0h 3m 0° 30′		0h 5m 1° 0′		0h 7m 1° 30′		0h 9m 2° 0′		s
0+15	4.67757	0.00000	5.63181	0.00004	6.07550	0.00012	6.36774	0.00023	6.58600	0.00039	60
2	.70605	.00000	.64141	.00004	.08127	.00012	.37186	.00024	.58921	.00039	58
4+16	.73363	.00001	.65090	.00004	.08700	.00012	.37597	.00024	.59241	.00039	56
6	.76036	.00001	.66029	.00005	.09270	.00012	.38006	.00024	.59560	.00039	54
8+17	4.78629	0.00001	5.66958	0.00005	6.09836	0.00013	6.38412	0.00024	6.59878	0.00040	52
10	.81147	.00001	.67877	.00005	.10398	.00013	.38817	.00024	.60194	.00040	50
12+18	.83594	.00001	.68787	.00005	.10956	.00013	.39220	.00025	.60509	.00040	48
14	.85973	.00001	.69687	.00005	.11511	.00013	.39622	.00025	.60823	.00041	46
16+19	4.88290	0.00001	5.70578	0.00005	6.12063	0.00013	6.40021	0.00025	6.61136	0.00041	44
18	.90546	.00001	.71460	.00005	.12611	.00013	.40418	.00025	.61448	.00041	42
20+20	.92745	.00001	.72332	.00005	.13155	.00014	.40814	.00026	.61759	.00041	40
22	.94890	.00001	.73197	.00005	.13696	.00014	.41208	.00026	.62068	.00042	38
24+21	4.96983	0.00001	5.74052	0.00006	6.14234	0.00014	6.41600	0.00026	6.62377	0.00042	36
26	4.99027	.00001	.74900	.00006	.14769	.00014	.41990	.00026	.62684	.00042	34
28+22	5.01024	.00001	.75739	.00006	.15300	.00014	.42379	.00027	.62991	.00043	32
30	.02976	.00001	.76570	.00006	.15828	.00014	.42766	.00027	.63296	.00043	30
32+23	5.04885	0.00001	5.77394	0.00006	6.16353	0.00015	6.43151	0.00027	6.63600	0.00043	28
34	.06753	.00001	.78209	.00006	.16874	.00015	.43534	.00027	.63903	.00044	26
36+24	.08581	.00001	.79017	.00006	.17393	.00015	.43916	.00027	.64205	.00044	24
38	.10372	.00001	.79818	.00006	.17908	.00015	.44296	.00028	.64504	.00044	22
40+25	5.12127	0.00001	5.80611	0.00006	6.18421	0.00015	6.44675	0.00028	6.64806	0.00044	20
42	.13847	.00001	.81397	.00007	.18930	.00015	.45052	.00028	.65105	.00045	18
44+26	.15534	.00001	.82176	.00007	.19437	.00016	.45427	.00028	.65403	.00045	16
46	.17188	.00001	.82948	.00007	.19940	.00016	.45800	.00029	.65700	.00045	14
48+27	5.18812	0.00002	5.83713	0.00007	6.20441	0.00016	6.46172	0.00029	6.65996	0.00046	12
50	.20406	.00002	.84472	.00007	.20938	.00016	.46543	.00029	.66291	.00046	10
52+28	.21971	.00002	.85224	.00007	.21433	.00016	.46911	.00029	.66585	.00046	8
54	.23508	.00002	.85969	.00007	.21925	.00017	.47279	.00030	.66878	.00047	6
56+29	5.25019	0.00002	5.86709	0.00007	6.22415	0.00017	6.47644	0.00030	6.67170	0.00047	4
58	.26503	.00002	.87442	.00008	.22901	.00017	.48008	.00030	.67461	.00047	2
60+30	5.27963	0.00002	5.88168	0.00008	6.23385	0.00017	6.48371	0.00030	6.67751	0.00048	0
	23h 58m		23h 56m		23h 54m		23h 52m		23h 50m		

TABLE 34.

Haversines.

s ′	$0^h\ 10^m$ 2° 30′		$0^h\ 12^m$ 3° 0′		$0^h\ 14^m$ 3° 30′		$0^h\ 16^m$ 4° 0′		$0^h\ 18^m$ 4° 30′		s
	Log. Hav.	Nat. Hav.	Log. Hav.	Nat. Hav.	Log. Hav.	Nat. Hav.	Log. Hav.	Nat. Hav.	Log. Hav.	Nat. Hav.	
0 0	6.67751	**0.00048**	6.83584	**0.00069**	6.96970	**0.00093**	7.08564	**0.00122**	7.18790	**0.00154**	60
2	.68040	**.00048**	.83825	**.00069**	.97176	**.00094**	.08745	**.00122**	.18950	**.00155**	58
4+ 1	.68328	**.00048**	.84065	**.00069**	.97382	**.00094**	.08925	**.00123**	.19111	**.00155**	56
6	.68615	**.00049**	.84304	**.00070**	.97588	**.00095**	.09105	**.00123**	.19271	**.00156**	54
8+ 2	6.68901	**0.00049**	6.84543	**0.00070**	6.97793	**0.00095**	7.09284	**0.00124**	7.19430	**0.00156**	52
10	.69186	**.00049**	.84782	**.00070**	.97997	**.00095**	.09464	**.00124**	.19590	**.00157**	50
12+ 3	.69470	**.00050**	.85019	**.00071**	.98201	**.00096**	.09642	**.00125**	.19749	**.00158**	48
14	.69754	**.00050**	.85256	**.00071**	.98405	**.00096**	.09821	**.00125**	.19908	**.00158**	46
16+ 4	6.70036	**0.00050**	6.85492	**0.00072**	6.98608	**0.00097**	7.09999	**0.00126**	7.20066	**0.00159**	44
18	.70318	**.00050**	.85728	**.00072**	.98811	**.00097**	.10177	**.00126**	.20225	**.00159**	42
20+ 5	.70598	**.00051**	.85963	**.00072**	.99013	**.00098**	.10354	**.00127**	.20383	**.00160**	40
22	.70878	**.00051**	.86197	**.00073**	.99214	**.00098**	.10531	**.00127**	.20540	**.00160**	38
24+ 6	6.71157	**0.00051**	6.86431	**0.00073**	6.99416	**0.00099**	7.10708	**0.00128**	7.20698	**0.00161**	36
26	.71435	**.00052**	.86664	**.00074**	6.99616	**.00099**	.10884	**.00128**	.20855	**.00162**	34
28+ 7	.71712	**.00052**	.86897	**.00074**	6.99817	**.00100**	.11060	**.00129**	.21012	**.00162**	32
30	.71988	**.00052**	.87129	**.00074**	7.00017	**.00100**	.11236	**.00130**	.21168	**.00163**	30
32+ 8	6.72263	**0.00053**	6.87360	**0.00075**	7.00216	**0.00101**	7.11411	**0.00130**	7.21325	**0.00163**	28
34	.72537	**.00053**	.87591	**.00075**	.00415	**.00101**	.11586	**.00131**	.21481	**.00164**	26
36+ 9	.72811	**.00053**	.87821	**.00076**	.00613	**.00101**	.11760	**.00131**	.21636	**.00165**	24
38	.73084	**.00054**	.88050	**.00076**	.00811	**.00102**	.11934	**.00132**	.21792	**.00165**	22
40+10	6.73355	**0.00054**	6.88279	**0.00076**	7.01009	**0.00102**	7.12108	**0.00132**	7.21947	**0.00166**	20
42	.73626	**.00054**	.88507	**.00077**	.01206	**.00103**	.12282	**.00133**	.22102	**.00166**	18
44+11	.73896	**.00055**	.88735	**.00077**	.01403	**.00103**	.12455	**.00133**	.22256	**.00167**	16
46	.74166	**.00055**	.88962	**.00078**	.01599	**.00104**	.12627	**.00134**	.22411	**.00168**	14
48+12	6.74434	**0.00056**	6.89188	**0.00078**	7.01795	**0.00104**	7.12800	**0.00134**	7.22565	**0.00168**	12
50	.74702	**.00056**	.89414	**.00078**	.01990	**.00105**	.12972	**.00135**	.22718	**.00169**	10
52+13	.74969	**.00056**	.89639	**.00079**	.02185	**.00105**	.13144	**.00135**	.22872	**.00169**	8
54	.75235	**.00057**	.89864	**.00079**	.02379	**.00106**	.13315	**.00136**	.23025	**.00170**	6
56+14	6.75500	**0.00057**	6.90088	**0.00080**	7.02573	**0.00106**	7.13486	**0.00136**	7.23178	**0.00171**	4
58	6.75764	**0.00057**	6.90312	**0.00080**	7.02767	**0.00107**	7.13657	**0.00137**	7.23331	**0.00171**	2
	$23^h\ 49^m$		$23^h\ 47^m$		$23^h\ 45^m$		$23^h\ 43^m$		$23^h\ 41^m$		

s ′	$0^h\ 11^m$ 2° 30′		$0^h\ 13^m$ 3° 0′		$0^h\ 15^m$ 3° 30′		$0^h\ 17^m$ 4° 0′		$0^h\ 19^m$ 4° 30′		s
0+15	6.76028	**0.00058**	6.90535	**0.00080**	7.02960	**0.00107**	7.13827	**0.00137**	7.23483	**0.00172**	60
2	.76290	**.00058**	.90757	**.00081**	.03153	**.00108**	.13997	**.00138**	.23635	**.00172**	58
4+16	.76552	**.00058**	.90979	**.00081**	.03345	**.00108**	.14167	**.00139**	.23787	**.00173**	56
6	.76814	**.00059**	.91200	**.00082**	.03537	**00108**	.14337	**.00139**	.23939	**.00174**	54
8+17	6.77074	**0.00059**	6.91421	**0.00082**	7.03729	**0.00109**	7.14506	**0.00140**	7.24090	**0.00174**	52
10	.77334	**.00059**	.91641	**.00082**	.03920	**.00109**	.14674	**.00140**	.24241	**.00175**	50
12+18	.77592	**.00060**	.91860	**.00083**	.04110	**.00110**	.14843	**.00141**	.24392	**.00175**	48
14	.77851	**.00060**	.92079	**.00083**	.04300	**.00110**	.15011	**.00141**	.24543	**.00176**	46
16+19	6.78108	**0.00060**	6.92298	**0.00084**	7.04490	**0.00111**	7.15179	**0.00142**	7.24693	**0.00177**	44
18	.78364	**.00061**	.92516	**.00084**	.04680	**.00111**	.15346	**.00142**	.24843	**.00177**	42
20+20	.78620	**.00061**	.92733	**.00085**	.04869	**.00112**	.15513	**.00143**	.24993	**.00178**	40
22	.78875	**.00061**	.92950	**.00085**	.05057	**.00112**	.15680	**.00143**	.25143	**.00178**	38
24+21	6.79129	**0.00062**	6.93166	**0.00085**	7.05245	**0.00113**	7.15846	**0.00144**	7.25292	**0.00179**	36
26	.79383	**.00062**	.93382	**.00086**	.05433	**.00113**	.16013	**.00145**	.25441	**.00180**	34
28+22	.79630	**.00063**	.93597	**.00086**	.05620	**.00114**	.16178	**.00145**	.25590	**.00180**	32
30	.79888	**.00063**	.93812	**.00087**	.05807	**.00114**	.16344	**.00146**	.25738	**.00181**	30
32+23	6.80139	**0.00063**	6.94026	**0.00087**	7.05994	**0.00115**	7.16509	**0.00146**	7.25886	**0.00181**	28
34	.80390	**.00064**	.94239	**.00088**	.06180	**.00115**	.16674	**.00147**	.26034	**.00182**	26
36+24	.80640	**.00064**	.94453	**.00088**	.06366	**.00116**	.16839	**.00147**	.26182	**.00183**	24
38	.80889	**.00064**	.94665	**.00088**	.06551	**.00116**	.17003	**.00148**	.26330	**.00183**	22
40+25	6.81137	**0.00065**	6.94877	**0.00089**	7.06736	**0.00117**	7.17167	**0.00148**	7.26477	**0.00184**	20
42	.81385	**.00065**	.95089	**.00089**	.06920	**.00117**	.17331	**.00149**	.26624	**.00185**	18
44+26	.81632	**.00066**	.95300	**.00090**	.07105	**.00118**	.17494	**.00150**	.26771	**.00185**	16
46	.81879	**.00066**	.95510	**.00090**	.07288	**.00118**	.17657	**.00150**	.26917	**.00186**	14
48+27	6.82124	**0.00066**	6.95720	**0.00091**	7.07472	**0.00119**	7.17820	**0.00151**	7.27064	**0.00186**	12
50	.82369	**.00067**	.95930	**.00091**	.07655	**.00119**	.17982	**.00151**	.27210	**.00187**	10
52+28	.82614	**.00067**	.96139	**.00091**	.07837	**.00120**	.18144	**.00152**	.27355	**.00188**	8
54	.82857	**.00067**	.96347	**.00092**	.08019	**.00120**	.18306	**.00152**	.27501	**.00188**	6
56+29	6.83100	**0.00068**	6.96555	**0.00092**	7.08201	**0.00121**	7.18468	**0.00153**	7.27646	**0.00189**	4
58	.83342	**.00068**	.96763	**.00093**	.08383	**.00121**	.18629	**.00154**	.27791	**.00190**	2
60+30	6.83584	**0.00069**	6.96970	**0.00093**	7.08564	**0.00122**	7.18790	**0.00154**	7.27936	**0.00190**	0
	$23^h\ 48^m$		$23^h\ 46^m$		$23^h\ 44^m$		$23^h\ 42^m$		$23^h\ 40^m$		

TABLE 34.

Haversines.

s	′	0h 20m 5° 0′ Log. Hav.	Nat. Hav.	0h 22m 5° 30′ Log. Hav.	Nat. Hav.	0h 24m 6° 0′ Log. Hav.	Nat. Hav.	0h 26m 6° 30′ Log. Hav.	Nat. Hav.	0h 28m 7° 0′ Log. Hav.	Nat. Hav.	s
0	0	7.27936	**0.00190**	7.36209	**0.00230**	7.43760	**0.00274**	7.50706	**0.00321**	7.57135	**0.00373**	60
2		.28080	**.00191**	.36340	**.00231**	.43880	**.00275**	.50817	**.00322**	.57238	**.00374**	58
4+	1	.28225	**.00192**	.36471	**.00232**	.44001	**.00275**	.50928	**.00323**	.57341	**.00374**	56
6		.28369	**.00192**	.36602	**.00232**	.44121	**.00276**	.51039	**.00324**	.57444	**.00375**	54
8+	2	7.28513	**0.00193**	7.36733	**0.00233**	7.44241	**0.00277**	7.51149	**0.00325**	7.57547	**0.00376**	52
10		.28656	**.00193**	.36864	**.00234**	.44361	**.00278**	.51260	**.00326**	.57650	**.00377**	50
12+	3	.28800	**.00194**	.36994	**.00234**	.44480	**.00278**	.51370	**.00326**	.57752	**.00378**	48
14		.28943	**.00195**	.37124	**.00235**	.44600	**.00279**	.51481	**.00327**	.57855	**.00379**	46
16+	4	7.29086	**0.00195**	7.37254	**0.00236**	7.44719	**0.00280**	7.51591	**0.00328**	7.57957	**0.00380**	44
18		.29228	**.00196**	.37384	**.00237**	.44838	**.00281**	.51701	**.00329**	.58060	**.00381**	42
20+	5	.29371	**.00197**	.37514	**.00237**	.44957	**.00282**	.51811	**.00330**	.58162	**.00382**	40
22		.29513	**.00197**	.37643	**.00238**	.45076	**.00282**	.51921	**.00331**	.58264	**.00383**	38
24+	6	7.29655	**0.00198**	7.37773	**0.00239**	7.45194	**0.00283**	7.52030	**0.00331**	7.58366	**0.00383**	36
26		.29797	**.00199**	.37902	**.00239**	.45313	**.00284**	.52140	**.00332**	.58467	**.00384**	34
28+	7	.29938	**.00199**	.38030	**.00240**	.45431	**.00285**	.52249	**.00333**	.58569	**.00385**	32
30		.30079	**.00200**	.38159	**.00241**	.45549	**.00285**	.52358	**.00334**	.58670	**.00386**	30
32+	8	7.30220	**0.00201**	7.38288	**0.00241**	7.45667	**0.00286**	7.52467	**0.00335**	7.58772	**0.00387**	28
34		.30361	**.00201**	.38416	**.00242**	.45785	**.00287**	.52576	**.00336**	.58873	**.00388**	26
36+	9	.30502	**.00202**	.38544	**.00243**	.45903	**.00288**	.52685	**.00336**	.58974	**.00389**	24
38		.30642	**.00203**	.38672	**.00244**	.46020	**.00289**	.52794	**.00337**	.59075	**.00390**	22
40+	10	7.30782	**0.00203**	7.38800	**0.00244**	7.46138	**0.00289**	7.52902	**0.00338**	7.59176	**0.00391**	20
42		.30922	**.00204**	.38927	**.00245**	.46255	**.00290**	.53011	**.00339**	.59277	**.00392**	18
44+	11	.31062	**.00204**	.39054	**.00246**	.46372	**.00291**	.53119	**.00340**	.59378	**.00392**	16
46		.31201	**.00205**	.39182	**.00247**	.46489	**.00292**	.53227	**.00341**	.59478	**.00393**	14
48+	12	7.31340	**0.00206**	7.39309	**0.00247**	7.46605	**0.00292**	7.53335	**0.00341**	7.59579	**0.00394**	12
50		.31479	**.00206**	.39435	**.00248**	.46722	**.00293**	.53443	**.00342**	.59679	**.00395**	10
52+	13	.31618	**.00207**	.39562	**.00249**	.46838	**.00294**	.53550	**.00343**	.59779	**.00396**	8
54		.31757	**.00208**	.39688	**.00249**	.46955	**.00295**	.53658	**.00344**	.59879	**.00397**	6
56+	14	7.31895	**0.00208**	7.39815	**0.00250**	7.47071	**0.00296**	7.53766	**0.00345**	7.59979	**0.00398**	4
58		7.32033	**0.00209**	7.39941	**0.00251**	7.47187	**0.00296**	7.53873	**0.00346**	7.60079	**0.00399**	2
		23h 39m		23h 37m		23h 35m		23h 33m		23h 31m		

s	′	0h 21m 5° 0′ Log. Hav.	Nat. Hav.	0h 23m 5° 30′ Log. Hav.	Nat. Hav.	0h 25m 6° 0′ Log. Hav.	Nat. Hav.	0h 27m 6° 30′ Log. Hav.	Nat. Hav.	0h 29m 7° 0′ Log. Hav.	Nat. Hav.	s
0+	15	7.32171	**0.00210**	7.40067	**0.00252**	7.47302	**0.00297**	7.53980	**0.00347**	7.60179	**0.00400**	60
2		.32309	**.00210**	.40192	**.00252**	.47418	**.00298**	.54087	**.00347**	.60279	**.00401**	58
4+	16	.32446	**.00211**	.40318	**.00253**	.47533	**.00299**	.54194	**.00348**	.60378	**.00402**	56
6		,32583	**.00212**	.40443	**.00254**	.47649	**.00300**	.54301	**.00349**	.60478	**.00403**	54
8+	17	7.32720	**0.00212**	7.40568	**0.00255**	7.47764	**0.00300**	7.54407	**0.00350**	7.60577	**0.00403**	52
10		.32857	**.00213**	.40693	**.00255**	.47879	**.00301**	.54514	**.00351**	.60676	**.00404**	50
12+	18	.32994	**.00214**	.40818	**.00256**	.47994	**.00302**	.54620	**.00352**	.60775	**.00405**	48
14		.33130	**.00214**	.40943	**.00257**	.48109	**.00303**	.54727	**.00353**	.60874	**.00406**	46
16+	19	7.33266	**0.00215**	7.41067	**0.00257**	7.48223	**0.00304**	7.54833	**0.00353**	7.60973	**0.00407**	44
18		.33402	**.00216**	.41191	**.00258**	.48337	**.00304**	.54939	**.00354**	.61072	**.00408**	42
20+	20	.33538	**.00216**	.41315	**.00259**	.48452	**.00305**	.55045	**.00355**	.61170	**.00409**	40
22		.33673	**.00217**	.41439	**.00260**	.48566	**.00306**	.55150	**.00356**	.61269	**.00410**	38
24+	21	7.33809	**0.00218**	7.41563	**0.00260**	7.48680	**0.00307**	7.55256	**0.00357**	7.61367	**0.00411**	36
26		.33944	**.00218**	.41686	**.00261**	.48794	**.00308**	.55361	**.00358**	.61466	**.00412**	34
28+	22	.34079	**.00219**	.41810	**.00262**	.48907	**.00308**	.55467	**.00359**	.61564	**.00413**	32
30		.34213	**.00220**	.41933	**.00263**	.49021	**.00309**	.55572	**.00360**	.61662	**.00414**	30
32+	23	7.34348	**0.00221**	7.42056	**0.00263**	7.49134	**0.00310**	7.55677	**0.00360**	7.61760	**0.00415**	28
34		.34482	**.00221**	.42179	**.00264**	.49247	**.00311**	.55782	**.00361**	.61858	**.00416**	26
36+	24	.34616	**.00222**	.42301	**.00265**	.49360	**.00312**	.55887	**.00362**	.61955	**.00416**	24
38		.34750	**.00223**	.42424	**.00266**	.49473	**.00312**	.55992	**.00363**	.62053	**.00417**	22
40+	25	7.34884	**0.00223**	7.42546	**0.00266**	7.49586	**0.00313**	7.56096	**0.00364**	7.62151	**0.00418**	20
42		.35017	**.00224**	.42668	**.00267**	.49699	**.00314**	.56201	**.00365**	.62248	**.00419**	18
44+	26	.35150	**.00225**	.42790	**.00268**	.49811	**.00315**	.56305	**.00366**	.62345	**.00420**	16
46		.35283	**.00225**	.42912	**.00269**	.49923	**.00316**	.56409	**.00367**	.62442	**.00421**	14
48+	27	7.35416	**0.00226**	7.43034	**0.00269**	7.50036	**0.00316**	7.56513	**0.00367**	7.62540	**0.00422**	12
50		.35549	**.00227**	.43155	**.00270**	.50148	**.00317**	.56617	**.00368**	.62636	**.00423**	10
52+	28	.35681	**.00227**	.43277	**.00271**	.50259	**.00318**	.56721	**.00369**	.62733	**.00424**	8
54		.35813	**.00228**	.43398	**.00272**	.50371	**.00319**	.56825	**.00370**	.62830	**.00425**	6
56+	29	7.35945	**0.00229**	7.43519	**0.00272**	7.50483	**0.00320**	7.56928	**0.00371**	7.62927	**0.00426**	4
58		.36077	**.00229**	.43639	**.00273**	.50594	**.00321**	.57032	**.00372**	.63023	**.00427**	2
60+	30	7.36209	**0.00230**	7.43760	**0.00274**	7.50706	**0.00321**	7.57135	**0.00373**	7.63120	**0.00428**	0
		23h 38m		23h 36m		23h 34m		23h 32m		23h 30m		

TABLE 34.

Haversines.

s	′	$0^h\,30^m$ 7° 30′ Log. Hav.	Nat. Hav.	$0^h\,32^m$ 8° 0′ Log. Hav.	Nat. Hav.	$0^h\,34^m$ 8° 30′ Log. Hav.	Nat. Hav.	$0^h\,36^m$ 9° 0′ Log. Hav.	Nat. Hav.	$0^h\,38^m$ 9° 30′ Log. Hav.	Nat. Hav.	s
0	0	7.63120	0.00428	7.68717	0.00487	7.73974	0.00549	7.78929	0.00616	7.83615	0.00686	60
2		.63216	.00429	.68807	.00488	.74059	.00550	.79009	.00617	.83691	.00687	58
4+	1	.63312	.00430	.68897	.00489	.74143	.00551	.79089	.00618	.83767	.00688	56
6		.63408	.00431	.68987	.00490	.74228	.00552	.79169	.00619	.83842	.00689	54
8+	2	7.63504	0.00432	7.69077	0.00491	7.74313	0.00554	7.79249	0.00620	7.83918	0.00691	52
10		.63600	.00433	.69167	.00492	.74398	.00555	.79329	.00621	.83994	.00692	50
12+	3	.63696	.00433	.69257	.00493	.74482	.00556	.79409	.00622	.84070	.00693	48
14		.63792	.00434	.69347	.00494	.74567	.00557	.79489	.00624	.84145	.00694	46
16+	4	7.63887	0.00435	7.69437	0.00495	7.74651	0.00558	7.79568	0.00625	7.84221	0.00695	44
18		.63983	.00436	.69526	.00496	74735	.00559	.79648	.00626	.84296	.00697	42
20+	5	.64078	.00437	.69616	.00497	.74819	.00560	.79728	.00627	.84372	.00698	40
22		.64173	.00438	.69705	.00498	.74904	.00561	.79807	.00628	.84447	.00699	38
24+	6	7.64269	0.00439	7.69794	0.00499	7.74988	0.00562	7.79886	0.00629	7.84522	0.00700	36
26		.64364	.00440	.69883	.00500	.75072	.00563	.79966	.00630	.84597	.00701	34
28+	7	.64458	.00441	.69972	.00501	.75155	.00564	.80045	.00632	.84672	.00703	32
30		.64553	.00442	.70061	.00502	.75239	.00565	.80124	.00633	.84747	.00704	30
32+	8	7.64648	0.00443	7.70150	0.00503	7.75323	0.00567	7.80203	0.00634	7.84822	0.00705	28
34		.64743	.00444	.70239	.00504	.75407	.00568	.80282	.00635	.84897	.00706	26
36+	9	.64837	.00445	.70328	.00505	.75490	.00569	.80361	.00636	.84972	.00707	24
38		.64932	.00446	.70416	.00506	.75574	.00570	.80440	.00637	.85047	.00709	22
40+	10	7.65026	0.00447	7.70505	0.00507	7.75657	0.00571	7.80519	0.00639	7.85122	0.00710	20
42		.65120	.00448	.70593	.00508	.75740	.00572	.80598	.00640	.85196	.00711	18
44+	11	.65214	.00449	.70682	.00509	.75824	.00573	.80677	.00641	.85271	.00712	16
46		.65308	.00450	.70770	.00510	.75907	.00574	.80755	.00642	.85346	.00714	14
48+	12	7.65402	0.00451	7.70858	0.00511	7.75990	0.00575	7.80834	0.00643	7.85420	0.00715	12
50		.65496	.00452	.70946	.00512	.76073	.00576	.80912	.00644	.85494	.00716	10
52+	13	.65590	.00453	.71034	.00513	.76156	.00578	.80991	.00646	.85569	.00717	8
54		.65683	.00454	.71122	.00514	.76239	.00579	.81069	.00647	.85643	.00719	6
56+	14	7.65777	0.00455	7.71210	0.00515	7.76321	0.00580	7.81147	0.00648	7.85717	0.00720	4
58		7.65870	0.00456	7.71298	0.00516	7.76404	0.00581	7.81225	0.00649	7.85791	0.00721	2
		$23^h\,29^m$		$23^h\,27^m$		$23^h\,25^m$		$23^h\,23^m$		$23^h\,21^m$		

s	′	$0^h\,31^m$ 7° 30′ Log. Hav.	Nat. Hav.	$0^h\,33^m$ 8° 0′ Log. Hav.	Nat. Hav.	$0^h\,35^m$ 8° 30′ Log. Hav.	Nat. Hav.	$0^h\,37^m$ 9° 0′ Log. Hav.	Nat. Hav.	$0^h\,39^m$ 9° 30′ Log. Hav.	Nat. Hav.	s
0+	15	7.65964	0.00457	7.71385	0.00517	7.76487	0.00582	7.81303	0.00650	7.85866	0.00722	60
2		.66057	.00458	.71473	.00518	.76569	.00583	.81382	.00651	.85940	.00723	58
4+	16	.66150	.00459	.71560	.00520	.76652	.00584	.81459	.00653	.86014	.00725	56
6		.66243	.00460	.71648	.00521	.76734	.00585	.81537	.00654	.86087	.00726	54
8+	17	7.66336	0.00461	7.71735	0.00522	7.76816	0.00586	7.81615	0.00655	7.86161	0.00727	52
10		.66429	.00462	.71822	.00523	.76898	.00587	.81693	.00656	.86235	.00728	50
12+	18	.66521	.00463	.71909	.00524	.76981	.00589	.81771	.00657	.86309	.00730	48
14		.66614	.00464	.71996	.00525	.77063	.00590	.81848	.00658	.86382	.00731	46
16+	19	7.66706	0.00465	7.72083	0.00526	7.77145	0.00591	7.81926	0.00660	7.86456	0.00732	44
18		.66799	.00466	.72170	.00527	.77227	.00592	.82003	.00661	.86530	.00733	42
20+	20	.66891	.00467	.72257	.00528	.77308	.00593	.82081	.00662	.86603	.00735	40
22		.66983	.00468	.72343	.00529	.77390	.00594	.82158	.00663	.86676	.00736	38
24+	21	7.67075	0.00469	7.72430	0.00530	7.77472	0.00595	7.82235	0.00664	7.86750	0.00737	36
26		.67167	.00470	.72516	.00531	.77553	.00596	.82313	.00665	.86823	.00738	34
28+	22	.67259	.00471	.72603	.00532	.77635	.00598	.82390	.00667	.86896	.00740	32
30		.67351	.00472	.72689	.00533	.77716	.00599	.82467	.00668	.86969	.00741	30
32+	23	7.67443	0.00473	7.72775	0.00534	7.77798	0.00600	7.82544	0.00669	7.87042	0.00742	28
34		.67535	.00474	.72861	.00535	.77879	.00601	.82621	.00670	.87115	.00743	26
36+	24	.67626	.00475	.72948	.00536	.77960	.00602	.82698	.00671	.87188	.00745	24
38		.67718	.00476	.73034	.00537	.78041	.00603	.82774	.00673	.87261	.00746	22
40+	25	7.67809	0.00477	7.73119	0.00539	7.78122	0.00604	7.82851	0.00674	7.87334	0.00747	20
42		.67900	.00478	.73205	.00540	.78203	.00605	.82928	.00675	.87407	.00748	18
44+	26	.67991	.00479	.73291	.00541	.78284	.00607	.83004	.00676	.87480	.00750	16
46		.68082	.00480	.73377	.00542	.78365	.00608	.83081	.00677	.87552	.00751	14
48+	27	7.68173	0.00481	7.73462	0.00543	7.78446	0.00609	7.83157	0.00679	7.87625	0.00752	12
50		.68264	.00482	.73548	.00544	.78526	.00610	.83234	.00680	.87697	.00753	10
52+	28	.68355	.00483	.73633	.00545	.78607	.00611	.83310	.00681	.87770	.00755	8
54		.68445	.00484	.73718	.00546	.78688	.00612	.83386	.00682	.87842	.00756	6
56+	29	7.68536	0.00485	7.73803	0.00547	7.78768	0.00613	7.83463	0.00683	7.87915	0.00757	4
58		.68627	.00486	.73889	.00548	.78848	.00614	.83539	.00685	.87987	.00758	2
60+	30	7.68717	0.00487	7.73974	0.00549	7.78929	0.00616	7.83615	0.00686	7.88059	0.00760	0
		$23^h\,28^m$		$23^h\,26^m$		$23^h\,24^m$		$23^h\,22^m$		$23^h\,20^m$		

TABLE 34.

Haversines.

s	′	0h 40m 10° 0′ Log. Hav.	Nat. Hav.	0h 42m 10° 30′ Log. Hav.	Nat. Hav.	0h 44m 11° 0′ Log. Hav.	Nat. Hav.	0h 46m 11° 30′ Log. Hav.	Nat. Hav.	0h 48m 12° 0′ Log. Hav.	Nat. Hav.	s
0	0	7.88059	**0.00760**	7.92286	**0.00837**	7.96315	**0.00919**	8.00163	**0.01004**	8.03847	**0.01093**	60
2		.88131	**.00761**	.92354	**.00839**	.96380	**.00920**	.00226	**.01005**	.03907	**.01094**	58
4+	1	.88203	**.00762**	.92423	**.00840**	.96446	**.00921**	.00289	**.01007**	.03967	**.01096**	56
6		.88276	**.00763**	.92492	**.00841**	.96511	**.00923**	.00351	**.01008**	.04027	**.01097**	54
8+	2	7.88348	**0.00765**	7.92560	**0.00843**	7.96577	**0.00924**	8.00414	**0.01010**	8.04087	**0.01099**	52
10		.88419	**.00766**	.92629	**.00844**	.96642	**.00926**	.00476	**.01011**	.04147	**.01100**	50
12+	3	.88491	**.00767**	.92697	**.00845**	.96707	**.00927**	.00539	**.01012**	.04207	**.01102**	48
14		.88563	**.00768**	.92766	**.00847**	.96773	**.00928**	.00601	**.01014**	.04267	**.01103**	46
16+	4	7.88635	**0.00770**	7.92834	**0.00848**	7.96838	**0.00930**	8.00664	**0.01015**	8.04326	**0.01105**	44
18		.88707	**.00771**	.92902	**.00849**	.96903	**.00931**	.00726	**.01017**	.04386	**.01106**	42
20+	5	88778	**.00772**	.92970	**.00851**	.96968	**.00933**	.00788	**.01018**	.04446	**.01108**	40
22		.88850	**.00774**	.93039	**.00852**	.97033	**.00934**	.00851	**.01020**	.04506	**.01109**	38
24+	6	7.88921	**0.00775**	7.93107	**0.00853**	7.97098	**0.00935**	8.00913	**0.01021**	8.04565	**0.01111**	36
26		.88993	**.00776**	.93175	**.00855**	.97163	**.00937**	.00975	**.01023**	.04625	**.01112**	34
28+	7	.89064	**.00777**	.93243	**.00856**	.97228	**.00938**	.01037	**.01024**	.04684	**.01114**	32
30		.89135	**.00779**	.93311	**.00857**	.97293	**.00940**	.01099	**.01026**	.04744	**.01115**	30
32+	8	7.89207	**0.00780**	7.93379	**0.00859**	7.97358	**0.00941**	8.01161	**0.01027**	8.04803	**0.01117**	28
34		.89278	**.00781**	.93447	**.00860**	.97423	**.00942**	.01223	**.01029**	.04863	**.01118**	26
36+	9	.89349	**.00783**	.93514	**.00861**	.97478	**.00944**	.01285	**.01030**	.04922	**.01120**	24
38		.89420	**.00784**	.93582	**.00863**	.97552	**.00945**	.01347	**.01032**	.04981	**.01122**	22
40+	10	7.89491	**0.00785**	7.93650	**0.00864**	7.97617	**0.00947**	8.01409	**0.01033**	8.05041	**0.01123**	20
42		.89562	**.00786**	.93717	**.00865**	.97681	**.00948**	.01471	**.01034**	.05100	**.01125**	18
44+	11	.89633	**.00788**	.93785	**.00867**	.97746	**.00949**	.01532	**.01036**	.05159	**.01126**	16
46		.89704	**.00789**	.93852	**.00868**	.97810	**.00951**	.01594	**.01037**	.05218	**.01128**	14
48+	12	7.89775	**0.00790**	7.93920	**0.00869**	7.97875	**0.00952**	8.01656	**0.01039**	8.05277	**0.01129**	12
50		.89846	**.00792**	.93987	**.00871**	.97939	**.00954**	.01717	**.01040**	.05336	**.01131**	10
52+	13	.89916	**.00793**	.94055	**.00872**	.98003	**.00955**	.01779	**.01042**	.05395	**.01132**	8
54		.89987	**.00794**	.94122	**.00873**	.98068	**.00956**	.01840	**.01043**	.05454	**.01134**	6
56+	14	7.90057	**0.00795**	7.94189	**0.00875**	7.98132	**0.00958**	8.01902	**0.01045**	8.05513	**0.01135**	4
58		7.90128	**0.00797**	7.94257	**0.00876**	7.98196	**0.00959**	8.01963	**0.01046**	8.05572	**0.01137**	2
		23h 19m		23h 17m		23h 15m		23h 13m		23h 11m		

s	′	0h 41m 10° 0′ Log. Hav.	Nat. Hav.	0h 43m 10° 30′ Log. Hav.	Nat. Hav.	0h 45m 11° 0′ Log. Hav.	Nat. Hav.	0h 47m 11° 30′ Log. Hav.	Nat. Hav.	0h 49m 12° 0′ Log. Hav.	Nat. Hav.	s
0+	15	7.90198	**0.00798**	7.94324	**0.00877**	7.98260	**0.00961**	8.02025	**0.01048**	8.05631	**0.01138**	60
2		.90269	**.00799**	.94391	**.00879**	.98325	**.00962**	.02086	**.01049**	.05690	**.01140**	58
4+	16	.90339	**.00801**	.94458	**.00880**	.98389	**.00964**	.02148	**.01051**	.05749	**.01142**	56
6		.90409	**.00802**	.94525	**.00882**	.98453	**.00965**	.02209	**.01052**	.05808	**.01143**	54
8+	17	7.90480	**0.00803**	7.94592	**0.00883**	7.98517	**0.00966**	8.02270	**0.01054**	8.05866	**0.01145**	52
10		.90550	**.00804**	.94659	**.00884**	.98581	**.00968**	.02331	**.01055**	.05925	**.01146**	50
12+	18	.90620	**.00806**	.94726	**.00886**	.98644	**.00969**	.02392	**.01057**	.05984	**.01148**	48
14		.90690	**.00807**	.94792	**.00887**	.98708	**.00971**	.02453	**.01058**	.06042	**.01149**	46
16+	19	7.90760	**0.00808**	7.94859	**0.00888**	7.98772	**0.00972**	8.02515	**0.01060**	8.06101	**0.01151**	44
18		.90830	**.00810**	.94926	**.00890**	.98836	**.00974**	.02576	**.01061**	.06159	**.01152**	42
20+	20	.90900	**.00811**	.94992	**.00891**	.98899	**.00975**	.02637	**.01063**	.06218	**.01154**	40
22		.90970	**.00812**	.95059	**.00892**	.98963	**.00976**	.02697	**.01064**	.06276	**.01155**	38
24+	21	7.91039	**0.00814**	7.95126	**0.00894**	7.99027	**0.00978**	8.02758	**0.01066**	8.06335	**0.01157**	36
26		.91109	**.00815**	.95192	**.00895**	99090	**.00979**	.02819	**.01067**	.06393	**.01159**	34
28+	22	.91179	**.00816**	.95259	**.00897**	.99154	**.00981**	.02880	**.01069**	.06451	**.01160**	32
30		.91248	**.00817**	.95325	**.00898**	.99217	**.00982**	.02941	**.01070**	.06510	**.01162**	30
32+	23	7.91318	**0.00819**	7.95391	**0.00899**	7.99281	**0.00984**	8.03001	**0.01072**	8.06568	**0.01163**	28
34		.91387	**.00820**	.95458	**.00901**	.99344	**.00985**	.03062	**.01073**	.06626	**.01165**	26
36+	24	.91457	**.00821**	.95524	**.00902**	.99407	**.00986**	.03123	**.01075**	.06684	**.01166**	24
38		.91526	**.00823**	.95590	**.00903**	.99470	**.00988**	.03183	**.01076**	.06742	**.01168**	22
40+	25	7.91596	**0.00824**	7.95656	**0.00905**	7.99534	**0.00989**	8.03244	**0.01078**	8.06800	**0.01170**	20
42		.91665	**.00825**	.95722	**.00906**	.99597	**.00991**	.03304	**.01079**	.06859	**.01171**	18
44+	26	.91734	**.00827**	.95788	**.00908**	.99660	**.00992**	.03365	**.01081**	.06917	**.01173**	16
46		.91803	**.00828**	.95854	**.00909**	.99723	**.00994**	.03425	**.01082**	.06975	**.01174**	14
48+	27	7.91872	**0.00829**	7.95920	**0.00910**	7.99786	**0.00995**	8.03486	**0.01084**	8.07032	**0.01176**	12
50		.91941	**.00831**	.95986	**.00912**	.99849	**.00997**	.03546	**.01085**	.07090	**.01177**	10
52+	28	.92010	**.00832**	.96052	**.00913**	.99912	**.00998**	.03606	**.01087**	.07148	**.01179**	8
54		.92079	**.00833**	.96118	**.00914**	7.99975	**.00999**	.03666	**.01088**	.07206	**.01180**	6
56+	29	7.92148	**0.00835**	7.96183	**0.00916**	8.00038	**0.01001**	8.03727	**0.01090**	8.07264	**0.01182**	4
58		.92217	**.00836**	.96249	**.00917**	.00100	**.01002**	.03787	**.01091**	.07322	**.01184**	2
60+	30	7.92286	**0.00837**	7.96315	**0.00919**	8.00163	**0.01004**	8.03847	**0.01093**	8.07379	**0.01185**	0
		23h 18m		23h 16m		23h 14m		23h 12m		23h 10m		

TABLE 34.

Haversines.

s ′	0h 50m 12° 30′		0h 52m 13° 0′		0h 54m 13° 30′		0h 56m 14° 0′		0h 58m 14° 30′		s
	Log. Hav.	Nat. Hav.	Log. Hav.	Nat. Hav.	Log. Hav.	Nat. Hav.	Log. Hav.	Nat. Hav.	Log. Hav.	Nat. Hav.	
0 0	8.07379	0.01185	8.10772	0.01282	8.14035	0.01382	8.17179	0.01485	8.20211	0.01593	60
2	.07437	.01187	.10827	.01283	.14089	.01383	.17230	.01487	.20261	.01594	58
4+ 1	.07494	.01188	.10883	.01285	.14142	.01385	.17282	.01489	.20310	.01596	56
6	.07552	.01190	.10938	.01286	.14195	.01387	.17333	.01491	.20360	.01598	54
8+ 2	8.07610	0.01192	8.10993	0.01288	8.14248	0.01388	8.17384	0.01492	8.20410	0.01600	52
10	.07667	.01193	.11049	.01290	.14302	.01390	.17436	.01494	.20459	.01602	50
12+ 3	.07725	.01195	.11104	.01291	.14355	.01392	.17487	.01496	.20509	.01604	48
14	.07782	.01196	.11159	.01293	.14408	.01393	.17538	.01498	.20558	.01605	46
16+ 4	8.07839	0.01198	8.11214	0.01295	8.14461	0.01395	8.17590	0.01499	8.20608	0.01607	44
18	.07897	.01199	.11269	.01296	.14514	.01397	.17641	.01501	.20657	.01609	42
20+ 5	.07954	.01201	.11324	.01298	.14567	.01399	.17692	.01503	.20706	.01611	40
22	.08011	.01203	.11379	.01300	.14620	.01400	.17743	.01505	.20756	.01613	38
24+ 6	8.08069	0.01204	8.11435	0.01301	8.14673	0.01402	8.17794	0.01506	8.20805	0.01615	36
26	.08126	.01206	.11490	.01303	.14726	.01404	.17845	.01508	.20854	.01616	34
28+ 7	.08183	.01207	.11544	.01305	.14779	.01405	.17896	.01510	.20904	.01618	32
30	.08240	.01209	.11599	.01306	.14832	.01407	.17947	.01512	.20953	.01620	30
32+ 8	8.08297	0.01211	8.11654	0.01308	8.14885	0.01409	8.17998	0.01513	8.21002	0.01622	28
34	.08354	.01212	.11709	.01309	.14938	.01411	.18049	.01515	.21051	.01624	26
36+ 9	.08411	.01214	.11764	.01311	.14991	.01412	.18100	.01517	.21100	.01626	24
38	.08468	.01215	.11819	.01313	.15043	.01414	.18151	.01519	.21149	.01627	22
40+10	8.08525	0.01217	8.11873	0.01314	8.15096	0.01416	8.18202	0.01521	8.21199	0.01629	20
42	.08582	.01218	.11928	.01316	.15149	.01417	.18253	.01522	.21248	.01631	18
44+11	.08639	.01220	.11983	.01317	.15201	.01419	.18303	.01524	.21297	.01633	16
46	.08696	.01222	.12038	.01319	.15254	.01421	.18354	.01526	.21346	.01635	14
48+12	8.08752	0.01223	8.12092	0.01321	8.15307	0.01423	8.18405	0.01528	8.21395	0.01637	12
50	.08809	.01225	.12147	.01323	.15359	.01424	.18455	.01530	.21444	.01638	10
52+13	.08866	.01226	.12201	.01324	.15412	.01426	.18506	.01531	.21493	.01640	8
54	.08922	.01228	.12256	.01326	.15464	.01428	.18557	.01533	.21541	.01642	6
56+14	8.08979	0.01230	8.12310	0.01328	8.15517	0.01429	8.18607	0.01535	8.21590	0.01644	4
58	8.09036	0.01231	8.12365	0.01329	8.15569	0.01431	8.18658	0.01537	8.21639	0.01646	2
	23h 9m		23h 7m		23h 5m		23h 3m		23h 1m		

s ′	0h 51m 12° 30′		0h 53m 13° 0′		0h 55m 13° 30′		0h 57m 14° 0′		0h 59m 14° 30′		s
0+15	8.09092	0.01233	8.12419	0.01331	8.15622	0.01433	8.18709	0.01538	8.21688	0.01648	60
2	.09149	.01234	.12473	.01333	.15674	.01435	.18759	.01540	.21737	.01650	58
4+16	.09205	.01236	.12528	.01334	.15726	.01436	.18810	.01542	.21785	.01651	56
6	.09262	.01238	.12582	.01336	.15779	.01438	.18860	.01544	.21834	.01653	54
8+17	8.09318	0.01239	8.12636	0.01338	8.15831	0.01440	8.18910	0.01546	8.21883	0.01655	52
10	.09374	.01241	.12691	.01339	.15883	.01442	.18961	.01547	.21932	.01657	50
12+18	.09431	.01243	.12745	.01341	.15935	.01443	.19011	.01549	.21980	.01659	48
14	.09487	.01244	.12799	.01343	.15987	.01445	.19062	.01551	.22029	.01661	46
16+19	8.09543	0.01246	8.12853	0.01344	8.16040	0.01447	8.19112	0.01553	8.22077	0.01663	44
18	.09600	.01247	.12907	.01346	.16092	.01448	.19162	.01555	.22126	.01664	42
20+20	.09656	.01249	.12961	.01348	.16144	.01450	.19212	.01556	.22175	.01666	40
22	.09712	.01251	.13015	.01349	.16196	.01452	.19263	.01558	.22223	.01668	38
24+21	8.09768	0.01252	8.13069	0.01351	8.16248	0.01454	8.19313	0.01560	8.22272	0.01670	36
26	.09824	.01254	.13123	.01353	.16300	.01455	.19363	.01562	.22320	.01672	34
28+22	.09880	.01255	.13177	.01354	.16352	.01457	.19413	.01564	.22368	.01674	32
30	.09936	.01257	.13231	.01356	.16404	.01459	.19463	.01565	.22417	.01676	30
32+23	8.09992	0.01259	8.13285	0.01358	8.16456	0.01461	8.19513	0.01567	8.22465	0.01677	28
34	.10048	.01260	.13339	.01360	.16508	.01462	.19563	.01569	.22514	.01679	26
36+24	.10104	.01262	.13392	.01361	.16559	.01464	.19613	.01571	.22562	.01681	24
38	.10160	.01264	.13446	.01363	.16611	.01466	.19663	.01573	.22610	.01683	22
40+25	8.10216	0.01265	8.13500	0.01365	8.16663	0.01468	8.19713	0.01574	8.22658	0.01685	20
42	.10271	.01267	.13554	.01366	.16715	.01469	.19763	.01576	.22707	.01687	18
44+26	.10327	.01268	.13607	.01368	.16766	.01471	.19813	.01578	.22755	.01689	16
46	.10383	.01270	.13661	.01370	.16818	.01473	.19863	.01580	.22803	.01691	14
48+27	8.10439	0.01272	8.13714	0.01371	8.16870	0.01475	8.19913	0.01582	8.22851	0.01692	12
50	.10494	.01273	.13768	.01373	.16921	.01476	.19963	.01584	.22899	.01694	10
52+28	.10550	.01275	.13822	.01375	.16973	.01478	.20012	.01585	.22947	.01696	8
54	.10605	.01277	.13875	.01376	.17024	.01480	.20062	.01587	.22996	.01698	6
56+29	8.10661	0.01278	8.13928	0.01378	8.17076	0.01482	8.20112	0.01589	8.23044	0.01700	4
58	.10716	.01280	.13982	.01380	.17127	.01483	.20162	.01591	.23092	.01702	2
60+30	8.10772	0.01282	8.14035	0.01382	8.17179	0.01485	8.20211	0.01593	8.23140	0.01704	0
	23h 8m		23h 6m		23h 4m		23h 2m		23h 0m		

TABLE 34.

Haversines.

s	1h 0m 15° 0′		1h 1m 15° 15′		1h 2m 15° 30′		1h 3m 15° 45′		1h 4m 16° 0′		s
	Log. Hav.	Nat. Hav.	Log. Hav.	Nat. Hav.	Log. Hav.	Nat. Hav.	Log. Hav.	Nat. Hav.	Log. Hav.	Nat. Hav.	
0	8.23140	**.01704**	8.24567	**.01761**	8.25971	**.01818**	8.27352	**.01877**	8.28711	**.01937**	60
1	.23164	**.01705**	.24591	**.01762**	.25994	**.01819**	.27375	**.01878**	.28734	**.01938**	59
2	.23188	**.01706**	.24614	**.01763**	.26017	**.01820**	.27398	**.01879**	.28756	**.01939**	58
3	.23212	**.01707**	.24638	**.01764**	.26040	**.01821**	.27420	**.01880**	.28779	**.01940**	57
+ 1′	8.23235	**.01707**	8.24661	**.01764**	8.26064	**.01822**	8.27443	**.01881**	8.28801	**.01941**	56
5	.23259	**.01708**	.24685	**.01765**	.26087	**.01823**	.27466	**.01882**	.28823	**.01942**	55
6	.23283	**.01709**	.24708	**.01766**	.26110	**.01824**	.27489	**.01883**	.28846	**.01943**	54
7	.23307	**.01710**	.24732	**.01767**	.26133	**.01825**	.27512	**.01884**	.28868	**.01944**	53
+ 2′	8.23331	**.01711**	8.24755	**.01768**	8.26156	**.01826**	8.27534	**.01885**	8.28891	**.01945**	52
9	.23355	**.01712**	.24779	**.01769**	.26179	**.01827**	.27557	**.01886**	.28913	**.01946**	51
10	.23379	**.01713**	.24803	**.01770**	.26203	**.01828**	.27580	**.01887**	.28936	**.01947**	50
11	.23403	**.01714**	.24826	**.01771**	.26226	**.01829**	.27603	**.01888**	.28958	**.01948**	49
+ 3′	8.23427	**.01715**	8.24850	**.01772**	8.26249	**.01830**	8.27626	**.01889**	8.28980	**.01949**	48
13	.23451	**.01716**	.24873	**.01773**	.26272	**.01831**	.27648	**.01890**	.29003	**.01950**	47
14	.23475	**.01717**	.24897	**.01774**	.26295	**.01832**	.27671	**.01891**	.29025	**.01951**	46
15	.23499	**.01718**	.24920	**.01775**	.26318	**.01833**	.27694	**.01892**	.29048	**.01952**	45
+ 4′	8.23523	**.01719**	8.24944	**.01776**	8.26341	**.01834**	8.27717	**.01893**	8.29070	**.01953**	44
17	.23546	**.01720**	.24967	**.01777**	.26364	**.01835**	.27739	**.01894**	.29092	**.01954**	43
18	.23570	**.01721**	.24991	**.01778**	.26388	**.01836**	.27762	**.01895**	.29115	**.01955**	42
19	.23594	**.01722**	.25014	**.01779**	.26411	**.01837**	.27785	**.01896**	.29137	**.01956**	41
+ 5′	8.23618	**.01723**	8.25037	**.01780**	8.26434	**.01838**	8.27807	**.01897**	8.29159	**.01957**	40
21	.23642	**.01724**	.25061	**.01781**	.26457	**.01839**	.27830	**.01898**	.29182	**.01958**	39
22	.23666	**.01724**	.25084	**.01782**	.26480	**.01840**	.27853	**.01899**	.29204	**.01959**	38
23	.23690	**.01725**	.25108	**.01783**	.26503	**.01841**	.27876	**.01900**	.29226	**.01960**	37
+ 6′	8.23713	**.01726**	8.25131	**.01784**	8.26526	**.01842**	8.27898	**.01901**	8.29249	**.01961**	36
25	.23737	**.01727**	.25155	**.01785**	.26549	**.01843**	.27921	**.01902**	.29271	**.01962**	35
26	.23761	**.01728**	.25178	**.01786**	.26572	**.01844**	.27944	**.01903**	.29293	**.01963**	34
27	.23785	**.01729**	.25202	**.01787**	.26595	**.01845**	.27966	**.01904**	.29316	**.01964**	33
+ 7′	8.23809	**.01730**	8.25225	**.01788**	8.26618	**.01846**	8.27989	**.01905**	8.29338	**.01965**	32
29	.23832	**.01731**	.25248	**.01789**	.26641	**.01847**	.28012	**.01906**	.29360	**.01966**	31
30	.23856	**.01732**	.25272	**.01789**	.26664	**.01848**	.28034	**.01907**	.29383	**.01967**	30
31	.23880	**.01733**	.25295	**.01790**	.26687	**.01849**	.28057	**.01908**	.29405	**.01968**	29
+ 8′	8.23904	**.01734**	8.25319	**.01791**	8.26710	**.01850**	8.28080	**.01909**	8.29427	**.01969**	28
33	.23928	**.01735**	.25342	**.01792**	.26733	**.01851**	.28102	**.01910**	.29449	**.01970**	27
34	.23951	**.01736**	.25365	**.01793**	.26756	**.01852**	.28125	**.01911**	.29472	**.01971**	26
35	.23975	**.01737**	.25389	**.01794**	.26779	**.01853**	.28147	**.01912**	.29494	**.01972**	25
+ 9′	8.23999	**.01738**	8.25412	**.01795**	8.26802	**.01854**	8.28170	**.01913**	8.29516	**.01973**	24
37	.24022	**.01739**	.25435	**.01796**	.26825	**.01855**	.28193	**.01914**	.29539	**.01974**	23
38	.24046	**.01740**	.25459	**.01797**	.26848	**.01856**	.28215	**.01915**	.29561	**.01975**	22
39	.24070	**.01741**	.25482	**.01798**	.26871	**.01857**	.28238	**.01916**	.29583	**.01976**	21
+ 10′	8.24094	**.01742**	8.25505	**.01799**	8.26894	**.01858**	8.28260	**.01917**	8.29605	**.01977**	20
41	.24118	**.01743**	.25529	**.01800**	.26917	**.01859**	.28283	**.01918**	.29628	**.01978**	19
42	.24141	**.01743**	.25552	**.01801**	.26940	**.01860**	.28306	**.01919**	.29650	**.01979**	18
43	.24165	**.01744**	.25575	**.01802**	.26963	**.01861**	.28328	**.01920**	.29672	**.01980**	17
+ 11′	8.24189	**.01745**	8.25599	**.01803**	8.26986	**.01861**	8.28351	**.01921**	8.29694	**.01981**	16
45	.24212	**.01746**	.25622	**.01804**	.27009	**.01862**	.28373	**.01922**	.29716	**.01982**	15
46	.24236	**.01747**	.25645	**.01805**	.27032	**.01863**	.28396	**.01923**	.29739	**.01983**	14
47	.24260	**.01748**	.25669	**.01806**	.27055	**.01864**	.28418	**.01924**	.29761	**.01984**	13
+ 12′	8.24283	**.01749**	8.25692	**.01807**	8.27078	**.01865**	8.28441	**.01925**	8.29783	**.01985**	12
49	.24307	**.01750**	.25715	**.01808**	.27100	**.01866**	.28464	**.01926**	.29805	**.01986**	11
50	.24331	**.01751**	.25738	**.01809**	.27123	**.01867**	.28486	**.01927**	.29827	**.01987**	10
51	.24354	**.01752**	.25762	**.01810**	.27146	**.01868**	.28509	**.01928**	.29850	**.01988**	9
+ 13′	8.24378	**.01753**	8.25785	**.01811**	8.27169	**.01869**	8.28531	**.01929**	8.29872	**.01989**	8
53	.24402	**.01754**	.25808	**.01812**	.27192	**.01870**	.28554	**.01930**	.29894	**.01990**	7
54	.24425	**.01755**	.25831	**.01813**	.27215	**.01871**	.28576	**.01931**	.29916	**.01991**	6
55	.24449	**.01756**	.25855	**.01814**	.27238	**.01872**	.28599	**.01932**	.29938	**.01992**	5
+ 14′	8.24473	**.01757**	8.25878	**.01815**	8.27261	**.01873**	8.28621	**.01933**	8.29960	**.01993**	4
57	.24496	**.01758**	.25901	**.01816**	.27283	**.01874**	.28644	**.01934**	.29982	**.01994**	3
58	.24520	**.01759**	.25924	**.01817**	.27306	**.01875**	.28666	**.01935**	.30005	**.01995**	2
59	.24543	**.01760**	.25948	**.01818**	.27329	**.01876**	.28689	**.01936**	.30027	**.01997**	1
+ 15′	8.24567	**.01761**	8.25971	**.01818**	8.27352	**.01877**	8.28711	**.01937**	8.30049	**.01998**	0
	22h 59m		22h 58m		22h 57m		22h 56m		22h 55m		

TABLE 34.

Haversines.

s	$1^h 5^m$ 16° 15′		$1^h 6^m$ 16° 30′		$1^h 7^m$ 16° 45′		$1^h 8^m$ 17° 0′		$1^h 9^m$ 17° 15′		s
	Log. Hav.	Nat. Hav.	Log. Hav.	Nat. Hav.	Log. Hav.	Nat. Hav.	Log. Hav.	Nat. Hav.	Log. Hav.	Nat. Hav.	
0	8.30049	**.01998**	8.31366	**.02059**	8.32663	**.02121**	8.33940	**.02185**	8.35199	**.02249**	60
1	.30071	**.01999**	.31388	**.02060**	.32684	**.02122**	.33962	**.02186**	.35220	**.02250**	59
2	.30093	**.02000**	.31410	**.02061**	.32706	**.02124**	.33983	**.02187**	.35241	**.02251**	58
3	.30115	**.02001**	.31431	**.02062**	.32727	**.02125**	.34004	**.02188**	.35261	**.02252**	57
+ 1′	8.30137	**.02002**	8.31453	**.02063**	8.32749	**.02126**	8.34025	**.02189**	8.35282	**.02253**	56
5	.30159	**.02003**	.31475	**.02064**	.32770	**.02127**	.34046	**.02190**	.35303	**.02254**	55
6	.30182	**.02004**	.31497	**.02065**	.32792	**.02128**	.34067	**.02191**	.35324	**.02255**	54
7	.30204	**.02005**	.31518	**.02066**	.32813	**.02129**	.34088	**.02192**	.35345	**.02257**	53
+ 2′	8.30226	**.02006**	8.31540	**.02067**	8.32834	**.02130**	8.34109	**.02193**	8.35365	**.02258**	52
9	.30248	**.02007**	.31562	**.02068**	.32856	**.02131**	.34130	**.02194**	.35386	**.02259**	51
10	.30270	**.02008**	.31584	**.02069**	.32877	**.02132**	.34152	**.02195**	.35407	**.02260**	50
11	.30292	**.02009**	.31605	**.02070**	.32899	**.02133**	.34173	**.02196**	.35428	**.02261**	49
+ 3′	8.30314	**.02010**	8.31627	**.02071**	8.32920	**.02134**	8.34194	**.02198**	8.35449	**.02262**	48
13	.30336	**.02011**	.31649	**.02072**	.32941	**.02135**	.34215	**.02199**	.35469	**.02263**	47
14	.30358	**.02012**	.31670	**.02074**	.32963	**.02136**	.34236	**.02200**	.35490	**.02264**	46
15	.30380	**.02013**	.31692	**.02075**	.32984	**.02137**	.34257	**.02201**	.35511	**.02265**	45
+ 4′	8.30402	**.02014**	8.31714	**.02076**	8.33006	**.02138**	8.34278	**.02202**	8.35532	**.02266**	44
17	.30424	**.02015**	.31735	**.02077**	.33027	**.02139**	.34299	**.02203**	.35552	**.02267**	43
18	.30446	**.02016**	.31757	**.02078**	.33048	**.02140**	.34320	**.02204**	.35573	**.02268**	42
19	.30468	**.02017**	.31779	**.02079**	.33070	**.02141**	.34341	**.02205**	.35594	**.02270**	41
+ 5′	8.30490	**.02018**	8.31800	**.02080**	8.33091	**.02142**	8.34362	**.02206**	8.35614	**.02271**	40
21	.30512	**.02019**	.31822	**.02081**	.33112	**.02143**	.34383	**.02207**	.35635	**.02272**	39
22	.30534	**.02020**	.31844	**.02082**	.33134	**.02145**	.34404	**.02208**	.35656	**.02273**	38
23	.30556	**.02021**	.31865	**.02083**	.33155	**.02146**	.34425	**.02209**	.35677	**.02274**	37
+ 6′	8.30578	**.02022**	8.31887	**.02084**	8.33176	**.02147**	8.34446	**.02210**	8.35697	**.02275**	36
25	.30600	**.02023**	.31909	**.02085**	.33198	**.02148**	.34467	**.02211**	.35718	**.02276**	35
26	.30622	**.02024**	.31930	**.02086**	.33219	**.02149**	.34488	**.02212**	.35739	**.02277**	34
27	.30644	**.02025**	.31952	**.02087**	.33240	**.02150**	.34509	**.02214**	.35759	**.02278**	33
+ 7′	8.30666	**.02026**	8.31974	**.02088**	8.33262	**.02151**	8.34530	**.02215**	8.35780	**.02279**	32
29	.30688	**.02027**	.31995	**.02089**	.33283	**.02152**	.34551	**.02216**	.35801	**.02280**	31
30	.30710	**.02028**	.32017	**.02090**	.33304	**.02153**	.34572	**.02217**	.35821	**.02281**	30
31	.30732	**.02029**	.32039	**.02091**	.33325	**.02154**	.34593	**.02218**	.35842	**.02283**	29
+ 8′	8.30754	**.02030**	8.32060	**.02092**	8.33347	**.02155**	8.34614	**.02219**	8.35863	**.02284**	28
33	.30776	**.02031**	.32082	**.02093**	.33368	**.02156**	.34635	**.02220**	.35883	**.02285**	27
34	.30798	**.02032**	.32103	**.02094**	.33389	**.02157**	.34656	**.02221**	.35904	**.02286**	26
35	.30820	**.02033**	.32125	**.02095**	.33411	**.02158**	.34677	**.02222**	.35925	**.02287**	25
+ 9′	8.30842	**.02034**	8.32147	**.02096**	8.33432	**.02159**	8.34698	**.02223**	8.35945	**.02288**	24
37	.30863	**.02035**	.32168	**.02097**	.33453	**.02160**	.34719	**.02224**	.35966	**.02289**	23
38	.30885	**.02036**	.32190	**.02098**	.33474	**.02161**	.34740	**.02225**	.35987	**.02290**	22
39	.30907	**.02037**	.32211	**.02099**	.33496	**.02162**	.34761	**.02226**	.36007	**.02291**	21
+ 10′	8.30929	**.02038**	8.32233	**.02101**	8.33517	**.02164**	8.34782	**.02227**	8.36028	**.02292**	20
41	.30951	**.02039**	.32254	**.02102**	.33538	**.02165**	.34803	**.02229**	.36048	**.02293**	19
42	.30973	**.02040**	.32276	**.02103**	.33559	**.02166**	.34823	**.02230**	.36069	**.02295**	18
43	.30995	**.02042**	.32297	**.02104**	.33580	**.02167**	.34844	**.02231**	.36090	**.02296**	17
+ 11′	8.31017	**.02043**	8.32319	**.02105**	8.33602	**.02168**	8.34865	**.02232**	8.36110	**.02297**	16
45	.31039	**.02044**	.32341	**.02106**	.33623	**.02169**	.34886	**.02233**	.36131	**.02298**	15
46	.31060	**.02045**	.32362	**.02107**	.33644	**.02170**	.34907	**.02234**	.36151	**.02299**	14
47	.31082	**.02046**	.32384	**.02108**	.33665	**.02171**	.34928	**.02235**	.36172	**.02300**	13
+ 12′	8.31104	**.02047**	8.32405	**.02109**	8.33686	**.02172**	8.34949	**.02236**	8.36193	**.02301**	12
49	.31126	**.02048**	.32427	**.02110**	.33708	**.02173**	.34970	**.02237**	.36213	**.02302**	11
50	.31148	**.02049**	.32448	**.02111**	.33729	**.02174**	.34991	**.02238**	.36234	**.02303**	10
51	.31170	**.02050**	.32470	**.02112**	.33750	**.02175**	.35011	**.02239**	.36254	**.02304**	9
+ 13′	8.31192	**.02051**	8.32491	**.02113**	8.33771	**.02176**	8.35032	**.02240**	8.36275	**.02305**	8
53	.31213	**.02052**	.32513	**.02114**	.33792	**.02177**	.35053	**.02241**	.36295	**.02307**	7
54	.31235	**.02053**	.32534	**.02115**	.33814	**.02178**	.35074	**.02243**	.36316	**.02308**	6
55	.31257	**.02054**	.32556	**.02116**	.33835	**.02179**	.35095	**.02244**	.36337	**.02309**	5
+ 14′	8.31279	**.02055**	8.32577	**.02117**	8.33856	**.02181**	8.35116	**.02245**	8.36357	**.02310**	4
57	.31301	**.02056**	.32599	**.02118**	.33877	**.02182**	.35137	**.02246**	.36378	**.02311**	3
58	.31322	**.02057**	.32620	**.02119**	.33898	**.02183**	.35157	**.02247**	.36398	**.02312**	2
59	.31344	**.02058**	.32642	**.02120**	.33919	**.02184**	.35178	**.02248**	.36419	**.02313**	1
+ 15′	8.31366	**.02059**	8.32663	**.02121**	8.33940	**.02185**	8.35199	**.02249**	8.36439	**.02314**	0
	$22^h 54^m$		$22^h 53^m$		$22^h 52^m$		$22^h 51^m$		$22^h 50^m$		

541524°—43——43

TABLE 34.

Haversines.

s	1h 10m 17° 30′ Log. Hav.	1h 10m 17° 30′ Nat. Hav.	1h 11m 17° 45′ Log. Hav.	1h 11m 17° 45′ Nat. Hav.	1h 12m 18° 0′ Log. Hav.	1h 12m 18° 0′ Nat. Hav.	1h 13m 18° 15′ Log. Hav.	1h 13m 18° 15′ Nat. Hav.	1h 14m 18° 30′ Log. Hav.	1h 14m 18° 30′ Nat. Hav.	s
0	8.36439	**.02314**	8.37662	**.02380**	8.38867	**.02447**	8.40055	**.02515**	8.41226	**.02584**	60
1	.36460	**.02315**	.37682	**.02381**	.38886	**.02448**	.40074	**.02516**	.41246	**.02585**	59
2	.36480	**.02316**	.37702	**.02382**	.38906	**.02449**	.40094	**.02517**	.41265	**.02586**	58
3	.36501	**.02317**	.37722	**.02384**	.38926	**.02451**	.40114	**.02518**	.41284	**.02587**	57
+ 1′	8.36521	**.02319**	8.37742	**.02385**	8.38946	**.02452**	8.40133	**.02520**	8.41304	**.02588**	56
5	.36542	**.02320**	.37763	**.02386**	.38966	**.02453**	.40153	**.02521**	.41323	**.02590**	55
6	.36562	**.02321**	.37783	**.02387**	.38986	**.02454**	.40172	**.02522**	.41343	**.02591**	54
7	.36583	**.02322**	.37803	**.02388**	.39006	**.02455**	.40192	**.02523**	.41362	**.02592**	53
+ 2′	8.36603	**.02323**	8.37823	**.02389**	8.39026	**.02456**	8.40212	**.02524**	8.41381	**.02593**	52
9	.36624	**.02324**	.37843	**.02390**	.39046	**.02457**	.40231	**.02525**	.41401	**.02594**	51
10	.36644	**.02325**	.37864	**.02391**	.39066	**.02458**	.40251	**.02526**	.41420	**.02595**	50
11	.36665	**.02326**	.37884	**.02392**	.39086	**.02460**	.40271	**.02528**	.41439	**.02597**	49
+ 3′	8.36685	**.02327**	8.37904	**.02394**	8.39105	**.02461**	8.40290	**.02529**	8.41459	**.02598**	48
13	.36706	**.02328**	.37924	**.02395**	.39125	**.02462**	.40310	**.02530**	.41478	**.02599**	47
14	.36726	**.02329**	.37944	**.02396**	.39145	**.02463**	.40329	**.02531**	.41497	**.02600**	46
15	.36746	**.02331**	.37964	**.02397**	.39165	**.02464**	.40349	**.02532**	.41517	**.02601**	45
+ 4′	8.36767	**.02332**	8.37985	**.02398**	8.39185	**.02465**	8.40369	**.02533**	8.41536	**.02602**	44
17	.36787	**.02333**	.38005	**.02399**	.39205	**.02466**	.40388	**.02534**	.41555	**.02603**	43
18	.36808	**.02334**	.38025	**.02400**	.39225	**.02467**	.40408	**.02536**	.41575	**.02605**	42
19	.36828	**.02335**	.38045	**.02401**	.39245	**.02469**	.40427	**.02537**	.41594	**.02606**	41
+ 5′	8.36849	**.02336**	8.38065	**.02402**	8.39264	**.02470**	8.40447	**.02538**	8.41613	**.02607**	40
21	.36869	**.02337**	.38085	**.02404**	.39284	**.02471**	.40467	**.02539**	.41632	**.02608**	39
22	.36889	**.02338**	.38105	**.02405**	.39304	**.02472**	.40486	**.02540**	.41652	**.02609**	38
23	.36910	**.02339**	.38126	**.02406**	.39324	**.02473**	.40506	**.02541**	.41671	**.02610**	37
+ 6′	8.36930	**.02340**	8.38146	**.02407**	8.39344	**.02474**	8.40525	**.02542**	8.41690	**.02612**	36
25	.36951	**.02342**	.38166	**.02408**	.39364	**.02475**	.40545	**.02544**	.41710	**.02613**	35
26	.36971	**.02343**	.38186	**.02409**	.39384	**.02476**	.40564	**.02545**	.41729	**.02614**	34
27	.36991	**.02344**	.38206	**.02410**	.39403	**.02478**	.40584	**.02546**	.41748	**.02615**	33
+ 7′	8.37012	**.02345**	8.38226	**.02411**	8.39423	**.02479**	8.40603	**.02547**	8.41767	**.02616**	32
29	.37032	**.02346**	.38246	**.02412**	.39443	**.02480**	.40623	**.02548**	.41787	**.02617**	31
30	.37053	**.02347**	.38266	**.02414**	.39463	**.02481**	.40642	**.02549**	.41806	**.02619**	30
31	.37073	**.02348**	.38286	**.02415**	.39482	**.02482**	.40662	**.02550**	.41825	**.02620**	29
+ 8′	8.37093	**.02349**	8.38306	**.02416**	8.39502	**.02483**	8.40681	**.02552**	8.41845	**.02621**	28
33	.37114	**.02350**	.38326	**.02417**	.39522	**.02484**	.40701	**.02553**	.41864	**.02622**	27
34	.37134	**.02351**	.38346	**.02418**	.39542	**.02486**	.40721	**.02554**	.41883	**.02623**	26
35	.37154	**.02353**	.38367	**.02419**	.39562	**.02487**	.40740	**.02555**	.41902	**.02624**	25
+ 9′	8.37175	**.02354**	8.38387	**.02420**	8.39581	**.02488**	8.40760	**.02556**	8.41921	**.02626**	24
37	.37195	**.02355**	.38407	**.02421**	.39601	**.02489**	.40779	**.02557**	.41941	**.02627**	23
38	.37215	**.02356**	.38427	**.02423**	.39621	**.02490**	.40799	**.02559**	.41960	**.02628**	22
39	.37236	**.02357**	.38447	**.02424**	.39641	**.02491**	.40818	**.02560**	.41979	**.02629**	21
+ 10′	8.37256	**.02358**	8.38467	**.02425**	8.39660	**.02492**	8.40837	**.02561**	8.41998	**.02630**	20
41	.37276	**.02359**	.38487	**.02426**	.39680	**.02493**	.40857	**.02562**	.42018	**.02631**	19
42	.37297	**.02360**	.38507	**.02427**	.39700	**.02495**	.40876	**.02563**	.42037	**.02633**	18
43	.37317	**.02361**	.38527	**.02428**	.39720	**.02496**	.40896	**.02564**	.42056	**.02634**	17
+ 11′	8.37337	**.02363**	8.38547	**.02429**	8.39739	**.02497**	8.40915	**.02565**	8.42075	**.02635**	16
45	.37358	**.02364**	.38567	**.02430**	.39759	**.02498**	.40935	**.02567**	.42095	**.02636**	15
46	.37378	**.02365**	.38587	**.02431**	.39779	**.02499**	.40954	**.02568**	.42114	**.02637**	14
47	.37398	**.02366**	.38607	**.02433**	.39799	**.02500**	.40974	**.02569**	.42133	**.02638**	13
+ 12′	8.37419	**.02367**	8.38627	**.02434**	8.39818	**.02501**	8.40993	**.02570**	8.42152	**.02639**	12
49	.37439	**.02368**	.38647	**.02435**	.39838	**.02503**	.41013	**.02571**	.42171	**.02641**	11
50	.37459	**.02369**	.38667	**.02436**	.39858	**.02504**	.41032	**.02572**	.42190	**.02642**	10
51	.37479	**.02370**	.38687	**.02437**	.39877	**.02505**	.41052	**.02573**	.42210	**.02643**	9
+ 13′	8.37500	**.02371**	8.38707	**.02438**	8.39897	**.02506**	8.41071	**.02575**	8.42229	**.02644**	8
53	.37520	**.02372**	.38727	**.02439**	.39917	**.02507**	.41090	**.02576**	.42248	**.02645**	7
54	.37540	**.02374**	.38747	**.02440**	.39937	**.02508**	.41110	**.02577**	.42267	**.02646**	6
55	.37560	**.02375**	.38767	**.02442**	.39956	**.02509**	.41129	**.02578**	.42286	**.02648**	5
+ 14′	8.37581	**.02376**	8.38787	**.02443**	8.39976	**.02510**	8.41149	**.02579**	8.42305	**.02649**	4
57	.37601	**.02377**	.38807	**.02444**	.39996	**.02512**	.41168	**.02580**	.42324	**.02650**	3
58	.37621	**.02378**	.38827	**.02445**	.40015	**.02513**	.41187	**.02582**	.42344	**.02651**	2
59	.37641	**.02379**	.38847	**.02446**	.40035	**.02514**	.41207	**.02583**	.42363	**.02652**	1
+ 15′	8.37662	**.02380**	8.38867	**.02447**	8.40055	**.02515**	8.41226	**.02584**	8.42382	**.02653**	0
	22h 49m		22h 48m		22h 47m		22h 46m		22h 45m		

TABLE 34.

Haversines.

	$1^h\,15^m$ 18° 45′		$1^h\,16^m$ 19° 0′		$1^h\,17^m$ 19° 15′		$1^h\,18^m$ 19° 30′		$1^h\,19^m$ 19° 45′		
s	Log. Hav.	Nat. Hav.	Log. Hav.	Nat. Hav.	Log. Hav.	Nat. Hav.	Log. Hav.	Nat. Hav.	Log. Hav.	Nat. Hav.	s
0	8.42382	**.02653**	8.43522	**.02724**	8.44647	**.02796**	8.45757	**.02868**	8.46852	**.02941**	60
1	.42401	**.02655**	.43541	**.02725**	.44665	**.02797**	.45775	**.02869**	.46871	**.02942**	59
2	.42420	**.02656**	.43560	**.02726**	.44684	**.02798**	.45794	**.02870**	.46889	**.02944**	58
3	.42439	**.02657**	.43578	**.02728**	.44703	**.02799**	.45812	**.02871**	.46907	**.02945**	57
+ 1′	8.42458	**.02658**	8.43597	**.02729**	8.44721	**.02800**	8.45830	**.02873**	8.46925	**.02946**	56
5	.42477	**.02659**	.43616	**.02730**	.44740	**.02802**	.45849	**.02874**	.46943	**.02947**	55
6	.42497	**.02661**	.43635	**.02731**	.44758	**.02803**	.45867	**.02875**	.46961	**.02949**	54
7	.42516	**.02662**	.43654	**.02732**	.44777	**.02804**	.45885	**.02876**	.46979	**.02950**	53
+ 2′	8.42535	**.02663**	8.43673	**.02734**	8.44796	**.02805**	8.45904	**.02878**	8.46998	**.02951**	52
9	.42554	**.02664**	.43692	**.02735**	.44814	**.02806**	.45922	**.02879**	.47016	**.02952**	51
10	.42573	**.02665**	.43710	**.02736**	.44833	**.02808**	.45940	**.02880**	.47034	**.02954**	50
11	.42592	**.02666**	.43729	**.02737**	.44851	**.02809**	.45959	**.02881**	.47052	**.02955**	49
+ 3′	8.42611	**.02668**	8.43748	**.02738**	8.44870	**.02810**	8.45977	**.02883**	8.47070	**.02956**	48
13	.42630	**.02669**	.43767	**.02739**	.44889	**.02811**	.45995	**.02884**	.47088	**.02957**	47
14	.42649	**.02670**	.43786	**.02741**	.44907	**.02812**	.46014	**.02885**	.47106	**.02958**	46
15	.42668	**.02671**	.43805	**.02742**	.44926	**.02814**	.46032	**.02886**	.47124	**.02960**	45
+ 4′	8.42687	**.02672**	8.43823	**.02743**	8.44944	**.02815**	8.46050	**.02887**	8.47142	**.02961**	44
17	.42706	**.02673**	.43842	**.02744**	.44963	**.02816**	.46069	**.02889**	.47160	**.02962**	43
18	.42725	**.02675**	.43861	**.02745**	.44981	**.02817**	.46087	**.02890**	.47178	**.02963**	42
19	.42745	**.02676**	.43880	**.02747**	.45000	**.02818**	.46105	**.02891**	.47197	**.02965**	41
+ 5′	8.42764	**.02677**	8.43899	**.02748**	8.45018	**.02820**	8.46124	**.02892**	8.47215	**.02966**	40
21	.42783	**.02678**	.43917	**.02749**	.45037	**.02821**	.46142	**.02893**	.47233	**.02967**	39
22	.42802	**.02679**	.43936	**.02750**	.45055	**.02822**	.46160	**.02895**	.47251	**.02968**	38
23	.42821	**.02680**	.43955	**.02751**	.45074	**.02823**	.46179	**.02896**	.47269	**.02970**	37
+ 6′	8.42840	**.02682**	8.43974	**.02753**	8.45093	**.02824**	8.46197	**.02897**	8.47287	**.02971**	36
25	.42859	**.02683**	.43992	**.02754**	.45111	**.02826**	.46215	**.02898**	.47305	**.02972**	35
26	.42878	**.02684**	.44011	**.02755**	.45130	**.02827**	.46233	**.02900**	.47323	**.02973**	34
27	.42897	**.02685**	.44030	**.02756**	.45148	**.02828**	.46252	**.02901**	.47341	**.02974**	33
+ 7′	8.42916	**.02686**	8.44049	**.02757**	8.45167	**.02829**	8.46270	**.02902**	8.47359	**.02976**	32
29	.42935	**.02688**	.44067	**.02759**	.45185	**.02830**	.46288	**.02903**	.47377	**.02977**	31
30	.42954	**.02689**	.44086	**.02760**	.45204	**.02832**	.46306	**.02904**	.47395	**.02978**	30
31	.42973	**.02690**	.44105	**.02761**	.45222	**.02833**	.46325	**.02906**	.47413	**.02979**	29
+ 8′	8.42992	**.02691**	8.44124	**.02762**	8.45241	**.02834**	8.46343	**.02907**	8.47431	**.02981**	28
33	.43011	**.02692**	.44142	**.02763**	.45259	**.02835**	.46361	**.02908**	.47449	**.02982**	27
34	.43030	**.02693**	.44161	**.02764**	.45278	**.02836**	.46379	**.02909**	.47467	**.02983**	26
35	.43049	**.02695**	.44180	**.02766**	.45296	**.02838**	.46398	**.02911**	.47485	**.02984**	25
+ 9′	8.43068	**.02696**	8.44199	**.02767**	8.45315	**.02839**	8.46416	**.02912**	8.47503	**.02986**	24
37	.43087	**.02697**	.44217	**.02768**	.45333	**.02840**	.46434	**.02913**	.47521	**.02987**	23
38	.43106	**.02698**	.44236	**.02769**	.45352	**.02841**	.46452	**.02914**	.47539	**.02988**	22
39	.43125	**.02699**	.44255	**.02771**	.45370	**.02842**	.46471	**.02915**	.47557	**.02989**	21
+ 10′	8.43144	**.02700**	8.44273	**.02772**	8.45388	**.02844**	8.46489	**.02917**	8.47575	**.02991**	20
41	.43163	**.02702**	.44292	**.02773**	.45407	**.02845**	.46507	**.02918**	.47593	**.02992**	19
42	.43181	**.02703**	.44311	**.02774**	.45425	**.02846**	.46525	**.02919**	.47611	**.02993**	18
43	.43200	**.02704**	.44330	**.02775**	.45444	**.02847**	.46544	**.02920**	.47629	**.02994**	17
+ 11′	8.43219	**.02705**	8.44348	**.02776**	8.45462	**.02849**	8.46562	**.02922**	8.47647	**.02996**	16
45	.43238	**.02706**	.44367	**.02778**	.45481	**.02850**	.46580	**.02923**	.47665	**.02997**	15
46	.43257	**.02708**	.44386	**.02779**	.45499	**.02851**	.46598	**.02924**	.47683	**.02998**	14
47	.43276	**.02709**	.44404	**.02780**	.45518	**.02852**	.46616	**.02925**	.47701	**.02999**	13
+ 12′	8.43295	**.02710**	8.44423	**.02781**	8.45536	**.02853**	8.46634	**.02926**	8.47719	**.03000**	12
49	.43314	**.02711**	.44442	**.02782**	.45554	**.02855**	.46653	**.02928**	.47737	**.03002**	11
50	.43333	**.02712**	.44460	**.02784**	.45573	**.02856**	.46671	**.02929**	.47755	**.03003**	10
51	.43352	**.02713**	.44479	**.02785**	.45591	**.02857**	.46689	**.02930**	.47773	**.03004**	9
+ 13′	8.43371	**.02715**	8.44498	**.02786**	8.45610	**.02858**	8.46707	**.02931**	8.47791	**.03005**	8
53	.43390	**.02716**	.44516	**.02787**	.45628	**.02859**	.46725	**.02933**	.47809	**.03007**	7
54	.43409	**.02717**	.44535	**.02788**	.45646	**.02861**	.46744	**.02934**	.47827	**.03008**	6
55	.43427	**.02718**	.44554	**.02790**	.45665	**.02862**	.46762	**.02935**	.47844	**.03009**	5
+ 14′	8.43446	**.02719**	8.44572	**.02791**	8.45683	**.02863**	8.46780	**.02936**	8.47862	**.03010**	4
57	.43465	**.02721**	.44591	**.02792**	.45702	**.02864**	.46798	**.02938**	.47880	**.03012**	3
58	.43484	**.02722**	.44610	**.02793**	.45720	**.02866**	.46816	**.02939**	.47898	**.03013**	2
59	.43503	**.02723**	.44628	**.02794**	.45738	**.02867**	.46834	**.02940**	.47916	**.03014**	1
+ 15′	8.43522	**.02724**	8.44647	**.02796**	8.45757	**.02868**	8.46852	**.02941**	8.47934	**.03015**	0
	$22^h\,44^m$		$22^h\,43^m$		$22^h\,42^m$		$22^h\,41^m$		$22^h\,40^m$		

TABLE 34.

Haversines.

s	1h 20m 20° 0′ Log. Hav.	Nat. Hav.	1h 21m 20° 15′ Log. Hav.	Nat. Hav.	1h 22m 20° 30′ Log. Hav.	Nat. Hav.	1h 23m 20° 45′ Log. Hav.	Nat. Hav.	1h 24m 21° 0′ Log. Hav.	Nat. Hav.	s
0	8.47934	.03015	8.49002	.03090	8.50056	.03166	8.51098	.03243	8.52127	.03321	60
1	.47952	.03017	.49020	.03092	.50074	.03168	.51115	.03245	.52144	.03322	59
2	.47970	.03018	.49037	.03093	.50091	.03169	.51132	.03246	.52161	.03324	58
3	.47988	.03019	.49055	.03094	.50109	.03170	.51150	.03247	.52178	.03325	57
+ 1′	8.48006	.03020	8.49073	.03095	8.50126	.03171	8.51167	.03248	8.52195	.03326	56
5	.48024	.03022	.49090	.03097	.50144	.03173	.51184	.03250	.52212	.03328	55
6	.48041	.03023	.49108	.03098	.50161	.03174	.51201	.03251	.52229	.03329	54
7	.48059	.03024	.49126	.03099	.50179	.03175	.51219	.03252	.52246	.03330	53
+ 2′	8.48077	.03025	8.49143	.03101	8.50196	.03177	8.51236	.03254	8.52263	.03331	52
9	.48095	.03027	.49161	.03102	.50214	.03178	.51253	.03255	.52280	.03333	51
10	.48113	.03028	.49179	.03103	.50231	.03179	.51270	.03256	.52297	.03334	50
11	.48131	.03029	.49196	.03104	.50248	.03180	.51287	.03257	.52314	.03335	49
+ 3′	8.48149	.03030	8.49214	.03106	8.50266	.03182	8.51305	.03259	8.52331	.03337	48
13	.48167	.03032	.49232	.03107	.50283	.03183	.51322	.03260	.52348	.03338	47
14	.48184	.03033	.49249	.03108	.50301	.03184	.51339	.03261	.52365	.03339	46
15	.48202	.03034	.49267	.03109	.50318	.03186	.51356	.03263	.52382	.03341	45
+ 4′	8.48220	.03035	8.49284	.03111	8.50335	.03187	8.51374	.03264	8.52399	.03342	44
17	.48238	.03037	.49302	.03112	.50353	.03188	.51391	.03265	.52416	.03343	43
18	.48256	.03038	.49320	.03113	.50370	.03189	.51408	.03266	.52433	.03344	42
19	.48274	.03039	.49337	.03114	.50388	.03191	.51425	.03268	.52450	.03346	41
+ 5′	8.48292	.03040	8.49355	.03116	8.50405	.03192	8.51442	.03269	8.52467	.03347	40
21	.48309	.03042	.49373	.03117	.50422	.03193	.51459	.03270	.52484	.03348	39
22	.48327	.03043	.49390	.03118	.50440	.03194	.51477	.03272	.52501	.03350	38
23	.48345	.03044	.49408	.03119	.50457	.03196	.51494	.03273	.52518	.03351	37
+ 6′	8.48363	.03045	8.49425	.03121	8.50475	.03197	8.51511	.03274	8.52535	.03352	36
25	.48381	.03047	.49443	.03122	.50492	.03198	.51528	.03275	.52552	.03354	35
26	.48399	.03048	.49461	.03123	.50509	.03200	.51545	.03277	.52569	.03355	34
27	.48416	.03049	.49478	.03125	.50527	.03201	.51562	.03278	.52585	.03356	33
+ 7′	8.48434	.03050	8.49496	.03126	8.50544	.03202	8.51580	.03279	8.52602	.03358	32
29	.48452	.03052	.49513	.03127	.50561	.03204	.51597	.03281	.52619	.03359	31
30	.48470	.03053	.49531	.03128	.50579	.03205	.51614	.03282	.52636	.03360	30
31	.48488	.03054	.49548	.03130	.50596	.03206	.51631	.03283	.52653	.03361	29
+ 8′	8.48505	.03055	8.49566	.03131	8.50614	.03207	8.51648	.03285	8.52670	.03363	28
33	.48523	.03057	.49584	.03132	.50631	.03209	.51665	.03286	.52687	.03364	27
34	.48541	.03058	.49601	.03133	.50648	.03210	.51682	.03287	.52704	.03365	26
35	.48559	.03059	.49619	.03135	.50666	.03211	.51700	.03288	.52721	.03367	25
+ 9′	8.48576	.03060	8.49636	.03136	8.50683	.03212	8.51717	.03290	8.52738	.03368	24
37	.48594	.03062	.49654	.03137	.50700	.03214	.51734	.03291	.52755	.03369	23
38	.48612	.03063	.49671	.03138	.50718	.03215	.51751	.03292	.52772	.03371	22
39	.48630	.03064	.49689	.03140	.50735	.03216	.51768	.03294	.52789	.03372	21
+ 10′	8.48648	.03065	8.49706	.03141	8.50752	.03218	8.51785	.03295	8.52806	.03373	20
41	.48665	.03067	.49724	.03142	.50770	.03219	.51802	.03296	.52822	.03375	19
42	.48683	.03068	.49742	.03144	.50787	.03220	.51819	.03298	.52839	.03376	18
43	.48701	.03069	.49759	.03145	.50804	.03221	.51836	.03299	.52856	.03377	17
+ 11′	8.48719	.03070	8.49777	.03146	8.50821	.03223	8.51854	.03300	8.52873	.03379	16
45	.48736	.03072	.49794	.03147	.50839	.03224	.51871	.03301	.52890	.03380	15
46	.48754	.03073	.49812	.03149	.50856	.03225	.51888	.03303	.52907	.03381	14
47	.48772	.03074	.49829	.03150	.50873	.03227	.51905	.03304	.52924	.03382	13
+ 12′	8.48789	.03075	8.49847	.03151	8.50891	.03228	8.51922	.03305	8.52941	.03384	12
49	.48807	.03077	.49864	.03152	.50908	.03229	.51939	.03307	.52958	.03385	11
50	.48825	.03078	.49882	.03154	.50925	.03230	.51956	.03308	.52974	.03386	10
51	.48843	.03079	.49899	.03155	.50943	.03232	.51973	.03309	.52991	.03388	9
+ 13′	8.48860	.03080	8.49917	.03156	8.50960	.03233	8.51990	.03311	8.53008	.03389	8
53	.48878	.03082	.49934	.03157	.50977	.03234	.52007	.03312	.53025	.03390	7
54	.48896	.03083	.49952	.03159	.50994	.03236	.52024	.03313	.53042	.03392	6
55	.48914	.03084	.49969	.03160	.51012	.03237	.52041	.03314	.53059	.03393	5
+ 14′	8.48931	.03085	8.49987	.03161	8.51029	.03238	8.52058	.03316	8.53076	.03394	4
57	.48949	.03087	.50004	.03163	.51046	.03239	.52076	.03317	.53092	.03396	3
58	.48967	.03088	.50022	.03164	.51063	.03241	.52093	.03318	.53109	.03397	2
59	.48984	.03089	.50039	.03165	.51081	.03242	.52110	.03320	.53126	.03398	1
+ 15′	8.49002	.03090	8.50056	.03166	8.51098	.03243	8.52127	.03321	8.53143	.03400	0
	22h 39m		22h 38m		22h 37m		22h 36m		22h 35m		

TABLE 34.

Haversines.

	1h 35m 23° 45′		1h 36m 24° 0′		1h 37m 24° 15′		1h 38m 24° 30′		1h 39m 24° 45′		
s	Log. Hav.	Nat. Hav.	Log. Hav.	Nat. Hav.	Log. Hav.	Nat. Hav.	Log. Hav.	Nat. Hav.	Log. Hav.	Nat. Hav.	s
0	8.62680	**.04234**	8.63576	**.04323**	8.64463	**.04412**	8.65340	**.04502**	8.66208	**.04593**	60
1	.62695	**.04236**	.63591	**.04324**	.64477	**.04413**	.65355	**.04503**	.66223	**.04594**	59
2	.62710	**.04237**	.63606	**.04326**	.64492	**.04415**	.65369	**.04505**	.66237	**.04596**	58
3	.62725	**.04239**	.63620	**.04327**	.64507	**.04416**	.65384	**.04506**	.66251	**.04597**	57
+ 1′	8.62740	**.04240**	8.63635	**.04329**	8.64521	**.04418**	8.65398	**.04508**	8.66266	**.04599**	56
5	.62755	**.04242**	.63650	**.04330**	.64536	**.04419**	.65413	**.04509**	.66280	**.04600**	55
6	.62770	**.04243**	.63665	**.04332**	.64551	**.04421**	.65427	**.04511**	.66295	**.04602**	54
7	.62785	**.04245**	.63680	**.04333**	.64565	**.04422**	.65442	**.04512**	.66309	**.04604**	53
+ 2′	8.62800	**.04246**	8.63695	**.04335**	8.64580	**.04424**	8.65456	**.04514**	8.66323	**.04605**	52
9	.62815	**.04248**	.63709	**.04336**	.64595	**.04425**	.65471	**.04516**	.66338	**.04607**	51
10	.62830	**.04249**	.63724	**.04338**	.64609	**.04427**	.65485	**.04517**	.66352	**.04608**	50
11	.62845	**.04251**	.63739	**.04339**	.64624	**.04428**	.65500	**.04519**	.66366	**.04610**	49
+ 3′	8.62860	**.04252**	8.63754	**.04340**	8.64639	**.04430**	8.65514	**.04520**	8.66381	**.04611**	48
13	.62875	**.04253**	.63769	**.04342**	.64653	**.04431**	.65529	**.04522**	.66395	**.04613**	47
14	.62890	**.04255**	.63784	**.04343**	.64668	**.04433**	.65543	**.04523**	.66409	**.04614**	46
15	.62904	**.04256**	.63798	**.04345**	.64683	**.04434**	.65558	**.04525**	.66424	**.04616**	45
+ 4′	8.62919	**.04258**	8.63813	**.04346**	8.64697	**.04436**	8.65572	**.04526**	8.66438	**.04617**	44
17	.62934	**.04259**	.63828	**.04348**	.64712	**.04437**	.65587	**.04528**	.66453	**.04619**	43
18	.62949	**.04261**	.63843	**.04349**	.64727	**.04439**	.65601	**.04529**	.66467	**.04620**	42
19	.62964	**.04262**	.63858	**.04351**	.64741	**.04440**	.65616	**.04531**	.66481	**.04622**	41
+ 5′	8.62979	**.04264**	8.63872	**.04352**	8.64756	**.04442**	8.65630	**.04532**	8.66496	**.04623**	40
21	.62994	**.04265**	.63887	**.04354**	.64771	**.04443**	.65645	**.04534**	.66510	**.04625**	39
22	.63009	**.04267**	.63902	**.04355**	.64785	**.04445**	.65659	**.04535**	.66524	**.04626**	38
23	.63024	**.04268**	.63917	**.04357**	.64800	**.04446**	.65674	**.04537**	.66539	**.04628**	37
+ 6′	8.63039	**.04270**	8.63932	**.04358**	8.64815	**.04448**	8.65688	**.04538**	8.66553	**.04629**	36
25	.63054	**.04271**	.63946	**.04360**	.64829	**.04449**	.65703	**.04540**	.66567	**.04631**	35
26	.63069	**.04273**	.63961	**.04361**	.64844	**.04451**	.65717	**.04541**	.66582	**.04633**	34
27	.63084	**.04274**	.63976	**.04363**	.64859	**.04452**	.65732	**.04543**	.66596	**.04634**	33
+ 7′	8.63099	**.04276**	8.63991	**.04364**	8.64873	**.04454**	8.65746	**.04544**	8.66610	**.04636**	32
29	.63114	**.04277**	.64006	**.04366**	.64888	**.04455**	.65761	**.04546**	.66625	**.04637**	31
30	.63129	**.04278**	.64020	**.04367**	.64902	**.04457**	.65775	**.04547**	.66639	**.04639**	30
31	.63144	**.04280**	.64035	**.04369**	.64917	**.04458**	.65790	**.04549**	.66653	**.04640**	29
+ 8′	8.63159	**.04281**	8.64050	**.04370**	8.64932	**.04460**	8.65804	**.04550**	8.66668	**.04642**	28
33	.63174	**.04283**	.64065	**.04372**	.64946	**.04461**	.65819	**.04552**	.66682	**.04643**	27
34	.63189	**.04284**	.64079	**.04373**	.64961	**.04463**	.65833	**.04553**	.66696	**.04645**	26
35	.63204	**.04286**	.64094	**.04375**	.64976	**.04464**	.65848	**.04555**	.66710	**.04646**	25
+ 9′	8.63218	**.04287**	8.64109	**.04376**	8.64990	**.04466**	8.65862	**.04556**	8.66725	**.04648**	24
37	.63233	**.04289**	.64124	**.04378**	.65005	**.04467**	.65876	**.04558**	.66739	**.04649**	23
38	.63248	**.04290**	.64139	**.04379**	.65019	**.04469**	.65891	**.04559**	.66753	**.04651**	22
39	.63263	**.04292**	.64153	**.04381**	.65034	**.04470**	.65905	**.04561**	.66768	**.04652**	21
+ 10′	8.63278	**.04293**	8.64168	**.04382**	8.65049	**.04472**	8.65920	**.04562**	8.66782	**.04654**	20
41	.63293	**.04295**	.64183	**.04384**	.65063	**.04473**	.65934	**.04564**	.66796	**.04655**	19
42	.63308	**.04296**	.64198	**.04385**	.65078	**.04475**	.65949	**.04565**	.66811	**.04657**	18
43	.63323	**.04298**	.64212	**.04387**	.65092	**.04476**	.65963	**.04567**	.66825	**.04659**	17
+ 11′	8.63338	**.04299**	8.64227	**.04388**	8.65107	**.04478**	8.65978	**.04569**	8.66839	**.04660**	16
45	.63353	**.04301**	.64242	**.04390**	.65122	**.04479**	.65992	**.04570**	.66853	**.04662**	15
46	.63368	**.04302**	.64257	**.04391**	.65136	**.04481**	.66006	**.04572**	.66868	**.04663**	14
47	.63382	**.04304**	.64271	**.04393**	.65151	**.04482**	.66021	**.04573**	.66882	**.04665**	13
+ 12′	8.63397	**.04305**	8.64286	**.04394**	8.65165	**.04484**	8.66035	**.04575**	8.66896	**.04666**	12
49	.63412	**.04306**	.64301	**.04395**	.65180	**.04485**	.66050	**.04576**	.66911	**.04668**	11
50	.63427	**.04308**	.64315	**.04397**	.65194	**.04487**	.66064	**.04578**	.66925	**.04669**	10
51	.63442	**.04309**	.64330	**.04398**	.65209	**.04488**	.66079	**.04579**	.66939	**.04671**	9
+ 13′	8.63457	**.04311**	8.64345	**.04400**	8.65224	**.04490**	8.66093	**.04581**	8.66953	**.04672**	8
53	.63472	**.04312**	.64360	**.04401**	.65238	**.04491**	.66107	**.04582**	.66968	**.04674**	7
54	.63487	**.04314**	.64374	**.04403**	.65253	**.04493**	.66122	**.04584**	.66982	**.04675**	6
55	.63502	**.04315**	.64389	**.04404**	.65267	**.04494**	.66136	**.04585**	.66996	**.04677**	5
+ 14′	8.63516	**.04317**	8.64404	**.04405**	8.65282	**.04496**	8.66151	**.04587**	8.67010	**.04678**	4
57	.63531	**.04318**	.64418	**.04407**	.65296	**.04497**	.66165	**.04588**	.67025	**.04680**	3
58	.63546	**.04320**	.64433	**.04409**	.65311	**.04499**	.66179	**.04590**	.67039	**.04682**	2
59	.63561	**.04321**	.64448	**.04410**	.65325	**.04500**	.66194	**.04591**	.67053	**.04683**	1
+ 15′	8.63576	**.04323**	8.64463	**.04412**	8.65340	**.04502**	8.66208	**.04593**	8.67067	**.04685**	0
	22h 24m		22h 23m		22h 22m		22h 21m		22h 20m		

TABLE 34.

Haversines.

	1h 40m 25° 0′		1h 41m 25° 15′		1h 42m 25° 30′		1h 43m 25° 45′		1h 44m 26° 0′		
s	Log. Hav.	Nat. Hav.	Log. Hav.	Nat. Hav.	Log. Hav.	Nat. Hav.	Log. Hav.	Nat. Hav.	Log. Hav.	Nat. Hav.	s
0	8.67067	**.04685**	8.67918	**.04777**	8.68760	**.04871**	8.69593	**.04965**	8.70418	**.05060**	60
1	.67082	**.04686**	.67932	**.04779**	.68773	**.04872**	.69607	**.04967**	.70431	**.05062**	59
2	.67096	**.04688**	.67946	**.04780**	.68787	**.04874**	.69620	**.04968**	.70445	**.05063**	58
3	.67110	**.04689**	.67960	**.04782**	.68801	**.04875**	.69634	**.04970**	.70459	**.05065**	57
+ 1′	8.67124	**.04691**	8.67974	**.04783**	8.68815	**.04877**	8.69648	**.04971**	8.70472	**.05067**	56
5	.67139	**.04692**	.67988	**.04785**	.68829	**.04879**	.69662	**.04973**	.70486	**.05068**	55
6	.67153	**.04694**	.68002	**.04787**	.68843	**.04880**	.69676	**.04975**	.70500	**.05070**	54
7	.67167	**.04695**	.68016	**.04788**	.68857	**.04882**	.69690	**.04976**	.70513	**.05071**	53
+ 2′	8.67181	**.04697**	8.68030	**.04790**	8.68871	**.04883**	8.69703	**.04978**	8.70527	**.05073**	52
9	.67196	**.04698**	.68045	**.04791**	.68885	**.04885**	.69717	**.04979**	.70541	**.05075**	51
10	.67210	**.04700**	.68059	**.04793**	.68899	**.04886**	.69731	**.04981**	.70554	**.05076**	50
11	.67224	**.04702**	.68073	**.04794**	.68913	**.04888**	.69745	**.04982**	.70568	**.05078**	49
+ 3′	8.67238	**.04703**	8.68087	**.04796**	8.68927	**.04890**	8.69758	**.04984**	8.70582	**.05079**	48
13	.67252	**.04705**	.68101	**.04797**	.68941	**.04891**	.69772	**.04986**	.70595	**.05081**	47
14	.67267	**.04706**	.68115	**.04799**	.68955	**.04893**	.69786	**.04987**	.70609	**.05083**	46
15	.67281	**.04708**	.68129	**.04801**	.68969	**.04894**	.69800	**.04989**	.70623	**.05084**	45
+ 4′	8.67295	**.04709**	8.68143	**.04802**	8.68983	**.04896**	8.69814	**.04990**	8.70636	**.05086**	44
17	.67309	**.04711**	.68157	**.04804**	.68996	**.04897**	.69827	**.04992**	.70650	**.05087**	43
18	.67323	**.04712**	.68171	**.04805**	.69010	**.04899**	.69841	**.04994**	.70664	**.05089**	42
19	.67338	**.04714**	.68185	**.04807**	.69024	**.04901**	.69855	**.04995**	.70677	**.05091**	41
+ 5′	8.67352	**.04715**	8.68199	**.04808**	8.69038	**.04902**	8.69869	**.04997**	8.70691	**.05092**	40
21	.67366	**.04717**	.68213	**.04810**	.69052	**.04904**	.69882	**.04998**	.70704	**.05094**	39
22	.67380	**.04718**	.68227	**.04811**	.69066	**.04905**	.69896	**.05000**	.70718	**.05095**	38
23	.67394	**.04720**	.68241	**.04813**	.69080	**.04907**	.69910	**.05001**	.70732	**.05097**	37
+ 6′	8.67409	**.04722**	8.68256	**.04815**	8.69094	**.04908**	8.69924	**.05003**	8.70745	**.05099**	36
25	.67423	**.04723**	.68270	**.04816**	.69108	**.04910**	.69937	**.05005**	.70759	**.05100**	35
26	.67437	**.04725**	.68284	**.04818**	.69122	**.04912**	.69951	**.05006**	.70773	**.05102**	34
27	.67451	**.04726**	.68298	**.04819**	.69136	**.04913**	.69965	**.05008**	.70786	**.05104**	33
+ 7′	8.67465	**.04728**	8.68312	**.04821**	8.69149	**.04915**	8.69979	**.05009**	8.70800	**.05105**	32
29	.67480	**.04729**	.68326	**.04822**	.69163	**.04916**	.69992	**.05011**	.70813	**.05107**	31
30	.67494	**.04731**	.68340	**.04824**	.69177	**.04918**	.70006	**.05013**	.70827	**.05108**	30
31	.67508	**.04732**	.68354	**.04825**	.69191	**.04919**	.70020	**.05014**	.70841	**.05110**	29
+ 8′	8.67522	**.04734**	8.68368	**.04827**	8.69205	**.04921**	8.70034	**.05016**	8.70854	**.05111**	28
33	.67536	**.04735**	.68382	**.04829**	.69219	**.04923**	.70047	**.05017**	.70868	**.05113**	27
34	.67550	**.04737**	.68396	**.04830**	.69233	**.04924**	.70061	**.05019**	.70881	**.05115**	26
35	.67565	**.04739**	.68410	**.04832**	.69247	**.04926**	.70075	**.05021**	.70895	**.05116**	25
+ 9′	8.67579	**.04740**	8.68424	**.04833**	8.69260	**.04927**	8.70089	**.05022**	8.70909	**.05118**	24
37	.67593	**.04742**	.68438	**.04835**	.69274	**.04929**	.70102	**.05024**	.70922	**.05119**	23
38	.67607	**.04743**	.68452	**.04836**	.69288	**.04930**	.70116	**.05025**	.70936	**.05121**	22
39	.67621	**.04745**	.68466	**.04838**	.69302	**.04932**	.70130	**.05027**	.70949	**.05123**	21
+ 10′	8.67635	**.04746**	8.68480	**.04839**	8.69316	**.04934**	8.70144	**.05028**	8.70963	**.05124**	20
41	.67649	**.04748**	.68494	**.04841**	.69330	**.04935**	.70157	**.05030**	.70977	**.05126**	19
42	.67664	**.04749**	.68508	**.04843**	.69344	**.04937**	.70171	**.05032**	.70990	**.05127**	18
43	.67678	**.04751**	.68522	**.04844**	.69358	**.04938**	.70185	**.05033**	.71004	**.05129**	17
+ 11′	8.67692	**.04752**	8.68536	**.04846**	8.69371	**.04940**	8.70198	**.05035**	8.71017	**.05131**	16
45	.67706	**.04754**	.68550	**.04847**	.69385	**.04941**	.70212	**.05036**	.71031	**.05132**	15
46	.67720	**.04756**	.68564	**.04849**	.69399	**.04943**	.70226	**.05038**	.71045	**.05134**	14
47	.67734	**.04757**	.68578	**.04850**	.69413	**.04945**	.70240	**.05040**	.71058	**.05135**	13
+ 12′	8.67748	**.04759**	8.68592	**.04852**	8.69427	**.04946**	8.70253	**.05041**	8.71072	**.05137**	12
49	.67763	**.04760**	.68606	**.04854**	.69441	**.04948**	.70267	**.05043**	.71085	**.05139**	11
50	.67777	**.04762**	.68620	**.04855**	.69454	**.04949**	.70281	**.05044**	.71099	**.05140**	10
51	.67791	**.04763**	.68634	**.04857**	.69468	**.04951**	.70294	**.05046**	.71112	**.05142**	9
+ 13′	8.67805	**.04765**	8.68648	**.04858**	8.69482	**.04952**	8.70308	**.05048**	8.71126	**.05144**	8
53	.67819	**.04766**	.68662	**.04860**	.69496	**.04954**	.70322	**.05049**	.71140	**.05145**	7
54	.67833	**.04768**	.68676	**.04861**	.69510	**.04956**	.70336	**.05051**	.71153	**.05147**	6
55	.67847	**.04769**	.68690	**.04863**	.69524	**.04957**	.70349	**.05052**	.71167	**.05148**	5
+ 14′	8.67861	**.04771**	8.68704	**.04864**	8.69537	**.04959**	8.70363	**.05054**	8.71180	**.05150**	4
57	.67875	**.04773**	.68718	**.04866**	.69551	**.04960**	.70377	**.05055**	.71194	**.05152**	3
58	.67890	**.04774**	.68732	**.04868**	.69565	**.04962**	.70390	**.05057**	.71207	**.05153**	2
59	.67904	**.04776**	.68746	**.04869**	.69579	**.04964**	.70404	**.05059**	.71221	**.05155**	1
+ 15′	8.67918	**.04777**	8.68760	**.04871**	8.69593	**.04965**	8.70418	**.05060**	8.71234	**.05156**	0
	22h 19m		22h 18m		22h 17m		22h 16m		22h 15m		

TABLE 34.

Haversines.

s	$1^h\ 45^m$ 26° 15′		$1^h\ 46^m$ 26° 30′		$1^h\ 47^m$ 26° 45′		$1^h\ 48^m$ 27° 0′		$1^h\ 49^m$ 27° 15′		s
s	Log. Hav.	Nat. Hav.	Log. Hav	Nat. Hav.	Log. Hav.	Nat. Hav.	Log. Hav.	Nat. Hav.	Log. Hav.	Nat. Hav.	s
0	8.71234	**.05156**	8.72043	**.05253**	8.72844	**.05351**	8.73637	**.05450**	8.74423	**.05549**	60
1	.71248	**.05158**	.72057	**.05255**	.72857	**.05353**	.73650	**.05451**	.74436	**.05551**	59
2	.71261	**.05160**	.72070	**.05257**	.72871	**.05354**	.73663	**.05453**	.74449	**.05552**	58
3	.71275	**.05161**	.72083	**.05258**	.72884	**.05356**	.73677	**.05455**	.74462	**.05554**	57
+ 1′	8.71289	**.05163**	8.72097	**.05260**	8.72897	**.05358**	8.73690	**.05456**	8.74475	**.05556**	56
5	.71302	**.05164**	.72110	**.05261**	.72910	**.05359**	.73703	**.05458**	.74488	**.05557**	55
6	.71316	**.05166**	.72124	**.05263**	.72924	**.05361**	.73716	**.05460**	.74501	**.05559**	54
7	.71329	**.05168**	.72137	**.05265**	.72937	**.05363**	.73729	**.05461**	.74514	**.05561**	53
+ 2′	8.71343	**.05169**	8.72150	**.05266**	8.72950	**.05364**	8.73742	**.05463**	8.74527	**.05562**	52
9	.71356	**.05171**	.72164	**.05268**	.72963	**.05366**	.73755	**.05464**	.74540	**.05564**	51
10	.71370	**.05172**	.72177	**.05270**	.72977	**.05367**	.73769	**.05466**	.74553	**.05566**	50
11	.71383	**.05174**	.72191	**.05271**	.72990	**.05369**	.73782	**.05468**	.74566	**.05567**	49
+ 3′	8.71397	**.05176**	8.72204	**.05273**	8.73003	**.05371**	8.73795	**.05470**	8.74579	**.05569**	48
13	.71410	**.05177**	.72217	**.05274**	.73016	**.05372**	.73808	**.05471**	.74592	**.05571**	47
14	.71424	**.05179**	.72231	**.05276**	.73030	**.05374**	.73821	**.05473**	.74605	**.05572**	46
15	.71437	**.05181**	.72244	**.05278**	.73043	**.05376**	.73834	**.05474**	.74618	**.05574**	45
+ 4′	8.71451	**.05182**	8.72257	**.05279**	8.73056	**.05377**	8.73847	**.05476**	8.74631	**.05576**	44
17	.71464	**.05184**	.72271	**.05281**	.73069	**.05379**	.73860	**.05478**	.74644	**.05577**	43
18	.71478	**.05185**	.72284	**.05283**	.73083	**.05381**	.73874	**.05479**	.74657	**.05579**	42
19	.71491	**.05187**	.72298	**.05284**	.73096	**.05382**	.73887	**.05481**	.74670	**.05581**	41
+ 5′	8.71505	**.05189**	8.72311	**.05286**	8.73109	**.05384**	8.73900	**.05483**	8.74683	**.05582**	40
21	.71518	**.05190**	.72324	**.05287**	.73122	**.05385**	.73913	**.05484**	.74696	**.05584**	39
22	.71532	**.05192**	.72338	**.05289**	.73136	**.05387**	.73926	**.05486**	.74709	**.05586**	38
23	.71545	**.05193**	.72351	**.05291**	.73149	**.05389**	.73939	**.05488**	.74722	**.05587**	37
+ 6′	8.71559	**.05195**	8.72364	**.05292**	8.73162	**.05390**	8.73952	**.05489**	8.74735	**.05589**	36
25	.71572	**.05197**	.72378	**.05294**	.73175	**.05392**	.73965	**.05491**	.74748	**.05591**	35
26	.71586	**.05198**	.72391	**.05296**	.73189	**.05394**	.73978	**.05493**	.74761	**.05593**	34
27	.71599	**.05200**	.72404	**.05297**	.73202	**.05395**	.73992	**.05494**	.74774	**.05594**	33
+ 7′	8.71613	**.05201**	8.72418	**.05299**	8.73215	**.05397**	8.74005	**.05496**	8.74787	**.05596**	32
29	.71626	**.05203**	.72431	**.05300**	.73228	**.05399**	.74018	**.05498**	.74800	**.05597**	31
30	.71640	**.05205**	.72445	**.05302**	.73241	**.05400**	.74031	**.05499**	.74813	**.05599**	30
31	.71653	**.05206**	.72458	**.05304**	.73255	**.05402**	.74044	**.05501**	.74826	**.05601**	29
+ 8′	8.71667	**.05208**	8.72471	**.05305**	8.73268	**.05404**	8.74057	**.05503**	8.74839	**.05603**	28
33	.71680	**.05210**	.72485	**.05307**	.73281	**.05405**	.74070	**.05504**	.74852	**.05604**	27
34	.71694	**.05211**	.72498	**.05309**	.73294	**.05407**	.74083	**.05506**	.74864	**.05606**	26
35	.71707	**.05213**	.72511	**.05310**	.73308	**.05408**	.74096	**.05508**	.74877	**.05607**	25
+ 9′	8.71721	**.05214**	8.72525	**.05312**	8.73321	**.05410**	8.74109	**.05509**	8.74890	**.05609**	24
37	.71734	**.05216**	.72538	**.05314**	.73334	**.05412**	.74122	**.05511**	.74903	**.05611**	23
38	.71748	**.05218**	.72551	**.05315**	.73347	**.05413**	.74135	**.05513**	.74916	**.05613**	22
39	.71761	**.05219**	.72565	**.05317**	.73360	**.05415**	.74149	**.05514**	.74929	**.05614**	21
+ 10′	8.71774	**.05221**	8.72578	**.05318**	8.73374	**.05417**	8.74162	**.05516**	8.74942	**.05616**	20
41	.71788	**.05222**	.72591	**.05320**	.73387	**.05418**	.74175	**.05518**	.74955	**.05618**	19
42	.71801	**.05224**	.72605	**.05322**	.73400	**.05420**	.74188	**.05519**	.74968	**.05619**	18
43	.71815	**.05226**	.72618	**.05323**	.73413	**.05422**	.74201	**.05521**	.74981	**.05621**	17
+ 11′	8.71828	**.05227**	8.72631	**.05325**	8.73426	**.05423**	8.74214	**.05523**	8.74994	**.05623**	16
45	.71842	**.05229**	.72644	**.05326**	.73440	**.05425**	.74227	**.05524**	.75007	**.05624**	15
46	.71855	**.05231**	.72658	**.05328**	.73453	**.05427**	.74240	**.05526**	.75020	**.05626**	14
47	.71869	**.05232**	.72671	**.05330**	.73466	**.05428**	.74253	**.05528**	.75033	**.05628**	13
+ 12′	8.71882	**.05234**	8.72684	**.05331**	8.73479	**.05430**	8.74266	**.05529**	8.75046	**.05629**	12
49	.71895	**.05235**	.72698	**.05333**	.73492	**.05431**	.74279	**.05531**	.75059	**.05631**	11
50	.71909	**.05237**	.72711	**.05335**	.73505	**.05433**	.74292	**.05533**	.75072	**.05633**	10
51	.71922	**.05239**	.72724	**.05336**	.73519	**.05435**	.74305	**.05534**	.75084	**.05634**	9
+ 13′	8.71936	**.05240**	8.72738	**.05338**	8.73532	**.05436**	8.74318	**.05536**	8.75097	**.05636**	8
53	.71949	**.05242**	.72751	**.05340**	.73545	**.05438**	.74331	**.05537**	.75110	**.05638**	7
54	.71963	**.05244**	.72764	**.05341**	.73558	**.05440**	.74344	**.05539**	.75123	**.05639**	6
55	.71976	**.05245**	.72778	**.05343**	.73571	**.05441**	.74357	**.05541**	.75136	**.05641**	5
+ 14′	8.71989	**.05247**	8.72791	**.05345**	8.73584	**.05443**	8.74371	**.05542**	8.75149	**.05643**	4
57	.72003	**.05248**	.72804	**.05346**	.73598	**.05445**	.74384	**.05544**	.75162	**.05644**	3
58	.72016	**.05250**	.72817	**.05348**	.73611	**.05446**	.74397	**.05546**	.75175	**.05646**	2
59	.72030	**.05252**	.72831	**.05349**	.73624	**.05448**	.74410	**.05547**	.75188	**.05648**	1
+ 15′	8.72043	**.05253**	8.72844	**.05351**	8.73637	**.05450**	8.74423	**.05549**	8.75201	**.05649**	0
	$22^h\ 14^m$		$22^h\ 13^m$		$22^h\ 12^m$		$22^h\ 11^m$		$22^h\ 10^m$		

TABLE 34.

Haversines.

s	1h 50m 27° 30′ Log. Hav.	Nat. Hav.	1h 51m 27° 45′ Log. Hav.	Nat. Hav.	1h 52m 28° 0′ Log. Hav.	Nat. Hav.	1h 53m 28° 15′ Log. Hav.	Nat. Hav.	1h 54m 28° 30′ Log. Hav.	Nat. Hav.	s
0	8.75201	**.05649**	8.75972	**.05751**	8.76735	**.05853**	8.77492	**.05955**	8.78241	**.06059**	60
1	.75214	**.05651**	.75984	**.05752**	.76748	**.05854**	.77504	**.05957**	.78254	**.06061**	59
2	.75227	**.05653**	.75997	**.05754**	.76760	**.05856**	.77517	**.05959**	.78266	**.06063**	58
3	.75239	**.05655**	.76010	**.05756**	.76773	**.05858**	.77529	**.05961**	.78278	**.06064**	57
+ 1′	8.75252	**.05656**	8.76023	**.05757**	8.76786	**.05859**	8.77542	**.05962**	8.78291	**.06066**	56
5	.75265	**.05658**	.76035	**.05759**	.76798	**.05861**	.77554	**.05964**	.78303	**.06068**	55
6	.75278	**.05660**	.76048	**.05761**	76811	**.05863**	.77567	**.05966**	.78316	**.06070**	54
7	.75291	**.05661**	.76061	**.05762**	.76824	**.05865**	.77579	**.05968**	.78328	**.06071**	53
+ 2′	8.75304	**.05663**	8.76074	**.05764**	8.76836	**.05866**	8.77592	**.05969**	8.78341	**.06073**	52
9	.75317	**.05665**	.76086	**.05766**	.76849	**.05868**	.77604	**.05971**	.78353	**.06075**	51
10	.75330	**.05666**	.76099	**.05768**	.76862	**.05870**	.77617	**.05973**	.78365	**.06077**	50
11	.75343	**.05668**	.76112	**.05769**	.76874	**.05871**	.77630	**.05974**	.78378	**.06078**	49
+ 3′	8.75355	**.05670**	8.76125	**.05771**	8.76887	**.05873**	8.77642	**.05976**	8.78390	**.06080**	48
13	.75368	**.05671**	.76138	**.05773**	.76900	**.05875**	.77655	**.05978**	.78403	**.06082**	47
14	.75381	**.05673**	.76150	**.05774**	.76912	**.05877**	.77667	**.05980**	.78415	**.06083**	46
15	.75394	**.05675**	.76163	**.05776**	.76925	**.05878**	.77680	**.05981**	.78428	**.06085**	45
+ 4′	8.75407	**.05676**	8.76176	**.05778**	8.76938	**.05880**	8.77692	**.05983**	8.78440	**.06087**	44
17	.75420	**.05678**	.76189	**.05779**	.76950	**.05882**	.77705	**.05985**	.78452	**.06089**	43
18	.75433	**.05680**	.76201	**.05781**	.76963	**.05883**	.77717	**.05986**	.78465	**.06090**	42
19	.75446	**.05681**	.76214	**.05783**	.76975	**.05885**	.77730	**.05988**	.78477	**.06092**	41
+ 5′	8.75458	**.05683**	8.76227	**.05785**	8.76988	**.05887**	8.77742	**.05990**	8.78490	**.06094**	40
21	.75471	**.05685**	.76240	**.05786**	.77001	**.05888**	.77755	**.05992**	.78502	**.06096**	39
22	.75484	**.05686**	.76252	**.05788**	.77013	**.05890**	.77767	**.05993**	.78514	**.06097**	38
23	.75497	**.05688**	.76265	**.05790**	.77026	**.05892**	.77780	**.05995**	.78527	**.06099**	37
+ 6′	8.75510	**.05690**	8.76278	**.05791**	8.77039	**.05894**	8.77792	**.05997**	8.78539	**.06101**	36
25	.75523	**.05691**	.76291	**.05793**	.77051	**.05895**	.77805	**.05999**	.78551	**.06103**	35
26	.75536	**.05693**	.76303	**.05795**	.77064	**.05897**	.77817	**.06000**	.78564	**.06104**	34
27	.75548	**.05695**	.76316	**.05796**	.77076	**.05899**	.77830	**.06002**	.78576	**.06106**	33
+ 7′	8.75561	**.05697**	8.76329	**.05798**	8.77089	**.05901**	8.77842	**.06004**	8.78589	**.06108**	32
29	.75574	**.05698**	.76341	**.05800**	.77102	**.05902**	.77855	**.06005**	.78601	**.06110**	31
30	.75587	**.05700**	.76354	**.05802**	.77114	**.05904**	.77867	**.06007**	.78613	**.06111**	30
31	.75600	**.05702**	.76367	**.05803**	.77127	**.05906**	.77880	**.06009**	.78626	**.06113**	29
+ 8′	8.75613	**.05703**	8.76380	**.05805**	8.77139	**.05907**	8.77892	**.06011**	8.78638	**.06115**	28
33	.75626	**.05705**	.76392	**.05807**	.77152	**.05909**	.77905	**.06012**	.78651	**.06117**	27
34	.75638	**.05707**	.76405	**.05808**	.77165	**.05911**	.77917	**.06014**	.78663	**.06118**	26
35	.75651	**.05708**	.76418	**.05810**	.77177	**.05913**	.77930	**.06016**	.78675	**.06120**	25
+ 9′	8.75664	**.05710**	8.76431	**.05812**	8.77190	**.05914**	8.77942	**.06018**	8.78688	**.06122**	24
37	.75677	**.05712**	.76443	**.05813**	.77202	**.05916**	.77955	**.06019**	.78700	**.06124**	23
38	.75690	**.05713**	.76456	**.05815**	.77215	**.05918**	.77967	**.06021**	.78712	**.06125**	22
39	.75703	**.05715**	.76469	**.05817**	.77228	**.05919**	.77980	**.06023**	.78725	**.06127**	21
+ 10′	8.75715	**.05717**	8.76481	**.05819**	8.77240	**.05921**	8.77992	**.06024**	8.78737	**.06129**	20
41	.75728	**.05718**	.76494	**.05820**	.77253	**.05923**	.78005	**.06026**	.78749	**.06130**	19
42	.75741	**.05720**	.76507	**.05822**	.77265	**.05925**	.78017	**.06028**	.78762	**.06132**	18
43	.75754	**.05722**	.76519	**.05824**	.77278	**.05926**	.78029	**.06030**	.78774	**.06134**	17
+ 11′	8.75767	**.05724**	8.76532	**.05825**	8.77291	**.05928**	8.78042	**.06031**	8.78787	**.06136**	16
45	.75779	**.05725**	.76545	**.05827**	.77303	**.05930**	.78054	**.06033**	.78799	**.06137**	15
46	.75792	**.05727**	.76558	**.05829**	.77316	**.05931**	.78067	**.06035**	.78811	**.06139**	14
47	.75805	**.05729**	.76570	**.05830**	.77328	**.05933**	.78079	**.06037**	.78824	**.06141**	13
+ 12′	8.75818	**.05730**	8.76583	**.05832**	8.77341	**.05935**	8.78092	**.06038**	8.78836	**.06143**	12
49	.75831	**.05732**	.76596	**.05834**	.77353	**.05936**	.78104	**.06040**	.78848	**.06144**	11
50	.75844	**.05734**	.76608	**.05836**	.77366	**.05938**	.78117	**.06042**	.78861	**.06146**	10
51	.75856	**.05735**	.76621	**.05837**	.77379	**.05940**	.78129	**.06044**	.78873	**.06148**	9
+ 13′	8.75869	**.05737**	8.76634	**.05839**	8.77391	**.05942**	8.78142	**.06045**	8.78885	**.06150**	8
53	.75882	**.05739**	.76646	**.05841**	.77404	**.05943**	.78154	**.06047**	.78898	**.06151**	7
54	.75895	**.05740**	.76659	**.05842**	.77416	**.05945**	.78167	**.06049**	.78910	**.06153**	6
55	.75908	**.05742**	.76672	**.05844**	.77429	**.05947**	.78179	**.06050**	.78922	**.06155**	5
+ 14′	8.75920	**.05744**	8.76684	**.05846**	8.77441	**.05949**	8.78191	**.06052**	8.78935	**.06157**	4
57	.75933	**.05745**	.76697	**.05847**	.77454	**.05950**	.78204	**.06054**	.78947	**.06158**	3
58	.75946	**.05747**	.76710	**.05849**	.77466	**.05952**	.78216	**.06056**	.78959	**.06160**	2
59	.75959	**.05749**	.76722	**.05851**	.77479	**.05954**	.78229	**.06057**	.78972	**.06162**	1
+ 15′	8.75972	**.05751**	8.76735	**.05853**	8.77492	**.05955**	8.78241	**.06059**	8.78984	**.06164**	0
	22h 9m		22h 8m		22h 7m		22h 6m		22h 5m		

TABLE 34.

Haversines.

	$1^h\ 55^m$ 28° 45′		$1^h\ 56^m$ 29° 0′		$1^h\ 57^m$ 29° 15′		$1^h\ 58^m$ 29° 30′		$1^h\ 59^m$ 29° 45′		
s	Log. Hav.	Nat. Hav.	Log. Hav.	Nat. Hav.	Log. Hav.	Nat. Hav.	Log. Hav.	Nat. Hav.	Log. Hav.	Nat. Hav.	s
0	8.78984	.06164	8.79720	.06269	8.80449	.06375	8.81172	.06482	8.81889	.06590	60
1	.78996	.06165	.79732	.06271	.80462	.06377	.81184	.06484	.81901	.06592	59
2	.79009	.06167	.79744	.06273	.80474	.06379	.81196	.06486	.81913	.06594	58
3	.79021	.06169	.79757	.06274	.80486	.06381	.81208	.06488	.81925	.06595	57
+ 1′	8.79033	.06171	8.79769	.06276	8.80498	.06382	8.81220	.06489	8.81937	.06597	56
5	.79046	.06172	.79781	.06278	.80510	.06384	.81232	.06491	.81948	.06599	55
6	.79058	.06174	.79793	.06280	.80522	.06386	.81244	.06493	.81960	.06601	54
7	.79070	.06176	.79805	.06281	.80534	.06388	.81256	.06495	.81972	.06603	53
+ 2′	8.79082	.06178	8.79818	.06283	8.80546	.06389	8.81268	.06497	8.81984	.06605	52
9	.79095	.06179	.79830	.06285	.80558	.06391	.81280	.06498	.81996	.06606	51
10	.79107	.06181	79842	.06287	.80570	.06393	.81292	.06500	.82008	.06608	50
11	.79119	.06183	.79854	.06288	.80582	.06395	.81304	.06502	.82020	.06610	49
+ 3′	8.79132	.06185	8.79866	.06290	8.80595	.06397	8.81316	.06504	8.82032	.06612	48
13	.79144	.06186	.79879	.06292	.80607	.06398	.81328	.06505	.82043	.06614	47
14	.79156	.06188	.79891	.06294	.80619	.06400	.81340	.06507	.82055	.06615	46
15	.79169	.06190	.79903	.06295	.80631	.06402	.81352	.06509	.82067	.06617	45
+ 4′	8.79181	.06192	8.79915	.06297	8.80643	.06404	8.81364	.06511	8.82079	.06619	44
17	.79193	.06193	.79927	.06299	.80655	.06405	.81376	.06513	.82091	.06621	43
18	.79205	.06195	.79940	.06301	.80667	.06407	.81388	.06514	.82103	.06623	42
19	.79218	.06197	.79952	.06303	.80679	.06409	.81400	.06516	.82115	.06624	41
+ 5′	8.79230	.06199	8.79964	.06304	8.80691	.06411	8.81412	.06518	8.82126	.06626	40
21	.79242	.06200	.79976	.06306	.80703	.06413	.81424	.06520	.82138	.06628	39
22	.79255	.06202	.79988	.06308	.80715	.06414	.81436	.06522	.82150	.06630	38
23	.79267	.06204	.80000	.06310	.80727	.06416	.81448	.06523	.82162	.06632	37
+ 6′	8.79279	.06206	8.80013	.06311	8.80739	.06418	8.81460	.06525	8.82174	.06633	36
25	.79291	.06207	.80025	.06313	.80751	.06420	.81472	.06527	.82186	.06635	35
26	.79304	.06209	.80037	.06315	.80764	.06421	.81484	.06529	.82198	.06637	34
27	.79316	.06211	.80049	.06317	.80776	.06423	.81496	.06531	.82209	.06639	33
+ 7′	8.79328	.06213	8.80061	.06318	8.80788	.06425	8.81508	.06532	8.82221	.06641	32
29	.79341	.06214	.80073	.06320	.80800	.06427	.81520	.06534	.82233	.06642	31
30	.79353	.06216	.80086	.06322	.80812	.06429	.81531	.06536	.82245	.06644	30
31	.79365	.06218	.80098	.06324	.80824	.06430	.81543	.06538	.82257	.06646	29
+ 8′	8.79377	.06220	8.80110	.06326	8.80836	.06432	8.81555	.06540	8.82269	.06648	28
33	.79390	.06221	.80122	.06327	.80848	.06434	.81567	.06541	.82280	.06650	27
34	.79402	.06223	.80134	.06329	.80860	.06436	.81579	.06543	.82292	.06652	26
35	.79414	.06225	.80146	.06331	.80872	.06438	.81591	.06545	.82304	.06653	25
+ 9′	8.79426	.06227	8.80158	.06333	8.80884	.06439	8.81603	.06547	8.82316	.06655	24
37	.79439	.06229	.80171	.06334	.80896	.06441	.81615	.06549	.82328	.06657	23
38	.79451	.06230	.80183	.06336	.80908	.06443	.81627	.06550	.82340	.06659	22
39	.79463	.06232	.80195	.06338	.80920	.06445	.81639	.06552	.82351	.06661	21
+ 10′	8.79475	.06234	8.80207	.06340	8.80932	.06446	8.81651	.06554	8.82363	.06662	20
41	.79488	.06236	.80219	.06341	.80944	.06448	.81663	.06556	.82375	.06664	19
42	.79500	.06237	.80231	.06343	.80956	.06450	.81675	.06558	.82387	.06666	18
43	.79512	.06239	.80243	.06345	.80968	.06452	.81687	.06559	.82399	.06668	17
+ 11′	8.79524	.06241	8.80256	.06347	8.80980	.06454	8.81699	.06561	8.82410	.06670	16
45	.79537	.06243	.80268	.06349	.80992	.06455	.81710	.06563	.82422	.06671	15
46	.79549	.06244	.80280	.06350	.81004	.06457	.81722	.06565	.82434	.06673	14
47	.79561	.06246	.80292	.06352	.81016	.06459	.81734	.06567	.82446	.06675	13
+ 12′	8.79573	.06248	8.80304	.06354	8.81028	.06461	8.81746	.06568	8.82458	.06677	12
49	.79586	.06250	.80316	.06356	.81040	.06463	.81758	.06570	.82470	.06679	11
50	.79598	.06251	.80328	.06357	.81052	.06464	.81770	.06572	.82481	.06681	10
51	.79610	.06253	.80340	.06359	.81064	.06466	.81782	.06574	.82493	.06682	9
+ 13′	8.79622	.06255	8.80353	.06361	8.81076	.06468	8.81794	.06576	8.82505	.06684	8
53	.79634	.06257	.80365	.06363	.81088	.06470	.81806	.06577	.82517	.06686	7
54	.79647	.06258	.80377	.06365	.81100	.06471	.81818	.06579	.82529	.06688	6
55	.79659	.06260	.80389	.06366	.81112	.06473	.81830	.06581	.82540	.06690	5
+ 14′	8.79671	.06262	8.80401	.06368	8.81124	.06475	8.81841	.06583	8.82552	.06691	4
57	.79683	.06264	.80413	.06370	.81136	.06477	.81853	.06585	.82564	.06693	3
58	.79696	.06265	.80425	.06372	.81148	.06479	.81865	.06586	.82576	.06695	2
59	.79708	.06267	.80437	.06373	.81160	.06480	.81877	.06588	.82588	.06697	1
+ 15′	8.79720	.06269	8.80449	.06375	8.81172	.06482	8.81889	.06590	8.82599	.06699	0
	$22^h\ 4^m$		$22^h\ 3^m$		$22^h\ 2^m$		$22^h\ 1^m$		$22^h\ 0^m$		

TABLE 34.

Haversines.

	$2^h 0^m$ 30° 0′		$2^h 1^m$ 30° 15′		$2^h 2^m$ 30° 30′		$2^h 3^m$ 30° 45′		$2^h 4^m$ 31° 0′		
s	Log. Hav.	Nat. Hav.	Log. Hav.	Nat. Hav.	Log. Hav.	Nat. Hav.	Log. Hav.	Nat. Hav.	Log. Hav.	Nat. Hav.	s
0	8.82599	**.06699**	8.83303	**.06808**	8.84002	**.06919**	8.84694	**.07030**	8.85380	**.07142**	*60*
1	.82611	**.06701**	.83315	**.06810**	.84013	**.06920**	.84705	**.07032**	.85391	**.07144**	*59*
2	.82623	**.06702**	.83327	**.06812**	.84025	**.06922**	.84717	**.07033**	.85403	**.07145**	*58*
3	.82635	**.06704**	.83338	**.06814**	.84036	**.06924**	.84728	**.07035**	.85414	**.07147**	*57*
+ 1′	8.82646	**.06706**	8.83350	**.06816**	8.84048	**.06926**	8.84740	**.07037**	8.85425	**.07149**	*56*
5	.82658	**.06708**	.83362	**.06817**	.84059	**.06928**	.84751	**.07039**	.85437	**.07151**	*55*
6	.82670	**.06710**	.83374	**.06819**	.84071	**.06930**	.84762	**.07041**	.85448	**.07153**	*54*
7	.82682	**.06711**	.83385	**.06821**	.84083	**.06931**	.84774	**.07043**	.85459	**.07155**	*53*
+ 2′	8.82694	**.06713**	8.83397	**.06823**	8.84094	**.06933**	8.84785	**.07045**	8.85471	**.07157**	*52*
9	.82705	**.06715**	.83409	**.06825**	.84106	**.06935**	.84797	**.07046**	.85482	**.07158**	*51*
10	.82717	**.06717**	.83420	**.06826**	.84117	**.06937**	.84808	**.07048**	.85494	**.07160**	*50*
11	.82729	**.06719**	.83432	**.06828**	.84129	**.06939**	.84820	**.07050**	.85505	**.07162**	*49*
+ 3′	8.82741	**.06721**	8.83444	**.06830**	8.84140	**.06941**	8.84831	**.07052**	8.85516	**.07164**	*48*
13	.82752	**.06722**	.83455	**.06832**	.84152	**.06943**	.84843	**.07054**	.85528	**.07166**	*47*
14	.82764	**.06724**	.83467	**.06834**	.84164	**.06944**	.84854	**.07056**	.85539	**.07168**	*46*
15	.82776	**.06726**	.83479	**.06836**	.84175	**.06946**	.84866	**.07058**	.85550	**.07170**	*45*
+ 4′	8.82788	**.06728**	8.83490	**.06838**	8.84187	**.06948**	8.84877	**.07059**	8.85562	**.07172**	*44*
17	.82799	**.06730**	.83502	**.06839**	.84198	**.06950**	.84889	**.07061**	.85573	**.07173**	*43*
18	.82811	**.06731**	.83513	**.06841**	.84210	**.06952**	.84900	**.07063**	.85585	**.07175**	*42*
19	.82823	**.06733**	.83525	**.06843**	.84221	**.06954**	.84912	**.07065**	.85596	**.07177**	*41*
+ 5′	8.82835	**.06735**	8.83537	**.06845**	8.84233	**.06956**	8.84923	**.07067**	8.85607	**.07179**	*40*
21	.82846	**.06737**	.83548	**.06847**	.84244	**.06957**	.84934	**.07069**	.85619	**.07181**	*39*
22	.82858	**.06739**	.83560	**.06849**	.84256	**.06959**	.84946	**.07071**	.85630	**.07183**	*38*
23	.82870	**.06741**	.83572	**.06850**	.84268	**.06961**	.84957	**.07073**	.85641	**.07185**	*37*
+ 6′	8.82882	**.06742**	8.83583	**.06852**	8.84279	**.06963**	8.84969	**.07074**	8.85653	**.07187**	*36*
25	.82893	**.06744**	.83595	**.06854**	.84291	**.06965**	.84980	**.07076**	.85664	**.07189**	*35*
26	.82905	**.06746**	.83607	**.06856**	.84302	**.06967**	.84992	**.07078**	.85675	**.07190**	*34*
27	.82917	**.06748**	.83618	**.06858**	.84314	**.06968**	.85003	**.07080**	.85687	**.07192**	*33*
+ 7′	8.82929	**.06750**	8.83630	**.06860**	8.84325	**.06970**	8.85015	**.07082**	8.85698	**.07194**	*32*
29	.82940	**.06752**	.83642	**.06861**	.84337	**.06972**	.85026	**.07084**	.85709	**.07196**	*31*
30	.82952	**.06753**	.83653	**.06863**	.84348	**.06974**	.85037	**.07086**	.85721	**.07198**	*30*
31	.82964	**.06755**	.83665	**.06865**	.84360	**.06976**	.85049	**.07087**	.85732	**.07200**	*29*
+ 8′	8.82976	**.06757**	8.83676	**.06867**	8.84371	**.06978**	8.85060	**.07089**	8.85743	**.07202**	*28*
33	.82987	**.06759**	.83688	**.06869**	.84383	**.06980**	.85072	**.07091**	.85755	**.07204**	*27*
34	.82999	**.06761**	.83700	**.06871**	.84394	**.06981**	.85083	**.07093**	.85766	**.07205**	*26*
35	.83011	**.06763**	.83711	**.06872**	.84406	**.06983**	.85095	**.07095**	.85777	**.07207**	*25*
+ 9′	8.83023	**.06764**	8.83723	**.06874**	8.84417	**.06985**	8.85106	**.07097**	8.85789	**.07209**	*24*
37	.83034	**.06766**	.83735	**.06876**	.84429	**.06987**	.85117	**.07099**	.85800	**.07211**	*23*
38	.83046	**.06768**	.83746	**.06878**	.84441	**.06989**	.85129	**.07100**	.85811	**.07213**	*22*
39	.83058	**.06770**	.83758	**.06880**	.84452	**.06991**	.85140	**.07102**	.85823	**.07215**	*21*
+ 10′	8.83069	**.06772**	8.83769	**.06882**	8.84464	**.06993**	8.85152	**.07104**	8.85834	**.07217**	*20*
41	.83081	**.06773**	.83781	**.06884**	.84475	**.06994**	.85163	**.07106**	.85845	**.07219**	*19*
42	.83093	**.06775**	.83793	**.06885**	.84487	**.06996**	.85175	**.07108**	.85857	**.07220**	*18*
43	.83105	**.06777**	.83804	**.06887**	.84498	**.06998**	.85186	**.07110**	.85868	**.07222**	*17*
+ 11′	8.83116	**.06779**	8.83816	**.06889**	8.84510	**.07000**	8.85197	**.07112**	8.85879	**.07224**	*16*
45	.83128	**.06781**	.83828	**.06891**	.84521	**.07002**	.85209	**.07114**	.85891	**.07226**	*15*
46	.83140	**.06783**	.83839	**.06893**	.84533	**.07004**	.85220	**.07115**	.85902	**.07228**	*14*
47	.83151	**.06784**	.83851	**.06895**	.84544	**.07006**	.85232	**.07117**	.85913	**.07230**	*13*
+ 12′	8.83163	**.06786**	8.83862	**.06896**	8.84556	**.07007**	8.85243	**.07119**	8.85925	**.07232**	*12*
49	.83175	**.06788**	.83874	**.06898**	.84567	**.07009**	.85254	**.07121**	.85936	**.07234**	*11*
50	.83187	**.06790**	.83886	**.06900**	.84579	**.07011**	.85266	**.07123**	.85947	**.07236**	*10*
51	.83198	**.06792**	.83897	**.06902**	.84590	**.07013**	.85277	**.07125**	.85959	**.07237**	*9*
+ 13′	8.83210	**.06794**	8.83909	**.06904**	8.84602	**.07015**	8.85289	**.07127**	8.85970	**.07239**	*8*
53	.83222	**.06795**	.83920	**.06906**	.84613	**.07017**	.85300	**.07129**	.85981	**.07241**	*7*
54	.83233	**.06797**	.83932	**.06907**	.84625	**.07019**	.85311	**.07130**	.85992	**.07243**	*6*
55	.83245	**.06799**	.83944	**.06909**	.84636	**.07020**	.85323	**.07132**	.86004	**.07245**	*5*
+ 14′	8.83257	**.06801**	8.83955	**.06911**	8.84648	**.07022**	8.85334	**.07134**	8.86015	**.07247**	*4*
57	.83268	**.06803**	.83967	**.06913**	.84659	**.07024**	.85346	**.07136**	.86026	**.07249**	*3*
58	.83280	**.06805**	.83978	**.06915**	.84671	**.07026**	.85357	**.07138**	.86038	**.07251**	*2*
59	.83292	**.06806**	.83990	**.06917**	.84682	**.07028**	.85368	**.07140**	.86049	**.07253**	*1*
+ 15′	8.83303	**.06808**	8.84002	**.06919**	8.84694	**.07030**	8.85380	**.07142**	8.86060	**.07254**	*0*
	$21^h 59^m$		$21^h 58^m$		$21^h 57^m$		$21^h 56^m$		$21^h 55^m$		

TABLE 34.

Haversines.

s	$2^h\ 5^m$ 31° 15′		$2^h\ 6^m$ 31° 30′		$2^h\ 7^m$ 31° 45′		$2^h\ 8^m$ 32° 0′		$2^h\ 9^m$ 32° 15′		s
	Log. Hav.	Nat. Hav.	Log. Hav.	Nat. Hav.	Log. Nav.	Nat. Hav.	Log. Hav.	Nat. Hav.	Log. Hav.	Nat. Hav.	
0	8.86060	.07254	8.86735	.07368	8.87404	.07482	8.88068	.07598	8.88726	.07714	60
1	.86072	.07256	.86746	.07370	.87415	.07484	.88079	.07600	.88737	.07716	59
2	.86085	.07258	.86757	.07372	.87426	.07486	.88090	.07601	.88748	.07717	58
3	.86094	.07260	.86769	.07374	.87437	.07488	.88101	.07603	.88759	.07719	57
+ 1′	8.86105	.07262	8.86780	.07376	8.87448	.07490	8.88112	.07605	8.88769	.07721	56
5	.86117	.07264	.86791	.07377	.87460	.07492	.88123	.07607	.88780	.07723	55
6	.86128	.07266	.86802	.07379	.87471	.07494	.88134	.07609	.88791	.07725	54
7	.86139	.07268	.86813	.07381	.87482	.07496	.88145	.07611	.88802	.07727	53
+ 2′	8.86151	.07270	8.86825	.07383	8.87493	.07498	8.88156	.07613	8.88813	.07729	52
9	.86162	.07271	.86836	.07385	.87504	.07500	.88167	.07615	.88824	.07731	51
10	.86173	.07273	.86847	.07387	.87515	.07502	.88178	.07617	.88835	.07733	50
11	.86184	.07275	.86858	.07389	.87526	.07503	.88189	.07619	.88846	.07735	49
+ 3′	8.86196	.07277	8.86869	.07391	8.87537	.07505	8.88200	.07621	8.88857	.07737	48
13	.86207	.07279	.86880	.07393	.87548	.07507	.88211	.07623	.88868	.07739	47
14	.86218	.07281	.86892	.07395	.87559	.07509	.88222	.07625	.88879	.07741	46
15	.86229	.07283	.86903	.07397	.87570	.07511	.88233	.07627	.88890	.07743	45
+ 4′	8.86241	.07285	8.86914	.07398	8.87582	.07513	8.88244	.07628	8.88900	.07745	44
17	.86252	.07287	.86925	.07400	.87593	.07515	.88255	.07630	.88911	.07747	43
18	.86263	.07288	.86936	.07402	.87604	.07517	.88266	.07632	.88922	.07749	42
19	.86275	.07290	.86947	.07404	.87615	.07519	.88277	.07634	.88933	.07751	41
+ 5′	8.86286	.07292	8.86959	.07406	8.87626	.07521	8.88288	.07636	8.88944	.07752	40
21	.86297	.07294	.86970	.07408	.87637	.07523	.88299	.07638	.88955	.07754	39
22	.86308	.07296	.86981	.07410	.87648	.07525	.88310	.07640	.88966	.07756	38
23	.86320	.07298	.86992	.07412	.87659	.07527	.88321	.07642	.88977	.07758	37
+ 6′	8.86331	.07300	8.87003	.07414	8.87670	.07528	8.88332	.07644	8.88988	.07760	36
25	.86342	.07302	.87014	.07416	.87681	.07530	.88343	.07646	.88998	.07762	35
26	.86353	.07304	.87026	.07417	.87692	.07532	.88354	.07648	.89009	.07764	34
27	.86365	.07305	.87037	.07419	.87703	.07534	.88364	.07650	.89020	.07766	33
+ 7′	8.86376	.07307	8.87048	.07421	8.87714	.07536	8.88375	.07652	8.89031	.07768	32
29	.86387	.07309	.87059	.07423	.87725	.07538	.88386	.07654	.89042	.07770	31
30	.86398	.07311	.87070	.07425	.87737	.07540	.88397	.07656	.89053	.07772	30
31	.86410	.07313	.87081	.07427	.87748	.07542	.88408	.07657	.89064	.07774	29
+ 8′	8.86421	.07315	8.87093	.07429	8.87759	.07544	8.88419	.07659	8.89075	.07776	28
33	.86432	.07317	.87104	.07431	.87770	.07546	.88430	.07661	.89086	.07778	27
34	.86443	.07319	.87115	.07433	.87781	.07548	.88441	.07663	.89096	.07780	26
35	.86455	.07321	.87126	.07435	.87792	.07549	.88452	.07665	.89107	.07782	25
+ 9′	8.86466	.07322	8.87137	.07437	8.87803	.07551	8.88463	.07667	8.89118	.07784	24
37	.86477	.07324	.87148	.07438	.87814	.07553	.88474	.07669	.89129	.07786	23
38	.86488	.07326	.87159	.07440	.87825	.07555	.88485	.07671	.89140	.07788	22
39	.86499	.07328	.87171	.07442	.87836	.07557	.88496	.07673	.89151	.07789	21
+ 10′	8.86511	.07330	8.87182	.07444	8.87847	.07559	8.88507	.07675	8.89162	.07791	20
41	.86522	.07332	.87193	.07446	.87858	.07561	.88518	.07677	.89172	.07793	19
42	.86533	.07334	.87204	.07448	.87869	.07563	.88529	.07679	.89183	.07795	18
43	.86544	.07336	.87215	.07450	.87880	.07565	.88540	.07681	.89194	.07797	17
+ 11′	8.86556	.07338	8.87226	.07452	8.87891	.07567	8.88551	.07683	8.89205	.07799	16
45	.86567	.07340	.87237	.07454	.87902	.07569	.88562	.07685	.89216	.07801	15
46	.86578	.07341	.87248	.07456	.87913	.07571	.88573	.07686	.89227	.07803	14
47	.86589	.07343	.87260	.07458	.87924	.07573	.88584	.07688	.89238	.07805	13
+ 12′	8.86600	.07345	8.87271	.07459	8.87935	.07574	8.88595	.07690	8.89248	.07807	12
49	.86611	.07347	.87282	.07461	.87946	.07576	.88606	.07692	.89259	.07809	11
50	.86623	.07349	.87293	.07463	.87957	.07578	.88616	.07694	.89270	.07811	10
51	.86634	.07351	.87304	.07465	.87968	.07580	.88627	.07696	.89281	.07813	9
+ 13′	8.86645	.07353	8.87315	.07467	8.87980	.07582	8.88638	.07698	8.89292	.07815	8
53	.86657	.07355	.87326	.07469	.87991	.07584	.88649	.07700	.89303	.07817	7
54	.86668	.07357	.87337	.07471	.88002	.07586	.88660	.07702	.89314	.07819	6
55	.86679	.07359	.87349	.07473	.88013	.07588	.88671	.07704	.89324	.07821	5
+ 14′	8.86690	.07360	8.87360	.07475	8.88024	.07590	8.88682	.07706	8.89335	.07823	4
57	.86701	.07362	.87371	.07477	.88035	.07592	.88693	.07708	.89346	.07825	3
58	.86713	.07364	.87382	.07479	.88046	.07594	.88704	.07710	.89357	.07827	2
59	.86724	.07366	.87393	.07480	.88057	.07596	.88715	.07712	.89368	.07829	1
+ 15′	8.86735	.07368	8.87404	.07482	8.88068	.07598	8.88726	.07714	8.89379	.07830	0
	$21^h\ 54^m$		$21^h\ 53^m$		$21^h\ 52^m$		$21^h\ 51^m$		$21^h\ 50^m$		

TABLE 34.

Haversines.

s	2h 10m 32° 30′ Log. Hav.	Nat. Hav.	2h 11m 32° 45′ Log. Hav.	Nat. Hav.	2h 12m 33° 0′ Log. Hav.	Nat. Hav.	2h 13m 33° 15′ Log. Hav.	Nat. Hav.	2h 14m 33° 30′ Log. Hav.	Nat. Hav.	s
0	8.89379	**.07830**	8.90026	**.07948**	8.90668	**.08066**	8.91306	**.08186**	8.91938	**.08306**	60
1	.89389	**.07832**	.90037	**.07950**	.90679	**.08068**	.91316	**.08188**	.91948	**.08308**	59
2	.89400	**.07834**	.90048	**.07952**	.90690	**.08070**	.91327	**.08190**	.91959	**.08310**	58
3	.89411	**.07836**	.90058	**.07954**	.90700	**.08072**	.91337	**.08192**	.91969	**.08312**	57
+ 1′	8.89422	**.07838**	8.90069	**.07956**	8.90711	**.08074**	8.91348	**.08194**	8.91980	**.08314**	56
5	.89433	**.07840**	.90080	**.07958**	.90722	**.08076**	.91358	**.08196**	.91990	**.08316**	55
6	.89444	**.07842**	.90091	**.07960**	.90732	**.08078**	.91369	**.08198**	.92001	**.08318**	54
7	.89454	**.07844**	.90101	**.07962**	.90743	**.08080**	.91380	**.08200**	.92011	**.08320**	53
+ 2′	8.89465	**.07846**	8.90112	**.07964**	8.90754	**.08082**	8.91390	**.08202**	8.92022	**.08322**	52
9	.89476	**.07848**	.90123	**.07966**	.90764	**.08084**	.91401	**.08204**	.92032	**.08324**	51
10	.89487	**.07850**	.90134	**.07968**	.90775	**.08086**	.91411	**.08206**	.92043	**.08326**	50
11	.89498	**.07852**	.90144	**.07970**	.90786	**.08088**	.91422	**.08208**	.92053	**.08328**	49
+ 3′	8.89509	**.07854**	8.90155	**.07972**	8.90796	**.08090**	8.91432	**.08210**	8.92064	**.08330**	48
13	.89519	**.07856**	.90166	**.07974**	.90807	**.08092**	.91443	**.08212**	.92074	**.08332**	47
14	.89530	**.07858**	.90176	**.07976**	.90818	**.08094**	.91454	**.08214**	.92084	**.08334**	46
15	.89541	**.07860**	.90187	**.07978**	.90828	**.08096**	.91464	**.08216**	.92095	**.08336**	45
+ 4′	8.89552	**.07862**	8.90198	**.07980**	8.90839	**.08098**	8.91475	**.08218**	8.92105	**.08338**	44
17	.89563	**.07864**	.90209	**.07982**	.90849	**.08100**	.91485	**.08220**	.92116	**.08340**	43
18	.89573	**.07866**	.90219	**.07983**	.90860	**.08102**	.91496	**.08222**	.92126	**.08342**	42
19	.89584	**.07868**	.90230	**.07985**	.90871	**.08104**	.91506	**.08224**	.92137	**.08344**	41
+ 5′	8.89595	**.07870**	8.90241	**.07987**	8.90881	**.08106**	8.91517	**.08226**	8.92147	**.08346**	40
21	.89606	**.07872**	.90252	**.07989**	.90892	**.08108**	.91527	**.08228**	.92158	**.08348**	39
22	.89617	**.07873**	.90262	**.07991**	.90903	**.08110**	.91538	**.08230**	.92168	**.08350**	38
23	.89627	**.07875**	.90273	**.07993**	.90913	**.08112**	.91549	**.08232**	.92179	**.08352**	37
+ 6′	8.89638	**.07877**	8.90284	**.07995**	8.90924	**.08114**	8.91559	**.08234**	8.92189	**.08354**	36
25	.89649	**.07879**	.90294	**.07997**	.90935	**.08116**	.91570	**.08236**	.92200	**.08356**	35
26	.89660	**.07881**	.90305	**.07999**	.90945	**.08118**	.91580	**.08238**	.92210	**.08358**	34
27	.89671	**.07883**	.90316	**.08001**	.90956	**.08120**	.91591	**.08240**	.92221	**.08360**	33
+ 7′	8.89681	**.07885**	8.90326	**.08003**	8.90966	**.08122**	8.91601	**.08242**	8.92231	**.08362**	32
29	.89692	**.07887**	.90337	**.08005**	.90977	**.08124**	.91612	**.08244**	.92241	**.08364**	31
30	.89703	**.07889**	.90348	**.08007**	.90988	**.08126**	.91622	**.08246**	.92252	**.08366**	30
31	.89714	**.07891**	.90359	**.08009**	.90998	**.08128**	.91633	**.08248**	.92262	**.08368**	29
+ 8′	8.89725	**.07893**	8.90369	**.08011**	8.91009	**.08130**	8.91643	**.08250**	8.92273	**.08370**	28
33	.89735	**.07895**	.90380	**.08013**	.91019	**.08132**	.91654	**.08252**	.92283	**.08372**	27
34	.89746	**.07897**	.90391	**.08015**	.91030	**.08134**	.91664	**.08254**	.92294	**.08374**	26
35	.89757	**.07899**	.90401	**.08017**	.91041	**.08136**	.91675	**.08256**	.92304	**.08376**	25
+ 9′	8.89768	**.07901**	8.90412	**.08019**	8.91051	**.08138**	8.91685	**.08258**	8.92315	**.08378**	24
37	.89779	**.07903**	.90423	**.08021**	.91062	**.08140**	.91696	**.08260**	.92325	**.08380**	23
38	.89789	**.07905**	.90433	**.08023**	.91073	**.08142**	.91707	**.08262**	.92335	**.08382**	22
39	.89800	**.07907**	.90444	**.08025**	.91083	**.08144**	.91717	**.08264**	.92346	**.08384**	21
+ 10′	8.89811	**.07909**	8.90455	**.08027**	8.91094	**.08146**	8.91728	**.08266**	8.92356	**.08386**	20
41	.89822	**.07911**	.90466	**.08029**	.91104	**.08148**	.91738	**.08268**	.92367	**.08388**	19
42	.89832	**.07913**	.90476	**.08031**	.91115	**.08150**	.91749	**.08270**	.92377	**.08390**	18
43	.89843	**.07915**	.90487	**.08033**	.91126	**.08152**	.91759	**.08272**	.92388	**.08392**	17
+ 11′	8.89854	**.07917**	8.90498	**.08035**	8.91136	**.08154**	8.91770	**.08274**	8.92398	**.08394**	16
45	.89865	**.07919**	.90508	**.08037**	.91147	**.08156**	.91780	**.08276**	.92409	**.08396**	15
46	.89875	**.07921**	.90519	**.08039**	.91157	**.08158**	.91791	**.08278**	.92419	**.08398**	14
47	.89886	**.07923**	.90530	**.08041**	.91168	**.08160**	.91801	**.08280**	.92429	**.08400**	13
+ 12′	8.89897	**.07924**	8.90540	**.08043**	8.91179	**.08162**	8.91812	**.08282**	8.92440	**.08402**	12
49	.89908	**.07926**	.90551	**.08045**	.91189	**.08164**	.91822	**.08284**	.92450	**.08404**	11
50	.89919	**.07928**	.90562	**.08047**	.91200	**.08166**	.91833	**.08286**	.92461	**.08406**	10
51	.89929	**.07930**	.90572	**.08049**	.91210	**.08168**	.91843	**.08288**	.92471	**.08408**	9
+ 13′	8.89940	**.07932**	8.90583	**.08051**	8.91221	**.08170**	8.91854	**.08290**	8.92482	**.08410**	8
53	.89951	**.07934**	.90594	**.08053**	.91232	**.08172**	.91864	**.08292**	.92492	**.08412**	7
54	.89962	**.07936**	.90604	**.08055**	.91242	**.08174**	.91875	**.08294**	.92502	**.08414**	6
55	.89972	**.07938**	.90615	**.08057**	.91253	**.08176**	.91885	**.08296**	.92513	**.08416**	5
+ 14′	8.89983	**.07940**	8.90626	**.08059**	8.91263	**.08178**	8.91896	**.08298**	8.92523	**.08418**	4
57	.89994	**.07942**	.90636	**.08061**	.91274	**.08180**	.91906	**.08300**	.92534	**.08420**	3
58	.90005	**.07944**	.90647	**.08063**	.91284	**.08182**	.91917	**.08302**	.92544	**.08422**	2
59	.90015	**.07946**	.90658	**.08065**	.91295	**.08184**	.91927	**.08304**	.92554	**.08425**	1
+ 15′	8.90026	**.07948**	8.90668	**.08066**	8.91306	**.08186**	8.91938	**.08306**	8.92565	**.08427**	0
	21h 49m		21h 48m		21h 47m		21h 46m		21h 45m		

TABLE 34.

Haversines.

s	$2^h\,15^m$ **33° 45′**		$2^h\,16^m$ **34° 0′**		$2^h\,17^m$ **34° 15′**		$2^h\,18^m$ **34° 30′**		$2^h\,19^m$ **34° 45′**		s
	Log. Hav.	Nat. Hav.	Log. Hav.	Nat. Hav.	Log. Hav.	Nat. Hav.	Log. Hav.	Nat. Hav.	Log. Hav.	Nat. Hav.	
0	8.92565	**.08427**	8.93187	**.08548**	8.93805	**.08671**	8.94417	**.08794**	8.95025	**.08918**	*60*
1	.92575	**.08429**	.93197	**.08550**	.93815	**.08673**	.94427	**.08796**	.95035	**.08920**	*59*
2	.92586	**.08431**	.93208	**.08552**	.93825	**.08675**	.94438	**.08798**	.95045	**.08922**	*58*
3	.92596	**.08433**	.93218	**.08554**	.93835	**.08677**	.94448	**.08800**	.95055	**.08924**	*57*
+ **1′**	8.92607	**.08435**	8.93228	**.08556**	8.93846	**.08679**	8.94458	**.08802**	8.95065	**.08926**	*56*
5	.92617	**.08437**	.93239	**.08558**	.93856	**.08681**	.94468	**.08804**	.95076	**.08928**	*55*
6	.92627	**.08439**	.93249	**.08560**	.93866	**.08683**	.94478	**.08806**	.95086	**.08930**	*54*
7	.92638	**.08441**	.93259	**.08562**	.93876	**.08685**	.94488	**.08808**	.95096	**.08932**	*53*
+ **2′**	8.92648	**.08443**	8.93270	**.08564**	8.93886	**.08687**	8.94498	**.08810**	8.95106	**.08934**	*52*
9	.92659	**.08445**	.93280	**.08566**	.93897	**.08689**	.94509	**.08812**	.95116	**.08936**	*51*
10	.92669	**.08447**	.93290	**.08568**	.93907	**.08691**	.94519	**.08814**	.95126	**.08938**	*50*
11	.92679	**.08449**	.93301	**.08571**	.93917	**.08693**	.94529	**.08816**	.95136	**.08940**	*49*
+ **3′**	8.92690	**.08451**	8.93311	**.08573**	8.93927	**.08695**	8.94539	**.08818**	8.95146	**.08943**	*48*
13	.92700	**.08453**	.93321	**.08575**	.93938	**.08697**	.94549	**.08820**	.95156	**.08945**	*47*
14	.92710	**.08455**	.93332	**.08577**	.93948	**.08699**	.94559	**.08823**	.95166	**.08947**	*46*
15	.92721	**.08457**	.93342	**.08579**	.93958	**.08701**	.94570	**.08825**	.95176	**.08949**	*45*
+ **4′**	8.92731	**.08459**	8.93352	**.08581**	8.93968	**.08703**	8.94580	**.08827**	8.95186	**.08951**	*44*
17	.92742	**.08461**	.93363	**.08583**	.93979	**.08705**	.94590	**.08829**	.95197	**.08953**	*43*
18	.92752	**.08463**	.93373	**.08585**	.93989	**.08707**	.94600	**.08831**	.95207	**.08955**	*42*
19	.92762	**.08465**	.93383	**.08587**	.93999	**.08709**	.94610	**.08833**	.95217	**.08957**	*41*
+ **5′**	8.92773	**.08467**	8.93393	**.08589**	8.94009	**.08711**	8.94620	**.08835**	8.95227	**.08959**	*40*
21	.92783	**.08469**	.93404	**.08591**	.94019	**.08714**	.94630	**.08837**	.95237	**.08961**	*39*
22	.92794	**.08471**	.93414	**.08593**	.94030	**.08716**	.94641	**.08839**	.95247	**.08963**	*38*
23	.92804	**.08473**	.93424	**.08595**	.94040	**.08718**	.94651	**.08841**	.95257	**.08965**	*37*
+ **6′**	8.92814	**.08475**	8.93435	**.08597**	8.94050	**.08720**	8.94661	**.08843**	8.95267	**.08967**	*36*
25	.92825	**.08477**	.93445	**.08599**	.94060	**.08722**	.94671	**.08845**	.95277	**.08970**	*35*
26	.92835	**.08479**	.93455	**.08601**	.94071	**.08724**	.94681	**.08847**	.95287	**.08972**	*34*
27	.92845	**.08481**	.93466	**.08603**	.94081	**.08726**	.94691	**.08849**	.95297	**.08974**	*33*
+ **7′**	8.92856	**.08483**	8.93476	**.08605**	8.94091	**.08728**	8.94701	**.08851**	8.95307	**.08976**	*32*
29	.92866	**.08485**	.93486	**.08607**	.94101	**.08730**	.94712	**.08853**	.95317	**.08978**	*31*
30	.92877	**.08487**	.93496	**.08609**	.94111	**.08732**	.94722	**.08856**	.95327	**.08980**	*30*
31	.92887	**.08489**	.93507	**.08611**	.94122	**.08734**	.94732	**.08858**	.95337	**.08982**	*29*
+ **8′**	8.92897	**.08491**	8.93517	**.08613**	8.94132	**.08736**	8.94742	**.08860**	8.95347	**.08984**	*28*
33	.92908	**.08493**	.93527	**.08615**	.94142	**.08738**	.94752	**.08862**	.95357	**.08986**	*27*
34	.92918	**.08495**	.93538	**.08617**	.94152	**.08740**	.94762	**.08864**	.95368	**.08988**	*26*
35	.92928	**.08497**	.93548	**.08619**	.94162	**.08742**	.94772	**.08866**	.95378	**.08990**	*25*
+ **9′**	8.92939	**.08499**	8.93558	**.08621**	8.94173	**.08744**	8.94782	**.08868**	8.95388	**.08992**	*24*
37	.92949	**.08501**	.93568	**.08624**	.94183	**.08746**	.94793	**.08870**	.95398	**.08994**	*23*
38	.92960	**.08503**	.93579	**.08626**	.94193	**.08748**	.94803	**.08872**	.95408	**.08997**	*22*
39	.92970	**.08505**	.93589	**.08628**	.94203	**.08750**	.94813	**.08874**	.95418	**.08999**	*21*
+ **10′**	8.92980	**.08508**	8.93599	**.08630**	8.94213	**.08753**	8.94823	**.08876**	8.95428	**.09001**	*20*
41	.92991	**.08510**	.93610	**.08632**	.94224	**.08755**	.94833	**.08878**	.95438	**.09003**	*19*
42	.93001	**.08512**	.93620	**.08634**	.94234	**.08757**	.94843	**.08880**	.95448	**.09005**	*18*
43	.93011	**.08514**	.93630	**.08636**	.94244	**.08759**	.94853	**.08882**	.95458	**.09007**	*17*
+ **11′**	8.93022	**.08516**	8.93640	**.08638**	8.94254	**.08761**	8.94863	**.08885**	8.95468	**.09009**	*16*
45	.93032	**.08518**	.93651	**.08640**	.94264	**.08763**	.94874	**.08887**	.95478	**.09011**	*15*
46	.93042	**.08520**	.93661	**.08642**	.94275	**.08765**	.94884	**.08889**	.95488	**.09013**	*14*
47	.93053	**.08522**	.93671	**.08644**	.94285	**.08767**	.94894	**.08891**	.95498	**.09015**	*13*
+ **12′**	8.93063	**.08524**	8.93681	**.08646**	8.94295	**.08769**	8.94904	**.08893**	8.95508	**.09017**	*12*
49	.93073	**.08526**	.93692	**.08648**	.94305	**.08771**	.94914	**.08895**	.95518	**.09019**	*11*
50	.93084	**.08528**	.93702	**.08650**	.94315	**.08773**	.94924	**.08897**	.95528	**.09022**	*10*
51	.93094	**.08530**	.93712	**.08652**	.94326	**.08775**	.94934	**.08899**	.95538	**.09024**	*9*
+ **13′**	8.93104	**.08532**	8.93722	**.08654**	8.94336	**.08777**	8.94944	**.08901**	8.95548	**.09026**	*8*
53	.93115	**.08534**	.93733	**.08656**	.94346	**.08779**	.94954	**.08903**	.95558	**.09028**	*7*
54	.93125	**.08536**	.93743	**.08658**	.94356	**.08781**	.94965	**.08905**	.95568	**.09030**	*6*
55	.93135	**.08538**	.93753	**.08660**	.94366	**.08783**	.94975	**.08907**	.95578	**.09032**	*5*
+ **14′**	8.93146	**.08540**	8.93764	**.08662**	8.94376	**.08785**	8.94985	**.08909**	8.95588	**.09034**	*4*
57	.93156	**.08542**	.93774	**.08664**	.94387	**.08788**	.94995	**.08911**	.95598	**.09036**	*3*
58	.93166	**.08544**	.93784	**.08666**	.94397	**.08790**	.95005	**.08914**	.95608	**.09038**	*2*
59	.93177	**.08546**	.93794	**.08668**	.94407	**.08792**	.95015	**.08916**	.95618	**.09040**	*1*
+ **15′**	8.93187	**.08548**	8.93805	**.08671**	8.94417	**.08794**	8.95025	**.08918**	8.95628	**.09042**	*0*
	$21^h\,44^m$		$21^h\,43^m$		$21^h\,42^m$		$21^h\,41^m$		$21^h\,40^m$		

TABLE 34.

Haversines.

s	$2^h\ 20^m$ 35° 0′		$2^h\ 21^m$ 35° 15′		$2^h\ 22^m$ 35° 30′		$2^h\ 23^m$ 35° 45′		$2^h\ 24^m$ 36° 0′		s
	Log. Hav.	Nat. Hav.	Log. Hav.	Nat. Hav.	Log. Hav.	Nat. Hav.	Log. Hav.	Nat. Hav.	Log. Hav.	Nat. Hav.	
0	8.95628	**.09042**	8.96227	**.09168**	8.96821	**.09294**	8.97411	**.09421**	8.97997	**.09549**	60
1	.95638	**.09044**	.96237	**.09170**	.96831	**.09296**	.97421	**.09423**	.98006	**.09551**	59
2	.95648	**.09047**	.96247	**.09172**	.96841	**.09298**	.97431	**.09426**	.98016	**.09553**	58
3	.95658	**.09049**	.96257	**.09174**	.96851	**.09301**	.97441	**.09428**	.98026	**.09556**	57
+ 1′	8.95668	**.09051**	8.96267	**.09176**	8.96861	**.09303**	8.97450	**.09430**	8.98035	**.09558**	56
5	.95678	**.09053**	.96277	**.09178**	.96871	**.09305**	.97460	**.09432**	.98045	**.09560**	55
6	.95688	**.09055**	.96287	**.09181**	.96881	**.09307**	.97470	**.09434**	.98055	**.09562**	54
7	.95698	**.09057**	.96297	**.09183**	.96890	**.09309**	.97480	**.09436**	.98065	**.09564**	53
+ 2′	8.95709	**.09059**	8.96307	**.09185**	8.96900	**.09311**	8.97489	**.09438**	8.98074	**.09566**	52
9	.95719	**.09061**	.96317	**.09187**	.96910	**.09313**	.97499	**.09440**	.98084	**.09568**	51
10	.95729	**.09063**	.96326	**.09189**	.96920	**.09315**	.97509	**.09443**	.98094	**.09571**	50
11	.95739	**.09065**	.96336	**.09191**	.96930	**.09317**	.97519	**.09445**	.98103	**.09573**	49
+ 3′	8.95749	**.09067**	8.96346	**.09193**	8.96940	**.09320**	8.97529	**.09447**	8.98113	**.09575**	48
13	.95759	**.09070**	.96356	**.09195**	.96950	**.09322**	.97538	**.09449**	.98123	**.09577**	47
14	.95769	**.09072**	.96366	**.09197**	.96959	**.09324**	.97548	**.09451**	.98132	**.09579**	46
15	.95779	**.09074**	.96376	**.09199**	.96969	**.09326**	.97558	**.09453**	.98142	**.09581**	45
+ 4′	8.95789	**.09076**	8.96386	**.09202**	8.96979	**.09328**	8.97568	**.09455**	8.98152	**.09583**	44
17	.95799	**.09078**	.96396	**.09204**	.96989	**.09330**	.97577	**.09457**	.98162	**.09586**	43
18	.95809	**.09080**	.96406	**.09206**	.96999	**.09332**	.97587	**.09460**	.98171	**.09588**	42
19	.95819	**.09082**	.96416	**.09208**	.97009	**.09334**	.97597	**.09462**	.98181	**.09590**	41
+ 5′	8.95828	**.09084**	8.96426	**.09210**	8.97018	**.09337**	8.97607	**.09464**	8.98191	**.09592**	40
21	.95838	**.09086**	.96436	**.09212**	.97028	**.09339**	.97617	**.09466**	.98200	**.09594**	39
22	.95848	**.09088**	.96446	**.09214**	.97038	**.09341**	.97626	**.09468**	.98210	**.09596**	38
23	.95858	**.09090**	.96455	**.09216**	.97048	**.09343**	.97636	**.09470**	.98220	**.09598**	37
+ 6′	8.95868	**.09093**	8.96465	**.09218**	8.97058	**.09345**	8.97646	**.09472**	8.98229	**.09601**	36
25	.95878	**.09095**	.96475	**.09220**	.97068	**.09347**	.97656	**.09474**	.98239	**.09603**	35
26	.95888	**.09097**	.96485	**.09223**	.97077	**.09349**	.97665	**.09477**	.98249	**.09605**	34
27	.95898	**.09099**	.96495	**.09225**	.97087	**.09351**	.97675	**.09479**	.98259	**.09607**	33
+ 7′	8.95908	**.09101**	8.96505	**.09227**	8.97097	**.09353**	8.97685	**.09481**	8.98268	**.09609**	32
29	.95918	**.09103**	.96515	**.09229**	.97107	**.09356**	.97695	**.09483**	.98278	**.09611**	31
30	.95928	**.09105**	.96525	**.09231**	.97117	**.09358**	.97704	**.09485**	.98288	**.09613**	30
31	.95938	**.09107**	.96535	**.09233**	.97127	**.09360**	.97714	**.09487**	.98297	**.09616**	29
+ 8′	8.95948	**.09109**	8.96545	**.09235**	8.97136	**.09362**	8.97724	**.09489**	8.98307	**.09618**	28
33	.95958	**.09111**	.96555	**.09237**	.97146	**.09364**	.97734	**.09492**	.98317	**.09620**	27
34	.95968	**.09113**	.96564	**.09239**	.97156	**.09366**	.97743	**.09494**	.98326	**.09622**	26
35	.95978	**.09116**	.96574	**.09242**	.97166	**.09368**	.97753	**.09496**	.98336	**.09624**	25
+ 9′	8.95988	**.09118**	8.96584	**.09244**	8.97176	**.09370**	8.97763	**.09498**	8.98346	**.09626**	24
37	.95998	**.09120**	.96594	**.09246**	.97186	**.09372**	.97773	**.09500**	.98355	**.09628**	23
38	.96008	**.09122**	.96604	**.09248**	.97195	**.09375**	.97782	**.09502**	.98365	**.09631**	22
39	.96018	**.09124**	.96614	**.09250**	.97205	**.09377**	.97792	**.09504**	.98375	**.09633**	21
+ 10′	8.96028	**.09126**	8.96624	**.09252**	8.97215	**.09379**	8.97802	**.09506**	8.98384	**.09635**	20
41	.96038	**.09128**	.96634	**.09254**	.97225	**.09381**	.97812	**.09509**	.98394	**.09637**	19
42	.96048	**.09130**	.96644	**.09256**	.97235	**.09383**	.97821	**.09511**	.98404	**.09639**	18
43	.96058	**.09132**	.96653	**.09258**	.97244	**.09385**	.97831	**.09513**	.98413	**.09641**	17
+ 11′	8.96068	**.09134**	8.96663	**.09260**	8.97254	**.09387**	8.97841	**.09515**	8.98423	**.09643**	16
45	.96078	**.09136**	.96673	**.09263**	.97264	**.09389**	.97851	**.09517**	.98433	**.09646**	15
46	.96088	**.09139**	.96683	**.09265**	.97274	**.09392**	.97860	**.09519**	.98442	**.09648**	14
47	.96098	**.09141**	.96693	**.09267**	.97284	**.09394**	.97870	**.09521**	.98452	**.09650**	13
+ 12′	8.96108	**.09143**	8.96703	**.09269**	8.97294	**.09396**	8.97880	**.09524**	8.98462	**.09652**	12
49	.96118	**.09145**	.96713	**.09271**	.97303	**.09398**	.97890	**.09526**	.98471	**.09654**	11
50	.96128	**.09147**	.96723	**.09273**	.97313	**.09400**	.97899	**.09528**	.98481	**.09656**	10
51	.96138	**.09149**	.96733	**.09275**	.97323	**.09402**	.97909	**.09530**	.98491	**.09658**	9
+ 13′	8.96148	**.09151**	8.96742	**.09277**	8.97333	**.09404**	8.97919	**.09532**	8.98500	**.09661**	8
53	.96158	**.09153**	.96752	**.09280**	.97343	**.09406**	.97928	**.09534**	.98510	**.09663**	7
54	.96167	**.09155**	.96762	**.09282**	.97352	**.09409**	.97938	**.09536**	.98520	**.09665**	6
55	.96177	**.09157**	.96772	**.09284**	.97362	**.09411**	.97948	**.09538**	.98529	**.09667**	5
+ 14′	8.96187	**.09160**	8.96782	**.09286**	8.97372	**.09413**	8.97958	**.09541**	8.98539	**.09669**	4
57	.96197	**.09162**	.96792	**.09288**	.97382	**.09415**	.97967	**.09543**	.98549	**.09671**	3
58	.96207	**.09164**	.96802	**.09290**	.97392	**.09417**	.97977	**.09545**	.98558	**.09673**	2
59	.96217	**.09166**	.96812	**.09292**	.97401	**.09419**	.97987	**.09547**	.98568	**.09676**	1
+ 15′	8.96227	**.09168**	8.96821	**.09294**	8.97411	**.09421**	8.97997	**.09549**	8.98578	**.09678**	0
	$21^h\ 39^m$		$21^h\ 38^m$		$21^h\ 37^m$		$21^h\ 36^m$		$21^h\ 35^m$		

TABLE 34.

Haversines.

	$2^h\ 25^m$ 36° 15′		$2^h\ 26^m$ 36° 30′		$2^h\ 27^m$ 36° 45′		$2^h\ 28^m$ 37° 0′		$2^h\ 29^m$ 37° 15′		
s	Log. Hav.	Nat. Hav.	Log. Hav.	Nat. Hav.	Log. Hav.	Nat. Hav.	Log. Hav.	Nat. Hav.	Log. Hav.	Nat. Hav.	s
0	8.98578	.09678	8.99154	.09807	8.99727	.09937	9.00295	.10068	9.00860	.10200	60
1	.98587	.09680	.99164	.09809	.99736	.09939	.00305	.10070	.00869	.10202	59
2	.98597	.09682	.99173	.09811	.99746	.09942	.00314	.10073	.00878	.10204	58
3	.98606	.09684	.99183	.09814	.99755	.09944	.00324	.10075	.00888	.10206	57
+ 1′	8.98616	.09686	8.99193	.09816	8.99765	.09946	9.00333	.10077	9.00897	.10209	56
5	.98626	.09689	.99202	.09818	.99774	.09948	.00342	.10079	.00906	.10211	55
6	.98635	.09691	.99212	.09820	.99784	.09950	.00352	.10081	.00916	.10213	54
7	.98645	.09693	.99221	.09822	.99793	.09953	.00361	.10084	.00925	.10215	53
+ 2′	8.98655	.09695	8.99231	.09824	8.99803	.09955	9.00371	.10086	9.00935	.10218	52
9	.98664	.09697	.99240	.09827	.99812	.09957	.00380	.10088	.00944	.10220	51
10	.98674	.09699	.99250	.09829	.99822	.09959	.00390	.10090	.00953	.10222	50
11	.98684	.09701	.99260	.09831	.99831	.09961	.00399	.10092	.00963	.10224	49
+ 3′	8.98693	.09704	8.99269	.09833	8.99841	.09963	9.00408	.10095	9.00972	.10226	48
13	.98703	.09706	.99279	.09835	.99850	.09966	.00418	.10097	.00981	.10228	47
14	.98712	.09708	.99288	.09837	.99860	.09968	.00427	.10099	.00991	.10231	46
15	.98722	.09710	.99298	.09840	.99869	.09970	.00437	.10101	.01000	.10233	45
+ 4′	8.98732	.09712	8.99307	.09842	8.99879	.09972	9.00446	.10103	9.01009	.10235	44
17	.98741	.09714	.99317	.09844	.99888	.09974	.00456	.10105	.01019	.10237	43
18	.98751	.09717	.99327	.09846	.99898	.09977	.00465	.10108	.01028	.10240	42
19	.98761	.09719	.99336	.09848	.99907	.09979	.00474	.10110	.01037	.10242	41
+ 5′	8.98770	.09721	8.99346	.09850	8.99917	.09981	9.00484	.10112	9.01047	.10244	40
21	.98780	.09723	.99355	.09853	.99926	.09983	.00493	.10114	.01056	.10246	39
22	.98790	.09725	.99365	.09855	.99936	.09985	.00503	.10116	.01065	.10248	38
23	.98799	.09727	.99374	.09857	.99945	.09987	.00512	.10119	.01075	.10251	37
+ 6′	8.98809	.09729	8.99384	.09859	8.99955	.09990	9.00522	.10121	9.01084	.10253	36
25	.98818	.09732	.99393	.09861	.99964	.09992	.00531	.10123	.01094	.10255	35
26	.98828	.09734	.99403	.09863	.99974	.09994	.00540	.10125	.01103	.10257	34
27	.98838	.09736	.99412	.09866	.99983	.09996	.00550	.10127	.01112	.10259	33
+ 7′	8.98847	.09738	8.99422	.09868	8.99993	.09998	9.00559	.10130	9.01122	.10262	32
29	.98857	.09740	.99432	.09870	9.00002	.10000	.00569	.10132	.01131	.10264	31
30	.98866	.09742	.99441	.09872	.00012	.10003	.00578	.10134	.01140	.10266	30
31	.98876	.09745	.99451	.09874	.00021	.10005	.00587	.10136	.01150	.10268	29
+ 8′	8.98886	.09747	8.99460	.09876	9.00031	.10007	9.00597	.10138	9.01159	.10270	28
33	.98895	.09749	.99470	.09879	.00040	.10009	.00606	.10141	.01168	.10273	27
34	.98905	.09751	.99479	.09881	.00049	.10011	.00616	.10143	.01178	.10275	26
35	.98915	.09753	.99489	.09883	.00059	.10014	.00625	.10145	.01187	.10277	25
+ 9′	8.98924	.09755	8.99498	.09885	9.00068	.10016	9.00634	.10147	9.01196	.10279	24
37	.98934	.09757	.99508	.09887	.00078	.10018	.00644	.10149	.01206	.10281	23
38	.98943	.09760	.99517	.09890	.00087	.10020	.00653	.10152	.01215	.10284	22
39	.98953	.09762	.99527	.09892	.00097	.10022	.00663	.10154	.01224	.10286	21
+ 10′	8.98963	.09764	8.99536	.09894	9.00106	.10025	9.00672	.10156	9.01234	.10288	20
41	.98972	.09766	.99546	.09896	.00116	.10027	.00681	.10158	.01243	.10290	19
42	.98982	.09768	.99556	.09898	.00125	.10029	.00691	.10160	.01252	.10293	18
43	.98991	.09770	.99565	.09900	.00135	.10031	.00700	.10163	.01262	.10295	17
+ 11′	8.99001	.09773	8.99575	.09903	9.00144	.10033	9.00710	.10165	9.01271	.10297	16
45	.99011	.09775	.99584	.09905	.00154	.10035	.00719	.10167	.01280	.10299	15
46	.99020	.09777	.99594	.09907	.00163	.10038	.00728	.10169	.01289	.10301	14
47	.99030	.09779	.99603	.09909	.00172	.10040	.00738	.10171	.01299	.10304	13
+ 12′	8.99039	.09781	8.99613	.09911	9.00182	.10042	9.00747	.10174	9.01308	.10306	12
49	.99049	.09783	.99622	.09913	.00191	.10044	.00756	.10176	.01317	.10308	11
50	.99058	.09786	.99632	.09916	.00201	.10046	.00766	.10178	.01327	.10310	10
51	.99068	.09788	.99641	.09918	.00210	.10049	.00775	.10180	.01336	.10312	9
+ 13′	8.99078	.09790	8.99651	.09920	9.00220	.10051	9.00785	.10182	9.01345	.10315	8
53	.99087	.09792	.99660	.09922	.00229	.10053	.00794	.10184	.01355	.10317	7
54	.99097	.09794	.99670	.09924	.00239	.10055	.00803	.10187	.01364	.10319	6
55	.99106	.09796	.99679	.09926	.00248	.10057	.00813	.10189	.01373	.10321	5
+ 14′	8.99116	.09799	8.99689	.09929	9.00258	.10059	9.00822	.10191	9.01383	.10323	4
57	.99126	.09801	.99698	.09931	.00267	.10062	.00831	.10193	.01392	.10326	3
58	.99135	.09803	.99708	.09933	.00276	.10064	.00841	.10196	.01401	.10328	2
59	.99145	.09805	.99717	.09935	.00286	.10066	.00850	.10198	.01411	.10330	1
+ 15′	8.99154	.09807	8.99727	.09937	9.00295	.10068	9.00860	.10200	9.01420	.10332	0
	$21^h\ 34^m$		$21^h\ 33^m$		$21^h\ 32^m$		$21^h\ 31^m$		$21^h\ 30^m$		

541524°—43——44

TABLE 34.

Haversines.

s	*2h 30m* **37° 30′**		*2h 31m* **37° 45′**		*2h 32m* **38° 0′**		*2h 33m* **38° 15′**		*2h 34m* **38° 30′**		
s	Log. Hav.	Nat. Hav.	Log. Hav.	Nat. Hav.	Log. Nav.	Nat. Hav.	Log. Hav.	Nat. Hav.	Log. Hav.	Nat. Hav.	s
0	9.01420	**.10332**	9.01976	**.10466**	9.02528	**.10599**	9.03077	**.10734**	9.03621	**.10870**	*60*
1	.01429	**.10335**	.01985	**.10468**	.02538	**.10602**	.03086	**.10736**	.03630	**.10872**	*59*
2	.01438	**.10337**	.01995	**.10470**	.02547	**.10604**	.03095	**.10739**	.03639	**.10874**	*58*
3	.01448	**.10339**	.02004	**.10472**	.02556	**.10606**	.03104	**.10741**	.03648	**.10876**	*57*
+ **1′**	9.01457	**.10341**	9.02013	**.10474**	9.02565	**.10608**	9.03113	**.10743**	9.03657	**.10879**	*56*
5	.01466	**.10343**	.02022	**.10477**	.02574	**.10611**	.03122	**.10745**	.03667	**.10881**	*55*
6	.01476	**.10346**	.02031	**.10479**	.02583	**.10613**	.03131	**.10748**	.03676	**.10883**	*54*
7	.01485	**.10348**	.02041	**.10481**	.02593	**.10615**	.03141	**.10750**	.03685	**.10885**	*53*
+ **2′**	9.01494	**.10350**	9.02050	**.10483**	9.02602	**.10617**	9.03150	**.10752**	9.03694	**.10888**	*52*
9	.01504	**.10352**	.02059	**.10486**	.02611	**.10620**	.03159	**.10754**	.03703	**.10890**	*51*
10	.01513	**.10354**	.02068	**.10488**	.02620	**.10622**	.03168	**.10757**	.03712	**.10892**	*50*
11	.01522	**.10357**	.02078	**.10490**	.02629	**.10624**	.03177	**.10759**	.03721	**.10895**	*49*
+ **3′**	9.01531	**.10359**	9.02087	**.10492**	9.02638	**.10626**	9.03186	**.10761**	9.03730	**.10897**	*48*
13	.01541	**.10361**	.02096	**.10494**	.02648	**.10629**	.03195	**.10763**	.03739	**.10899**	*47*
14	.01550	**.10363**	.02105	**.10497**	.02657	**.10631**	.03204	**.10766**	.03748	**.10901**	*46*
15	.01559	**.10366**	.02115	**.10499**	.02666	**.10633**	.03213	**.10768**	.03757	**.10904**	*45*
+ **4′**	9.01569	**.10368**	9.02124	**.10501**	9.02675	**.10635**	9.03222	**.10770**	9.03766	**.10906**	*44*
17	.01578	**.10370**	.02133	**.10503**	.02684	**.10638**	.03231	**.10772**	.03775	**.10908**	*43*
18	.01587	**.10372**	.02142	**.10506**	.02693	**.10640**	.03241	**.10775**	.03784	**.10910**	*42*
19	.01596	**.10374**	.02151	**.10508**	.02702	**.10642**	.03250	**.10777**	.03793	**.10913**	*41*
+ **5′**	9.01606	**.10377**	9.02161	**.10510**	9.02712	**.10644**	9.03259	**.10779**	9.03802	**.10915**	*40*
21	.01615	**.10379**	.02170	**.10512**	.02721	**.10647**	.03268	**.10781**	.03811	**.10917**	*39*
22	.01624	**.10381**	.02179	**.10515**	.02730	**.10649**	.03277	**.10784**	.03820	**.10919**	*38*
23	.01634	**.10383**	.02188	**.10517**	.02739	**.10651**	.03286	**.10786**	.03829	**.10922**	*37*
+ **6′**	9.01643	**.10386**	9.02197	**.10519**	9.02748	**.10653**	9.03295	**.10788**	9.03838	**.10924**	*36*
25	.01652	**.10388**	.02207	**.10521**	.02757	**.10655**	.03304	**.10790**	.03847	**.10926**	*35*
26	.01661	**.10390**	.02216	**.10523**	.02767	**.10658**	.03313	**.10793**	.03856	**.10929**	*34*
27	.01671	**.10392**	.02225	**.10526**	.02776	**.10660**	.03322	**.10795**	.03865	**.10931**	*33*
+ **7′**	9.01680	**.10394**	9.02234	**.10528**	9.02785	**.10662**	9.03331	**.10797**	9.03874	**.10933**	*32*
29	.01689	**.10397**	.02244	**.10530**	.02794	**.10664**	.03340	**.10799**	.03883	**.10935**	*31*
30	.01698	**.10399**	.02253	**.10532**	.02803	**.10667**	.03350	**.10802**	.03892	**.10938**	*30*
31	.01708	**.10401**	.02262	**.10535**	.02812	**.10669**	.03359	**.10804**	.03901	**.10940**	*29*
+ **8′**	9.01717	**.10403**	9.02271	**.10537**	9.02821	**.10671**	9.03368	**.10806**	9.03910	**.10942**	*28*
33	.01726	**.10405**	.02280	**.10539**	.02830	**.10673**	.03377	**.10809**	.03919	**.10944**	*27*
34	.01736	**.10408**	.02290	**.10541**	.02840	**.10676**	.03386	**.10811**	.03928	**.10947**	*26*
35	.01745	**.10410**	.02299	**.10544**	.02849	**.10678**	.03395	**.10813**	.03937	**.10949**	*25*
+ **9′**	9.01754	**.10412**	9.02308	**.10546**	9.02858	**.10680**	9.03404	**.10815**	9.03946	**.10951**	*24*
37	.01763	**.10414**	.02317	**.10548**	.02867	**.10682**	.03413	**.10818**	.03955	**.10953**	*23*
38	.01773	**.10417**	.02326	**.10550**	.02876	**.10685**	.03422	**.10820**	.03964	**.10956**	*22*
39	.01782	**.10419**	.02336	**.10552**	.02885	**.10687**	.03431	**.10822**	.03973	**.10958**	*21*
+ **10′**	9.01791	**.10421**	9.02345	**.10555**	9.02894	**.10689**	9.03440	**.10824**	9.03982	**.10960**	*20*
41	.01800	**.10423**	.02354	**.10557**	.02904	**.10691**	.03449	**.10827**	.03991	**.10963**	*19*
42	.01810	**.10425**	.02363	**.10559**	.02913	**.10694**	.03458	**.10829**	.04000	**.10965**	*18*
43	.01819	**.10428**	.02372	**.10561**	.02922	**.10696**	.03467	**.10831**	.04009	**.10967**	*17*
+ **11′**	9.01828	**.10430**	9.02381	**.10564**	9.02931	**.10698**	9.03476	**.10833**	9.04018	**.10969**	*16*
45	.01837	**.10432**	.02391	**.10566**	.02940	**.10700**	.03486	**.10836**	.04027	**.10972**	*15*
46	.01847	**.10434**	.02400	**.10568**	.02949	**.10703**	.03495	**.10838**	.04036	**.10974**	*14*
47	.01856	**.10436**	.02409	**.10570**	.02958	**.10705**	.03504	**.10840**	.04045	**.10976**	*13*
+ **12′**	9.01865	**.10439**	9.02418	**.10573**	9.02967	**.10707**	9.03513	**.10842**	9.04054	**.10978**	*12*
49	.01874	**.10441**	.02427	**.10575**	.02977	**.10709**	.03522	**.10845**	.04063	**.10981**	*11*
50	.01884	**.10443**	.02437	**.10577**	.02986	**.10712**	.03531	**.10847**	.04072	**.10983**	*10*
51	.01893	**.10445**	.02446	**.10579**	.02995	**.10714**	.03540	**.10849**	.04081	**.10985**	*9*
+ **13′**	9.01902	**.10448**	9.02455	**.10582**	9.03004	**.10716**	9.03549	**.10851**	9.04090	**.10988**	*8*
53	.01911	**.10450**	.02464	**.10584**	.03013	**.10718**	.03558	**.10854**	.04099	**.10990**	*7*
54	.01921	**.10452**	.02473	**.10586**	.03022	**.10721**	.03567	**.10856**	.04108	**.10992**	*6*
55	.01930	**.10454**	.02483	**.10588**	.03031	**.10723**	.03576	**.10858**	.04117	**.10994**	*5*
+ **14′**	9.01939	**.10457**	9.02492	**.10591**	9.03040	**.10725**	9.03585	**.10861**	9.04126	**.10997**	*4*
57	.01948	**.10459**	.02501	**.10593**	.03050	**.10727**	.03594	**.10863**	.04135	**.10999**	*3*
58	.01958	**.10461**	.02510	**.10595**	.03059	**.10730**	.03603	**.10865**	.04144	**.11001**	*2*
59	.01967	**.10463**	.02519	**.10597**	.03068	**.10732**	.03612	**.10867**	.04153	**.11004**	*1*
+ **15′**	9.01976	**.10466**	9.02528	**.10599**	9.03077	**.10734**	9.03621	**.10870**	9.04162	**.11006**	*0*
	21h 29m		*21h 28m*		*21h 27m*		*21h 26m*		*21h 25m*		

TABLE 34.

Haversines.

s	$2^h\ 35^m$ 38° 45′		$2^h\ 36^m$ 39° 0′		$2^h\ 37^m$ 39° 15′		$2^h\ 38^m$ 39° 30′		$2^h\ 39^m$ 39° 45′		s
	Log. Hav.	Nat. Hav.	Log. Hav.	Nat. Hav.	Log. Hav.	Nat. Hav.	Log. Hav.	Nat. Hav.	Log. Hav.	Nat. Hav.	
0	9.04162	**.11006**	9.04699	**.11143**	9.05232	**.11280**	9.05762	**.11419**	9.06288	**.11558**	*60*
1	.04171	**.11008**	.04708	**.11145**	.05241	**.11283**	.05771	**.11421**	.06297	**.11560**	*59*
2	.04180	**.11010**	.04717	**.11147**	.05250	**.11285**	.05780	**.11423**	.06305	**.11563**	*58*
3	.04189	**.11013**	.04726	**.11150**	.05259	**.11287**	.05788	**.11426**	:06314	**.11565**	*57*
+ 1′	9.04198	**.11015**	9.04735	**.11152**	9.05268	**.11290**	9.05797	**.11428**	9.06323	**.11567**	*56*
5	.04207	**.11017**	.04744	**.11154**	.05277	**.11292**	.05806	**.11430**	.06332	**.11569**	*55*
6	.04216	**.11019**	.04753	**.11156**	.05285	**.11294**	.05815	**.11433**	.06340	**.11572**	*54*
7	.04225	**.11022**	.04761	**.11159**	.05294	**.11296**	.05823	**.11435**	.06349	**.11574**	*53*
+ 2′	9.04234	**.11024**	9.04770	**.11161**	9.05303	**.11299**	9.05832	**.11437**	9.06358	**.11577**	*52*
9	.04243	**.11026**	.04779	**.11163**	.05312	**.11301**	.05841	**.11440**	.06367	**.11579**	*51*
10	.04252	**.11029**	.04788	**.11166**	.05321	**.11303**	.05850	**.11442**	.06375	**.11581**	*50*
11	.04261	**.11031**	.04797	**.11168**	.05330	**.11306**	.05859	**.11444**	.06384	**.11584**	*49*
+ 3′	9.04270	**.11033**	9.04806	**.11170**	9.05339	**.11308**	9.05867	**.11447**	9.06393	**.11586**	*48*
13	.04279	**.11035**	.04815	**.11172**	.05347	**.11310**	.05876	**.11449**	.06401	**.11588**	*47*
14	.04288	**.11038**	.04824	**.11175**	.05356	**.11313**	.05885	**.11451**	.06410	**.11590**	*46*
15	.04297	**.11040**	.04833	**.11177**	.05365	**.11315**	.05894	**.11453**	.06419	**.11593**	*45*
+ 4′	9.04306	**.11042**	9.04842	**.11179**	9.05374	**.11317**	9.05903	**.11456**	9.06428	**.11595**	*44*
17	.04315	**.11044**	.04851	**.11182**	.05383	**.11320**	.05911	**.11458**	.06436	**.11597**	*43*
18	.04324	**.11047**	.04859	**.11184**	.05392	**.11322**	.05920	**.11460**	.06445	**.11600**	*42*
19	.04333	**.11049**	.04868	**11186**	.05400	**.11324**	.05929	**.11463**	.06454	**.11602**	*41*
+ 5′	9.04341	**.11051**	9.04877	**.11189**	9.05409	**.11326**	9.05938	**.11465**	9.06462	**.11604**	*40*
21	.04350	**.11054**	.04886	**.11191**	.05418	**.11329**	.05946	**.11467**	.06471	**.11607**	*39*
22	.04359	**.11056**	.04895	**.11193**	.05427	**.11331**	.05955	**.11470**	.06480	**.11609**	*38*
23	.04368	**.11058**	.04904	**.11195**	.05436	**.11333**	.05964	**.11472**	.06489	**.11611**	*37*
+ 6′	9.04377	**.11060**	9.04913	**.11198**	9.05445	**.11336**	9.05973	**.11474**	9.06497	**.11614**	*36*
25	.04386	**.11063**	.04922	**.11200**	.05453	**.11338**	.05982	**.11477**	.06506	**.11616**	*35*
26	.04395	**.11065**	.04931	**.11202**	.05462	**.11340**	.05990	**.11479**	.06515	**.11618**	*34*
27	.04404	**.11067**	.04939	**.11205**	.05471	**.11343**	.05999	**.11481**	.06523	**.11621**	*33*
+ 7′	9.04413	**.11070**	9.04948	**.11207**	9.05480	**.11345**	9.06008	**.11484**	9.06532	**.11623**	*32*
29	.04422	**.11072**	.04957	**.11209**	.05489	**.11347**	.06017	**.11486**	.06541	**.11625**	*31*
30	.04431	**.11074**	.04966	**.11211**	.05498	**.11349**	.06025	**.11488**	.06550	**.11628**	*30*
31	.04440	**.11076**	.04975	**.11214**	.05506	**.11352**	.06034	**.11491**	.06558	**.11630**	*29*
+ 8′	9.04449	**.11079**	9.04984	**.11216**	9.05515	**.11354**	9.06043	**.11493**	9.06567	**.11632**	*28*
33	.04458	**.11081**	.04993	**.11218**	.05524	**.11356**	.06052	**.11495**	.06576	**.11635**	*27*
34	.04467	**.11083**	.05002	**.11221**	.05533	**.11359**	.06060	**.11498**	.06584	**.11637**	*26*
35	.04476	**.11086**	.05011	**.11223**	.05542	**.11361**	.06069	**.11500**	.06593	**.11639**	*25*
+ 9′	9.04485	**.11088**	9.05019	**.11225**	9.05551	**.11363**	9.06078	**.11502**	9.06602	**.11642**	*24*
37	.04494	**.11090**	.05028	**.11228**	.05559	**.11366**	.06087	**.11504**	.06611	**.11644**	*23*
38	.04503	**.11092**	.05037	**.11230**	.05568	**.11368**	.06095	**.11507**	.06619	**.11646**	*22*
39	.04512	**.11095**	.05046	**.11232**	.05577	**.11370**	.06104	**.11509**	.06628	**.11649**	*21*
+ 10′	9.04520	**.11097**	9.05055	**.11234**	9.05586	**.11373**	9.06113	**.11511**	9.06637	**.11651**	*20*
41	.04529	**.11099**	.05064	**.11237**	.05595	**.11375**	.06122	**.11514**	.06645	**.11653**	*19*
42	.04538	**.11102**	.05073	**.11239**	.05603	**.11377**	.06131	**.11516**	.06654	**.11656**	*18*
43	.04547	**.11104**	.05082	**.11241**	.05612	**.11379**	.06139	**.11518**	.06663	**.11658**	*17*
+ 11′	9.04556	**.11106**	9.05090	**.11244**	9.05621	**.11382**	9.06148	**.11521**	9.06671	**.11660**	*16*
45	.04565	**.11108**	.05099	**.11246**	.05630	**.11384**	.06157	**.11523**	.06680	**.11663**	*15*
46	.04574	**.11111**	.05108	**.11248**	.05639	**.11386**	.06166	**.11525**	.06689	**.11665**	*14*
47	.04583	**.11113**	.05117	**.11251**	.05648	**.11389**	.06174	**.11528**	.06697	**.11667**	*13*
+ 12′	9.04592	**.11115**	9.05126	**.11253**	9.05656	**.11391**	9.06183	**.11530**	9.06706	**.11670**	*12*
49	.04601	**.11117**	.05135	**.11255**	.05665	**.11393**	.06192	**.11532**	.06715	**.11672**	*11*
50	.04610	**.11120**	.05144	**.11257**	.05674	**.11396**	.06201	**.11535**	.06724	**.11674**	*10*
51	.04619	**.11122**	.05153	**.11260**	.05683	**.11398**	.06209	**.11537**	.06732	**.11677**	*9*
+ 13′	9.04628	**.11124**	9.05161	**.11262**	9.05692	**.11400**	9.06218	**.11539**	9.06741	**.11679**	*8*
53	.04637	**.11127**	.05170	**.11264**	.05700	**.11403**	.06227	**.11542**	.06750	**.11681**	*7*
54	.04646	**.11129**	.05179	**.11267**	.05709	**.11405**	.06235	**.11544**	.06758	**.11684**	*6*
55	.04654	**.11131**	.05188	**.11269**	.05718	**.11407**	.06244	**.11546**	.06767	**.11686**	*5*
+ 14′	9.04663	**.11134**	9.05197	**.11271**	9.05727	**.11410**	9.06253	**.11549**	9.06776	**.11688**	*4*
57	.04672	**.11136**	.05206	**.11274**	.05736	**.11412**	.06262	**.11551**	.06784	**.11691**	*3*
58	.04681	**.11138**	.05215	**.11276**	.05744	**.11414**	.06270	**.11553**	.06793	**.11693**	*2*
59	.04690	**.11140**	.05223	**.11278**	.05753	**.11416**	.06279	**.11556**	.06802	**.11695**	*1*
+ 15′	9.04699	**.11143**	9.05232	**.11280**	9.05762	**.11419**	9.06288	**.11558**	9.06810	**.11698**	*0*
	$21^h\ 24^m$		$21^h\ 23^m$		$21^h\ 22^m$		$21^h\ 21^m$		$21^h\ 20^m$		

TABLE 34.

Haversines.

	$2^h\ 40^m$ 40° 0′		$2^h\ 41^m$ 40° 15′		$2^h\ 42^m$ 40° 30′		$2^h\ 43^m$ 40° 45′		$2^h\ 44^m$ 41° 0′		
s	Log. Hav.	Nat. Hav.	Log. Hav.	Nat. Hav.	Log. Hav.	Nat. Hav.	Log. Hav.	Nat. Hav.	Log. Hav.	Nat. Hav.	s
0	9.06810	**.11698**	9.07329	**.11838**	9.07845	**.11980**	9.08357	**.12122**	9.08865	**.12265**	60
1	.06819	**.11700**	.07338	**.11841**	.07853	**.11982**	.08365	**.12124**	.08874	**.12267**	59
2	.06828	**.11702**	.07346	**.11843**	.07862	**.11984**	.08374	**.12127**	.08882	**.12269**	58
3	.06836	**.11705**	.07355	**.11845**	.07870	**.11987**	.08382	**.12129**	.08890	**.12272**	57
+ 1′	9.06845	**.11707**	9.07364	**.11848**	9.07879	**.11989**	9.08391	**.12131**	9.08899	**.12274**	56
5	.06854	**.11709**	.07372	**.11850**	.07887	**.11992**	.08399	**.12134**	.08907	**.12276**	55
6	.06862	**.11712**	.07381	**.11852**	.07896	**.11994**	.08408	**.12136**	.08916	**.12279**	54
7	.06871	**.11714**	.07390	**.11855**	.07905	**.11996**	.08416	**.12138**	.08924	**.12281**	53
+ 2′	9.06880	**.11716**	9.07398	**.11857**	9.07913	**.11999**	9.08425	**.12141**	9.08933	**.12284**	52
9	.06888	**.11719**	.07407	**.11860**	.07922	**.12001**	.08433	**.12143**	.08941	**.12286**	51
10	.06897	**.11721**	.07415	**.11862**	.07930	**.12003**	.08442	**.12146**	.08949	**.12288**	50
11	.06906	**.11724**	.07424	**.11864**	.07939	**.12006**	.08450	**.12148**	.08958	**.12291**	49
+ 3′	9.06914	**.11726**	9.07433	**.11867**	9.07947	**.12008**	9.08459	**.12150**	9.08966	**.12293**	48
13	.06923	**.11728**	.07441	**.11869**	.07956	**.12010**	.08467	**.12153**	.08975	**.12296**	47
14	.06932	**.11731**	.07450	**.11871**	.07964	**.12013**	.08475	**.12155**	.08983	**.12298**	46
15	.06940	**.11733**	.07458	**.11874**	.07973	**.12015**	.08484	**.12157**	.08992	**.12300**	45
+ 4′	9.06949	**.11735**	9.07467	**.11876**	9.07981	**.12018**	9.08492	**.12160**	9.09000	**.12303**	44
17	.06958	**.11738**	.07476	**.11878**	.07990	**.12020**	.08501	**.12162**	.09009	**.12305**	43
18	.06966	**.11740**	.07484	**.11881**	.07999	**.12022**	.08509	**.12165**	.09017	**.12307**	42
19	.06975	**.11742**	.07493	**.11883**	.08007	**.12025**	.08518	**.12167**	.09025	**.12310**	41
+ 5′	9.06984	**.11745**	9.07501	**.11885**	9.08016	**.12027**	9.08526	**.12169**	9.09034	**.12312**	40
21	.06992	**.11747**	.07510	**.11888**	.08024	**.12029**	.08535	**.12172**	.09042	**.12315**	39
22	.07001	**.11749**	.07519	**.11890**	.08033	**.12032**	.08543	**.12174**	.09051	**.12317**	38
23	.07010	**.11752**	.07527	**.11892**	.08041	**.12034**	.08552	**.12176**	.09059	**.12319**	37
+ 6′	9.07018	**.11754**	9.07536	**.11895**	9.08050	**.12036**	9.08560	**.12179**	9.09068	**.12322**	36
25	.07027	**.11756**	.07544	**.11897**	.08058	**.12039**	.08569	**.12181**	.09076	**.12324**	35
26	.07036	**.11759**	.07553	**.11900**	.08067	**.12041**	.08577	**.12184**	.09084	**.12327**	34
27	.07044	**.11761**	.07562	**.11902**	.08075	**.12044**	.08586	**.12186**	.09093	**.12329**	33
+ 7′	9.07053	**.11763**	9.07570	**.11904**	9.08084	**.12046**	9.08594	**.12188**	9.09101	**.12331**	32
29	.07062	**.11766**	.07579	**.11907**	.08092	**.12048**	.08603	**.12191**	.09110	**.12334**	31
30	.07070	**.11768**	.07587	**.11909**	.08101	**.12051**	.08611	**.12193**	.09118	**.12336**	30
31	.07079	**.11770**	.07596	**.11911**	.08110	**.12053**	.08620	**.12195**	.09126	**.12339**	29
+ 8′	9.07088	**.11773**	9.07605	**.11914**	9.08118	**.12055**	9.08628	**.12198**	9.09135	**.12341**	28
33	.07096	**.11775**	.07613	**.11916**	.08127	**.12058**	.08637	**.12200**	.09143	**.12343**	27
34	.07105	**.11777**	.07622	**.11918**	.08135	**.12060**	.08645	**.12203**	.09152	**.12346**	26
35	.07113	**.11780**	.07630	**.11921**	.08144	**.12062**	.08654	**.12205**	.09160	**.12348**	25
+ 9′	9.07122	**.11782**	9.07639	**.11923**	9.08152	**.12065**	9.08662	**.12207**	9.09169	**.12351**	24
37	.07131	**.11784**	.07647	**.11925**	.08161	**.12067**	.08671	**.12210**	.09177	**.12353**	23
38	.07139	**.11787**	.07656	**.11928**	.08169	**.12070**	.08679	**.12212**	.09185	**.12355**	22
39	.07148	**.11789**	.07665	**.11930**	.08178	**.12072**	.08687	**.12214**	.09194	**.12358**	21
+ 10′	9.07157	**.11791**	9.07673	**.11933**	9.08186	**.12074**	9.08696	**.12217**	9.09202	**.12360**	20
41	.07165	**.11794**	.07682	**.11935**	.08195	**.12077**	.08704	**.12219**	.09211	**.12363**	19
42	.07174	**.11796**	.07690	**.11937**	.08203	**.12079**	.08713	**.12222**	.09219	**.12365**	18
43	.07183	**.11798**	.07699	**.11940**	.08212	**.12081**	.08721	**.12224**	.09227	**.12367**	17
+ 11′	9.07191	**.11801**	9.07708	**.11942**	9.08220	**.12084**	9.08730	**.12226**	9.09236	**.12370**	16
45	.07200	**.11803**	.07716	**.11944**	.08229	**.12086**	.08738	**.12229**	.09244	**.12372**	15
46	.07208	**.11806**	.07725	**.11947**	.08237	**.12089**	.08747	**.12231**	.09253	**.12374**	14
47	.07217	**.11808**	.07733	**.11949**	.08246	**.12091**	.08755	**.12233**	.09261	**.12377**	13
+ 12′	9.07226	**.11810**	9.07742	**.11951**	9.08254	**.12093**	9.08764	**.12236**	9.09269	**.12379**	12
49	.07234	**.11813**	.07750	**.11954**	.08263	**.12096**	.08772	**.12238**	.09278	**.12382**	11
50	.07243	**.11815**	.07759	**.11956**	.08271	**.12098**	.08781	**.12241**	.09286	**.12384**	10
51	.07252	**.11817**	.07768	**.11958**	.08280	**.12100**	.08789	**.12243**	.09295	**.12386**	9
+ 13′	9.07260	**.11820**	9.07776	**.11961**	9.08288	**.12103**	9.08797	**.12245**	9.09303	**.12389**	8
53	.07269	**.11822**	.07785	**.11963**	.08297	**.12105**	.08806	**.12248**	.09311	**.12391**	7
54	.07277	**.11824**	.07793	**.11966**	.08306	**.12108**	.08814	**.12250**	.09320	**.12394**	6
55	.07286	**.11827**	.07802	**.11968**	.08314	**.12110**	.08823	**.12253**	.09328	**.12396**	5
+ 14′	9.07295	**.11829**	9.07810	**.11970**	9.08323	**.12112**	9.08831	**.12255**	9.09337	**.12398**	4
57	.07303	**.11831**	.07819	**.11973**	.08331	**.12115**	.08840	**.12257**	.09345	**.12401**	3
58	.07312	**.11834**	.07827	**.11975**	.08340	**.12117**	.08848	**.12260**	.09353	**.12403**	2
59	.07321	**.11836**	.07836	**.11977**	.08348	**.12119**	.08857	**.12262**	.09362	**.12406**	1
+ 15′	9.07329	**.11838**	9.07845	**.11980**	9.08357	**.12122**	9.08865	**.12265**	9.09370	**.12408**	0
	$21^h\ 19^m$		$21^h\ 18^m$		$21^h\ 17^m$		$21^h\ 16^m$		$21^h\ 15^m$		

TABLE 34.

Haversines.

s	$2^h\ 45^m$ 41° 15′		$2^h\ 46^m$ 41° 30′		$2^h\ 47^m$ 41° 45′		$2^h\ 48^m$ 42° 0′		$2^h\ 49^m$ 42° 15′		s
	Log. Hav.	Nat. Hav.	Log. Hav.	Nat. Hav.	Log. Hav.	Nat. Hav.	Log. Hav.	Nat. Hav.	Log. Hav.	Nat. Hav.	
0	9.09370	.12408	9.09872	.12552	9.10371	.12697	9.10866	.12843	9.11358	.12989	60
1	.09379	.12410	.09880	.12555	.10379	.12700	.10874	.12845	.11366	.12992	59
2	.09387	.12413	.09889	.12557	.10387	.12702	.10882	.12848	.11374	.12994	58
3	.09395	.12415	.09897	.12559	.10395	.12704	.10891	.12850	.11382	.12996	57
+ 1′	9.09404	.12418	9.09905	.12562	9.10404	.12707	9.10899	.12852	9.11391	.12999	56
5	.09412	.12420	.09914	.12564	.10412	.12709	.10907	.12855	.11399	.13001	55
6	.09421	.12422	.09922	.12567	.10420	.12712	.10915	.12857	.11407	.13004	54
7	.09429	.12425	.09930	.12569	.10429	.12714	.10923	.12860	.11415	.13006	53
+ 2′	9.09437	.12427	9.09939	.12572	9.10437	.12717	9.10932	.12862	9.11423	.13009	52
9	.09446	.12430	.09947	.12574	.10445	.12719	.10940	.12865	.11431	.13011	51
10	.09454	.12432	.09955	.12576	.10453	.12721	.10948	.12867	.11440	.13014	50
11	.09462	.12434	.09964	.12579	.10462	.12724	.10956	.12870	.11448	.13016	49
+ 3′	9.09471	.12437	9.09972	.12581	9.10470	.12726	9.10965	.12872	9.11456	.13018	48
13	.09479	.12439	.09980	.12584	.10478	.12729	.10973	.12874	.11464	.13021	47
14	.09488	.12442	.09989	.12586	.10486	.12731	.10981	.12877	.11472	.13023	46
15	.09496	.12444	.09997	.12588	.10495	.12733	.10989	.12879	.11480	.13026	45
+ 4′	9.09504	.12446	9.10005	.12591	9.10503	.12736	9.10997	.12882	9.11489	.13028	44
17	.09513	.12449	.10014	.12593	.10511	.12738	.11006	.12884	.11497	.13031	43
18	.09521	.12451	.10022	.12596	.10519	.12741	.11014	.12887	.11505	.13033	42
19	.09529	.12454	.10030	.12598	.10528	.12743	.11022	.12889	.11513	.13036	41
+ 5′	9.09538	.12456	9.10039	.12600	9.10536	.12746	9.11030	.12891	9.11521	.13038	40
21	.09546	.12458	.10047	.12603	.10544	.12748	.11038	.12894	.11529	.13041	39
22	.09555	.12461	.10055	.12605	.10553	.12750	.11047	.12896	.11538	.13043	38
23	.09563	.12463	.10064	.12608	.10561	.12753	.11055	.12899	.11546	.13045	37
+ 6′	9.09571	.12466	9.10072	.12610	9.10569	.12755	9.11063	.12901	9.11554	.13048	36
25	.09580	.12468	.10080	.12613	.10577	.12758	.11071	.12904	.11562	.13050	35
26	.09588	.12470	.10088	.12615	.10586	.12760	.11079	.12906	.11570	.13053	34
27	.09596	.12473	.10097	.12617	.10594	.12763	.11088	.12909	.11578	.13055	33
+ 7′	9.09605	.12475	9.10105	.12620	9.10602	.12765	9.11096	.12911	9.11586	.13058	32
29	.09613	.12478	.10113	.12622	.10610	.12767	.11104	.12913	.11595	.13060	31
30	.09622	.12480	.10122	.12625	.10619	.12770	.11112	.12916	.11603	.13063	30
31	.09630	.12482	.10130	.12627	.10627	.12772	.11120	.12918	.11611	.13065	29
+ 8′	9.09638	.12485	9.10138	.12629	9.10635	.12775	9.11129	.12921	9.11619	.13067	28
33	.09647	.12487	.10147	.12632	.10643	.12777	.11137	.12923	.11627	.13070	27
34	.09655	.12490	.10155	.12634	.10652	.12780	.11145	.12926	.11635	.13072	26
35	.09663	.12492	.10163	.12637	.10660	.12782	.11153	.12928	.11643	.13075	25
+ 9′	9.09672	.12494	9.10172	.12639	9.10668	.12784	9.11161	.12930	9.11652	.13077	24
37	.09680	.12497	.10180	.12641	.10676	.12787	.11170	.12933	.11660	.13080	23
38	.09688	.12499	.10188	.12644	.10685	.12789	.11178	.12935	.11668	.13082	22
39	.09697	.12502	.10196	.12646	.10693	.12792	.11186	.12938	.11676	.13085	21
+ 10′	9.09705	.12504	9.10205	.12649	9.10701	.12794	9.11194	.12940	9.11684	.13087	20
41	.09713	.12506	.10213	.12651	.10709	.12797	.11202	.12943	.11692	.13090	19
42	.09722	.12509	.10221	.12654	.10718	.12799	.11211	.12945	.11700	.13092	18
43	.09730	.12511	.10230	.12656	.10726	.12801	.11219	.12948	.11709	.13095	17
+ 11′	9.09739	.12514	9.10238	.12658	9.10734	.12804	9.11227	.12950	9.11717	.13097	16
45	.09747	.12516	.10246	.12661	.10742	.12806	.11235	.12952	.11725	.13099	15
46	.09755	.12519	.10255	.12663	.10751	.12809	.11243	.12955	.11733	.13102	14
47	.09764	.12521	.10263	.12666	.10759	.12811	.11252	.12957	.11741	.13104	13
+ 12′	9.09772	.12523	9.10271	.12668	9.10767	.12814	9.11260	.12960	9.11749	.13107	12
49	.09780	.12526	.10279	.12671	.10775	.12816	.11268	.12962	.11757	.13109	11
50	.09789	.12528	.10288	.12673	.10784	.12818	.11276	.12965	.11766	.13112	10
51	.09797	.12531	.10296	.12675	.10792	.12821	.11284	.12967	.11774	.13114	9
+ 13′	9.09805	.12533	9.10304	.12678	9.10800	.12823	9.11292	.12970	9.11782	.13116	8
53	.09814	.12536	.10313	.12680	.10808	.12826	.11301	.12972	.11790	.13119	7
54	.09822	.12538	.10321	.12683	.10816	.12828	.11309	.12974	.11798	.13121	6
55	.09830	.12540	.10329	.12685	.10825	.12831	.11317	.12977	.11806	.13124	5
+ 14′	9.09839	.12543	9.10337	.12687	9.10833	.12833	9.11325	.12979	9.11814	.13126	4
57	.09847	.12545	.10346	.12690	.10841	.12836	.11333	.12982	.11822	.13129	3
58	.09856	.12547	.10354	.12692	.10849	.12838	.11342	.12984	.11831	.13131	2
59	.09864	.12550	.10362	.12695	.10858	.12840	.11350	.12987	.11839	.13134	1
+ 15′	9.09872	.12552	9.10371	.12697	9.10866	.12843	9.11358	.12989	9.11847	.13136	0
	$21^h\ 14^m$		$21^h\ 13^m$		$21^h\ 12^m$		$21^h\ 11^m$		$21^h\ 10^m$		

TABLE 34.

Haversines.

s	2h 50m 42° 30′		2h 51m 42° 45′		2h 52m 43° 0′		2h 53m 43° 15′		2h 54m 43° 30′		s
	Log. Hav.	Nat. Hav.	Log. Hav.	Nat. Hav.	Log. Hav.	Nat. Hav.	Log. Hav.	Nat. Hav.	Log. Hav.	Nat. Hav.	
0	9.11847	**.13136**	9.12332	**.13284**	9.12815	**.13432**	9.13295	**.13581**	9.13771	**.13731**	60
1	.11855	**.13139**	.12341	**.13286**	.12823	**.13435**	.13303	**.13584**	.13779	**.13734**	59
2	.11863	**.13141**	.12349	**.13289**	.12831	**.13437**	.13311	**.13586**	.13787	**.13736**	58
3	.11871	**.13143**	.12357	**.13291**	.12839	**.13440**	.13319	**.13589**	.13795	**.13739**	57
+ 1′	9.11879	**.13146**	9.12365	**.13294**	9.12847	**.13442**	9.13326	**.13591**	9.13803	**.13741**	56
5	.11887	**.13148**	.12373	**.13296**	.12855	**.13445**	.13334	**.13594**	.13811	**.13744**	55
6	.11895	**.13151**	.12381	**.13299**	.12863	**.13447**	.13342	**.13596**	.13819	**.13746**	54
7	.11904	**.13153**	.12389	**.13301**	.12871	**.13450**	.13350	**.13599**	.13827	**.13749**	53
+ 2′	9.11912	**.13156**	9.12397	**.13304**	9.12879	**.13452**	9.13358	**.13601**	9.13834	**.13751**	52
9	.11920	**.13158**	.12405	**.13306**	.12887	**.13455**	.13366	**.13604**	.13842	**.13754**	51
10	.11928	**.13161**	.12413	**.13309**	.12895	**.13457**	.13374	**.13607**	.13850	**.13756**	50
11	.11936	**.13163**	.12421	**.13311**	.12903	**.13460**	.13382	**.13609**	.13858	**.13759**	49
+ 3′	9.11944	**.13166**	9.12429	**.13314**	9.12911	**.13462**	9.13390	**.13611**	9.13866	**.13761**	48
13	.11952	**.13168**	.12437	**.13316**	.12919	**.13465**	.13398	**.13614**	.13874	**.13764**	47
14	.11960	**.13171**	.12445	**.13318**	.12927	**.13467**	.13406	**.13616**	.13882	**.13766**	46
15	.11968	**.13173**	.12453	**.13321**	.12935	**.13470**	.13414	**.13619**	.13890	**.13769**	45
+ 4′	9.11977	**.13175**	9.12461	**.13323**	9.12943	**.13472**	9.13422	**.13621**	9.13898	**.13771**	44
17	.11985	**.13178**	.12470	**.13326**	.12951	**.13474**	.13430	**.13624**	.13906	**.13774**	43
18	.11993	**.13180**	.12478	**.13328**	.12959	**.13477**	.13438	**.13626**	.13913	**.13776**	42
19	.12001	**.13183**	.12486	**.13331**	.12967	**.13479**	.13446	**.13629**	.13921	**.13779**	41
+ 5′	9.12009	**.13185**	9.12494	**.13333**	9.12975	**.13482**	9.13454	**.13631**	9.13929	**.13781**	40
21	.12017	**.13188**	.12502	**.13336**	.12983	**.13484**	.13462	**.13634**	.13937	**.13784**	39
22	.12025	**.13190**	.12510	**.13338**	.12991	**.13487**	.13470	**.13636**	.13945	**.13786**	38
23	.12033	**.13193**	.12518	**.13341**	.12999	**.13489**	.13478	**.13639**	.13953	**.13789**	37
+ 6′	9.12041	**.13195**	9.12526	**.13343**	9.13007	**.13492**	9.13486	**.13641**	9.13961	**.13791**	36
25	.12050	**.13198**	.12534	**.13346**	.13015	**.13494**	.13494	**.13644**	.13969	**.13794**	35
26	.12058	**.13200**	.12542	**.13348**	.13023	**.13497**	.13501	**.13646**	.13977	**.13796**	34
27	.12066	**.13203**	.12550	**.13351**	.13031	**.13499**	.13509	**.13649**	.13985	**.13799**	33
+ 7′	9.12074	**.13205**	9.12558	**.13353**	9.13039	**.13502**	9.13517	**.13651**	9.13992	**.13801**	32
29	.12082	**.13207**	.12566	**.13356**	.13047	**.13504**	.13525	**.13654**	.14000	**.13804**	31
30	.12090	**.13210**	.12574	**.13358**	.13055	**.13507**	.13533	**.13656**	.14008	**.13806**	30
31	.12098	**.13212**	.12582	**.13360**	.13063	**.13509**	.13541	**.13659**	.14016	**.13809**	29
+ 8′	9.12106	**.13215**	9.12590	**.13363**	9.13071	**.13512**	9.13549	**.13661**	9.14024	**.13811**	28
33	.12114	**.13217**	.12598	**.13365**	.13079	**.13514**	.13557	**.13664**	.14032	**.13814**	27
34	.12122	**.13220**	.12606	**.13368**	.13087	**.13517**	.13565	**.13666**	.14040	**.13816**	26
35	.12130	**.13222**	.12614	**.13370**	.13095	**.13519**	.13573	**.13669**	.14048	**.13819**	25
+ 9′	9.12139	**.13225**	9.12622	**.13373**	9.13103	**.13522**	9.13581	**.13671**	9.14056	**.13822**	24
37	.12147	**.13227**	.12630	**.13375**	.13111	**.13524**	.13589	**.13674**	.14063	**.13824**	23
38	.12155	**.13230**	.12638	**.13378**	.13119	**.13527**	.13597	**.13676**	.14071	**.13827**	22
39	.12163	**.13232**	.12647	**.13380**	.13127	**.13529**	.13605	**.13679**	.14079	**.13829**	21
+ 10′	9.12171	**.13235**	9.12655	**.13383**	9.13135	**.13532**	9.13613	**.13681**	9.14087	**.13832**	20
41	.12179	**.13237**	.12663	**.13385**	.13143	**.13534**	.13621	**.13684**	.14095	**.13834**	19
42	.12187	**.13239**	.12671	**.13388**	.13151	**.13537**	.13628	**.13686**	.14103	**.13837**	18
43	.12195	**.13242**	.12679	**.13390**	.13159	**.13539**	.13636	**.13689**	.14111	**.13839**	17
+ 11′	9.12203	**.13244**	9.12687	**.13393**	9.13167	**.13542**	9.13644	**.13691**	9.14119	**.13842**	16
45	.12211	**.13247**	.12695	**.13395**	.13175	**.13544**	.13652	**.13694**	.14127	**.13844**	15
46	.12219	**.13249**	.12703	**.13398**	.13183	**.13547**	.13660	**.13696**	.14134	**.13847**	14
47	.12228	**.13252**	.12711	**.13400**	.13191	**.13549**	.13668	**.13699**	.14142	**.13849**	13
+ 12′	9.12236	**.13254**	9.12719	**.13403**	9.13199	**.13552**	9.13676	**.13701**	9.14150	**.13852**	12
49	.12244	**.13257**	.12727	**.13405**	.13207	**.13554**	.13684	**.13704**	.14158	**.13854**	11
50	.12252	**.13259**	.12735	**.13408**	.13215	**.13557**	.13692	**.13706**	.14166	**.13857**	10
51	.12260	**.13262**	.12743	**.13410**	.13223	**.13559**	.13700	**.13709**	.14174	**.13859**	9
+ 13′	9.12268	**.13264**	9.12751	**.13412**	9.13231	**.13562**	9.13708	**.13711**	9.14182	**.13862**	8
53	.12276	**.13267**	.12759	**.13415**	.13239	**.13564**	.13716	**.13714**	.14190	**.13864**	7
54	.12284	**.13269**	.12767	**.13417**	.13247	**.13567**	.13724	**.13716**	.14197	**.13867**	6
55	.12292	**.13272**	.12775	**.13420**	.13255	**.13569**	.13732	**.13719**	.14205	**.13869**	5
+ 14′	9.12300	**.13274**	9.12783	**.13422**	9.13263	**.13571**	9.13739	**.13721**	9.14213	**.13872**	4
57	.12308	**.13276**	.12791	**.13425**	.13271	**.13574**	.13747	**.13724**	.14221	**.13874**	3
58	.12316	**.13279**	.12799	**.13427**	.13279	**.13576**	.13755	**.13726**	.14229	**.13877**	2
59	.12324	**.13281**	.12807	**.13430**	.13287	**.13579**	.13763	**.13729**	.14237	**.13879**	1
+ 15′	9.12332	**.13284**	9.12815	**.13432**	9.13295	**.13581**	9.13771	**.13731**	9.14245	**.13882**	0
	21h 9m		21h 8m		21h 7m		21h 6m		21h 5m		

TABLE 34.

Haversines.

s	$2^h\ 55^m$ 43° 45′		$2^h\ 56^m$ 44° 0′		$2^h\ 57^m$ 44° 15′		$2^h\ 58^m$ 44° 30′		$2^h\ 59^m$ 44° 45′		s
s	Log. Hav.	Nat. Hav.	Log. Hav.	Nat. Hav.	Log. Hav.	Nat. Hav.	Log. Hav.	Nat. Hav.	Log. Hav.	Nat. Hav.	s
0	9.14245	**.13882**	9.14715	**.14033**	9.15183	**.14185**	9.15647	**.14337**	9.16109	**.14491**	60
1	.14252	**.13884**	.14723	**.14035**	.15190	**.14187**	.15655	**.14340**	.16117	**.14493**	59
2	.14260	**.13887**	.14731	**.14038**	.15198	**.14190**	.15663	**.14343**	.16124	**.14496**	58
3	.14268	**.13889**	.14739	**.14041**	.15206	**.14192**	.15670	**.14345**	.16132	**.14498**	57
+ 1′	9.14276	**.13892**	9.14746	**.14043**	9.15214	**.14195**	9.15678	**.14348**	9.16140	**.14501**	56
5	.14284	**.13894**	.14754	**.14046**	.15221	**.14198**	.15686	**.14350**	.16147	**.14504**	55
6	.14292	**.13897**	.14762	**.14048**	.15229	**.14200**	.15694	**.14353**	.16155	**.14506**	54
7	.14300	**.13899**	.14770	**.14051**	.15237	**.14203**	.15701	**.14355**	.16163	**.14509**	53
+ 2′	9.14307	**.13902**	9.14778	**.14053**	9.15245	**.14205**	9.15709	**.14358**	9.16170	**.14511**	52
9	.14315	**.13904**	.14785	**.14056**	.15253	**.14208**	.15717	**.14360**	.16178	**.14514**	51
10	.14323	**.13907**	.14793	**.14058**	.15260	**.14210**	.15724	**.14363**	.16186	**.14516**	50
11	.14331	**.13909**	.14801	**.14061**	.15268	**.14213**	.15732	**.14366**	.16193	**.14519**	49
+ 3′	9.14339	**.13912**	9.14809	**.14063**	9.15276	**.14215**	9.15740	**.14368**	9.16201	**.14521**	48
13	.14347	**.13914**	.14817	**.14066**	.15284	**.14218**	.15748	**.14371**	.16209	**.14524**	47
14	.14355	**.13917**	.14824	**.14068**	.15291	**.14220**	.15755	**.14373**	.16216	**.14527**	46
15	.14362	**.13920**	.14832	**.14071**	.15299	**.14223**	.15763	**.14376**	.16224	**.14529**	45
+ 4′	9.14370	**.13922**	9.14840	**.14073**	9.15307	**.14226**	9.15771	**.14378**	9.16232	**.14532**	44
17	.14378	**.13925**	.14848	**.14076**	.15315	**.14228**	.15778	**.14381**	.16239	**.14534**	43
18	.14386	**.13927**	.14856	**.14079**	.15322	**.14231**	.15786	**.14383**	.16247	**.14537**	42
19	.14394	**.13930**	.14863	**.14081**	.15330	**.14233**	.15794	**.14386**	.16255	**.14539**	41
+ 5′	9.14402	**.13932**	9.14871	**.14084**	9.15338	**.14236**	9.15802	**.14388**	9.16262	**.14542**	40
21	.14410	**.13935**	.14879	**.14086**	.15346	**.14238**	.15809	**.14391**	.16270	**.14545**	39
22	.14417	**.13937**	.14887	**.14089**	.15353	**.14241**	.15817	**.14394**	.16278	**.14547**	38
23	.14425	**.13940**	.14895	**.14091**	.15361	**.14243**	.15825	**.14396**	.16285	**.14550**	37
+ 6′	9.14433	**.13942**	9.14902	**.14094**	9.15369	**.14246**	9.15832	**.14399**	9.16293	**.14552**	36
25	.14441	**.13945**	.14910	**.14096**	.15377	**.14248**	.15840	**.14401**	.16301	**.14555**	35
26	.14449	**.13947**	.14918	**.14099**	.15384	**.14251**	.15848	**.14404**	.16308	**.14557**	34
27	.14457	**.13950**	.14926	**.14101**	.15392	**.14253**	.15855	**.14406**	.16316	**.14560**	33
+ 7′	9.14465	**.13952**	9.14934	**.14104**	9.15400	**.14256**	9.15863	**.14409**	9.16324	**.14562**	32
29	.14472	**.13955**	.14941	**.14106**	.15408	**.14259**	.15871	**.14411**	.16331	**.14565**	31
30	.14480	**.13957**	.14949	**.14109**	.15415	**.14261**	.15879	**.14414**	.16339	**.14568**	30
31	.14488	**.13960**	.14957	**.14111**	.15423	**.14264**	.15886	**.14417**	.16346	**.14570**	29
+ 8′	9.14496	**.13962**	9.14965	**.14114**	9.15431	**.14266**	9.15894	**.14419**	9.16354	**.14573**	28
33	.14504	**.13965**	.14973	**.14116**	.15439	**.14269**	.15902	**.14422**	.16362	**.14575**	27
34	.14512	**.13967**	.14980	**.14119**	.15446	**.14271**	.15909	**.14424**	.16369	**.14578**	26
35	.14519	**.13970**	.14988	**.14122**	.15454	**.14274**	.15917	**.14427**	.16377	**.14580**	25
+ 9′	9.14527	**.13972**	9.14996	**.14124**	9.15462	**.14276**	9.15925	**.14429**	9.16385	**.14583**	24
37	.14535	**.13975**	.15004	**.14127**	.15470	**.14279**	.15932	**.14432**	.16392	**.14586**	23
38	.14543	**.13977**	.15012	**.14129**	.15477	**.14281**	.15940	**.14434**	.16400	**.14588**	22
39	.14551	**.13980**	.15019	**.14132**	.15485	**.14284**	.15948	**.14437**	.16408	**.14591**	21
+ 10′	9.14559	**.13983**	9.15027	**.14134**	9.15493	**.14287**	9.15955	**.14440**	9.16415	**.14593**	20
41	.14566	**.13985**	.15035	**.14137**	.15500	**.14289**	.15963	**.14442**	.16423	**.14596**	19
42	.14574	**.13988**	.15043	**.14139**	.15508	**.14292**	.15971	**.14445**	.16431	**.14598**	18
43	.14582	**.13990**	.15050	**.14142**	.15516	**.14294**	.15978	**.14447**	.16438	**.14601**	17
+ 11′	9.14590	**.13993**	9.15058	**.14144**	9.15524	**.14297**	9.15986	**.14450**	9.16446	**.14604**	16
45	.14598	**.13995**	.15066	**.14147**	.15531	**.14299**	.15994	**.14452**	.16453	**.14606**	15
46	.14606	**.13998**	.15074	**.14149**	.15539	**.14302**	.16002	**.14455**	.16461	**.14609**	14
47	.14613	**.14000**	.15082	**.14152**	.15547	**.14304**	.16009	**.14457**	.16469	**.14611**	13
+ 12′	9.14621	**.14003**	9.15089	**.14154**	9.15555	**.14307**	9.16017	**.14460**	9.16476	**.14614**	12
49	.14629	**.14005**	.15097	**.14157**	.15562	**.14309**	.16025	**.14463**	.16484	**.14616**	11
50	.14637	**.14008**	.15105	**.14160**	.15570	**.14312**	.16032	**.14465**	.16492	**.14619**	10
51	.14645	**.14010**	.15113	**.14162**	.15578	**.14315**	.16040	**.14468**	.16499	**.14622**	9
+ 13′	9.14653	**.14013**	9.15120	**.14165**	9.15585	**.14317**	9.16048	**.14470**	9.16507	**.14624**	8
53	.14660	**.14015**	.15128	**.14167**	.15593	**.14320**	.16055	**.14473**	.16515	**.14627**	7
54	.14668	**.14018**	.15136	**.14170**	.15601	**.14322**	.16063	**.14475**	.16522	**.14629**	6
55	.14676	**.14020**	.15144	**.14172**	.15609	**.14325**	.16071	**.14478**	.16530	**.14632**	5
+ 14′	9.14684	**.14023**	9.15152	**.14175**	9.15616	**.14327**	9.16078	**.14480**	9.16537	**.14634**	4
57	.14692	**.14025**	.15159	**.14177**	.15624	**.14330**	.16086	**.14483**	.16545	**.14637**	3
58	.14699	**.14028**	.15167	**.14180**	.15632	**.14332**	.16094	**.14486**	.16553	**.14639**	2
59	.14707	**.14030**	.15175	**.14182**	.15640	**.14335**	.16101	**.14488**	.16560	**.14642**	1
+ 15′	9.14715	**.14033**	9.15183	**.14185**	9.15647	**.14337**	9.16109	**.14491**	9.16568	**.14645**	0
	$21^h\ 4^m$		$21^h\ 3^m$		$21^h\ 2^m$		$21^h\ 1^m$		$21^h\ 0^m$		

TABLE 34.

Haversines.

s	3h 0m 45° 0′		3h 1m 45° 15′		3h 2m 45° 30′		3h 3m 45° 45′		3h 4m 46° 0′		s
	Log. Hav.	Nat. Hav.	Log. Hav.	Nat. Hav.	Log. Hav.	Nat. Hav.	Log. Hav.	Nat. Hav.	Log. Hav.	Nat. Hav.	
0	9.16568	**.14645**	9.17024	**.14799**	9.17477	**.14955**	9.17928	**.15110**	9.18376	**.15267**	60
1	.16576	**.14647**	.17032	**.14802**	.17485	**.14957**	.17935	**.15113**	.18383	**.15270**	59
2	.16583	**.14650**	.17039	**.14804**	.17492	**.14960**	.17943	**.15116**	.18390	**.15272**	58
3	.16591	**.14652**	.17047	**.14807**	.17500	**.14962**	.17950	**.15118**	.18398	**.15275**	57
+ 1′	9.16598	**.14655**	9.17054	**.14810**	9.17507	**.14965**	9.17958	**.15121**	9.18405	**.15278**	56
5	.16606	**.14658**	.17062	**.14812**	.17515	**.14968**	.17965	**.15123**	.18413	**.15280**	55
6	.16614	**.14660**	.17069	**.14815**	.17522	**.14970**	.17973	**.15126**	.18420	**.15283**	54
7	.16621	**.14663**	.17077	**.14817**	.17530	**.14973**	.17980	**.15129**	.18428	**.15285**	53
+ 2′	9.16629	**.14665**	9.17085	**.14820**	9.17538	**.14975**	9.17988	**.15131**	9.18435	**.15288**	52
9	.16637	**.14668**	.17092	**.14822**	.17545	**.14978**	.17995	**.15134**	.18443	**.15291**	51
10	.16644	**.14670**	.17100	**.14825**	.17553	**.14981**	.18003	**.15137**	.18450	**.15293**	50
11	.16652	**.14673**	.17107	**.14828**	.17560	**.14983**	.18010	**.15139**	.18457	**.15296**	49
+ 3′	9.16659	**.14676**	9.17115	**.14830**	9.17568	**.14986**	9.18018	**.15142**	9.18465	**.15298**	48
13	.16667	**.14678**	.17122	**.14833**	.17575	**.14988**	.18025	**.15144**	.18472	**.15301**	47
14	.16675	**.14681**	.17130	**.14835**	.17583	**.14991**	.18033	**.15147**	.18480	**.15304**	46
15	.16682	**.14683**	.17138	**.14838**	.17590	**.14993**	.18040	**.15150**	.18487	**.15306**	45
+ 4′	9.16690	**.14686**	9.17145	**.14841**	9.17598	**.14996**	9.18048	**.15152**	9.18495	**.15309**	44
17	.16697	**.14688**	.17153	**.14843**	.17605	**.14999**	.18055	**.15155**	.18502	**.15312**	43
18	.16705	**.14691**	.17160	**.14846**	.17613	**.15001**	.18062	**.15157**	.18509	**.15314**	42
19	.16713	**.14693**	.17168	**.14848**	.17620	**.15004**	.18070	**.15160**	.18517	**.15316**	41
+ 5′	9.16720	**.14696**	9.17175	**.14851**	9.17628	**.15006**	9.18077	**.15163**	9.18524	**.15319**	40
21	.16728	**.14699**	.17183	**.14853**	.17635	**.15009**	.18085	**.15165**	.18532	**.15322**	39
22	.16735	**.14701**	.17191	**.14856**	.17643	**.15012**	.18092	**.15168**	.18539	**.15325**	38
23	.16743	**.14704**	.17198	**.14859**	.17650	**.15014**	.18100	**.15170**	.18547	**.15327**	37
+ 6′	9.16751	**.14706**	9.17206	**.14861**	9.17658	**.15017**	9.18107	**.15173**	9.18554	**.15330**	36
25	.16758	**.14709**	.17213	**.14864**	.17665	**.15019**	.18115	**.15176**	.18561	**.15333**	35
26	.16766	**.14712**	.17221	**.14866**	.17673	**.15022**	.18122	**.15178**	.18569	**.15335**	34
27	.16774	**.14714**	.17228	**.14869**	.17680	**.15025**	.18130	**.15181**	.18576	**.15337**	33
+ 7′	9.16781	**.14717**	9.17236	**.14872**	9.17688	**.15027**	9.18137	**.15183**	9.18584	**.15340**	32
29	.16789	**.14719**	.17243	**.14874**	.17695	**.15030**	.18145	**.15186**	.18591	**.15343**	31
30	.16796	**.14722**	.17251	**.14877**	.17703	**.15032**	.18152	**.15189**	.18598	**.15346**	30
31	.16804	**.14724**	.17259	**.14879**	.17710	**.15035**	.18160	**.15191**	.18606	**.15348**	29
+ 8′	9.16812	**.14727**	9.17266	**.14882**	9.17718	**.15038**	9.18167	**.15194**	9.18613	**.15351**	28
33	.16819	**.14730**	.17274	**.14885**	.17725	**.15040**	.18174	**.15197**	.18621	**.15353**	27
34	.16827	**.14732**	.17281	**.14887**	.17733	**.15043**	.18182	**.15199**	.18628	**.15356**	26
35	.16834	**.14735**	.17289	**.14890**	.17740	**.15045**	.18189	**.15202**	.18636	**.15359**	25
+ 9′	9.16842	**.14737**	9.17296	**.14892**	9.17748	**.15048**	9.18197	**.15204**	9.18643	**.15361**	24
37	.16850	**.14740**	.17304	**.14895**	.17755	**.15051**	.18204	**.15207**	.18650	**.15364**	23
38	.16857	**.14743**	.17311	**.14898**	.17763	**.15053**	.18212	**.15210**	.18658	**.15367**	22
39	.16865	**.14745**	.17319	**.14900**	.17770	**.15056**	.18219	**.15212**	.18665	**.15369**	21
+ 10′	9.16872	**.14748**	9.17327	**.14903**	9.17778	**.15058**	9.18227	**.15215**	9.18673	**.15372**	20
41	.16880	**.14750**	.17334	**.14905**	.17785	**.15061**	.18234	**.15217**	.18680	**.15374**	19
42	.16887	**.14753**	.17342	**.14908**	.17793	**.15064**	.18242	**.15220**	.18687	**.15377**	18
43	.16895	**.14755**	.17349	**.14910**	.17800	**.15066**	.18249	**.15222**	.18695	**.15379**	17
+ 11′	9.16903	**.14758**	9.17357	**.14913**	9.17808	**.15069**	9.18256	**.15225**	9.18702	**.15382**	16
45	.16910	**.14760**	.17364	**.14916**	.17815	**.15071**	.18264	**.15228**	.18710	**.15385**	15
46	.16918	**.14763**	.17372	**.14918**	.17823	**.15074**	.18271	**.15230**	.18717	**.15388**	14
47	.16925	**.14766**	.17379	**.14921**	.17830	**.15077**	.18279	**.15233**	.18724	**.15390**	13
+ 12′	9.16933	**.14768**	9.17387	**.14923**	9.17838	**.15079**	9.18286	**.15236**	9.18732	**.15393**	12
49	.16941	**.14771**	.17394	**.14926**	.17845	**.15082**	.18294	**.15238**	.18739	**.15395**	11
50	.16948	**.14773**	.17402	**.14929**	.17853	**.15084**	.18301	**.15241**	.18747	**.15398**	10
51	.16956	**.14776**	.17409	**.14931**	.17860	**.15087**	.18309	**.15244**	.18754	**.15401**	9
+ 13′	9.16963	**.14779**	9.17417	**.14934**	9.17868	**.15090**	9.18316	**.15246**	9.18762	**.15403**	8
53	.16971	**.14781**	.17425	**.14936**	.17875	**.15092**	.18324	**.15249**	.18769	**.15406**	7
54	.16979	**.14784**	.17432	**.14939**	.17883	**.15095**	.18331	**.15251**	.18776	**.15409**	6
55	.16986	**.14786**	.17440	**.14942**	.17890	**.15097**	.18338	**.15254**	.18784	**.15411**	5
+ 14′	9.16994	**.14789**	9.17447	**.14944**	9.17898	**.15100**	9.18346	**.15257**	9.18791	**.15414**	4
57	.17001	**.14791**	.17455	**.14947**	.17905	**.15103**	.18353	**.15259**	.18798	**.15416**	3
58	.17009	**.14794**	.17462	**.14949**	.17913	**.15105**	.18361	**.15262**	.18806	**.15419**	2
59	.17016	**.14797**	.17470	**.14952**	.17920	**.15108**	.18368	**.15264**	.18813	**.15422**	1
+ 15′	9.17024	**.14799**	9.17477	**.14955**	9.17928	**.15110**	9.18376	**.15267**	9.18821	**.15424**	0
	20h 59m		20h 58m		20h 57m		20h 56m		20h 55m		

TABLE 34.

Haversines.

s	3h 5m 46° 15′		3h 6m 46° 30′		3h 7m 46° 45′		3h 8m 47° 0′		3h 9m 47° 15′		
s	Log. Hav.	Nat. Hav.	Log. Hav.	Nat. Hav.	Log. Hav.	Nat. Hav.	Log. Hav.	Nat. Hav.	Log. Hav.	Nat. Hav.	s
0	9.18821	**.15424**	9.19263	**.15582**	9.19703	**.15741**	9.20140	**.15900**	9.20574	**.16060**	60
1	.18828	**.15427**	.19270	**.15585**	.19710	**.15743**	.20147	**.15903**	.20582	**.16063**	59
2	.18835	**.15430**	.19278	**.15588**	.19717	**.15746**	.20154	**.15905**	.20589	**.16065**	58
3	.18843	**.15432**	.19285	**.15590**	.19725	**.15748**	.20162	**.15908**	.20596	**.16068**	57
+ 1′	9.18850	**.15435**	9.19292	**.15593**	9.19732	**.15751**	9.20169	**.15911**	9.20603	**.16071**	56
5	.18858	**.15437**	.19300	**.15595**	.19739	**.15754**	.20176	**.15913**	.20611	**.16073**	55
6	.18865	**.15440**	.19307	**.15598**	.19747	**.15757**	.20184	**.15916**	.20618	**.16076**	54
7	.18872	**.15443**	.19315	**.15601**	.19754	**.15759**	.20191	**.15919**	.20625	**.16079**	53
+ 2′	9.18880	**.15445**	9.19322	**.15603**	9.19761	**.15762**	9.20198	**.15921**	9.20632	**.16081**	52
9	.18887	**.15448**	.19329	**.15606**	.19769	**.15765**	.20205	**.15924**	.20639	**.16084**	51
10	.18895	**.15451**	.19337	**.15609**	.19776	**.15767**	.20213	**.15927**	.20647	**.16087**	50
11	.18902	**.15453**	.19344	**.15611**	.19783	**.15770**	.20220	**.15929**	.20654	**.16089**	49
+ 3′	9.18909	**.15456**	9.19351	**.15614**	9.19790	**.15773**	9.20227	**.15932**	9.20661	**.16092**	48
13	.18917	**.15458**	.19359	**.15617**	.19798	**.15775**	.20234	**.15935**	.20668	**.16095**	47
14	.18924	**.15461**	.19366	**.15619**	.19805	**.15778**	.20242	**.15937**	.20675	**.16097**	46
15	.18932	**.15464**	.19373	**.15622**	.19812	**.15781**	.20249	**.15940**	.20683	**.16100**	45
+ 4′	9.18939	**.15466**	9.19381	**.15625**	9.19820	**.15783**	9.20256	**.15943**	9.20690	**.16103**	44
17	.18946	**.15469**	.19388	**.15627**	.19827	**.15786**	.20263	**.15945**	.20697	**.16105**	43
18	.18954	**.15472**	.19395	**.15630**	.19834	**.15789**	.20271	**.15948**	.20704	**.16108**	42
19	.18961	**.15474**	.19403	**.15632**	.19842	**.15791**	.20278	**.15951**	.20712	**.16111**	41
+ 5′	9.18968	**.15477**	9.19410	**.15635**	9.19849	**.15794**	9.20285	**.15953**	9.20719	**.16113**	40
21	.18976	**.15479**	.19417	**.15638**	.19856	**.15796**	.20292	**.15956**	.20726	**.16116**	39
22	.18983	**.15482**	.19425	**.15640**	.19863	**.15799**	.20300	**.15959**	.20733	**.16119**	38
23	.18991	**.15485**	.19432	**.15643**	.19871	**.15802**	.20307	**.15961**	.20740	**.16121**	37
+ 6′	9.18998	**.15487**	9.19439	**.15646**	9.19878	**.15804**	9.20314	**.15964**	9.20748	**.16124**	36
25	.19005	**.15490**	.19447	**.15648**	.19885	**.15807**	.20321	**.15967**	.20755	**.16127**	35
26	.19013	**.15493**	.19454	**.15651**	.19893	**.15810**	.20329	**.15969**	.20762	**.16129**	34
27	.19020	**.15495**	.19461	**.15654**	.19900	**.15812**	.20336	**.15972**	.20769	**.16132**	33
+ 7′	9.19027	**.15498**	9.19469	**.15656**	9.19907	**.15815**	9.20343	**.15975**	9.20776	**.16135**	32
29	.19035	**.15501**	.19476	**.15659**	.19914	**.15818**	.20350	**.15977**	.20784	**.16137**	31
30	.19042	**.15503**	.19483	**.15662**	.19922	**.15820**	.20358	**.15980**	.20791	**.16140**	30
31	.19050	**.15506**	.19491	**.15664**	.19929	**.15823**	.20365	**.15983**	.20798	**.16143**	29
+ 8′	9.19057	**.15509**	9.19498	**.15667**	9.19936	**.15826**	9.20372	**.15985**	9.20805	**.16146**	28
33	.19064	**.15511**	.19505	**.15670**	.19944	**.15828**	.20379	**.15988**	.20812	**.16148**	27
34	.19072	**.15514**	.19513	**.15672**	.19951	**.15831**	.20386	**.15991**	.20820	**.16151**	26
35	.19079	**.15516**	.19520	**.15675**	.19958	**.15834**	.20394	**.15993**	.20827	**.16154**	25
+ 9′	9.19086	**.15519**	9.19527	**.15677**	9.19965	**.15836**	9.20401	**.15996**	9.20834	**.16156**	24
37	.19094	**.15522**	.19535	**.15680**	.19973	**.15839**	.20408	**.15999**	.20841	**.16159**	23
38	.19101	**.15524**	.19542	**.15683**	.19980	**.15842**	.20415	**.16001**	.20848	**.16162**	22
39	.19109	**.15527**	.19549	**.15685**	.19987	**.15844**	.20423	**.16004**	.20856	**.16164**	21
+ 10′	9.19116	**.15530**	9.19557	**.15688**	9.19995	**.15847**	9.20430	**.16007**	9.20863	**.16167**	20
41	.19123	**.15532**	.19564	**.15691**	.20002	**.15850**	.20437	**.16009**	.20870	**.16170**	19
42	.19131	**.15535**	.19571	**.15693**	.20009	**.15852**	.20444	**.16012**	.20877	**.16172**	18
43	.19138	**.15537**	.19579	**.15696**	.20016	**.15855**	.20452	**.16015**	.20884	**.16175**	17
+ 11′	9.19145	**.15540**	9.19586	**.15699**	9.20024	**.15858**	9.20459	**.16017**	9.20891	**.16178**	16
45	.19153	**.15543**	.19593	**.15701**	.20031	**.15860**	.20466	**.16020**	.20899	**.16180**	15
46	.19160	**.15545**	.19600	**.15704**	.20038	**.15863**	.20473	**.16023**	.20906	**.16183**	14
47	.19167	**.15548**	.19608	**.15706**	.20045	**.15866**	.20481	**.16025**	.20913	**.16186**	13
+ 12′	9.19175	**.15551**	9.19615	**.15709**	9.20053	**.15868**	9.20488	**.16028**	9.20920	**.16188**	12
49	.19182	**.15553**	.19622	**.15712**	.20060	**.15871**	.20495	**.16031**	.20927	**.16191**	11
50	.19190	**.15556**	.19630	**.15714**	.20067	**.15874**	.20502	**.16033**	.20935	**.16194**	10
51	.19197	**.15559**	.19637	**.15717**	.20075	**.15876**	.20509	**.16036**	.20942	**.16196**	9
+ 13′	9.19204	**.15561**	9.19644	**.15720**	9.20082	**.15879**	9.20517	**.16039**	9.20949	**.16199**	8
53	.19212	**.15564**	19652	**.15722**	.20089	**.15881**	.20524	**.16041**	.20956	**.16202**	7
54	.19219	**.15566**	.19659	**.15725**	.20096	**.15884**	.20531	**.16044**	.20963	**.16204**	6
55	.19226	**.15569**	.19666	**.15728**	.20104	**.15887**	.20538	**.16047**	.20971	**.16207**	5
+ 14′	9.19234	**.15572**	9.19674	**.15730**	9.20111	**.15889**	9.20546	**.16049**	9.20978	**.16210**	4
57	.19241	**.15574**	.19681	**.15733**	.20118	**.15892**	.20553	**.16052**	.20985	**.16212**	3
58	.19248	**.15577**	.19688	**.15736**	.20125	**.15895**	.20560	**.16055**	.20992	**.16215**	2
59	.19256	**.15580**	.19696	**.15738**	.20133	**.15898**	.20567	**.16057**	.20999	**.16218**	1
+ 15′	9.19263	**.15582**	9.19703	**.15741**	9.20140	**.15900**	9.20574	**.16060**	9.21006	**.16220**	0
	20h 54m		20h 53m		20h 52m		20h 51m		20h 50m		

TABLE 34.

Haversines.

s	$3^h 10^m$ 47° 30′		$3^h 11^m$ 47° 45′		$3^h 12^m$ 48° 0′		$3^h 13^m$ 48° 15′		$3^h 14^m$ 48° 30′		s
	Log. Hav.	Nat. Hav.	Log. Hav.	Nat. Hav.	Log. Hav.	Nat. Hav.	Log. Hav.	Nat. Hav.	Log. Hav.	Nat. Hav.	
0	9.21006	**.16220**	9.21436	**.16382**	9.21863	**.16543**	9.22287	**.16706**	9.22709	**.16869**	60
1	.21014	**.16223**	.21443	**.16384**	.21870	**.16546**	.22294	**.16709**	.22716	**.16872**	59
2	.21021	**.16226**	.21450	**.16387**	.21877	**.16549**	.22301	**.16711**	.22723	**.16874**	58
3	.21028	**.16229**	.21457	**.16390**	.21884	**.16552**	.22308	**.16714**	.22730	**.16877**	57
+ 1′	9.21035	**.16231**	9.21464	**.16392**	9.21891	**.16554**	9.22315	**.16717**	9.22737	**.16880**	56
5	.21042	**.16234**	.21471	**.16395**	.21898	**.16557**	.22322	**.16720**	.22744	**.16883**	55
6	.21049	**.16237**	.21479	**.16398**	.21905	**.16560**	.22329	**.16722**	.22751	**.16885**	54
7	.21057	**.16239**	.21486	**.16401**	.21912	**.16562**	.22336	**.16725**	.22758	**.16888**	53
+ 2′	9.21064	**.16242**	9.21493	**.16403**	9.21919	**.16565**	9.22343	**.16728**	9.22765	**.16891**	52
9	.21071	**.16245**	.21500	**.16406**	.21926	**.16568**	.22350	**.16730**	.22772	**.16893**	51
10	.21078	**.16247**	.21507	**.16409**	.21934	**.16571**	.22358	**.16733**	.22779	**.16896**	50
11	.21085	**.16250**	.21514	**.16411**	.21941	**.16573**	.22365	**.16736**	.22786	**.16899**	49
+ 3′	9.21092	**.16253**	9.21521	**.16414**	9.21948	**.16576**	9.22372	**.16738**	9.22793	**.16902**	48
13	.21100	**.16255**	.21529	**.16417**	.21955	**.16579**	.22379	**.16741**	.22800	**.16904**	47
14	.21107	**.16258**	.21536	**.16419**	.21962	**.16581**	.22386	**.16744**	.22807	**.16907**	46
15	.21114	**.16261**	.21543	**.16422**	.21969	**.16584**	.22393	**.16747**	.22814	**.16910**	45
+ 4′	9.21121	**.16263**	9.21550	**.16425**	9.21976	**.16587**	9.22400	**.16749**	9.22821	**.16913**	44
17	.21128	**.16266**	.21557	**.16427**	.21983	**.16589**	.22407	**.16752**	.22828	**.16915**	43
18	.21135	**.16269**	.21564	**.16430**	.21990	**.16592**	.22414	**.16755**	.22835	**.16918**	42
19	.21143	**.16271**	.21571	**.16433**	.21997	**.16595**	.22421	**.16757**	.22842	**.16921**	41
+ 5′	9.21150	**.16274**	9.21578	**.16436**	9.22004	**.16598**	9.22428	**.16760**	9.22849	**.16924**	40
21	.21157	**.16277**	.21585	**.16438**	.22011	**.16600**	.22435	**.16763**	.22856	**.16926**	39
22	.21164	**.16280**	.21593	**.16441**	.22019	**.16603**	.22442	**.16766**	.22863	**.16929**	38
23	.21171	**.16282**	.21600	**.16444**	.22026	**.16606**	.22449	**.16768**	.22870	**.16932**	37
+ 6′	9.21178	**.16285**	9.21607	**.16446**	9.22033	**.16608**	9.22456	**.16771**	9.22877	**.16934**	36
25	.21186	**.16288**	.21614	**.16449**	.22040	**.16611**	.22463	**.16774**	.22884	**.16937**	35
26	.21193	**.16290**	.21621	**.16452**	.22047	**.16614**	.22470	**.16777**	.22891	**.16940**	34
27	.21200	**.16293**	.21628	**.16454**	.22054	**.16616**	.22477	**.16779**	.22898	**.16943**	33
+ 7′	9.21207	**.16296**	9.21635	**.16457**	9.22061	**.16619**	9.22484	**.16782**	9.22905	**.16945**	32
29	.21214	**.16298**	.21642	**.16460**	.22068	**.16622**	.22491	**.16785**	.22912	**.16948**	31
30	.21221	**.16301**	.21650	**.16462**	.22075	**.16625**	.22498	**.16787**	.22919	**.16951**	30
31	.21229	**.16304**	.21657	**.16465**	.22082	**.16627**	.22505	**.16790**	.22926	**.16953**	29
+ 8′	9.21236	**.16306**	9.21664	**.16468**	9.22089	**.16630**	9.22512	**.16793**	9.22933	**.16956**	28
33	.21243	**.16309**	.21671	**.16471**	.22096	**.16633**	.22519	**.16795**	.22940	**.16959**	27
34	.21250	**.16312**	.21678	**.16473**	.22103	**.16635**	.22526	**.16798**	.22947	**.16962**	26
35	.21257	**.16314**	.21685	**.16476**	.22111	**.16638**	.22533	**.16801**	.22954	**.16964**	25
+ 9′	9.21264	**.16317**	9.21692	**.16479**	9.22118	**.16641**	9.22540	**.16804**	9.22961	**.16967**	24
37	.21272	**.16320**	.21699	**.16481**	.22125	**.16644**	.22547	**.16806**	.22968	**.16970**	23
38	.21279	**.16323**	.21706	**.16484**	.22132	**.16646**	.22555	**.16809**	.22975	**.16973**	22
39	.21286	**.16325**	.21714	**.16487**	.22139	**.16649**	.22562	**.16812**	.22982	**.16975**	21
+ 10′	9.21293	**.16328**	9.21721	**.16489**	9.22146	**.16652**	9.22569	**.16815**	9.22989	**.16978**	20
41	.21300	**.16331**	.21728	**.16492**	.22153	**.16654**	.22576	**.16817**	.22996	**.16981**	19
42	.21307	**.16333**	.21735	**.16495**	.22160	**.16657**	.22583	**.16820**	.23003	**.16984**	18
43	.21314	**.16336**	.21742	**.16498**	.22167	**.16660**	.22590	**.16823**	.23010	**.16986**	17
+ 11′	9.21322	**.16339**	9.21749	**.16500**	9.22174	**.16663**	9.22597	**.16825**	9.23017	**.16989**	16
45	.21329	**.16341**	.21756	**.16503**	.22181	**.16665**	.22604	**.16828**	.23024	**.16992**	15
46	.21336	**.16344**	.21763	**.16506**	.22188	**.16668**	.22611	**.16831**	.23031	**.16994**	14
47	.21343	**.16347**	.21770	**.16508**	.22195	**.16671**	.22618	**.16834**	.23038	**.16997**	13
+ 12′	9.21350	**.16349**	9.21778	**.16511**	9.22202	**.16673**	9.22625	**.16836**	9 23045	**.17000**	12
49	.21357	**.16352**	.21785	**.16514**	.22209	**.16676**	.22632	**.16839**	.23052	**.17003**	11
50	.21364	**.16355**	.21792	**.16516**	.22216	**.16679**	.22639	**.16842**	.23059	**.17005**	10
51	.21372	**.16357**	.21799	**.16519**	.22224	**.16681**	.22646	**.16844**	.23066	**.17008**	9
+ 13′	9.21379	**.16360**	9.21806	**.16522**	9.22231	**.16684**	9.22653	**.16847**	9.23073	**.17011**	8
53	.21386	**.16363**	.21813	**.16524**	.22238	**.16687**	.22660	**.16850**	.23080	**.17014**	7
54	.21393	**.16366**	.21820	**.16527**	.22245	**.16690**	.22667	**.16853**	.23087	**.17016**	6
55	.21400	**.16368**	.21827	**.16530**	.22252	**.16692**	.22674	**.16855**	.23094	**.17019**	5
+ 14′	9.21407	**.16371**	9.21834	**.16533**	9.22259	**.16695**	9.22681	**.16858**	9.23100	**.17022**	4
57	.21414	**.16374**	.21841	**.16535**	.22266	**.16698**	.22688	**.16861**	.23107	**.17024**	3
58	.21422	**.16376**	.21848	**.16538**	.22273	**.16701**	.22695	**.16864**	.23114	**.17027**	2
59	.21429	**.16379**	.21856	**.16541**	.22280	**.16703**	.22702	**.16866**	.23121	**.17030**	1
+ 15′	9.21436	**.16382**	9.21863	**.16543**	9.22287	**.16706**	9.22709	**.16869**	9.23128	**.17033**	0
	$20^h 49^m$		$20^h 48^m$		$20^h 47^m$		$20^h 46^m$		$20^h 45^m$		

TABLE 34.

Haversines.

s	$3^h\ 15^m$ 48° 45′		$3^h\ 16^m$ 49° 0′		$3^h\ 17^m$ 49° 15′		$3^h\ 18^m$ 49° 30′		$3^h\ 19^m$ 49° 45′		s
	Log. Hav.	Nat. Hav.	Log. Hav.	Nat. Hav.	Log. Hav.	Nat. Hav.	Log. Hav.	Nat. Hav.	Log. Hav.	Nat. Hav.	
0	9.23128	**.17033**	9.23545	**.17197**	9.23960	**.17362**	9.24372	**.17528**	9.24782	**.17694**	60
1	.23135	**.17035**	.23552	**.17200**	.23967	**.17365**	.24379	**.17530**	.24789	**.17697**	59
2	.23142	**.17038**	.23559	**.17203**	.23974	**.17368**	.24386	**.17533**	.24796	**.17699**	58
3	.23149	**.17041**	.23566	**.17205**	.23981	**.17370**	.24393	**.17536**	.24803	**.17702**	57
+ 1′	9.23156	**.17044**	9.23573	**.17208**	9.23988	**.17373**	9.24400	**.17539**	9.24809	**.17705**	56
5	.23163	**.17046**	.23580	**.17211**	.23994	**.17376**	.24406	**.17541**	.24816	**.17708**	55
6	.23170	**.17049**	.23587	**.17214**	.24001	**.17379**	.24413	**.17544**	.24823	**.17710**	54
7	.23177	**.17052**	.23594	**.17216**	.24008	**.17381**	.24420	**.17547**	.24830	**.17713**	53
+ 2′	9.23184	**.17055**	9.23601	**.17219**	9.24015	**.17384**	9.24427	**.17550**	9.24837	**.17716**	52
9	.23191	**.17057**	.23608	**.17222**	.24022	**.17387**	.24434	**.17552**	.24843	**.17719**	51
10	.23198	**.17060**	.23615	**.17225**	.24029	**.17390**	.24441	**.17555**	.24850	**.17722**	50
11	.23205	**.17063**	.23622	**.17227**	.24036	**.17392**	.24448	**.17558**	.24857	**.17724**	49
+ 3′	9.23212	**.17066**	9.23629	**.17230**	9.24043	**.17395**	9.24454	**.17561**	9.24864	**.17727**	48
13	.23219	**.17068**	.23635	**.17233**	.24050	**.17398**	.24461	**.17563**	.24871	**.17730**	47
14	.23226	**.17071**	.23642	**.17235**	.24056	**.17401**	.24468	**.17566**	.24877	**.17733**	46
15	.23233	**.17074**	.23649	**.17238**	.24063	**.17403**	.24475	**.17569**	.24884	**.17735**	45
+ 4′	9.23240	**.17076**	9.23656	**.17241**	9.24070	**.17406**	9.24482	**.17572**	9.24891	**.17738**	44
17	.23247	**.17079**	.23663	**.17244**	.24077	**.17409**	.24489	**.17575**	.24898	**.17741**	43
18	.23254	**.17082**	.23670	**.17246**	.24084	**.17412**	.24495	**.17577**	.24905	**.17744**	42
19	.23261	**.17085**	.23677	**.17249**	.24091	**.17414**	.24502	**.17580**	.24911	**.17746**	41
+ 5′	9.23268	**.17087**	9.23684	**.17252**	9.24098	**.17417**	9.24509	**.17583**	9.24918	**.17749**	40
21	.23275	**.17090**	.23691	**.17255**	.24105	**.17420**	.24516	**.17586**	.24925	**.17752**	39
22	.23282	**.17093**	.23698	**.17257**	.24111	**.17423**	.24523	**.17588**	.24932	**.17755**	38
23	.23289	**.17096**	.23705	**.17260**	.24118	**.17425**	.24530	**.17591**	.24939	**.17758**	37
+ 6′	9.23295	**.17098**	9.23712	**.17263**	9.24125	**.17428**	9.24536	**.17594**	9.24945	**.17760**	36
25	.23302	**.17101**	.23718	**.17266**	.24132	**.17431**	.24543	**.17597**	.24952	**.17763**	35
26	.23309	**.17104**	.23725	**.17268**	.24139	**.17434**	.24550	**.17600**	.24959	**.17766**	34
27	.23316	**.17107**	.23732	**.17271**	.24146	**.17436**	.24557	**.17602**	.24966	**.17769**	33
+ 7′	9.23323	**.17109**	9.23739	**.17274**	9.24153	**.17439**	9.24564	**.17605**	9.24973	**.17772**	32
29	.23330	**.17112**	.23746	**.17277**	.24160	**.17442**	.24571	**.17608**	.24979	**.17774**	31
30	.23337	**.17115**	.23753	**.17279**	.24166	**.17445**	.24577	**.17611**	.24986	**.17777**	30
31	.23344	**.17117**	.23760	**.17282**	.24173	**.17447**	.24584	**.17613**	.24993	**.17780**	29
+ 8′	9.23351	**.17120**	9.23767	**.17285**	9.24180	**.17450**	9.24591	**.17616**	9.25000	**.17783**	28
33	.23358	**.17123**	.23774	**.17288**	.24187	**.17453**	.24598	**.17619**	.25007	**.17785**	27
34	.23365	**.17126**	.23781	**.17290**	.24194	**.17456**	.24605	**.17622**	.25013	**.17788**	26
35	.23372	**.17128**	.23788	**.17293**	.24201	**.17458**	.24612	**.17624**	.25020	**.17791**	25
+ 9′	9.23379	**.17131**	9.23794	**.17296**	9.24208	**.17461**	9.24618	**.17627**	9.25027	**.17794**	24
37	.23386	**.17134**	.23801	**.17299**	.24215	**.17464**	.24625	**.17630**	.25034	**.17797**	23
38	.23393	**.17137**	.23808	**.17301**	.24221	**.17467**	.24632	**.17633**	.25040	**.17799**	22
39	.23400	**.17139**	.23815	**.17304**	.24228	**.17470**	.24639	**.17636**	.25047	**.17802**	21
+ 10′	9.23407	**.17142**	9.23822	**.17307**	9.24235	**.17472**	9.24646	**.17638**	9.25054	**.17805**	20
41	.23414	**.17145**	.23829	**.17310**	.24242	**.17475**	.24653	**.17641**	.25061	**.17808**	19
42	.23421	**.17148**	.23836	**.17313**	.24249	**.17478**	.24659	**.17644**	.25068	**.17811**	18
43	.23427	**.17150**	.23843	**.17315**	.24256	**.17481**	.24666	**.17647**	.25074	**.17813**	17
+ 11′	9.23434	**.17153**	9.23850	**.17318**	9.24263	**.17483**	9.24673	**.17649**	9.25081	**.17816**	16
45	.23441	**.17156**	.23857	**.17321**	.24269	**.17486**	.24680	**.17652**	.25088	**.17819**	15
46	.23448	**.17159**	.23863	**.17323**	.24276	**.17489**	.24687	**.17655**	.25095	**.17822**	14
47	.23455	**.17161**	.23870	**.17326**	.24283	**.17492**	.24694	**.17658**	.25102	**.17824**	13
+ 12′	9.23462	**.17164**	9.23877	**.17329**	9.24290	**.17494**	9.24700	**.17661**	9.25108	**.17827**	12
49	.23469	**.17167**	.23884	**.17332**	.24297	**.17497**	.24707	**.17663**	.25115	**.17830**	11
50	.23476	**.17170**	.23891	**.17335**	.24304	**.17500**	.24714	**.17666**	.25122	**.17833**	10
51	.23483	**.17172**	.23898	**.17337**	.24311	**.17503**	.24721	**.17669**	.25129	**.17836**	9
+ 13′	9.23490	**.17175**	9.23905	**.17340**	9.24317	**.17505**	9.24728	**.17672**	9.25135	**.17838**	8
53	.23497	**.17178**	.23912	**.17343**	.24324	**.17508**	.24734	**.17674**	.25142	**.17841**	7
54	.23504	**.17181**	.23919	**.17346**	.24331	**.17511**	.24741	**.17677**	.25149	**.17844**	6
55	.23511	**.17183**	.23926	**.17348**	.24338	**.17514**	.24748	**.17680**	.25156	**.17847**	5
+ 14′	9.23518	**.17186**	9.23932	**.17351**	9.24345	**.17517**	9.24755	**.17683**	9.25163	**.17849**	4
57	.23525	**.17189**	.23939	**.17354**	.24352	**.17519**	.24762	**.17686**	.25169	**.17852**	3
58	.23532	**.17192**	.23946	**.17357**	.24359	**.17522**	.24768	**.17688**	.25176	**.17855**	2
59	.23538	**.17194**	.23953	**.17359**	.24365	**.17525**	.24775	**.17691**	.25183	**.17858**	1
+ 15′	9.23545	**.17197**	9.23960	**.17362**	9.24372	**.17528**	9.24782	**.17694**	9.25190	**.17861**	0
	$20^h\ 44^m$		$20^h\ 43^m$		$20^h\ 42^m$		$20^h\ 41^m$		$20^h\ 40^m$		

TABLE 34.

Haversines.

s	3h 20m 50° 0′		3h 21m 50° 15′		3h 22m 50° 30′		3h 23m 50° 45′		3h 24m 51° 0′		s
	Log. Hav.	Nat. Hav.	Log. Hav.	Nat. Hav.	Log. Hav.	Nat. Hav.	Log. Hav.	Nat. Hav.	Log. Hav.	Nat. Hav.	
0	9.25190	**.17861**	9.25595	**.18028**	9.25998	**.18196**	9.26398	**.18365**	9.26797	**.18534**	60
1	.25196	**.17863**	.25602	**.18031**	.26005	**.18199**	.26405	**.18368**	.26804	**.18537**	59
2	.25203	**.17866**	.25608	**.18034**	.26011	**.18202**	.26412	**.18370**	.26810	**.18540**	58
3	.25210	**.17869**	.25615	**.18036**	.26018	**.18205**	.26418	**.18373**	.26817	**.18542**	57
+ 1′	9.25217	**.17872**	9.25622	**.18039**	9.26025	**.18207**	9.26425	**.18376**	9.26823	**.18545**	56
5	.25224	**.17875**	.25629	**.18042**	.26031	**.18210**	.26432	**.18379**	.26830	**.18548**	55
6	.25230	**.17877**	.25635	**.18045**	.26038	**.18213**	.26438	**.18382**	.26837	**.18551**	54
7	.25237	**.17880**	.25642	**.18048**	.26045	**.18216**	.26445	**.18384**	.26843	**.18554**	53
+ 2′	9.25244	**.17883**	9.25649	**.18050**	9.26051	**.18219**	9.26452	**.18387**	9.26850	**.18557**	52
9	.25251	**.17886**	.25655	**.18053**	.26058	**.18221**	.26458	**.18390**	.26856	**.18559**	51
10	.25257	**.17888**	.25662	**.18056**	.26065	**.18224**	.26465	**.18393**	.26863	**.18562**	50
11	.25264	**.17891**	.25669	**.18059**	.26071	**.18227**	.26472	**.18396**	.26870	**.18565**	49
+ 3′	9.25271	**.17894**	9.25676	**.18062**	9.26078	**.18230**	9.26478	**.18399**	9.26876	**.18568**	48
13	.25278	**.17897**	.25682	**.18064**	.26085	**.18233**	.26485	**.18401**	.26883	**.18571**	47
14	.25284	**.17900**	.25689	**.18067**	.26091	**.18235**	.26492	**.18404**	.26890	**.18574**	46
15	.25291	**.17902**	.25696	**.18070**	.26098	**.18238**	.26498	**.18407**	.26896	**.18576**	45
+ 4′	9.25298	**.17905**	9.25703	**.18073**	9.26105	**.18241**	9.26505	**.18410**	9.26903	**.18579**	44
17	.25305	**.17908**	.25709	**.18076**	.26112	**.18244**	.26512	**.18413**	.26909	**.18582**	43
18	.25311	**.17911**	.25716	**.18078**	.26118	**.18247**	.26518	**.18415**	.26916	**.18585**	42
19	.25318	**.17914**	.25723	**.18081**	.26125	**.18249**	.26525	**.18418**	.26923	**.18588**	41
+ 5′	9.25325	**.17916**	9.25729	**.18084**	9.26132	**.18252**	9.26532	**.18421**	9.26929	**.18591**	40
21	.25332	**.17919**	.25736	**.18087**	.26138	**.18255**	.26538	**.18424**	.26936	**.18593**	39
22	.25339	**.17922**	.25743	**.18090**	.26145	**.18258**	.26545	**.18427**	.26942	**.18596**	38
23	.25345	**.17925**	.25750	**.18092**	.26152	**.18261**	.26551	**.18430**	.26949	**.18599**	37
+ 6′	9.25352	**.17928**	9.25756	**.18095**	9.26158	**.18263**	9.26558	**.18432**	9.26956	**.18602**	36
25	.25359	**.17930**	.25763	**.18098**	.26165	**.18266**	.26565	**.18435**	.26962	**.18605**	35
26	.25366	**.17933**	.25770	**.18101**	.26172	**.18269**	.26571	**.18438**	.26969	**.18608**	34
27	.25372	**.17936**	.25776	**.18104**	.26178	**.18272**	.26578	**.18441**	.26975	**.18610**	33
+ 7′	9.25379	**.17939**	9.25783	**.18106**	9.26185	**.18275**	9.26585	**.18444**	9.26982	**.18613**	32
29	.25386	**.17941**	.25790	**.18109**	.26192	**.18277**	.26591	**.18446**	.26989	**.18616**	31
30	.25393	**.17944**	.25797	**.18112**	.26198	**.18280**	.26598	**.18449**	.26995	**.18619**	30
31	.25399	**.17947**	.25803	**.18115**	.26205	**.18283**	.26605	**.18452**	.27002	**.18622**	29
+ 8′	9.25406	**.17950**	9.25810	**.18118**	9.26212	**.18286**	9.26611	**.18455**	9.27008	**.18624**	28
33	.25413	**.17953**	.25817	**.18120**	.26218	**.18289**	.26618	**.18458**	.27015	**.18627**	27
34	.25420	**.17955**	.25823	**.18123**	.26225	**.18292**	.26625	**.18461**	.27022	**.18630**	26
35	.25426	**.17958**	.25830	**.18126**	.26232	**.18294**	.26631	**.18463**	.27028	**.18633**	25
+ 9′	9.25433	**.17961**	9.25837	**.18129**	9.26238	**.18297**	9.26638	**.18466**	9.27035	**.18636**	24
37	.25440	**.17964**	.25844	**.18132**	.26245	**.18300**	.26644	**.18469**	.27041	**.18639**	23
38	.25447	**.17967**	.25850	**.18134**	.26252	**.18303**	.26651	**.18472**	.27048	**.18641**	22
39	.25453	**.17969**	.25857	**.18137**	.26259	**.18306**	.26658	**.18475**	.27055	**.18644**	21
+ 10′	9.25460	**.17972**	9.25864	**.18140**	9.26265	**.18308**	9.26664	**.18478**	9.27061	**.18647**	20
41	.25467	**.17975**	.25870	**.18143**	.26272	**.18311**	.26671	**.18480**	.27068	**.18650**	19
42	.25474	**.17978**	.25877	**.18146**	.26279	**.18314**	.26678	**.18483**	.27074	**.18653**	18
43	.25480	**.17981**	.25884	**.18148**	.26285	**.18317**	.26684	**.18486**	.27081	**.18656**	17
+ 11′	9.25487	**.17983**	9.25891	**.18151**	9.26292	**.18320**	9.26691	**.18489**	9.27088	**.18658**	16
45	.25494	**.17986**	.25897	**.18154**	.26299	**.18323**	.26697	**.18492**	.27094	**.18661**	15
46	.25500	**.17989**	.25904	**.18157**	.26305	**.18325**	.26704	**.18494**	.27101	**.18664**	14
47	.25507	**.17992**	.25911	**.18160**	.26312	**.18328**	.26711	**.18497**	.27107	**.18667**	13
+ 12′	9.25514	**.17995**	9.25917	**.18162**	9.26319	**.18331**	9.26717	**.18500**	9.27114	**.18670**	12
49	.25521	**.17997**	.25924	**.18165**	.26325	**.18334**	.26724	**.18503**	.27121	**.18673**	11
50	.25528	**.18000**	.25931	**.18168**	.26332	**.18337**	.26731	**.18506**	.27127	**.18675**	10
51	.25534	**.18003**	.25938	**.18171**	.26339	**.18339**	.26737	**.18509**	.27134	**.18678**	9
+ 13′	9.25541	**.18006**	9.25944	**.18174**	9.26345	**.18342**	9.26744	**.18511**	9.27140	**.18681**	8
53	.25548	**.18008**	.25951	**.18176**	.26352	**.18345**	.26751	**.18514**	.27147	**.18684**	7
54	.25554	**.18011**	.25958	**.18179**	.26359	**.18348**	.26757	**.18517**	.27154	**.18687**	6
55	.25561	**.18014**	.25964	**.18182**	.26365	**.18351**	.26764	**.18520**	.27160	**.18690**	5
+ 14′	9.25568	**.18017**	9.25971	**.18185**	9.26372	**.18353**	9.26770	**.18523**	9.27167	**.18692**	4
57	.25575	**.18020**	.25978	**.18188**	.26378	**.18356**	.26777	**.18526**	.27173	**.18695**	3
58	.25581	**.18022**	.25984	**.18190**	.26385	**.18359**	.26784	**.18528**	.27180	**.18698**	2
59	.25588	**.18025**	.25991	**.18193**	.26392	**.18362**	.26790	**.18531**	.27186	**.18701**	1
+ 15′	9.25595	**.18028**	9.25998	**.18196**	9.26398	**.18365**	9.26797	**.18534**	9.27193	**.18704**	0
	20h 39m		20h 38m		20h 37m		20h 36m		20h 35m		

TABLE 34.

Haversines.

s	3h 25m 51° 15′ Log. Hav.	Nat. Hav.	3h 26m 51° 30′ Log. Hav.	Nat. Hav.	3h 27m 51° 45′ Log. Hav.	Nat. Hav.	3h 28m 52° 0′ Log. Hav.	Nat. Hav.	3h 29m 52° 15′ Log. Hav.	Nat. Hav.	s
0	9.27193	**.18704**	9.27587	**.18874**	9.27979	**.19045**	9.28368	**.19217**	9.28756	**.19389**	60
1	.27200	**.18707**	.27594	**.18877**	.27985	**.19048**	.28375	**.19220**	.28762	**.19392**	59
2	.27206	**.18710**	.27600	**.18880**	.27992	**.19051**	.28381	**.19223**	.28769	**.19395**	58
3	.27213	**.18712**	.27607	**.18883**	.27998	**.19054**	.28388	**.19226**	.28775	**.19398**	57
+ 1′	9.27219	**.18715**	9.27613	**.18886**	9.28005	**.19057**	9.28394	**.19228**	9.28782	**.19401**	56
5	.27226	**.18718**	.27620	**.18888**	.28011	**.19060**	.28401	**.19231**	.28788	**.19404**	55
6	.27233	**.18721**	.27626	**.18891**	.28018	**.19062**	.28407	**.19234**	.28794	**.19406**	54
7	.27239	**.18724**	.27633	**.18894**	.28024	**.19065**	.28414	**.19237**	.28801	**.19409**	53
+ 2′	9.27246	**.18727**	9.27639	**.18897**	9.28031	**.19068**	9.28420	**.19240**	9.28807	**.19412**	52
9	.27252	**.18729**	.27646	**.18900**	.28037	**.19071**	.28427	**.19243**	.28814	**.19415**	51
10	.27259	**.18732**	.27652	**.18903**	.28044	**.19074**	.28433	**.19246**	.28820	**.19418**	50
11	.27265	**.18735**	.27659	**.18906**	.28050	**.19077**	.28440	**.19248**	.28827	**.19421**	49
+ 3′	9.27272	**.18738**	9.27666	**.18908**	9.28057	**.19080**	9.28446	**.19251**	9.28833	**.19424**	48
13	.27279	**.18741**	.27672	**.18912**	.28063	**.19082**	.28453	**.19254**	.28840	**.19427**	47
14	.27285	**.18744**	.27679	**.18914**	.28070	**.19085**	.28459	**.19257**	.28846	**.19429**	46
15	.27292	**.18746**	.27685	**.18917**	.28076	**.19088**	.28465	**.19260**	.28852	**.19432**	45
+ 4′	9.27298	**.18749**	9.27692	**.18920**	9.28083	**.19091**	9.28472	**.19263**	9.28859	**.19435**	44
17	.27305	**.18752**	.27698	**.18923**	.28089	**.19094**	.28478	**.19266**	.28865	**.19438**	43
18	.27311	**.18755**	.27705	**.18926**	.28096	**.19097**	.28485	**.19269**	.28872	**.19441**	42
19	.27318	**.18758**	.27711	**.18928**	.28102	**.19100**	.28491	**.19271**	.28878	**.19444**	41
+ 5′	9.27325	**.18761**	9.27718	**.18931**	9.28109	**.19102**	9.28498	**.19274**	9.28885	**.19447**	40
21	.27331	**.18763**	.27724	**.18934**	.28115	**.19105**	.28504	**.19277**	.28891	**.19450**	39
22	.27338	**.18766**	.27731	**.18937**	.28122	**.19108**	.28511	**.19280**	.28897	**.19452**	38
23	.27344	**.18769**	.27737	**.18940**	.28128	**.19111**	.28517	**.19283**	.28904	**.19455**	37
+ 6′	9.27351	**.18772**	9.27744	**.18943**	9.28135	**.19114**	9.28524	**.19286**	9.28910	**.19458**	36
25	.27357	**.18775**	.27751	**.18945**	.28141	**.19117**	.28530	**.19289**	.28917	**.19461**	35
26	.27364	**.18778**	.27757	**.18948**	.28148	**.19120**	.28537	**.19291**	.28923	**.19464**	34
27	.27371	**.18780**	.27764	**.18951**	.28154	**.19122**	.28543	**.19294**	.28930	**.19467**	33
+ 7′	9.27377	**.18783**	9.27770	**.18954**	9.28161	**.19125**	9.28549	**.19297**	9.28936	**.19470**	32
29	.27384	**.18786**	.27777	**.18957**	.28167	**.19128**	.28556	**.19300**	.28942	**.19473**	31
30	.27390	**.18789**	.27783	**.18960**	.28174	**.19131**	.28562	**.19303**	.28949	**.19475**	30
31	.27397	**.18792**	.27790	**.18963**	.28180	**.19134**	.28569	**.19306**	.28955	**.19478**	29
+ 8′	9.27403	**.18795**	9.27796	**.18965**	9.28187	**.19137**	9.28575	**.19309**	9.28962	**.19481**	28
33	.27410	**.18797**	.27803	**.18968**	.28193	**.19140**	.28582	**.19311**	.28968	**.19484**	27
34	.27417	**.18800**	.27809	**.18971**	.28200	**.19142**	.28588	**.19314**	.28974	**.19487**	26
35	.27423	**.18803**	.27816	**.18974**	.28206	**.19145**	.28595	**.19317**	.28981	**.19490**	25
+ 9′	9.27430	**.18806**	9.27822	**.18977**	9.28213	**.19148**	9.28601	**.19320**	9.28987	**.19493**	24
37	.27436	**.18809**	.27829	**.18980**	.28219	**.19151**	.28608	**.19323**	.28994	**.19496**	23
38	.27443	**.18812**	.27835	**.18983**	.28226	**.19154**	.28614	**.19326**	.29000	**.19499**	22
39	.27449	**.18815**	.27842	**.18985**	.28232	**.19157**	.28620	**.19329**	.29007	**.19501**	21
+ 10′	9.27456	**.18817**	9.27848	**.18988**	9.28239	**.19160**	9.28627	**.19332**	9.29013	**.19504**	20
41	.27463	**.18820**	.27855	**.18991**	.28245	**.19163**	.28633	**.19335**	.29019	**.19507**	19
42	.27469	**.18823**	.27861	**.18994**	.28252	**.19165**	.28640	**.19337**	.29026	**.19510**	18
43	.27476	**.18826**	.27868	**.18997**	.28258	**.19168**	.28646	**.19340**	.29032	**.19513**	17
+ 11′	9.27482	**.18829**	9.27875	**.19000**	9.28265	**.19171**	9.28653	**.19343**	9.29039	**.19516**	16
45	.27489	**.18832**	.27881	**.19002**	.28271	**.19174**	.28659	**.19346**	.29045	**.19519**	15
46	.27495	**.18834**	.27888	**.19005**	.28278	**.19177**	.28666	**.19349**	.29051	**.19522**	14
47	.27502	**.18837**	.27894	**.19008**	.28284	**.19180**	.28672	**.19352**	.29058	**.19524**	13
+ 12′	9.27508	**.18840**	9.27901	**.19011**	9.28291	**.19183**	9.28679	**.19355**	9.29064	**.19527**	12
49	.27515	**.18843**	.27907	**.19014**	.28297	**.19185**	.28685	**.19358**	.29071	**.19530**	11
50	.27522	**.18846**	.27914	**.19017**	.28304	**.19188**	.28691	**.19360**	.29078	**.19533**	10
51	.27528	**.18849**	.27920	**.19020**	.28310	**.19191**	.28698	**.19363**	.29084	**.19536**	9
+ 13′	9.27535	**.18852**	9.27927	**.19022**	9.28317	**.19194**	9.28704	**.19366**	9.29090	**.19539**	8
53	.27541	**.18854**	.27933	**.19025**	.28323	**.19197**	.28711	**.19369**	.29096	**.19542**	7
54	.27548	**.18857**	.27940	**.19028**	.28330	**.19200**	.28717	**.19372**	.29103	**.19545**	6
55	.27554	**.18860**	.27946	**.19031**	.28336	**.19203**	.28724	**.19375**	.29109	**.19548**	5
+ 14′	9.27561	**.18863**	9.27953	**.19034**	9.28342	**.19205**	9.28730	**.19378**	9.29116	**.19550**	4
57	.27567	**.18866**	.27959	**.19037**	.28349	**.19208**	.28737	**.19381**	.29122	**.19553**	3
58	.27574	**.18869**	.27966	**.19040**	.28355	**.19211**	.28743	**.19383**	.29128	**.19556**	2
59	.27580	**.18871**	.27972	**.19042**	.28362	**.19214**	.28749	**.19386**	.29135	**.19559**	1
+ 15′	9.27587	**.18874**	9.27979	**.19045**	9.28368	**.19217**	9.28756	**.19389**	9.29141	**.19562**	0
	20h 34m		20h 33m		20h 32m		20h 31m		20h 30m		

TABLE 34.

Haversines.

s	$3^h\ 30^m$ 52° 30′		$3^h\ 31^m$ 52° 45′		$3^h\ 32^m$ 53° 0′		$3^h\ 33^m$ 53° 15′		$3^h\ 34^m$ 53° 30′		s
	Log. Hav.	Nat. Hav.	Log. Hav.	Nat. Hav.	Log. Hav.	Nat. Hav.	Log. Hav.	Nat. Hav.	Log. Hav.	Nat. Hav.	
0	9.29141	**.19562**	9.29524	**.19735**	9.29906	**.19909**	9.30285	**.20084**	9.30662	**.20259**	60
1	.29148	**.19565**	.29531	**.19738**	.29912	**.19912**	.30291	**.20087**	.30668	**.20262**	59
2	.29154	**.19568**	.29537	**.19741**	.29918	**.19915**	.30297	**.20090**	.30674	**.20265**	58
3	.29160	**.19571**	.29543	**.19744**	.29925	**.19918**	.30303	**.20093**	.30680	**.20268**	57
+ 1′	9.29167	**.19573**	9.29550	**.19747**	9.29931	**.19921**	9.30310	**.20095**	9.30687	**.20271**	56
5	.29173	**.19576**	.29556	**.19750**	.29937	**.19924**	.30316	**.20098**	.30693	**.20273**	55
6	.29180	**.19579**	.29563	**.19753**	.29943	**.19927**	.30322	**.20101**	.30699	**.20276**	54
7	.29186	**.19582**	.29569	**.19756**	.29950	**.19930**	.30329	**.20104**	.30705	**.20279**	53
+ 2′	9.29192	**.19585**	9.29575	**.19758**	9.29956	**.19932**	9.30335	**.20107**	9.30712	**.20282**	52
9	.29199	**.19588**	.29582	**.19761**	.29962	**.19935**	.30341	**.20110**	.30718	**.20285**	51
10	.29205	**.19591**	.29588	**.19764**	.29969	**.19938**	.30348	**.20113**	.30724	**.20288**	50
11	.29212	**.19594**	.29594	**.19767**	.29975	**.19941**	.30354	**.20116**	.30730	**.20291**	49
+ 3′	9.29218	**.19597**	9.29601	**.19770**	9.29981	**.19944**	9.30360	**.20119**	9.30737	**.20294**	48
13	.29224	**.19599**	.29607	**.19773**	.29988	**.19947**	.30366	**.20122**	.30743	**.20297**	47
14	.29231	**.19602**	.29614	**.19776**	.29994	**.19950**	.30373	**.20125**	.30749	**.20300**	46
15	.29237	**.19605**	.29620	**.19779**	.30000	**.19953**	.30379	**.20127**	.30755	**.20303**	45
+ 4′	9.29244	**.19608**	9.29626	**.19782**	9.30007	**.19956**	9.30385	**.20130**	9.30762	**.20306**	44
17	.29250	**.19611**	.29633	**.19785**	.30013	**.19959**	.30392	**.20133**	.30768	**.20309**	43
18	.29256	**.19614**	.29639	**.19787**	.30019	**.19962**	.30398	**.20136**	.30774	**.20312**	42
19	.29263	**.19617**	.29645	**.19790**	.30026	**.19964**	.30404	**.20139**	.30780	**.20314**	41
+ 5′	9.29269	**.19620**	9.29652	**.19793**	9.30032	**.19967**	9.30410	**.20142**	9.30787	**.20317**	40
21	.29276	**.19623**	.29658	**.19796**	.30038	**.19970**	.30417	**.20145**	.30793	**.20320**	39
22	.29282	**.19625**	.29664	**.19799**	.30045	**.19973**	.30423	**.20148**	.30799	**.20323**	38
23	.29288	**.19628**	.29671	**.19802**	.30051	**.19976**	.30429	**.20151**	.30805	**.20326**	37
+ 6′	9.29295	**.19631**	9.29677	**.19805**	9.30057	**.19979**	9.30436	**.20154**	9.30812	**.20329**	36
25	.29301	**.19634**	.29683	**.19808**	.30064	**.19982**	.30442	**.20157**	.30818	**.20332**	35
26	.29307	**.19637**	.29690	**.19811**	.30070	**.19985**	.30448	**.20160**	.30824	**.20335**	34
27	.29314	**.19640**	.29696	**.19814**	.30076	**.19988**	.30454	**.20162**	.30830	**.20338**	33
+ 7′	9.29320	**.19643**	9.29703	**.19816**	9.30083	**.19991**	9.30461	**.20165**	9.30837	**.20341**	32
29	.29327	**.19646**	.29709	**.19819**	.30089	**.19994**	.30467	**.20168**	.30843	**.20344**	31
30	.29333	**.19649**	.29715	**.19822**	.30095	**.19996**	.30473	**.20171**	.30849	**.20347**	30
31	.29339	**.19651**	.29722	**.19825**	.30102	**.19999**	.30480	**.20174**	.30855	**.20350**	29
+ 8′	9.29346	**.19654**	9.29728	**.19828**	9.30108	**.20002**	9.30486	**.20177**	9.30862	**.20352**	28
33	.29352	**.19657**	.29734	**.19831**	.30114	**.20005**	.30492	**.20180**	.30868	**.20355**	27
34	.29359	**.19660**	.29741	**.19834**	.30121	**.20008**	.30498	**.20183**	.30874	**.20358**	26
35	.29365	**.19663**	.29747	**.19837**	.30127	**.20011**	.30505	**.20186**	.30880	**.20361**	25
+ 9′	9.29371	**.19666**	9.29753	**.19840**	9.30133	**.20014**	9.30511	**.20189**	9.30887	**.20364**	24
37	.29378	**.19669**	.29760	**.19842**	.30139	**.20017**	.30517	**.20192**	.30893	**.20367**	23
38	.29384	**.19672**	.29766	**.19845**	.30146	**.20020**	.30524	**.20195**	.30899	**.20370**	22
39	.29391	**.19675**	.29772	**.19848**	.30152	**.20023**	.30530	**.20198**	.30905	**.20373**	21
+ 10′	9.29397	**.19677**	9.29779	**.19851**	9.30158	**.20026**	9.30536	**.20200**	9.30912	**.20376**	20
41	.29403	**.19680**	.29785	**.19854**	.30165	**.20028**	.30542	**.20203**	.30918	**.20379**	19
42	.29410	**.19683**	.29791	**.19857**	.30171	**.20031**	.30549	**.20206**	.30924	**.20382**	18
43	.29416	**.19686**	.29798	**.19860**	.30177	**.20034**	.30555	**.20209**	.30930	**.20385**	17
+ 11′	9.29422	**.19689**	9.29804	**.19863**	9.30184	**.20037**	9.30561	**.20212**	9.30937	**.20388**	16
45	.29429	**.19692**	.29810	**.19866**	.30190	**.20040**	.30567	**.20215**	.30943	**.20391**	15
46	.29435	**.19695**	.29817	**.19869**	.30196	**.20043**	.30574	**.20218**	.30949	**.20393**	14
47	.29442	**.19698**	.29823	**.19872**	.30203	**.20046**	.30580	**.20221**	.30955	**.20396**	13
+ 12′	9.29448	**.19701**	9.29829	**.19874**	9.30209	**.20049**	9.30586	**.20224**	9.30962	**.20399**	12
49	.29454	**.19703**	.29836	**.19877**	.30215	**.20052**	.30593	**.20227**	.30968	**.20402**	11
50	.29461	**.19706**	.29842	**.19880**	.30222	**.20055**	.30599	**.20230**	.30974	**.20405**	10
51	.29467	**.19709**	.29848	**.19883**	.30228	**.20058**	.30605	**.20233**	.30980	**.20408**	9
+ 13′	9.29473	**.19712**	9.29855	**.19886**	9.30234	**.20060**	9.30611	**.20235**	9.30987	**.20411**	8
53	.29480	**.19715**	.29861	**.19889**	.30240	**.20063**	.30618	**.20238**	.30993	**.20414**	7
54	.29486	**.19718**	.29867	**.19892**	.30247	**.20066**	.30624	**.20241**	.30999	**.20417**	6
55	.29493	**.19721**	.29874	**.19895**	.30253	**.20069**	.30630	**.20244**	.31005	**.20420**	5
+ 14′	9.29499	**.19724**	9.29880	**.19898**	9.30259	**.20072**	9.30636	**.20247**	9.31012	**.20423**	4
57	.29505	**.19727**	.29886	**.19901**	.30266	**.20075**	.30643	**.20250**	.31018	**.20426**	3
58	.29512	**.19730**	.29893	**.19903**	.30272	**.20078**	.30649	**.20253**	.31024	**.20429**	2
59	.29518	**.19732**	.29899	**.19906**	.30278	**.20081**	.30655	**.20256**	.31030	**.20432**	1
+ 15′	9.29524	**.19735**	9.29906	**.19909**	9.30285	**.20084**	9.30662	**.20259**	9.31036	**.20435**	0
	$20^h\ 29^m$		$20^h\ 28^m$		$20^h\ 27^m$		$20^h\ 26^m$		$20^h\ 25^m$		

TABLE 34.

Haversines.

s	3h 35m 53° 45′		3h 36m 54° 0′		3h 37m 54° 15′		3h 38m 54° 30′		3h 39m 54° 45′		s
	Log. Hav.	Nat. Hav.	Log. Hav.	Nat. Hav.	Log. Hav.	Nat. Hav.	Log. Hav.	Nat. Hav.	Log. Hav.	Nat. Hav.	
0	9.31036	**.20435**	9.31409	**.20611**	9.31780	**.20788**	9.32149	**.20965**	9.32516	**.21143**	60
1	.31043	**.20437**	.31416	**.20614**	.31786	**.20790**	.32155	**.20968**	.32522	**.21146**	59
2	.31049	**.20440**	.31422	**.20617**	.31793	**.20793**	.32161	**.20971**	.32528	**.21149**	58
3	.31055	**.20443**	.31428	**.20620**	.31799	**.20796**	.32168	**.20974**	.32534	**.21152**	57
+ 1′	9.31061	**.20446**	9.31434	**.20623**	9.31805	**.20799**	9.32174	**.20977**	9.32541	**.21155**	56
5	.31068	**.20449**	.31440	**.20626**	.31811	**.20802**	.32180	**.20980**	.32547	**.21158**	55
6	.31074	**.20452**	.31447	**.20629**	.31817	**.20805**	.32186	**.20983**	.32553	**.21161**	54
7	.31080	**.20455**	.31453	**.20631**	.31823	**.20808**	.32192	**.20986**	.32559	**.21164**	53
+ 2′	9.31086	**.20458**	9.31459	**.20634**	9.31830	**.20811**	9.32198	**.20989**	9.32565	**.21167**	52
9	.31093	**.20461**	.31465	**.20637**	.31836	**.20814**	.32204	**.20991**	.32571	**.21169**	51
10	.31099	**.20464**	.31471	**.20640**	.31842	**.20817**	.32210	**.20994**	.32577	**.21172**	50
11	.31105	**.20467**	.31478	**.20643**	.31848	**.20820**	.32217	**.20997**	.32583	**.21175**	49
+ 3′	9.31111	**.20470**	9.31484	**.20646**	9.31854	**.20823**	9.32223	**.21000**	9.32589	**.21178**	48
13	.31117	**.20473**	.31490	**.20649**	.31860	**.20826**	.32229	**.21003**	.32595	**.21181**	47
14	.31124	**.20476**	.31496	**.20652**	.31867	**.20829**	.32235	**.21006**	.32601	**.21184**	46
15	.31130	**.20479**	.31502	**.20655**	.31873	**.20832**	.32241	**.21009**	.32608	**.21187**	45
+ 4′	9.31136	**.20481**	9.31508	**.20658**	9.31879	**.20835**	9.32247	**.21012**	9.32614	**.21190**	44
17	.31142	**.20484**	.31515	**.20661**	.31885	**.20838**	.32253	**.21015**	.32620	**.21193**	43
18	.31149	**.20487**	.31521	**.20664**	.31891	**.20841**	.32259	**.21018**	.32626	**.21196**	42
19	.31155	**.20490**	.31527	**.20667**	.31897	**.20844**	.32266	**.21021**	.32632	**.21199**	41
+ 5′	9.31161	**.20493**	9.31533	**.20670**	9.31903	**.20847**	9.32272	**.21024**	9.32638	**.21202**	40
21	.31167	**.20496**	.31539	**.20673**	.31910	**.20850**	.32278	**.21027**	.32644	**.21205**	39
22	.31173	**.20499**	.31546	**.20675**	.31916	**.20852**	.32284	**.21030**	.32650	**.21208**	38
23	.31180	**.20502**	.31552	**.20678**	.31922	**.20855**	.32290	**.21033**	.32656	**.21211**	37
+ 6′	9.31186	**.20505**	9.31558	**.20681**	9.31928	**.20858**	9.32296	**.21036**	9.32662	**.21214**	36
25	.31192	**.20508**	.31564	**.20684**	.31934	**.20861**	.32302	**.21039**	.32668	**.21217**	35
26	.31198	**.20511**	.31570	**.20687**	.31940	**.20864**	.32308	**.21042**	.32675	**.21220**	34
27	.31205	**.20514**	.31577	**.20690**	.31947	**.20867**	.32315	**.21045**	.32681	**.21223**	33
+ 7′	9.31211	**.20517**	9.31583	**.20693**	9.31953	**.20870**	9.32321	**.21048**	9.32687	**.21226**	32
29	.31217	**.20520**	.31589	**.20696**	.31959	**.20873**	.32327	**.21051**	.32693	**.21229**	31
30	.31223	**.20523**	.31595	**.20699**	.31965	**.20876**	.32333	**.21054**	.32699	**.21232**	30
31	.31229	**.20525**	.31601	**.20702**	.31971	**.20879**	.32339	**.21057**	.32705	**.21235**	29
+ 8′	9.31236	**.20528**	9.31607	**.20705**	9.31977	**.20882**	9.32345	**.21060**	9.32711	**.21238**	28
33	.31242	**.20531**	.31614	**.20708**	.31983	**.20885**	.32351	**.21063**	.32717	**.21241**	27
34	.31248	**.20534**	.31620	**.20711**	.31990	**.20888**	.32357	**.21066**	.32723	**.21244**	26
35	.31254	**.20537**	.31626	**.20714**	.31996	**.20891**	.32363	**.21069**	.32729	**.21247**	25
+ 9′	9.31260	**.20540**	9.31632	**.20717**	9.32002	**.20894**	9.32370	**.21072**	9.32735	**.21250**	24
37	.31267	**.20543**	.31638	**.20720**	.32008	**.20897**	.32376	**.21074**	.32741	**.21253**	23
38	.31273	**.20546**	.31644	**.20723**	.32014	**.20900**	.32382	**.21077**	.32748	**.21256**	22
39	.31279	**.20549**	.31651	**.20726**	.32020	**.20903**	.32388	**.21080**	.32754	**.21259**	21
+ 10′	9.31285	**.20552**	9.31657	**.20729**	9.32026	**.20906**	9.32394	**.21083**	9.32760	**.21262**	20
41	.31291	**.20555**	.31663	**.20731**	.32033	**.20909**	.32400	**.21086**	.32766	**.21265**	19
42	.31298	**.20558**	.31669	**.20734**	.32039	**.20912**	.32406	**.21089**	.32772	**.21268**	18
43	.31304	**.20561**	.31675	**.20737**	.32045	**.20915**	.32412	**.21092**	.32778	**.21271**	17
+ 11′	9.31310	**.20564**	9.31682	**.20740**	9.32051	**.20918**	9.32418	**.21095**	9.32784	**.21274**	16
45	.31316	**.20567**	.31688	**.20743**	.32057	**.20920**	.32425	**.21098**	.32790	**.21277**	15
46	.31323	**.20570**	.31694	**.20746**	.32063	**.20923**	.32431	**.21101**	.32796	**.21280**	14
47	.31329	**.20573**	.31700	**.20749**	.32069	**.20926**	.32437	**.21104**	.32802	**.21282**	13
+ 12′	9.31335	**.20575**	9.31706	**.20752**	9.32076	**.20929**	9.32443	**.21107**	9.32808	**.21285**	12
49	.31341	**.20578**	.31712	**.20755**	.32082	**.20932**	.32449	**.21110**	.32814	**.21288**	11
50	.31347	**.20581**	.31719	**.20758**	.32088	**.20935**	.32455	**.21113**	.32820	**.21291**	10
51	.31354	**.20584**	.31725	**.20761**	.32094	**.20938**	.32461	**.21116**	.32827	**.21294**	9
+ 13′	9.31360	**.20587**	9.31731	**.20764**	9.32100	**.20941**	9.32467	**.21119**	9.32833	**.21297**	8
53	.31366	**.20590**	.31737	**.20767**	.32106	**.20944**	.32473	**.21122**	.32839	**.21300**	7
54	.31372	**.20593**	.31743	**.20770**	.32112	**.20947**	.32480	**.21125**	.32845	**.21303**	6
55	.31378	**.20596**	.31749	**.20773**	.32119	**.20950**	.32486	**.21128**	.32851	**.21306**	5
+ 14′	9.31385	**.20599**	9.31756	**.20776**	9.32125	**.20953**	9.32492	**.21131**	9.32857	**.21309**	4
57	.31391	**.20602**	.31762	**.20779**	.32131	**.20956**	.32498	**.21134**	.32863	**.21312**	3
58	.31397	**.20605**	.31768	**.20782**	.32137	**.20959**	.32504	**.21137**	.32869	**.21315**	2
59	.31403	**.20608**	.31774	**.20785**	.32143	**.20962**	.32510	**.21140**	.32875	**.21318**	1
+ 15′	9.31409	**.20611**	9.31780	**.20788**	9.32149	**.20965**	9.32516	**.21143**	9.32881	**.21321**	0
	20h 24m		20h 23m		20h 22m		20h 21m		20h 20m		

TABLE 34.

Haversines.

	3h 40m **55° 0′**		*3h 41m* **55° 15′**		*3h 42m* **55° 30′**		*3h 43m* **55° 45′**		*3h 44m* **56° 0′**		
s	Log. Hav.	Nat. Hav.	Log. Hav.	Nat. Hav.	Log. Hav.	Nat. Hav.	Log. Hav.	Nat. Hav.	Log. Hav.	Nat. Hav.	s
0	9.32881	**.21321**	9.33244	**.21500**	9.33605	**.21680**	9.33965	**.21860**	9.34322	**.22040**	*60*
1	.32887	**.21324**	.33250	**.21503**	.33611	**.21683**	.33971	**.21863**	.34328	**.22043**	*59*
2	.32893	**.21327**	.33256	**.21506**	.33617	**.21686**	.33976	**.21866**	.34334	**.22046**	*58*
3	.32899	**.21330**	.33262	**.21509**	.33623	**.21689**	.33982	**.21869**	.34340	**.22049**	*57*
+ **1′**	9.32905	**.21333**	9.33268	**.21512**	9.33629	**.21692**	9.33988	**.21872**	9.34346	**.22052**	*56*
5	.32911	**.21336**	.33274	**.21515**	.33635	**.21695**	.33994	**.21875**	.34352	**.22055**	*55*
6	.32918	**.21339**	.33280	**.21518**	.33641	**.21698**	.34000	**.21878**	.34358	**.22058**	*54*
7	.32924	**.21342**	.33286	**.21521**	.33647	**.21701**	.34006	**.21881**	.34363	**.22061**	*53*
+ **2′**	9.32930	**.21345**	9.33292	**.21524**	9.33653	**.21704**	9.34012	**.21884**	9.34369	**.22064**	*52*
9	.32936	**.21348**	.33298	**.21527**	.33659	**.21707**	.34018	**.21887**	.34375	**.22067**	*51*
10	.32942	**.21351**	.33305	**.21530**	.33665	**.21710**	.34024	**.21890**	.34381	**.22071**	*50*
11	.32948	**.21354**	.33311	**.21533**	.33671	**.21713**	.34030	**.21893**	.34387	**.22074**	*49*
+ **3′**	9.32954	**.21357**	9.33317	**.21536**	9.33677	**.21716**	9.34036	**.21896**	9.34393	**.22077**	*48*
13	.32960	**.21360**	.33323	**.21539**	.33683	**.21719**	.34042	**.21899**	.34399	**.22080**	*47*
14	.32966	**.21363**	.33329	**.21542**	.33689	**.21722**	.34048	**.21902**	.34405	**.22083**	*46*
15	.32972	**.21366**	.33335	**.21545**	.33695	**.21725**	.34054	**.21905**	.34411	**.22086**	*45*
+ **4′**	9.32978	**.21369**	9.33341	**.21548**	9.33701	**.21728**	9.34060	**.21908**	9.34417	**.22089**	*44*
17	.32984	**.21372**	.33347	**.21551**	.33707	**.21731**	.34066	**.21911**	.34423	**.22092**	*43*
18	.32990	**.21375**	.33353	**.21554**	.33713	**.21734**	.34072	**.21914**	.34429	**.22095**	*42*
19	.32996	**.21378**	.33359	**.21557**	.33719	**.21737**	.34078	**.21917**	.34435	**.22098**	*41*
+ **5′**	9.33002	**.21381**	9.33365	**.21560**	9.33725	**.21740**	9.34084	**.21920**	9.34441	**.22101**	*40*
21	.33008	**.21384**	.33371	**.21563**	.33731	**.21743**	.34090	**.21923**	.34446	**.22104**	*39*
22	.33014	**.21387**	.33377	**.21566**	.33737	**.21746**	.34096	**.21926**	.34452	**.22107**	*38*
23	.33021	**.21390**	.33383	**.21569**	.33743	**.21749**	.34102	**.21929**	.34458	**.22110**	*37*
+ **6′**	9.33027	**.21393**	9.33389	**.21572**	9.33749	**.21752**	9.34108	**.21932**	9.34464	**.22113**	*36*
25	.33033	**.21396**	.33395	**.21575**	.33755	**.21755**	.34114	**.21935**	.34470	**.22116**	*35*
26	.33039	**.21399**	.33401	**.21578**	.33761	**.21758**	.34120	**.21938**	.34476	**.22119**	*34*
27	.33045	**.21402**	.33407	**.21581**	.33767	**.21761**	.34126	**.21941**	.34482	**.22122**	*33*
+ **7′**	9.33051	**.21405**	9.33413	**.21584**	9.33773	**.21764**	9.34132	**.21944**	9.34488	**.22125**	*32*
29	.33057	**.21408**	.33419	**.21587**	.33779	**.21767**	.34137	**.21947**	.34494	**.22128**	*31*
30	.33063	**.21411**	.33425	**.21590**	.33785	**.21770**	.34143	**.21950**	.34500	**.22131**	*30*
31	.33069	**.21414**	.33431	**.21593**	.33791	**.21773**	.34149	**.21953**	.34506	**.22134**	*29*
+ **8′**	9.33075	**.21417**	9.33437	**.21596**	9.33797	**.21776**	9.34155	**.21956**	9.34512	**.22137**	*28*
33	.33081	**.21420**	.33443	**.21599**	.33803	**.21779**	.34161	**.21959**	.34518	**.22140**	*27*
34	.33087	**.21423**	.33449	**.21602**	.33809	**.21782**	.34167	**.21962**	.34524	**.22143**	*26*
35	.33093	**.21426**	.33455	**.21605**	.33815	**.21785**	.34173	**.21965**	.34529	**.22146**	*25*
+ **9′**	9.33099	**.21429**	9.33461	**.21608**	9.33821	**.21788**	9.34179	**.21968**	9.34535	**.22149**	*24*
37	.33105	**.21431**	.33467	**.21611**	.33827	**.21791**	.34185	**.21971**	.34541	**.22152**	*23*
38	.33111	**.21434**	.33473	**.21614**	.33833	**.21794**	.34191	**.21974**	.34547	**.22155**	*22*
39	.33117	**.21437**	.33479	**.21617**	.33839	**.21797**	.34197	**.21977**	.34553	**.22158**	*21*
+ **10′**	9.33123	**.21440**	9.33485	**.21620**	9.33845	**.21800**	9.34203	**.21980**	9.34559	**.22161**	*20*
41	.33129	**.21443**	.33491	**.21623**	.33851	**.21803**	.34209	**.21983**	.34565	**.22164**	*19*
42	.33135	**.21446**	.33497	**.21626**	.33857	**.21806**	.34215	**.21986**	.34571	**.22167**	*18*
43	.33142	**.21449**	.33503	**.21629**	.33863	**.21809**	.34221	**.21989**	.34577	**.22170**	*17*
+ **11′**	9.33148	**.21452**	9.33509	**.21632**	9.33869	**.21812**	9.34227	**.21992**	9.34583	**.22173**	*16*
45	.33154	**.21455**	.33515	**.21635**	.33875	**.21815**	.34233	**.21995**	.34589	**.22176**	*15*
46	.33160	**.21458**	.33521	**.21638**	.33881	**.21818**	.34239	**.21998**	.34595	**.22179**	*14*
47	.33166	**.21461**	.33527	**.21641**	.33887	**.21821**	.34245	**.22001**	.34600	**.22182**	*13*
+ **12′**	9.33172	**.21464**	9.33533	**.21644**	9.33893	**.21824**	9.34251	**.22004**	9.34606	**.22185**	*12*
49	.33178	**.21467**	.33539	**.21647**	.33899	**.21827**	.34256	**.22007**	.34612	**.22188**	*11*
50	.33184	**.21470**	.33545	**.21650**	.33905	**.21830**	.34262	**.22010**	.34618	**.22191**	*10*
51	.33190	**.21473**	.33551	**.21653**	.33911	**.21833**	.34268	**.22013**	.34624	**.22194**	*9*
+ **13′**	9.33196	**.21476**	9.33557	**.21656**	9.33917	**.21836**	9.34274	**.22016**	9.34630	**.22197**	*8*
53	.33202	**.21479**	.33563	**.21659**	.33923	**.21839**	.34280	**.22019**	.34636	**.22200**	*7*
54	.33208	**.21482**	.33569	**.21662**	.33929	**.21842**	.34286	**.22022**	.34642	**.22203**	*6*
55	.33214	**.21485**	.33575	**.21665**	.33935	**.21845**	.34292	**.22025**	.34648	**.22206**	*5*
+ **14′**	9.33220	**.21488**	9.33581	**.21668**	9.33941	**.21848**	9.34298	**.22028**	9.34654	**.22209**	*4*
57	.33226	**.21491**	.33587	**.21671**	.33947	**.21851**	.34304	**.22031**	.34660	**.22212**	*3*
58	.33232	**.21494**	.33593	**.21674**	.33953	**.21854**	.34310	**.22034**	.34666	**.22215**	*2*
59	.33238	**.21497**	.33599	**.21677**	.33959	**.21857**	.34316	**.22037**	.34671	**.22218**	*1*
+ **15′**	9.33244	**.21500**	9.33605	**.21680**	9.33965	**.21860**	9.34322	**.22040**	9.34677	**.22221**	*0*
	20h 19m		*20h 18m*		*20h 17m*		*20h 16m*		*20h 15m*		

TABLE 34.

Haversines.

s	3h 45m 56° 15′		3h 46m 56° 30′		3h 47m 56° 45′		3h 48m 57° 0′		3h 49m 57° 15′		s
	Log. Hav.	Nat. Hav.	Log. Hav.	Nat. Hav.	Log. Hav.	Nat. Hav.	Log. Hav.	Nat. Hav.	Log. Hav.	Nat. Hav.	
0	9.34677	**.22221**	9.35031	**.22403**	9.35383	**.22585**	9.35733	**.22768**	9.36081	**.22951**	60
1	.34683	**.22225**	.35037	**.22406**	.35389	**.22588**	.35738	**.22771**	.36086	**.22954**	59
2	.34689	**.22228**	.35043	**.22409**	.35394	**.22591**	.35744	**.22774**	.36092	**.22957**	58
3	.34695	**.22231**	.35049	**.22412**	.35400	**.22594**	.35750	**.22777**	.36098	**.22960**	57
+ 1′	9.34701	**.22234**	9.35054	**.22415**	9.35406	**.22598**	9.35756	**.22780**	9.36104	**.22964**	56
5	.34707	**.22237**	.35060	**.22418**	.35412	**.22601**	.35762	**.22783**	.36110	**.22967**	55
6	.34713	**.22240**	.35066	**.22421**	.35418	**.22604**	.35767	**.22786**	.36115	**.22970**	54
7	.34719	**.22243**	.35072	**.22424**	.35424	**.22607**	.35773	**.22789**	.36121	**.22973**	53
+ 2′	9.34725	**.22246**	9.35078	**.22427**	9.35429	**.22610**	9.35779	**.22792**	9.36127	**.22976**	52
9	.34730	**.22249**	.35084	**.22430**	.35435	**.22613**	.35785	**.22795**	.36133	**.22979**	51
10	.34736	**.22252**	.35090	**.22433**	.35441	**.22616**	.35791	**.22799**	.36139	**.22982**	50
11	.34742	**.22255**	.35096	**.22437**	.35447	**.22619**	.35797	**.22802**	.36144	**.22985**	49
+ 3′	9.34748	**.22258**	9.35101	**.22440**	9.35453	**.22622**	9.35802	**.22805**	9.36150	**.22988**	48
13	.34754	**.22261**	.35107	**.22443**	.35459	**.22625**	.35808	**.22808**	.36156	**.22991**	47
14	.34760	**.22264**	.35113	**.22446**	.35464	**.22628**	.35814	**.22811**	.36162	**.22994**	46
15	.34766	**.22267**	.35119	**.22449**	.35470	**.22631**	.35820	**.22814**	.36167	**.22997**	45
+ 4′	9.34772	**.22270**	9.35125	**.22452**	9.35476	**.22634**	9.35826	**.22817**	9.36173	**.23000**	44
17	.34778	**.22273**	.35131	**.22455**	.35482	**.22637**	.35831	**.22820**	.36179	**.23003**	43
18	.34784	**.22276**	.35137	**.22458**	.35488	**.22640**	.35837	**.22823**	.36185	**.23006**	42
19	.34789	**.22279**	.35143	**.22461**	.35494	**.22643**	.35843	**.22826**	.36191	**.23009**	41
+ 5′	9.34795	**.22282**	9.35148	**.22464**	9.35500	**.22646**	9.35849	**.22829**	9.36196	**.23012**	40
21	.34801	**.22285**	.35154	**.22467**	.35505	**.22649**	.35855	**.22832**	.36202	**.23016**	39
22	.34807	**.22288**	.35160	**.22470**	.35511	**.22652**	.35860	**.22835**	.36208	**.23019**	38
23	.34813	**.22291**	.35166	**.22473**	.35517	**.22655**	.35866	**.22838**	.36214	**.23022**	37
+ 6′	9.34819	**.22294**	9.35172	**.22476**	9.35523	**.22658**	9.35872	**.22841**	9.36219	**.23025**	36
25	.34825	**.22297**	.35178	**.22479**	.35529	**.22661**	.35878	**.22844**	.36225	**.23028**	35
26	.34831	**.22300**	.35184	**.22482**	.35535	**.22664**	.35884	**.22847**	.36231	**.23031**	34
27	.34837	**.22303**	.35189	**.22485**	.35540	**.22667**	.35889	**.22850**	.36237	**.23034**	33
+ 7′	9.34843	**.22306**	9.35195	**.22488**	9.35546	**.22671**	9.35895	**.22853**	9.36243	**.23037**	32
29	.34848	**.22309**	.35201	**.22491**	.35552	**.22674**	.35901	**.22857**	.36248	**.23040**	31
30	.34854	**.22312**	.35207	**.22494**	.35558	**.22677**	.35907	**.22860**	.36254	**.23043**	30
31	.34860	**.22315**	.35213	**.22497**	.35564	**.22680**	.35913	**.22863**	.36260	**.23046**	29
+ 8′	9.34866	**.22318**	9.35219	**.22500**	9.35570	**.22683**	9.35918	**.22866**	9.36266	**.23049**	28
33	.34872	**.22321**	.35225	**.22503**	.35575	**.22686**	.35924	**.22869**	.36271	**.23052**	27
34	.34878	**.22324**	.35230	**.22506**	.35581	**.22689**	.35930	**.22872**	.36277	**.23055**	26
35	.34884	**.22327**	.35236	**.22509**	.35587	**.22692**	.35936	**.22875**	.36283	**.23058**	25
+ 9′	9.34890	**.22330**	9.35242	**.22512**	9.35593	**.22695**	9.35942	**.22878**	9.36289	**.23061**	24
37	.34896	**.22333**	.35248	**.22515**	.35599	**.22698**	.35947	**.22881**	.36294	**.23065**	23
38	.34901	**.22336**	.35254	**.22518**	.35604	**.22701**	.35953	**.22884**	.36300	**.23068**	22
39	.34907	**.22340**	.35260	**.22522**	.35610	**.22704**	.35959	**.22887**	.36306	**.23071**	21
+ 10′	9.34913	**.22343**	9.35266	**.22525**	9.35616	**.22707**	9.35965	**.22890**	9.36312	**.23074**	20
41	.34919	**.22346**	.35271	**.22528**	.35622	**.22710**	.35971	**.22893**	.36318	**.23077**	19
42	.34925	**.22349**	.35277	**.22531**	.35628	**.22713**	.35976	**.22896**	.36323	**.23080**	18
43	.34931	**.22352**	.35283	**.22534**	.35634	**.22716**	.35982	**.22899**	.36329	**.23083**	17
+ 11′	9.34937	**.22355**	9.35289	**.22537**	9.35639	**.22719**	9.35988	**.22902**	9.36335	**.23086**	16
45	.34943	**.22358**	.35295	**.22540**	.35645	**.22722**	.35994	**.22905**	.36341	**.23089**	15
46	.34949	**.22361**	.35301	**.22543**	.35651	**.22725**	.36000	**.22908**	.36346	**.23092**	14
47	.34954	**.22364**	.35307	**.22546**	.35657	**.22728**	.36005	**.22912**	.36352	**.23095**	13
+ 12′	9.34960	**.22367**	9.35312	**.22549**	9.35663	**.22731**	9.36011	**.22915**	9.36358	**.23098**	12
49	.34966	**.22370**	.35318	**.22552**	.35669	**.22735**	.36017	**.22918**	.36364	**.23101**	11
50	.34972	**.22373**	.35324	**.22555**	.35674	**.22738**	.36023	**.22921**	.36369	**.23104**	10
51	.34978	**.22376**	.35330	**.22558**	.35680	**.22741**	.36029	**.22924**	.36375	**.23107**	9
+ 13′	9.34984	**.22379**	9.35336	**.22561**	9.35686	**.22744**	9.36034	**.22927**	9.36381	**.23110**	8
53	.34990	**.22382**	.35342	**.22564**	.35692	**.22747**	.36040	**.22930**	.36387	**.23114**	7
54	.34996	**.22385**	.35348	**.22567**	.35698	**.22750**	.36046	**.22933**	.36392	**.23117**	6
55	.35002	**.22388**	.35353	**.22570**	.35703	**.22753**	.36052	**.22936**	.36398	**.23120**	5
+ 14′	9.35007	**.22391**	9.35359	**.22573**	9.35709	**.22756**	9.36058	**.22939**	9.36404	**.23123**	4
57	.35013	**.22394**	.35365	**.22576**	.35715	**.22759**	.36063	**.22942**	.36410	**.23126**	3
58	.35019	**.22397**	.35371	**.22579**	.35721	**.22762**	.36069	**.22945**	.36415	**.23129**	2
59	.35025	**.22400**	.35377	**.22582**	.35727	**.22765**	.36075	**.22948**	.36421	**.23132**	1
+ 15′	9.35031	**.22403**	9.35383	**.22585**	9.35733	**.22768**	9.36081	**.22951**	9.36427	**.23135**	0
	20h 14m		20h 13m		20h 12m		20h 11m		20h 10m		

541524°—43——45

TABLE 34.

Haversines.

	$3^h\ 50^m$ 57° 30′		$3^h\ 51^m$ 57° 45′		$3^h\ 52^m$ 58° 0′		$3^h\ 53^m$ 58° 15′		$3^h\ 54^m$ 58° 30′		
s	Log. Hav.	Nat. Hav.	Log. Hav.	Nat. Hav.	Log. Nav.	Nat. Hav.	Log. Hav.	Nat. Hav.	Log. Hav.	Nat. Hav.	s
0	9.36427	.23135	9.36772	.23319	9.37114	.23504	9.37455	.23689	9.37794	.23875	60
1	.36433	.23138	.36777	.23322	.37120	.23507	.37461	.23692	.37800	.23878	59
2	.36439	.23141	.36783	.23325	.37126	.23510	.37467	.23695	.37806	.23881	58
3	.36444	.23144	.36789	.23329	.37131	.23513	.37472	.23699	.37811	.23884	57
+ 1′	9.36450	.23147	9.36794	.23332	9.37137	.23516	9.37478	.23702	9.37817	.23887	56
5	.36456	.23150	.36800	.23335	.37143	.23519	.37484	.23705	.37823	.23891	55
6	.36462	.23153	.36806	.23338	.37148	.23523	.37489	.23708	.37828	.23894	54
7	.36467	.23156	.36812	.23341	.37154	.23526	.37495	.23711	.37834	.23897	53
+ 2′	9.36473	.23160	9.36817	.23344	9.37160	.23529	9.37501	.23714	9.37840	.23900	52
9	.36479	.23163	.36823	.23347	.37166	.23532	.37506	.23717	.37845	.23903	51
10	.36485	.23166	.36829	.23350	.37171	.23535	.37512	.23720	.37851	.23906	50
11	.36490	.23169	.36834	.23353	.37177	.23538	.37518	.23723	.37856	.23909	49
+ 3′	9.36496	.23172	9.36840	.23356	9.37183	.23541	9.37523	.23726	9.37862	.23912	48
13	.36502	.23175	.36846	.23359	.37188	.23544	.37529	.23729	.37868	.23915	47
14	.36508	.23178	.36852	.23362	.37194	.23547	.37535	.23733	.37873	.23918	46
15	.36513	.23181	.36857	.23365	.37200	.23550	.37540	.23736	.37879	.23922	45
+ 4′	9.36519	.23184	9.36863	.23368	9.37205	.23553	9.37546	.23739	9.37885	.23925	44
17	.36525	.23187	.36869	.23372	.37211	.23556	.37552	.23742	.37890	.23928	43
18	.36531	.23190	.36875	.23375	.37217	.23560	.37557	.23745	.37896	.23931	42
19	.36536	.23193	.36880	.23378	.37222	.23563	.37563	.23748	.37902	.23934	41
+ 5′	9.36542	.23196	9.36886	.23381	9.37228	.23566	9.37569	.23751	9.37907	.23937	40
21	.36548	.23199	.36892	.23384	.37234	.23569	.37574	.23754	.37913	.23940	39
22	.36554	.23203	.36897	.23387	.37239	.23572	.37580	.23757	.37918	.23943	38
23	.36559	.23206	.36903	.23390	.37245	.23575	.37585	.23760	.37924	.23946	37
+ 6′	9.36565	.23209	9.36909	.23393	9:37251	.23578	9.37591	.23764	9.37930	.23950	36
25	.36571	.23212	.36915	.23396	.37257	.23581	.37597	.23767	.37935	.23953	35
26	.36577	.23215	.36920	.23399	.37262	.23584	.37602	.23770	.37941	.23956	34
27	.36582	.23218	.36926	.23402	.37268	.23587	.37608	.23773	.37947	.23959	33
+ 7′	9.36588	.23221	9.36932	.23405	9.37274	.23590	9.37614	.23776	9.37952	.23962	32
29	.36594	.23224	.36937	.23409	.37279	.23594	.37619	.23779	.37958	.23965	31
30	.36599	.23227	.36943	.23412	.37285	.23597	.37625	.23782	.37963	.23968	30
31	.36605	.23230	.36949	.23415	.37291	.23600	.37631	.23785	.37969	.23971	29
+ 8′	9.36611	.23233	9.36955	.23418	9.37296	.23603	9.37636	.23788	9.37975	.23974	28
33	.36617	.23236	.36960	.23421	.37302	.23606	.37642	.23791	.37980	.23977	27
34	.36622	.23239	.36966	.23424	.37308	.23609	.37648	.23795	.37986	.23981	26
35	.36628	.23242	.36972	.23427	.37313	.23612	.37653	.23798	.37992	.23984	25
+ 9′	9.36634	.23246	9.36977	.23430	9.37319	.23615	9.37659	.23801	9.37997	.23987	24
37	.36640	.23249	.36983	.23433	.37325	.23618	.37665	.23804	.38003	.23990	23
38	.36645	.23252	.36989	.23436	.37330	.23621	.37670	.23807	.38008	.23993	22
39	.36651	.23255	.36995	.23439	.37336	.23624	.37676	.23810	.38014	.23996	21
+ 10′	9.36657	.23258	9.37000	.23442	9.37342	.23627	9.37682	.23813	9.38020	.23999	20
41	.36663	.23261	.37006	.23445	.37347	.23631	.37687	.23816	.38025	.24002	19
42	.36668	.23264	.37012	.23449	.37353	.23634	.37693	.23819	.38031	.24005	18
43	.36674	.23267	.37017	.23452	.37359	.23637	.37699	.23822	.38037	.24009	17
+ 11′	9.36680	.23270	9.37023	.23455	9.37364	.23640	9.37704	.23825	9.38042	.24012	16
45	.36686	.23273	.37029	.23458	.37370	.23643	.37710	.23829	.38048	.24015	15
46	.36691	.23276	.37034	.23461	.37376	.23646	.37715	.23832	.38053	.24018	14
47	.36697	.23279	.37040	.23464	.37382	.23649	.37721	.23835	.38059	.24021	13
+ 12′	9.36703	.23282	9.37046	.23467	9.37387	.23652	9.37727	.23838	9.38065	.24024	12
49	.36708	.23285	.37052	.23470	.37393	.23655	.37732	.23841	.38070	.24027	11
50	.36714	.23289	.37057	.23473	.37399	.23658	.37738	.23844	.38076	.24030	10
51	.36720	.23292	.37063	.23476	.37404	.23661	.37744	.23847	.38081	.24033	9
+ 13′	9.36726	.23295	9.37069	.23479	9.37410	.23665	9.37749	.23850	9.38087	.24036	8
53	.36731	.23298	.37074	.23482	.37416	.23668	.37755	.23853	.38093	.24040	7
54	.36737	.23301	.37080	.23486	.37421	.23671	.37761	.23856	.38098	.24043	6
55	.36743	.23304	.37086	.23489	.37427	.23674	.37766	.23860	.38104	.24046	5
+ 14′	9.36749	.23307	9.37091	.23492	9.37433	.23677	9.37772	.23863	9.38110	.24049	4
57	.36754	.23310	.37097	.23495	.37438	.23680	.37778	.23866	.38115	.24052	3
58	.36760	.23313	.37103	.23498	.37444	.23683	.37783	.23869	.38121	.24055	2
59	.36766	.23316	.37109	.23501	.37450	.23686	.37789	.23872	.38126	.24058	1
+ 15′	9.36772	.23319	9.37114	.23504	9.37455	.23689	9.37794	.23875	9.38132	.24061	0
	$20^h\ 9^m$		$20^h\ 8^m$		$20^h\ 7^m$		$20^h\ 6^m$		$20^h\ 5^m$		

TABLE 34.

Haversines.

s	*3h 55m* **58° 45′**		*3h 56m* **59° 0′**		*3h 57m* **59° 15′**		*3h 58m* **59° 30′**		*3h 59m* **59° 45′**		s
	Log. Hav.	Nat. Hav.	Log. Hav.	Nat. Hav.	Log. Hav.	Nat. Hav.	Log. Hav.	Nat. Hav.	Log. Hav.	Nat. Hav.	
0	9.38132	**.24061**	9.38468	**.24248**	9.38802	**.24435**	9.39134	**.24623**	9.39465	**.24811**	60
1	.38138	**.24064**	.38473	**.24251**	.38807	**.24438**	.39140	**.24626**	.39470	**.24814**	59
2	.38143	**.24068**	.38479	**.24254**	.38813	**.24442**	.39145	**.24629**	.39476	**.24818**	58
3	.38149	**.24071**	.38485	**.24257**	.38819	**.24445**	.39151	**.24632**	.39481	**.24821**	57
+ 1′	9.38154	**.24074**	9.38490	**.24261**	9.38824	**.24448**	9.39156	**.24636**	9.39487	**.24824**	56
5	.38160	**.24077**	.38496	**.24264**	.38830	**.24451**	.39162	**.24639**	.39492	**.24827**	55
6	.38166	**.24080**	.38501	**.24267**	.38835	**.24454**	.39167	**.24642**	.39498	**.24830**	54
7	.38171	**.24083**	.38507	**.24270**	.38841	**.24457**	.39173	**.24645**	.39503	**.24833**	53
+ 2′	9.38177	**.24086**	9.38512	**.24273**	9.38846	**.24460**	9.39178	**.24648**	9.39509	**.24836**	52
9	.38182	**.24089**	.38518	**.24276**	.38852	**.24463**	.39184	**.24651**	.39514	**.24840**	51
10	.38188	**.24092**	.38524	**.24279**	.38857	**.24467**	.39189	**.24654**	.39520	**.24843**	50
11	.38194	**.24096**	.38529	**.24282**	.38863	**.24470**	.39195	**.24658**	.39525	**.24846**	49
+ 3′	9.38199	**.24099**	9.38535	**.24286**	9.38868	**.24473**	9.39201	**.24661**	9.39531	**.24849**	48
13	.38205	**.24102**	.38540	**.24289**	.38874	**.24476**	.39206	**.24664**	.39536	**.24852**	47
14	.38210	**.24105**	.38546	**.24292**	.38880	**.24479**	.39212	**.24667**	.39542	**.24855**	46
15	.38216	**.24108**	.38551	**.24295**	.38885	**.24482**	.39217	**.24670**	.39547	**.24858**	45
+ 4′	9.38222	**.24111**	9.38557	**.24298**	9.38891	**.24485**	9.39223	**.24673**	9.39553	**.24862**	44
17	.38227	**.24114**	.38563	**.24301**	.38896	**.24488**	.39228	**.24676**	.39558	**.24865**	43
18	.38233	**.24117**	.38568	**.24304**	.38902	**.24492**	.39234	**.24680**	.39564	**.24868**	42
19	.38239	**.24120**	.38574	**.24307**	.38907	**.24495**	.39239	**.24683**	.39569	**.24871**	41
+ 5′	9.38244	**.24124**	9.38579	**.24310**	9.38913	**.24498**	9.39245	**.24686**	9.39575	**.24874**	40
21	.38250	**.24127**	.38585	**.24314**	.38918	**.24501**	.39250	**.24689**	.39580	**.24877**	39
22	.38255	**.24130**	.38590	**.24317**	.38924	**.24504**	.39256	**.24692**	.39586	**.24880**	38
23	.38261	**.24133**	.38596	**.24320**	.38929	**.24507**	.39261	**.24695**	.39591	**.24884**	37
+ 6′	9.38267	**.24136**	9.38602	**.24323**	9.38935	**.24510**	9.39267	**.24698**	9.39597	**.24887**	36
25	.38272	**.24139**	.38607	**.24326**	.38941	**.24514**	.39272	**.24701**	.39602	**.24890**	35
26	.38278	**.24142**	.38613	**.24329**	.38946	**.24517**	.39278	**.24705**	.39608	**.24893**	34
27	.38283	**.24145**	.38618	**.24332**	.38952	**.24520**	.39283	**.24708**	.39613	**.24896**	33
+ 7′	9.38289	**.24148**	9.38624	**.24335**	9.38957	**.24523**	9.39289	**.24711**	9.39619	**.24899**	32
29	.38295	**.24152**	.38629	**.24339**	.38963	**.24526**	.39294	**.24714**	.39624	**.24902**	31
30	.38300	**.24155**	.38635	**.24342**	.38968	**.24529**	.39300	**.24717**	.39630	**.24906**	30
31	.38306	**.24158**	.38641	**.24345**	.38974	**.24532**	.39305	**.24720**	.39635	**.24909**	29
+ 8′	9.38311	**.24161**	9.38646	**.24348**	9.38979	**.24535**	9.39311	**.24723**	9.39641	**.24912**	28
33	.38317	**.24164**	.38652	**.24351**	.38985	**.24539**	.39316	**.24727**	.39646	**.24915**	27
34	.38322	**.24167**	.38657	**.24354**	.38990	**.24542**	.39322	**.24730**	.39652	**.24918**	26
35	.38328	**.24170**	.38663	**.24357**	.38996	**.24545**	.39327	**.24733**	.39657	**.24921**	25
+ 9′	9.38334	**.24173**	9.38668	**.24360**	9.39002	**.24548**	9.39333	**.24736**	9.39663	**.24924**	24
37	.38339	**.24176**	.38674	**.24364**	.39007	**.24551**	.39338	**.24739**	.39668	**.24928**	23
38	.38345	**.24180**	.38680	**.24367**	.39013	**.24554**	.39344	**.24742**	.39674	**.24931**	22
39	.38350	**.24183**	.38685	**.24370**	.39018	**.24557**	.39349	**.24745**	.39679	**.24934**	21
+ 10′	9.38356	**.24186**	9.38691	**.24373**	9.39024	**.24560**	9.39355	**.24749**	9.39685	**.24937**	20
41	.38362	**.24189**	.38696	**.24376**	.39029	**.24564**	.39360	**.24752**	.39690	**.24940**	19
42	.38367	**.24192**	.38702	**.24379**	.39035	**.24567**	.39366	**.24755**	.39695	**.24943**	18
43	.38373	**.24195**	.38707	**.24382**	.39040	**.24570**	.39371	**.24758**	.39701	**.24946**	17
+ 11′	9.38378	**.24198**	9.38713	**.24385**	9.39046	**.24573**	9.39377	**.24761**	9.39706	**.24950**	16
45	.38384	**.24201**	.38719	**.24388**	.39051	**.24576**	.39382	**.24764**	.39712	**.24953**	15
46	.38390	**.24204**	.38724	**.24392**	.39057	**.24579**	.39388	**.24767**	.39717	**.24956**	14
47	.38395	**.24208**	.38730	**.24395**	.39062	**.24582**	.39393	**.24770**	.39723	**.24959**	13
+ 12′	9.38401	**.24211**	9.38735	**.24398**	9.39068	**.24586**	9.39399	**.24774**	9.39728	**.24962**	12
49	.38406	**.24214**	.38741	**.24401**	.39073	**.24589**	.39404	**.24777**	.39734	**.24965**	11
50	.38412	**.24217**	.38746	**.24404**	.39079	**.24592**	.39410	**.24780**	.39739	**.24969**	10
51	.38418	**.24220**	.38752	**.24407**	.39085	**.24595**	.39415	**.24783**	.39745	**.24972**	9
+ 13′	9.38423	**.24223**	9.38757	**.24410**	9.39090	**.24598**	9.39421	**.24786**	9.39750	**.24975**	8
53	.38429	**.24226**	.38763	**.24413**	.39096	**.24601**	.39426	**.24789**	.39756	**.24978**	7
54	.38434	**.24229**	.38769	**.24417**	.39101	**.24604**	.39432	**.24792**	.39761	**.24981**	6
55	.38440	**.24233**	.38774	**.24420**	.39107	**.24607**	.39437	**.24796**	.39767	**.24984**	5
+ 14′	9.38445	**.24236**	9.38780	**.24423**	9.39112	**.24611**	9.39443	**.24799**	9.39772	**.24987**	4
57	.38451	**.24239**	.38785	**.24426**	.39118	**.24614**	.39448	**.24802**	.39778	**.24991**	3
58	.38457	**.24242**	.38791	**.24429**	.39123	**.24617**	.39454	**.24805**	.39783	**.24994**	2
59	.38462	**.24245**	.38796	**.24432**	.39129	**.24620**	.39459	**.24808**	.39789	**.24997**	1
+ 15′	9.38468	**.24248**	9.38802	**.24435**	9.39134	**.24623**	9.39465	**.24811**	9.39794	**.25000**	0
	20h 4m		*20h 3m*		*20h 2m*		*20h 1m*		*20h 0m*		

TABLE 34.

Haversines.

s	$4^h 0^m$ 60° 0′ Log. Hav.	Nat. Hav.	$4^h 1^m$ 60° 15′ Log. Hav.	Nat. Hav.	$4^h 2^m$ 60° 30′ Log. Hav.	Nat. Hav.	$4^h 3^m$ 60° 45′ Log. Hav.	Nat. Hav.	$4^h 4^m$ 61° 0′ Log. Hav.	Nat. Hav.	s
0	9.39794	**.25000**	9.40121	**.25189**	9.40447	**.25379**	9.40771	**.25569**	9.41094	**.25760**	60
1	.39799	**.25003**	.40127	**.25192**	.40453	**.25382**	.40777	**.25572**	.41099	**.25763**	59
2	.39805	**.25006**	.40132	**.25195**	.40458	**.25385**	.40782	**.25575**	.41105	**.25766**	58
3	.39810	**.25009**	.40138	**.25199**	.40463	**.25388**	.40787	**.25578**	.41110	**.25769**	57
+ 1′	9.39816	**.25013**	9.40143	**.25202**	9.40469	**.25391**	9.40793	**.25582**	9.41115	**.25772**	56
5	.39821	**.25016**	.40149	**.25205**	.40474	**.25395**	.40798	**.25585**	.41121	**.25775**	55
6	.39827	**.25019**	.40154	**.25208**	.40480	**.25398**	.40804	**.25588**	.41126	**.25779**	54
7	.39832	**.25022**	.40159	**.25211**	.40485	**.25401**	.40809	**.25591**	.41131	**.25782**	53
+ 2′	9.39838	**.25025**	9.40165	**.25214**	9.40490	**.25404**	9.40814	**.25594**	9.41137	**.25785**	52
9	.39843	**.25028**	.40170	**.25218**	.40496	**.25407**	.40820	**.25597**	.41142	**.25788**	51
10	.39849	**.25032**	.40176	**.25221**	.40501	**.25410**	.40825	**.25601**	.41147	**.25791**	50
11	.39854	**.25035**	.40181	**.25224**	.40507	**.25414**	.40831	**.25604**	.41153	**.25795**	49
+ 3′	9.39860	**.25038**	9.40187	**.25227**	9.40512	**.25417**	9.40836	**.25607**	9.41158	**.25798**	48
13	.39865	**.25041**	.40192	**.25230**	.40518	**.25420**	.40841	**.25610**	.41163	**.25801**	47
14	.39871	**.25044**	.40198	**.25233**	.40523	**.25423**	.40847	**.25613**	.41169	**.25804**	46
15	.39876	**.25047**	.40203	**.25237**	.40528	**.25426**	.40852	**.25617**	.41174	**.25807**	45
+ 4′	9.39881	**.25050**	9.40208	**.25240**	9.40534	**.25429**	9.40858	**.25620**	9.41180	**.25810**	44
17	.39887	**.25054**	.40214	**.25243**	.40539	**.25433**	.40863	**.25623**	.41185	**.25814**	43
18	.39892	**.25057**	.40219	**.25246**	.40545	**.25436**	.40868	**.25626**	.41190	**.25817**	42
19	.39898	**.25060**	.40225	**.25249**	.40550	**.25439**	.40874	**.25629**	.41196	**.25820**	41
+ 5′	9.39903	**.25063**	9.40230	**.25252**	9.40555	**.25442**	9.40879	**.25632**	9.41201	**.25823**	40
21	.39909	**.25066**	.40236	**.25255**	.40561	**.25445**	.40884	**.25636**	.41206	**.25826**	39
22	.39914	**.25069**	.40241	**.25259**	.40566	**.25448**	.40890	**.25639**	.41212	**.25830**	38
23	.39920	**.25072**	.40246	**.25262**	.40572	**.25452**	.40895	**.25642**	.41217	**.25833**	37
+ 6′	9.39925	**.25076**	9.40252	**.25265**	9.40577	**.25455**	9.40900	**.25645**	9.41222	**.25836**	36
25	.39931	**.25079**	.40257	**.25268**	.40582	**.25458**	.40906	**.25648**	.41228	**.25839**	35
26	.39936	**.25082**	.40263	**.25271**	.40588	**.25461**	.40911	**.25651**	.41233	**.25842**	34
27	.39942	**.25085**	.40268	**.25274**	.40593	**.25464**	40917	**.25655**	.41238	**.25845**	33
+ 7′	9.39947	**.25088**	9.40274	**.25278**	9.40599	**.25467**	9.40922	**.25658**	9.41244	**.25849**	32
29	.39952	**.25091**	.40279	**.25281**	.40604	**.25471**	.40927	**.25661**	.41249	**.25852**	31
30	.39958	**.25095**	.40284	**.25284**	.40609	**.25474**	.40933	**.25664**	.41254	**.25855**	30
31	.39963	**.25098**	.40290	**.25287**	.40615	**.25477**	.40938	**.25667**	.41260	**.25858**	29
+ 8′	9.39969	**.25101**	9.40295	**.25290**	9.40620	**.25480**	9.40943	**.25671**	9.41265	**.25861**	28
33	.39974	**.25104**	.40301	**.25293**	.40626	**.25483**	.40949	**.25674**	.41270	**.25865**	27
34	.39980	**.25107**	.40306	**.25297**	.40631	**.25487**	.40954	**.25677**	.41276	**.25868**	26
35	.39985	**.25110**	.40312	**.25300**	.40636	**.25490**	.40960	**.25680**	.41281	**.25871**	25
+ 9′	9.39991	**.25113**	9.40317	**.25303**	9.40642	**.25493**	9.40965	**.25683**	9.41287	**.25874**	24
37	.39996	**.25117**	.40322	**.25306**	.40647	**.25496**	.40970	**.25686**	.41292	**.25877**	23
38	.40002	**.25120**	.40328	**.25309**	.40653	**.25499**	.40976	**.25690**	.41297	**.25880**	22
39	.40007	**.25123**	.40333	**.25312**	.40658	**.25502**	.40981	**.25693**	.41303	**.25884**	21
+ 10′	9.40012	**.25126**	9.40339	**.25316**	9.40663	**.25506**	9.40986	**.25696**	9.41308	**.25887**	20
41	.40018	**.25129**	.40344	**.25319**	.40669	**.25509**	.40992	**.25699**	.41313	**.25890**	19
42	.40023	**.25132**	.40350	**.25322**	.40674	**.25512**	.40997	**.25702**	.41319	**.25893**	18
43	.40029	**.25136**	.40355	**.25325**	.40680	**.25515**	.41003	**.25705**	.41324	**.25896**	17
+ 11′	9.40034	**.25139**	9.40360	**.25328**	9.40685	**.25518**	9.41008	**.25709**	9.41329	**.25900**	16
45	.40040	**.25142**	.40366	**.25331**	.40690	**.25521**	.41013	**.25712**	.41335	**.25903**	15
46	.40045	**.25145**	.40371	**.25335**	.40696	**.25525**	.41019	**.25715**	.41340	**.25906**	14
47	.40051	**.25148**	.40377	**.25338**	.40701	**.25528**	.41024	**.25718**	.41345	**.25909**	13
+ 12′	9.40056	**.25151**	9.40382	**.25341**	9.40707	**.25531**	9.41029	**.25721**	9.41351	**.25912**	12
49	.40062	**.25154**	.40388	**.25344**	.40712	**.25534**	.41035	**.25724**	.41356	**.25915**	11
50	.40067	**.25158**	.40393	**.25347**	.40717	**.25537**	.41040	**.25728**	.41361	**.25919**	10
51	.40072	**.25161**	.40398	**.25350**	.40723	**.25540**	.41046	**.25731**	.41367	**.25922**	9
+ 13′	9.40078	**.25164**	9.40404	**.25354**	9.40728	**.25544**	9.41051	**.25734**	9.41372	**.25925**	8
53	.40083	**.25167**	.40409	**.25357**	.40734	**.25547**	.41056	**.25737**	.41377	**.25928**	7
54	.40089	**.25170**	.40415	**.25360**	.40739	**.25550**	.41062	**.25740**	.41383	**.25931**	6
55	.40094	**.25173**	.40420	**.25363**	.40744	**.25553**	.41067	**.25744**	.41388	**.25935**	5
+ 14′	9.40100	**.25177**	9.40425	**.25366**	9.40750	**.25556**	9.41072	**.25747**	9.41393	**.25938**	4
57	.40105	**.25180**	.40431	**.25369**	.40755	**.25559**	.41078	**.25750**	.41399	**.25941**	3
58	.40111	**.25183**	.40436	**.25372**	.40761	**.25563**	.41083	**.25753**	.41404	**.25944**	2
59	.40116	**.25186**	.40442	**.25376**	.40766	**.25566**	.41088	**.25756**	.41409	**.25947**	1
+ 15′	9.40121	**.25189**	9.40447	**.25379**	9.40771	**.25569**	9.41094	**.25760**	9.41415	**.25951**	0
	$19^h 59^m$		$19^h 58^m$		$19^h 57^m$		$19^h 56^m$		$19^h 55^m$		

TABLE 34.

Haversines.

s	4h 5m 61° 15′ Log. Hav.	Nat. Hav.	4h 6m 61° 30′ Log. Hav.	Nat. Hav.	4h 7m 61° 45′ Log. Hav.	Nat. Hav.	4h 8m 62° 0′ Log. Hav.	Nat. Hav.	4h 9m 62° 15′ Log. Hav.	Nat. Hav.	s
0	9.41415	**.25951**	9.41734	**.26142**	9.42052	**.26334**	9.42368	**.26526**	9.42682	**.26719**	60
1	.41420	**.25954**	.41739	**.26145**	.42057	**.26337**	.42373	**.26530**	.42688	**.26722**	59
2	.41425	**.25957**	.41745	**.26148**	.42062	**.26340**	.42378	**.26533**	.42693	**.26726**	58
3	.41431	**.25960**	.41750	**.26152**	.42068	**.26344**	.42384	**.26536**	.42698	**.26729**	57
+ 1′	9.41436	**.25963**	9.41755	**.26155**	9.42073	**.26347**	9.42389	**.26539**	9.42703	**.26732**	56
5	.41441	**.25966**	.41761	**.26158**	.42078	**.26350**	.42394	**.26543**	.42709	**.26735**	55
6	.41447	**.25970**	.41766	**.26161**	.42083	**.26353**	.42399	**.26546**	.42714	**.26739**	54
7	.41452	**.25973**	.41771	**.26164**	.42089	**.26356**	.42405	**.26549**	.42719	**.26742**	53
+ 2′	9.41457	**.25976**	9.41776	**.26168**	9.42094	**.26360**	9.42410	**.26552**	9.42724	**.26745**	52
9	.41463	**.25979**	.41782	**.26171**	.42099	**.26363**	.42415	**.26555**	.42730	**.26748**	51
10	.41468	**.25982**	.41787	**.26174**	.42105	**.26366**	.42420	**.26559**	.42735	**.26751**	50
11	.41473	**.25986**	.41792	**.26177**	.42110	**.26369**	.42426	**.26562**	.42740	**.26755**	49
+ 3′	9.41479	**.25989**	9.41798	**.26180**	9.42115	**.26372**	9.42431	**.26565**	9.42745	**.26758**	48
13	.41484	**.25992**	.41803	**.26184**	.42120	**.26376**	.42436	**.26568**	.42750	**.26761**	47
14	.41489	**.25995**	.41808	**.26187**	.42126	**.26379**	.42441	**.26571**	.42756	**.26764**	46
15	.41495	**.25998**	.41814	**.26190**	.42131	**.26382**	.42447	**.26575**	.42761	**.26768**	45
+ 4′	9.41500	**.26002**	9.41819	**.26193**	9.42136	**.26385**	9.42452	**.26578**	9.42766	**.26771**	44
17	.41505	**.26005**	.41824	**.26196**	.42141	**.26389**	.42457	**.26581**	.42771	**.26774**	43
18	.41511	**.26008**	.41829	**.26200**	.42147	**.26392**	.42462	**.26584**	.42777	**.26777**	42
19	.41516	**.26011**	.41835	**.26203**	.42152	**.26395**	.42468	**.26587**	.42782	**.26780**	41
+ 5′	9.41521	**.26014**	9.41840	**.26206**	9.42157	**.26398**	9.42473	**.26591**	9.42787	**.26784**	40
21	.41527	**.26017**	.41845	**.26209**	.42163	**.26402**	.42478	**.26594**	.42792	**.26787**	39
22	.41532	**.26021**	.41851	**.26212**	.42168	**.26405**	.42483	**.26597**	.42797	**.26790**	38
23	.41537	**.26024**	.41856	**.26216**	.42173	**.26408**	.42489	**.26600**	.42803	**.26793**	37
+ 6′	9.41543	**.26027**	9.41861	**.26219**	9.42178	**.26411**	9.42494	**.26604**	9.42808	**.26797**	36
25	.41548	**.26030**	.41867	**.26222**	.42184	**.26414**	.42499	**.26607**	.42813	**.26800**	35
26	.41553	**.26033**	.41872	**.26225**	.42189	**.26417**	.42504	**.26610**	.42818	**.26803**	34
27	.41559	**.26037**	.41877	**.26228**	.42194	**.26421**	.42510	**.26613**	.42824	**.26806**	33
+ 7′	9.41564	**.26040**	9.41882	**.26232**	9.42199	**.26424**	9.42515	**.26616**	9.42829	**.26809**	32
29	.41569	**.26043**	.41888	**.26235**	.42205	**.26427**	.42520	**.26620**	.42834	**.26813**	31
30	.41575	**.26046**	.41893	**.26238**	.42210	**.26430**	.42525	**.26623**	.42839	**.26816**	30
31	.41580	**.26049**	.41898	**.26241**	.42215	**.26433**	.42531	**.26626**	.42844	**.26819**	29
+ 8′	9.41585	**.26053**	9.41904	**.26244**	9.42221	**.26437**	9.42536	**.26629**	9.42850	**.26822**	28
33	.41590	**.26056**	.41909	**.26248**	.42226	**.26440**	.42541	**.26632**	.42855	**.26826**	27
34	.41596	**.26059**	.41914	**.26251**	.42231	**.26443**	.42546	**.26636**	.42860	**.26829**	26
35	.41601	**.26062**	.41920	**.26254**	.42236	**.26446**	.42552	**.26639**	.42865	**.26832**	25
+ 9′	9.41606	**.26065**	9.41925	**.26257**	9.42242	**.26449**	9.42557	**.26642**	9.42870	**.26835**	24
37	.41612	**.26069**	.41930	**.26260**	.42247	**.26453**	.42562	**.26645**	.42876	**.26838**	23
38	.41617	**.26072**	.41935	**.26264**	.42252	**.26456**	.42567	**.26649**	.42881	**.26842**	22
39	.41622	**.26075**	.41941	**.26267**	.42257	**.26459**	.42573	**.26652**	.42886	**.26845**	21
+ 10′	9.41628	**.26078**	9.41946	**.26270**	9.42263	**.26462**	9.42578	**.26655**	9.42891	**.26848**	20
41	.41633	**.26081**	.41951	**.26273**	.42268	**.26465**	.42583	**.26658**	.42897	**.26851**	19
42	.41638	**.26085**	.41957	**.26276**	.42273	**.26469**	.42588	**.26661**	.42902	**.26855**	18
43	.41644	**.26088**	.41962	**.26280**	.42278	**.26472**	.42593	**.26665**	.42907	**.26858**	17
+ 11′	9.41649	**.26091**	9.41967	**.26283**	9.42284	**.26475**	9.42599	**.26668**	9.42912	**.26861**	16
45	.41654	**.26094**	.41972	**.26286**	.42289	**.26478**	.42604	**.26671**	.42917	**.26864**	15
46	.41660	**.26097**	.41978	**.26289**	.42294	**.26481**	.42609	**.26674**	.42923	**.26867**	14
47	.41665	**.26101**	.41983	**.26292**	.42300	**.26485**	.42614	**.26677**	.42928	**.26871**	13
+ 12′	9.41670	**.26104**	9.41988	**.26296**	9.42305	**.26488**	9.42620	**.26681**	9.42933	**.26874**	12
49	.41676	**.26107**	.41994	**.26299**	.42310	**.26491**	.42625	**.26684**	.42938	**.26877**	11
50	.41681	**.26110**	.41999	**.26302**	.42315	**.26494**	.42630	**.26687**	.42943	**.26880**	10
51	.41686	**.26113**	.42004	**.26305**	.42321	**.26498**	.42635	**.26690**	.42949	**.26883**	9
+ 13′	9.41692	**.26117**	9.42009	**.26308**	9.42326	**.26501**	9.42641	**.26694**	9.42954	**.26887**	8
53	.41697	**.26120**	.42015	**.26312**	.42331	**.26504**	.42646	**.26697**	.42959	**.26890**	7
54	.41702	**.26123**	.42020	**.26315**	.42336	**.26507**	.42651	**.26700**	.42964	**.26893**	6
55	.41707	**.26126**	.42025	**.26318**	.42342	**.26510**	.42656	**.26703**	.42969	**.26896**	5
+ 14′	9.41713	**.26129**	9.42031	**.26321**	9.42347	**.26514**	9.42662	**.26706**	9.42975	**.26900**	4
57	.41718	**.26132**	.42036	**.26324**	.42352	**.26517**	.42667	**.26710**	.42980	**.26903**	3
58	.41723	**.26136**	.42041	**.26328**	.42357	**.26520**	.42672	**.26713**	.42985	**.26906**	2
59	.41729	**.26139**	.42046	**.26331**	.42363	**.26523**	.42677	**.26716**	.42990	**.26909**	1
+ 15′	9.41734	**.26142**	9.42052	**.26334**	9.42368	**.26526**	9.42682	**.26719**	9.42996	**.26913**	0
	19h 54m		19h 53m		19h 52m		19h 51m		19h 50m		

TABLE 34.

Haversines.

s	4h 10m 62° 30′		4h 11m 62° 45′		4h 12m 63° 0′		4h 13m 63° 15′		4h 14m 63° 30′		s
	Log. Hav.	Nat. Hav.	Log. Hav.	Nat. Hav.	Log. Hav.	Nat. Håv.	Log. Hav.	Nat. Hav.	Log. Hav.	Nat. Hav.	
0	9.42996	**.26913**	9.43307	**.27106**	9.43617	**.27300**	9.43926	**.27495**	9.44232	**.27690**	60
1	.43001	**.26916**	.43312	**.27110**	.43622	**.27304**	.43931	**.27498**	.44238	**.27693**	59
2	.43006	**.26919**	.43317	**.27113**	.43627	**.27307**	.43936	**.27502**	.44243	**.27697**	58
3	.43011	**.26922**	.43323	**.27116**	.43632	**.27310**	.43941	**.27505**	.44248	**.27700**	57
+ 1′	9.43016	**.26925**	9.43328	**.27119**	9.43638	**.27313**	9.43946	**.27508**	9.44253	**.27703**	56
5	.43022	**.26929**	.43333	**.27122**	.43643	**.27317**	.43951	**.27511**	.44258	**.27706**	55
6	.43027	**.26932**	.43338	**.27126**	.43648	**.27320**	.43956	**.27515**	.44263	**.27710**	54
7	.43032	**.26935**	.43343	**.27129**	.43653	**.27323**	.43961	**.27518**	.44268	**.27713**	53
+ 2′	9.43037	**.26938**	9.43348	**.27132**	9.43658	**.27326**	9.43967	**.27521**	9.44273	**.27716**	52
9	.43042	**.26942**	.43354	**.27135**	.43663	**.27330**	.43972	**.27524**	.44278	**.27719**	51
10	.43048	**.26945**	.43359	**.27139**	.43669	**.27333**	.43977	**.27528**	.44283	**.27723**	50
11	.43053	**.26948**	.43364	**.27142**	.43674	**.27336**	.43982	**.27531**	.44289	**.27726**	49
+ 3′	9.43058	**.26951**	9.43369	**.27145**	9.43679	**.27339**	9.43987	**.27534**	9.44294	**.27729**	48
13	.43063	**.26955**	.43374	**.27148**	.43684	**.27343**	.43992	**.27537**	.44299	**.27732**	47
14	.43068	**.26958**	.43380	**.27152**	.43689	**.27346**	.43997	**.27541**	.44304	**.27736**	46
15	.43074	**.26961**	.43385	**.27155**	.43694	**.27349**	.44002	**.27544**	.44309	**.27739**	45
+ 4′	9.43079	**.26964**	9.43390	**.27158**	9.43699	**.27352**	9.44008	**.27547**	9.44314	**.27742**	44
17	.43084	**.26967**	.43395	**.27161**	.43705	**.27356**	.44013	**.27550**	.44319	**.27745**	43
18	.43089	**.26971**	.43400	**.27165**	.43710	**.27359**	.44018	**.27554**	.44324	**.27749**	42
19	.43094	**.26974**	.43405	**.27168**	.43715	**.27362**	.44023	**.27557**	.44329	**.27752**	41
+ 5′	9.43100	**.26977**	9.43411	**.27171**	9.43720	**.27365**	9.44028	**.27560**	9.44334	**.27755**	40
21	.43105	**.26980**	.43416	**.27174**	.43725	**.27369**	.44033	**.27563**	.44340	**.27758**	39
22	.43110	**.26984**	.43421	**.27177**	.43730	**.27372**	.44038	**.27567**	.44345	**.27762**	38
23	.43115	**.26987**	.43426	**.27181**	.43735	**.27375**	.44043	**.27570**	.44350	**.27765**	37
+ 6′	9.43120	**.26990**	9.43431	**.27184**	9.43741	**.27378**	9.44048	**.27573**	9.44355	**.27768**	36
25	.43126	**.26993**	.43436	**.27187**	.43746	**.27382**	.44054	**.27576**	.44360	**.27772**	35
26	.43131	**.26996**	.43442	**.27190**	.43751	**.27385**	.44059	**.27580**	.44365	**.27775**	34
27	.43136	**.27000**	.43447	**.27194**	.43756	**.27388**	.44064	**.27583**	.44370	**.27778**	33
+ 7′	9.43141	**.27003**	9.43452	**.27197**	9.43761	**.27391**	9.44069	**.27586**	9.44375	**.27781**	32
29	.43146	**.27006**	.43457	**.27200**	.43766	**.27394**	.44074	**.27589**	.44380	**.27785**	31
30	.43151	**.27009**	.43462	**.27203**	.43771	**.27398**	.44079	**.27593**	.44385	**.27788**	30
31	43157	**.27013**	.43467	**.27207**	.43777	**.27401**	.44084	**.27596**	.44390	**.27791**	29
+ 8′	9.43162	**.27016**	9.43473	**.27210**	9.43782	**.27404**	9.44089	**.27599**	9.44396	**.27794**	28
33	.43167	**.27019**	.43478	**.27213**	.43787	**.27407**	.44095	**.27602**	.44401	**.27798**	27
34	.43172	**.27022**	.43483	**.27216**	.43792	**.27411**	.44100	**.27606**	.44406	**.27801**	26
35	.43177	**.27025**	.43488	**.27220**	.43797	**.27414**	.44105	**.27609**	.44411	**.27804**	25
+ 9′	9.43183	**.27029**	9.43493	**.27223**	9.43802	**.27417**	9.44110	**.27612**	9.44416	**.27807**	24
37	.43188	**.27032**	.43498	**.27226**	.43807	**.27420**	.44115	**.27615**	.44421	**.27811**	23
38	.43193	**.27035**	.43504	**.27229**	.43813	**.27424**	.44120	**.27619**	.44426	**.27814**	22
39	.43198	**.27038**	.43509	**.27232**	.43818	**.27427**	.44125	**.27622**	.44431	**.27817**	21
+ 10′	9.43203	**.27042**	9.43514	**.27236**	9.43823	**.27430**	9.44130	**.27625**	9.44436	**.27820**	20
41	.43209	**.27045**	.43519	**.27239**	.43828	**.27433**	.44135	**.27628**	.44441	**.27824**	19
42	.43214	**.27048**	.43524	**.27242**	.43833	**.27437**	.44141	**.27632**	.44446	**.27827**	18
43	.43219	**.27051**	.43529	**.27245**	.43838	**.27440**	.44146	**.27635**	.44452	**.27830**	17
+ 11′	9.43224	**.27055**	9.43535	**.27249**	9.43843	**.27443**	9.44151	**.27638**	9.44457	**.27833**	16
45	.43229	**.27058**	.43540	**.27252**	.43849	**.27446**	.44156	**.27641**	.44462	**.27837**	15
46	.43234	**.27061**	.43545	**.27255**	.43854	**.27450**	.44161	**.27645**	.44467	**.27840**	14
47	.43240	**.27064**	.43550	**.27258**	.43859	**.27453**	.44166	**.27648**	.44472	**.27843**	13
+ 12′	9.43245	**.27068**	9.43555	**.27262**	9.43864	**.27456**	9.44171	**.27651**	9.44477	**.27846**	12
49	.43250	**.27071**	.43560	**.27265**	.43869	**.27459**	44176	**.27654**	.44482	**.27850**	11
50	.43255	**.27074**	.43565	**.27268**	.43874	**.27463**	.44181	**.27658**	.44487	**.27853**	10
51	.43260	**.27077**	.43571	**.27271**	.43879	**.27466**	.44187	**.27661**	.44492	**.27856**	9
+ 13′	9.43266	**.27080**	9.43576	**.27275**	9.43884	**.27469**	9.44192	**.27664**	9.44497	**.27859**	8
53	.43271	**.27084**	.43581	**.27278**	.43890	**.27472**	.44197	**.27667**	.44502	**.27863**	7
54	.43276	**.27087**	.43586	**.27281**	.43895	**.27476**	.44202	**.27671**	.44507	**.27866**	6
55	.43281	**.27090**	.43591	**.27284**	.43900	**.27479**	.44207	**.27674**	.44513	**.27869**	5
+ 14′	9.43286	**.27093**	9.43596	**.27288**	9.43905	**.27482**	9.44212	**.27677**	9.44518	**.27873**	4
57	.43291	**.27097**	.43602	**.27291**	.43910	**.27485**	.44217	**.27680**	.44523	**.27876**	3
58	.43297	**.27100**	.43607	**.27294**	.43915	**.27489**	.44222	**.27684**	.44528	**.27879**	2
59	.43302	**.27103**	.43612	**.27297**	.43920	**.27492**	.44227	**.27687**	.44533	**.27882**	1
+ 15′	9.43307	**.27106**	9.43617	**.27300**	9.43926	**.27495**	9.44232	**.27690**	9.44538	**.27886**	0
	19h 49m		19h 48m		19h 47m		19h 46m		19h 45m		

TABLE 34.

Haversines.

	$4^h\ 15^m$ 63° 45′		$4^h\ 16^m$ 64° 0′		$4^h\ 17^m$ 64° 15′		$4^h\ 18^m$ 64° 30′		$4^h\ 19^m$ 64° 45′		
s	Log. Hav.	Nat. Hav.	Log. Hav.	Nat. Hav.	Log. Hav.	Nat. Hav.	Log. Hav.	Nat. Hav.	Log. Hav.	Nat. Hav.	s
0	9.44538	**.27886**	9.44842	**.28081**	9.45144	**.28278**	9.45446	**.28474**	9.45745	**.28672**	60
1	.44543	**.27889**	.44847	**.28085**	.45149	**.28281**	.45451	**.28478**	.45750	**.28675**	59
2	.44548	**.27892**	.44852	**.28088**	.45155	**.28284**	.45456	**.28481**	.45755	**.28678**	58
3	.44553	**.27895**	.44857	**.28091**	.45160	**.28288**	.45461	**.28484**	.45760	**.28681**	57
+ 1′	9.44558	**.27899**	9.44862	**.28095**	9.45165	**.28291**	9.45466	**.28488**	9.45765	**.28685**	56
5	.44563	**.27902**	.44867	**.28098**	.45170	**.28294**	.45471	**.28491**	.45770	**.28688**	55
6	.44568	**.27905**	.44872	**.28101**	.45175	**.28297**	.45476	**.28494**	.45775	**.28691**	54
7	.44573	**.27908**	.44877	**.28104**	.45180	**.28301**	.45481	**.28497**	.45780	**.28695**	53
+ 2′	9.44579	**.27912**	9.44882	**.28108**	9.45185	**.28304**	9.45486	**.28501**	9.45785	**.28698**	52
9	.44584	**.27915**	.44887	**.28111**	.45190	**.28307**	.45491	**.28504**	.45790	**.28701**	51
10	.44589	**.27918**	.44892	**.28114**	.45195	**.28310**	.45496	**.28507**	.45795	**.28704**	50
11	.44594	**.27921**	.44898	**.28117**	.45200	**.28314**	.45501	**.28511**	.45800	**.28708**	49
+ 3′	9.44599	**.27925**	9.44903	**.28121**	9.45205	**.28317**	9.45506	**.28514**	9.45805	**.28711**	48
13	.44604	**.27928**	.44908	**.28124**	.45210	**.28320**	.45511	**.28517**	.45810	**.28714**	47
14	.44609	**.27931**	.44913	**.28127**	.45215	**.28324**	.45516	**.28520**	.45815	**.28718**	46
15	.44614	**.27935**	.44918	**.28130**	.45220	**.28327**	.45521	**.28524**	.45820	**.28721**	45
+ 4′	9.44619	**.27938**	9.44923	**.28134**	9.45225	**.28330**	9.45526	**.28527**	9.45825	**.28724**	44
17	.44624	**.27941**	.44928	**.28137**	.45230	**.28333**	.45531	**.28530**	.45830	**.28727**	43
18	.44629	**.27944**	.44933	**.28140**	.45235	**.28337**	.45536	**.28534**	.45835	**.28731**	42
19	.44634	**.27948**	.44938	**.28144**	.45240	**.28340**	.45541	**.28537**	.45840	**.28734**	41
+ 5′	9.44639	**.27951**	9.44943	**.28147**	9.45245	**.28343**	9.45546	**.28540**	9.45845	**.28737**	40
21	.44645	**.27954**	.44948	**.28150**	.45250	**.28347**	.45551	**.28543**	.45850	**.28741**	39
22	.44650	**.27957**	.44953	**.28153**	.45255	**.28350**	.45556	**.28547**	.45855	**.28744**	38
23	.44655	**.27961**	.44958	**.28157**	.45260	**.28353**	.45561	**.28550**	.45860	**.28747**	37
+ 6′	9.44660	**.27964**	9.44963	**.28160**	9.45265	**.28356**	9.45566	**.28553**	9.45865	**.28751**	36
25	.44665	**.27967**	.44968	**.28163**	.45270	**.28360**	.45571	**.28557**	.45870	**.28754**	35
26	.44670	**.27970**	.44973	**.28166**	.45275	**.28363**	.45576	**.28560**	.45875	**.28757**	34
27	.44675	**.27974**	.44978	**.28170**	.45280	**.28366**	.45581	**.28563**	.45879	**.28760**	33
+ 7′	9.44680	**.27977**	9.44983	**.28173**	9.45285	**.28369**	9.45586	**.28566**	9.45884	**.28764**	32
29	.44685	**.27980**	.44988	**.28176**	.45290	**.28373**	.45591	**.28570**	.45889	**.28767**	31
30	.44690	**.27983**	.44993	**.28180**	.45295	**.28376**	.45596	**.28573**	.45894	**.28770**	30
31	.44695	**.27987**	.44998	**.28183**	.45300	**.28379**	.45601	**.28576**	.45899	**.28774**	29
+ 8′	9.44700	**.27990**	9.45003	**.28186**	9.45305	**.28383**	9.45606	**.28580**	9.45904	**.28777**	28
33	.44705	**.27993**	.45009	**.28189**	.45310	**.28386**	.45610	**.28583**	.45909	**.28780**	27
34	.44710	**.27997**	.45014	**.28193**	.45315	**.28389**	.45615	**.28586**	.45914	**.28783**	26
35	.44715	**.28000**	.45019	**.28196**	.45320	**.28392**	.45620	**.28589**	.45919	**.28787**	25
+ 9′	9.44721	**.28003**	9.45024	**.28199**	9.45325	**.28396**	9.45625	**.28593**	9.45924	**.28790**	24
37	.44726	**.28006**	.45029	**.28202**	.45330	**.28399**	.45630	**.28596**	.45929	**.28793**	23
38	.44731	**.28010**	.45034	**.28206**	.45335	**.28402**	.45635	**.28599**	.45934	**.28797**	22
39	.44736	**.28013**	.45039	**.28209**	.45340	**.28406**	.45640	**.28603**	.45939	**.28800**	21
+ 10′	9.44741	**.28016**	9.45044	**.28212**	9.45345	**.28409**	9.45645	**.28606**	9.45944	**.28803**	20
41	.44746	**.28019**	.45049	**.28216**	.45350	**.28412**	.45650	**.28609**	.45949	**.28807**	19
42	.44751	**.28023**	.45054	**.28219**	.45355	**.28415**	.45655	**.28612**	.45954	**.28810**	18
43	.44756	**.28026**	.45059	**.28222**	.45360	**.28419**	.45660	**.28616**	.45959	**.28813**	17
+ 11′	9.44761	**.28029**	9.45064	**.28225**	9.45365	**.28422**	9.45665	**.28619**	9.45964	**.28816**	16
45	.44766	**.28032**	.45069	**.28229**	.45370	**.28425**	.45670	**.28622**	.45969	**.28820**	15
46	.44771	**.28036**	.45074	**.28232**	.45375	**.28429**	.45675	**.28626**	.45974	**.28823**	14
47	.44776	**.28039**	.45079	**.28235**	.45380	**.28432**	.45680	**.28629**	.45979	**.28826**	13
+ 12′	9.44781	**.28042**	9.45084	**.28238**	9.45385	**.28435**	9.45685	**.28632**	9.45984	**.28830**	12
49	.44786	**.28046**	.45089	**.28242**	.45390	**.28438**	.45690	**.28635**	.45989	**.28833**	11
50	.44791	**.28049**	.45094	**.28245**	.45395	**.28442**	.45695	**.28639**	.45994	**.28836**	10
51	.44796	**.28052**	.45099	**.28248**	.45400	**.28445**	.45700	**.28642**	.45999	**.28839**	9
+ 13′	9.44801	**.28055**	9.45104	**.28252**	9.45405	**.28448**	9.45705	**.28645**	9.46004	**.28843**	8
53	.44807	**.28059**	.45109	**.28255**	.45410	**.28451**	.45710	**.28649**	.46009	**.28846**	7
54	.44812	**.28062**	.45114	**.28258**	.45415	**.28455**	.45715	**.28652**	.46014	**.28849**	6
55	.44817	**.28065**	.45119	**.28261**	.45420	**.28458**	.45720	**.28655**	.46019	**.28853**	5
+ 14′	9.44822	**.28068**	9.45124	**.28265**	9.45426	**.28461**	9.45725	**.28658**	9.46023	**.28856**	4
57	.44827	**.28072**	.45129	**.28268**	.45431	**.28465**	.45730	**.28662**	.46028	**.28859**	3
58	.44832	**.28075**	.45134	**.28271**	.45436	**.28468**	.45735	**.28665**	.46033	**.28863**	2
59	.44837	**.28078**	.45139	**.28274**	.45441	**.28471**	.45740	**.28668**	.46038	**.28866**	1
+ 15′	9.44842	**.28081**	9.45144	**.28278**	9.45446	**.28474**	9.45745	**.28672**	9.46043	**.28869**	0
	$19^h\ 44^m$		$19^h\ 43^m$		$19^h\ 42^m$		$19^h\ 41^m$		$19^h\ 40^m$		

TABLE 34.

Haversines.

	$4^h\ 20^m$ 65° 0′		$4^h\ 21^m$ 65° 15′		$4^h\ 22^m$ 65° 30′		$4^h\ 23^m$ 65° 45′		$4^h\ 24^m$ 66° 0′		
s	Log. Hav.	Nat. Hav.	Log. Hav.	Nat. Hav.	Log. Hav.	Nat. Hav.	Log. Hav.	Nat. Hav.	Log. Hav.	Nat. Hav.	s
0	9.46043	.28869	9.46340	.29067	9.46635	.29265	9.46929	.29464	9.47222	.29663	60
1	.46048	.28872	.46345	.29070	.46640	.29269	.46934	.29467	.47227	.29666	59
2	.46053	.28876	.46350	.29074	.46645	.29272	.46939	.29471	.47231	.29670	58
3	.46058	.28879	.46355	.29077	.46650	.29275	.46944	.29474	.47236	.29673	57
+ 1′	9.46063	.28882	9.46360	.29080	9.46655	.29279	9.46949	.29477	9.47241	.29676	56
5	.46068	.28886	.46365	.29084	.46660	.29282	.46954	.29481	.47246	.29680	55
6	.46073	.28889	.46370	.29087	.46665	.29285	.46959	.29484	.47251	.29683	54
7	.46078	.28892	.46375	.29090	.46670	.29289	.46963	.29487	.47256	.29686	53
+ 2′	9.46083	.28895	9.46380	.29093	9.46675	.29292	9.46968	.29491	9.47261	.29690	52
9	.46088	.28899	.46384	.29097	.46680	.29295	.46973	.29494	.47266	.29693	51
10	.46093	.28902	.46389	.29100	.46684	.29298	.46978	.29497	.47270	.29696	50
11	.46098	.28905	.46394	.29103	.46689	.29302	.46983	.29501	.47275	.29700	49
+ 3′	9.46103	.28909	9.46399	.29107	9.46694	.29305	9.46988	.29504	9.47280	.29703	48
13	.46108	.28912	.46404	.29110	.46699	.29308	.46993	.29507	.47285	.29706	47
14	.46113	.28915	.46409	.29113	.46704	.29312	.46998	.29510	.47290	.29710	46
15	.46118	.28918	.46414	.29117	.46709	.29315	.47003	.29514	.47295	.29713	45
+ 4′	9.46123	.28922	9.46419	.29120	9.46714	.29318	9.47007	.29517	9.47300	.29716	44
17	.46128	.28925	.46424	.29123	.46719	.29322	.47012	.29520	.47304	.29720	43
18	.46132	.28928	.46429	.29126	.46724	.29325	.47017	.29524	.47309	.29723	42
19	.46137	.28932	.46434	.29130	.46729	.29328	.47022	.29527	.47314	.29726	41
+ 5′	9.46142	.28935	9.46439	.29133	9.46733	.29332	9.47027	.29530	9.47319	.29730	40
21	.46147	.28938	.46444	.29136	.46738	.29335	.47032	.29534	.47324	.29733	39
22	.46152	.28942	.46448	.29140	.46743	.29338	.47037	.29537	.47329	.29736	38
23	.46157	.28945	.46453	.29143	.46748	.29341	.47042	.29540	.47334	.29740	37
+ 6′	9.46162	.28948	9.46458	.29146	9.46753	.29345	9.47046	.29544	9.47338	.29743	36
25	.46167	.28952	.46463	.29150	.46758	.29348	.47051	.29547	.47343	.29746	35
26	.46172	.28955	.46468	.29153	.46763	.29351	.47056	.29550	.47348	.29750	34
27	.46177	.28958	.46473	.29156	.46768	.29355	.47061	.29554	.47353	.29753	33
+ 7′	9.46182	.28961	9.46478	.29160	9.46773	.29358	9.47066	.29557	9.47358	.29756	32
29	.46187	.28965	.46483	.29163	.46778	.29361	.47071	.29560	.47363	.29760	31
30	.46192	.28968	.46488	.29166	.46782	.29365	.47076	.29564	.47367	.29763	30
31	.46197	.28971	.46493	.29169	.46787	.29368	.47081	.29567	.47372	.29766	29
+ 8′	9.46202	.28975	9.46498	.29173	9.46792	.29371	9.47085	.29570	9.47377	.29770	28
33	.46207	.28978	.46503	.29176	.46797	.29375	.47090	.29573	.47382	.29773	27
34	.46212	.28981	.46508	.29179	.46802	.29378	.47095	.29577	.47387	.29776	26
35	.46217	.28985	.46512	.29183	.46807	.29381	.47100	.29580	.47392	.29779	25
+ 9′	9.46222	.28988	9.46517	.29186	9.46812	.29385	9.47105	.29583	9.47397	.29783	24
37	.46226	.28991	.46522	.29189	.46817	.29388	.47110	.29587	.47401	.29786	23
38	.46231	.28994	.46527	.29193	.46822	.29391	.47115	.29590	.47406	.29789	22
39	.46236	.28998	.46532	.29196	.46827	.29394	.47120	.29593	.47411	.29793	21
+ 10′	9.46241	.29001	9.46537	.29199	9.46831	.29398	9.47124	.29597	9.47416	.29796	20
41	.46246	.29004	.46542	.29202	.46836	.29401	.47129	.29600	.47421	.29799	19
42	.46251	.29008	.46547	.29206	.46841	.29404	.47134	.29603	.47426	.29803	18
43	.46256	.29011	.46552	.29209	.46846	.29408	.47139	.29607	.47431	.29806	17
+ 11′	9.46261	.29014	9.46557	.29212	9.46851	.29411	9.47144	.29610	9.47435	.29809	16
45	.46266	.29017	.46562	.29216	.46856	.29414	.47149	.29613	.47440	.29813	15
46	.46271	.29021	.46567	.29219	.46861	.29418	.47154	.29617	.47445	.29816	14
47	.46276	.29024	.46571	.29222	.46866	.29421	.47159	.29620	.47450	.29819	13
+ 12′	9.46281	.29027	9.46576	.29226	9.46871	.29424	9.47163	.29623	9.47455	.29823	12
49	.46286	.29031	.46581	.29229	.46875	.29428	.47168	.29627	.47460	.29826	11
50	.46291	.29034	.46586	.29232	.46880	.29431	.47173	.29630	.47464	.29829	10
51	.46296	.29037	.46591	.29236	.46885	.29434	.47178	.29633	.47469	.29833	9
+ 13′	9.46301	.29041	9.46596	.29239	9.46890	.29438	9.47183	.29637	9.47474	.29836	8
53	.46305	.29044	.46601	.29242	.46895	.29441	.47188	.29640	.47479	.29839	7
54	.46310	.29047	.46606	.29245	.46900	.29444	.47193	.29643	.47484	.29843	6
55	.46315	.29051	.46611	.29249	.46905	.29447	.47197	.29647	.47489	.29846	5
+ 14′	9.46320	.29054	9.46616	.29252	9.46910	.29451	9.47202	.29650	9.47493	.29849	4
57	.46325	.29057	.46621	.29255	.46915	.29454	.47207	.29653	.47498	.29853	3
58	.46330	.29060	.46626	.29259	.46919	.29457	.47212	.29657	.47503	.29856	2
59	.46335	.29064	.46630	.29262	.46924	.29461	.47217	.29660	.47508	.29859	1
+ 15′	9.46340	.29067	9.46635	.29265	9.46929	.29464	9.47222	.29663	9.47513	.29863	0
	$19^h\ 39^m$		$19^h\ 38^m$		$19^h\ 37^m$		$19^h\ 36^m$		$19^h\ 35^m$		

TABLE 34.

Haversines.

	$4^h 25^m$ 66° 15′		$4^h 26^m$ 66° 30′		$4^h 27^m$ 66° 45′		$4^h 28^m$ 67° 0′		$4^h 29^m$ 67° 15′		
s	Log. Hav.	Nat. Hav.	Log. Hav.	Nat. Hav.	Log. Hav.	Nat. Hav.	Log. Hav.	Nat. Hav.	Log. Hav.	Nat. Hav.	s
0	9.47513	**.29863**	9.47803	**.30063**	9.48091	**.30263**	9.48378	**.30463**	9.48664	**.30664**	60
1	.47518	**.29866**	.47807	**.30066**	.48096	**.30266**	.48383	**.30467**	.48668	**.30668**	59
2	.47523	**.29869**	.47812	**.30069**	.48101	**.30269**	.48387	**.30470**	.48673	**.30671**	58
3	.47527	**.29873**	.47817	**.30073**	.48105	**.30273**	.48392	**.30473**	.48678	**.30675**	57
+ 1′	9.47532	**.29876**	9.47822	**.30076**	9.48110	**.30276**	9.48397	**.30477**	9.48683	**.30678**	56
5	.47537	**.29879**	.47827	**.30079**	.48115	**.30280**	.48402	**.30480**	.48687	**.30681**	55
6	.47542	**.29883**	.47831	**.30083**	.48120	**.30283**	.48407	**.30484**	.48692	**.30685**	54
7	.47547	**.29886**	.47836	**.30086**	.48124	**.30286**	.48411	**.30487**	.48697	**.30688**	53
+ 2′	9.47552	**.29889**	9.47841	**.30089**	9.48129	**.30290**	9.48416	**.30490**	9.48702	**.30691**	52
9	.47556	**.29893**	.47846	**.30093**	.48134	**.30293**	.48421	**.30494**	.48706	**.30695**	51
10	.47561	**.29896**	.47851	**.30096**	.48139	**.30296**	.48426	**.30497**	.48711	**.30698**	50
11	.47566	**.29899**	.47856	**.30099**	.48144	**.30300**	.48430	**.30500**	.48716	**.30701**	49
+ 3′	9.47571	**.29903**	9.47860	**.30103**	9.48148	**.30303**	9.48435	**.30504**	9.48720	**.30705**	48
13	.47576	**.29906**	.47865	**.30106**	.48153	**.30306**	.48440	**.30507**	.48725	**.30708**	47
14	.47581	**.29909**	.47870	**.30109**	.48158	**.30310**	.48445	**.30510**	.48730	**.30711**	46
15	.47585	**.29913**	.47875	**.30113**	.48163	**.30313**	.48449	**.30514**	.48735	**.30715**	45
+ 4′	9.47590	**.29916**	9.47880	**.30116**	9.48168	**.30316**	9.48454	**.30517**	9.48739	**.30718**	44
17	.47595	**.29919**	.47884	**.30119**	.48172	**.30320**	.48459	**.30520**	.48744	**.30721**	43
18	.47600	**.29923**	.47889	**.30123**	.48177	**.30323**	.48464	**.30524**	.48749	**.30725**	42
19	.47605	**.29926**	.47894	**.30126**	.48182	**.30326**	.48468	**.30527**	.48754	**.30728**	41
+ 5′	9.47610	**.29929**	9.47899	**.30129**	9.48187	**.30330**	9.48473	**.30530**	9.48758	**.30732**	40
21	.47614	**.29933**	.47904	**.30133**	.48192	**.30333**	.48478	**.30534**	.48763	**.30735**	39
22	.47619	**.29936**	.47908	**.30136**	.48196	**.30336**	.48483	**.30537**	.48768	**.30738**	38
23	.47624	**.29939**	.47913	**.30139**	.48201	**.30340**	.48488	**.30540**	.48773	**.30742**	37
+ 6′	9.47629	**.29943**	9.47918	**.30143**	9.48206	**.30343**	9.48492	**.30544**	9.48777	**.30745**	36
25	.47634	**.29946**	.47923	**.30146**	.48211	**.30346**	.48497	**.30547**	.48782	**.30748**	35
26	.47639	**.29949**	.47928	**.30149**	.48215	**.30350**	.48502	**.30551**	.48787	**.30752**	34
27	.47643	**.29953**	.47933	**.30153**	.48220	**.30353**	.48507	**.30554**	.48792	**.30755**	33
+ 7′	9.47648	**.29956**	9.47937	**.30156**	9.48225	**.30356**	9.48511	**.30557**	9.48796	**.30758**	32
29	.47653	**.29959**	.47942	**.30159**	.48230	**.30360**	.48516	**.30561**	.48801	**.30762**	31
30	.47658	**.29963**	.47947	**.30163**	.48235	**.30363**	.48521	**.30564**	.48806	**.30765**	30
31	.47663	**.29966**	.47952	**.30166**	.48239	**.30366**	.48526	**.30567**	.48811	**.30768**	29
+ 8′	9.47668	**.29969**	9.47957	**.30169**	9.48244	**.30370**	9.48530	**.30571**	9.48815	**.30772**	28
33	.47672	**.29973**	.47961	**.30173**	.48249	**.30373**	.48535	**.30574**	.48820	**.30775**	27
34	.47677	**.29976**	.47966	**.30176**	.48254	**.30376**	.48540	**.30577**	.48825	**.30779**	26
35	.47682	**.29979**	.47971	**.30179**	.48258	**.30380**	.48545	**.30581**	.48830	**.30782**	25
+ 9′	9.47687	**.29983**	9.47976	**.30183**	9.48263	**.30383**	9.48549	**.30584**	9.48834	**.30785**	24
37	.47692	**.29986**	.47981	**.30186**	.48268	**.30386**	.48554	**.30587**	.48839	**.30789**	23
38	.47697	**.29989**	.47985	**.30189**	.48273	**.30390**	.48559	**.30591**	.48844	**.30792**	22
39	.47701	**.29993**	.47990	**.30193**	.48278	**.30393**	.48564	**.30594**	.48848	**.30795**	21
+ 10′	9.47706	**.29996**	9.47995	**.30196**	9.48282	**.30397**	9.48568	**.30597**	9.48853	**.30799**	20
41	.47711	**.29999**	.48000	**.30199**	.48287	**.30400**	.48573	**.30601**	.48858	**.30802**	19
42	.47716	**.30003**	.48005	**.30203**	.48292	**.30403**	.48578	**.30604**	.48863	**.30805**	18
43	.47721	**.30006**	.48009	**.30206**	.48297	**.30407**	.48583	**.30607**	.48867	**.30809**	17
+ 11′	9.47725	**.30009**	9.48014	**.30209**	9.48302	**.30410**	9.48587	**.30611**	9.48872	**.30812**	16
45	.47730	**.30013**	.48019	**.30213**	.48306	**.30413**	.48592	**.30614**	.48877	**.30815**	15
46	.47735	**.30016**	.48024	**.30216**	.48311	**.30417**	.48597	**.30618**	.48882	**.30819**	14
47	.47740	**.30019**	.48029	**.30219**	.48316	**.30420**	.48602	**.30621**	.48886	**.30822**	13
+ 12′	9.47745	**.30023**	9.48033	**.30223**	9.48321	**.30423**	9.48607	**.30624**	9.48891	**.30826**	12
49	.47750	**.30026**	.48038	**.30226**	.48325	**.30427**	.48611	**.30628**	.48896	**.30829**	11
50	.47754	**.30029**	.48043	**.30229**	.48330	**.30430**	.48616	**.30631**	.48901	**.30832**	10
51	.47759	**.30033**	.48048	**.30233**	.48335	**.30433**	.48621	**.30634**	.48905	**.30836**	9
+ 13′	9.47764	**.30036**	9.48053	**.30236**	9.48340	**.30437**	9.48626	**.30638**	9.48910	**.30839**	8
53	.47769	**.30039**	.48057	**.30239**	.48344	**.30440**	.48630	**.30641**	.48915	**.30842**	7
54	.47774	**.30043**	.48062	**.30243**	.48349	**.30443**	.48635	**.30644**	.48919	**.30846**	6
55	.47778	**.30046**	.48067	**.30246**	.48354	**.30447**	.48640	**.30648**	.48924	**.30849**	5
+ 14′	9.47783	**.30049**	9.48072	**.30249**	9.48359	**.30450**	9.48645	**.30651**	9.48929	**.30852**	4
57	.47788	**.30053**	.48077	**.30253**	.48364	**.30453**	.48649	**.30655**	.48934	**.30856**	3
58	.47793	**.30056**	.48081	**.30256**	.48368	**.30457**	.48654	**.30658**	.48938	**.30859**	2
59	.47798	**.30059**	.48086	**.30259**	.48373	**.30460**	.48659	**.30661**	.48943	**.30862**	1
+ 15′	9.47803	**.30063**	9.48091	**.30263**	9.48378	**.30463**	9.48664	**.30664**	9.48948	**.30866**	0
	$19^h 34^m$		$19^h 33^m$		$19^h 32^m$		$19^h 31^m$		$19^h 30^m$		

TABLE 34.

Haversines.

s	4h 30m 67° 30′		4h 31m 67° 45′		4h 32m 68° 0′		4h 33m 68° 15′		4h 34m 68° 30′		s
	Log. Hav.	Nat. Hav.	Log. Hav.	Nat. Hav.	Log. Hav.	Nat. Hav.	Log. Hav.	Nat. Hav.	Log. Hav.	Nat. Hav.	
0	9.48948	.30866	9.49231	.31068	9.49512	.31270	9.49793	.31472	9.50072	.31675	60
1	.48953	.30869	.49235	.31071	.49517	.31273	.49797	.31475	.50076	.31678	59
2	.48957	.30873	.49240	.31074	.49522	.31276	.49802	.31479	.50081	.31682	58
3	.48962	.30876	.49245	.31078	.49526	.31280	.49807	.31482	.50085	.31685	57
+ 1′	9.48967	.30879	9.49250	.31081	9.49531	.31283	9.49811	.31486	9.50090	.31688	56
5	.48971	.30883	.49254	.31084	.49536	.31287	.49816	.31489	.50095	.31692	55
6	.48976	.30886	.49259	.31088	.49540	.31290	.49821	.31492	.50099	.31695	54
7	.48981	.30889	.49264	.31091	.49545	.31293	.49825	.31496	.50104	.31699	53
+ 2′	9.48986	.30893	9.49268	.31095	9.49550	.31297	9.49830	.31499	9.50109	.31702	52
9	.48990	.30896	.49273	.31098	.49554	.31300	.49835	.31503	.50113	.31705	51
10	.48995	.30899	.49278	.31101	.49559	.31303	.49839	.31506	.50118	.31709	50
11	.49000	.30903	.49282	.31105	.49564	.31307	.49844	.31509	.50123	.31712	49
+ 3′	9.49004	.30906	9.49287	.31108	9.49568	.31310	9.49849	.31513	9.50127	.31716	48
13	.49009	.30910	.49292	.31111	.49573	.31314	.49853	.31516	.50132	.31719	47
14	.49014	.30913	.49297	.31115	.49578	.31317	.49858	.31519	.50136	.31722	46
15	.49019	.30916	.49301	.31118	.49583	.31320	.49862	.31523	.50141	.31726	45
+ 4′	9.49023	.30920	9.49306	.31121	9.49587	.31324	9.49867	.31526	9.50146	.31729	44
17	.49028	.30923	.49311	.31125	.49592	.31327	.49872	.31530	.50150	.31732	43
18	.49033	.30926	.49315	.31128	.49597	.31330	.49876	.31533	.50155	.31736	42
19	.49038	.30930	.49320	.31132	.49601	.31334	.49881	.31536	.50160	.31739	41
+ 5′	9.49042	.30933	9.49325	.31135	9.49606	.31337	9.49886	.31540	9.50164	.31742	40
21	.49047	.30936	.49329	.31138	.49611	.31341	.49890	.31543	.50169	.31746	39
22	.49052	.30940	.49334	.31142	.49615	.31344	.49895	.31546	.50174	.31749	38
23	.49056	.30943	.49339	.31145	.49620	.31347	.49900	.31550	.50178	.31753	37
+ 6′	9.49061	.30946	9.49344	.31148	9.49625	.31351	9.49904	.31553	9.50183	.31756	36
25	.49066	.30950	.49348	.31152	.49629	.31354	.49909	.31557	.50187	.31760	35
26	.49071	.30953	.49353	.31155	.49634	.31357	.49914	.31560	.50192	.31763	34
27	.49075	.30957	.49358	.31158	.49639	.31361	.49918	.31563	.50197	.31766	33
+ 7′	9.49080	.30960	9.49362	.31162	9.49643	.31364	9.49923	.31567	9.50201	.31770	32
29	.49085	.30963	.49367	.31165	.49648	.31367	.49928	.31570	.50206	.31773	31
30	.49089	.30967	.49372	.31169	.49653	.31371	.49932	.31573	.50211	.31776	30
31	.49094	.30970	.49376	.31172	.49657	.31374	.49937	.31577	.50215	.31780	29
+ 8′	9.49099	.30973	9.49381	.31175	9.49662	.31378	9.49942	.31580	9.50220	.31783	28
33	.49104	.30977	.49386	.31179	.49667	.31381	.49946	.31584	.50224	.31787	27
34	.49108	.30980	.49390	.31182	.49671	.31384	.49951	.31587	.50229	.31790	26
35	.49113	.30983	.49395	.31185	.49676	.31388	.49956	.31590	.50234	.31793	25
+ 9′	9.49118	.30987	9.49400	.31189	9.49681	.31391	9.49960	.31594	9.50238	.31797	24
37	.49122	.30990	.49405	.31192	.49685	.31394	.49965	.31597	.50243	.31800	23
38	.49127	.30994	.49409	.31196	.49690	.31398	.49969	.31601	.50248	.31804	22
39	.49132	.30997	.49414	.31199	.49695	.31401	.49974	.31604	.50252	.31807	21
+ 10′	9.49137	.31000	9.49419	.31202	9.49699	.31405	9.49979	.31607	9.50257	.31810	20
41	.49141	.31004	.49423	.31206	.49704	.31408	.49983	.31611	.50261	.31814	19
42	.49146	.31007	.49428	.31209	.49709	.31411	.49988	.31614	.50266	.31817	18
43	.49151	.31010	.49433	.31212	.49713	.31415	.49993	.31617	.50271	.31820	17
+ 11′	9.49155	.31014	9.49437	.31216	9.49718	.31418	9.49997	.31621	9.50275	.31824	16
45	.49160	.31017	.49442	.31219	.49723	.31421	.50002	.31624	.50280	.31827	15
46	.49165	.31020	.49447	.31222	.49727	.31425	.50007	.31628	.50284	.31831	14
47	.49170	.31024	.49451	.31226	.49732	.31428	.50011	.31631	.50289	.31834	13
+ 12′	9.49174	.31027	9.49456	.31229	9.49737	.31432	9.50016	.31634	9.50294	.31837	12
49	.49179	.31031	.49461	.31233	.49741	.31435	.50021	.31638	.50298	.31841	11
50	.49184	.31034	.49465	.31236	.49746	.31438	.50025	.31641	.50303	.31844	10
51	.49188	.31037	.49470	.31239	.49751	.31442	.50030	.31644	.50308	.31848	9
+ 13′	9.49193	.31041	9.49475	.31243	9.49755	.31445	9.50034	.31648	9.50312	.31851	8
53	.49198	.31044	.49480	.31246	.49760	.31448	.50039	.31651	.50317	.31854	7
54	.49202	.31047	.49484	.31249	.49765	.31452	.50044	.31655	.50322	.31858	6
55	.49207	.31051	.49489	.31253	.49769	.31455	.50048	.31658	.50326	.31861	5
+ 14′	9.49212	.31054	9.49494	.31256	9.49774	.31459	9.50053	.31661	9.50331	.31865	4
57	.49217	.31057	.49498	.31260	.49779	.31462	.50058	.31665	.50335	.31868	3
58	.49221	.31061	.49503	.31263	.49783	.31465	.50062	.31668	.50340	.31871	2
59	.49226	.31064	.49508	.31266	.49788	.31469	.50067	.31672	.50345	.31875	1
+ 15′	9.49231	.31068	9.49512	.31270	9.49793	.31472	9.50072	.31675	9.50349	.31878	0
	19h 29m		19h 28m		19h 27m		19h 26m		19h 25m		

Haversines.

s	$4^h 35^m$ 68° 45′		$4^h 36^m$ 69° 0′		$4^h 37^m$ 69° 15′		$4^h 38^m$ 69° 30′		$4^h 39^m$ 69° 45′		
s	Log. Hav.	Nat. Hav.	Log. Hav.	Nat. Hav.	Log. Hav.	Nat. Hav.	Log. Hav.	Nat. Hav.	Log. Hav.	Nat. Hav.	s
0	9.50349	**.31878**	9.50626	**.32082**	9.50901	**.32285**	9.51174	**.32490**	9.51447	**.32694**	60
1	.50354	**.31881**	.50630	**.32085**	.50905	**.32289**	.51179	**.32493**	.51452	**.32698**	59
2	.50358	**.31885**	.50635	**.32088**	.50910	**.32292**	.51184	**.32496**	.51456	**.32701**	58
3	.50363	**.31888**	.50639	**.32092**	.50914	**.32296**	.51188	**.32500**	.51461	**.32704**	57
+ 1′	9.50368	**.31892**	9.50644	**.32095**	9.50919	**.32299**	9.51193	**.32503**	9.51465	**.32708**	56
5	.50372	**.31895**	.50649	**.32099**	.50924	**.32302**	.51197	**.32507**	.51470	**.32711**	55
6	.50377	**.31898**	.50653	**.32102**	.50928	**.32306**	.51202	**.32510**	.51474	**.32715**	54
7	.50382	**.31902**	.50658	**.32105**	.50933	**.32309**	.51206	**.32513**	.51479	**.32718**	53
+ 2′	9.50386	**.31905**	9.50662	**.32109**	9.50937	**.32313**	9.51211	**.32517**	9.51483	**.32721**	52
9	.50391	**.31909**	.50667	**.32112**	.50942	**.32316**	.51215	**.32520**	.51488	**.32725**	51
10	.50395	**.31912**	.50672	**.32116**	.50946	**.32319**	.51220	**.32524**	.51492	**.32728**	50
11	.50400	**.31915**	.50676	**.32119**	.50951	**.32323**	.51225	**.32527**	.51497	**.32732**	49
+ 3′	9.50405	**.31919**	9.50681	**.32122**	9.50956	**.32326**	9.51229	**.32531**	9.51501	**.32735**	48
13	.50409	**.31922**	.50685	**.32126**	.50960	**.32330**	.51234	**.32534**	.51506	**.32738**	47
14	.50414	**.31926**	.50690	**.32129**	.50965	**.32333**	.51238	**.32537**	.51510	**.32742**	46
15	.50418	**.31929**	.50694	**.32133**	.50969	**.32336**	.51243	**.32541**	.51515	**.32745**	45
+ 4′	9.50423	**.31932**	9.50699	**.32136**	9.50974	**.32340**	9.51247	**.32544**	9.51519	**.32749**	44
17	.50428	**.31936**	.50704	**.32139**	.50978	**.32343**	.51252	**.32547**	.51524	**.32752**	43
18	.50432	**.31939**	.50708	**.32143**	.50983	**.32347**	.51256	**.32551**	.51529	**.32756**	42
19	.50437	**.31942**	.50713	**.32146**	.50988	**.32350**	.51261	**.32554**	.51533	**.32759**	41
+ 5′	9.50442	**.31946**	9.50717	**.32150**	9.50992	**.32353**	9.51265	**.32558**	9.51538	**.32762**	40
21	.50446	**.31949**	.50722	**.32153**	.50997	**.32357**	.51270	**.32561**	.51542	**.32766**	39
22	.50451	**.31953**	.50727	**.32156**	.51001	**.32360**	.51275	**.32565**	.51547	**.32769**	38
23	.50455	**.31956**	.50731	**.32160**	.51006	**.32364**	.51279	**.32568**	.51551	**.32773**	37
+ 6′	9.50460	**.31959**	9.50736	**.32163**	9.51010	**.32367**	9.51284	**.32571**	9.51556	**.32776**	36
25	.50465	**.31963**	.50740	**.32166**	.51015	**.32370**	.51288	**.32575**	.51560	**.32779**	35
26	.50469	**.31966**	.50745	**.32170**	.51019	**.32374**	.51293	**.32578**	.51565	**.32783**	34
27	.50474	**.31970**	.50750	**.32173**	.51024	**.32377**	.51297	**.32582**	.51569	**.32786**	33
+ 7′	9.50478	**.31973**	9.50754	**.32177**	9.51029	**.32381**	9.51302	**.32585**	9.51574	**.32790**	32
29	.50483	**.31976**	.50759	**.32180**	.51033	**.32384**	.51306	**.32588**	.51578	**.32793**	31
30	.50488	**.31980**	.50763	**.32183**	.51038	**.32388**	.51311	**.32592**	.51583	**.32797**	30
31	.50492	**.31983**	.50768	**.32187**	.51042	**.32391**	.51315	**.32595**	.51587	**.32800**	29
+ 8′	9.50497	**.31987**	9.50772	**.32190**	9.51047	**.32394**	9.51320	**.32599**	9.51592	**.32803**	28
33	.50501	**.31990**	.50777	**.32194**	.51051	**.32398**	.51325	**.32602**	.51596	**.32807**	27
34	.50506	**.31993**	.50782	**.32197**	.51056	**.32401**	.51329	**.32605**	.51601	**.32810**	26
35	.50511	**.31997**	.50786	**.32200**	.51061	**.32405**	.51334	**.32609**	.51605	**.32814**	25
+ 9′	9.50515	**.32000**	9.50791	**.32204**	9.51065	**.32408**	9.51338	**.32612**	9.51610	**.32817**	24
37	.50520	**.32004**	.50795	**.32207**	.51070	**.32411**	.51343	**.32616**	.51614	**.32820**	23
38	.50524	**.32007**	.50800	**.32211**	.51074	**.32415**	.51347	**.32619**	.51619	**.32824**	22
39	.50529	**.32010**	.50805	**.32214**	.51079	**.32418**	.51352	**.32623**	.51623	**.32827**	21
+ 10′	9.50534	**.32014**	9.50809	**.32217**	9.51083	**.32422**	9.51356	**.32626**	9.51628	**.32831**	20
41	.50538	**.32017**	.50814	**.32221**	.51088	**.32425**	.51361	**.32629**	.51633	**.32834**	19
42	.50543	**.32021**	.50818	**.32224**	.51092	**.32428**	.51365	**.32633**	.51637	**.32838**	18
43	.50547	**.32024**	.50823	**.32228**	.51097	**.32432**	.51370	**.32636**	.51642	**.32841**	17
+ 11′	9.50552	**.32027**	9.50827	**.32231**	9.51102	**.32435**	9.51374	**.32640**	9.51646	**.32844**	16
45	.50557	**.32031**	.50832	**.32235**	.51106	**.32438**	.51379	**.32643**	.51651	**.32848**	15
46	.50561	**.32034**	.50837	**.32238**	.51111	**.32442**	.51384	**.32646**	.51655	**.32851**	14
47	.50566	**.32037**	.50841	**.32241**	.51115	**.32445**	.51388	**.32650**	.51660	**.32855**	13
+ 12′	9.50570	**.32041**	9.50846	**.32245**	9.51120	**.32449**	9.51393	**.32653**	9.51664	**.32858**	12
49	.50575	**.32044**	.50850	**.32248**	.51124	**.32452**	.51397	**.32657**	.51669	**.32861**	11
50	.50580	**.32048**	.50855	**.32251**	.51129	**.32456**	.51402	**.32660**	.51673	**.32865**	10
51	.50584	**.32051**	.50860	**.32255**	.51133	**.32459**	.51406	**.32663**	.51678	**.32868**	9
+ 13′	9.50589	**.32054**	9.50864	**.32258**	9.51138	**.32462**	9.51411	**.32667**	9.51682	**.32872**	8
53	.50593	**.32058**	.50869	**.32262**	.51143	**.32466**	.51415	**.32670**	.51687	**.32875**	7
54	.50598	**.32061**	.50873	**.32265**	.51147	**.32469**	.51420	**.32674**	.51691	**.32878**	6
55	.50603	**.32065**	.50878	**.32268**	.51152	**.32473**	.51424	**.32677**	.51696	**.32882**	5
+ 14′	9.50607	**.32068**	9.50882	**.32272**	9.51156	**.32476**	9.51429	**.32681**	9.51700	**.32885**	4
57	.50612	**.32071**	.50887	**.32275**	.51161	**.32479**	.51433	**.32684**	.51705	**.32889**	3
58	.50616	**.32075**	.50892	**.32279**	.51165	**.32483**	.51438	**.32687**	.51709	**.32892**	2
59	.50621	**.32078**	.50896	**.32282**	.51170	**.32486**	.51442	**.32691**	.51714	**.32896**	1
+ 15′	9.50626	**.32082**	9.50901	**.32285**	9.51174	**.32490**	9.51447	**.32694**	9.51718	**.32899**	0
	$19^h 24^m$		$19^h 23^m$		$19^h 22^m$		$19^h 21^m$		$19^h 20^m$		

TABLE 34.

Haversines.

s	$4^h 40^m$ 70° 0′ Log. Hav.	Nat. Hav.	$4^h 41^m$ 70° 15′ Log. Hav.	Nat. Hav.	$4^h 42^m$ 70° 30′ Log. Hav.	Nat. Hav.	$4^h 43^m$ 70° 45′ Log. Hav.	Nat. Hav.	$4^h 44^m$ 71° 0′ Log. Hav.	Nat. Hav.	s
0	9.51718	**.32899**	9.51988	**.33104**	9.52257	**.33310**	9.52525	**.33515**	9.52791	**.33722**	60
1	.51723	**.32902**	.51993	**.33108**	.52261	**.33313**	.52529	**.33519**	.52795	**.33725**	59
2	.51727	**.32906**	.51997	**.33111**	.52266	**.33317**	.52533	**.33522**	.52800	**.33728**	58
3	.51732	**.32909**	.52002	**.33114**	.52270	**.33320**	.52538	**.33526**	.52804	**.33732**	57
+ 1′	9.51736	**.32913**	9.52006	**.33118**	9.52275	**.33323**	9.52542	**.33529**	9.52809	**.33735**	56
5	.51741	**.32916**	.52011	**.33121**	.52279	**.33327**	.52547	**.33533**	.52813	**.33739**	55
6	.51745	**.32920**	.52015	**.33125**	.52284	**.33330**	.52551	**.33536**	.52817	**.33742**	54
7	.51750	**.32923**	.52020	**.33128**	.52288	**.33334**	.52556	**.33540**	.52822	**.33746**	53
+ 2′	9.51754	**.32926**	9.52024	**.33132**	9.52293	**.33337**	9.52560	**.33543**	9.52826	**.33749**	52
9	.51759	**.32930**	.52029	**.33135**	.52297	**.33341**	.52565	**.33546**	.52831	**.33753**	51
10	.51763	**.32933**	.52033	**.33138**	.52302	**.33344**	.52569	**.33550**	.52835	**.33756**	50
11	.51768	**.32937**	.52038	**.33142**	.52306	**.33347**	.52573	**.33553**	.52839	**.33759**	49
+ 3′	9.51772	**.32940**	9.52042	**.33145**	9.52311	**.33351**	9.52578	**.33557**	9.52844	**.33763**	48
13	.51777	**.32943**	.52047	**.33149**	.52315	**.33354**	.52582	**.33560**	.52848	**.33766**	47
14	.51781	**.32947**	.52051	**.33152**	.52320	**.33358**	.52587	**.33564**	.52853	**.33770**	46
15	.51786	**.32950**	.52056	**.33156**	.52324	**.33361**	.52591	**.33567**	.52857	**.33773**	45
+ 4′	9.51790	**.32954**	9.52060	**.33159**	9.52328	**.33365**	9.52596	**.33570**	9.52862	**.33777**	44
17	.51795	**.32957**	.52065	**.33162**	.52333	**.33368**	.52600	**.33574**	.52866	**.33780**	43
18	.51799	**.32961**	.52069	**.33166**	.52337	**.33371**	.52605	**.33577**	.52870	**.33783**	42
19	.51804	**.32964**	.52074	**.33169**	.52342	**.33375**	.52609	**.33581**	.52875	**.33787**	41
+ 5′	9.51808	**.32967**	9.52078	**.33173**	9.52346	**.33378**	9.52613	**.33584**	9.52879	**.33790**	40
21	.51813	**.32971**	.52082	**.33176**	.52351	**.33382**	.52618	**.33588**	.52884	**.33794**	39
22	.51817	**.32974**	.52087	**.33179**	.52355	**.33385**	.52622	**.33591**	.52888	**.33797**	38
23	.51822	**.32978**	.52091	**.33183**	.52360	**.33389**	.52627	**.33594**	.52893	**.33801**	37
+ 6′	9.51826	**.32981**	9.52096	**.33186**	9.52364	**.33392**	9.52631	**.33598**	9.52897	**.33804**	36
25	.51831	**.32984**	.52100	**.33190**	.52369	**.33395**	.52636	**.33601**	.52901	**.33808**	35
26	.51835	**.32988**	.52105	**.33193**	.52373	**.33399**	.52640	**.33605**	.52906	**.33811**	34
27	.51840	**.32991**	.52109	**.33197**	.52378	**.33402**	.52645	**.33608**	.52910	**.33814**	33
+ 7′	9.51844	**.32995**	9.52114	**.33200**	9.52382	**.33406**	9.52649	**.33612**	9.52915	**.33818**	32
29	.51849	**.32998**	.52118	**.33203**	.52386	**.33409**	.52653	**.33615**	.52919	**.33821**	31
30	.51853	**.33002**	.52123	**.33207**	.52391	**.33413**	.52658	**.33618**	.52923	**.33825**	30
31	.51858	**.33005**	.52127	**.33210**	.52395	**.33416**	.52662	**.33622**	.52928	**.33828**	29
+ 8′	9.51862	**.33008**	9.52132	**.33214**	9.52400	**.33419**	9.52667	**.33625**	9.52932	**.33832**	28
33	.51867	**.33012**	.52136	**.33217**	.52404	**.33423**	.52671	**.33629**	.52937	**.33835**	27
34	.51871	**.33015**	.52141	**.33221**	.52409	**.33426**	.52676	**.33632**	.52941	**.33839**	26
35	.51876	**.33019**	.52145	**.33224**	.52413	**.33430**	.52680	**.33636**	.52946	**.33842**	25
+ 9′	9.51880	**.33022**	9.52150	**.33227**	9.52418	**.33433**	9.52684	**.33639**	9.52950	**.33845**	24
37	.51885	**.33025**	.52154	**.33231**	.52422	**.33436**	.52689	**.33642**	.52954	**.33849**	23
38	.51889	**.33029**	.52159	**.33234**	.52427	**.33440**	.52693	**.33646**	.52959	**.33852**	22
39	.51894	**.33032**	.52163	**.33238**	.52431	**.33444**	.52698	**.33649**	.52963	**.33856**	21
+ 10′	9.51898	**.33036**	9.52168	**.33241**	9.52436	**.33447**	9.52702	**.33653**	9.52968	**.33859**	20
41	.51903	**.33039**	.52172	**.33245**	.52440	**.33450**	.52707	**.33656**	.52972	**.33863**	19
42	.51907	**.33043**	.52177	**.33248**	.52444	**.33454**	.52711	**.33660**	.52976	**.33866**	18
43	.51912	**.33046**	.52181	**.33251**	.52449	**.33457**	.52715	**.33663**	.52981	**.33869**	17
+ 11′	9.51916	**.33049**	9.52185	**.33255**	9.52453	**.33461**	9.52720	**.33667**	9.52985	**.33873**	16
45	.51921	**.33053**	.52190	**.33258**	.52458	**.33464**	.52724	**.33670**	.52990	**.33876**	15
46	.51925	**.33056**	.52194	**.33262**	.52462	**.33467**	.52729	**.33673**	.52994	**.33880**	14
47	.51930	**.33060**	.52199	**.33265**	.52467	**.33471**	.52733	**.33677**	.52999	**.33883**	13
+ 12′	9.51934	**.33063**	9.52203	**.33269**	9.52471	**.33474**	9.52738	**.33680**	9.53003	**.33887**	12
49	.51939	**.33067**	.52208	**.33272**	.52476	**.33478**	.52742	**.33684**	.53007	**.33890**	11
50	.51943	**.33070**	.52212	**.33275**	.52480	**.33481**	.52747	**.33687**	.53012	**.33894**	10
51	.51948	**.33073**	.52217	**.33279**	.52484	**.33485**	.52751	**.33691**	.53016	**.33897**	9
+ 13′	9.51952	**.33077**	9.52221	**.33282**	9.52489	**.33488**	9.52755	**.33694**	9.53021	**.33900**	8
53	.51957	**.33080**	.52226	**.33286**	.52493	**.33491**	.52760	**.33698**	.53025	**.33904**	7
54	.51961	**.33084**	.52230	**.33289**	.52498	**.33495**	.52764	**.33701**	.53029	**.33907**	6
55	.51966	**.33087**	.52235	**.33293**	.52502	**.33498**	.52769	**.33704**	.53034	**.33911**	5
+ 14′	9.51970	**.33090**	9.52239	**.33296**	9.52507	**.33502**	9.52773	**.33708**	9.53038	**.33914**	4
57	.51975	**.33094**	.52244	**.33299**	.52511	**.33505**	.52778	**.33711**	.53043	**.33918**	3
58	.51979	**.33097**	.52248	**.33303**	.52516	**.33509**	.52782	**.33715**	.53047	**.33921**	2
59	.51984	**.33101**	.52253	**.33306**	.52520	**.33512**	.52786	**.33718**	.53051	**.33925**	1
+ 15′	9.51988	**.33104**	9.52257	**.33310**	9.52525	**.33515**	9.52791	**.33722**	9.53056	**.33928**	0
	$19^h 19^m$		$19^h 18^m$		$19^h 17^m$		$19^h 16^m$		$19^h 15^m$		

TABLE 34.

Haversines.

s	$4^h 45^m$ 71° 15′ Log. Hav.	Nat. Hav.	$4^h 46^m$ 71° 30′ Log. Hav.	Nat. Hav.	$4^h 47^m$ 71° 45′ Log. Hav.	Nat. Hav.	$4^h 48^m$ 72° 0′ Log. Hav.	Nat. Hav.	$4^h 49^m$ 72° 15′ Log. Hav.	Nat. Hav.	s
0	9.53056	**.33928**	9.53320	**.34135**	9.53582	**.34342**	9.53844	**.34549**	9.54104	**.34757**	60
1	.53060	**.33931**	.53324	**.34138**	.53587	**.34345**	.53848	**.34553**	.54108	**.34760**	59
2	.53065	**.33935**	.53328	**.34142**	.53591	**.34349**	.53852	**.34556**	.54113	**.34764**	58
3	.53069	**.33938**	.53333	**.34145**	.53595	**.34352**	.53857	**.34560**	.54117	**.34767**	57
+ 1′	9.53073	**.33942**	9.53337	**.34149**	9.53600	**.34356**	9.53861	**.34563**	9.54121	**.34771**	56
5	.53078	**.33945**	.53342	**.34152**	.53604	**.34359**	.53865	**.34566**	.54126	**.34774**	55
6	.53082	**.33949**	.53346	**.34155**	.53609	**.34363**	.53870	**.34570**	.54130	**.34778**	54
7	.53087	**.33952**	.53350	**.34159**	.53613	**.34366**	.53874	**.34573**	.54134	**.34781**	53
+ 2′	9.53091	**.33956**	9.53355	**.34162**	9.53617	**.34369**	9.53879	**.34577**	9.54139	**.34784**	52
9	.53096	**.33959**	.53359	**.34166**	.53622	**.34373**	.53883	**.34580**	.54143	**.34788**	51
10	.53100	**.33962**	.53364	**.34169**	.53626	**.34376**	.53887	**.34584**	.54147	**.34791**	50
11	.53104	**.33966**	.53368	**.34173**	.53630	**.34380**	.53892	**.34587**	.54152	**.34795**	49
+ 3′	9.53109	**.33969**	9.53372	**.34176**	9.53635	**.34383**	9.53896	**.34591**	9.54156	**.34798**	48
13	.53113	**.33973**	.53377	**.34180**	.53639	**.34387**	.53900	**.34594**	.54160	**.34802**	47
14	.53118	**.33976**	.53381	**.34183**	.53643	**.34390**	.53905	**.34598**	.54165	**.34805**	46
15	.53122	**.33980**	.53385	**.34186**	.53648	**.34394**	.53909	**.34601**	.54169	**.34809**	45
+ 4′	9.53126	**.33983**	9.53390	**.34190**	9.53652	**.34397**	9.53913	**.34604**	9.54173	**.34812**	44
17	.53131	**.33986**	.53394	**.34193**	.53657	**.34400**	.53918	**.34608**	.54177	**.34816**	43
18	.53135	**.33990**	.53399	**.34197**	.53661	**.34404**	.53922	**.34611**	.54182	**.34819**	42
19	.53140	**.33993**	.53403	**.34200**	.53665	**.34407**	.53926	**.34615**	.54186	**.34823**	41
+ 5′	9.53144	**.33997**	9.53407	**.34204**	9.53670	**.34411**	9.53931	**.34618**	9.54190	**.34826**	40
21	.53148	**.34000**	.53412	**.34207**	.53674	**.34414**	.53935	**.34622**	.54195	**.34830**	39
22	.53153	**.34004**	.53416	**.34211**	.53678	**.34418**	.53939	**.34625**	.54199	**.34833**	38
23	.53157	**.34007**	.53421	**.34214**	.53683	**.34421**	.53944	**.34629**	.54203	**.34836**	37
+ 6′	9.53162	**.34011**	9.53425	**.34218**	9.53687	**.34425**	9.53948	**.34632**	9.54208	**.34840**	36
25	.53166	**.34014**	.53429	**.34221**	.53691	**.34428**	.53952	**.34636**	.54212	**.34843**	35
26	.53170	**.34018**	.53434	**.34224**	.53696	**.34432**	.53957	**.34639**	.54216	**.34847**	34
27	.53175	**.34021**	.53438	**.34228**	.53700	**.34435**	.53961	**.34643**	.54221	**.34850**	33
+ 7′	9.53179	**.34024**	9.53442	**.34231**	9.53704	**.34439**	9.53966	**.34646**	9.54225	**.34854**	32
29	.53184	**.34028**	.53447	**.34235**	.53709	**.34442**	.53970	**.34649**	.54229	**.34857**	31
30	.53188	**.34031**	.53451	**.34238**	.53713	**.34445**	.53974	**.34653**	.54234	**.34861**	30
31	.53192	**.34035**	.53456	**.34242**	.53718	**.34449**	.53978	**.34656**	.54238	**.34864**	29
+ 8′	9.53197	**.34038**	9.53460	**.34245**	9.53722	**.34452**	9.53983	**.34660**	9.54242	**.34868**	28
33	.53201	**.34042**	.53464	**.34249**	.53726	**.34456**	.53987	**.34663**	.54247	**.34871**	27
34	.53206	**.34045**	.53469	**.34252**	.53731	**.34459**	.53991	**.34667**	.54251	**.34875**	26
35	.53210	**.34049**	.53473	**.34256**	.53735	**.34463**	.53996	**.34670**	.54255	**.34878**	25
+ 9′	9.53214	**.34052**	9.53477	**.34259**	9.53739	**.34466**	9.54000	**.34674**	9.54260	**.34882**	24
37	.53219	**.34055**	.53482	**.34262**	.53744	**.34470**	.54004	**.34677**	.54264	**.34885**	23
38	.53223	**.34059**	.53486	**.34266**	.53748	**.34473**	.54009	**.34681**	.54268	**.34888**	22
39	.53228	**.34062**	.53491	**.34269**	.53752	**.34477**	.54013	**.34684**	.54272	**.34892**	21
+ 10′	9.53232	**.34066**	9.53495	**.34273**	9.53757	**.34480**	9.54017	**.34688**	9.54277	**.34895**	20
41	.53236	**.34069**	.53499	**.34276**	.53761	**.34483**	.54022	**.34691**	.54281	**.34899**	19
42	.53241	**.34073**	.53504	**.34280**	.53765	**.34487**	.54026	**.34694**	.54285	**.34902**	18
43	.53245	**.34076**	.53508	**.34283**	.53770	**.34490**	.54030	**.34698**	.54290	**.34906**	17
+ 11′	9.53249	**.34080**	9.53512	**.34287**	9.53774	**.34494**	9.54035	**.34701**	9.54294	**.34909**	16
45	.53254	**.34083**	.53517	**.34290**	.53778	**.34497**	.54039	**.34705**	.54298	**.34913**	15
46	.53258	**.34087**	.53521	**.34293**	.53783	**.34501**	.54043	**.34708**	.54303	**.34916**	14
47	.53263	**.34090**	.53526	**.34297**	.53787	**.34504**	.54048	**.34712**	.54307	**.34920**	13
+ 12′	9.53267	**.34093**	9.53530	**.34300**	9.53792	**.34508**	9.54052	**.34715**	9.54311	**.34923**	12
49	.53271	**.34097**	.53534	**.34304**	.53796	**.34511**	.54056	**.34719**	.54316	**.34927**	11
50	.53276	**.34100**	.53539	**.34307**	.53800	**.34515**	.54061	**.34722**	.54320	**.34930**	10
51	.53280	**.34104**	.53543	**.34311**	.53805	**.34518**	.54065	**.34726**	.54324	**.34933**	9
+ 13′	9.53285	**.34107**	9.53547	**.34314**	9.53809	**.34521**	9.54069	**.34729**	9.54329	**.34937**	8
53	.53289	**.34111**	.53552	**.34318**	.53813	**.34525**	.54074	**.34733**	.54333	**.34940**	7
54	.53293	**.34114**	.53556	**.34321**	.53818	**.34528**	.54078	**.34736**	.54337	**.34944**	6
55	.53298	**.34118**	.53560	**.34325**	.53822	**.34532**	.54082	**.34739**	.54341	**.34947**	5
+ 14′	9.53302	**.34121**	9.53565	**.34328**	9.53826	**.34535**	9.54087	**.34743**	9.54346	**.34951**	4
57	.53307	**.34124**	.53569	**.34331**	.53831	**.34539**	.54091	**.34746**	.54350	**.34954**	3
58	.53311	**.34128**	.53574	**.34335**	.53835	**.34542**	.54095	**.34750**	.54354	**.34958**	2
59	.53315	**.34131**	.53578	**.34338**	.53839	**.34546**	.54100	**.34753**	.54359	**.34961**	1
+ 15′	9.53320	**.34135**	9.53582	**.34342**	9.53844	**.34549**	9.54104	**.34757**	9.54363	**.34965**	0
	$19^h 14^m$		$19^h 13^m$		$19^h 12^m$		$19^h 11^m$		$19^h 10^m$		

TABLE 34.

Haversines.

s	$4^h 50^m$ 72° 30′		$4^h 51^m$ 72° 45′		$4^h 52^m$ 73° 0′		$4^h 53^m$ 73° 15′		$4^h 54^m$ 73° 30′		s
	Log. Hav.	Nat. Hav.	Log. Hav.	Nat. Hav.	Log. Hav.	Nat. Hav.	Log. Hav.	Nat. Hav.	Log. Hav.	Nat. Hav.	
0	9.54363	**.34965**	9.54621	**.35173**	9.54878	**.35381**	9.55133	**.35590**	9.55387	**.35799**	60
1	.54367	**.34968**	.54625	**.35176**	.54882	**.35385**	.55137	**.35594**	.55392	**.35803**	59
2	.54372	**.34972**	.54629	**.35180**	.54886	**.35388**	.55142	**.35597**	.55396	**.35806**	58
3	.54376	**.34975**	.54634	**.35183**	.54890	**.35392**	.55146	**.35601**	.55400	**.35810**	57
+ 1′	9.54380	**.34979**	9.54638	**.35187**	9.54895	**.35395**	9.55150	**.35604**	9.55404	**.35813**	56
5	.54385	**.34982**	.54642	**.35190**	.54899	**.35399**	.55154	**.35608**	.55409	**.35817**	55
6	.54389	**.34986**	.54647	**.35194**	.54903	**.35402**	.55159	**.35611**	.55413	**.35820**	54
7	.54393	**.34989**	.54651	**.35197**	.54907	**.35406**	.55163	**.35615**	.55417	**.35824**	53
+ 2′	9.54397	**.34992**	9.54655	**.35201**	9.54912	**.35409**	9.55167	**.35618**	9.55421	**.35827**	52
9	.54402	**.34996**	.54659	**.35204**	.54916	**.35413**	.55171	**.35622**	.55425	**.35831**	51
10	.54406	**.34999**	.54664	**.35208**	.54920	**.35416**	.55176	**.35625**	.55430	**.35834**	50
11	.54410	**.35003**	.54668	**.35211**	.54924	**.35420**	.55180	**.35628**	.55434	**.35838**	49
+ 3′	9.54415	**.35006**	9.54672	**.35215**	9.54929	**.35423**	9.55184	**.35632**	9.55438	**.35841**	48
13	.54419	**.35010**	.54677	**.35218**	.54933	**.35427**	.55188	**.35635**	.55442	**.35845**	47
14	.54423	**.35013**	.54681	**.35222**	.54937	**.35430**	.55192	**.35639**	.55447	**.35848**	46
15	.54428	**.35017**	.54685	**.35225**	.54942	**.35434**	.55197	**.35642**	.55451	**.35852**	45
+ 4′	9.54432	**.35020**	9.54689	**.35228**	9.54946	**.35437**	9.55201	**.35646**	9.55455	**.35855**	44
17	.54436	**.35024**	.54694	**.35232**	.54950	**.35441**	.55205	**.35649**	.55459	**.35859**	43
18	.54440	**.35027**	.54698	**.35235**	.54954	**.35444**	.55209	**.35653**	.55463	**.35862**	42
19	.54445	**.35031**	.54702	**.35239**	.54959	**.35448**	.55214	**.35656**	.55468	**.35865**	41
+ 5′	9.54449	**.35034**	9.54707	**.35242**	9.54963	**.35451**	9.55218	**.35660**	9.55472	**.35869**	40
21	.54453	**.35038**	.54711	**.35246**	.54967	**.35454**	.55222	**.35663**	.55476	**.35872**	39
22	.54458	**.35041**	.54715	**.35249**	.54971	**.35458**	.55226	**.35667**	.55480	**.35876**	38
23	.54462	**.35044**	.54719	**.35253**	.54976	**.35461**	.55231	**.35670**	.55485	**.35879**	37
+ 6′	9.54466	**.35048**	9.54724	**.35256**	9.54980	**.35465**	9.55235	**.35674**	9.55489	**.35883**	36
25	.54471	**.35051**	.54728	**.35260**	.54984	**.35468**	.55239	**.35677**	.55493	**.35886**	35
26	.54475	**.35055**	.54732	**.35263**	.54988	**.35472**	.55243	**.35681**	.55497	**.35890**	34
27	.54479	**.35058**	.54736	**.35267**	.54993	**.35475**	.55248	**.35684**	.55501	**.35893**	33
+ 7′	9.54483	**.35062**	9.54741	**.35270**	9.54997	**.35479**	9.55252	**.35688**	9.55506	**.35897**	32
29	.54488	**.35065**	.54745	**.35274**	.55001	**.35482**	.55256	**.35691**	.55510	**.35900**	31
30	.54492	**.35069**	.54749	**.35277**	.55005	**.35486**	.55260	**.35695**	.55514	**.35904**	30
31	.54496	**.35072**	.54754	**.35281**	.55010	**.35489**	.55265	**.35698**	.55518	**.35907**	29
+ 8′	9.54501	**.35076**	9.54758	**.35284**	9.55014	**.35493**	9.55269	**.35702**	9.55523	**.35911**	28
33	.54505	**.35079**	.54762	**.35288**	.55018	**.35496**	.55273	**.35705**	.55527	**.35914**	27
34	.54509	**.35083**	.54766	**.35291**	.55022	**.35500**	.55277	**.35709**	.55531	**.35918**	26
35	.54514	**.35086**	.54771	**.35294**	.55027	**.35503**	.55282	**.35712**	.55535	**.35921**	25
+ 9′	9.54518	**.35090**	9.54775	**.35298**	9.55031	**.35507**	9.55286	**.35716**	9.55539	**.35925**	24
37	.54522	**.35093**	.54779	**.35301**	.55035	**.35510**	.55290	**.35719**	.55544	**.35928**	23
38	.54526	**.35097**	.54784	**.35305**	.55039	**.35514**	.55294	**.35723**	.55548	**.35932**	22
39	.54531	**.35100**	.54788	**.35308**	.55044	**.35517**	.55298	**.35726**	.55552	**.35935**	21
+ 10′	9.54535	**.35103**	9.54792	**.35312**	9.55048	**.35521**	9.55303	**.35730**	9.55556	**.35939**	20
41	.54539	**.35107**	.54796	**.35315**	.55052	**.35524**	.55307	**.35733**	.55561	**.35942**	19
42	.54544	**.35110**	.54801	**.35319**	.55057	**.35528**	.55311	**.35737**	.55565	**.35946**	18
43	.54548	**.35114**	.54805	**.35322**	.55061	**.35531**	.55315	**.35740**	.55569	**.35949**	17
+ 11′	9.54552	**.35117**	9.54809	**.35326**	9.55065	**.35534**	9.55320	**.35743**	9.55573	**.35953**	16
45	.54556	**.35121**	.54813	**.35329**	.55069	**.35538**	.55324	**.35747**	.55577	**.35956**	15
46	.54561	**.35124**	.54818	**.35333**	.55074	**.35541**	.55328	**.35750**	.55582	**.35960**	14
47	.54565	**.35128**	.54822	**.35336**	.55078	**.35545**	.55332	**.35754**	.55586	**.35963**	13
+ 12′	9.54569	**.35131**	9.54826	**.35340**	9.55082	**.35548**	9.55337	**.35757**	9.55590	**.35967**	12
49	.54574	**.35135**	.54831	**.35343**	.55086	**.35552**	.55341	**.35761**	.55594	**.35970**	11
50	.54578	**.35138**	.54835	**.35347**	.55091	**.35555**	.55345	**.35764**	.55598	**.35974**	10
51	.54582	**.35142**	.54839	**.35350**	.55095	**.35559**	.55349	**.35768**	.55603	**.35977**	9
+ 13′	9.54587	**.35145**	9.54843	**.35354**	9.55099	**.35562**	9.55354	**.35771**	9.55607	**.35981**	8
53	.54591	**.35149**	.54848	**.35357**	.55103	**.35566**	.55358	**.35775**	.55611	**.35984**	7
54	.54595	**.35152**	.54852	**.35361**	.55108	**.35569**	.55362	**.35778**	.55615	**.35988**	6
55	.54599	**.35156**	.54856	**.35364**	.55112	**.35573**	.55366	**.35782**	.55620	**.35991**	5
+ 14′	9.54604	**.35159**	9.54860	**.35368**	9.55116	**.35576**	9.55370	**.35785**	9.55624	**.35995**	4
57	.54608	**.35162**	.54865	**.35371**	.55120	**.35580**	.55375	**.35789**	.55628	**.35998**	3
58	.54612	**.35166**	.54869	**.35374**	.55125	**.35583**	.55379	**.35792**	.55632	**.36002**	2
59	.54617	**.35169**	.54873	**.35378**	.55129	**.35587**	.55383	**.35796**	.55636	**.36005**	1
+ 15′	9.54621	**.35173**	9.54878	**.35381**	9.55133	**.35590**	9.55387	**.35799**	9.55641	**.36009**	0
	$19^h 9^m$		$19^h 8^m$		$19^h 7^m$		$19^h 6^m$		$19^h 5^m$		

TABLE 34.

Haversines.

s	$4^h 55^m$ 73° 45′		$4^h 56^m$ 74° 0′		$4^h 57^m$ 74° 15′		$4^h 58^m$ 74° 30′		$4^h 59^m$ 74° 45′		s
	Log. Hav.	Nat. Hav.	Log. Hav.	Nat. Hav.	Log. Hav.	Nat. Hav.	Log. Hav.	Nat. Hav.	Log. Hav.	Nat. Hav.	
0	9.55641	**.36009**	9.55893	**.36218**	9.56144	**.36428**	9.56393	**.36638**	9.56642	**.36848**	60
1	.55645	**.36012**	.55897	**.36222**	.56148	**.36431**	.56397	**.36642**	.56646	**.36852**	59
2	.55649	**.36016**	.55901	**.36225**	.56152	**.36435**	.56402	**.36645**	.56650	**.36855**	58
3	.55653	**.36019**	.55905	**.36229**	.56156	**.36438**	.56406	**.36649**	.56654	**.36859**	57
+ 1′	9.55657	**.36023**	9.55909	**.36232**	9.56160	**.36442**	9.56410	**.36652**	9.56658	**.36862**	56
5	.55662	**.36026**	.55914	**.36236**	.56164	**.36445**	.56414	**.36656**	.56663	**.36866**	55
6	.55666	**.36030**	.55918	**.36239**	.56169	**.36449**	.56418	**.36659**	.56667	**.36869**	54
7	.55670	**.36033**	.55922	**.36243**	.56173	**.36452**	.56422	**.36663**	.56671	**.36873**	53
+ 2′	9.55674	**.36036**	9.55926	**.36246**	9.56177	**.36456**	9.56426	**.36666**	9.56675	**.36877**	52
9	.55678	**.36040**	.55930	**.36250**	.56181	**.36459**	.56431	**.36670**	.56679	**.36880**	51
10	.55683	**.36043**	.55935	**.36253**	.56185	**.36463**	.56435	**.36673**	.56683	**.36884**	50
11	.55687	**.36047**	.55939	**.36257**	.56189	**.36466**	.56439	**.36677**	.56687	**.36887**	49
+ 3′	9.55691	**.36050**	9.55943	**.36260**	9.56194	**.36470**	9.56443	**.36680**	9.56692	**.36891**	48
13	.55695	**.36054**	.55947	**.36264**	.56198	**.36473**	.56447	**.36684**	.56696	**.36894**	47
14	.55699	**.36057**	.55951	**.36267**	.56202	**.36477**	.56451	**.36687**	.56700	**.36898**	46
15	.55704	**.36061**	.55955	**.36271**	.56206	**.36480**	.56456	**.36691**	.56704	**.36901**	45
+ 4′	9.55708	**.36064**	9.55960	**.36274**	9.56210	**.36484**	9.56460	**.36694**	9.56708	**.36905**	44
17	.55712	**.36068**	.55964	**.36278**	.56214	**.36487**	.56464	**.36698**	.56712	**.36908**	43
18	.55716	**.36071**	.55968	**.36281**	.56219	**.36491**	.56468	**.36701**	.56716	**.36912**	42
19	.55721	**.36075**	.55972	**.36285**	.56223	**.36494**	.56472	**.36705**	.56720	**.36915**	41
+ 5′	9.55725	**.36078**	9.55976	**.36288**	9.56227	**.36498**	9.56476	**.36708**	9.56725	**.36919**	40
21	.55729	**.36082**	.55981	**.36292**	.56231	**.36501**	.56480	**.36712**	.56729	**.36922**	39
22	.55733	**.36085**	.55985	**.36295**	.56235	**.36505**	.56485	**.36715**	.56733	**.36926**	38
23	.55737	**.36089**	.55989	**.36299**	.56239	**.36508**	.56489	**.36719**	.56737	**.36929**	37
+ 6′	9.55742	**.36092**	9.55993	**.36302**	9.56244	**.36512**	9.56493	**.36722**	9.56741	**.36933**	36
25	.55746	**.36096**	.55997	**.36306**	.56248	**.36515**	.56497	**.36726**	.56745	**.36936**	35
26	.55750	**.36099**	.56001	**.36309**	.56252	**.36519**	.56501	**.36729**	.56749	**.36940**	34
27	.55754	**.36103**	.56006	**.36313**	.56256	**.36522**	.56505	**.36733**	.56753	**.36943**	33
+ 7′	9.55758	**.36106**	9.56010	**.36316**	9.56260	**.36526**	9.56509	**.36736**	9.56758	**.36947**	32
29	.55763	**.36110**	.56014	**.36320**	.56264	**.36529**	.56514	**.36740**	.56762	**.36950**	31
30	.55767	**.36113**	.56018	**.36323**	.56269	**.36533**	.56518	**.36743**	.56766	**.36954**	30
31	.55771	**.36117**	.56022	**.36327**	.56273	**.36536**	.56522	**.36747**	.56770	**.36957**	29
+ 8′	9.55775	**.36120**	9.56027	**.36330**	9.56277	**.36540**	9.56526	**.36750**	9.56774	**.36961**	28
33	.55779	**.36124**	.56031	**.36334**	.56281	**.36543**	.56530	**.36754**	.56778	**.36964**	27
34	.55784	**.36127**	.56035	**.36337**	.56285	**.36547**	.56534	**.36757**	.56782	**.36968**	26
35	.55788	**.36131**	.56039	**.36341**	.56289	**.36551**	.56538	**.36761**	.56786	**.36971**	25
+ 9′	9.55792	**.36134**	9.56043	**.36344**	9.56294	**.36554**	9.56543	**.36764**	9.56791	**.36975**	24
37	.55796	**.36138**	.56047	**.36348**	.56298	**.36558**	.56547	**.36768**	.56795	**.36978**	23
38	.55800	**.36141**	.56052	**.36351**	.56302	**.36561**	.56551	**.36771**	.56799	**.36982**	22
39	.55805	**.36145**	.56056	**.36355**	.56306	**.36565**	.56555	**.36775**	.56803	**.36985**	21
+ 10′	9.55809	**.36148**	9.56060	**.36358**	9.56310	**.36568**	9.56559	**.36778**	9.56807	**.36989**	20
41	.55813	**.36152**	.56064	**.36362**	.56314	**.36572**	.56563	**.36782**	.56811	**.36992**	19
42	.55817	**.36155**	.56068	**.36365**	.56318	**.36575**	.56567	**.36785**	.56815	**.36996**	18
43	.55821	**.36159**	.56073	**.36368**	.56323	**.36579**	.56572	**.36789**	.56819	**.36999**	17
+ 11′	9.55826	**.36162**	9.56077	**.36372**	9.56327	**.36582**	9.56576	**.36792**	9.56824	**.37003**	16
45	.55830	**.36166**	.56081	**.36376**	.56331	**.36586**	.56580	**.36796**	.56828	**.37006**	15
46	.55834	**.36169**	.56085	**.36379**	.56335	**.36589**	.56584	**.36799**	.56832	**.37010**	14
47	.55838	**.36173**	.56089	**.36382**	.56339	**.36593**	.56588	**.36803**	.56836	**.37013**	13
+ 12′	9.55842	**.36176**	9.56093	**.36386**	9.56343	**.36596**	9.56592	**.36806**	9.56840	**.37017**	12
49	.55846	**.36180**	.56098	**.36389**	.56348	**.36600**	.56596	**.36810**	.56844	**.37020**	11
50	.55851	**.36183**	.56102	**.36393**	.56352	**.36603**	.56601	**.36813**	.56848	**.37024**	10
51	.55855	**.36187**	.56106	**.36396**	.56356	**.36607**	.56605	**.36817**	.56852	**.37027**	9
+ 13′	9.55859	**.36190**	9.56110	**.36400**	9.56360	**.36610**	9.56609	**.36820**	9.56856	**.37031**	8
53	.55863	**.36194**	.56114	**.36403**	.56364	**.36614**	.56613	**.36824**	.56861	**.37034**	7
54	.55867	**.36197**	.56118	**.36407**	.56368	**.36617**	.56617	**.36827**	.56865	**.37038**	6
55	.55872	**.36201**	.56123	**.36410**	.56373	**.36621**	.56621	**.36831**	.56869	**.37041**	5
+ 14′	9.55876	**.36204**	9.56127	**.36414**	9.56377	**.36624**	9.56625	**.36834**	9.56873	**.37045**	4
57	.55880	**.36208**	.56131	**.36417**	.56381	**.36628**	.56630	**.36838**	.56877	**.37049**	3
58	.55884	**.36211**	.56135	**.36421**	.56385	**.36631**	.56634	**.36841**	.56881	**.37052**	2
59	.55888	**.36215**	.56139	**.36424**	.56389	**.36635**	.56638	**.36845**	.56885	**.37055**	1
+ 15′	9.55893	**.36218**	9.56144	**.36428**	9.56393	**.36638**	9.56642	**.36848**	9.56889	**.37059**	0
	$19^h 4^m$		$19^h 3^m$		$19^h 2^m$		$19^h 1^m$		$19^h 0^m$		

TABLE 34.

Haversines.

s	$5^h\ 0^m$ 75° 0′ Log. Hav.	Nat. Hav.	$5^h\ 1^m$ 75° 15′ Log. Hav.	Nat. Hav.	$5^h\ 2^m$ 75° 30′ Log. Hav.	Nat. Hav.	$5^h\ 3^m$ 75° 45′ Log. Hav.	Nat. Hav.	$5^h\ 4^m$ 76° 0′ Log. Hav.	Nat. Hav.	s
0	9.56889	**.37059**	9.57136	**.37270**	9.57381	**.37481**	9.57625	**.37692**	9.57868	**.37904**	60
1	.56893	**.37063**	.57140	**.37273**	.57385	**.37485**	.57629	**.37696**	.57872	**.37907**	59
2	.56898	**.37066**	.57144	**.37277**	.57389	**.37488**	.57633	**.37699**	.57876	**.37911**	58
3	.56902	**.37070**	.57148	**.37280**	.57393	**.37492**	.57637	**.37703**	.57881	**.37914**	57
+ 1′	9.56906	**.37073**	9.57152	**.37284**	9.57397	**.37495**	9.57642	**.37706**	9.57885	**.37918**	56
5	.56910	**.37077**	.57156	**.37287**	.57402	**.37499**	.57646	**.37710**	.57889	**.37922**	55
6	.56914	**.37080**	.57160	**.37291**	.57406	**.37502**	.57650	**.37713**	.57893	**.37925**	54
7	.56918	**.37084**	.57165	**.37295**	.57410	**.37506**	.57654	**.37717**	.57897	**.37929**	53
+ 2′	9.56922	**.37087**	9.57169	**.37298**	9.57414	**.37509**	9.57658	**.37721**	9.57901	**.37932**	52
9	.56926	**.37091**	.57173	**.37302**	.57418	**.37513**	.57662	**.37724**	.57905	**.37936**	51
10	.56931	**.37094**	.57177	**.37305**	.57422	**.37516**	.57666	**.37728**	.57909	**.37939**	50
11	.56935	**.37098**	.57181	**.37309**	.57426	**.37520**	.57670	**.37731**	.57913	**.37943**	49
+ 3′	9.56939	**.37101**	9.57185	**.37312**	9.57430	**.37523**	9.57674	**.37735**	9.57917	**.37946**	48
13	.56943	**.37105**	.57189	**.37316**	.57434	**.37527**	.57678	**.37738**	.57921	**.37950**	47
14	.56947	**.37108**	.57193	**.37319**	.57438	**.37530**	.57682	**.37742**	.57925	**.37953**	46
15	.56951	**.37112**	.57197	**.37323**	.57442	**.37534**	.57686	**.37745**	.57929	**.37957**	45
+ 4′	9.56955	**.37115**	9.57201	**.37326**	9.57446	**.37537**	9.57690	**.37749**	9.57933	**.37960**	44
17	.56959	**.37119**	.57205	**.37330**	.57450	**.37541**	.57694	**.37752**	.57937	**.37964**	43
18	.56963	**.37122**	.57210	**.37333**	.57454	**.37544**	.57698	**.37756**	.57941	**.37967**	42
19	.56968	**.37126**	.57214	**.37337**	.57459	**.37548**	.57702	**.37759**	.57945	**.37971**	41
+ 5′	9.56972	**.37129**	9.57218	**.37340**	9.57463	**.37551**	9.57706	**.37763**	9.57949	**.37974**	40
21	.56976	**.37133**	.57222	**.37344**	.57467	**.37555**	.57711	**.37766**	.57953	**.37978**	39
22	.56980	**.37136**	.57226	**.37347**	.57471	**.37558**	.57715	**.37770**	.57957	**.37982**	38
23	.56984	**.37140**	.57230	**.37351**	.57475	**.37562**	.57719	**.37773**	.57961	**.37985**	37
+ 6′	9.56988	**.37143**	9.57234	**.37354**	9.57479	**.37566**	9.57723	**.37777**	9.57965	**.37989**	36
25	.56992	**.37147**	.57238	**.37358**	.57483	**.37569**	.57727	**.37780**	.57969	**.37992**	35
26	.56996	**.37150**	.57242	**.37361**	.57487	**.37573**	.57731	**.37784**	.57973	**.37996**	34
27	.57000	**.37154**	.57246	**.37365**	.57491	**.37576**	.57735	**.37788**	.57977	**.37999**	33
+ 7′	9.57005	**.37157**	9.57250	**.37368**	9.57495	**.37580**	9.57739	**.37791**	9.57981	**.38003**	32
29	.57009	**.37161**	.57255	**.37372**	.57499	**.37583**	.57743	**.37794**	.57986	**.38006**	31
30	.57013	**.37164**	.57259	**.37375**	.57503	**.37587**	.57747	**.37798**	.57990	**.38010**	30
31	.57017	**.37168**	.57263	**.37379**	.57507	**.37590**	.57751	**.37802**	.57994	**.38013**	29
+ 8′	9.57021	**.37171**	9.57267	**.37382**	9.57511	**.37594**	9.57755	**.37805**	9.57998	**.38017**	28
33	.57025	**.37175**	.57271	**.37386**	.57516	**.37597**	.57759	**.37809**	.58002	**.38020**	27
34	.57029	**.37179**	.57275	**.37389**	.57520	**.37601**	.57763	**.37812**	.58006	**.38024**	26
35	.57033	**.37182**	.57279	**.37393**	.57524	**.37604**	.57767	**.37816**	.58010	**.38027**	25
+ 9′	9.57037	**.37186**	9.57283	**.37397**	9.57528	**.37608**	9.57771	**.37819**	9.58014	**.38031**	24
37	.57042	**.37189**	.57287	**.37400**	.57532	**.37611**	.57775	**.37823**	.58018	**.38034**	23
38	.57046	**.37193**	.57291	**.37404**	.57536	**.37615**	.57779	**.37826**	.58022	**.38038**	22
39	.57050	**.37196**	.57295	**.37407**	.57540	**.37618**	.57783	**.37830**	.58026	**.38042**	21
+ 10′	9.57054	**.37200**	9.57299	**.37411**	9.57544	**.37622**	9.57787	**.37833**	9.58030	**.38045**	20
41	.57058	**.37203**	.57304	**.37414**	.57548	**.37625**	.57792	**.37837**	.58034	**.38049**	19
42	.57062	**.37207**	.57308	**.37418**	.57552	**.37629**	.57796	**.37840**	.58038	**.38052**	18
43	.57066	**.37210**	.57312	**.37421**	.57556	**.37632**	.57800	**.37844**	.58042	**.38056**	17
+ 11′	9.57070	**.37214**	9.57316	**.37425**	9.57560	**.37636**	9.57804	**.37847**	9.58046	**.38059**	16
45	.57074	**.37217**	.57320	**.37428**	.57564	**.37639**	.57808	**.37851**	.58050	**.38063**	15
46	.57078	**.37221**	.57324	**.37432**	.57568	**.37643**	.57812	**.37855**	.58054	**.38066**	14
47	.57083	**.37224**	.57328	**.37435**	.57572	**.37647**	.57816	**.37858**	.58058	**.38070**	13
+ 12′	9.57087	**.37228**	9.57332	**.37439**	9.57577	**.37650**	9.57820	**.37862**	9.58062	**.38073**	12
49	.57091	**.37231**	.57336	**.37442**	.57581	**.37654**	.57824	**.37865**	.58066	**.38077**	11
50	.57095	**.37235**	.57340	**.37446**	.57585	**.37657**	.57828	**.37869**	.58070	**.38080**	10
51	.57099	**.37238**	.57344	**.37449**	.57589	**.37661**	.57832	**.37872**	.58074	**.38084**	9
+ 13′	9.57103	**.37242**	9.57348	**.37453**	9.57593	**.37664**	9.57836	**.37876**	9.58078	**.38087**	8
53	.57107	**.37245**	.57353	**.37456**	.57597	**.37668**	.57840	**.37879**	.58082	**.38091**	7
54	.57111	**.37249**	.57357	**.37460**	.57601	**.37671**	.57844	**.37883**	.58086	**.38095**	6
55	.57115	**.37252**	.57361	**.37463**	.57605	**.37675**	.57848	**.37886**	.58090	**.38098**	5
+ 14′	9.57119	**.37256**	9.57365	**.37467**	9.57609	**.37678**	9.57852	**.37890**	9.58094	**.38102**	4
57	.57124	**.37259**	.57369	**.37470**	.57613	**.37682**	.57856	**.37893**	.58098	**.38105**	3
58	.57128	**.37263**	.57373	**.37474**	.57617	**.37685**	.57860	**.37897**	.58102	**.38109**	2
59	.57132	**.37266**	.57377	**.37477**	.57621	**.37689**	.57864	**.37900**	.58106	**.38112**	1
+ 15′	9.57136	**.37270**	9.57381	**.37481**	9.57625	**.37692**	9.57868	**.37904**	9.58110	**.38116**	0
	$18^h\ 59^m$		$18^h\ 58^m$		$18^h\ 57^m$		$18^h\ 56^m$		$18^h\ 55^m$		

Haversines.

s	$5^h 5^m$ 76° 15′ Log. Hav.	Nat. Hav.	$5^h 6^m$ 76° 30′ Log. Hav.	Nat. Hav.	$5^h 7^m$ 76° 45′ Log. Hav.	Nat. Hav.	$5^h 8^m$ 77° 0′ Log. Hav.	Nat. Hav.	$5^h 9^m$ 77° 15′ Log. Hav.	Nat. Hav.	s
0	9.58110	**.38116**	9.58351	**.38328**	9.58591	**.38540**	9.58830	**.38752**	9.59068	**.38965**	60
1	.58114	**.38119**	.58355	**.38331**	.58595	**.38544**	.58834	**.38756**	.59072	**.38969**	59
2	.58118	**.38123**	.58359	**.38335**	.58599	**.38547**	.58838	**.38760**	.59076	**.38972**	58
3	.58122	**.38126**	.58363	**.38338**	.58603	**.38551**	.58842	**.38763**	.59079	**.38976**	57
+ 1′	9.58126	**.38130**	9.58367	**.38342**	9.58607	**.38554**	9.58846	**.38767**	9.59083	**.38979**	56
5	.58131	**.38133**	.58371	**.38345**	.58611	**.38558**	.58850	**.38770**	.59087	**.38983**	55
6	.58135	**.38137**	.58375	**.38349**	.58615	**.38561**	.58854	**.38774**	.59091	**.38986**	54
7	.58139	**.38140**	.58379	**.38352**	.58619	**.38565**	.58858	**.38777**	.59095	**.38990**	53
+ 2′	9.58143	**.38144**	9.58383	**.38356**	9.58623	**.38568**	9.58862	**.38781**	9.59099	**.38994**	52
9	.58147	**.38148**	.58387	**.38360**	.58627	**.38572**	.58866	**.38784**	.59103	**.38997**	51
10	.58151	**.38151**	.58391	**.38363**	.58631	**.38575**	.58870	**.38788**	.59107	**.39001**	50
11	.58155	**.38155**	.58395	**.38367**	.58635	**.38579**	.58874	**.38791**	.59111	**.39004**	49
+ 3′	9.58159	**.38158**	9.58399	**.38370**	9.58639	**.38582**	9.58878	**.38795**	9.59115	**.39008**	48
13	.58163	**.38162**	.58403	**.38374**	.58643	**.38586**	.58882	**.38799**	.59119	**.39011**	47
14	.58167	**.38165**	.58407	**.38377**	.58647	**.38590**	.58885	**.38802**	.59123	**.39015**	46
15	.58171	**.38169**	.58411	**.38381**	.58651	**.38593**	.58889	**.38806**	.59127	**.39018**	45
+ 4′	9.58175	**.38172**	9.58415	**.38384**	9.58655	**.38597**	9.58893	**.38809**	9.59131	**.39022**	44
17	.58179	**.38176**	.58419	**.38388**	.58659	**.38600**	.58897	**.38813**	.59135	**.39025**	43
18	.58183	**.38179**	.58423	**.38391**	.58663	**.38604**	.58901	**.38816**	.59139	**.39029**	42
19	.58187	**.38183**	.58427	**.38395**	.58667	**.38607**	.58905	**.38820**	.59143	**.39033**	41
+ 5′	9.58191	**.38186**	9.58431	**.38398**	9.58671	**.38611**	9.58909	**.38823**	9.59147	**.39036**	40
21	.58195	**.38190**	.58435	**.38402**	.58675	**.38614**	.58913	**.38827**	.59151	**.39040**	39
22	.58199	**.38193**	.58439	**.38406**	.58679	**.38618**	.58917	**.38830**	.59155	**.39043**	38
23	.58203	**.38197**	.58443	**.38409**	.58683	**.38621**	.58921	**.38834**	.59158	**.39047**	37
+ 6′	9.58207	**.38200**	9.58447	**.38413**	9.58687	**.38625**	9.58925	**.38837**	9.59162	**.39050**	36
25	.58211	**.38204**	.58451	**.38416**	.58691	**.38628**	.58929	**.38841**	.59166	**.39054**	35
26	.58215	**.38208**	.58455	**.38420**	.58695	**.38632**	.58933	**.38845**	.59170	**.39057**	34
27	.58219	**.38211**	.58459	**.38423**	.58699	**.38636**	.58937	**.38848**	.59174	**.39061**	33
+ 7′	9.58223	**.38215**	9.58463	**.38427**	9.58703	**.38639**	9.58941	**.38852**	9.59178	**.39064**	32
29	.58227	**.38218**	.58467	**.38430**	.58707	**.38643**	.58945	**.38855**	.59182	**.39068**	31
30	.58231	**.38222**	.58471	**.38434**	.58711	**.38646**	.58949	**.38859**	.59186	**.39072**	30
31	.58235	**.38225**	.58475	**.38437**	.58715	**.38650**	.58953	**.38862**	.59190	**.39075**	29
+ 8′	9.58239	**.38229**	9.58479	**.38441**	9.58719	**.38653**	9.58957	**.38866**	9.59194	**.39079**	28
33	.58243	**.38232**	.58483	**.38444**	.58723	**.38657**	.58961	**.38869**	.59198	**.39082**	27
34	.58247	**.38236**	.58487	**.38448**	.58727	**.38660**	.58965	**.38873**	.59202	**.39086**	26
35	.58251	**.38239**	.58491	**.38451**	.58731	**.38664**	.58969	**.38876**	.59206	**.39089**	25
+ 9′	9.58255	**.38243**	9.58495	**.38455**	9.58735	**.38667**	9.58973	**.38880**	9.59210	**.39093**	24
37	.58259	**.38246**	.58499	**.38459**	.58739	**.38671**	.58977	**.38884**	.59214	**.39096**	23
38	.58263	**.38250**	.58503	**.38462**	.58742	**.38675**	.58981	**.38887**	.59218	**.39100**	22
39	.58267	**.38254**	.58507	**.38466**	.58746	**.38678**	.58985	**.38891**	.59222	**.39103**	21
+ 10′	9.58271	**.38257**	9.58511	**.38469**	9.58750	**.38682**	9.58989	**.38894**	9.59225	**.39107**	20
41	.58275	**.38261**	.58515	**.38473**	.58754	**.38685**	.58992	**.38898**	.59229	**.39111**	19
42	.58279	**.38264**	.58519	**.38476**	.58758	**.38689**	.58996	**.38901**	.59233	**.39114**	18
43	.58283	**.38268**	.58523	**.38480**	.58762	**.38692**	.59000	**.38905**	.59237	**.39118**	17
+ 11′	9.58287	**.38271**	9.58527	**.38483**	9.58766	**.38696**	9.59004	**.38908**	9.59241	**.39121**	16
45	.58291	**.38275**	.58531	**.38487**	.58770	**.38699**	.59008	**.38912**	.59245	**.39125**	15
46	.58295	**.38278**	.58535	**.38490**	.58774	**.38703**	.59012	**.38915**	.59249	**.39128**	14
47	.58299	**.38282**	.58539	**.38494**	.58778	**.38706**	.59016	**.38919**	.59253	**.39132**	13
+ 12′	9.58303	**.38285**	9.58543	**.38498**	9.58782	**.38710**	9.59020	**.38923**	9.59257	**.39135**	12
49	.58307	**.38289**	.58547	**.38501**	.58786	**.38713**	.59024	**.38926**	.59261	**.39139**	11
50	.58311	**.38292**	.58551	**.38505**	.58790	**.38717**	.59028	**.38930**	.59265	**.39143**	10
51	.58315	**.38296**	.58555	**.38508**	.58794	**.38721**	.59032	**.38933**	.59269	**.39146**	9
+ 13′	9.58319	**.38299**	9.58559	**.38512**	9.58798	**.38724**	9.59036	**.38937**	9.59273	**.39150**	8
53	.58323	**.38303**	.58563	**.38515**	.58802	**.38728**	.59040	**.38940**	.59277	**.39153**	7
54	.58327	**.38307**	.58567	**.38519**	.58806	**.38731**	.59044	**.38944**	.59281	**.39157**	6
55	.58331	**.38310**	.58571	**.38522**	.58810	**.38735**	.59048	**.38947**	.59285	**.39160**	5
+ 14′	9.58335	**.38314**	9.58575	**.38526**	9.58814	**.38738**	9.59052	**.38951**	9.59289	**.39164**	4
57	.58339	**.38317**	.58579	**.38529**	.58818	**.38742**	.59056	**.38954**	.59292	**.39167**	3
58	.58343	**.38321**	.58583	**.38533**	.58822	**.38745**	.59060	**.38958**	.59296	**.39171**	2
59	.58347	**.38324**	.58587	**.38536**	.58826	**.38749**	.59064	**.38962**	.59300	**.39174**	1
+ 15′	9.58351	**.38328**	9.58591	**.38540**	9.58830	**.38752**	9.59068	**.38965**	9.59304	**.39178**	0
	$18^h 54^m$		$18^h 53^m$		$18^h 52^m$		$18^h 51^m$		$18^h 50^m$		

541524°—43——46

TABLE 34.

Haversines.

s	$5^h 10^m$ 77° 30′ Log. Hav.	Nat. Hav.	$5^h 11^m$ 77° 45′ Log. Hav.	Nat. Hav.	$5^h 12^m$ 78° 0′ Log. Hav.	Nat. Hav.	$5^h 13^m$ 78° 15′ Log. Hav.	Nat. Hav.	$5^h 14^m$ 78° 30′ Log. Hav.	Nat. Hav.	s
0	9.59304	**.39178**	9.59540	**.39391**	9.59774	**.39604**	9.60008	**.39818**	9.60240	**.40032**	60
1	.59308	**.39182**	.59544	**.39395**	.59778	**.39608**	.60012	**.39821**	.60244	**.40035**	59
2	.59312	**.39185**	.59548	**.39398**	.59782	**.39612**	.60016	**.39825**	.60248	**.40039**	58
3	.59316	**.39189**	.59552	**.39402**	.59786	**.39615**	.60020	**.39829**	.60252	**.40042**	57
+ 1′	9.59320	**.39192**	9.59556	**.39405**	9.59790	**.39619**	9.60023	**.39832**	9.60256	**.40046**	56
5	.59324	**.39196**	.59559	**.39409**	.59794	**.39622**	.60027	**.39836**	.60260	**.40049**	55
6	.59328	**.39199**	.59563	**.39412**	.59798	**.39626**	.60031	**.39839**	.60263	**.40053**	54
7	.59332	**.39203**	.59567	**.39416**	.59802	**.39629**	.60035	**.39843**	.60267	**.40057**	53
+ 2′	9.59336	**.39206**	9.59571	**.39420**	9.59806	**.39633**	9.60039	**.39846**	9.60271	**.40060**	52
9	.59340	**.39210**	.59575	**.39423**	.59809	**.39636**	.60043	**.39850**	.60275	**.40064**	51
10	.59344	**.39214**	.59579	**.39427**	.59813	**.39640**	.60047	**.39854**	.60279	**.40067**	50
11	.59348	**.39217**	.59583	**.39430**	.59817	**.39644**	.60051	**.39857**	.60283	**.40071**	49
+ 3′	9.59351	**.39221**	9.59587	**.39434**	9.59821	**.39647**	9.60054	**.39861**	9.60287	**.40074**	48
13	.59355	**.39224**	.59591	**.39437**	.59825	**.39651**	.60058	**.39864**	.60291	**.40078**	47
14	.59359	**.39228**	.59595	**.39441**	.59829	**.39654**	.60062	**.39868**	.60294	**.40081**	46
15	.59363	**.39231**	.59599	**.39444**	.59833	**.39658**	.60066	**.39871**	.60298	**.40085**	45
+ 4′	9.59367	**.39235**	9.59602	**.39448**	9.59837	**.39661**	9.60070	**.39875**	9.60302	**.40089**	44
17	.59371	**.39238**	.59606	**.39451**	.59841	**.39665**	.60074	**.39878**	.60306	**.40092**	43
18	.59375	**.39242**	.59610	**.39455**	.59845	**.39668**	.60078	**.39882**	.60310	**.40096**	42
19	.59379	**.39245**	.59614	**.39459**	.59848	**.39672**	.60082	**.39886**	.60314	**.40099**	41
+ 5′	9.59383	**.39249**	9.59618	**.39462**	9.59852	**.39676**	9.60085	**.39889**	9.60318	**.40103**	40
21	.59387	**.39253**	.59622	**.39466**	.59856	**.39679**	.60089	**.39893**	.60321	**.40106**	39
22	.59391	**.39256**	.59626	**.39469**	.59860	**.39683**	.60093	**.39896**	.60325	**.40110**	38
23	.59395	**.39260**	.59630	**.39473**	.59864	**.39686**	.60097	**.39900**	.60329	**.40114**	37
+ 6′	9.59399	**.39263**	9.59634	**.39476**	9.59868	**.39690**	9.60101	**.39903**	9.60333	**.40117**	36
25	.59403	**.39267**	.59638	**.39480**	.59872	**.39693**	.60105	**.39907**	.60337	**.40121**	35
26	.59406	**.39270**	.59642	**.39484**	.59876	**.39697**	.60109	**.39910**	.60341	**.40124**	34
27	.59410	**.39274**	.59646	**.39487**	.59880	**.39700**	.60113	**.39914**	.60345	**.40128**	33
+ 7′	9.59414	**.39277**	9.59649	**.39491**	9.59883	**.39704**	9.60116	**.39918**	9.60348	**.40131**	32
29	.59418	**.39281**	.59653	**.39494**	.59887	**.39708**	.60120	**.39921**	.60352	**.40135**	31
30	.59422	**.39285**	.59657	**.39498**	.59891	**.39711**	.60124	**.39925**	.60356	**.40139**	30
31	.59426	**.39288**	.59661	**.39501**	.59895	**.39715**	.60128	**.39928**	.60360	**.40142**	29
+ 8′	9.59430	**.39292**	9.59665	**.39505**	9.59899	**.39718**	9.60132	**.39932**	9.60364	**.40146**	28
33	.59434	**.39295**	.59669	**.39508**	.59903	**.39722**	.60136	**.39935**	.60368	**.40149**	27
34	.59438	**.39299**	.59673	**.39512**	.59907	**.39725**	.60140	**.39939**	.60372	**.40153**	26
35	.59442	**.39302**	.59677	**.39516**	.59911	**.39729**	.60144	**.39943**	.60375	**.40156**	25
+ 9′	9.59446	**.39306**	9.59681	**.39519**	9.59915	**.39732**	9.60147	**.39946**	9.60379	**.40160**	24
37	.59450	**.39309**	.59685	**.39523**	.59918	**.39736**	.60151	**.39950**	.60383	**.40163**	23
38	.59454	**.39313**	.59688	**.39526**	.59922	**.39739**	.60155	**.39953**	.60387	**.40167**	22
39	.59458	**.39317**	.59692	**.39530**	.59926	**.39743**	.60159	**.39957**	.60391	**.40171**	21
+ 10′	9.59461	**.39320**	9.59696	**.39533**	9.59930	**.39746**	9.60163	**.39960**	9.60395	**.40174**	20
41	.59465	**.39324**	.59700	**.39537**	.59934	**.39750**	.60167	**.39964**	.60399	**.40178**	19
42	.59469	**.39327**	.59704	**.39540**	.59938	**.39754**	.60171	**.39967**	.60402	**.40181**	18
43	.59473	**.39331**	.59708	**.39544**	.59942	**.39757**	.60175	**.39971**	.60406	**.40185**	17
+ 11′	9.59477	**.39334**	9.59712	**.39548**	9.59946	**.39761**	9.60178	**.39975**	9.60410	**.40188**	16
45	.59481	**.39338**	.59716	**.39551**	.59950	**.39765**	.60182	**.39978**	.60414	**.40192**	15
46	.59485	**.39341**	.59720	**.39555**	.59953	**.39768**	.60186	**.39982**	.60418	**.40196**	14
47	.59489	**.39345**	.59724	**.39558**	.59957	**.39772**	.60190	**.39985**	.60422	**.40199**	13
+ 12′	9.59493	**.39348**	9.59728	**.39562**	9.59961	**.39775**	9.60194	**.39989**	9.60426	**.40203**	12
49	.59497	**.39352**	.59731	**.39565**	.59965	**.39779**	.60198	**.39992**	.60429	**.40206**	11
50	.59501	**.39356**	.59735	**.39569**	.59969	**.39782**	.60202	**.39996**	.60433	**.40210**	10
51	.59505	**.39359**	.59739	**.39572**	.59973	**.39786**	.60206	**.40000**	.60437	**.40213**	9
+ 13′	9.59508	**.39363**	9.59743	**.39576**	9.59977	**.39789**	9.60209	**.40003**	9.60441	**.40217**	8
53	.59512	**.39366**	.59747	**.39580**	.59981	**.39793**	.60213	**.40007**	.60445	**.40220**	7
54	.59516	**.39370**	.59751	**.39583**	.59985	**.39796**	.60217	**.40010**	.60449	**.40224**	6
55	.59520	**.39373**	.59755	**.39587**	.59988	**.39800**	.60221	**.40014**	.60452	**.40228**	5
+ 14′	9.59524	**.39377**	9.59759	**.39590**	9.59992	**.39803**	9.60225	**.40017**	9.60456	**.40231**	4
57	.59528	**.39380**	.59763	**.39594**	.59996	**.39807**	.60229	**.40021**	.60460	**.40235**	3
58	.59532	**.39384**	.59767	**.39597**	.60000	**.39811**	.60233	**.40024**	.60464	**.40238**	2
59	.59536	**.39388**	.59770	**.39601**	.60004	**.39814**	.60236	**.40028**	.60468	**.40242**	1
+ 15′	9.59540	**.39391**	9.59774	**.39604**	9.60008	**.39818**	9.60240	**.40032**	9.60472	**.40245**	0
	$18^h 49^m$		$18^h 48^m$		$18^h 47^m$		$18^h 46^m$		$18^h 45^m$		

TABLE 34.

Haversines.

s	5h 15m 78° 45′ Log. Hav.	Nat. Hav.	5h 16m 79° 0′ Log. Hav.	Nat. Hav.	5h 17m 79° 15′ Log. Hav.	Nat. Hav.	5h 18m 79° 30′ Log. Hav.	Nat. Hav.	5h 19m 79° 45′ Log. Hav.	Nat. Hav.	s
0	9.60472	.40245	9.60702	.40460	9.60931	.40674	9.61160	.40888	9.61387	.41103	60
1	.60476	.40249	.60706	.40463	.60935	.40677	.61164	.40892	.61391	.41106	59
2	.60479	.40253	.60710	.40467	.60939	.40681	.61167	.40895	.61395	.41110	58
3	.60483	.40256	.60714	.40470	.60943	.40685	.61171	.40899	.61399	.41114	57
+ 1′	9.60487	.40260	9.60717	.40474	9.60947	.40688	9.61175	.40903	9.61402	.41117	56
5	.60491	.40263	.60721	.40477	.60951	.40692	.61179	.40906	.61406	.41121	55
6	.60495	.40267	.60725	.40481	.60954	.40695	.61183	.40910	.61410	.41124	54
7	.60499	.40270	.60729	.40485	.60958	.40699	.61186	.40913	.61414	.41128	53
+ 2′	9.60502	.40274	9.60733	.40488	9.60962	.40702	9.61190	.40917	9.61417	.41131	52
9	.60506	.40277	.60737	.40492	.60966	.40706	.61194	.40920	.61421	.41135	51
10	.60510	.40281	.60740	.40495	.60970	.40710	.61198	.40924	.61425	.41139	50
11	.60514	.40285	.60744	.40499	.60973	.40713	.61202	.40928	.61429	.41142	49
+ 3′	9.60518	.40288	9.60748	.40502	9.60977	.40717	9.61205	.40931	9.61433	.41146	48
13	.60522	.40292	.60752	.40506	.60981	.40720	.61209	.40935	.61436	.41149	47
14	.60526	.40295	.60756	.40510	.60985	.40724	.61213	.40938	.61440	.41153	46
15	.60529	.40299	.60760	.40513	.60989	.40727	.61217	.40942	.61444	.41156	45
+ 4′	9.60533	.40303	9.60763	.40517	9.60992	.40731	9.61221	.40945	9.61448	.41160	44
17	.60537	.40306	.60767	.40520	.60996	.40735	.61224	.40949	.61451	.41164	43
18	.60541	.40310	.60771	.40524	.61000	.40738	.61228	.40953	.61455	.41167	42
19	.60545	.40313	.60775	.40527	.61004	.40742	.61232	.40956	.61459	.41171	41
+ 5′	9.60549	.40317	9.60779	.40531	9.61008	.40745	9.61236	.40960	9.61463	.41174	40
21	.60552	.40320	.60783	.40535	.61012	.40749	.61240	.40963	.61467	.41178	39
22	.60556	.40324	.60786	.40538	.61015	.40752	.61243	.40967	.61470	.41182	38
23	.60560	.40328	.60790	.40542	.61019	.40756	.61247	.40970	.61474	.41185	37
+ 6′	9.60564	.40331	9.60794	.40545	9.61023	.40760	9.61251	.40974	9.61478	.41189	36
25	.60568	.40335	.60798	.40549	.61027	.40763	.61255	.40978	.61482	.41192	35
26	.60572	.40338	.60802	.40552	.61031	.40767	.61258	.40981	.61485	.41196	34
27	.60576	.40342	.60805	.40556	.61034	.40770	.61262	.40985	.61489	.41199	33
+ 7′	9.60579	.40345	9.60809	.40560	9.61038	.40774	9.61266	.40988	9.61493	.41203	32
29	.60583	.40349	.60813	.40563	.61042	.40777	.61270	.40992	.61497	.41207	31
30	.60587	.40352	.60817	.40567	.61046	.40781	.61274	.40996	.61500	.41210	30
31	.60591	.40356	.60821	.40570	.61050	.40785	.61277	.40999	.61504	.41214	29
+ 8′	9.60595	.40360	9.60825	.40574	9.61053	.40788	9.61281	.41003	9.61508	.41217	28
33	.60599	.40363	.60828	.40577	.61057	.40792	.61285	.41006	.61512	.41221	27
34	.60602	.40367	.60832	.40581	.61061	.40795	.61289	.41010	.61516	.41225	26
35	.60606	.40370	.60836	.40585	.61065	.40799	.61293	.41013	.61519	.41228	25
+ 9′	9.60610	.40374	9.60840	.40588	9.61069	.40802	9.61296	.41017	9.61523	.41232	24
37	.60614	.40377	.60844	.40592	.61072	.40806	.61300	.41021	.61527	.41235	23
38	.60618	.40381	.60847	.40595	.61076	.40810	.61304	.41024	.61531	.41239	22
39	.60622	.40385	.60851	.40599	.61080	.40813	.61308	.41028	.61534	.41242	21
+ 10′	9.60625	.40388	9.60855	.40602	9.61084	.40817	9.61312	.41031	9.61538	.41246	20
41	.60629	.40392	.60859	.40606	.61088	.40820	.61315	.41035	.61542	.41250	19
42	.60633	.40395	.60863	.40610	.61091	.40824	.61319	.41039	.61546	.41253	18
43	.60637	.40399	.60867	.40613	.61095	.40827	.61323	.41042	.61549	.41257	17
+ 11′	9.60641	.40402	9.60870	.40617	9.61099	.40831	9.61327	.41046	9.61553	.41260	16
45	.60645	.40406	.60874	.40620	.61103	.40835	.61330	.41049	.61557	.41264	15
46	.60648	.40410	.60878	.40624	.61107	.40838	.61334	.41053	.61561	.41267	14
47	.60652	.40413	.60882	.40627	.61110	.40842	.61338	.41056	.61565	.41271	13
+ 12′	9.60656	.40417	9.60886	.40631	9.61114	.40845	9.61342	.41060	9.61568	.41275	12
49	.60660	.40420	.60890	.40635	.61118	.40849	.61346	.41063	.61572	.41278	11
50	.60664	.40424	.60893	.40638	.61122	.40852	.61349	.41067	.61576	.41282	10
51	.60668	.40427	.60897	.40642	.61126	.40856	.61353	.41071	.61580	.41285	9
+ 13′	9.60671	.40431	9.60901	.40645	9.61129	.40860	9.61357	.41074	9.61583	.41289	8
53	.60675	.40434	.60905	.40649	.61133	.40863	.61361	.41078	.61587	.41293	7
54	.60679	.40438	.60909	.40652	.61137	.40867	.61364	.41082	.61591	.41296	6
55	.60683	.40442	.60912	.40656	.61141	.40870	.61368	.41085	.61595	.41300	5
+ 14′	9.60687	.40445	9.60916	.40660	9.61145	.40874	9.61372	.41089	9.61598	.41303	4
57	.60691	.40449	.60920	.40663	.61148	.40878	.61376	.41092	.61602	.41307	3
58	.60694	.40452	.60924	.40667	.61152	.40881	.61380	.41096	.61606	.41310	2
59	.60698	.40456	.60928	.40670	.61156	.40885	.61383	.41099	.61610	.41314	1
+ 15′	9.60702	.40460	9.60931	.40674	9.61160	.40888	9.61387	.41103	9.61614	.41318	0
	18h 44m		18h 43m		18h 42m		18h 41m		18h 40m		

TABLE 34.

Haversines.

s	$5^h\ 20^m$ 80° 0′		$5^h\ 21^m$ 80° 15′		$5^h\ 22^m$ 80° 30′		$5^h\ 23^m$ 80° 45′		$5^h\ 24^m$ 81° 0′		s
	Log. Hav.	Nat. Hav.	Log. Hav.	Nat. Hav.	Log. Hav.	Nat. Hav.	Log. Hav.	Nat. Hav.	Log. Hav.	Nat. Hav.	
0	9.61614	.41318	9.61839	.41533	9.62063	.41748	9.62287	.41963	9.62509	.42178	60
1	.61617	.41321	.61843	.41536	.62067	.41751	.62290	.41966	.62513	.42182	59
2	.61621	.41325	.61846	.41540	.62071	.41755	.62294	.41970	.62516	.42185	58
3	.61625	.41328	.61850	.41543	.62074	.41758	.62298	.41974	.62520	.42189	57
+ 1′	9.61629	.41332	9.61854	.41547	9.62078	.41762	9.62301	.41977	9.62524	.42193	56
5	.61632	.41335	.61858	.41550	.62082	.41766	.62305	.41981	.62527	.42196	55
6	.61636	.41339	.61861	.41554	.62086	.41769	.62309	.41984	.62531	.42200	54
7	.61640	.41343	.61865	.41558	.62089	.41773	.62313	.41988	.62535	.42203	53
+ 2′	9.61644	.41346	9.61869	.41561	9.62093	.41776	9.62316	.41992	9.62538	.42207	52
9	.61647	.41350	.61873	.41565	.62097	.41780	.62320	.41995	.62542	.42211	51
10	.61651	.41353	.61876	.41568	.62100	.41783	.62324	.41999	.62546	.42214	50
11	.61655	.41357	.61880	.41572	.62104	.41787	.62327	.42002	.62550	.42218	49
+ 3′	9.61659	.41361	9.61884	.41576	9.62108	.41791	9.62331	.42006	9.62553	.42221	48
13	.61662	.41364	.61888	.41579	.62112	.41794	.62335	.42010	.62557	.42225	47
14	.61666	.41368	.61891	.41583	.62115	.41798	.62338	.42013	.62561	.42229	46
15	.61670	.41371	.61895	.41586	.62119	.41801	.62342	.42017	.62564	.42232	45
+ 4′	9.61674	.41375	9.61899	.41590	9.62123	.41805	9.62346	.42020	9.62568	.42236	44
17	.61677	.41378	.61903	.41593	.62127	.41809	.62350	.42024	.62572	.42239	43
18	.61681	.41382	.61906	.41597	.62130	.41812	.62353	.42027	.62575	.42243	42
19	.61685	.41386	.61910	.41601	.62134	.41816	.62357	.42031	.62579	.42247	41
+ 5′	9.61689	.41389	9.61914	.41604	9.62138	.41819	9.62361	.42035	9.62583	.42250	40
21	.61692	.41393	.61917	.41608	.62141	.41823	.62364	.42038	.62586	.42254	39
22	.61696	.41396	.61921	.41611	.62145	.41827	.62368	.42042	.62590	.42257	38
23	.61700	.41400	.61925	.41615	.62149	.41830	.62372	.42045	.62594	.42261	37
+ 6′	9.61704	.41404	9.61929	.41619	9.62153	.41834	9.62376	.42049	9.62598	.42264	36
25	.61708	.41407	.61932	.41622	.62156	.41837	.62379	.42053	.62601	.42268	35
26	.61711	.41411	.61936	.41626	.62160	.41811	.62383	.42056	.62605	.42272	34
27	.61715	.41414	.61940	.41629	.62164	.41844	.62387	.42060	.62609	.42275	33
+ 7′	9.61719	.41418	9.61944	.41633	9.62168	.41848	9.62390	.42063	9.62612	.42279	32
29	.61723	.41421	.61947	.41636	.62171	.41852	.62394	.42067	.62616	.42282	31
30	.61726	.41425	.61951	.41640	.62175	.41855	.62398	.42071	.62620	.42286	30
31	.61730	.41429	.61955	.41644	.62179	.41859	.62402	.42074	.62623	.42290	29
+ 8′	9.61734	.41432	9.61959	.41647	9.62182	.41862	9.62405	.42078	9.62627	.42293	28
33	.61738	.41436	.61962	.41651	.62186	.41866	.62409	.42081	.62631	.42297	27
34	.61741	.41439	.61966	.41654	.62190	.41870	.62413	.42085	.62634	.42300	26
35	.61745	.41443	.61970	.41658	.62194	.41873	.62416	.42089	.62638	.42304	25
+ 9′	9.61749	.41447	9.61974	.41662	9.62197	.41877	9.62420	.42092	9.62642	.42308	24
37	.61753	.41450	.61977	.41665	.62201	.41880	.62424	.42096	.62646	.42311	23
38	.61756	.41454	.61981	.41669	.62205	.41884	.62427	.42099	.62649	.42315	22
39	.61760	.41457	.61985	.41672	.62208	.41888	.62431	.42103	.62653	.42318	21
+ 10′	9.61764	.41461	9.61989	.41676	9.62212	.41891	9.62435	.42106	9.62657	.42322	20
41	.61768	.41464	.61992	.41679	.62216	.41895	.62439	.42110	.62660	.42326	19
42	.61771	.41468	.61996	.41683	.62220	.41898	.62442	.42114	.62664	.42329	18
43	.61775	.41472	.62000	.41687	.62223	.41902	.62446	.42117	.62668	.42333	17
+ 11′	9.61779	.41475	9.62003	.41690	9.62227	.41905	9.62450	.42121	9.62671	.42336	16
45	.61783	.41479	.62007	.41694	.62231	.41909	.62453	.42124	.62675	.42340	15
46	.61786	.41482	.62011	.41697	.62234	.41913	.62457	.42128	.62679	.42344	14
47	.61790	.41486	.62015	.41701	.62238	.41916	.62461	.42132	.62682	.42347	13
+ 12′	9.61794	.41490	9.62018	.41705	9.62242	.41920	9.62464	.42135	9.62686	.42351	12
49	.61798	.41493	.62022	.41708	.62246	.41923	.62468	.42139	.62690	.42354	11
50	.61801	.41497	.62026	.41712	.62249	.41927	.62472	.42142	.62693	.42358	10
51	.61805	.41500	.62030	.41715	.62253	.41931	.62476	.42146	.62697	.42361	9
+ 13′	9.61809	.41504	9.62033	.41719	9.62257	.41934	9.62479	.42150	9.62701	.42365	8
53	.61813	.41507	.62037	.41722	.62261	.41938	.62483	.42153	.62704	.42369	7
54	.61816	.41511	.62041	.41726	.62264	.41941	.62487	.42157	.62708	.42372	6
55	.61820	.41515	.62045	.41730	.62268	.41945	.62490	.42160	.62712	.42376	5
+ 14′	9.61824	.41518	9.62048	.41733	9.62272	.41949	9.62494	.42164	9.62716	.42379	4
57	.61828	.41522	.62052	.41737	.62275	.41952	.62498	.42168	.62719	.42383	3
58	.61831	.41525	.62056	.41740	.62279	.41956	.62501	.42171	.62723	.42387	2
59	.61835	.41529	.62059	.41744	.62283	.41959	.62505	.42175	.62727	.42390	1
+ 15′	9.61839	.41533	9.62063	.41748	9.62287	.41963	9.62509	.42178	9.62730	.42394	0
	$18^h\ 39^m$		$18^h\ 38^m$		$18^h\ 37^m$		$18^h\ 36^m$		$18^h\ 35^m$		

TABLE 34.

Haversines.

s	$5^h\,25^m$ 81° 15′ Log. Hav.	Nat. Hav.	$5^h\,26^m$ 81° 30′ Log. Hav.	Nat. Hav.	$5^h\,27^m$ 81° 45′ Log. Hav.	Nat. Hav.	$5^h\,28^m$ 82° 0′ Log. Hav.	Nat. Hav.	$5^h\,29^m$ 82° 15′ Log. Hav	Nat. Hav.	s
0	9.62730	**.42394**	9.62951	**.42610**	9.63170	**.42825**	9.63389	**.43041**	9.63606	**.43257**	60
1	.62734	**.42397**	.62954	**.42613**	.63174	**.42829**	.63392	**.43045**	.63610	**.43261**	59
2	.62738	**.42401**	.62958	**.42617**	.63177	**.42833**	.63396	**.43049**	.63613	**.43265**	58
3	.62741	**.42405**	.62962	**.42620**	.63181	**.42836**	.63399	**.43052**	.63617	**.43268**	57
+ 1′	9.62745	**.42408**	9.62965	**.42624**	9.63185	**.42840**	9.63403	**.43056**	9.63621	**.43272**	56
5	.62749	**.42412**	.62969	**.42628**	.63188	**.42843**	.63407	**.43059**	.63624	**.43275**	55
6	.62752	**.42415**	.62973	**.42631**	.63192	**.42847**	.63410	**.43063**	.63628	**.43279**	54
7	.62756	**.42419**	.62976	**.42635**	.63196	**.42851**	.63414	**.43067**	.63631	**.43283**	53
+ 2′	9.62760	**.42423**	9.62980	**.42638**	9.63199	**.42854**	9.63418	**.43070**	9.63635	**.43286**	52
9	.62763	**.42426**	.62984	**.42642**	.63203	**.42858**	.63421	**.43074**	.63639	**.43290**	51
10	.62767	**.42430**	.62987	**.42645**	.63207	**.42861**	.63425	**.43077**	.63642	**.43293**	50
11	.62771	**.42433**	.62991	**.42649**	.63210	**.42865**	.63429	**.43081**	.63646	**.43297**	49
+ 3′	9.62774	**.42437**	9.62995	**.42653**	9.63214	**.42869**	9.63432	**.43085**	9.63649	**.43301**	48
13	.62778	**.42441**	.62998	**.42656**	.63218	**.42872**	.63436	**.43088**	.63653	**.43304**	47
14	.62782	**.42444**	.63002	**.42660**	.63221	**.42876**	.63439	**.43092**	.63657	**.43308**	46
15	.62785	**.42448**	.63006	**.42663**	.63225	**.42879**	.63443	**.43095**	.63660	**.43312**	45
+ 4′	9.62789	**.42451**	9.63009	**.42667**	9.63228	**.42883**	9.63447	**.43099**	9.63664	**.43315**	44
17	.62793	**.42455**	.63013	**.42671**	.63232	**.42887**	.63450	**.43103**	.63668	**.43319**	43
18	.62796	**.42459**	.63017	**.42674**	.63236	**.42890**	.63454	**.43106**	.63671	**.43322**	42
19	.62800	**.42462**	.63020	**.42678**	.63239	**.42894**	.63458	**.43110**	.63675	**.43326**	41
+ 5′	9.62804	**.42466**	9.63024	**.42681**	9.63243	**.42897**	9.63461	**.43113**	9.63678	**.43330**	40
21	.62808	**.42469**	.63028	**.42685**	.63247	**.42901**	.63465	**.43117**	.63682	**.43333**	39
22	.62811	**.42473**	.63031	**.42689**	.63250	**.42905**	.63468	**.43121**	.63686	**.43337**	38
23	.62815	**.42477**	.63035	**.42692**	.63254	**.42908**	.63472	**.43124**	.63689	**.43340**	37
+ 6′	9.62819	**.42480**	9.63039	**.42696**	9.63258	**.42912**	9.63476	**.43128**	9.63693	**.43344**	36
25	.62822	**.42484**	.63042	**.42699**	.63261	**.42915**	.63479	**.43131**	.63696	**.43348**	35
26	.62826	**.42487**	.63046	**.42703**	.63265	**.42919**	.63483	**.43135**	.63700	**.43351**	34
27	.62830	**.42491**	.63050	**.42707**	.63269	**.42923**	.63487	**.43139**	.63704	**.43355**	33
+ 7′	9.62833	**.42494**	9.63053	**.42710**	9.63272	**.42926**	9.63490	**.43142**	9.63707	**.43358**	32
29	.62837	**.42498**	.63057	**.42714**	.63276	**.42930**	.63494	**.43146**	.63711	**.43362**	31
30	.62841	**.42502**	.63061	**.42717**	.63279	**.42933**	.63497	**.43149**	.63714	**.43366**	30
31	.62844	**.42505**	.63064	**.42721**	.63283	**.42937**	.63501	**.43153**	.63718	**.43369**	29
+ 8′	9.62848	**.42509**	9.63068	**.42725**	9.63287	**.42941**	9.63505	**.43157**	9.63722	**.43373**	28
33	.62852	**.42512**	.63071	**.42728**	.63290	**.42944**	.63508	**.43160**	.63725	**.43376**	27
34	.62855	**.42516**	.63075	**.42732**	.63294	**.42948**	.63512	**.43164**	.63729	**.43380**	26
35	.62859	**.42520**	.63079	**.42735**	.63298	**.42951**	.63516	**.43167**	.63733	**.43384**	25
+ 9′	9.62863	**.42523**	9.63082	**.42739**	9.63301	**.42955**	9.63519	**.43171**	9.63736	**.43387**	24
37	.62866	**.42527**	.63086	**.42743**	.63305	**.42959**	.63523	**.43175**	.63740	**.43391**	23
38	.62870	**.42530**	.63090	**.42746**	.63309	**.42962**	.63526	**.43178**	.63743	**.43394**	22
39	.62874	**.42534**	.63093	**.42750**	.63312	**.42966**	.63530	**.43182**	.63747	**.43398**	21
+ 10′	9.62877	**.42538**	9.63097	**.42753**	9.63316	**.42969**	9.63534	**.43185**	9.63751	**.43402**	20
41	.62881	**.42541**	.63101	**.42757**	.63320	**.42973**	.63537	**.43189**	.63754	**.43405**	19
42	.62885	**.42545**	.63104	**.42761**	.63323	**.42977**	.63541	**.43193**	.63758	**.43409**	18
43	.62888	**.42548**	.63108	**.42764**	.63327	**.42980**	.63545	**.43196**	.63761	**.43412**	17
+ 11′	9.62892	**.42552**	9.63112	**.42768**	9.63330	**.42984**	9.63548	**.43200**	9.63765	**.43416**	16
45	.62896	**.42556**	.63115	**.42771**	.63334	**.42987**	.63552	**.43203**	.63769	**.43420**	15
46	.62899	**.42559**	.63119	**.42775**	.63338	**.42991**	.63555	**.43207**	.63772	**.43423**	14
47	.62903	**.42563**	.63123	**.42779**	.63341	**.42995**	.63559	**.43211**	.63776	**.43427**	13
+ 12′	9.62907	**.42566**	9.63126	**.42782**	9.63345	**.42998**	9.63563	**.43214**	9.63779	**.43430**	12
49	.62910	**.42570**	.63130	**.42786**	.63349	**.43002**	.63566	**.43218**	.63783	**.43434**	11
50	.62914	**.42574**	.63134	**.42789**	.63352	**.43005**	.63570	**.43221**	.63787	**.43438**	10
51	.62918	**.42577**	.63137	**.42793**	.63356	**.43009**	.63574	**.43225**	.63790	**.43441**	9
+ 13′	9.62921	**.42581**	9.63141	**.42797**	9.63360	**.43013**	9.63577	**.43229**	9.63794	**.43445**	8
53	.62925	**.42584**	.63145	**.42800**	.63363	**.43016**	.63581	**.43232**	.63797	**.43448**	7
54	.62929	**.42588**	.63148	**.42804**	.63367	**.43020**	.63584	**.43236**	.63801	**.43452**	6
55	.62932	**.42592**	.63152	**.42807**	.63370	**.43023**	.63588	**.43239**	.63805	**.43456**	5
+ 14′	9.62936	**.42595**	9.63156	**.42811**	9.63374	**.43027**	9.63592	**.43243**	9.63808	**.43459**	4
57	.62940	**.42599**	.63159	**.42815**	.63378	**.43031**	.63595	**.43247**	.63812	**.43463**	3
58	.62943	**.42602**	.63163	**.42818**	.63381	**.43034**	.63599	**.43250**	.63815	**.43466**	2
59	.62947	**.42606**	.63166	**.42822**	.63385	**.43038**	.63602	**.43254**	.63819	**.43470**	1
+ 15′	9.62951	**.42610**	9.63170	**.42825**	9.63389	**.43041**	9.63606	**.43257**	9.63823	**.43474**	0
	$18^h\,34^m$		$18^h\,33^m$		$18^h\,32^m$		$18^h\,31^m$		$18^h\,30^m$		

TABLE 34.

Haversines.

s	$5^h\,30^m$ 82° 30′		$5^h\,31^m$ 82° 45′		$5^h\,32^m$ 83° 0′		$5^h\,33^m$ 83° 15′		$5^h\,34^m$ 83° 30′		s
	Log. Hav.	Nat. Hav.	Log. Hav.	Nat. Hav.	Log. Hav.	Nat. Hav.	Log. Hav.	Nat. Hav.	Log. Hav.	Nat. Hav.	
0	9.63823	**.43474**	9.64038	**.43690**	9.64253	**.43907**	9.64467	**.44123**	9.64679	**.44340**	60
1	.63826	**.43477**	.64042	**.43694**	.64256	**.43910**	.64470	**.44127**	.64683	**.44343**	59
2	.63830	**.43481**	.64046	**.43697**	.64260	**.43914**	.64474	**.44130**	.64686	**.44347**	58
3	.63833	**.43485**	.64049	**.43701**	.64264	**.43917**	.64477	**.44134**	.64690	**.44351**	57
+ 1′	9.63837	**.43488**	9.64053	**.43704**	9.64267	**.43921**	9.64481	**.44138**	9.64694	**.44354**	56
5	.63841	**.43492**	.64056	**.43708**	.64271	**.43925**	.64484	**.44141**	.64697	**.44358**	55
6	.63844	**.43495**	.64060	**.43712**	.64274	**.43928**	.64488	**.44145**	.64701	**.44362**	54
7	.63848	**.43499**	.64063	**.43715**	.64278	**.43932**	.64492	**.44148**	.64704	**.44365**	53
+ 2′	9.63851	**.43503**	9.64067	**.43719**	9.64281	**.43935**	9.64495	**.44152**	9.64708	**.44369**	52
9	.63855	**.43506**	.64071	**.43723**	.64285	**.43939**	.64499	**.44156**	.64711	**.44372**	51
10	.63859	**.43510**	.64074	**.43726**	.64289	**.43943**	.64502	**.44159**	.64715	**.44376**	50
11	.63862	**.43513**	.64078	**.43730**	.64292	**.43946**	.64506	**.44163**	.64718	**.44380**	49
+ 3′	9.63866	**.43517**	9.64081	**.43733**	9.64296	**.43950**	9.64509	**.44166**	9.64722	**.44383**	48
13	.63869	**.43521**	.64085	**.43737**	.64299	**.43953**	.64513	**.44170**	.64725	**.44387**	47
14	.63873	**.43524**	.64088	**.43741**	.64303	**.43957**	.64516	**.44174**	.64729	**.44390**	46
15	.63877	**.43528**	.64092	**.43744**	.64306	**.43961**	.64520	**.44177**	.64732	**.44394**	45
+ 4′	9.63880	**.43531**	9.64096	**.43748**	9.64310	**.43964**	9.64523	**.44181**	9.64736	**.44398**	44
17	.63884	**.43535**	.64099	**.43751**	.64314	**.43968**	.64527	**.44185**	.64740	**.44401**	43
18	.63887	**.43539**	.64102	**.43755**	.64317	**.43972**	.64531	**.44188**	.64743	**.44405**	42
19	.63891	**.43542**	.64106	**.43759**	.64321	**.43975**	.64534	**.44192**	.64747	**.44408**	41
+ 5′	9.63895	**.43546**	9.64110	**.43762**	9.64324	**.43979**	9.64538	**.44195**	9.64750	**.44412**	40
21	.63898	**.43549**	.64113	**.43766**	.64328	**.43982**	.64541	**.44199**	.64754	**.44416**	39
22	.63902	**.43553**	.64117	**.43769**	.64331	**.43986**	.64545	**.44203**	.64757	**.44419**	38
23	.63905	**.43557**	.64121	**.43773**	.64335	**.43990**	.64548	**.44206**	.64761	**.44423**	37
+ 6′	9.63909	**.43560**	9.64124	**.43777**	9.64339	**.43993**	9.64552	**.44210**	9.64764	**.44427**	36
25	.63913	**.43564**	.64128	**.43780**	.64342	**.43997**	.64555	**.44213**	.64768	**.44430**	35
26	.63916	**.43567**	.64131	**.43784**	.64346	**.44000**	.64559	**.44217**	.64771	**.44434**	34
27	.63920	**.43571**	.64135	**.43787**	.64349	**.44004**	.64563	**.44221**	.64775	**.44437**	33
+ 7′	9.63923	**.43575**	9.64139	**.43791**	9.64353	**.44008**	9.64566	**.44224**	9.64778	**.44441**	32
29	.63927	**.43578**	.64142	**.43795**	.64356	**.44011**	.64570	**.44228**	.64782	**.44445**	31
30	.63931	**.43582**	.64146	**.43798**	.64360	**.44015**	.64573	**.44231**	.64785	**.44448**	30
31	.63934	**.43585**	.64149	**.43802**	.64363	**.44018**	.64577	**.44235**	.64789	**.44452**	29
+ 8′	9.63938	**.43589**	9.64153	**.43805**	9.64367	**.44022**	9.64580	**.44239**	9.64793	**.44455**	28
33	.63941	**.43593**	.64156	**.43809**	.64371	**.44026**	.64584	**.44242**	.64796	**.44459**	27
34	.63945	**.43596**	.64160	**.43813**	.64374	**.44029**	.64587	**.44246**	.64800	**.44463**	26
35	.63949	**.43600**	.64164	**.43816**	.64378	**.44033**	.64591	**.44250**	.64803	**.44466**	25
+ 9′	9.63952	**.43603**	9.64167	**.43820**	9.64381	**.44036**	9.64594	**.44253**	9.64807	**.44470**	24
37	.63956	**.43607**	.64171	**.43824**	.64385	**.44040**	.64598	**.44257**	.64810	**.44474**	23
38	.63959	**.43611**	.64174	**.43827**	.64388	**.44044**	.64602	**.44260**	.64814	**.44477**	22
39	.63963	**.43614**	.64178	**.43831**	.64392	**.44047**	.64605	**.44264**	.64817	**.44481**	21
+ 10′	9.63966	**.43618**	9.64181	**.43834**	9.64396	**.44051**	9.64609	**.44268**	9.64821	**.44484**	20
41	.63970	**.43622**	.64185	**.43838**	.64399	**.44055**	.64612	**.44271**	.64824	**.44488**	19
42	.63974	**.43625**	.64189	**.43842**	.64403	**.44058**	.64616	**.44275**	.64828	**.44492**	18
43	.63977	**.43629**	.64192	**.43845**	.64406	**.44062**	.64619	**.44278**	.64831	**.44495**	17
+ 11′	9.63981	**.43632**	9.64196	**.43849**	9.64410	**.44065**	9.64623	**.44282**	9.64835	**.44499**	16
45	.63984	**.43636**	.64199	**.43852**	.64413	**.44069**	.64626	**.44286**	.64838	**.44502**	15
46	.63988	**.43640**	.64203	**.43856**	.64417	**.44073**	.64630	**.44289**	.64842	**.44506**	14
47	.63992	**.43643**	.64206	**.43860**	.64420	**.44076**	.64633	**.44293**	.64845	**.44510**	13
+ 12′	9.63995	**.43647**	9.64210	**.43863**	9.64424	**.44080**	9.64637	**.44296**	9.64849	**.44513**	12
49	.63999	**.43650**	.64214	**.43867**	.64428	**.44083**	.64640	**.44300**	.64852	**.44517**	11
50	.64002	**.43654**	.64217	**.43870**	.64431	**.44087**	.64644	**.44304**	.64856	**.44521**	10
51	.64006	**.43658**	.64221	**.43874**	.64435	**.44091**	.64648	**.44307**	.64860	**.44524**	9
+ 13′	9.64010	**.43661**	9.64224	**.43878**	9.64438	**.44094**	9.64651	**.44311**	9.64863	**.44528**	8
53	.64013	**.43665**	.64228	**.43881**	.64442	**.44098**	.64655	**.44315**	.64867	**.44531**	7
54	.64017	**.43668**	.64231	**.43885**	.64445	**.44101**	.64658	**.44318**	.64870	**.44535**	6
55	.64020	**.43672**	.64235	**.43888**	.64449	**.44105**	.64662	**.44322**	.64874	**.44539**	5
+ 14′	9.64024	**.43676**	9.64239	**.43892**	9.64452	**.44109**	9.64665	**.44325**	9.64877	**.44542**	4
57	.64028	**.43679**	.64242	**.43896**	.64456	**.44112**	.64669	**.44329**	.64881	**.44546**	3
58	.64031	**.43683**	.64246	**.43899**	.64460	**.44116**	.64672	**.44333**	.64884	**.44549**	2
59	.64035	**.43686**	.64249	**.43903**	.64463	**.44120**	.64676	**.44336**	.64888	**.44553**	1
+ 15′	9.64038	**.43690**	9.64253	**.43907**	9.64467	**.44123**	9.64679	**.44340**	9.64891	**.44557**	0
	$18^h\,29^m$		$18^h\,28^m$		$18^h\,27^m$		$18^h\,26^m$		$18^h\,25^m$		

TABLE 34.

Haversines.

s	5h 35m 83° 45′ Log. Hav.	Nat. Hav.	5h 36m 84° 0′ Log. Hav.	Nat. Hav.	5h 37m 84° 15′ Log. Hav.	Nat. Hav.	5h 38m 84° 30′ Log. Hav.	Nat. Hav.	5h 39m 84° 45′ Log. Hav.	Nat. Hav.	s
0	9.64891	**.44557**	9.65102	**.44774**	9.65312	**.44991**	9.65521	**.45208**	9.65729	**.45425**	60
1	.64895	**.44560**	.65106	**.44777**	.65316	**.44994**	.65525	**.45211**	.65733	**.45429**	59
2	.64898	**.44564**	.65109	**.44781**	.65319	**.44998**	.65528	**.45215**	.65736	**.45432**	58
3	.64902	**.44568**	.65113	**.44784**	.65323	**.45001**	.65532	**.45219**	.65740	**.45436**	57
+ 1′	9.64905	**.44571**	9.65116	**.44788**	9.65326	**.45005**	9.65535	**.45222**	9.65743	**.45439**	56
5	.64909	**.44575**	.65120	**.44792**	.65330	**.45009**	.65539	**.45226**	.65747	**.45443**	55
6	.64912	**.44578**	.65123	**.44795**	.65333	**.45012**	.65542	**.45229**	.65750	**.45447**	54
7	.64916	**.44582**	.65127	**.44799**	.65337	**.45016**	.65546	**.45233**	.65754	**.45450**	53
+ 2′	9.64919	**.44586**	9.65130	**.44803**	9.65340	**.45020**	9.65549	**.45237**	9.65757	**.45454**	52
9	.64923	**.44589**	.65134	**.44806**	.65344	**.45023**	.65553	**.45240**	.65761	**.45458**	51
10	.64926	**.44593**	.65137	**.44810**	.65347	**.45027**	.65556	**.45244**	.65764	**.45461**	50
11	.64930	**.44596**	.65141	**.44813**	.65351	**.45030**	.65559	**.45248**	.65767	**.45465**	49
+ 3′	9.64934	**.44600**	9.65144	**.44817**	9.65354	**.45034**	9.65563	**.45251**	9.65771	**.45468**	48
13	.64937	**.44604**	.65148	**.44821**	.65358	**.45038**	.65566	**.45255**	.65774	**.45472**	47
14	.64941	**.44607**	.65151	**.44824**	.65361	**.45041**	.65570	**.45258**	.65778	**.45476**	46
15	.64944	**.44611**	.65155	**.44828**	.65365	**.45045**	.65573	**.45262**	.65781	**.45479**	45
+ 4′	9.64948	**.44614**	9.65158	**.44831**	9.65368	**.45048**	9.65577	**.45266**	9.65785	**.45483**	44
17	.64951	**.44618**	.65162	**.44835**	.65372	**.45052**	.65580	**.45269**	.65788	**.45486**	43
18	.64955	**.44622**	.65165	**.44839**	.65375	**.45056**	.65584	**.45273**	.65792	**.45490**	42
19	.64958	**.44625**	.65169	**.44842**	.65378	**.45059**	.65587	**.45276**	.65795	**.45494**	41
+ 5′	9.64962	**.44629**	9.65172	**.44846**	9.65382	**.45063**	9.65591	**.45280**	9.65799	**.45497**	40
21	.64965	**.44633**	.65176	**.44850**	.65385	**.45067**	.65594	**.45284**	.65802	**.45501**	39
22	.64969	**.44636**	.65179	**.44853**	.65389	**.45070**	.65598	**.45287**	.65806	**.45505**	38
23	.64972	**.44640**	.65183	**.44857**	.65392	**.45074**	.65601	**.45291**	.65809	**.45508**	37
+ 6′	9.64976	**.44643**	9.65186	**.44860**	9.65396	**.45077**	9.65605	**.45295**	9.65812	**.45512**	36
25	.64979	**.44647**	.65190	**.44864**	.65399	**.45081**	.65608	**.45298**	.65816	**.45515**	35
26	.64983	**.44651**	.65193	**.44868**	.65403	**.45085**	.65612	**.45302**	.65819	**.45519**	34
27	.64986	**.44654**	.65197	**.44871**	.65406	**.45088**	.65615	**.45305**	.65823	**.45523**	33
+ 7′	9.64990	**.44658**	9.65200	**.44875**	9.65410	**.45092**	9.65619	**.45309**	9.65826	**.45526**	32
29	.64993	**.44661**	.65204	**.44878**	.65413	**.45096**	.65622	**.45313**	.65830	**.45530**	31
30	.64997	**.44665**	.65207	**.44882**	.65417	**.45099**	.65625	**.45316**	.65833	**.45534**	30
31	.65000	**.44669**	.65211	**.44886**	.65421	**.45103**	.65629	**.45320**	.65837	**.45537**	29
+ 8′	9.65004	**.44672**	9.65214	**.44889**	9.65424	**.45106**	9.65632	**.45324**	9.65840	**.45541**	28
33	.65007	**.44676**	.65218	**.44893**	.65427	**.45110**	.65636	**.45327**	.65844	**.45544**	27
34	.65011	**.44680**	.65221	**.44897**	.65431	**.45114**	.65639	**.45331**	.65847	**.45548**	26
35	.65014	**.44683**	.65225	**.44900**	.65434	**.45117**	.65643	**.45334**	.65850	**.45552**	25
+ 9′	9.65018	**.44687**	9.65228	**.44904**	9.65438	**.45121**	9.65646	**.45338**	9.65854	**.45555**	24
37	.65021	**.44690**	.65232	**.44907**	.65441	**.45124**	.65650	**.45342**	.65857	**.45559**	23
38	.65025	**.44694**	.65235	**.44911**	.65445	**.45128**	.65653	**.45345**	.65861	**.45563**	22
39	.65028	**.44698**	.65239	**.44915**	.65448	**.45132**	.65657	**.45349**	.65864	**.45566**	21
+ 10′	9.65032	**.44701**	9.65242	**.44918**	9.65452	**.45135**	9.65660	**.45353**	9.65868	**.45570**	20
41	.65035	**.44705**	.65246	**.44922**	.65455	**.45139**	.65664	**.45356**	.65871	**.45573**	19
42	.65039	**.44708**	.65249	**.44925**	.65459	**.45143**	.65667	**.45360**	.65875	**.45577**	18
43	.65043	**.44712**	.65253	**.44929**	.65462	**.45146**	.65671	**.45363**	.65878	**.45581**	17
+ 11′	9.65046	**.44716**	9.65256	**.44933**	9.65466	**.45150**	9.65674	**.45367**	9.65881	**.45584**	16
45	.65050	**.44719**	.65260	**.44936**	.65469	**.45153**	.65677	**.45371**	.65885	**.45588**	15
46	.65053	**.44723**	.65263	**.44940**	.65473	**.45157**	.65681	**.45374**	.65888	**.45592**	14
47	.65057	**.44727**	.65267	**.44944**	.65476	**.45161**	.65684	**.45378**	.65892	**.45595**	13
+ 12′	9.65060	**.44730**	9.65270	**.44947**	9.65480	**.45164**	9.65688	**.45381**	9.65895	**.45599**	12
49	.65064	**.44734**	.65274	**.44951**	.65483	**.45168**	.65691	**.45385**	.65899	**.45602**	11
50	.65067	**.44737**	.65277	**.44954**	.65486	**.45172**	.65695	**.45389**	.65902	**.45606**	10
51	.65071	**.44741**	.65281	**.44958**	.65490	**.45175**	.65698	**.45392**	.65906	**.45610**	9
+ 13′	9.65074	**.44745**	9.65284	**.44962**	9.65493	**.45179**	9.65702	**.45396**	9.65909	**.45613**	8
53	.65078	**.44748**	.65288	**.44965**	.65497	**.45182**	.65705	**.45400**	.65913	**.45617**	7
54	.65081	**.44752**	.65291	**.44969**	.65500	**.45186**	.65709	**.45403**	.65916	**.45620**	6
55	.65085	**.44755**	.65295	**.44973**	.65504	**.45190**	.65712	**.45407**	.65919	**.45624**	5
+ 14′	9.65088	**.44759**	9.65298	**.44976**	9.65507	**.45193**	9.65716	**.45410**	9.65923	**.45628**	4
57	.65092	**.44763**	.65302	**.44980**	.65511	**.45197**	.65719	**.45414**	.65926	**.45631**	3
58	.65095	**.44766**	.65305	**.44983**	.65514	**.45200**	.65722	**.45418**	.65930	**.45635**	2
59	.65099	**.44770**	.65309	**.44987**	.65518	**.45204**	.65726	**.45421**	.65933	**.45639**	1
+ 15′	9.65102	**.44774**	9.65312	**.44991**	9.65521	**.45208**	9.65729	**.45425**	9.65937	**.45642**	0
	18h 24m		18h 23m		18h 22m		18h 21m		18h 20m		

TABLE 34.

Haversines.

s	$5^h 40^m$ 85° 0′		$5^h 41^m$ 85° 15′		$5^h 42^m$ 85° 30′		$5^h 43^m$ 85° 45′		$5^h 44^m$ 86° 0′		s
	Log. Hav.	Nat. Hav.	Log. Hav.	Nat. Hav.	Log. Hav.	Nat. Hav.	Log. Hav.	Nat. Hav.	Log. Hav.	Nat. Hav.	
0	9.65937	**.45642**	9.66143	**.45860**	9.66348	**.46077**	9.66553	**.46295**	9.66757	**.46512**	60
1	.65940	**.45646**	.66146	**.45863**	.66352	**.46081**	.66556	**.46298**	.66760	**.46516**	59
2	.65944	**.45649**	.66150	**.45867**	.66355	**.46084**	.66560	**.46302**	.66763	**.46519**	58
3	.65947	**.45653**	.66153	**.45870**	.66359	**.46088**	.66563	**.46305**	.66767	**.46523**	57
+ 1′	9.65950	**.45657**	9.66157	**.45874**	9.66362	**.46092**	9.66567	**.46309**	9.66770	**.46527**	56
5	.65954	**.45660**	.66160	**.45878**	.66366	**.46095**	.66570	**.46313**	.66774	**.46530**	55
6	.65957	**.45664**	.66164	**.45881**	.66369	**.46099**	.66573	**.46316**	.66777	**.46534**	54
7	.65961	**.45668**	.66167	**.45885**	.66372	**.46102**	.66577	**.46320**	.66780	**.46538**	53
+ 2′	9.65964	**.45671**	9.66170	**.45889**	9.66376	**.46106**	9.66580	**.46324**	9.66784	**.46541**	52
9	.65968	**.45675**	.66174	**.45892**	.66379	**.46110**	.66584	**.46327**	.66787	**.46545**	51
10	.65971	**.45678**	.66177	**.45896**	.66383	**.46113**	.66587	**.46331**	.66791	**.46548**	50
11	.65975	**.45682**	.66181	**.45899**	.66386	**.46117**	.66590	**.46334**	.66794	**.46552**	49
+ 3′	9.65978	**.45686**	9.66184	**.45903**	9.66389	**.46121**	9.66594	**.46338**	9.66797	**.46556**	48
13	.65981	**.45689**	.66188	**.45907**	.66393	**.46124**	.66597	**.46342**	.66801	**.46559**	47
14	.65985	**.45693**	.66191	**.45910**	.66396	**.46128**	.66601	**.46345**	.66804	**.46563**	46
15	.65988	**.45697**	.66194	**.45914**	.66400	**.46131**	.66604	**.46349**	.66807	**.46567**	45
+ 4′	9.65992	**.45700**	9.66198	**.45918**	9.66403	**.46135**	9.66607	**.46353**	9.66811	**.46570**	44
17	.65995	**.45704**	.66201	**.45921**	.66407	**.46139**	.66611	**.46356**	.66814	**.46574**	43
18	.65999	**.45707**	.66205	**.45925**	.66410	**.46142**	.66614	**.46360**	.66818	**.46577**	42
19	.66002	**.45711**	.66208	**.45928**	.66413	**.46146**	.66618	**.46363**	.66821	**.46581**	41
+ 5′	9.66006	**.45715**	9.66212	**.45932**	9.66417	**.46150**	9.66621	**.46367**	9.66824	**.46585**	40
21	.66009	**.45718**	.66215	**.45936**	.66420	**.46153**	.66624	**.46371**	.66828	**.46588**	39
22	.66012	**.45722**	.66218	**.45939**	.66424	**.46157**	.66628	**.46374**	.66831	**.46592**	38
23	.66016	**.45726**	.66222	**.45943**	.66427	**.46161**	.66631	**.46378**	.66835	**.46596**	37
+ 6′	9.66019	**.45729**	9.66225	**.45947**	9.66430	**.46164**	9.66635	**.46382**	9.66838	**.46599**	36
25	.66023	**.45733**	.66229	**.45950**	.66434	**.46168**	.66638	**.46385**	.66841	**.46603**	35
26	.66026	**.45736**	.66232	**.45954**	.66437	**.46171**	.66641	**.46389**	.66845	**.46606**	34
27	.66030	**.45740**	.66236	**.45957**	.66441	**.46175**	.66645	**.46392**	.66848	**.46610**	33
+ 7′	9.66033	**.45744**	9.66239	**.45961**	9.66444	**.46179**	9.66648	**.46396**	9.66851	**.46614**	32
29	.66037	**.45747**	.66242	**.45965**	.66447	**.46182**	.66652	**.46400**	.66855	**.46617**	31
30	.66040	**.45751**	.66246	**.45968**	.66451	**.46186**	.66655	**.46403**	.66858	**.46621**	30
31	.66043	**.45755**	.66249	**.45972**	.66454	**.46189**	.66658	**.46407**	.66862	**.46625**	29
+ 8′	9.66047	**.45758**	9.66253	**.45976**	9.66458	**.46193**	9.66662	**.46411**	9.66865	**.46628**	28
33	.66050	**.45762**	.66256	**.45979**	.66461	**.46197**	.66665	**.46414**	.66868	**.46632**	27
34	.66054	**.45765**	.66260	**.45983**	.66464	**.46200**	.66669	**.46418**	.66872	**.46636**	26
35	.66057	**.45769**	.66263	**.45986**	.66468	**.46204**	.66672	**.46421**	.66875	**.46639**	25
+ 9′	9.66061	**.45773**	9.66266	**.45990**	9.66471	**.46208**	9.66675	**.46425**	9.66878	**.46643**	24
37	.66064	**.45776**	.66270	**.45994**	.66475	**.46211**	.66679	**.46429**	.66882	**.46646**	23
38	.66067	**.45780**	.66273	**.45997**	.66478	**.46215**	.66682	**.46432**	.66885	**.46650**	22
39	.66071	**.45783**	.66277	**.46001**	.66482	**.46218**	.66685	**.46436**	.66889	**.46654**	21
+ 10′	9.66074	**.45787**	9.66280	**.46005**	9.66485	**.46222**	9.66689	**.46440**	9.66892	**.46657**	20
41	.66078	**.45791**	.66284	**.46008**	.66488	**.46226**	.66692	**.46443**	.66895	**.46661**	19
42	.66081	**.45794**	.66287	**.46012**	.66492	**.46229**	.66696	**.46447**	.66899	**.46665**	18
43	.66085	**.45798**	.66290	**.46015**	.66495	**.46233**	.66699	**.46451**	.66902	**.46668**	17
+ 11′	9.66088	**.45802**	9.66294	**.46019**	9.66499	**.46237**	9.66702	**.46454**	9.66905	**.46672**	16
45	.66092	**.45805**	.66297	**.46023**	.66502	**.46240**	.66706	**.46458**	.66909	**.46675**	15
46	.66095	**.45809**	.66301	**.46026**	.66505	**.46244**	.66709	**.46461**	.66912	**.46679**	14
47	.66098	**.45812**	.66304	**.46030**	.66509	**.46247**	.66713	**.46465**	.66916	**.46683**	13
+ 12′	9.66102	**.45816**	9.66307	**.46034**	9.66512	**.46251**	9.66716	**.46469**	9.66919	**.46686**	12
49	.66105	**.45820**	.66311	**.46037**	.66516	**.46255**	.66719	**.46472**	.66922	**.46690**	11
50	.66109	**.45823**	.66314	**.46041**	.66519	**.46258**	.66723	**.46476**	.66926	**.46694**	10
51	.66112	**.45827**	.66318	**.46044**	.66522	**.46262**	.66726	**.46480**	.66929	**.46697**	9
+ 13′	9.66116	**.45831**	9.66321	**.46048**	9.66526	**.46266**	9.66730	**.46483**	9.66932	**.46701**	8
53	.66119	**.45834**	.66325	**.46052**	.66529	**.46269**	.66733	**.46487**	.66936	**.46704**	7
54	.66122	**.45838**	.66328	**.46055**	.66533	**.46273**	.66736	**.46490**	.66939	**.46708**	6
55	.66126	**.45841**	.66331	**.46059**	.66536	**.46276**	.66740	**.46494**	.66943	**.46712**	5
+ 14′	9.66129	**.45845**	9.66335	**.46063**	9.66539	**.46280**	9.66743	**.46498**	9.66946	**.46715**	4
57	.66133	**.45849**	.66338	**.46066**	.66543	**.46284**	.66747	**.46501**	.66949	**.46719**	3
58	.66136	**.45852**	.66342	**.46070**	.66546	**.46287**	.66750	**.46505**	.66953	**.46723**	2
59	.66140	**.45856**	.66345	**.46073**	.66550	**.46291**	.66753	**.46509**	.66956	**.46726**	1
+ 15′	9.66143	**.45860**	9.66348	**.46077**	9.66553	**.46295**	9.66757	**.46512**	9.66959	**.46730**	0
	$18^h 19^m$		$18^h 18^m$		$18^h 17^m$		$18^h 16^m$		$18^h 15^m$		

TABLE 34.

Haversines.

s	$5^h 45^m$ 86° 15′		$5^h 46^m$ 86° 30′		$5^h 47^m$ 86° 45′		$5^h 48^m$ 87° 0′		$5^h 49^m$ 87° 15′		s
	Log. Hav.	Nat. Hav.	Log. Hav.	Nat. Hav.	Log. Hav.	Nat. Hav.	Log. Hav.	Nat. Hav.	Log. Hav.	Nat. Hav.	
0	9.66959	**.46730**	9.67161	**.46948**	9.67362	**.47165**	9.67562	**.47383**	9.67762	**.47601**	60
1	.66963	**.46733**	.67165	**.46951**	.67366	**.47169**	.67566	**.47387**	.67765	**.47605**	59
2	.66966	**.46737**	.67168	**.46955**	.67369	**.47173**	.67569	**.47390**	.67768	**.47608**	58
3	.66970	**.46741**	.67171	**.46958**	.67372	**.47176**	.67572	**.47394**	.67772	**.47612**	57
+ 1′	9.66973	**.46744**	9.67175	**.46962**	9.67376	**.47180**	9.67576	**.47398**	9.67775	**.47616**	56
5	.66976	**.46748**	.67178	**.46966**	.67379	**.47184**	.67579	**.47401**	.67778	**.47619**	55
6	.66980	**.46752**	.67181	**.46969**	.67382	**.47187**	.67582	**.47405**	.67782	**.47623**	54
7	.66983	**.46755**	.67185	**.46973**	.67386	**.47191**	.67586	**.47409**	.67785	**.47627**	53
+ 2′	9.66986	**.46759**	9.67188	**.46977**	9.67389	**.47194**	9.67589	**.47412**	9.67788	**.47630**	52
9	.66990	**.46762**	.67192	**.46980**	.67392	**.47198**	.67592	**.47416**	.67792	**.47634**	51
10	.66993	**.46766**	.67195	**.46984**	.67396	**.47202**	.67596	**.47420**	.67795	**.47637**	50
11	.66997	**.46770**	.67198	**.46987**	.67399	**.47205**	.67599	**.47423**	.67798	**.47641**	49
+ 3′	9.67000	**.46773**	9.67202	**.46991**	9.67402	**.47209**	9.67602	**.47427**	9.67801	**.47645**	48
13	.67003	**.46777**	.67205	**.46995**	.67406	**.47213**	.67606	**.47430**	.67805	**.47648**	47
14	.67007	**.46781**	.67208	**.46998**	.67409	**.47216**	.67609	**.47434**	.67808	**.47652**	46
15	.67010	**.46784**	.67212	**.47002**	.67412	**.47220**	.67612	**.47438**	.67811	**.47656**	45
+ 4′	9.67013	**.46788**	9.67215	**.47006**	9.67416	**.47223**	9.67616	**.47441**	9.67815	**.47659**	44
17	.67017	**.46792**	.67218	**.47009**	.67419	**.47227**	.67619	**.47445**	.67818	**.47663**	43
18	.67020	**.46795**	.67222	**.47013**	.67422	**.47231**	.67622	**.47449**	.67821	**.47666**	42
19	.67023	**.46799**	.67225	**.47017**	.67426	**.47234**	.67626	**.47452**	.67825	**.47670**	41
+ 5′	9.67027	**.46802**	9.67228	**.47020**	9.67429	**.47238**	9.67629	**.47456**	9.67828	**.47674**	40
21	.67030	**.46806**	.67232	**.47024**	.67432	**.47242**	.67632	**.47459**	.67831	**.47677**	39
22	.67034	**.46810**	.67235	**.47027**	.67436	**.47245**	.67636	**.47463**	.67835	**.47681**	38
23	.67037	**.46813**	.67238	**.47031**	.67439	**.47249**	.67639	**.47467**	.67838	**.47685**	37
+ 6′	9.67040	**.46817**	9.67242	**.47035**	9.67443	**.47252**	9.67642	**.47470**	9.67841	**.47688**	36
25	.67044	**.46821**	.67245	**.47038**	.67446	**.47256**	.67646	**.47474**	.67844	**.47692**	35
26	.67047	**.46824**	.67249	**.47042**	.67449	**.47260**	.67649	**.47478**	.67848	**.47696**	34
27	.67050	**.46828**	.67252	**.47046**	.67452	**.47263**	.67652	**.47481**	.67851	**.47699**	33
+ 7′	9.67054	**.46831**	9.67255	**.47049**	9.67456	**.47267**	9.67656	**.47485**	9.67854	**.47703**	32
29	.67057	**.46835**	.67259	**.47053**	.67459	**.47271**	.67659	**.47489**	.67858	**.47706**	31
30	.67060	**.46839**	.67262	**.47056**	.67462	**.47274**	.67662	**.47492**	.67861	**.47710**	30
31	.67064	**.46842**	.67265	**.47060**	.67466	**.47278**	.67666	**.47496**	.67864	**.47714**	29
+ 8′	9.67067	**.46846**	9.67269	**.47064**	9.67469	**.47282**	9.67669	**.47499**	9.67868	**.47717**	28
33	.67071	**.46850**	.67272	**.47067**	.67472	**.47285**	.67672	**.47503**	.67871	**.47721**	27
34	.67074	**.46853**	.67275	**.47071**	.67476	**.47289**	.67675	**.47507**	.67874	**.47725**	26
35	.67077	**.46857**	.67279	**.47075**	.67479	**.47292**	.67679	**.47510**	.67878	**.47728**	25
+ 9′	9.67081	**.46860**	9.67282	**.47078**	9.67483	**.47296**	9.67682	**.47514**	9.67881	**.47732**	24
37	.67084	**.46864**	.67285	**.47082**	.67486	**.47300**	.67685	**.47518**	.67884	**.47735**	23
38	.67087	**.46868**	.67289	**.47086**	.67489	**.47303**	.67689	**.47521**	.67887	**.47739**	22
39	.67091	**.46871**	.67292	**.47089**	.67493	**.47307**	.67692	**.47525**	.67891	**.47743**	21
+ 10′	9.67094	**.46875**	9.67295	**.47093**	9.67496	**.47311**	9.67695	**.47528**	9.67894	**.47746**	20
41	.67097	**.46879**	.67299	**.47096**	.67499	**.47314**	.67699	**.47532**	.67897	**.47750**	19
42	.67101	**.46882**	.67302	**.47100**	.67503	**.47318**	.67702	**.47536**	.67901	**.47754**	18
43	.67104	**.46886**	.67305	**.47104**	.67506	**.47321**	.67705	**.47539**	.67904	**.47757**	17
+ 11′	9.67108	**.46890**	9.67309	**.47107**	9.67509	**.47325**	9.67709	**.47543**	9.67907	**.47761**	16
45	.67111	**.46893**	.67312	**.47111**	.67512	**.47329**	.67712	**.47547**	.67911	**.47765**	15
46	.67114	**.46897**	.67315	**.47115**	.67516	**.47332**	.67715	**.47550**	.67914	**.47768**	14
47	.67118	**.46900**	.67319	**.47118**	.67519	**.47336**	.67719	**.47554**	.67917	**.47772**	13
+ 12′	9.67121	**.46904**	9.67322	**.47122**	9.67522	**.47340**	9.67722	**.47558**	9.67920	**.47775**	12
49	.67124	**.46908**	.67326	**.47125**	.67526	**.47343**	.67725	**.47561**	.67924	**.47779**	11
50	.67128	**.46911**	.67329	**.47129**	.67529	**.47347**	.67729	**.47565**	.67927	**.47783**	10
51	.67131	**.46915**	.67332	**.47133**	.67532	**.47351**	.67732	**.47568**	.67930	**.47786**	9
+ 13′	9.67134	**.46919**	9.67336	**.47136**	9.67536	**.47354**	9.67735	**.47572**	9.67934	**.47790**	8
53	.67138	**.46922**	.67339	**.47140**	.67539	**.47358**	.67738	**.47576**	.67937	**.47794**	7
54	.67141	**.46926**	.67342	**.47144**	.67542	**.47361**	.67742	**.47579**	.67940	**.47797**	6
55	.67145	**.46929**	.67346	**.47147**	.67546	**.47365**	.67745	**.47583**	.67944	**.47801**	5
+ 14′	9.67148	**.46933**	9.67349	**.47151**	9.67549	**.47369**	9.67748	**.47587**	9.67947	**.47805**	4
57	.67151	**.46937**	.67352	**.47155**	.67552	**.47372**	.67752	**.47590**	.67950	**.47808**	3
58	.67155	**.46940**	.67356	**.47158**	.67556	**.47376**	.67755	**.47594**	.67953	**.47812**	2
59	.67158	**.46944**	.67359	**.47162**	.67559	**.47380**	.67758	**.47597**	.67957	**.47815**	1
+ 15′	9.67161	**.46948**	9.67362	**.47165**	9.67562	**.47383**	9.67762	**.47601**	9.67960	**.47819**	0
	$18^h 14^m$		$18^h 13^m$		$18^h 12^m$		$18^h 11^m$		$18^h 10^m$		

TABLE 34.

Haversines.

s	$5^h 50^m$ 87° 30′		$5^h 51^m$ 87° 45′		$5^h 52^m$ 88° 0′		$5^h 53^m$ 88° 15′		$5^h 54^m$ 88° 30′		s
s	Log. Hav.	Nat. Hav.	Log. Hav.	Nat. Hav.	Log. Hav.	Nat. Hav.	Log. Hav.	Nat. Hav.	Log. Hav.	Nat. Hav.	s
0	9.67960	**.47819**	9.68158	**.48037**	9.68354	**.48255**	9.68550	**.48473**	9.68745	**.48691**	60
1	.67963	**.47823**	.68161	**.48041**	.68358	**.48259**	.68553	**.48477**	.68748	**.48695**	59
2	.67967	**.47826**	.68164	**.48044**	.68361	**.48262**	.68557	**.48480**	.68751	**.48698**	58
3	.67970	**.47830**	.68167	**.48048**	.68364	**.48266**	.68560	**.48484**	.68755	**.48702**	57
+ 1′	9.67973	**.47834**	9.68171	**.48052**	9.68367	**.48269**	9.68563	**.48488**	9.68758	**.48706**	56
5	.67977	**.47837**	.68174	**.48055**	.68371	**.48273**	.68566	**.48491**	.68761	**.48709**	55
6	.67980	**.47841**	.68177	**.48059**	.68374	**.48277**	.68570	**.48495**	.68764	**.48713**	54
7	.67983	**.47844**	.68181	**.48062**	.68377	**.48280**	.68573	**.48499**	.68768	**.48717**	53
+ 2′	9.67986	**.47848**	9.68184	**.48066**	9.68380	**.48284**	9.68576	**.48502**	9.68771	**.48720**	52
9	.67990	**.47852**	.68187	**.48070**	.68384	**.48288**	.68579	**.48506**	.68774	**.48724**	51
10	.67993	**.47855**	.68190	**.48073**	.68387	**.48291**	.68583	**.48509**	.68777	**.48728**	50
11	.67996	**.47859**	.68194	**.48077**	.68390	**.48295**	.68586	**.48513**	.68781	**.48731**	49
+ 3′	9.68000	**.47863**	9.68197	**.48081**	9.68393	**.48299**	9.68589	**.48517**	9.68784	**.48735**	48
13	.68003	**.47866**	.68200	**.48084**	.68397	**.48302**	.68592	**.48520**	.68787	**.48738**	47
14	.68006	**.47870**	.68204	**.48088**	.68400	**.48306**	.68596	**.48524**	.68790	**.48742**	46
15	.68010	**.47874**	.68207	**.48092**	.68403	**.48310**	.68599	**.48528**	.68794	**.48746**	45
+ 4′	9.68013	**.47877**	9.68210	**.48095**	9.68407	**.48313**	9.68602	**.48531**	9.68797	**.48749**	44
17	.68016	**.47881**	.68213	**.48099**	.68410	**.48317**	.68605	**.48535**	.68800	**.48753**	43
18	.68019	**.47884**	.68217	**.48102**	.68413	**.48320**	.68609	**.48538**	.68803	**.48757**	42
19	.68023	**.47888**	.68220	**.48106**	.68416	**.48324**	.68612	**.48542**	.68806	**.48760**	41
+ 5′	9.68026	**.47892**	9.68223	**.48110**	9.68420	**.48328**	9.68615	**.48546**	9.68810	**.48764**	40
21	.68029	**.47895**	.68227	**.48113**	.68423	**.48331**	.68618	**.48549**	.68813	**.48767**	39
22	.68033	**.47899**	.68230	**.48117**	.68426	**.48335**	.68622	**.48553**	.68816	**.48771**	38
23	.68036	**.47903**	.68233	**.48121**	.68429	**.48339**	.68625	**.48557**	.68820	**.48775**	37
+ 6′	9.68039	**.47906**	9.68236	**.48124**	9.68433	**.48342**	9.68628	**.48560**	9.68823	**.48778**	36
25	.68042	**.47910**	.68240	**.48128**	.68436	**.48346**	.68631	**.48564**	.68826	**.48782**	35
26	.68046	**.47913**	.68243	**.48131**	.68439	**.48350**	.68635	**.48568**	.68829	**.48786**	34
27	.68049	**.47917**	.68246	**.48135**	.68442	**.48353**	.68638	**.48571**	.68832	**.48789**	33
+ 7′	9.68052	**.47921**	9.68249	**.48139**	9.68446	**.48357**	9.68641	**.48575**	9.68836	**.48793**	32
29	.68056	**.47924**	.68253	**.48142**	.68449	**.48360**	.68644	**.48578**	.68839	**.48797**	31
30	.68059	**.47928**	.68256	**.48146**	.68452	**.48364**	.68648	**.48582**	.68842	**.48800**	30
31	.68062	**.47932**	.68259	**.48150**	.68456	**.48368**	.68651	**.48586**	.68845	**.48804**	29
+ 8′	9.68066	**.47935**	9.68263	**.48153**	9.68459	**.48371**	9.68654	**.48589**	9.68849	**.48807**	28
33	.68069	**.47939**	.68266	**.48157**	.68462	**.48375**	.68657	**.48593**	.68852	**.48811**	27
34	.68072	**.47943**	.68269	**.48161**	.68465	**.48379**	.68661	**.48597**	.68855	**.48815**	26
35	.68075	**.47946**	.68272	**.48164**	.68469	**.48382**	.68664	**.48600**	.68858	**.48818**	25
+ 9′	9.68079	**.47950**	9.68276	**.48168**	9.68472	**.48386**	9.68667	**.48604**	9.68862	**.48822**	24
37	.68082	**.47953**	.68279	**.48171**	.68475	**.48389**	.68670	**.48608**	.68865	**.48826**	23
38	.68085	**.47957**	.68282	**.48175**	.68478	**.48393**	.68674	**.48611**	.68868	**.48829**	22
39	.68089	**.47961**	.68286	**.48179**	.68482	**.48397**	.68677	**.48615**	.68871	**.48833**	21
+ 10′	9.68092	**.47964**	9.68289	**.48182**	9.68485	**.48400**	9.68680	**.48618**	9.68875	**.48837**	20
41	.68095	**.47968**	.68292	**.48186**	.68488	**.48404**	.68683	**.48622**	.68878	**.48840**	19
42	.68098	**.47972**	.68295	**.48190**	.68491	**.48408**	.68687	**.48626**	.68881	**.48844**	18
43	.68102	**.47975**	.68299	**.48193**	.68495	**.48411**	.68690	**.48629**	.68884	**.48847**	17
+ 11′	9.68105	**.47979**	9.68302	**.48197**	9.68498	**.48415**	9.68693	**.48633**	9.68887	**.48851**	16
45	.68108	**.47983**	.68305	**.48201**	.68501	**.48419**	.68696	**.48637**	.68891	**.48855**	15
46	.68112	**.47986**	.68308	**.48204**	.68504	**.48422**	.68700	**.48640**	.68894	**.48858**	14
47	.68115	**.47990**	.68312	**.48208**	.68508	**.48426**	.68703	**.48644**	.68897	**.48862**	13
+ 12′	9.68118	**.47993**	9.68315	**.48211**	9.68511	**.48429**	9.68706	**.48648**	9.68900	**.48866**	12
49	.68121	**.47997**	.68318	**.48215**	.68514	**.48433**	.68709	**.48651**	.68904	**.48869**	11
50	.68125	**.48001**	.68322	**.48219**	.68517	**.48437**	.68713	**.48655**	.68907	**.48873**	10
51	.68128	**.48004**	.68325	**.48222**	.68521	**.48440**	.68716	**.48658**	.68910	**.48877**	9
+ 13′	9.68131	**.48008**	9.68328	**.48226**	9.68524	**.48444**	9.68719	**.48662**	9.68913	**.48880**	8
53	.68135	**.48012**	.68331	**.48230**	.68527	**.48448**	.68722	**.48666**	.68917	**.48884**	7
54	.68138	**.48015**	.68335	**.48233**	.68531	**.48451**	.68726	**.48669**	.68920	**.48887**	6
55	.68141	**.48019**	.68338	**.48237**	.68534	**.48455**	.68729	**.48673**	.68923	**.48891**	5
+ 14′	9.68144	**.48022**	9.68341	**.48241**	9.68537	**.48459**	9.68732	**.48677**	9.68926	**.48895**	4
57	.68148	**.48026**	.68344	**.48244**	.68540	**.48462**	.68735	**.48680**	.68929	**.48898**	3
58	.68151	**.48030**	.68348	**.48248**	.68544	**.48466**	.68739	**.48684**	.68933	**.48902**	2
59	.68154	**.48033**	.68351	**.48251**	.68547	**.48469**	.68742	**.48688**	.68936	**.48906**	1
+ 15′	9.68158	**.48037**	9.68354	**.48255**	9.68550	**.48473**	9.68745	**.48691**	9.68939	**.48909**	0
	$18^h 9^m$		$18^h 8^m$		$18^h 7^m$		$18^h 6^m$		$18^h 5^m$		

TABLE 34.

Haversines.

s	$5^h\ 55^m$ 88° 45′		$5^h\ 56^m$ 89° 0′		$5^h\ 57^m$ 89° 15′		$5^h\ 58^m$ 89° 30′		$5^h\ 59^m$ 89° 45′		s
	Log. Hav.	Nat. Hav.	Log. Hav.	Nat. Hav.	Log. Hav.	Nat. Hav.	Log. Hav.	Nat. Hav.	Log. Hav.	Nat. Hav.	
0	9.68939	**.48909**	9.69132	**.49127**	9.69325	**.49346**	9.69516	**.49564**	9.69707	**.49782**	60
1	.68942	**.48913**	.69136	**.49131**	.69328	**.49349**	.69520	**.49567**	.69710	**.49785**	59
2	.68946	**.48917**	.69139	**.49135**	.69331	**.49353**	.69523	**.49571**	.69713	**.49789**	58
3	.68949	**.48920**	.69142	**.49138**	.69334	**.49356**	.69526	**.49575**	.69717	**.49793**	57
+ 1′	9.68952	**.48924**	9.69145	**.49142**	9.69338	**.49360**	9.69529	**.49578**	9.69720	**.49796**	56
5	.68955	**.48927**	.69148	**.49146**	.69341	**.49364**	.69532	**.49582**	.69723	**.49800**	55
6	.68958	**.48931**	.69152	**.49149**	.69344	**.49367**	.69535	**.49585**	.69726	**.49804**	54
7	.68962	**.48935**	.69155	**.49153**	.69347	**.49371**	.69539	**.49589**	.69729	**.49807**	53
+ 2′	9.68965	**.48938**	9.69158	**.49156**	9.69350	**.49375**	9.69542	**.49593**	9.69732	**.49811**	52
9	.68968	**.48942**	.69161	**.49160**	.69354	**.49378**	.69545	**.49596**	.69736	**.49815**	51
10	.68971	**.48946**	.69164	**.49164**	.69357	**.49382**	.69548	**.49600**	.69739	**.49818**	50
11	.68975	**.48949**	.69168	**.49167**	.69360	**.49386**	.69551	**.49604**	.69742	**.49822**	49
+ 3′	9.68978	**.48953**	9.69171	**.49171**	9.69363	**.49389**	9.69555	**.49607**	9.69745	**.49825**	48
13	.68981	**.48957**	.69174	**.49175**	.69366	**.49393**	.69558	**.49611**	.69748	**.49829**	47
14	.68984	**.48960**	.69177	**.49178**	.69370	**.49396**	.69561	**.49615**	.69751	**.49833**	46
15	.68988	**.48964**	.69181	**.49182**	.69373	**.49400**	.69564	**.49618**	.69755	**.49836**	45
+ 4′	9.68991	**.48967**	9.69184	**.49186**	9.69376	**.49404**	9.69567	**.49622**	9.69758	**.49840**	44
17	.68994	**.48971**	.69187	**.49189**	.69379	**.49407**	.69570	**.49625**	.69761	**.49844**	43
18	.68997	**.48975**	.69190	**.49193**	.69382	**.49411**	.69574	**.49629**	.69764	**.49847**	42
19	.69000	**.48978**	.69193	**.49196**	.69386	**.49415**	.69577	**.49633**	.69767	**.49851**	41
+ 5′	9.69004	**.48982**	9.69197	**.49200**	9.69389	**.49418**	9.69580	**.49636**	9.69770	**.49855**	40
21	.69007	**.48986**	.69200	**.49204**	.69392	**.49422**	.69583	**.49640**	.69774	**.49858**	39
22	.69010	**.48989**	.69203	**.49207**	.69395	**.49426**	.69586	**.49644**	.69777	**.49862**	38
23	.69013	**.48993**	.69206	**.49211**	.69398	**.49429**	.69590	**.49647**	.69780	**.49865**	37
+ 6′	9.69017	**.48997**	9.69209	**.49215**	9.69402	**.49433**	9.69593	**.49651**	9.69783	**.49869**	36
25	.69020	**.49000**	.69213	**.49218**	.69405	**.49436**	.69596	**.49655**	.69786	**.49873**	35
26	.69023	**.49004**	.69216	**.49222**	.69408	**.49440**	.69599	**.49658**	.69789	**.49876**	34
27	.69026	**.49007**	.69219	**.49226**	.69411	**.49444**	.69602	**.49662**	.69793	**.49880**	33
+ 7′	9.69029	**.49011**	9.69222	**.49229**	9.69414	**.49447**	9.69605	**.49665**	9.69796	**.49884**	32
29	.69033	**.49015**	.69225	**.49233**	.69417	**.49451**	.69609	**.49669**	.69799	**.49887**	31
30	.69036	**.49018**	.69229	**.49236**	.69421	**.49455**	.69612	**.49673**	.69802	**.49891**	30
31	.69039	**.49022**	.69232	**.49240**	.69424	**.49458**	.69615	**.49676**	.69805	**.49895**	29
+ 8′	9.69042	**.49026**	9.69235	**.49244**	9.69427	**.49462**	9.69618	**.49680**	9.69808	**.49898**	28
33	.69046	**.49029**	.69238	**.49247**	.69430	**.49465**	.69621	**.49684**	.69812	**.49902**	27
34	.69049	**.49033**	.69242	**.49251**	.69433	**.49469**	.69625	**.49687**	.69815	**.49905**	26
35	.69052	**.49036**	.69245	**.49255**	.69437	**.49473**	.69628	**.49691**	.69818	**.49909**	25
+ 9′	9.69055	**.49040**	9.69248	**.49258**	9.69440	**.49476**	9.69631	**.49695**	9.69821	**.49913**	24
37	.69058	**.49044**	.69251	**.49262**	.69443	**.49480**	.69634	**.49698**	.69824	**.49916**	23
38	.69062	**.49047**	.69254	**.49266**	.69446	**.49484**	.69637	**.49702**	.69827	**.49920**	22
39	.69065	**.49051**	.69258	**.49269**	.69449	**.49487**	.69640	**.49705**	.69831	**.49924**	21
+ 10′	9.69068	**.49055**	9.69261	**.49273**	9.69453	**.49491**	9.69644	**.49709**	9.69834	**.49927**	20
41	.69071	**.49058**	.69264	**.49276**	.69456	**.49495**	.69647	**.49713**	.69837	**.49931**	19
42	.69074	**.49062**	.69267	**.49280**	.69459	**.49498**	.69650	**.49716**	.69840	**.49935**	18
43	.69078	**.49066**	.69270	**.49284**	.69462	**.49502**	.69653	**.49720**	.69843	**.49938**	17
+ 11′	9.69081	**.49069**	9.69274	**.49287**	9.69465	**.49506**	9.69656	**.49724**	9.69846	**.49942**	16
45	.69084	**.49073**	.69277	**.49291**	.69469	**.49509**	.69659	**.49727**	.69850	**.49945**	15
46	.69087	**.49076**	.69280	**.49295**	.69472	**.49513**	.69663	**.49731**	.69853	**.49949**	14
47	.69091	**.49080**	.69283	**.49298**	.69475	**.49516**	.69666	**.49735**	.69856	**.49953**	13
+ 12′	9.69094	**.49084**	9.69286	**.49302**	9.69478	**.49520**	9.69669	**.49738**	9.69859	**.49956**	12
49	.69097	**.49087**	.69290	**.49306**	.69481	**.49524**	.69672	**.49742**	.69862	**.49960**	11
50	.69100	**.49091**	.69293	**.49309**	.69484	**.49527**	.69675	**.49745**	.69865	**.49964**	10
51	.69103	**.49095**	.69296	**.49313**	.69488	**.49531**	.69678	**.49749**	.69869	**.49967**	9
+ 13′	9.69107	**.49098**	9.69299	**.49316**	9.69491	**.49535**	9.69682	**.49753**	9.69872	**.49971**	8
53	.69110	**.49102**	.69302	**.49320**	.69494	**.49538**	.69685	**.49756**	.69875	**.49975**	7
54	.69113	**.49106**	.69306	**.49324**	.69497	**.49542**	.69688	**.49760**	.69878	**.49978**	6
55	.69116	**.49109**	.69309	**.49327**	.69500	**.49545**	.69691	**.49764**	.69881	**.49982**	5
+ 14′	9.69120	**.49113**	9.69312	**.49331**	9.69504	**.49549**	9.69694	**.49767**	9.69884	**.49985**	4
57	.69123	**.49116**	.69315	**.49335**	.69507	**.49553**	.69698	**.49771**	.69888	**.49989**	3
58	.69126	**.49120**	.69318	**.49338**	.69510	**.49556**	.69701	**.49775**	.69891	**.49993**	2
59	.69129	**.49124**	.69322	**.49342**	.69513	**.49560**	.69704	**.49778**	.69894	**.49997**	1
+ 15′	9.69132	**.49127**	9.69325	**.49346**	9.69516	**.49564**	9.69707	**.49782**	9.69897	**.50000**	0
	$18^h\ 4^m$		$18^h\ 3^m$		$18^h\ 2^m$		$18^h\ 1^m$		$18^h\ 0^m$		

TABLE 34.

Haversines.

s	6h 0m 90° 0′ Log. Hav.	Nat. Hav.	6h 1m 90° 15′ Log. Hav.	Nat. Hav.	6h 2m 90° 30′ Log. Hav.	Nat. Hav.	6h 3m 90° 45′ Log. Hav.	Nat. Hav.	6h 4m 91° 0′ Log. Hav.	Nat. Hav.	s
0	9.69897	**.50000**	9.70086	**.50218**	9.70274	**.50436**	9.70462	**.50654**	9.70648	**.50873**	60
1	.69900	**.50004**	.70089	**.50222**	.70277	**.50440**	.70465	**.50658**	.70652	**.50876**	59
2	.69903	**.50007**	.70092	**.50225**	.70281	**.50444**	.70468	**.50662**	.70655	**.50880**	58
3	.69906	**.50011**	.70096	**.50229**	.70284	**.50447**	.70471	**.50665**	.70658	**.50884**	57
+ 1′	9.69910	**.50015**	9.70099	**.50233**	9.70287	**.50451**	9.70474	**.50669**	9.70661	**.50887**	56
5	.69913	**.50018**	.70102	**.50236**	.70290	**.50455**	.70477	**.50673**	.70664	**.50891**	55
6	.69916	**.50022**	.70105	**.50240**	.70293	**.50458**	.70480	**.50676**	.70667	**.50894**	54
7	.69919	**.50025**	.70108	**.50244**	.70296	**.50462**	.70484	**.50680**	.70670	**.50898**	53
+ 2′	9.69922	**.50029**	9.70111	**.50247**	9.70299	**.50465**	9.70487	**.50684**	9.70673	**.50902**	52
9	.69925	**.50033**	.70114	**.50251**	.70303	**.50469**	.70490	**.50687**	.70676	**.50905**	51
10	.69929	**.50036**	.70118	**.50255**	.70306	**.50473**	.70493	**.50691**	.70679	**.50909**	50
11	.69932	**.50040**	.70121	**.50258**	.70309	**.50476**	.70496	**.50694**	.70683	**.50913**	49
+ 3′	9.69935	**.50044**	9.70124	**.50262**	9.70312	**.50480**	9.70499	**.50698**	9.70686	**.50916**	48
13	.69938	**.50047**	.70127	**.50265**	.70315	**.50484**	.70502	**.50702**	.70689	**.50920**	47
14	.69941	**.50051**	.70130	**.50269**	.70318	**.50487**	.70505	**.50705**	.70692	**.50924**	46
15	.69944	**.50055**	.70133	**.50273**	.70321	**.50491**	.70509	**.50709**	.70695	**.50927**	45
+ 4′	9.69948	**.50058**	9.70136	**.50276**	9.70324	**.50495**	9.70512	**.50713**	9.70698	**.50931**	44
17	.69951	**.50062**	.70140	**.50280**	.70328	**.50498**	.70515	**.50716**	.70701	**.50934**	43
18	.69954	**.50065**	.70143	**.50284**	.70331	**.50502**	.70518	**.50720**	.70704	**.50938**	42
19	.69957	**.50069**	.70146	**.50287**	.70334	**.50505**	.70521	**.50724**	.70707	**.50942**	41
+ 5′	9.69960	**.50073**	9.70149	**.50291**	9.70337	**.50509**	9.70524	**.50727**	9.70710	**.50945**	40
21	.69963	**.50076**	.70152	**.50295**	.70340	**.50513**	.70527	**.50731**	.70714	**.50949**	39
22	.69966	**.50080**	.70155	**.50298**	.70343	**.50516**	.70530	**.50734**	.70717	**.50953**	38
23	.69970	**.50084**	.70158	**.50302**	.70346	**.50520**	.70533	**.50738**	.70720	**.50956**	37
+ 6′	9.69973	**.50087**	9.70161	**.50305**	9.70349	**.50524**	9.70537	**.50742**	9.70723	**.50960**	36
25	.69976	**.50091**	.70165	**.50309**	.70353	**.50527**	.70540	**.50745**	.70726	**.50964**	35
26	.69979	**.50095**	.70168	**.50313**	.70356	**.50531**	.70543	**.50749**	.70729	**.50967**	34
27	.69982	**.50098**	.70171	**.50316**	.70359	**.50534**	.70546	**.50753**	.70732	**.50971**	33
+ 7′	9.69985	**.50102**	9.70174	**.50320**	9.70362	**.50538**	9.70549	**.50756**	9.70735	**.50974**	32
29	.69988	**.50105**	.70177	**.50324**	.70365	**.50542**	.70552	**.50760**	.70738	**.50978**	31
30	.69992	**.50109**	.70180	**.50327**	.70368	**.50545**	.70555	**.50764**	.70741	**.50982**	30
31	.69995	**.50113**	.70183	**.50331**	.70371	**.50549**	.70558	**.50767**	.70745	**.50985**	29
+ 8′	9.69998	**.50116**	9.70187	**.50335**	9.70374	**.50553**	9.70561	**.50771**	9.70748	**.50989**	28
33	.70001	**.50120**	.70190	**.50338**	.70378	**.50556**	.70565	**.50774**	.70751	**.50993**	27
34	.70004	**.50124**	.70193	**.50342**	.70381	**.50560**	.70568	**.50778**	.70754	**.50996**	26
35	.70007	**.50127**	.70196	**.50345**	.70384	**.50564**	.70571	**.50782**	.70757	**.51000**	25
+ 9′	9.70011	**.50131**	9.70199	**.50349**	9.70387	**.50567**	9.70574	**.50785**	9.70760	**.51004**	24
37	.70014	**.50135**	.70202	**.50353**	.70390	**.50571**	.70577	**.50789**	.70763	**.51007**	23
38	.70017	**.50138**	.70205	**.50356**	.70393	**.50574**	.70580	**.50793**	.70766	**.51011**	22
39	.70020	**.50142**	.70209	**.50360**	.70396	**.50578**	.70583	**.50796**	.70769	**.51014**	21
+ 10′	9.70023	**.50145**	9.70212	**.50364**	9.70399	**.50582**	9.70586	**.50800**	9.70772	**.51018**	20
41	.70026	**.50149**	.70215	**.50367**	.70402	**.50585**	.70589	**.50804**	.70775	**.51022**	19
42	.70029	**.50153**	.70218	**.50371**	.70406	**.50589**	.70593	**.50807**	.70779	**.51025**	18
43	.70033	**.50156**	.70221	**.50375**	.70409	**.50593**	.70596	**.50811**	.70782	**.51029**	17
+ 11′	9.70036	**.50160**	9.70224	**.50378**	9.70412	**.50596**	9.70599	**.50814**	9.70785	**.51033**	16
45	.70039	**.50164**	.70227	**.50382**	.70415	**.50600**	.70602	**.50818**	.70788	**.51036**	15
46	.70042	**.50167**	.70230	**.50385**	.70418	**.50604**	.70605	**.50822**	.70791	**.51040**	14
47	.70045	**.50171**	.70234	**.50389**	.70421	**.50607**	.70608	**.50825**	.70794	**.51043**	13
+ 12′	9.70048	**.50175**	9.70237	**.50393**	9.70424	**.50611**	9.70611	**.50829**	9.70797	**.51047**	12
49	.70051	**.50178**	.70240	**.50396**	.70427	**.50614**	.70614	**.50833**	.70800	**.51051**	11
50	.70055	**.50182**	.70243	**.50400**	.70431	**.50618**	.70617	**.50836**	.70803	**.51054**	10
51	.70058	**.50185**	.70246	**.50404**	.70434	**.50622**	.70620	**.50840**	.70806	**.51058**	9
+ 13′	9.70061	**.50189**	9.70249	**.50407**	9.70437	**.50625**	9.70624	**.50844**	9.70809	**.51062**	8
53	.70064	**.50193**	.70252	**.50411**	.70440	**.50629**	.70627	**.50847**	.70813	**.51065**	7
54	.70067	**.50196**	.70256	**.50415**	.70443	**.50633**	.70630	**.50851**	.70816	**.51069**	6
55	.70070	**.50200**	.70259	**.50418**	.70446	**.50636**	.70633	**.50854**	.70819	**.51073**	5
+ 14′	9.70074	**.50204**	9.70262	**.50422**	9.70449	**.50640**	9.70636	**.50858**	9.70822	**.51076**	4
57	.70077	**.50207**	.70265	**.50425**	.70452	**.50644**	.70639	**.50862**	.70825	**.51080**	3
58	.70080	**.50211**	.70268	**.50429**	.70456	**.50647**	.70642	**.50865**	.70828	**.51083**	2
59	.70083	**.50215**	.70271	**.50433**	.70459	**.50651**	.70645	**.50869**	.70831	**.51087**	1
+ 15′	9.70086	**.50218**	9.70274	**.50436**	9.70462	**.50654**	9.70648	**.50873**	9.70834	**.51091**	0
	17h 59m		17h 58m		17h 57m		17h 56m		17h 55m		

Haversines.

s	6h 5m 91° 15′		6h 6m 91° 30′		6h 7m 91° 45′		6h 8m 92° 0′		6h 9m 92° 15′		s
	Log. Hav.	Nat. Hav.	Log. Hav.	Nat. Hav.	Log. Hav.	Nat. Hav.	Log. Hav.	Nat. Hav.	Log. Hav.	Nat. Hav.	
0	9.70834	**.51091**	9.71019	**.51309**	9.71203	**.51527**	9.71387	**.51745**	9.71569	**.51963**	60
1	.70837	**.51094**	.71022	**.51312**	.71206	**.51531**	.71390	**.51749**	.71572	**.51967**	59
2	.70840	**.51098**	.71025	**.51316**	.71210	**.51534**	.71393	**.51752**	.71575	**.51970**	58
3	.70843	**.51102**	.71028	**.51320**	.71213	**.51538**	.71396	**.51756**	.71579	**.51974**	57
+ 1′	9.70847	**.51105**	9.71032	**.51323**	9.71216	**.51541**	9.71399	**.51760**	9.71582	**.51978**	56
5	.70850	**.51109**	.71035	**.51327**	.71219	**.51545**	.71402	**.51763**	.71585	**.51981**	55
6	.70853	**.51113**	.71038	**.51331**	.71222	**.51549**	.71405	**.51767**	.71588	**.51985**	54
7	.70856	**.51116**	.71041	**.51334**	.71225	**.51552**	.71408	**.51770**	.71591	**.51988**	53
+ 2′	9.70859	**.51120**	9.71044	**.51338**	9.71228	**.51556**	9.71411	**.51774**	9.71594	**.51992**	52
9	.70862	**.51123**	.71047	**.51342**	.71231	**.51560**	.71414	**.51778**	.71597	**.51996**	51
10	.70865	**.51127**	.71050	**.51345**	.71234	**.51563**	.71417	**.51781**	.71600	**.51999**	50
11	.70868	**.51131**	.71053	**.51349**	.71237	**.51567**	.71420	**.51785**	.71603	**.52003**	49
+ 3′	9.70871	**.51134**	9.71056	**.51352**	9.71240	**.51571**	9.71423	**.51789**	9.71606	**.52007**	48
13	.70874	**.51138**	.71059	**.51356**	.71243	**.51574**	.71426	**.51792**	.71609	**.52010**	47
14	.70877	**.51142**	.71062	**.51360**	.71246	**.51578**	.71430	**.51796**	.71612	**.52014**	46
15	.70881	**.51145**	.71065	**.51363**	.71249	**.51581**	.71433	**.51799**	.71615	**.52018**	45
+ 4′	9.70884	**.51149**	9.71068	**.51367**	9.71252	**.51585**	9.71436	**.51803**	9.71618	**.52021**	44
17	.70887	**.51153**	.71072	**.51371**	.71255	**.51589**	.71439	**.51807**	.71621	**.52025**	43
18	.70890	**.51156**	.71075	**.51374**	.71259	**.51592**	.71442	**.51810**	.71624	**.52028**	42
19	.70893	**.51160**	.71078	**.51378**	.71262	**.51596**	.71445	**.51814**	.71627	**.52032**	41
+ 5′	9.70896	**.51163**	9.71081	**.51382**	9.71265	**.51600**	9.71448	**.51818**	9.71630	**.52036**	40
21	.70899	**.51167**	.71084	**.51385**	.71268	**.51603**	.71451	**.51821**	.71633	**.52039**	39
22	.70902	**.51171**	.71087	**.51389**	.71271	**.51607**	.71454	**.51825**	.71636	**.52043**	38
23	.70905	**.51174**	.71090	**.51392**	.71274	**.51611**	.71457	**.51829**	.71639	**.52047**	37
+ 6′	9.70908	**.51178**	9.71093	**.51396**	9.71277	**.51614**	9.71460	**.51832**	9.71642	**.52050**	36
25	.70911	**.51182**	.71096	**.51400**	.71280	**.51618**	.71463	**.51836**	.71645	**.52054**	35
26	.70914	**.51185**	.71099	**.51403**	.71283	**.51621**	.71466	**.51839**	.71648	**.52057**	34
27	.70918	**.51189**	.71102	**.51407**	.71286	**.51625**	.71469	**.51843**	.71651	**.52061**	33
+ 7′	9.70921	**.51193**	9.71105	**.51411**	9.71289	**.51629**	9.71472	**.51847**	9.71654	**.52065**	32
29	.70924	**.51196**	.71108	**.51414**	.71292	**.51632**	.71475	**.51850**	.71657	**.52068**	31
30	.70927	**.51200**	.71111	**.51418**	.71295	**.51636**	.71478	**.51854**	.71660	**.52072**	30
31	.70930	**.51203**	.71114	**.51422**	.71298	**.51640**	.71481	**.51858**	.71663	**.52076**	29
+ 8′	9.70933	**.51207**	9.71118	**.51425**	9.71301	**.51643**	9.71484	**.51861**	9.71666	**.52079**	28
33	.70936	**.51211**	.71121	**.51429**	.71304	**.51647**	.71487	**.51865**	.71670	**.52083**	27
34	.70939	**.51214**	.71124	**.51432**	.71307	**.51650**	.71490	**.51869**	.71673	**.52087**	26
35	.70942	**.51218**	.71127	**.51436**	.71311	**.51654**	.71493	**.51872**	.71676	**.52090**	25
+ 9′	9.70945	**.51222**	9.71130	**.51440**	9.71314	**.51658**	9.71496	**.51876**	9.71679	**.52094**	24
37	.70948	**.51225**	.71133	**.51443**	.71317	**.51661**	.71500	**.51879**	.71682	**.52097**	23
38	.70951	**.51229**	.71136	**.51447**	.71320	**.51665**	.71503	**.51883**	.71685	**.52101**	22
39	.70955	**.51233**	.71139	**.51451**	.71323	**.51669**	.71506	**.51887**	.71688	**.52105**	21
+ 10′	9.70958	**.51236**	9.71142	**.51454**	9.71326	**.51672**	9.71509	**.51890**	9.71691	**.52108**	20
41	.70961	**.51240**	.71145	**.51458**	.71329	**.51676**	.71512	**.51894**	.71694	**.52112**	19
42	.70964	**.51243**	.71148	**.51462**	.71332	**.51680**	.71515	**.51898**	.71697	**.52116**	18
43	.70967	**.51247**	.71151	**.51465**	.71335	**.51683**	.71518	**.51901**	.71700	**.52119**	17
+ 11′	9.70970	**.51251**	9.71154	**.51469**	9.71338	**.51687**	9.71521	**.51905**	9.71703	**.52123**	16
45	.70973	**.51254**	.71157	**.51472**	.71341	**.51690**	.71524	**.51908**	.71706	**.52126**	15
46	.70976	**.51258**	.71161	**.51476**	.71344	**.51694**	.71527	**.51912**	.71709	**.52130**	14
47	.70979	**.51262**	.71164	**.51480**	.71347	**.51698**	.71530	**.51916**	.71712	**.52134**	13
+ 12′	9.70982	**.51265**	9.71167	**.51483**	9.71350	**.51701**	9.71533	**.51919**	9.71715	**.52137**	12
49	.70985	**.51269**	.71170	**.51487**	.71353	**.51705**	.71536	**.51923**	.71718	**.52141**	11
50	.70988	**.51273**	.71173	**.51491**	.71356	**.51709**	.71539	**.51927**	.71721	**.52145**	10
51	.70992	**.51276**	.71176	**.51494**	.71359	**.51712**	.71542	**.51930**	.71724	**.52148**	9
+ 13′	9.70995	**.51280**	9.71179	**.51498**	9.71362	**.51716**	9.71545	**.51934**	9.71727	**.52152**	8
53	.70998	**.51283**	.71182	**.51501**	.71365	**.51720**	.71548	**.51938**	.71730	**.52156**	7
54	.71001	**.51287**	.71185	**.51505**	.71369	**.51723**	.71551	**.51941**	.71733	**.52159**	6
55	.71004	**.51291**	.71188	**.51508**	.71372	**.51727**	.71554	**.51945**	.71736	**.52163**	5
+ 14′	9.71007	**.51294**	9.71191	**.51512**	9.71375	**.51730**	9.71557	**.51948**	9.71739	**.52166**	4
57	.71010	**.51298**	.71194	**.51516**	.71378	**.51734**	.71560	**.51952**	.71742	**.52170**	3
58	.71013	**.51302**	.71197	**.51520**	.71381	**.51738**	.71563	**.51956**	.71745	**.52174**	2
59	.71016	**.51305**	.71200	**.51523**	.71384	**.51741**	.71566	**.51959**	.71748	**.52177**	1
+ 15′	9.71019	**.51309**	9.71203	**.51527**	9.71387	**.51745**	9.71569	**.51963**	9.71751	**.52181**	0
	17h 54m		17h 53m		17h 52m		17h 51m		17h 50m		

TABLE 34.

Haversines.

s	6h 10m 92° 30′		6h 11m 92° 45′		6h 12m 93° 0′		6h 13m 93° 15′		6h 14m 93° 30′		s
	Log. Hav.	Nat. Hav.	Log. Hav.	Nat. Hav.	Log. Hav.	Nat. Hav.	Log. Hav.	Nat. Hav.	Log. Hav.	Nat. Hav.	
0	9.71751	**.52181**	9.71932	**.52399**	9.72112	**.52617**	9.72292	**.52835**	9.72471	**.53052**	60
1	.71754	**.52185**	.71935	**.52403**	.72115	**.52620**	.72295	**.52838**	.72474	**.53056**	59
2	.71757	**.52188**	.71938	**.52406**	.72118	**.52624**	.72298	**.52842**	.72476	**.53060**	58
3	.71760	**.52192**	.71941	**.52410**	.72121	**.52628**	.72301	**.52846**	.72479	**.53063**	57
+ 1′	9.71763	**.52196**	9.71944	**.52413**	9.72124	**.52631**	9.72304	**.52849**	9.72482	**.53067**	56
5	.71766	**.52199**	.71947	**.52417**	.72127	**.52635**	.72307	**.52853**	.72485	**.53071**	55
6	.71769	**.52203**	.71950	**.52421**	.72130	**.52639**	.72310	**.52856**	.72488	**.53074**	54
7	.71772	**.52206**	.71953	**.52424**	.72133	**.52642**	.72313	**.52860**	.72491	**.53078**	53
+ 2′	9.71775	**.52210**	9.71956	**.52428**	9.72136	**.52646**	9.72316	**.52864**	9.72494	**.53081**	52
9	.71778	**.52214**	.71959	**.52432**	.72139	**.52649**	.72319	**.52867**	.72497	**.53085**	51
10	.71781	**.52217**	.71962	**.52435**	.72142	**.52653**	.72322	**.52871**	.72500	**.53089**	50
11	.71784	**.52221**	.71965	**.52439**	.72145	**.52657**	.72325	**.52875**	.72503	**.53092**	49
+ 3′	9.71787	**.52225**	9.71968	**.52442**	9.72148	**.52660**	9.72328	**.52878**	9.72506	**.53096**	48
13	.71791	**.52228**	.71971	**.52446**	.72151	**.52664**	.72331	**.52882**	.72509	**.53100**	47
14	.71794	**.52232**	.71974	**.52450**	.72154	**.52668**	.72334	**.52885**	.72512	**.53103**	46
15	.71797	**.52235**	.71977	**.52453**	.72157	**.52671**	.72337	**.52889**	.72515	**.53107**	45
+ 4′	9.71800	**.52239**	9.71980	**.52457**	9.72160	**.52675**	9.72340	**.52893**	9.72518	**.53110**	44
17	.71803	**.52243**	.71983	**.52461**	.72163	**.52679**	.72343	**.52896**	.72521	**.53114**	43
18	.71806	**.52246**	.71986	**.52464**	.72166	**.52682**	.72346	**.52900**	.72524	**.53118**	42
19	.71809	**.52250**	.71989	**.52468**	.72169	**.52686**	.72349	**.52904**	.72527	**.53121**	41
+ 5′	9.71812	**.52254**	9 71992	**.52472**	9.72172	**.52689**	9.72352	**.52907**	9.72530	**.53125**	40
21	.71815	**.52257**	.71995	**.52475**	.72175	**.52693**	.72354	**.52911**	.72533	**.53129**	39
22	.71818	**.52261**	.71998	**.52479**	.72178	**.52697**	.72357	**.52915**	.72536	**.53132**	38
23	.71821	**.52264**	.72001	**.52482**	.72181	**.52700**	.72360	**.52918**	.72539	**.53136**	37
+ 6′	9.71824	**.52268**	9.72004	**.52486**	9.72184	**.52704**	9.72363	**.52922**	9.72542	**.53140**	36
25	.71827	**.52272**	.72007	**.52490**	.72187	**.52708**	.72366	**.52925**	.72545	**.53143**	35
26	.71830	**.52275**	.72010	**.52493**	.72190	**.52711**	.72369	**.52929**	.72548	**.53147**	34
27	.71833	**.52279**	.72013	**.52497**	.72193	**.52715**	.72372	**.52933**	.72551	**.53150**	33
+ 7′	9.71836	**.52283**	9.72016	**.52501**	9.72196	**.52718**	9.72375	**.52936**	9.72554	**.53154**	32
29	.71839	**.52286**	.72019	**.52504**	.72199	**.52722**	.72378	**.52940**	.72557	**.53158**	31
30	.71842	**.52290**	.72022	**.52508**	.72202	**.52726**	.72381	**.52944**	.72560	**.53161**	30
31	.71845	**.52294**	.72025	**.52511**	.72205	**.52729**	.72384	**.52947**	.72563	**.53165**	29
+ 8′	9.71848	**.52297**	9.72028	**.52515**	9.72208	**.52733**	9.72387	**.52951**	9.72565	**.53169**	28
33	.71851	**.52301**	.72031	**.52519**	.72211	**.52737**	.72390	**.52954**	.72568	**.53172**	27
34	.71854	**.52304**	.72034	**.52522**	.72214	**.52740**	.72393	**.52958**	.72571	**.53176**	26
35	.71857	**.52308**	.72037	**.52526**	.72217	**.52744**	.72396	**.52962**	.72574	**.53179**	25
+ 9′	9.71860	**.52312**	9.72040	**.52530**	9.72220	**.52748**	9.72399	**.52965**	9.72577	**.53183**	24
37	.71863	**.52315**	.72043	**.52533**	.72223	**.52751**	.72402	**.52969**	.72580	**.53187**	23
38	.71866	**.52319**	.72046	**.52537**	.72226	**.52755**	.72405	**.52973**	.72583	**.53190**	22
39	.71869	**.52323**	.72049	**.52541**	.72229	**.52758**	.72408	**.52976**	.72586	**.53194**	21
+ 10′	9.71872	**.52326**	9.72052	**.52544**	9.72232	**.52762**	9.72411	**.52980**	9.72589	**.53198**	20
41	.71875	**.52330**	.72055	**.52548**	.72235	**.52766**	.72414	**.52983**	.72592	**.53201**	19
42	.71878	**.52334**	.72058	**.52551**	.72238	**.52769**	.72417	**.52987**	.72595	**.53205**	18
43	.71881	**.52337**	.72061	**.52555**	.72241	**.52773**	.72420	**.52991**	.72598	**.53208**	17
+ 11′	9.71884	**.52341**	9.72064	**.52559**	9.72244	**.52776**	9.72423	**.52994**	9.72601	**.53212**	16
45	.71887	**.52344**	.72067	**.52562**	.72247	**.52780**	.72426	**.52998**	.72604	**.53216**	15
46	.71890	**.52348**	.72070	**.52566**	.72250	**.52784**	.72429	**.53002**	.72607	**.53219**	14
47	.71893	**.52352**	.72073	**.52570**	.72253	**.52787**	.72432	**.53005**	.72610	**.53223**	13
+ 12′	9.71896	**.52355**	9.72076	**.52573**	9.72256	**.52791**	9.72435	**.53009**	9.72613	**.53227**	12
49	.71899	**.52359**	.72079	**.52577**	.72259	**.52795**	.72438	**.53013**	.72616	**.53230**	11
50	.71902	**.52363**	.72082	**.52580**	.72262	**.52798**	.72441	**.53016**	.72619	**.53234**	10
51	.71905	**.52366**	.72085	**.52584**	.72265	**.52802**	.72444	**.53020**	.72622	**.53238**	9
+ 13′	9.71908	**.52370**	9.72088	**.52588**	9.72268	**.52806**	9.72447	**.53023**	9.72625	**.53241**	8
53	.71911	**.52373**	.72091	**.52591**	.72271	**.52809**	.72450	**.53027**	.72628	**.53245**	7
54	.71914	**.52377**	.72094	**.52595**	.72274	**.52813**	.72453	**.53031**	.72631	**.53248**	6
55	.71917	**.52381**	.72097	**.52599**	.72277	**.52816**	.72456	**.53034**	.72634	**.53252**	5
+ 14′	9.71920	**.52384**	9.72100	**.52602**	9.72280	**.52820**	9.72459	**.53038**	9.72637	**.53256**	4
57	.71923	**.52388**	.72103	**.52606**	.72283	**.52824**	.72462	**.53042**	.72640	**.53259**	3
58	.71926	**.52392**	.72106	**.52610**	.72286	**.52827**	.72465	**.53045**	.72642	**.53263**	2
59	.71929	**.52395**	.72109	**.52613**	.72289	**.52831**	.72468	**.53049**	.72645	**.53267**	1
+ 15′	9.71932	**.52399**	9.72112	**.52617**	9.72292	**.52835**	9.72471	**.53052**	9.72648	**.53270**	0
	17h 49m		17h 48m		17h 47m		17h 46m		17h 45m		

TABLE 34.

Haversines.

s	$6^h\ 15^m$ 93° 45′		$6^h\ 16^m$ 94° 0′		$6^h\ 17^m$ 94° 15′		$6^h\ 18^m$ 94° 30′		$6^h\ 19^m$ 94° 45		s
	Log. Hav.	Nat. Hav.	Log. Hav.	Nat. Hav.	Log. Hav.	Nat. Hav.	Log. Hav.	Nat. Hav.	Log. Hav.	Nat. Hav.	
0	9.72648	**.53270**	9.72825	**.53488**	9.73002	**.53705**	9.73177	**.53923**	9.73352	**.54140**	60
1	.72651	**.53274**	.72828	**.53491**	.73005	**.53709**	.73180	**.53927**	.73355	**.54144**	59
2	.72654	**.53277**	.72831	**.53495**	.73008	**.53713**	.73183	**.53930**	.73358	**.54148**	58
3	.72657	**.53281**	.72834	**.53499**	.73011	**.53716**	.73186	**.53934**	.73361	**.54151**	57
+ 1′	9.72660	**.53285**	9.72837	**.53502**	9.73014	**.53720**	9.73189	**.53937**	9.73364	**.54155**	56
5	.72663	**.53288**	.72840	**.53506**	.73016	**.53724**	.73192	**.53941**	.73367	**.54159**	55
6	.72666	**.53292**	.72843	**.53510**	.73019	**.53727**	.73195	**.53945**	.73370	**.54162**	54
7	.72669	**.53296**	.72846	**.53513**	.73022	**.53731**	.73198	**.53948**	.73373	**.54166**	53
+ 2′	9.72672	**.53299**	9.72849	**.53517**	9.73025	**.53734**	9.73201	**.53952**	9.73375	**.54169**	52
9	.72675	**.53303**	.72852	**.53520**	.73028	**.53738**	.73204	**.53956**	.73378	**.54173**	51
10	.72678	**.53306**	.72855	**.53524**	.73031	**.53742**	.73207	**.53959**	.73381	**.54177**	50
11	.72681	**.53310**	.72858	**.53528**	.73034	**.53745**	.73209	**.53963**	.73384	**.54180**	49
+ 3′	9.72684	**.53314**	9.72861.	**.53531**	9.73037	**.53749**	9.73212	**.53966**	9.73387	**.54184**	48
13	.72687	**.53317**	.72864	**.53535**	.73040	**.53753**	.73215	**.53970**	.73390	**.54188**	47
14	.72690	**.53321**	.72867	**.53539**	.73043	**.53756**	.73218	**.53974**	.73393	**.54191**	46
15	.72693	**.53325**	.72870	**.53542**	.73046	**.53760**	.73221	**.53977**	.73396	**.54195**	45
+ 4′	9.72696	**.53328**	9.72873	**.53546**	9.73049	**.53763**	9.73224	**.53981**	9.73399	**.54198**	44
17	.72699	**.53332**	.72876	**.53549**	.73052	**.53767**	.73227	**.53985**	.73402	**.54202**	43
18	.72702	**.53335**	.72878	**.53553**	.73055	**.53771**	.73230	**.53988**	.73404	**.54206**	42
19	.72705	**.53339**	.72881	**.53557**	.73057	**.53774**	.73233	**.53992**	.73407	**.54209**	41
+ 5′	9.72708	**.53343**	9.72884	**.53560**	9.73060	**.53778**	9.73236	**.53995**	9.73410	**.54213**	40
21	.72710	**.53346**	.72887	**.53564**	.73063	**.53782**	.73239	**.53999**	.73413	**.54217**	39
22	.72713	**.53350**	.72890	**.53568**	.73066	**.53785**	.73242	**.54003**	.73416	**.54220**	38
23	.72716	**.53354**	.72893	**.53571**	.73069	**.53789**	.73244	**.54006**	.73419	**.54224**	37
+ 6′	9.72719	**.53357**	9.72896	**.53575**	9.73072	**.53792**	9.73247	**.54010**	9.73422	**.54227**	36
25	.72722	**.53361**	.72899	**.53579**	.73075	**.53796**	.73250	**.54014**	.73425	**.54231**	35
26	.72725	**.53364**	.72902	**.53582**	.75078	**.53800**	.73253	**.54017**	.73428	**.54235**	34
27	.72728	**.53368**	.72905	**.53586**	.73081	**.53803**	.73256	**.54021**	.73431	**.54238**	33
+ 7′	9.72731	**.53372**	9.72908	**.53589**	9.73084	**.53807**	9.73259	**.54024**	9.73433	**.54242**	32
29	.72734	**.53375**	.72911	**.53593**	.73087	**.53811**	.73262	**.54028**	.73436	**.54245**	31
30	.72737	**.53379**	.72914	**.53597**	.73090	**.53814**	.73265	**.54032**	.73439	**.54249**	30
31	.72740	**.53383**	.72917	**.53600**	.73093	**.53818**	.73268	**.54035**	.73442	**.54253**	29
+ 8′	9.72743	**.53386**	9.72920	**.53604**	9.73096	**.53821**	9.73271	**.54039**	9.73445	**.54256**	28
33	.72746	**.53390**	.72923	**.53608**	.73098	**.53825**	.73274	**.54043**	.73448	**.54260**	27
34	.72749	**.53394**	.72926	**.53611**	.73101	**.53829**	.73277	**.54046**	.73451	**.54264**	26
35	.72752	**.53397**	.72928	**.53615**	.73104	**.53832**	.73280	**.54050**	.73454	**.54267**	25
+ 9′	9.72755	**.53401**	9.72931	**.53618**	9.73107	**.53836**	9.73282	**.54053**	9.73457	**.54271**	24
37	.72758	**.53404**	.72934	**.53622**	.73110	**.53840**	.73285	**.54057**	.73460	**.54274**	23
38	.72761	**.53408**	.72937	**.53626**	.73113	**.53843**	.73288	**.54061**	.73462	**.54278**	22
39	.72764	**.53412**	.72940	**.53629**	.73116	**.53847**	.73291	**.54064**	.73465	**.54282**	21
+ 10′	9.72767	**.53415**	9.72943	**.53633**	9.73119	**.53850**	9.73294	**.54068**	9.73468	**.54285**	20
41	.72770	**.53419**	.72946	**.53637**	.73122	**.53854**	.73297	**.54072**	.73471	**.54289**	19
42	.72772	**.53423**	.72949	**.53640**	.73125	**.53858**	.73300	**.54075**	.73474	**.54293**	18
43	.72775	**.53426**	.72952	**.53644**	.73128	**.53861**	.73303	**.54079**	.73477	**.54296**	17
+ 11′	9.72778	**.53430**	9.72955	**.53647**	9.73131	**.53865**	9.73306	**.54082**	9.73480	**.54300**	16
45	.72781	**.53433**	.72958	**.53651**	.73134	**.53869**	.73309	**.54086**	.73483	**.54303**	15
46	.72784	**.53437**	.72961	**.53655**	.73136	**.53872**	.73311	**.54090**	.73486	**.54307**	14
47	.72787	**.53441**	.72964	**.53658**	.73139	**.53876**	.73314	**.54093**	.73489	**.54311**	13
+ 12′	9.72790	**.53444**	9.72967	**.53662**	9.73142	**.53879**	9.73317	**.54097**	9.73491	**.54314**	12
49	.72793	**.53448**	.72970	**.53666**	.73145	**.53883**	.73320	**.54101**	.73494	**.54318**	11
50	.72796	**.53452**	.72972	**.53669**	.73148	**.53887**	.73323	**.54104**	.73497	**.54322**	10
51	.72799	**.53455**	.72975	**.53673**	.73151	**.53890**	.73326	**.54108**	.73500	**.54325**	9
+ 13′	9.72802	**.53459**	9.72978	**.53676**	9.73154	**.53894**	9.73329	**.54111**	9.73503	**.54329**	8
53	.72805	**.53462**	.72981	**.53680**	.73157	**.53898**	.73332	**.54115**	.73506	**.54332**	7
54	.72808	**.53466**	.72984	**.53684**	.73160	**.53901**	.73335	**.54119**	.73509	**.54336**	6
55	.72811	**.53470**	.72987	**.53687**	.73163	**.53905**	.73338	**.54122**	.73512	**.54340**	5
+ 14′	9.72814	**.53473**	9.72990	**.53691**	9.73166	**.53908**	9.73341	**.54126**	9.73515	**.54343**	4
57	.72817	**.53477**	.72993	**.53695**	.73169	**.53912**	.73343	**.54130**	.73517	**.54347**	3
58	.72820	**.53481**	.72996	**.53698**	.73172	**.53916**	.73346	**.54133**	.73520	**.54351**	2
59	.72823	**.53484**	.72999	**.53702**	.73174	**.53919**	.73349	**.54137**	.73523	**.54354**	1
+ 15′	9.72825	**.53488**	9.73002	**.53705**	9.73177	**.53923**	9.73352	**.54140**	9.73526	**.54358**	0
	$17^h\ 44^m$		$17^h\ 43^m$		$17^h\ 42^m$		$17^h\ 41^m$		$17^h\ 40^m$		

TABLE 34.

Haversines.

s	6h 20m 95° 0′ Log. Hav.	6h 20m 95° 0′ Nat. Hav.	6h 21m 95° 15′ Log. Hav.	6h 21m 95° 15′ Nat. Hav.	6h 22m 95° 30′ Log. Hav.	6h 22m 95° 30′ Nat. Hav.	6h 23m 95° 45′ Log. Hav.	6h 23m 95° 45′ Nat. Hav.	6h 24m 96° 0′ Log. Hav.	6h 24m 96° 0′ Nat. Hav.	s
0	9.73526	.54358	9.73699	.54575	9.73872	.54792	9.74044	.55009	9.74215	.55226	60
1	.73529	.54361	.73702	.54579	.73875	.54796	.74047	.55013	.74218	.55230	59
2	.73532	.54365	.73705	.54582	.73878	.54800	.74049	.55017	.74220	.55234	58
3	.73535	.54369	.73708	.54586	.73881	.54803	.74052	.55020	.74223	.55237	57
+ 1′	9.73538	.54372	9.73711	.54590	9.73883	.54807	9.74055	.55024	9.74226	.55241	56
5	.73541	.54376	.73714	.54593	.73886	.54810	.74058	.55028	.74229	.55245	55
6	.73544	.54380	.73717	.54597	.73889	.54814	.74061	.55031	.74232	.55248	54
7	.73546	.54383	.73720	.54600	.73892	.54818	.74064	.55035	.74235	.55252	53
+ 2′	9.73549	.54387	9.73722	.54604	9.73895	.54821	9.74067	.55038	9.74237	.55255	52
9	.73552	.54390	.73725	.54608	.73898	.54825	.74069	.55042	.74240	.55259	51
10	.73555	.54394	.73728	.54611	.73901	.54828	.74072	.55046	.74243	.55263	50
11	.73558	.54398	.73731	.54615	.73903	.54832	.74075	.55049	.74246	.55266	49
+ 3′	9.73561	.54401	9.73734	.54619	9.73906	.54836	9.74078	.55053	9.74249	.55270	48
13	.73564	.54405	.73737	.54622	.73909	.54839	.74081	.55056	.74252	.55273	47
14	.73567	.54409	.73740	.54626	.73912	.54843	.74084	.55060	.74254	.55277	46
15	.73570	.54412	.73743	.54629	.73915	.54847	.74087	.55064	.74257	.55281	45
+ 4′	9.73572	.54416	9.73746	.54633	9.73918	.54850	9.74089	.55067	9.74260	.55284	44
17	.73575	.54419	.73748	.54637	.73921	.54854	.74092	.55071	.74263	.55288	43
18	.73578	.54423	.73751	.54640	.73924	.54857	.74095	.55075	.74266	.55292	42
19	.73581	.54427	.73754	.54644	.73926	.54861	.74098	.55078	.74269	.55295	41
+ 5′	9.73584	.54430	9.73757	.54647	9.73929	.54865	9.74101	.55082	9.74272	.55299	40
21	.73587	.54434	.73760	.54651	.73932	.54868	.74104	.55085	.74274	.55302	39
22	.73590	.54437	.73763	.54655	.73935	.54872	.74106	.55089	.74277	.55306	38
23	.73593	.54441	.73766	.54658	.73938	.54876	.74109	.55093	.74280	.55310	37
+ 6′	9.73596	.54445	9.73769	.54662	9.73941	.54879	9.74112	.55096	9.74283	.55313	36
25	.73598	.54448	.73771	.54666	.73944	.54883	.74115	.55100	.74286	.55317	35
26	.73601	.54452	.73774	.54669	.73946	.54886	.74118	.55103	.74289	.55320	34
27	.73604	.54456	.73777	.54673	.73949	.54890	.74121	.55107	.74291	.55324	33
+ 7′	9.73607	.54459	9.73780	.54676	9.73952	.54894	9.74124	.55111	9.74294	.55328	32
29	.73610	.54463	.73783	.54680	.73955	.54897	.74126	.55114	.74297	.55331	31
30	.73613	.54466	.73786	.54684	.73958	.54901	.74129	.55118	.74300	.55335	30
31	.73616	.54470	.73789	.54687	.73961	.54904	.74132	.55122	.74303	.55339	29
+ 8′	9.73619	.54474	9.73792	.54691	9.73964	.54908	9.74135	.55125	9.74306	.55342	28
33	.73622	.54477	.73794	.54695	.73967	.54912	.74138	.55129	.74308	.55346	27
34	.73624	.54481	.73797	.54698	.73969	.54915	.74141	.55132	.74311	.55349	26
35	.73627	.54485	.73800	.54702	.73972	.54919	.74144	.55136	.74314	.55353	25
+ 9′	9.73630	.54488	9.73803	.54705	9.73975	.54923	9.74146	.55140	9.74317	.55357	24
37	.73633	.54492	.73806	.54709	.73978	.54926	.74149	.55143	.74320	.55360	23
38	.73636	.54495	.73809	.54713	.73981	.54930	.74152	.55147	.74323	.55364	22
39	.73639	.54499	.73812	.54716	.73984	.54933	.74155	.55150	.74325	.55367	21
+ 10′	9.73642	.54503	9.73815	.54720	9.73987	.54937	9.74158	.55154	9.74328	.55371	20
41	.73645	.54506	.73817	.54724	.73989	.54941	.74161	.55158	.74331	.55375	19
42	.73648	.54510	.73820	.54727	.73992	.54944	.74163	.55161	.74334	.55378	18
43	.73650	.54514	.73823	.54731	.73995	.54948	.74166	.55165	.74337	.55382	17
+ 11′	9.73653	.54517	9.73826	.54734	9.73998	.54952	9.74169	.55169	9.74340	.55386	16
45	.73656	.54521	.73829	.54738	.74001	.54955	.74172	.55172	.74342	.55389	15
46	.73659	.54524	.73832	.54742	.74004	.54959	.74175	.55176	.74345	.55393	14
47	.73662	.54528	.73835	.54745	.74007	.54963	.74178	.55179	.74348	.55396	13
+ 12′	9.73665	.54532	9.73838	.54749	9.74009	.54966	9.74181	.55183	9.74351	.55400	12
49	.73668	.54535	.73840	.54752	.74012	.54970	.74183	.55187	.74354	.55404	11
50	.73671	.54539	.73843	.54756	.74015	.54973	.74186	.55190	.74357	.55407	10
51	.73674	.54542	.73846	.54760	.74018	.54977	.74189	.55194	.74359	.55411	9
+ 13′	9.73676	.54546	9.73849	.54763	9.74021	.54980	9.74192	.55197	9.74362	.55414	8
53	.73679	.54550	.73852	.54767	.74024	.54984	.74195	.55201	.74365	.55418	7
54	.73682	.54553	.73855	.54771	.74027	.54988	.74198	.55205	.74368	.55422	6
55	.73685	.54557	.73858	.54774	.74029	.54991	.74200	.55208	.74371	.55425	5
+ 14′	9.73688	.54561	9.73860	.54778	9.74032	.54995	9.74203	.55212	9.74374	.55429	4
57	.73691	.54564	.73863	.54781	.74035	.54999	.74206	.55216	.74376	.55433	3
58	.73694	.54568	.73866	.54785	.74038	.55002	.74209	.55219	.74379	.55436	2
59	.73697	.54571	.73869	.54789	.74041	.55006	.74212	.55223	.74382	.55440	1
+ 15′	9.73699	.54575	9.73872	.54792	9.74044	.55009	9.74215	.55226	9.74385	.55443	0
	17h 39m		17h 38m		17h 37m		17h 36m		17h 35m		

TABLE 34.

Haversines.

s	6h 25m 96° 15′		6h 26m 96° 30′		6h 27m 96° 45′		6h 28m 97° 0′		6h 29m 97° 15′		s
	Log. Hav.	Nat. Hav.	Log. Hav.	Nat. Hav.	Log. Hav.	Nat. Hav.	Log. Hav.	Nat. Hav.	Log. Hav.	Nat. Hav.	
0	9.74385	**.55443**	9.74554	**.55660**	9.74723	**.55877**	9.74891	**.56093**	9.75059	**.56310**	60
1	.74388	**.55447**	.74557	**.55664**	.74726	**.55880**	.74894	**.56097**	.75061	**.56314**	59
2	.74391	**.55451**	.74560	**.55667**	.74729	**.55884**	.74897	**.56101**	.75064	**.56317**	58
3	.74393	**.55454**	.74563	**.55671**	.74732	**.55888**	.74900	**.56104**	.75067	**.56321**	57
+ 1′	9.74396	**.55458**	9.74566	**.55675**	9.74734	**.55891**	9.74902	**.56108**	9.75070	**.56324**	56
5	.74399	**.55461**	.74569	**.55678**	.74737	**.55895**	.74905	**.56112**	.75072	**.56328**	55
6	.74402	**.55465**	.74571	**.55682**	.74740	**.55899**	.74908	**.56115**	.75075	**.56332**	54
7	.74405	**.55469**	.74574	**.55685**	.74743	**.55902**	.74911	**.56119**	.75078	**.56335**	53
+ 2′	9.74408	**.55472**	9.74577	**.55689**	9.74746	**.55906**	9.74914	**.56122**	9.75081	**.56339**	52
9	.74410	**.55476**	.74580	**.55693**	.74748	**.55909**	.74916	**.56126**	.75084	**.56342**	51
10	.74413	**.55479**	.74583	**.55696**	.74751	**.55913**	.74919	**.56130**	.75086	**.56346**	50
11	.74416	**.55483**	.74585	**.55700**	.74754	**.55917**	.74922	**.56133**	.75089	**.56350**	49
+ 3′	9 74419	**.55487**	9.74588	**.55704**	9.74757	**.55920**	9.74925	**.56137**	9.75092	**.56353**	48
13	.74422	**.55490**	.74591	**.55707**	.74760	**.55924**	.74928	**.56140**	.75095	**.56357**	47
14	.74425	**.55494**	.74594	**.55711**	.74762	**.55927**	.74930	**.56144**	.75097	**.56360**	46
15	.74427	**.55498**	.74597	**.55714**	.74765	**.55931**	.74933	**.56147**	.75100	**.56364**	45
+ 4′	9.74430	**.55501**	9.74600	**.55718**	9.74768	**.55935**	9.74936	**.56151**	9.75103	**.56368**	44
17	.74433	**.55505**	.74602	**.55722**	.74771	**.55938**	.74939	**.56155**	.75106	**.56371**	43
18	.74436	**.55508**	.74605	**.55725**	.74774	**.55942**	.74941	**.56158**	.75109	**.56375**	42
19	.74439	**.55512**	.74608	**.55729**	.74776	**.55945**	.74944	**.56162**	.75111	**.56378**	41
+ 5′	9.74442	**.55516**	9.74611	**.55732**	9.74779	**.55949**	9.74947	**.56166**	9.75114	**.56382**	40
21	.74444	**.55519**	.74614	**.55736**	.74782	**.55953**	.74950	**.56169**	.75117	**.56386**	39
22	.74447	**.55523**	.74616	**.55740**	.74785	**.55956**	.74953	**.56173**	.75120	**.56389**	38
23	.74450	**.55526**	.74619	**.55743**	.74788	**.55960**	.74955	**.56176**	.75122	**.56393**	37
+ 6′	9.74453	**.55530**	9.74622	**.55747**	9.74791	**.55964**	9.74958	**.56180**	9.75125	**.56397**	36
25	.74456	**.55534**	.74625	**.55750**	.74793	**.55967**	.74961	**.56184**	.75128	**.56400**	35
26	.74458	**.55537**	.74628	**.55754**	.74796	**.55971**	.74964	**.56187**	.75131	**.56404**	34
27	.74461	**.55541**	.74630	**.55758**	.74799	**.55974**	.74967	**.56191**	.75134	**.56407**	33
+ 7′	9.74464	**.55545**	9.74633	**.55761**	9.74802	**.55978**	9.74969	**.56195**	9.75136	**.56411**	32
29	.74467	**.55548**	.74636	**.55765**	.74805	**.55982**	.74972	**.56198**	.75139	**.56415**	31
30	.74470	**.55552**	.74639	**.55769**	.74807	**.55985**	.74975	**.56202**	.75142	**.56418**	30
31	.74473	**.55555**	.74642	**.55772**	.74810	**.55989**	.74978	**.56205**	.75145	**.56422**	29
+ 8′	9.74475	**.55559**	9.74645	**.55776**	9.74813	**.55992**	9.74981	**.56209**	9.75147	**.56425**	28
33	.74478	**.55563**	.74647	**.55779**	.74816	**.55996**	.74983	**.56213**	.75150	**.56429**	27
34	.74481	**.55566**	.74650	**.55783**	.74819	**.56000**	.74986	**.56216**	.75153	**.56433**	26
35	.74484	**.55570**	.74653	**.55787**	.74821	**.56003**	.74989	**.56220**	.75156	**.56436**	25
+ 9′	9.74487	**.55573**	9.74656	**.55790**	9.74824	**.56007**	9.74992	**.56223**	9.75159	**.56440**	24
37	.74490	**.55577**	.74659	**.55794**	.74827	**.56010**	.74994	**.56227**	.75161	**.56443**	23
38	.74492	**.55581**	.74661	**.55797**	.74830	**.56014**	.74997	**.56231**	.75164	**.56447**	22
39	.74495	**.55584**	.74664	**.55801**	.74833	**.56018**	.75000	**.56234**	.75167	**.56451**	21
+ 10′	9.74498	**.55588**	9.74667	**.55805**	9.74835	**.56021**	9.75003	**.56238**	9.75170	**.56454**	20
41	.74501	**.55592**	.74670	**.55808**	.74838	**.56025**	.75006	**.56241**	.75172	**.56458**	19
42	.74504	**.55595**	.74673	**.55812**	.74841	**.56029**	.75008	**.56245**	.75175	**.56461**	18
43	.74506	**.55599**	.74675	**.55815**	.74844	**.56032**	.75011	**.56249**	.75178	**.56465**	17
+ 11′	9.74509	**.55602**	9.74678	**.55819**	9.74846	**.56036**	9.75014	**.56252**	9.75181	**.56469**	16
45	.74512	**.55606**	.74681	**.55823**	.74849	**.56039**	.75017	**.56256**	.75183	**.56472**	15
46	.74515	**.55610**	.74684	**.55826**	.74852	**.56043**	.75020	**.56259**	.75186	**.56476**	14
47	.74518	**.55613**	.74687	**.55830**	.74855	**.56047**	.75022	**.56263**	.75189	**.56479**	13
+ 12′	9.74521	**.55617**	9.74690	**.55834**	9.74858	**.56050**	9.75025	**.56267**	9.75192	**.56483**	12
49	.74523	**.55620**	.74692	**.55837**	.74860	**.56054**	.75028	**.56270**	.75195	**.56487**	11
50	.74526	**.55624**	.74695	**.55841**	.74863	**.56057**	.75031	**.56274**	.75197	**.56490**	10
51	.74529	**.55628**	.74698	**.55844**	.74866	**.56061**	.75033	**.56277**	.75200	**.56494**	9
+ 13′	9.74532	**.55631**	9.74701	**.55848**	9.74869	**.56065**	9.75036	**.56281**	9.75203	**.56497**	8
53	.74535	**.55635**	.74704	**.55852**	.74872	**.56068**	.75039	**.56285**	.75206	**.56501**	7
54	.74538	**.55638**	.74706	**.55855**	.74874	**.56072**	.75042	**.56288**	.75208	**.56505**	6
55	.74540	**.55642**	.74709	**.55859**	.74877	**.56075**	.75045	**.56292**	.75211	**.56508**	5
+ 14′	9.74543	**.55646**	9.74712	**.55862**	9.74880	**.56079**	9.75047	**.56296**	9.75214	**.56512**	4
57	.74546	**.55649**	.74715	**.55866**	.74883	**.56083**	.75050	**.56299**	.75217	**.56516**	3
58	.74549	**.55653**	.74718	**.55870**	.74886	**.56086**	.75053	**.56303**	.75220	**.56519**	2
59	.74552	**.55657**	.74720	**.55873**	.74888	**.56090**	.75056	**.56306**	.75222	**.56523**	1
+ 15′	9.74554	**.55660**	9.74723	**.55877**	9.74891	**.56093**	9.75059	**.56310**	9.75225	**.56526**	0
	17h 34m		17h 33m		17h 32m		17h 31m		17h 30m		

541524°—43——47

TABLE 34.

Haversines.

s	6h 30m 97° 30′ Log. Hav.	Nat. Hav.	6h 31m 97° 45′ Log. Hav.	Nat. Hav.	6h 32m 98° 0′ Log. Hav.	Nat. Hav.	6h 33m 98° 15′ Log. Hav.	Nat. Hav.	6h 34m 98° 30′ Log. Hav.	Nat. Hav.	s
0	9.75225	.56526	9.75391	.56743	9.75556	.56959	9.75720	.57175	9.75884	.57390	60
1	.75228	.56530	.75394	.56746	.75559	.56962	.75723	.57178	.75887	.57394	59
2	.75231	.56534	.75396	.56750	.75561	.56966	.75726	.57182	.75889	.57398	58
3	.75233	.56537	.75399	.56753	.75564	.56969	.75729	.57185	.75892	.57401	57
+ 1′	9.75236	.56541	9.75402	.56757	9.75567	.56973	9.75731	.57189	9.75895	.57405	56
5	.75239	.56544	.75405	.56761	.75570	.56977	.75734	.57193	.75898	.57408	55
6	.75242	.56548	.75407	.56764	.75572	.56980	.75737	.57196	.75900	.57412	54
7	.75244	.56552	.75410	.56768	.75575	.56984	.75739	.57200	.75903	.57416	53
+ 2′	9.75247	.56555	9.75413	.56771	9.75578	.56987	9.75742	.57203	9.75906	.57419	52
9	.75250	.56559	.75416	.56775	.75581	.56991	.75745	.57207	.75908	.57423	51
10	.75253	.56562	.75418	.56779	.75583	.56994	.75748	.57211	.75911	.57426	50
11	.75256	.56566	.75421	.56782	.75586	.56998	.75750	.57214	.75914	.57430	49
+ 3′	9.75258	.56570	9.75424	.56786	9.75589	.57002	9.75753	.57218	9.75917	.57434	48
13	.75261	.56573	.75427	.56789	.75592	.57005	.75756	.57221	.75919	.57437	47
14	.75264	.56577	.75429	.56793	.75594	.57009	.75759	.57225	.75922	.57441	46
15	.75267	.56580	.75432	.56797	.75597	.57012	.75761	.57229	.75925	.57444	45
+ 4′	9.75269	.56584	9.75435	.56800	9.75600	.57016	9.75764	.57232	9.75927	.57448	44
17	.75272	.56588	.75438	.56804	.75603	.57020	.75767	.57236	.75930	.57452	43
18	.75275	.56591	.75440	.56807	.75605	.57023	.75770	.57239	.75933	.57455	42
19	.75278	.56595	.75443	.56811	.75608	.57027	.75772	.57243	.75936	.57459	41
+ 5′	9.75280	.56598	9.75446	.56815	9.75611	.57031	9.75775	.57247	9.75938	.57462	40
21	.75283	.56602	.75449	.56818	.75614	.57034	.75778	.57250	.75941	.57466	39
22	.75286	.56606	.75452	.56822	.75616	.57038	.75780	.57254	.75944	.57470	38
23	.75289	.56609	.75454	.56825	.75619	.57041	.75783	.57257	.75947	.57473	37
+ 6′	9.75291	.56613	9.75457	.56829	9.75622	.57045	9.75786	.57261	9.75949	.57477	36
25	.75294	.56616	.75460	.56833	.75625	.57049	.75789	.57265	.75952	.57480	36
26	.75297	.56620	.75463	.56836	.75627	.57052	.75791	.57268	.75955	.57484	34
27	.75300	.56624	.75465	.56840	.75630	.57056	.75794	.57272	.75957	.57488	33
+ 7′	9.75303	.56627	9.75468	.56843	9.75633	.57059	9.75797	.57275	9.75960	.57491	32
29	.75305	.56631	.75471	.56847	.75636	.57063	.75800	.57279	.75963	.57495	31
30	.75308	.56634	.75474	.56851	.75638	.57067	.75802	.57283	.75966	.57498	30
31	.75311	.56638	.75476	.56854	.75641	.57070	.75805	.57286	.75968	.57502	29
+ 8′	9.75314	.56642	9.75479	.56858	9.75644	.57074	9.75808	.57290	9.75971	.57506	28
33	.75316	.56645	.75482	.56861	.75646	.57077	.75810	.57293	.75974	.57509	27
34	.75319	.56649	.75485	.56865	.75649	.57081	.75813	.57297	.75976	.57513	26
35	.75322	.56652	.75487	.56869	.75652	.57085	.75816	.57301	.75979	.57516	25
+ 9′	9.75325	.56656	9.75490	.56872	9.75655	.57088	9.75819	.57304	9.75982	.57520	24
37	.75327	.56660	.75493	.56876	.75657	.57092	.75821	.57308	.75985	.57524	23
38	.75330	.56663	.75496	.56879	.75660	.57095	.75824	.57311	.75987	.57527	22
39	.75333	.56667	.75498	.56883	.75663	.57099	.75827	.57315	.75990	.57531	21
+ 10′	9.75336	.56670	9.75501	.56887	9.75666	.57103	9.75830	.57318	9.75993	.57534	20
41	.75338	.56674	.75504	.56890	.75668	.57106	.75832	.57322	.75995	.57538	19
42	.75341	.56678	.75507	.56894	.75671	.57110	.75835	.57326	.75998	.57541	18
43	.75344	.56681	.75509	.56897	.75674	.57114	.75838	.57329	.76001	.57545	17
+ 11′	9.75347	.56685	9.75512	.56901	9.75677	.57117	9.75840	.57333	9.76004	.57549	16
45	.75350	.56689	.75515	.56905	.75679	.57121	.75843	.57337	.76006	.57552	15
46	.75352	.56692	.75518	.56908	.75682	.57124	.75846	.57340	.76009	.57556	14
47	.75355	.56696	.75520	.56912	.75685	.57128	.75849	.57344	.76012	.57559	13
+ 12′	9.75358	.56699	9.75523	.56915	9.75688	.57131	9.75851	.57347	9.76014	.57563	12
49	.75361	.56703	.75526	.56919	.75690	.57135	.75854	.57351	.76017	.57567	11
50	.75363	.56707	.75529	.56923	.75693	.57139	.75857	.57355	.76020	.57570	10
51	.75366	.56710	.75531	.56926	.75696	.57142	.75859	.57358	.76023	.57574	9
+ 13′	9.75369	.56714	9.75534	.56930	9.75698	.57146	9.75862	.57362	9.76025	.57577	8
53	.75372	.56717	.75537	.56933	.75701	.57149	.75865	.57365	.76028	.57581	7
54	.75374	.56721	.75540	.56937	.75704	.57153	.75868	.57369	.76031	.57585	6
55	.75377	.56725	.75542	.56941	.75707	.57157	.75870	.57373	.76033	.57588	5
+ 14′	9.75380	.56728	9.75545	.56944	9.75709	.57160	9.75873	.57376	9.76036	.57592	4
57	.75383	.56732	.75548	.56948	.75712	.57164	.75876	.57380	.76039	.57595	3
58	.75385	.56735	.75550	.56951	.75715	.57167	.75879	.57383	.76041	.57599	2
59	.75388	.56739	.75553	.56955	.75718	.57171	.75881	.57387	.76044	.57603	1
+ 15′	9.75391	.56743	9.75556	.56959	9.75720	.57175	9.75884	.57390	9.76047	.57606	0
	17h 29m		17h 28m		17h 27m		17h 26m		17h 25m		

TABLE 34.

Haversines.

s	$6^h\ 35^m$ 98° 45′		$6^h\ 36^m$ 99° 0′		$6^h\ 37^m$ 99° 15′		$6^h\ 38^m$ 99° 30′		$6^h\ 39^m$ 99° 45′		s
	Log. Hav.	Nat. Hav.	Log. Hav.	Nat. Hav.	Log. Hav.	Nat. Hav.	Log. Hav.	Nat. Hav.	Log. Hav.	Nat. Hav.	
0	9.76047	**.57606**	9.76209	**.57822**	9.76371	**.58037**	9.76531	**.58252**	9.76691	**.58467**	60
1	.76050	**.57610**	.76212	**.57825**	.76373	**.58041**	.76534	**.58256**	.76694	**.58471**	59
2	.76052	**.57613**	.76215	**.57829**	.76376	**.58044**	.76537	**.58260**	.76697	**.58475**	58
3	.76055	**.57617**	.76217	**.57833**	.76379	**.58048**	.76539	**.58263**	.76699	**.58478**	57
+ 1′	9.76058	**.57621**	9.76220	**.57836**	9.76381	**.58051**	9.76542	**.58267**	9.76702	**.58482**	56
5	.76060	**.57624**	.76223	**.57840**	.76384	**.58055**	.76545	**.58270**	.76705	**.58485**	55
6	.76063	**.57628**	.76225	**.57843**	.76387	**.58059**	.76547	**.58274**	.76707	**.58489**	54
7	.76066	**.57631**	.76228	**.57847**	.76389	**.58062**	.76550	**.58277**	.76710	**.58493**	53
+ 2′	9.76069	**.57635**	9.76231	**.57850**	9.76392	**.58066**	9.76553	**.58281**	9.76713	**.58496**	52
9	.76071	**.57639**	.76233	**.57854**	.76395	**.58069**	.76555	**.58285**	.76715	**.58500**	51
10	.76074	**.57642**	.76236	**.57858**	.76397	**.58073**	.76558	**.58288**	.76718	**.58503**	50
11	.76077	**.57646**	.76239	**.57861**	.76400	**.58077**	.76561	**.58292**	.76721	**.58507**	49
+ 3′	9.76079	**.57649**	9.76241	**.57865**	9.76403	**.58080**	9.76563	**.58295**	9.76723	**.58510**	48
13	.76082	**.57653**	.76244	**.57868**	.76405	**.58084**	.76566	**.58299**	.76726	**.58514**	47
14	.76085	**.57656**	.76247	**.57872**	.76408	**.58087**	.76569	**.58303**	.76729	**.58518**	46
15	.76088	**.57660**	.76250	**.57876**	.76411	**.58091**	.76571	**.58306**	.76731	**.58521**	45
+ 4′	9.76090	**.57664**	9.76252	**.57879**	9.76414	**.58095**	9.76574	**.58310**	9.76734	**.58525**	44
17	.76093	**.57667**	.76255	**.57883**	.76416	**.58098**	.76577	**.58313**	.76737	**.58528**	43
18	.76096	**.57671**	.76258	**.57886**	.76419	**.58102**	.76579	**.58317**	.76739	**.58532**	42
19	.76098	**.57675**	.76260	**.57890**	.76422	**.58105**	.76582	**.58321**	.76742	**.58536**	41
+ 5′	9.76101	**.57678**	9.76263	**.57894**	9.76424	**.58109**	9.76585	**.58324**	9.76745	**.58539**	40
21	.76104	**.57682**	.76266	**.57897**	.76427	**.58112**	.76587	**.58328**	.76747	**.58543**	39
22	.76106	**.57685**	.76268	**.57901**	.76430	**.58116**	.76590	**.58331**	.76750	**.58546**	38
23	.76109	**.57689**	.76271	**.57904**	.76432	**.58120**	.76593	**.58335**	.76753	**.58550**	37
+ 6′	9.76112	**.57692**	9.76274	**.57908**	9.76435	**.58123**	9.76595	**.58338**	9.76755	**.58553**	36
25	.76115	**.57696**	.76276	**.57911**	.76438	**.58127**	.76598	**.58342**	.76758	**.58557**	35
26	.76117	**.57700**	.76279	**.57915**	.76440	**.58130**	.76601	**.58346**	.76761	**.58561**	34
27	.76120	**.57703**	.76282	**.57919**	.76443	**.58134**	.76603	**.58349**	.76763	**.58564**	33
+ 7′	9.76123	**.57707**	9.76285	**.57922**	9.76446	**.58138**	9.76606	**.58353**	9.76766	**.58568**	32
29	.76125	**.57710**	.76287	**.57926**	.76448	**.58141**	.76609	**.58356**	.76769	**.58571**	31
30	.76128	**.57714**	.76290	**.57929**	.76451	**.58145**	.76611	**.58360**	.76771	**.58575**	30
31	.76131	**.57718**	.76293	**.57933**	.76454	**.58148**	.76614	**.58364**	.76774	**.58579**	29
+ 8′	9.76134	**.57721**	9.76296	**.57937**	9.76456	**.58152**	9.76617	**.58367**	9.76777	**.58582**	28
33	.76136	**.57725**	.76298	**.57940**	.76459	**.58156**	.76619	**.58371**	.76779	**.58586**	27
34	.76139	**.57728**	.76301	**.57944**	.76462	**.58159**	.76622	**.58374**	.76782	**.58589**	26
35	.76142	**.57732**	.76303	**.57947**	.76464	**.58163**	.76625	**.58378**	.76784	**.58593**	25
+ 9′	9.76144	**.57736**	9.76306	**.57951**	9.76467	**.58166**	9.76627	**.58381**	9.76787	**.58596**	24
37	.76147	**.57739**	.76309	**.57955**	.76470	**.58170**	.76630	**.58385**	.76790	**.58600**	23
38	.76150	**.57743**	.76311	**.57958**	.76473	**.58173**	.76633	**.58389**	.76792	**.58604**	22
39	.76152	**.57746**	.76314	**.57962**	.76475	**.58177**	.76635	**.58392**	.76795	**.58607**	21
+ 10′	9.76155	**.57750**	9.76317	**.57965**	9.76478	**.58181**	9.76638	**.58396**	9.76798	**.58611**	20
41	.76158	**.57753**	.76320	**.57969**	.76481	**.58184**	.76641	**.58399**	.76800	**.58614**	19
42	.76161	**.57757**	.76322	**.57973**	.76483	**.58188**	.76643	**.58403**	.76803	**.58618**	18
43	.76163	**.57761**	.76325	**.57976**	.76486	**.58191**	.76646	**.58407**	.76806	**.58622**	17
+ 11′	9.76166	**.57764**	9.76328	**.57980**	9.76489	**.58195**	9.76649	**.58410**	9.76808	**.58625**	16
45	.76169	**.57768**	.76330	**.57983**	.76491	**.58199**	.76651	**.58414**	.76811	**.58629**	15
46	.76171	**.57771**	.76333	**.57987**	.76494	**.58202**	.76654	**.58417**	.76814	**.58632**	14
47	.76174	**.57775**	.76336	**.57990**	.76497	**.58206**	.76657	**.58421**	.76816	**.58636**	13
+ 12′	9.76177	**.57779**	9.76338	**.57994**	9.76499	**.58209**	9.76659	**.58424**	9.76819	**.58639**	12
49	.76179	**.57782**	.76341	**.57998**	.76502	**.58213**	.76662	**.58428**	.76822	**.58643**	11
50	.76182	**.57786**	.76344	**.58001**	.76505	**.58217**	.76665	**.58432**	.76824	**.58647**	10
51	.76185	**.57789**	.76346	**.58005**	.76507	**.58220**	.76667	**.58435**	.76827	**.58650**	9
+ 13′	9.76188	**.57793**	9.76349	**.58008**	9.76510	**.58224**	9.76670	**.58439**	9.76830	**.58654**	8
53	.76190	**.57797**	.76352	**.58012**	.76513	**.58227**	.76673	**.58442**	.76832	**.58657**	7
54	.76193	**.57800**	.76354	**.58016**	.76515	**.58231**	.76675	**.58446**	.76835	**.58661**	6
55	.76196	**.57804**	.76357	**.58019**	.76518	**.58234**	.76678	**.58450**	.76838	**.58665**	5
+ 14′	9.76198	**.57807**	9.76360	**.58023**	9.76521	**.58238**	9.76681	**.58453**	9.76840	**.58668**	4
57	.76201	**.57811**	.76363	**.58026**	.76523	**.58242**	.76683	**.58457**	.76843	**.58671**	3
58	.76204	**.57815**	.76365	**.58030**	.76526	**.58245**	.76686	**.58460**	.76845	**.58675**	2
59	.76206	**.57818**	.76368	**.58034**	.76529	**.58249**	.76689	**.58464**	.76848	**.58679**	1
+ 15′	9.76209	**.57822**	9.76371	**.58037**	9.76531	**.58252**	9.76691	**.58467**	9.76851	**.58682**	0
	$17^h\ 24^m$		$17^h\ 23^m$		$17^h\ 22^m$		$17^h\ 21^m$		$17^h\ 20^m$		

TABLE 34.

Haversines.

s	6h 40m 100° 0′		6h 41m 100° 15′		6h 42m 100° 30′		6h 43m 100° 45′		6h 44m 101° 0′		s
	Log. Hav.	Nat. Hav.	Log. Hav.	Nat. Hav.	Log. Hav.	Nat. Hav.	Log. Hav.	Nat. Hav.	Log. Hav.	Nat. Hav.	
0	9.76851	**.58682**	9.77009	**.58897**	9.77167	**.59112**	9.77325	**.59326**	9.77481	**.59540**	60
1	.76853	**.58686**	.77012	**.58901**	.77170	**.59115**	.77327	**.59330**	.77484	**.59544**	59
2	.76856	**.58690**	.77015	**.58904**	.77173	**.59119**	.77330	**.59333**	.77486	**.59548**	58
3	.76859	**.58693**	.77017	**.58908**	.77175	**.59122**	.77333	**.59337**	.77489	**.59551**	57
+ 1′	9.76861	**.58697**	9.77020	**.58911**	9.77178	**.59126**	9.77335	**.59340**	9.77492	**.59555**	56
5	.76864	**.58700**	.77023	**.58915**	.77181	**.59130**	.77338	**.59344**	.77494	**.59558**	55
6	.76867	**.58704**	.77025	**.58919**	.77183	**.59133**	.77340	**.59348**	.77497	**.59562**	54
7	.76869	**.58707**	.77028	**.58922**	.77186	**.59137**	.77343	**.59351**	.77499	**.59565**	53
+ 2′	9.76872	**.58711**	9.77031	**.58926**	9.77188	**.59140**	9.77346	**.59355**	9.77502	**.59569**	52
9	.76875	**.58714**	.77033	**.58929**	.77191	**.59144**	.77348	**.59358**	.77505	**.59573**	51
10	.76877	**.58718**	.77036	**.58933**	.77194	**.59148**	.77351	**.59362**	.77507	**.59576**	50
11	.76880	**.58722**	.77038	**.58937**	.77196	**.59151**	.77353	**.59365**	.77510	**.59580**	49
+ 3′	9.76883	**.58725**	9.77041	**.58940**	9.77199	**.59155**	9.77356	**.59369**	9.77512	**.59583**	48
13	.76885	**.58729**	.77044	**.58944**	.77202	**.59158**	.77359	**.59373**	.77515	**.59587**	47
14	.76888	**.58733**	.77046	**.58947**	.77204	**.59162**	.77361	**.59376**	.77518	**.59590**	46
15	.76891	**.58736**	.77049	**.58951**	.77207	**.59165**	.77364	**.59380**	.77520	**.59594**	45
+ 4′	9.76893	**.58740**	9.77052	**.58954**	9.77209	**.59169**	9.77366	**.59383**	9.77523	**.59598**	44
17	.76896	**.58743**	.77054	**.58958**	.77212	**.59173**	.77369	**.59387**	.77525	**.59601**	43
18	.76898	**.58747**	.77057	**.58962**	.77215	**.59176**	.77372	**.59391**	.77528	**.59605**	42
19	.76901	**.58750**	.77060	**.58965**	.77217	**.59180**	.77374	**.59394**	.77531	**.59608**	41
+ 5′	9.76904	**.58754**	9.77062	**.58969**	9.77220	**.59183**	9.77377	**.59398**	9.77533	**.59612**	40
21	.76906	**.58758**	.77065	**.58972**	.77223	**.59187**	.77380	**.59401**	.77536	**.59615**	39
22	.76909	**.58761**	.77067	**.58976**	.77225	**.59190**	.77382	**.59405**	.77538	**.59619**	38
23	.76912	**.58765**	.77070	**.58979**	.77228	**.59194**	.77385	**.59408**	.77541	**.59623**	37
+ 6′	9.76914	**.58768**	9.77073	**.58983**	9.77230	**.59198**	9.77387	**.59412**	9.77544	**.59626**	36
25	.76917	**.58772**	.77075	**.58987**	.77233	**.59201**	.77390	**.59416**	.77546	**.59630**	35
26	.76920	**.58776**	.77078	**.58990**	.77236	**.59205**	.77393	**.59419**	.77549	**.59633**	34
27	.76922	**.58779**	.77081	**.58994**	.77238	**.59208**	.77395	**.59423**	.77551	**.59637**	33
+ 7′	9.76925	**.58783**	9.77083	**.58997**	9.77241	**.59212**	9.77398	**.59426**	9.77554	**.59640**	32
29	.76928	**.58786**	.77086	**.59001**	.77243	**.59215**	.77400	**.59430**	.77557	**.59644**	31
30	.76930	**.58790**	.77089	**.59005**	.77246	**.59219**	.77403	**.59433**	.77559	**.59648**	30
31	.76933	**.58793**	.77091	**.59008**	.77249	**.59223**	.77406	**.59437**	.77562	**.59651**	29
+ 8′	9.76936	**.58797**	9.77094	**.59012**	9.77251	**.59226**	9.77408	**.59440**	9.77564	**.59655**	28
33	.76938	**.58801**	.77096	**.59015**	.77254	**.59230**	.77411	**.59444**	.77567	**.59658**	27
34	.76941	**.58804**	.77099	**.59019**	.77257	**.59233**	.77413	**.59448**	.77570	**.59662**	26
35	.76943	**.58808**	.77102	**.59022**	.77259	**.59237**	.77416	**.59451**	.77572	**.59665**	25
+ 9′	9.76946	**.58811**	9.77104	**.59026**	9.77262	**.59240**	9.77419	**.59455**	9.77575	**.59669**	24
37	.76949	**.58815**	.77107	**.59030**	.77264	**.59244**	.77421	**.59458**	.77577	**.59672**	23
38	.76951	**.58818**	.77110	**.59033**	.77267	**.59248**	.77424	**.59462**	.77580	**.59676**	22
39	.76954	**.58822**	.77112	**.59037**	.77270	**.59251**	.77427	**.59465**	.77583	**.59680**	21
+ 10′	9.76957	**.58826**	9.77115	**.59040**	9.77272	**.59255**	9.77429	**.59469**	9.77585	**.59683**	20
41	.76959	**.58829**	.77117	**.59044**	.77275	**.59258**	.77432	**.59473**	.77588	**.59687**	19
42	.76962	**.58833**	.77120	**.59047**	.77278	**.59262**	.77434	**.59476**	.77590	**.59690**	18
43	.76965	**.58836**	.77123	**.59051**	.77280	**.59265**	.77437	**.59480**	.77593	**.59694**	17
+ 11′	9.76967	**.58840**	9.77125	**.59055**	9.77283	**.59269**	9.77440	**.59483**	9.77596	**.59697**	16
45	.76970	**.58843**	.77128	**.59058**	.77285	**.59273**	.77442	**.59487**	.77598	**.59701**	15
46	.76972	**.58847**	.77131	**.59062**	.77288	**.59276**	.77445	**.59490**	.77601	**.59705**	14
47	.76975	**.58851**	.77133	**.59065**	.77291	**.59280**	.77447	**.59494**	.77603	**.59708**	13
+ 12′	9.76978	**.58854**	9.77136	**.59069**	9.77293	**.59283**	9.77450	**.59498**	9.77606	**.59712**	12
49	.76980	**.58858**	.77139	**.59072**	.77296	**.59287**	.77453	**.59501**	.77609	**.59715**	11
50	.76983	**.58861**	.77141	**.59076**	.77298	**.59290**	.77455	**.59505**	.77611	**.59719**	10
51	.76986	**.58865**	.77144	**.59080**	.77301	**.59294**	.77458	**.59508**	.77614	**.59722**	9
+ 13′	9.76988	**.58869**	9.77146	**.59083**	9.77304	**.59298**	9.77460	**.59512**	9.77616	**.59726**	8
53	.76991	**.58872**	.77149	**.59087**	.77306	**.59301**	.77463	**.59515**	.77619	**.59730**	7
54	.76994	**.58876**	.77152	**.59090**	.77309	**.59305**	.77466	**.59519**	.77622	**.59733**	6
55	.76996	**.58879**	.77154	**.59094**	.77312	**.59308**	.77468	**.59523**	.77624	**.59737**	5
+ 14′	9.76999	**.58883**	9.77157	**.59097**	9.77314	**.59312**	9.77471	**.59526**	9.77627	**.59740**	4
57	.77002	**.58886**	.77160	**.59101**	.77317	**.59315**	.77473	**.59530**	.77629	**.59744**	3
58	.77004	**.58890**	.77162	**.59105**	.77319	**.59319**	.77476	**.59533**	.77632	**.59747**	2
59	.77007	**.58894**	.77165	**.59108**	.77322	**.59323**	.77479	**.59537**	.77634	**.59751**	1
+ 15′	9.77009	**.58897**	9.77167	**.59112**	9.77325	**.59326**	9.77481	**.59540**	9.77637	**.59755**	0
	17h 19m		17h 18m		17h 17m		17h 16m		17h 15m		

TABLE 34.

Haversines.

s	$6^h\,45^m$ 101° 15′		$6^h\,46^m$ 101° 30′		$6^h\,47^m$ 101° 45′		$6^h\,48^m$ 102° 0′		$6^h\,49^m$ 102° 15′		s
	Log. Hav.	Nat. Hav.	Log. Hav.	Nat. Hav.	Log. Hav.	Nat. Hav.	Log. Hav.	Nat. Hav.	Log. Hav.	Nat. Hav.	
0	9.77637	.59755	9.77792	.59968	9.77947	.60182	9.78101	.60396	9.78254	.60609	60
1	.77640	.59758	.77795	.59972	.77949	.60185	.78103	.60399	.78256	.60612	59
2	.77642	.59762	.77797	.59976	.77952	.60189	.78106	.60403	.78259	.60616	58
3	.77645	.59765	.77800	.59979	.77954	.60193	.78108	.60406	.78261	.60620	57
+ 1′	9.77647	.59769	9.77803	.59983	9.77957	.60196	9.78111	.60410	9.78264	.60623	56
5	.77650	.59772	.77805	.59986	.77960	.60200	.78113	.60414	.78266	.60627	55
6	.77653	.59776	.77808	.59990	.77962	.60203	.78116	.60417	.78269	.60630	54
7	.77655	.59779	.77810	.59993	.77965	.60207	.78118	.60420	.78271	.60634	53
+ 2′	9.77658	.59783	9.77813	.59997	9.77967	.60211	9.78121	.60424	9.78274	.60637	52
9	.77660	.59787	.77815	.60000	.77970	.60214	.78124	.60428	.78277	.60641	51
10	.77663	.59790	.77818	.60004	.77972	.60218	.78126	.60431	.78279	.60644	50
11	.77666	.59794	.77821	.60008	.77975	.60221	.78129	.60435	.78282	.60648	49
+ 3′	9.77668	.59797	9.77823	.60011	9.77978	.60225	9.78131	.60438	9.78284	.60652	48
13	.77671	.59801	.77826	.60015	.77980	.60228	.78134	.60442	.78287	.60655	47
14	.77673	.59804	.77828	.60018	.77983	.60232	.78136	.60445	.78289	.60659	46
15	.77676	.59808	.77831	.60022	.77985	.60235	.78139	.60449	.78292	.60662	45
+ 4′	9.77679	.59812	9.77834	.60025	9.77988	.60239	9.78141	.60452	9.78294	.60666	44
17	.77681	.59815	.77836	.60029	.77990	.60243	.78144	.60456	.78297	.60669	43
18	.77684	.59819	.77839	.60033	.77993	.60246	.78147	.60460	.78299	.60673	42
19	.77686	.59822	.77841	.60036	.77996	.60250	.78149	.60463	.78302	.60676	41
+ 5′	9.77689	.59826	9.77844	.60040	9.77998	.60253	9.78152	.60467	9.78305	.60680	40
21	.77691	.59829	.77846	.60043	.78001	.60257	.78154	.60470	.78307	.60684	39
22	.77694	.59833	.77849	.60047	.78003	.60260	.78157	.60474	.78310	.60687	38
23	.77697	.59837	.77852	.60050	.78006	.60264	.78159	.60477	.78312	.60691	37
+ 6′	9.77699	.59840	9.77854	.60054	9.78008	.60268	9.78162	.60481	9.78315	.60694	36
25	.77702	.59844	.77857	.60057	.78011	.60271	.78164	.60484	.78317	.60698	35
26	.77704	.59847	.77859	.60061	.78013	.60275	.78167	.60488	.78320	.60701	34
27	.77707	.59851	.77862	.60065	.78016	.60278	.78170	.60492	.78322	.60705	33
+ 7′	9.77710	.59854	9.77864	.60068	9.78019	.60282	9.78172	.60495	9.78325	.60708	32
29	.77712	.59858	.77867	.60072	.78021	.60285	.78175	.60499	.78327	.60712	31
30	.77715	.59861	.77870	.60075	.78024	.60289	.78177	.60502	.78330	.60715	30
31	.77717	.59865	.77872	.60079	.78026	.60292	.78180	.60506	.78332	.60719	29
+ 8′	9.77720	.59869	9.77875	.60082	9.78029	.60296	9.78182	.60509	9.78335	.60723	28
33	.77723	.59872	.77877	.60086	.78031	.60300	.78185	.60513	.78338	.60726	27
34	.77725	.59876	.77880	.60090	.78034	.60303	.78187	.60516	.78340	.60730	26
35	.77728	.59879	.77882	.60093	.78037	.60307	.78190	.60520	.78343	.60733	25
+ 9′	9.77730	.59883	9.77885	.60097	9.78039	.60310	9.78192	.60524	9.78345	.60737	24
37	.77733	.59886	.77888	.60100	.78042	.60314	.78195	.60527	.78348	.60740	23
38	.77735	.59890	.77890	.60104	.78044	.60317	.78198	.60531	.78350	.60744	22
39	.77738	.59894	.77893	.60107	.78047	.60321	.78200	.60534	.78353	.60747	21
+ 10′	9.77741	.59897	9.77895	.60111	9.78049	.60324	9.78203	.60538	9.78355	.60751	20
41	.77743	.59901	.77898	.60114	.78052	.60328	.78205	.60541	.78358	.60755	19
42	.77746	.59904	.77900	.60118	.78054	.60332	.78208	.60545	.78360	.60758	18
43	.77748	.59908	.77903	.60122	.78057	.60335	.78210	.60548	.78363	.60762	17
+ 11′	9.77751	.59911	9.77906	.60125	9.78060	.60339	9.78213	.60552	9.78365	.60765	16
45	.77754	.59915	.77908	.60129	.78062	.60342	.78215	.60556	.78368	.60769	15
46	.77756	.59919	.77911	.60132	.78065	.60346	.78218	.60559	.78371	.60772	14
47	.77759	.59922	.77913	.60136	.78067	.60349	.78221	.60563	.78373	.60776	13
+ 12′	9.77761	.59926	9.77916	.60139	9.78070	.60353	9.78223	.60566	9.78376	.60779	12
49	.77764	.59929	.77918	.60143	.78072	.60356	.78226	.60570	.78378	.60783	11
50	.77766	.59933	.77921	.60146	.78075	.60360	.78228	.60573	.78381	.60786	10
51	.77769	.59936	.77924	.60150	.78077	.60364	.78231	.60577	.78383	.60790	9
+ 13′	9.77772	.59940	9.77926	.60154	9.78080	.60367	9.78233	.60580	9.78386	.60794	8
53	.77774	.59943	.77929	.60157	.78083	.60371	.78236	.60584	.78388	.60797	7
54	.77777	.59947	.77931	.60161	.78085	.60374	.78238	.60588	.78391	.60801	6
55	.77779	.59951	.77934	.60164	.78088	.60378	.78241	.60591	.78393	.60804	5
+ 14′	9.77782	.59954	9.77936	.60168	9.78090	.60381	9.78243	.60595	9.78396	.60808	4
57	.77785	.59958	.77939	.60171	.78093	.60385	.78246	.60598	.78398	.60811	3
58	.77787	.59961	.77942	.60175	.78095	.60388	.78249	.60602	.78401	.60815	2
59	.77790	.59965	.77944	.60179	.78098	.60392	.78251	.60605	.78404	.60818	1
+ 15′	9.77792	.59968	9.77947	.60182	9.78101	.60396	9.78254	.60609	9.78406	.60822	0
	$17^h\,14^m$		$17^h\,13^m$		$17^h\,12^m$		$17^h\,11^m$		$17^h\,10^m$		

TABLE 34.

Haversines.

	$6^h\ 50^m$ **102° 30′**		$6^h\ 51^m$ **102° 45′**		$6^h\ 52^m$ **103° 0′**		$6^h\ 53^m$ **103° 15′**		$6^h\ 54^m$ **103° 30′**		
s	Log. Hav.	Nat. Hav.	Hav.Log.	Nat. Hav.	Log. Hav.	Nat. Hav.	Log. Hav.	Nat. Hav.	Log. Hav.	Nat. Hav.	s
0	9.78406	**.60822**	9.78558	**.61035**	9.78709	**.61248**	9.78859	**.61460**	9.79009	**.61672**	60
1	.78409	**.60825**	.78560	**.61038**	.78711	**.61251**	.78862	**.61464**	.79011	**.61676**	59
2	.78411	**.60829**	.78563	**.61042**	.78714	**.61255**	.78864	**.61467**	.79014	**.61679**	58
3	.78414	**.60833**	.78565	**.61046**	.78716	**.61258**	.78867	**.61471**	.79016	**.61683**	57
+ 1′	9.78416	**.60836**	9.78568	**.61049**	9.78719	**.61262**	9.78869	**.61474**	9.79019	**.61686**	56
5	.78419	**.60840**	.78570	**.61053**	.78721	**.61265**	.78872	**.61478**	.79021	**.61690**	55
6	.78421	**.60843**	.78573	**.61056**	.78724	**.61269**	.78874	**.61481**	.79024	**.61693**	54
7	.78424	**.60847**	.78575	**.61060**	.78726	**.61272**	.78877	**.61485**	.79026	**.61697**	53
+ 2′	9.78426	**.60850**	9.78578	**.61063**	9.78729	**.61276**	9.78879	**.61488**	9.79029	**.61701**	52
9	.78429	**.60854**	.78581	**.61067**	.78731	**.61279**	.78882	**.61492**	.79031	**.61704**	51
10	.78431	**.60857**	.78583	**.61070**	.78734	**.61283**	.78884	**.61495**	.79034	**.61708**	50
11	.78434	**.60861**	.78586	**.61074**	.78737	**.61287**	.78887	**.61499**	.79036	**.61711**	49
+ 3′	9.78436	**.60865**	9.78588	**.61077**	9.78739	**.61290**	9.78889	**.61502**	9.79039	**.61715**	48
13	.78439	**.60868**	.78591	**.61081**	.78742	**.61294**	.78892	**.61506**	.79041	**.61718**	47
14	.78442	**.60872**	.78593	**.61085**	.78744	**.61297**	.78894	**.61510**	.79044	**.61722**	46
15	.78444	**.60875**	.78596	**.61088**	.78747	**.61301**	.78897	**.61513**	.79046	**.61725**	45
+ 4′	9.78447	**.60879**	9.78598	**.61092**	9.78749	**.61304**	9.78899	**.61517**	9.79049	**.61729**	44
17	.78449	**.60882**	.78601	**.61095**	.78752	**.61308**	.78902	**.61520**	.79051	**.61732**	43
18	.78452	**.60886**	.78603	**.61099**	.78754	**.61311**	.78904	**.61524**	.79054	**.61736**	42
19	.78454	**.60889**	.78606	**.61102**	.78757	**.61315**	.78907	**.61527**	.79056	**.61739**	41
+ 5′	9.78457	**.60893**	9.78608	**.61106**	9.78759	**.61318**	9.78909	**.61531**	9.79059	**.61743**	40
21	.78459	**.60897**	.78611	**.61109**	.78762	**.61322**	.78912	**.61534**	.79061	**.61747**	39
22	.78462	**.60900**	.78613	**.61113**	.78764	**.61325**	.78914	**.61538**	.79064	**.61750**	38
23	.78464	**.60904**	.78616	**.61116**	.78767	**.61329**	.78917	**.61541**	.79066	**.61754**	37
+ 6′	9.78467	**.60907**	9.78618	**.61120**	9.78769	**.61333**	9.78919	**.61545**	9.79069	**.61757**	36
25	.78469	**.60911**	.78621	**.61124**	.78772	**.61336**	.78922	**.61548**	.79071	**.61761**	35
26	.78472	**.60914**	.78623	**.61127**	.78774	**.61340**	.78924	**.61552**	.79074	**.61764**	34
27	.78474	**.60918**	.78626	**.61131**	.78777	**.61343**	.78927	**.61556**	.79076	**.61768**	33
+ 7′	9.78477	**.60921**	9.78628	**.61134**	9.78779	**.61347**	9.78929	**.61559**	9.79079	**.61771**	32
29	.78479	**.60925**	.78631	**.61138**	.78782	**.61350**	.78932	**.61563**	.79081	**.61775**	31
30	.78482	**.60928**	.78633	**.61141**	.78784	**.61354**	.78934	**.61566**	.79084	**.61778**	30
31	.78485	**.60932**	.78636	**.61145**	.78787	**.61357**	.78937	**.61570**	.79086	**.61782**	29
+ 8′	9.78487	**.60936**	9.78638	**.61148**	9.78789	**.61361**	9.78939	**.61573**	9.79089	**.61785**	28
33	.78490	**.60939**	.78641	**.61152**	.78792	**.61364**	.78942	**.61577**	.79091	**.61789**	27
34	.78492	**.60943**	.78643	**.61155**	.78794	**.61368**	.78944	**.61580**	.79094	**.61792**	26
35	.78495	**.60946**	.78646	**.61159**	.78797	**.61372**	.78947	**.61584**	.79096	**.61796**	25
+ 9′	9.78497	**.60950**	9.78649	**.61163**	9.78799	**.61375**	9.78949	**.61587**	9.79099	**.61800**	24
37	.78500	**.60953**	.78651	**.61166**	.78802	**.61379**	.78952	**.61591**	.79101	**.61803**	23
38	.78502	**.60957**	.78654	**.61170**	.78804	**.61382**	.78954	**.61594**	.79103	**.61807**	22
39	.78505	**.60960**	.78656	**.61173**	.78807	**.61386**	.78957	**.61598**	.79106	**.61810**	21
+ 10′	9.78507	**.60964**	9.78659	**.61177**	9.78809	**.61389**	9.78959	**.61602**	9.79108	**.61814**	20
41	.78510	**.60967**	.78661	**.61180**	.78812	**.61393**	.78962	**.61605**	.79111	**.61817**	19
42	.78512	**.60971**	.78664	**.61184**	.78814	**.61396**	.78964	**.61609**	.79113	**.61821**	18
43	.78515	**.60975**	.78666	**.61187**	.78817	**.61400**	.78967	**.61612**	.79116	**.61824**	17
+ 11′	9.78517	**.60978**	9.78669	**.61191**	9.78819	**.61403**	9.78969	**.61616**	9.79118	**.61828**	16
45	.78520	**.60982**	.78671	**.61194**	.78822	**.61407**	.78972	**.61619**	.79121	**.61831**	15
46	.78522	**.60985**	.78674	**.61198**	.78824	**.61410**	.78974	**.61623**	.79123	**.61835**	14
47	.78525	**.60989**	.78676	**.61201**	.78827	**.61414**	.78977	**.61626**	.79126	**.61838**	13
+ 12′	9.78528	**.60992**	9.78679	**.61205**	9.78829	**.61418**	9.78979	**.61630**	9.79128	**.61842**	12
49	.78530	**.60996**	.78681	**.61209**	.78832	**.61421**	.78982	**.61633**	.79131	**.61845**	11
50	.78533	**.60999**	.78684	**.61212**	.78834	**.61425**	.78984	**.61637**	.79133	**.61849**	10
51	.78535	**.61003**	.78686	**.61216**	.78837	**.61428**	.78987	**.61640**	.79136	**.61853**	9
+ 13′	9.78538	**.61007**	9.78689	**.61219**	9.78839	**.61432**	9.78989	**.61644**	9.79138	**.61856**	8
53	.78540	**.61010**	.78691	**.61223**	.78842	**.61435**	.78992	**.61648**	.79141	**.61860**	7
54	.78543	**.61014**	.78694	**.61226**	.78844	**.61439**	.78994	**.61651**	.79143	**.61863**	6
55	.78545	**.61017**	.78696	**.61230**	.78847	**.61442**	.78997	**.61655**	.79146	**.61867**	5
+ 14′	9.78548	**.61021**	9.78699	**.61233**	9.78849	**.61446**	9.78999	**.61658**	9.79148	**.61870**	4
57	.78550	**.61024**	.78701	**.61237**	.78852	**.61449**	.79002	**.61662**	.79151	**.61874**	3
58	.78553	**.61028**	.78704	**.61240**	.78854	**.61453**	.79004	**.61665**	.79153	**.61877**	2
59	.78555	**.61032**	.78706	**.61244**	.78857	**.61456**	.79007	**.61669**	.79156	**.61881**	1
+ 15′	9.78558	**.61035**	9.78709	**.61248**	9.78859	**.61460**	9.79009	**.61672**	9.79158	**.61884**	0
	$17^h\ 9^m$		$17^h\ 8^m$		$17^h\ 7^m$		$17^h\ 6^m$		$17^h\ 5^m$		

TABLE 34.

Haversines.

	6ʰ 55ᵐ 103° 45′		6ʰ 56ᵐ 104° 0′		6ʰ 57ᵐ 104° 15′		6ʰ 58ᵐ 104° 30′		6ʰ 59ᵐ 104° 45′		
s	Log. Hav.	Nat. Hav.	Log. Hav.	Nat. Hav.	Log. Hav.	Nat. Hav.	Log. Hav.	Nat. Hav.	Log. Hav.	Nat. Hav.	s
0	9.79158	**.61884**	9.79306	**.62096**	9.79454	**.62308**	9.79601	**.62519**	9.79748	**.62730**	60
1	.79161	**.61888**	.79309	**.62100**	.79457	**.62311**	.79604	**.62522**	.79750	**.62734**	59
2	.79163	**.61891**	.79311	**.62103**	.79459	**.62315**	.79606	**.62526**	.79752	**.62737**	58
3	.79165	**.61895**	.79314	**.62107**	.79462	**.62318**	.79609	**.62530**	.79755	**.62741**	57
+ 1′	9.79168	**.61898**	9.79316	**.62110**	9.79464	**.62322**	9.79611	**.62533**	9.79757	**.62744**	56
5	.79170	**.61902**	.79319	**.62114**	.79466	**.62325**	.79613	**.62537**	.79760	**.62748**	55
6	.79173	**.61905**	.79321	**.62117**	.79469	**.62329**	.79616	**.62540**	.79762	**.62751**	54
7	.79175	**.61909**	.79324	**.62121**	.79471	**.62332**	.79618	**.62544**	.79765	**.62755**	53
+ 2′	9.79178	**.61913**	9.79326	**.62124**	9.79474	**.62336**	9.79621	**.62547**	9.79767	**.62758**	52
9	.79180	**.61916**	.79329	**.62128**	.79476	**.62339**	.79623	**.62551**	.79770	**.62762**	51
10	.79183	**.61920**	.79331	**.62131**	.79479	**.62343**	.79626	**.62554**	.79772	**.62765**	50
11	.79185	**.61923**	.79334	**.62135**	.79481	**.62346**	.79628	**.62558**	.79774	**.62769**	49
+ 3′	9.79188	**.61927**	9.79336	**.62138**	9.79484	**.62350**	9.79631	**.62561**	9.79777	**.62772**	48
13	.79190	**.61930**	.79339	**.62142**	.79486	**.62353**	.79633	**.62565**	.79779	**.62776**	47
14	.79193	**.61934**	.79341	**.62145**	.79489	**.62357**	.79635	**.62568**	.79782	**.62779**	46
15	.79195	**.61937**	.79343	**.62149**	.79491	**.62361**	.79638	**.62572**	.79784	**.62783**	45
+ 4′	9.79198	**.61941**	9.79346	**.62153**	9.79493	**.62364**	9.79640	**.62575**	9.79787	**.62786**	44
17	.79200	**.61944**	.79348	**.62156**	.79496	**.62368**	.79643	**.62579**	.79789	**.62790**	43
18	.79203	**.61948**	.79351	**.62160**	.79498	**.62371**	.79645	**.62582**	.79791	**.62793**	42
19	.79205	**.61951**	.79353	**.62163**	.79501	**.62375**	.79648	**.62586**	.79794	**.62797**	41
+ 5′	9.79208	**.61955**	9.79356	**.62167**	9.79503	**.62378**	9.79650	**.62589**	9.79796	**.62800**	40
21	.79210	**.61958**	.79358	**.62170**	.79506	**.62382**	.79653	**.62593**	.79799	**.62804**	39
22	.79213	**.61962**	.79361	**.62174**	.79508	**.62385**	.79655	**.62596**	.79801	**.62807**	38
23	.79215	**.61966**	.79363	**.62177**	.79511	**.62389**	.79657	**.62600**	.79804	**.62811**	37
+ 6′	9.79217	**.61969**	9.79366	**.62181**	9.79513	**.62392**	9.79660	**.62603**	9.79806	**.62814**	36
25	.79220	**.61973**	.79368	**.62184**	.79516	**.62396**	.79662	**.62607**	.79808	**.62818**	35
26	.79222	**.61976**	.79371	**.62188**	.79518	**.62399**	.79665	**.62611**	.79811	**.62822**	34
27	.79225	**.61980**	.79373	**.62191**	.79520	**.62403**	.79667	**.62614**	.79813	**.62825**	33
+ 7′	9.79227	**.61983**	9.79376	**.62195**	9.79523	**.62406**	9.79670	**.62618**	9.79816	**.62829**	32
29	.79230	**.61987**	.79378	**.62198**	.79525	**.62410**	.79672	**.62621**	.79818	**.62832**	31
30	.79232	**.61990**	.79380	**.62202**	.79528	**.62413**	.79674	**.62625**	.79821	**.62836**	30
31	.79235	**.61994**	.79383	**.62205**	.79530	**.62417**	.79677	**.62628**	.79823	**.62839**	29
+ 8′	9.79237	**.61997**	9.79385	**.62209**	9.79533	**.62420**	9.79679	**.62632**	9.79825	**.62843**	28
33	.79240	**.62001**	.79388	**.62213**	.79535	**.62424**	.79682	**.62635**	.79828	**.62846**	27
34	.79242	**.62004**	.79390	**.62216**	.79538	**.62427**	.79684	**.62639**	.79830	**.62850**	26
35	.79245	**.62008**	.79393	**.62220**	.79540	**.62431**	.79687	**.62642**	.79833	**.62853**	25
+ 9′	9.79247	**.62011**	9.79395	**.62223**	9.79542	**.62434**	9.79689	**.62646**	9.79835	**.62857**	24
37	.79250	**.62015**	.79398	**.62227**	.79545	**.62438**	.79692	**.62649**	.79838	**.62860**	23
38	.79252	**.62018**	.79400	**.62230**	.79547	**.62442**	.79694	**.62653**	.79840	**.62864**	22
39	.79255	**.62022**	.79403	**.62234**	.79550	**.62445**	.79696	**.62656**	.79842	**.62867**	21
+ 10′	9.79257	**.62026**	9.79405	**.62237**	9.79552	**.62449**	9.79699	**.62660**	9.79845	**.62871**	20
41	.79260	**.62029**	.79407	**.62241**	.79555	**.62452**	.79701	**.62663**	.79847	**.62874**	19
42	.79262	**.62033**	.79410	**.62244**	.79557	**.62456**	.79704	**.62667**	.79850	**.62878**	18
43	.79264	**.62036**	.79412	**.62248**	.79560	**.62459**	.79706	**.62670**	.79852	**.62881**	17
+ 11′	9.79267	**.62040**	9.79415	**.62251**	9.79562	**.62463**	9.79709	**.62674**	9.79855	**.62885**	16
45	.79269	**.62043**	.79417	**.62255**	.79565	**.62466**	.79711	**.62677**	.79857	**.62888**	15
46	.79272	**.62047**	.79420	**.62258**	.79567	**.62470**	.79714	**.62681**	.79859	**.62892**	14
47	.79274	**.62050**	.79422	**.62262**	.79569	**.62473**	.79716	**.62684**	.79862	**.62895**	13
+ 12′	9.79277	**.62054**	9.79425	**.62265**	9.79572	**.62477**	9.79718	**.62688**	9.79864	**.62899**	12
49	.79279	**.62057**	.79427	**.62269**	.79574	**.62480**	.79721	**.62691**	.79867	**.62902**	11
50	.79282	**.62061**	.79430	**.62272**	.79577	**.62484**	.79723	**.62695**	.79869	**.62906**	10
51	.79284	**.62064**	.79432	**.62276**	.79579	**.62487**	.79726	**.62698**	.79872	**.62909**	9
+ 13′	9.79287	**.62068**	9.79434	**.62279**	9.79582	**.62491**	9.79728	**.62702**	9.79874	**.62913**	8
53	.79289	**.62071**	.79437	**.62283**	.79584	**.62494**	.79731	**.62706**	.79876	**.62916**	7
54	.79292	**.62075**	.79439	**.62287**	.79587	**.62498**	.79733	**.62709**	.79879	**.62920**	6
55	.79294	**.62078**	.79442	**.62290**	.79589	**.62501**	.79735	**.62713**	.79881	**.62923**	5
+ 14′	9.79297	**.62082**	9.79444	**.62294**	9.79591	**.62505**	9.79738	**.62716**	9.79884	**.62927**	4
57	.79299	**.62086**	.79447	**.62297**	.79594	**.62508**	.79740	**.62720**	.79886	**.62930**	3
58	.79301	**.62089**	.79449	**.62301**	.79596	**.62512**	.79743	**.62723**	.79888	**.62934**	2
59	.79304	**.62093**	.79452	**.62304**	.79599	**.62515**	.79745	**.62727**	.79891	**.62937**	1
+ 15′	9.79306	**.62096**	9.79454	**.62308**	9.79601	**.62519**	9.79748	**.62730**	9.79893	**.62941**	0
	17ʰ 4ᵐ		17ʰ 3ᵐ		17ʰ 2ᵐ		17ʰ 1ᵐ		17ʰ 0ᵐ		

TABLE 34.

Haversines.

s	$7^h\,0^m$ 105° 0′ Log. Hav.	Nat. Hav.	$7^h\,1^m$ 105° 15′ Log. Hav.	Nat. Hav.	$7^h\,2^m$ 105° 30′ Log. Hav.	Nat. Hav.	$7^h\,3^m$ 105° 45′ Log. Hav.	Nat. Hav.	$7^h\,4^m$ 106° 0′ Log. Hav.	Nat. Hav.	s
0	9.79893	**.62941**	9.80038	**.63152**	9.80183	**.63362**	9.80327	**.63572**	9.80470	**.63782**	60
1	.79896	**.62944**	.80041	**.63155**	.80185	**.63365**	.80329	**.63576**	.80472	**.63785**	59
2	.79898	**.62948**	.80043	**.63159**	.80188	**.63369**	.80331	**.63579**	.80474	**.63789**	58
3	.79901	**.62951**	.80046	**.63162**	.80190	**.63372**	.80334	**.63583**	.80477	**.63792**	57
+ 1′	9.79903	**.62955**	9.80048	**.63166**	9.80192	**.63376**	9.80336	**.63586**	9.80479	**.63796**	56
5	.79905	**.62958**	.80050	**.63169**	.80195	**.63379**	.80339	**.63590**	.80482	**.63799**	55
6	.79908	**.62962**	.80053	**.63173**	.80197	**.63383**	.80341	**.63593**	.80484	**.63803**	54
7	.79910	**.62965**	.80055	**.63176**	.80200	**.63386**	.80343	**.63597**	.80486	**.63806**	53
+ 2′	9.79913	**.62969**	9.80058	**.63180**	9.80202	**.63390**	9.80346	**.63600**	9.80489	**.63810**	52
9	.79915	**.62973**	.80060	**.63183**	.80204	**.63393**	.80348	**.63604**	.80491	**.63813**	51
10	.79918	**.62976**	.80063	**.63187**	.80207	**.63397**	.80351	**.63607**	.80494	**.63817**	50
11	.79920	**.62980**	.80065	**.63190**	.80209	**.63400**	.80353	**.63611**	.80496	**.63820**	49
+ 3′	9.79922	**.62983**	9.80067	**.63194**	9.80212	**.63404**	9.80355	**.63614**	9.80498	**.63824**	48
13	.79925	**.62987**	.80070	**.63197**	.80214	**.63407**	.80358	**.63618**	.80501	**.63827**	47
14	.79927	**.62990**	.80072	**.63201**	.80216	**.63411**	.80360	**.63621**	.80503	**.63831**	46
15	.79930	**.62994**	.80075	**.63204**	.80219	**.63414**	.80362	**.63625**	.80505	**.63834**	45
+ 4′	9.79932	**.62997**	9.80077	**.63208**	9.80221	**.63418**	9.80365	**.63628**	9.80508	**.63838**	44
17	.79935	**.63001**	.80079	**.63211**	.80224	**.63421**	.80367	**.63632**	.80510	**.63841**	43
18	.79937	**.63004**	.80082	**.63215**	.80226	**.63425**	.80370	**.63635**	.80513	**.63845**	42
19	.79939	**.63008**	.80084	**.63218**	.80228	**.63428**	.80372	**.63639**	.80515	**.63848**	41
+ 5′	9.79942	**.63011**	9.80087	**.63222**	9.80231	**.63432**	9.80374	**.63642**	9.80517	**.63852**	40
21	.79944	**.63015**	.80089	**.63225**	.80233	**.63435**	.80377	**.63646**	.80520	**.63855**	39
22	.79947	**.63018**	.80091	**.63229**	.80236	**.63439**	.80379	**.63649**	.80522	**.63859**	38
23	.79949	**.63022**	.80094	**.63232**	.80238	**.63442**	.80382	**.63653**	.80524	**.63862**	37
+ 6′	9.79951	**.63025**	9.80096	**.63236**	9.80240	**.63446**	9.80384	**.63656**	9.80527	**.63866**	36
25	.79954	**.63029**	.80099	**.63239**	.80243	**.63450**	.80386	**.63660**	.80529	**.63869**	35
26	.79956	**.63032**	.80101	**.63243**	.80245	**.63453**	.80389	**.63663**	.80532	**.63873**	34
27	.79959	**.63036**	.80103	**.63246**	.80248	**.63457**	.80391	**.63666**	.80534	**.63876**	33
+ 7′	9.79961	**.63039**	9.80106	**.63250**	9.80250	**.63460**	9.80393	**.63670**	9.80536	**.63880**	32
29	.79964	**.63043**	.80108	**.63253**	.80252	**.63464**	.80396	**.63673**	.80539	**.63883**	31
30	.79966	**.63046**	.80111	**.63257**	.80255	**.63467**	.80398	**.63677**	.80541	**.63887**	30
31	.79968	**.63050**	.80113	**.63260**	.80257	**.63471**	.80401	**.63680**	.80543	**.63890**	29
+ 8′	9.79971	**.63053**	9.80116	**.63264**	9.80260	**.63474**	9.80403	**.63684**	9.80546	**.63894**	28
33	.79973	**.63057**	.80118	**.63267**	.80262	**.63478**	.80405	**.63687**	.80548	**.63897**	27
34	.79976	**.63060**	.80120	**.63271**	.80264	**.63481**	.80408	**.63691**	.80551	**.63901**	26
35	.79978	**.63064**	.80123	**.63274**	.80267	**.63485**	.80410	**.63694**	.80553	**.63904**	25
+ 9′	9.79980	**.63067**	9.80125	**.63278**	9.80269	**.63488**	9.80413	**.63698**	9.80555	**.63908**	24
37	.79983	**.63071**	.80128	**.63281**	.80272	**.63492**	.80415	**.63701**	.80558	**.63911**	23
38	.79985	**.63074**	.80130	**.63285**	.80274	**.63495**	.80417	**.63705**	.80560	**.63915**	22
39	.79988	**.63078**	.80132	**.63288**	.80276	**.63499**	.80420	**.63708**	.80562	**.63918**	21
+ 10′	9.79990	**.63081**	9.80135	**.63292**	9.80279	**.63502**	9.80422	**.63712**	9.80565	**.63922**	20
41	.79993	**.63085**	.80137	**.63295**	.80281	**.63506**	.80424	**.63715**	.80567	**.63925**	19
42	.79995	**.63088**	.80140	**.63299**	.80284	**.63509**	.80427	**.63719**	.80570	**.63929**	18
43	.79997	**.63092**	.80142	**.63302**	.80286	**.63513**	.80429	**.63722**	.80572	**.63932**	17
+ 11′	9.80000	**.63095**	9.80144	**.63306**	9.80288	**.63516**	9.80432	**.63726**	9.80574	**.63936**	16
45	.80002	**.63099**	.80147	**.63309**	.80291	**.63520**	.80434	**.63729**	.80577	**.63939**	15
46	.80005	**.63102**	.80149	**.63313**	.80293	**.63523**	.80436	**.63733**	.80579	**.63943**	14
47	.80007	**.63106**	.80152	**.63316**	.80296	**.63527**	.80439	**.63736**	.80581	**.63946**	13
+ 12′	9.80009	**.63109**	9.80154	**.63320**	9.80298	**.63530**	9.80441	**.63740**	9.80584	**.63950**	12
49	.80012	**.63113**	.80156	**.63323**	.80300	**.63534**	.80444	**.63743**	.80586	**.63953**	11
50	.80014	**.63116**	.80159	**.63327**	.80303	**.63537**	.80446	**.63747**	.80589	**.63957**	10
51	.80017	**.63120**	.80161	**.63330**	.80305	**.63541**	.80448	**.63750**	.80591	**.63960**	9
+ 13′	9.80019	**.63123**	9.80164	**.63334**	9.80307	**.63544**	9.80451	**.63754**	9.80593	**.63964**	8
53	.80022	**.63127**	.80166	**.63337**	.80310	**.63548**	.80453	**.63757**	.80596	**.63967**	7
54	.80024	**.63131**	.80168	**.63341**	.80312	**.63551**	.80455	**.63761**	.80598	**.63971**	6
55	.80026	**.63134**	.80171	**.63344**	.80315	**.63555**	.80458	**.63764**	.80600	**.63974**	5
+ 14′	9.80029	**.63138**	9.80173	**.63348**	9.80317	**.63558**	9.80460	**.63768**	9.80603	**.63977**	4
57	.80031	**.63142**	.80176	**.63351**	.80319	**.63562**	.80463	**.63771**	.80605	**.63981**	3
58	.80034	**.63145**	.80178	**.63355**	.80322	**.63565**	.80465	**.63775**	.80607	**.63984**	2
59	.80036	**.63148**	.80180	**.63358**	.80324	**.63569**	.80467	**.63778**	.80610	**.63988**	1
+ 15′	9.80038	**.63152**	9.80183	**.63362**	9.80327	**.63572**	9.80470	**.63782**	9.80612	**.63991**	0
	$16^h\,59^m$		$16^h\,58^m$		$16^h\,57^m$		$16^h\,56^m$		$16^h\,55^m$		

TABLE 34.

Haversines.

	$7^h 5^m$ 106° 15′		$7^h 6^m$ 106° 30′		$7^h 7^m$ 106° 45′		$7^h 8^m$ 107° 0′		$7^h 9^m$ 107° 15′		
	Log. Hav.	Nat. Hav.	Log. Hav.	Nat. Hav.	Log. Hav.	Nat. Hav.	Log. Hav.	Nat. Hav.	Log. Hav.	Nat. Hav.	s
0	9.80612	**.63991**	9.80754	**.64201**	9.80895	**.64410**	9.81036	**.64619**	9.81176	**.64827**	60
1	.80615	**.63995**	.80756	**.64204**	.80898	**.64413**	.81038	**.64622**	.81178	**.64831**	59
2	.80617	**.63998**	.80759	**.64208**	.80900	**.64417**	.81040	**.64626**	.81180	**.64834**	58
3	.80619	**.64002**	.80761	**.64211**	.80902	**.64420**	.81043	**.64629**	.81183	**.64838**	57
+ 1′	9.80622	**.64005**	9.80763	**.64215**	9.80905	**.64424**	9.81045	**.64632**	9.81185	**.64841**	56
5	.80624	**.64009**	.80766	**.64218**	.80907	**.64427**	.81047	**.64636**	.81187	**.64844**	55
6	.80626	**.64012**	.80768	**.64222**	.80909	**.64431**	.81050	**.64639**	.81190	**.64848**	54
7	.80629	**.64016**	.80771	**.64225**	.80912	**.64434**	.81052	**.64643**	.81192	**.64851**	53
+ 2′	9.80631	**.64019**	9.80773	**.64229**	9.80914	**.64438**	9.81054	**.64646**	9.81194	**.64855**	52
9	.80634	**.64023**	.80775	**.64232**	.80916	**.64441**	.81057	**.64650**	.81197	**.64858**	51
10	.80636	**.64026**	.80778	**.64236**	.80919	**.64445**	.81059	**.64653**	.81199	**.64862**	50
11	.80638	**.64030**	.80780	**.64239**	.80921	**.64448**	.81061	**.64657**	.81201	**.64865**	49
+ 3′	9.80641	**.64033**	9.80782	**.64243**	9.80923	**.64452**	9.81064	**.64660**	9.81204	**.64869**	48
13	.80643	**.64037**	.80785	**.64246**	.80926	**.64455**	.81066	**.64664**	.81206	**.64872**	47
14	.80645	**.64040**	.80787	**.64250**	.80928	**.64459**	.81068	**.64667**	.81208	**.64876**	46
15	.80648	**.64044**	.80789	**.64253**	.80930	**.64462**	.81071	**.64671**	.81211	**.64879**	45
+ 4′	9.80650	**.64047**	9.80792	**.64257**	9.80933	**.64466**	.81073	**.64674**	9.81213	**.64883**	44
17	.80652	**.64051**	.80794	**.64260**	.80935	**.64469**	.81075	**.64678**	.81215	**.64886**	43
18	.80655	**.64054**	.80796	**.64264**	.80937	**.64472**	.81078	**.64681**	.81217	**.64890**	42
19	.80657	**.64058**	.80799	**.64267**	.80940	**.64476**	.81080	**.64685**	.81220	**.64893**	41
+ 5′	9.80660	**.64061**	9.80801	**.64270**	9.80942	**.64479**	9.81082	**.64688**	9.81222	**.64897**	40
21	.80662	**.64065**	.80804	**.64274**	.80944	**.64483**	.81085	**.64692**	.81224	**.64900**	39
22	.80664	**.64068**	.80806	**.64277**	.80947	**.64486**	.81087	**.64695**	.81227	**.64903**	38
23	.80667	**.64072**	.80808	**.64281**	.80949	**.64490**	.81089	**.64699**	.81229	**.64907**	37
+ 6′	9.80669	**.64075**	9.80811	**.64284**	9.80952	**.64493**	9.81092	**.64702**	9.81231	**.64910**	36
25	.80671	**.64079**	.80813	**.64288**	.80954	**.64497**	.81094	**.64705**	.81234	**.64914**	35
26	.80674	**.64082**	.80815	**.64291**	.80956	**.64500**	.81096	**.64709**	.81236	**.64917**	34
27	.80676	**.64086**	.80818	**.64295**	.80959	**.64504**	.81099	**.64712**	.81238	**.64921**	33
+ 7′	9.80678	**.64089**	9.80820	**.64298**	9.80961	**.64507**	9.81101	**.64716**	9.81241	**.64924**	32
29	.80681	**.64093**	.80822	**.64302**	.80963	**.64511**	.81103	**.64719**	.81243	**.64928**	31
30	.80683	**.64096**	.80825	**.64305**	.80966	**.64514**	.81106	**.64723**	.81245	**.64931**	30
31	.80686	**.64100**	.80827	**.64309**	.80968	**.64518**	.81108	**.64726**	.81248	**.64935**	29
+ 8′	9.80688	**.64103**	9.80829	**.64312**	9.80970	**.64521**	9.81110	**.64730**	9.81250	**.64938**	28
33	.80690	**.64107**	.80832	**.64316**	.80973	**.64525**	.81113	**.64733**	.81252	**.64942**	27
34	.80693	**.64110**	.80834	**.64319**	.80975	**.64528**	.81115	**.64737**	.81255	**.64945**	26
35	.80695	**.64114**	.80836	**.64323**	.80977	**.64532**	.81117	**.64740**	.81257	**.64949**	25
+ 9′	9.80697	**.64117**	9.80839	**.64326**	9.80980	**.64535**	9.81120	**.64744**	9.81259	**.64952**	24
37	.80700	**.64121**	.80841	**.64330**	.80982	**.64539**	.81122	**.64747**	.81262	**.64956**	23
38	.80702	**.64124**	.80844	**.64333**	.80984	**.64542**	.81124	**.64751**	.81264	**.64959**	22
39	.80704	**.64128**	.80846	**.64337**	.80987	**.64546**	.81127	**.64754**	.81266	**.64962**	21
+ 10′	9.80707	**.64131**	9.80848	**.64340**	9.80989	**.64549**	9.81129	**.64758**	9.81269	**.64966**	20
41	.80709	**.64135**	.80851	**.64344**	.80991	**.64552**	.81131	**.64761**	.81271	**.64969**	19
42	.80712	**.64138**	.80853	**.64347**	.80994	**.64556**	.81134	**.64765**	.81273	**.64973**	18
43	.80714	**.64142**	.80855	**.64351**	.80996	**.64559**	.81136	**.64768**	.81276	**.64976**	17
+ 11′	9.80716	**.64145**	9.80858	**.64354**	9.80998	**.64563**	9.81138	**.64772**	9.81278	**.64980**	16
45	.80719	**.64148**	.80860	**.64358**	.81001	**.64566**	.81141	**.64775**	.81280	**.64983**	15
46	.80721	**.64152**	.80862	**.64361**	.81003	**.64570**	.81143	**.64778**	.81282	**.64987**	14
47	.80723	**.64155**	.80865	**.64365**	.81005	**.64573**	.81145	**.64782**	.81285	**.64990**	13
+ 12′	9.80726	**.64159**	9.80867	**.64368**	9.81008	**.64577**	9.81148	**.64785**	9.81287	**.64994**	12
49	.80728	**.64162**	.80869	**.64372**	.81010	**.64580**	.81150	**.64789**	.81289	**.64997**	11
50	.80730	**.64166**	.80872	**.64375**	.81012	**.64584**	.81152	**.64792**	.81292	**.65001**	10
51	.80733	**.64169**	.80874	**.64378**	.81015	**.64587**	.81155	**.64796**	.81294	**.65004**	9
+ 13′	9.80735	**.64173**	9.80876	**.64382**	9.81017	**.64591**	9.81157	**.64799**	9.81296	**.65008**	8
53	.80738	**.64176**	.80879	**.64385**	.81019	**.64594**	.81159	**.64803**	.81299	**.65011**	7
54	.80740	**.64180**	.80881	**.64389**	.81022	**.64598**	.81162	**.64806**	.81301	**.65014**	6
55	.80742	**.64183**	.80883	**.64392**	.81024	**.64601**	.81164	**.64810**	.81303	**.65018**	5
+ 14′	9.80745	**.64187**	9.80886	**.64396**	9.81026	**.64605**	9.81166	**.64813**	9.81306	**.65021**	4
57	.80747	**.64190**	.80888	**.64399**	.81029	**.64608**	.81169	**.64817**	.81308	**.65025**	3
58	.80749	**.64194**	.80891	**.64403**	.81031	**.64612**	.81171	**.64820**	.81310	**.65028**	2
59	.80752	**.64197**	.80893	**.64406**	.81033	**.64615**	.81173	**.64824**	.81313	**.65032**	1
+ 15′	9.80754	**.64201**	9.80895	**.64410**	9.81036	**.64619**	9.81176	**.64827**	9.81315	**.65035**	0
	$16^h 54^m$		$16^h 53^m$		$16^h 52^m$		$16^h 51^m$		$16^h 50^m$		

TABLE 34.

Haversines.

s	7h 10m 107° 30′ Log. Hav.	Nat. Hav.	7h 11m 107° 45′ Log. Hav.	Nat. Hav.	7h 12m 108° 0′ Log. Hav.	Nat. Hav.	7h 13m 108° 15′ Log. Hav.	Nat. Hav.	7h 14m 108° 30′ Log. Hav.	Nat. Hav.	s
0	9.81315	.65035	9.81454	.65243	9.81592	.65451	9.81729	.65658	9.81866	.65865	60
1	.81317	.65039	.81456	.65247	.81594	.65454	.81731	.65662	.81868	.65869	59
2	.81320	.65042	.81458	.65250	.81596	.65458	.81733	.65665	.81870	.65872	58
3	.81322	.65046	.81460	.65254	.81598	.65461	.81736	.65668	.81872	.65876	57
+ 1′	9.81324	.65049	9.81463	.65257	9.81601	.65465	9.81738	.65672	9.81875	.65879	56
5	.81326	.65053	.81465	.65261	.81603	.65468	.81740	.65675	.81877	.65882	55
6	.81329	.65056	.81467	.65264	.81605	.65472	.81743	.65679	.81879	.65886	54
7	.81331	.65060	.81470	.65267	.81608	.65475	.81745	.65682	.81882	.65889	53
+ 2′	9.81333	.65063	9.81472	.65271	9.81610	.65479	9.81747	.65686	9.81884	.65893	52
9	.81336	.65066	.81474	.65274	.81612	.65482	.81749	.65689	.81886	.65896	51
10	.81338	.65070	.81477	.65278	.81614	.65485	.81752	.65693	.81888	.65900	50
11	.81340	.65073	.81479	.65281	.81617	.65489	.81754	.65696	.81891	.65903	49
+ 3′	9.81343	.65077	9.81481	.65285	9.81619	.65492	9.81756	.65700	9.81893	.65907	48
13	.81345	.65080	.81483	.65288	.81621	.65496	.81759	.65703	.81895	.65910	47
14	.81347	.65084	.81486	.65292	.81624	.65499	.81761	.65707	.81897	.65914	46
15	.81350	.65087	.81488	.65295	.81626	.65503	.81763	.65710	.81900	.65917	45
+ 4′	9.81352	.65091	9.81490	.65299	9.81628	.65506	9.81765	.65713	9.81902	.65920	44
17	.81354	.65094	.81493	.65302	.81631	.65510	.81768	.65717	.81904	.65924	43
18	.81357	.65098	.81495	.65306	.81633	.65513	.81770	.65720	.81907	.65927	42
19	.81359	.65101	.81497	.65309	.81635	.65516	.81772	.65724	.81909	.65931	41
+ 5′	9.81361	.65105	9.81500	.65312	9.81637	.65520	9.81775	.65727	9.81911	.65934	40
21	.81364	.65108	.81502	.65316	.81640	.65523	.81777	.65731	.81913	.65938	39
22	.81366	.65112	.81505	.65319	.81642	.65527	.81779	.65734	.81916	.65941	38
23	.81368	.65115	.81507	.65323	.81644	.65530	.81781	.65738	.81918	.65944	37
+ 6′	9.81370	.65118	9.81509	.65326	9.81647	.65534	9.81784	.65741	9.81920	.65948	36
25	.81373	.65122	.81511	.65330	.81649	.65537	.81786	.65744	.81922	.65951	35
26	.81375	.65125	.81513	.65333	.81651	.65541	.81788	.65748	.81925	.65955	34
27	.81377	.65129	.81516	.65337	.81653	.65544	.81791	.65751	.81927	.65958	33
+ 7′	9.81380	.65132	9.81518	.65340	9.81656	.65548	9.81793	.65755	9.81929	.65962	32
29	.81382	.65136	.81520	.65344	.81658	.65551	.81795	.65758	.81931	.65965	31
30	.81384	.65139	.81523	.65347	.81660	.65555	.81797	.65762	.81934	.65969	30
31	.81387	.65143	.81525	.65351	.81663	.65558	.81800	.65765	.81936	.65972	29
+ 8′	9.81389	.65146	9.81527	.65354	9.81665	.65561	9.81802	.65769	9.81938	.65976	28
33	.81391	.65150	.81530	.65357	.81667	.65565	.81804	.65772	.81941	.65979	27
34	.81394	.65153	.81532	.65361	.81669	.65568	.81806	.65776	.81943	.65982	26
35	.81396	.65157	.81534	.65364	.81672	.65572	.81809	.65779	.81945	.65986	25
+ 9′	9.81398	.65160	9.81536	.65368	9.81674	.65575	9.81811	.65782	9.81947	.65989	24
37	.81400	.65164	.81539	.65372	.81676	.65579	.81813	.65786	.81950	.65993	23
38	.81403	.65167	.81541	.65375	.81679	.65582	.81816	.65789	.81952	.65996	22
39	.81405	.65171	.81543	.65378	.81681	.65586	.81818	.65793	.81954	.66000	21
+ 10′	9.81407	.65174	9.81546	.65382	9.81683	.65589	9.81820	.65796	9.81956	.66003	20
41	.81410	.65177	.81548	.65385	.81685	.65593	.81822	.65800	.81959	.66006	19
42	.81412	.65181	.81550	.65389	.81688	.65596	.81825	.65803	.81961	.66010	18
43	.81414	.65184	.81552	.65392	.81690	.65599	.81827	.65807	.81963	.66013	17
+ 11′	9.81417	.65188	9.81555	.65396	9.81692	.65603	.81829	.65810	9.81965	.66017	16
45	.81419	.65191	.81557	.65399	.81695	.65606	.81832	.65813	.81968	.66020	15
46	.81421	.65195	.81559	.65402	.81697	.65610	.81834	.65817	.81970	.66024	14
47	.81424	.65198	.81562	.65406	.81699	.65613	.81836	.65820	.81972	.66027	13
+ 12′	9.81426	.65202	9.81564	.65409	9.81701	.65617	9.81838	.65824	9.81975	.66031	12
49	.81428	.65205	.81566	.65413	.81704	.65620	.81841	.65827	.81977	.66034	11
50	.81430	.65209	.81569	.65416	.81706	.65624	.81843	.65831	.81979	.66038	10
51	.81433	.65212	.81571	.65420	.81708	.65627	.81845	.65834	.81981	.66041	9
+ 13′	9.81435	.65216	9.81573	.65423	9.81711	.65630	9.81847	.65838	9.81984	.66044	8
53	.81437	.65219	.81575	.65427	.81713	.65634	.81850	.65841	.81986	.66048	7
54	.81440	.65222	.81578	.65430	.81715	.65637	.81852	.65845	.81988	.66051	6
55	.81442	.65226	.81580	.65434	.81717	.65641	.81854	.65848	.81990	.66055	5
+ 14′	9.81444	.65229	9.81582	.65437	9.81720	.65644	9.81857	.65851	9.81993	.66058	4
57	.81447	.65233	.81585	.65440	.81722	.65648	.81859	.65855	.81995	.66062	3
58	.81449	.65236	.81587	.65444	.81724	.65651	.81861	.65858	.81997	.66065	2
59	.81451	.65240	.81589	.65447	.81727	.65655	.81863	.65862	.81999	.66068	1
+ 15′	9.81454	.65243	9.81592	.65451	9.81729	.65658	9.81866	.65865	9.82002	.66072	0
	16h 49m		16h 48m		16h 47m		16h 46m		16h 45m		

TABLE 34.

Haversines.

s	7h 15m 108° 45′ Log. Hav.	Nat. Hav.	7h 16m 109° 0′ Log. Hav.	Nat. Hav.	7h 17m 109° 15′ Log. Hav.	Nat. Hav.	7h 18m 109° 30′ Log. Hav.	Nat. Hav.	7h 19m 109° 45′ Log. Hav.	Nat. Hav.	s
0	9.82002	**.66072**	9.82137	**.66278**	9.82272	**.66485**	9.82406	**.66690**	9.82540	**.66896**	60
1	.82004	**.66075**	.82139	**.66282**	.82274	**.66488**	.82409	**.66694**	.82542	**.66899**	59
2	.82006	**.66079**	.82142	**.66285**	.82277	**.66491**	.82411	**.66697**	.82544	**.66903**	58
3	.82009	**.66082**	.82144	**.66289**	.82279	**.66495**	.82413	**.66701**	.82547	**.66906**	57
+ 1′	9.82011	**.66086**	9.82146	**.66292**	9.82281	**.66498**	9.82415	**.66704**	9.82549	**.66910**	56
5	.82013	**.66089**	.82148	**.66296**	.82283	**.66502**	.82417	**.66707**	.82551	**.66913**	55
6	.82015	**.66093**	.82151	**.66299**	.82286	**.66505**	.82420	**.66711**	.82553	**.66916**	54
7	.82018	**.66096**	.82153	**.66302**	.82288	**.66508**	.82422	**.66714**	.82555	**.66920**	53
+ 2′	9.82020	**.66100**	9.82155	**.66306**	9.82290	**.66512**	9.82424	**.66718**	9.82558	**.66923**	52
9	.82022	**.66103**	.82157	**.66309**	.82292	**.66515**	.82426	**.66721**	.82560	**.66927**	51
10	.82024	**.66106**	.82160	**.66313**	.82294	**.66519**	.82429	**.66725**	.82562	**.66930**	50
11	.82027	**.66110**	.82162	**.66316**	.82297	**.66522**	.82431	**.66728**	.82564	**.66933**	49
+ 3′	9.82029	**.66113**	9.82164	**.66320**	9.82299	**.66526**	9.82433	**.66731**	9.82567	**.66937**	48
13	.82031	**.66117**	.82166	**.66323**	.82301	**.66529**	.82435	**.66735**	.82569	**.66940**	47
14	.82033	**.66120**	.82169	**.66327**	.82303	**.66533**	.82438	**.66738**	.82571	**.66944**	46
15	.82036	**.66124**	.82171	**.66330**	.82306	**.66536**	.82440	**.66742**	.82573	**.66947**	45
+ 4′	9.82038	**.66127**	9.82173	**.66333**	9.82308	**.66539**	9.82442	**.66745**	9.82575	**.66951**	44
17	.82040	**.66130**	.82175	**.66337**	.82310	**.66543**	.82444	**.66749**	.82578	**.66954**	43
18	.82042	**.66134**	.82178	**.66340**	.82312	**.66546**	.82446	**.66752**	.82580	**.66957**	42
19	.82045	**.66137**	.82180	**.66344**	.82315	**.66550**	.82449	**.66755**	.82582	**.66961**	41
+ 5′	9.82047	**.66141**	9.82182	**.66347**	9.82317	**.66553**	9.82451	**.66759**	9.82584	**.66964**	40
21	.82049	**.66144**	.82184	**.66351**	.82319	**.66557**	.82453	**.66762**	.82587	**.66968**	39
22	.82051	**.66148**	.82187	**.66354**	.82321	**.66560**	.82455	**.66766**	.82589	**.66971**	38
23	.82054	**.66151**	.82189	**.66357**	.82324	**.66563**	.82458	**.66769**	.82591	**.66975**	37
+ 6′	9.82056	**.66155**	9.82191	**.66361**	9.82326	**.66567**	9.82460	**.66773**	9.82593	**.66978**	36
25	.82058	**.66158**	.82193	**.66364**	.82328	**.66570**	.82462	**.66776**	.82595	**.66981**	35
26	.82061	**.66161**	.82196	**.66368**	.82330	**.66574**	.82464	**.66779**	.82598	**.66985**	34
27	.82063	**.66165**	.82198	**.66371**	.82333	**.66577**	.82467	**.66783**	.82600	**.66988**	33
+ 7′	9.82065	**.66168**	9.82200	**.66375**	9.82335	**.66581**	9.82469	**.66786**	9.82602	**.66992**	32
29	.82067	**.66172**	.82202	**.66378**	.82337	**.66584**	.82471	**.66790**	.82604	**.66995**	31
30	.82070	**.66175**	.82205	**.66382**	.82339	**.66587**	.82473	**.66793**	.82606	**.66998**	30
31	.82072	**.66179**	.82207	**.66385**	.82341	**.66591**	.82475	**.66797**	.82609	**.67002**	29
+ 8′	9.82074	**.66182**	9.82209	**.66388**	9.82344	**.66594**	9.82478	**.66800**	9.82611	**.67005**	28
33	.82076	**.66186**	.82211	**.66392**	.82346	**.66598**	.82480	**.66803**	.82613	**.67009**	27
34	.82079	**.66189**	.82214	**.66395**	.82348	**.66601**	.82482	**.66807**	.82615	**.67012**	26
35	.82081	**.66192**	.82216	**.66399**	.82350	**.66605**	.82484	**.66810**	.82618	**.67016**	25
+ 9′	9.82083	**.66196**	9.82218	**.66402**	9.82353	**.66608**	9.82487	**.66814**	9.82620	**.67019**	24
37	.82085	**.66199**	.82220	**.66406**	.82355	**.66611**	.82489	**.66817**	.82622	**.67022**	23
38	.82088	**.66203**	.82223	**.66409**	.82357	**.66615**	.82491	**.66821**	.82624	**.67026**	22
39	.82090	**.66206**	.82225	**.66412**	.82359	**.66618**	.82493	**.66824**	.82627	**.67029**	21
+ 10′	9.82092	**.66210**	9.82227	**.66416**	9.82362	**.66622**	9.82495	**.66827**	9.82629	**.67033**	20
41	.82094	**.66213**	.82229	**.66419**	.82364	**.66625**	.82498	**.66831**	.82631	**.67036**	19
42	.82097	**.66217**	.82232	**.66423**	.82366	**.66629**	.82500	**.66834**	.82633	**.67039**	18
43	.82099	**.66220**	.82234	**.66426**	.82368	**.66632**	.82502	**.66838**	.82635	**.67043**	17
+ 11′	9.82101	**.66223**	9.82236	**.66430**	9.82371	**.66635**	9.82504	**.66841**	9.82638	**.67046**	16
45	.82103	**.66227**	.82238	**.66433**	.82373	**.66639**	.82507	**.66844**	.82640	**.67050**	15
46	.82106	**.66230**	.82241	**.66436**	.82375	**.66642**	.82509	**.66848**	.82642	**.67053**	14
47	.82108	**.66234**	.82243	**.66440**	.82377	**.66646**	.82511	**.66851**	.82644	**.67057**	13
+ 12′	9.82110	**.66237**	9.82245	**.66443**	9.82380	**.66649**	9.82513	**.66855**	9.82646	**.67060**	12
49	.82112	**.66241**	.82247	**.66447**	.82382	**.66653**	.82515	**.66858**	.82649	**.67063**	11
50	.82115	**.66244**	.82250	**.66450**	.82384	**.66656**	.82518	**.66862**	.82651	**.67067**	10
51	.82117	**.66247**	.82252	**.66454**	.82386	**.66659**	.82520	**.66865**	.82653	**.67070**	9
+ 13′	9.82119	**.66251**	9.82254	**.66457**	9.82388	**.66663**	9.82522	**.66868**	9.82655	**.67074**	8
53	.82121	**.66254**	.82256	**.66460**	.82391	**.66666**	.82524	**.66872**	.82657	**.67077**	7
54	.82124	**.66258**	.82259	**.66464**	.82393	**.66670**	.82527	**.66875**	.82660	**.67081**	6
55	.82126	**.66261**	.82261	**.66467**	.82395	**.66673**	.82529	**.66879**	.82662	**.67084**	5
+ 14′	9.82128	**.66265**	9.82263	**.66471**	9.82397	**.66677**	9.82531	**.66882**	9.82664	**.67087**	4
57	.82130	**.66268**	.82265	**.66474**	.82400	**.66680**	.82533	**.66886**	.82666	**.67091**	3
58	.82133	**.66272**	.82268	**.66478**	.82402	**.66683**	.82535	**.66889**	.82668	**.67094**	2
59	.82135	**.66275**	.82270	**.66481**	.82404	**.66687**	.82538	**.66892**	.82671	**.67098**	1
+ 15′	9.82137	**.66278**	9.82272	**.66485**	9.82406	**.66690**	9.82540	**.66896**	9.82673	**.67101**	0
	16h 44m		16h 43m		16h 42m		16h 41m		16h 40m		

TABLE 34.

Haversines.

s	7h 20m 110° 0′ Log. Hav.	Nat. Hav.	7h 21m 110° 15′ Log. Hav.	Nat. Hav.	7h 22m 110° 30′ Log. Hav.	Nat. Hav.	7h 23m 110° 45′ Log. Hav.	Nat. Hav.	7h 24m 111° 0′ Log. Hav.	Nat. Hav.	s
0	9.82673	**.67101**	9.82805	**.67306**	9.82937	**.67510**	9.83068	**.67715**	9.83199	**.67918**	60
1	.82675	**.67104**	.82807	**.67309**	.82939	**.67514**	.83070	**.67718**	.83201	**.67922**	59
2	.82677	**.67108**	.82810	**.67313**	.82941	**.67517**	.83073	**.67721**	.83203	**.67925**	58
3	.82680	**.67111**	.82812	**.67316**	.82944	**.67521**	.83075	**.67725**	.83205	**.67929**	57
+ 1′	9.82682	**.67115**	9.82814	**.67320**	9.82946	**.67524**	9.83077	**.67728**	9.83207	**.67932**	56
5	.82684	**.67118**	.82816	**.67323**	.82948	**.67527**	.83079	**.67732**	.83210	**.67935**	55
6	.82686	**.67122**	.82818	**.67326**	.82950	**.67531**	.83081	**.67735**	.83212	**.67939**	54
7	.82688	**.67125**	.82821	**.67330**	.82952	**.67534**	.83083	**.67738**	.83214	**.67942**	53
+ 2′	9.82691	**.67128**	9.82823	**.67333**	9.82955	**.67538**	9.83086	**.67742**	9.83216	**.67946**	52
9	.82693	**.67132**	.82825	**.67337**	.82957	**.67541**	.83088	**.67745**	.83218	**.67949**	51
10	.82695	**.67135**	.82827	**.67340**	.82959	**.67544**	.83090	**.67749**	.83220	**.67952**	50
11	.82697	**.67139**	.82829	**.67343**	.82961	**.67548**	.83092	**.67752**	.83223	**.67956**	49
+ 3′	9.82699	**.67142**	9.82832	**.67347**	9.82963	**.67551**	9.83094	**.67755**	9.83225	**.67959**	48
13	.82702	**.67145**	.82834	**.67350**	.82966	**.67555**	.83097	**.67759**	.83227	**.67963**	47
14	.82704	**.67149**	.82836	**.67354**	.82968	**.67558**	.83099	**.67762**	.83229	**.67966**	46
15	.82706	**.67152**	.82838	**.67357**	.82970	**.67561**	.83101	**.67766**	.83231	**.67969**	45
+ 4′	9.82708	**.67156**	9.82840	**.67360**	9.82972	**.67565**	9.83103	**.67769**	9.83233	**.67973**	44
17	.82710	**.67159**	.82843	**.67364**	.82974	**.67568**	.83105	**.67772**	.83236	**.67976**	43
18	.82713	**.67163**	.82845	**.67367**	.82976	**.67572**	.83107	**.67776**	.83238	**.67979**	42
19	.82715	**.67166**	.82847	**.67371**	.82979	**.67575**	.83110	**.67779**	.83240	**.67983**	41
+ 5′	9.82717	**.67169**	9.82849	**.67374**	9.82981	**.67578**	9.83112	**.67783**	9.83242	**.67986**	40
21	.82719	**.67173**	.82851	**.67377**	.82983	**.67582**	.83114	**.67786**	.83244	**.67990**	39
22	.82722	**.67176**	.82854	**.67381**	.82985	**.67585**	.83116	**.67789**	.83246	**.67993**	38
23	.82724	**.67180**	.82856	**.67384**	.82987	**.67589**	.83118	**.67793**	.83249	**.67996**	37
+ 6′	9.82726	**.67183**	9.82858	**.67388**	9.82990	**.67592**	9.83120	**.67796**	9.83251	**.68000**	36
25	.82728	**.67186**	.82860	**.67391**	.82992	**.67595**	.83123	**.67800**	.83253	**.68003**	35
26	.82730	**.67190**	.82862	**.67395**	.82994	**.67599**	.83125	**.67803**	.83255	**.68007**	34
27	.82733	**.67193**	.82865	**.67398**	.82996	**.67602**	.83127	**.67806**	.83257	**.68010**	33
+ 7′	9.82735	**.67197**	9.82867	**.67401**	9.82998	**.67606**	9.83129	**.67810**	9.83259	**.68013**	32
29	.82737	**.67200**	.82869	**.67405**	.83001	**.67609**	.83131	**.67813**	.83262	**.68017**	31
30	.82739	**.67203**	.82871	**.67408**	.83003	**.67613**	.83134	**.67817**	.83264	**.68020**	30
31	.82741	**.67207**	.82873	**.67412**	.83005	**.67616**	.83136	**.67820**	.83266	**.68024**	29
+ 8′	9.82744	**.67210**	9.82876	**.67415**	9.83007	**.67619**	9.83138	**.67823**	9.83268	**.68027**	28
33	.82746	**.67214**	.82878	**.67418**	.83009	**.67623**	.83140	**.67827**	.83270	**.68030**	27
34	.82748	**.67217**	.82880	**.67422**	.83011	**.67626**	.83142	**.67830**	.83272	**.68034**	26
35	.82750	**.67221**	.82882	**.67425**	.83014	**.67630**	.83144	**.67834**	.83275	**.68037**	25
+ 9′	9.82752	**.67224**	9.82884	**.67429**	9.83016	**.67633**	9.83147	**.67837**	9.83277	**.68041**	24
37	.82755	**.67227**	.82887	**.67432**	.83018	**.67636**	.83149	**.67840**	.83279	**.68044**	23
38	.82757	**.67231**	.82889	**.67435**	.83020	**.67640**	.83151	**.67844**	.83281	**.68047**	22
39	.82759	**.67234**	.82891	**.67439**	.83022	**.67643**	.83153	**.67847**	.83283	**.68051**	21
+ 10′	9.82761	**.67238**	9.82893	**.67442**	9.83025	**.67647**	9.83155	**.67850**	9.83285	**.68054**	20
41	.82763	**.67241**	.82895	**.67446**	.83027	**.67650**	.83157	**.67854**	.83288	**.68058**	19
42	.82766	**.67244**	.82898	**.67449**	.83029	**.67653**	.83160	**.67857**	.83290	**.68061**	18
43	.82768	**.67248**	.82900	**.67452**	.83031	**.67657**	.83162	**.67861**	.83292	**.68064**	17
+ 11′	9.82770	**.67251**	9.82902	**.67456**	9.83033	**.67660**	9.83164	**.67864**	9.83294	**.68068**	16
45	.82772	**.67255**	.82904	**.67459**	.83035	**.67664**	.83166	**.67868**	.83296	**.68071**	15
46	.82774	**.67258**	.82906	**.67463**	.83038	**.67667**	.83168	**.67871**	.83298	**.68074**	14
47	.82777	**.67261**	.82909	**.67466**	.83040	**.67670**	.83170	**.67874**	.83301	**.68078**	13
+ 12′	9.82779	**.67265**	9.82911	**.67469**	9.83042	**.67674**	9.83173	**.67878**	9.83303	**.68081**	12
49	.82781	**.67268**	.82913	**.67473**	.83044	**.67677**	.83175	**.67881**	.83305	**.68085**	11
50	.82783	**.67272**	.82915	**.67476**	.83046	**.67681**	.83177	**.67884**	.83307	**.68088**	10
51	.82785	**.67275**	.82917	**.67480**	.83049	**.67684**	.83179	**.67888**	.83309	**.68091**	9
+ 13′	9.82788	**.67279**	9.82920	**.67483**	9.83051	**.67687**	9.83181	**.67891**	9.83311	**.68095**	8
53	.82790	**.67282**	.82922	**.67487**	.83053	**.67691**	.83184	**.67895**	.83314	**.68098**	7
54	.82792	**.67285**	.82924	**.67490**	.83055	**.67694**	.83186	**.67898**	.83316	**.68102**	6
55	.82794	**.67289**	.82926	**.67493**	.83057	**.67698**	.83188	**.67901**	.83318	**.68105**	5
+ 14′	9.82796	**.67292**	9.82928	**.67497**	9.83059	**.67701**	9.83190	**.67905**	9.83320	**.68108**	4
57	.82799	**.67296**	.82930	**.67500**	.83062	**.67704**	.83192	**.67908**	.83322	**.68112**	3
58	.82801	**.67299**	.82933	**.67504**	.83064	**.67708**	.83194	**.67912**	.83324	**.68115**	2
59	.82803	**.67302**	.82935	**.67507**	.83066	**.67711**	.83197	**.67915**	.83327	**.68119**	1
+ 15′	9.82805	**.67306**	9.82937	**.67510**	9.83068	**.67715**	9.83199	**.67918**	9.83329	**.68122**	0
	16h 39m		16h 38m		16h 37m		16h 36m		16h 35m		

TABLE 34.

Haversines.

s	7h 25m 111° 15′ Log. Hav.	Nat. Hav.	7h 26m 111° 30′ Log. Hav.	Nat. Hav.	7h 27m 111° 45′ Log. Hav.	Nat. Hav.	7h 28m 112° 0′ Log. Hav.	Nat. Hav.	7h 29m 112° 15′ Log. Hav.	Nat. Hav.	s
0	9.83329	**.68122**	9.83458	**.68325**	9.83587	**.68528**	9.83715	**.68730**	9.83842	**.68932**	60
1	.83331	**.68125**	.83460	**.68328**	.83589	**.68531**	.83717	**.68734**	.83844	**.68936**	59
2	.83333	**.68129**	.83462	**.68332**	.83591	**.68535**	.83719	**.68737**	.83847	**.68939**	58
3	.83335	**.68132**	.83464	**.68335**	.83593	**.68538**	.83721	**.68740**	.83849	**.68943**	57
+ 1′	9.83337	**.68135**	9.83467	**.68339**	9.83595	**.68541**	9.83723	**.68744**	9.83851	**.68946**	56
5	.83339	**.68139**	.83469	**.68342**	.83597	**.68545**	.83725	**.68747**	.83853	**.68949**	55
6	.83342	**.68142**	.83471	**.68345**	.83600	**.68548**	.83728	**.68751**	.83855	**.68953**	54
7	.83344	**.68146**	.83473	**.68349**	.83602	**.68552**	.83730	**.68754**	.83857	**.68956**	53
+ 2′	9.83346	**.68149**	9.83475	**.68352**	9.83604	**.68555**	9.83732	**.68757**	9.83859	**.68959**	52
9	.83348	**.68152**	.83477	**.68356**	.83606	**.68558**	.83734	**.68761**	.83861	**.68963**	51
10	.83350	**.68156**	.83480	**.68359**	.83608	**.68562**	.83736	**.68764**	.83864	**.68966**	50
11	.83352	**.68159**	.83482	**.68362**	.83610	**.68565**	.83738	**.68767**	.83866	**.68969**	49
+ 3′	9.83355	**.68163**	9.83484	**.68366**	9.83612	**.68568**	9.83740	**.68771**	9.83868	**.68973**	48
13	.83357	**.68166**	.83486	**.68369**	.83615	**.68572**	.83743	**.68774**	.83870	**.68976**	47
14	.83359	**.68169**	.83488	**.68372**	.83617	**.68575**	.83745	**.68778**	.83872	**.68980**	46
15	.83361	**.68173**	.83490	**.68376**	.83619	**.68579**	.83747	**.68781**	.83874	**.68983**	45
+ 4′	9.83363	**.68176**	9.83492	**.68379**	9.83621	**.68582**	9.83749	**.68784**	9.83876	**.68986**	44
17	.83365	**.68180**	.83495	**.68383**	.83623	**.68585**	.83751	**.68788**	.83878	**.68990**	43
18	.83368	**.68183**	.83497	**.68386**	.83625	**.68589**	.83753	**.68791**	.83881	**.68993**	42
19	.83370	**.68186**	.83499	**.68389**	.83627	**.68592**	.83755	**.68794**	.83883	**.68996**	41
+ 5′	9.83372	**.68190**	9.83501	**.68393**	9.83630	**.68595**	9.83757	**.68798**	9.83885	**.69000**	40
21	.83374	**.68193**	.83503	**.68396**	.83632	**.68599**	.83760	**.68801**	.83887	**.69003**	39
22	.83376	**.68196**	.83505	**.68399**	.83634	**.68602**	.83762	**.68804**	.83889	**.69006**	38
23	.83378	**.68200**	.83507	**.68403**	.83636	**.68606**	.83764	**.68808**	.83891	**.69010**	37
+ 6′	9.83380	**.68203**	9.83510	**.68406**	9.83638	**.68609**	9.83766	**.68811**	9.83893	**.69013**	36
25	.83383	**.68207**	.83512	**.68410**	.83640	**.68612**	.83768	**.68815**	.83895	**.69017**	35
26	.83385	**.68210**	.83514	**.68413**	.83642	**.68616**	.83770	**.68818**	.83897	**.69020**	34
27	.83387	**.68213**	.83516	**.68416**	.83644	**.68619**	.83772	**.68821**	.83900	**.69023**	33
+ 7′	9.83389	**.68217**	9.83518	**.68420**	9.83647	**.68622**	9.83774	**.68825**	9.83902	**.69027**	32
29	.83391	**.68220**	.83520	**.68423**	.83649	**.68626**	.83777	**.68828**	.83904	**.69030**	31
30	.83393	**.68224**	.83522	**.68427**	.83651	**.68629**	.83779	**.68831**	.83906	**.69033**	30
31	.83396	**.68227**	.83525	**.68430**	.83653	**.68633**	.83781	**.68835**	.83908	**.69037**	29
+ 8′	9.83398	**.68230**	9.83527	**.68433**	9.83655	**.68636**	9.83783	**.68838**	9.83910	**.69040**	28
33	.83400	**.68234**	.83529	**.68437**	.83657	**.68639**	.83785	**.68842**	.83912	**.69044**	27
34	.83402	**.68237**	.83531	**.68440**	.83659	**.68643**	.83787	**.68845**	.83914	**.69047**	26
35	.83404	**.68240**	.83533	**.68443**	.83662	**.68646**	.83789	**.68848**	.83916	**.69050**	25
+ 9′	9.83406	**.68244**	9.83535	**.68447**	9.83664	**.68649**	9.83791	**.68852**	9.83919	**.69054**	24
37	.83409	**.68247**	.83537	**.68450**	.83666	**.68653**	.83794	**.68855**	.83921	**.69057**	23
38	.83411	**.68251**	.83540	**.68454**	.83668	**.68656**	.83796	**.68858**	.83923	**.69060**	22
39	.83413	**.68254**	.83542	**.68457**	.83670	**.68660**	.83798	**.68862**	.83925	**.69064**	21
+ 10′	9.83415	**.68257**	9.83544	**.68460**	9.83672	**.68663**	9.83800	**.68865**	9.83927	**.69067**	20
41	.83417	**.68261**	.83546	**.68464**	.83674	**.68666**	.83802	**.68869**	.83929	**.69070**	19
42	.83419	**.68264**	.83548	**.68467**	.83676	**.68670**	.83804	**.68872**	.83931	**.69074**	18
43	.83421	**.68268**	.83550	**.68470**	.83679	**.68673**	.83806	**.68875**	.83933	**.69077**	17
+ 11′	9.83424	**.68271**	9.83552	**.68474**	9.83681	**.68676**	9.83808	**.68879**	9.83935	**.69080**	16
45	.83426	**.68274**	.83555	**.68477**	.83683	**.68680**	.83811	**.68882**	.83938	**.69084**	15
46	.83428	**.68278**	.83557	**.68481**	.83685	**.68683**	.83813	**.68885**	.83940	**.69087**	14
47	.83430	**.68281**	.83559	**.68484**	.83687	**.68687**	.83815	**.68889**	.83942	**.69091**	13
+ 12′	9.83432	**.68284**	9.83561	**.68487**	9.83689	**.68690**	9.83817	**.68892**	9.83944	**.69094**	12
49	.83434	**.68288**	.83563	**.68491**	.83691	**.68693**	.83819	**.68895**	.83946	**.69097**	11
50	.83436	**.68291**	.83565	**.68494**	.83694	**.68697**	.83821	**.68899**	.83948	**.69101**	10
51	.83439	**.68295**	.83567	**.68497**	.83696	**.68700**	.83823	**.68902**	.83950	**.69104**	9
+ 13′	9.83441	**.68298**	9.83570	**.68501**	9.83698	**.68703**	9.83825	**.68906**	9.83952	**.69107**	8
53	.83443	**.68301**	.83572	**.68504**	.83700	**.68707**	.83828	**.68909**	.83955	**.69111**	7
54	.83445	**.68305**	.83574	**.68508**	.83702	**.68710**	.83830	**.68912**	.83957	**.69114**	6
55	.83447	**.68308**	.83576	**.68511**	.83704	**.68713**	.83832	**.68916**	.83959	**.69117**	5
+ 14′	9.83449	**.68312**	9.83578	**.68515**	9.83706	**.68717**	9.83834	**.68919**	9.83961	**.69121**	4
57	.83452	**.68315**	.83580	**.68518**	.83708	**.68720**	.83836	**.68922**	.83963	**.69124**	3
58	.83454	**.68318**	.83582	**.68521**	.83711	**.68724**	.83838	**.68926**	.83965	**.69127**	2
59	.83456	**.68322**	.83585	**.68525**	.83713	**.68727**	.83840	**.68929**	.83967	**.69131**	1
+ 15′	9.83458	**.68325**	9.83587	**.68528**	9.83715	**.68730**	9.83842	**.68932**	9.83969	**.69134**	0
	16h 34m		16h 33m		16h 32m		16h 31m		16h 30m		

TABLE 34.

Haversines.

s	*7h 30m* **112° 30′**		*7h 31m* **112° 45′**		*7h 32m* **113° 0′**		*7h 33m* **113° 15′**		*7h 34m* **113° 30′**		
s	Log. Hav.	Nat. Hav.	Log. Hav.	Nat. Hav.	Log. Hav.	Nat. Hav.	Log. Hav.	Nat. Hav.	Log. Hav.	Nat. Hav.	s
0	9.83969	**.69134**	9.84096	**.69336**	9.84221	**.69537**	9.84346	**.69737**	9.84471	**.69937**	*60*
1	.83971	**.69138**	.84098	**.69339**	.84223	**.69540**	.84349	**.69741**	.84473	**.69941**	*59*
2	.83974	**.69141**	.84100	**.69342**	.84226	**.69543**	.84351	**.69744**	.84475	**.69944**	*58*
3	.83976	**.69144**	.84102	**.69346**	.84228	**.69547**	.84353	**.69747**	.84477	**.69947**	*57*
+ **1′**	9.83978	**.69148**	9.84104	**.69349**	9.84230	**.69550**	9.84355	**.69751**	9.84479	**.69951**	*56*
5	.83980	**.69151**	.84106	**.69352**	.84232	**.69553**	.84357	**.69754**	.84481	**.69954**	*55*
6	.83982	**.69154**	.84108	**.69356**	.84234	**.69557**	.84359	**.69757**	.84483	**.69957**	*54*
7	.83984	**.69158**	.84110	**.69359**	.84236	**.69560**	.84361	**.69761**	.84485	**.69961**	*53*
+ **2′**	9.83986	**.69161**	9.84112	**.69362**	9.84238	**.69563**	9.84363	**.69764**	9.84488	**.69964**	*52*
9	.83988	**.69164**	.84114	**.69366**	.84240	**.69567**	.84365	**.69767**	.84490	**.69967**	*51*
10	.83990	**.69168**	.84117	**.69369**	.84242	**.69570**	.84367	**.69771**	.84492	**.69971**	*50*
11	.83992	**.69171**	.84119	**.69372**	.84244	**.69573**	.84369	**.69774**	.84494	**.69974**	*49*
+ **3′**	9.83995	**.69174**	9.84121	**.69376**	9.84246	**.69577**	9.84371	**.69777**	9.84496	**.69977**	*48*
13	.83997	**.69178**	.84123	**.69379**	.84248	**.69580**	.84373	**.69781**	.84498	**.69981**	*47*
14	.83999	**.69181**	.84125	**.69382**	.84251	**.69583**	.84376	**.69784**	.84500	**.69984**	*46*
15	.84001	**.69185**	.84127	**.69386**	.84253	**.69587**	.84378	**.69787**	.84502	**.69987**	*45*
+ **4′**	9.84003	**.69188**	9.84129	**.69389**	9.84255	**.69590**	9.84380	**.69791**	9.84504	**.69991**	*44*
17	.84005	**.69191**	.84131	**.69393**	.84257	**.69593**	.84382	**.69794**	.84506	**.69994**	*43*
18	.84007	**.69195**	.84133	**.69396**	.84259	**.69597**	.84384	**.69797**	.84508	**.69997**	*42*
19	.84009	**.69198**	.84135	**.69399**	.84261	**.69600**	.84386	**.69801**	.84510	**.70001**	*41*
+ **5′**	9.84011	**.69201**	9.84138	**.69403**	9.84263	**.69603**	9.84388	**.69804**	9.84512	**.70004**	*40*
21	.84014	**.69205**	.84140	**.69406**	.84265	**.69607**	.84390	**.69807**	.84514	**.70007**	*39*
22	.84016	**.69208**	.84142	**.69409**	.84267	**.69610**	.84392	**.69811**	.84517	**.70011**	*38*
23	.84018	**.69211**	.84144	**.69413**	.84269	**.69614**	.84394	**.69814**	.84519	**.70014**	*37*
+ **6′**	9.84020	**.69215**	9.84146	**.69416**	9.84271	**.69617**	9.84396	**.69817**	9.84521	**.70017**	*36*
25	.84022	**.69218**	.84148	**.69419**	.84274	**.69620**	.84398	**.69821**	.84523	**.70021**	*35*
26	.84024	**.69221**	.84150	**.69423**	.84276	**.69624**	.84400	**.69824**	.84525	**.70024**	*34*
27	.84026	**.69225**	.84152	**.69426**	.84278	**.69627**	.84403	**.69827**	.84527	**.70027**	*33*
+ **7′**	9.84028	**.69228**	9.84154	**.69429**	9.84280	**.69630**	9.84405	**.69831**	9.84529	**.70031**	*32*
29	.84030	**.69232**	.84156	**.69433**	.84282	**.69634**	.84407	**.69834**	.84531	**.70034**	*31*
30	.84033	**.69235**	.84159	**.69436**	.84284	**.69637**	.84409	**.69837**	.84533	**.70037**	*30*
31	.84035	**.69238**	.84161	**.69439**	.84286	**.69640**	.84411	**.69841**	.84535	**.70041**	*29*
+ **8′**	9.84037	**.69242**	9.84163	**.69443**	9.84288	**.69644**	9.84413	**.69844**	9.84537	**.70044**	*28*
33	.84039	**.69245**	.84165	**.69446**	.84290	**.69647**	.84415	**.69847**	.84539	**.70047**	*27*
34	.84041	**.69248**	.84167	**.69450**	.84292	**.69650**	.84417	**.69851**	.84541	**.70051**	*26*
35	.84043	**.69252**	.84169	**.69453**	.84294	**.69654**	.84419	**.69854**	.84543	**.70054**	*25*
+ **9′**	9.84045	**.69255**	9.84171	**.69456**	9.84296	**.69657**	9.84421	**.69857**	9.84545	**.70057**	*24*
37	.84047	**.69258**	.84173	**.69460**	.84299	**.69660**	.84423	**.69861**	.84547	**.70061**	*23*
38	.84049	**.69262**	.84175	**.69463**	.84301	**.69664**	.84425	**.69864**	.84550	**.70064**	*22*
39	.84051	**.69265**	.84177	**.69466**	.84303	**.69667**	.84427	**.69867**	.84552	**.70067**	*21*
+ **10′**	9.84054	**.69268**	9.84179	**.69470**	9.84305	**.69670**	9.84430	**.69871**	9.84554	**.70071**	*20*
41	.84056	**.69272**	.84182	**.69473**	.84307	**.69674**	.84432	**.69874**	.84556	**.70074**	*19*
42	.84058	**.69275**	.84184	**.69476**	.84309	**.69677**	.84434	**.69877**	.84558	**.70077**	*18*
43	.84060	**.69279**	.84186	**.69480**	.84311	**.69680**	.84436	**.69881**	.84560	**.70081**	*17*
+ **11′**	9.84062	**.69282**	9.84188	**.69483**	9.84313	**.69684**	9.84438	**.69884**	9.84562	**.70084**	*16*
45	.84064	**.69285**	.84190	**.69486**	.84315	**.69687**	.84440	**.69887**	.84564	**.70087**	*15*
46	.84066	**.69289**	.84192	**.69490**	.84317	**.69690**	.84442	**.69891**	.84566	**.70091**	*14*
47	.84068	**.69292**	.84194	**.69493**	.84319	**.69694**	.84444	**.69894**	.84568	**.70094**	*13*
+ **12′**	9.84070	**.69295**	9.84196	**.69496**	9.84321	**.69697**	9.84446	**.69897**	9.84570	**.70097**	*12*
49	.84072	**.69299**	.84198	**.69500**	.84324	**.69700**	.84448	**.69901**	.84572	**.70101**	*11*
50	.84075	**.69302**	.84200	**.69503**	.84326	**.69704**	.84450	**.69904**	.84574	**.70104**	*10*
51	.84077	**.69305**	.84203	**.69506**	.84328	**.69707**	.84452	**.69907**	.84576	**.70107**	*9*
+ **13′**	9.84079	**.69309**	9.84205	**.69510**	9.84330	**.69710**	9.84454	**.69911**	9.84578	**.70111**	*8*
53	.84081	**.69312**	.84207	**.69513**	.84332	**.69714**	.84456	**.69914**	.84581	**.70114**	*7*
54	.84083	**.69315**	.84209	**.69516**	.84334	**.69717**	.84459	**.69917**	.84583	**.70117**	*6*
55	.84085	**.69319**	.84211	**.69520**	.84336	**.69720**	.84461	**.69921**	.84585	**.70121**	*5*
+ **14′**	9.84087	**.69322**	9.84213	**.69523**	9.84338	**.69724**	9.84463	**.69924**	9.84587	**.70124**	*4*
57	.84089	**.69326**	.84215	**.69527**	.84340	**.69727**	.84465	**.69927**	.84589	**.70127**	*3*
58	.84091	**.69329**	.84217	**.69530**	.84342	**.69731**	.84467	**.69931**	.84591	**.70131**	*2*
59	.84093	**.69332**	.84219	**.69533**	.84344	**.69734**	.84469	**.69934**	.84593	**.70134**	*1*
+ **15′**	9.84096	**.69336**	9.84221	**.69537**	9.84346	**.69737**	9.84471	**.69937**	9.84595	**.70137**	*0*
	16h 29m		*16h 28m*		*16h 27m*		*16h 26m*		*16h 25m*		

TABLE 34.

Haversines.

s	7h 35m 113° 45′		7h 36m 114° 0′		7h 37m 114° 15′		7h 38m 114° 30′		7h 39m 114° 45′		s
	Log. Hav.	Nat. Hav.	Log. Hav.	Nat. Hav.	Log. Hav.	Nat. Hav.	Log. Hav.	Nat. Hav.	Log. Hav.	Nat. Hav.	
0	9.84595	.70137	9.84718	.70337	9.84841	.70536	9.84963	.70735	9.85085	.70933	60
1	.84597	.70141	.84720	.70340	.84843	.70539	.84965	.70738	.85087	.70936	59
2	.84599	.70144	.84722	.70343	.84845	.70543	.84967	.70741	.85089	.70940	58
3	.84601	.70147	.84724	.70347	.84847	.70546	.84969	.70745	.85091	.70943	57
+ 1′	9.84603	.70151	9.84726	.70350	9.84849	.70549	9.84971	.70748	9.85093	.70946	56
5	.84605	.70154	.84729	.70353	.84851	.70553	.84973	.70751	.85095	.70950	55
6	.84607	.70157	.84731	.70357	.84853	.70556	.84975	.70755	.85097	.70953	54
7	.84609	.70161	.84733	.70360	.84855	.70559	.84977	.70758	.85099	.70956	53
+ 2′	9.84611	.70164	9.84735	.70363	9.84857	.70562	9.84979	.70761	9.85101	.70959	52
9	.84613	.70167	.84737	.70367	.84859	.70566	.84982	.70764	.85103	.70963	51
10	.84616	.70171	.84739	.70370	.84861	.70569	.84984	.70768	.85105	.70966	50
11	.84618	.70174	.84741	.70373	.84863	.70572	.84986	.70771	.85107	.70969	49
+ 3′	9.84620	.70177	9.84743	.70377	9.84866	.70576	9.84988	.70774	9.85109	.70973	48
13	.84622	.70181	.84745	.70380	.84868	.70579	.84990	.70778	.85111	.70976	47
14	.84624	.70184	.84747	.70383	.84870	.70582	.84992	.70781	.85113	.70979	46
15	.84626	.70187	.84749	.70387	.84872	.70586	.84994	.70784	.85115	.70983	45
+ 4′	9.84628	.70191	9.84751	.70390	9.84874	.70589	9.84996	.70788	9.85117	.70986	44
17	.84630	.70194	.84753	.70393	.84876	.70592	.84998	.70791	.85119	.70989	43
18	.84632	.70197	.84755	.70397	.84878	.70596	.85000	.70794	.85121	.70992	42
19	.84634	.70201	.84757	.70400	.84880	.70599	.85002	.70798	.85123	.70996	41
+ 5′	9.84636	.70204	9.84759	.70403	9.84882	.70602	9.85004	.70801	9.85125	.70999	40
21	.84638	.70207	.84761	.70407	.84884	.70606	.85006	.70804	.85127	.71002	39
22	.84640	.70211	.84763	.70410	.84886	.70609	.85008	.70807	.85129	.71006	38
23	.84642	.70214	.84765	.70413	.84888	.70612	.85010	.70811	.85131	.71009	37
+ 6′	9.84644	.70217	9.84767	.70417	9.84890	.70615	9.85012	.70814	9.85133	.71012	36
25	.84646	.70221	.84770	.70420	.84892	.70619	.85014	.70817	.85135	.71016	35
26	.84648	.70224	.84772	.70423	.84894	.70622	.85016	.70821	.85137	.71019	34
27	.84651	.70227	.84774	.70426	.84896	.70625	.85018	.70824	.85139	.71022	33
+ 7′	9.84653	.70230	9.84776	.70430	9.84898	.70629	9.85020	.70827	9.85141	.71025	32
29	.84655	.70234	.84778	.70433	.84900	.70632	.85022	.70831	.85143	.71029	31
30	.84657	.70237	.84780	.70436	.84902	.70635	.85024	.70834	.85145	.71032	30
31	.84659	.70240	.84782	.70440	.84904	.70639	.85026	.70837	.85147	.71035	29
+ 8′	9.84661	.70244	9.84784	.70443	9.84906	.70642	9.85028	.70840	9.85149	.71039	28
33	.84663	.70247	.84786	.70446	.84908	.70645	.85030	.70844	.85151	.71042	27
34	.84665	.70250	.84788	.70450	.84910	.70649	.85032	.70847	.85153	.71045	26
35	.84667	.70254	.84790	.70453	.84912	.70652	.85034	.70850	.85155	.71049	25
+ 9′	9.84669	.70257	9.84792	.70456	9.84914	.70655	9.85036	.70854	9.85158	.71052	24
37	.84671	.70260	.84794	.70460	.84916	.70659	.85038	.70857	.85160	.71055	23
38	.84673	.70264	.84796	.70463	.84919	.70662	.85040	.70860	.85162	.71058	22
39	.84675	.70267	.84798	.70466	.84921	.70665	.85042	.70864	.85164	.71062	21
+ 10′	9.84677	.70270	9.84800	.70470	9.84923	.70668	9.85044	.70867	9.85166	.71065	20
41	.84679	.70274	.84802	.70473	.84925	.70672	.85046	.70870	.85168	.71068	19
42	.84681	.70277	.84804	.70476	.84927	.70675	.85048	.70874	.85170	.71072	18
43	.84683	.70280	.84806	.70480	.84929	.70678	.85050	.70877	.85172	.71075	17
+ 11′	9.84685	.70284	9.84808	.70483	9.84931	.70682	9.85052	.70880	9.85174	.71078	16
45	.84688	.70287	.84810	.70486	.84933	.70685	.85054	.70884	.85176	.71082	15
46	.84690	.70290	.84812	.70490	.84935	.70688	.85057	.70887	.85178	.71085	14
47	.84692	.70294	.84815	.70493	.84937	.70692	.85059	.70890	.85180	.71088	13
+ 12′	9.84694	.70297	9.84817	.70496	9.84939	.70695	9.85061	.70893	9.85182	.71091	12
49	.84696	.70300	.84819	.70499	.84941	.70698	.85063	.70897	.85184	.71095	11
50	.84698	.70304	.84821	.70503	.84943	.70702	.85065	.70900	.85186	.71098	10
51	.84700	.70307	.84823	.70506	.84945	.70705	.85067	.70903	.85188	.71101	9
+ 13′	9.84702	.70310	9.84825	.70509	9.84947	.70708	9.85069	.70907	9.85190	.71105	8
53	.84704	.70314	.84827	.70513	.84949	.70712	.85071	.70910	.85192	.71108	7
54	.84706	.70317	.84829	.70516	.84951	.70715	.85073	.70913	.85194	.71111	6
55	.84708	.70320	.84831	.70519	.84953	.70718	.85075	.70916	.85196	.71114	5
+ 14′	9.84710	.70324	9.84833	.70523	9.84955	.70721	9.85077	.70920	9.85198	.71118	4
57	.84712	.70327	.84835	.70526	.84957	.70725	.85079	.70923	.85200	.71121	3
58	.84714	.70330	.84837	.70529	.84959	.70729	.85081	.70926	.85202	.71124	2
59	.84716	.70333	.84839	.70533	.84961	.70731	.85083	.70930	.85204	.71128	1
+ 15′	9.84718	.70337	9.84841	.70536	9.84963	.70735	9.85085	.70933	9.85206	.71131	0
	16h 24m		16h 23m		16h 22m		16h 21m		16h 20m		

TABLE 34.

Haversines.

s	$7^h 40^m$ 115° 0′ Log. Hav.	Nat. Hav.	$7^h 41^m$ 115° 15′ Log. Hav.	Nat. Hav.	$7^h 42^m$ 115° 30′ Log. Hav.	Nat. Hav.	$7^h 43^m$ 115° 45′ Log. Hav.	Nat. Hav.	$7^h 44^m$ 116° 0′ Log. Hav.	Nat. Hav.	s
0	9.85206	**.71131**	9.85326	**.71328**	9.85446	**.71526**	9.85565	**.71722**	9.85684	**.71919**	60
1	.85208	**.71134**	.85328	**.71332**	.85448	**.71529**	.85567	**.71726**	.85686	**.71922**	59
2	.85210	**.71138**	.85330	**.71335**	.85450	**.71532**	.85569	**.71729**	.85688	**.71925**	58
3	.85212	**.71141**	.85332	**.71338**	.85452	**.71535**	.85571	**.71732**	.85690	**.71928**	57
+ 1′	9.85214	**.71144**	9.85334	**.71342**	9.85454	**.71539**	9.85573	**.71735**	9.85692	**.71932**	56
5	.85216	**.71147**	.85336	**.71345**	.85456	**.71542**	.85575	**.71739**	.85694	**.71935**	55
6	.85218	**.71151**	.85338	**.71348**	.85458	**.71545**	.85577	**.71742**	.85696	**.71938**	54
7	.85220	**.71154**	.85340	**.71351**	.85460	**.71549**	.85579	**.71745**	.85698	**.71941**	53
+ 2′	9.85222	**.71157**	9.85342	**.71355**	9.85462	**.71552**	9.85581	**.71748**	9.85700	**.71945**	52
9	.85224	**.71161**	.85344	**.71358**	.85464	**.71555**	.85583	**.71752**	.85702	**.71948**	51
10	.85226	**.71164**	.85346	**.71361**	.85466	**.71558**	.85585	**.71755**	.85704	**.71951**	50
11	.85228	**.71167**	.85348	**.71365**	.85468	**.71562**	.85587	**.71758**	.85706	**.71955**	49
+ 3′	9.85230	**.71170**	9.85350	**.71368**	9.85470	**.71565**	9.85589	**.71762**	9.85708	**.71958**	48
13	.85232	**.71174**	.85352	**.71371**	.85472	**.71568**	.85591	**.71765**	.85710	**.71961**	47
14	.85234	**.71177**	.85354	**.71374**	.85474	**.71571**	.85593	**.71768**	.85712	**.71964**	46
15	.85236	**.71180**	.85356	**.71378**	.85476	**.71575**	.85595	**.71771**	.85714	**.71968**	45
+ 4′	9.85238	**.71184**	9.85358	**.71381**	9.85478	**.71578**	9.85597	**.71775**	9.85716	**.71971**	44
17	.85240	**.71187**	.85360	**.71384**	.85480	**.71581**	.85599	**.71778**	.85718	**.71974**	43
18	.85242	**.71190**	.85362	**.71388**	.85482	**.71585**	.85601	**.71781**	.85720	**.71977**	42
19	.85244	**.71194**	.85364	**.71391**	.85484	**.71588**	.85603	**.71784**	.85722	**.71981**	41
+ 5′	9.85246	**.71197**	9.85366	**.71394**	9.85486	**.71591**	9.85605	**.71788**	9.85724	**.71984**	40
21	.85248	**.71200**	.85368	**.71397**	.85488	**.71594**	.85607	**.71791**	.85726	**.71987**	39
22	.85250	**.71203**	.85370	**.71401**	.85490	**.71598**	.85609	**.71794**	.85727	**.71990**	38
23	.85252	**.71207**	.85372	**.71404**	.85492	**.71601**	.85611	**.71798**	.85729	**.71994**	37
+ 6′	9.85254	**.71210**	9.85374	**.71407**	9.85494	**.71604**	9.85613	**.71801**	9.85731	**.71997**	36
25	.85256	**.71213**	.85376	**.71411**	.85496	**.71608**	.85615	**.71804**	.85733	**.72000**	35
26	.85258	**.71217**	.85378	**.71414**	.85498	**.71611**	.85617	**.71807**	.85735	**.72003**	34
27	.85260	**.71220**	.85380	**.71417**	.85500	**.71614**	.85619	**.71811**	.85737	**.72007**	33
+ 7′	9.85262	**.71223**	9.85382	**.71420**	9.85502	**.71617**	9.85621	**.71814**	9.85739	**.72010**	32
29	.85264	**.71226**	.85384	**.71424**	.85504	**.71621**	.85623	**.71817**	.85741	**.72013**	31
30	.85266	**.71230**	.85386	**.71427**	.85506	**.71624**	.85625	**.71820**	.85743	**.72017**	30
31	.85268	**.71233**	.85388	**.71430**	.85508	**.71627**	.85627	**.71824**	.85745	**.72020**	29
+ 8′	9.85270	**.71236**	9.85390	**.71434**	9.85510	**.71631**	9.85629	**.71827**	9.85747	**.72023**	28
33	.85272	**.71240**	.85392	**.71437**	.85512	**.71634**	.85631	**.71830**	.85749	**.72026**	27
34	.85274	**.71243**	.85394	**.71440**	.85514	**.71637**	.85633	**.71834**	.85751	**.72030**	26
35	.85276	**.71246**	.85396	**.71443**	.85516	**.71640**	.85635	**.71837**	.85753	**.72033**	25
+ 9′	9.85278	**.71249**	9.85398	**.71447**	9.85518	**.71644**	9.85637	**.71840**	9.85755	**.72036**	24
37	.85280	**.71253**	.85400	**.71450**	.85520	**.71647**	.85639	**.71843**	.85757	**.72039**	23
38	.85282	**.71256**	.85402	**.71453**	.85522	**.71650**	.85641	**.71847**	.85759	**.72043**	22
39	.85284	**.71259**	.85404	**.71456**	.85524	**.71653**	.85643	**.71850**	.85761	**.72046**	21
+ 10′	9.85286	**.71263**	9.85406	**.71460**	9.85526	**.71657**	9.85645	**.71853**	9.85763	**.72049**	20
41	.85288	**.71266**	.85408	**.71463**	.85528	**.71660**	.85647	**.71856**	.85765	**.72052**	19
42	.85290	**.71269**	.85410	**.71466**	.85530	**.71663**	.85649	**.71860**	.85767	**.72056**	18
43	.85292	**.71273**	.85412	**.71470**	.85532	**.71667**	.85651	**.71863**	.85769	**.72059**	17
+ 11′	9.85294	**.71276**	9.85414	**.71473**	9.85534	**.71670**	9.85653	**.71866**	9.85771	**.72062**	16
45	.85296	**.71279**	.85416	**.71476**	.85536	**.71673**	.85654	**.71870**	.85773	**.72066**	15
46	.85298	**.71282**	.85418	**.71480**	.85538	**.71676**	.85656	**.71873**	.85775	**.72069**	14
47	.85300	**.71286**	.85420	**.71483**	.85540	**.71680**	.85658	**.71876**	.85777	**.72072**	13
+ 12′	9.85302	**.71289**	9.85422	**.71486**	9.85542	**.71683**	9.85660	**.71879**	9.85779	**.72075**	12
49	.85304	**.71292**	.85424	**.71489**	.85544	**.71686**	.85662	**.71883**	.85781	**.72079**	11
50	.85306	**.71296**	.85426	**.71493**	.85546	**.71690**	.85664	**.71886**	.85783	**.72082**	10
51	.85308	**.71299**	.85428	**.71496**	.85548	**.71693**	.85666	**.71889**	.85785	**.72085**	9
+ 13′	9.85310	**.71302**	9.85430	**.71499**	9.85550	**.71696**	9.85668	**.71892**	9.85787	**.72088**	8
53	.85312	**.71305**	.85432	**.71503**	.85552	**.71699**	.85670	**.71896**	.85788	**.72092**	7
54	.85314	**.71309**	.85434	**.71506**	.85554	**.71703**	.85672	**.71899**	.85790	**.72095**	6
55	.85316	**.71312**	.85436	**.71509**	.85555	**.71706**	.85674	**.71902**	.85792	**.72098**	5
+ 14′	9.85318	**.71315**	9.85438	**.71512**	9.85557	**.71709**	9.85676	**.71905**	9.85794	**.72101**	4
57	.85320	**.71319**	.85440	**.71516**	.85559	**.71712**	.85678	**.71909**	.85796	**.72105**	3
58	.85322	**.71322**	.85442	**.71519**	.85561	**.71716**	.85680	**.71912**	.85798	**.72108**	2
59	.85324	**.71325**	.85444	**.71522**	.85563	**.71719**	.85682	**.71915**	.85800	**.72111**	1
+ 15′	9.85326	**.71328**	9.85446	**.71526**	9.85565	**.71722**	9.85684	**.71919**	9.85802	**.72114**	0
	$16^h 19^m$		$16^h 18^m$		$16^h 17^m$		$16^h 16^m$		$16^h 15^m$		

TABLE 34.

Haversines.

s	$7^h 45^m$ 116° 15′		$7^h 46^m$ 116° 30′		$7^h 47^m$ 116° 45′		$7^h 48^m$ 117° 0′		$7^h 49^m$ 117° 15′		
s	Log. Hav.	Nat. Hav.	Log. Hav.	Nat. Hav.	Log. Hav.	Nat. Hav.	Log. Hav.	Nat. Hav.	Log. Hav.	Nat. Hav.	s
0	9.85802	.72114	9.85920	.72310	9.86037	.72505	9.86153	.72700	9.86269	.72894	60
1	.85804	.72118	.85922	.72313	.86039	.72508	.86155	.72703	.86271	.72897	59
2	.85806	.72121	.85924	.72316	.86041	.72511	.86157	.72706	.86273	.72900	58
3	.85808	.72124	.85926	.72320	.86043	.72515	.86159	.72709	.86275	.72903	57
+ 1′	9.85810	.72127	9.85928	.72323	9.86045	.72518	9.86161	.72712	9.86277	.72907	56
5	.85812	.72131	.85930	.72326	.86046	.72521	.86163	.72716	.86279	.72910	55
6	.85814	.72134	.85931	.72329	.86048	.72524	.86165	.72719	.86281	.72913	54
7	.85816	.72137	.85933	.72333	.86050	.72528	.86167	.72722	.86282	.72916	53
+ 2′	9.85818	.72141	9.85935	.72336	9.86052	.72531	9.86169	.72725	9.86284	.72920	52
9	.85820	.72144	.85937	.72339	.86054	.72534	.86171	.72729	.86286	.72923	51
10	.85822	.72147	.85939	.72342	.86056	.72537	.86173	.72732	.86288	.72926	50
11	.85824	.72150	.85941	.72346	.86058	.72541	.86174	.72735	.86290	.72929	49
+ 3′	9.85826	.72154	9.85943	.72349	9.86060	.72544	9.86176	.72738	9.86292	.72932	48
13	.85828	.72157	.85945	.72352	.86062	.72547	.86178	.72742	.86294	.72936	47
14	.85830	.72160	.85947	.72355	.86064	.72550	.86180	.72745	.86296	.72939	46
15	.85832	.72163	.85949	.72359	.86066	.72554	.86182	.72748	.86298	.72942	45
+ 4′	9.85834	.72167	9.85951	.72362	9.86068	.72557	9.86184	.72751	9.86300	.72945	44
17	.85836	.72170	.85953	.72365	.86070	.72560	.86186	.72755	.86302	.72949	43
18	.85838	.72173	.85955	.72368	.86072	.72563	.86188	.72758	.86304	.72953	42
19	.85840	.72176	.85957	.72372	.86074	.72567	.86190	.72761	.86306	.72955	41
+ 5′	9.85841	.72180	9.85959	.72375	9.86076	.72570	9.86192	.72764	9.86307	.72958	40
21	.85843	.72183	.85961	.72378	.86078	.72573	.86194	.72768	.86309	.72962	39
22	.85845	.72186	.85963	.72381	.86080	.72576	.86196	.72771	.86311	.72965	38
23	.85847	.72189	.85965	.72385	.86081	.72580	.86198	.72774	.86313	.72968	37
+ 6′	9.85849	.72193	9.85967	.72388	9.86083	.72583	9.86200	.72777	9.86315	.72971	36
25	.85851	.72196	.85969	.72391	.86085	.72586	.86201	.72780	.86317	.72974	35
26	.85853	.72199	.85971	.72394	.86087	.72589	.86203	.72784	.86319	.72978	34
27	.85855	.72202	.85972	.72398	.86089	.72593	.86205	.72787	.86321	.72981	33
+ 7′	9.85857	.72206	9.85974	.72401	9.86091	.72596	9.86207	.72790	9.86323	.72984	32
29	.85859	.72209	.85976	.72404	.86093	.72599	.86209	.72793	.86325	.72987	31
30	.85861	.72212	.85978	.72407	.86095	.72602	.86211	.72797	.86327	.72991	30
31	.85863	.72215	.85980	.72411	.86097	.72606	.86213	.72800	.86329	.72994	29
+ 8′	9.85865	.72219	9.85982	.72414	9.86099	.72609	9.86215	.72803	9.86331	.72997	28
33	.85867	.72222	.85984	.72417	.86101	.72612	.86217	.72806	.86332	.73000	27
34	.85869	.72225	.85986	.72420	.86103	.72615	.86219	.72810	.86334	.73004	26
35	.85871	.72229	.85988	.72424	.86105	.72618	.86221	.72813	.86336	.73007	25
+ 9′	9.85873	.72232	9.85990	.72427	9.86107	.72622	9.86223	.72816	9.86338	.73010	24
37	.85875	.72235	.85992	.72430	.86109	.72625	.86225	.72819	.86340	.73013	23
38	.85877	.72238	.85994	.72433	.86111	.72628	.86227	.72823	.86342	.73016	22
39	.85879	.72242	.85996	.72437	.86112	.72631	.86229	.72826	.86344	.73020	21
+ 10′	9.85881	.72245	9.85998	.72440	9.86114	.72635	9.86230	.72829	9.86346	.73023	20
41	.85883	.72248	.86000	.72443	.86116	.72638	.86232	.72832	.86348	.73026	19
42	.85885	.72251	.86002	.72446	.86118	.72641	.86234	.72835	.86350	.73029	18
43	.85887	.72255	.86004	.72450	.86120	.72644	.86236	.72839	.86352	73033	17
+ 11′	9.85888	.72258	9.86006	.72453	9.86122	.72648	9.86238	.72842	9.86354	.73036	16
45	.85890	.72261	.86008	.72456	.86124	.72651	.86240	.72845	.86355	.73039	15
46	.85892	.72264	.86010	.72459	.86126	.72654	.86242	.72848	.86357	.73042	14
47	.85894	.72268	.86011	.72463	.86128	.72657	.86244	.72852	.86359	.73046	13
+ 12′	9.85896	.72271	9.86013	.72466	9.86130	.72661	9.86246	.72855	9.86361	.73049	12
49	.85898	.72274	.86015	.72469	.86132	.72664	.86248	.72858	.86363	.73052	11
50	.85900	.72277	.86017	.72472	.86134	.72667	.86250	.72861	.86365	.73055	10
51	.85902	.72281	.86019	72476	.86136	.72670	.86252	.72865	.86367	.73058	9
+ 13′	9.85904	.72284	9.86021	.72479	9.86138	.72674	9.86254	.72868	9.86369	.73062	8
53	.85906	.72287	.86023	.72482	.86140	.72677	.86256	.72871	.86371	.73065	7
54	.85908	.72290	.86025	.72485	.86142	.72680	.86257	.72874	.86373	.73068	6
55	.85910	.72294	.86027	.72489	.86143	.72683	.86259	.72878	.86375	.73071	5
+ 14′	9.85912	.72297	9.86029	.72492	9.86145	.72687	9.86261	.72881	9.86377	.73076	4
57	.85914	.72300	.86031	.72495	.86147	.72690	.86263	.72884	.86379	.73078	3
58	.85916	.72303	.86033	.72498	.86149	.72693	.86265	.72887	.86380	.73081	2
59	.85918	72307	.86035	.72502	.86151	.72696	.86267	.72890	.86382	.73084	1
+ 15′	9.85920	.72310	9.86037	.72505	9.86153	.72700	9.86269	.72894	9.86384	.73087	0
	$16^h 14^m$		$16^h 13^m$		$16^h 12^m$		$16^h 11^m$		$16^h 10^m$		

541524°—43——48

TABLE 34.

Haversines.

s	7h 50m 117° 30′		7h 51m 117° 45′		7h 52m 118° 0′		7h 53m 118° 15′		7h 54m 118° 30′		s
	Log. Hav.	Nat. Hav.	Log. Hav.	Nat. Hav.	Log. Hav	Nat. Hav	Log. Hav.	Nat. Hav.	Log. Hav.	Nat. Hav.	
0	9.86384	.73087	9.86499	.73281	9.86613	.73474	9.86727	.73666	9.86840	.73858	60
1	.86386	.73091	.86501	.73284	.86615	.73477	.86729	.73669	.86842	.73861	59
2	.86388	.73094	.86503	.73287	.86617	.73480	.86730	.73672	.86843	.73864	58
3	.86390	.73097	.86505	.73290	.86619	.73483	.86732	.73676	.86845	.73868	57
+ 1′	9.86392	.73100	9.86507	.73294	9.86621	.73486	9.86734	.73679	9.86847	.73871	56
5	.86394	.73104	.86509	.73297	.86623	.73490	.86736	.73682	.86849	.73874	55
6	.86396	.73107	.86510	.73300	.86625	.73493	.86738	.73685	.86851	.73877	54
7	.86398	.73110	.86512	.73303	.86626	.73496	.86740	.73688	.86853	.73880	53
+ 2′	9.86400	.73113	9.86514	.73306	9.86628	.73499	9.86742	.73692	9.86855	.73884	52
9	.86401	.73116	.86516	.73310	.86630	.73502	.86744	.73695	.86857	.73887	51
10	.86403	.73120	.86518	.73313	.86632	.73506	.86746	.73698	.86859	.73890	50
11	.86405	.73123	.86520	.73316	.86634	.73509	.86747	.73701	.86860	.73893	49
+ 3′	9.86407	.73126	9.86522	.73319	9.86636	.73512	9.86749	.73704	9.86862	.73896	48
13	.86409	.73129	.86524	.73323	.86638	.73515	.86751	.73708	.86864	.73899	47
14	.86411	.73133	.86526	.73326	.86640	.73519	.86753	.73711	.86866	.73903	46
15	.86413	.73136	.86528	.73329	.86642	.73522	.86755	.73714	.86868	.73906	45
+ 4′	9.86415	.73139	9.86529	.73332	9.86643	.73525	9.86757	.73717	9.86870	.73909	44
17	.86417	.73142	.86531	.73335	.86645	.73528	.86759	.73720	.86872	.73912	43
18	.86419	.73145	.86533	.73339	.86647	.73531	.86761	.73724	.86874	.73915	42
19	.86421	.73149	.86535	.73342	.86649	.73535	.86763	.73727	.86875	.73919	41
+ 5′	9.86423	.73152	9.86537	.73345	9.86651	.73538	9.86764	.73730	9.86877	.73922	40
21	.86424	.73155	.86539	.73348	.86653	.73541	.86766	.73733	.86879	.73925	39
22	.86426	.73158	.86541	.73351	.86655	.73544	.86768	.73736	.86881	.73928	38
23	.86428	.73162	.86543	.73355	.86657	.73547	.86770	.73740	.86883	.73931	37
+ 6′	9.86430	.73165	9.86545	.73358	9.86659	.73551	9.86772	.73743	9.86885	.73935	36
25	.86432	.73168	.86547	.73361	.86661	.73554	.86774	.73746	.86887	.73938	35
26	.86434	.73171	.86549	.73364	.86662	.73557	.86776	.73749	.86889	.73941	34
27	.86436	.73174	.86550	.73368	.86664	.73560	.86778	.73752	.86890	.73944	33
+ 7′	9.86438	.73178	9.86552	.73371	9.86666	.73563	9.86780	.73756	9.86892	.73947	32
29	.86440	.73181	.86554	.73374	.86668	.73567	.86781	.73759	.86894	.73951	31
30	.86442	.73184	.86556	.73377	.86670	.73570	.86783	.73762	.86896	.73954	30
31	.86444	.73187	.86558	.73380	.86672	.73573	.86785	.73765	.86898	.73957	29
+ 8′	9.86446	.73191	9.86560	.73384	9.86674	.73576	9.86787	.73768	9.86900	.73960	28
33	.86447	.73194	.86562	.73387	.86676	.73579	.86789	.73772	.86902	.73963	27
34	.86449	.73197	.86564	.73390	.86678	.73583	.86791	.73775	.86904	.73967	26
35	.86451	.73200	.86566	.73393	.86679	.73586	.86793	.73778	.86905	.73970	25
+ 9′	9.86453	.73203	9.86568	.73396	9.86681	.73589	9.86795	.73781	9.86907	.73973	24
37	.86455	.73207	.86569	.73400	.86683	.73592	.86796	.73784	.86909	.73976	23
38	.86457	.73210	.86571	.73403	.86685	.73595	.86798	.73788	.86911	.73979	22
39	.86459	.73213	.86573	.73406	.86687	.73599	.86800	.73791	.86913	.73982	21
+ 10′	9.86461	.73216	9.86575	.73409	9.86689	.73602	9.86802	.73794	9.86915	.73986	20
41	.86463	.73220	.86577	.73413	.86691	.73605	.86804	.73797	.86917	.73989	19
42	.86465	.73223	.86579	.73416	.86693	.73608	.86806	.73800	.86919	.73992	18
43	.86467	.73226	.86581	.73419	.86695	.73611	.86808	.73804	.86920	.73995	17
+ 11′	9.86468	.73229	9.86583	.73422	9.86696	.73615	9.86810	.73807	9.86922	.73998	16
45	.86470	.73232	.86585	.73425	.86698	.73618	.86812	.73810	.86924	.74002	15
46	.86472	.73236	.86587	.73429	.86700	.73621	.86813	.73813	.86926	.74005	14
47	.86474	.73239	.86588	.73432	.86702	.73624	.86815	.73816	.86928	.74008	13
+ 12′	9.86476	.73242	9.86590	.73435	9.86704	.73628	9.86817	.73820	9.86930	.74011	12
49	.86478	.73245	.86592	.73438	.86706	.73631	.86819	.73823	.86932	.74014	11
50	.86480	.73249	.86594	.73441	.86708	.73634	.86821	.73826	.86933	.74018	10
51	.86482	.73252	.86596	.73445	.86710	.73637	.86823	.73829	.86935	.74021	9
+ 13′	9.86484	.73255	9.86598	.73448	9.86712	.73640	9.86825	.73832	9.86937	.74024	8
53	.86486	.73258	.86600	.73451	.86713	.73644	.86827	.73836	.86939	.74027	7
54	.86488	.73261	.86602	.73454	.86715	.73647	.86828	.73839	.86941	.74030	6
55	.86489	.73265	.86604	.73458	.86717	.73650	.86830	.73842	.86943	.74033	5
+ 14′	9.86491	.73268	9.86606	.73461	9.86719	.73653	9.86832	.73845	9.86945	.74037	4
57	.86493	.73271	.86607	.73464	.86721	.73656	.86834	.73848	.86947	.74040	3
58	.86495	.73274	.86609	.73467	.86723	.73660	.86836	.73852	.86948	.74043	2
59	.86497	.73278	.86611	.73470	.86725	.73663	.86838	.73855	.86950	.74046	1
+ 15′	9.86499	.73281	9.86613	.73474	9.86727	.73666	9.86840	.73858	9.86952	.74049	0
	16h 9m		16h 8m		16h 7m		16h 6m		16h 5m		

TABLE 34.

Haversines.

s	$7^h 55^m$ 118° 45′		$7^h 56^m$ 119° 0′		$7^h 57^m$ 119° 15′		$7^h 58^m$ 119° 30′		$7^h 59^m$ 119° 45′		
s	Log. Hav.	Nat. Hav.	Log. Hav.	Nat. Hav.	Log. Hav.	Nat. Hav.	Log. Hav.	Nat. Hav.	Log. Hav.	Nat. Hav.	s
0	9.86952	.74049	9.87064	.74240	9.87175	.74431	9.87286	.74621	9.87396	.74811	60
1	.86954	.74052	.87066	.74244	.87177	.74434	.87288	.74624	.87398	.74814	59
2	.86956	.74056	.87068	.74247	.87179	.74437	.87290	.74628	.87400	.74817	58
3	.86958	.74059	.87070	.74250	.87181	.74441	.87292	.74631	.87402	.74820	57
+ 1′	9.86960	.74062	9.87072	.74253	9.87183	.74444	9.87294	.74634	9.87404	.74823	56
5	.86962	.74065	.87073	.74256	.87185	.74447	.87295	.74637	.87406	.74827	55
6	.86963	.74069	.87075	.74260	.87187	.74450	.87297	.74640	.87407	.74830	54
7	.86965	.74072	.87077	.74263	.87188	.74453	.87299	.74643	.87409	.74833	53
+ 2′	9.86967	.74075	9.87079	.74266	9.87190	.74456	9.87301	.74646	9.87411	.74836	52
9	.86969	.74078	.87081	.74269	.87192	.74460	.87303	.74650	.87413	.74839	51
10	.86971	.74081	.87083	.74272	.87194	.74463	.87305	.74653	.87415	.74842	50
11	.86973	.74084	.87085	.74275	.87196	.74466	.87306	.74656	.87417	.74846	49
+ 3′	9.86975	.74088	9.87086	.74279	9.87198	.74469	9.87308	.74659	9.87418	.74849	48
13	.86977	.74091	.87088	.74282	.87199	.74472	.87310	.74662	.87420	.74852	47
14	.86978	.74094	.87090	.74285	.87201	.74475	.87312	.74665	.87422	.74855	46
15	.86980	.74097	.87092	.74288	.87203	.74479	.87314	.74669	.87424	.74858	45
+ 4′	9.86982	.74100	9.87094	.74291	9.87205	.74482	9.87316	.74672	9.87426	.74861	44
17	.86984	.74104	.87096	.74294	.87207	.74485	.87318	.74675	.87428	.74864	43
18	.86986	.74107	.87098	.74298	.87209	.74488	.87319	.74678	.87429	.74868	42
19	.86988	.74110	.87100	.74301	.87211	.74491	.87321	.74681	.87431	74871	41
+ 5′	9.86990	.74113	9.87101	.74304	9.87212	.74494	9.87323	.74684	9.87433	.74874	40
21	.86991	.74116	.87103	.74307	.87214	.74498	.87325	.74688	.87435	.74877	39
22	.86993	.74120	.87105	.74310	.87216	.74501	.87327	.74691	.87437	.74880	38
23	.86995	.74123	.87107	.74314	.87218	.74504	.87329	.74694	.87439	.74883	37
+ 6′	9.86997	.74126	9.87109	.74317	9.87220	.74507	9.87330	.74697	9.87440	.74887	36
25	.86999	.74129	.87111	.74320	.87222	.74510	.87332	.74700	.87442	.74890	35
26	.87001	.74132	.87112	.74323	.87224	.74514	.87334	.74703	.87444	.74893	34
27	.87003	.74135	.87114	.74326	.87225	.74517	.87336	.74707	.87446	.74896	33
+ 7′	9.87004	.74139	9.87116	.74329	9.87227	.74520	9.87338	.74710	9.87448	.74899	32
29	.87006	.74142	.87118	.74333	.87229	.74523	.87340	.74713	.87450	.74902	31
30	.87008	.74145	.87120	.74336	.87231	.74526	.87341	.74716	.87451	.74905	30
31	.87010	.74148	.87122	.74339	.87233	.74529	.87343	.74719	.87453	.74908	29
+ 8′	9.87012	.74151	9.87124	.74342	9.87235	.74533	9.87345	.74722	9.87455	.74912	28
33	.87014	.74155	.87125	.74345	.87236	.74536	.87347	.74726	.87457	.74915	27
34	.87016	.74158	.87127	.74349	.87238	.74539	.87349	.74729	.87459	.74918	26
35	.87018	.74161	.87129	.74352	.87240	.74542	.87351	.74732	.87460	.74921	25
+ 9′	9.87019	.74164	9.87131	.74355	9.87242	.74545	9.87352	.74735	9.87462	.74924	24
37	.87021	.74167	.87133	.74358	.87244	.74548	.87354	.74738	.87464	.74928	23
38	.87023	.74170	.87135	.74361	.87246	.74552	.87356	.74741	.87466	.74931	22
39	.87025	.74174	.87137	.74364	.87248	.74555	.87358	.74744	.87468	.74934	21
+ 10′	9.87027	.74177	9.87138	.74368	9.87249	.74558	9.87360	.74748	9.87470	.74937	20
41	.87029	.74180	.87140	.74371	.87251	.74561	.87362	.74751	.87471	.74940	19
42	.87031	.74183	.87142	.74374	.87253	.74564	.87363	.74754	.87473	.74943	18
43	.87032	.74186	.87144	.74377	.87255	.74567	.87365	.74757	.87475	.74946	17
+ 11′	9.87034	.74190	9.87146	.74380	9.87257	.74571	9.87367	.74760	9.87477	.74950	16
45	.87036	.74193	.87148	.74383	.87259	.74574	.87369	.74763	.87479	.74953	15
46	.87038	.74196	.87149	.74387	.87260	.74577	.87371	.74767	.87481	.74956	14
47	.87040	.74199	.87151	.74390	.87262	.74580	.87373	.74770	.87482	.74959	13
+ 12′	9.87042	.74202	9.87153	.74393	9.87264	.74583	9.87374	.74773	9.87484	.74962	12
49	.87044	.74205	.87155	.74396	.87266	.74586	.87376	.74776	.87486	.74965	11
50	.87045	.74209	.87157	.74399	.87268	.74590	.87378	.74779	.87488	.74969	10
51	.87047	.74212	.87159	.74402	.87270	.74593	.87380	.74782	.87490	.74972	9
+ 13′	9.87049	.74215	9.87161	.74406	9.87271	.74596	9.87382	.74786	9.87492	.74975	8
53	.87051	.74218	.87162	.74409	.87273	.74599	.87384	.74789	.87493	.74978	7
54	.87053	.74221	.87164	.74412	.87275	.74602	.87385	.74792	.87495	.74981	6
55	.87055	.74225	.87166	.74415	.87277	.74605	.87387	.74795	.87497	.74984	5
+ 14′	9.87057	.74228	9.87168	.74418	9.87279	.74609	9.87389	.74798	9.87499	.74987	4
57	.87059	.74231	.87170	.74422	.87281	.74612	.87391	.74801	.87501	.74991	3
58	.87060	.74234	.87172	.74425	.87283	.74615	.87393	.74805	.87502	.74994	2
59	.87062	.74237	.87174	.74428	.87284	.74618	.87395	.74808	.87504	.74997	1
+ 15′	9.87064	.74240	9.87175	.74431	9.87286	.74621	9.87396	.74811	9.87506	.75000	0
	$16^h 4^m$		$16^h 3^m$		$16^h 2^m$		$16^h 1^m$		$16^h 0^m$		

TABLE 34.

Haversines.

s ′	8h 0m 120° 0′ Log. Hav.	Nat. Hav.	8h 2m 120° 30′ Log. Hav.	Nat. Hav.	8h 4m 121° 0′ Log. Hav.	Nat. Hav.	8h 6m 121° 30′ Log. Hav.	Nat. Hav.	8h 8m 122° 0′ Log. Hav.	Nat. Hav.	s
0 0	9.87506	**0.75000**	9.87724	**0.75377**	9.87939	**0.75752**	9.88153	**0.76125**	9.88364	**0.76496**	60
2	.87510	**.75006**	.87727	**.75383**	.87943	**.75758**	.88156	**.76131**	.88367	**.76502**	58
4+ 1	.87513	**.75013**	.87731	**.75389**	.87947	**.75764**	.88160	**.76137**	.88371	**.76508**	56
6	.87517	**.75019**	.87735	**.75396**	.87950	**.75771**	.88163	**.76144**	.88374	**.76514**	54
8+ 2	9.87521	**0.75025**	9.87738	**0.75402**	9.87954	**0.75777**	9.88167	**0.76150**	9.88378	**0.76521**	52
10	.87524	**.75032**	.87742	**.75408**	.87957	**.75783**	.88170	**.76156**	.88381	**.76527**	50
12+ 3	.87528	**.75038**	.87745	**.75415**	.87961	**.75789**	.88174	**.76162**	.88385	**.76533**	48
14	.87532	**.75044**	.87749	**.75421**	.87964	**.75795**	.88177	**.76168**	.88388	**.76539**	46
16+ 4	9.87535	**0.75050**	9.87753	**0.75427**	9.87968	**0.75802**	9.88181	**0.76175**	9.88392	**0.76545**	44
18	.87539	**.75057**	.87756	**.75433**	.87971	**.75808**	.88185	**.76181**	.88395	**.76551**	42
20+ 5	.87543	**.75063**	.87760	**.75440**	.87975	**.75814**	.88188	**.76187**	.88399	**.76558**	40
22	.87546	**.75069**	.87764	**.75446**	.87979	**.75820**	.88192	**.76193**	.88402	**.76564**	38
24+ 6	9.87550	**0.75075**	9.87767	**0.75452**	9.87982	**0.75827**	9.88195	**0.76199**	9.88406	**0.76570**	36
26	.87553	**.75082**	.87771	**.75458**	.87986	**.75833**	.88199	**.76205**	.88409	**.76576**	34
28+ 7	.87557	**.75088**	.87774	**.75465**	.87989	**.75839**	.88202	**.76212**	.88413	**.76582**	32
30	.87561	**.75094**	.87778	**.75471**	.87993	**.75845**	.88206	**.76218**	.88416	**.76588**	30
32+ 8	9.87564	**0.75101**	9.87782	**0.75477**	9.87996	**0.75852**	9.88209	**0.76224**	9.88420	**0.76595**	28
34	.87568	**.75107**	.87785	**.75483**	.88000	**.75858**	.88213	**.76230**	.88423	**.76601**	26
36+ 9	.87572	**.75113**	.87789	**.75490**	.88004	**.75864**	.88216	**.76236**	.88427	**.76607**	24
38	.87575	**.75120**	.87792	**.75496**	.88007	**.75870**	.88220	**.76243**	.88430	**.76613**	22
40+10	9.87579	**0.75126**	9.87796	**0.75502**	9.88011	**0.75876**	9.88223	**0.76249**	9.88434	**0.76619**	20
42	.87583	**.75132**	.87800	**.75508**	.88014	**.75883**	.88227	**.76255**	.88437	**.76625**	18
44+11	.87586	**.75138**	.87803	**.75515**	.88018	**.75889**	.88230	**.76261**	.88441	**.76632**	16
46	.87590	**.75145**	.87807	**.75521**	.88021	**.75895**	.88234	**.76267**	.88444	**.76638**	14
48+12	9.87593	**0.75151**	9.87810	**0.75527**	9.88025	**0.75901**	9.88237	**0.76274**	9.88448	**0.76644**	12
50	.87597	**.75157**	.87814	**.75533**	.88029	**.75908**	.88241	**.76280**	.88451	**.76650**	10
52+13	.87601	**.75164**	.87818	**.75540**	.88032	**.75914**	.88244	**.76286**	.88455	**.76656**	8
54	.87604	**.75170**	.87821	**.75546**	.88036	**.75920**	.88248	**.76292**	.88458	**.76662**	6
56+14	9.87608	**0.75176**	9.87825	**0.75552**	9.88039	**0.75926**	9.88252	**0.76298**	9.88462	**0.76668**	4
58	9.87612	**0.75182**	9.87828	**0.75558**	9.88043	**0.75932**	9.88255	**0.76305**	9.88465	**0.76675**	2
	15h 59m		15h 57m		15h 55m		15h 53m		15h 51m		

s ′	8h 1m 120° 0′ Log. Hav.	Nat. Hav.	8h 3m 120° 30′ Log. Hav.	Nat. Hav.	8h 5m 121° 0′ Log. Hav.	Nat. Hav.	8h 7m 121° 30′ Log. Hav.	Nat. Hav.	8h 9m 122° 0′ Log. Hav.	Nat. Hav.	s
0+15	9.87615	**0.75189**	9.87832	**0.75565**	9.88046	**0.75939**	9.88259	**0.76311**	9.88469	**0.76681**	60
2	.87619	**.75195**	.87835	**.75571**	.88050	**.75945**	.88262	**.76317**	.88472	**.76687**	58
4+16	.87623	**.75201**	.87839	**.75577**	.88053	**.75951**	.88266	**.76323**	.88476	**.76693**	56
6	.87626	**.75208**	.87843	**.75583**	.88057	**.75957**	.88269	**.76329**	.88479	**.76699**	54
8+17	9.87630	**0.75214**	9.87846	**0.75590**	9.88061	**0.75964**	9.88273	**0.76335**	9.88483	**0.76705**	52
10	.87633	**.75220**	.87850	**.75596**	.88064	**.75970**	.88276	**.76342**	.88486	**.76711**	50
12+18	.87637	**.75226**	.87853	**.75602**	.88068	**.75976**	.88280	**.76348**	.88490	**.76718**	48
14	.87641	**.75233**	.87857	**.75608**	.88071	**.75982**	.88283	**.76354**	.88493	**.76724**	46
16+19	9.87644	**0.75239**	9.87861	**0.75615**	9.88075	**0.75988**	9.88287	**0.76360**	9.88496	**0.76730**	44
18	.87648	**.75245**	.87864	**.75621**	.88078	**.75995**	.88290	**.76366**	.88500	**.76736**	42
20+20	.87652	**.75251**	.87868	**.75627**	.88082	**.76001**	.88294	**.76373**	.88503	**.76742**	40
22	.87655	**.75258**	.87871	**.75633**	.88085	**.76007**	.88297	**.76379**	.88507	**.76748**	38
24+21	9.87659	**0.75264**	9.87875	**0.75640**	9.88089	**0.76013**	9.88301	**0.76385**	9.88510	**0.76754**	36
26	.87662	**.75270**	.87879	**.75646**	.88092	**.76019**	.88304	**.76391**	.88514	**.76761**	34
28+22	.87666	**.75277**	.87882	**.75652**	.88096	**.76026**	.88308	**.76397**	.88517	**.76767**	32
30	.87670	**.75283**	.87886	**.75658**	.88100	**.76032**	.88311	**.76403**	.88521	**.76773**	30
32+23	9.87673	**0.75289**	9.87889	**0.75665**	9.88103	**0.76038**	9.88315	**0.76410**	9.88524	**0.76779**	28
34	.87677	**.75295**	.87893	**.75671**	.88107	**.76044**	.88318	**.76416**	.88528	**.76785**	26
36+24	.87680	**.75302**	.87896	**.75677**	.88110	**.76050**	.88322	**.76422**	.88531	**.76791**	24
38	.87684	**.75308**	.87900	**.75683**	.88114	**.76057**	.88325	**.76428**	.88535	**.76797**	22
40+25	9.87688	**0.75314**	9.87904	**0.75690**	9.88117	**0.76063**	9.88329	**0.76434**	9.88538	**0.76804**	20
42	.87691	**.75321**	.87907	**.75696**	.88121	**.76069**	.88332	**.76440**	.88542	**.76810**	18
44+26	.87695	**.75327**	.87911	**.75702**	.88124	**.76075**	.88336	**.76447**	.88545	**.76816**	16
46	.87699	**.75333**	.87914	**.75708**	.88128	**.76082**	.88339	**.76453**	.88549	**.76822**	14
48+27	9.87702	**0.75339**	9.87918	**0.75714**	9.88131	**0.76088**	9.88343	**0.76459**	9.88552	**0.76828**	12
50	.87706	**.75346**	.87921	**.75721**	.88135	**.76094**	.88346	**.76465**	.88556	**.76834**	10
52+28	.87709	**.75352**	.87925	**.75727**	.88139	**.76100**	.88350	**.76471**	.88559	**.76840**	8
54	.87713	**.75358**	.87929	**.75733**	.88142	**.76106**	.88353	**.76477**	.88562	**.76847**	6
56+29	9.87717	**0.75364**	9.87932	**0.75739**	9.88146	**0.76113**	9.88357	**0.76484**	9.88566	**0.76853**	4
58	.87720	**.75371**	.87936	**.75746**	.88149	**.76119**	.88360	**.76490**	.88569	**.76859**	2
60+30	9.87724	**0.75377**	9.87939	**0.75752**	9.88153	**0.76125**	9.88364	**0.76496**	9.88573	**0.76865**	0
	15h 58m		15h 56m		15h 54m		15h 52m		15h 50m		

TABLE 34.

Haversines.

s ′	$8^h 10^m$ 122° 30′		$8^h 12^m$ 123° 0′		$8^h 14^m$ 123° 30′		$8^h 16^m$ 124° 0′		$8^h 18^m$ 124° 30′		s
	Log. Hav.	Nat. Hav.	Log. Hav.	Nat. Hav.	Log. Hav.	Nat. Hav.	Log. Hav.	Nat. Hav.	Log. Hav.	Nat. Hav.	
0 0	9.88573	**0.76865**	9.88780	**0.77232**	9.88984	**0.77597**	9.89187	**0.77960**	9.89387	**0.78320**	60
2	.88576	**.76871**	.88783	**.77238**	.88988	**.77603**	.89190	**.77966**	.89391	**.78326**	58
4+ 1	.88580	**.76877**	.88787	**.77244**	.88991	**.77609**	.89194	**.77972**	.89394	**.78332**	56
6	.88583	**.76883**	.88790	**.77250**	.88995	**.77615**	.89197	**.77978**	.89397	**.78338**	54
8+ 2	9.88587	**0.76890**	9.88793	**0.77256**	9.88998	**0.77621**	9.89200	**0.77984**	9.89400	**0.78344**	52
10	.88590	**.76896**	.88797	**.77262**	.89001	**.77627**	.89204	**.77990**	.89404	**.78350**	50
12+ 3	.88594	**.76902**	.88800	**.77269**	.89005	**.77633**	.89207	**.77996**	.89407	**.78356**	48
14	.88597	**.76908**	.88804	**.77275**	.89008	**.77639**	.89210	**.78002**	.89411	**.78362**	46
16+ 4	9.88600	**0.76914**	9.88807	**0.77281**	9.89012	**0.77645**	9.89214	**0.78008**	9.89414	**0.78368**	44
18	.88604	**.76920**	.88811	**.77287**	.89015	**.77651**	.89217	**.78014**	.89417	**.78374**	42
20+ 5	.88607	**.76926**	.88814	**.77293**	.89018	**.77657**	.89221	**.78020**	.89421	**.78380**	40
22	.88611	**.76932**	.88817	**.77299**	.89022	**.77664**	.89224	**.78026**	.89424	**.78386**	38
24+ 6	9.88614	**.076939**	9.88821	**0.77305**	9.89025	**0.77670**	9.89227	**0.78032**	9.89427	**0.78392**	36
26	.88618	**.76945**	.88824	**.77311**	.89028	**.77676**	.89231	**.78038**	.89431	**.78398**	34
28+ 7	.88621	**.76951**	.88828	**.77317**	.89032	**.77682**	.89234	**.78044**	.89434	**.78404**	32
30	.88625	**.76957**	.88831	**.77323**	.89035	**.77688**	.89237	**.78050**	.89437	**.78410**	30
32+ 8	9.88628	**0.76963**	9.88835	**0.77329**	9.89039	**0.77694**	9.89241	**0.78056**	9.89441	**0.78416**	28
34	.88632	**.76969**	.88838	**.77336**	.89042	**.77700**	.89244	**.78062**	.89444	**.78422**	26
36+ 9	.88635	**.76975**	.88841	**.77342**	.89045	**.77706**	.89247	**.78068**	.89447	**.78428**	24
38	.88639	**.76981**	.88845	**.77348**	.89049	**.77712**	.89251	**.78074**	.89450	**.78434**	22
40+10	9.88642	**0.76988**	.9.88848	**0.77354**	9.89052	**0.77718**	9.89254	**0.78080**	9.89454	**0.78440**	20
42	.88645	**.76994**	.88852	**.77360**	.89056	**.77724**	.89257	**.78086**	.89457	**.78446**	18
44+11	.88649	**.77000**	.88855	**.77366**	.89059	**.77730**	.89261	**.78092**	.89460	**.78452**	16
46	.88652	**.77006**	.88858	**.77372**	.89062	**.77736**	.89264	**.78098**	.89464	**.78458**	14
48+12	9.88656	**0.77012**	9.88862	**0.77378**	9.89066	**0.77742**	9.89267	**0.78104**	9.89467	**0.78464**	12
50	.88659	**.77018**	.88865	**.77384**	.89069	**.77748**	.89271	**.78110**	.89470	**.78470**	10
52+13	.88663	**.77024**	.88869	**.77390**	.89072	**.77754**	.89274	**.78116**	.89474	**.78476**	8
54	.88666	**.77030**	.88872	**.77396**	.89076	**.77760**	.89277	**.78122**	.89477	**.78482**	6
56+14	9.88670	**0.77036**	9.88876	**0.77403**	9.89079	**0.77766**	9.89281	**0.78128**	9.89480	**0.78488**	4
58	9.88673	**0.77043**	9.88879	**0.77409**	9.89083	**0.77772**	9.89284	**0.78134**	.9.89484	**0.78494**	2
	$15^h 49^m$		$15^h 47^m$		$15^h 45^m$		$15^h 43^m$		$15^h 41^m$		

s ′	$8^h 11^m$ 122° 30′		$8^h 13^m$ 123° 0′		$8^h 15^m$ 123° 30′		$8^h 17^m$ 124° 0′		$8^h 19^m$ 124° 30′		s
0+15	9.88677	**0.77049**	9.88882	**0.77415**	9.89086	**0.77779**	9.89287	**0.78140**	9.89487	**0.78500**	60
2	.88680	**.77055**	.88886	**.77412**	.89089	**.77785**	.89291	**.78146**	.89490	**.78506**	58
4+16	.88683	**.77061**	.88889	**.77427**	.89093	**.77791**	.89294	**.78152**	.89493	**.78512**	56
6	.88687	**.77067**	.88893	**.77433**	.89096	**.77797**	.89298	**.78158**	.89497	**.78518**	54
8+17	9.88690	**0.77073**	9.88896	**0.77439**	9.89099	**0.77803**	9.89301	**0.78164**	9.89500	**0.78524**	52
10	.88694	**.77079**	.88899	**.77445**	.89102	**.77809**	.89304	**.78170**	.89503	**.78530**	50
12+18	.88697	**.77085**	.88903	**.77451**	.89106	**.77815**	.89308	**.78176**	.89507	**.78536**	48
14	.88701	**.77092**	.88906	**.77457**	.89110	**.77821**	.89311	**.78182**	.89510	**.78542**	46
16+19	9.88704	**0.77098**	9.88910	**0.77463**	9.89113	**0.77827**	9.89314	**0.78188**	9.89513	**0.78548**	44
18	.88708	**.77104**	.88913	**.77469**	.89116	**.77833**	.89318	**.78194**	.89517	**.78554**	42
20+20	.88711	**.77110**	.88916	**.77475**	.89120	**.77839**	.89321	**.78200**	.89520	**.78560**	40
22	.88714	**.77116**	.88920	**.77482**	.89123	**.77845**	.89324	**.78206**	.89523	**.78566**	38
24+21	9.88718	**0.77122**	9.88923	**0.77488**	9.89126	**0.77851**	9.89328	**0.78212**	9.89527	**0.78572**	36
26	.88721	**.77128**	.88927	**.77494**	.89130	**.77857**	.89331	**.78218**	.89530	**.78577**	34
28+22	.88725	**.77134**	.88930	**.77500**	.89133	**.77863**	.89334	**.78224**	.89533	**.78583**	32
30	.88728	**.77140**	.88933	**.77506**	.89137	**.77869**	.89338	**.78230**	.89536	**.78589**	30
32+23	9.88732	**0.77147**	9.88937	**0.77512**	9.89140	**0.77875**	9.89341	**0.78236**	9.89540	**0.78595**	28
34	.88735	**.77153**	.88940	**.77518**	.89143	**.77881**	.89344	**.78242**	.89543	**.78601**	26
36+24	.88739	**.77159**	.88944	**.77524**	.89147	**.77887**	.89348	**.78248**	.89546	**.78607**	24
38	.88742	**.77165**	.88947	**.77530**	.89150	**.77893**	.89351	**.78254**	.89550	**.78613**	22
40+25	9.88745	**0.77171**	9.88950	**0.77536**	9.89153	**0.77899**	9.89354	**0.78260**	9.89553	**0.78619**	20
42	.88749	**.77177**	.88954	**.77542**	.89157	**.77905**	.89358	**.78266**	.89556	**.78625**	18
44+26	.88752	**.77183**	.88957	**.77548**	.89160	**.77911**	.89361	**.78272**	.89559	**.78531**	16
46	.88756	**.77189**	.88961	**.77554**	.89163	**.77917**	.89364	**.78278**	.89563	**.78637**	14
48+27	9.88759	**0.77195**	9.88964	**0.77560**	9.89167	**0.77923**	9.89368	**0.78284**	9.89566	**0.78643**	12
50	.88763	**.77201**	.88967	**.77567**	.89170	**.77929**	.89371	**.78290**	.89569	**.78649**	10
52+28	.88766	**.77208**	.88971	**.77573**	.89174	**.77936**	.89374	**.78296**	.89573	**.78655**	8
54	.88769	**.77214**	.88974	**.77579**	.89177	**.77942**	.89378	**.78302**	.89576	**.78661**	6
56+29	9.88773	**0.77220**	9.88978	**0.77585**	9.89180	**0.77948**	9.89381	**0.78308**	9.89579	**0.78667**	4
58	.88776	**.77226**	.88981	**.77591**	.89184	**.77954**	.89384	**.78314**	.89583	**.78673**	2
60+30	9.88780	**0.77232**	9.88984	**0.77597**	9.89187	**0.77960**	9.89387	**0.78320**	9.89586	**0.78679**	0
	$15^h 48^m$		$15^h 46^m$		$15^h 44^m$		$15^h 42^m$		$15^h 40^m$		

TABLE 34.

Haversines.

s	′	8h 20m 125° 0′ Log. Hav.	8h 20m 125° 0′ Nat. Hav.	8h 22m 125° 30′ Log. Hav.	8h 22m 125° 30′ Nat. Hav.	8h 24m 126° 0′ Log. Hav.	8h 24m 126° 0′ Nat. Hav.	8h 26m 126° 30′ Log. Hav.	8h 26m 126° 30′ Nat. Hav.	8h 28m 127° 0′ Log. Hav.	8h 28m 127° 0′ Nat. Hav.	s
0	0	9.89586	**0.78679**	9.89782	**0.79035**	9.89976	**0.79389**	9.90168	**0.79741**	9.90358	**0.80091**	60
2		.89589	**.78685**	.89785	**.79041**	.89979	**.79395**	.90171	**.79747**	.90361	**.80097**	58
4+	1	.89592	**.78691**	.89789	**.79047**	.89983	**.79401**	.90175	**.79753**	.90365	**.80102**	56
6		.89596	**.78697**	.89792	**.79053**	.89986	**.79407**	.90178	**.79759**	.90368	**.80108**	54
8+	2	9.89599	**0.78703**	9.89795	**0.79059**	9.89989	**0.79413**	9.90181	**0.79765**	9.90371	**0.80114**	52
10		.89602	**.78709**	.89798	**.79065**	.89992	**.79419**	.90184	**.79770**	.90374	**.80120**	50
12+	3	.89606	**.78715**	.89802	**.79071**	.89995	**.79425**	.90187	**.79776**	.90377	**.80126**	48
14		.89609	**.78721**	.89805	**.79077**	.89999	**.79430**	.90191	**.79782**	.90380	**.80131**	46
16+	4	9.89612	**0.78726**	9.89808	**0.79082**	9.90002	**0.79436**	9.90194	**0.79788**	9.90383	**0.80137**	44
18		.89615	**.78732**	.89811	**.79088**	.90005	**.79442**	.90197	**.79794**	.90387	**.80143**	42
20+	5	.89619	**.78738**	.89815	**.79094**	.90008	**.79448**	.90200	**.79800**	.90390	**.80149**	40
22		.89622	**.78744**	.89818	**.79100**	.90012	**.79454**	.90203	**.79805**	.90393	**.80155**	38
24+	6	9.89625	**0.78750**	9.89821	**0.79106**	9.90015	**0.79460**	9.90206	**0.79811**	9.90396	**0.80160**	36
26		.89628	**.78756**	.89824	**.79112**	.90018	**.79466**	.90210	**.79817**	.90399	**.80166**	34
28+	7	.89632	**.78762**	.89828	**.79118**	.90021	**.79471**	.90213	**.79823**	.90402	**.80172**	32
30		.89635	**.78768**	.89831	**.79124**	.90024	**.79477**	.90216	**.79829**	.90405	**.80178**	30
32+	8	9.89638	**0.78774**	9.89834	**0.79130**	9.90028	**0.79483**	9.90219	**0.79835**	9.90409	**0.80184**	28
34		.89642	**.78780**	.89837	**.79136**	.90031	**.79489**	.90222	**.79840**	.90412	**.80189**	26
36+	9	.89645	**.78786**	.89840	**.79142**	.90034	**.79495**	.90225	**.79846**	.90415	**.80195**	24
38		.89648	**.78792**	.89844	**.79148**	.90037	**.79501**	.90229	**.79852**	.90418	**.80201**	22
40+	10	9.89651	**0.78798**	9.89847	**0.79153**	9.90040	**0.79507**	9.90232	**0.79858**	9.90421	**0.80207**	20
42		.89655	**.78804**	.89850	**.79159**	.90044	**.79513**	.90235	**.79864**	.90425	**.80213**	18
44+	11	.89658	**.78810**	.89853	**.79165**	.90047	**.79519**	.90238	**.79870**	.90428	**.80218**	16
46		.89661	**.78816**	.89857	**.79171**	.90050	**.79524**	.90241	**.79875**	.90431	**.80224**	14
48+	12	9.89665	**0.78822**	9.89860	**0.79177**	9.90053	**0.79530**	9.90244	**0.79881**	9.90434	**0.80230**	12
50		.89668	**.78828**	.89863	**.79183**	.90056	**.79536**	.90248	**.79887**	.90437	**.80236**	10
52+	13	.89671	**.78834**	.89866	**.79189**	.90060	**.79542**	.90251	**.79893**	.90440	**.80242**	8
54		.89674	**.78839**	.89870	**.79195**	.90063	**.79548**	.90254	**.79899**	.90443	**.80247**	6
56+	14	9.89678	**0.78845**	9.89873	**0.79201**	9.90066	**0.79554**	9.90257	**0.79905**	9.90446	**0.80253**	4
58		9.89681	**0.78851**	9.89876	**0.79207**	9.90069	**0.79560**	9.90260	**0.79910**	9.90449	**0.80259**	2
		15h 39m		15h 37m		15h 35m		15h 33m		15h 31m		

s	′	8h 21m 125° 0′ Log. Hav.	8h 21m 125° 0′ Nat. Hav.	8h 23m 125° 30′ Log. Hav.	8h 23m 125° 30′ Nat. Hav.	8h 25m 126° 0′ Log. Hav.	8h 25m 126° 0′ Nat. Hav.	8h 27m 126° 30′ Log. Hav.	8h 27m 126° 30′ Nat. Hav.	8h 29m 127° 0′ Log. Hav.	8h 29m 127° 0′ Nat. Hav.	s
0+	15	9.89684	**0.78857**	9.89879	**0.79212**	9.90072	**0.79565**	9.90264	**0.79916**	9.90452	**0.80265**	60
2		.89687	**.78863**	.89883	**.79218**	.90076	**.79571**	.90267	**.79922**	.90456	**.80270**	58
4+	16	.89691	**.78869**	.89886	**.79224**	.90079	**.79577**	.90270	**.79928**	.90459	**.80276**	56
6		.89694	**.78875**	.89889	**.79230**	.90082	**.79583**	.90273	**.79934**	.90462	**.80282**	54
8+	17	9.89697	**0.78881**	9.89892	**0.79236**	9.90085	**0.79589**	9.90276	**0.79940**	9.90465	**0.80288**	52
10		.89701	**.78887**	.89896	**.79242**	.90088	**.79595**	.90279	**.79945**	.90468	**.80294**	50
12+	18	.89704	**.78893**	.89899	**.79248**	.90092	**.79601**	.90282	**.79951**	.90471	**.80299**	48
14		.89707	**.78899**	.89902	**.79254**	.90095	**.79607**	.90286	**.79957**	.90475	**.80305**	46
16+	19	9.89710	**0.78905**	9.89905	**0.79260**	9.90098	**0.79612**	9.90289	**0.79963**	9.90478	**0.80311**	44
18		.89714	**.78911**	.89908	**.79266**	.90101	**.79618**	.90292	**.79969**	.90481	**.80317**	42
20+	20	.89717	**.78917**	.89912	**.79271**	.90104	**.79624**	.90295	**.79974**	.90484	**.80323**	40
22		.89720	**.78923**	.89915	**.79277**	.90108	**.79630**	.90298	**.79980**	.90487	**.80328**	38
24+	21	9.89723	**0.78928**	9.89918	**0.79283**	9.90111	**0.79636**	9.90301	**0.79986**	9.90490	**0.80334**	36
26		.89727	**.78934**	.89921	**.79289**	.90114	**.79642**	.90305	**.79992**	.90493	**.80340**	34
28+	22	.89730	**.78940**	.89925	**.79295**	.90117	**.79648**	.90308	**.79998**	.90496	**.80346**	32
30		.89733	**.78946**	.89928	**.79301**	.90120	**.79653**	.90311	**.80004**	.90499	**.80351**	30
32+	23	9.89736	**0.78952**	9.89931	**0.79307**	9.90124	**0.79659**	9.90314	**0.80009**	9.90503	**0.80357**	28
34		.89740	**.78958**	.89934	**.79313**	.90127	**.79665**	.90317	**.80015**	.90506	**.80363**	26
36+	24	.89743	**.78964**	.89938	**.79319**	.90130	**.79671**	.90320	**.80021**	.90509	**.80369**	24
38		.89746	**.78970**	.89941	**.79325**	.90133	**.79677**	.90324	**.80027**	.90512	**.80375**	22
40+	25	9.89749	**0.78976**	9.89944	**0.79330**	9.90136	**0.79683**	9.90327	**0.80033**	9.90515	**0.80380**	20
42		.89753	**.78982**	.89947	**.79336**	.90140	**.79688**	.90330	**.80038**	.90518	**.80386**	18
44+	26	.89756	**.78988**	.89950	**.79342**	.90143	**.79694**	.90333	**.80044**	.90521	**.80392**	16
46		.89759	**.78994**	.89954	**.79348**	.90146	**.79700**	.90336	**.80050**	.90524	**.80398**	14
48+	27	9.89763	**0.79000**	9.89957	**0.79354**	9.90149	**0.79706**	9.90339	**0.80056**	9.90527	**0.80403**	12
50		.89766	**.79006**	.89960	**.79360**	.90152	**.79712**	.90342	**.80062**	.90531	**.80409**	10
52+	28	.89769	**.79011**	.89963	**.79366**	.90356	**.79718**	.90346	**.80068**	.90534	**.80415**	8
54		.89772	**.79017**	.89966	**.79372**	.90159	**.79724**	.90349	**.80073**	.90537	**.80421**	6
56+	29	9.89776	**0.79023**	9.89970	**0.79377**	9.90162	**0.79729**	9.90352	**0.80079**	9.90540	**0.80427**	4
58		.89779	**.79029**	.89973	**.79383**	.90165	**.79735**	.90355	**.80085**	.90543	**.80432**	2
60+	30	9.89782	**0.79035**	9.89976	**0.79389**	9.90168	**0.79741**	9.90358	**0.80091**	9.90546	**0.80438**	0
		15h 38m		15h 36m		15h 34m		15h 32m		15h 30m		

TABLE 34.

Haversines.

s	′	8h 30m 127° 30′ Log. Hav.	Nat. Hav.	8h 32m 128° 0′ Log. Hav.	Nat. Hav.	8h 34m 128° 30′ Log. Hav.	Nat. Hav.	8h 36m 129° 0′ Log. Hav.	Nat. Hav.	8h 38m 129° 30′ Log. Hav.	Nat. Hav.	s
0	0	9.90546	**0.80438**	9.90732	**0.80783**	9.90916	**0.81126**	9.91098	**0.81466**	9.91277	**0.81804**	60
2		.90549	**.80444**	.90735	**.80789**	.90919	**.81131**	.91101	**.81472**	.91280	**.81810**	58
4+	1	.90552	**.80450**	.90738	**.80795**	.90922	**.81137**	.91104	**.81477**	.91283	**.81815**	56
6		.90556	**.80455**	.90741	**.80800**	.90925	**.81143**	.91107	**.81483**	.91286	**.81821**	54
8+	2	9.90559	**0.80461**	9.90744	**0.80806**	9.90928	**0.81148**	9.91110	**0.81489**	9.91289	**0.81826**	52
10		.90562	**.80467**	.90747	**.80812**	.90931	**.81154**	.91113	**.81494**	.91292	**.81832**	50
12+	3	.90565	**.80473**	.90751	**.80817**	.90934	**.81160**	.91116	**.81500**	.91295	**.81838**	48
14		.90568	**.80478**	.90754	**.80823**	.90937	**.81165**	.91119	**.81506**	.91298	**.81843**	46
16+	4	9.90571	**0.80484**	9.90757	**0.80829**	9.90940	**0.81171**	9.91122	**0.81511**	9.91301	**0.81849**	44
18		.90574	**.80490**	.90760	**.80835**	.90943	**.81177**	.91125	**.81517**	.91304	**.81854**	42
20+	5	.90577	**.80496**	.90763	**.80840**	.90946	**.81183**	.91128	**.81523**	.91307	**.81860**	40
22		.90580	**.80502**	.90766	**.80846**	.90949	**.81188**	.91131	**.81528**	.91310	**.81866**	38
24+	6	9.90584	**0.80507**	9.90769	**0.80852**	9.90952	**0.81194**	9.91134	**0.81534**	9.91313	**0.81871**	36
26		.90587	**.80513**	.90772	**.80858**	.90955	**.81200**	.91137	**.81539**	.91316	**.81877**	34
28+	7	.90590	**.80519**	.90775	**.80863**	.90958	**.81205**	.91140	**.81545**	.91319	**.81882**	32
30		.90593	**.80525**	.90778	**.80869**	.90962	**.81211**	.91143	**.81551**	.91322	**.81888**	30
32+	8	9.90596	**0.80530**	9.90781	**0.80875**	9.90965	**0.81217**	9.91146	**0.81556**	9.91325	**0.81894**	28
34		.90599	**.80536**	.90784	**.80880**	.90968	**.81222**	.91149	**.81562**	.91328	**.81899**	26
36+	9	.90602	**.80542**	.90787	**.80886**	.90971	**.81228**	.91152	**.81568**	.91331	**.81905**	24
38		.90605	**.80548**	.90790	**.80892**	.90974	**.81234**	.91155	**.81573**	.91334	**.81910**	22
40+	10	9.90608	**0.80553**	9.90794	**0.80898**	9.90977	**0.81239**	9.91158	**0.81579**	9.91337	**0.81916**	20
42		.90611	**.80559**	.90797	**.80903**	.90980	**.81245**	.91161	**.81585**	.91340	**.81922**	18
44+	11	.90615	**.80565**	.90800	**.80909**	.90983	**.81251**	.91164	**.81590**	.91343	**.81927**	16
46		.90618	**.80571**	.90803	**.80915**	.90986	**.81256**	.91167	**.81596**	.91346	**.81933**	14
48+	12	9.90621	**0.80576**	9.90806	**0.80920**	9.90989	**0.81262**	9.91170	**0.81601**	9.91349	**0.81938**	12
50		.90624	**.80582**	.90809	**.80926**	.90992	**.81268**	.91173	**.81607**	.91352	**.81944**	10
52+	13	.90627	**.80588**	.90812	**.80932**	.90995	**.81273**	.91176	**.81613**	.91355	**.81950**	8
54		.90630	**.80594**	.90815	**.80938**	.90998	**.81279**	.91179	**.81618**	.91358	**.81955**	6
56+	14	9.90633	**0.80599**	9.90818	**0.80943**	9.91001	**0.81285**	9.91182	**0.81624**	9.91361	**0.81961**	4
58		9.90636	**0.80605**	9.90821	**0.80949**	9.91004	**0.81291**	9.91185	**0.81630**	9.91364	**0.81966**	2
		15h 29m		15h 27m		15h 25m		15h 23m		15h 21m		

s	′	8h 31m 127° 30′ Log. Hav.	Nat. Hav.	8h 33m 128° 0′ Log. Hav.	Nat. Hav.	8h 35m 128° 30′ Log. Hav.	Nat. Hav.	8h 37m 129° 0′ Log. Hav.	Nat. Hav.	8h 39m 129° 30′ Log. Hav.	Nat. Hav.	s
0+	15	9.90639	**0.80611**	9.90824	**0.80955**	9.91007	**0.81296**	9.91188	**0.81635**	9.91367	**0.81972**	60
2		.90642	**.80617**	.90827	**.80960**	.91010	**.81302**	.91191	**.81641**	.91369	**.81978**	58
4+	16	.90646	**.80622**	.90830	**.80966**	.91013	**.81308**	.91194	**.81647**	.91372	**.81983**	56
6		.90646	**.80628**	.90833	**.80972**	.91016	**.81313**	.91197	**.81652**	.91375	**.81989**	54
8+	17	9.90652	**0.80634**	9.90836	**0.80978**	9.91019	**0.81319**	9.91200	**0.81658**	9.91378	**0.81994**	52
10		.90655	**.80640**	.90840	**.80983**	.91022	**.81325**	.91203	**.81663**	.91381	**.82000**	50
12+	18	.90658	**.80645**	.90843	**.80989**	.91025	**.81330**	.91206	**.81669**	.91384	**.82005**	48
14		.90661	**.80651**	.90846	**.80995**	.91028	**.81336**	.91209	**.81675**	.91387	**.82011**	46
16+	19	9.90664	**0.80657**	9.90849	**0.81000**	9.91031	**0.81342**	9.91212	**0.81680**	9.91390	**0.82017**	44
18		.90667	**.80663**	.90852	**.81006**	.91034	**.81347**	.91215	**.81686**	.91393	**.82022**	42
20+	20	.90670	**.80668**	.90855	**.81012**	.91037	**.81353**	.91218	**.81692**	.91396	**.82028**	40
22		.90673	**.80674**	.90858	**.81017**	.91040	**.81359**	.91221	**.81697**	.91399	**.82033**	38
24+	21	9.90676	**0.80680**	9.90861	**0.81023**	9.91043	**0.81364**	9.91224	**0.81703**	9.91402	**0.82039**	36
26		.90680	**.80686**	.90864	**.81029**	.91046	**.81370**	.91227	**.81708**	.91405	**.82045**	34
28+	22	.90683	**.80691**	.90867	**.81035**	.91049	**.81376**	.91230	**.81714**	.91408	**.82050**	32
30		.90686	**.80697**	.90870	**.81040**	.91052	**.81381**	.91233	**.81720**	.91411	**.82056**	30
32+	23	9.90689	**0.80703**	9.90873	**0.81046**	9.91055	**0.81387**	9.91236	**0.81725**	9.91414	**0.82061**	28
34		.90692	**.80709**	.90876	**.81052**	.91058	**.81392**	.91239	**.81731**	.91417	**.82067**	26
36+	24	.90695	**.80714**	.90879	**.81057**	.91061	**.81398**	.91242	**.81737**	.91420	**.82072**	24
38		.90698	**.80720**	.90882	**.81063**	.91064	**.81404**	.91245	**.81742**	.91423	**.82078**	22
40+	25	9.90701	**0.80726**	9.90885	**0.81068**	9.91067	**0.81409**	9.91248	**0.81748**	9.91426	**0.82084**	20
42		.90704	**.80731**	.90888	**.81074**	.91071	**.81415**	.91251	**.81753**	.91429	**.82089**	18
44+	26	.90707	**.80737**	.90892	**.81080**	.91074	**.81421**	.91254	**.81759**	.91432	**.82095**	16
46		.90710	**.80743**	.90895	**.81086**	.91077	**.81426**	.91257	**.81765**	.91435	**.82100**	14
48+	27	9.90714	**0.80749**	9.90898	**0.81092**	9.91080	**0.81432**	9.91260	**0.81770**	9.91437	**0.82106**	12
50		.90717	**.80754**	.90901	**.81097**	.91083	**.81438**	.91263	**.81776**	.91440	**.82112**	10
52+	28	.90720	**.80760**	.90904	**.81103**	.91086	**.81443**	.91265	**.81781**	.91443	**.82117**	8
54		.90723	**.80766**	.90907	**.81109**	.91089	**.81449**	.91268	**.81787**	.91446	**.82123**	6
56+	29	9.90726	**0.80772**	9.90910	**0.81114**	9.91092	**0.81455**	9.91271	**0.81793**	9.91449	**0.82128**	4
58		.90729	**.80777**	.90913	**.81120**	.91095	**.81460**	.91274	**.81798**	.91452	**.82134**	2
60+	30	9.90732	**0.80783**	9.90916	**0.81126**	9.91098	**0.81466**	9.91277	**0.81804**	9.91455	**0.82139**	0
		15h 28m		15h 26m		15h 24m		15h 22m		15h 20m		

TABLE 34.

Haversines.

s ′	$8^h 40^m$ 130° 0′ Log. Hav.	Nat. Hav.	$8^h 42^m$ 130° 30′ Log. Hav.	Nat. Hav.	$8^h 44^m$ 131° 0′ Log. Hav.	Nat. Hav.	$8^h 46^m$ 131° 30′ Log. Hav.	Nat. Hav.	$8^h 48^m$ 132° 0′ Log. Hav.	Nat. Hav.	s
0 0	9.91455	**0.82139**	9.91631	**0.82472**	9.91805	**0.82803**	9.91976	**0.83131**	9.92146	**0.83457**	60
2	.91458	**.82145**	.91634	**.82478**	.91807	**.82808**	.91979	**.83136**	.92149	**.83462**	58
4+ 1	.91461	**.82151**	.91637	**.82483**	.91810	**.82814**	.91982	**.83142**	.92152	**.83467**	56
6	.91464	**.82156**	.91640	**.82489**	.91813	**.82819**	.91985	**.83147**	.92154	**.83473**	54
8+ 2	9.91467	**0.82162**	9.91643	**0.82495**	9.91816	**0.82825**	9.91988	**0.83153**	9.92157	**0.83478**	52
10	.91470	**.82167**	.91645	**.82500**	.91819	**.82830**	.91991	**.83158**	.92160	**.83484**	50
12+ 3	.91473	**.82173**	.91648	**.82506**	.91822	**.82836**	.91993	**.83164**	.92163	**.83489**	48
14	.91476	**.82178**	.91651	**.82511**	.91825	**.82841**	.91996	**.83169**	.92166	**.83494**	46
16+ 4	9.91479	**0.82184**	9.91654	**0.82517**	9.91828	**0.82847**	9.91999	**0.83175**	9.92169	**0.83500**	44
18	.91482	**.82189**	.91657	**.82522**	.91830	**.82852**	.92002	**.83180**	.92171	**.83505**	42
20+ 5	.91485	**.82195**	.91660	**.82528**	.91833	**.82858**	.92005	**.83185**	.92174	**.83511**	40
22	.91488	**.82200**	.91663	**.82533**	.91836	**.82863**	.92008	**.83191**	.92177	**.83516**	38
24+ 6	9.91490	**0.82206**	9.91666	**0.82539**	9.91839	**0.82869**	9.92010	**0.83196**	9.92180	**0.83521**	36
26	.91493	**.82212**	.91669	**.82544**	.91842	**.82874**	.92013	**.83202**	.92183	**.83527**	34
28+ 7	.91496	**.82217**	.91672	**.82550**	.91845	**.82880**	.92016	**.83207**	.92185	**.83532**	32
30	.91499	**.82223**	.91674	**.82555**	.91848	**.82885**	.92019	**.83213**	.92188	**.83538**	30
32+ 8	9.91502	**0.82228**	9.91677	**0.82561**	9.91851	**0.82891**	9.92022	**0.83218**	9.92191	**0.83543**	28
34	.91505	**.82234**	.91680	**.82566**	.91853	**.82896**	.92025	**.83224**	.92194	**.83548**	26
36+ 9	.91508	**.82240**	.91683	**.82572**	.91856	**.82902**	.92027	**.83229**	.92197	**.83554**	24
38	.91511	**.82245**	.91686	**.82577**	.91859	**.82907**	.92030	**.83234**	.92199	**.83559**	22
40+10	9.91514	**0.82251**	9.91689	**0.82583**	9.91862	**0.82913**	9.92033	**0.83240**	9.92202	**0.83564**	20
42	.91517	**.82256**	.91692	**.82588**	.91865	**.82918**	.92036	**.83245**	.92205	**.83570**	18
44+11	.91520	**.82262**	.91695	**.82594**	.91868	**.82924**	.92039	**.83251**	.92208	**.83575**	16
46	.91523	**.82267**	.91698	**.82599**	.91871	**.82929**	.92042	**.83256**	.92211	**.83581**	14
48+12	9.91526	**0.82273**	9.91701	**0.82605**	9.91874	**0.82934**	9.92044	**0.83262**	9.92213	**0.83586**	12
50	.91529	**.82278**	.91703	**.82610**	.91876	**.82940**	.92047	**.83267**	.92216	**.83591**	10
52+13	.91532	**.82284**	.91706	**.82616**	.91879	**.82945**	.92050	**.83272**	.92219	**.83597**	8
54	.91534	**.82290**	.91709	**.82621**	.91882	**.82951**	.92053	**.83278**	.92222	**.83602**	6
56+14	9.91537	**0.82295**	9.91712	**0.82627**	9.91885	**0.82956**	9.92056	**0.83283**	9.92225	**0.83608**	4
58	9.91540	**0.82301**	9.91715	**0.82632**	9.91888	**0.82962**	9.92059	**0.83289**	9.92227	**0.83613**	2
	$15^h 19^m$		$15^h 17^m$		$15^h 15^m$		$15^h 13^m$		$15^h 11^m$		

s ′	$8^h 41^m$ 130° 0′ Log. Hav.	Nat. Hav.	$8^h 43^m$ 130° 30′ Log. Hav.	Nat. Hav.	$8^h 45^m$ 131° 0′ Log. Hav.	Nat. Hav.	$8^h 47^m$ 131° 30: Log. Hav.	Nat. Hav.	$8^h 49^m$ 132° 0′ Log. Hav.	Nat. Hav.	s
0+15	9.91543	**0.82306**	9.91718	**0.82638**	9.91891	**0.82967**	9.92061	**0.83294**	9.92230	**0.83618**	60
2	.91546	**.82312**	.91721	**.82644**	.91894	**.82973**	.92064	**.83300**	.92233	**.83624**	58
4+16	.91549	**.82317**	.91724	**.82649**	.91896	**.82978**	.92067	**.83305**	.92236	**.83629**	56
6	.91552	**.82323**	.91727	**.82655**	.91899	**.82984**	.92070	**.83310**	.92239	**.83635**	54
8+17	9.91555	**0.82328**	9.91730	**0.82660**	9.91902	**0.82989**	9.92073	**0.83316**	9.92241	**0.83640**	52
10	.91558	**.82334**	.91732	**.82666**	.91905	**.82995**	.92076	**.83321**	.92244	**.83645**	50
12+18	.91561	**.82339**	.91735	**.82671**	.91908	**.83000**	.92078	**.83327**	.92247	**.83651**	48
14	.91564	**.82345**	.91738	**.82677**	.91911	**.83006**	.92081	**.83332**	.92250	**.83656**	46
16+19	9.91567	**0.82351**	9.91741	**0.82682**	9.91914	**0.83011**	9.92084	**0.83337**	9.92253	**0.83661**	44
18	.91570	**.82356**	.91744	**.82688**	.91916	**.83016**	.92087	**.83343**	.92255	**.83667**	42
20+20	.91573	**.82362**	.91747	**.82693**	.91919	**.83022**	.92090	**.83348**	.92258	**.83672**	40
22	.91575	**.82367**	.91750	**.82699**	.91922	**.83027**	.92093	**.83354**	.92261	**.83678**	38
24+21	9.91578	**0.82373**	9.91753	**0.82704**	9.91925	**0.83033**	9.92095	**0.83359**	9.92264	**0.83683**	36
26	.91581	**.82378**	.91756	**.82710**	.91928	**.83038**	.92098	**.83365**	.92266	**.83688**	34
28+22	.91584	**.82384**	.91758	**.82715**	.91931	**.83044**	.92101	**.83370**	.92269	**.83694**	32
30	.91587	**.82389**	.91761	**.82721**	.91934	**.83049**	.92104	**.83375**	.92272	**.83699**	30
32+23	9.91590	**0.82395**	9.91764	**0.82726**	9.91936	**0.83055**	9.92107	**0.83381**	9.92275	**0.83704**	28
34	.91593	**.82400**	.91767	**.82732**	.91939	**.83060**	.92109	**.83386**	.92278	**.83710**	26
36+24	.91596	**.82406**	.91770	**.82737**	.91942	**.83066**	.92112	**.83392**	.92280	**.83715**	24
38	.91599	**.82412**	.91773	**.82743**	.91945	**.83071**	.92115	**.83397**	.92283	**.83720**	22
40+25	9.91602	**0.82417**	9.91776	**0.82748**	9.91948	**0.83077**	9.92118	**0.83402**	9.92286	**0.83726**	20
42	.91605	**.82423**	.91779	**.82754**	.91951	**.83082**	.92121	**.83408**	.92289	**.83731**	18
44+26	.91608	**.82428**	.91782	**.82759**	.91954	**.83087**	.92124	**.83413**	.92292	**.83737**	16
46	.91610	**.82434**	.91784	**.82765**	.91956	**.83093**	.92126	**.83419**	.92294	**.83742**	14
48+27	9.91613	**0.82439**	9.91787	**0.82770**	9.91959	**0.83098**	9.92129	**0.83424**	9.92297	**0.83747**	12
50	.91616	**.82445**	.91790	**.82776**	.91962	**.83104**	.92132	**.83430**	.92300	**.83753**	10
52+28	.91619	**.82450**	.91793	**.82781**	.91965	**.83109**	.92135	**.83435**	.92303	**.83758**	8
54	.91622	**.82456**	.91796	**.82786**	.91968	**.83115**	.92138	**.83440**	.92305	**.83763**	6
56+29	9.91625	**0.82461**	9.91799	**0.82792**	9.91971	**0.83120**	9.92140	**0.83446**	9.92308	**0.83769**	4
58	.91628	**.82467**	.91802	**.82797**	.91973	**.83126**	.92143	**.83451**	.92311	**.83774**	2
60+30	9.91631	**0.82472**	9.91805	**0.82803**	9.91976	**0.83131**	9.92146	**0.83457**	9.92314	**0.83780**	0
	$15^h 18^m$		$15^h 16^m$		$15^h 14^m$		$15^h 12^m$		$15^h 10^m$		

TABLE 34.

Haversines.

s ′	8h 50m 132° 30′		8h 52m 133° 0′		8h 54m 133° 30′		8h 56m 134° 0′		8h 58m 134° 30′		s
	Log. Hav.	Nat. Hav.	Log. Hav.	Nat. Hav.	Log. Hav.	Nat. Hav.	Log. Hav.	Nat. Hav.	Log. Hav.	Nat. Hav.	
0 0	9.92314	**0.83780**	9.92480	**0.84100**	9.92643	**0.84418**	9.92805	**0.84733**	9.92965	**0.85045**	60
2	.92317	**.83785**	.92482	**.84105**	.92646	**.84423**	.92808	**.84738**	.92968	**.85051**	58
4+ 1	.92319	**.83790**	.92485	**.84111**	.92649	**.84428**	.92811	**.84743**	.92970	**.85056**	56
6	.92322	**.83796**	.92488	**.84116**	.92652	**.84434**	.92813	**.84749**	.92973	**.85061**	54
8+ 2	9.92325	**0.83801**	9.92491	**0.84121**	9.92654	**0.84439**	9.92816	**0.84754**	9.92975	**0.85066**	52
10	.92328	**.83806**	.92493	**.84127**	.92657	**.84444**	.92819	**.84759**	.92978	**.85071**	50
12+ 3	.92330	**.83812**	.92496	**.84132**	.92660	**.84449**	.92821	**.84764**	.92981	**.85077**	48
14	.92333	**.83817**	.92499	**.84137**	.92662	**.84455**	.92824	**.84770**	.92984	**.85082**	46
16+ 4	9.92336	**0.83822**	9.92502	**0.84142**	9 92665	**0.84460**	9.92827	**0.84775**	9.92986	**0.85087**	44
18	.92339	**.83828**	.92504	**.84148**	.92668	**.84465**	.92829	**.84780**	.92989	**.85092**	42
20+ 5	.92342	**.83833**	.92507	**.84153**	.92670	**.84470**	.92832	**.84785**	.92992	**.85097**	40
22	.92344	**.83838**	.92510	**.84158**	.92673	**.84476**	.92835	**.84790**	.92994	**.85102**	38
24+ 6	9.92347	**0.83844**	9.92512	**0.84164**	9.92676	**0.84481**	9.92837	**0.84796**	9.92997	**0.85108**	36
26	.92350	**.83849**	.92515	**.84169**	.92679	**.84486**	.92840	**.84801**	.93001	**.85113**	34
28+ 7	.92353	**.83855**	.92518	**.84174**	.92681	**.84492**	.92843	**.84806**	.93002	**.85118**	32
30	.92355	**.83860**	.92521	**.84180**	.92684	**.84497**	.92845	**.84811**	.93005	**.85123**	30
32+ 8	9.92358	**0.83865**	9.92523	**0.84185**	9.92687	**0.84502**	9.92848	**0.84817**	9.93007	**0.85128**	28
34	.92361	**.83871**	.92526	**.84190**	.92689	**.84507**	.92851	**.84822**	.93010	**.85134**	26
36+ 9	.92364	**.83876**	.92529	**.84196**	.92692	**.84513**	.92853	**.84827**	.93013	**.85139**	24
38	.92366	**.83881**	.92532	**.84201**	.92695	**.84518**	.92856	**.84832**	.93015	**.85144**	22
40+10	9.92369	**0.83887**	9.92534	**0.84206**	9.92698	**0.84523**	9.92859	**0.84837**	9.93018	**0.85149**	20
42	.92372	**.83892**	.92537	**.84211**	.92700	**.84528**	.92861	**.84843**	.93021	**.85154**	18
44+11	.92375	**.83897**	.92540	**.84217**	.92703	**.84534**	.92864	**.84848**	.93023	**.85159**	16
46	.92378	**.83903**	.92543	**.84222**	.92706	**.84539**	.92867	**.84853**	.93026	**.85165**	14
48+12	9.92380	**0.83908**	9.92545	**0.84227**	9.92708	**0.84544**	9.92869	**0.84858**	9.93029	**0.85170**	12
50	.92383	**.83913**	.92548	**.84233**	.92711	**.84549**	.92872	**.84863**	.93031	**.85175**	10
52+13	.92386	**.83919**	.92551	**.84238**	.92714	**.84555**	.92875	**.84869**	.93034	**.85180**	8
54	.92389	**.83924**	.92554	**.84243**	.92716	**.84560**	.92877	**.84874**	.93036	**.85185**	6
56+14	9.92391	**0.83929**	9.92556	**0.84249**	9.92719	**0.84565**	9.92880	**0.84879**	9.93039	**0.85190**	4
58	9.92394	**0.83935**	9.92559	**0.84254**	9.92722	**0.84570**	9.92883	**0.84884**	9.93042	**0.85196**	2
	15h 9m		15h 7m		15h 5m		15h 3m		15h 1m		

s ′	8h 51m 132° 30′		8h 53m 133° 0′		8h 55m 133° 30′		8h 57m 134° 0′		8h 59m 134° 30′		s
0+15	9.92397	**0.83940**	9.92562	**0.84259**	9.92725	**0.84576**	9.92885	**0.84890**	9.93044	**0.85201**	60
2	.92400	**.83945**	.92564	**.84264**	.92727	**.84581**	.92888	**.84895**	.93047	**.85206**	58
4+16	.92402	**.83951**	.92567	**.84270**	.92730	**.84586**	.92891	**.84900**	.93050	**.85211**	56
6	.92405	**.83956**	.92570	**.84275**	.92733	**.84591**	.92893	**.84905**	.93052	**.85216**	54
8+17	9.92408	**0.83961**	9.92573	**0.84280**	9.92735	**0.84597**	9.92896	**0.84910**	9.93055	**0.85221**	52
10	.92411	**.83967**	.92575	**.84286**	.92738	**.84602**	.92899	**.84916**	.93057	**.85227**	50
12+18	.92413	**.83972**	.92578	**.84291**	.92741	**.84607**	.92901	**.84921**	.93060	**.85232**	48
14	.92416	**.83977**	.92581	**.84296**	.92743	**.84612**	.92904	**.84926**	.93063	**.85237**	46
16+19	9.92419	**0.83983**	9.92584	**0.84302**	9.92746	**0.84618**	9.92907	**0.84931**	9.93065	**0.85242**	44
18	.92422	**.83988**	.92586	**.84307**	.92749	**.84623**	.92909	**.84936**	.93068	**.85247**	42
20+20	.92425	**.83993**	.92589	**.84312**	.92751	**.84628**	.92912	**.84942**	.93071	**.85252**	40
22	.92427	**.83999**	.92592	**.84317**	.92754	**.84633**	.92915	**.84947**	.93073	**.85258**	38
24+21	9.92430	**0.84004**	9.92594	**0.84323**	9.92757	**0.84639**	9.92917	**0.84952**	9.93076	**0.85263**	36
26	.92433	**.84009**	.92597	**.84328**	.92760	**.84644**	.92920	**.84957**	.93079	**.85268**	34
28+22	.92436	**.84015**	.92600	**.84333**	.92762	**.84649**	.92923	**.84962**	.93081	**.85273**	32
30	.92438	**.84020**	.92603	**.84339**	.92765	**.84654**	.92925	**.84968**	.93084	**.85278**	30
32+23	9.92441	**0.84025**	9.92605	**0.84344**	9.92768	**0.84660**	9.92928	**0.84973**	9.93086	**0.85283**	28
34	.92444	**.84031**	.92608	**.84349**	.92770	**.84665**	.92931	**.84978**	.93089	**.85288**	26
36+24	.92447	**.84036**	.92611	**.84354**	.92773	**.84670**	.92933	**.84983**	.93092	**.85294**	24
38	.92449	**.84041**	.92613	**.84360**	.92776	**.84675**	.92936	**.84988**	.93094	**.85299**	22
40+25	9.92452	**0.84047**	9.92616	**0.84365**	9.92778	**0.84681**	9.92939	**0.84994**	9.93097	**0.85304**	20
42	.92455	**.84052**	.92619	**.84370**	.92781	**.84686**	.92941	**.84999**	.93100	**.85309**	18
44+26	.92458	**.84057**	.92622	**.84376**	.92784	**.84691**	.92944	**.85004**	.93102	**.85314**	16
46	.92460	**.84063**	.92624	**.84381**	.92786	**.84696**	.92947	**.85009**	.93105	**.85319**	14
48+27	9.92463	**0.84068**	9.92627	**0.84386**	9.92789	**0.84702**	9.92949	**0.85014**	9.93107	**0.85324**	12
50	.92466	**.84073**	.92630	**.84391**	.92792	**.84707**	.92952	**.85020**	.93110	**.85330**	10
52+28	.92469	**.84079**	.92633	**.84397**	.92794	**.84712**	.92955	**.85025**	.93113	**.85335**	8
54	.92471	**.84084**	.92635	**.84402**	.92797	**.84717**	.92957	**.85030**	.93115	**.85340**	6
56+29	9.92474	**0.84089**	9.92638	**0.84407**	9.92800	**0.84722**	9.92960	**0.85035**	9.93118	**0.85345**	4
58	.92477	**.84095**	.92641	**.84412**	.92802	**.84728**	.92962	**.85040**	.93120	**.85350**	2
60+30	9.92480	**0.84100**	9.92643	**0.84418**	9.92805	**0.84733**	9.92965	**0.85045**	9.93123	**0.85355**	0
	15h 8m		15h 6m		15h 4m		15h 2m		15h 0m		

TABLE 34.

Haversines.

s	′	9h 0m Log. Hav.	135° Nat. Hav.	9h 4m Log. Hav.	136° Nat. Hav.	9h 8m Log. Hav.	137° Nat. Hav.	9h 12m Log. Hav.	138° Nat. Hav.	9h 16m Log. Hav.	139° Nat. Hav.	s
0	0	9.93123	0.85355	9.93433	0.85967	9.93736	0.86568	9.94030	0.87157	9.94318	0.87735	60
4	1	.93128	.85366	.93438	.85977	.93741	.86578	.94035	.87167	.94322	.87745	56
8	2	.93134	.85376	.93443	.85987	.93746	.86588	.94040	.87177	.94327	.87755	52
12	3	.93139	.85386	.93448	.85997	.93751	.86597	.94045	.87186	.94332	.87764	48
16	4	9.93144	0.85396	9.93454	0.86007	9.93755	0.86607	9.94050	0.87196	9.94336	0.87774	44
20	5	.93149	.85407	.93459	.86017	.93760	.86617	.94055	.87206	.94341	.87783	40
24	6	.93154	.85417	.93464	.86028	.93765	.86627	.94059	.87216	.94346	.87793	36
28	7	.93160	.85427	.93469	.86038	.93770	.86637	.94064	.87225	.94351	.87802	32
32	8	9.93165	0.85438	9.93474	0.86048	9.93775	0.86647	9.94069	0.87235	9.94355	0.87812	28
36	9	.93170	.85448	.93479	.86058	.93780	.86657	.94074	.87245	.94360	.87821	24
40	10	.93175	.85458	.93484	.86068	.93785	.86667	.94079	.87254	.94365	.87831	20
44	11	.93181	.85468	.93489	.86078	.93790	.86677	.94084	.87264	.94369	.87840	16
48	12	9.93186	0.85479	9.93494	0.86088	9.93795	0.86686	9.94088	0.87274	9.94374	0.87850	12
52	13	.93191	.85489	.93499	.86098	.93800	.86696	.94093	.87283	.94379	.87859	8
56	14	9.93196	0.85499	9.93504	0.86108	9.93805	0.86706	9.94098	0.87293	9.94383	0.87869	4
		14h 59m		14h 55m		14h 51m		14h 47m		14h 43m		

s	′	9h 1m Log. Hav.	135° Nat. Hav.	9h 5m Log. Hav.	136° Nat. Hav.	9h 9m Log. Hav.	137° Nat. Hav.	9h 13m Log. Hav.	138° Nat. Hav.	9h 17m Log. Hav.	139° Nat. Hav.	s
0	15	9.93201	0.85509	9.93509	0.86118	9.93810	0.86716	9.94103	0.87303	9.94388	0.87878	60
4	16	.93207	.85520	.93515	.86128	.93815	.86726	.94108	.87313	.94393	.87888	56
8	17	.93212	.85530	.93520	.86138	.93820	.86736	.94112	.87322	.94398	.87897	52
12	18	.93217	.85540	.93525	.86148	.93825	.86746	.94117	.87332	.94402	.87907	48
16	19	9.93222	0.85550	9.93530	0.86158	9.93830	0.86756	9.94122	0.87342	9.94407	0.87916	44
20	20	.93227	.85560	.93535	.86168	.93835	.86765	.94127	.87351	.94412	.87926	40
24	21	.93232	.85571	.93540	.86178	.93840	.86775	.94132	.87361	.94416	.87935	36
28	22	.93238	.85581	.93545	.86189	.93845	.86785	.94137	.87371	.94421	.87945	32
32	23	9.93243	0.85591	9.93550	0.86199	9.93849	0.86795	9.94141	0.87380	9.94426	0.87954	28
36	24	.93248	.85601	.93555	.86209	.93854	.86805	.94146	.87390	.94430	.87964	24
40	25	.93253	.85612	.93560	.86219	.93859	.86815	.94151	.87400	.94435	.87973	20
44	26	.93258	.85622	.93565	.86229	.93864	.86825	.94156	.87409	.94440	.87983	16
48	27	9.93264	0.85632	9.93570	0.86239	9.93869	0.86834	9.94161	0.87419	9.94444	0.87992	12
52	28	.93269	.85642	.93575	.86249	.93874	.86844	.94165	.87428	.94449	.88001	8
56	29	9.93274	0.85652	9.93580	0.86259	9.93879	0.86854	9.94170	0.87438	9.94454	0.88011	4
		14h 58m		14h 54m		14h 50m		14h 46m		14h 42m		

s	′	9h 2m Log. Hav.	135° Nat. Hav.	9h 6m Log. Hav.	136° Nat. Hav.	9h 10m Log. Hav.	137° Nat. Hav.	9h 14m Log. Hav.	138° Nat. Hav.	9h 18m Log. Hav.	139° Nat. Hav.	s
0	30	9.93279	0.85663	9.93585	0.86269	9.93884	0.86864	9.94175	0.87448	9.94458	0.88020	60
4	31	.93284	.85673	.93590	.86279	.93889	.86874	.94180	.87457	.94463	.88030	56
8	32	.93289	.85683	.93595	.86289	.93894	.86884	.94184	.87467	.94468	.88039	52
12	33	.93295	.85693	.93600	.86299	.93899	.86893	.94189	.87477	.94472	.88049	48
16	34	9.93300	0.85703	9.93605	0.86309	9.93904	0.86903	9.94194	0.87486	9.94477	0.88058	44
20	35	.93305	.85713	.93611	.86319	.93908	.86913	.94199	.87496	.94482	.88068	40
24	36	.93310	.85724	.93616	.86329	.93913	.86923	.94204	.87505	.94486	.88077	36
28	37	.93315	.85734	.93621	.86339	.93918	.86933	.94208	.87515	.94491	.88086	32
32	38	9.93320	0.85744	9.93626	0.86349	9.93923	0.86942	9.94213	0.87525	9.94496	0.88096	28
36	39	.93326	.85754	.93631	.86359	.93928	.86952	.94218	.87534	.94500	.88105	24
40	40	.93331	.85764	.93636	.86369	.93933	.86962	.94223	.87544	.94505	.88115	20
44	41	.93336	.85774	.93641	.86379	.93938	.86972	.94227	.87554	.94509	.88124	16
48	42	9.93341	0.85785	9.93646	0.86389	9.93943	0.86982	9.94232	0.87563	9.94514	0.88133	12
52	43	.93346	.85795	.93651	.86399	.93948	.86991	.94237	.87573	.94519	.88143	8
56	44	9.93351	0.85805	9.93656	0.86409	9.93952	0.87001	9.94242	0.87582	9.94523	0.88152	4
		14h 57m		14h 53m		14h 49m		14h 45m		14h 41m		

s	′	9h 3m Log. Hav.	135° Nat. Hav.	9h 7m Log. Hav.	136° Nat. Hav.	9h 11m Log. Hav.	137° Nat. Hav.	9h 15m Log. Hav.	138° Nat. Hav.	9h 19m Log. Hav.	139° Nat. Hav.	s
0	45	9.93356	0.85815	9.93661	0.86419	9.93957	0.87011	9.94246	0.87592	9.94528	0.88162	60
4	46	.93362	.85825	.93666	.86429	.93962	.87021	.94251	.87602	.94533	.88171	56
8	47	.93367	.85835	.93671	.86438	.93967	.87030	.94256	.87611	.94537	.88180	52
12	48	.93372	.85846	.93676	.86448	.93972	.87040	.94261	.87621	.94542	.88190	48
16	49	9.93377	0.85856	9.93681	0.86458	9.93977	0.87050	9.94265	0.87630	9.94546	0.88199	44
20	50	.93382	.85866	.93686	.86468	.93982	.87060	.94270	.87640	.94551	.88209	40
24	51	.93387	.85876	.93691	.86478	.93987	.87070	.94275	.87649	.94556	.88218	36
28	52	.93392	.85886	.93696	.86488	.93991	.87079	.94280	.87659	.94560	.88227	32
32	53	9.93397	0.85896	9.93701	0.86498	9.93996	0.87089	9.94284	0.87669	9.94565	0.88237	28
36	54	.93403	.85906	.93706	.86508	.94001	.87099	.94289	.87678	.94570	.88246	24
40	55	.93408	.85916	.93711	.86518	.94006	.87109	.94294	.87688	.94574	.88255	20
44	56	.93413	.85926	.93716	.86528	.94011	.87118	.94299	.87697	.94579	.88265	16
48	57	9.93418	0.85937	9.93721	0.86538	9.94016	0.87128	9.94303	0.87707	9.94583	0.88274	12
52	58	.93423	.85947	.93726	.86548	.94021	.87138	.94308	.87716	.94588	.88284	8
56	59	.93428	.85957	.93731	.86558	.94026	.87148	.94313	.87726	.94593	.88293	4
60	60	9.93433	0.85967	9.93736	0.86568	9.94030	0.87157	9.94318	0.87735	9.94597	0.88302	0
		14h 56m		14h 52m		14h 48m		14h 44m		14h 40m		

TABLE 34.

Haversines.

s	′	9h 20m 140° Log. Hav.	Nat. Hav.	9h 24m 141° Log. Hav.	Nat. Hav.	9h 28m 142° Log. Hav.	Nat. Hav.	9h 32m 143° Log. Hav.	Nat. Hav.	9h 36m 144° Log. Hav.	Nat. Hav.	s
0	0	9.94597	0.88302	9.94869	0.88857	9.95134	0.89401	9.95391	0.89932	9.95641	0.90451	60
4	1	.94602	.88312	.94874	.88866	.95138	.89409	.95396	.89941	.95645	.90459	56
8	2	.94606	.88321	.94878	.88876	.95143	.89418	.95400	.89949	.95649	.90468	52
12	3	.94611	.88330	.94883	.88885	.95147	.89427	.95404	.89958	.95654	.90476	48
16	4	9.94616	0.88340	9.94887	0.88894	9.95151	0.89436	9.95408	0.89967	9.95658	0.90485	44
20	5	.94620	.88349	.94892	.88903	.95156	.89445	.95412	.89976	.95662	.90494	40
24	6	.94625	.88358	.94896	.88912	.95160	.89454	.95417	.89984	.95666	.90502	36
28	7	.94629	.88368	.94901	.88921	.95164	.89463	.95421	.89993	.95670	.90511	32
32	8	9.94634	0.88377	9.94905	0.88930	9.95169	0.89472	9.95425	0.90002	9.95674	0.90519	28
36	9	.94638	.88386	.94909	.88940	.95173	.89481	.95429	.90010	.95678	.90528	24
40	10	.94643	.88396	.94914	.88949	.95177	.89490	.95433	.90019	.95682	.90537	20
44	11	.94648	.88405	.94918	.88958	.95182	.89499	.95438	.90028	.95686	.90545	16
48	12	9.94652	0.88414	9.94923	0.88967	9.95186	0.89508	9.95442	0.90037	9.95690	0.90553	12
52	13	.94657	.88423	.94927	.88976	.95190	.89517	.95446	.90045	.95694	.90562	8
56	14	9.94661	0.88433	9.94932	0.88985	9.95195	0.89526	9.95450	0.90054	9.95699	0.90570	4
		14h 39m		14h 35m		14h 31m		14h 27m		14h 23m		

s	′	9h 21m 140° Log. Hav.	Nat. Hav.	9h 25m 141° Log. Hav.	Nat. Hav.	9h 29m 142° Log. Hav.	Nat. Hav.	9h 33m 143° Log. Hav.	Nat. Hav.	9h 37m 144° Log. Hav.	Nat. Hav.	s
0	15	9.94666	0.88442	9.94936	0.88994	9.95199	0.89534	9.95454	0.90063	9.95703	0.90579	60
4	16	.94670	.88451	.94941	.89003	.95203	.89543	.95459	.90071	.95707	.90588	56
8	17	.94675	.88461	.94945	.89012	.95208	.89552	.95463	.90080	.95711	.90596	52
12	18	.94680	.88470	.94950	.89022	.95212	.89561	.95467	.90089	.95715	.90604	48
16	19	9.94684	0.88479	9.94954	0.89031	9.95216	0.89570	9.95471	0.90097	9.95719	0.90613	44
20	20	.94689	.88489	.94958	.89040	.95221	.89579	.95475	.90106	.95723	.90621	40
24	21	.94693	.88498	.94963	.89049	.95225	.89588	.95480	.90115	.95727	.90630	36
28	22	.94698	.88507	.94967	.89058	.95229	.89597	.95484	.90124	.95731	.90638	32
32	23	9.94702	0.88516	9.94972	0.89067	o.95234	0.89606	9.95488	0.90132	9.95735	0.90647	28
36	24	.94707	.88526	.94976	.89076	.95238	.89614	.95492	.90141	.95739	.90655	24
40	25	.94711	.88535	.94981	.89085	.95242	.89623	.95496	.90150	.95743	.90664	20
44	26	.94716	.88544	.94985	.89094	.95246	.89632	.95501	.90158	.95747	.90672	16
48	27	9.94721	0.88553	9.94989	0.89103	9.95251	0.89641	9.95505	0.90167	9.95751	0.90680	12
52	28	.94725	.88563	.94994	.89112	.95255	.89650	.95509	.90176	.95755	.90689	8
56	29	9.94730	0.88572	9.94998	0.89121	9.95259	0.89659	9.95513	0.90184	9.95759	0.90697	4
		14h 38m		14h 34m		14h 30m		14h 26m		14h 22m		

s	′	9h 22m 140° Log. Hav.	Nat. Hav.	9h 26m 141° Log. Hav.	Nat. Hav.	9h 30m 142° Log. Hav.	Nat. Hav.	9h 34m 143° Log. Hav.	Nat. Hav.	9h 38m 144° Log. Hav.	Nat. Hav.	s
0	30	9.94734	0.88581	9.95003	0.89130	9.95264	0.89668	9.95517	0.90193	9.95763	0.90706	60
4	31	.94739	.88590	.95007	.89139	.95268	.89677	.95521	.90201	.95768	.90714	56
8	32	.94743	.88600	.95011	.89149	.95272	.89685	.95526	.90210	.95772	.90723	52
12	33	.94748	.88609	.95016	.89158	.95276	.89694	.95530	.90219	.95776	.90731	48
16	34	9.94752	0.88618	9.95020	0.89167	9.95281	0.89703	9.95534	0.90227	9.95780	0.90740	44
20	35	.94757	.88627	.95025	.89176	.95285	.89712	.95538	.90236	.95784	.90748	40
24	36	.94761	.88637	.95029	.89185	.95289	.89721	.95542	.90245	.95788	.90756	36
28	37	.94766	.88646	.95033	.89194	.95294	.89730	.95546	.90253	.95792	.90765	32
32	38	9.94770	0.88655	9.95038	0.89203	9.95298	0.89738	9.95550	0.90262	9.95796	0.90773	28
36	39	.94774	.88664	.95042	.89212	.95302	.89747	.95555	.90271	.95800	.90792	24
40	40	.94779	.88674	.95047	.89221	.95306	.89756	.95559	.90279	.95804	.90790	20
44	41	.94784	.88683	.95051	.89230	.95311	.89765	.95563	.90288	.95808	.90798	16
48	42	9.94788	0.88692	9.95055	0.89239	9.95315	0.89774	9.95567	0.90296	9.95812	0.90807	12
52	43	.94793	.88701	.95060	.89248	.95319	.89783	.95571	.90305	.95816	.90815	8
56	44	9.94797	0.88710	9.95064	0.89257	9.95323	0.89791	9.95575	0.90314	9.95820	0.90824	4
		14h 37m		14h 33m		14h 29m		14h 25m		14h 21m		

s	′	9h 23m 140° Log. Hav.	Nat. Hav.	9h 27m 141° Log. Hav.	Nat. Hav.	9h 31m 142° Log. Hav.	Nat. Hav.	9h 35m 143° Log. Hav.	Nat. Hav.	9h 39m 144° Log. Hav.	Nat. Hav.	s
0	45	9.94802	0.88720	9.95069	0.89266	9.95328	0.89800	9.95579	0.90322	9.95824	0.90832	60
4	46	.94806	.88729	.95073	.89275	.95332	.89809	.95584	.90331	.95828	.90840	56
8	47	.94811	.88738	.95077	.89284	.95336	.89818	.95588	.90339	.95832	.90849	52
12	48	.94815	.88747	.95082	.89293	.95340	.89827	.95592	.90348	.95836	.90857	48
16	49	9.94820	0.88756	9.95086	0.89302	9.95345	0.89835	9.95596	0.90357	9.95840	0.90866	44
20	50	.94824	.88766	.95090	.89311	.95349	.89844	.95600	.90365	.95844	.90874	40
24	51	.94829	.88775	.95095	.89320	.95353	.89853	.95604	.90374	.95848	.90882	36
28	52	.94833	.88784	.95099	.89329	.95357	.89862	.95608	.90382	.95852	.90891	32
32	53	9.94838	0.88793	9.95104	0.89338	9.95362	0.89870	9.95613	0.90391	9.95856	0.90899	28
36	54	.94842	.88802	.95108	.89347	.95366	.89879	.95617	.90399	.95860	.90907	24
40	55	.94847	.88811	.95112	.89356	.95370	.89888	.95621	.90408	.95864	.90916	20
44	56	.94851	.88821	.95117	.89365	.95374	.89897	.95625	.90417	.95868	.90924	16
48	57	9.94856	0.88830	9.95121	0.89374	9.95379	0.89906	9.95629	0.90425	9.95872	0.90933	12
52	58	.94860	.88839	.95125	.89383	.95383	.89914	.95633	.90434	.95876	.90941	8
56	59	.94865	.88848	.95130	.89392	.95387	.89923	.95637	.90442	.95880	.90949	4
60	60	9.94869	0.88857	9.95134	0.89401	9.95391	0.89932	9.95641	0.90451	9.95884	0.90958	0
		14h 36m		14h 32m		14h 28m		14h 24m		14h 20m		

TABLE 34.

Haversines.

s	′	9h 40m Log. Hav.	145° Nat. Hav.	9h 44m Log. Hav.	146° Nat. Hav.	9h 48m Log. Hav.	147° Nat. Hav.	9h 52m Log. Hav.	148° Nat. Hav.	9h 56m Log. Hav.	149° Nat. Hav.	s
0	0	9.95884	**0.90958**	9.96119	**0.91452**	9.96347	**0.91934**	9.96568	**0.92402**	9.96782	**0.92858**	60
4	1	.95888	**.90966**	.96123	**.91460**	.96351	**.91941**	.96572	**.92410**	.96786	**.92866**	56
8	2	.95892	**.90974**	.96127	**.91468**	.96355	**.91949**	.96576	**.92418**	.96789	**.92873**	52
12	3	.95896	**.90983**	.96131	**.91476**	.96359	**.91957**	.96579	**.92426**	.96793	**.92881**	48
16	4	9.95900	**0.90991**	9.96135	**0.91484**	9.96362	**0.91965**	9.96583	**0.92433**	9.96796	**0.92888**	44
20	5	.95904	**.90999**	.96139	**.91493**	.96366	**.91973**	.96586	**.92441**	.96800	**.92896**	40
24	6	.95908	**.91008**	.96142	**.91501**	.96370	**.91981**	.96590	**.92449**	.96803	**.92903**	36
28	7	.95912	**.91016**	.96146	**.91509**	.96374	**.91989**	.96594	**.92456**	.96807	**.92911**	32
32	8	9.95916	**0.91024**	9.96150	**0.91517**	9.96377	**0.91997**	9.96597	**0.92464**	9.96810	**0.92918**	28
36	9	.95920	**.91033**	.96154	**.91525**	.96381	**.92005**	.96601	**.92472**	.96814	**.92926**	24
40	10	.95924	**.91041**	.96158	**.91533**	.96385	**.92013**	.96604	**.92479**	.96817	**.92933**	20
44	11	.95928	**.91049**	.96162	**.91541**	.96388	**.92020**	.96608	**.92487**	.96821	**.92941**	16
48	12	9.95932	**0.91057**	9.96165	**0.91549**	9.96392	**0.92028**	9.96612	**0.92495**	9.96824	**0.92948**	12
52	13	.95936	**.91066**	.96169	**.91557**	.96396	**.92036**	.96615	**.92502**	.96827	**.92955**	8
56	14	9.95939	**0.91074**	9.96173	**0.91565**	9.96400	**0.92044**	9.96619	**0.92510**	9.96831	**0.92963**	4
		14h 19m		14h 15m		14h 11m		14h 7m		14h 3m		

s	′	9h 41m Log. Hav.	145° Nat. Hav.	9h 45m Log. Hav.	146° Nat. Hav.	9h 49m Log. Hav.	147° Nat. Hav.	9h 53m Log. Hav.	148° Nat. Hav.	9h 57m Log. Hav.	149° Nat. Hav.	s
0	15	9.95943	**0.91082**	9.96177	**0.91574**	9.96403	**0.92052**	9.96622	**0.92518**	9.96834	**0.92970**	60
4	16	.95947	**.91091**	.96181	**.91582**	.96407	**.92060**	.96626	**.92525**	.96837	**.92978**	56
8	17	.95951	**.91099**	.96185	**.91590**	.96411	**.92068**	.96630	**.92533**	.96841	**.92985**	52
12	18	.95955	**.91107**	.96188	**.91598**	.96414	**.92076**	.96633	**.92541**	.96845	**.92993**	48
16	19	9.95959	**0.91115**	9.96192	**0.91606**	9.96418	**0.92083**	9.96637	**0.92548**	9.96848	**0.93000**	44
20	20	.95963	**.91124**	.96196	**.91614**	.96422	**.92091**	.96640	**.92556**	.96852	**.93007**	40
24	21	.95967	**.91132**	.96200	**.91622**	.96426	**.92099**	.96644	**.92563**	.96855	**.93015**	36
28	22	.95971	**.91140**	.96204	**.91630**	.96429	**.92107**	.96648	**.92571**	.96859	**.93022**	32
32	23	9.95975	**0.91149**	9.96208	**0.91638**	9.96433	**0.92115**	9.96651	**0.92579**	9.96862	**0.93030**	28
36	24	.95979	**.91157**	.96211	**.91646**	.96437	**.92123**	.96655	**.92586**	.96866	**.93037**	24
40	25	.95983	**.91165**	.96215	**.91654**	.96440	**.92130**	.96658	**.92594**	.96869	**.93045**	20
44	26	.95987	**.91173**	.96219	**.91662**	.96444	**.92138**	.96662	**.92602**	.96873	**.93052**	16
48	27	9.95991	**0.91182**	9.96223	**0.91670**	9.96448	**0.92146**	9.96665	**0.92609**	9.96876	**0.93059**	12
52	28	.95995	**.91190**	.96227	**.91678**	.96451	**.92154**	.96669	**.92617**	.96879	**.93067**	8
56	29	9.95999	**0.91198**	9.96230	**0.91686**	9.96455	**0.92162**	9.96673	**0.92624**	9.96883	**0.93074**	4
		14h 18m		14h 14m		14h 10m		14h 6m		14h 2m		

s	′	9h 42m Log. Hav.	145° Nat. Hav.	9h 46m Log. Hav.	146° Nat. Hav.	9h 50m Log. Hav.	147° Nat. Hav.	9h 54m Log. Hav.	148° Nat. Hav.	9h 58m Log. Hav.	149° Nat. Hav.	s
0	30	9.96002	**0.91206**	9.96234	**0.91694**	9.96459	**0.92170**	9.96676	**0.92632**	9.96886	**0.93081**	60
4	31	.96006	**.91215**	.96238	**.91702**	.96462	**.92177**	.96680	**.92640**	.96890	**.93089**	56
8	32	.96010	**.91223**	.96242	**.91710**	.96466	**.92185**	.96683	**.92647**	.96894	**.93096**	52
12	33	.96014	**.91231**	.96246	**.91718**	.96470	**.92193**	.96687	**.92655**	.96897	**.93104**	48
16	34	9.96018	**0.91239**	9.96249	**0.91726**	9.96473	**0.92201**	9.96690	**0.92662**	9.96900	**0.93111**	44
20	35	.96022	**.91247**	.96253	**.91734**	.96477	**.92209**	.96694	**.92670**	.96904	**.93118**	40
24	36	.96026	**.91256**	.96257	**.91742**	.96481	**.92216**	.96697	**.92678**	.96907	**.93126**	36
28	37	.96030	**.91264**	.96261	**.91750**	.96484	**.92224**	.96701	**.92685**	.96910	**.93133**	32
32	38	9.96034	**0.91272**	9.96265	**0.91758**	9.96488	**0.92232**	9.96705	**0.92693**	9.96914	**0.93140**	28
36	39	.96038	**.91280**	.96268	**.91766**	.96492	**.92240**	.96708	**.92700**	.96917	**.93148**	24
40	40	.96042	**.91289**	.96272	**.91774**	.96495	**.92248**	.96712	**.92708**	.96921	**.93155**	20
44	41	.96046	**.91297**	.96276	**.91782**	.96499	**.92255**	.96715	**.92715**	.96924	**.93162**	16
48	42	9.96049	**0.91305**	9.96280	**0.91790**	9.96503	**0.92263**	9.96719	**0.92723**	9.96928	**0.93170**	12
52	43	.96053	**.91313**	.96283	**.91798**	.96506	**.92271**	.96722	**.92731**	.96931	**.93177**	8
56	44	9.96057	**0.91321**	9.96287	**0.91806**	9.96510	**0.92279**	9.96726	**0.92738**	9.96934	**0.93184**	4
		14h 17m		14h 13m		14h 9m		14h 5m		14h 1m		

s	′	9h 43m Log. Hav.	145° Nat. Hav.	9h 47m Log. Hav.	146° Nat. Hav.	9h 51m Log. Hav.	147° Nat. Hav.	9h 55m Log. Hav.	148° Nat. Hav.	9h 59m Log. Hav.	149° Nat. Hav.	s
0	45	9.96061	**0.91329**	9.96291	**0.91814**	9.96514	**0.92286**	9.96729	**0.92746**	9.96938	**0.93192**	60
4	46	.96065	**.91338**	.96295	**.91822**	.96517	**.92294**	.96733	**.92753**	.96941	**.93199**	56
8	47	.96069	**.91346**	.96299	**.91830**	.96521	**.92302**	.96736	**.92761**	.96945	**.93206**	52
12	48	.96073	**.91354**	.96302	**.91838**	.96525	**.92310**	.96740	**.92768**	.96948	**.93214**	48
16	49	9.96077	**0.91362**	9.96306	**0.91846**	9.96528	**0.92317**	9.96743	**0.92776**	9.96951	**0.93221**	44
20	50	.96081	**.91370**	.96310	**.91854**	.96532	**.92325**	.96747	**.92783**	.96955	**.93228**	40
24	51	.96084	**.91379**	.96314	**.91862**	.96536	**.92333**	.96750	**.92791**	.96958	**.93236**	36
28	52	.96088	**.91387**	.96317	**.91870**	.96539	**.92341**	.96754	**.92798**	.96962	**.93243**	32
32	53	9.96092	**0.91395**	9.96321	**0.91878**	9.96543	**0.92348**	9.96758	**0.92806**	9.96965	**0.93250**	28
36	54	.96096	**.91403**	.96325	**.91886**	.96547	**.92356**	.96761	**.92813**	.96968	**.93258**	24
40	55	.96100	**.91411**	.96329	**.91894**	.96550	**.92364**	.96765	**.92821**	.96972	**.93265**	20
44	56	.96104	**.91419**	.96332	**.91902**	.96554	**.92372**	.96768	**.92828**	.96975	**.93272**	16
48	57	9.96108	**0.91427**	9.96336	**0.91910**	9.96557	**0.92379**	9.96772	**0.92836**	9.96979	**0.93279**	12
52	58	.96112	**.91436**	.96340	**.91918**	.96561	**.92387**	.96775	**.92843**	.96982	**.93287**	8
56	59	.96115	**.91444**	.96344	**.91926**	.96565	**.92394**	.96779	**.92851**	.96985	**.93294**	4
60	60	9.96119	**0.91452**	9.96347	**0.91934**	9.96568	**0.92402**	9.96782	**0.92858**	9.96989	**0.93301**	0
		14h 16m		14h 12m		14h 8m		14h 4m		14h 0m		

Haversines.

s	′	10h 0m 150° Log. Hav.	Nat. Hav.	10h 4m 151° Log. Hav.	Nat. Hav.	10h 8m 152° Log. Hav.	Nat. Hav.	10h 12m 153° Log. Hav.	Nat. Hav.	10h 16m 154° Log. Hav.	Nat. Hav.	s
0	0	9.96989	**0.93301**	9.97188	**0.93731**	9.97381	**0.94147**	9.97566	**0.94550**	9.97745	**0.94940**	60
4	1	.96992	**.93309**	.97192	**.93738**	.97384	**.94154**	.97569	**.95557**	.97748	**.94946**	56
8	2	.96996	**.93316**	.97195	**.93745**	.97387	**.94161**	.97572	**.94564**	.97751	**.94952**	52
12	3	.96999	**.93323**	.97198	**.93752**	.97390	**.94168**	.97575	**.94570**	.97754	**.94959**	48
16	4	9.97002	**0.93330**	9.97201	**0.93759**	9.97393	**0.94175**	9.97578	**0.94577**	9.97756	**0.94965**	44
20	5	.97006	**.93338**	.97205	**.93766**	.97397	**.94181**	.97581	**.94583**	.97759	**.94972**	40
24	6	.97009	**.93345**	.97208	**.93773**	.97400	**.94188**	.97584	**.94590**	.97762	**.94978**	36
28	7	.97012	**.93352**	.97211	**.93780**	.97403	**.94195**	.97587	**.94596**	.97765	**.94984**	32
32	8	9.97016	**0.93359**	9.97214	**0.93787**	9.97406	**0.94202**	9.97591	**0.94603**	9.97768	**0.94991**	28
36	9	.97019	**.93367**	.97218	**.93794**	.97409	**.94209**	.97594	**.94610**	.97771	**.94997**	24
40	10	.97022	**.93374**	.97221	**.93801**	.97412	**.94215**	.97597	**.94616**	.97774	**.95003**	20
44	11	.97026	**.93381**	.97224	**.93808**	.97415	**.94222**	.97600	**.94623**	.97777	**.95010**	16
48	12	9.97029	**0.93388**	9.97227	**0.93815**	9.97418	**0.94229**	9.97603	**0.94629**	9.97780	**0.95016**	12
52	13	.97033	**.93395**	.97231	**.93822**	.97422	**.94236**	.97606	**.94636**	.97783	**.95022**	8
56	14	9.97036	**0.93403**	9.97234	**0.93829**	9.97425	**0.94243**	9.97609	**0.94642**	9.97785	**0.95029**	4
		13h 59m		13h 55m		13h 51m		13h 47m		13h 43m		

s	′	10h 1m 150° Log. Hav.	Nat. Hav.	10h 5m 151° Log. Hav.	Nat. Hav.	10h 9m 152° Log. Hav.	Nat. Hav.	10h 13m 153° Log. Hav.	Nat. Hav.	10h 17m 154° Log. Hav.	Nat. Hav.	s
0	15	9.97039	**0.93410**	9.97237	**0.93836**	9.97428	**0.94249**	9.97612	**0.94649**	9.97788	**0.95035**	60
4	16	.97043	**.93417**	.97240	**.93843**	.97431	**.94256**	.97615	**.94655**	.97791	**.95041**	56
8	17	.97046	**.93424**	.97244	**.93850**	.97434	**.94263**	.97618	**.94662**	.97794	**.95048**	52
12	18	.97049	**.93432**	.97247	**.93857**	.97437	**.94270**	.97621	**.94669**	.97797	**.95054**	48
16	19	9.97052	**0.93439**	9.97250	**0.93864**	9.97440	**0.94276**	9.97624	**0.94675**	9.97800	**0.95060**	44
20	20	.97056	**.93446**	.97253	**.93871**	.97443	**.94283**	.97627	**.94682**	.97803	**.95066**	40
24	21	.97059	**.93453**	.97257	**.93878**	.97447	**.94290**	.97630	**.94688**	.97806	**.95073**	36
28	22	.97063	**.93460**	.97260	**.93885**	.97450	**.94297**	.97633	**.94695**	.97808	**.95079**	32
32	23	9.97066	**0.93468**	9.97263	**0.93892**	9.97453	**0.94303**	9.97636	**0.94701**	9.97811	**0.95085**	28
36	24	.97069	**.93475**	.97266	**.93899**	.97456	**.94310**	.97639	**.94708**	.97814	**.95092**	24
40	25	.97073	**.93482**	.97269	**.93906**	.97459	**.94317**	.97642	**.94714**	.97817	**.95098**	20
44	26	.97076	**.93489**	.97273	**.93913**	.97462	**.94324**	.97645	**.94721**	.97820	**.95104**	16
48	27	9.97079	**0.93496**	9.97276	**0.93920**	9.97465	**0.94330**	9.97647	**0.94727**	9.97823	**0.95111**	12
52	28	.97083	**.93503**	.97279	**.93927**	.97468	**.94337**	.97650	**.94734**	.97826	**.95117**	8
56	29	9.97086	**0.93511**	9.97282	**0.93934**	9.97471	**0.94344**	9.97653	**0.94740**	9.97829	**0.95123**	4
		13h 58m		13h 54m		13h 50m		13h 46m		13h 42m		

s	′	10h 2m 150° Log. Hav.	Nat. Hav.	10h 6m 151° Log. Hav.	Nat. Hav.	10h 10m 152° Log. Hav.	Nat. Hav.	10h 14m 153° Log. Hav.	Nat. Hav.	10h 18m 154° Log. Hav.	Nat. Hav.	s
0	30	9.97089	**0.93518**	9.97285	**0.93941**	9.97474	**0.94351**	9.97656	**0.94747**	9.97831	**0.95129**	60
4	31	.97093	**.93525**	.97289	**.93948**	.97478	**.94357**	.97659	**.94753**	.97834	**.95136**	56
8	32	.97096	**.93532**	.97292	**.93955**	.97481	**.94364**	.97662	**.94760**	.97837	**.95142**	52
12	33	.97099	**.93539**	.97295	**.93962**	.97484	**.94371**	.97665	**.94766**	.97840	**.95148**	48
16	34	9.97103	**0.93546**	9.97298	**0.93969**	9.97487	**0.94377**	9.97668	**0.94773**	9.97843	**0.95154**	44
20	35	.97106	**.93554**	.97301	**.93976**	.97490	**.94384**	.97671	**.94779**	.97846	**.95161**	40
24	36	.97109	**.93561**	.97305	**.93982**	.97493	**.94391**	.97674	**.94786**	.97849	**.95167**	36
28	37	.97113	**.93568**	.97308	**.93989**	.97496	**.94397**	.97677	**.94792**	.97851	**.95173**	32
32	38	9.97116	**0.93575**	9.97311	**0.93996**	9.97499	**0.94404**	9.97680	**0.94799**	9.97854	**0.95179**	28
36	39	.97119	**.93582**	.97314	**.94003**	.97502	**.94411**	.97683	**.94805**	.97857	**.95185**	24
40	40	.97123	**.93589**	.97317	**.94010**	.97505	**.94418**	.97686	**.94811**	.97860	**.95192**	20
44	41	.97126	**.93596**	.97321	**.94017**	.97508	**.94424**	.97689	**.94818**	.97863	**.95198**	16
48	42	9.97129	**0.93603**	9.97324	**0.94024**	9.97511	**0.94431**	9.97692	**0.94824**	9.97866	**0.95204**	12
52	43	.97132	**.93611**	.97327	**.94031**	.97514	**.94438**	.97695	**.94831**	.97868	**.95210**	8
56	44	9.97136	**0.93618**	9.97330	**0.94038**	9.97518	**0.94444**	9.97698	**0.94837**	9.97871	**0.95217**	4
		13h 57m		13h 53m		13h 49m		13h 45m		13h 41m		

s	′	10h 3m 150° Log. Hav.	Nat. Hav.	10h 7m 151° Log. Hav.	Nat. Hav.	10h 11m 152° Log. Hav.	Nat. Hav.	10h 15m 153° Log. Hav.	Nat. Hav.	10h 19m 154° Log. Hav.	Nat. Hav.	s
0	45	9.97139	**0.93625**	9.97333	**0.94045**	9.97521	**0.94451**	9.97701	**0.94844**	9.97874	**0.95223**	60
4	46	.97142	**.93632**	.97337	**.94051**	.97524	**.94458**	.97704	**.94850**	.97877	**.95229**	56
8	47	.97146	**.93639**	.97340	**.94058**	.97527	**.94464**	.97707	**.94857**	.97880	**.95235**	52
12	48	.97149	**.93646**	.97343	**.94065**	.97530	**.94471**	.97710	**.94863**	.97883	**.95241**	48
16	49	9.97152	**0.93653**	9.97346	**0.94072**	9.97533	**0.94477**	9.97713	**0.94869**	9.97885	**0.95248**	44
20	50	.97156	**.93660**	.97349	**.94079**	.97536	**.94484**	.97716	**.94876**	.97888	**.95254**	40
24	51	.97159	**.93667**	.97352	**.94086**	.97539	**.94491**	.97718	**.94882**	.97891	**.95260**	36
28	52	.97162	**.93674**	.97356	**.94093**	.97542	**.94497**	.97721	**.94889**	.97894	**.95266**	32
32	53	9.97165	**0.93682**	9.97359	**0.94099**	9.97545	**0.94504**	9.97724	**0.94895**	9.97897	**0.95272**	28
36	54	.97169	**.93689**	.97362	**.94106**	.97548	**.94511**	.97727	**.94901**	.97899	**.95278**	24
40	55	.97172	**.93696**	.97365	**.94113**	.97551	**.94517**	.97730	**.94908**	.97902	**.95285**	20
44	56	.97175	**.93703**	.97368	**.94120**	.97554	**.94524**	.97733	**.94914**	.97905	**.95291**	16
48	57	9.97179	**0.93710**	9.97371	**0.94127**	9.97557	**0.94531**	9.97736	**0.94921**	9.97908	**0.95297**	12
52	58	.97182	**.93717**	.97375	**.94134**	.97560	**.94537**	.97739	**.94927**	.97911	**.95303**	8
56	59	.97185	**.93724**	.97378	**.94141**	.97563	**.94544**	.97742	**.94933**	.97914	**.95309**	4
60	60	9.97188	**0.93731**	9.97381	**0.94147**	9.97566	**0.94550**	9.97745	**0.94940**	9.97916	**0.95315**	0
		13h 56m		13h 52m		13h 48m		13h 44m		13h 40m		

TABLE 34.

Haversines.

s	′	10h 20m 155° Log. Hav.	Nat. Hav.	10h 24m 156° Log. Hav.	Nat. Hav.	10h 28m 157° Log. Hav.	Nat. Hav.	10h 32m 158° Log. Hav.	Nat. Hav.	10h 36m 159° Log. Hav.	Nat. Hav.	s
0	**0**	9.97916	**0.95315**	9.98081	**0.95677**	9.98239	**0.96025**	9.98389	**0.96359**	9.98533	**0.96679**	*60*
4	**1**	.97919	**.95322**	.98084	**.95683**	.98241	**.96031**	.98392	**.96365**	.98536	**.96684**	*56*
8	**2**	.97922	**.95328**	.98086	**.95689**	.98244	**.96037**	.98394	**.96370**	.98538	**.96689**	*52*
12	**3**	.97925	**.95334**	.98089	**.95695**	.98246	**.96042**	.98397	**.96376**	.98540	**.96695**	*48*
16	**4**	9.97927	**0.95340**	9.98092	**0.95701**	9.98249	**0.96048**	9.98399	**0.96381**	9.98543	**0.96700**	*44*
20	**5**	.97930	**.95346**	.98094	**.95707**	.98251	**.96054**	.98402	**.96386**	.98545	**.96705**	*40*
24	**6**	.97933	**.95352**	.98097	**.95713**	.98254	**.96059**	.98404	**.96392**	.98547	**.96710**	*36*
28	**7**	.97936	**.95358**	.98100	**.95719**	.98256	**.96065**	.98406	**.96397**	.98550	**.96715**	*32*
32	**8**	9.97939	**0.95364**	9.98102	**0.95724**	9.98259	**0.96071**	9.98409	**0.96403**	9.98552	**0.96721**	*28*
36	**9**	.97941	**.95371**	.98105	**.95730**	.98262	**.96076**	.98411	**.96408**	.98554	**.96726**	*24*
40	**10**	.97944	**.95377**	.98108	**.95736**	.98264	**.96082**	.98414	**.96413**	.98557	**.96731**	*20*
44	**11**	.97947	**.95383**	.98110	**.95742**	.98267	**.96088**	.98416	**.96419**	.98559	**.96736**	*16*
48	**12**	9.97950	**0.95389**	9.98113	**0.95748**	9.98269	**0.96093**	9.98419	**0.96424**	9.98561	**0.96741**	*12*
52	**13**	.97953	**.95395**	.98116	**.95754**	.98272	**.96099**	.98421	**.96430**	.98564	**.96746**	*8*
56	**14**	9.97955	**0.95401**	9.98118	**0.95760**	9.98274	**0.96104**	9.98424	**0.96435**	9.98566	**0.96752**	*4*
		13h 39m		*13h 35m*		*13h 31m*		*13h 27m*		*13h 23m*		

s	′	10h 21m 155°		10h 25m 156°		10h 29m 157°		10h 33m 158°		10h 37m 159°		s
0	**15**	9.97958	**0.95407**	9.98121	**0.95766**	9.98277	**0.96110**	9.98426	**0.96440**	9.98568	**0.96757**	*60*
4	**16**	.97961	**.95413**	.98124	**.95771**	.98279	**.96116**	.98428	**.96446**	.98570	**.96762**	*56*
8	**17**	.97964	**.95419**	.98126	**.95777**	.98282	**.96121**	.98431	**.96451**	.98573	**.96767**	*52*
12	**18**	.97966	**.95425**	.98129	**.95783**	.98285	**.96127**	.98433	**.96457**	.98575	**.96772**	*48*
16	**19**	9.97969	**0.95431**	9.98132	**0.95789**	9.98287	**0.96133**	9.98436	**0.96462**	9.98577	**0.96777**	*44*
20	**20**	.97972	**.95438**	.98134	**.95795**	.98290	**.96138**	.98438	**.96467**	.98580	**.96782**	*40*
24	**21**	.97975	**.95444**	.98137	**.95801**	.98292	**.96144**	.98440	**.96473**	.98582	**.96788**	*36*
28	**22**	.97977	**.95450**	.98139	**.95806**	.98295	**.96149**	.98443	**.96478**	.98584	**.96793**	*32*
32	**23**	9.97980	**0.95456**	9.98142	**0.95812**	9.98297	**0.96155**	9.98445	**0.96483**	9.98587	**0.96798**	*28*
36	**24**	.97983	**.95462**	.98145	**.95818**	.98300	**.96161**	.98448	**.96489**	.98589	**.96803**	*24*
40	**25**	.97986	**.95468**	.98147	**.95824**	.98302	**.96166**	.98450	**.96494**	.98591	**.96808**	*20*
44	**26**	.97988	**.95474**	.98150	**.95830**	.98305	**.96172**	.98453	**.96500**	.98593	**.96813**	*16*
48	**27**	9.97991	**0.95480**	9.98153	**0.95836**	9.98307	**0.96177**	9.98455	**0.96505**	9.98596	**0.96818**	*12*
52	**28**	.97994	**.95486**	.98155	**.95841**	.98310	**.96183**	.98457	**.96510**	.98598	**.96823**	*8*
56	**29**	9.97997	**0.95492**	9.98158	**0.95847**	9.98312	**0.96188**	9.98460	**0.96516**	9.98600	**0.96829**	*4*
		13h 38m		*13h 34m*		*13h 30m*		*13h 26m*		*13h 22m*		

s	′	10h 22m 155°		10h 26m 156°		10h 30m 157°		10h 34m 158°		10h 38m 159°		s
0	**30**	9.97999	**0.95498**	9.98161	**0.95853**	9.98315	**0.96194**	9.98462	**0.96521**	9.98603	**0.96834**	*60*
4	**31**	.98002	**.95504**	.98163	**.95859**	.98317	**.96200**	.98465	**.96526**	.98605	**.96839**	*56*
8	**32**	.98005	**.95510**	.98166	**.95865**	.98320	**.96205**	.98467	**.96532**	.98607	**.96844**	*52*
12	**33**	.98008	**.95516**	.98168	**.95870**	.98322	**.96211**	.98469	**.96537**	.98609	**.96849**	*48*
16	**34**	9.98010	**0.95522**	9.98171	**0.95876**	9.98325	**0.96216**	9.98472	**0.96542**	9.98612	**0.96854**	*44*
20	**35**	.98013	**.95528**	.98174	**.95882**	.98327	**.96222**	.98474	**.96547**	.98614	**.96859**	*40*
24	**36**	.98016	**.95534**	.98176	**.95888**	.98330	**.96227**	.98476	**.96553**	.98616	**.96864**	*36*
28	**37**	.98019	**.95540**	.98179	**.95894**	.98332	**.96223**	.98479	**.96558**	.98619	**.96869**	*32*
32	**38**	9.98021	**0.95546**	9.98182	**0.95899**	9.98335	**0.96238**	9.98481	**0.96563**	9.98621	**0.96874**	*28*
36	**39**	.98024	**.95552**	.98184	**.95905**	.98337	**.96244**	.98484	**.96569**	.98623	**.96879**	*24*
40	**40**	.98027	**.95558**	.98187	**.95911**	.98340	**.96249**	.98486	**.96574**	.98625	**.96884**	*20*
44	**41**	.98030	**.95564**	.98189	**.95917**	.98342	**.96255**	.98488	**.96579**	.98628	**.96889**	*16*
48	**42**	9.98032	**0.95570**	9.98192	**0.95922**	9.98345	**0.96260**	9.98491	**0.96585**	9.98630	**0.96894**	*12*
52	**43**	.98035	**.95576**	.98195	**.95928**	.98347	**.96266**	.98493	**.96590**	.98632	**.96899**	*8*
56	**44**	9.98038	**0.95582**	9.98197	**0.95934**	9.98350	**0.96272**	9.98496	**0.96595**	9.98634	**0.96905**	*4*
		13h 37m		*13h 33m*		*13h 29m*		*13h 25m*		*13h 21m*		

s	′	10h 23m 155°		10h 27m 156°		10h 31m 157°		10h 35m 158°		10h 39m 159°		s
0	**45**	9.98040	**0.95588**	9.98200	**0.95940**	9.98352	**0.96277**	9.98498	**0.96600**	9.98637	**0.96910**	*60*
4	**46**	.98043	**.95594**	.98202	**.95945**	.98355	**.96283**	.98500	**.96606**	.98639	**.96915**	*56*
8	**47**	.98046	**.95600**	.98205	**.95951**	.98357	**.96288**	.98503	**.96611**	.98641	**.96920**	*52*
12	**48**	.98049	**.95606**	.98208	**.95957**	.98360	**.96294**	.98505	**.96616**	.98643	**.96925**	*48*
16	**49**	9.98051	**0.95612**	9.98210	**0.95962**	9.98362	**0.96299**	9.98507	**0.96621**	9.98646	**0.96930**	*44*
20	**50**	.98054	**.95618**	.98213	**.95968**	.98365	**.96305**	.98510	**.96627**	.98648	**.96935**	*40*
24	**51**	.98057	**.95624**	.98215	**.95974**	.98367	**.96310**	.98512	**.96632**	.98650	**.96940**	*36*
28	**52**	.98059	**.95630**	.98218	**.95980**	.98370	**.96315**	.98514	**.96637**	.98652	**.96945**	*32*
32	**53**	9.98062	**0.95636**	9.98221	**0.95985**	9.98372	**0.96321**	9.98517	**0.96642**	9.98655	**0.96950**	*28*
36	**54**	.98065	**.95642**	.98223	**.95991**	.98375	**.96326**	.98519	**.96648**	.98657	**.96955**	*24*
40	**55**	.98067	**.95648**	.98226	**.95997**	.98377	**.96332**	.98521	**.96653**	.98659	**.96960**	*20*
44	**56**	.98070	**.95654**	.98228	**.96002**	.98379	**.96337**	.98524	**.96658**	.98661	**.96965**	*16*
48	**57**	9.98073	**0.95660**	9.98231	**0.96008**	9.98382	**0.96343**	9.98526	**0.96663**	9.98664	**0.96970**	*12*
52	**58**	.98076	**.95665**	.98233	**.96014**	.98384	**.96348**	.98529	**.96669**	.98666	**.96975**	*8*
56	**59**	.98078	**.95671**	.98236	**.96020**	.98387	**.96354**	.98531	**.96674**	.98668	**.96980**	*4*
60	**60**	9.98081	**0.95677**	9.98239	**0.96025**	9.98389	**0.96359**	9.98533	**0.96679**	9.98670	**0.96985**	*0*
		13h 36m		*13h 32m*		*13h 28m*		*13h 24m*		*13h 20m*		

TABLE 34.

Haversines.

s	′	10h 40m 160° Log. Hav.	Nat. Hav.	10h 44m 161° Log. Hav.	Nat. Hav.	10h 48m 162° Log. Hav.	Nat. Hav.	10h 52m 163° Log. Hav.	Nat. Hav.	10h 56m 164° Log. Hav.	Nat. Hav.	s
0	0	9.98670	**0.96985**	9.98801	**0.97276**	9.98924	**0.97553**	9.99041	**0.97815**	9.99151	**0.98063**	60
4	1	.98673	**.96990**	.98803	**.97281**	.98926	**.97557**	.99043	**.97819**	.99152	**.98067**	56
8	2	.98675	**.96995**	.98805	**.97285**	.98928	**.97562**	.99044	**.97824**	.99154	**.98071**	52
12	3	.98677	**.97000**	.98807	**.97290**	.98930	**.97566**	.99046	**.97828**	.99156	**.98075**	48
16	4	9.98679	**0.97005**	9.98809	**0.97295**	9.98932	**0.97571**	9.99048	**0.97832**	9.99158	**0.98079**	44
20	5	.98681	**.97009**	.98811	**.97300**	.98934	**.97575**	.99050	**.97836**	.99159	**.98083**	40
24	6	.98684	**.97014**	.98813	**.97304**	.98936	**.97580**	.99052	**.97841**	.99161	**.98087**	36
28	7	.98686	**.97019**	.98815	**.97309**	.98938	**.97584**	.99054	**.97845**	.99163	**.98091**	32
32	8	9.98688	**0.97024**	9.98817	**0.97314**	9.98940	**0.97589**	9.99056	**0.97849**	9.99165	**0.98095**	28
36	9	.98690	**.97029**	.98819	**.97318**	.98942	**.97593**	.99058	**.97853**	.99166	**.98099**	24
40	10	.98692	**.97034**	.98822	**.97323**	.98944	**.97598**	.99059	**.97858**	.99168	**.98103**	20
44	11	.98695	**.97039**	.98824	**.97328**	.98946	**.97602**	.99061	**.97862**	.99170	**.98107**	16
48	12	9.98697	**0.97044**	9.98826	**0.97332**	9.98948	**0.97606**	9.99063	**0.97866**	9.99172	**0.98111**	12
52	13	.98699	**.97049**	.98828	**.97337**	.98950	**.97611**	.99065	**.97870**	.99173	**.98115**	8
56	14	9.98701	**0.97054**	9.98830	**0.97342**	9.98952	**0.97615**	9.99067	**0.97874**	9.99175	**0.98119**	4
		13h 19m		13h 15m		13h 11m		13h 7m		13h 3m		

s	′	10h 41m 160° Log. Hav.	Nat. Hav.	10h 45m 161° Log. Hav.	Nat. Hav.	10h 49m 162° Log. Hav.	Nat. Hav.	10h 53m 163° Log. Hav.	Nat. Hav.	10h 57m 164° Log. Hav.	Nat. Hav.	s
0	15	9.98703	**0.97059**	9.98832	**0.97347**	9.98954	**0.97620**	9.99069	**0.97879**	9.99177	**0.98123**	60
4	16	.98706	**.97064**	.98834	**.97351**	.98956	**.97624**	.99071	**.97883**	.99179	**.98127**	56
8	17	.98708	**.97069**	.98836	**.97356**	.98958	**.97629**	.99072	**.97887**	.99180	**.98131**	52
12	18	.98710	**.97074**	.98838	**.97361**	.98960	**.97633**	.99074	**.97891**	.99182	**.98135**	48
16	19	9.98712	**0.97078**	9.98840	**0.97365**	9.98962	**0.97637**	9.99076	**0.97895**	9.99184	**0.98139**	44
20	20	.98714	**.97083**	.98842	**.97370**	.98964	**.97642**	.99078	**.97899**	.99186	**.98142**	40
24	21	.98717	**.97088**	.98845	**.97374**	.98966	**.97646**	.99080	**.97904**	.99187	**.98146**	36
28	22	.98719	**.97093**	.98847	**.97379**	.98968	**.97651**	.99082	**.97908**	.99189	**.98150**	32
32	23	9.98721	**0.97098**	9.98849	**0.97384**	9.98970	**0.97655**	9.99084	**0.97912**	9.99191	**0.98154**	28
36	24	.98723	**.97103**	.98851	**.97388**	.98971	**.97660**	.99085	**.97916**	.99193	**.98158**	24
40	25	.98725	**.97108**	.98853	**.97393**	.98973	**.97664**	.99087	**.97920**	.99194	**.98162**	20
44	26	.98728	**.97113**	.98855	**.97398**	.98975	**.97668**	.99089	**.97924**	.99196	**.98166**	16
48	27	9.98730	**0.97117**	9.98857	**0.97402**	9.98977	**0.97673**	9.99091	**0.97929**	9.99198	**0.98170**	12
52	28	.98732	**.97122**	.98859	**.97407**	.98979	**.97677**	.99093	**.97933**	.99200	**.98174**	8
56	29	9.98734	**0.97127**	9.98861	**0.97412**	9.98981	**0.97681**	9.99095	**0.97937**	9.99201	**0.98178**	4
		13h 18m		13h 14m		13h 10m		13h 6m		13h 2m		

s	′	10h 42m 160° Log. Hav.	Nat. Hav.	10h 46m 161° Log. Hav.	Nat. Hav.	10h 50m 162° Log. Hav.	Nat. Hav.	10h 54m 163° Log. Hav.	Nat. Hav.	10h 58m 164° Log. Hav.	Nat. Hav.	s
0	30	9.98736	**0.97132**	9.98863	**0.97416**	9.98983	**0.97686**	9.99096	**0.97941**	9.99203	**0.98182**	60
4	31	.98738	**.97137**	.98865	**.97421**	.98985	**.97690**	.99098	**.97945**	.99205	**.98185**	56
8	32	.98741	**.97142**	.98867	**.97425**	.98987	**.97695**	.99100	**.97949**	.99206	**.98189**	52
12	33	.98743	**.97147**	.98869	**.97430**	.98989	**.97699**	.99102	**.97953**	.99208	**.98193**	48
16	34	9.98745	**0.97151**	9.98871	**0.97435**	9.98991	**0.97703**	9.99104	**0.97957**	9.99210	**0.98197**	44
20	35	.98747	**.97156**	.98873	**.97439**	.98993	**.97708**	.99106	**.97962**	.99212	**.98201**	40
24	36	.98749	**.97161**	.98875	**.97444**	.98995	**.97712**	.99107	**.97966**	.99213	**.98205**	36
28	37	.98751	**.97166**	.98877	**.97448**	.98997	**.97716**	.99109	**.97970**	.99215	**.98209**	32
32	38	9.98754	**0.97171**	9.98880	**0.97453**	9.98999	**0.97721**	9.99111	**0.97974**	9.99217	**0.98212**	28
36	39	.98756	**.97176**	.98882	**.97458**	.99001	**.97725**	.99113	**.97978**	.99218	**.98216**	24
40	40	.98758	**.97180**	.98884	**.97462**	.99003	**.97729**	.99115	**.97982**	.99220	**.98220**	20
44	41	.98760	**.97185**	.98886	**.97467**	.99004	**.97734**	.99116	**.97986**	.99222	**.98224**	16
48	42	9.98762	**0.97190**	9.98888	**0.97471**	9.99006	**0.97738**	9.99118	**0.97990**	9.99223	**0.98228**	12
52	43	.98764	**.97195**	.98890	**.97476**	.99008	**.97742**	.99120	**.97994**	.99225	**.98232**	8
56	44	9.98766	**0.97200**	9.98892	**0.97480**	9.99010	**0.97747**	9.99122	**0.97998**	9.99227	**0.98236**	4
		13h 17m		13h 13m		13h 9m		13h 5m		13h 1m		

s	′	10h 43m 160° Log. Hav.	Nat. Hav.	10h 47m 161° Log. Hav.	Nat. Hav.	10h 51m 162° Log. Hav.	Nat. Hav.	10h 55m 163° Log. Hav.	Nat. Hav.	10h 59m 164° Log. Hav.	Nat. Hav.	s
0	45	9.98769	**0.97204**	9.98894	**0.97485**	9.99012	**0.97751**	9.99124	**0.98002**	9.99229	**0.98239**	60
4	46	.98771	**.97209**	.98896	**.97490**	.99014	**.97755**	.99126	**.98007**	.99230	**.98243**	56
8	47	.98773	**.97214**	.98898	**.97494**	.99016	**.97760**	.99127	**.98011**	.99232	**.98247**	52
12	48	.98775	**.97219**	.98900	**.97499**	.99018	**.97764**	.99129	**.98015**	.99234	**.98251**	48
16	49	9.98777	**0.97224**	9.98902	**0.97503**	9.99020	**0.97768**	9.99131	**0.98019**	9.99235	**0.98255**	44
20	50	98779	**.97228**	.98904	**.97508**	.99022	**.97773**	.99133	**.98023**	.99237	**.98258**	40
24	51	.98781	**.97233**	.98906	**.97512**	.99024	**.97777**	.99135	**.98027**	.99239	**.98262**	36
28	52	.98784	**.97238**	.98908	**.97517**	.99026	**.97781**	.99136	**.98031**	.99240	**.98266**	32
32	53	9.98786	**0.97243**	9.98910	**0.97521**	9.99027	**0.97785**	9.99138	**0.98035**	9.99242	**0.98270**	28
36	54	.98788	**.97247**	.98912	**.97526**	.99029	**.97790**	.99140	**.98039**	.99244	**.98274**	24
40	55	.98790	**.97252**	.98914	**.97530**	.99031	**.97794**	.99142	**.98043**	.99245	**.98277**	20
44	56	.98792	**.97257**	.98916	**.97535**	.99033	**.97798**	.99143	**.98047**	.99247	**.98281**	16
48	57	9.98794	**0.97262**	9.98918	**0.97539**	9.99035	**0.97802**	9.99145	**0.98051**	9.99249	**0.98285**	12
52	58	.98796	**.97266**	.98920	**.97544**	.99037	**.97807**	.99147	**.98055**	.99250	**.98289**	8
56	59	.98798	**.97271**	.98922	**.97548**	.99039	**.97811**	.99149	**.98059**	.99252	**.98293**	4
60	60	9.98801	**0.97276**	9.98924	**0.97553**	9.99041	**0.97815**	9.99151	**0.98063**	9.99254	**0.98296**	0
		13h 16m		13h 12m		13h 8m		13h 4m		13h 0m		

TABLE 34.

Haversines.

s	′	$11^h 0^m$ 165° Log. Hav.	Nat. Hav.	$11^h 4^m$ 166° Log. Hav.	Nat. Hav.	$11^h 8^m$ 167° Log. Hav.	Nat. Hav.	$11^h 12^m$ 168° Log. Hav.	Nat. Hav.	$11^h 16^m$ 169° Log. Hav.	Nat. Hav.	s
0	0	9.99254	**0.98296**	9.99350	**0.98515**	9.99440	**0.98719**	9.99523	**0.98907**	9.99599	**0.99081**	60
4	1	.99255	**.98300**	.99352	**.98518**	.99441	**.98722**	.99524	**.98910**	.99600	**.99084**	56
8	2	.99257	**.98304**	.99353	**.98522**	.99443	**.98725**	.99526	**.98913**	.99602	**.99087**	52
12	3	.99259	**.98308**	.99355	**.98525**	.99444	**.98728**	.99527	**.98916**	.99603	**.99090**	48
16	4	9.99260	**0.98311**	9.99356	**0.98529**	9.99446	**0.98732**	9.99528	**0.98919**	9.99604	**0.99092**	44
20	5	.99262	**.98315**	.99358	**.98532**	.99447	**.98735**	.99529	**.98922**	.99605	**.99095**	40
24	6	.99264	**.98319**	.99359	**.98536**	.99448	**.98738**	.99531	**.98925**	.99606	**.99098**	36
28	7	.99265	**.98323**	.99361	**.98539**	.99450	**.98741**	.99532	**.98928**	.99608	**.99101**	32
32	8	9.99267	**0.98326**	9.99362	**0.98543**	9.99451	**0.98745**	9.99533	**0.98931**	9.99609	**0.99103**	28
36	9	.99269	**.98330**	.99364	**.98546**	.99453	**.98748**	.99535	**.98934**	.99610	**.99106**	24
40	10	.99270	**.98334**	.99366	**.98550**	.99454	**.98751**	.99536	**.98937**	.99611	**.99109**	20
44	11	.99272	**.98337**	.99367	**.98553**	.99456	**.98754**	.99537	**.98940**	.99612	**.99112**	16
48	12	9.99274	**0.98341**	9.99369	**0.98557**	9.99457	**0.98757**	9.99539	**0.98943**	9.99614	**0.99114**	12
52	13	.99275	**.98345**	.99370	**.98560**	.99458	**.98761**	.99540	**.98946**	.99615	**.99117**	8
56	14	9.99277	**0.98349**	9.99372	**0.98564**	9.99460	**0.98764**	9.99541	**0.98949**	9.99616	**0.99120**	4
		$12^h 59^m$		$12^h 55^m$		$12^h 51^m$		$12^h 47^m$		$12^h 43^m$		

s	′	$11^h 1^m$ 165°		$11^h 5^m$ 166°		$11^h 9^m$ 167°		$11^h 13^m$ 168°		$11^h 17^m$ 169°		s
0	15	9.99278	**0.98352**	9.99373	**0.98567**	9.99461	**0.98767**	9.99543	**0.98952**	9.99617	**0.99123**	60
4	16	.99280	**.98356**	.99375	**.98571**	.99463	**.98770**	.99544	**.98955**	.99618	**.99125**	56
8	17	.99282	**.98360**	.99376	**.98574**	.99464	**.98774**	.99545	**.98958**	.99620	**.99128**	52
12	18	.99283	**.98363**	.99378	**.98577**	.99465	**.98777**	.99546	**.98961**	.99621	**.99131**	48
16	19	9.99285	**0.98367**	9.99379	**0.98581**	9.99467	**0.98780**	9.99548	**0.98964**	9.99622	**0.99133**	44
20	20	.99287	**.98371**	.99381	**.98584**	.99468	**.98783**	.99549	**.98967**	.99623	**.99136**	40
24	21	.99288	**.98374**	.99382	**.98588**	.99470	**.98786**	.99550	**.98970**	.99624	**.99139**	36
28	22	.99290	**.98378**	.99384	**.98591**	.99471	**.98789**	.99552	**.98973**	.99626	**.99141**	32
32	23	9.99291	**0.98382**	9.99385	**0.98595**	9.99472	**0.98793**	9.99553	**0.98976**	9.99627	**0.99144**	28
36	24	.99293	**.98385**	.99387	**.98598**	.99474	**.98796**	.99554	**.98979**	.99628	**.99147**	24
40	25	.99295	**.98389**	.99388	**.98601**	.99475	**.98799**	.99555	**.98982**	.99629	**.99149**	20
44	26	.99296	**.98393**	.99390	**.98605**	.99477	**.98802**	.99557	**.98985**	.99630	**.99152**	16
48	27	9.99298	**0.98396**	9.99391	**0.98608**	9.99478	**0.98805**	9.99558	**0.98987**	9.99631	**0.99155**	12
52	28	.99300	**.98400**	.99393	**.98611**	.99479	**.98809**	.99559	**.98990**	.99633	**.99157**	8
56	29	9.99301	**0.98404**	9.99394	**0.98615**	9.99481	**0.98812**	9.99561	**0.98993**	9.99634	**0.99160**	4
		$12^h 58^m$		$12^h 54^m$		$12^h 50^m$		$12^h 46^m$		$12^h 42^m$		

s	′	$11^h 2^m$ 165°		$11^h 6^m$ 166°		$11^h 10^m$ 167°		$11^h 14^m$ 168°		$11^h 18^m$ 169°		s
0	30	9.99303	**0.98407**	9.99396	**0.98619**	9.99482	**0.98815**	9.99562	**0.98996**	9.99635	**0.99163**	60
4	31	.99304	**.98411**	.99397	**.98622**	.99484	**.98818**	.99563	**.98999**	.99636	**.99165**	56
8	32	.99306	**.98415**	.99399	**.98625**	.99485	**.98821**	.99564	**.99002**	.99637	**.99168**	52
12	33	.99308	**.98418**	.99400	**.98629**	.99486	**.98824**	.99566	**.99005**	.99638	**.99171**	48
16	34	9.99309	**0.98422**	9.99402	**0.98632**	9.99488	**0.98827**	9.99567	**0.99008**	9.99639	**0.99173**	44
20	35	.99311	**.98426**	.99403	**.98635**	.99489	**.98830**	.99568	**.99011**	.99641	**.99176**	40
24	36	.99312	**.98429**	.99405	**.98639**	.99490	**.98834**	.99569	**.99014**	.99642	**.99179**	36
28	37	.99314	**.98433**	.99406	**.98642**	.99492	**.98837**	.99571	**.99016**	.99643	**.99181**	32
32	38	9.99316	**0.98436**	9.99408	**0.98646**	9.99493	**0.98840**	9.99572	**0.99019**	9.99644	**0.99184**	28
36	39	.99317	**.98440**	.99409	**.98649**	.99495	**.98843**	.99573	**.99022**	.99645	**.99186**	24
40	40	.99319	**.98444**	.99411	**.98652**	.99496	**.98846**	.99575	**.99025**	.99646	**.99189**	20
44	41	.99320	**.98447**	.99412	**.98656**	.99497	**.98849**	.99576	**.99028**	.99648	**.99192**	16
48	42	9.99322	**0.98451**	9.99414	**0.98659**	9.99499	**0.98852**	9.99577	**0.99031**	9.99649	**0.99194**	12
52	43	.99324	**.98454**	.99415	**.98662**	.99500	**.98855**	.99578	**.99034**	.99650	**.99197**	8
56	44	9.99325	**0.98458**	9.99417	**0.98666**	9.99501	**0.98858**	9.99580	**0.99036**	9.99651	**0.99199**	4
		$12^h 57^m$		$12^h 53^m$		$12^h 49^m$		$12^h 45^m$		$12^h 41^m$		

s	′	$11^h 3^m$ 165°		$11^h 7^m$ 166°		$11^h 11^m$ 167°		$11^h 15^m$ 168°		$11^h 19^m$ 169°		s
0	45	9.99327	**0.98462**	9.99418	**0.98669**	9.99503	**0.98862**	9.99581	**0.99039**	9.99652	**0.99202**	60
4	46	.99328	**.98465**	.99420	**.98672**	.99504	**.98865**	.99582	**.99042**	.99653	**.99205**	56
8	47	.99330	**.98469**	.99421	**.98676**	.99505	**.98868**	.99583	**.99045**	.99654	**.99207**	52
12	48	.99331	**.98472**	.99422	**.98679**	.99507	**.98871**	.99584	**.99048**	.99655	**.99210**	48
16	49	9.99333	**0.98476**	9.99424	**0.98682**	9.99508	**0.98874**	9.99586	**0.99051**	9.99657	**0.99212**	44
20	50	.99335	**.98479**	.99425	**.98686**	.99510	**.98877**	.99587	**.99053**	99658	**.99215**	40
24	51	.99336	**.98483**	.99427	**.98689**	.99511	**.98880**	.99588	**.99056**	.99659	**.99217**	36
28	52	.99338	**.98487**	.99429	**.98692**	.99512	**.98883**	.99589	**.99059**	.99660	**.99220**	32
32	53	9.99339	**0.98490**	9.99430	**0.98696**	9.99514	**0.98886**	9.99591	**0.99062**	9.99661	**0.99223**	28
36	54	.99341	**.98494**	.99431	**.98699**	.99515	**.98889**	.99592	**.99065**	.99662	**.99225**	24
40	55	.99342	**.98497**	.99433	**.98702**	.99516	**.98892**	.99593	**.99067**	.99663	**.99228**	20
44	56	.99344	**.98501**	.99434	**.98705**	.99518	**.98895**	.99594	**.99070**	.99664	**.99230**	16
48	57	9.99345	**0.98504**	9.99436	**0.98709**	9.99519	**0.98898**	9.99596	**0.99073**	9.99666	**0.99233**	12
52	58	.99347	**.98508**	.99437	**.98712**	.99520	**.98901**	.99597	**.99076**	.99667	**.99235**	8
56	59	.99349	**.98511**	.99438	**.98715**	.99522	**.98904**	.99598	**.99079**	.99668	**.99238**	4
60	60	9.99350	**0.98515**	9.99440	**0.98719**	9.99523	**0.98907**	9.99599	**0.99081**	9.99669	**0.99240**	0
		$12^h 56^m$		$12^h 52^m$		$12^h 48^m$		$12^h 44^m$		$12^h 40^m$		

TABLE 34.

Haversines.

s	′	11h 20m 170° Log. Hav.	Nat. Hav.	11h 24m 171° Log. Hav.	Nat. Hav.	11h 28m 172° Log. Hav.	Nat. Hav.	11h 32m 173° Log. Hav.	Nat. Hav.	11h 36m 174° Log. Hav.	Nat. Hav.	s
0	0	9.99669	0.99240	9.99732	0.99384	9.99788	0.99513	9.99838	0.99627	9.99881	0.99726	60
4	1	.99670	.99243	.99733	.99387	.99789	.99515	.99839	.99629	.99882	.99728	56
8	2	.99671	.99245	.99734	.99389	.99790	.99517	.99839	.99631	.99882	.99729	52
12	3	.99672	.99248	.99735	.99391	.99791	.99519	.99840	.99633	.99883	.99731	48
16	4	9.99673	0.99250	9.99736	0.99393	9.99792	0.99521	9.99841	0.99634	9.99884	0.99732	44
20	5	.99674	.99253	.99737	.99396	.99793	.99523	.99842	.99636	.99884	.99734	40
24	6	.99675	.99255	.99738	.99398	.99793	.99525	.99842	.99638	.99885	.99735	36
28	7	.99677	.99258	.99739	.99400	.99794	.99527	.99843	.99640	.99885	.99737	32
32	8	9.99678	0.99260	9.99740	0.99402	9.99795	0.99529	9.99844	0.99641	9.99886	0.99738	28
36	9	.99679	.99263	.99741	.99405	.99796	.99531	.99845	.99643	.99887	.99740	24
40	10	.99680	.99265	.99742	.99407	.99797	.99533	.99845	.99645	.99887	.99741	20
44	11	.99681	.99268	.99743	.99409	.99798	.99535	.99846	.99647	.99888	.99743	16
48	12	9.99682	0.99270	9.99744	0.99411	9.99799	0.99537	9.99847	0.99648	9.99889	0.99744	12
52	13	.99683	.99273	.99745	.99414	.99800	.99539	.99848	.99650	.99889	.99746	8
56	14	9.99684	0.99275	9.99746	0.99416	9.99800	0.99541	9.99848	0.99652	9.99890	0.99747	4
		12h 39m		12h 35m		12h 31m		12h 27m		12h 23m		

s	′	11h 21m 170° Log. Hav.	Nat. Hav.	11h 25m 171° Log. Hav.	Nat. Hav.	11h 29m 172° Log. Hav.	Nat. Hav.	11h 33m 173° Log. Hav.	Nat. Hav.	11h 37m 174° Log. Hav.	Nat. Hav.	s
0	15	9.99685	0.99278	9.99747	0.99418	9.99801	0.99543	9.99849	0.99653	9.99891	0.99748	60
4	16	.99686	.99280	.99748	.99420	.99802	.99545	.99850	.99655	.99891	.99750	56
8	17	.99687	.99283	.99748	.99422	.99803	.99547	.99851	.99657	.99892	.99751	52
12	18	.99688	.99285	.99749	.99425	.99804	.99549	.99851	.99659	.99893	.99753	48
16	19	9.99690	0.99288	9.99750	0.99427	9.99805	0.99551	9.99852	0.99660	9.99893	0.99754	44
20	20	.99691	.99290	.99751	.99429	.99805	.99553	.99853	.99662	.99894	.99756	40
24	21	.99692	.99293	.99752	.99431	.99806	.99555	.99854	.99664	.99894	.99757	36
28	22	.99693	.99295	.99753	.99433	.99807	.99557	.99854	.99665	.99895	.99759	32
32	23	9.99694	0.99297	9.99754	0.99436	9.99808	0.99559	9.99855	0.99667	9.99896	0.99760	28
36	24	.99695	.99300	.99755	.99438	.99809	.99561	.99856	.99669	.99896	.99761	24
40	25	.99696	.99302	.99756	.99440	.99810	.99563	.99857	.99670	.99897	.99763	20
44	26	.99697	.99305	.99757	.99442	.99811	.99565	.99857	.99672	.99897	.99764	16
48	27	9.99698	0.99307	9.99758	0.99444	9.99811	0.99567	9.99858	0.99674	9.99898	0.99766	12
52	28	.99699	.99309	.99759	.99446	.99812	.99568	.99859	.99675	.99899	.99767	8
56	29	9.99700	0.99312	9.99760	0.99449	9.99813	0.99570	9.99859	0.99677	9.99899	0.99768	4
		12h 38m		12h 34m		12h 30m		12h 26m		12h 22m		

s	′	11h 22m 170° Log. Hav.	Nat. Hav.	11h 26m 171° Log. Hav.	Nat. Hav.	11h 30m 172° Log. Hav.	Nat. Hav.	11h 34m 173° Log. Hav.	Nat. Hav.	11h 38m 174° Log. Hav.	Nat. Hav.	s
0	30	9.99701	0.99314	9.99761	0.99451	9.99814	0.99572	9.99860	0.99679	9.99900	0.99770	60
4	31	.99702	.99317	.99762	.99453	.99815	.99574	.99861	.99680	.99901	.99771	56
8	32	.99703	.99319	.99763	.99455	.99815	.99576	.99862	.99682	.99901	.99773	52
12	33	.99704	.99321	.99764	.99457	.99816	.99578	.99862	.99684	.99902	.99774	48
16	34	9.99705	0.99324	9.99765	0.99459	9.99817	0.99580	9.99863	0.99685	9.99902	0.99775	44
20	35	.99706	.99326	.99766	.99461	.99818	.99582	.99864	.99687	.99903	.99777	40
24	36	.99707	.99329	.99766	.99464	.99819	.99584	.99864	.99688	.99904	.99778	36
28	37	.99708	.99331	.99767	.99466	.99820	.99585	.99865	.99690	.99904	.99780	32
32	38	9.99710	0.99333	9.99768	0.99468	9.99820	0.99587	9.99866	0.99692	9.99905	0.99781	28
36	39	.99711	.99336	.99769	.99470	.99821	.99589	.99867	.99693	.99905	.99782	24
40	40	.99712	.99338	.99770	.99472	.99822	.99591	.99867	.99695	.99906	.99784	20
44	41	.99713	.99340	.99771	.99474	.99823	.99593	.99868	.99696	.99906	.99785	16
48	42	9.99714	0.99343	9.99772	0.99476	9.99824	0.99595	9.99869	0.99698	9.99907	0.99786	12
52	43	.99715	.99345	.99773	.99478	.99824	.99597	.99869	.99700	.99908	.99788	8
56	44	9.99716	0.99347	9.99774	0.99480	9.99825	0.99598	9.99870	0.99701	9.99908	0.99789	4
		12h 37m		12h 33m		12h 29m		12h 25m		12h 21m		

s	′	11h 23m 170° Log. Hav.	Nat. Hav.	11h 27m 171° Log. Hav.	Nat. Hav.	11h 31m 172° Log. Hav.	Nat. Hav.	11h 35m 173° Log. Hav.	Nat. Hav.	11h 39m 174° Log. Hav.	Nat. Hav.	s
0	45	9.99717	0.99350	9.99774	0.99483	9.99826	0.99600	9.99871	0.99703	9.99909	0.99790	60
4	46	.99718	.99352	.99775	.99485	.99827	.99602	.99871	.99704	.99909	.99792	56
8	47	.99719	.99354	.99776	.99487	.99828	.99604	.99872	.99706	.99910	.99793	52
12	48	.99720	.99357	.99777	.99489	.99828	.99606	.99873	.99708	.99911	.99794	48
16	49	9.99721	0.99359	9.99778	0.99491	9.99829	0.99608	9.99874	0.99709	9.99911	0.99796	44
20	50	.99722	.99361	.99779	.99493	.99830	.99609	.99874	.99711	.99912	.99797	40
24	51	.99723	.99364	.99780	.99495	.99831	.99611	.99875	.99712	.99912	.99798	36
28	52	.99724	.99366	.99781	.99497	.99832	.99613	.99876	.99714	.99913	.99799	32
32	53	9.99725	0.99368	9.99782	0.99499	9.99832	0.99615	9.99876	0.99715	9.99913	0.99801	28
36	54	.99726	.99371	.99783	.99501	.99833	.99617	.99877	.99717	.99914	.99802	24
40	55	.99727	.99373	.99784	.99503	.99834	.99618	.99878	.99719	.99915	.99803	20
44	56	.99728	.99375	.99785	.99505	.99835	.99620	.99878	.99720	.99915	.99805	16
48	57	9.99729	0.99378	9.99786	0.99507	9.99836	0.99622	9.99879	0.99722	9.99916	0.99806	12
52	58	.99730	.99380	.99786	.99509	.99836	.99624	.99880	.99723	.99916	.99807	8
56	59	.99731	.99382	.99787	.99511	.99837	.99626	.99880	.99725	.99917	.99808	4
60	60	9.99732	0.99384	9.99788	0.99513	9.99838	0.99627	9.99881	0.99726	9.99917	0.99810	0
		12h 36m		12h 32m		12h 28m		12h 24m		12h 20m		

541524°—43——49

TABLE 34.

Haversines.

s	′	$11^h 40^m$	175°	$11^h 44^m$	176°	$11^h 48^m$	177°	$11^h 52^m$	178°	$11^h 56^m$	179°	
		Log. Hav.	Nat. Hav.	Log. Hav.	Nat. Hav.	Log. Hav.	Nat. Hav.	Log. Hav.	Nat. Hav.	Log. Hav.	Nat. Hav.	s
0	**0**	9.99917	**0.99810**	9.99947	**0.99878**	9.99970	**0.99931**	9.99987	**0.99970**	9.99997	**0.99992**	*60*
4	**1**	.99918	**.99811**	.99948	**.99879**	.99971	**.99932**	.99987	**.99971**	.99997	**.99993**	*56*
8	**2**	.99918	**.99812**	.99948	**.99880**	.99971	**.99933**	.99987	**.99971**	.99997	**.99993**	*52*
12	**3**	.99919	**.99814**	.99948	**.99881**	.99971	**.99934**	.99987	**.99971**	.99997	**.99993**	*48*
16	**4**	9.99919	**0.99815**	9.99949	**0.99882**	9.99972	**0.99934**	9.99988	**0.99972**	9.99997	**0.99994**	*44*
20	**5**	.99920	**.99816**	.99949	**.99883**	.99972	**.99935**	.99988	**.99972**	.99997	**.99994**	*40*
24	**6**	.99921	**.99817**	.99950	**.99884**	.99972	**.99936**	.99988	**.99973**	.99997	**.99994**	*36*
28	**7**	.99921	**.99819**	.99950	**.99885**	.99973	**.99937**	.99988	**.99973**	.99997	**.99994**	*32*
32	**8**	9.99922	**0.99820**	9.99951	**0.99886**	9.99973	**0.99937**	9.99988	**0.99973**	9.99998	**0.99994**	*28*
36	**9**	.99922	**.99821**	.99951	**.99887**	.99973	**.99938**	.99989	**.99974**	.99998	**.99995**	*24*
40	**10**	.99923	**.99822**	.99951	**.99888**	.99973	**.99939**	.99989	**.99974**	.99998	**.99995**	*20*
44	**11**	.99923	**.99823**	.99952	**.99889**	.99974	**.99940**	.99989	**.99975**	.99998	**.99995**	*16*
48	**12**	9.99924	**0.99825**	9.99952	**0.99890**	9.99974	**0.99940**	9.99989	**0.99975**	9.99998	**0.99995**	*12*
52	**13**	.99924	**.99826**	.99953	**.99891**	.99974	**.99941**	.99989	**.99976**	.99998	**.99995**	*8*
56	**14**	9.99925	**0.99827**	9.99953	**0.99892**	9.99975	**0.99942**	9.99990	**0.99976**	9.99998	**0.99996**	*4*
		$12^h 19^m$		$12^h 15^m$		$12^h 11^m$		$12^h 7^m$		$12^h 3^m$		

s	′	$11^h 41^m$	175°	$11^h 45^m$	176°	$11^h 49^m$	177	$11^h 53^m$	178°	$11^h 57^m$	179°	s
0	**15**	9.99925	**0.99828**	9.99953	**0.99893**	9.99975	**0.99942**	9.99990	**0.99977**	9.99998	**0.99996**	*60*
4	**16**	.99926	**.99829**	.99954	**.99894**	.99975	**.99943**	.99990	**.99977**	.99998	**.99996**	*56*
8	**17**	.99926	**.99831**	.99954	**.99895**	.99976	**.99944**	.99990	**.99978**	.99998	**.99996**	*52*
12	**18**	.99927	**.99832**	.99954	**.99896**	.99976	**.99944**	.99990	**.99978**	.99998	**.99996**	*48*
16	**19**	9.99927	**0.99833**	9.99955	**0.99897**	9.99976	**0.99945**	9.99991	**0.99978**	9.99998	**0.99996**	*44*
20	**20**	.99928	**.99834**	.99955	**.99898**	.99976	**.99946**	.99991	**.99979**	.99999	**.99997**	*40*
24	**21**	.99928	**.99835**	.99956	**.99899**	.99977	**.99947**	.99991	**.99979**	.99999	**.99997**	*36*
28	**22**	.99929	**.99837**	.99956	**.99900**	.99977	**.99947**	.99991	**.99980**	.99999	**.99997**	*32*
32	**23**	9.99929	**0.99838**	9.99957	**0.99900**	9.99977	**0.99948**	9.99991	**0.99980**	9.99999	**0.99997**	*28*
36	**24**	.99930	**.99839**	.99957	**.99901**	.99978	**.99949**	.99992	**.99981**	.99999	**.99997**	*24*
40	**25**	.99931	**.99840**	.99958	**.99902**	.99978	**.99949**	.99992	**.99981**	.99999	**.99997**	*20*
44	**26**	.99931	**.99841**	.99958	**.99903**	.99978	**.99950**	.99992	**.99981**	.99999	**.99998**	*16*
48	**27**	9.99932	**0.99842**	9.99958	**0.99904**	9.99978	**0.99950**	9.99992	**0.99982**	9.99999	**0.99998**	*12*
52	**28**	.99932	**.99844**	.99959	**.99905**	.99979	**.99951**	.99992	**.99982**	.99999	**.99998**	*8*
56	**29**	9.99933	**0.99845**	9.99959	**0.99906**	9.99979	**0.99952**	9.99992	**0.99982**	9.99999	**0.99998**	*4*
		$12^h 18^m$		$12^h 14^m$		$12^h 10^m$		$12^h 6^m$		$12^h 2^m$		

s	′	$11^h 42^m$	175°	$11^h 46^m$	176°	$11^h 50^m$	177°	$11^h 54^m$	178°	$11^h 58^m$	179°	s
0	**30**	9.99933	**0.99846**	9.99959	**0.99907**	9.99979	**0.99952**	9.99993	**0.99983**	9.99999	**0.99998**	*60*
4	**31**	.99934	**.99847**	.99960	**.99908**	.99980	**.99953**	.99993	**.99983**	.99999	**.99998**	*56*
8	**32**	.99934	**.99848**	.99960	**.99909**	.99980	**.99954**	.99993	**.99984**	.99999	**.99998**	*52*
12	**33**	.99935	**.99849**	.99961	**.99909**	.99980	**.99954**	.99993	**.99984**	.99999	**.99998**	*48*
16	**34**	9.99935	**0.99850**	9.99961	**0.99910**	9.99980	**0.99955**	9.99993	**0.99984**	9.99999	**0.99999**	*44*
20	**35**	.99935	**.99851**	.99961	**.99911**	.99981	**.99956**	.99993	**.99985**	.99999	**.99999**	*40*
24	**36**	.99936	**.99853**	.99962	**.99912**	.99981	**.99956**	.99994	**.99985**	9.99999	**.99999**	*36*
28	**37**	.99936	**.99854**	.99962	**.99913**	.99981	**.99957**	.99994	**.99985**	0.00000	**.99999**	*32*
32	**38**	9.99937	**0.99855**	9.99963	**0.99914**	9.99981	**0.99957**	9.99994	**0.99986**	0.00000	**0.99999**	*28*
36	**39**	.99937	**.99856**	.99963	**.99915**	.99982	**.99958**	.99994	**.99986**	.00000	**.99999**	*24*
40	**40**	.99938	**.99857**	.99963	**.99915**	.99982	**.99959**	.99994	**.99986**	.00000	**.99999**	*20*
44	**41**	.99938	**.99858**	.99964	**.99916**	.99982	**.99959**	.99994	**.99987**	.00000	**.99999**	*16*
48	**42**	9.99939	**0.99859**	9.99964	**0.99917**	9.99983	**0.99960**	9.99994	**0.99987**	0.00000	**0.99999**	*12*
52	**43**	.99939	**.99860**	.99964	**.99918**	.99983	**.99960**	.99995	**.99987**	.00000	**.99999**	*8*
56	**44**	9.99940	**0.99861**	9.99965	**0.99919**	9.99983	**0.99961**	9.99995	**0.99988**	0.00000	**0.99999**	*4*
		$12^h 17^m$		$12^h 13^m$		$12^h 9^m$		$12^h 5^m$		$12^h 1^m$		

s	′	$11^h 43^m$	175°	$11^h 47^m$	176°	$11^h 51^m$	177°	$11^h 55^m$	178°	$11^h 59^m$	179°	s
0	**45**	9.99940	**0.99863**	9.99965	**0.99920**	9.99983	**0.99961**	9.99995	**0.99988**	0.00000	**1.00000**	*60*
4	**46**	.99941	**.99864**	.99965	**.99920**	.99983	**.99962**	.99995	**.99988**	.00000	**.00000**	*56*
8	**47**	.99941	**.99865**	.99966	**.99921**	.99984	**.99963**	.99995	**.99989**	.00000	**.00000**	*52*
12	**48**	.99942	**.99866**	.99966	**.99922**	.99984	**.99963**	.99995	**.99989**	.00000	**.00000**	*48*
16	**49**	9.99942	**0.99867**	9.99966	**0.99923**	9.99984	**0.99964**	9.99995	**0.99989**	0.00000	**1.00000**	*44*
20	**50**	.99943	**.99868**	.99967	**.99924**	.99984	**.99964**	.99996	**.99990**	.00000	**.00000**	*40*
24	**51**	.99943	**.99869**	.99967	**.99924**	.99985	**.99965**	.99996	**.99990**	.00000	**.00000**	*36*
28	**52**	.99943	**.99870**	.99968	**.99925**	.99985	**.99965**	.99996	**.99990**	.00000	**.00000**	*32*
32	**53**	9.99944	**0.99871**	9.99968	**0.99926**	9.99985	**0.99966**	9.99996	**0.99991**	0.00000	**1.00000**	*28*
36	**54**	.99944	**.99872**	.99968	**.99927**	.99985	**.99966**	.99996	**.99991**	.00000	**.00000**	*24*
40	**55**	.99945	**.99873**	.99969	**.99928**	.99986	**.99967**	.99996	**.99991**	.00000	**.00000**	*20*
44	**56**	.99945	**.99874**	.99969	**.99928**	.99986	**.99967**	.99996	**.99991**	.00000	**.00000**	*16*
48	**57**	9.99946	**0.99875**	9.99969	**0.99929**	9.99986	**0.99968**	9.99996	**0.99992**	0.00000	**1.00000**	*12*
52	**58**	.99946	**.99876**	.99970	**.99930**	.99986	**.99969**	.99996	**.99992**	.00000	**.00000**	*8*
56	**59**	.99947	**.99877**	.99970	**.99931**	.99987	**.99969**	.99997	**.99992**	.00000	**.00000**	*4*
60	**60**	9.99947	**0.99878**	9.99970	**0.99931**	9.99987	**0.99970**	9.99997	**0.99992**	0.00000	**1.00000**	*0*
		$12^h 16^m$		$12^h 12^m$		$12^h 8^m$		$12^h 4^m$		$12^h 0^m$		

TABLE 35.

Longitude Factors.

F is the change in longitude due to a change of 1′ in latitude.

Latitude.

Bear-ing.	0°	1°	2°	4°	6°	8°	10°	12°	Bear-ing.
°	′	′	′	′	′	′	′	′	°
1	57.29	57.30	57.32	57.43	57.61	57.85	58.17	58.57	1
2	28.64	28.64	28.65	28.71	28.79	28.92	29.08	29.28	2
3	19.08	19.08	19.09	19.13	19.19	19.27	19.38	19.51	3
4	14.30	14.30	14.31	14.34	14.38	14.44	14.52	14.62	4
5	11.43	11.43	11.44	11.46	11.49	11.54	11.61	11.69	5
6	9.51	9.52	9.52	9.54	9.57	9.61	9.66	9.73	6
7	8.14	8.15	8.15	8.16	8.19	8.22	8.27	8.33	7
8	7.12	7.12	7.12	7.13	7.15	7.18	7.22	7.27	8
10	5.67	5.67	5.68	5.69	5.70	5.73	5.76	5.80	10
12	4.71	4.71	4.71	4.72	4.73	4.75	4.78	4.81	12
14	4.01	4.01	4.01	4.02	4.03	4.05	4.07	4.10	14
16	3.49	3.49	3.49	3.50	3.51	3.52	3.54	3.56	16
18	3.08	3.08	3.08	3.08	3.10	3.11	3.13	3.15	18
20	2.75	2.75	2.75	2.75	2.76	2.77	2.79	2.81	20
22	2.47	2.47	2.48	2.48	2.49	2.50	2.51	2.53	22
24	2.25	2.25	2.25	2.25	2.26	2.27	2.28	2.30	24
26	2.05	2.05	2.05	2.05	2.06	2.07	2.08	2.10	26
28	1.88	1.88	1.88	1.88	1.89	1.90	1.91	1.92	28
30	1.73	1.73	1.73	1.74	1.74	1.75	1.76	1.77	30
32	1.60	1.60	1.60	1.60	1.61	1.62	1.63	1.64	32
34	1.48	1.48	1.48	1.49	1.49	1.50	1.50	1.52	34
36	1.38	1.38	1.38	1.38	1.38	1.39	1.40	1.41	36
38	1.28	1.28	1.28	1.28	1.29	1.29	1.30	1.31	38
40	1.19	1.19	1.19	1.19	1.20	1.20	1.21	1.22	40
42	1.11	1.11	1.11	1.11	1.12	1.12	1.13	1.14	42
44	1.04	1.04	1.04	1.04	1.04	1.05	1.05	1.06	44
46	.97	.97	.97	.97	.97	.98	.98	.99	46
48	.90	.90	.90	.90	.90	.91	.91	.92	48
50	.84	.84	.84	.84	.84	.85	.85	.86	50
52	.78	.78	.78	.78	.79	.79	.79	.80	52
54	.73	.73	.73	.73	.73	.73	.74	.74	54
56	.67	.67	.67	.68	.68	.68	.68	.69	56
58	.63	.63	.63	.63	.63	.63	.63	.64	58
60	.58	.58	.58	.58	.58	.58	.59	.59	60
62	.53	.53	.53	.53	.53	.54	.54	.54	62
64	.49	.49	.49	.49	.49	.49	.50	.50	64
66	.45	.45	.45	.45	.45	.45	.45	.46	66
68	.40	.40	.40	.40	.40	.41	.41	.41	68
70	.36	.36	.36	.36	.37	.37	.37	.37	70
72	.33	.33	.33	.33	.33	.33	.33	.33	72
74	.29	.29	.29	.29	.29	.29	.29	.29	74
76	.25	.25	.25	.25	.25	.25	.25	.25	76
78	.21	.21	.21	.21	.21	.21	.22	.22	78
80	.18	.18	.18	.18	.18	.18	.18	.18	80
81	.16	.16	.16	.16	.16	.16	.16	.16	81
82	.14	.14	.14	.14	.14	.14	.14	.14	82
83	.12	.12	.12	.12	.12	.12	.12	.13	83
84	.10	.10	.10	.10	.10	.10	.11	.11	84
85	.09	.09	.09	.09	.09	.09	.09	.09	85
86	.07	.07	.07	.07	.07	.07	.07	.07	86
87	.05	.05	.05	.05	.05	.05	.05	.05	87
88	.03	.03	.03	.03	.03	.03	.03	.04	88
89	.02	.02	.02	.02	.02	.02	.02	.02	89
90	.00	.00	.00	.00	.00	.00	.00	.00	90
	0°	1°	2°	4°	6°	8°	10°	12°	

Corr. to Long. = Error in Lat. × F.

TABLE 35.

Longitude Factors.

F is the change in longitude due to a change of 1′ in latitude.

Bearing.	14°	16°	18°	20°	22°	24°	26°	28°	Bearing.
°	′	′	′	′	′	′	′	′	°
1	59.04	59.60	60.24	60.97	61.79	62.71	63.74	64.88	**1**
2	29.51	29.79	30.11	30.47	30.89	31.35	31.86	32.43	**2**
3	19.67	19.85	20.06	20.31	20.58	20.89	21.23	21.61	**3**
4	14.74	14.88	15.04	15.22	15.42	15.65	15.91	16.20	**4**
5	11.78	11.89	12.02	12.16	12.33	12.51	12.72	12.95	**5**
6	9.81	9.90	10.00	10.12	10.26	10.41	10.59	10.78	**6**
7	8.39	8.47	8.56	8.67	8.78	8.91	9.06	9.22	**7**
8	7.33	7.40	7.48	7.57	7.67	7.79	7.92	8.06	**8**
10	5.85	5.90	5.96	6.03	6.12	6.21	6.31	6.42	**10**
12	4.85	4.89	4.95	5.01	5.07	5.15	5.23	5.33	**12**
14	4.13	4.17	4.22	4.27	4.33	4.39	4.46	4.54	**14**
16	3.59	3.63	3.67	3.71	3.76	3.82	3.88	3.95	**16**
18	3.17	3.20	3.24	3.28	3.32	3.37	3.42	3.49	**18**
20	2.83	2.86	2.89	2.92	2.96	3.01	3.06	3.11	**20**
22	2.55	2.58	2.60	2.63	2.67	2.71	2.75	2.80	**22**
24	2.32	2.34	2.36	2.39	2.42	2.46	2.50	2.54	**24**
26	2.11	2.13	2.16	2.18	2.21	2.24	2.28	2.32	**26**
28	1.94	1.96	1.98	2.00	2.03	2.06	2.09	2.13	**28**
30	1.78	1.80	1.82	1.84	1.87	1.90	1.93	1.96	**30**
32	1.65	1.66	1.68	1.70	1.73	1.75	1.78	1.81	**32**
34	1.53	1.54	1.56	1.58	1.60	1.62	1.65	1.68	**34**
36	1.42	1.43	1.45	1.47	1.48	1.51	1.53	1.56	**36**
38	1.32	1.33	1.35	1.36	1.38	1.40	1.42	1.45	**38**
40	1.23	1.24	1.25	1.27	1.28	1.30	1.33	1.35	**40**
42	1.14	1.15	1.17	1.18	1.20	1.22	1.24	1.26	**42**
44	1.07	1.08	1.09	1.10	1.12	1.13	1.15	1.17	**44**
46	1.00	1.01	1.02	1.03	1.04	1.06	1.07	1.09	**46**
48	.93	.94	.95	.96	.97	.99	1.00	1.02	**48**
50	.87	.87	.88	.89	.91	.92	.93	.95	**50**
52	.80	.81	.82	.83	.84	.85	.87	.88	**52**
54	.75	.76	.76	.77	.78	.79	.81	.82	**54**
56	.69	.70	.71	.72	.73	.74	.75	.76	**56**
58	.64	.65	.66	.66	.67	.68	.69	.71	**58**
60	.60	.60	.61	.61	.62	.63	.64	.65	**60**
62	.55	.55	.56	.57	.57	.58	.59	.60	**62**
64	.50	.51	.51	.52	.53	.53	.54	.55	**64**
66	.46	.46	.47	.47	.48	.49	.50	.50	**66**
68	.42	.42	.42	.43	.44	.44	.45	.46	**68**
70	.37	.38	.38	.39	.39	.40	.40	.41	**70**
72	.34	.34	.34	.35	.35	.36	.36	.37	**72**
74	.30	.30	.30	.31	.31	.31	.32	.33	**74**
76	.26	.26	.26	.27	.27	.27	.28	.28	**76**
78	.22	.22	.22	.23	.23	.23	.24	.24	**78**
80	.18	.18	.18	.19	.19	.19	.20	.20	**80**
81	.16	.16	.17	.17	.17	.17	.18	.18	**81**
82	.14	.15	.15	.15	.15	.15	.16	.16	**82**
83	.13	.13	.13	.13	.13	.13	.14	.14	**83**
84	.11	.11	.11	.11	.11	.11	.12	.12	**84**
85	.09	.09	.09	.09	.09	.10	.10	.10	**85**
86	.07	.07	.07	.07	.08	.08	.08	.08	**86**
87	.05	.05	.05	.06	.06	.06	.06	.06	**87**
88	.04	.04	.04	.04	.04	.04	.04	.04	**88**
89	.02	.02	.02	.02	.02	.02	.02	.02	**89**
90	.00	.00	.00	.00	.00	.00	.00	.00	**90**
	14°	**16°**	**18°**	**20°**	**22°**	**24°**	**26°**	**28°**	

Corr. to Long. = Error in Lat. × F.

TABLE 35.

Longitude Factors.

F is the change in longitude due to a change of 1′ in latitude.

Bearing.	Latitude. 30°	32°	34°	36°	38°	40°	42°	44°	Bearing.
°	′	′	′	′	′	′	′	′	°
1	66.15	67.56	69.10	70.81	72.70	74.79	77.09	79.64	1
2	33.07	33.77	34.54	35.40	36.34	37.38	38.53	39.81	2
3	22.03	22.50	23.02	23.59	24.21	24.91	25.68	26.53	3
4	16.51	16.86	17.25	17.68	18.15	18.67	19.24	19.88	4
5	13.20	13.48	13.79	14.13	14.50	14.92	15.38	15.89	5
6	10.99	11.22	11.48	11.76	12.07	12.42	12.80	13.23	6
7	9.40	9.60	9.82	10.07	10.34	10.63	10.96	11.32	7
8	8.22	8.39	8.58	8.79	9.03	9.29	9.57	9.89	8
10	6.55	6.69	6.84	7.01	7.20	7.40	7.63	7.88	10
12	5.43	5.55	5.67	5.81	5.97	6.14	6.33	6.54	12
14	4.63	4.73	4.84	4.96	5 09	5.24	5.40	5.58	14
16	4.03	4.11	4.21	4.31	4.43	4.55	4.69	4.85	16
18	3.55	3.63	3.71	3.80	3.91	4.02	4.14	4.28	18
20	3.17	3.24	3.31	3.40	3.49	3.59	3.70	3.82	20
22	2.86	2.92	2.98	3.06	3.14	3.23	3.33	3.44	22
24	2.59	2.65	2.71	2.78	2.85	2.93	3.02	3.12	24
26	2.37	2.42	2.47	2.53	2.60	2.68	2.76	2.85	26
28	2.17	2.22	2.27	2.32	2.39	2.45	2.53	2.61	28
30	2.00	2.04	2.09	2.14	2.20	2.26	2.33	2.41	30
32	1.85	1.89	1.93	1.98	2.03	2.09	2.15	2.22	32
34	1.71	1.75	1.79	1.83	1.88	1.93	1.99	2.06	34
36	1.59	1.62	1.66	1.70	1.75	1.80	1.85	1.91	36
38	1.48	1.51	1.54	1.58	1.62	1.67	1.72	1.78	38
40	1.38	1.41	1.44	1.47	1.51	1.56	1.60	1.66	40
42	1.28	1.31	1.34	1.37	1.41	1.45	1.49	1.54	42
44	1.20	1.22	1.25	1.28	1.31	1.35	1.39	1.44	44
46	1.11	1.14	1.16	1.19	1.23	1.26	1.30	1.34	46
48	1.04	1.06	1.09	1.11	1.14	1.17	1.21	1.25	48
50	.97	.99	1.01	1.04	1.06	1.09	1.13	1.17	50
52	.90	.92	.94	.97	.99	1.02	1.05	1.09	52
54	.84	.86	.88	.90	.92	.95	.98	1.01	54
56	.78	.79	.81	.83	.86	.88	.91	.94	56
58	.72	.74	.75	.77	.79	.82	.84	.87	58
60	.67	.68	.70	.71	.73	.75	.78	.80	60
62	.61	.63	.64	.66	.67	.69	.72	.74	62
64	.56	.57	.59	.60	.62	.64	.66	.68	64
66	.51	.52	.54	.55	.56	.58	.60	.62	66
68	.47	.48	.49	.50	.51	.53	.54	.56	68
70	.42	.43	.44	.45	.46	.47	.49	.51	70
72	.37	.38	.39	.40	.41	.42	.44	.45	72
74	.33	.34	.35	.35	.36	.37	.39	.40	74
76	.29	.29	.30	.31	.32	.32	.34	.35	76
78	.24	.25	.26	.26	.27	.28	.29	.29	78
80	.20	.21	.21	.22	.22	.23	.24	.24	80
81	.18	.19	.19	.20	.20	.21	.21	.22	81
82	.16	.17	.17	.17	.18	.18	.19	.19	82
83	.14	.14	.15	.15	.16	.16	.16	.17	83
84	.12	.12	.13	.13	.13	.14	.14	.15	84
85	.10	.10	.11	.11	.11	.11	.12	.12	85
86	.08	.08	.08	.09	.09	.09	.09	.10	86
87	.06	.06	.06	.06	.07	.07	.07	.07	87
88	.04	.04	.04	.04	.04	.05	.05	.05	88
89	.02	.02	.02	.02	.02	.02	.02	.02	89
90	.00	.00	.00	.00	.00	.00	.00	.00	90
	30°	32°	34°	36°	38°	40°	42°	44°	

Corr. to Long. = Error in Lat. × F.

TABLE 35.

Longitude Factors.

F is the change in longitude due to a change of 1′ in latitude.

Bearing.	46°	48°	50°	52°	54°	56°	58°	60°	Bearing.
°	′	′	′	′	′	′	′	′	°
1	82.47	85.62	89.13	93.05	97.47	102.5	108.1	114.6	1
2	41.22	42.80	44.55	46.51	48.72	51.21	54.04	57.27	2
3	27.47	28.52	29.68	30.99	32.46	34.12	36.01	38.16	3
4	20.59	21.37	22.25	23.23	24.33	25.57	26.99	28.60	4
5	16.45	17.08	17.78	18.57	19.45	20.44	21.57	22.86	5
6	13.70	14.22	14.80	15.45	16.19	17.01	17.95	19.03	6
7	11.72	12.17	12.67	13.23	13.86	14.56	15.37	16.29	7
8	10.24	10.63	11.07	11.56	12.11	12.72	13.43	14.23	8
10	8.16	8.48	8.82	9.21	9.65	10.14	10.70	11.34	10
12	6.77	7.03	7.32	7.64	8.00	8.41	8.88	9.41	12
14	5.77	5.99	6.24	6.51	6.82	7.17	7.57	8.02	14
16	5.02	5.21	5.42	5.66	5.93	6.24	6.58	6.97	16
18	4.43	4.60	4.79	5.00	5.24	5.50	5.81	6.15	18
20	3.95	4.11	4.27	4.46	4.67	4.91	5.19	5.49	20
22	3.56	3.70	3.85	4.02	4.21	4.43	4.67	4.95	22
24	3.23	3.36	3.49	3.65	3.82	4.02	4.24	4.49	24
26	2.95	3.06	3.19	3.33	3.49	3.66	3.87	4.10	26
28	2.71	2.81	2.93	3.05	3.20	3.36	3.55	3.76	28
30	2.49	2.59	2.69	2.81	2.95	3.10	3.27	3.46	30
32	2.30	2.39	2.49	2.60	2.72	2.86	3.02	3.20	32
34	2.13	2.22	2.31	2.41	2.52	2.65	2.80	2.96	34
36	1.98	2.06	2.14	2.24	2.34	2.46	2.60	2.75	36
38	1.84	1.91	1.99	2.08	2.18	2.29	2.41	2.56	38
40	1.71	1.78	1.85	1.94	2.03	2.13	2.25	2.38	40
42	1.60	1.66	1.73	1.80	1.89	1.99	2.09	2.22	42
44	1.49	1.55	1.61	1.68	1.76	1.85	1.95	2.07	44
46	1.39	1.44	1.50	1.57	1.64	1.73	1.82	1.93	46
48	1.30	1.35	1.40	1.46	1.53	1.61	1.70	1.80	48
50	1.21	1.25	1.31	1.36	1.43	1.50	1.58	1.68	50
52	1.12	1.17	1.22	1.27	1.33	1.40	1.47	1.56	52
54	1.05	1.09	1.13	1.18	1.23	1.30	1.37	1.45	54
56	.97	1.01	1.05	1.10	1.15	1.21	1.27	1.35	56
58	.90	.93	.97	1.01	1.06	1.12	1.18	1.25	58
60	.83	.86	.90	.94	.98	1.03	1.09	1.15	60
62	.77	.79	.83	.86	.90	.95	1.00	1.06	62
64	.70	.73	.76	.79	.83	.87	.92	.97	64
66	.64	.66	.69	.72	.76	.79	.84	.89	66
68	.58	.60	.63	.65	.69	.72	.76	.81	68
70	.52	.54	.57	.59	.62	.65	.68	.73	70
72	.47	.49	.51	.53	.55	.58	.61	.65	72
74	.41	.43	.45	.46	.49	.51	.54	.57	74
76	.36	.37	.39	.40	.42	.45	.47	.50	76
78	.31	.32	.33	.34	.36	.38	.40	.42	78
80	.25	.26	.27	.29	.30	.31	.33	.35	80
81	.23	.24	.25	.26	.27	.28	.30	.32	81
82	.20	.21	.22	.23	.24	.25	.26	.28	82
83	.18	.18	.19	.20	.21	.22	.23	.25	83
84	.15	.16	.16	.17	.18	.19	.20	.21	84
85	.13	.13	.14	.14	.15	.16	.16	.17	85
86	.10	.10	.11	.11	.12	.12	.13	.14	86
87	.08	.08	.08	.08	.09	.09	.10	.10	87
88	.05	.05	.05	.06	.06	.06	.07	.07	88
89	.02	.03	.03	.03	.03	.03	.03	.03	89
90	.00	.00	.00	.00	.00	.00	.00	.00	90
	46°	48°	50°	52°	54°	56°	58°	60°	

Corr. to Long. = Error in Lat. × F.

TABLE 36.

Latitude Factors.

f is the change in latitude due to a change of 1′ in longitude.

Bearing.	Latitude. 0°	1°	2°	4°	6°	8°	10°	12°	Bearing.
°	′	′	′	′	′	′	′	′	°
1	0.02	0.02	0.02	0.02	0.02	0.02	0.02	0.02	**1**
2	.03	.03	.03	.03	.03	.03	.03	.03	**2**
3	.05	.05	.05	.05	.05	.05	.05	.05	**3**
4	.07	.07	.07	.07	.07	.07	.07	.07	**4**
5	.09	.09	.09	.09	.09	.09	.09	.09	**5**
6	.11	.11	.11	.10	.10	.10	.10	.10	**6**
7	.12	.12	.12	.12	.12	.12	.12	.12	**7**
8	.14	.14	.14	.14	.14	.14	.14	.14	**8**
10	.18	.18	.18	.18	.18	.17	.17	.17	**10**
12	.21	.21	.21	.21	.21	.21	.21	.21	**12**
14	.25	.25	.25	.25	.25	.25	.25	.24	**14**
16	.29	.29	.29	.29	.28	.28	.28	.28	**16**
18	.32	.32	.32	.32	.32	.32	.32	.32	**18**
20	.36	.36	.36	.36	.36	.36	.36	.36	**20**
22	.40	.40	.40	.40	.40	.40	.40	.40	**22**
24	.44	.44	.44	.44	.44	.44	.44	.43	**24**
26	.49	.49	.49	.49	.49	.48	.48	.48	**26**
28	.53	.53	.53	.53	.53	.53	.52	.52	**28**
30	.58	.58	.58	.57	.57	.57	.57	.56	**30**
32	.63	.63	.63	.63	.62	.62	.61	.61	**32**
34	.68	.68	.68	.67	.67	.67	.67	.66	**34**
36	.72	.72	.72	.72	.72	.72	.71	.71	**36**
38	.78	.78	.78	.78	.78	.78	.77	.76	**38**
40	.84	.84	.84	.84	.83	.83	.83	.82	**40**
42	.90	.90	.90	.90	.89	.89	.88	.88	**42**
44	.96	.96	.96	.96	.96	.95	.95	.94	**44**
46	1.04	1.04	1.04	1.03	1.03	1.03	1.02	1.01	**46**
48	1.11	1.11	1.11	1.11	1.11	1.10	1.10	1.09	**48**
50	1.19	1.19	1.19	1.19	1.19	1.18	1.17	1.17	**50**
52	1.28	1.28	1.28	1.28	1.27	1.27	1.26	1.25	**52**
54	1.38	1.38	1.38	1.37	1.37	1.36	1.36	1.35	**54**
56	1.48	1.48	1.48	1.48	1.47	1.47	1.46	1.45	**56**
58	1.60	1.60	1.60	1.60	1.59	1.58	1.58	1.57	**58**
60	1.73	1.73	1.73	1.73	1.72	1.72	1.71	1.69	**60**
62	1.88	1.88	1.88	1.88	1.87	1.86	1.85	1.84	**62**
64	2.05	2.05	2.05	2.05	2.04	2.03	2.02	2.01	**64**
66	2.25	2.25	2.24	2.24	2.23	2.22	2.21	2.20	**66**
68	2.48	2.48	2.47	2.47	2.46	2.45	2.44	2.42	**68**
70	2.75	2.75	2.75	2.74	2.73	2.72	2.71	2.69	**70**
72	3.08	3.08	3.08	3.07	3.06	3.05	3.03	3.01	**72**
74	3.49	3.49	3.49	3.48	3.47	3.45	3.43	3.41	**74**
76	4.01	4.01	4.01	4.00	3.99	3.97	3.95	3.92	**76**
78	4.70	4.70	4.70	4.69	4.68	4.66	4.63	4.60	**78**
80	5.67	5.67	5.67	5.66	5.64	5.62	5.59	5.55	**80**
81	6.31	6.31	6.31	6.30	6.28	6.25	6.22	6.18	**81**
82	7.12	7.11	7.11	7.10	7.07	7.05	7.01	6.96	**82**
83	8.15	8.14	8.14	8.13	8.10	8.07	8.02	7.97	**83**
84	9.52	9.51	9.51	9.49	9.46	9.42	9.37	9.31	**84**
85	11.43	11.43	11.42	11.40	11.37	11.32	11.25	11.18	**85**
86	14.30	14.30	14.29	14.27	14.22	14.16	14.08	13.99	**86**
87	19.08	19.08	19.07	19.03	18.98	18.91	18.79	18.66	**87**
88	28.63	28.63	28.62	28.57	28.48	28.35	28.20	28.01	**88**
89	57.29	57.28	57.26	57.15	56.98	56.73	56.42	56.04	**89**
	0°	1°	2°	4°	6°	8°	10°	12°	

Cor. to Lat. = Error in Long. × f.

TABLE 36.

Latitude Factors.

f is the change in latitude due to a change of 1′ in longitude.

Bear-ing.	Latitude. 14°	16°	18°	20°	22°	24°	26°	28°	Bear-ing.
°	′	′	′	′	′	′	′	′	°
1	0.02	0.02	0.02	0.02	0.02	0.02	0.02	0.02	**1**
2	.03	.03	.03	.03	.03	.03	.03	.03	**2**
3	.05	.05	.05	.05	.05	.05	.05	.05	**3**
4	.07	.07	.07	.07	.06	.06	.06	.06	**4**
5	.08	.08	.08	.08	.08	.08	.08	.08	**5**
6	.10	.10	.10	.10	.10	.10	.09	.09	**6**
7	.12	.12	.12	.12	.11	.11	.11	.11	**7**
8	.14	.14	.13	.13	.13	.13	.13	.12	**8**
10	.17	.17	.17	.17	.16	.16	.16	.16	**10**
12	.21	.20	.20	.20	.20	.19	.19	.19	**12**
14	.24	.24	.24	.23	.23	.23	.22	.22	**14**
16	.28	.28	.27	.27	.27	.26	.26	.25	**16**
18	.32	.31	.31	.30	.30	.30	.29	.29	**18**
20	.35	.35	.35	.34	.34	.33	.33	.32	**20**
22	.39	.39	.38	.38	.38	.37	.36	.36	**22**
24	.43	.43	.42	.42	.41	.41	.40	.39	**24**
26	.47	.47	.46	.46	.45	.45	.44	.43	**26**
28	.52	.51	.51	.50	.49	.49	.48	.47	**28**
30	.56	.56	.55	.54	.53	.53	.52	.51	**30**
32	.61	.60	.60	.59	.58	.57	.56	.55	**32**
34	.65	.65	.64	.63	.63	.62	.61	.59	**34**
36	.70	.70	.69	.68	.68	.66	.65	.64	**36**
38	.76	.75	.74	.74	.72	.71	.70	.69	**38**
40	.81	.81	.80	.79	.78	.77	.75	.74	**40**
42	.88	.87	.85	.85	.83	.82	.81	.79	**42**
44	.93	.93	.92	.91	.89	.88	.87	.85	**44**
46	1.01	1.00	.99	.97	.96	.95	.93	.91	**46**
48	1.08	1.07	1.06	1.04	1.03	1.02	1.00	.98	**48**
50	1.16	1.15	1.13	1.12	1.10	1.09	1.07	1.05	**50**
52	1.24	1.23	1.22	1.20	1.19	1.17	1.15	1.13	**52**
54	1.34	1.32	1.31	1.29	1.28	1.26	1.24	1.22	**54**
56	1.44	1.43	1.41	1.39	1.38	1.35	1.33	1.31	**56**
58	1.55	1.54	1.52	1.50	1.48	1.46	1.44	1.41	**58**
60	1.68	1.67	1.65	1.63	1.61	1.58	1.56	1.53	**60**
62	1.83	1.81	1.79	1.77	1.74	1.72	1.69	1.66	**62**
64	1.99	1.97	1.95	1.93	1.90	1.87	1.84	1.81	**64**
66	2.18	2.16	2.14	2.11	2.08	2.05	2.02	1.98	**66**
68	2.40	2.38	2.35	2.33	2.30	2.26	2.23	2.18	**68**
70	2.67	2.64	2.61	2.58	2.55	2.51	2.47	2.43	**70**
72	2.99	2.96	2.93	2.89	2.85	2.81	2.77	2.72	**72**
74	3.38	3.35	3.32	3.28	3.23	3.19	3.14	3.08	**74**
76	3.89	3.86	3.81	3.77	3.72	3.66	3.61	3.54	**76**
78	4.56	4.52	4.47	4.42	4.36	4.30	4.23	4.15	**78**
80	5.50	5.45	5.39	5.33	5.26	5.18	5.10	5.01	**80**
81	6.13	6.07	6.01	5.93	5.86	5.77	5.68	5.58	**81**
82	6.90	6.84	6.77	6.69	6.60	6.50	6.40	6.28	**82**
83	7.90	7.83	7.75	7.65	7.55	7.44	7.32	7.19	**83**
84	9.23	9.15	9.05	8.94	8.82	8.69	8.55	8.40	**84**
85	11.09	10.99	10.87	10.74	10.60	10.44	10.26	10.09	**85**
86	13.88	13.75	13.60	13.44	13.26	13.07	12.86	12.63	**86**
87	18.51	18.34	18.15	17.93	17.69	17.43	17.15	16.85	**87**
88	27.78	27.52	27.23	26.91	26.55	26.16	25.74	25.28	**88**
89	55.59	55.07	54.49	53.84	53.12	52.33	51.50	50.58	**89**
	14°	**16°**	**18°**	**20°**	**22°**	**24°**	**26°**	**28°**	

Corr. to Lat.=Error in Long.×f.

TABLE 36.

Latitude Factors.

f is the change in latitude due to a change of 1′ in longitude.

Bearing.	Latitude. 30°	32°	34°	36°	38°	40°	42°	44°	Bearing.
°	′	′	′	′	′	′	′	′	°
1	0.02	0.01	0.01	0.01	0.01	0.01	0.01	0.01	1
2	.03	.03	.03	.03	.03	.03	.03	.03	2
3	.05	.05	.04	.04	.04	.04	.04	.04	3
4	.06	.06	.06	.06	.06	.05	.05	.05	4
5	.08	.07	.07	.07	.07	.07	.07	.06	5
6	.09	.09	.09	.09	.08	.08	.08	.08	6
7	.11	.10	.10	.10	.10	.09	.09	.09	7
8	.12	.12	.12	.11	.11	.11	.10	.10	8
10	.15	.15	.15	.14	.14	.14	.13	.13	10
12	.18	.18	.18	.17	.17	.16	.16	.15	12
14	.22	.21	.21	.20	.20	.19	.19	.18	14
16	.25	.24	.24	.23	.23	.22	.21	.21	16
18	.28	.28	.27	.26	.26	.25	.24	.23	18
20	.32	.31	.30	.29	.29	.28	.27	.26	20
22	.35	.34	.34	.33	.32	.31	.30	.29	22
24	.39	.38	.37	.36	.35	.34	.33	.32	24
26	.42	.41	.40	.40	.38	.37	.36	.35	26
28	.46	.45	.44	.43	.42	.41	.40	.38	28
30	.50	.49	.48	.47	.45	.44	.43	.41	30
32	.54	.53	.52	.51	.49	.48	.47	.45	32
34	.58	.57	.56	.55	.53	.52	.50	.49	34
36	.63	.62	.60	.59	.57	.56	.54	.52	36
38	.68	.66	.65	.63	.62	.60	.58	.56	38
40	.72	.71	.69	.68	.66	.64	.63	.60	40
42	.78	.76	.75	.73	.71	.69	.67	.65	42
44	.83	.82	.80	.78	.76	.74	.72	.69	44
46	.90	.88	.86	.84	.82	.79	.77	.74	46
48	.96	.94	.92	.90	.88	.85	.83	.80	48
50	1.03	1.01	.99	.96	.94	.91	.88	.86	50
52	1.11	1.09	1.06	1.04	1.01	.98	.95	.92	52
54	1.19	1.16	1.14	1.11	1.08	1.05	1.02	.99	54
56	1.28	1.26	1.23	1.20	1.17	1.14	1.10	1.07	56
58	1.39	1.36	1.33	1.30	1.26	1.23	1.19	1.15	58
60	1.49	1.47	1.44	1.40	1.37	1.33	1.29	1.25	60
62	1.63	1.59	1.56	1.52	1.48	1.44	1.40	1.35	62
64	1.78	1.74	1.70	1.66	1.62	1.57	1.52	1.48	64
66	1.95	1.91	1.85	1.82	1.77	1.72	1.67	1.62	66
68	2.14	2.10	2.05	2.00	1.95	1.90	1.84	1.78	68
70	2.38	2.33	2.28	2.22	2.17	2.10	2.04	1.98	70
72	2.67	2.61	2.55	2.50	2.43	2.36	2.29	2.21	72
74	3.02	2.96	2.89	2.82	2.75	2.67	2.59	2.51	74
76	3.47	3.40	3.33	3.25	3.16	3.07	2.98	2.89	76
78	4.07	3.99	3.90	3.81	3.71	3.60	3.50	3.38	78
80	4.91	4.81	4.70	4.59	4.47	4.34	4.22	4.08	80
81	5.47	5.35	5.24	5.11	4.98	4.84	4.69	4.54	81
82	6.16	6.03	5.90	5.76	5.61	5.45	5.29	5.12	82
83	7.05	6.91	6.75	6.59	6.42	6.24	6.05	5.86	83
84	8.24	8.07	7.93	7.70	7.50	7.29	7.07	6.84	84
85	9.90	9.69	9.48	9.25	9.01	8.75	8.49	8.22	85
86	12.39	12.13	11.86	11.57	11.27	10.95	10.63	10.29	86
87	16.52	16.18	15.82	15.44	15.04	14.62	14.18	13.73	87
88	24.80	24.28	23.74	23.17	22.56	21.93	21.28	20.60	88
89	49.61	48.58	47.50	46.36	45.14	43.98	42.58	41.21	89
	30°	32°	34°	36°	38°	40°	42°	44°	

Corr. to Lat. = Error in Long. × f.

TABLE 36.

Latitude Factors.

f is the change in latitude due to a change of 1′ in longitude.

Bearing.	Latitude. 46°	48°	50°	52°	54°	56°	58°	60°	Bearing.
°	′	′	′	′	′	′	′	′	°
1	0.01	0.01	0.01	0.01	0.01	0.01	0.01	0.01	1
2	.02	.02	.02	.02	.02	.02	.02	.02	2
3	.04	.03	.03	.03	.03	.03	.03	.03	3
4	.05	.05	.04	.04	.04	.04	.04	.03	4
5	.06	.06	.06	.05	.05	.05	.05	.04	5
6	.07	.07	.07	.06	.06	.06	.06	.05	6
7	.08	.08	.08	.08	.07	.07	.06	.06	7
8	.10	.09	.09	.08	.08	.08	.07	.07	8
10	.12	.12	.11	.11	.10	.10	.09	.09	10
12	.15	.14	.14	.13	.13	.12	.11	.11	12
14	.17	.17	.16	.15	.15	.14	.13	.12	14
16	.20	.19	.18	.18	.17	.16	.15	.14	16
18	.23	.22	.21	.20	.19	.18	.17	.16	18
20	.25	.24	.23	.22	.21	.20	.19	.18	20
22	.28	.27	.26	.25	.24	.23	.21	.20	22
24	.31	.30	.29	.27	.26	.25	.24	.22	24
26	.34	.33	.31	.30	.29	.27	.26	.24	26
28	.37	.36	.34	.33	.31	.30	.28	.27	28
30	.40	.39	.37	.36	.34	.32	.31	.29	30
32	.43	.42	.40	.38	.37	.35	.33	.31	32
34	.47	.45	.43	.41	.40	.38	.36	.34	34
36	.51	.49	.47	.45	.43	.41	.38	.36	36
38	.54	.52	.50	.48	.46	.44	.41	.39	38
40	.58	.56	.54	.52	.49	.47	.44	.42	40
42	.63	.60	.58	.56	.53	.50	.48	.45	42
44	.67	.65	.62	.60	.57	.54	.51	.48	44
46	.72	.69	.67	.64	.61	.58	.55	.52	46
48	.77	.74	.71	.68	.65	.62	.59	.56	48
50	.83	.80	.77	.73	.70	.67	.63	.60	50
52	.89	.86	.82	.79	.75	.72	.68	.64	52
54	.96	.92	.88	.85	.81	.77	.73	.69	54
56	1.03	.99	.95	.91	.87	.83	.79	.74	56
58	1.11	1.07	1.03	.99	.94	.89	.85	.80	58
60	1.20	1.16	1.11	1.07	1.02	.97	.92	.87	60
62	1.31	1.26	1.21	1.16	1.11	1.05	1.00	.94	62
64	1.42	1.37	1.32	1.26	1.20	1.15	1.09	1.03	64
66	1.56	1.50	1.44	1.38	1.32	1.26	1.19	1.12	66
68	1.72	1.66	1.59	1.52	1.45	1.38	1.31	1.24	68
70	1.91	1.84	1.77	1.69	1.61	1.54	1.45	1.37	70
72	2.14	2.06	1.99	1.89	1.81	1.72	1.63	1.54	72
74	2.42	2.33	2.24	2.15	2.05	1.95	1.85	1.74	74
76	2.79	2.68	2.58	2.47	2.36	2.24	2.13	2.01	76
78	3.27	3.15	3.02	2.90	2.77	2.63	2.49	2.35	78
80	3.94	3.80	3.70	3.49	3.33	3.17	3.01	2.84	80
81	4.39	4.23	4.06	3.89	3.71	3.53	3.35	3.16	81
82	4.94	4.76	4.57	4.38	4.18	3.98	3.77	3.56	82
83	5.66	5.45	5.24	5.01	4.79	4.56	4.32	4.07	83
84	6.61	6.37	6.12	5.86	5.59	5.32	5.04	4.76	84
85	7.94	7.65	7.35	7.04	6.72	6.39	6.06	5.72	85
86	9.94	9.57	9.19	8.81	8.41	8.00	7.58	7.15	86
87	13.26	12.77	12.27	11.75	11.22	10.67	10.11	9.54	87
88	19.89	19.16	18.41	17.64	16.83	16.01	15.17	14.32	88
89	39.80	38.34	36.83	35.24	33.68	32.04	30.36	28.65	89
	46°	48°	50°	52°	54°	56°	58°	60°	

Corr. to Lat. = Error in Long. × f.

TABLE 37.

Noon Interval Factor.

Easterly hourly change in longitude.

M	.0	.1	.2	.3	.4	.5	.6	.7	.8	.9
0	1. 00000	0. 99989	0. 99978	0. 99967	0. 99956	0. 99944	0. 99933	0. 99922	0. 99911	0. 99900
1	. 99889	. 99878	. 99867	. 99856	. 99845	. 99834	. 99823	. 99812	. 99801	. 99790
2	. 99778	. 99767	. 99756	. 99745	. 99734	. 99723	. 99712	. 99701	. 99690	. 99679
3	. 99668	. 99657	. 99646	. 99635	. 99624	. 99613	. 99602	. 99591	. 99580	. 99569
4	. 99558	. 99547	. 99536	. 99525	. 99514	. 99503	. 99492	. 99481	. 99470	. 99459
5	. 99448	. 99437	. 99426	. 99415	. 99404	. 99393	. 99382	. 99371	. 99360	. 99349
6	. 99338	. 99327	. 99316	. 99305	. 99294	. 99283	. 99272	. 99261	. 99250	. 99239
7	. 99228	. 99217	. 99206	. 99196	. 99185	. 99174	. 99163	. 99152	. 99141	. 99130
8	. 99119	. 99108	. 99097	. 99086	. 99075	. 99064	. 99054	. 99043	. 99032	. 99021
9	. 99010	. 98999	. 98988	. 98977	. 98966	. 98956	. 98945	. 98934	. 98923	. 98912
10	. 98901	. 98890	. 98879	. 98868	. 98857	. 98847	. 98836	. 98825	. 98814	. 98803
11	. 98793	. 98782	. 98771	. 98760	. 98749	. 98738	. 98727	. 98717	. 98706	. 98695
12	. 98684	. 98674	. 98663	. 98652	. 98641	. 98630	. 98620	. 98609	. 98598	. 98587
13	. 98576	. 98565	. 98555	. 98544	. 98533	. 98522	. 98511	. 98501	. 98490	. 98479
14	. 98468	. 98457	. 98447	. 98436	. 98425	. 98414	. 98404	. 98393	. 98382	. 98371
15	. 98361	. 98350	. 98339	. 98329	. 98318	. 98307	. 98296	. 98285	. 98275	. 98264
16	. 98253	. 98242	. 98232	. 98221	. 98210	. 98200	. 98189	. 98178	. 98168	. 98157
17	. 98146	. 98135	. 98125	. 98114	. 98103	. 98093	. 98082	. 98071	. 98061	. 98050
18	. 98039	. 98028	. 98018	. 98007	. 97997	. 97986	. 97975	. 97964	. 97954	. 97943
19	. 97933	. 97922	. 97911	. 97901	. 97890	. 97879	. 97869	. 97858	. 97847	. 97836
20	. 97826	. 97816	. 97805	. 97794	. 97784	. 97773	. 97762	. 97752	. 97741	. 97731
21	. 97720	. 97709	. 97698	. 97688	. 97678	. 97667	. 97657	. 97646	. 97635	. 97624
22	. 97614	. 97603	. 97593	. 97582	. 97572	. 97561	. 97550	. 97540	. 97530	. 97519
23	. 97508	. 97498	. 97487	. 97477	. 97466	. 97455	. 97445	. 97434	. 97424	. 97413
24	. 97402	. 97391	. 97381	. 97371	. 97360	. 97350	. 97339	. 97329	. 97318	. 97308
25	. 97298	. 97287	. 97276	. 97266	. 97255	. 97245	. 97234	. 97224	. 97213	. 97203
26	. 97192	. 97182	. 97171	. 97161	. 97150	. 97140	. 97130	. 97119	. 97108	. 97098
27	. 97088	. 97077	. 97067	. 97056	. 97045	. 97035	. 97025	. 97014	. 97004	. 96993
28	. 96983	. 96972	. 96962	. 96952	. 96941	. 96931	. 96920	. 96910	. 96899	. 96889
29	. 96878	. 96868	. 96858	. 96847	. 96837	. 96826	. 96816	. 96806	. 96795	. 96785
30	. 96774	. 96764	. 96754	. 96743	. 96733	. 96722	. 96712	. 96702	. 96691	. 96681
31	. 96670	. 96660	. 96650	. 96639	. 96629	. 96618	. 96608	. 96598	. 96587	. 96577
32	. 96567	. 96556	. 96546	. 96535	. 96525	. 96515	. 96505	. 96494	. 96484	. 96473
33	. 96463	. 96453	. 96442	. 96432	. 96422	. 96411	. 96401	. 96391	. 96380	. 96370
34	. 96360	. 96350	. 96339	. 96329	. 96319	. 96308	. 96298	. 96288	. 96277	. 96267
35	. 96257	. 96247	. 96236	. 96226	. 96216	. 96205	. 96195	. 96185	. 96175	. 96164
36	. 96154	. 96144	. 96133	. 96123	. 96113	. 96103	. 96092	. 96082	. 96072	. 96061
37	. 96051	. 96041	. 96031	. 96021	. 96010	. 96000	. 95990	. 95979	. 95969	. 95959
38	. 95949	. 95939	. 95929	. 95918	. 95908	. 95898	. 95888	. 95877	. 95867	. 95857
39	. 95847	. 95837	. 95826	. 95816	. 95806	. 95796	. 95786	. 95775	. 95765	. 95755
40	. 95745	. 95734	. 95724	. 95714	. 95704	. 95694	. 95684	. 95674	. 95663	. 95653
41	. 95643	. 95633	. 95623	. 95613	. 95602	. 95592	. 95582	. 95572	. 95562	. 95552
42	. 95541	. 95531	. 95521	. 95511	. 95501	. 95491	. 95481	. 95471	. 95460	. 95450
43	. 95440	. 95430	. 95420	. 95410	. 95400	. 95390	. 95380	. 95369	. 95359	. 95349
44	. 95339	. 95329	. 95319	. 95309	. 95299	. 95289	. 95279	. 95268	. 95258	. 95248
45	. 95238	. 95228	. 95218	. 95208	. 95198	. 95188	. 95178	. 95168	. 95158	. 95148
46	. 95137	. 95127	. 95117	. 95107	. 95097	. 95087	. 95077	. 95067	. 95057	. 95047
47	. 95037	. 95027	. 95017	. 95007	. 94997	. 94987	. 94977	. 94967	. 94957	. 94947
48	. 94937	. 94927	. 94917	. 94907	. 94897	. 94887	. 94877	. 94867	. 94857	. 94847
49	. 94837	. 94827	. 94817	. 94807	. 94797	. 94787	. 94777	. 94767	. 94757	. 94747
50	. 94737	. 94727	. 94717	. 94707	. 94697	. 94687	. 94677	. 94667	. 94657	. 94647
51	. 94637	. 94627	. 94617	. 94607	. 94597	. 94587	. 94577	. 94568	. 94558	. 94548
52	. 94538	. 94528	. 94518	. 94508	. 94498	. 94488	. 94478	. 94468	. 94459	. 94449
53	. 94438	. 94429	. 94419	. 94409	. 94399	. 94389	. 94379	. 94369	. 94359	. 94349
54	. 94339	. 94329	. 94320	. 94310	. 94300	. 94290	. 94280	. 94270	. 94261	. 94251
55	. 94241	. 94231	. 94221	. 94211	. 94201	. 94191	. 94181	. 94171	. 94162	. 94152
56	. 94142	. 94133	. 94123	. 94113	. 94103	. 94093	. 94083	. 94073	. 94064	. 94054
57	. 94044	. 94034	. 94024	. 94014	. 94005	. 93995	. 93985	. 93975	. 93965	. 93956
58	. 93946	. 93936	. 93926	. 93916	. 93906	. 93897	. 93887	. 93877	. 93868	. 93858
59	. 93848	. 93838	. 93828	. 93818	. 93809	. 93799	. 93789	. 93779	. 93769	. 93759
60	. 93750	. 93740	. 93730	. 93721	. 93711	. 93701	. 93691	. 93682	. 93672	. 93662

Combine change in longitude due to vessels course and speed, with change due to current, take factor from table and multiply it by hour angle obtained from morning observation. For time of transit of star or planet multiply its hour angle by factor.

TABLE 37.

Noon Interval Factor.

Westerly hourly change in longitude.

M	.0	.1	.2	.3	.4	.5	.6	.7	.8	.9
0	1. 0000	1. 0001	1. 0002	1. 0003	1. 0005	1. 0006	1. 0007	1. 0008	1. 0009	1. 0010
1	1. 0011	1. 0012	1. 0013	1. 0014	1. 0016	1. 0017	1. 0018	1. 0019	1. 0020	1. 0021
2	1. 0022	1. 0023	1. 0025	1. 0026	1. 0027	1. 0028	1. 0029	1. 0030	1. 0031	1. 0032
3	1. 0034	1. 0035	1. 0036	1. 0037	1. 0038	1. 0039	1. 0040	1. 0041	1. 0042	1. 0043
4	1. 0045	1. 0046	1. 0047	1. 0048	1. 0049	1. 0050	1. 0051	1. 0053	1. 0054	1. 0055
5	1. 0056	1. 0057	1. 0058	1. 0059	1. 0060	1. 0062	1. 0063	1. 0064	1. 0065	1. 0066
6	1. 0067	1. 0068	1. 0070	1. 0071	1. 0072	1. 0073	1. 0074	1. 0075	1. 0076	1. 0077
7	1. 0078	1. 0079	1. 0080	1. 0082	1. 0083	1. 0084	1. 0085	1. 0086	1. 0087	1. 0089
8	1. 0090	1. 0091	1. 0092	1. 0093	1. 0094	1. 0095	1. 0096	1. 0098	1. 0099	1. 0100
9	1. 0101	1. 0102	1. 0103	1. 0104	1. 0105	1. 0106	1. 0108	1. 0109	1. 0110	1. 0111
10	1. 0112	1. 0113	1. 0115	1. 0116	1. 0117	1. 0118	1. 0119	1. 0120	1. 0121	1. 0123
11	1. 0124	1. 0125	1. 0126	1. 0127	1. 0128	1. 0129	1. 0130	1. 0131	1. 0133	1. 0134
12	1. 0135	1. 0136	1. 0137	1. 0139	1. 0140	1. 0141	1. 0142	1. 0143	1. 0144	1. 0145
13	1. 0146	1. 0148	1. 0149	1. 0150	1. 0151	1. 0152	1. 0154	1. 0155	1. 0156	1. 0157
14	1. 0158	1. 0159	1. 0161	1. 0162	1. 0163	1. 0164	1. 0165	1. 0166	1. 0167	1. 0168
15	1. 0169	1. 0171	1. 0172	1. 0173	1. 0174	1. 0175	1. 0177	1. 0178	1. 0179	1. 0180
16	1. 0181	1. 0182	1. 0183	1. 0184	1. 0185	1. 0186	1. 0187	1. 0188	1. 0190	1. 0191
17	1. 0193	1. 0194	1. 0195	1. 0196	1. 0197	1. 0198	1. 0199	1. 0201	1. 0202	1. 0203
18	1. 0204	1. 0205	1. 0206	1. 0208	1. 0209	1. 0210	1. 0211	1. 0212	1. 0213	1. 0214
19	1. 0216	1. 0217	1. 0218	1. 0219	1. 0220	1. 0222	1. 0223	1. 0224	1. 0225	1. 0226
20	1. 0227	1. 0228	1. 0229	1. 0231	1. 0232	1. 0233	1. 0234	1. 0235	1. 0236	1. 0238
21	1. 0239	1. 0240	1. 0241	1. 0242	1. 0244	1. 0245	1. 0246	1. 0247	1. 0248	1. 0249
22	1. 0250	1. 0252	1. 0253	1. 0254	1. 0255	1. 0256	1. 0258	1. 0259	1. 0260	1. 0261
23	1. 0262	1. 0263	1. 0265	1. 0266	1. 0267	1. 0268	1. 0269	1. 0270	1. 0271	1. 0273
24	1. 0274	1. 0275	1. 0276	1. 0277	1. 0279	1. 0280	1. 0281	1. 0282	1. 0283	1. 0285
25	1. 0286	1. 0287	1. 0288	1. 0289	1. 0291	1. 0292	1. 0293	1. 0294	1. 0295	1. 0296
26	1. 0297	1. 0299	1. 0300	1. 0301	1. 0302	1. 0303	1. 0304	1. 0306	1. 0307	1. 0308
27	1. 0309	1. 0311	1. 0312	1. 0313	1. 0314	1. 0315	1. 0316	1. 0318	1. 0319	1. 0320
28	1. 0321	1. 0322	1. 0324	1. 0325	1. 0326	1. 0327	1. 0328	1. 0329	1. 0330	1. 0332
29	1. 0333	1. 0334	1. 0335	1. 0336	1. 0338	1. 0339	1. 0340	1. 0341	1. 0342	1. 0344
30	1. 0345	1. 0346	1. 0347	1. 0348	1. 0350	1. 0351	1. 0352	1. 0353	1. 0354	1. 0355
31	1. 0357	1. 0358	1. 0359	1. 0360	1. 0362	1. 0363	1. 0364	1. 0365	1. 0366	1. 0367
32	1. 0369	1. 0370	1. 0371	1. 0372	1. 0374	1. 0375	1. 0376	1. 0377	1. 0378	1. 0379
33	1. 0381	1. 0382	1. 0383	1. 0384	1. 0386	1. 0387	1. 0388	1. 0389	1. 0390	1. 0391
34	1. 0393	1. 0394	1. 0395	1. 0396	1. 0397	1. 0399	1. 0400	1. 0401	1. 0402	1. 0403
35	1. 0405	1. 0406	1. 0407	1. 0408	1. 0409	1. 0411	1. 0412	1. 0413	1. 0414	1. 0415
36	1. 0416	1. 0418	1. 0419	1. 0420	1. 0421	1. 0422	1. 0424	1. 0425	1. 0426	1. 0427
37	1. 0429	1. 0430	1. 0431	1. 0432	1. 0433	1. 0435	1. 0436	1. 0437	1. 0438	1. 0439
38	1. 0441	1. 0442	1. 0443	1. 0445	1. 0446	1. 0447	1. 0448	1. 0449	1. 0451	1. 0452
39	1. 0453	1. 0454	1. 0455	1. 0457	1. 0458	1. 0459	1. 0460	1. 0462	1. 0463	1. 0464
40	1. 0465	1. 0466	1. 0468	1. 0469	1. 0470	1. 0471	1. 0472	1. 0474	1. 0475	1. 0476
41	1. 0477	1. 0478	1. 0480	1. 0481	1. 0482	1. 0483	1. 0485	1. 0486	1. 0487	1. 0488
42	1. 0489	1. 0491	1. 0492	1. 0493	1. 0494	1. 0496	1. 0497	1. 0498	1. 0499	1. 0500
43	1. 0502	1. 0503	1. 0504	1. 0505	1. 0507	1. 0508	1. 0509	1. 0510	1. 0511	1. 0513
44	1. 0514	1. 0515	1. 0517	1. 0518	1. 0519	1. 0520	1. 0522	1. 0523	1. 0524	1. 0525
45	1. 0526	1. 0528	1. 0529	1. 0530	1. 0531	1. 0532	1. 0534	1. 0535	1. 0536	1. 0537
46	1. 0539	1. 0540	1. 0541	1. 0542	1. 0543	1. 0545	1. 0546	1. 0547	1. 0549	1. 0550
47	1. 0551	1. 0552	1. 0553	1. 0555	1. 0556	1. 0557	1. 0558	1. 0560	1. 0561	1. 0562
48	1. 0564	1. 0565	1. 0566	1. 0567	1. 0569	1. 0570	1. 0571	1. 0572	1. 0573	1. 0575
49	1. 0576	1. 0577	1. 0578	1. 0580	1. 0581	1. 0582	1. 0583	1. 0585	1. 0586	1. 0587
50	1. 0588	1. 0589	1. 0591	1. 0592	1. 0593	1. 0594	1. 0596	1. 0597	1. 0598	1. 0599
51	1. 0601	1. 0602	1. 0603	1. 0604	1. 0605	1. 0607	1. 0608	1. 0609	1. 0611	1. 0612
52	1. 0613	1. 0614	1. 0616	1. 0617	1. 0618	1. 0620	1. 0621	1. 0622	1. 0623	1. 0624
53	1. 0626	1. 0627	1. 0628	1. 0630	1. 0631	1. 0632	1. 0633	1. 0635	1. 0636	1. 0637
54	1. 0638	1. 0639	1. 0641	1. 0642	1. 0643	1. 0644	1. 0646	1. 0647	1. 0648	1. 0650
55	1. 0651	1. 0652	1. 0653	1. 0655	1. 0656	1. 0657	1. 0658	1. 0660	1. 0661	1. 0662
56	1. 0664	1. 0665	1. 0666	1. 0667	1. 0668	1. 0670	1. 0671	1. 0672	1. 0674	1. 0675
57	1. 0676	1. 0677	1. 0678	1. 0680	1. 0681	1. 0683	1. 0684	1. 0685	1. 0686	1. 0688
58	1. 0689	1. 0690	1. 0691	1. 0693	1. 0694	1. 0695	1. 0696	1. 0698	1. 0699	1. 0700
59	1. 0701	1. 0703	1. 0704	1. 0705	1. 0707	1. 0708	1. 0709	1. 0710	1. 0712	1. 0713
60	1. 0714	1. 0716	1. 0717	1. 0718	1. 0719	1. 0721	1. 0722	1. 0723	1. 0724	1. 0726

Combine change in longitude due to vessel's course and speed with change due to current, take factor from table and multiply it by hour angle obtained from morning observation. For W. T. of transit of star or planet, multiply star's H. A. by factor.

TABLE 38.

Sidereal into Mean Solar Time.

To be subtracted from a sidereal time interval.

Sidereal.	0h	1h	2h	3h	4h	5h	6h	7h	For seconds.	
m.	m. s.	m. s.	m. s.	m. s.	m. s.	m. s.	m. s.	m. s.	s.	s.
0	0 0.000	0 9.830	0 19.659	0 29.489	0 39.318	0 49.148	0 58.977	1 8.807		
1	0 0.164	0 9.993	0 19.823	0 29.653	0 39.482	0 49.312	0 59.141	1 8.971	1	0.003
2	0 0.328	0 10.157	0 19.987	0 29.816	0 39.646	0 49.475	0 59.305	1 9.135	2	.005
3	0 0.491	0 10.321	0 20.151	0 29.980	0 39.810	0 49.639	0 59.469	1 9.298	3	.008
4	0 0.655	0 10.485	0 20.314	0 30.144	0 39.974	0 49.803	0 59.633	1 9.462	4	.011
5	0 0.819	0 10.649	0 20.478	0 30.308	0 40.137	0 49.967	0 59.796	1 9.626	5	.014
6	0 0.983	0 10.813	0 20.642	0 30.472	0 40.301	0 50.131	0 59.960	1 9.790	6	.016
7	0 1.147	0 10.976	0 20.806	0 30.635	0 40.465	0 50.295	1 0.124	1 9.954	7	.019
8	0 1.311	0 11.140	0 20.970	0 30.799	0 40.629	0 50.458	1 0.288	1 10.118	8	.022
9	0 1.474	0 11.304	0 21.134	0 30.963	0 40.793	0 50.622	1 0.452	1 10.281	9	.025
10	0 1.638	0 11.468	0 21.297	0 31.127	0 40.956	0 50.786	1 0.616	1 10.445	10	.027
11	0 1.802	0 11.632	0 21.461	0 31.291	0 41.120	0 50.950	1 0.779	1 10.609	11	.030
12	0 1.966	0 11.795	0 21.625	0 31.455	0 41.284	0 51.114	1 0.943	1 10.773	12	.033
13	0 2.130	0 11.959	0 21.789	0 31.618	0 41.448	0 51.278	1 1.107	1 10.937	13	.035
14	0 2.294	0 12.123	0 21.953	0 31.782	0 41.612	0 51.441	1 1.271	1 11.100	14	.038
15	0 2.457	0 12.287	0 22.117	0 31.946	0 41.776	0 51.605	1 1.435	1 11.264	15	.041
16	0 2.621	0 12.451	0 22.280	0 32.110	0 41.939	0 51.769	1 1.599	1 11.428	16	.044
17	0 2.785	0 12.615	0 22.444	0 32.274	0 42.103	0 51.933	1 1.762	1 11.592	17	.046
18	0 2.949	0 12.778	0 22.608	0 32.438	0 42.267	0 52.097	1 1.926	1 11.756	18	.049
19	0 3.113	0 12.942	0 22.772	0 32.601	0 42.431	0 52.260	1 2.090	1 11.920	19	.052
20	0 3.277	0 13.106	0 22.936	0 32.765	0 42.595	0 52.424	1 2.254	1 12.083	20	.055
21	0 3.440	0 13.270	0 23.099	0 32.929	0 42.759	0 52.588	1 2.418	1 12.247	21	.057
22	0 3.604	0 13.434	0 23.263	0 33.093	0 42.922	0 52.752	1 2.582	1 12.411	22	.060
23	0 3.768	0 13.598	0 23.427	0 33.257	0 43.086	0 52.916	1 2.745	1 12.575	23	.063
24	0 3.932	0 13.761	0 23.591	0 33.420	0 43.250	0 53.080	1 2.909	1 12.739	24	.066
25	0 4.096	0 13.925	0 23.755	0 33.584	0 43.414	0 53.243	1 3.073	1 12.903	25	.068
26	0 4.259	0 14.089	0 23.919	0 33.748	0 43.578	0 53.407	1 3.237	1 13.066	26	.071
27	0 4.423	0 14.253	0 24.082	0 33.912	0 43.742	0 53.571	1 3.401	1 13.230	27	.074
28	0 4.587	0 14.417	0 24.246	0 34.076	0 43.905	0 53.735	1 3.564	1 13.394	28	.076
29	0 4.751	0 14.581	0 24.410	0 34.240	0 44.069	0 53.899	1 3.728	1 13.558	29	.079
30	0 4.915	0 14.744	0 24.574	0 34.403	0 44.233	0 54.063	1 3.892	1 13.722	30	.082
31	0 5.079	0 14.908	0 24.738	0 34.567	0 44.397	0 54.226	1 4.056	1 13.886	31	.085
32	0 5.242	0 15.072	0 24.902	0 34.731	0 44.561	0 54.390	1 4.220	1 14.049	32	.087
33	0 5.406	0 15.236	0 25.065	0 34.895	0 44.724	0 54.554	1 4.384	1 14.213	33	.090
34	0 5.570	0 15.400	0 25.229	0 35.059	0 44.888	0 54.718	1 4.547	1 14.377	34	.093
35	0 5.734	0 15.563	0 25.393	0 35.223	0 45.052	0 54.882	1 4.711	1 14.541	35	.096
36	0 5.898	0 15.727	0 25.557	0 35.386	0 45.216	0 55.046	1 4.875	1 14.705	36	.098
37	0 6.062	0 15.891	0 25.721	0 35.550	0 45.380	0 55.209	1 5.039	1 14.868	37	.101
38	0 6.225	0 16.055	0 25.885	0 35.714	0 45.544	0 55.373	1 5.203	1 15.032	38	.104
39	0 6.389	0 16.219	0 26.048	0 35.878	0 45.707	0 55.537	1 5.367	1 15.196	39	.106
40	0 6.553	0 16.383	0 26.212	0 36.042	0 45.871	0 55.701	1 5.530	1 15.360	40	.109
41	0 6.717	0 16.546	0 26.376	0 36.206	0 46.035	0 55.865	1 5.694	1 15.524	41	.112
42	0 6.881	0 16.710	0 26.540	0 36.369	0 46.199	0 56.028	1 5.858	1 15.688	42	.115
43	0 7.045	0 16.874	0 26.704	0 36.533	0 46.363	0 56.192	1 6.022	1 15.851	43	.117
44	0 7.208	0 17.038	0 26.867	0 36.697	0 46.527	0 56.356	1 6.186	1 16.015	44	.120
45	0 7.372	0 17.202	0 27.031	0 36.861	0 46.690	0 56.520	1 6.350	1 16.179	45	.123
46	0 7.536	0 17.366	0 27.195	0 37.025	0 46.854	0 56.684	1 6.513	1 16.343	46	.126
47	0 7.700	0 17.529	0 27.359	0 37.188	0 47.018	0 56.848	1 6.677	1 16.507	47	.128
48	0 7.864	0 17.693	0 27.523	0 37.352	0 47.182	0 57.011	1 6.841	1 16.671	48	.131
49	0 8.027	0 17.857	0 27.687	0 37.516	0 47.346	0 57.175	1 7.005	1 16.834	49	.134
50	0 8.191	0 18.021	0 27.850	0 37.680	0 47.510	0 57.339	1 7.169	1 16.998	50	.137
51	0 8.355	0 18.185	0 28.014	0 37.844	0 47.673	0 57.503	1 7.332	1 17.162	51	.139
52	0 8.519	0 18.349	0 28.178	0 38.008	0 47.837	0 57.667	1 7.496	1 17.326	52	.142
53	0 8.683	0 18.512	0 28.342	0 38.171	0 48.001	0 57.831	1 7.660	1 17.490	53	.145
54	0 8.847	0 18.676	0 28.506	0 38.335	0 48.165	0 57.994	1 7.824	1 17.654	54	.147
55	0 9.010	0 18.840	0 28.670	0 38.499	0 48.329	0 58.158	1 7.988	1 17.817	55	.150
56	0 9.174	0 19.004	0 28.833	0 38.663	0 48.492	0 58.322	1 8.152	1 17.981	56	.153
57	0 9.338	0 19.168	0 28.997	0 38.827	0 48.656	0 58.486	1 8.315	1 18.145	57	.156
58	0 9.502	0 19.331	0 29.161	0 38.991	0 48.820	0 58.650	1 8.479	1 18.309	58	.158
59	0 9.666	0 19.495	0 29.325	0 39.154	0 48.984	0 58.814	1 8.643	1 18.473	59	0.161

TABLE 38.

Sidereal into Mean Solar Time.

To be subtracted from a sidereal time interval.

Sidereal.	8h	9h	10h	11h	12h	13h	14h	15h	For seconds.	
m.	m. s.	m. s.	m. s.	m. s.	m. s.	m. s.	m. s.	m. s.	s.	s.
0	1 18.636	1 28.466	1 38.296	1 48.125	1 57.955	2 7.784	2 17.614	2 27.443		
1	1 18.800	1 28.630	1 38.459	1 48.289	1 58.119	2 7.948	2 17.778	2 27.607	1	0.003
2	1 18.964	1 28.794	1 38.623	1 48.453	1 58.282	2 8.112	2 17.941	2 27.771	2	.005
3	1 19.128	1 28.958	1 38.787	1 48.617	1 58.446	2 8.276	2 18.105	2 27.935	3	.008
4	1 19.292	1 29.121	1 38.951	1 48.780	1 58.610	2 8.440	2 18.269	2 28.099	4	.011
5	1 19.456	1 29.285	1 39.115	1 48.944	1 58.774	2 8.603	2 18.433	2 28.263	5	.014
6	1 19.619	1 29.449	1 39.279	1 49.108	1 58.938	2 8.767	2 18.597	2 28.426	6	.016
7	1 19.783	1 29.613	1 39.442	1 49.272	1 59.101	2 8.931	2 18.761	2 28.590	7	.019
8	1 19.947	1 29.777	1 39.606	1 49.436	1 59.265	2 9.095	2 18.924	2 28.754	8	.022
9	1 20.111	1 29.940	1 39.770	1 49.600	1 59.429	2 9.259	2 19.088	2 28.918	9	.025
10	1 20.275	1 30.104	1 39.934	1 49.763	1 59.593	2 9.423	2 19.252	2 29.082	10	.027
11	1 20.439	1 30.268	1 40.098	1 49.927	1 59.757	2 9.586	2 19.416	2 29.245	11	.030
12	1 20.602	1 30.432	1 40.261	1 50.091	1 59.921	2 9.750	2 19.580	2 29.409	12	.033
13	1 20.766	1 30.596	1 40.425	1 50.255	2 0.084	2 9.914	2 19.744	2 29.573	13	.035
14	1 20.930	1 30.760	1 40.589	1 50.419	2 0.248	2 10.078	2 19.907	2 29.737	14	.038
15	1 21.094	1 30.923	1 40.753	1 50.583	2 0.412	2 10.242	2 20.071	2 29.901	15	.041
16	1 21.258	1 31.087	1 40.917	1 50.746	2 0.576	2 10.405	2 20.235	2 30.065	16	.044
17	1 21.422	1 31.251	1 41.081	1 50.910	2 0.740	2 10.569	2 20.399	2 30.228	17	.046
18	1 21.585	1 31.415	1 41.244	1 51.074	2 0.904	2 10.733	2 20.563	2 30.392	18	.049
19	1 21.749	1 31.579	1 41.408	1 51.238	2 1.067	2 10.897	2 20.727	2 30.556	19	.052
20	1 21.913	1 31.743	1 41.572	1 51.402	2 1.231	2 11.061	2 20.890	2 30.720	20	.055
21	1 22.077	1 31.906	1 41.736	1 51.565	2 1.395	2 11.225	2 21.054	2 30.884	21	.057
22	1 22.241	1 32.070	1 41.900	1 51.729	2 1.559	2 11.388	2 21.218	2 31.048	22	.060
23	1 22.404	1 32.234	1 42.064	1 51.893	2 1.723	2 11.552	2 21.382	2 31.211	23	.063
24	1 22.568	1 32.398	1 42.227	1 52.057	2 1.887	2 11.716	2 21.546	2 31.375	24	.066
25	1 22.732	1 32.562	1 42.391	1 52.221	2 2.050	2 11.880	2 21.709	2 31.539	25	.068
26	1 22.896	1 32.726	1 42.555	1 52.385	2 2.214	2 12.044	2 21.873	2 31.703	26	.071
27	1 23.060	1 32.889	1 42.719	1 52.548	2 2.378	2 12.208	2 22.037	2 31.867	27	.074
28	1 23.224	1 33.053	1 42.883	1 52.712	2 2.542	2 12.371	2 22.201	2 32.031	28	.076
29	1 23.387	1 33.217	1 43.047	1 52.876	2 2.706	2 12.535	2 22.365	2 32.194	29	.079
30	1 23.551	1 33.381	1 43.210	1 53.040	2 2.869	2 12.699	2 22.529	2 32.358	30	.082
31	1 23.715	1 33.545	1 43.374	1 53.204	2 3.033	2 12.863	2 22.692	2 32.522	31	.085
32	1 23.879	1 33.708	1 43.538	1 53.368	2 3.197	2 13.027	2 22.856	2 32.686	32	.087
33	1 24.043	1 33.872	1 43.702	1 53.531	2 3.361	2 13.191	2 23.020	2 32.850	33	.090
34	1 24.207	1 34.036	1 43.866	1 53.695	2 3.525	2 13.354	2 23.184	2 33.013	34	.093
35	1 24.370	1 34.200	1 44.029	1 53.859	2 3.689	2 13.518	2 23.348	2 33.177	35	.096
36	1 24.534	1 34.364	1 44.193	1 54.023	2 3.852	2 13.682	2 23.512	2 33.341	36	.098
37	1 24.698	1 34.528	1 44.357	1 54.187	2 4.016	2 13.846	2 23.675	2 33.505	37	.101
38	1 24.862	1 34.691	1 44.521	1 54.351	2 4.180	2 14.010	2 23.839	2 33.669	38	.104
39	1 25.026	1 34.855	1 44.685	1 54.514	2 4.344	2 14.173	2 24.003	2 33.833	39	.106
40	1 25.190	1 35.019	1 44.849	1 54.678	2 4.508	2 14.337	2 24.167	2 33.996	40	.109
41	1 25.353	1 35.183	1 45.012	1 54.842	2 4.672	2 14.501	2 24.331	2 34.160	41	.112
42	1 25.517	1 35.347	1 45.176	1 55.006	2 4.835	2 14.665	2 24.495	2 34.324	42	.115
43	1 25.681	1 35.511	1 45.340	1 55.170	2 4.999	2 14.829	2 24.658	2 34.488	43	.117
44	1 25.845	1 35.674	1 45.504	1 55.333	2 5.163	2 14.993	2 24.822	2 34.652	44	.120
45	1 26.009	1 35.838	1 45.668	1 55.497	2 5.327	2 15.156	2 24.986	2 34.816	45	.123
46	1 26.172	1 36.002	1 45.832	1 55.661	2 5.491	2 15.320	2 25.150	2 34.979	46	.126
47	1 26.336	1 36.166	1 45.995	1 55.825	2 5.655	2 15.484	2 25.314	2 35.143	47	.128
48	1 26.500	1 36.330	1 46.159	1 55.989	2 5.818	2 15.648	2 25.477	2 35.307	48	.131
49	1 26.664	1 36.493	1 46.323	1 56.153	2 5.982	2 15.812	2 25.641	2 35.471	49	.134
50	1 26.828	1 36.657	1 46.487	1 56.316	2 6.146	2 15.976	2 25.805	2 35.635	50	.137
51	1 26.992	1 36.821	1 46.651	1 56.480	2 6.310	2 16.139	2 25.969	2 35.798	51	.139
52	1 27.155	1 36.985	1 46.815	1 56.644	2 6.474	2 16.303	2 26.133	2 35.962	52	.142
53	1 27.319	1 37.149	1 46.978	1 56.808	2 6.637	2 16.467	2 26.297	2 36.126	53	.145
54	1 27.483	1 37.313	1 47.142	1 56.972	2 6.801	2 16.631	2 26.460	2 36.290	54	.147
55	1 27.647	1 37.476	1 47.306	1 57.136	2 6.965	2 16.795	2 26.624	2 36.454	55	.150
56	1 27.811	1 37.640	1 47.470	1 57.299	2 7.129	2 16.959	2 26.788	2 36.618	56	.153
57	1 27.975	1 37.804	1 47.634	1 57.463	2 7.293	2 17.122	2 26.952	2 36.781	57	.156
58	1 28.138	1 37.968	1 47.797	1 57.627	2 7.457	2 17.286	2 27.116	2 36.945	58	.158
59	1 28.302	1 38.132	1 47.961	1 57.791	2 7.620	2 17.450	2 27.280	2 37.109	59	0.161

TABLE 38.

Sidereal into Mean Solar Time.

To be subtracted from a sidereal time interval.

Sidereal.	16ʰ	17ʰ	18ʰ	19ʰ	20ʰ	21ʰ	22ʰ	23ʰ	For seconds.	
m.	*m. s.*	*m. s.*	*m. s.*	*m. s.*	*m. s.*	*m. s.*	*m. s.*	*m. s.*	*s.*	*s.*
0	2 37.273	2 47.102	2 56.932	3 6.762	3 16.591	3 26.421	3 36.250	3 46.080		
1	2 37.437	2 47.266	2 57.096	3 6.925	3 16.755	3 26.585	3 36.414	3 46.244	1	0.003
2	2 37.601	2 47.430	2 57.260	3 7.089	3 16.919	3 26.748	3 36.578	3 46.407	2	.005
3	2 37.764	2 47.594	2 57.424	3 7.253	3 17.083	3 26.912	3 36.742	3 46.571	3	.008
4	2 37.928	2 47.758	2 57.587	3 7.417	3 17.246	3 27.076	3 36.906	3 46.735	4	.011
5	2 38.092	2 47.922	2 57.751	3 7.581	3 17.410	3 27.240	3 37.069	3 46.899	5	.014
6	2 38.256	2 48.085	2 57.915	3 7.745	3 17.574	3 27.404	3 37.233	3 47.063	6	.016
7	2 38.420	2 48.249	2 58.079	3 7.908	3 17.738	3 27.568	3 37.397	3 47.227	7	.019
8	2 38.584	2 48.413	2 58.243	3 8.072	3 17.902	3 27.731	3 37.561	3 47.390	8	.022
9	2 38.747	2 48.577	2 58.406	3 8.236	3 18.066	3 27.895	3 37.725	3 47.554	9	.025
10	2 38.911	2 48.741	2 58.570	3 8.400	3 18.229	3 28.059	3 37.889	3 47.718	10	.027
11	2 39.075	2 48.905	2 58.734	3 8.564	3 18.393	3 28.223	3 38.052	3 47.882	11	.030
12	2 39.239	2 49.068	2 58.898	3 8.728	3 18.557	3 28.387	3 38.216	3 48.046	12	.033
13	2 39.403	2 49.232	2 59.062	3 8.891	3 18.721	3 28.550	3 38.380	3 48.210	13	.035
14	2 39.566	2 49.396	2 59.226	3 9.055	3 18.885	3 28.714	3 38.544	3 48.373	14	.038
15	2 39.730	2 49.560	2 59.389	3 9.219	3 19.049	3 28.878	3 38.708	3 48.537	15	.041
16	2 39.894	2 49.724	2 59.553	3 9.383	3 19.212	3 29.042	3 38.871	3 48.701	16	.044
17	2 40.058	2 49.888	2 59.717	3 9.547	3 19.376	3 29.206	3 39.035	3 48.865	17	.046
18	2 40.222	2 50.051	2 59.881	3 9.710	3 19.540	3 29.370	3 39.199	3 49.029	18	.049
19	2 40.386	2 50.215	3 0.045	3 9.874	3 19.704	3 29.533	3 39.363	3 49.193	19	.052
20	2 40.549	2 50.379	3 0.209	3 10.038	3 19.868	3 29.697	3 39.527	3 49.356	20	.055
21	2 40.713	2 50.543	3 0.372	3 10.202	3 20.032	3 29.861	3 39.691	3 49.520	21	.057
22	2 40.877	2 50.707	3 0.536	3 10.366	3 20.195	3 30.025	3 39.854	3 49.684	22	.060
23	2 41.041	2 50.870	3 0.700	3 10.530	3 20.359	3 30.189	3 40.018	3 49.848	23	.063
24	2 41.205	2 51.034	3 0.864	3 10.693	3 20.523	3 30.353	3 40.182	3 50.012	24	.066
25	2 41.369	2 51.198	3 1.028	3 10.857	3 20.687	3 30.516	3 40.346	3 50.175	25	.068
26	2 41.532	2 51.362	3 1.192	3 11.021	3 20.851	3 30.680	3 40.510	3 50.339	26	.071
27	2 41.696	2 51.526	3 1.355	3 11.185	3 21.014	3 30.844	3 40.674	3 50.503	27	.074
28	2 41.860	2 51.690	3 1.519	3 11.349	3 21.178	3 31.008	3 40.837	3 50.667	28	.076
29	2 42.024	2 51.853	3 1.683	3 11.513	3 21.342	3 31.172	3 41.001	3 50.831	29	.079
30	2 42.188	2 52.017	3 1.847	3 11.676	3 21.506	3 31.336	3 41.165	3 50.995	30	.082
31	2 42.352	2 52.181	3 2.011	3 11.840	3 21.670	3 31.499	3 41.329	3 51.158	31	.085
32	2 42.515	2 52.345	3 2.174	3 12.004	3 21.834	3 31.663	3 41.493	3 51.322	32	.087
33	2 42.679	2 52.509	3 2.338	3 12.168	3 21.997	3 31.827	3 41.657	3 51.486	33	.090
34	2 42.843	2 52.673	3 2.502	3 12.332	3 22.161	3 31.991	3 41.820	3 51.650	34	.093
35	2 43.007	2 52.836	3 2.666	3 12.496	3 22.325	3 32.155	3 41.984	3 51.814	35	.096
36	2 43.171	2 53.000	3 2.830	3 12.659	3 22.489	3 32.318	3 42.148	3 51.978	36	.098
37	2 43.334	2 53.164	3 2.994	3 12.823	3 22.653	3 32.482	3 42.312	3 52.141	37	.101
38	2 43.498	2 53.328	3 3.157	3 12.987	3 22.817	3 32.646	3 42.476	3 52.305	38	.104
39	2 43.662	2 53.492	3 3.321	3 13.151	3 22.980	3 32.810	3 42.639	3 52.469	39	.106
40	2 43.826	2 53.656	3 3.485	3 13.315	3 23.144	3 32.974	3 42.803	3 52.633	40	.109
41	2 43.990	2 53.819	3 3.649	3 13.478	3 23.308	3 33.138	3 42.967	3 52.797	41	.112
42	2 44.154	2 53.983	3 3.813	3 13.642	3 23.472	3 33.301	3 43.131	3 52.961	42	.115
43	2 44.317	2 54.147	3 3.977	3 13.806	3 23.636	3 33.465	3 43.295	3 53.124	43	.117
44	2 44.481	2 54.311	3 4.140	3 13.970	3 23.800	3 33.629	3 43.459	3 53.288	44	.120
45	2 44.645	2 54.475	3 4.304	3 14.134	3 23.963	3 33.793	3 43.622	3 53.452	45	.123
46	2 44.809	2 54.638	3 4.468	3 14.298	3 24.127	3 33.957	3 43.786	3 53.616	46	.126
47	2 44.973	2 54.802	3 4.632	3 14.461	3 24.291	3 34.121	3 43.950	3 53.780	47	.128
48	2 45.137	2 54.966	3 4.796	3 14.625	3 24.455	3 34.284	3 44.114	3 53.943	48	.131
49	2 45.300	2 55.130	3 4.960	3 14.789	3 24.619	3 34.448	3 44.278	3 54.107	49	.134
50	2 45.464	2 55.294	3 5.123	3 14.953	3 24.782	3 34.612	3 44.442	3 54.271	50	.137
51	2 45.628	2 55.458	3 5.287	3 15.117	3 24.946	3 34.776	3 44.605	3 54.435	51	.139
52	2 45.792	2 55.621	3 5.451	3 15.281	3 25.110	3 34.940	3 44.769	3 54.599	52	.142
53	2 45.956	2 55.785	3 5.615	3 15.444	3 25.274	3 35.104	3 44.933	3 54.763	53	.145
54	2 46.120	2 55.949	3 5.779	3 15.608	3 25.438	3 35.267	3 45.097	3 54.926	54	.147
55	2 46.283	2 56.113	3 5.942	3 15.772	3 25.602	3 35.431	3 45.261	3 55.090	55	.150
56	2 46.447	2 56.277	3 6.106	3 15.936	3 25.765	3 35.595	3 45.425	3 55.254	56	.153
57	2 46.611	2 56.441	3 6.270	3 16.100	3 25.929	3 35.759	3 45.588	3 55.418	57	.156
58	2 46.755	2 56.604	3 6.434	3 16.264	3 26.093	3 35.923	3 45.752	3 55.582	58	.158
59	2 46.939	2 56.768	3 6.598	3 16.427	3 26.257	3 36.086	3 45.916	3 55.746	59	0.161

TABLE 39.

Mean Solar into Sidereal Time.

To be added to a mean time interval.

Mean.	0h	1h	2h	3h	4h	5h	6h	7h	For seconds.	
m.	m. s.	m. s.	m. s.	m. s.	m. s.	m. s.	m. s.	m. s.	s.	s.
0	0 0.000	0 9.856	0 19.713	0 29.569	0 39.426	0 49.282	0 59.139	1 8.995		
1	0 0.164	0 10.021	0 19.877	0 29.734	0 39.590	0 49.447	0 59.303	1 9.160	1	0.003
2	0 0.329	0 10.185	0 20.041	0 29.898	0 39.764	0 49.611	0 59.467	1 9.324	2	.005
3	0 0.493	0 10.349	0. 20.206	0 30.062	0 39.919	0 49.775	0 59.632	1 9.488	3	.008
4	0 0.657	0 10.514	0 20.370	0 30.227	0 40.083	0 49.939	0 59.796	1 9.652	4	.011
5	0 0.821	0 10.678	0 20.534	0 30.391	0 40.247	0 50.104	0 59.960	1 9.817	5	.014
6	0 0.986	0 10.842	0 20.699	0 30.555	0 40.412	0 50.268	1 0.124	1 9.981	6	.016
7	0 1.150	0 11.006	0 20.863	0 30.719	0 40.576	0 50.432	1 0.289	1 10.145	7	.019
8	0 1.314	0 11.171	0 21.027	0 30.884	0 40.740	0 50.597	1 0.453	1 10.310	8	.022
9	0 1.478	0 11.335	0 21.191	0 31.048	0 40.904	0 50.761	1 0.617	1 10.474	9	.025
10	0 1.643	0 11.499	0 21.356	0 31.212	0 41.069	0 50.925	1 0.782	1 10.638	10	.027
11	0 1.807	0 11.663	0 21.520	0 31.376	0 41.233	0 51.089	1 0.946	1 10.802	11	.030
12	0 1.971	0 11.828	0 21.684	0 31.541	0 41.397	0 51.254	1 1.110	1 10.967	12	.033
13	0 2.136	0 11.992	0 21.849	0 31.705	0 41.561	0 51.418	1 1.274	1 11.131	13	.036
14	0 2.300	0 12.156	0 22.013	0 31.869	0 41.726	0 51.582	1 1.439	1 11.295	14	.038
15	0 2.464	0 12.321	0 22.177	0 32.034	0 41.890	0 51.746	1 1.603	1 11.459	15	.041
16	0 2.628	0 12.485	0 22.341	0 32.198	0 42.054	0 51.911	1 1.767	1 11.624	16	.044
17	0 2.793	0 12.649	0 22.506	0 32.362	0 42.219	0 52.075	1 1.932	1 11.788	17	.047
18	0 2.957	0 12.813	0 22.670	0 32.526	0 42.383	0 52.239	1 2.096	1 11.952	18	.049
19	0 3.121	0 12.978	0 22.834	0 32.691	0 42.547	0 52.404	1 2.260	1 12.117	19	.052
20	0 3.285	0 13.142	0 22.998	0 32.855	0 42.711	0 52.568	1 2.424	1 12.281	20	.055
21	0 3.450	0 13.306	0 23.163	0 33.019	0 42.876	0 52.732	1 2.589	1 12.445	21	.057
22	0 3.614	0 13.471	0 23.327	0 33.183	0 43.040	0 52.896	1 2.753	1 12.609	22	.060
23	0 3.778	0 13.635	0 23.491	0 33.348	0 43.204	0 53.061	1 2.917	1 12.774	23	.063
24	0 3.943	0 13.799	0 23.656	0 33.512	0 43.368	0 53.225	1 3.081	1 12.938	24	.066
25	0 4.107	0 13.963	0 23.820	0 33.676	0 43.533	0 53.389	1 3.246	1 13.102	25	.068
26	0 4.271	0 14.128	0 23.984	0 33.841	0 43.697	0 53.554	1 3.410	1 13.266	26	.071
27	0 4.435	0 14.292	0 24.148	0 34.005	0 43.861	0 53.718	1 3.574	1 13.431	27	.074
28	0 4.600	0 14.456	0 24.313	0 34.169	0 44.026	0 53.882	1 3.739	1 13.595	28	.077
29	0 4.764	0 14.620	0 24.477	0 34.333	0 44.190	0 54.046	1 3.903	1 13.759	29	.079
30	0 4.928	0 14.785	0 24.641	0 34.498	0 44.354	0 54.211	1 4.067	1 13.924	30	.082
31	0 5.093	0 14.949	0 24.805	0 34.662	0 44.518	0 54.375	1 4.231	1 14.088	31	.085
32	0 5.257	0 15.113	0 24.970	0 34.826	0 44.683	0 54.539	1 4.396	1 14.252	32	.088
33	0 5.421	0 15.278	0 25.134	0 34.990	0 44.847	0 54.703	1 4.560	1 14.416	33	.090
34	0 5.585	0 15.442	0 25.298	0 35.155	0 45.011	0 54.868	1 4.724	1 14.581	34	.093
35	0 5.750	0 15.606	0 25.463	0 35.319	0 45.176	0 55.032	1 4.888	1 14.745	35	.096
36	0 5.914	0 15.770	0 25.627	0 35.483	0 45.340	0 55.196	1 5.053	1 14.909	36	.099
37	0 6.078	0 15.935	0 25.791	0 35.648	0 45.504	0 55.361	1 5.217	1 15.073	37	.101
38	0 6.242	0 16.099	0 25.955	0 35.812	0 45.668	0 55.525	1 5.381	1 15.238	38	.104
39	0 6.407	0 16.263	0 26.120	0 35.976	0 45.833	0 55.689	1 5.546	1 15.402	39	.107
40	0 6.571	0 16.427	0 26.284	0 36.140	0 45.997	0 55.853	1 5.710	1 15.566	40	.110
41	0 6.735	0 16.592	0 26.448	0 36.305	0 46.161	0 56.018	1 5.874	1 15.731	41	.112
42	0 6.900	0 16.756	0 26.612	0 36.469	0 46.325	0 56.182	1 6.038	1 15.895	42	.115
43	0 7.064	0 16.920	0 26.777	0 36.633	0 46.490	0 56.346	1 6.203	1 16.059	43	.118
44	0 7.228	0 17.085	0 26.941	0 36.798	0 46.654	0 56.510	1 6.367	1 16.223	44	.120
45	0 7.392	0 17.249	0 27.105	0 36.962	0 46.818	0 56.675	1 6.531	1 16.388	45	.123
46	0 7.557	0 17.413	0 27.270	0 37.126	0 46.983	0 56.839	1 6.695	1 16.552	46	.126
47	0 7.721	0 17.577	0 27.434	0 37.290	0 47.147	0 57.003	1 6.860	1 16.716	47	.129
48	0 7.885	0 17.742	0 27.598	0 37.455	0 47.311	0 57.168	1 7.024	1 16.881	48	.131
49	0 8.049	0 17.906	0 27.762	0 37.619	0 47.475	0 57.332	1 7.188	1 17.045	49	.134
50	0 8.214	0 18.070	0 27.927	0 37.783	0 47.640	0 57.496	1 7.353	1 17.209	50	.137
51	0 8.378	0 18.234	0 28.091	0 37.947	0 47.804	0 57.660	1 7.517	1 17.373	51	.140
52	0 8.542	0 18.399	0 28.255	0 38.112	0 47.968	0 57.825	1 7.681	1 17.538	52	.142
53	0 8.707	0 18.563	0 28.420	0 38.276	0 48.132	0 57.989	1 7.845	1 17.702	53	.145
54	0 8.871	0 18.727	0 28.584	0 38.440	0 48.297	0 58.153	1 8.010	1 17.866	54	.148
55	0 9.035	0 18.892	0 28.748	0 38.605	0 48.461	0 58.317	1 8.174	1 18.030	55	.151
56	0 9.199	0 19.056	0 28.912	0 38.769	0 48.625	0 58.482	1 8.338	1 18.195	56	.153
57	0 9.364	0 19.220	0 29.077	0 38.933	0 48.790	0 58.646	1 8.502	1 18.359	57	.156
58	0 9.528	0 19.384	0 29.241	0 39.097	0 48.954	0 58.810	1 8.667	1 18.523	58	.159
59	0 9.692	0 19.549	0 29.405	0 39.262	0 49.118	0 58.975	1 8.831	1 18.688	59	0.162

TABLE 39.

Mean Solar into Sidereal Time.

To be added to a mean time interval.

Mean.	8h	9h	10h	11h	12h	13h	14h	15h	For seconds.	
m.	m. s.	m. s.	m. s.	m. s.	m. s.	m. s.	m. s.	m. s.	s.	s.
0	1 18.852	1 28.708	1 38.565	1 48.421	1 58.278	2 8.134	2 17.991	2 27.847		
1	1 19.016	1 28.873	1 38.729	1 48.585	1 58.442	2 8.298	2 18.155	2 28.011	1	0.003
2	1 19.180	1 29.037	1 38.893	1 48.750	1 58.606	2 8.463	2 18.319	2 28.176	2	.005
3	1 19.345	1 29.201	1 39.058	1 48.914	1 58.771	2 8.627	2 18.483	2 28.340	3	.008
4	1 19.509	1 29.365	1 39.222	1 49.078	1 58.935	2 8.791	2 18.648	2 28.504	4	.011
5	1 19.673	1 29.530	1 39.386	1 49.243	1 59.099	2 8.956	2 18.812	2 28.668	5	.014
6	1 19.837	1 29.694	1 39.550	1 49.407	1 59.263	2 9.120	2 18.976	2 28.833	6	.016
7	1 20.002	1 29.858	1 39.715	1 49.571	1 59.428	2 9.284	2 19.141	2 28.997	7	.019
8	1 20.166	1 30.022	1 39.879	1 49.735	1 59.592	2 9.448	2 19.305	2 29.161	8	.022
9	1 20.330	1 30.187	1 40.043	1 49.900	1 59.756	2 9.613	2 19.469	2 29.326	9	.025
10	1 20.495	1 30.351	1 40.207	1 50.064	1 59.920	2 9.777	2 19.633	2 29.490	10	.027
11	1 20.659	1 30.515	1 40.372	1 50.228	2 0.085	2 9.941	2 19.798	2 29.654	11	.030
12	1 20.823	1 30.680	1 40.536	1 50.393	2 0.249	2 10.105	2 19.962	2 29.818	12	.033
13	1 20.987	1 30.844	1 40.700	1 50.557	2 0.413	2 10.270	2 20.126	2 29.983	13	.036
14	1 21.152	1 31.008	1 40.865	1 50.721	2 0.578	2 10.434	2 20.290	2 30.147	14	.038
15	1 21.316	1 31.172	1 41.029	1 50.885	2 0.742	2 10.598	2 20.455	2 30.311	15	.041
16	1 21.480	1 31.337	1 41.193	1 51.050	2 0.906	2 10.763	2 20.619	2 30.476	16	.044
17	1 21.644	1 31.501	1 41.357	1 51.214	2 1.070	2 10.927	2 20.783	2 30.640	17	.047
18	1 21.809	1 31.665	1 41.522	1 51.378	2 1.235	2 11.091	2 20.948	2 30.804	18	.049
19	1 21.973	1 31.829	1 41.686	1 51.542	2 1.399	2 11.255	2 21.112	2 30.968	19	.052
20	1 22.137	1 31.994	1 41.850	1 51.707	2 1.563	2 11.420	2 21.276	2 31.133	20	.055
21	1 22.302	1 32.158	1 42.015	1 51.871	2 1.727	2 11.584	2 21.440	2 31.297	21	.057
22	1 22.466	1 32.322	1 42.179	1 52.035	2 1.892	2 11.748	2 21.605	2 31.461	22	.060
23	1 22.630	1 32.487	1 42.343	1 52.200	2 2.056	2 11.912	2 21.769	2 31.625	23	.063
24	1 22.794	1 32.651	1 42.507	1 52.364	2 2.220	2 12.077	2 21.933	2 31.790	24	.066
25	1 22.959	1 32.815	1 42.672	1 52.528	2 2.385	2 12.241	2 22.098	2 31.954	25	.068
26	1 23.123	1 32.979	1 42.836	1 52.692	2 2.549	2 12.405	2 22.262	2 32.118	26	.071
27	1 23.287	1 33.144	1 43.000	1 52.857	2 2.713	2 12.570	2 22.426	2 32.283	27	.074
28	1 23.451	1 33.308	1 43.164	1 53.021	2 2.877	2 12.734	2 22.590	2 32.447	28	.077
29	1 23.616	1 33.472	1 43.329	1 53.185	2 3.042	2 12.898	2 22.755	2 32.611	29	.079
30	1 23.780	1 33.637	1 43.493	1 53.349	2 3.206	2 13.062	2 22.919	2 32.775	30	.082
31	1 23.944	1 33.801	1 43.657	1 53.514	2 3.370	2 13.227	2 23.083	2 32.940	31	.085
32	1 24.109	1 33.965	1 43.822	1 53.678	2 3.534	2 13.391	2 23.247	2 33.104	32	.088
33	1 24.273	1 34.129	1 43.986	1 53.842	2 3.699	2 13.555	2 23.412	2 33.268	33	.090
34	1 24.437	1 34.294	1 44.150	1 54.007	2 3.863	2 13.720	2 23.576	2 33.432	34	.093
35	1 24.601	1 34.458	1 44.314	1 54.171	2 4.027	2 13.884	2 23.740	2 33.597	35	.096
36	1 24.766	1 34.622	1 44.479	1 54.335	2 4.192	2 14.048	2 23.905	2 33.761	36	.099
37	1 24.930	1 34.786	1 44.643	1 54.499	2 4.356	2 14.212	2 24.069	2 33.925	37	.101
38	1 25.094	1 34.951	1 44.807	1 54.664	2 4.520	2 14.377	2 24.233	2 34.090	38	.104
39	1 25.259	1 35.115	1 44.971	1 54.828	2 4.684	2 14.541	2 24.397	2 34.254	39	.107
40	1 25.423	1 35.279	1 45.136	1 54.992	2 4.849	2 14.705	2 24.562	2 34.418	40	.110
41	1 25.587	1 35.444	1 45.300	1 55.156	2 5.013	2 14.869	2 24.726	2 34.582	41	.112
42	1 25.751	1 35.608	1 45.464	1 55.321	2 5.177	2 15.034	2 24.890	2 34.747	42	.115
43	1 25.916	1 35.772	1 45.629	1 55.485	2 5.342	2 15.198	2 25.054	2 34.911	43	.118
44	1 26.080	1 35.936	1 45.793	1 55.649	2 5.506	2 15.362	2 25.219	2 35.075	44	.120
45	1 26.244	1 36.101	1 45.957	1 55.814	2 5.670	2 15.527	2 25.383	2 35.239	45	.123
46	1 26.408	1 36.265	1 46.121	1 55.978	2 5.834	2 15.691	2 25.547	2 35.404	46	.126
47	1 26.573	1 36.429	1 46.286	1 56.142	2 5.999	2 15.855	2 25.712	2 35.568	47	.129
48	1 26.737	1 36.593	1 46.450	1 56.306	2 6.163	2 16.019	2 25.876	2 35.732	48	.131
49	1 26.901	1 36.758	1 46.614	1 56.471	2 6.327	2 16.184	2 26.040	2 35.897	49	.134
50	1 27.066	1 36.922	1 46.778	1 56.635	2 6.491	2 16.348	2 26.204	2 36.061	50	.137
51	1 27.230	1 37.086	1 46.943	1 56.799	2 6.656	2 16.512	2 26.369	2 36.225	51	.140
52	1 27.394	1 37.251	1 47.107	1 56.964	2 6.820	2 16.676	2 26.533	2 36.389	52	.142
53	1 27.558	1 37.415	1 47.271	1 57.128	2 6.984	2 16.841	2 26.697	2 36.554	53	.145
54	1 27.723	1 37.579	1 47.436	1 57.292	2 7.149	2 17.005	2 26.861	2 36.718	54	.148
55	1 27.887	1 37.743	1 47.600	1 57.456	2 7.313	2 17.169	2 27.026	2 36.882	55	.151
56	1 28.051	1 37.908	1 47.764	1 57.621	2 7.477	2 17.334	2 27.190	2 37.047	56	.153
57	1 28.215	1 38.072	1 47.928	1 57.785	2 7.641	2 17.498	2 27.354	2 37.211	57	.156
58	1 28.380	1 38.236	1 48.093	1 57.949	2 7.806	2 17.662	2 27.519	2 37.375	58	.159
59	1 28.544	1 38.400	1 48.257	1 58.113	2 7.970	2 17.826	2 27.683	2 37.539	59	0.162

541524°—43——50

TABLE 39.

Mean Solar into Sidereal time.

To be added to a mean time interval.

Mean.	16h	17h	18h	19h	20h	21h	22h	23h	For seconds.	
m.	m. s.	m. s.	m. s.	m. s.	m. s.	m. s.	m. s.	m. s.	s.	s.
0	2 37.704	2 47.560	2 57.417	3 7.273	3 17.129	3 26.986	3 36.842	3 46.699		
1	2 37.868	2 47.724	2 57.581	3 7.437	3 17.294	3 27.150	3 37.007	3 46.863	1	0.003
2	2 38.032	2 47.889	2 57.745	3 7.602	3 17.458	3 27.315	3 37.171	3 47.027	2	.005
3	2 38.196	2 48.053	2 57.909	3 7.766	3 17.622	3 27.479	3 37.335	3 47.192	3	.008
4	2 38.361	2 48.217	2 58.074	3 7.930	3 17.787	3 27.643	3 37.500	3 47.356	4	.011
5	2 38.525	2 48.381	2 58.238	3 8.094	3 17.951	3 27.807	3 37.664	3 47.520	5	.014
6	2 38.689	2 48.546	2 58.402	3 8.259	3 18.115	3 27.972	3 37.828	3 47.685	6	.016
7	2 38.854	2 48.710	2 58.566	3 8.423	3 18.279	3 28.136	3 37.992	3 47.849	7	.019
8	2 39.018	2 48.874	2 58.731	3 8.587	3 18.444	3 28.300	3 38.157	3 48.013	8	.022
9	2 39.182	2 49.039	2 58.895	3 8.751	3 18.608	3 28.464	3 38.321	3 48.177	9	.025
10	2 39.346	2 49.203	2 59.059	3 8.916	3 18.772	3 28.629	3 38.485	3 48.342	10	.027
11	2 39.511	2 49.367	2 59.224	3 9.080	3 18.937	3 28.793	3 38.649	3 48.506	11	.030
12	2 39.675	2 49.531	2 59.388	3 9.244	3 19.101	3 28.957	3 38.814	3 48.670	12	.033
13	2 39.839	2 49.696	2 59.552	3 9.409	3 19.265	3 29.122	3 38.978	3 48.834	13	.036
14	2 40.003	2 49.860	2 59.716	3 9.573	3 19.429	3 29.286	3 39.142	3 48.999	14	.038
15	2 40.168	2 50.024	2 59.881	3 9.737	3 19.594	3 29.450	3 39.307	3 49.163	15	.041
16	2 40.332	2 50.188	3 0.045	3 9.901	3 19.758	3 29.614	3 39.471	3 49.327	16	.044
17	2 40.496	2 50.353	3 0.209	3 10.066	3 19.922	3 29.779	3 39.635	3 49.492	17	.047
18	2 40.661	2 50.517	3 0.373	3 10.230	3 20.086	3 29.943	3 39.799	3 49.656	18	.049
19	2 40.825	2 50.681	3 0.538	3 10.394	3 20.251	3 30.107	3 39.964	3 49.820	19	.052
20	2 40.989	2 50.846	3 0.702	3 10.559	3 20.415	3 30.271	3 40.128	3 49.984	20	.055
21	2 41.153	2 51.010	3 0.866	3 10.723	3 20.579	3 30.436	3 40.292	3 50.149	21	.057
22	2 41.318	2 51.174	3 1.031	3 10.887	3 20.744	3 30.600	3 40.456	3 50.313	22	.060
23	2 41.482	2 51.338	3 1.195	3 11.051	3 20.908	3 30.764	3 40.621	3 50.477	23	.063
24	2 41.646	2 51.503	3 1.359	3 11.216	3 21.072	3 30.929	3 40.785	3 50.642	24	.066
25	2 41.810	2 51.667	3 1.523	3 11.380	3 21.236	3 31.093	3 40.949	3 50.806	25	.068
26	2 41.975	2 51.831	3 1.688	3 11.544	3 21.401	3 31.257	3 41.114	3 50.970	26	.071
27	2 42.139	2 51.995	3 1.852	3 11.708	3 21.565	3 31.421	3 41.278	3 51.134	27	.074
28	2 42.303	2 52.160	3 2.016	3 11.873	3 21.729	3 31.586	3 41.442	3 51.299	28	.077
29	2 42.468	2 52.324	3 2.181	3 12.037	3 21.893	3 31.750	3 41.606	3 51.463	29	.079
30	2 42.632	2 52.488	3 2.345	3 12.201	3 22.058	3 31.914	3 41.771	3 51.627	30	.082
31	2 42.796	2 52.653	3 2.509	3 12.366	3 22.222	3 32.078	3 41.935	3 51.791	31	.085
32	2 42.960	2 52.817	3 2.673	3 12.530	3 22.386	3 32.243	3 42.099	3 51.956	32	.088
33	2 43.125	2 52.981	3 2.838	3 12.694	3 22.551	3 32.407	3 42.264	3 52.120	33	.090
34	2 43.289	2 53.145	3 3.002	3 12.858	3 22.715	3 32.571	3 42.428	3 52.284	34	.093
35	2 43.453	2 53.310	3 3.166	3 13.023	3 22.879	3 32.736	3 42.592	3 52.449	35	.096
36	2 43.617	2 53.474	3 3.330	3 13.187	3 23.043	3 32.900	3 42.756	3 52.613	36	.099
37	2 43.782	2 53.638	3 3.495	3 13.351	3 23.208	3 33.064	3 42.921	3 52.777	37	.101
38	2 43.946	2 53.803	3 3.659	3 13.515	3 23.372	3 33.228	3 43.085	3 52.941	38	.104
39	2 44.110	2 53.967	3 3.823	3 13.680	3 23.536	3 33.393	3 43.249	3 53.106	39	.107
40	2 44.275	2 54.131	3 3.988	3 13.844	3 23.700	3 33.557	3 43.413	3 53.270	40	.110
41	2 44.439	2 54.295	3 4.152	3 14.008	3 23.865	3 33.721	3 43.578	3 53.434	41	.112
42	2 44.603	2 54.460	3 4.316	3 14.173	3 24.029	3 33.886	3 43.742	3 53.598	42	.115
43	2 44.767	2 54.624	3 4.480	3 14.337	3 24.193	3 34.050	3 43.906	3 53.763	43	.118
44	2 44.932	2 54.788	3 4.645	3 14.501	3 24.358	3 34.214	3 44.071	3 53.927	44	.120
45	2 45.096	2 54.952	3 4.809	3 14.665	3 24.522	3 34.378	3 44.235	3 54.091	45	.123
46	2 45.260	2 55.117	3 4.973	3 14.830	3 24.686	3 34.543	3 44.399	3 54.256	46	.126
47	2 45.425	2 55.281	3 5.137	3 14.994	3 24.850	3 34.707	3 44.563	3 54.420	47	.129
48	2 45.589	2 55.445	3 5.302	3 15.158	3 25.015	3 34.871	3 44.728	3 54.584	48	.131
49	2 45.753	2 55.610	3 5.466	3 15.322	3 25.179	3 35.035	3 44.892	3 54.748	49	.134
50	2 45.917	2 55.774	3 5.630	3 15.487	3 25.343	3 35.200	3 45.056	3 54.913	50	.137
51	2 46.082	2 55.938	3 5.795	3 15.651	3 25.508	3 35.364	3 45.220	3 55.077	51	.140
52	2 46.246	2 56.102	3 5.959	3 15.815	3 25.672	3 35.528	3 45.385	3 55.241	52	.142
53	2 46.410	2 56.267	3 6.123	3 15.980	3 25.836	3 35.693	3 45.549	3 55.405	53	.145
54	2 46.574	2 56.431	3 6.287	3 16.144	3 26.000	3 35.857	3 45.713	3 55.570	54	.148
55	2 46.739	2 56.595	3 6.452	3 16.308	3 26.165	3 36.021	3 45.878	3 55.734	55	.151
56	2 46.903	2 56.759	3 6.616	3 16.472	3 26.329	3 36.185	3 46.042	3 55.898	56	.153
57	2 47.067	2 56.924	3 6.780	3 16.637	3 26.493	3 36.350	3 46.206	3 56.063	57	.156
58	2 47.232	2 57.088	3 6.944	3 16.801	3 26.657	3 36.514	3 46.370	3 56.227	58	.159
59	2 47.396	2 57.252	3 7.109	3 16.965	3 26.822	3 36.678	3 46.535	3 56.391	59	0.162

TABLE 40.

Corrections To Be Applied to the Observed Altitude of a Star or of the Sun's Lower Limb, To Find the True Altitude.

Observed Altitude.	☉ Sun's Corr.	★ Star's Corr.
° ′	′	′
6 30	+ 8. 2	−7. 9
6 40	8. 4	7. 7
6 50	8. 6	7. 6
7 0	8. 7	7. 4
7 10	8. 9	7. 2
7 20	+ 9. 0	−7. 1
7 30	9. 2	7. 0
7 40	9. 3	6. 8
7 50	9. 5	6. 7
8 0	9. 6	6. 6
8 10	+ 9. 7	−6. 4
8 20	9. 8	6. 3
8 30	10. 0	6. 2
8 40	10. 1	6. 1
8 50	10. 2	6. 0
9 0	+10. 3	−5. 9
9 20	10. 5	5. 7
9 40	10. 6	5. 5
10 0	10. 8	5. 3
10 20	11. 0	5. 2
10 40	+11. 2	−5. 0
11 0	11. 3	4. 9
11 30	11. 5	4. 7
12 0	11. 7	4. 5
12 30	11. 9	4. 3
13 0	+12. 0	−4. 1
13 30	12. 2	4. 0
14 0	12. 3	3. 8
15 0	12. 6	3. 6
16 0	12. 8	3. 4
17 0	+13. 0	−3. 2
18 0	13. 2	3. 0
19 0	13. 3	2. 8
20 0	13. 5	2. 6
22 0	13. 7	2. 4
24 0	+14. 0	−2. 2
26 0	14. 1	2. 0
28 0	14. 3	1. 8
30 0	14. 4	1. 7
32 0	14. 6	1. 6
34 0	+14. 7	−1. 4
36 0	14. 8	1. 3
38 0	14. 9	1. 3
40 0	15. 0	1. 2
45 0	15. 1	1. 0
50 0	+15. 3	−0. 8
55 0	15. 4	0. 7
60 0	15. 5	0. 6
65 0	15. 6	0. 5
70 0	15. 7	0. 4
75 0	+15. 8	−0. 3
80 0	15. 8	0. 2
85 0	15. 9	−0. 1
90 0	+16. 0	0. 0

Date.	☉ Additional Sun's Corr.
	′
Jan. 1	+0. 3
15	+0. 3
Feb. 1	+0. 3
15	+0. 2
Mar. 1	+0. 2
15	+0. 1
Apr. 1	0. 0
15	0. 0
May 1	−0. 1
15	−0. 1
June 1	−0. 2
15	−0. 2
July 1	−0. 2
15	−0. 2
Aug. 1	−0. 2
15	−0. 2
Sept. 1	−0. 1
15	−0. 1
Oct. 1	0. 0
15	+0. 1
Nov. 1	+0. 2
15	+0. 2
Dec. 1	+0. 3
15	+0. 3
31	+0. 3

In case the sun's upper limb is observed, then twice the semidiameter obtained from the nautical almanac is subtracted from the resulting altitude. This gives the sextant altitude of the lower limb, then the corrections are obtained from the above table in the usual way.

Correction for Height of Eye.	
Height of Eye (feet).	Corr.
	′
0	0. 0
1	−1. 0
2	1. 4
3	1. 7
4	2. 0
5	−2. 2
6	2. 4
7	2. 6
8	2. 8
9	2. 9
10	−3. 1
11	3. 2
12	3. 4
13	3. 5
14	3. 7
15	−3. 8
16	3. 9
17	4. 0
18	4. 1
19	4. 3
20	−4. 4
21	4. 5
22	4. 6
23	4. 7
24	4. 8
25	−4. 9
26	5. 0
27	5. 1
28	5. 2
29	5. 3
30	−5. 4
31	5. 4
32	5. 5
33	5. 6
34	5. 7
35	−5. 8
37	6. 0
39	6. 1
41	6. 3
43	6. 4
45	−6. 6
47	6. 7
49	6. 9
51	7. 0
53	7. 1
55	−7. 3
60	7. 6
65	7. 9
70	8. 2
75	8. 5
80	−8. 8
85	9. 0
90	9. 3
95	9. 6
100	−9. 8

TABLE 41.

Correction to the Observed Altitude of the Moon.

FOR REFRACTION, PARALLAX, AND SEMIDIAMETER.

Lower Limb.								
Obs. Alt. Lower Limb.	Horizontal Parallax.							
	54′	55′	56′	57′	58′	59′	60′	61′
°	′	′	′	′	′	′	′	′
5.5	+59.6	+60.9	+62.1	+63.4	+64.7	+66.0	+67.3	+68.5
6.0	60.2	61.4	62.7	64.0	65.3	66.5	67.8	69.1
6.5	60.7	61.9	63.2	64.5	65.8	67.0	68.3	69.6
7.0	61.1	62.4	63.6	64.9	66.2	67.4	68.7	70.0
7.5	61.5	62.7	64.0	65.3	66.5	67.8	69.1	70.4
8.0	+61.8	+63.1	+64.3	+65.6	+66.9	+68.1	+69.4	+70.7
8.5	62.1	63.3	64.6	65.9	67.1	68.4	69.7	70.9
9.0	62.3	63.6	64.8	66.1	67.4	68.6	69.9	71.1
9.5	62.5	63.8	65.0	66.3	67.6	68.8	70.1	71.3
10.0	62.7	64.0	65.2	66.5	67.7	69.0	70.3	71.5
11	+63.0	+64.2	+65.5	+66.7	+68.0	+69.3	+70.5	+71.8
12	63.2	64.4	65.7	66.9	68.2	69.5	70.7	72.0
13	63.3	64.6	65.8	67.0	68.3	69.6	70.8	72.1
14	63.4	64.6	65.9	67.1	68.4	69.6	70.9	72.1
15	63.4	64.6	65.9	67.1	68.4	69.6	70.9	72.1
16	+63.4	+64.6	+65.8	+67.1	+68.3	+69.6	+70.8	+72.0
17	63.3	64.5	65.8	67.0	68.2	69.5	70.7	71.9
18	63.2	64.4	65.6	66.9	68.1	69.3	70.6	71.8
19	63.1	64.3	65.5	66.7	67.9	69.2	70.4	71.6
20	62.9	64.1	65.3	66.5	67.8	69.0	70.2	71.4
21	+62.7	+63.9	+65.1	+66.3	+67.5	+68.7	+70.0	+71.2
22	62.5	63.7	64.9	66.1	67.3	68.5	69.7	70.9
23	62.2	63.4	64.6	65.9	67.0	68.2	69.4	70.6
24	62.0	63.1	64.3	65.5	66.7	67.9	69.1	70.3
25	61.7	62.9	64.0	65.2	66.4	67.6	68.8	69.9
26	+61.3	+62.5	+63.7	+64.9	+66.0	+67.2	+68.4	+69.6
27	61.0	62.2	63.3	64.5	65.7	66.8	68.0	69.2
28	60.7	61.8	63.0	64.1	65.3	66.4	67.6	68.8
29	60.3	61.4	62.6	63.7	64.9	66.0	67.2	68.4
30	59.9	61.0	62.2	63.3	64.4	65.6	66.7	67.9
31	+59.5	+60.6	+61.7	+62.9	+64.0	+65.1	+66.3	+67.4
32	59.0	60.2	61.3	62.4	63.5	64.7	65.8	66.9
33	58.6	59.7	60.8	61.9	63.1	64.2	65.3	66.4
34	58.1	59.2	60.3	61.4	62.5	63.6	64.8	65.9
35	57.7	58.7	59.8	60.9	62.0	63.1	64.2	65.3
36	+57.2	+58.2	+59.3	+60.4	+61.5	+62.6	+63.7	+64.7
37	56.7	57.7	58.8	59.8	60.9	62.0	63.1	64.2
38	56.1	57.2	58.2	59.3	60.4	61.4	62.5	63.6
39	55.6	56.6	57.7	58.7	59.8	60.8	61.9	62.9
40	55.0	56.1	57.1	58.1	59.2	60.2	61.3	62.3
41	+54.4	+55.5	+56.5	+57.5	+58.6	+59.6	+60.6	+61.6
42	53.9	54.9	55.9	56.9	57.9	59.0	60.0	61.0
43	53.3	54.3	55.3	56.3	57.3	58.3	59.3	60.3
44	52.7	53.7	54.6	55.6	56.6	57.6	58.6	59.6
45	52.0	53.0	54.0	55.0	56.0	56.9	57.9	58.9

Lower Limb.								
Obs. Alt. Lower Limb.	Horizontal Parallax.							
	54′	55′	56′	57′	58′	59′	60′	61′
°	′	′	′	′	′	′	′	′
46	+51.4	+52.4	+53.3	+54.3	+55.3	+56.2	+57.2	+58.2
47	50.7	51.7	52.6	53.6	54.6	55.5	56.5	57.4
48	50.1	51.0	52.0	52.9	53.9	54.8	55.7	56.7
49	49.4	50.3	51.3	52.2	53.1	54.1	55.0	55.9
50	48.7	49.6	50.5	51.5	52.4	53.3	54.2	55.1
51	+48.0	+48.9	+49.8	+50.7	+51.6	+52.5	+53.4	+54.3
52	47.3	48.2	49.1	50.0	50.9	51.8	52.7	53.5
53	46.6	47.5	48.3	49.2	50.1	51.0	51.8	52.7
54	45.8	46.7	47.6	48.4	49.3	50.2	51.0	51.9
55	45.1	46.0	46.8	47.6	48.5	49.3	50.2	51.0
56	+44.4	+45.2	+46.0	+46.8	+47.7	+48.5	+49.4	+50.2
57	43.6	44.4	45.2	46.0	46.9	47.7	48.5	49.3
58	42.8	43.6	44.4	45.2	46.0	46.9	47.7	48.5
59	42.1	42.9	43.6	44.4	45.2	46.0	46.8	47.6
60	41.3	42.1	42.8	43.6	44.4	45.1	45.9	46.7
61	+40.5	+41.2	+42.0	+42.7	+43.5	+44.3	+45.0	+45.8
62	39.6	40.4	41.1	41.9	42.6	43.4	44.1	44.9
63	38.8	39.6	40.3	41.0	41.8	42.5	43.2	43.9
64	38.0	38.7	39.4	40.2	40.9	41.6	42.3	43.0
65	37.2	37.9	38.6	39.3	40.0	40.7	41.4	42.1
66	+36.4	+37.0	+37.7	+38.4	+39.1	+39.8	+40.4	+41.1
67	35.5	36.2	36.8	37.5	38.2	38.8	39.5	40.2
68	34.7	35.3	36.0	36.6	37.3	37.9	38.6	39.2
69	33.8	34.4	35.1	35.7	36.3	37.0	37.6	38.2
70	32.9	33.6	34.2	34.8	35.4	36.0	36.7	37.3
71	+32.1	+32.7	+33.3	+33.9	+34.5	+35.1	+35.7	+36.3
72	31.2	31.8	32.3	32.9	33.5	34.1	34.7	35.3
73	30.3	30.9	31.4	32.0	32.6	33.2	33.7	34.3
74	29.4	30.0	30.5	31.1	31.6	32.2	32.7	33.3
75	28.5	29.1	29.6	30.1	30.7	31.2	31.8	32.3
76	+27.7	+28.2	+28.7	+29.2	+29.7	+30.2	+30.8	+31.3
77	26.8	27.3	27.7	28.2	28.8	29.3	29.8	30.2
78	25.8	26.3	26.8	27.3	27.8	28.3	28.7	29.2
79	24.9	25.4	25.9	26.3	26.8	27.3	27.7	28.2
80	24.0	24.5	24.9	25.4	25.8	26.3	26.7	27.2
81	+23.1	+23.6	+24.0	+24.4	+24.8	+25.3	+25.7	+26.2
82	22.2	22.6	23.0	23.4	23.9	24.3	24.7	25.1
83	21.3	21.7	22.1	22.5	22.9	23.3	23.7	24.1
84	20.4	20.8	21.1	21.5	21.9	22.3	22.6	23.0
85	19.4	19.8	20.2	20.5	20.9	21.3	21.6	22.0
86	+18.5	+18.9	+19.2	+19.6	+19.9	+20.3	+20.6	+20.9
87	17.6	17.9	18.2	18.6	18.9	19.2	19.6	19.9
88	16.7	17.0	17.3	17.6	17.9	18.2	18.5	18.8
89	15.7	16.0	16.3	16.6	16.9	17.2	17.5	17.8
90	+14.7	+15.0	+15.3	+15.6	+15.8	+16.1	+16.4	+16.7

Height of Eye Correction.

H. E. feet.	Corr.	H. E. feet.	Corr.	H. E. feet.	Corr.	H. E. feet.	Corr.	H. E. feet.	Corr.	H. E. feet.	Corr.
	′		′		′		′		′		′
0	0.0	10	−3.1	20	−4.4	30	−5.4	45	−6.6	80	−8.8
1	−1.0	11	−3.2	21	−4.5	31	−5.4	47	−6.7	85	−9.0
2	−1.4	12	−3.4	22	−4.6	32	−5.5	49	−6.9	90	−9.3
3	−1.7	13	−3.5	23	−4.7	33	−5.6	51	−7.0	95	−9.6
4	−2.0	14	−3.7	24	−4.8	34	−5.7	53	−7.1	100	−9.8
5	−2.2	15	−3.8	25	−4.9	35	−5.8	55	−7.3	105	−10.0
6	−2.4	16	−3.9	26	−5.0	37	−6.0	60	−7.6	110	−10.3
7	−2.6	17	−4.0	27	−5.1	39	−6.1	65	−7.9	115	−10.5
8	−2.8	18	−4.1	28	−5.2	41	−6.3	70	−8.2	120	−10.7
9	−2.9	19	−4.3	29	−5.3	43	−6.4	75	−8.5	125	−11.0

TABLE 41.

Correction to the Observed Altitude of the Moon.

FOR REFRACTION, PARALLAX, AND SEMIDIAMETER.

UPPER LIMB.

Obs. Alt. Upper Limb.	Horizontal Parallax.							
	54′	55′	56′	57′	58′	59′	60′	61′
°	′	′	′	′	′	′	′	′
5.5	+29.4	+30.2	+30.9	+31.6	+32.3	+33.0	+33.7	+34.4
6.0	30.1	30.8	31.5	32.3	33.0	33.7	34.4	35.1
6.5	30.7	31.4	32.1	32.8	33.5	34.3	35.0	35.7
7.0	31.2	31.9	32.6	33.3	34.0	34.8	35.5	36.2
7.5	31.6	32.3	33.0	33.7	34.5	35.2	35.9	36.6
8.0	+32.0	+32.7	+33.4	+34.1	+34.8	+35.5	+36.3	+37.0
8.5	32.3	33.0	33.7	34.4	35.1	35.9	36.6	37.3
9.0	32.6	33.3	34.0	34.7	35.4	36.1	36.8	37.5
9.5	32.8	33.5	34.2	34.9	35.6	36.3	37.1	37.8
10.0	33.0	33.7	34.4	35.1	35.8	36.5	37.3	38.0
11	+33.3	+34.0	+34.7	+35.4	+36.2	+36.9	+37.6	+38.3
12	33.6	34.3	35.0	35.7	36.4	37.1	37.8	38.5
13	33.7	34.4	35.1	35.8	36.5	37.2	37.9	38.6
14	33.8	34.5	35.2	35.9	36.6	37.3	38.0	38.7
15	33.8	34.5	35.2	35.9	36.6	37.3	38.0	38.7
16	+33.8	+34.5	+35.2	+35.9	+36.6	+37.3	+38.0	+38.6
17	33.8	34.5	35.1	35.8	36.5	37.2	37.9	38.6
18	33.7	34.3	35.0	35.7	36.4	37.1	37.7	38.4
19	33.5	34.2	34.9	35.6	36.2	36.9	37.6	38.2
20	33.4	34.0	34.7	35.4	36.0	36.7	37.4	38.1
21	+33.2	+33.9	+34.5	+35.2	+35.8	+36.5	+37.2	+37.8
22	33.0	33.6	34.3	34.9	35.6	36.3	36.9	37.6
23	32.7	33.4	34.0	34.7	35.3	36.0	36.6	37.3
24	32.5	33.1	33.7	34.4	35.0	35.7	36.3	37.0
25	32.2	32.8	33.4	34.1	34.7	35.4	36.0	36.6
26	+31.9	+32.5	+33.1	+33.7	+34.4	+35.0	+35.6	+36.2
27	31.5	32.1	32.8	33.4	34.0	34.6	35.2	35.9
28	31.2	31.8	32.4	33.0	33.6	34.2	34.9	35.5
29	30.8	31.4	32.0	32.6	33.2	33.8	34.4	35.0
30	30.4	31.0	31.6	32.2	32.8	33.4	34.0	34.6
31	+30.0	+30.6	+31.2	+31.8	+32.3	+32.9	+33.5	+34.1
32	29.6	30.1	30.7	31.3	31.9	32.5	33.0	33.6
33	29.1	29.7	30.3	30.8	31.4	32.0	32.5	33.1
34	28.7	29.2	29.8	30.3	30.9	31.5	32.0	32.6
35	28.2	28.7	29.3	29.8	30.4	30.9	31.5	32.0
36	+27.7	+28.2	+28.8	+29.3	+29.8	+30.4	+30.9	+31.5
37	27.2	27.7	28.2	28.8	29.3	29.8	30.3	30.9
38	26.7	27.2	27.7	28.2	28.7	29.2	29.7	30.3
39	26.1	26.6	27.1	27.6	28.1	28.6	29.1	29.6
40	25.6	26.1	26.6	27.1	27.6	28.0	28.5	29.0
41	+25.0	+25.5	+26.0	+26.4	+26.9	+27.4	+27.9	+28.4
42	24.4	24.9	25.4	25.8	26.3	26.8	27.2	27.7
43	23.8	24.3	24.7	25.2	25.6	26.1	26.6	27.0
44	23.2	23.6	24.1	24.6	25.0	25.4	25.9	26.3
45	22.6	23.0	23.4	23.9	24.3	24.7	25.2	25.6

UPPER LIMB.

Obs. Alt. Upper Limb.	Horizontal Parallax.							
	54′	55′	56′	57′	58′	59′	60′	61′
°	′	′	′	′	′	′	′	′
46	+21.9	+22.4	+22.8	+23.2	+23.6	+24.0	+24.5	+24.9
47	21.3	21.7	22.1	22.5	22.9	23.3	23.8	24.2
48	20.6	21.0	21.4	21.8	22.2	22.6	23.0	23.4
49	19.9	20.3	20.7	21.1	21.5	21.9	22.3	22.6
50	19.2	19.6	20.0	20.4	20.7	21.1	21.5	21.9
51	+18.5	+18.9	+19.3	+19.6	+20.0	+20.3	+20.7	+21.1
52	17.8	18.2	18.5	18.9	19.2	19.6	19.9	20.3
53	17.1	17.5	17.8	18.1	18.4	18.8	19.1	19.4
54	16.4	16.7	17.0	17.3	17.7	18.0	18.3	18.6
55	15.7	16.0	16.3	16.6	16.9	17.2	17.5	17.8
56	+14.9	+15.2	+15.5	+15.8	+16.1	+16.3	+16.6	+16.9
57	14.2	14.4	14.7	15.0	15.2	15.5	15.8	16.1
58	13.4	13.6	13.9	14.2	14.4	14.7	14.9	15.2
59	12.6	12.8	13.1	13.3	13.6	13.8	14.1	14.3
60	11.8	12.0	12.3	12.5	12.7	13.0	13.2	13.4
61	+11.0	+11.2	+11.4	+11.6	+11.9	+12.1	+12.3	+12.5
62	10.2	10.4	10.6	10.8	11.0	11.2	11.4	11.6
63	9.4	9.6	9.8	9.9	10.1	10.3	10.5	10.7
64	8.6	8.7	8.9	9.1	9.2	9.4	9.6	9.7
65	7.7	7.9	8.0	8.2	8.3	8.5	8.7	8.8
66	+ 6.9	+ 7.0	+ 7.2	+ 7.3	+ 7.5	+ 7.6	+ 7.7	+ 7.9
67	6.1	6.2	6.3	6.4	6.5	6.7	6.8	6.9
68	5.2	5.3	5.4	5.5	5.6	5.7	5.8	5.9
69	4.3	4.4	4.5	4.6	4.7	4.8	4.8	4.9
70	3.5	3.5	3.6	3.7	3.8	3.8	3.9	4.0
71	+ 2.6	+ 2.7	+2.7	+ 2.8	+ 2.8	+ 2.9	+ 2.9	+ 3.0
72	1.7	1.8	1.8	1.9	1.9	1.9	2.0	2.0
73	+ 0.9	+ 0.9	+ 0.9	+ 0.9	+ 0.9	+ 1.0	+ 1.0	+ 1.0
74	0.0	0.0	0.0	0.0	0.0	0.0	0.0	0.0
75	− 0.9	− 0.9	− 0.9	− 1.0	− 1.0	− 1.0	− 1.0	− 1.0
76	− 1.8	− 1.9	− 1.9	− 1.9	− 1.9	− 2.0	− 2.0	− 2.0
77	2.7	2.8	2.8	2.9	2.9	2.9	3.0	3.0
78	3.6	3.7	3.8	3.8	3.9	3.9	4.0	4.1
79	4.5	4.6	4.7	4.8	4.8	4.9	5.0	5.1
80	5.4	5.5	5.6	5.7	5.8	5.9	6.0	6.1
81	− 6.3	− 6.5	− 6.6	− 6.7	− 6.8	− 6.9	− 7.0	− 7.2
82	7.3	7.4	7.5	7.7	7.8	7.9	8.1	8.2
83	8.2	8.3	8.5	8.6	8.8	8.9	9.1	9.2
84	9.1	9.3	9.4	9.6	9.8	9.9	10.1	10.3
85	10.0	10.2	10.4	10.6	10.8	10.9	11.1	11.3
86	−10.9	−11.2	−11.4	−11.5	−11.7	−12.0	−12.2	−12.3
87	11.9	12.1	12.3	12.5	12.7	13.0	13.2	13.4
88	12.8	13.0	13.3	13.5	13.7	14.0	14.2	14.4
89	13.7	14.0	14.3	14.5	14.7	15.0	15.3	15.5
90	−14.7	−15.0	−15.3	−15.6	−15.8	−16.1	−16.4	−16.7

Height of Eye Correction.

H. E. feet.	Corr.	H. E. feet.	Corr.	H. E. feet.	Corr.	H. E. feet.	Corr.	H. E. feet.	Corr.	H. E. feet.	Corr.
	′		′		′		′		′		′
0	0.0	10	−3.1	20	−4.4	30	−5.4	45	−6.6	80	−8.8
1	−1.0	11	−3.2	21	−4.5	31	−5.4	47	−6.7	85	−9.0
2	−1.4	12	−3.4	22	−4.6	32	−5.5	49	−6.9	90	−9.3
3	−1.7	13	−3.5	23	−4.7	33	−5.6	51	−7.0	95	−9.6
4	−2.0	14	−3.7	24	−4.8	34	−5.7	53	−7.1	100	−9.8
5	−2.2	15	−3.8	25	−4.9	35	−5.8	55	−7.3	105	−10.0
6	−2.4	16	−3.9	26	−5.0	37	−6.0	60	−7.6	110	−10.3
7	−2.6	17	−4.0	27	−5.1	39	−6.1	65	−7.9	115	−10.5
8	−2.8	18	−4.1	28	−5.2	41	−6.3	70	−8.2	120	−10.7
9	−2.9	19	−4.3	29	−5.3	43	−6.4	75	−8.5	125	−11.0

TABLE 42.

For Conversion of Arc and Time.

°	h. m.	°	h. m.	°	h. m.	°	h. m.	°	h. m.	°	h. m.	′	m. s.	″	s.
0	0 0	**60**	4 0	**120**	8 0	**180**	12 0	**240**	16 0	**300**	20 0	**0**	0 0	**0**	0.00
1	0 4	**61**	4 4	**121**	8 4	**181**	12 4	**241**	16 4	**301**	20 4	**1**	0 4	**1**	0.07
2	0 8	**62**	4 8	**122**	8 8	**182**	12 8	**242**	16 8	**302**	20 8	**2**	0 8	**2**	0.13
3	0 12	**63**	4 12	**123**	8 12	**183**	12 12	**243**	16 12	**303**	20 12	**3**	0 12	**3**	0.20
4	0 16	**64**	4 16	**124**	8 16	**184**	12 16	**244**	16 16	**304**	20 16	**4**	0 16	**4**	0.27
5	0 20	**65**	4 20	**125**	8 20	**185**	12 20	**245**	16 20	**305**	20 20	**5**	0 20	**5**	0.33
6	0 24	**66**	4 24	**126**	8 24	**186**	12 24	**246**	16 24	**306**	20 24	**6**	0 24	**6**	0.40
7	0 28	**67**	4 28	**127**	8 28	**187**	12 28	**247**	16 28	**307**	20 28	**7**	0 28	**7**	0.47
8	0 32	**68**	4 32	**128**	8 32	**188**	12 32	**248**	16 32	**308**	20 32	**8**	0 32	**8**	0.53
9	0 36	**69**	4 36	**129**	8 36	**189**	12 36	**249**	16 36	**309**	20 36	**9**	0 36	**9**	0.60
10	0 40	**70**	4 40	**130**	8 40	**190**	12 40	**250**	16 40	**310**	20 40	**10**	0 40	**10**	0.67
11	0 44	**71**	4 44	**131**	8 44	**191**	12 44	**251**	16 44	**311**	20 44	**11**	0 44	**11**	0.73
12	0 48	**72**	4 48	**132**	8 48	**192**	12 48	**252**	16 48	**312**	20 48	**12**	0 48	**12**	0.80
13	0 52	**73**	4 52	**133**	8 52	**193**	12 52	**253**	16 52	**313**	20 52	**13**	0 52	**13**	0.87
14	0 56	**74**	4 56	**134**	8 56	**194**	12 56	**254**	16 56	**314**	20 56	**14**	0 56	**14**	0.93
15	1 0	**75**	5 0	**135**	9 0	**195**	13 0	**255**	17 0	**315**	21 0	**15**	1 0	**15**	1.00
16	1 4	**76**	5 4	**136**	9 4	**196**	13 4	**256**	17 4	**316**	21 4	**16**	1 4	**16**	1.07
17	1 8	**77**	5 8	**137**	9 8	**197**	13 8	**257**	17 8	**317**	21 8	**17**	1 8	**17**	1.13
18	1 12	**78**	5 12	**138**	9 12	**198**	13 12	**258**	17 12	**318**	21 12	**18**	1 12	**18**	1.20
19	1 16	**79**	5 16	**139**	9 16	**199**	13 16	**259**	17 16	**319**	21 16	**19**	1 16	**19**	1.27
20	1 20	**80**	5 20	**140**	9 20	**200**	13 20	**260**	17 20	**320**	21 20	**20**	1 20	**20**	1.33
21	1 24	**81**	5 24	**141**	9 24	**201**	13 24	**261**	17 24	**321**	21 24	**21**	1 24	**21**	1.40
22	1 28	**82**	5 28	**142**	9 28	**202**	13 28	**262**	17 28	**322**	21 28	**22**	1 28	**22**	1.47
23	1 32	**83**	5 32	**143**	9 32	**203**	13 32	**263**	17 32	**323**	21 32	**23**	1 32	**23**	1.53
24	1 36	**84**	5 36	**144**	9 36	**204**	13 36	**264**	17 36	**324**	21 36	**24**	1 36	**24**	1.60
25	1 40	**85**	5 40	**145**	9 40	**205**	13 40	**265**	17 40	**325**	21 40	**25**	1 40	**25**	1.67
26	1 44	**86**	5 44	**146**	9 44	**206**	13 44	**266**	17 44	**326**	21 44	**26**	1 44	**26**	1.73
27	1 48	**87**	5 48	**147**	9 48	**207**	13 48	**267**	17 48	**327**	21 48	**27**	1 48	**27**	1.80
28	1 52	**88**	5 52	**148**	9 52	**208**	13 52	**268**	17 52	**328**	21 52	**28**	1 52	**28**	1.87
29	1 56	**89**	5 56	**149**	9 56	**209**	13 56	**269**	17 56	**329**	21 56	**29**	1 56	**29**	1.93
30	2 0	**90**	6 0	**150**	10 0	**210**	14 0	**270**	18 0	**330**	22 0	**30**	2 0	**30**	2.00
31	2 4	**91**	6 4	**151**	10 4	**211**	14 4	**271**	18 4	**331**	22 4	**31**	2 4	**31**	2.07
32	2 8	**92**	6 8	**152**	10 8	**212**	14 8	**272**	18 8	**332**	22 8	**32**	2 8	**32**	2.13
33	2 12	**93**	6 12	**153**	10 12	**213**	14 12	**273**	18 12	**333**	22 12	**33**	2 12	**33**	2.20
34	2 16	**94**	6 16	**154**	10 16	**214**	14 16	**274**	18 16	**334**	22 16	**34**	2 16	**34**	2.27
35	2 20	**95**	6 20	**155**	10 20	**215**	14 20	**275**	18 20	**335**	22 20	**35**	2 20	**35**	2.33
36	2 24	**96**	6 24	**156**	10 24	**216**	14 24	**276**	18 24	**336**	22 24	**36**	2 24	**36**	2.40
37	2 28	**97**	6 28	**157**	10 28	**217**	14 28	**277**	18 28	**337**	22 28	**37**	2 28	**37**	2.47
38	2 32	**98**	6 32	**158**	10 32	**218**	14 32	**278**	18 32	**338**	22 32	**38**	2 32	**38**	2.53
39	2 36	**99**	6 36	**159**	10 36	**219**	14 36	**279**	18 36	**339**	22 36	**39**	2 36	**39**	2.60
40	2 40	**100**	6 40	**160**	10 40	**220**	14 40	**280**	18 40	**340**	22 40	**40**	2 40	**40**	2.67
41	2 44	**101**	6 44	**161**	10 44	**221**	14 44	**281**	18 44	**341**	22 44	**41**	2 44	**41**	2.73
42	2 48	**102**	6 48	**162**	10 48	**222**	14 48	**282**	18 48	**342**	22 48	**42**	2 48	**42**	2.80
43	2 52	**103**	6 52	**163**	10 52	**223**	14 52	**283**	18 52	**343**	22 52	**43**	2 52	**43**	2.87
44	2 56	**104**	6 56	**164**	10 56	**224**	14 56	**284**	18 56	**344**	22 56	**44**	2 56	**44**	2.93
45	3 0	**105**	7 0	**165**	11 0	**225**	15 0	**285**	19 0	**345**	23 0	**45**	3 0	**45**	3.00
46	3 4	**106**	7 4	**166**	11 4	**226**	15 4	**286**	19 4	**346**	23 4	**46**	3 4	**46**	3.07
47	3 8	**107**	7 8	**167**	11 8	**227**	15 8	**287**	19 8	**347**	23 8	**47**	3 8	**47**	3.13
48	3 12	**108**	7 12	**168**	11 12	**228**	15 12	**288**	19 12	**348**	23 12	**48**	3 12	**48**	3.20
49	3 16	**109**	7 16	**169**	11 16	**229**	15 16	**289**	19 16	**349**	23 16	**49**	3 16	**49**	3.27
50	3 20	**110**	7 20	**170**	11 20	**230**	15 20	**290**	19 20	**350**	23 20	**50**	3 20	**50**	3.33
51	3 24	**111**	7 24	**171**	11 24	**231**	15 24	**291**	19 24	**351**	23 24	**51**	3 24	**51**	3.40
52	3 28	**112**	7 28	**172**	11 28	**232**	15 28	**292**	19 28	**352**	23 28	**52**	3 28	**52**	3.47
53	3 32	**113**	7 32	**173**	11 32	**233**	15 32	**293**	19 32	**353**	23 32	**53**	3 32	**53**	3.53
54	3 36	**114**	7 36	**174**	11 36	**234**	15 36	**294**	19 36	**354**	23 36	**54**	3 36	**54**	3.60
55	3 40	**115**	7 40	**175**	11 40	**235**	15 40	**295**	19 40	**355**	23 40	**55**	3 40	**55**	3.67
56	3 44	**116**	7 44	**176**	11 44	**236**	15 44	**296**	19 44	**356**	23 44	**56**	3 44	**56**	3.73
57	3 48	**117**	7 48	**177**	11 48	**237**	15 48	**297**	19 48	**357**	23 48	**57**	3 48	**57**	3.80
58	3 52	**118**	7 52	**178**	11 52	**238**	15 52	**298**	19 52	**358**	23 52	**58**	3 52	**58**	3.87
59	3 56	**119**	7 56	**179**	11 56	**239**	15 56	**299**	19 56	**359**	23 56	**59**	3 56	**59**	3.93
60	4 0	**120**	8 0	**180**	12 0	**240**	16 0	**300**	20 0	**360**	24 0	**60**	4 0	**60**	4.00

TABLE 43.

For conversion of Local civil time to Greenwich civil time

Long. W. / L. C. T.	180°	165°	150°	135°	120°	105°	90°	75°	60°	45°	30°	15°	0°
	G.C.T.	*G.C.T.*	*G.C.T.*	*G.C.T.*	*G.C.T.*	*G.C.T.*	*G.C.T.*	*G.C.T.*	*G.C.T.*	*G.C.T.*	*G.C.T.*	*G.C.T.*	*G.C.T.*
00 00	12 00	11 00	10 00	09 00	08 00	07 00	06 00	05 00	04 00	03 00	02 00	01 00	00 00
01 00	13 00	12 00	11 00	10 00	09 00	08 00	07 00	06 00	05 00	04 00	03 00	02 00	01 00
02 00	14 00	13 00	12 00	11 00	10 00	09 00	08 00	07 00	06 00	05 00	04 00	03 00	02 00
03 00	15 00	14 00	13 00	12 00	11 00	10 00	09 00	08 00	07 00	06 00	05 00	04 00	03 00
04 00	16 00	15 00	14 00	13 00	12 00	11 00	10 00	09 00	08 00	07 00	06 00	05 00	04 00
05 00	17 00	16 00	15 00	14 00	13 00	12 00	11 00	10 00	09 00	08 00	07 00	06 00	05 00
06 00	18 00	17 00	16 00	15 00	14 00	13 00	12 00	11 00	10 00	09 00	08 00	07 00	06 00
07 00	19 00	18 00	17 00	16 00	15 00	14 00	13 00	12 00	11 00	10 00	09 00	08 00	07 00
08 00	20 00	19 00	18 00	17 00	16 00	15 00	14 00	13 00	12 00	11 00	10 00	09 00	08 00
09 00	21 00	20 00	19 00	18 00	17 00	16 00	15 00	14 00	13 00	12 00	11 00	10 00	09 00
10 00	22 00	21 00	20 00	19 00	18 00	17 00	16 00	15 00	14 00	13 00	12 00	11 00	10 00
11 00	23 00	22 00	21 00	20 00	19 00	18 00	17 00	16 00	15 00	14 00	13 00	12 00	11 00
12 00	24 00	23 00	22 00	21 00	20 00	19 00	18 00	17 00	16 00	15 00	14 00	13 00	12 00
13 00	*01 00*	24 00	23 00	22 00	21 00	20 00	19 00	18 00	17 00	16 00	15 00	14 00	13 00
14 00	*02 00*	*01 00*	24 00	23 00	22 00	21 00	20 00	19 00	18 00	17 00	16 00	15 00	14 00
15 00	*03 00*	*02 00*	*01 00*	24 00	23 00	22 00	21 00	20 00	19 00	18 00	17 00	16 00	15 00
16 00	*04 00*	*03 00*	*02 00*	*01 00*	24 00	23 00	22 00	21 00	20 00	19 00	18 00	17 00	16 00
17 00	*05 00*	*04 00*	*03 00*	*02 00*	*01 00*	24 00	23 00	22 00	21 00	20 00	19 00	18 00	17 00
18 00	*06 00*	*05 00*	*04 00*	*03 00*	*02 00*	*01 00*	24 00	23 00	22 00	21 00	20 00	19 00	18 00
19 00	*07 00*	*06 00*	*05 00*	*04 00*	*03 00*	*02 00*	*01 00*	24 00	23 00	22 00	21 00	20 00	19 00
20 00	*08 00*	*07 00*	*06 00*	*05 00*	*04 00*	*03 00*	*02 00*	*01 00*	24 00	23 00	22 00	21 00	20 00
21 00	*09 00*	*08 00*	*07 00*	*06 00*	*05 00*	*04 00*	*03 00*	*02 00*	*01 00*	24 00	23 00	22 00	21 00
22 00	*10 00*	*09 00*	*08 00*	*07 00*	*06 00*	*05 00*	*04 00*	*03 00*	*02 00*	*01 00*	24 00	23 00	22 00
23 00	*11 00*	*10 00*	*09 00*	*08 00*	*07 00*	*06 00*	*05 00*	*04 00*	*03 00*	*02 00*	*01 00*	24 00	23 00
24 00	*12 00*	*11 00*	*10 00*	*09 00*	*08 00*	*07 00*	*06 00*	*05 00*	*04 00*	*03 00*	*02 00*	*01 00*	24 00
Zone--	+12	+11	+10	+9	+8	+7	+6	+5	+4	+3	+2	+1	0

When G. C. T. is found in italic type, the Greenwich date is one day ahead of the local date in west longitude

0°	15°	30°	45°	60°	75°	90°	105°	120°	135°	150°	165°	180°	Long. E. / L. C. T.
G.C.T.	*G.C.T.*	*G.C.T.*	*G.C.T.*	*G.C.T.*	*G.C.T.*	*G.C.T.*	*G.C.T.*	*G.C.T.*	*G.C.T.*	*G.C.T.*	*G.C.T.*	*G.C.T.*	
00 00	*23 00*	*22 00*	*21 00*	*20 00*	*19 00*	*18 00*	*17 00*	*16 00*	*15 00*	*14 00*	*13 00*	*12 00*	**00 00**
01 00	24 00	*23 00*	*22 00*	*21 00*	*20 00*	*19 00*	*18 00*	*17 00*	*16 00*	*15 00*	*14 00*	*13 00*	**01 00**
02 00	01 00	24 00	*23 00*	*22 00*	*21 00*	*20 00*	*19 00*	*18 00*	*17 00*	*16 00*	*15 00*	*14 00*	**02 00**
03 00	02 00	01 00	24 00	*23 00*	*22 00*	*21 00*	*20 00*	*19 00*	*18 00*	*17 00*	*16 00*	*15 00*	**03 00**
04 00	03 00	02 00	01 00	24 00	*23 00*	*22 00*	*21 00*	*20 00*	*19 00*	*18 00*	*17 00*	*16 00*	**04 00**
05 00	04 00	03 00	02 00	01 00	24 00	*23 00*	*22 00*	*21 00*	*20 00*	*19 00*	*18 00*	*17 00*	**05 00**
06 00	05 00	04 00	03 00	02 00	01 00	24 00	*23 00*	*22 00*	*21 00*	*20 00*	*19 00*	*18 00*	**06 00**
07 00	06 00	05 00	04 00	03 00	02 00	01 00	24 00	*23 00*	*22 00*	*21 00*	*20 00*	*19 00*	**07 00**
08 00	07 00	06 00	05 00	04 00	03 00	02 00	01 00	24 00	*23 00*	*22 00*	*21 00*	*20 00*	**08 00**
09 00	08 00	07 00	06 00	05 00	04 00	03 00	02 00	01 00	24 00	*23 00*	*22 00*	*21 00*	**09 00**
10 00	09 00	08 00	07 00	06 00	05 00	04 00	03 00	02 00	01 00	24 00	*23 00*	*22 00*	**10 00**
11 00	10 00	09 00	08 00	07 00	06 00	05 00	04 00	03 00	02 00	01 00	24 00	*23 00*	**11 00**
12 00	11 00	10 00	09 00	08 00	07 00	06 00	05 00	04 00	03 00	02 00	01 00	24 00	**12 00**
13 00	12 00	11 00	10 00	09 00	08 00	07 00	06 00	05 00	04 00	03 00	02 00	01 00	**13 00**
14 00	13 00	12 00	11 00	10 00	09 00	08 00	07 00	06 00	05 00	04 00	03 00	02 00	**14 00**
15 00	14 00	13 00	12 00	11 00	10 00	09 00	08 00	07 00	06 00	05 00	04 00	03 00	**15 00**
16 00	15 00	14 00	13 00	12 00	11 00	10 00	09 00	08 00	07 00	06 00	05 00	04 00	**16 00**
17 00	16 00	15 00	14 00	13 00	12 00	11 00	10 00	09 00	08 00	07 00	06 00	05 00	**17 00**
18 00	17 00	16 00	15 00	14 00	13 00	12 00	11 00	10 00	09 00	08 00	07 00	06 00	**18 00**
19 00	18 00	17 00	16 00	15 00	14 00	13 00	12 00	11 00	10 00	09 00	08 00	07 00	**19 00**
20 00	19 00	18 00	17 00	16 00	15 00	14 00	13 00	12 00	11 00	10 00	09 00	08 00	**20 00**
21 00	20 00	19 00	18 00	17 00	16 00	15 00	14 00	13 00	12 00	11 00	10 00	09 00	**21 00**
22 00	21 00	20 00	19 00	18 00	17 00	16 00	15 00	14 00	13 00	12 00	11 00	10 00	**22 00**
23 00	22 00	21 00	20 00	19 00	18 00	17 00	16 00	15 00	14 00	13 00	12 00	11 00	**23 00**
24 00	23 00	22 00	21 00	20 00	19 00	18 00	17 00	16 00	15 00	14 00	13 00	12 00	**24 00**
0	−1	−2	−3	−4	−5	−6	−7	−8	−9	−10	−11	−12	**Zone**

When G. C. T. is found in italic type, the Greenwich date is one day before the local date in east longitude